Wave motion in elastic solids

Wave motion in elastic solids

KARL F. GRAFF

OHIO STATE UNIVERSITY PRESS

LIBRARY OF CONGRESS CATALOGING IN PUBLICATION DATA

Graff, Karl F

Wave motion in elastic solids.

Bibliography: p.
1. Solids. 2. Elastic waves. I. Title.
QC176.8.W3G7 531′.33 74–3040
ISBN 0–8142–0232–2

PRINTED IN NORTHERN IRELAND
AT THE UNIVERSITIES PRESS
BELFAST NORTHERN IRELAND

TO MARTHA

Preface

THE purpose of this book is to present, in one place and in a fairly comprehensive manner, an intermediate-level coverage of nearly all of the major topics of elastic wave propagation in solids. Thus subjects range from the elementary theory of waves and vibrations in strings to the three-dimensional theory of waves in thick plates. It is hoped that the result will find application not only as a textbook for a wide audience of engineering students, but also as a general reference for workers in vibrations and acoustics.

The book is organized into eight chapters and three appendices. The first four chapters cover wave motion in the simple structural shapes, namely strings (Chapter 1), longitudinal rod motion (Chapter 2), beams (Chapter 3), and membranes, plates, and (cylindrical) shells (Chapter 4). In these chapters, the so-called 'strength-of-materials' theories provide the governing equations. Chapter 1, dealing with waves in strings, is used to introduce nearly all of the basic wave propagation concepts used throughout the remainder of the book. There is also some material included in each of the first four chapters on steady vibrations of structural shapes.

Chapters 5–8 deal with wave propagation as governed by the three-dimensional equations of elasticity and cover waves in infinite media, waves in a half-space, scattering and diffraction, and waves in thick rods, plates, and shells. The appendices of the book cover the topics of the elasticity equations, integral transforms, and experimental methods.

An effort has been made to make the book as self-contained as possible. This is in part reflected by the contents of the appendices, where introductory material is included, as indicated above, on elasticity, transforms, and experimental techniques. It is further reflected by fairly complete development of a number of topics in the mechanics and mathematics of the subject, such as simple transform solutions, orthogonality conditions, approximate theories of plates, and asymptotic methods.

Throughout the book, emphasis has been placed on showing results, in addition to mere theoretical development of the subject. This has taken the form of results from both theoretical and experimental studies. The intent in doing so has been twofold. On the one hand, presentation of specific results from a range of studies should assist the student in reaching a better physical understanding of the response of systems to transients. On the other hand, the availability of a basic catalogue of results should be of some assistance to workers in the field charged with analysing waves in more complex systems. Finally, in particular reference to the inclusion of experimental results, it is hoped that the role played by better physical appreciation for wave propagation, a partial substitute for actual laboratory work and verification (or lack thereof) of theoretical results, will be brought out.

It is hoped that the book will find various uses as text or reference. The inclusion of over one hundred problems should assist its use as a textbook. As a text, it has three main uses. For use as an upper-level undergraduate book, the material would be drawn primarily from large parts of the first four chapters. For lower-level graduate use, where prior exposure to the elasticity equations could be assumed, material could be drawn from all of the first five chapters and parts of Chapters 6 and 8. For upper-level graduate use, material could be drawn from the entire book. Again, it is hoped that the somewhat self-contained nature of the book and the emphasis on results will make it of use as a reference book.

Finally, it should be noted that, as is the case for many books, this was an outgrowth of notes prepared for courses of instruction. Specifically, notes prepared over several years of teaching two graduate-level courses in the Department of Engineering Mechanics at the Ohio State University served as the basis. The courses, 'Vibrations of continuous systems' and 'Elastic wave propagation', covered both steady-state vibration phenomena and propagation of transients. Needless to say, acknowledgement to the many students taking these courses is in order. Their comments, sometimes diplomatic, sometimes otherwise, but always constructive, were of considerable help in the notes-to-book evolutionary process.

K. F. G.

Columbus, Ohio
October, 1973

Acknowledgements

Figs 2.33 and 6.35 are reproduced with the permission of Microform International Marketing Corporation, exclusive copyright licensee of Pergamon Press journal back files.

Figs 8.6, 8.8, 8.9, 8.10, and 8.11 are reproduced with permission from *Structural Mechanics* (ed. Goodier and Hoff) Pergamon Press Inc. (1960).

Fig. 6.33 is reproduced with permission from H. E. Tatel, *Journal of Geophysical Research*, vol. 75 (1970) copyright by American Geophysical Union.

Fig. 6.36 is reproduced with permission from D. Lewis and J. W. Dally, *Journal of Geophysical Research*, vol. 75 (1970) copyright by American Geophysical Union.

Figs 3.3, 4.3, 4.4, 4.8, 4.9, 4.17, and 7.2 are from P. M. Morse, *Vibration and Sound*, copyright 1948 McGraw-Hill. Fig. 6.27 is from W. M. Ewing, W. S. Jardetzky, and F. Press, *Elastic Waves in layered media* copyright 1957 McGraw-Hill. Fig. 4.13 is from I. N. Sneddon, *Fourier Transforms*, copyright 1951 McGraw-Hill. All used with permission of McGraw-Hill Book Company.

Fig. 8.52 is reproduced with permission from D. Y. Hseih and H. Kolsky, *Proceedings of the Physical Society*, vol. 71 (1958), copyright by the Institute of Physics.

Contents

Introduction

I.1 General aspects of wave propagation

The effect of a sharply applied, localized disturbance in a medium soon transmits or 'spreads' to other parts of the medium. This simple fact forms a basis for study of the fascinating subject known as *wave propagation*. The manifestation of this phenomenon are familiar to everyone in forms such as the transmission of sound in air, the spreading of ripples on a pond of water, the transmission of seismic tremors in the earth, or the transmission of radio waves. These and many other examples could be cited to illustrate the propagation of waves through gaseous, liquid, and solid media and free space.

The propagation of disturbances in the various media mentioned share many common features, so that a person versed in the science of one understands much about the others. There are sufficient differences, however, as to make a completely general development of the subject impractical and to thus require concentration on a single topic. Our attention in this development will be focused on the propagation of waves in solids. We will thus be considering solely mechanical disturbances in contrast, say, to electromagnetic or acoustic disturbances.

The physical basis for the propagation of a disturbance ultimately lies in the interaction of the discrete atoms of the solid. Investigations along such lines are more atuned to physics than mechanics, however. In solid and fluid mechanics, the medium is regarded as *continuous*, so that properties such as density or elastic constants are considered to be continuous functions representing averages of microscopic quantities. Nevertheless, in envisaging the basis for propagation of a disturbance it is helpful to first consider a model composed of discrete elements consisting of a series of interconnected masses and springs. If a disturbance is imparted to a mass particle, it is transmitted to the next mass by the intervening spring. In this manner the disturbance is soon transmitted to a remote point, although any given particle of the system will have moved only a small amount. The role of the mass and stiffness parameters in affecting the speed of propagation is quite clear in such a model. If the stiffness of the connecting springs is increased or the particle masses decreased, or both, the speed of propagation would be expected to increase. Weaker springs and/or larger masses would slow the propagation velocity. Extreme values of the parameters could lead to instantaneous or zero propagation of disturbances. So in the case of a continuous media. The mass and elastic parameters are now distributed in terms of mass density and the elastic moduli. The interaction from one part of the system to the next is the interaction of one differential element on the next. Instead of the simple push-pull motion along a series of springs and masses, the disturbance spreads outward in a three-dimensional sense. A wavefront will be associated with the outward spreading disturbance. Particles ahead of the front will have experienced no motion, while particles behind the front will have experienced motion and may in fact continue to oscillate for some time.

In the case of a solid, two distinct types of action will be possible in a wave. In one case, the solid will transmit tensile and compressive stress and the motion of particles will be in the direction of the wave motion. This behaviour is analogous to that of fluids. In addition, the solid may transmit shear stress, and the motion of particles is transverse to the direction of propagation. There is no analogue to this behaviour in fluids, although the transverse nature of the wave bears close resemblance to electromagnetic waves.

The outward propagation of waves from a disturbance is one aspect of wave motion. Inevitably, the waves encounter and interact with boundaries. In this area, the behaviour of waves in solids differs considerably from that of fluids. In a solid a single wave, be it compression or shear, will generally produce both compression and shear waves on striking a boundary, whereas acoustic and electromagnetic waves will only generate waves of their own type.

It is the continual propagation and reflection of waves in a bounded solid that brings about the state of static equilibrium. Speaking in these terms, every process of loading a solid is a dynamic process involving the propagation and reflection of waves. However, if the rate of onset of the load is slow compared with many transit times of waves within the solid, static equilibrium effectively prevails and wave effects are of no consequence. It is only when loading rates are comparable with transit times of waves that the mechanics of wave propagation must be considered.

In many problems of waves in solids, the preceding description of wave motion is too detailed, somewhat in analogy to attempting to describe waves in a solid through the motion of the atoms. The motion of simple structural shapes such as rods, beams, and plates may be described adequately in many instances without resort to considering the propagation and reflection of individual waves within the specimen. Instead, so called 'strength-of-material' theories may be devised, based on various assumptions on how these solids deform, that approximate the detailed behaviour of the solid. The first four chapters of this book will be devoted to such considerations. Such theories, while most useful, have inherent limitations as loading transients become more severe, or frequencies of excitation become higher or as the necessary assumptions on deformations become less obvious. At this stage, analysis based on the exact equations of elasticity becomes necessary, and it is this area to which the last four chapters of the book will be devoted.

The propagation of waves in solids may be divided roughly into three categories. The first is elastic waves, where the stresses in the material obey Hooke's law. The considerations of this book, whether concerned with simple structures or with analysis based on the exact equations, will assume such elastic behaviour. The two other main categories, visco-elastic waves, where viscous as well as elastic stresses act, and plastic waves in which the yield stress of the material is exceeded, will not be covered here. These subjects are sufficiently broad in themselves to warrant entire books.

The study of wave propagation is far from an abstract mathematical subject. The experimental measurements of wave phenomena furnish us with much of our information on the properties of solids, be these solids the earth, pure crystals of metal, or other substances. The deliberate introduction of stress waves in materials finds many applications in structures, electronic technology, and testing. For this reason, it is considered useful to review a range of experimental results in stress waves at the conclusion of several of the chapters.

I.2. Applications of wave phenomena

The practical applications of wave phenomena surely go back to the early history of man. The shaping of stone implements, for example, consists of striking sharp, carefully placed blows along the edges of a flint. The resulting stress waves in the 'cone of percussion' break out fragments of rock in very specific patterns. Starting at this early time, it may be safely said that interest in wave phenomena has been increasing ever since.

The motivations for the current high level of interest in the subject are the many practical applications in science and industry. In the area of *structures*, for example, the interest is mainly in the response to impact or blast loads. Under transient loads of moderate strength, completely elastic conditions may prevail throughout the structure and elastic wave theory may suffice to predict all aspects of the response. Under more severe loads, local permanent deformation, fracture, or perforation of the structure may occur. Elastic wave theory often still finds application under such conditions in predicting the response away from the area of impact.

The behaviour of structural *materials* under loads severe enough to cause permanent damage is an area of very great interest. Studies in this area generally fall in the category of *anelastic wave propagation*. Some of the techniques used in the study of these properties use elastic waves, such as waves in a high-strength steel rod, to dynamically load-test specimens of weaker materials. Most of the applications in this area are in various aspects of military and space technology. However, a number of metal forming processes, such as explosive forming, high energy rate forming, or sonic riveting and forging, find use for similar information.

Another area in the study of structures involving wave phenomena is that of crack propagation or the interaction of dynamic stress fields with existing cracks, voids, or inclusions in a material. The concept of a dynamic stress concentration factor, for example, finds application in this area. Problems in this area are the analogue of scattering and diffraction problems arising in acoustics and electromagnetics.

The field of *ultrasonics* represents another major area of application of wave phenomena. The general aspects of this area involve introducing a very low energy-level, high-frequency stress pulse or 'wave packet' into a material and observing the subsequent propagation and reflection of this energy. The means for introducing and detecting the stress waves are based on the *piezoelectric effect* in certain crystals and ceramics, whereby an electrical field applied to the material causes a mechanical strain or the inverse effect where a strain produces an electric field. Thus an electrical pulse is capable of lauching a mechanical pulse. Detection is accomplished when a mechanical pulse strikes a piezoelectric crystal and generates an electrical signal.

A host of applications are based on this reciprocal effect. For example, by studying the propagation, reflection, and attenuation of ultrasonic pulses, it is possible to determine many fundamental properties of materials such as elastic constants and damping characteristics. The field of non-destructive testing makes wide use of ultrasonics to detect defects in materials. By launching a pulse into a solid, it is possible to locate defects by the reflection of pulse energy from the defect much in the manner of underwater sonar detection. Various detection applications use longitudinal waves, shear waves, or surface waves.

Ultrasonic *delay lines* find wide application in the field of electronics. The objective of such devices is to provide a means to delay an electrical signal for a short time interval (such as a few microseconds), as dictated by signal-processing considerations. With the extremely high propagation velocity of electrical signals, it becomes impractical to accomplish this delay using purely electronic components. The relatively slow velocity of mechanical disturbances makes such time delays easily obtained. The procedure is to convert the electrical signal to a mechanical pulse using a piezoelectric transducer, to propagate the signal in some type of solid media, and to recover it a specified time later with another transducer. A wide variety of types of delay lines exist. Some are based on the propagation of longitudinal or torsional waves in thin wires, some on the propagation of shear waves in thin strips, others on the propagation of longitudinal waves in bulk solids, and still others on the propagation of waves along a surface.

The general subject of *waves in the earth* covers many interesting propagation phenomena. Earthquakes generate waves that may travel thousands of miles. Study of the propagation of such waves or tremors artificially produced have provided the most knowledge on the interior construction of the earth. Waves in the earth generated by blast are of concern from the standpoint either of blast detection or the protection of underground structures. The matter of distinguishing blast and earthquake 'signatures' is also of concern. Other aspects of waves in the earth involve less catastrophic considerations and pertain to oil and gas exploration. By studying the reflection of waves from underground discontinuities, it is possible to locate possible oil-bearing deposits.

Consider the areas of mining and quarrying where numerous applications of *waves in rock* are found. The blasting that is used in these operations has the purpose of producing intense stress waves. It is the interaction of these waves with each other and with boundaries that is responsible for the fracture and removal of the large quantities of rock. For example, in quarrying, a typical operation is to drill a series of blast holes parallel to the exposed rock face. The ensuing stress waves from the blast propagate to the exposed face and reflect, creating tensile stresses that fracture the rock. The drilling of the blast holes referred to is generally by *percussive drilling*. This process operates by transmitting longitudinal waves created by an air hammer down drill rod into the rock. Many interesting problems on reflection and transmission of waves at discontinuities exist in this application.

The phenomenon of *acoustic emission* is a producer of stress waves and hence of potential applications. It is observed that the motion of dislocations during plastic deformation produce very high-frequency, low-energy stress waves that may be detected with sensitive transducers. Waves of greater energy are created by cracking in materials in a microscopic analogue to energy release occurring in earthquakes. The study of acoustic emission waves enables some deductions to be made on the fundamental processes occurring within the material. Of at least equal interest is that monitoring of such waves enables structural integrity to be assessed by passive means.

The cataloguing of applications of elastic and anelastic wave phenomena could easily stretch on, but it is hoped that the point has been made that applications are many and widespread and that interest in the subject stems from practical considerations.

I.3. Historical background

The history of the study of wave and vibration phenomena goes back hundreds of years. Most early studies were naturally more observational than quantitative and frequently were concerned with musical tones or water waves, two of the most common associations with wave motion. From the time of Galileo onward, the science of vibrations and waves progressed rapidly in association with developments in the statics of solids. Some of the major developments in the area over the years are chronologically ordered in the following.

Sixth Century B.C.: Pythagoras studied the origin of musical sounds and the vibrations of strings.

1636: Mersenne presented the first correct published account on the vibrations of strings.

1638: Galileo described the vibrations of pendulums, the phenomenon of resonance, and the factors influencing the vibrations of strings.

1678: Robert Hooke formulated the law of proportionality between stress and strain for elastic bodies. This law forms the basis for the static and dynamic theory of elasticity.

1686: Newton investigated the speed of water waves and the speed of sound in air.

1700: Sauveur calculated vibrational frequency of a stretched string.

1713: Taylor worked out a completely dynamical solution for the vibrations of a string.

1744: Leonard Euler (1744) and Daniel Bernoulli (1751) developed the equation for the vibrations of beams and obtained the normal modes for various boundary conditions.

1747: D'Alembert derived the equation of motion of the string and solved the initial-value problem.

1755: D. Bernoulli developed the principle of superposition and applied it to the vibrations of strings.

1759: Lagrange analysed the string as a system of discrete mass particles.

1766: Euler attempted to analyse the vibrations of a bell on the basis of the behaviour of curved bars. James Bernoulli (1789) also attempted analysis of this problem.

1802: E. F. F. Chladni reported experimental investigations on the vibrations of beams and on the longitudinal and torsional vibrations of rods.

1815: Madame Sophie Germain developed the equation for the vibrations of a plate.

1821: Navier investigated the general equations of equilibrium and vibration of elastic solids. Although not all of the developments of the work met with complete acceptance, it represented one of the most important developments in mechanics.

1822: Cauchy developed most of the aspects of the pure theory of elasticity including the dynamical equations of motion for a solid. Poisson (1829) also investigated the general equations.

1828: Poisson investigated the propagation of waves through an elastic solid. He found that two wave types, longitudinal and transverse, could exist. Cauchy (1830) obtained a similar result. Poisson also solved the problem of the radial vibrations of a sphere.

1828: Poisson developed approximate theories for the vibrations of rods.

1862: Clebsch founded the general theory for the free vibrations of solid bodies using normal modes.

1872: J. Hopkinson performed the first experiments on plastic wave propagation in wires.

1876: Pochhammer obtained the frequency equation for the propagation of waves in rods according to the exact equations of elasticity. Chree (1889) carried out similar studies.

1880: Jaerisch analysed the general problem of the vibrations of a sphere. The result was obtained independently by Lamb (1882).

1882: Hertz developed the first successful theory for impact.

1883: St. Venant summarized the work on impact of earlier investigators and presented his results on transverse impact.

1887: Rayleigh investigated the propagation of surface waves on a solid.

1888: Rayleigh and Lamb (1889) developed the frequency equation for waves in a plate according to exact elasticity theory.

1904: Lamb made the first investigation of pulse propagation in a semi-infinite solid.

1911: Love developed the theory of waves in a thin layer overlying a solid and showed that such waves accounted for certain anomalies in seismogram records.

1914: B. Hopkinson performed experiments on the propagation of elastic pulses in bars.

1921: Timoshenko developed a theory for beams that accounted for shearing deformation.

1930: Donnell studied the effect of a non-linear stress–strain law on the propagation of stress waves in a bar.

1942: von Karman, Taylor (1942), and Rakmatulin developed a one-dimensional finite-amplitude plastic wave theory.

1949: Davies published an extensive theoretical and experimental study on waves in bars.

1951: Mindlin presented an approximate theory for waves in a plate that provided a general basis for development of higher-order plate and rod theories.

1951: Malvern developed a rate-dependent theory for plastic wave propagation.

1955: Perkeris presented the solution to Lamb's problem of pulse propagation in a semi-infinite solid.

Developments in wave propagation did not, of course, cease in 1955; the date only represents the author's desire not to offend more recent significant contributors to the field through inadvertent omission from a mere listing. Recent activities in the field of wave propagation have dealt with formulating various approximate theories for plates and rods and with the analysis of transient loading situations. In the latter regard, the analysis of pulse propagation in the half-space and in plates and rods has received considerable attention. The development of approximate techniques for diffraction analysis have been successfully carried out. The application of the digital computer has enabled a number of otherwise intractable problems to be solved.

1 Waves and vibrations in strings

In beginning the analysis of wave propagation in solids, we strive for mathematical simplicity. However, many of the applications of wave phenomena involve quite complicated mathematical analyses that arise from the geometric complexities of the physical system. The taut string, on the other hand, represents a physical system whose governing equation is rather simple, yet basic to many wave propagation problems. Nearly all of the basic concepts of propagation, such as dispersion and group velocity as well as certain techniques of analysis can and will be introduced, unobscured by the complexities involved in more complicated elastic systems.

While it is sufficient to rest the case for analysing the taut string on mathematical grounds alone, it should be appreciated that practical motivations also exist. The characteristics of many musical instruments are based on the vibrations of strings. The dynamics of electrical transmission lines may be modelled on the basis of strings. Problems in the dynamics of strings arise in the manufacture of thread. Nevertheless, it is primarily for mathematical reasons that we are presently interested in the elastic string.

1.1. Waves in long strings

The basic governing equation for the taut string must first be developed. Since boundaries inevitably introduce complications in wave propagation due to reflection phenomena, the first considerations will involve 'long' strings, that is, infinite or semi-infinite strings where the problem of boundary reflection will not arise. The basic propagation characteristics of free waves and waves resulting from forced motion will be studied under these conditions.

1.1.1. *The governing equation*

Consider a differential element of taut string under tension T as shown in Fig. 1.1. It is assumed that any variation in the tension due to the displacement of the string is negligible. The mass density per unit length is ρ and the body force or external loading is $q(x, t)$. The resulting equation of motion in the

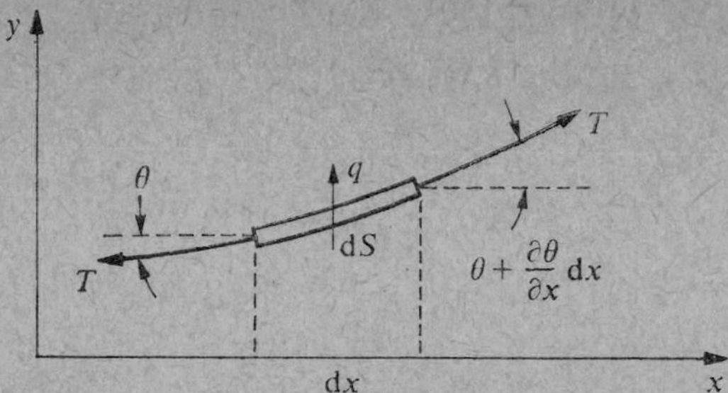

FIG 1.1. Differential element of taut string.

vertical direction is then

$$-T\sin\theta+T\sin\left(\theta+\frac{\partial\theta}{\partial x}\,dx\right)+q\,ds=\rho\,ds\frac{\partial^2 y}{\partial t^2}. \tag{1.1.1}$$

The arc length ds is given by d$s=(1+y'^2)^{\frac{1}{2}}$ dx. If we assume small deflections of the string, we may write that d$s \simeq$ dx. Furthermore, for small deflections, we approximate $\sin\theta$ by θ and note that $\theta \simeq \partial y/\partial x$. The preceding equation then reduces to

$$T\frac{\partial^2 y}{\partial x^2}+q=\rho\frac{\partial^2 y}{\partial t^2}. \tag{1.1.2}$$

A number of solutions to this non-homogeneous second-order partial differential equation will be investigated in later sections. Of particular interest is the form of the homogeneous equation obtained by setting $q=0$, giving

$$\frac{\partial^2 y}{\partial x^2}=\frac{1}{c_0^2}\frac{\partial^2 y}{\partial t^2}, \qquad c_0=\left(\frac{T}{\rho}\right)^{\frac{1}{2}}. \tag{1.1.3}$$

This resulting equation governing the free transverse motion of the string is known as the *wave equation*. It possesses a number of interesting properties and will be found to govern the motion of a number of other elastic systems.

1.1.2. *Harmonic waves*

We shall first investigate the propagation of simple harmonic waves in a string. Using the separation of variables approach, we let $y=Y(x)T(t)$ and substitute in the wave equation (1.1.3), giving

$$\frac{Y''}{Y}=\frac{T''}{c_0^2 T}=-\gamma^2. \tag{1.1.4}$$

The resulting solution for $y(x,t)$ is then

$$y=(A_1\sin\gamma x+A_2\cos\gamma x)(A_3\sin\omega t+A_4\cos\omega t), \tag{1.1.5}$$

where the *radial frequency* is given as $\omega = \gamma c_0$. Regrouping, the solution may be written as

$$y = A_1A_4 \sin \gamma x \cos \omega t + A_2A_3 \cos \gamma x \sin \omega t + A_2A_4 \cos \gamma x \cos \omega t + \\ + A_1A_3 \sin \gamma x \sin \omega t. \qquad (1.1.6)$$

Consider a typical term of this solution written in the form

$$y = A \cos \gamma x \sin \omega t. \qquad (1.1.7)$$

The deflections of the string at successive instants of time as governed by (1.1.7) are shown in Fig. 1.2. We note that points of zero vibration amplitude,

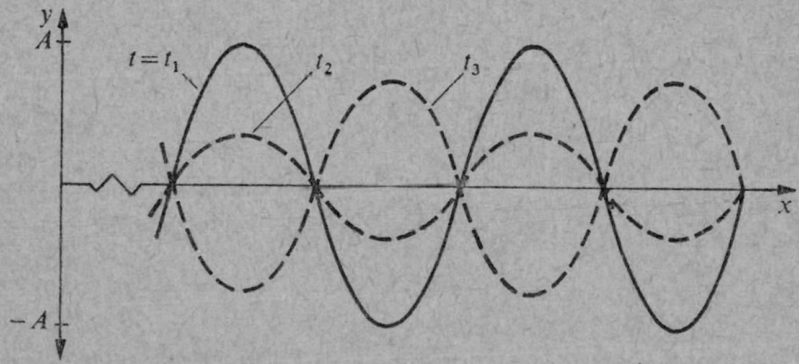

FIG. 1.2. Vibrational patterns of the string due to the standing wave $y = A \cos \gamma x \sin \omega t$.

called *nodes*, and of maximum amplitude, called the *antinodes*, occur at regular intervals along the string and remained fixed in that position with the passage of time. A vibration of this type and governed by results of the form (1.1.7) is called a stationary or *standing wave.*

Using trigonometric identities, the solution (1.1.6) may be put in the form

$$y = B_1 \sin (\gamma x + \omega t) + B_2 \sin (\gamma x - \omega t) + \\ + B_3 \cos (\gamma x + \omega t) - B_4 \cos (\gamma x - \omega t). \qquad (1.1.8)$$

Consider a typical term in the solution, given by

$$y = A \cos (\gamma x - \omega t) = A \cos \gamma (x - c_0 t). \qquad (1.1.9)$$

This may be shown to represent a wave *propagating* in the positive x direction. If we designate the argument of (1.1.9) as the *phase* ϕ, where

$$\phi = \gamma x - \omega t = \gamma (x - c_0 t), \qquad (1.1.10)$$

then we may note that for increasing time, increasing values of x are required to maintain the phase constant. The appearance of the deflection at successive instants of time would be as shown in Fig. 1.3. The propagation velocity of the constant phase is c_0, defined as the *phase velocity*. It is seen that constancy

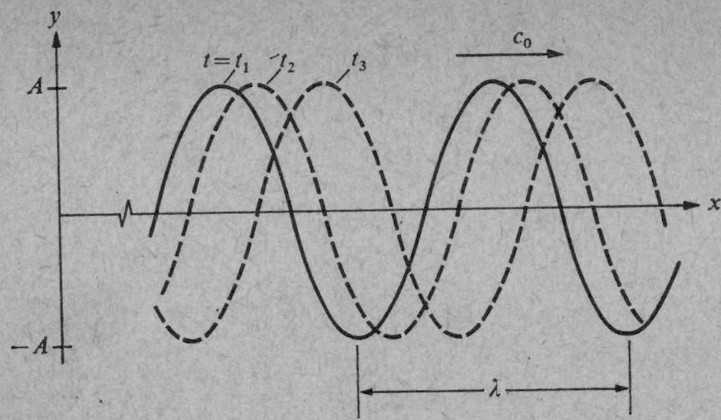

FIG. 1.3. Transverse string deflections at successive times resulting from the propagating wave $y = A\cos(\gamma x - \omega t)$.

of phase for increasing time requires $x = c_0 t$. It should be noted that (1.1.9) represents a wave of infinite length. It thus has no 'wavefront' or beginning, so that it is only by considering the phase that enables a propagation velocity to be associated with the motion.

Referring to Fig. 1.3, we define the distance between two successive points of constant phase as the *wavelength* λ. This is shown as the distance between two minimum points, or 'troughs' in the diagram, but could as well refer to successive maxima, points of zero amplitude or intermediate phase points. From (1.1.10) it is seen that the wavelength is related to γ by $\lambda = 2\pi/\gamma$. The parameter γ will be designated the *wavenumber*.

Other quantities that frequently arise in describing wave motion are the *cyclic frequency* f, where $\omega = 2\pi f$, and the *period*, T, of the wave, where $T = 1/f$. It is of value to summarize these various definitions and relations as follows:

$$\begin{aligned} A &= \text{amplitude of wave (length)} \\ \omega &= \text{radial frequency of wave (radians/time)} \\ f &= \text{cyclic frequency of wave (cycles/time)} \\ \lambda &= \text{wavelength of wave (length)} \\ \gamma &= \text{wavenumber of wave (1/length)} \\ c_0 &= \text{phase velocity of wave (length/time)} \\ T &= \text{period of wave (time)} \end{aligned} \tag{1.1.11}$$

$$\omega = \gamma c_0, \qquad \omega = 2\pi f, \qquad T = 1/f, \qquad \lambda = 2\pi/\gamma. \tag{1.1.12}$$

Having considered the characteristics of a typical harmonic wave, it is seen that the remaining terms of the solution (1.1.8) are similar in nature. The major point of difference is that terms having the argument $(\gamma x + \omega t)$ are propagating in the negative x direction. The general result (1.1.8) may be described as a propagating wave solution. It has been developed from (1.1.6), which may be described as a standing-wave solution. It may be said that the standing waves result from constructive and destructive interference of leftward and rightward propagating waves. This particular aspect is emphasized by considering two propagating waves of equal amplitude. Thus,

$$y = \frac{A}{2}\cos(\gamma x+\omega t)+\frac{A}{2}\cos(\gamma x-\omega t) = A\cos\gamma x\cos\omega t. \quad (1.1.13)$$

Finally, we consider alternate forms of representing harmonic waves. Instead of using $\sin\omega t$ or $\cos\omega t$ to represent the time dependence, we could use the exponential representation. Thus, let

$$y = Y(x)e^{i\omega t}. \quad (1.1.14)$$

Substituting in (1.1.3) and solving gives the solutions

$$y = A_1 e^{i(\gamma x+\omega t)}+B_1 e^{-i(\gamma x-\omega t)}. \quad (1.1.15)$$

These results are recognized as harmonic waves propagating in the negative and positive x direction respectively. Considering an initial time behaviour of the form $\exp(-i\omega t)$ leads to the solutions

$$y = A_2 e^{i(\gamma x-\omega t)}+B_2 e^{-i(\gamma x+\omega t)}. \quad (1.1.16)$$

1.1.3. *The D'Alembert solution*

It is possible to derive a general solution to the wave equation using Fourier superposition of harmonic waves, and this will be done in a later section. A classical solution by D'Alembert (1747) will be investigated, at this stage, that will provide considerable insight into wave-propagation phenomena. Thus, consider the wave equation (1.1.3) and introduce the change of variables

$$\xi = x-c_0 t, \qquad \eta = x+c_0 t. \quad (1.1.17)$$

By chain-rule differentiation, we have

$$\frac{\partial y}{\partial x} = \frac{\partial y}{\partial \xi}\frac{\partial \xi}{\partial x}+\frac{\partial y}{\partial \eta}\frac{\partial \eta}{\partial x} = \frac{\partial y}{\partial \xi}+\frac{\partial y}{\partial \eta},$$

$$\frac{\partial y}{\partial t} = \frac{\partial y}{\partial \xi}\frac{\partial \xi}{\partial t}+\frac{\partial y}{\partial \eta}\frac{\partial \eta}{\partial t} = -c_0\frac{\partial y}{\partial \xi}+c_0\frac{\partial y}{\partial \eta}. \quad (1.1.18)$$

The second derivatives give

$$\frac{\partial^2 y}{\partial x^2} = \frac{\partial^2 y}{\partial \xi^2}+2\frac{\partial^2 y}{\partial \xi\,\partial \eta}+\frac{\partial^2 y}{\partial \eta^2}, \qquad \frac{\partial^2 y}{\partial t^2} = c_0^2\left(\frac{\partial^2 y}{\partial \xi^2}-2\frac{\partial^2 y}{\partial \xi\,\partial \eta}+\frac{\partial^2 y}{\partial \eta^2}\right). \quad (1.1.19)$$

Substituting (1.1.19) in the wave equation gives

$$\frac{\partial^2 y(\xi,\eta)}{\partial \xi\,\partial \eta} = 0. \quad (1.1.20)$$

This may be integrated directly to give

$$\frac{\partial y}{\partial \xi} = F(\xi), \qquad y(\xi, \eta) = f(\xi) + g(\eta). \tag{1.1.21}$$

Finally, changing back to x,t variables gives the classical D'Alembert solution to the wave equation,

$$y(x, t) = f(x - c_0 t) + g(x + c_0 t). \tag{1.1.22}$$

In considering these results, we first note that f and g are arbitrary functions of integration that will be specifically determined by the initial conditions or forcing function of a given problem. More important at this stage is to note that these functions represent *propagating disturbances*. Thus, in the case of $f(x-c_0t)$, if $x-c_0t$ = constant, the function is obviously constant. Arguing in the same manner as for harmonic waves, increasing time requires increasing values of x to maintain the argument of the function constant. This corresponds to a wave propagating in the positive x direction. Similarly, $g(x+c_0t)$ is a disturbance propagating in the negative x direction.

The second point to emphasize regarding the solution (1.1.22) is that whatever the shape of the disturbances $f(x-c_0t)$, $g(x+c_0t)$ initially, that shape is maintained during the propagation. Thus, the waves propagate *without distortion*. The resulting nature of the propagation for a disturbance moving in the positive x direction is shown in Fig. 1.4. Appreciation of the undistorted nature of the wave propagation is important for two reasons. First, it represents a fundamental characteristic of the one-dimensional wave equation. Second, it will serve as a comparison against many physical systems where the opposite is true and where pulse distortion occurs during propagation.

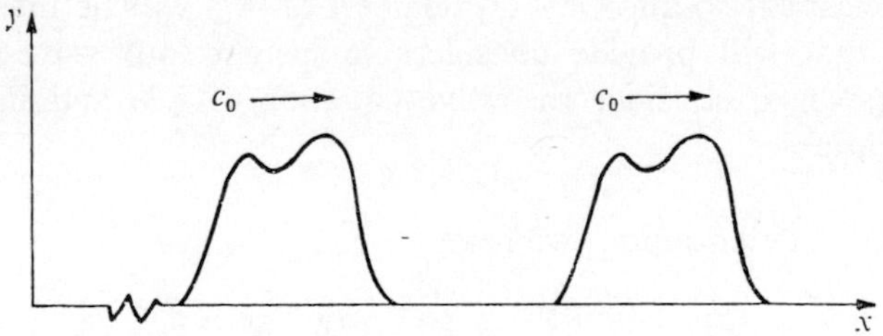

FIG. 1.4. Undistorted propagation of a pulse $f(x-c_0t)$.

1.1.4. *The initial-value problem*

We now wish to determine the form of the functions arising in the general solution (1.1.22) under prescribed initial conditions in the string. Let

$$y(x, 0) = U(x), \qquad \dot{y}(x, 0) = V(x). \tag{1.1.23}$$

Substituting the result (1.1.43) in these conditions gives the values of A and B as

$$A = B = \bar{U}(\gamma)/2. \tag{1.1.45}$$

The transformed solution is then

$$\bar{Y}(\gamma, t) = \frac{\bar{U}(\gamma)}{2}\{\exp(i\gamma c_0 t)+\exp(-i\gamma c_0 t)\}. \tag{1.1.46}$$

Taking the inverse Fourier transform of this result gives

$$y(x, t) = \frac{1}{2\sqrt{(2\pi)}}\int_{-\infty}^{\infty} \bar{U}(\gamma)\{\exp(i\gamma c_0 t)+\exp(-i\gamma c_0 t)\}\exp(-i\gamma x)\, d\gamma$$

$$= \frac{1}{2\sqrt{(2\pi)}}\int_{-\infty}^{\infty} \bar{U}(\gamma)[\exp\{-i\gamma(x-c_0 t)\}+\exp\{-i\gamma(x+c_0 t)\}]\, d\gamma. \tag{1.1.47}$$

Proceeding now in a manner similar to that used in the Fourier integral approach, we temporarily replace $x-c_0t$ and $x+c_0t$ by ξ and η in (1.1.47). In the one case, we then have

$$\frac{1}{\sqrt{(2\pi)}}\int_{-\infty}^{\infty} \bar{U}(\gamma)\exp(-i\gamma\xi)\, d\gamma = U(\xi), \tag{1.1.48}$$

simply from the definition of the inverse Fourier transform. Replacing ξ by η in (1.1.48) gives $U(\eta)$. Then the result (1.1.47) takes the form

$$y(x, t) = \tfrac{1}{2}\{U(\xi)+U(\eta)\} = \tfrac{1}{2}\{U(x-c_0t)+U(x+c_0t)\}, \tag{1.1.49}$$

and the D'Alembert form of the solution is again recovered.

1.1.6. *Energy in a string*

We have considered only the propagation of transverse displacements in a string up to this point. In considering the propagation of energy, we must first develop an expression for the kinetic and potential energy in a string. The kinetic energy in a differential element of string as shown in Fig. 1.1 would be given by

$$dK = \rho\, ds\dot{y}^2/2. \tag{1.1.50}$$

The total kinetic energy in a segment of string between x_1 and x_2 would then be

$$K(t) = \frac{1}{2}\int_{x_1}^{x_2} \rho\dot{y}^2\left\{1+\left(\frac{\partial y}{\partial x}\right)^2\right\}^{\frac{1}{2}} dx. \tag{1.1.51}$$

It is permissible to neglect the term $(\partial y/\partial x)^2$ in comparison to unity for small deflections of the string so that

$$K(t) = \frac{1}{2}\int_{x_1}^{x_2} \rho \dot{y}^2 \, dx. \tag{1.1.52}$$

We then define the kinetic energy density $k(x, t)$ as

$$k(x, t) = \rho \dot{y}^2/2. \tag{1.1.53}$$

The computation of the potential energy in a length of string is slightly more involved. In particular, the higher-order term just neglected in the kinetic-energy calculation provides the contribution to the potential energy. Thus, the change in length of the string between x_1 and x_2 due to stretching will be given by

$$\Delta l = \int_{x_1}^{x_2} ds - (x_2 - x_1) = \int_{x_1}^{x_2} \left\{1 + \left(\frac{\partial y}{\partial x}\right)^2\right\}^{\frac{1}{2}} dx - (x_2 - x_1). \tag{1.1.54}$$

We make the approximation $\{1+(\partial y/\partial x)^2\}^{\frac{1}{2}} \cong 1+(\partial y/\partial x)^2/2$. Using this in (1.1.54) gives

$$\Delta l \cong \frac{1}{2}\int_{x_1}^{x_2} \left(\frac{\partial y}{\partial x}\right)^2 dx. \tag{1.1.55}$$

The potential energy $V(t)$ in the length x_1 to x_2 will be given by $T\Delta l$ so that

$$V(t) = \frac{1}{2}\int_{x_1}^{x_2} T\left(\frac{\partial y}{\partial x}\right)^2 dx. \tag{1.1.56}$$

We define the potential energy density $v(x, t)$ as

$$v(x, t) = \frac{T}{2}\left(\frac{\partial y}{\partial x}\right)^2. \tag{1.1.57}$$

The total energy of the system in the region x_1 to x_2 is then given by

$$E(t) = K(t) + V(t), \tag{1.1.58}$$

and the energy density is given by

$$\varepsilon(x, t) = k(x, t) + v(x, t) = \frac{\rho \dot{y}^2}{2} + \frac{T}{2}\left(\frac{\partial y}{\partial x}\right)^2. \tag{1.1.59}$$

Consider now a wave, propagating in the positive x direction, given by $y = f(x - c_0 t)$. The kinetic and potential energy densities are given by

$$k = \rho c_0^2 f'^2/2, \qquad v = T f'^2/2. \tag{1.1.60}$$

Since $c_0^2 = T/\rho$, we see that the two expressions are equal. Thus a propagating wave in a string has its energy equally divided into kinetic and potential energies.

In addition to the energy density of the string, one is often interested in the power flow, or rate of transfer of energy past a given point or, still equivalently, the rate of doing work at a given point of the string. This quantity may be readily established by noting that the rate of doing work, or power, is given by

$$P(x_0, t) = -T\frac{\partial y}{\partial x}\dot{y}\bigg|_{x=x_0}. \tag{1.1.61}$$

Suppose that a wave having the general form $y = g(x+c_0t)$ is propagating to the left. Then we have

$$P(x_0, t) = -Tc_0g'^2 \leqslant 0. \tag{1.1.62}$$

If a wave of the form $y = f(x-c_0t)$ is travelling to the right, we have

$$P(x_0, t) = Tc_0f'^2 \geqslant 0. \tag{1.1.63}$$

We see that in thc first case, power is leaving the portion of string $x > x_0$, while in the second case it is entering that region. Thus, we say that power flows in the direction of the wave.

1.1.7. *Forced motion of a semi-infinite string*

We now give our first attention to the forced motion of strings. The two basic ways of imparting energy to the string are through boundary forcing or through motion imparted in regions along the length of string. We will consider the former problem first since the governing differential equation is still homogeneous.

As a simple first example, consider the semi-infinite string $x \geqslant 0$ to be excited at the boundary by the harmonic displacement $y(0, t) = y_0 \exp(i\omega t)$. The most straightforward approach here is to assume a solution of the form previously given by (1.1.14) and substitute in the wave equation. The results are (also previously given by (1.1.15))

$$y = A_1e^{i(\gamma x+\omega t)}+B_1e^{-i(\gamma x-\omega t)}, \qquad \gamma = \omega/c_0. \tag{1.1.64}$$

The constants A_1, B_1 must be determined from the boundary conditions of the problem. From the condition at $y(0, t)$ we obtain $y_0 = A_1+B_1$, so that we have

$$y = A_1e^{i(\gamma x+\omega t)}+(y_0-A_1)e^{-i(\gamma x-\omega t)}. \tag{1.1.65}$$

The establishment of the second condition is, in fact, the whole point of this otherwise trivial example. There are no further conditions at $x = 0$. On the other hand there is, effectively, a condition at infinity. Specificially, we again note that the result (1.1.65) contains both leftward and rightward propagating waves. However, unless there is an energy source radiating waves in from infinity or a boundary that is reflecting waves back to the origin, there is no physical basis for the leftward propagating term $\exp\{i(\gamma x+\omega t)\}$ in the result. So, on the basis of a *radiation condition* we set $A_1 = 0$. Then we have

$$y = y_0 e^{-i(\gamma x-\omega t)}. \tag{1.1.66}$$

The radiation condition introduced in this problem will be used repeatedly in the analysis of future wave problems. It functions in the manner of a boundary condition, enabling certain solutions of a differential equation to be discarded. We note that the solution selected depends on the nature of the initial time dependence. Thus, if a time dependence $\exp(-i\omega t)$ had been used in the problem, the radiation condition would have resulted in $B_1 = 0$ instead of $A_1 = 0$.

We now consider the response of a string subjected to a general transient displacement

$$y(0, t) = g(t). \tag{1.1.67}$$

We again use the Fourier transform approach, applying the exponential transform to the wave equation on the time variable. This gives

$$\frac{d^2\bar{y}}{dx^2}+\frac{\omega^2}{c_0^2}\bar{y} = 0, \tag{1.1.68}$$

where $\bar{y} = \bar{y}(x, \omega)$ is the transformed displacement and ω is the transform variable. Solving (1.1.68) we obtain

$$\bar{y} = A\exp(i\omega x/c_0)+B\exp(-i\omega x/c_0). \tag{1.1.69}$$

The transformed boundary condition is given by

$$\bar{y}(0, \omega) = \bar{g}(\omega). \tag{1.1.70}$$

Substituting (1.1.69) in this condition gives $A+B = \bar{g}(\omega)$. The second boundary condition will be on the radiation, as in the preceding simple example. This is made explicit by taking the inverse transform, giving

$$y(x, t) = \frac{1}{\sqrt{(2\pi)}}\int_{-\infty}^{\infty} [\{\bar{g}(\omega)-B\}\exp(i\omega x/c_0)+B\exp(-i\omega x/c_0)]\exp(-i\omega t)\, d\omega. \tag{1.1.71}$$

We again recognize incoming radiation from infinity in the term

$$\exp\{-i(\omega x/c_0+\omega t)\}$$

and set $B = 0$. This gives

$$y(x, t) = \frac{1}{\sqrt{(2\pi)}}\int_{-\infty}^{\infty} \bar{g}(\omega)\exp\{i\omega(x/c_0-t)\}\, d\omega. \tag{1.1.72}$$

It should be immediately recognized that this result has the form

$$y(x, t) = g(x/c_0 - t). \tag{1.1.73}$$

Thus, the disturbance created at the origin propagates outward without change of shape.

We return to the solution form (1.1.72) and note for future reference that many wave-propagation problems result in solutions of this general form. Thus, given an input $y(0, t)$, find the response or output $y(x, t)$. The result is obviously the superposition of many propagating harmonic waves where the amplitudes of the various frequency components are determined by the transform $\bar{g}(\omega)$ of the input. This quantity is usually designated the *frequency spectrum* of the input. Now, in the case of the string where each frequency component propagates with the same velocity c_0 the undistorted pulse propagation (1.1.73) is predicted. However, this same solution form will provide the basis for considering more complex wave phenomena where the relationships between phase velocity, frequency, and wavenumber are not so simple as in the present case.

1.1.8. *Forced motion of an infinite string*

Our considerations thus far have been with free motion in an infinite string (the initial-value problem) and with boundary forcing of a semi-infinite string. As such we have only considered the homogeneous equation for the string. We now consider the forced motion of an infinite string such that the non-homogeneous equation (1.1.2) governs. Rewritten slightly, we thus have

$$\frac{\partial^2 y}{\partial x^2} - \frac{1}{c_0^2}\frac{\partial^2 y}{\partial t^2} = p(x, t), \tag{1.1.74}$$

where $p(x, t) = -q(x, t)/T$.

It was possible, in the analysis of the semi-infinite string, to develop a general solution for arbitrary forcing (1.1.72) and to still render some interpretation of the results. In the present problem, the forcing $p(x, t)$ may be arbitrary in both space and time. Consequently, a general solution of (1.1.74), while obtainable, is not so amenable to similar interpretation and is more a formal mathematical exercise. The approach taken in this type of problem is to replace $p(x, t)$ by special loadings, solve the resulting special problem, and obtain solutions to more general cases by superposition.

As our first special loading, replace $p(x, t)$ by the load $\delta(x-\xi)\delta(t-\tau)$. This represents a unit load occurring at time $t = \tau$ at a location $x = \xi$ on the string. The practice of replacing general loads with an impulse load and determining the system response to this load is widely used in applied mathematics. The resulting system response is usually designated as the *Green's function* of the system. For the present one-dimensional problem, this would be written as

$$G = G(x, t/\xi, \tau). \tag{1.1.75}$$

The problem is thus one of considering

$$\frac{\partial^2 G}{\partial x^2} - \frac{1}{c_0^2}\frac{\partial^2 G}{\partial t^2} = \delta(x-\xi)\,\delta(t-\tau). \tag{1.1.76}$$

A double-transform approach will be taken. We first take the Fourier transform on the space variable, giving

$$-\gamma^2 \bar{G} - \frac{1}{c_0^2}\frac{\partial^2 \bar{G}}{\partial t^2} = \frac{e^{i\gamma\xi}}{\sqrt{(2\pi)}}\,\delta(t-\tau). \tag{1.1.77}$$

We assume the system is initially at rest, so that $y(x, 0) = \dot{y}(x, 0) = 0$. Taking the Laplace transform of (1.1.77) gives

$$-\gamma^2 \bar{G}_L - \frac{s^2}{c_0^2}\bar{G}_L = \frac{1}{\sqrt{(2\pi)}} e^{i\gamma\xi} e^{-s\tau}, \tag{1.1.78}$$

where $\bar{G}_L = \bar{G}_L(\gamma, s/\xi, \tau)$. The transformed solution is then

$$\bar{G}_L = \frac{-c_0^2}{\sqrt{(2\pi)}}\frac{e^{i\gamma\xi}e^{-s\tau}}{s^2+c_0^2\gamma^2}. \tag{1.1.79}$$

In inverting the above, we first consider the Laplace inversion. We note from tables that

$$\mathscr{L}^{-1}\left\{\frac{1}{s^2+c_0^2\gamma^2}\right\} = \frac{1}{c_0\gamma}\sin c_0\gamma t, \tag{1.1.80}$$

and that in general

$$\mathscr{L}^{-1}\{e^{-s\tau}F_L(s)\} = F(t-\tau), \qquad F(t) = 0, \qquad t < 0. \tag{1.1.81}$$

The Laplace inverted result is then

$$\bar{G} = -\frac{c_0^2}{\sqrt{(2\pi)}}\frac{e^{i\gamma\xi}}{c_0\gamma}\sin c_0\gamma(t-\tau)H\langle t-\tau\rangle, \tag{1.1.82}$$

where $H\langle t-\tau\rangle$ is the Heaviside step function. Next taking the inverse Fourier transform we obtain

$$G = \frac{-c_0^2}{2\pi}H\langle t-\tau\rangle \int_{-\infty}^{\infty} \frac{\sin c_0\gamma(t-\tau)}{c_0\gamma} e^{-i\gamma(x-\xi)}\,d\gamma. \tag{1.1.83}$$

The inversion of this part is also fairly simple. We know† that

$$\mathscr{F}^{-1}\left\{\sqrt{\left(\frac{2}{\pi}\right)}\frac{\sin a\gamma}{\gamma}\right\} = \begin{cases} 1, & |x| < a \\ 0, & |x| > a \end{cases}. \tag{1.1.84}$$

† See, for example, Appendix B.3.

To use this result, we rewrite (1.1.83) as

$$G = \frac{-c_0}{2} H\langle t'/c_0\rangle \frac{1}{\sqrt{(2\pi)}} \int_{-\infty}^{\infty} \sqrt{\left(\frac{2}{\pi}\right)} \frac{\sin t'\gamma}{\gamma} \exp(-i\gamma x')\, d\gamma, \tag{1.1.85}$$

where $t' = c_0(t-\tau)$, $x' = x-\xi$. Applying (1.1.84) to this gives

$$G = -\frac{c_0}{2} H\langle t'/c_0\rangle (H\langle x'+t'\rangle - H\langle x'-t'\rangle). \tag{1.1.86}$$

In this result, two Heaviside functions have been superimposed to provide the representation of a rectangular pulse. Now, changing back to the original x,t variables, we have

$$G(x, t/\xi, \tau) = -\frac{c_0}{2} H\langle t-\tau\rangle \{H\langle x-\xi+c_0(t-\tau)\rangle - H\langle x-\xi-c_0(t-\tau)\rangle\}. \tag{1.1.87}$$

The ensuing motion of the string predicted by this result is shown in Fig. 1.7.

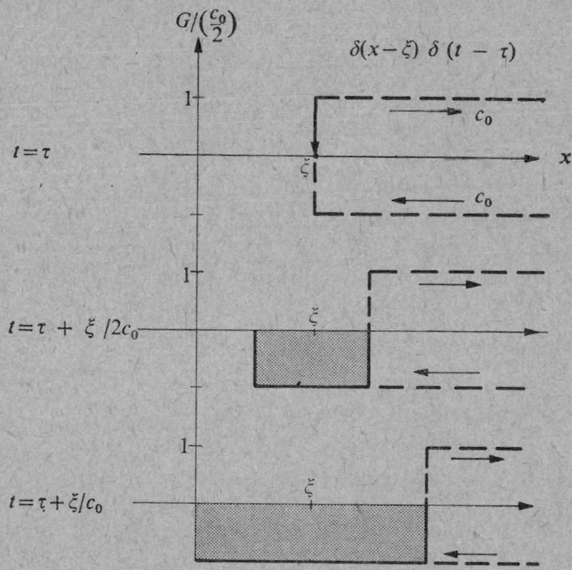

FIG. 1.7. Motion of a string subjected to the impulse loading of $\delta(x-\xi)\,\delta(t-\tau)$.

The solution for the response of the string to a general loading $p(x, t)$ is obtained from the Green's function result by the following double integral:

$$y(x, t) = \int_0^t d\tau \int_{-\infty}^{\infty} G(x, t/\xi, \tau) p(\xi, \tau)\, d\xi. \tag{1.1.88}$$

For the second special case of loading on the string, we assume the time variation is simple harmonic so that $p(x,t) = f(x)\exp(-i\omega t)$. If we assume the response to have a similar form, so that $y = Y(x)\exp(-i\omega t)$, the governing equation (1.1.74) reduces to the ordinary differential equation

$$\frac{d^2Y}{dx^2}+\frac{\omega^2}{c_0^2}Y = f(x). \tag{1.1.89}$$

We now specialize the spatial variation of the load to that of a unit concentrated load acting at $x = \xi$, so that $f(x) = \delta(x-\xi)$. We thus will be seeking the Green's function of the system for harmonic loading. We denote the response as $G = G(x/\xi)$ and write (1.1.89) as

$$\frac{d^2G}{dx^2}+\frac{\omega^2}{c_0^2}G = \delta(x-\xi). \tag{1.1.90}$$

We now apply the Fourier transform to this, resulting in the transformed solution

$$\bar{G} = -\frac{1}{\sqrt{(2\pi)}}\frac{e^{i\gamma\xi}}{\gamma^2-\gamma_0^2}, \qquad \gamma_0 = \omega/c_0. \tag{1.1.91}$$

The Fourier inversion gives

$$G = \frac{-1}{2\pi}\int_{-\infty}^{\infty}\frac{e^{-i\gamma(x-\xi)}}{\gamma^2-\gamma_0^2}\,d\gamma. \tag{1.1.92}$$

We will now take the time to evaluate the above integral from first principles by carrying out the integration in the complex plane. At least two aspects of the analysis that arise in this problem occur repeatedly in more general problems of wave propagation. Before proceeding, we simplify (1.1.92) slightly by letting $\xi = 0$, corresponding to the load being applied at the origin. We thus have

$$G(x/0) = -\frac{1}{2\pi}\int_{-\infty}^{\infty}\frac{e^{-i\gamma x}}{\gamma^2-\gamma_0^2}\,d\gamma. \tag{1.1.93}$$

Considering γ complex, we have from the calculus of residues that

$$\int_C \frac{e^{-i\gamma x}}{\gamma^2-\gamma_0^2}\,d\gamma = 2\pi i\sum \text{Res}, \tag{1.1.94}$$

where C is a closed contour in the complex plane. The first step in evaluating (1.1.94) is to select the general contour in the complex plane. The two obvious possibilities are shown in Fig. 1.8 where, for the moment, the poles $\gamma = \pm\gamma_0$ located on the real axis have been ignored. Along the semicircular

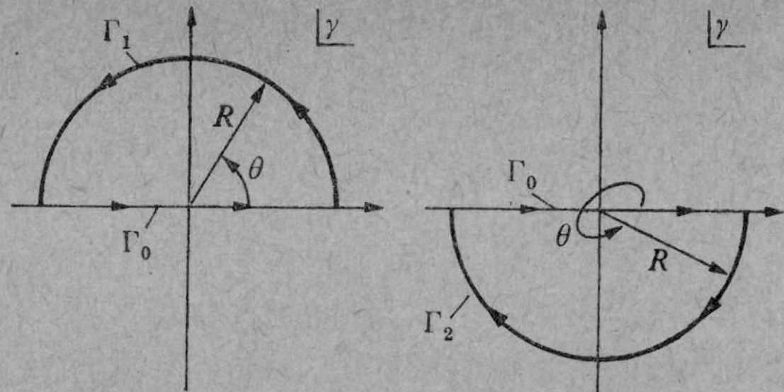

FIG. 1.8. Two possible choices of contour for evaluating (1.1.94).

path, be it Γ_1 or Γ_2, we let $\gamma = R\exp(i\theta)$. If we define I_1 to be the form of the integral (1.1.94) along Γ_1, and substitute the polar representation of γ in the integral, we have

$$I_1 = \lim_{R\to\infty} \int_0^\pi \frac{e^{xR\sin\theta}e^{-ixR\cos\theta}}{R^2e^{2i\theta}-\gamma_0^2} iRe^{i\theta}\, d\theta. \tag{1.1.95}$$

The important term in (1.1.95) is $\exp(xR\sin\theta)$. Along Γ_1 we have $\sin\theta > 0$ always. Then, if $x < 0$, the exponential rapidly decays for large values of R and, in fact, as $R \to \infty$ we have $I_1 \to 0$. If, on the other hand, $x > 0$ then I_1 would become infinite as $R \to \infty$. Similar arguments can be applied to the integral I_2 along Γ_2 to show that the integral vanishes for $R \to \infty$ as long as $x > 0$.

The conclusion we reach is that either contour could be selected, as long as the resulting restriction on x is specifically recognized. In our analysis of the infinite string, where $-\infty < x < \infty$, the selection of a specific contour will limit the results to $-\infty < x < 0$ or to $0 < x < \infty$ for a load applied at the origin. If the load is placed at $x = \xi$, such as for the result (1.1.92) the regions of validity would simply become $-\infty < x < \xi$ or $\xi < x < \infty$. This, then, is the first aspect of the inversion that arises in many wave propagation problems.

The second aspect relates to the poles of (1.1.94) that are located on the real axis. If this were merely a pathological circumstance of this problem, there would be possibly no need for great concern over the matter, circumventing it possibly by working a 'nicer' example. It is a fact of analysis, however, that this situation arises repeatedly in wave problems and must be accounted for.

The first step is to avoid the singularity on the path of integration by deforming the contour in a small, semicircular path either above or below the poles, as shown in Fig. 1.9 for $\gamma = \gamma_0$. Such an indentation will include or exclude a singularity from within the contour of integration depending on whether the over-all closure of the contour is above or below the real axis.

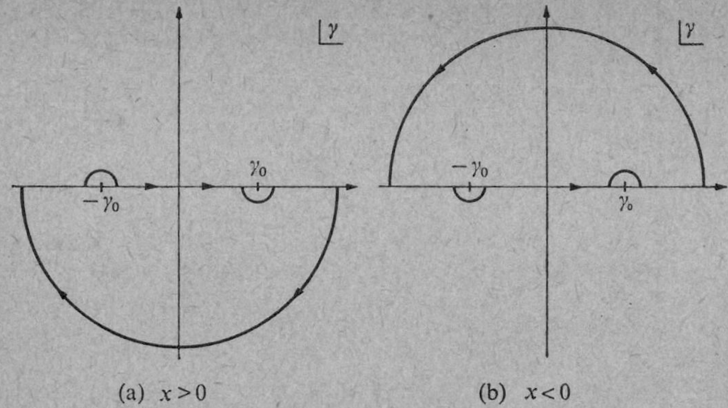

FIG. 1.9. The required contours and indentations for (a) $x > 0$ and (b) $x < 0$.

The residues of the singularities are found to be

$$\text{Res}\big|_{\gamma=-\gamma_0} = -\frac{\exp(\mathrm{i}\gamma_0 x)}{2\gamma_0}, \qquad \text{Res}\big|_{\gamma=\gamma_0} = \frac{\exp(-\mathrm{i}\gamma_0 x)}{2\gamma_0}. \tag{1.1.96}$$

We now recall that the time dependence in this problem is $\exp(-\mathrm{i}\omega t)$. This dependence combined with either of (1.1.96) can give leftward or rightward propagating waves, depending on whether $x \gtrless 0$ and depending on with which residue it is combined. Thus which indentations are used will be governed ultimately by the radiation condition. Indentations selected must yield outgoing waves.

To illustrate this, we suppose $x > 0$ is the region of interest. On the basis of earlier discussion, we know the general contour is closed below the real axis, as is Γ_2 of Fig. 1.8. In order to have outward propagating waves in $x > 0$, we must have behaviour of the form $\exp\{\mathrm{i}(\gamma x - \omega t)\}$. From the residues (1.1.96) it is seen that the pole at $\gamma = -\gamma_0$ must be included *within* the general contour and the pole at $\gamma = \gamma_0$ must be *excluded*. This requires indentations as shown in Fig. 1.9(a). We thus have that

$$G(x/0) = -\frac{1}{2\pi}(-2\pi\mathrm{i}\ \text{Res}\big|_{\gamma=-\gamma_0}). \tag{1.1.97}$$

The minus sign within the parentheses of the result accounts for the fact that the path of integration of Fig. 1.9(a) is counterclockwise. As a final result, we have

$$G(x/0) = -\frac{\mathrm{i}}{2\gamma_0}\exp(\mathrm{i}\gamma_0 x), \qquad x > 0. \tag{1.1.98}$$

The proper contour for the region $x < 0$ is shown, without further discussion, in Fig. 1.9(b).

This concludes consideration of the second major aspect of the problem. We see that the proper contour selection, including indentations, is based on the range of x (thus $x > 0$ or $x < 0$ for this simple example) and the nature of the time dependence, with the radiation condition dictating the final choices. The difficulty with this problem has resulted from poles being on the axis of integration. It turns out that the whole problem vanishes nicely when there is damping in the system, as analysis in § 1.7 p. 70) will show.

The basis for extending the Green's function result to general loading situations lies in the convolution theorem (see Appendix B). If $G(x/\xi)$ is the Green's function and $f(x)$ is the loading function, we have

$$Y(x) = \frac{1}{\sqrt{(2\pi)}} \int_{-\infty}^{\infty} G(\gamma/\xi) f(x-\gamma)\, \mathrm{d}\gamma. \tag{1.1.99}$$

If the convolution approach is not used, results for more general loadings could be considered by attempting to directly invert the transformed solution of (1.1.89), which would give an integral of the form

$$Y(x) = -\frac{1}{\sqrt{(2\pi)}} \int_{-\infty}^{\infty} \frac{\bar{f}(\gamma)}{\gamma^2-\gamma_0^2} \mathrm{e}^{-\mathrm{i}\gamma x}\, \mathrm{d}\gamma. \tag{1.1.100}$$

1.2. Reflection and transmission at boundaries

Our considerations thus far have dealt with waves in infinite or semi-infinite strings. Thus, the conditions were such that the interaction of waves with boundaries did not enter. We now wish to consider waves incident on a boundary of the string. When this situation arises, wave reflection occurs with the nature of the reflected wave being determined by the nature of the boundary or 'boundary condition.'

1.2.1. *Types of boundaries*

One of the simplest types of end boundary condition would be the case of a string attached to a rigid support. Supposing this support to be at the origin, the condition would thus be $y(0, t) = 0$. Another type of constraint could be given by the end of the string sliding on a frictionless slot, shown as the free end condition in Table 1.1. The component of force in the vertical direction at $x = 0$ would be given by

$$F_{\mathrm{v}}(0, t) = T\, \partial y(0, t)/\partial x. \tag{1.2.1}$$

Since the slot is frictionless and the end of the string is without mass, the net vertical force component must be zero. Thus, the case of a free end condition is specified by $\partial y(0, t)/\partial x = 0$.

It is possible to devise numerous other conditions corresponding to an attached end mass, a spring, or a dashpot. The mathematical statements of these conditions are arrived at by equating the vertical component of string tension to the forces on these elements. Table 1.1 summarizes these various

TABLE 1.1

Type	Diagram	Equation
Fixed	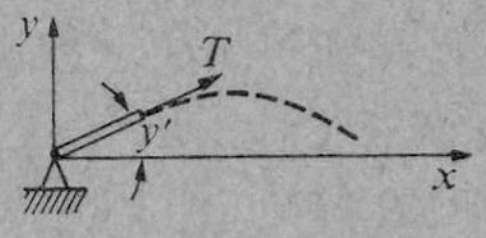	$y(0,t)=0$
Free	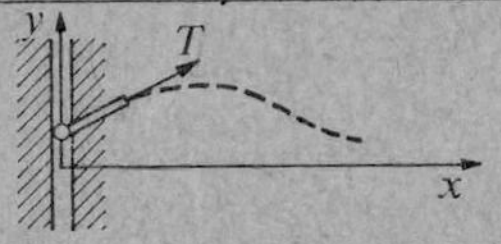	$\dfrac{\partial y(0,t)}{\partial x}=0$
Mass	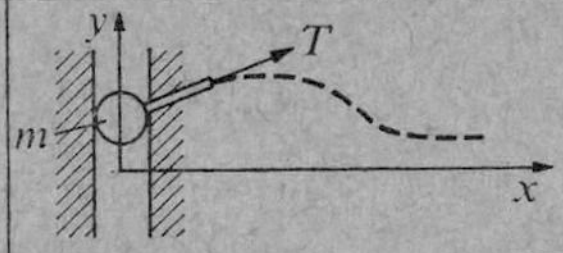	$m\ddot{y}(0,t)=T\dfrac{\partial y(0,t)}{\partial x}$
Spring	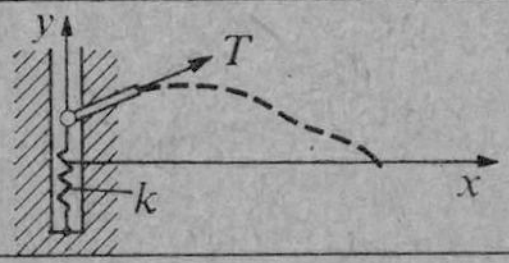	$ky(0,t)=T\dfrac{\partial y(0,t)}{\partial x}$
Dashpot	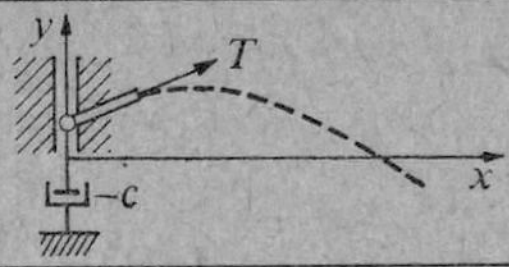	$c\dot{y}(0,t)=T\dfrac{\partial y(0,t)}{\partial x}$

conditions. More complicated conditions could be obtained by combining the spring–mass–dashpot elements.

1.2.2. *Reflection from a fixed boundary*

The reflection of an incident wave from a fixed boundary represents the simplest type of boundary interaction. All wave-reflection problems can be approached in a purely mathematical way, and the present case is no exception. However, the simple end condition permits a somewhat intuitive approach to be used, called the method of images, and saves formalism for more complicated problems.

Consider a displacement pulse $f(x+c_0t)$ propagating to the left and incident on a fixed boundary, as shown in Fig. 1.10(a). Imagine now removing

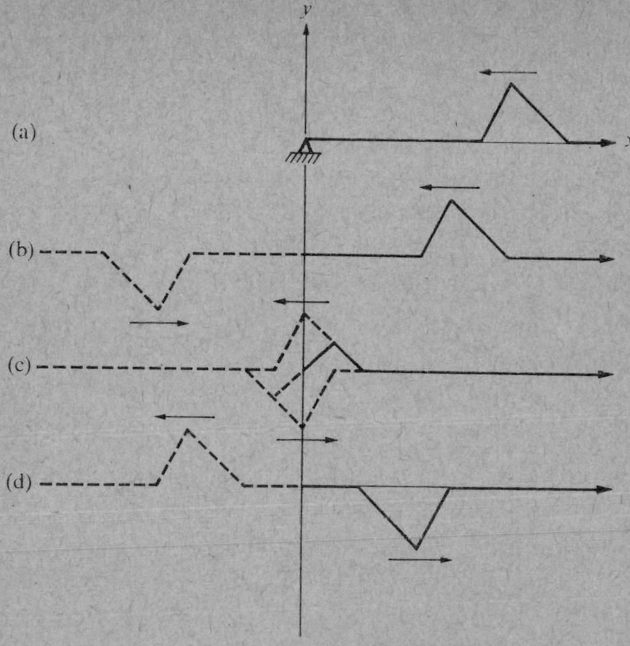

FIG. 1.10. Sequence of events during pulse reflection from a fixed boundary.

the boundary at $x = 0$ but extending the string to negative infinity. Now construct an 'image' pulse to $f(x+c_0t)$. This pulse is symmetrically placed with respect to $x = 0$, is opposite in sense to $f(x+c_0t)$, and is propagating to the right, as shown in Fig. 1.10(b). As these pulses approach the origin, they will interact, as shown in Fig. 1.10(c). It should be clear that, as they pass, their displacements will mutually cancel at $x = 0$, giving $y(0, t) = 0$ always. Thus the fixed end boundary condition for the semi-infinite string is always satisfied by the image pulse system in the infinite string. As time passes the interaction stage is completed and the image pulse propagates into the region $x > 0$, while the original 'real' pulse propagates into $x < 0$, as shown in Fig. 1.10(d). After the completion of the process, it is seen that the sign of the original pulse has been reversed. This is characteristic of the fixed boundary.

1.2.3. *Reflection from an elastic boundary*

As an example of a more complicated reflection problem, we consider the wave incident on an elastic boundary, as shown in Table 1.1 for the spring end condition. The problem is thus one of requiring the solution of the wave equation

$$y = f(c_0t-x)+g(c_0t+x) \tag{1.2.2}$$

to satisfy the boundary condition

$$ky(0, t) = T\,\partial y(0, t)/\partial x. \tag{1.2.3}$$

The change in the representation of the argument of the wave in (1.2.2) in contrast to the earlier representation (1.1.22) is merely for convenience in using the Laplace transform approach. It is presumed in (1.2.2) that the incident wave $g(c_0t+x)$ is prescribed. It is thus a matter of finding the reflected wave $f(c_0t-x)$.

In substituting (1.2.2) in (1.2.3) we note that

$$\left.\frac{\partial y(x, t)}{\partial x}\right|_{x=0} = -f'(c_0t-x)+g'(c_0t+x)\big|_{x=0} = -f'(c_0t)+g'(c_0t), \tag{1.2.4}$$

so that (1.2.3) becomes

$$k\{f(c_0t)+g(c_0t)\} = T\{-f'(c_0t)+g'(c_0t)\}. \tag{1.2.5}$$

Making the change of variables $\tau = c_0t$ and rearranging gives

$$f'(\tau)+\frac{k}{T}f(\tau) = g'(\tau)-\frac{k}{T}g(\tau). \tag{1.2.6}$$

We apply the Laplace transform to (1.2.6), obtaining

$$\left(s+\frac{k}{T}\right)\bar{f} = \left(s-\frac{k}{T}\right)\bar{g}. \tag{1.2.7}$$

We note that (1.2.6) holds only for $x = 0$. In obtaining the result (1.2.7) we have assumed xero initial conditions. If we express $s-k/T = s+k/T-2k/T$, the transformed solution may be written as

$$\bar{f} = \bar{g}-2\frac{k}{T}\frac{\bar{g}}{s+k/T}. \tag{1.2.8}$$

For the inverted solution we may formally write

$$f(\tau) = g(\tau)-\frac{2k}{T}\mathscr{L}^{-1}\left\{\frac{\bar{g}(s)}{s+k/T}\right\}. \tag{1.2.9}$$

The formal solution could be carried one step further by using the convolution integral to express the inverse transform of the product term in (1.2.9). In either case, there is little further that can be done without considering a specific form of the incident wave.

As an example, let the incident wave be a rectangular pulse defined by

$$g(c_0t+x) = H\langle c_0t+x-L\rangle - H\langle c_0t+x-(L+a)\rangle. \tag{1.2.10}$$

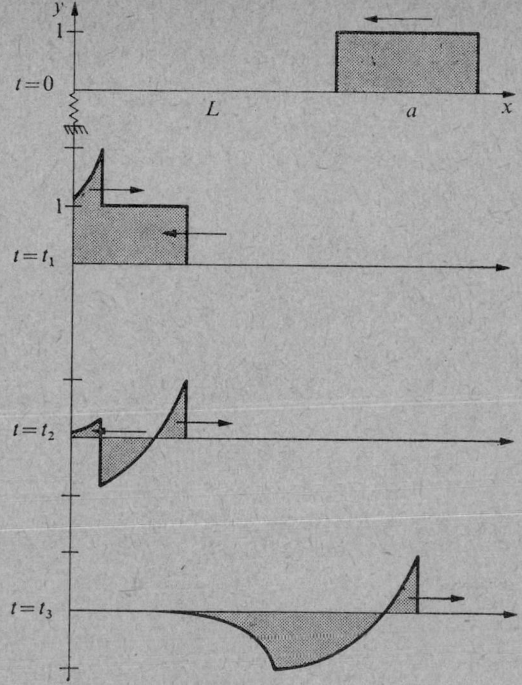

FIG. 1.11. Motion of the string during reflection of a rectangular pulse from an elastic boundary.

This combination of step functions gives a pulse of length a that, at $t = 0$, is a distance L from the origin, as shown in Fig. 1.11. It is the value of this function at $x = 0$ that is required in (1.2.9). We have that

$$g(\tau) = H\langle\tau-L\rangle-H\langle\tau-(L+a)\rangle. \tag{1.2.11}$$

Noting the Laplace transform relation

$$\mathscr{L}\{H\langle t\rangle\} = 1/s, \tag{1.2.12}$$

and recalling the previously used result (1.1.81), we obtain the transform of (1.2.10) as

$$\bar{g} = \frac{\exp(-Ls)}{s}-\frac{\exp\{-(L+a)\}}{s}. \tag{1.2.13}$$

The inverted solution (1.2.9) then becomes

$$f(\tau) = g(\tau)-\frac{2k}{T}\mathscr{L}^{-1}\left[\frac{\exp(-Ls)}{s(s+k/T)}-\frac{\exp\{-(L+a)s\}}{s(s+k/T)}\right]. \tag{1.2.14}$$

To invert the expression within the brackets, we first use the result

$$\mathscr{L}^{-1}\left\{\frac{1}{s(s+k/T)}\right\} = \frac{T}{k}\left\{1-\exp\left(-\frac{k}{T}\tau\right)\right\}. \tag{1.2.15}$$

Again using the just cited result (1.1.81), we are then able to write

$$\mathscr{L}^{-1}\left\{\frac{\exp(-Ls)}{s(s+k/T)}\right\} = \frac{T}{k}\left[1-\exp\left\{-\frac{k}{T}(\tau-L)\right\}\right]H\langle\tau-L\rangle. \tag{1.2.16}$$

The complete result, expressed in terms of t, is

$$f(c_0t) = g(c_0t)-2\left[1-\exp\left\{-\frac{k}{T}(c_0t-L)\right\}\right]H\langle c_0t-L\rangle+$$
$$+2\left[1-\exp\left\{-\frac{k}{T}(c_0t-L-a)\right\}\right]H\langle c_0t-L-a\rangle. \tag{1.2.17}$$

The response away from the origin is obtained by replacing c_0t by c_0t-x in the result (1.2.17).

The general motion of the string predicted by this result is shown in Fig. 1.11. Without assigning specific values to the parameters k, T, and a, the results must be accepted as highly qualitative. It is quite obvious, nevertheless, that the incident wave has undergone considerable distortion during the reflection process.

1.2.4. *Reflection of harmonic waves*

A procedure that is frequently used in studying the reflection characteristics of boundaries is to consider the incident wave to be a pure harmonic. Thus, instead of considering each reflection problem on an *ad hoc* basis, general, frequency-dependent relationships for the amplitude and phase of the reflected waves are obtained. We will again consider the elastic boundary to illustrate the procedure.

Consider the harmonic wave solution to the wave equation given by

$$y = Ae^{i(\gamma x+\omega t)}+Be^{-i(\gamma x-\omega t)}. \tag{1.2.18}$$

We presume the incident wave, which is the A coefficient term in the above solution, to be specified. Substituting (1.2.18) in the boundary condition (1.2.3) we obtain

$$k(A+B) = Ti\gamma(A-B). \tag{1.2.19}$$

Solving for the amplitude ratio B/A we obtain

$$\frac{B}{A} = -\frac{k-Ti\gamma}{k+Ti\gamma}. \tag{1.2.20}$$

The frequency dependence of the above may be displayed explicitly using $\omega = \gamma c_0$ to give

$$\frac{B}{A} = -\frac{kc_0 - Ti\omega}{kc_0 + Ti\omega}. \tag{1.2.21}$$

This complex quantity may be given the general representation

$$\frac{B}{A} = M(\omega)e^{i\phi(\omega)}, \tag{1.2.22}$$

where $M(\omega)$ is the real, frequency-dependent amplitude and $\phi(\omega)$ is the frequency-dependent phase angle. Thus, the reflected and incident waves will be out of phase with one another. In the present problem it is found that $M(\omega) = -1$, indicating that the amplitude of the reflected wave is the same as the incident wave. This is to be expected here since there is no loss of energy in the system.

1.2.5. *Reflection and transmission at discontinuities*

A wave propagating in a string may encounter a discontinuity such as a change in string density or an attached mass or spring. Such situations are capable of producing reflected waves. In addition, energy may also transmit across the discontinuity. Let us consider the case of a string with an abrupt change in mass per unit length, as shown in Fig. 1.12.

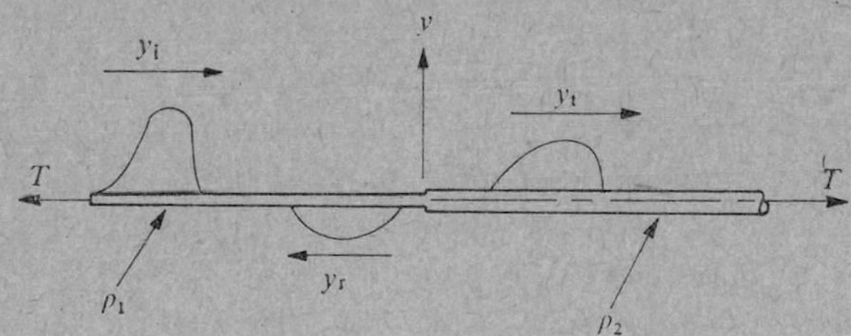

FIG. 1.12. Incident, reflected, and transmitted waves at a discontinuity in the string.

The incident, reflected, and transmitted waves may be expressed as

$$y_i = f_1(x - c_1 t), \qquad y_r = g_1(x + c_1 t), \qquad y_t = f_2(x - c_2 t). \tag{1.2.23}$$

where $c_1 = \sqrt{(T/\rho_1)}$, $c_2 = \sqrt{(T/\rho_2)}$. We presume the incident wave to be specified and wish to determine y_r and y_t. The boundary conditions at the discontinuity require that the velocity and vertical component of string tension be continuous. Thus,

$$\dot{y}_i + \dot{y}_r = \dot{y}_t, \qquad \frac{\partial y_i}{\partial x} + \frac{\partial y_r}{\partial x} = \frac{\partial y_t}{\partial x}, \qquad x = 0. \tag{1.2.24}$$

Substituting (1.2.23) in (1.2.24) gives

$$-c_1(f_1' - g_1') = -c_2 f_2', \; f_1' + g_1' = f_2'. \tag{1.2.25}$$

Solving the two equations simultaneously for f_2', g_2' gives

$$f_2' = \frac{2c_1}{c_1+c_2} f_1', \qquad g_2' = \frac{c_1-c_2}{c_1+c_2} f_1'. \tag{1.2.26}$$

This establishes the reflected and transmitted waves.

When point inhomogeneities, such as a mass, spring, or a dashpot are present, continuity of velocity and balance-of-force considerations still apply. The considerations used in expressing the force boundary conditions of the various elements in Table 1.1 can be extended for the present case. Thus, suppose a mass m is located at $x = 0$. The resulting force boundary condition would be

$$m\ddot{y}(0, t) = -T\frac{\partial y_1(0, t)}{\partial x} + T\frac{\partial y_2(0, t)}{\partial x}. \tag{1.2.27}$$

1.3. Free vibration of a finite string

We now will consider the free vibrations of a completely bounded string. The motion as described by propagating waves will be presented. However, the more useful approach to such problems will be the determination of the natural frequencies and normal modes of the system.

1.3.1. *Waves in a finite string*

Consider a finite string of length l subjected to an initial disturbance, such as an imposed displacement field. We recall from § 1.1 (see Fig. 1.5) that, when the string is released, waves will propagate both to the left and right. When each wave encounters a boundary, reflection back into the string interior will occur. This process will continually repeat itself in the case of a finite string. If the boundaries are fixed or free, the image method may be readily used to describe the motion.

Considering the string ends to be fixed, the field of image waves necessary to satisfy the boundary conditions for all time is shown in Fig. 1.13 for $t = 0$.

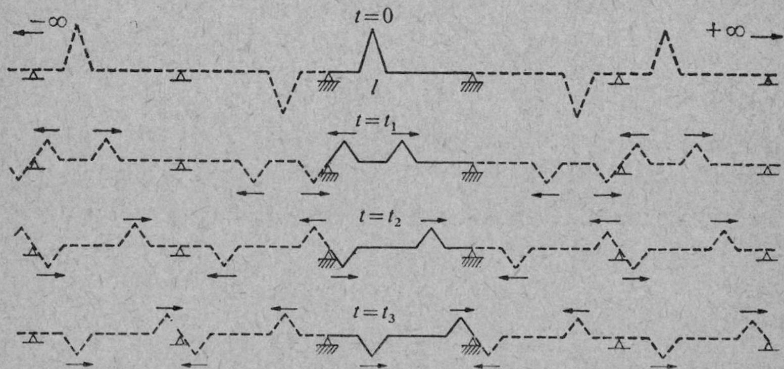

FIG. 1.13. Initial image wavefield ($t = 0$) necessary to satisfy fixed end conditions and resulting propagation at later instants of time $t = t_1, t_2, t_3$.

Thus, it is necessary to construct an infinite set of image strings in order to provide a description of the response for all time.

It is possible to give a mathematical prescription for the preceding pulse system. Thus, suppose the initial conditions are $y(x, 0) = U(x)$, $\dot{y}(x, 0) = 0$. Then we define $\bar{U}(x)$, where

$$\bar{U}(x) = \begin{cases} U(x), & 0 < x < l \\ -U(-x), & -l < x < 0, \end{cases} \tag{1.3.1}$$

and where

$$\bar{U}(x) = \bar{U}(x+2ml) \qquad (m = 0, 1, 2, \ldots). \tag{1.3.2}$$

This serves to define the pulse system shown in Fig. 1.13 for $t = 0$. For $t > 0$, we then have that

$$y(x, t) = \tfrac{1}{2}\{\bar{U}(x-c_0t)+\bar{U}(x+c_0t)\}. \tag{1.3.3}$$

As in the case of reflection from a single boundary in a semi-infinite string, a formal mathematical analysis will yield equivalent results to those obtained by 'inspection' in formulating the image approach.

The image or D'Alembert approach to waves in finite strings is only applicable to simple boundary conditions and is mainly useful to give an understanding to the basis for periodic motion in such a system. For more general analysis, other techniques are now developed.

1.3.2. *Vibrations of a fixed–fixed string*

We now apply the method of separation of variables to the free-vibrations problem. As before, consider a string of length l, fixed at both ends. Consider, as a solution to the wave equation (1.1.3),

$$y = Y(x)\psi(t). \tag{1.3.4}$$

Substituting in the wave equation gives

$$c_0^2\frac{Y''}{Y} = \frac{\ddot{\psi}}{\psi} = -\omega^2, \tag{1.3.5}$$

or

$$Y''+\frac{\omega^2}{c_0^2}Y = 0, \tag{1.3.6}$$

$$\ddot{\psi}+\omega^2\psi = 0, \tag{1.3.7}$$

where, momentarily, ω merely represents a separation of variables constant.

Considering (1.3.7) first, we have

$$\psi = A\sin\omega t+B\cos\omega t, \tag{1.3.8}$$

or, in exponential form,

$$\psi = A_1e^{i\omega t}+B_1e^{-i\omega t}. \tag{1.3.9}$$

This form of the solution represents simple harmonic motion at the frequency ω. If we had selected a separation constant less than zero in (1.3.5), thus

$\bar{\omega}^2 < 0$, we would then obtain the non-harmonic solution,

$$y = A_1 e^{\bar{\omega}t} + B_1 e^{-\bar{\omega}t}. \tag{1.3.10}$$

This is definitely incapable of representing the periodic motion that we know occurs in the fixed–fixed string.

Now considering (1.3.6), we have

$$Y = C \sin \beta x + D \cos \beta x, \; \beta^2 = \omega^2/c_0^2. \tag{1.3.11}$$

The boundary conditions for the problem are

$$y(0, t) = y(l, t) = 0. \tag{1.3.12}$$

Applying these to (1.3.11) gives the conditions that $D = 0$ and the *frequency equation* (also called the characteristic equation) for the system

$$\sin \beta l = 0, \qquad \beta l = n\pi \qquad (n = 1, 2, \ldots). \tag{1.3.13}$$

Thus we obtain the *natural frequencies* (also called the *eigenvalues*) of the system, given by

$$\omega_n = c_0 \beta_n = n\pi c_0/l \qquad (n = 1, 2, \ldots). \tag{1.3.14}$$

These represent the discrete frequencies at which the system is capable of undergoing harmonic motion. For a given value of n, we thus have the vibrational pattern of the string described by

$$Y_n(x) = C_n \sin \beta_n x, \qquad (n = 1, 2, \ldots), \tag{1.3.15}$$

where Y_n are usually called the *normal modes* (also called the *eigenfunctions*) of the system.

Several of the resulting vibration patterns are shown in Fig. 1.14. We note

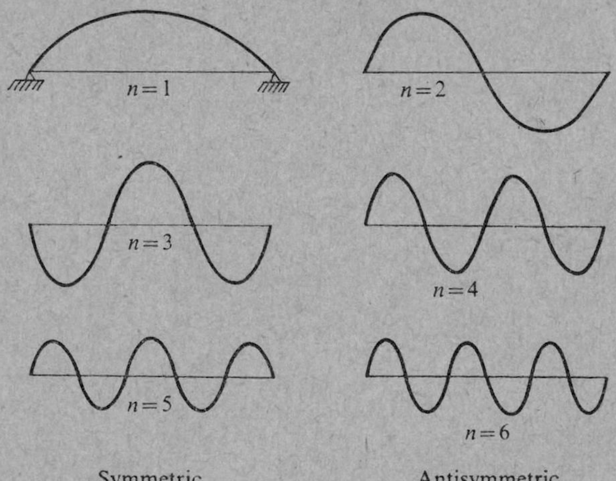

FIG. 1.14. Symmetric ($n = 1, 3, 5$) and antisymmetric ($n = 2, 4, 6$) modes of a fixed–fixed string.

that the modes for $n = 1, 3, 5, \ldots$ give *symmetric* motion while *antisymmetric* modes result from $n = 2, 4, 6 \ldots$. The points of zero displacement are called the *nodes* of vibration, while points of maximum vibration are called the *antinodes*.

Combining the time and spatial dependence for a given value of n, we obtain

$$y_n(x, t) = (A_n \sin \omega_n t + B_n \cos \omega_n t)\sin \beta_n x, \tag{1.3.16}$$

where the constant C_n of (1.3.15) has been absorbed in the constants A_n and B_n. The general solution is then obtained by the superposition of all particular solutions to give

$$y(x, t) = \sum_{n=1}^{\infty} (A_n \sin \omega_n t + B_n \cos \omega_n t)\sin \beta_n x. \tag{1.3.17}$$

The most general consideration in the free vibrations of strings is the initial value problem. Thus, we wish to determine the motion for all time given the initial conditions,

$$y(x, 0) = U(x), \qquad \dot{y}(x, 0) = V(x). \tag{1.3.18}$$

Substituting the solution (1.3.17) in the above, we obtain

$$U(x) = \sum_{n=1}^{\infty} B_n \sin \beta_n x, \tag{1.3.19}$$

$$V(x) = \sum_{n=1}^{\infty} A_n \omega_n \sin \beta_n x. \tag{1.3.20}$$

The constants A_n, B_n are found in the manner used in Fourier series analysis. Thus, multiply (1.3.19) and (1.3.20) by $\sin \beta_m x$ and integrate over the interval $0 \leqslant x \leqslant l$. Noting that

$$\int_0^l \sin \beta_n x \sin \beta_m x \, dx = \begin{cases} l/2, & m = n, \\ 0, & m \neq n, \end{cases} \tag{1.3.21}$$

we obtain

$$A_n = \frac{2}{l\omega_n} \int_0^l V(x) \sin \beta_n x \, dx, \tag{1.3.22}$$

$$B_n = \frac{2}{l} \int_0^l U(x) \sin \beta_n x \, dx. \tag{1.3.23}$$

This establishes the motion of the system.

Referring back to (1.3.17), we note that we may write

$$A_n \sin \omega_n t \sin \beta_n x = \frac{A_n}{2} \cos(\beta_n x - \omega_n t) - \frac{A_n}{2} \cos(\beta_n x + \omega_n t), \tag{1.3.24}$$

$$B_n \cos \omega_n t \sin \beta_n x = \frac{B_n}{2} \sin(\beta_n x + \omega_n t) + \frac{B_n}{2} \sin(\beta_n x - \omega_n t), \tag{1.3.25}$$

which are travelling-wave expressions. This representation merely re-emphasizes the underlying unity between wave propagation and vibrations in systems.

Finally, we note that (1.3.17) is effectively a statement that the string is a system having infinite degrees of freedom. We recall that in the vibrations of discrete element systems (that is, spring–mass systems), the problem is to describe the motion of each mass element. If there are n elements, there will be approximately n degrees of freedom to the system and the motion will be described by displacements $u_1(t)$, $u_2(t)$, . . . , $u_n(t)$. In a continuous system as the number of elements increases to infinity there becomes an infinite number of degrees of freedom. In the normal mode representation (1.3.17), each mode represents a single degree of freedom. Thus, although a given mode is a continuous curve, it represents constraint for every particle on the curve to follow a certain vibration.

1.3.3. *The general normal mode solution*

The fixed–fixed string is but one of a number of combinations of boundary constraints that can be imposed on finite strings. Referring to Table 1.1, we could have free–free, fixed–free, fixed–elastic, and so on as support conditions. Rather than consider all of the possible combinations of boundary conditions, we seek to obtain a more general solution.

Again considering separation of variables, and deleting a few of the preliminary steps of the previous development, we obtain the general solution form

$$y = \sum_{n=1}^{\infty} (A_n \sin \omega_n t + B_n \cos \omega_n t) Y_n(x), \tag{1.3.26}$$

where $Y_n(x)$ are the normal modes satisfying the differential equation

$$Y_n''(x) + \beta_n^2 Y_n(x) = 0, \qquad \beta_n^2 = \omega_n^2/c_0^2, \tag{1.3.27}$$

and the particular boundary conditions of the problem. The problem is to determine the A_n and B_n for the general initial value problem. As it turns out, the principle used for the fixed–fixed string may be generalized due to the important property of *orthogonality* of the normal modes.

To develop this aspect, consider a solution $Y_m(x)$ which also, of course, satisfies (1.3.27) with n replaced by m. We may then form the following set of equations.

$$\begin{aligned} Y_m Y_n'' + \beta_n^2 Y_m Y_n &= 0, \\ Y_n Y_m'' + \beta_m^2 Y_n Y_m &= 0. \end{aligned} \tag{1.3.28}$$

The first equation has been formed by multiplying (1.3.27) by Y_m, the second in a similar fashion except for interchanging m and n. Subtracting the two equations of (1.3.27) and integrating over the interval $0 \leqslant x \leqslant l$, we obtain

$$\int_0^l (Y_m Y_n'' - Y_n Y_m'')\, dx + (\beta_n^2 - \beta_m^2) \int_0^l Y_m Y_n \, dx = 0. \tag{1.3.29}$$

Integrating the first term of the first integral by parts gives

$$\int_0^l Y_m Y_n'' \, dx = [Y_m Y_n' - Y_m' Y_n]_0^l + \int_0^l Y_m'' Y_n \, dx. \tag{1.3.30}$$

Inserting this result in (1.3.29) gives

$$[Y_m(x) Y_n'(x) - Y_m'(x) Y_n(x)]_0^l + (\beta_n^2 - \beta_m^2) \int_0^l Y_m Y_n \, dx = 0. \tag{1.3.31}$$

Now, the expression in brackets will obviously vanish if the ends of the string are any combination of fixed–free conditions. In fact, the brackets vanish for any combinations of end conditions such that

$$\begin{aligned} a_1 Y(0) + b_1 Y'(0) &= 0, \\ a_2 Y(l) + b_2 Y'(l) &= 0, \end{aligned} \tag{1.3.32}$$

where fixed, free, or elastic conditions may be obtained by letting the constants a_1, a_2, b_1, b_2 be zero or non-zero, depending on the condition desired. Assuming that (1.3.32) holds, we obtain from (1.3.31)

$$(\beta_n^2 - \beta_m^2) \int_0^l Y_m Y_n \, dx = 0. \tag{1.3.33}$$

Since $\beta_n \neq \beta_m$ except for $n = m$, we obtain

$$\int_0^l Y_m Y_n \, dx = 0 \qquad (m \neq n). \tag{1.3.34}$$

This is the important orthogonality property of the normal modes.† It represents the generalization of (1.3.21) for the fixed–fixed string and enables the coefficients A_n, B_n to be established. Thus, using (1.3.34), it is readily obtained that

$$A_n = \frac{1}{\omega_n N} \int_0^l V(x) Y_n(x) \, dx, \qquad B_n = \frac{1}{N} \int_0^l U(x) Y_n(x) \, dx, \tag{1.3.35}$$

† The procedure and results (1.3.28) to (1.3.34) are, of course, standard results from the theory of Sturm–Liouville systems.

where N is the normalizing factor given by

$$N = \int_0^l Y_n^2(x)\,dx. \qquad (1.3.36)$$

We briefly consider the situation not accounted for by boundary conditions of the form (1.3.32). Such would be the case for mass or dashpot terminations. Thus, for a mass termination at $x=0$, we have from Table 1.1 that

$$m\ddot{y}(0,t) - T\frac{\partial y(0,t)}{\partial x} = 0. \qquad (1.3.37)$$

Substituting (1.3.26) in the above gives

$$\omega_n^2 Y_n(0) + TY_n'(0) = 0. \qquad (1.3.38)$$

At first glance, this appears to satisfy the general form of (1.3.32). However, ω_n is not a constant, taking on new values for different modes. Specifically, it results that the bracketed term of (1.3.31) does not vanish, and the orthogonality property of the modes does not exist. The basic difficulty arises in the *time dependent* nature of the boundary conditions. For such problems, simple orthogonality breaks down and other means of analysis must be brought to bear.†

1.4. Forced vibrations of a string

The general problem under consideration will be the forced vibrations of a finite length string, described by

$$T\frac{\partial^2 y}{\partial x^2} - \rho\frac{\partial^2 y}{\partial t^2} = -q(x,t). \qquad (1.4.1)$$

The techniques developed for solving the forced-vibrations problem for the string will be applicable generally to more difficult problems arising in beam and plate vibrations. Many aspects of analysis of the finite string are similar to the techniques previously applied to forced motion of an infinite string, so that analyses will be rather briefly presented.

In (1.4.1), $q(x, t)$ may be considered a general loading in space and time. However, to arrive at a solution for such conditions, the solutions to particular loadings in space and in time will first be derived. By considering the case of harmonic loading, the solution to the case of arbitrary time variation may be found by means of the Fourier integral. Furthermore, by specializing the spatial variation of loading to the case of a concentrated load, the solution to the more general problem will also be found by a Fourier superposition.

In the case of a harmonically varying forcing function, it will be found that two distinct problem-types arise. When the forcing function is applied

† See Tong [9, pp. 260–8] and, more extensively, Berry and Naghdi [1].

at the boundaries, the differential equation becomes homogeneous but the boundary conditions are inhomogeneous. If, on the other hand, the forcing function is acting on the interior of the system, the equation is non-homogeneous, but the boundary conditions become homogeneous.

1.4.1. *Solution by Green's function*

Let us consider the case of a harmonically varying force acting at a single point $x = \xi$. Then

$$q(x, t) = P\delta(x-\xi)e^{-i\omega t}, \tag{1.4.2}$$

and the differential equation becomes

$$\frac{\partial^2 y}{\partial x^2} - \frac{1}{c_0^2}\frac{\partial^2 y}{\partial t^2} = -\frac{P}{T}\delta(x-\xi)e^{-i\omega t}. \tag{1.4.3}$$

The response may be written as

$$y(x, t) = \psi(x)e^{-i\omega t}, \tag{1.4.4}$$

giving

$$\psi'' + \beta^2\psi = \delta(x-\xi), \qquad \beta^2 = \omega^2/c_0^2, \tag{1.4.5}$$

where $P/T = -1$ has been selected to provide a positive unit impulse on the right-hand side. Assuming simple, rigid supports at the ends, the boundary conditions are

$$\psi(0) = \psi(l) = 0. \tag{1.4.6}$$

Now, recalling that $\delta(x-\xi) = 0$, $x \neq \xi$, we see that two solutions to the homogeneous equation may be found; one valid for $x < \xi$, the other for $x > \xi$. Thus

$$\psi_1 = A_1 \sin \beta x + B_1 \cos \beta x \qquad (0 \leqslant x < \xi), \tag{1.4.7}$$

$$\psi_2 = A_2 \sin \beta x + B_2 \cos \beta x \qquad (\xi < x \leqslant l). \tag{1.4.8}$$

Substituting these in the boundary conditions (1.4.6) we obtain

$$\psi_1 = A_1 \sin \beta x \qquad (0 \leqslant x < \xi), \tag{1.4.9}$$

$$\psi_2 = A_2(\sin \beta x - \tan \beta l \cos \beta x) \qquad (\xi < x \leqslant l). \tag{1.4.10}$$

To match the solutions at the load discontinuity, two conditions are required, one of which is $\psi_1(\xi) = \psi_2(\xi)$, corresponding to continuity of displacement. To establish the second, we integrate (1.4.5) across the load discontinuity, giving

$$\int_{\xi-\varepsilon}^{\xi+\varepsilon} \psi''\, dx + \beta^2 \int_{\xi-\varepsilon}^{\xi+\varepsilon} \psi\, dx = \int_{\xi-\varepsilon}^{\xi+\varepsilon} \delta(x-\xi)\, dx = 1. \tag{1.4.11}$$

Since $\psi(x)$ is continuous across $x = \xi$, the second integral on the left-hand side of (1.4.11) vanishes. The remaining integral gives

$$\int_{-\varepsilon}^{\xi+\varepsilon} \psi''\, dx = \psi'\Big|_{\xi-\varepsilon}^{\xi+\varepsilon} = \psi_2'(\xi) - \psi_1'(\xi) = 1. \tag{1.4.12}$$

This establishes the second boundary condition and represents the discontinuity in slope of the string. Substituting the solutions (1.4.9) and (1.4.10) in the boundary conditions at $x = \xi$ we obtain

$$\begin{aligned} A_1 \sin \beta\xi &= A_2(\sin \beta\xi - \tan \beta l \cos \beta\xi), \\ A_2(\cos \beta\xi + \tan \beta l \sin \beta\xi) - A_1 \cos \beta\xi &= 1/\beta, \end{aligned} \tag{1.4.13}$$

from which we obtain

$$\begin{aligned} \psi_1(x) &= -\frac{\sin \beta x \sin \beta(l-\xi)}{\beta \sin \beta l} \qquad (0 \leqslant x < \xi) \\ \psi_2(x) &= -\frac{\sin \beta\xi \sin \beta(l-x)}{\beta \sin \beta l} \qquad (\xi < x \leqslant l). \end{aligned} \tag{1.4.14}$$

This solution is called the Green's function for the problem and is denoted as $G(x/\xi)$. Thus

$$G(x/\xi) = \begin{cases} -\dfrac{\sin \beta x \sin \beta(l-\xi)}{\beta \sin \beta l}, & (0 \leqslant x < \xi) \\ -\dfrac{\sin \beta\xi \sin \beta(l-x)}{\beta \sin \beta l}, & (\xi < x \leqslant l). \end{cases} \tag{1.4.15}$$

The response of the system to a concentrated, harmonic load of magnitude $P = -T$ applied at $x = \xi$ is thus

$$y(x, t) = G(x/\xi)e^{-i\omega t}. \tag{1.4.16}$$

The above approach to the problem of forced vibration is quite powerful. The extension to general loading in space is possible using the superposition principle, but it is best to postpone this until the transform techniques are brought to bear on the problem.

1.4.2. *Solution by transform techniques*

The application of the Fourier and Laplace transform techniques to problems in forced vibrations may take several routes, applying one or the other transform or both to a given problem. Several approaches will be illustrated in the following.

1. *Application of the Laplace transform.* Consider again the case of loading $P\delta(x-\xi)\exp(-i\omega t)$, so that

$$\frac{\partial^2 y}{\partial x^2} - \frac{1}{c_0^2}\frac{\partial^2 y}{\partial t^2} = \delta(x-\xi)e^{-i\omega t}, \tag{1.4.17}$$

where $P = -T$ has again been selected. Let $y(x, t) = \psi(x)\exp(-i\omega t)$ as before, so that

$$\psi''(x) + \beta^2\psi(x) = \delta(x-\xi), \qquad \beta^2 = \omega^2/c_0^2 \tag{1.4.18}$$

must be solved. Taking the Laplace transform on the spatial variable of the preceding gives

$$s^2\bar{\Psi}(s)-s\psi(0)-\psi'(0)+\beta^2\bar{\Psi} = \mathscr{L}\{\delta(x-\xi)\}, \tag{1.4.19}$$

where

$$\mathscr{L}\{\delta(x-\xi)\} = \int_0^\infty \delta(x-\xi)e^{-sx}\,dx = e^{-s\xi}. \tag{1.4.20}$$

Solving for $\bar{\Psi}(s)$, we have

$$\bar{\Psi}(s) = \frac{s\psi(0)+\psi'(0)}{s^2+\beta^2}+\frac{e^{-s\xi}}{s^2+\beta^2}. \tag{1.4.21}$$

Inverting, we obtain

$$\psi(x) = \psi(0)\mathscr{L}^{-1}\left(\frac{s}{s^2+\beta^2}\right)+\psi'(0)\mathscr{L}^{-1}\left(\frac{1}{s^2+\beta^2}\right)+\mathscr{L}^{-1}\left(\frac{e^{-s\xi}}{s^2+\beta^2}\right). \tag{1.4.22}$$

Now

$$\mathscr{L}^{-1}\left(\frac{s}{s^2+\beta^2}\right) = \cos\beta x, \qquad \mathscr{L}^{-1}\left(\frac{1}{s^2+\beta^2}\right) = \frac{\sin\beta x}{\beta}. \tag{1.4.23}$$

To invert the last term in the solution, we regard $\exp(-s\xi)/(s^2+\beta^2)$ as the product of two functions $f_1(s)$, $f_2(s)$. Although the first impulse is to select these as $\exp(-s\xi)$ and $(s^2+\beta^2)^{-1}$, consulting tables of Laplace transforms reveals the former to have no inverse, whereas $\exp(-s\xi)/s$ does. So we let

$$f_1(s) = \frac{e^{-s\xi}}{s}, \qquad f_2(s) = \frac{s}{s^2+\beta^2}, \tag{1.4.24}$$

for which

$$\mathscr{L}^{-1}\left(\frac{e^{-s\xi}}{s}\right) = \begin{cases} 0, & 0<x<\xi \\ 1, & \xi<x \end{cases}, \tag{1.4.25}$$

$$\mathscr{L}^{-1}\left(\frac{s}{s^2+\beta^2}\right) = \cos\beta x. \tag{1.4.26}$$

Then, by the convolution theorem,

$$\mathscr{L}^{-1}\left(\frac{e^{-s\xi}}{s^2+\beta^2}\right) = \begin{cases} 0 & (0\leqslant x<\xi) \\ \displaystyle\int_0^x \cos\beta(x-u)\,du & (\xi<x\leqslant l). \end{cases} \tag{1.4.27}$$

Hence

$$\psi(x) = \psi(0)\cos\beta x+\psi'(0)\frac{\sin\beta x}{\beta}+\frac{1}{\beta}\begin{cases} 0 & (0\leqslant x<\xi) \\ \sin\beta(x-\xi) & (\xi<x\leqslant l). \end{cases} \tag{1.4.28}$$

Assuming that the ends of the string are fixed, we have the boundary conditions

$$\psi(0) = \psi(l) = 0. \tag{1.4.29}$$

From the second condition we have

$$\psi(l) = \psi'(0)\frac{\sin\beta l}{\beta}+\frac{\sin\beta(l-\xi)}{\beta} = 0, \tag{1.4.30}$$

so that $\psi'(0)$ may be found. Then

$$\psi(x) = -\frac{\sin\beta(l-\xi)}{\beta\sin\beta l}\sin\beta x+\frac{1}{\beta}\begin{cases}0 & (0 \leqslant x < \xi)\\ \sin\beta(x-\xi) & (\xi < x \leqslant l).\end{cases} \tag{1.4.31}$$

These results may be combined to give the alternate formulation,

$$\psi(x) = \begin{cases}-\dfrac{\sin\beta(l-\xi)}{\beta\sin\beta l}\sin\beta x & (0 \leqslant x < \xi)\\[2ex] -\dfrac{\sin\beta\xi\,\sin\beta(l-x)}{\beta\sin\beta l} & (\xi < x \leqslant l).\end{cases} \tag{1.4.32}$$

This result corresponds to the Green's function $G(x/\xi)$.

SKIP

2. *Solution by finite Fourier transform.* Consider the loading to be of the general form

$$q(x, t) = TW(x)e^{i\omega t}, \tag{1.4.33}$$

so that the governing equation is

$$\frac{\partial^2 y}{\partial x^2}-\frac{1}{c_0^2}\frac{\partial^2 y}{\partial t^2} = -W(x)e^{i\omega t}. \tag{1.4.34}$$

Assuming $y(x, t) = Y(x)\exp(i\omega t)$, we have

$$Y''(x)+\beta^2 Y(x)+W(x) = 0. \tag{1.4.35}$$

The finite Fourier transform will be applied to the above (it must be the finite transform since x is bounded, $0 \leqslant x \leqslant l$). The nature of the boundary condition will determine whether the sine or cosine transform is appropriate. We first attempt the sine transform.

$$F_s\{Y''(x)\} = \frac{1}{l}\int_0^l Y''(x)\sin\frac{n\pi}{l}x\,dx. \tag{1.4.36}$$

Integrating by parts gives

$$F_s\{Y''(x)\} = \frac{1}{l}\left[Y'(x)\sin\frac{n\pi}{l}x-\frac{n\pi}{l}Y(x)\cos\frac{n\pi}{l}x\right]_0^l - \\ -\frac{1}{l}\left(\frac{n\pi}{l}\right)^2\int_0^l Y(x)\sin\frac{n\pi}{l}x\,dx. \tag{1.4.37}$$

For a string fixed at both ends, $Y(0) = Y(l) = 0$, while $\sin n\pi x/l = 0$, at $x = 0, l$. Thus the expression in brackets in (1.4.37) vanishes and

$$F_s\{Y''(x)\} = -\left(\frac{n\pi}{l}\right)^2 \bar{Y}(n), \tag{1.4.38}$$

where

$$\bar{Y}(n) = \frac{1}{l}\int_0^l Y(x)\sin\frac{n\pi}{l}x\,dx. \tag{1.4.39}$$

Then the transformed equation is

$$\bar{Y}(n) = \frac{\overline{W}(n)}{\alpha_n^2-\beta^2}, \qquad \alpha_n = \frac{n\pi}{l}. \tag{1.4.40}$$

We note that, had the finite cosine transform been attempted, the expression in brackets of (1.4.37) would not vanish for the given boundary conditions. The inverse transform is then (see Appendix B)

$$Y(x) = 2\sum_{n=1}^{\infty}\frac{\overline{W}(n)\sin\alpha_n x}{\alpha_n^2-\beta^2} = \frac{2}{l}\sum_{n=1}^{\infty}\frac{\sin\alpha_n x}{\alpha_n^2-\beta^2}\int_0^l W(u)\sin\alpha_n u\,du. \tag{1.4.41}$$

Then

$$y(x,t) = Y(x)e^{i\omega t}. \tag{1.4.42}$$

The special case of $W(x) = \delta(x-\xi)$ will give the previously obtained results of (1.4.32).

3. *Laplace and finite Fourier transforms.* We again consider the forced vibration of a string fixed at $x = 0, l$, where the loading is considered to be a variable in x and t, so that

$$T\frac{\partial^2 y}{\partial x^2}-\rho\frac{\partial^2 y}{\partial t^2}+q(x,t) = 0, \tag{1.4.43}$$

and

$$y(0,t) = y(l,t) = 0. \tag{1.4.44}$$

The case of non-zero initial conditions may also be included, so that

$$y(x,0) = h(x), \qquad \dot{y}(x,0) = g(x). \tag{1.4.45}$$

First apply the Laplace transform,

$$c_0^2\bar{y}''(x,s)-s^2\bar{y}(x,s) = -\frac{1}{\rho}\bar{q}(x,s)-sh(x)-g(x). \tag{1.4.46}$$

Now apply the finite Fourier sine transform, giving

$$(c_0^2\alpha_n^2+s^2)\,\bar{Y}(n,s) = \frac{\bar{Q}(n,s)}{\rho}+sH(n)+G(n). \tag{1.4.47}$$

The transformed solution is then

$$\bar{Y}(n, s) = \frac{\bar{Q}/\rho + sH + G}{c_0^2\alpha_n^2 + s^2}, \qquad \alpha_n = \frac{n\pi}{l}. \tag{1.4.48}$$

The inverse Fourier sine transform gives

$$\bar{y}(x, s) = \frac{2}{l}\sum_{n=1}^{\infty} \frac{\sin \alpha_n x}{c_0^2\alpha_n^2 + s^2}\left\{\frac{1}{\rho}\int_0^l \bar{q}(u, s)\sin \alpha_n u \, du + \right.$$

$$\left. + s\int_0^l h(u)\sin \alpha_n u \, du + \int_0^l g(u)\sin \alpha_n u \, du\right\}. \tag{1.4.49}$$

The convolution theorem is used in carrying out the Laplace inversion, since the product $\bar{Q}/(c_0^2\alpha_n^2 + s^2)$ arises, as well as the function $s/(c_0^2\alpha_n^2 + s^2)$. We have

$$\mathscr{L}^{-1}\left(\frac{1}{s^2 + c_0^2\alpha_n^2}\right) = \frac{1}{\omega_n}\sin \omega_n t,$$

$$\mathscr{L}^{-1}\left(\frac{s}{s^2 + c_0^2\alpha_n^2}\right) = \cos \omega_n t, \qquad \omega = c_0\alpha_n. \tag{1.4.50}$$

The convolution theorem is

$$\mathscr{L}^{-1}\{\bar{f}(s)\bar{g}(s)\} = \bar{f} * \bar{g} = \int_0^t f(\tau)g(t-\tau)\, d\tau. \tag{1.4.51}$$

Hence we have

$$\mathscr{L}^{-1}\left\{\frac{\bar{q}(u, s)}{s^2 + \omega_n^2}\right\} = \frac{1}{\omega_n}\int_0^t q(u, \tau)\sin \omega_n(t-\tau)\, d\tau. \tag{1.4.52}$$

Applying a term-by-term inversion to $\bar{y}(x, s)$, we obtain

$$y(x, t) = \frac{2}{\rho c_0 l}\sum_{n=1}^{\infty} \frac{\sin \alpha_n x}{\alpha_n} \times$$

$$\times \int_0^l \sin \alpha_n u \, du \int_0^t q(u, \tau)\sin \omega_n(t-\tau)\, d\tau + \frac{2}{l}\sum_{n=1}^{\infty} \sin \alpha_n x \times$$

$$\times \left\{\cos \omega_n t \int_0^l h(u)\sin \alpha_n u \, du + \frac{\sin \omega_n t}{\omega_n}\int_0^l g(u)\sin \alpha_n u \, du\right\}. \tag{1.4.53}$$

The case of zero initial conditions, $g(x) = h(x) = 0$, and

$$q(x, t) = Q(t)\delta(x-\xi), \tag{1.4.54}$$

gives

$$y(x, t) = \frac{2}{\rho c_0 l}\sum_{n=1}^{\infty}\frac{\sin\alpha_n x \sin\alpha_n\xi}{\alpha_n}\int_0^t Q(\tau)\sin\omega_n(t-\tau)\,d\tau. \qquad (1.4.55)$$

If, as a further specialization, we let $Q(\tau) = \delta(\tau)$, so that the loading represents an impulse load applied at $x = \xi$, the preceding reduces to

$$y(x, t) = \frac{2}{\rho c_0 l}\sum_{n=1}^{\infty}\frac{\sin\alpha_n x \sin\alpha_n\xi}{\alpha_n}\sin\omega_n t = G(x, t/\xi). \qquad (1.4.56)$$

The above solution could be regarded as a 'double' Green's function for the string fixed at $x = 0,l$. The response to an arbitrary loading $q(x, t)$ is then

$$y(x, t) = \int_0^l d\xi\int_0^t G(x, t-\tau/\xi)q(\xi, \tau)\,d\tau. \qquad (1.4.57)$$

1.4.3. *Solution by normal modes*

Consider again the problem of forced vibration of a finite string, governed by the equation

$$T\frac{\partial^2 y}{\partial x^2}-\rho\frac{\partial^2 y}{\partial t^2}+q(x, t) = 0. \qquad (1.4.58)$$

Let us assume that the problem of free vibrations of the string has already been solved and that a set of normal modes $Y_n(x)$ $(n = 1, 2, \ldots)$ has been determined. That is, Y_n are such that

$$Y_n''(x)+\beta_n^2 Y_n = 0, \qquad \beta_n^2 = \omega_n^2/c_0^2, \qquad (1.4.59)$$

is satisfied. Furthermore, let us assume that the boundary conditions of the problem are such that $Y_n(x)$ form an orthogonal set, as described in § 1.3. Then the configuration of the string at any point x and time t may be represented by a normal-mode expansion,

$$y(x, t) = \sum_{n=1}^{\infty} q_n(t)Y_n(x), \qquad (1.4.60)$$

where the coefficients $q_n(t)$, being functions of time, represent the time-varying character of the expansion needed to represent $y(x, t)$ at successive periods of time.

Substitution of the series representation into the equation of motion gives

$$\sum_{n=1}^{\infty}(Tq_n(t)Y_n''-\rho\ddot{q}_n(t)Y_n) = -q(x, t) \qquad (1.4.61)$$

or

$$\sum_{n=1}^{\infty}\{\ddot{q}_n(t)+\omega_n^2 q_n(t)\}Y_n(x) = \frac{1}{\rho}q(x, t), \qquad (1.4.62)$$

where the relation $Y_n'' = -(\omega_n/c_0)^2 Y_n$ has been used. Then, multiplying by $Y_n(x)$ and integrating, we have

$$\sum_{n=1}^{\infty} (\ddot{q}_n + \omega_n^2 q_n) \int_0^l Y_m Y_n \, dx = \frac{1}{\rho} \int_0^l Y_m q(x, t) \, dx, \tag{1.4.63}$$

which gives

$$\ddot{q}_n(t) + \omega_n^2 q_n(t) = \frac{1}{\rho N} \int_0^l Y_n(x) q(x, t) \, dx = Q_n(t). \tag{1.4.64}$$

Thus, we must solve

$$\ddot{q}_n(t) + \omega_n^2 q_n(t) = Q_n(t), \qquad (n = 1, 2, 3, \ldots). \tag{1.4.65}$$

The solution of this ordinary differential equation may be found by using the Laplace transform and the convolution theorem or by using variation of parameters. In either case, the solution is

$$q_n(t) = q_n(0) \cos \omega_n t + \frac{\dot{q}_n(0)}{\omega_n} \sin \omega_n t -$$

$$-\frac{1}{\omega_n} \int_0^t Q_n(\tau) \sin \omega_n (t - \tau) \, d\tau \qquad (n = 1, 2, \ldots), \tag{1.4.66}$$

where $q_n(0)$, $\dot{q}_n(0)$ represent the initial conditions. This establishes the total solution to the problem, since

$$y(x, t) = \sum_{n=1}^{\infty} q_n(t) Y_n(x), \tag{1.4.67}$$

and both $q_n(t)$, $Y_n(x)$ are known.

Sometimes the solution procedure is altered slightly by assuming both $y(x, t)$, $q(x, t)$ have the normal mode expansions

$$y(x, t) = \sum_{n=1}^{\infty} q_n(t) Y_n(x), \qquad q(x, t) = \sum_{n=1}^{\infty} b_n(t) Y_n(x), \tag{1.4.68}$$

where $b_n(t)$ are known and given by

$$b_n(t) = \int_0^l q(x, t) Y_n(x) \, dx. \tag{1.4.69}$$

Then substitution in the differential equation gives

$$\sum_{n=1}^{\infty} \{T q_n(t) Y_n'' - \rho \ddot{q}_n Y_n\} = -\sum_{n=1}^{\infty} b_n(t) Y_n(x). \tag{1.4.70}$$

Using (1.4.59), we obtain

$$\sum_{n=1}^{\infty}\{\ddot{q}_n(t)+\omega_n^2 q_n(t)\}Y_n(x) = \frac{1}{\rho}\sum_{n=1}^{\infty} b_n(t)Y_n(x). \tag{1.4.71}$$

Equating coefficients, we have

$$\ddot{q}_n(t)+\omega_n^2 q_n(t) = \frac{1}{\rho}b_n(t), \quad (n = 1, 2, 3,...), \tag{1.4.72}$$

which puts us in the same place as (1.4.65) so that the remaining steps are clear. Thus the two procedures are completely equivalent.

1.5. The string on an elastic base—dispersion

Up to this point, we have been considering vibrations and waves in a system where the governing equation, denoted as the 'wave equation', is particularly simple. One of the particular attributes of the system has been that pulses propagate without distortion, as evidenced by the D'Alembert solution. We now consider a slightly more complicated situation in which the string rests on an elastic foundation. The resulting equation will not be of wave equation form and will cause an effect known as *dispersion*. Many of the concepts developed here will find wide application to wave propagation in other elastic systems.

1.5.1. *The governing equation*

We refer back to the initial derivation of the wave equation and Fig. 1.1. The effects of an elastic foundation may be rather easily included by noting that a foundation of elastic modulus k (force length^{-2}) will result in a vertical force component of $(-ky\,dx)$ on the left-hand side of (1.1.3). Alternatively, the external load $q(x, t)$ may be interpreted as that due to the foundation, so that $q(x, t) = -ky(x, t)$. By either means, the resulting governing equation, in the absence of other body or external forces, is

$$T\frac{\partial^2 y}{\partial x^2}-ky = \rho\frac{\partial^2 y}{\partial t^2}, \tag{1.5.1}$$

or

$$\frac{\partial^2 y}{\partial x^2}-\frac{k}{T}y = \frac{1}{c_0^2}\frac{\partial^2 y}{\partial t^2}, \qquad c_0 = \sqrt{(T/\rho)}. \tag{1.5.2}$$

1.5.2. *Propagation of harmonic waves*

The first and obvious remark on the result of adding foundation stiffness is that the governing equation is no longer of simple wave equation form. Thus, a solution of the form $f(x \pm c_0 t)$ will not satisfy (1.5.2). Since the major characteristic of such a solution is undistorted pulse propagation, it is now logical to expect some type of pulse distortion to occur in a system governed by (1.5.2).

A first step in assessing this effect is to determine the necessary conditions for the propagation of harmonic waves. Thus, under what conditions will a solution

$$y = Ae^{i(\gamma x-\omega t)} \tag{1.5.3}$$

satisfy (1.5.2)? The propagation direction has arbitrarily been selected in (1.5.3). Substituting in (1.5.2) gives

$$\left(-\gamma^2-\frac{k}{T}+\frac{\omega^2}{c_0^2}\right)Ae^{i(\gamma x-\omega t)} = 0. \tag{1.5.4}$$

In order for this to be satisfied non-trivially, we must have

$$\omega^2 = c_0^2(\gamma^2+k/T) \tag{1.5.5}$$

or, alternatively,

$$\gamma^2 = \frac{\omega^2}{c_0^2}-\frac{k}{T}. \tag{1.5.6}$$

Symbolically, we represent the relationships (1.5.5) and (1.5.6) respectively by

$$\omega = \omega(\gamma), \qquad \gamma = \gamma(\omega). \tag{1.5.7}$$

An alternative form of the results may be obtained by noting that

$$e^{i(\gamma x-\omega t)} = e^{i\gamma(x-ct)}, \tag{1.5.8}$$

where $c = \omega/\gamma$ is the phase velocity of the wave. In the simple string, this has the specific value of $c = c_0$, whereas in the present case it is initially unspecified. Substituting a solution

$$y = Ae^{i\gamma(x-ct)} \tag{1.5.9}$$

in (1.5.2) gives the result

$$c^2 = c_0^2(1+k/T\gamma^2), \tag{1.5.10}$$

or, alternatively,

$$\gamma^2 = \frac{k/T}{(c^2/c_0^2)-1}. \tag{1.5.11}$$

Symbolically, we represent the relations (1.5.10) and (1.5.11) respectively by

$$c = c(\gamma), \qquad \gamma = \gamma(c). \tag{1.5.12}$$

These last results, it is seen, could be obtained directly from (1.5.5) or (1.5.6) by using the basic relation that holds between frequency, wave number and phase velocity, $\omega = \gamma c$.

Finally, by using the relation $\omega = \gamma c$, a third set of relations could be obtained by eliminating γ from (1.5.5) or ω from (1.5.11) to give

$$\omega^2 = \frac{kTc^2}{(c^2/c_0^2)-1}, \qquad \gamma^2 = \frac{\omega^2 c_0^2}{\omega^2-(kc_0^2/T)}, \tag{1.5.13}$$

or in symbolic form

$$\omega = \omega(c), \qquad \gamma = \gamma(\omega). \tag{1.5.14}$$

We now inquire into the implications of the results obtained, represented as specific relations by (1.5.5), (1.5.6), (1.5.10), and (1.5.11), or in symbolic form by (1.5.7) and (1.5.12). In fact, these results give us our first insight into the mechanism of pulse distortion which we know must occur. The results show that: *a harmonic wave of frequency ω can propagate only at specific velocity c as governed by $\omega = \omega(c)$*. Suppose we consider a pulse shape at a given time $t = t_0$ to be a Fourier superposition of harmonic waves. Then, as time advances, each Fourier component of the original pulse will propagate with its own individual velocity. The various components will become increasingly out of phase relative to their original position so that the original pulse shape will become increasingly distorted.

The preceding interpretation also gives the basis for the fact that no distortion occurs in the simple string, where the foundation is absent. While the direct prediction of this lack of distortion is given by the D'Alembert solution, the indirect prediction arises in the fact that frequency, wavenumber, and wave velocity are related by $\omega = \gamma c_0$, where c_0 is a constant. Thus, each harmonic component propagates with the same velocity, so that the phase relationships of an original Fourier superposition are maintained for all time. We note, incidentally, that this result is obtained by letting $k = 0$ in the various relations between frequency, wavenumber, and wave velocity.

Consider now the roots of the preceding relations between ω, γ, and c. The most useful interpretation will come from (1.5.6). We have that

$$\gamma = \pm\left(\frac{\omega^2}{c_0^2} - \frac{k}{T}\right)^{\frac{1}{2}}. \tag{1.5.15}$$

The above roots are real if $\omega^2/c_0^2 > k/T$. Referring back to (1.5.3), we have

$$y = Ae^{-i(\pm\gamma x + \omega t)}. \tag{1.5.16}$$

Thus, the two real roots yield leftward or rightward-propagating waves, depending on which sign is selected.

We next note that if $\omega^2/c_0^2 < k/T$, then the wavenumber predicted by (1.5.15) becomes imaginary. Defining $\bar{\gamma}^2 = -\gamma^2$, we have the motion given by

$$y = Ae^{\pm\bar{\gamma}x}e^{-i\omega t}. \tag{1.5.17}$$

This corresponds to a spatially varying but non-propagating disturbance. Now, the original question posed was to establish the conditions under which a harmonic wave (1.5.3) could exist. In this context, the results for imaginary wavenumber are not acceptable since they are non-propagating. However, it will be found that imaginary wavenumbers and results of the form (1.5.17) will play important roles in problems of transient loading and boundary interaction.

Finally, the special case of $\omega^2/c_0^2 = k/T$ should be noted. This, of course, represents the transition from propagation to non-propagation. From (1.5.6) we have that $\gamma = 0$ at the frequency $\omega_c = c_0\sqrt{(k/T)}$, and the string motion to be of the form†

$$y = A\exp(-i\omega_c t). \tag{1.5.18}$$

The frequency ω_c is designated as the *cutoff* frequency of the propagating mode. There is no spatial variation in the motion, so the string is basically vibrating as a simple spring–mass system.

1.5.3. *Frequency spectrum and the dispersion curve*

The basic factors governing propagation in a string on an elastic foundation have been presented in the formulas relating frequency, wavenumber, and velocity and in the interpretations of the propagation. It is still useful, however, to display these results in graphical form for easier interpretation. Typically, two types of displays are used: one is a plot of frequency versus wavenumber and is called the *frequency spectrum* of the system; the other is a plot of phase velocity versus wavenumber and is called the *dispersion curve* of the system.

To plot the frequency spectrum, we refer to (1.5.15). We assume the frequency to be real and positive. We have established that γ is imaginary for $\omega < \omega_c$ and real for $\omega > \omega_c$. The results are shown in Fig. 1.15. The curves

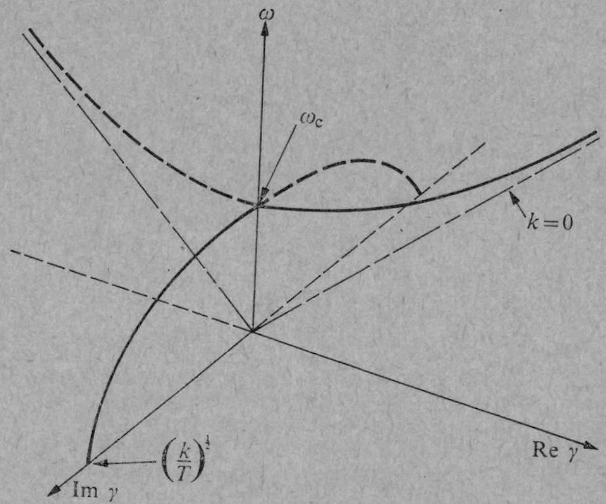

FIG. 1.15. Frequency spectrum for a string on an elastic foundation.

or branches in the real plane are hyperbolas, while the imaginary branches are ellipses. The line $k = 0$ in the figure is the non-dispersive result for the classical string. Thus, no dispersion is manifested as a straight line in the frequency spectrum.

† See problem 1.17.

It is possible to obtain phase velocity information from the frequency spectrum by the relation $\omega = \gamma c$. Thus, given a point on the real branch of the spectrum, the slope of the chord between the point and the origin is given by $\omega/\gamma = c$, the phase velocity for that particular frequency. This relation is shown in Fig. 1.16, where the frequency spectrum has been shown in slightly

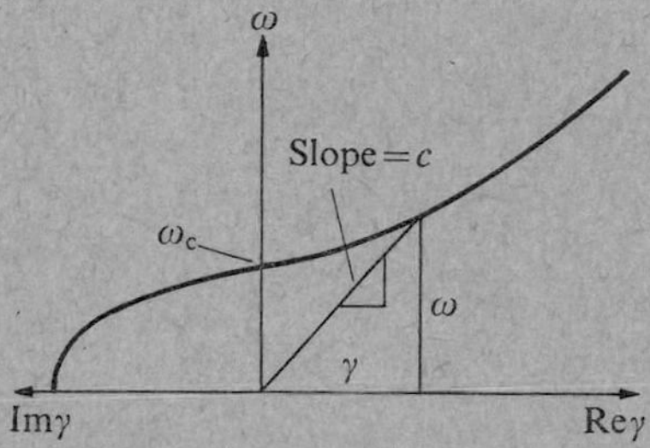

FIG. 1.16. Two-dimensional representation of the frequency spectrum showing relation between chord slope and phase velocity.

different form. Since the spectrum is usually symmetric with respect to the $\text{Re}\gamma = 0$ and the $\text{Im}\gamma = 0$ planes, it is sufficient to present a two-dimensional plot containing the ω, $\text{Re}\gamma > 0$ and $\text{Im}\gamma > 0$ axes.

Instead of deriving phase velocity information from the frequency spectrum, it is often presented independently, as previously mentioned, by dispersion curves. For this purpose, eqn (1.5.10) is required. Although it is possible to consider c as positive, negative, real, and imaginary, depending on γ, the most physically meaningful information is contained in a simple plot of $\text{Re}c > 0$ versus $\text{Re}\gamma > 0$ as shown in Fig. 1.17. The horizontal line of the

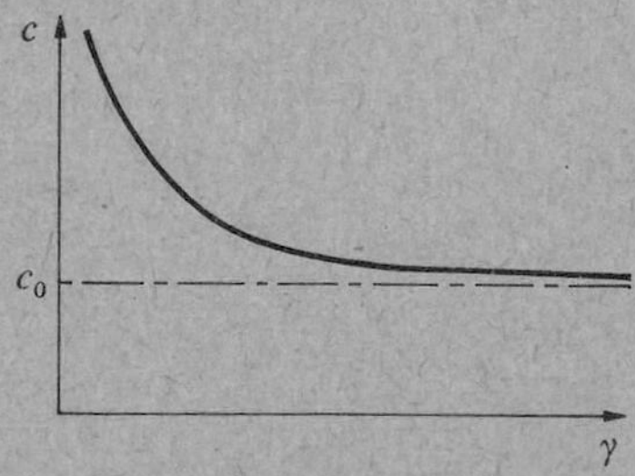

FIG. 1.17. Dispersion curve for a string on an elastic foundation.

figure is the result for the non-dispersive string where all wavelengths propagate with the same velocity c_0. At larger values of the wavenumber, corresponding to short wavelengths and high frequency, it is seen that the solid curve approaches the classical result, indicating that the foundation effect is minimal. However, at small values of wavenumber, corresponding to long wavelengths, the phase velocity increases rapidly, approaching infinity as $\gamma \to 0$. Referring back to Fig. 1.15 or Fig. 1.16, we note that as $\gamma \to 0$, $\omega \to \omega_c$, the cutoff frequency. We recall the result (1.5.18) indicating the system is in uniform vibration. The fact that $\gamma = 0$ also indicates uniform vibration since the wavelength is infinitely long. The basis for the apparently anamolous behaviour of the phase velocity is then clear, since the uniform vibration may be interpreted as a disturbance propagating with infinite speed through the medium.

1.5.4. *Harmonic and pulse excitation of a semi-infinite string*

Two examples of forced motion of a semi-infinite, dispersive string will be considered, one quite simple, the other not so simple. Each will illustrate particular aspects of propagation in dispersive media. So first consider a string $x > 0$ to be subjected to the harmonic end motion

$$y(0, t) = y_0 e^{-i\omega t}. \tag{1.5.19}$$

Considering a solution

$$y = Y(x)e^{-i\omega t}, \tag{1.5.20}$$

we rather straightforwardly can obtain

$$y = Ae^{i(\gamma x - \omega t)} + Be^{-i(\gamma x + \omega t)}, \tag{1.5.21}$$

where, as previously derived,

$$\gamma^2 = \left(\frac{\omega^2}{c_0^2} - \frac{k}{T}\right) > 0. \tag{1.5.22}$$

From the radiation condition, we set $B = 0$. Applying the boundary condition (1.5.19) we obtain $A = y_0$, so that the solution is simply

$$y(x, t) = y_0 e^{i(\gamma x - \omega t)}. \tag{1.5.23}$$

The resulting motion is the propagation of simple harmonic waves, as shown in Fig. 1.18(a). Now, if the excitation drops below the cutoff frequency,

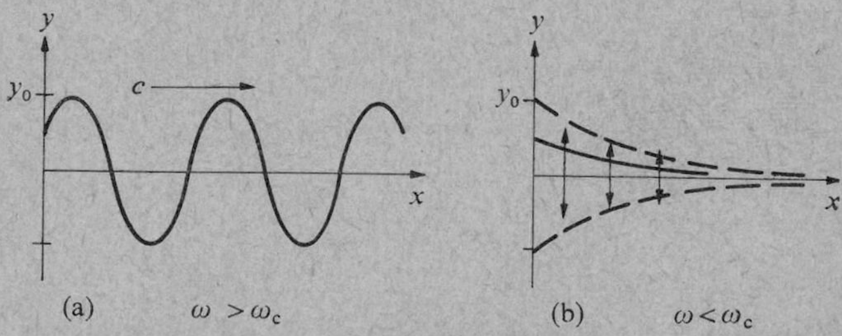

FIG. 1.18. Forced motion of a semi-infinite string (a) above and (b) below the cutoff frequency.

we have $\gamma^2 < 0$ in (1.5.22) and the resulting motion described by

$$y = y_0 e^{-\bar{\gamma}x} e^{-i\omega t}, \tag{1.5.24}$$

where $\bar{\gamma}^2 = -\gamma^2$. The motion is shown in Fig. 1.18(b). The point of this analysis is that the spatially decaying, non-propagating (or 'evanescent') mode that was not an acceptable solution for the harmonic-wave investigation is, in fact, a proper solution in the present problem for a range of forcing frequencies.

As a second example, consider that an applied force $F(t)$ is acting at the origin. The homogeneous differential equation (1.5.2) still governs the motion, now subjected to the boundary condition

$$-T\frac{\partial y(0, t)}{\partial t} = F(t), \tag{1.5.25}$$

where $F(t)$ is assumed positive in the upward direction.

The Laplace transform approach will be used. Transforming (1.5.2) gives

$$\frac{d^2\bar{y}}{dx^2} - m^2\bar{y} = 0, \tag{1.5.26}$$

where

$$m^2 = \frac{1}{c_0^2}(s^2 + k/\rho), \tag{1.5.27}$$

and $\bar{y} = \bar{y}(x, s)$. The solution of (1.5.26) is

$$\bar{y} = Ae^{-mx} + Be^{mx}. \tag{1.5.28}$$

We set $B = 0$ because of the increasing exponential behaviour. Actually, this is a bit too superficial an explanation for what actually must be ascertained by an inspection of the Laplace inversion integral for boundedness in the complex s-plane. The considerations are similar to those used in § 1.1 in closing the Fourier inversion contour. Omitting these details, we proceed to transform the force boundary condition (1.5.25), giving

$$-T\frac{d\bar{y}(0, s)}{dx} = \bar{F}(s). \tag{1.5.29}$$

Applying the solution to this, we obtain

$$A = \bar{F}(s)/mT. \tag{1.5.30}$$

This gives the transformed result

$$\bar{y}(x, s) = \frac{\bar{F}(s)}{mT} e^{-mx}. \tag{1.5.31}$$

The formal inversion of this could be expressed in terms of the convolution theorem.

To proceed further, a specific form for the forcing function must be given. Let us specify that the load be an impulse, given by

$$F(t) = P\delta(t). \tag{1.5.32}$$

Then the transform of this is $\bar{F}(s) = P$. The transformed solution (1.5.31) then takes the form

$$\bar{y}(x, s) = \frac{Pc_0}{T} \frac{\exp\{-(s^2+k/\rho)^{\frac{1}{2}}x/c_0\}}{(s^2+k/\rho)^{\frac{1}{2}}}. \tag{1.5.33}$$

The inversion of this would be no small task. Fortunately, the results

$$\mathscr{L}^{-1}\left\{\frac{1}{\sqrt{(s^2+a^2)}}\right\} = J_0(at), \tag{1.5.34}$$

have been tabulated, where $J_0(at)$ is the zero-order Bessel function. Employing the translation theorem enables (1.5.33) to be easily evaluated, giving

$$y(x, t) = \begin{cases} 0, & t < x/c_0 \\ \dfrac{Pc_0}{T} J_0\left\{\dfrac{k}{\rho}\sqrt{(t^2-x^2/c_0^2)}\right\}, & t > x/c_0. \end{cases} \tag{1.5.35}$$

The general form of the response predicted by (1.5.35) is shown in Fig. 1.19.

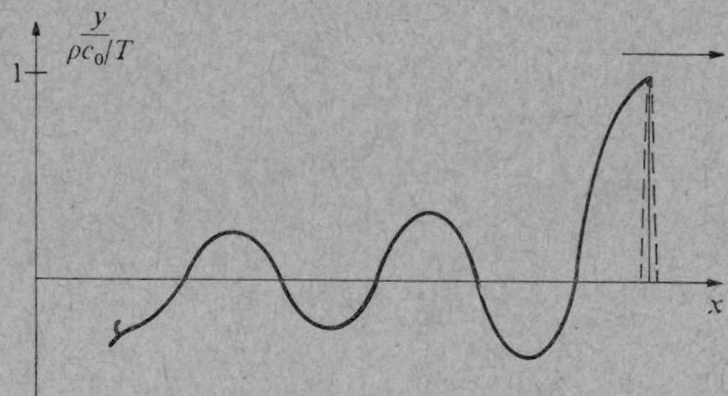

FIG. 1.19. Wave motion in a semi-infinite, elastically-supported string subjected to an impulse loading.

The main aspect to note is that the propagating pulse bears no resemblance to the input pulse, a direct consequence of dispersion. The pulse shape indicated by the dashed line in the figure is meant to illustrate a delta-function impulse, the waveform that would be propagated if the foundation were absent. We note that the head of the pulse propagates with the classical string velocity c_0.

1.6. Pulses in a dispersive media—group velocity

On the one hand, we have the wave equation and the propagation of pulses without distortion. On the other, we have the non-wave equation, the resulting frequency dependence of propagation velocity, the expected distortion of pulses, and the confirmation of this by specific example. With the string on the elastic foundation, we have been introduced to a dispersive system, the first of many to be encountered in our study of elastic waves. Because such systems are so prevalent, there is motivation for obtaining some general understanding of the consequences of dispersion and to develop techniques of analysis that will be applicable to a wide variety of situations. Work in this area represents an effort of long standing in wave-propagation theory and warrants considerable attention here. The general, unifying concept that will emerge from our study will be that of *group velocity*. The general technique of analysis will be the method of stationary phase.

1.6.1. *The concept of group velocity*

We initiate the discussion in this area by describing ripples in a pool of water, a physical situation familiar to everyone, including the earliest investigators in this area who used this example as the basis for further development. Thus it is observed that a stone dropped in a pool of still water creates an intense local disturbance (a 'splash' to the layman) which does not remain localized but spreads outward over the pool as a train of ripples as artistically depicted in Fig. 1.20. The ensuing behaviour of the ripple train

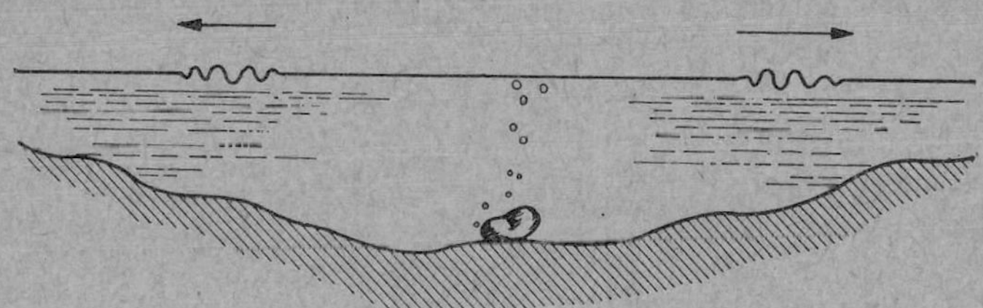

FIG. 1.20. Ripples on a pond of water resulting from a local splash.

is the aspect that drew the attention of early investigators. Quoting directly from Rayleigh.†

> It has often been remarked that, when a group of waves advances into still water, the velocity of the group is less than that of the individual waves of which it is composed; the waves appear to advance through the group, dying away as they approach its anterior limit.

Rephrasing only slightly, we say that ripples appear to originate at the rear of the group, propagate to the front, and disappear. Thus, the ripples have a higher velocity than the over-all group.

A simple analytical explanation of this behaviour was evidently first given by Stokes [8] and remains as the classical illustration of the phenomenon.

† Volume I, pp. 474 of reference [6]. A similar statement appears in Lamb's book [4, p. 380]. Evidently both statements were inspired by a paper by Scott Russell (1844), Report on waves, *Br. Assoc. Rep.* p. 369.

Thus, consider two propagating harmonic waves of equal amplitude but slightly different frequency ω_1 and ω_2, given by

$$y = A\cos(\gamma_1 x - \omega_1 t) + A\cos(\gamma_2 x - \omega_2 t), \tag{1.6.1}$$

where $\omega_1 = \gamma_1 c_1$, $\omega_2 = \gamma_2 c_2$. We may rewrite this as

$$y = 2A\cos\{\tfrac{1}{2}(\gamma_2 - \gamma_1)x - \tfrac{1}{2}(\omega_2 - \omega_1)t\} \times \\ \times \cos\{\tfrac{1}{2}(\gamma_1 + \gamma_2)x - (\omega_1 + \omega_2)t\}. \tag{1.6.2}$$

Since the frequencies are only slightly different, the wavenumbers also will only slightly differ. We write these differences as

$$\omega_2 - \omega_1 = \Delta\omega, \qquad \gamma_2 - \gamma_1 = \Delta\gamma. \tag{1.6.3}$$

Similarly, we define the average frequency and wavenumber as

$$\omega = \tfrac{1}{2}(\omega_1 + \omega_2), \qquad \gamma = \tfrac{1}{2}(\gamma_1 + \gamma_2), \tag{1.6.4}$$

and the resulting average velocity by $c = \omega/\gamma$. Thus (1.6.2) may be written as

$$y = 2A\cos(\tfrac{1}{2}\Delta\gamma x - \tfrac{1}{2}\Delta\omega t)\cos(\gamma x - \omega t). \tag{1.6.5}$$

Now, the cosine term containing the difference terms $\Delta\gamma, \Delta\omega$ is a low-frequency term since $\Delta\omega$ is a small number. It will have a propagation velocity c_g where

$$c_g = \frac{\Delta\omega}{\Delta\gamma}. \tag{1.6.6}$$

The cosine term containing the average wavenumber and frequency γ and ω will be a high-frequency term, propagating at the averge velocity c. The effect of the low-frequency term will be to act as a *modulation* on the high-frequency *carrier*. The appearance of the motion is as shown in Fig. 1.21.

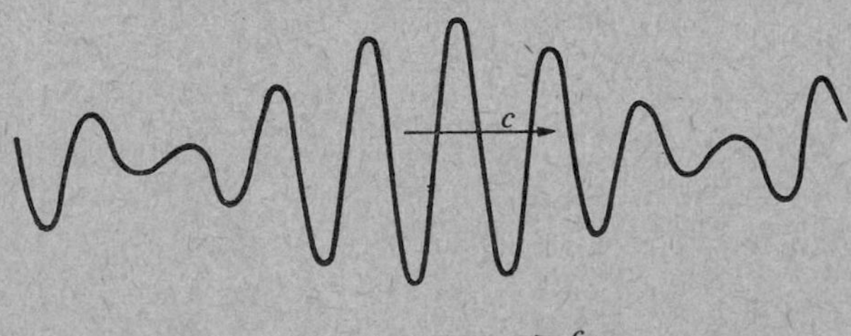

FIG. 1.21. Simple wave group formed by two waves of slightly different frequency.

It is the over-all wave group that propagates at the velocity c_g in the figure. The velocity of the high-frequency carrier may actually be greater than, equal to, or less than the velocity c_g. Whichever occurs will depend on the dispersion situation for the elastic system. For the various cases, we will have

$c > c_g$: waves will appear to originate at the rear of the group, travel to the front and disappear;

$c = c_g$: no relative motion of the group and carrier occurs and the group travels along without distortion of the wave shape.

$c < c_g$: waves will appear to originate at the front of the group, travel to the rear and disappear.

The velocity c_g that has been introduced by (1.6.6) is called the *group velocity*.

The preceding example illustrates the basic aspects of wave groups and group velocity as being formed by harmonic waves of only slightly different frequencies and wave speeds. Since only two waves were used, the results appear as a succession of groups. The existence of an isolated wave group, as illustrated in Fig. 1.20, is a consequence of many waves having slightly different frequencies and velocities interacting. Seeking to generalize along these lines, we consider a superposition of a number of waves†

$$y = \sum_{i=1}^{n} A_i \cos(\gamma_i x - \omega_i t + \phi_i), \tag{1.6.7}$$

where γ_i and ω_i differ only slightly. The phase angle of a given disturbance is ϕ_i (not to be confused with the phase $(\gamma_i x - \omega_i t + \phi_i)$).

We suppose that at some time $t = t_0$ and location $x = x_0$, the phases of the various wave trains are approximately the same so that a wave group has been formed. At a time $t = t_0 + \mathrm{d}t$ and location $x = x_0 + \mathrm{d}x$, the change in phase $\mathrm{d}P_i$ of any individual component is

$$\mathrm{d}P_i = \{\gamma_i(x_0 + \mathrm{d}x) - \omega_i(t_0 + \mathrm{d}t) + \phi_i\} - \{\gamma_i x_0 - \omega_i t_0 + \phi_i\} = \gamma_i\,\mathrm{d}x - \omega_i\,\mathrm{d}t. \tag{1.6.8}$$

In order for the wave group to be maintained, the change in phase for all of the terms must be approximately the same. This restriction is enforced by requiring that $\mathrm{d}P_j - \mathrm{d}P_i = 0$, which gives

$$(\gamma_j - \gamma_i)\,\mathrm{d}x - (\omega_j - \omega_i)\,\mathrm{d}t = 0. \tag{1.6.9}$$

Since γ_i, γ_j and ω_i, ω_j differ only slightly, we let $\mathrm{d}\gamma = \gamma_j - \gamma_i$, $\mathrm{d}\omega = \omega_j - \omega_i$. Thus (1.6.9) becomes

$$\mathrm{d}\gamma\,\mathrm{d}x - \mathrm{d}\omega\,\mathrm{d}t = 0. \tag{1.6.10}$$

The velocity of the group is then given by

$$c_g = \frac{\mathrm{d}x}{\mathrm{d}t} = \frac{\mathrm{d}\omega}{\mathrm{d}\gamma}. \tag{1.6.11}$$

This expression, which agrees in form with (1.6.6), is taken as the definition of group velocity.

† Havelock [2, p. 3].

The definition of group velocity may be expressed in alternate forms using the fundamental relation $\omega = \gamma c$. Thus

$$c_g = \frac{d(\gamma c)}{d\gamma} = c + \frac{\gamma\, dc}{d\gamma}, \tag{1.6.12}$$

where $c = c(\gamma)$. Also, since $\gamma = 2\pi/\lambda$, the results may be expressed in terms of wavelength, giving

$$c_g = c - \lambda \frac{dc}{d\lambda}. \tag{1.6.13}$$

The basic definition (1.6.11) permits a direct graphical interpretation to be made using the frequency spectrum of the system. Since the frequency spectrum is a plot of ω versus γ, the group velocity at any frequency is given by the slope of the branch of the frequency spectrum. This is illustrated in Fig. 1.22 for a hypothetical spectrum. The group velocity is indicated by the

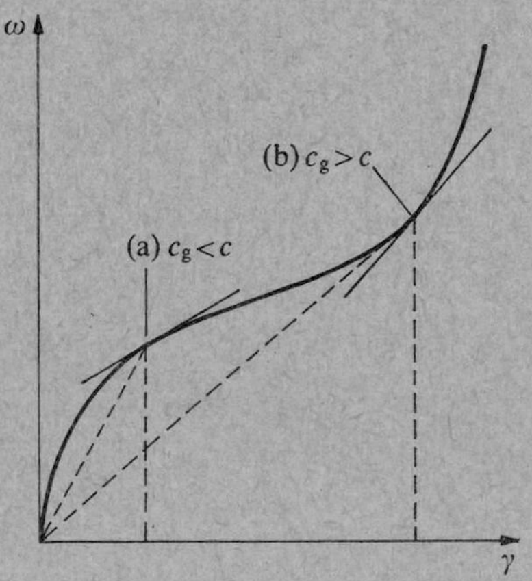

FIG. 1.22. Hypothetical frequency spectrum showing points (a) where $c_g < c$ and (b) where $c_g > c$.

local slopes to the curve of points (a) and (b). Recalling that the slope of a chord to a point is the phase velocity, it is seen that at point (a), $c_g < c$, while at point (b), $c_g > c$.

1.6.2. *Propagation of narrow-band pulses*

Having established the concepts of dispersion and group velocity, we wish to study the effects of these phenomena on pulse propagation in terms as general as possible. Now, a pulse may be characterized by its Fourier spectrum (see Appendix B) and, speaking in these terms, two possible extremes of behaviour are: (1) the pulse has a narrow frequency spectrum and is a 'narrow-band' pulse; (2) the pulse has a wide frequency band and is a 'wide-band' pulse. We will consider a technique for handling the first case in this section.

Suppose that we have applied the Fourier transform approach to the problem of forced motion of a semi-infinite string on an elastic foundation.† The inverse transform would then have the general form

$$y = \frac{1}{\sqrt{(2\pi)}} \int_{-\infty}^{\infty} f(\omega) e^{i(\gamma x - \omega t)} \, d\omega. \tag{1.6.14}$$

The above general form arises in many one-dimensional wave propagation problems. It is understood that $\gamma = \gamma(\omega)$ in the above, corresponding to a dispersive system. The nature of the forcing applied to the system is carried by $f(\omega)$. Thus, the inherent characteristics of the individual system as well as the peculiarities of the loading pulse are contained in the general solution form.

We have stated that the input is narrow-band, implying that its frequency spectrum, given by

$$f(\omega) = \frac{1}{\sqrt{(2\pi)}} \int_{-\infty}^{\infty} F(t) e^{i\omega t} \, dt, \tag{1.6.15}$$

is narrow. To interpret this more precisely, we note that a simple harmonic signal $\exp(-i\omega_0 t)$ has a spectrum given by‡

$$f(\omega_0) = \frac{1}{\sqrt{(2\pi)}} \int_{-\infty}^{\infty} \exp(-i\omega_0 t)\exp(i\omega t) \, d\omega = \sqrt{(2\pi)}\, \delta(\omega - \omega_0). \tag{1.6.16}$$

Thus, in the frequency domain, the harmonic wave shown in Fig. 1.23(a) is represented by a single line as shown in Fig. 1.23(b). Now suppose that $F(t)$ is a finite-duration oscillatory pulse having the time characteristics shown in Fig. 1.23(c). The frequency of oscillation within the 'packet' is ω_0. Then the Fourier spectrum of such a pulse is shown in Fig. 1.23(d). While not a delta function, the spectrum is sharply peaked at ω_0 with a bandwidth $\Delta\omega$ that is small relative to ω_0.

With these aspects in mind, we return to the solution form (1.6.15). We now expand $\gamma = \gamma(\omega)$ about the centre frequency ω_0. Thus

$$\gamma(\omega) = \gamma_0 + \left.\frac{d\gamma}{d\omega}\right|_{\omega_0} (\omega - \omega_0) + \ldots, \tag{1.6.17}$$

† See Problem 1.16.

‡ Most easily verified by substituting $\delta(\omega - \omega_0)$ in the inverse transform.

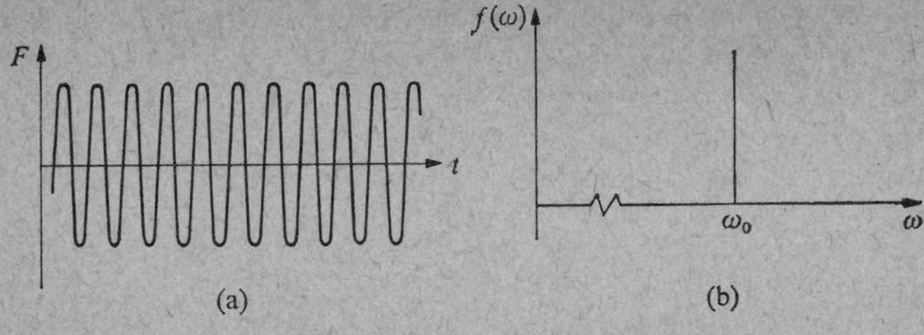

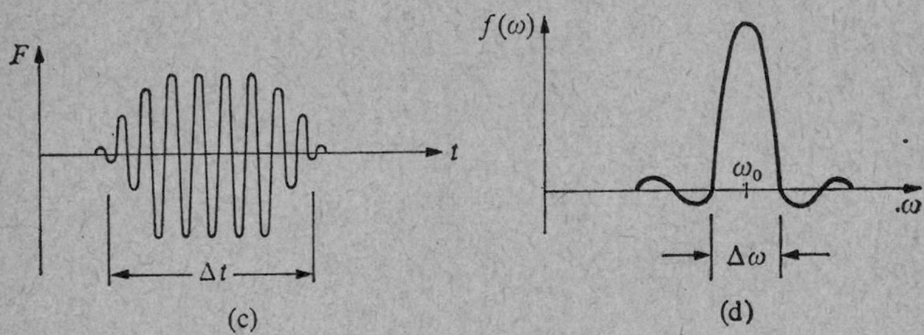

FIG. 1.23. Time behaviour and corresponding frequency spectrum for harmonic and narrow-band signals.

These first two terms will adequately represent $\gamma(\omega)$ for a narrow-band pulse. Substituting this in the solution, we have

$$y = \frac{\exp\left\{i\left(\gamma_0 - \frac{d\gamma}{d\omega}\bigg|_0 \omega_0\right)x\right\}}{\sqrt{(2\pi)}} \int_{-\infty}^{\infty} f(\omega)\exp\left\{i\left(x\frac{d\gamma}{d\omega}\bigg|_0 - t\right)\omega\right\} d\omega. \quad (1.6.18)$$

In interpreting this result, we first recall the definition of group velocity being $c_g = d\omega/d\gamma$. We thus see that $d\gamma/d\omega\,|_{\omega=\omega_0}$ is merely the reciprocal of the group velocity at the frequency ω_0. We designate this as c_g^0. We next make the change of variables,

$$t' = x/c_g^0 - t. \quad (1.6.19)$$

The integral that remains in (1.6.18) then takes the form

$$F(t') = \frac{1}{\sqrt{(2\pi)}} \int_{-\infty}^{\infty} f(\omega)\exp(i\omega t')\, d\omega. \quad (1.6.20)$$

Thus the result (1.6.18) becomes

$$y = \exp\{i(\gamma_0 - \omega_0/c_g^0)x\}F(t'). \quad (1.6.21)$$

The exponential occurring in (1.6.21) contributes nothing more than a phase angle for any given value of x. The important result is that $F(t')$, the original excitation waveform, propagates undistorted in shape and at the group velocity.

1.6.3. *Wide-band pulses—the method of stationary phase*

We have pointed out the widespread occurrence of the integral form (1.6.4) in wave-propagation problems and have presented a method for approximately evaluating it for narrow-band pulses. When the excitation is wide-band, the problem of evaluation often becomes rather formidable, even by numerical techniques, owing to the large range of the integral.

An approximate method for evaluating the integral is known as the *stationary-phase* method, or as Kelvin's method of stationary phase. The method is generally concerned with integrals of the type

$$y(x) = \int_a^b f(\omega)e^{ixh(\omega)}\,d\omega, \tag{1.6.22}$$

where $f(\omega)$ and $h(\omega)$ are real functions. The basis of the method is that for large, positive values of x, there will exist values of ω at which the major contributions to the integral occur and that, away from these critical points, the contributions of the integrand are negligible, owing to its self-cancelling oscillatory nature. This argument, and method, was first used by Stokes [7] to obtain an asymptotic representation for the function

$$y(x) = \int_0^\infty \cos x(\omega^3-\omega)\,d\omega. \tag{1.6.23}$$

Kelvin [3] first applied this principle in his consideration of a hydrodynamics problem.

In the context of wave propagation, the basis of the principle lies in the wave-group concept. Thus, the Fourier representation of the wave propagation shows a disturbance to be comprised of waves of all frequencies and wavelengths. Initially, the wave trains superimpose to give the applied disturbance. At any subsequent time, the existing disturbance is obtained by again summing the contributions of the propagating harmonic components. Because of dispersion, it is clear that the phases of the waves will no longer agree. However, there will be positions and times at which a number of waves have the same or nearly the same phase. These elements will thus re-inforce one another and produce the predominant part of the disturbance. This is again the basic argument used in the development of this section.

The basis of the preceding argument may be better understood by considering the properties of the integrand of (1.6.22). Considering only the real part, we have

$$I = f(\omega)\cos xh(\omega). \tag{1.6.24}$$

We first plot the phase $xh(\omega)$ versus ω in Fig. 1.24(a) in the vicinity of a maximum or stationary point of $h(\omega)$. Fig. 1.24(b) shows that for ω in the vicinity of the maximum, $\cos xh(\omega)$ oscillates slowly whereas for ω away from the stationary point, there are many oscillation for small changes in ω. Fig. 1.24(c) shows the resulting behaviour of $\cos xh(\omega)$. The necessity for having x large should be apparent from Fig. 1.24(a). Large x accentuates the

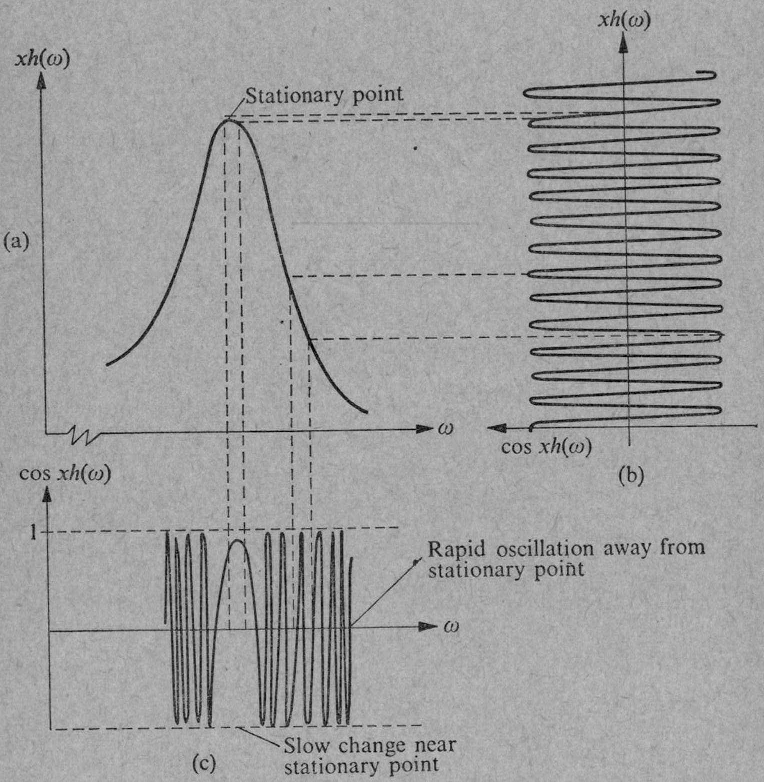

FIG. 1.24. The behaviour of $\cos xh(\omega)$ near a stationary point of $h(\omega)$.

maximum of $h(\omega)$ which increases the oscillatory nature of $\cos xh(\omega)$ away from the critical point.

To evaluate (1.6.22), making use of the ideas just described, we first expand $h(\omega)$ about ω_0. This gives

$$h(\omega) = h(\omega_0)+h'(\omega_0)(\omega-\omega_0)+(\tfrac{1}{2})h''(\omega_0)(\omega-\omega_0)^2+\ldots. \tag{1.6.25}$$

If ω_0 is a stationary point, then $h'(\omega_0) = 0$ and the phase is given by

$$xh(\omega) \simeq x\{h(\omega_0)+(\tfrac{1}{2})h''(\omega_0)(\omega-\omega_0)^2\}, \tag{1.6.26}$$

where the series has been truncated at the quadratic term. Then (1.6.22) becomes

$$y(x) = \int_{-\infty}^{\infty} f(\omega_0)\exp[\mathrm{i}x\{h(\omega_0)+\tfrac{1}{2}h''(\omega_0)(\omega-\omega_0)^2\}]\,\mathrm{d}\omega, \qquad (1.6.27)$$

where the limits of integration have been extended to infinity. This is justified because of the expected negligible contributions away from the stationary point. Then

$$y(x) = f(\omega_0)\exp\{\mathrm{i}xh(\omega_0)\}\int_{-\infty}^{\infty} \exp\left\{\frac{\mathrm{i}xh''(\omega_0)}{2}(\omega-\omega_0)^2\right\}\mathrm{d}\omega. \qquad (1.6.28)$$

The integral in this result may be found in tables and is given by

$$\int_{-\infty}^{\infty} \exp\left\{\frac{\mathrm{i}xh''(\omega_0)}{2}(\omega-\omega_0)^2\right\}\mathrm{d}\omega = \sqrt{\left\{\frac{2\pi}{xh''(\omega_0)}\right\}}\exp\left(\frac{\mathrm{i}\pi}{4}\right). \qquad (1.6.29)$$

Thus we have

$$y(x) = \left\{\frac{2\pi}{xh''(\omega_0)}\right\}^{\frac{1}{2}} f(\omega_0)\exp[\mathrm{i}\{xh(\omega_0)+\pi/4\}]. \qquad (1.6.30)$$

This result represents the approximate evaluation of the integral form (1.6.22) by the method of stationary phase.

We now relate the basic result (1.6.30) with the general integral form (1.6.14) arising in wave propagation. Comparing (1.6.22) and (1.6.14), we see that

$$h(\omega) = \gamma-\omega t/x. \qquad (1.6.31)$$

To find the stationary point such that $h'(\omega_0) = 0$ we differentiate this, giving

$$\frac{\mathrm{d}h(\omega)}{\mathrm{d}\omega} = \frac{\mathrm{d}\gamma}{\mathrm{d}\omega}-\frac{t}{x} = 0 \qquad (1.6.32)$$

or

$$\frac{\mathrm{d}\omega}{\mathrm{d}\gamma} = \frac{x}{t}. \qquad (1.6.33)$$

But $\mathrm{d}\omega/\mathrm{d}\gamma$ is the definition of group velocity. Basically, the stationary-phase result states that the dominant part of the disturbance that arrives at a particular point x at time t will have travelled with a group velocity $c_g = x/t$ and will consist of the dominant frequency component ω_0 determined from (1.6.32). This aspect is illustrated in Fig. 1.25 for a given location x_0 at time t_0. Thus, in Fig. 1.25(a) a hypothetical frequency spectrum is shown and the frequency ω_0 corresponding to $c_g = x_0/t_0$ indicated. At that instant of time, a disturbance having that frequency arrives at x_0 as shown in Fig. 1.25(b). The wavelength of the disturbance is given by $\lambda_0 = 2\pi/\gamma_0$. Other details of the disturbance at that location and time will depend on the form of $h(\omega)$ and $f(\omega)$ and will be given by (1.6.30). The former quantity will characterize

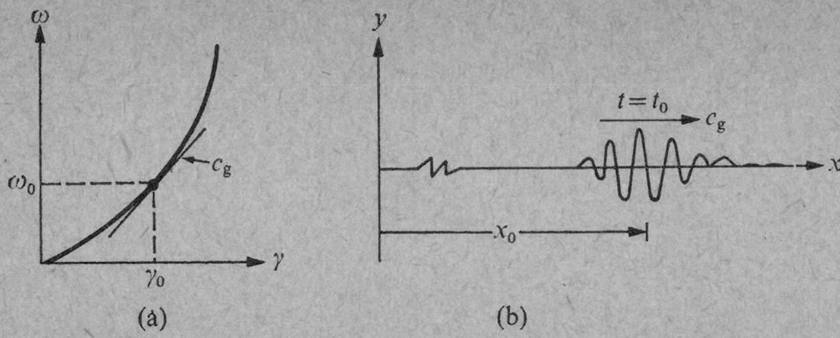

FIG. 1.25. Signal arriving at x_0 at time t_0 and having frequency ω_0.

the dispersive characteristics of the media while the latter will describe the input.

A concluding remark is in order regarding the method of stationary phase. The basis of the method is the supposed self-cancelling oscillations of the integrand. This provides the nulling mechanism for the integral away from the critical points. Other methods for obtaining asymptotic values of the integrals allow $h(\omega)$ and $f(\omega)$ to be complex and employ stronger mechanisms, involving exponential decay, than those used in the stationary-phase method. The method of steepest descent is one such technique that will be presented in a later chapter.

1.7. The string on a viscous subgrade

Our considerations thus far have been with purely elastic systems, and this will be the case for the major part of this book. Some brief attention, however, will be given here to a system exhibiting losses. Such is the case for a string on a viscous foundation. The effects of viscous damping significantly alters many basic aspects of string response.

1.7.1. *The governing equation*

The effects of a simple viscous foundation can be included in the governing equation in the same fashion used to include elastic-foundation effects. Thus, assuming a simple dashpot model for the forces, we assume a resistive force to the motion given by $q(x, t) = -\zeta\dot{y}(x, t)$. The resulting governing equation is

$$T\frac{\partial^2 y}{\partial x^2}-\zeta\frac{\partial y}{\partial t} = \rho\frac{\partial^2 y}{\partial t^2}. \tag{1.7.1}$$

There is little to remark on the equation other than it is not of the wave-equation form. It is also a matter of possible interest to note that as $\rho \to 0$, the equation passes over into the diffusion equation. Physically, this might correspond to the viscous effects of a foundation predominating over the mass effects of the string.

1.7.2. *Harmonic wave propagation*

Proceeding in somewhat the usual manner of investigating new mechanical systems, we consider the string to be infinite in length and seek to determine the conditions for propagation of free harmonic waves of the form

$$y = Ae^{i(\gamma x-\omega t)}. \tag{1.7.2}$$

Substitution in (1.7.1) gives

$$\gamma^2 = \frac{i\zeta\omega}{T}+\frac{\omega^2}{c_0^2}. \tag{1.7.3}$$

This is a complex quantity, the roots of which are given by

$$\gamma = M^{\frac{1}{2}}\exp(i\phi/2), \qquad M^{\frac{1}{2}}\exp\left\{i\left(\frac{\phi}{2}+\pi\right)\right\}, \tag{1.7.4}$$

where

$$M = \frac{1}{T}(\zeta^2\omega^2+\rho^2\omega^4)^{\frac{1}{2}}, \qquad \tan\phi = \frac{\zeta}{\rho\omega}. \tag{1.7.5}$$

We replace (1.7.4) with the more convenient notation

$$\gamma = \gamma_R+i\alpha, \quad -\gamma_R-i\alpha, \tag{1.7.6}$$

where

$$\gamma_R = M^{\frac{1}{2}}\cos\tfrac{1}{2}\phi, \qquad \alpha = M^{\frac{1}{2}}\sin\tfrac{1}{2}\phi. \tag{1.7.7}$$

Then the original waveform (1.7.2) becomes

$$y = A\exp[i\{\pm(\gamma_R+i\alpha)x-\omega t\}], \tag{1.7.8}$$

or

$$y = A\exp(\mp\alpha x)\exp\{i(\pm\gamma_R x-\omega t)\}. \tag{1.7.9}$$

If we assume $x > 0$, we are led to discard the lower (—) sign of (1.7.8), giving the final form

$$y = A\exp(-\alpha x)\exp\{i(\gamma_R x-\omega t)\}. \tag{1.7.10}$$

Interpreting this result, we conclude that the free propagation of harmonic waves of the form (1.7.2) is not possible in a damped string. Thus, in the context of the original question, the matter is closed and other aspects must be considered.

1.7.3. *Forced motion of a string*

The form of the results (1.7.10) is hardly surprising, and merely reflects the energy loss due to viscous damping. The negative answer to the matter of free wave propagation merely means that it makes no sense to consider such matters. The question of wave motion in a damped string only makes sense in the context of steady, forced vibration, where there is an energy source to maintain motion or in the context of transient response to initial conditions or applied load. With this in mind, the solution (1.7.10) is perfectly acceptable.

We note the occurrence for the first time of a complex wavenumber and see the implications on the waveform.

We can consider a very simple example of forced motion of a string to which (1.7.10) is directly applicable. Thus, consider the semi-infinite string $x > 0$ on a viscous foundation, subjected to the forced end motion

$$y(0, t) = y_0 \exp(-\mathrm{i}\omega t).$$

By inspection we can write immediately

$$y = y_0 \exp(-\alpha x)\exp\{\mathrm{i}(\gamma_{\mathrm{R}} x - \omega t)\}. \tag{1.7.11}$$

A second problem to consider is that of an infinite string subjected to the harmonically varying concentrated load at the origin given by

$$q(x, t) = -\frac{1}{T}\,\delta(x)\mathrm{e}^{-\mathrm{i}\omega t}. \tag{1.7.12}$$

Consider a solution to the governing eqn (1.7.1), with this term on the right-hand side, of the form

$$y = Y(x)\mathrm{e}^{-\mathrm{i}\omega t}. \tag{1.7.13}$$

We obtain the ordinary differential equation

$$\frac{\mathrm{d}^2 Y}{\mathrm{d}x^2} + \left(\frac{\mathrm{i}\zeta\omega}{T} + \frac{\omega^2}{c_0^2}\right) Y = \delta(x). \tag{1.7.14}$$

We now state the motivation for considering this otherwise commonplace problem. Except for the addition of damping, it is identical to the problem discussed at some length in § 1.1.8. Specifically, the Fourier transform was applied and the problem was the inversion of (1.1.93). Likewise the Fourier transform can be applied to (1.7.14), giving the solution

$$Y(x) = -\frac{1}{2\pi} \int_{-\infty}^{\infty} \frac{\mathrm{e}^{-\mathrm{i}\gamma x}}{\gamma^2 - \bar{\gamma}_0^2}\,\mathrm{d}\gamma, \tag{1.7.15}$$

where $\bar{\gamma}_0^2$ in the above is given by

$$\bar{\gamma}_0^2 = \frac{\mathrm{i}\zeta\omega}{T} + \frac{\omega^2}{c_0^2}. \tag{1.7.16}$$

We recall the rather lengthy discussion concerning the poles of (1.1.93) located on the real axis, and the proper indentation about the poles, resulting in Fig. 1.9. The whole point of this exercise is to show that when damping is included in the system, the matter of pole indentation does not even arise. This is because the poles are no longer located on the real axis, but are displaced above and below it as given by (1.7.6). If the damping is quite small, the pole locations are given by†

$$\bar{\gamma} \cong \pm(\gamma_0 + i\varepsilon), \tag{1.7.17}$$

where ε is a small quantity. The resulting locations are shown in Fig. 1.26. Also shown is the contour appropriate for determining the response for $x > 0$. The dashed semicircles in the figure represent the indentations selected on the basis of the radiation condition for the undamped problem. It is seen that damping automatically shifts the poles in the proper direction.

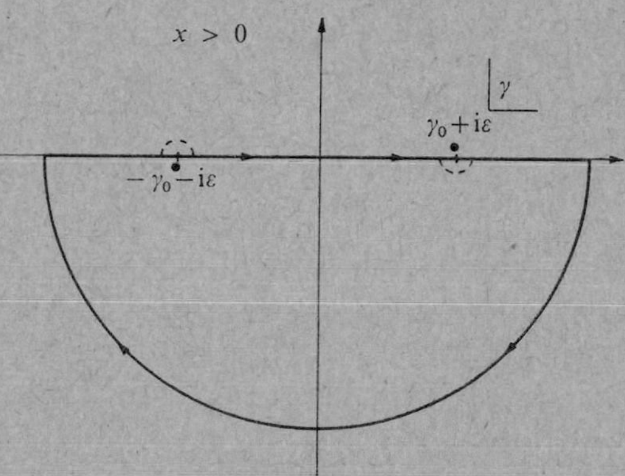

FIG. 1.26. Movement of poles off the real axis due to slight damping.

With this result pointed out, analysis will not be pursued further. It often occurs that investigators of wave problems will artificially include damping in the problem as a quick means of determining pole behaviour, then delete it from the problem.

References

1. BERRY, J. G. and NAGHDI, P. M. On the vibration of elastic bodies having time-dependent boundary conditions. *Q. J. appl. Math.* **14,** 43 (1956).
2. HAVELOCK, T. H. *The propagation of disturbances in dispersive media.* Cambridge University Press (1914).
3. KELVIN, LORD. *Phil. Mag.* **22,** 252–5 (1887).
4. LAMB, SIR H. *Hydrodynamics.* Dover Publications, New York (1945).
5. MORSE, P. M. and INGARD, K. U. *Theoretical acoustics.* McGraw-Hill, New York (1968).
6. RAYLEIGH, J. W. S. *The theory of sound*, Vols I and II. Dover Publications, New York (1945).
7. STOKES, G. G. *Mathematical and physical papers*, Vol. 2, p. 329. Cambridge University Press (1883).
8. —. *Smith's prize examination*, Cambridge, 1876. Reprinted in *Mathematics and Physics Papers*, Vol. 5, p. 362. Cambridge University Press (1905).

† Problem 1.21 pertains to specifically determining γ_0 and ε.

9. TONG, K. N. *Theory of mechanical vibration.* John Wiley and Sons, New York (1960)

Problems

1.1. Consider an infinite string which is given an initial velocity impulse over the length l as defined by

$$y(x, 0) = 0,\ \dot{y}(x, 0) = \begin{cases} V_0\, \delta(t), & |x| < l/2 \\ 0, & |x| > l/2. \end{cases}$$

Obtain the D'Alembert solution and plot the waveform for various values of time.

1.2. The infinite string is subjected to the distributed loading,

$$q(x, t) = \begin{cases} q_0 e^{-i\omega t}, & |x| < a \\ 0, & |x| > a. \end{cases}$$

Apply the Fourier transform method to this problem and determine the response for $x > a$. Recover the concentrated load results by letting $a \to 0$ in a 'proper' way.

1.3. Recover the D'Alembert results for the initial-value problem by applying the Laplace transform method.

1.4. Consider a semi-infinite, classical string, initially at rest and subjected to the harmonic end load $y(0, t) = y_0 \sin \omega t$ beginning at $t = 0$. Apply the Laplace transform method, obtaining the inversion by using integration in the complex plane. In particular, determine which way the Bromwich countour must be closed. Show that this depends on whether $x \gtrless c_0 t$.

1.5. Consider a taut string travelling at the translational velocity V_0 to the right. Develop the equation for the transverse motion of the string by introducing a moving coordinate system. Show that a resonance effect, leading to unbounded wave amplitudes, can occur if $V_0 \to c_0$. Consider also the case of a concentrated load P moving at velocity V_0. Note that with respect to the moving coordinate system $\partial/\partial t = 0$.

1.6. Apply the method of images to the reflection of a pulse from a free-end boundary condition of a semi-infinite string. Contrast the behaviour to the case of the fixed end.

1.7. Consider an infinite string with an elastic spring located at $x = 0$ and let a step pulse be incident on this discontinuity. Determine the reflected and transmitted wave system.

1.8. Consider harmonic waves in a semi-infinite string incident, respectively, on an elastic, mass, and dashpot end condition. Obtain the reflected wave amplitude ratio B/A for each case.

1.9. Consider a rectangular pulse incident on a fixed boundary of a semi-infinite string. Apply the Laplace transform approach to the problem. Show that the image pulse arises as a natural result of the analysis.

1.10. Consider the problem of a rectangular pulse incident on an elastic boundary of a semi-infinite string. The Laplace transform was applied to this problem in § 1.2, but less powerful techniques are quite sufficient here. Solve for the reflected wave using simple first-order differential equations.

1.11. *Impedance concepts for strings.* The concept of the mechanical impedance of a system is borrowed from electrical circuit theory. The impedance of an electrical circuit at a terminal is defined as the driving voltage divided by the current flow. Making the analogue of force to voltage and velocity to current, we have the impedance given by $Z = F/v$. The driving force (and voltage) is assumed harmonic. Determine the driving-point impedance of the following systems, assuming a concentrated force of $F_0 \exp(-i\omega t)$ to be applied at the appropriate location: (a) a semi-infinite classical string driven at the end; (b) a semi-infinite string on an elastic foundation driven at the end; (c) a finite string of length l, fixed at both ends, with the load applied at $x = \xi$; (d) a finite string of length l, fixed at one end, elastically supported at the other end and driven at that point.

In certain frequency ranges, distributed systems often behave like lumped parameter systems. Write the impedance expressions for a spring, a mass, and a dashpot. With which of these elements is (a) similar? Can you give a physical explanation for this?

1.12. Determine the equations governing the natural frequencies of strings of length l constrained as follows: (a) fixed-elastically supported; (b) fixed-end mass; (c) end mass–elastic support.

1.13. A taut string of length l, fixed at each end, is subjected to the initial conditions

$$y(x, 0) = \begin{cases} hx/\xi, & (0 \leq x < \xi) \\ h(l-x)/(l-\xi), & (\xi < x \leq l); \quad \dot{y}(x, 0) = 0. \end{cases}$$

Show that the solution for this initial-value problem is given by

$$y(x, t) = \frac{2hl^2}{\pi^2 \xi(l-\xi)} \sum_{n=1}^{\infty} \frac{1}{n^2} \sin\frac{n\pi\xi}{l} \sin\frac{n\pi x}{l} \cos\frac{n\pi c_0 t}{l}.$$

1.14. A taut string of length l is subjected to the distributed steady-state forcing $q(x, t) = q_0 \sin \omega t$. Solve the problem seeking a solution of the form $y(x, t) = Y(x)\sin \omega t$.

1.15. Sketch the curve of group velocity versus wavenumber for the infinite string on an elastic foundation.

1.16. Consider the semi-infinite string on an elastic foundation subjected to the end transient $y(0, t) = y_0(t)$. Apply the Fourier transform to this problem and thus obtain the specific form of the response integral (1.6.14) for this problem. Find the stationary points for the system, and, in general, determine the form taken by the integral.

1.17. For the string on an elastic foundation, re-examine the behaviour at the cutoff frequency. Specifically, show that at $\omega = \omega_c$, a response of the form

$$y(x, t) = (A+Bx)\exp(i\omega_c t)$$

is predicted. The B term of the result is subsequently discarded on physical grounds.

1.18. When a taut wire under tension T and carrying a current I is placed between two magnetic coils, a restoring force similar to that of an elastic foundation acts on the wire when the current flows in one direction in the coils. When the current is reversed, a negative restoring force acts on the wire. Thus an effective negative spring modulus is created. Study the propagation of harmonic waves in a string on a foundation having this characteristic. Sketch the frequency spectrum. An unstable wave motion should result.

1.19. Consider two harmonic waves of slightly differing frequency propagating in a string on an elastic foundation, in the manner of the Kelvin illustration of group velocity. Is $c \gtrless c_g$ for this system? Does the particular inequality hold for the entire range of ω?

1.20. A taut, semi-infinite string rests on an elastic foundation and is subjected to the end transient

$$y(0, t) = A \exp(-4t^2/\tau^2)\cos \omega_0 t,$$

where $\omega_0 = 2\omega_c$ and ω_c is the system cutoff frequency. The modulation is the Gaussian pulse, where the time constant τ is equal to $20/\omega_c$. Other parameters are $\rho = 0{\cdot}52$ kg m^{-1}, $c_0 = 50{\cdot}8$ m s^{-1}, $k = 20{\cdot}7\pi^2$ N m^{-2}. (a) On the basis of group velocity considerations, when would the signal arrive at a station $x = 25$ cm? (b) On the basis of the phase velocity of ω_0, when would the signal arrive at $x = 25$ cm? (c) For (a), what would be the wavelength of the received signal?

1.21. In the case of a string on a viscous foundation, suppose damping is small. Show that, for these conditions,

$$\gamma_R \cong \omega/c_0, \qquad \alpha \cong \zeta\omega/2T,$$

thus indicating that the propagation velocity is unaffected by the damping and only amplitude attenuation occurs.

2 Longitudinal waves in thin rods

PHYSICALLY longitudinal wave motion in a thin rod and the transverse wave motion of a taut string are quite different. Mathematically, however, the two systems are quite similar. It turns out that the wave equation which governs the motion of the string also governs the longitudinal rod motion, at least within a range of circumstances. It is to be expected, therefore, that many results obtained for the string, such as the D'Alembert solution, will apply directly to the rod.

Despite this apparent great similarity, considerable attention is devoted to problems involving the thin rod in the following. There are several reasons for this. The first is that the inherent physical difference between the two systems results in practical applications, and hence problems of analysis, of the rod structure that have no logical counterpart in the string. Problems involving mechanical impact are a case in point. Secondly, because the rod is a practical structural system, it is important to obtain a direct appreciation of such variables as stress, particle velocity, and energy. Finally, 'other' effects which cause the governing equation to depart from the wave equation form in the string (for example, the elastic foundation) also exist for the rod (for example, lateral inertia), and these must be considered in their own right.

The thin rod represents the first of several elastic systems considered where the governing theory is based on 'strength-of-materials' considerations. Other cases are the thin beam, the thin plate, and the thin shell. Such theories do not originate from the exact equations of elasticity but from considering the motion of an element of the structure. The distinguishing characteristics of all such theories is that certain assumptions on the kinematics of deformation are made, such as 'plane sections remain plane' for the thin beam. Chapters 2–4 will be concerned with such theories.

The contents of this chapter will digress from its title in the last section, where torsional waves in thin rods are briefly covered. It will be found that the governing equation, developed on the basis of strength-of-materials considerations, is again in the form of the wave equation. Other than presenting basic data on typical wave velocities, the analysis of this system will not be pursued further.

2.1. Waves in long rods

The governing equation for the thin rod will be derived and the basic propagation characteristics considered. Since most aspects are similar to the case of waves in strings, coverage will be rather brief.

2.1.1. *The governing equation*

Consider a straight, prismatic rod as shown in Fig. 2.1(a). The coordinate

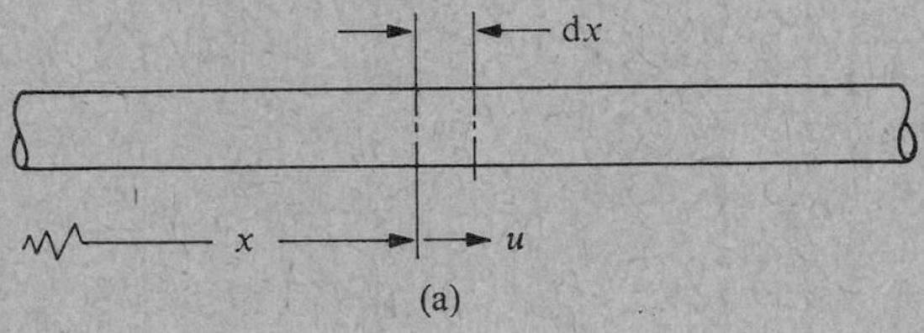

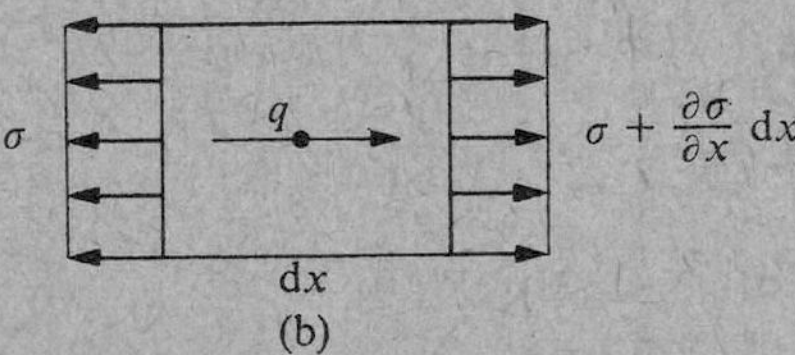

FIG. 2.1. A thin rod (a) with coordinate x and displacement u of a section and (b) the stresses acting on a differential element of rod.

x refers to a cross-section of the rod, while the longitudinal displacement of that section is given by $u(x, t)$. We presume the rod to be under a dynamically-varying stress field $\sigma(x, t)$, so that adjacent sections are subjected to varying stresses. A body force $q(x, t)$ per unit volume is also assumed present. The equation of motion in the x direction then becomes

$$-\sigma A+\left(\sigma+\frac{\partial\sigma}{\partial x}\,\mathrm{d}x\right)A+qA\,\mathrm{d}x = \rho A\,\mathrm{d}x\frac{\partial^2 u}{\partial t^2}, \tag{2.1.1}$$

where A is the cross-sectional area of the rod. We are considering a prismatic rod, so this parameter is a constant in this development. We note that tensile stress is assumed positive. Eqn (2.1.1) reduces to

$$\frac{\partial\sigma}{\partial x}+q = \rho\frac{\partial^2 u}{\partial t^2}. \tag{2.1.2}$$

Material effects have not been introduced, so at this stage the equation is applicable to non-elastic as well as elastic problems. We now presume that the material behaves elastically and follows the simple Hooke's law

$$\sigma = E\varepsilon, \tag{2.1.3}$$

where E is Young's modulus and ε is the axial strain, defined by

$$\varepsilon = \partial u/\partial x. \tag{2.1.4}$$

Using (2.1.3) and (2.1.4) in the equation of motion, we obtain

$$\frac{\partial}{\partial x}\left(E\frac{\partial u}{\partial x}\right)+q = \rho\frac{\partial^2 u}{\partial t^2}. \tag{2.1.5}$$

If the rod is homogeneous so that E (and ρ) do not vary with x, the equation reduces to

$$E\frac{\partial^2 u}{\partial x^2}+q = \rho\frac{\partial^2 u}{\partial t^2}. \tag{2.1.6}$$

We recognize this to be identical in form to (1.1.1) derived for the taut string.

There are several assumptions implicit in the development of (2.1.6), some of which have been mentioned, such as the prismatic shape and homogeneity. The former restriction will be relaxed somewhat in a later section. It is also assumed that plane, parallel cross-sections remain plane and parallel and that a uniform distribution of stress exists. Finally, we note that a very important assumption regarding lateral effects has been made. While we have assumed uniaxial stress, we have not assumed uniaxial strain. Thus, owing to the Poisson effect, there are lateral expansions and contractions arising from the axial stress. In fact, using the generalized Hooke's law we could determine these quantities. The important point is that we have neglected the *lateral inertia* effects associated with these contraction–expansions. This restriction will also be re-examined in a later section.

Continuing, we see that in the absence of body forces, eqn (2.1.6) reduces to

$$E\frac{\partial^2 u}{\partial x^2} = \rho\frac{\partial^2 u}{\partial t^2} \tag{2.1.7}$$

or

$$\frac{\partial^2 u}{\partial x^2} = \frac{1}{c_0^2}\frac{\partial^2 u}{\partial t^2}, \qquad c_0 = \sqrt{\left(\frac{E}{\rho}\right)}, \tag{2.1.8}$$

which is, of course, the familiar wave equation.

2.1.2. *Basic propagation characteristics*

It is desirable to review briefly the basic propagation aspects as governed by (2.1.8) in the context of thin rods. We know immediately that the D'Alembert solution pertains. Thus

$$u(x, t) = f(x-c_0 t)+g(x+c_0 t), \tag{2.1.9}$$

so that longitudinal waves propagate at the velocity c_0 in a thin rod and without distortion. Fig. 1.4 still nicely illustrates the behaviour. Typical propagation velocities in most metals are quite high, of the order of 5×10^3 m s^{-1}, compared to the velocity of sound in air of about 250 m s^{-1}.

The velocity c_0 is frequently designated the *bar velocity* or thin-rod velocity, to distinguish it from other propagation velocities for materials such as shear-wave velocity. Table 2.1 presents nominal bar velocity data for a number of materials.

TABLE 2.1
Bar velocity data for materials (nominal)

Material	Bar velocity	
	$\text{m s}^{-1}\times10^{-3}$	$\text{in. s}^{-1}\times10^{-4}$
Aluminum	5·23	20·6
Brass	3·43	13·5
Cadmium	2·39	9·4
Copper	3·58	14·1
Gold	2·03	8·0
Iron	5·18	20·4
Lead	1·14	4·5
Magnesium	4·90	19·3
Nickel	4·75	18·7
Silver	2·64	10·4
Steel	5·06	19·9
Tin	2·72	10·7
Tungsten	4·29	16·9
Zinc	3·81	15·0

Let us briefly consider the physical behaviour of the rod under a propagating pulse $u = f(x - c_0t)$. Recalling that $\sigma = E\,\partial u/\partial x$, we see that the stress configuration along the bar at any instant of time will be given by the slope of the displacement wave. Several pulse configurations are shown in a qualitative manner in Fig. 2.2. We see the displacement waveforms (a) and (b) of the

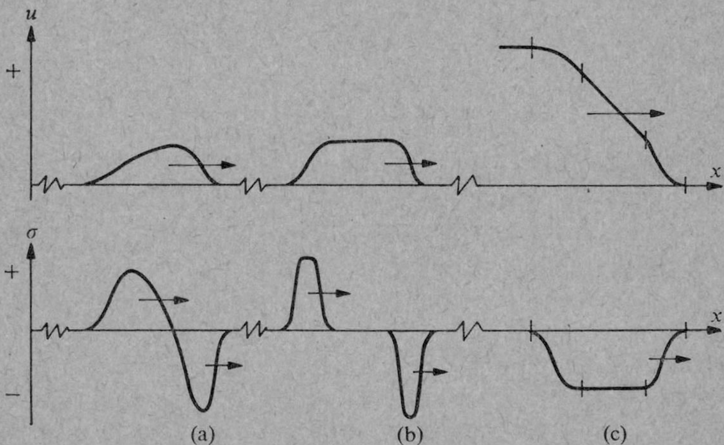

FIG. 2.2. Various displacement waveforms and the corresponding stress pulses.

figure are always positive, and that this leads to stress pulses having both tensile and compressive components. A plateau in the displacement wave, as in case (b), yields a region of zero stress. Case (c) of the figure is best considered by assuming the stress wave as prescribed, and that the displacements shown are the consequence of the stress wave. This latter waveform is commonly encountered in longitudinal impact of rods and will be studied in an idealized form in § 2.4.

As mentioned in discussing the assumptions of the theory, the Poisson effect causes lateral expansions and contractions under a propagating pulse. This effect is illustrated in greatly exaggerated form in Fig. 2.3.

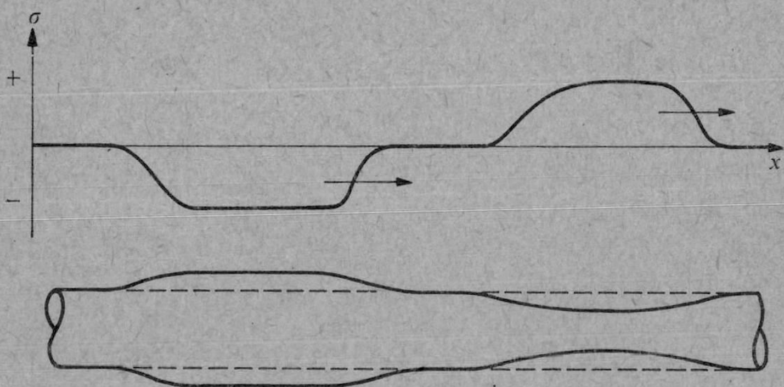

FIG. 2.3. Exaggerated illustration of Poisson expansion and contraction resulting from longitudinal stress pulses.

The particle velocity in the bar is given by

$$v(x, t) = \partial u/\partial t = -c_0 f'(x-c_0 t). \tag{2.1.10}$$

This may be expressed in terms of the stress, since

$$\sigma(x, t) = E\frac{\partial u}{\partial x} = Ef'(x-c_0 t). \tag{2.1.11}$$

Then we directly obtain

$$v(x, t) = -\frac{c_0}{E}\sigma(x, t). \tag{2.1.12}$$

Under elastic conditions, the stress is always much less than the elastic modulus, so the particle velocity will be much less than the propagation velocity. As an example, suppose a pulse of magnitude $\sigma = 10^8 \text{N m}^{-2}$ is propagating in steel. From Table 2.1 we have that $c_0 \simeq 5{\cdot}1\times10^3 \text{ m s}^{-1}$ and, for steel, $E \simeq 20{\cdot}7\times10^{10} \text{ N m}^{-2}$. This gives a particle velocity of $v = 2{\cdot}5 \text{ m s}^{-1}$. Not only is the particle velocity less than the propagation velocity, it is less by several orders of magnitude.

2.2. Reflection and transmission at boundaries

We forego repeating many of the results obtained for waves in strings, such as the initial-value problem, the characteristics plane representation, and other items covered in § 1.1, and proceed to the matter of reflection and transmission of waves. In fact, many of these results are contained in the first chapter and will be taken over rather directly. Most attention will be devoted to those areas peculiar to the rod, such as determining boundary conditions by reflected waves.

2.2.1. *Reflection from fixed and free ends*

Boundary conditions for a semi-infinite rod analogous to those for a string (see Table 1.1) can be formulated. The image method can be applied to the two simplest cases of end termination—the free and fixed ends. Again, the string results can be directly applied. However, there are one or two aspects of the phenomena in rods that deserve further emphasis. Consider first an incident pulse on a fixed boundary. The boundary condition is given by

$$u(0, t) = 0. \tag{2.2.1}$$

An image displacement pulse system is set up that will satisfy these boundary conditions and is shown in Fig. 2.4(a). Also shown is the corresponding stress

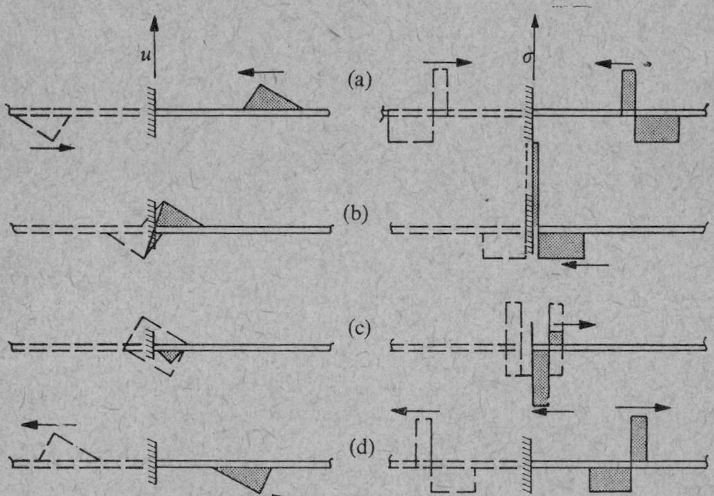

FIG. 2.4. Image displacement and stress pulse propagation, interaction, and reflection from a fixed boundary.

pulse situation. During steps (b) and (c) in the figure, interaction at the boundary occurs. The main point of this study is brought out in the stress-wave interaction in step (b). It is seen that the stresses superimpose to give double peak value. This is also occurring in step (c), where double the value of the compressive part is evident. This *stress multiplication* phenomenon is characteristic of the fixed boundary. Proceeding to part (d), after interaction has occurred, it is seen that the reflected stress pulse is identical to the incident pulse. Thus, compression has reflected as compression and tension as tension. This also is a characteristic of the fixed boundary.

Now consider a free-end boundary condition, as given by

$$\partial u(0, t)/\partial x = 0. \tag{2.2.2}$$

Again apply the image method to the reflection problem. The appropriate image system is shown in Fig. 2.5(a). As is evident in the interaction steps (b)

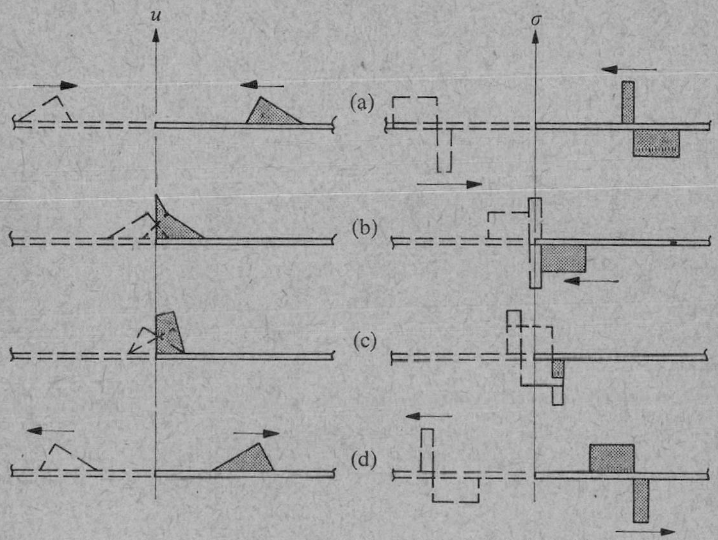

FIG. 2.5. Image displacement and stress pulse system for propagation, interaction, and reflection from a free end.

and (c), there is a doubling effect, but the doubling is associated with the *displacement* at the end and not the stress. This latter is, of course, always zero. Continuing to step (d), it is seen that the reflected stress pulse is opposite to the incident pulse; thus compression has reflected as tension and vice versa. This *stress reversal* is a characteristic of the free end.

There are several practical implications of the stress-reversal phenomenon for a free end, all basically related to the fact that if the incident wave is compressive, it will reflect as a tension wave. For example, one of the earliest experimental techniques for determining pulse characteristics employed this phenomenon.† Briefly, the method involves attaching a small pellet or 'time

† Hopkinson, B. (1914). *Phil. Trans. R. Soc.* A **213,** 437. This is mentioned in the *Introduction* (§ I.3). See Kolsky [18, pp. 87–91] for a more detailed description of the method.

piece' to the end of a rod using a thin layer of grease. Such an interface is capable of transmitting compression but not tension. When a compressive wave reaches the end of the rod, it transmits across the interface and then reverses sign. At the moment the interface stress drops from compression to zero and attempts to pass into tension, the pellet flys off due to the trapped wave momentum in the pellet. From a knowledge of the pellet length and flyoff velocity, it is possible to deduce many of the pulse characteristics.

A second application of the phenomenon is the determination of the dynamic tensile strengths of brittle materials [1, 15]. When the reflected wave causes the tensile strength of material to be reached, fracture abruptly occurs and the end of the test rod flys off in the manner of the time piece. The stress reversal phenomenon is of great importance in ballistic impact situations. Stress waves propagating through thick slabs behave in the same manner as in the rod on encountering a free boundary. It is possible, under the stress reversal, for a 'spall' to be torn from the free surface and to fly off with high velocity again due to tensile failure of the material.

2.2.2. *Reflection from other end conditions*

The elastic, mass, and dashpot end conditions for the string could be analogously formulated and analysed for the rod. Let us take a slightly more general viewpoint here that finds practical application in experimental studies involving dynamic loading of materials. Consider a semi-infinite rod in which the propagating wavefield is given by the D'Alembert solution. Thus

$$u = f(x-c_0t)+g(x+c_0t). \tag{2.2.3}$$

We suppose some force $F(t)$ to be acting on the end of the rod, such as that due to the resistance of some load against which the rod end is moving. The situation is shown in Fig. 2.6, where the dashed line indicates some hypothetical load. The velocity of the rod end is $V(t)$. The stress field in the rod will be given by

$$\begin{aligned}\sigma(x, t) &= E\{f'(x-c_0t)+g'(x+c_0t)\},\\ &= \sigma_r(x-c_0t)+\sigma_i(x+c_0t).\end{aligned} \tag{2.2.4}$$

Thus σ_i and σ_r are the incident and reflected stress pulses. Similarly, the velocity field in the rod is

$$\begin{aligned}v(x, t) &= c_0\{-f'(x-c_0t)+g'(x+c_0t)\},\\ &= \frac{c_0}{E}\{-\sigma_r(x-c_0t)+\sigma_i(x+c_0t)\}.\end{aligned} \tag{2.2.5}$$

Then, balance of force at the end of the rod requires

$$F(t) = -A\{\sigma_r(0, t)+\sigma_i(0, t)\}. \tag{2.2.6}$$

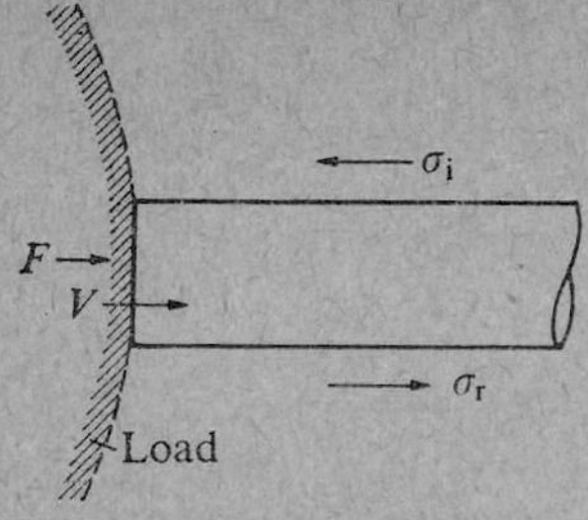

FIG. 2.6. Force F acting on the end of a rod due to the resistance of a load.

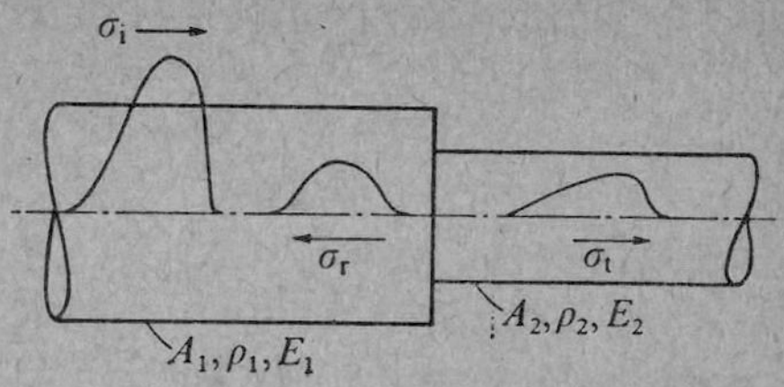

FIG. 2.7. Incident, reflected, and transmitted waves at the junction between two rods.

The velocity of the rod tip will be

$$V(t) = \frac{c_0}{E}\{-\sigma_r(0, t)+\sigma_i(0, t)\}. \tag{2.2.7}$$

These results may be used to determine the characteristics of a load by experimental means. Thus, by placing strain gauges† on the rod at some location x_0, it is a simple matter to measure the wave incident on a boundary and the wave reflected from it, so that $\sigma_i(x_0, t)$ and $\sigma_r(x_0, t)$ are known. Since the waves propagate from $x = 0$ to $x = x_0$ non-dispersively, the values of $\sigma_i(0, t)$ and $\sigma_r(0, t)$ are also known. From (2.2.6) and (2.2.7), the force and velocity at the interface are established. If the velocity results are integrated, displacement–time information is obtained. This data, combined with the force data enables the force-deformation characteristics of the load to be established.‡ While such a procedure is approximate, ignoring, for example, the inertia effects of the load, it finds application in percussive drilling studies and elsewhere.

2.2.3. *Transmission into another rod*

As in the case of the string, reflection of waves may occur at discontinuities other than a termination of the rod. In particular, we are interested here in the case of a junction between two semi-infinite rods, where there is a discontinuity in cross-section, in material properties or both. The situation is shown in Fig. 2.7. Proceeding in a manner similar to that used for the analogous case of the string (see Fig. 1.12 and eqns (1.2.23)–(1.2.26)), we have from balance of force and continuity of velocity at the junction

$$A_1(\sigma_i+\sigma_r) = A_2\sigma_t, \qquad v_i+v_r = v_t, \tag{2.2.8}$$

where the stresses and velocities are determined from the wavefields

$$u_i = f_1(x-c_1t), \qquad u_r = g_2(x+c_1t), \qquad u_t = f_2(x-c_2t). \tag{2.2.9}$$

† See Appendix C for a brief discussion of these devices.
‡ Problem 2.8 bears on this subject.

The results for the transmitted and reflected waves are then

$$\sigma_t = \frac{2A_1\rho_2c_2}{A_1\rho_1c_1 + A_2\rho_2c_2}\sigma_i, \qquad \sigma_r = \frac{A_2\rho_2c_2 - A_1\rho_1c_1}{A_1\rho_1c_1 + A_2\rho_2c_2}\sigma_i. \tag{2.2.10}$$

Problems involving transmission across junctions are often spoken of in terms of *impedance*.† This term and concept, borrowed from electric circuit theory, expresses the ratio of a driving force to the resulting velocity at a given point of the structure. For a semi-infinite rod, it is easily shown‡ that the driving point impedance is given by

$$Z = F/V = A\sqrt{(\rho E)}. \tag{2.2.11}$$

Using this parameter, it is possible to express the results (2.2.10) as

$$\sigma_t = \frac{2(Z_2/Z_1)(A_1/A_2)}{1+(Z_2/Z_1)}\sigma_i, \qquad \sigma_r = \frac{(Z_2/Z_1)-1}{1+(Z_2/Z_1)}\sigma_i \tag{2.2.12}$$

where $Z_1 = A_1\sqrt{(\rho_1 E_1)}$ and $Z_2 = A_2\sqrt{(\rho_2 E_2)}$. A number of interesting reflection–transmission situations arise as Z_1, Z_2, A_1, and A_2 are varied.§

2.3. Waves and vibrations in a finite rod

Our coverage of waves and vibrations in a finite rod will be fairly brief because of much applicable work in the area of strings. Again, the distinguishing aspects of the rod versus the string will be emphasized.

2.3.1. *Waves in a finite rod—history of a stress pulse*

From the work in strings, we are aware that the image method may be extended to describe waves in a finite rod (see Fig. 1.13). Instead of an initial-value problem, we wish here to consider a rod, having free end conditions, subjected to a pressure pulse at one end. Physically, we may imagine the rod to be freely suspended by two light strings, so that it is free to swing under the action of applied loads. This configuration has no counterpart in the case of the string. Thus, while free-end boundary conditions exist, the string is incapable of translation as a whole.

Consider the applied pressure to be a step pulse described by

$$p(t) = \begin{cases} -p_0, & 0 < t < T \\ 0, & T < t, \end{cases} \tag{2.3.1}$$

† First introduced in Problem 1.11.

‡ See Problem 2.3.

§ See Problem 2.6.

where the negative sign indicates compression. The propagating stress wave will be given by

$$\sigma(x, t) = p(x - c_0 t), \tag{2.3.2}$$

before the first end reflection. Now the response of a particle at a typical point to this stress pulse can be deduced from the results presented in § 2.1. In particular, eqn (2.1.12) shows that when the step stress pulse reaches $x = x_0$, the particle will be brought from rest to the velocity

$$v(x_0, t) = -c_0 p(x_0 - c_0 t)/E$$

instantaneously and will remain at this constant velocity until the pulse passes, at which point the velocity will again be zero. The displacement will increase according to the relation $u(x_0, t) = c_0 p_0 t/E$ while the pulse passes, and will remain constant after passage.

The preceding paragraph describes the motion of a single particle under a single passage of the step pulse. The pulse will traverse the bar repeatedly, owing to end reflections, thus subjecting the particle repeatedly to similar behaviour. The response at the ends will differ slightly from this behaviour owing to the 'velocity doubling' that occurs at reflection from a free end (see Fig. 2.5). The resulting behaviour of three particles of the bar during this multiple reflection process is shown in Fig. 2.8. Also shown is the loading and suspension configuration of the bar.

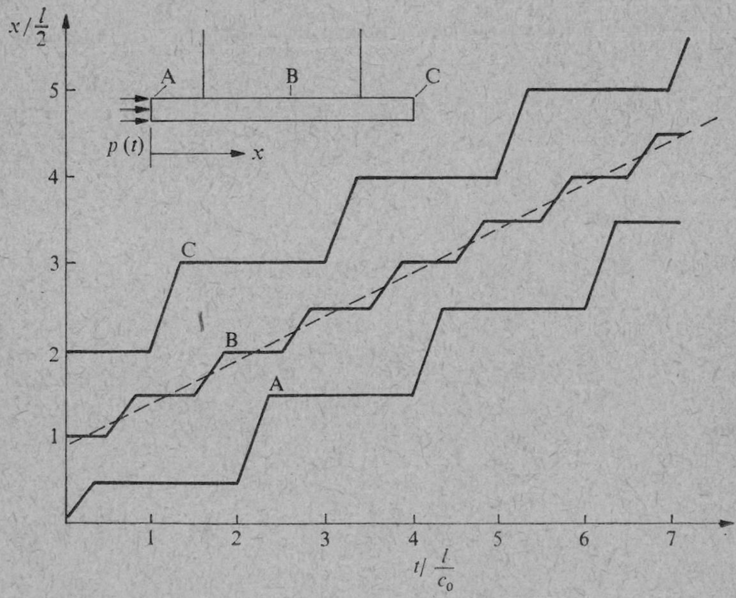

FIG. 2.8. The response of three points along a bar subjected to a step pressure pulse. (Based on Kolsky [18, p. 46].)

It is seen that point B moves to the right in a series of 'jerky' movements. The dashed line in the figure represents the average motion of B, which is located at the centre of gravity of the bar. Now, as time passes, the effects of slight damping in the material, as well as slight dispersive effects, will cause the various curves A, B, and C to be smoothed out. Specifically, curve B will approach the dashed line shown. There will then be no internal vibrations of the bar—in other words, no relative particle motions. Instead, each particle will have a uniform translational velocity given by the slope of the dashed line. This velocity will be that predicted by the simple impulse-momentum considerations of rigid-body dynamics. This example should serve to illustrate the connection between the detailed considerations of wave propagation and the gross motion considerations of rigid-body dynamics.

2.3.2. *Free vibrations of a finite rod*

The analysis of the free vibrations of finite rods closely follows the considerations for strings. Thus a rod of length l, constrained in some manner at $x = 0$ and $x = l$, has the motion predicted by

$$u(x, t) = \sum_{n=1}^{\infty}(A_n \sin \omega_n t + B_n \cos \omega_n t)U_n(x). \tag{2.3.3}$$

The functions $U_n(x)$ correspond to the normal modes of the rod at the natural frequencies ω_n. A variety of constraints, such as free–free, free–fixed, fixed–elastically supported, and so forth, are possible. As in the case of the string, the normal modes are orthogonal if the boundary conditions are of the form

$$aU(x_0) + bU'(x_0) = 0. \tag{2.3.4}$$

Let us consider one simple example of determining the normal modes and natural frequencies. The reasons for this are several: it is desirable to interpret the modes in terms of longitudinal rod displacements; this particular example has a slight distinguishing characteristic from anything in strings; and finally, it relates to a field of interesting applications of longitudinal resonance phenomena.

The example is the free–free rod, described by the boundary conditions

$$\frac{\partial u(0, t)}{\partial x} = \frac{\partial u(l, t)}{\partial x} = 0. \tag{2.3.5}$$

Using separation of variables in the homogeneous wave equation (for a discussion of this, see § 1.3) gives

$$U'' + \beta^2 U = 0, \qquad \beta^2 = \omega^2/c_0^2 \tag{2.3.6}$$

and

$$U = C \sin \beta x + D \cos \beta x. \tag{2.3.7}$$

Substituting this in the boundary conditions gives $C = 0$ and

$$\sin \beta l = 0, \qquad \beta l = n\pi \qquad (n = 0, 1, 2,\ldots). \tag{2.3.8}$$

The natural frequencies are thus

$$\omega_n = \frac{n\pi c_0}{l} \qquad (n = 0, 1, 2,\ldots). \tag{2.3.9}$$

The distinguishing characteristic of this result over the analogous string problem is the $n = 0$ root of the frequency equation. This is a perfectly acceptable root in the present problem, even though it predicts $U_0(x) = 0$. In fact, eqn (2.3.6) must be re-examined with $\beta = 0$, and the solution $U = U_0$, a constant, retained. This term corresponds to the rigid-body motion† of the bar, if there is any. For this particular set of boundary conditions, the general solution (2.3.7) must be supplemented by the additional U_0 term.

The normal modes for the first three natural frequencies are shown in Fig. 2.9. The longitudinal displacements along the rod are plotted on the

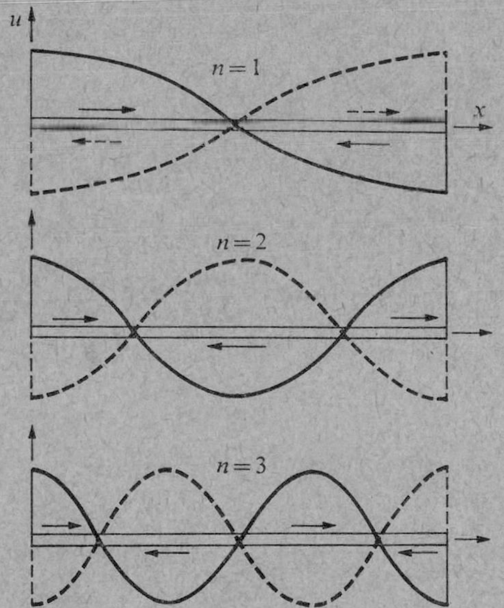

FIG. 2.9. The first three modes of a free–free rod.

vertical coordinate, while the arrows give a direct indication of particle motion. To obtain some appreciation of numbers, suppose the rod is steel and 25 cm long. For steel, $c_0 \simeq 5{\cdot}1 \times 10^3$ m s^{-1}, so (2.3.9) becomes

$$\omega_n = 20{\cdot}4 \times 10^3 \pi n \qquad (n = 1, 2,\ldots). \tag{2.3.10}$$

† See, for example, Timoshenko [38, p. 309].

The frequency in Hertz is given by $f_n = \omega_n/2\pi$, so that

$$f_n = 10{\cdot}2\times 10^3 n \cong 10^4 n, \qquad (n = 1, 2,\ldots). \tag{2.3.11}$$

We thus see that the first mode ($n = 1$), called the 'half-wave' mode, has a frequency $f_1 = 10^4$ Hz. This is, of course, a rather high frequency. A bar vibrating in this range emits a very high pitched acoustical tone. The point to be made here is that longitudinal resonance phenomena generally occur at very high frequencies compared, say, to the bending vibrations (to be studied in the next chapter) of the same element.

The phenomena of longitudinal resonance of rods finds considerable practical application in the field of power ultrasonics. Electro-mechanical devices, usually called simply 'transducers' or 'resonators', that convert electrical energy to longitudinal mechanical vibrations are designed to a large extent on the basis of longitudinal rod theory. The usual procedure is to place one or several piezoelectric discs at the displacement node of a half-wavelength bar, as shown in Fig. 2.10. A piezoelectric material has the property of undergoing mechanical displacement when an electric field is applied. By applying a driving voltage at the resonant frequency of the system, the discs act as a forcing function on the system and a strong vibration is set up. The inclusion of the piezoelectric discs at the node destroys the homogeneity of the rod, of course, so that precise prediction of resonance of the system based on formulas such as (2.3.8) is not possible and more elaborate analyses are necessary.

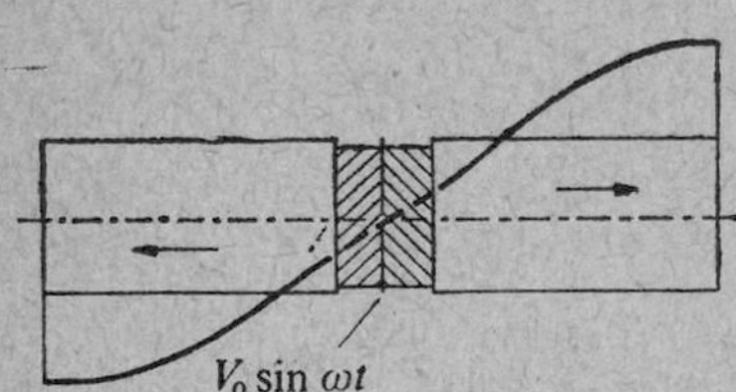

FIG. 2.10. Simplified illustration of a half wavelength ultrasonic transducer driven at a voltage $V_0 \sin \omega t$.

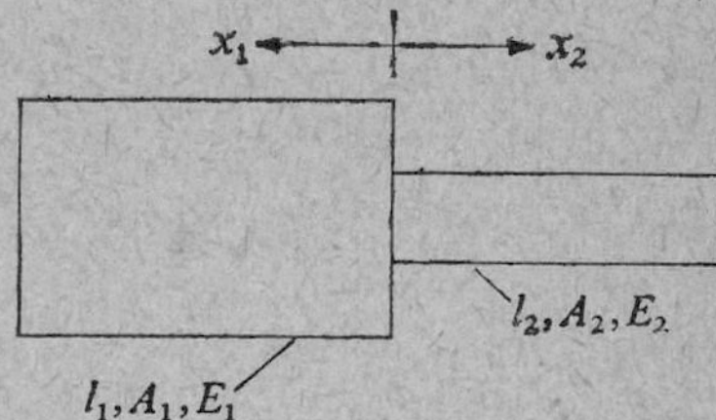

FIG. 2.11. Simple two-part composite rod.

It is possible to predict the resonant frequencies of composite rods made by connecting uniform rods together. This also has considerable application in the previously described area of power ultrasonics. To illustrate this, consider a simple two-part composite rod, as shown in Fig. 2.11. Two coordinate systems x_1 and x_2 are employed. It is presumed that the rods differ in length, cross-section, and material. Two governing equations must be used,

$$\frac{\partial^2 u_1}{\partial x_1^2} = \frac{1}{c_1^2}\frac{\partial^2 u_1}{\partial t^2}, \qquad \frac{\partial^2 u_2}{\partial x_2^2} = \frac{1}{c_2^2}\frac{\partial^2 u_2}{\partial t^2}, \tag{2.3.12}$$

where c_1, c_2 are the bar velocities of the respective materials. Seeking harmonic solutions, we write directly

$$U_1 = A \sin \beta_1 x_1 + B \cos \beta_1 x_1,$$
$$U_2 = C \sin \beta_2 x_2 + D \cos \beta_2 x_2, \tag{2.3.13}$$

where $\beta_1 = \omega/c_1$, $\beta_2 = \omega/c_2$. The boundary conditions for the problem are

$$x_1 = l_1, \qquad dU_1/dx_1 = 0,$$
$$x_1 = x_2 = 0, \qquad U_1 = -U_2, \qquad E_1 A_1 \frac{dU_1}{dx_1} = E_2 A_2 \frac{dU_2}{dx_2}, \tag{2.3.14}$$
$$x_2 = l_2, \qquad dU_2/dx_2 = 0.$$

The conditions at $x_1 = x_2 = 0$ express continuity of displacement and force at the junction. Applying these conditions to the solutions (2.3.13) gives the equations

$$A \cos \beta_1 l_1 - B \sin \beta_1 l_1 = 0,$$
$$B = -D,$$
$$E_1 A_1 A = E_2 A_2 C,$$
$$C \cos \beta_2 l_2 - D \sin \beta_2 l_2 = 0. \tag{2.3.15}$$

In order for these four homogeneous equations in A, B, C, and D to have a solution, the determinant of coefficients must vanish, giving the frequency equation

$$\frac{E_2 A_2}{E_1 A_1} \cos \beta_1 l_1 \sin \beta_2 l_2 + \cos \beta_2 l_2 \sin \beta_1 l_1 = 0. \tag{2.3.16}$$

In a general problem, this would have to be solved numerically for given values of the material and geometry parameters. A special case of interest in power ultrasonics may be easily examined, however. Suppose $E_1 = E_2$, so that the material of the two parts is the same (hence $\beta_1 = \beta_2 = \beta$) and that $l_1 = l_2$. Then (2.3.16) reduces to

$$\left(\frac{A_2}{A_1} + 1\right) \cos \beta l_1 \sin \beta l_1 = 0. \tag{2.3.17}$$

It may easily be shown that the roots corresponding to $\cos \beta l_1 = 0$ give modes of vibration antisymmetric with respect to $x_1 = x_2 = 0$, while $\sin \beta l_1 = 0$ gives symmetric modes. The first antisymmetric mode in particular is often used as a basis for transducer design. For this mode, the displacements of the two parts are given by

$$u_1 = A \sin \beta x_1, \qquad u_2 = C \sin \beta x_2, \tag{2.3.18}$$

where $C = (A_1/A_2)A$. If $A_1 > A_2$, it is seen that the displacement of u_1 is amplified relative to u_2.

2.3.3. *Forced vibrations of rods*

On the basis of the governing equation for rods, (2.1.6) where forcing effects are included, and on the basis of analogy with forced motion of strings, there would appear to be a wide class of problems associated with forced motion of rods. In a practical sense, this is not the case, however. Whereas the physical application of a transverse load at any point along the taut string is easily visualized, the means for applying longitudinal loads along a homogeneous rod are less easily imagined. While various circumstances can be contrived for such loadings, the most common means of load application is through longitudinal forcing at the ends of the rod. Thus, the concern here is with the homogeneous differential equation and inhomogeneous boundary conditions.

Consider, as a simple example of harmonic forcing, the case of a rod free at one end and subjected to the end force $F_0 \exp(i\omega t)$. Assuming a solution to the homogeneous wave equation of $U(x)\exp(i\omega t)$, we are again led to the solution form

$$U = C \sin \beta x + D \cos \beta x. \tag{2.3.19}$$

The boundary conditions are

$$EA\frac{dU}{dx}\bigg|_{x=0} = -F_0, \qquad \frac{dU}{dx}\bigg|_{x=l} = 0. \tag{2.3.20}$$

This gives

$$C = -\frac{F_0}{EA\beta}, \qquad D = -\frac{F_0}{EA\beta}\cot \beta l. \tag{2.3.21}$$

The resulting forced motion is

$$u(x, t) = -\frac{F_0}{EA\beta}(\sin \beta x + \cot \beta l \cos \beta x)e^{i\omega t}. \tag{2.3.22}$$

It is seen that the response becomes unbounded at the frequencies corresponding to $\sin \beta l = 0$, or

$$\omega_R = \frac{n\pi c_0}{l} \qquad (n = 1, 2, \ldots). \tag{2.3.23}$$

These are the resonant frequencies of the rod. We see they correspond to the natural frequencies of a free–free rod.

Velocity or displacement forcing conditions are also possible. Suppose we consider a rod, fixed at one end and subjected to the velocity forcing $V_0\exp(i\omega t)$. The boundary conditions for this case would be

$$i\omega U(0) = V_0, \qquad U(l) = 0. \tag{2.3.24}$$

It would be found that this system would be resonant at frequencies given again, coincidentally, by $\sin \beta l = 0$. The natural frequency counterpart to this problem would be found to be the fixed–fixed rod. Table 2.2 shows

TABLE 2.2

Forced	Free	Frequency
F_0		$\sin \beta l = 0$
V_0		$\sin \beta l = 0$
F_0		$\cos \beta l = 0$
V_0		$\cos \beta l = 0$

four common forced vibration situations, the resonant frequencies and the corresponding free vibration cases having the same natural frequencies. Harmonic forcing is understood.

2.3.4. *Impulse loading of a rod—two approaches*

We wish now to analyse the response of a rod to a transient load. The objective will not be to introduce new methods of analysis, but to compare presently known methods. Specifically, a wave propagation and a normal-mode method will be used and some general conclusions drawn.

The problem will be that of a rod, fixed at $x = 0$ and subjected to a transient pressure pulse at $x = l$, as shown in Fig. 2.12. The normal-mode

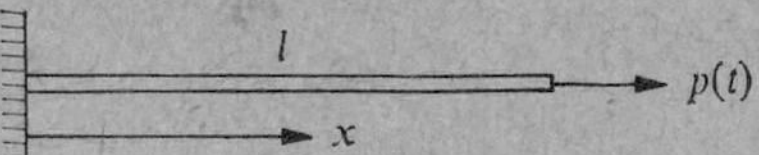

FIG. 2.12. Rod fixed at $x = 0$ subjected to a pressure pulse.

method of analysis will first be employed. Referring back to § 1.4, we have that

$$u(x, t) = \sum_{n=1}^{\infty} q_n(t) U_n(x), \tag{2.3.25}$$

where, for the fixed–free rod, the normal modes are given by

$$U_n(x) = \sin \beta_n x, \qquad \beta_n = \frac{n\pi}{2l} \qquad (n = 1, 3, \ldots). \tag{2.3.26}$$

The functions describing the time variation $q_n(t)$ are obtained from (see (1.4.64)),

$$\ddot{q}_n(t) + \omega_n^2 q_n(t) = \frac{2}{\rho l} \int_0^l U_n(x) q(x, t)\, dx, \tag{2.3.27}$$

where $q(x, t)$ is the longitudinal loading of the rod. It is possible to express the end loading as

$$q(x, t) = P\delta(l)f(t). \tag{2.3.28}$$

Then (2.3.27) becomes

$$\ddot{q}_n(t)+\omega_n^2 q_n(t) = \frac{2P}{\rho l}(-1)^{(n-1)/2}f(t) \qquad (n = 1, 3,...). \tag{2.3.29}$$

We solve this ordinary differential equation by Laplace transforms. Noting that the initial conditions are zero, the transformed solution is

$$\bar{q}_n(s) = \frac{k\bar{f}(s)}{s^2+\omega_n^2}, \qquad k = \frac{2P(-1)^{(n-1)/2}}{\rho l}. \tag{2.3.30}$$

We now specialize the time variation $f(t)$ to the delta function $\delta(t)$. Then, since $\mathscr{L}\{\delta(t)\} = 1$, we have that

$$\bar{q}_n(s) = \frac{k}{s^2+\omega_n^2}. \tag{2.3.31}$$

From Laplace transform tables, we have that

$$\mathscr{L}^{-1}\left(\frac{1}{s^2+\omega_n^2}\right) = \frac{1}{\omega_n}\sin \omega_n t. \tag{2.3.32}$$

We thus have for our final solution

$$u(x, t) = \frac{2P}{\rho c_0 l}\sum_{1,3,..}^{\infty}\frac{(-1)^{(n-1)/2}}{\beta_n}\sin \beta_n x \sin \omega_n t. \tag{2.3.33}$$

Without pausing to discuss the normal-mode results just obtained, we proceed to reconsider the same problem, applying the Laplace transform method directly. We first summarize the governing equation and conditions that set forth the problem. We have

$$\frac{\partial^2 u}{\partial x^2} = \frac{1}{c_0^2}\frac{\partial^2 u}{\partial t^2},$$

$$u(0, t) = 0, \qquad E\frac{\partial u(l, t)}{\partial x} = p(t),$$

$$u(x, 0) = \dot{u}(x, 0) = 0. \tag{2.3.34}$$

Applying the Laplace transform to the governing equation gives

$$\frac{d^2\bar{u}}{dx^2} - \frac{s^2}{c_0^2}\bar{u} = 0. \tag{2.3.35}$$

This has the solution

$$\bar{u}(x, s) = A\cosh\left(\frac{s}{c_0}x\right)+B\sinh\left(\frac{s}{c_0}x\right). \tag{2.3.36}$$

The transformed boundary conditions are

$$\bar{u}(0, s) = 0, \qquad E\,\mathrm{d}\bar{u}(l, s)/\mathrm{d}x = \bar{p}(s). \tag{2.3.37}$$

Applying these conditions to the solution (2.3.36) gives

$$A = 0, \qquad B = \frac{1}{E}\bar{p}(s)\bigg/\left(\frac{s}{c_0}\cosh\frac{s}{c_0}l\right), \tag{2.3.38}$$

resulting in the transformed solution

$$\bar{u}(x, s) = \frac{\bar{p}(s)}{\rho c_0}\left\{\sinh\left(\frac{s}{c_0}x\right)\bigg/ s\cosh\left(\frac{s}{c_0}l\right)\right\}. \tag{2.3.39}$$

To invert this, we apply the convolution integral, giving

$$u(x, t) = \frac{1}{\rho c_0}\int_0^t p(\tau)g(x, t-\tau)\,\mathrm{d}\tau, \tag{2.3.40}$$

where

$$g(x, t) = \mathscr{L}^{-1}\left\{\sinh\left(\frac{s}{c_0}x\right)\bigg/ s\cosh\left(\frac{s}{c_0}l\right)\right\}. \tag{2.3.41}$$

The problem, then, is the inversion of this function. We express $\bar{g}(x, s)$ in exponential form as

$$\begin{aligned}\bar{g}(x, s) &= \sinh\left(\frac{s}{c_0}x\right)\bigg/ s\cosh\left(\frac{s}{c_0}l\right)\\ &= \left[\exp\left\{\frac{s}{c_0}(x-l)\right\} - \exp\left\{\frac{s}{c_0}(x+l)\right\}\right]\bigg/ s\left\{1 + \exp\left(-\frac{2ls}{c_0}\right)\right\}\end{aligned} \tag{2.3.42}$$

We write the expression

$$1\bigg/\left\{1 + \exp\left(-\frac{2ls}{c_0}\right)\right\} = \sum_{n=0}^{\infty}(-1)^n\exp\left(-\frac{2lns}{c_0}\right). \tag{2.3.43}$$

Hence $\bar{g}(x, s)$ may be put in the form

$$\bar{g}(x, s) = \sum_{n=0}^{\infty}(-1)^n\left(\frac{1}{s}\mathrm{e}^{-\alpha s} - \frac{1}{s}\mathrm{e}^{-\beta s}\right), \tag{2.3.44}$$

where

$$\alpha = \{(2n+1)l-x\}/c_0, \qquad \beta = \{(2n+1)l+x\}/c_0. \tag{2.3.45}$$

From Laplace transform tables, we have that

$$\mathscr{L}^{-1}\left\{\frac{1}{s}\mathrm{e}^{-as}\right\} = H\langle t-a\rangle. \tag{2.3.46}$$

Then a term-by-term inversion of (2.3.44) gives

$$g(x,t) = \left\{H\left\langle t-\frac{(l-x)}{c_0}\right\rangle - H\left\langle t-\frac{(l+x)}{c_0}\right\rangle\right\} - \\ -\left\{H\left\langle t-\frac{(3l-x)}{c_0}\right\rangle - H\left\langle t-\frac{(3l+x)}{c_0}\right\rangle\right\} + \\ +\left\{H\left\langle t-\frac{(5l-x)}{c_0}\right\rangle - H\left\langle t-\frac{(5l+x)}{c_0}\right\rangle\right\} - \dots \quad (2.3.47)$$

This corresponds to a series of rectangular pulses.

Referring back to the convolution form (2.3.40) we see that $p(t)$ must still be specified. For a general loading, the integral would have to be evaluated numerically. However, for the special case of $p(t) = P\delta(t)$, we obtain from the convolution integral directly

$$u(x,t) = \frac{P}{\rho c_0} g(x,t), \quad (2.3.48)$$

where $g(x, t)$ is given by (2.3.47).

We now have two results to the same problem, being given by (2.3.33) and (2.3.48). The first is a normal-mode solution and the second, for want of a better term, we designate a wave-propagation solution. The response at a given point $x = x_0$ of the rod as predicted by the wave solution is shown in Fig. 2.13. The response clearly is one of a wave being reflected back and

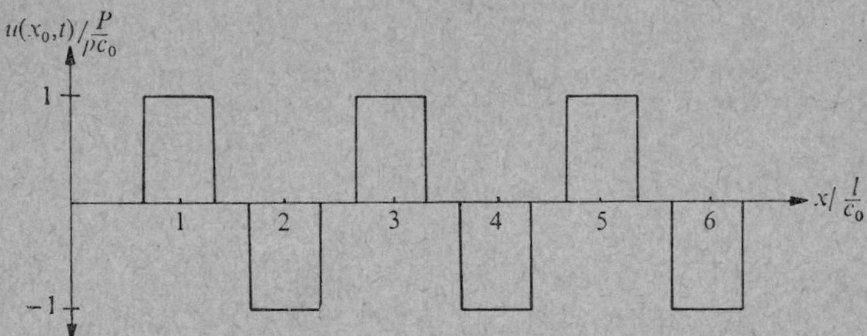

FIG. 2.13. Reflected waves in a rod subjected to a pulse load.

forth within the bar.

We note that each solution is in the form of an infinite series. Yet the two series are fundamentally different in the way in which they predict the response of the rod to this loading. Suppose we wish to predict the short-time response of the system to the load. It is seen that the normal-mode solution represents a rather slowly converging series. Thus, many terms would be required to obtain an accurate time prediction. The wave-propagation solution, on the other hand, has only to be summed to a term or so to reach the desired time at which response is sought. It provides a very accurate answer with minimal labour. On the other hand, if the long-time response is desired, many terms of the wave solution would be required. In the normal-mode case, physical intuition would lead us to discard all but the fundamental-mode term, since over long times the higher modes would damp out. Thus the normal-mode approach would prove more attractive. This example thus brings out the differing characteristics of the two approaches. For short time, the wave approach—for long time, the modal approach.

2.4. Longitudinal impact

Stress waves are produced by the mechanical impact of solids. Several situations of longitudinal impact in rods will be considered in this section and will represent first efforts at analysis in this area. Up to this stage, all of the considerations have been for prescribed loads, with no questions as to how these loads might be generated. Certainly mechanical impact represents one of the ways. In impact, however, one prescribes the material properties and geometries of the impacting solids as well as the velocity of impact. The impact force is not prescribed but is, in fact, the result to be established, as well as the ensuing wave propagation.

2.4.1. *Longitudinal collinear impact of two rods*

One of the simplest impact situations is the longitudinal impact of two flat-ended rods. It is, of course, possible to analyse the rod geometry completely, so one would suspect that such an impact situation would prove tractable. This is a technically important problem, since it provides the basis for many experimental studies of wave propagation. In the general impact cases, the bars would be of dissimilar lengths, areas, and materials, and would be travelling at two different velocities. Such a situation, at the instant of contact, is shown in Fig. 2.14(a). The analysis of such a general problem at

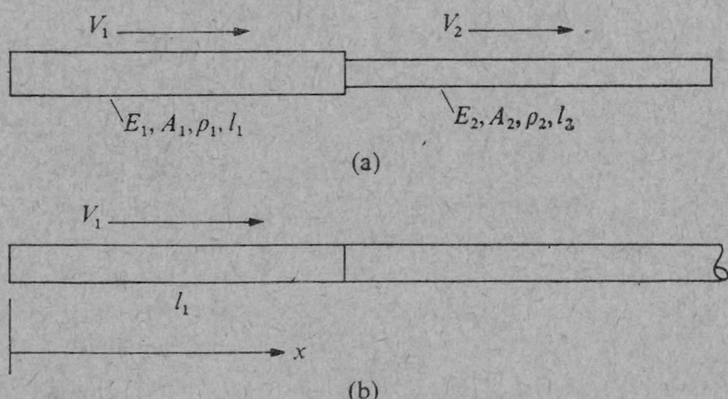

FIG. 2.14. (a) General collinear impact situation between two rods and (b) impact against a stationary semi-infinite rod.

the outset, while possible, would prove tedious. A more restricted problem will be considered first, as shown in Fig. 2.14(b).

We let the two rods be of identical materials and cross-sections, so that $E_1 = E_2$, $\rho_1 = \rho_2$, $A_1 = A_2$ in Fig. 2.14(b). Further, let the second rod be stationary ($V_2 = 0$) and of semi-infinite length ($l_2 \to \infty$). When the rods collide at $t = 0$, stress waves will propagate to the right and left from the point of contact. These wave functions may be found from the applicable initial conditions and boundary conditions for the process. From our previous work we know these functions have the form

$$\begin{aligned} u_1(x, t) &= f_1(x-c_1t)+g_1(x+c_1t), \\ u_2(x, t) &= f_2(x-c_1t)+g_2(x+c_1t). \end{aligned} \tag{2.4.1}$$

Initially, we have that both rods are stress free, that the velocity of the long rod is zero, and that the velocity of the moving rod is V_1. Recalling that the general expressions for velocity and stress are

$$\begin{aligned} v(x, t) &= -c_1f'(x-c_1t)+c_1g'(x+c_1t), \\ \sigma(x, t) &= E\{f'(x-c_1t)+g'(x+c_1t)\}, \end{aligned} \tag{2.4.2}$$

the initial condition statements take the form

$$\begin{aligned} -c_1f_1'(x)+c_1g_1'(x) &= V_1, \\ E_1A_1f_1'(x)+E_1A_1g_1'(x) &= 0, \\ -c_1f_2'(x)+c_1g_2'(x) &= 0, \\ E_1A_1f_2'(x)+E_1A_1g_2'(x) &= 0. \end{aligned} \tag{2.4.3}$$

These simultaneous equations may be solved for f_1', g_1', f_2', g_2', giving

$$\begin{aligned} f_2' &= g_2' = 0, \\ f_1' &= -g_1' = -\frac{V_1}{2c_1} \quad (0 < x < l_1). \end{aligned} \tag{2.4.4}$$

Thus at the instant of impact, the constant velocity–no stress situation existing in the left-hand rod is represented by two rectangular wave shapes, as shown in Fig. 2.15 for $t = 0$.

The two waves f_1', g_1' have been 'frozen' at $t = 0$, but it should be recalled that f_1' is a rightward-propagating wave and g_1' a leftward-propagating one. The wave action occurring for $t > 0$ will be governed by the interaction of these propagating waves with the various boundaries and discontinuities. In the case of f_1', this will be the junction of the two rods. However, since the rods are identical in this problem, there is in effect no discontinuity and f_1 moves across $x = l_1$. The wave g_2', on the other hand, reflects from the free end on the left in the manner established for such an end condition by the

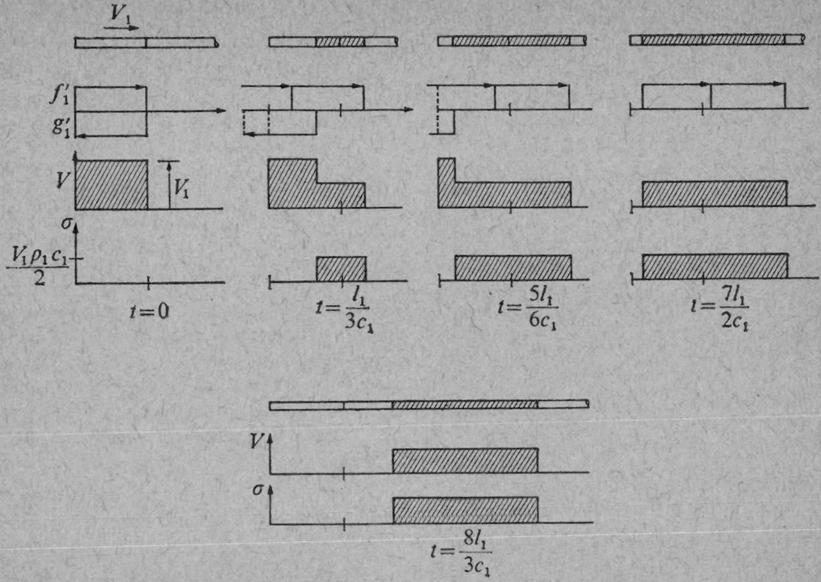

FIG. 2.15. Several stages of wave propagation in the collinear impact of two similar rods.

method of images (see Fig. 2.5). Several pertinent steps in the over-all wave process are shown in Fig. 2.15 for differing values of time. Three results are shown for each time: (1) the location of the wave functions f'_1 and g'_1; (2) the resulting velocity; (3) the resulting stress. As may be seen, a rectangular pulse of magnitude $\sigma = V_1\rho_1c_1/2$ and of duration $T = 2l_1/c_1$ is propagated into the semi-infinite rod. The length of the pulse is $2l_1$, twice the length of the impact bar. The impact bar is brought to rest for this case of identical cross-sections and materials.

As was mentioned, this configuration finds application in many studies of wave propagation.† It is a very simple configuration for generating a stress pulse of predictable shape and duration. In practice, imperfections in the physical system and inadequacies of the governing theory will cause deviations of the generated pulse from the ideal shape shown. It may be observed in experiments that the corners of the pulse are rather rounded and that the rise and fall of the pulse is not nearly as sharp as shown in the figure. Or there may be observed high-frequency oscillations on the rise and fall of the pulse. The first is generally a result of rounded contact surfaces of the impact bars and finite response time of the measuring system. The second is a consequence of lateral inertia and other higher-order effects neglected in the original development of the theory.

A somewhat more elaborate example of collinear impact will now be discussed. Referring to Fig. 2.14(a), we let both rods be of the same material

† See discussion in Appendix C.

(steel). Then let

$$\begin{aligned} l_1 &= 0{\cdot}457 \text{ m} = 18 \text{ in}, \qquad l_2 = 2l_1, \\ d_1 &= 1{\cdot}5\, d_2, \qquad d_2 = 2{\cdot}54 \text{ cm} = 1{\cdot}0 \text{ in}, \\ c_1 &= c_2 = 5{\cdot}08 \times 10^3 \text{ m s}^{-1} = 20 \times 10^4 \text{ in s}^{-1}, \\ V_1 &= V = 6{\cdot}10 \text{ m s}^{-1} = 240 \text{ in s}^{-1}, \qquad V_2 = 0, \end{aligned} \tag{2.4.5}$$

in which d_1, d_2 refer to the rod diameters. Following the procedures of the previous, simpler problem, we have at $t = 0$,

$$\begin{aligned} f_1'(x) &= -g_1'(x) = -V/2c_1, \\ f_2'(x) &= g_2'(x) = 0. \end{aligned} \tag{2.4.6}$$

This initial wave structure at the instant of collision is shown in Fig. 2.16 for

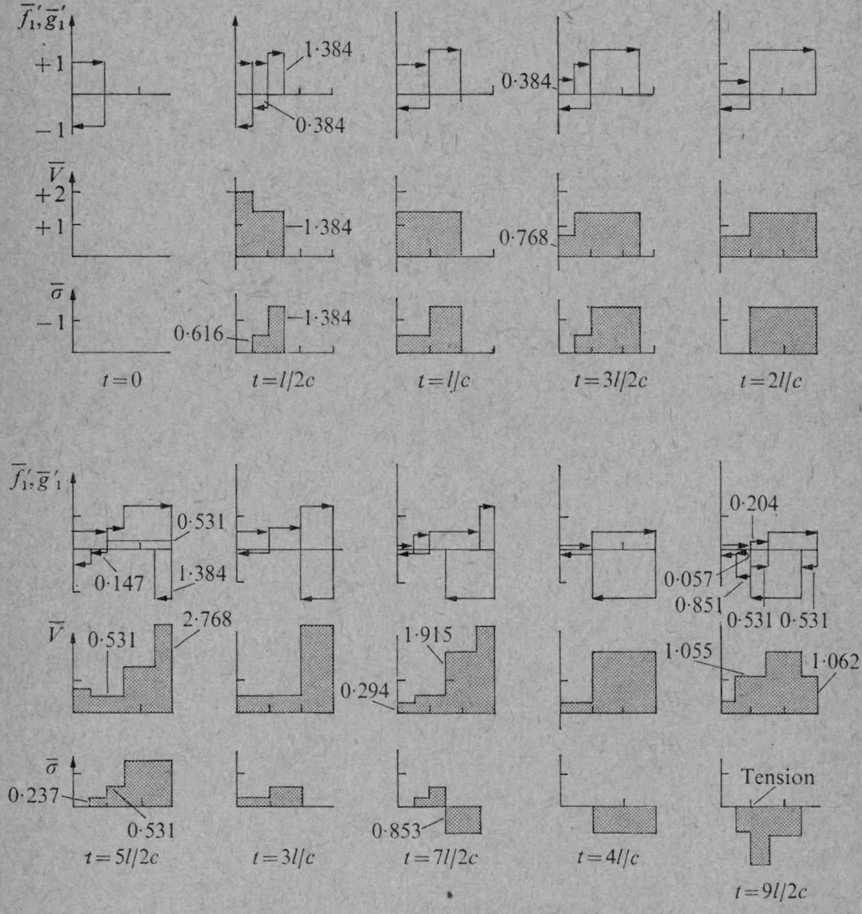

FIG. 2.16. Several stages in the wave propagation resulting from impact of two rods differing in cross-section and length.

$t = 0$. At $t > 0$, the rightward propagating component f'_1 encounters the cross-section discontuinuity. The transmitted component f'_2 and reflected component g'_2 are given by (see § 2.2)

$$f'_2 = \frac{2c_1 A_1 E_1}{A_1 E_1 c_2 + A_2 E_2 c_1} f'_1, \qquad g'_2 = \frac{c_1 A_2 E_2 - c_2 A_1 E_1}{A_1 E_1 c_2 + A_2 E_2 c_1} f'_1. \tag{2.4.7}$$

For the given values of the physical constants, these become,

$$f'_2 = 1{\cdot}384 f'_1, \qquad g'_2 = -0{\cdot}384 f'_1. \tag{2.4.8}$$

The wave structure after this first reflection and transmission is shown at $t = l_1/2c_1$. Note that the ordinates of the wavefunction, velocity, and stress diagrams have been non-dimensionalized as follows:

$$\bar{f}', \bar{g}' = \frac{2c_1}{V}(f', g'),$$
$$\bar{V} = \frac{2}{V}(f', g'), \tag{2.4.9}$$
$$\bar{\sigma} = \frac{2}{\rho_1 c_1 V}(f', g');$$

and that velocity continuity is maintained across the interface. The lack of stress continuity is a result of the area change. There is force continuity, however. A continuation of the wave process is shown in the $t = l_1/c_1$, $3l_1/2c_1$ figures. Nothing of particular significance occurs here other than the reflection of the leftward-propagating waves from the left free end.

At $t = 2l_1/c_1$, the stress waves generated by the impact have reflected from the left free end and returned to the interface. At this instant, the two bars have uniform but unequal velocities and, furthermore, the bar on the right has a greater velocity. Separation would occur except that the rightward-propagating wave in the right-hand bar (amplitude of 1·384) leaves the junction, bringing the left end of the bar momentarily to rest. The wave from the left bar immediately passes into the right bar, continuing the loading.

The situation is shown later at $t = 5l_1/2c_1$. The previously used ratios for transmitted and reflected waves still hold, only now new transmitted and reflected wave functions f'_3, g'_3 are computed, where

$$f'_3 = 1{\cdot}384 g'_2, \qquad g'_3 = -0{\cdot}384 g'_2, \tag{2.4.10}$$

and where $g'_3 = 0{\cdot}384 f'_1$. Thus

$$f'_3 = 0{\cdot}531 f'_1, \qquad g'_3 = 0{\cdot}148 f'_1. \tag{2.4.11}$$

The continuation of the propagation process at $t = 3l_1/c_1$, $7l_1/2c_1$ is shown. Again, the only significant aspects are the 0·384 and 0·147 amplitude waves reflecting from the left free end.

At $t = 4l_1/c_1$, the critical stage of the process is reached. Again, uniform velocities momentarily prevail in the two rods, with the rod on the right having the greater velocity. However, in contrast to the previous situation at $t = 2l_1/c_1$, the rod on the right is in tension. This tension cannot transmit across the interface to continue the wave process. It is easily shown that transmission would occur into the left bar if the interface were glued by considering the wave process at $t = 9l_1/2c_1$. The wave structure now becomes quite complicated since two waves, a rightward- (amplitude = 0·147) and a leftward- (amplitude = 1.384) propagating wave encounter the boundary simultaneously. The resulting structure is shown and it is seen that the interface is in tension.

Returning to $t = 4l_1/c_1$, it is of interest to note that the subsequent separation dynamics of the two bars differ. The left bar is in a uniform velocity state—and stays in that state since the leftward- and rightward-propagating waves have the same amplitude. The right bar, on the other hand, is only instantaneously in uniform motion. After separation, it continues to vibrate owing to the internal waves of 0·531 and 1·384 amplitudes.

The point of this lengthy and involved description of this more complicated impact is to gain some appreciation of the details of the wave propagation. In even slightly more complicated impacts, this procedure would not be feasible. An approach that eases the matter of following the multiple reflections within the system is to plot the characteristic plane representation of the wavefronts (see § 1.1 and Fig. 1.6 for first presentation of this scheme). This approach does not enable wave amplitudes to be established, however. The characteristics plane diagram for the impact situation just considered is shown in Fig. 2.17. If a horizontal line is drawn at any given time t, the intersection of that line with the characteristics establishes the positions of the wavefronts. Amplitude information must be determined using the procedures given in the previous example.

In practical analysis situations, the digital computer is employed, so that problems involving several cross-section changes and an extensive number of reflections are feasible to solve. One of the areas where this finds wide application is in percussive drilling, where impact of hammers of complicated geometries occur against rods having changes in cross-section.

2.4.2. *Rigid-mass impact against a rod*

The geometry of longitudinal rod impact is rather special, and we seek to widen our considerations. In some impact situations, the striking object may be approximated as a rigid mass, thus neglecting deformation and wave propagation in that part of the system. This approximation becomes more accurate when the impact mass is much greater than the local mass of the struck rod and when the material moduli of the impact mass is greater than the struck rod. This case of mechanical impact was first considered by St. Venant [36].

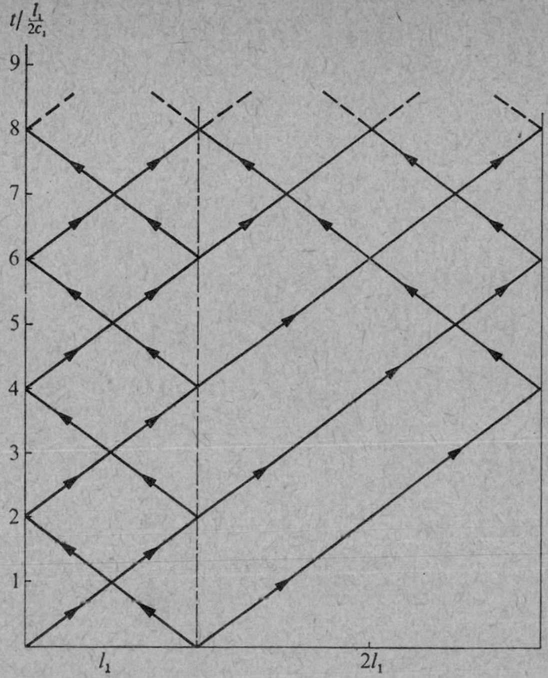

FIG. 2.17. Characteristics diagram of the wavefronts for impact of two dissimilar rods.

The case of a rigid mass impacting a semi-infinite rod is shown in Fig. 2.18. As a solution to the wave equation, we directly take

$$u(x, t) = f(c_0t - x), \tag{2.4.12}$$

corresponding to waves propagating away from the impact point. The main problem is the specification of boundary conditions. Impulse–momentum considerations applied to the mass are used for this purpose. Writing impulse-momentum, we have

$$mV_0 - \int_0^t F(\tau)\, d\tau = mV_f(t), \tag{2.4.13}$$

where $F(t)$ is the compressive force acting at the interface between mass and rod and t is the time after impact. In terms of the wave solution for the rod (2.4.12), we have the velocity and force at the interface given by

$$V_f(t) = c_0 f'(c_0 t), \qquad F(t) = -EAf'(c_0 t). \tag{2.4.14}$$

In substituting (2.4.14) into (2.4.13) we note that the velocity of the mass and rod tip are of the same sign, while the forces are of opposite sign. We obtain

$$-EA \int_0^t f'(c_0\tau)\, d\tau = m\{c_0 f'(c_0 t) - V_0\}. \tag{2.4.15}$$

The left-hand side may be integrated as follows

$$\int_0^t f'(c_0\tau)\,d\tau = \frac{1}{c_0}\int_0^{c_0 t} f'(\xi)\,d\xi = \frac{1}{c_0}\{f(c_0t)-f(0)\}. \tag{2.4.16}$$

Then (2.4.15) gives, upon substitution of (2.4.16) and rearranging terms

$$f'(c_0t)+\frac{EA}{mc_0^2}f(c_0t) = \frac{EA}{mc_0^2}f(0)+\frac{V_0}{c_0}. \tag{2.4.17}$$

The first-order differential equation has the complete solution

$$f(c_0t) = D\exp\left(-\frac{EA}{mc_0}t\right)+f(0)+\frac{mc_0}{EA}V_0. \tag{2.4.18}$$

The constant D is determined from the initial condition that the displacement is initially zero so that $f(0) = 0$. Using this in (2.4.18) we obtain

$$D = -mc_0V_0/EA,$$

so that $u(0, t)$ is given by

$$u(c_0t) = \frac{mc_0V_0}{EA}\left\{1-\exp\left(-\frac{EA}{mc_0}t\right)\right\}. \tag{2.4.19}$$

The general displacement field in the rod is given by

$$u(x, t) = \frac{mc_0V_0}{EA}H\langle c_0t-x\rangle[1-\exp\{-(c_0t-x)EA/mc_0^2\}]. \tag{2.4.20}$$

The velocity, strain, and force in the rod are given respectively by

$$v(x, t) = V_0H\langle c_0t-x\rangle\exp\{-(c_0t-x)EA/mc_0^2\},$$

$$\varepsilon(x, t) = -\frac{V}{c_0}H\langle c_0t-x\rangle\exp\{-(c_0t-x)EA/mc_0^2\},$$

$$F(x, t) = -\frac{EAV_0}{c_0}H\langle c_0t-x\rangle\exp\{-(c_0t-x)EA/mc_0^2\}. \tag{2.4.21}$$

The normalized displacement, velocity, and force, evaluated at $x = 0$, are plotted in Fig. 2.19, where

$$\bar{u} = EAu(0, t)/mc_0V_0, \qquad \bar{v} = v(0, t)/V_0,$$

$$\bar{F} = c_0F(0, t)/EAV_0, \qquad \bar{t} = EAt/mc_0. \tag{2.4.22}$$

In interpreting the results, we note that the time constant of the response is given by $T = mc_0/EA$. We recall from § 2.2 that the impedance of a rod is

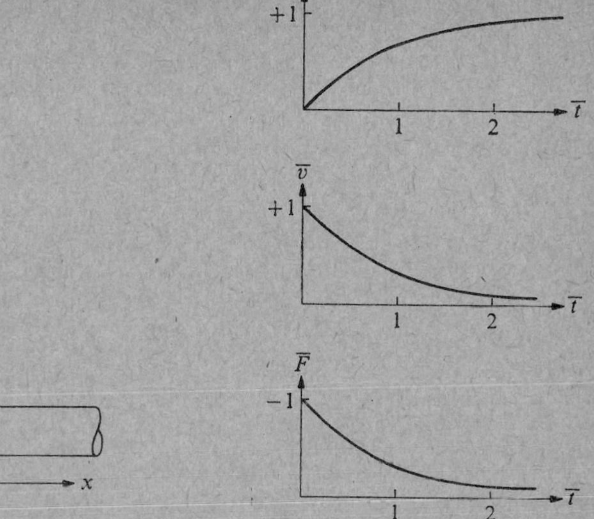

FIG. 2.18. Impact of a rigid mass against a semi-infinite rod.

FIG. 2.19. Normalized displacement, velocity, and force at the end of a rod impacted by a rigid mass.

given by $Z = \rho A c_0$. Thus, the time constant may be expressed as $T = m/Z$. We see that a smaller and smaller time constant is produced by a smaller mass and/or a greater rod impedance. Under these conditions, the force pulse begins to resemble an impulsive load for the rod.

It is of interest to compare the case of rigid-mass impact to that of one elastic rod impacting another. On the basis of previous work on impacting elastic rods, it is possible to show that the initial force generated by such an impact is given by

$$F_E(0, 0) = -\frac{Z_1}{1+Z_1/Z_2} V_0, \tag{2.4.23}$$

whereas for the rigid-mass impact, the initial force is (see (2.4.21)),

$$F_R(0, 0) = -Z_1 V_0. \tag{2.4.24}$$

The ratio of these two is then

$$\frac{F_E(0, 0)}{F_R(0, 0)} = \frac{1}{1+Z_1/Z_2}. \tag{2.4.25}$$

Thus, the rigid-mass situation always predicts a greater impact force, a hardly surprising result.

The case of rigid-mass impact against a finite rod, fixed at one end and struck at the free end, is a situation considered by St. Venant and others.† A motivation for interest in this problem is to assess the inertia effects of the rod on the dynamic response of the system. Thus the impact of a mass on a rod could be considered as a spring–mass system, the rod being the spring of the system and having a spring constant of $K = AE/l$. By then considering the wave propagation, the results of the two analyses could be compared and inertia effects assessed.

The cited references present many detailed results; only one or two major ones will be reviewed here. Results are presented for various mass ratios M, where

$$M = m_1/m_2 = \rho_1 A_1 l_1/m_2. \tag{2.4.26}$$

Thus m_2 is the impacting mass and m_1 is the total mass of the rod. The displacements occurring at the impacted end of the rod are shown in Fig. 2.20

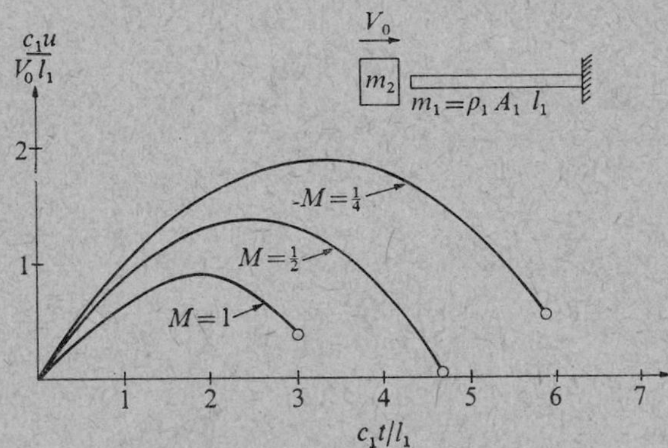

FIG. 2.20. Displacement at the end of a rod of length l struck by a rigid mass. (Based on Goldsmith [14, Fig. 26].)

for three mass ratios. The circles at the end of the curves indicate the termination of contact. To compare these results with those of a simple spring–mass model, we note that the frequency, spring constant, and period for such a system would be

$$\omega_n = \sqrt{\left(\frac{K_1}{m_2}\right)}, \qquad K_1 = \frac{A_1 E_1}{l_1}, \qquad T = 2\pi\sqrt{\left(\frac{m_2 l_1}{A_1 E_1}\right)}. \tag{2.4.27}$$

Taking one half the period, since this would be the contact time, and non-dimensionalizing it by c_1/l_1, we have for the spring–mass system

$$\bar{T}_c = \frac{c_1 T}{2 l_1} = \frac{\pi}{\sqrt{M}}. \tag{2.4.28}$$

† This problem is completely reviewed by Goldsmith [14, pp. 46–55]. Also see Timoshenko [37, pp. 498–504]. Todhunter and Pearson [39, Vol. II, Part 2, pp. 276–81], review St. Venant's work.

Calling $\tilde{T}_c$ the period of contact as established from Fig. 2.20, we have the results for the three mass ratios shown in Table 2.3.

TABLE 2.3
Contact time

M	$\tilde{T}_c$	$\bar{T}_c$
1	3·07	3·14
$\frac{1}{2}$	4·71	4·45
$\frac{1}{4}$	5·90	6·28

It is seen that periods of vibration of the two systems do not differ greatly. However, as shown in the previously cited references, more serious discrepancies occur in other parameters, such as the maximum strain.

2.4.3. *Impact of an elastic sphere against a rod*

The third impact situation that will be considered is that of a sphere in longitudinal collinear impact with a rod. In contrast to the case analysed in the preceding section, elastic deformation of the impacting solid will be accounted for using Hertz contact theory.† However, wave-propagation effects within the ball will be neglected. The approach to the problem thus combines classical longitudinal rod theory with elements of quasi-static elasticity analysis. This problem was evidently first solved by Eubanks, Muster, and Volterra [10] with experimental results later reported by Barton, Volterra, and Citron [3] and Ripperger and Abramson [35].

Consider the impact situation shown in Fig. 2.21. The displacement u_2

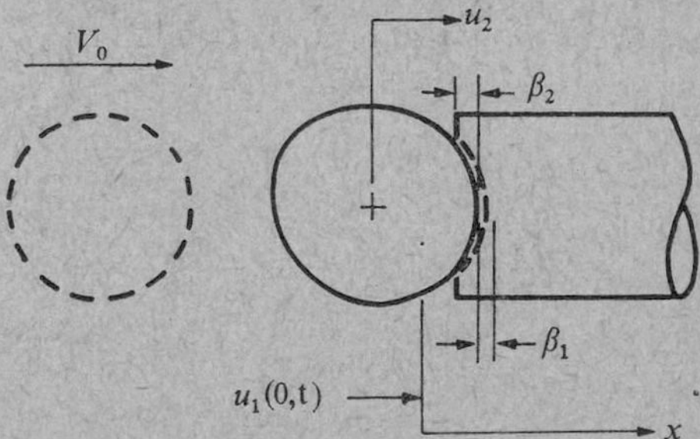

FIG. 2.21. Deformation kinematics during impact of a ball on a rod.

refers to the centre of the ball, while u_1 is the usual rod displacement. The parameters β_1 and β_2 measure the local deformation of the tip and ball respectively. As in the previous analysis of rigid-mass impact, we represent

† See, for example, Timoshenko [37, pp. 409–20].

the motion of the rod by

$$u_1(x, t) = f(c_0t - x). \tag{2.4.29}$$

We again apply impulse-momentum considerations, giving

$$m_2V_0 - \int_0^t F(\tau)\,d\tau = m_2\dot{u}_2, \tag{2.4.30}$$

where the contact force on the rod is given by

$$F(t) = -EAf'(c_0t). \tag{2.4.31}$$

The deformation–displacement condition at the contact surface now enters. The total motion of the rod contact surface consists of the gross displacement $u_1(0, t)$ plus an additional local deformation β_1. The motion of the ball contact surface is given by the gross forward motion of its centre $u_2(t)$ minus a local compression β_2. In order for the two surfaces to remain in contact, we must have

$$u_1(0, t) + \beta_1 = u_2(t) - \beta_2 \tag{2.4.32}$$

or

$$u_2(t) - u_1(0, t) = \beta_2 + \beta_1 = \alpha, \tag{2.4.33}$$

where α is defined as the 'approach,' as in Hertz contact theory.†

The governing equation for the problem is obtained by twice differentiating (2.4.33). The first differentiation gives

$$\dot{\alpha} = \dot{u}_2(t) - \dot{u}_1(0, t). \tag{2.4.34}$$

Substituting the expression for $\dot{u}_2(t)$, given by (2.4.30) and the result for $\dot{u}_1(0, t)$ obtained from (2.4.29) in (2.4.34) gives

$$\dot{\alpha} = V_0 - \frac{1}{m_2}\int_0^t F(\tau)\,d\tau - c_0f'(c_0t). \tag{2.4.35}$$

A second differentiation gives

$$\ddot{\alpha} = -\frac{F(t)}{m_2} - c_0^2f''(c_0t). \tag{2.4.36}$$

From the force expression (2.4.32) we have that

$$\dot{F}(t) = -EAc_0f''(c_0t). \tag{2.4.37}$$

Then (2.4.36) may be written as

$$\ddot{\alpha} - \frac{c_0}{EA}\dot{F}(t) + \frac{1}{m_2}F(t) = 0. \tag{2.4.38}$$

The relationship between the contact force and the local deformation must now be specified. This is determined from classical Hertz contact theory and

† Timoshenko [37, p. 410].

is given by

$$F = -K\alpha^{\frac{3}{2}}, \tag{2.4.39}$$

where K is a constant dependent on the elastic and geometric properties of the contact surfaces. For the case of a spherical ball in contact with a flat surface, the formula for K is

$$K = \frac{4}{3\pi}\frac{R^{\frac{1}{2}}}{k_1+k_2}, \tag{2.4.40}$$

where R is the radius of the ball and

$$k_1 = (1-\nu_1^2)/\pi E_1, \qquad k_2 = (1-\nu_2^2)/\pi E_2. \tag{2.4.41}$$

ν_1, E_1 and ν_2, E_2 are the Poisson's ratio and Young's modulus of rod and ball, respectively. Substituting in (2.4.38) gives

$$\frac{d^2\alpha}{dt^2}+\frac{Kc_0}{AE}\frac{d\alpha^{\frac{3}{2}}}{dt}+\frac{K}{m_2}\alpha^{\frac{3}{2}} = 0 \tag{2.4.42}$$

as the non-linear, ordinary differential equation governing impact against a rod. In addition, the initial conditions must be specified. In terms of the approach, we have that

$$\alpha(0) = u_2(0)-u_1(0, 0) = 0,$$
$$\dot{\alpha}(0) = \dot{u}_2(0)-\dot{u}_1(0, 0) = V_0. \tag{2.4.43}$$

Given the initial conditions, (2.4.42) must be solved numerically for specific values of the material and geometry parameters. The force generated is determined from (2.4.39), with the propagated stress pulse being given by

$$\alpha_1(x, t) = \frac{1}{A}F(c_0t-x). \tag{2.4.44}$$

If desired, the rebound velocity of the ball can be computed from (2.4.30). This latter calculation enables a coefficient of restitution for the impact to be established by the ratio $\dot{u}_2/V_0$.

Some numerical results are presented for the following parameters:

$$E = 20{\cdot}7 \times 10^{10}\ \mathrm{N\,m^{-2}} = 30 \times 10^6\ \mathrm{lb\,in^{-2}};$$

$$c_0 = 5{\cdot}08 \times 10^3\ \mathrm{m\,s^{-1}} = 20 \times 10^4\ \mathrm{in\,s^{-1}}; \qquad R = 0{\cdot}64\ \mathrm{cm} = 0{\cdot}25\ \mathrm{in}$$

$$m_2 = 0{\cdot}83 \times 10^{-3}\ \mathrm{kg} = 0{\cdot}57 \times 10^{-3}\ \mathrm{slug}; \qquad A = 1{\cdot}26\ \mathrm{cm^2} = 0{\cdot}196\ \mathrm{in^2}$$

$$K = 1{\cdot}20 \times 10^{10}\ \mathrm{N\,m^{-\frac{3}{2}}} = 345\ \mathrm{lb\,ml^{-\frac{3}{2}}} \tag{2.4.45}$$

The values for E, ν, c_0, m_2, and K all correspond to values for steel. The resulting stress pulses predicted for several impact velocities are shown in Fig. 2.22. It is seen that the duration of the impact is weakly dependent on the impact velocity. The relation between rebound velocity and impact

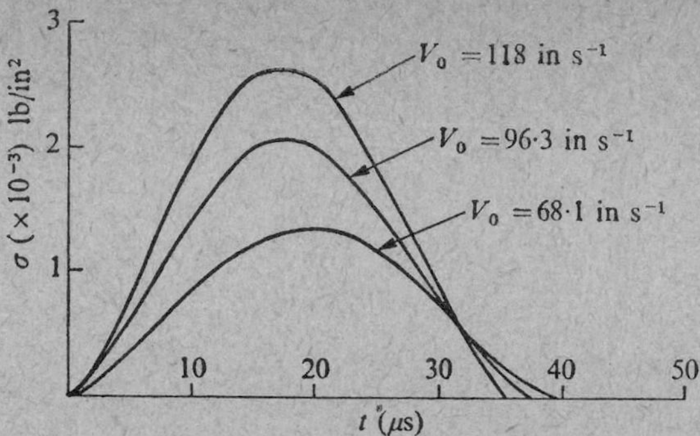

FIG. 2.22. Predicted stress pulses for impact of a ball against a rod (Feng [11], p. 18).

velocity is found to be, for all practical purposes, a linear one. For the parameters selected, it is found that $\dot{u}_2/V_0 = 0{\cdot}72$.

Because of the complicated, non-linear nature of the governing equation, it is not feasible to present general results for a wide class of impact situations. We note the relatively long period of impact compared to the ball dimensions. Thus, if impact duration were in accord with linear dimensions, as in the case of longitudinal rod impact, the duration would be an order of magnitude shorter than the resulting value of about 35 μs. This merely reflects the fundamentally different action occurring. Basically, the situation is analogous to a spring–mass system contacting the end of the rod, with the mass being that of the ball, the spring being that of the mutual deformation between the two surfaces. Considerations involving Hertz contact theory and longitudinal-rod theory have been applied to the case of collinear impact of two rods. This is reviewed extensively by Goldsmith [14, pp. 98–104].

2.5. Dispersive effects in rods

The wave equation governing the longitudinal motion of the rod predicts no distortion in a propagated wave. We shall investigate two sources of wave dispersion in this section. The first arises merely by allowing variation in cross section, but otherwise working within the assumptions of classical rod theory. The second involves including the lateral-inertia effect into the governing theory.

2.5.1. *Rods of variable cross-section—impedance*

A differential element, analogous to that shown in Fig. 2.1(b), isolated from a rod of variable cross-section is shown in Fig. 2.23. The equation of motion is given by

$$-\sigma A+\left(\sigma+\frac{\partial\sigma}{\partial x}\,\mathrm{d}x\right)\left(A+\frac{\mathrm{d}A}{\mathrm{d}x}\,\mathrm{d}x\right)=\tfrac{1}{2}\rho\left\{A+\left(A+\frac{\mathrm{d}A}{\mathrm{d}x}\,\mathrm{d}x\right)\right\}\mathrm{d}x\frac{\partial^2 u}{\partial t^2}. \quad (2.5.1)$$

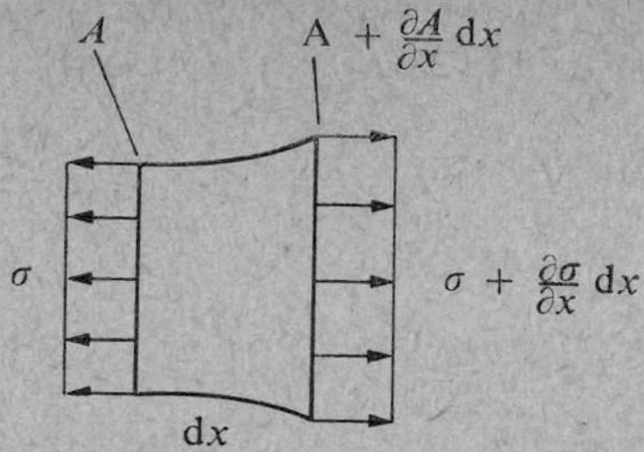

FIG. 2.23. Element from a variable cross-section rod.

The mass has been computed on the basis of the average area. Eqn (2.5.1) reduces to

$$A\frac{\partial\sigma}{\partial x}+\sigma\frac{\mathrm{d}A}{\mathrm{d}x} = \rho A\frac{\partial^2 u}{\partial t^2}. \tag{2.5.2}$$

where terms of the order of $\mathrm{d}x^2$ have been neglected. Noting that the left-hand side of (2.5.2) is given by $\partial(\sigma A)/\partial x$, we may write

$$\frac{1}{A}\frac{\partial}{\partial x}(\sigma A) = \rho\frac{\partial^2 u}{\partial t^2}. \tag{2.5.3}$$

From Hooke's law, $\sigma = E\,\partial u/\partial x$, giving

$$\frac{1}{A}\frac{\partial}{\partial x}\left(A\frac{\partial u}{\partial x}\right) = \frac{1}{c_0^2}\frac{\partial^2 u}{\partial t^2} \tag{2.5.4}$$

or

$$\frac{\partial^2 u}{\partial x^2}+\frac{1}{A}\frac{\mathrm{d}A}{\mathrm{d}x}\frac{\partial u}{\partial x} = \frac{1}{c_0^2}\frac{\partial^2 u}{\partial t^2}. \tag{2.5.5}$$

This last form clearly reveals the dispersive effects of variable cross-section. If A is constant $\mathrm{d}A/\mathrm{d}x = 0$, and the wave equation is recovered. Any variation $A = A(x)$ results in a non-wave equation. We also note that a uniform stress distribution is still assumed. In order for this assumption to remain valid, cross-sectional variation cannot be too drastic, since three-dimensional effects would enter.†

At this stage, it is seen that a cross-sectional variation must be specified before analysis can proceed further. In making some specifications, we point out that most problems in this area arise in the context of 'horn' problems. This refers to rods of tapered section that are frequently used in ultrasonics applications to achieve a high amplification of mechanical displacement (see § 2.3 and discussion pertaining to Figs. 2.10 and 2.11). Several common horn profiles, designated as linear, conical, exponential, and catenoidal are shown in Fig. 2.24. The equation governing the cross-sectional variations are

† See Morse [27, pp. 265–8] for relevant discussion of this matter in the analogous acoustic situation.

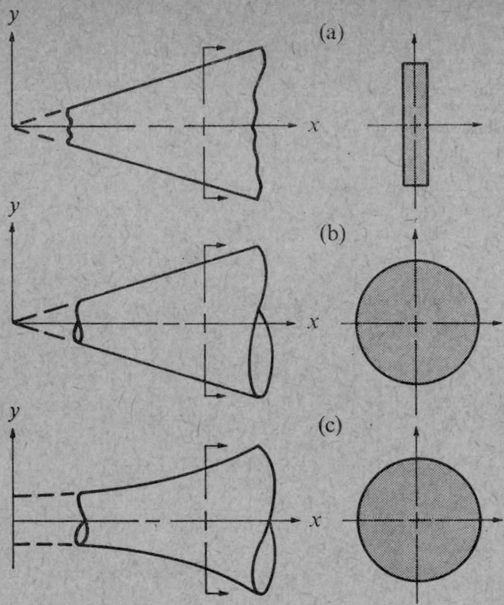

FIG. 2.24. (a) linear, (b) conical, and (c) exponential and catenoidal horn profiles.

given in the following:

linear: $$A(x) = \frac{A_0}{a}x \tag{2.5.6}$$

conical: $$A(x) = \frac{A_0}{a^2}x^2 \tag{2.5.7}$$

exponential: $$A(x) = A_0 e^{2x/h} \tag{2.5.8}$$

catenoidal: $$A(x) = A_0 \cosh^2\left(\frac{x}{h}\right). \tag{2.5.9}$$

For the linear and conical cones the one end of the horn is located at $x = a$, where the cross-sectional area is A_0 at that point. The exponential and catenoidal cases have the end of the horn located at the origin $x = 0$, where the area is A_0. The constant h governs the flair of the horn as x increases.

It is not particularly relevant to study the propagation of infinite harmonic wave trains in horn geometries, since only a few wavelengths of travel result in wavelengths comparable to the lateral dimensions, or in the area shrinking to zero, depending on the direction of propagation. It is somewhat more instructive to study the forced motion of semi-infinite horns where at least the last objection does not arise. This type of study is analogous to that carried out on acoustical horns in establishing the 'transmission coefficient'.†

† Morse [27, pp. 279–83].

As a first example, consider a horn governed by the linear area variation (2.5.6) subjected to a harmonic end forcing function $P_0 \exp(-i\omega t)$ at $x = a$. The governing equation, with the linear area variation substituted in (2.5.5), becomes

$$\frac{\partial^2 u}{\partial x^2}+\frac{1}{x}\frac{\partial u}{\partial x} = \frac{1}{c_0^2}\frac{\partial^2 u}{\partial t^2}. \tag{2.5.10}$$

Considering a solution of the form

$$u = U(x)e^{-i\omega t}, \tag{2.5.11}$$

we obtain the ordinary differential equation

$$\frac{d^2U}{dx^2}+\frac{1}{x}\frac{dU}{dx}+\beta^2 U = 0, \qquad \beta^2 = \frac{\omega^2}{c_0^2}. \tag{2.5.12}$$

This is the zeroth-order Bessel's equation, having the solution

$$U = A_1 J_0(\beta x)+B_1 Y_0(\beta x), \tag{2.5.13}$$

or, alternatively,

$$U = AH_0^{(1)}(\beta x)+BH_0^{(2)}(\beta x). \tag{2.5.14}$$

In (2.5.13), J_0 and Y_0 are Bessel's functions of the first and second kind, while (2.5.14) expresses the solution in terms of Bessel functions of the third kind, given by †

$$H_0^{(1)}(\beta x) = J_0(\beta x)+iY_0(\beta x),$$

$$H_0^{(2)}(\beta x) = J_0(\beta x)-iY_0(\beta x). \tag{2.5.15}$$

Now Bessel-function solutions will arise in a number of problems in wave propagation, with this merely being the first instance. The question that must be asked at this stage is the same arising in earlier problems of forced motion of simple systems; that is, 'which solution satisfies the radiation condition?' To establish this, the solution representation (2.5.15) is most convenient. For large values of the argument, the asymptotic representations of the functions of the third kind are‡

$$H_0^{(1)}(\beta x) \sim \sqrt{\left(\frac{2}{\pi\beta x}\right)}\exp\left\{i\left(\beta x-\frac{\pi}{4}\right)\right\}(1-\ldots),$$

$$H_0^{(2)}(\beta x) \sim \sqrt{\left(\frac{2}{\pi\beta x}\right)}\exp\left\{-i\left(\beta x-\frac{\pi}{4}\right)\right\}(1+\ldots). \tag{2.5.16}$$

Expressed in this form, it is immediately seen that the first of (2.5.16) in conjunction with the time behaviour $\exp(-i\omega t)$ gives outward-propagating waves. Consequently, this term should be retained in the solution (2.5.14) and B set equal to zero.

† See, for example, McLachlan [25, pp. 190–9].
‡ ibid., p. 198.

We now apply the boundary condition at the end of the horn, given by

$$EA_0\frac{\partial u(a,t)}{\partial x} = P_0\mathrm{e}^{-i\omega t}. \tag{2.5.17}$$

This gives

$$EA_0A\frac{\mathrm{d}H_0^{(1)}(\beta x)}{\mathrm{d}x}\bigg|_{x=a} = P_0. \tag{2.5.18}$$

We note that

$$\frac{\mathrm{d}H_0^{(1)}(\beta x)}{\mathrm{d}x} = -\beta H_1^{(1)}(\beta x). \tag{2.5.19}$$

The resulting solution for the displacement is given by

$$u(x,t) = -\frac{P_0}{EA_0\beta H_1^{(1)}(\beta a)}H_0^{(1)}(\beta x)\mathrm{e}^{-i\omega t}. \tag{2.5.20}$$

It is most useful to express the result in the form of the driving point impedance† of the horn and to refer this quantity to the impedance of a rod of uniform cross-section. Recalling that the impedance is defined as $\overline{Z}$ = force/velocity, we calculate the velocity from (2.5.20), giving

$$\dot{u}(x,t) = \frac{\mathrm{i}c_0P_0}{EA_0H_1^{(1)}(\beta a)}H_0^{(1)}(\beta x)\mathrm{e}^{-i\omega t}. \tag{2.5.21}$$

The impedance is then given by

$$Z = \frac{-\mathrm{i}EA_0H_1^{(1)}(\beta a)}{c_0H_0^{(1)}(\beta a)}. \tag{2.5.22}$$

The impedance of a rod is given by $Z_{\mathrm{R}} = A_0\sqrt{(\rho E)}$. Defining $\overline{Z}$ as the ratio of horn to rod impedances, we obtain

$$\overline{Z} = \frac{-\mathrm{i}H_1^{(1)}(\beta a)}{H_0^{(1)}(\beta a)}. \tag{2.5.23}$$

We make two observations on the results. First, the impedance is complex, as opposed to the purely real impedance of a prismatic rod. Thus the horn does not act as a pure resistance, simply absorbing energy. It has reactive components in its behaviour. Secondly, the impedance will be found to exhibit a cutoff frequency, below which energy is not propagated away from the end.‡

We now consider the case of a conical horn under forced end motion. With the cross-sectional area governed by (2.5.7), the equation of motion reduces

† See Problem 1.11 and § 2.2 for earlier discussion of this concept.
‡ Recall Problem 1.11 regarding resistive, reactive impedance aspects.

to†

$$\frac{\partial^2 u}{\partial x^2}+\frac{2}{x}\frac{\partial u}{\partial x}=\frac{1}{c_0^2}\frac{\partial^2 u}{\partial t^2}. \tag{2.5.24}$$

Again taking a solution of the form (2.5.11) we obtain

$$\frac{d^2U}{dx^2}+\frac{2}{x}\frac{dU}{dx}+\beta^2U=0. \tag{2.5.25}$$

This is again Bessel's equation having half-order Bessel functions as solutions

$$U=\frac{1}{\sqrt{x}}\{A_1J_{\frac{1}{2}}(\beta x)+BY_{\frac{1}{2}}(\beta x)\}. \tag{2.5.26}$$

The half-order Bessel functions have rather special properties and are known as spherical Bessel functions; the governing equation (2.5.25) is known as the zeroth-order spherical Bessel's equation. The standard form of the solution of (2.5.25) is given by

$$U=Ah_0^{(1)}(\beta x)+Bh_0^{(2)}(\beta x), \tag{2.5.27}$$

where $h_0^{(1)}(\beta x)$, $h_0^{(2)}(\beta x)$ are the spherical Bessel functions of the third kind.‡ These are defined in terms of spherical functions of the first and second kinds by

$$h_n^{(1)}(\beta x)=j_n(\beta x)+in_n(\beta x),$$

$$h_n^{(2)}(\beta x)=j_n(\beta x)-in_n(\beta x), \tag{2.5.28}$$

where

$$j_n(\beta x)=\sqrt{\left(\frac{2}{\pi\beta x}\right)}J_{n+\frac{1}{2}}(\beta x),$$

$$n_n(\beta x)=\sqrt{\left(\frac{2}{\pi\beta x}\right)}Y_{n+\frac{1}{2}}(\beta x). \tag{2.5.29}$$

† We note in passing that (2.5.24) may be expressed as

$$\frac{\partial^2(xu)}{\partial x^2}=\frac{1}{c_0^2}\frac{\partial^2(xu)}{\partial t^2},$$

which is the form taken by the wave equation for spherical waves, where x is replaced by the radius r. The solution is then

$$u=\frac{1}{x}f(x-c_0t)+\frac{1}{x}g(x+c_0t).$$

This solution form will find application in Chapter 5. A particular form, given by

$$u=\frac{A}{x}e^{i(\gamma x-\omega t)}+\frac{B}{x}e^{-i(\gamma x+\omega t)}$$

could be used in the present example instead of the equivalent, but more indirect, spherical Bessel function representation.

‡ See Morse and Feshbach [28, pp. 1465–8, 1573–4] for various aspects of the spherical Bessel functions.

The special feature of the spherical Bessel functions is that they may be represented by finite series, in contrast to infinite series representations necessary for the non-half-integer order functions. Thus, for $h_n^{(1)}(\beta x)$ we have

$$h_n^{(1)}(\beta x) = \frac{e^{i\beta x}(-i)^{-n+1}}{\beta x}\sum_{r=0}^{n}\frac{(n+r)!}{r!(n-r)}\left(\frac{i}{2\beta x}\right)^n. \tag{2.5.30}$$

Again, the radiation condition will establish which Bessel function must be retained in the solution (2.5.27). The asymptotic behaviour of the function $h_n^{(1)}$ is given in general by

$$h_n^{(1)}(\beta x) \sim \frac{i^{-n}}{i\beta x}e^{i\beta x}, \tag{2.5.31}$$

which yields outgoing waves for the particular time variation of this problem. Thus our solution is reduced to

$$u(x, t) = Ah_0^{(1)}(\beta x)e^{-i\omega t}. \tag{2.5.32}$$

The condition at the end of the rod is

$$EA_0\frac{\partial u}{\partial x}\bigg|_{x=a} = P_0e^{-i\omega t}. \tag{2.5.33}$$

Noting that

$$dh_0^{(1)}(\beta x)/dx = -\beta h_1^{(1)}(\beta x), \tag{2.5.34}$$

we evaluate A and obtain for the solution

$$u(x, t) = -\frac{P_0}{EA_0\beta h_1^{(1)}(\beta a)}h_0^{(1)}(\beta x)e^{-i\omega t}. \tag{2.5.35}$$

This result may be put in more specific form using (2.5.30). Thus we have that

$$h_0^{(1)}(\beta x) = -\frac{ie^{i\beta x}}{\beta x}, \qquad h_1^{(1)}(\beta x) = \frac{e^{i\beta x}}{\beta x}\left(1+\frac{i}{\beta x}\right). \tag{2.5.36}$$

Using these formulas, and calculating the impedance in the manner used for the rod of linearly varying section, it is possible to obtain

$$\bar{Z} = (1+i/\beta a), \tag{2.5.37}$$

where the impedance has been non-dimensionalized using the semi-infinite, prismatic rod.†

2.5.2. *Rods of variable section—horn resonance*

As was mentioned in the preliminary discussion of the previous section, rods of tapered section, or 'horns', find application in power ultrasonics. In this area, the interest is in the resonance characteristics of finite-length, tapered sections.

† See Problems 2.17, 2.18 for analogous studies on the exponential and catenoidal horn.

As a first and quite simple example, consider the resonance of a horn governed by the linear area variation (2.5.6), and fixed at $x = 0$ and $x = b$. The governing equation for the motion of such a system has been previously given by (2.5.10). For harmonic vibration, the ordinary differential equation (2.5.12) still pertains, as does the solution (2.5.13). We employ the Bessel functions of first and second kind instead of the third kind, since wave propagation is no longer a consideration. The boundary conditions are given by

$$U(a) = U(b) = 0. \tag{2.5.38}$$

This gives the two equations

$$\begin{aligned} A_1 J_0(\beta a) + B_1 Y_0(\beta a) &= 0, \\ A_1 J_0(\beta b) + B_1 Y_0(\beta b) &= 0, \end{aligned} \tag{2.5.39}$$

which, in turn, gives the frequency equation for the system

$$J_0(\beta a) Y_0(\beta b) - J_0(\beta b) Y_0(\beta a) = 0. \tag{2.5.40}$$

The values of a and b must be specified before the roots of this equation can be determined.

The preceding example was selected mainly for its simplicity and not for its applicability. In power ultrasonics, the interest is in determining the resonance frequencies and amplification characteristics of half-wavelength horns, under stress-free boundary conditions at either end. In practice, such a horn is driven at resonance by piezoelectric discs located at the node or, more commonly, by connecting to a half-wavelength resonator of the form shown in Fig. 2.10.

The determination of the resonance frequencies and mode shapes follows the methods used in the previous simple example. Thus, the governing equation for a particular area variation is established and a solution determined. The boundary conditions

$$\left.\frac{\mathrm{d}U}{\mathrm{d}x}\right|_{x=a} = \left.\frac{\mathrm{d}U}{\mathrm{d}x}\right|_{x=b} = 0 \tag{2.5.41}$$

are applied and a frequency equation analogous to (2.5.40) determined.

There are several ways of using the resulting formula for horn-design purposes. Fig. 2.25 presents data for conical, exponential, and catenoidal horns for a particular design procedure. This is based on specifying the ratio R of the large diameter to the small diameter of the horn and determining the resulting half-wavelength for a given resonant frequency. Thus, one specifies the desired ratio R and horn shape and obtains from the ordinate a resulting value of $2l/\lambda$. One then specifies the material of the horn and the desired operating frequency. This information is used to calculate the half-wave parameter $\lambda/2$. Thus the resulting length l of the horn is obtained.

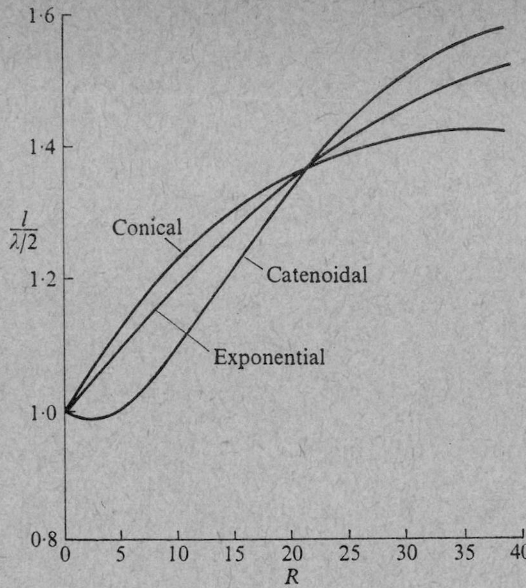

FIG. 2.25. A design chart for half-wavelength horns of conical, exponential, and catenoidal cross-section. (After Merkulov and Kharitonov [26].)

Other design parameters of interest are the amplification (ratio of small end to large end displacement), nodal location, and maximum stresses in the horn. The energy storage of the horn is also an important characteristic.

There is a large amount of literature in this area. Many aspects of horn and transducer design for ultrasonic applications are presented by Frederick [13, pp. 87–103] and by Eisner [8]. The latter author has also presented an extensive summary of the analyses of the horn problem [9].

2.5.3. *Effects of lateral inertia—dispersion*

In the derivation of the wave equation for the rod, several assumptions were mentioned, including uniform stress distribution, constant cross-section, and material homogeneity. It was also emphasized that the effects of lateral inertia were neglected. One purpose here is to re-examine this aspect and, specifically, to reformulate the theory with these effects included. Without knowing the specific form of the results, we suspect that a dispersive system will result. The fundamentally dispersive nature of the rod was first pointed out by Pochhammer† in conjunction with application of the exact theory of elasticity to wave propagation in the rod. An effort to assess the effects of lateral inertia on longitudinal vibrations was presented by Rayleigh [32,

† See Reference [31]. Note entry for 1876 in the *Introduction* (§ I.3). Also see Chapter 8, § 8.2.

Vol. 1, pp. 251–2]. Love [24, p. 428] presented the complete governing equation, and it is this development, based on energy considerations, that will be presented here.

We consider the rod and a typical cross-section as shown in Fig. 2.26, where

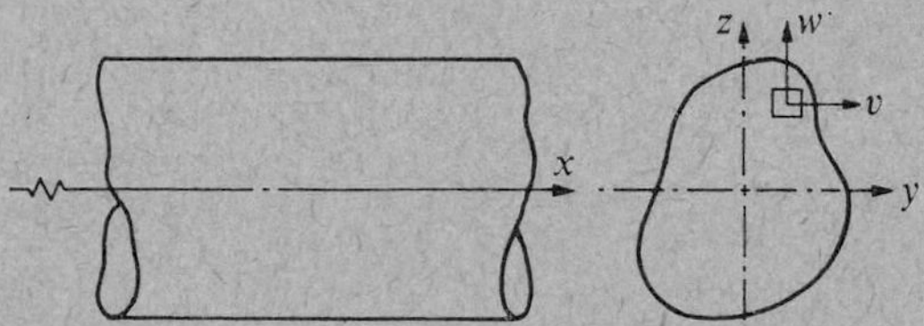

FIG. 2.26. Rod and cross-section showing lateral displacement components.

the origin is at the centroid of the rod. As a result of the longitudinal displacements u and the Poisson effect, lateral displacements v and w will occur at a typical point of the cross-section having coordinates y and z. The lateral strains existing in the rod will be given from the general Hooke's law as

$$\varepsilon_x = \frac{1}{E}\{\sigma_x - \nu(\sigma_y + \sigma_z)\},$$

$$\varepsilon_y = \frac{1}{E}\{\sigma_y - \nu(\sigma_x + \sigma_z)\},$$

$$\varepsilon_z = \frac{1}{E}\{\sigma_z - \nu(\sigma_x + \sigma_y)\}. \tag{2.5.42}$$

We assume that uniaxial stress still holds, so that $\sigma_y = \sigma_z = 0$. Hence we obtain from (2.5.42)

$$\varepsilon_y = \varepsilon_z = -\frac{\nu}{E}\sigma_x = -\nu\frac{\partial u}{\partial x}. \tag{2.5.43}$$

Now, the lateral displacements v and w are given by

$$v = \varepsilon_y y, \qquad w = \varepsilon_z z, \tag{2.5.44}$$

where y and z are the coordinates of a point in the cross-section. Substituting (2.5.43) in (2.5.44) enables the lateral displacements to be expressed in terms of the longitudinal motion as

$$v = -\nu y\frac{\partial u}{\partial x}, \qquad w = -\nu z\frac{\partial u}{\partial x}. \tag{2.5.45}$$

In applying the energy method† for the derivation of the equation of motion, expressions for the kinetic and potential energy are required. The

† Appendix A.8 briefly reviews energy considerations.

kinetic energy density is simply

$$T = \frac{\rho}{2}(\dot{u}^2+\dot{v}^2+\dot{w}^2), \qquad (2.5.46)$$

while the strain energy density is given by

$$V = \sigma\varepsilon/2, \qquad (2.5.47)$$

for uniaxial strain. Hamilton's equation then becomes

$$\delta \int_{t_0}^{t_1} (\tilde{T} - \tilde{V})\,\mathrm{d}t = 0, \qquad (2.5.48)$$

in the absence of external loads, where

$$\begin{aligned} \tilde{T} &= \int_V \frac{\rho}{2}(\dot{u}^2+\dot{v}^2+\dot{w}^2)\,\mathrm{d}V, \\ \tilde{V} &= \int_V \frac{\sigma\varepsilon}{2}\,\mathrm{d}V. \end{aligned} \qquad (2.5.49)$$

It is possible to integrate the preceding expressions over the area of the section. In first considering the kinetic energy integral, we note that

$$\dot{v} = -\nu y\frac{\partial^2 u}{\partial x\,\partial t}, \qquad \dot{w} = -\nu z\frac{\partial^2 u}{\partial x\,\partial t}. \qquad (2.5.50)$$

Then

$$\tilde{T} = \int_L \mathrm{d}x \int_A \frac{\rho}{2}\left\{\dot{u}^2+\nu^2(y^2+z^2)\left(\frac{\partial^2 u}{\partial x\,\partial t}\right)^2\right\}\mathrm{d}A. \qquad (2.5.51)$$

The longitudinal displacement $u(x, t)$ does not depend on the coordinates y and z, so the area integral may be evaluated exactly. The result is

$$\tilde{T} = \int_L \frac{\rho A}{2}\left\{\dot{u}^2+\nu^2k^2\left(\frac{\partial^2 u}{\partial x\,\partial t}\right)^2\right\}\mathrm{d}x, \qquad (2.5.52)$$

where k^2 is the polar radius of gyration of the cross-section, given in terms of the area and polar moment of inertia as $J = Ak^2$. The potential energy density is given by

$$\tilde{V} = \int_L \mathrm{d}x \int_A \left(\frac{E\varepsilon^2}{2}\right)\mathrm{d}A = \int_L \frac{EA}{2}\left(\frac{\partial u}{\partial x}\right)^2 \mathrm{d}x. \qquad (2.5.53)$$

Hamilton's equation then is

$$\delta \int_{t_0}^{t_1} \mathrm{d}t \int_L A\left[\frac{\rho}{2}\left\{\left(\frac{\partial u}{\partial t}\right)^2+\nu^2k^2\left(\frac{\partial^2 u}{\partial x\,\partial t}\right)^2\right\}-\frac{E}{2}\left(\frac{\partial u}{\partial x}\right)^2\right]\mathrm{d}x = 0. \qquad (2.5.54)$$

The procedures for carrying out this variation are presented in Love [24, pp. 166–7] and, in terms of the mathematics of the calculus of variations, in Langhaar [20, pp. 92–6]. Some of the steps will be presented here. The problem is one of obtaining the first variation δI of a double integral, where

$$I = \iint F\left(x, t, \frac{\partial u}{\partial x}, \frac{\partial u}{\partial t}, \frac{\partial^2 u}{\partial x\, \partial t}\right) \mathrm{d}x\, \mathrm{d}t, \tag{2.5.55}$$

and where

$$F = \frac{\rho A}{2}\left\{\left(\frac{\partial u}{\partial t}\right)^2 + \nu^2 k^2 \left(\frac{\partial^2 u}{\partial x\, \partial t}\right)^2\right\} - \frac{E}{2}\left(\frac{\partial u}{\partial x}\right)^2. \tag{2.5.56}$$

Carrying out the indicated variation, we obtain

$$\delta I = \int_t \int_L \left(\frac{\partial F}{\partial u_x}\, \delta u_x + \frac{\partial F}{\partial \dot{u}}\, \delta \dot{u} + \frac{\partial F}{\partial \dot{u}_x}\, \delta \dot{u}_x\right) \mathrm{d}t\, \mathrm{d}x = 0, \tag{2.5.57}$$

where $u_x = \partial u/\partial x$, $\dot{u} = \partial u/\partial t$, $\dot{u}_x = \partial^2 u/\partial x\, \partial t$ in the above. We integrate by parts in the usual manner, giving for the various terms of (2.5.57)

$$\int_{t_0}^{t_1}\int_L \frac{\partial F}{\partial u_x}\, \delta u_x\, \mathrm{d}t\, \mathrm{d}x = \int_{t_0}^{t_1} \mathrm{d}t \left\{\frac{\partial F}{\partial u_x}\, \delta u \bigg|_L - \int_L \frac{\partial}{\partial x}\left(\frac{\partial F}{\partial u_x}\right) \delta u\, \mathrm{d}x\right\},$$

$$\int_{t_0}^{t_1}\int_L \frac{\partial F}{\partial \dot{u}}\, \delta \dot{u}\, \mathrm{d}t\, \mathrm{d}x = \int_L \mathrm{d}x \left\{\frac{\partial F}{\partial \dot{u}}\, \delta u \bigg|_{t_0}^{t_1} - \int_{t_0}^{t_1} \frac{\partial}{\partial t}\left(\frac{\partial F}{\partial \dot{u}}\right) \delta u\, \mathrm{d}t\right\}$$

$$\int_{t_0}^{t_1}\int_L \frac{\partial F}{\partial \dot{u}_x}\, \delta \dot{u}_x\, \mathrm{d}t\, \mathrm{d}x = \int_{t_0}^{t_1} \mathrm{d}t \left(\frac{\partial F}{\partial \dot{u}_x}\, \delta \dot{u}\right)_L -$$

$$- \int_L \mathrm{d}x \left\{\frac{\partial}{\partial x}\left(\frac{\partial F}{\partial \dot{u}_x}\right) \delta u \bigg|_{t_0}^{t_1} - \int_{t_0}^{t_1} \frac{\partial^2}{\partial x\, \partial t}\left(\frac{\partial F}{\partial \dot{u}_x}\right) \delta u\, \mathrm{d}t\right\}. \tag{2.5.58}$$

The initial conditions and boundary conditions cause the various single integral terms in (2.5.58) to vanish, leaving

$$\int_t \int_L \left\{\frac{\partial}{\partial x}\left(\frac{\partial F}{\partial u_x}\right) + \frac{\partial}{\partial t}\left(\frac{\partial F}{\partial \dot{u}}\right) - \frac{\partial^2}{\partial x\, \partial t}\left(\frac{\partial F}{\partial \dot{u}_x}\right)\right\} \delta u\, \mathrm{d}x\, \mathrm{d}t = 0. \tag{2.5.59}$$

This gives the Euler equation of the problem,

$$\frac{\partial}{\partial x}\left(\frac{\partial F}{\partial u_x}\right) + \frac{\partial}{\partial t}\left(\frac{\partial F}{\partial \dot{u}}\right) - \frac{\partial^2}{\partial x\, \partial t}\left(\frac{\partial F}{\partial \dot{u}_x}\right) = 0. \tag{2.5.60}$$

Substituting (2.5.56) in the above gives Love's equation of motion

$$\frac{\partial^2 u}{\partial x^2}+\frac{\nu^2 k^2}{c_0^2}\frac{\partial^4 u}{\partial x^2\,\partial t^2}=\frac{1}{c_0^2}\frac{\partial^2 u}{\partial t^2}. \tag{2.5.61}$$

The first step is to determine the influence of lateral-inertia effects on the dispersion characteristics of the rod by considering a solution of the form

$$u = Ae^{i\gamma(x-ct)}, \tag{2.5.62}$$

where c is the general, frequency-dependent phase velocity. Substituting (2.5.62) in (2.5.61) gives

$$-\gamma^2+\frac{\nu^2 k^2}{c_0^2}\gamma^4 c^2+\frac{\gamma^2 c^2}{c_0^2}=0. \tag{2.5.63}$$

If we define the normalized phase velocity $\bar{c}$ and wavenumber $\bar{\gamma}$, where

$$\bar{c}=\frac{c}{c_0}, \qquad \bar{\gamma}=k\nu\gamma, \tag{2.5.64}$$

then (2.5.63) becomes

$$(1+\bar{\gamma}^2)\bar{c}^2=1 \tag{2.5.65}$$

or

$$\bar{c}=1/(1+\bar{\gamma}^2)^{\frac{1}{2}}. \tag{2.5.66}$$

We have neglected the negative root of (2.5.66), since it would only give waves propagating in the negative x direction.

In assessing the result (2.5.66) we first note that if $\bar{\gamma}=0$, the classical, 'inertialess' rod result is recovered. Tracing back a few steps, we see this would occur by setting $k=0$ in (2.5.61). The dispersion curve corresponding to (2.5.66) is plotted in Fig. 2.27. Also shown in the figure as dashed lines are

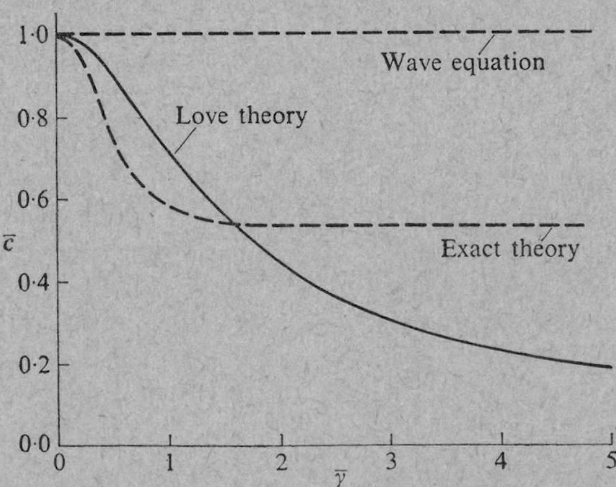

FIG. 2.27. Dispersion curve for Love's rod theory, wherein radial-inertia effects are included.

the dispersion curves for classical rod theory as governed by the wave equation, and the general shape of the curve as obtained by the exact equations of elasticity, if the cross-section of the rod were circular.

Recalling that $\bar{\gamma}$ is the reciprocal of wavelength, it is seen that, at low frequency and long wavelengths, all of the theories give the same propagation velocity c_0. For shorter wavelengths, the theories diverge, with classical rod theory breaking down seriously with respect to the Love results and exact theory for $\bar{\gamma} > 0{\cdot}3$. The Love theory at least approximates exact theory behaviour to the vicinity of $\bar{\gamma} = 2$, where departure then becomes more and more serious.

With this type of result available, it becomes possible to establish limitations of a theory in a fairly quantitative way. Thus, suppose on the basis of the dispersion curve, one imposes the restriction that $\bar{\gamma} < 0{\cdot}3$ as the wavenumber limit for the classical theory. This may be converted to frequency by noting that $\bar{\gamma}\bar{c} = \bar{\omega}$, where $\bar{\omega} = \nu k\omega/c_0$. For $\bar{\gamma} = 0{\cdot}3, \bar{c} \simeq 1$, so that $\bar{\omega} \simeq 0{\cdot}3$. Suppose our actual rod is of circular cross-section, 2·54 cm in diameter and made of steel. For these parameters, we would have $c_0 = 5{\cdot}08 \times 10^3\ \mathrm{m\ s^{-1}}$, $\nu = 0{\cdot}29$, $k = 2{\cdot}54/(2\sqrt{2})$. The resulting frequency is

$$f = 92\,800\ \mathrm{Hz}. \qquad (2.5.67)$$

In other words, the operating frequency of the system must be less than 90 000 Hz in order for classical theory to apply. In terms of a transient loading, there must not be significant components of the frequency spectrum of the loading pulse beyond 90 000 Hz. If one converts the wavenumber restriction to wavelength, it is found for the present example that $\lambda \geqslant 5$ cm must hold.

Our considerations in this section do not represent our first encounter with a dispersive system. However, they do represent our first encounter with an 'improved theory'. Thus, a basic characteristic of strength-of-materials type theories is that they contain assumptions of various forms on the kinematics of motion. In the case of the rod, they are regarding plane sections and the inertia contributions of certain components of motion. They are approximate theories. While the theories are approximate, they yield relatively simple governing equations. At the other extreme are the exact theories for various structures, such as rods and plates, that result from applying the equations of elasticity. Whilst having the virtue of exactness, they are often quite complicated. They often can serve, as was illustrated in Fig. 2.27, as a reference for an approximate theory. Attention will be given in several instances to the development of improvements on simple theories by comparing the results to those obtainable from exact analysis.

2.5.4. *Effects of lateral inertia—pulse propagation*

Davies [7, pp. 428–45] utilized Love's equation in analysing the propagation of sharp pulses in a cylindrical rod. This was only a part of a far-ranging study of the Hopkinson bar that also included extensive experiments and analyses based on the exact elasticity equations.† The problem considered was a bar of length l, free at the end $x = 0$ and subjected to a step pressure pulse P_0 at the end $x = l$. The initial conditions were taken to be zero. The basic steps of the Davies analysis will be presented in the following.

Taking the Laplace transform of (2.5.61) gives

$$\frac{d^2\bar{u}}{dx^2} - \frac{s^2}{c_0^2(1+H^2s^2)}\bar{u} = 0, \tag{2.5.68}$$

where $H^2 = \nu^2k^2/c_0^2$. This has the solution

$$\bar{u} = A \sinh \frac{s}{c_0\sqrt{(1+H^2s^2)}}x + B \cosh \frac{s}{c_0\sqrt{(1+H^2s^2)}}x. \tag{2.5.69}$$

The transformed boundary conditions of the problem are

$$\left.\frac{d\bar{u}}{dx}\right|_{x=0} = 0, \qquad E\left.\frac{d\bar{u}}{dx}\right|_{x=l} = \frac{P_0}{s}. \tag{2.5.70}$$

The first condition gives $A = 0$. Applying the second condition and solving for B yields the transformed solution

$$\bar{u} = \frac{P_0c_0\sqrt{(1+H^2s^2)}}{Es^2}\cosh\left\{\frac{sx}{c_0\sqrt{(1+H^2s^2)}}\right\}\Big/\sinh\left\{\frac{sl}{c_0\sqrt{(1+H^2s^2)}}\right\}. \tag{2.5.71}$$

The formal inversion gives

$$u(x,t) = \frac{P_0c_0}{2\pi iE}\int_{\alpha-i\infty}^{\alpha+i\infty} \frac{\sqrt{(1+H^2s^2)}}{s^2}\left[\cosh\left\{\frac{sx}{c_0\sqrt{(1+H^2s^2)}}\right\}\Big/\sinh\left\{\frac{sl}{c_0\sqrt{(1+H^2s^2)}}\right\}\right]e^{st}\,ds. \tag{2.5.72}$$

The inversion of the preceding result involves integration along the Bromwich line and closure of the contour in the left-hand plane. Three features of the integrand must be accounted for. First, at $s = 0$, a third-order pole exists owing to the s^2 and hyperbolic sine terms that approach zero. The residue of this pole is given by Davies as

$$\text{Res} = \frac{c_0t^2}{2l} + \frac{x^2}{2lc_0} - \frac{l}{6c_0} + \frac{H^2c_0}{l}. \tag{2.5.73}$$

Secondly, there are simple poles located at the zeros of the hyperbolic sine in (2.5.72), given by

$$\sinh \frac{sl}{c_0\sqrt{(1+H^2s^2)}} = 0, \qquad \frac{sl}{c_0\sqrt{(1+H^2s^2)}} = n\pi i. \tag{2.5.74}$$

† See the *Introduction* (of this book). This study will also be referred to in Chapter 8.

Solving for s gives

$$s = \frac{\pm n\pi i c_0}{(l^2+n^2\pi^2H^2c_0^2)^{\frac{1}{2}}}. \tag{2.5.75}$$

Davies gives the residues at these poles as

$$\text{Res} = -\frac{(-1)^n l}{\pi^2 n^2 c_0^2}\frac{l^2}{l^2+\pi^2n^2H^2c_0^2}\cos\frac{n\pi x}{l}\exp\{\pm n\pi i c_0 t/(l^2+\pi^2n^2H^2c_0^2)\}^{\frac{1}{2}}. \tag{2.5.76}$$

Finally, as $n \to \infty$, it is seen from (2.5.75) that $s \to \pm i/H$, corresponding to two essential singularities of the integrand. Davies states that these limit-point singularities can be excluded from within the contour by small circles and shown to make no contribution in the limit.

The resulting solution is given by $2\pi i\Sigma\text{Res}$, where only the real part of the solution is retained, giving

$$u(x,t) = \frac{P_0t^2}{2m}+\frac{P_0H^2}{m}+$$

$$+\frac{2P_0l^2}{\pi^2c_0^2m}\sum_{n=1}\frac{(-1)^n}{n^2}\cos\frac{n\pi x}{l}\left\{1-\frac{1}{1+n^2\psi^2}\cos\frac{n\pi c_0 t}{l\sqrt{(1+n^2\psi^2)}}\right\}. \tag{2.5.77}$$

In writing (2.5.77), the mass parameter $m = \rho l$ has been introducted and the parameter $\psi = \pi H c_0/l$ brought in. Finally, the Fourier-series identity

$$\frac{\pi^2}{4}\left(\frac{x^2}{l^2}-\frac{1}{3}\right) = \sum_{n=1}^{\infty}\frac{(-1)^n}{n^2}\cos\frac{n\pi x}{l}, \qquad (-l < x < l), \tag{2.5.78}$$

has been used in simplifying to the form (2.5.77).

In interpreting the result, we note that the first term corresponds to a rigid-body motion. Such a term has been previously pointed out as associated with a normal-mode type of representation† of the motion of a free–free rod, so it is not surprising to see it occur here. The second term P_0H^2/m is, according to Davies, a very small, time-independent constant displacement associated with the instantaneous propagation of disturbances which is implicit in the present theory. The remaining terms represent the normal modes of the bar.

Numerous results are presented by Davies on predicted displacements and pressures and comparison of results to experiment. Because the series in (2.5.77) is rather slowly convergent, many terms are required for accuracy (80–90 terms). In Fig. 2.28, the predicted displacement of the free end of the

† Recall § 2.3 and Timoshenko [38, pp. 309].

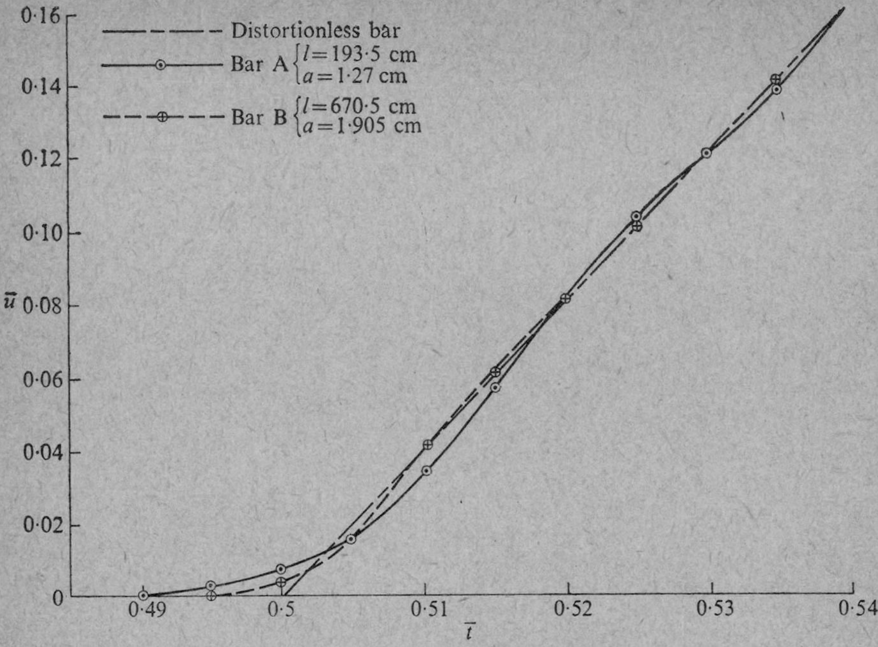

FIG. 2.28. Predicted displacement–time curves (solid lines) of the free end of a bar subjected to a step pressure pulse. [After Davies (7, Fig. 26).]

rod is shown. The displacement as predicted by classical theory is shown as the dashed line. The results have been non-dimensionalized as follows:

$$\bar{u} = \kappa\frac{u(0, t)}{u_s}, \qquad \bar{t} = \frac{t}{T_0}, \tag{2.5.79}$$

where u_s is the displacement under a static pressure of P_0 and T_0 is the time required for a pulse to travel twice the length of the bar. The parameter κ is an adjustment factor enabling data from two different bars (A and B) to be plotted on the same scale. For A, $\kappa = 1$ and for bar B, $\kappa = 3{\cdot}465$.

We have previously considered the case of a rectangular pressure pulse incident on the end of the bar and shown the displacement to be a ramp function like the dashed line of Fig. 2.28 (recall Fig. 2.8). It is seen that the effect of lateral inertia on the predicted response is to smooth the discontinuity at the base of the ramp. For later times, very slight oscillations about the classical result are predicted.

A second result presented by Davies was the predicted stress within the bar for a step pulse. This is shown in Fig. 2.29. The non-dimensional quantities are

$$\sigma = \frac{\sigma}{P_0}, \qquad \bar{t}' = \frac{2t}{T_0}. \tag{2.5.80}$$

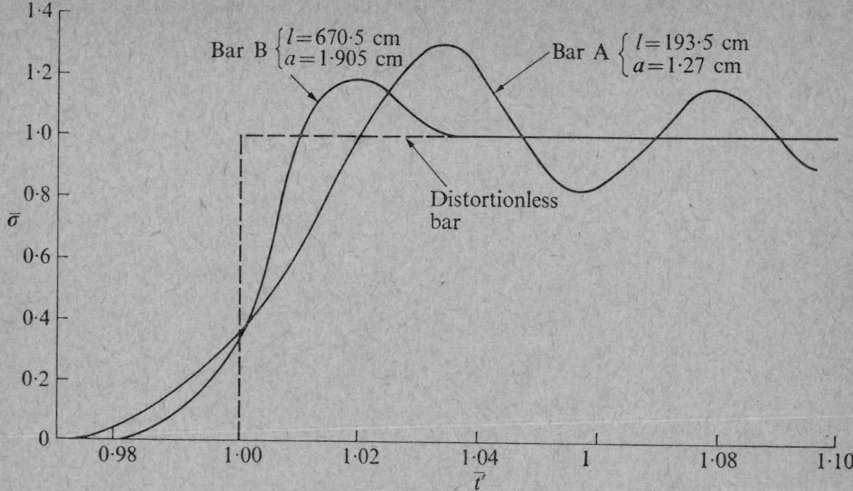

FIG. 2.29. Predicted stress–time curve of a bar subjected to a step pulse. [After Davies (7, Fig. 32).]

The predicted stress curve represents the stress that would exist at $x=0$ (the end of the bar) if the bar were continuous and not terminated at that point. Also shown as a dashed line is the undistorted step pulse that would be predicted by classical rod theory. The major item to note is the oscillatory nature of the response, with no sharp discontinuity of pulse arrival.

As mentioned earlier, the work Davies performed involved analysis based on exact theory, analysis based on Love theory, some of which has been reviewed here, and experimental studies. The experimental studies strongly confirmed the theoretical predictions shown in Fig. 2.28 and Fig. 2.29. A major consequence of the agreement of theory and experiment is that it may be concluded that lateral inertia effects alone account for the initial oscillatory behaviour of the pulse and that yet higher-order effects, such as radial shear stress, and other modes of deformation do not significantly affect this early-time behaviour. As will be shown in a later chapter, other oscillations, not accounted for by lateral inertia alone, are present in a transient and exact theory is required for their prediction.

2.6. Torsional vibrations

We now consider a digression from the study of longitudinal rod motion by reviewing the subject of torsional motion of rods. The governing equation for torsional motion in a rod, as will shortly be established, is identical in form to that of longitudinal motion, in the context of strength of materials development. In other words, the wave equation results. Without implying disfavour for this form of mechanical motion, it does not seem necessary, after the coverage of strings and longitudinal rod theory, to continue the analysis of this equation. The coverage therefore consists of development of the governing equation, plus brief remarks on application to various cross-sections.

2.6.1. *The governing equation*

Consider an element of a straight, prismatic rod subjected to variable end torques, as shown in Fig. 2.30. The equation of motion of the element, in

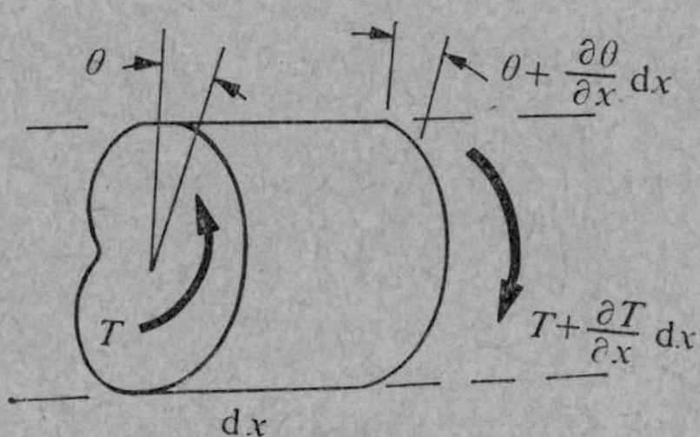

FIG. 2.30. Differential element of rod subjected to end torques.

the absence of body torques, is

$$-T+\left(T+\frac{\partial T}{\partial x}\,\mathrm{d}x\right)=\rho J\,\mathrm{d}x\frac{\partial^2\theta}{\partial t^2}, \tag{2.6.1}$$

where J is the polar moment of inertia. This reduces to

$$\frac{\partial T}{\partial x}=\rho J\frac{\partial^2\theta}{\partial t^2}. \tag{2.6.2}$$

The torque is related to the angle of twist by

$$T=C\frac{\partial\theta}{\partial x}, \tag{2.6.3}$$

where C is the torsional rigidity† of the bar. This quantity is dependent on the shear modulus G of the material and on the cross-sectional properties. Inserting (2.6.3) in (2.6.2) gives the resulting governing equation

$$\frac{\partial^2\theta}{\partial x^2}=\frac{\rho J}{C}\frac{\partial^2\theta}{\partial t^2}. \tag{2.6.4}$$

This result, except for dimensions, is the form of the wave equation derived for strings and longitudinal rod motion. It could be put into dimensional conformity merely by inserting a characteristic length of the rod, such as a diameter.

† Timoshenko [37, p. 298].

The torsional rigidity parameter appearing in the wave equation must be established from strength-of-material or elasticity considerations, depending on the complexity of the cross-section. For a rod of circular cross-section, we have $T = JG\,\partial\theta/\partial x$, where $J = \pi a^4/2$, and a is the radius of the rod. The governing equation becomes

$$\frac{\partial^2\theta}{\partial x^2} = \frac{1}{c_s^2}\frac{\partial^2\theta}{\partial t^2}, \qquad c_s = \sqrt{\left(\frac{G}{\rho}\right)}. \tag{2.6.5}$$

The propagation velocity c_s is that of shear waves in a material. The torsional rigidity of three other cross-sections as established from elasticity analysis are:

(1) ellipse: semi-major and minor axis of a and b,

$$C = \frac{\pi G a^3 b^3}{a^2+b^2}; \tag{2.6.6}$$

(2) triangle: equilateral, of height a,

$$C = \frac{Ga^4}{15\sqrt{3}}. \tag{2.6.7}$$

(3) narrow rectangular: width $2a$, depth $2b$, $b \gg a$,

$$C = \frac{a^3 b G}{3}. \tag{2.6.8}$$

For open, thin-walled cross-sections or thin-walled tubes, the torsional rigidity is fairly easily established by means of membrane-analogy analysis. For cross-sections having breadth and depth of comparable dimensions, elasticity analysis must be employed.

It should be noted that, for cross-sections lacking double axes of symmetry, it may be impossible for simple torsional vibrations to exist alone. That is torsional motion may be unavoidably coupled to bending motion through the deformation kinematics. Analysis may show the coupling to be weak and therefore negligible, but it is a consideration in torsional motion.

The case of the rod of circular cross-section is of particular interest. It may be recalled this is a case where elementary strength-of-materials considerations and those of exact elasticity yield the same results. Thus, in contrast to the theory for longitudinal motion in a circular cylindrical rod, which is approximate, the case of torsional motion in such a system should yield results in accord with exact analysis. However, exact analysis (Chapter 8) will reveal other modes of deformation not accounted for in the strength-of-materials theory.

2.7. Experimental studies in longitudinal waves

In this section, some of the experimental studies and applications of longitudinal waves in rods will be reviewed. The attempt will not be made to be comprehensive in this respect, but merely to bring out results and applications in areas related to the theoretical results of the chapter.

2.7.1. *Longitudinal impact of spheres on rods*

It will be recalled from § 2.4 that the longitudinal impact of an elastic sphere on a rod was considered on the basis of simple longitudinal rod theory and Hertzian contact theory. Theoretical results were presented for the predicted stress pulse in Fig. 2.22. Barton, Volterra, and Citron [3] obtained experimental results for this case and compared the results to theoretical predictions. A diagram of the experimental arrangement used is shown in Fig. 2.31 (a). The impacted rod was steel and 1 in. in diameter. The impact ball diameter ranged from 1 in. to 2 in. and impact velocities ranged from 121·30 cm s^{-1} to 242·61 cm s^{-1} (48–95 in. s^{-1}). The resulting stress pulses for the one-inch diameter ball impact are shown in Fig. 2.31 (b) for two different impact velocities. Waveform results are given also in Reference [3] for the case of a 2 in diameter ball. Tabular data on stress amplitudes and pulse duration is also given for other impact conditions. The quite apparent conclusion from the figure is that rather good agreement is obtained between experiment and theory. A slightly shorter pulse is predicted than observed. The peak amplitudes are only slightly different between theory and experiment.

Ripperger [34] conducted an extensive investigation of pulses in rods resulting from spherical ball impact. Various rod diameters ($\frac{1}{8}$ in., $\frac{1}{4}$ in., $\frac{1}{2}$ in. diameter) and impact ball diameters were considered as well as different impact velocities. Piezoelectric strain gauges were used to detect the strain signals. For strain-gauge stations several diameters from the impact end, the pulse shapes had the general form noted in Fig. 2.31 (b), and agreement between experiment and theory was quite good. For closer stations and for ball sizes considerably smaller than the rod diameter, a significant amount of high-frequency content was present. By using eccentric impact, bending waves were induced in some of the experimental studies.

2.7.2. *Longitudinal waves across discontinuities*

Ripperger and Abramson [35] presented experimential results for both longitudinal and flexural waves encountering a discontinuity in a rod in the form of a step change in cross-sectional area. The governing theoretical expressions, for transmitted and reflected longitudinal stress amplitudes, were derived in § 2.2, with the results being given by eqn (2.2.10). The geometry of the test bar studied by Ripperger and Abramson is shown in

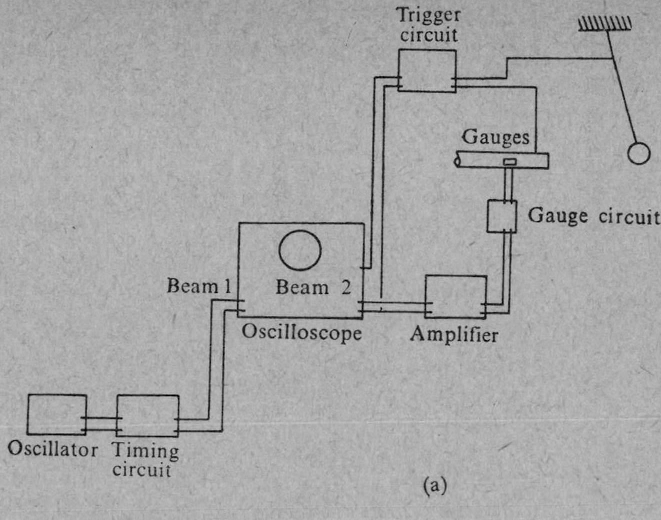

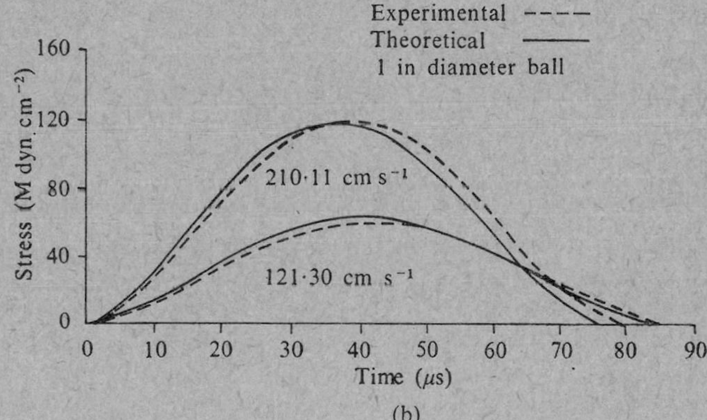

FIG. 2.31. (a) Experimental arrangement used for investigating the longitudinal impact of a ball on a rod and (b) results for the impact of a 1 in. diameter ball. (After Barton *et al.* [3], Figs. 2 and 4).

Fig. 2.32(a). In Fig. 2.32(b), the incident, reflected, and transmitted stress pulses are shown for propagation from the small end toward the large end. In Fig. 2.32(c), the case of propagation from the large end toward the small end is shown. It is seen that pulse shape and duration is maintained with only the amplitude being affected by the discontinuity.

Other studies related to this topic have also been made. Fischer [12] has obtained results for the case of a cylindrical bar having a short necked-down or swelled-out region. Some of the results obtained by Becker [4] are for a rectangular pulse reflecting off a step discontinuity.

2.7.3. *The split Hopkinson pressure bar*

An experimental apparatus for obtaining dynamic anelastic material properties that utilizes longitudinal elastic wave propagation in rods is called the split Hopkinson pressure bar. Kolsky [19] first proposed this modification of the basic Hopkinson bar. Basically, the method consists of sandwiching

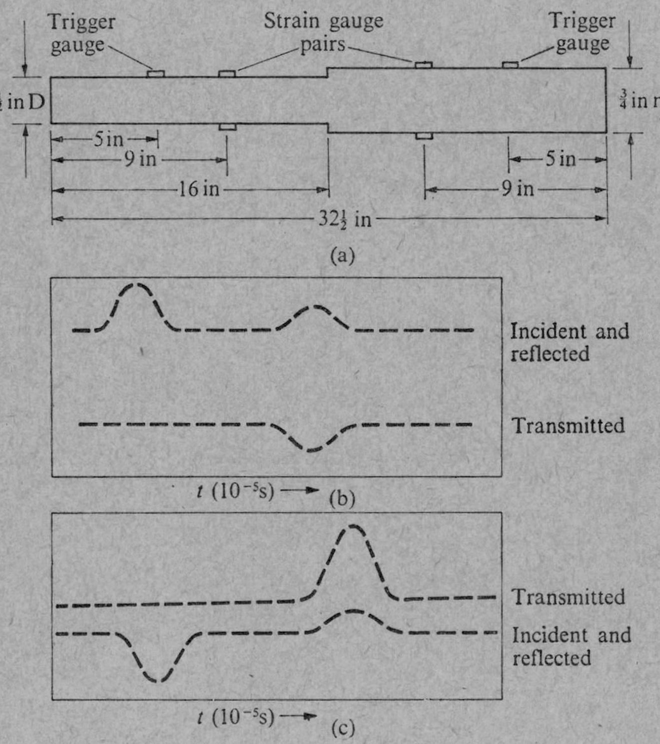

FIG. 2.32. (a) Geometry and arrangement of strain gauges on impact bar for study of longitudinal waves across a discontinuity; (b) experimental results for transmission from the small end toward the large end; (c) results for transmission from the large to the small end. (After Ripperger and Abramson [35], Figs. 2 and 4)

a short, cylindrical specimen of test material between two long rods of high-strength steel. A rectangular stress pulse is initiated in one of the elastic rods by the longitudinal impact of a striker bar. The stress wave dynamically loads the test specimen, with some of the incident wave energy being reflected from the specimen and some transmitting through the specimen to the second elastic rod. By using strain gauges to measure the incident, reflected, and transmitted waves, it is possible to determine the dynamic stress–strain relation for the material. A general schematic of the system is shown in Fig. 2.33.

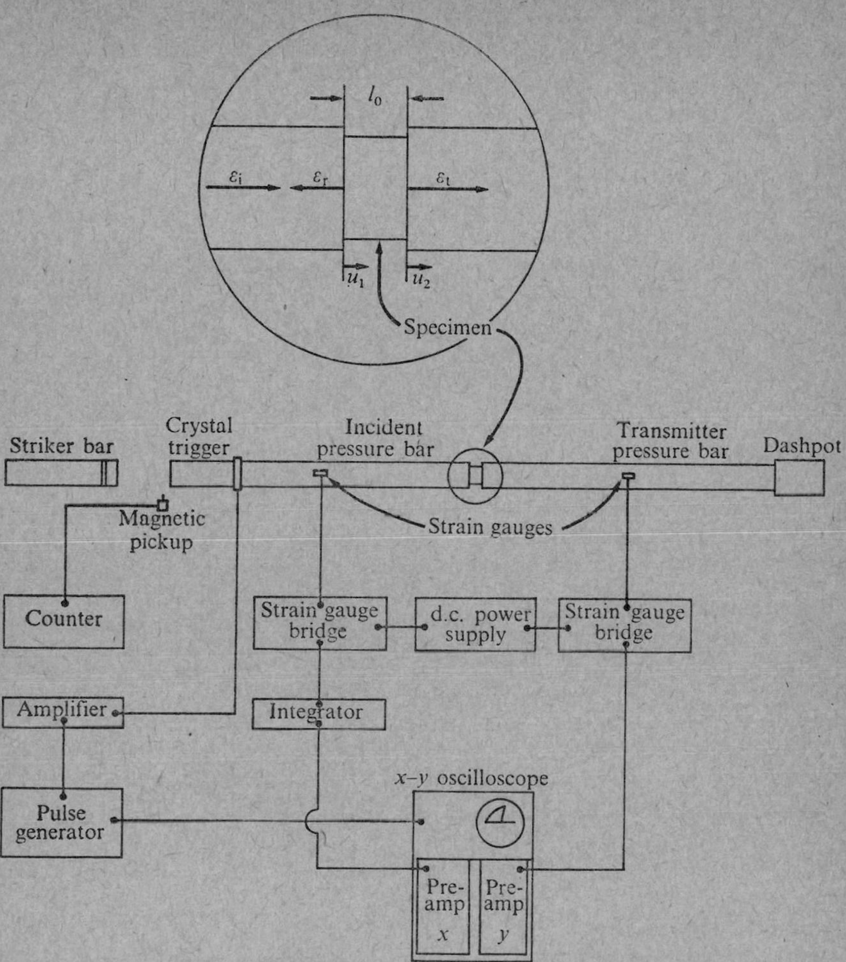

FIG. 2.33. Diagram of the split Hopkinson pressure bar apparatus. (After Lindholm [22], Fig. 1.)

The theory of the split Hopkinson bar is fairly simple and may be easily presented. From Fig. 2.33, it is supposed that the incident, reflected, and transmitted strain waves, ε_i, ε_r, ε_t are known from strain-gauge measurements. The displacements of the left and right interfaces of the specimen are denoted by u_1, u_2. From our previous work in one-dimensional rod theory, we have for the wave system in the incident bar

$$\begin{aligned} u &= f(x-c_0t)+g(x+c_0t) = u_i+u_r, \\ \epsilon &= f'+g' = \varepsilon_i+\varepsilon_r, \\ \dot{u} &= c_0(-f'+g') = c_0(-\varepsilon_i+\varepsilon_r). \end{aligned} \tag{2.7.1}$$

The displacement u_1 is then given by

$$u_1 = c_0 \int_0^t (-\varepsilon_i + \varepsilon_r)\, d\tau. \tag{2.7.2}$$

The transmitted wave system and the displacement u_2 are given by

$$u = h(x - c_0 t), \qquad \varepsilon = h' = \varepsilon_t,$$

$$\dot{u} = -c_0 h' = -c_0 \varepsilon_t, \qquad u_2 = -c_0 \int_0^t \varepsilon_t\, d\tau. \tag{2.7.3}$$

The average strain ε_s in the specimen is then given by

$$\varepsilon_s = \frac{u_2 - u_1}{l_0} = \frac{c_0}{l_0} \int_0^t (-\varepsilon_t + \varepsilon_i - \varepsilon_r)\, d\tau, \tag{2.7.4}$$

where l_0 is the original specimen length. The loads on each face of the specimen are given by

$$P_1 = AE(\varepsilon_i + \varepsilon_r), \qquad P_2 = AE\varepsilon_t, \tag{2.7.5}$$

where A is the rod cross-section. The important assumption is now made that wave-propagation effects within the short specimen may be neglected, so that $P_1 = P_2$. It follows that $\varepsilon_i + \varepsilon_r = \varepsilon_t$, so that (2.7.4) simplifies to

$$\varepsilon_s(t) = -\frac{2c_0}{l_0} \int_0^t \varepsilon_r\, d\tau. \tag{2.7.6}$$

The stress in the specimen is given by

$$\sigma_s = P_1/A_s = P_2/A_s, \tag{2.7.7}$$

where A_s is the specimen area. In practice, the strain ε_s is obtained by directly integrating the reflected strain ε_r and the stress is obtained directly from the transmitted strain signal ε_t.

Typical strain-gauge outputs for $\varepsilon_i(t)$, $\varepsilon_r(t)$, and $\varepsilon_t(t)$ are shown in Fig. 2.34.

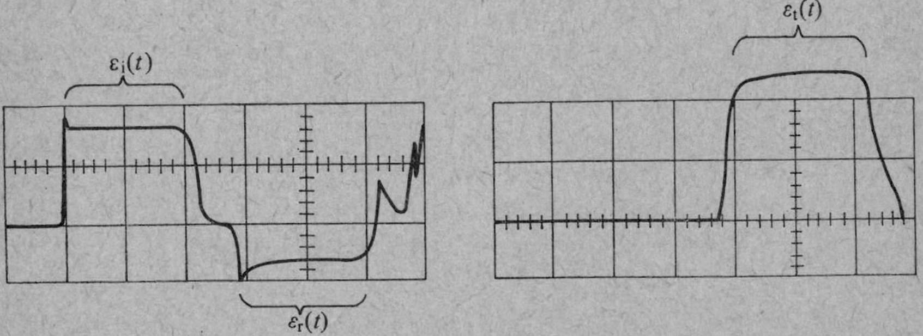

FIG. 2.34. Typical incident, reflected, and transmitted strain signals from a split Hopkinson bar test. (From Lindholm, Yeakley, and Bessey [23], Fig. 2).

Considering the incident wave in particular, it is seen that the wave is of nearly perfect rectangular shape, as predicted by simple longitudinal rod theory for the collision of two bars of identical cross-section and materials. There is, however, evidence of some high-frequency content at the start of the pulse. Results presented in Chapter 8 will bring this aspect out more clearly.

The split Hopkinson bar technique has been used by numerous investigators in studies of dynamic material properties. A fair amount of controversy has been associated with the test, mainly in conjunction with the quasi-static assumptions invoked in setting $P_1 = P_2$. The neglect of lateral-inertia effects in the specimen and the possible effects of interface friction at the specimen ends have also been the subject of discussion. Many contributions have been made here, but reference is made to Nicholas [29] for a survey of parts of this area and to Lindholm, Yeakley, and Bessey [23] and Nicholas [30] for discussion on the validity of the test technique.

2.7.4. *Lateral inertia effects*

The effect of lateral inertia on longitudinal waves was studied in § 2.5, where Love's development, also called Rayleigh's correction, was reviewed. Zemanek and Rudnick [40] have obtained results in this area confirming the validity of Love's theory for a limited range of wavelengths. Using the Love theory, it is not difficult to show that the longitudinal natural frequencies of a free–free rod are given by

$$\omega_n = n\pi c_0(l^2+n^2\pi^2\nu^2k^2)^{-\frac{1}{2}}, \tag{2.7.8}$$

where l is the rod length and k is the radius of gyration of the cross-section. Using an experimental setup as shown in Fig. 2.35(a), the rod natural frequencies (up to 140 modes) were measured. The phase velocity was then calculated from the formula

$$c = 2lf_n/n, \tag{2.7.9}$$

where $f_n = \omega_n/2\pi$. A plot of the resulting dispersion curve is shown in Fig. 2.26(b). Only a very limited range of wavenumber is shown. The case of a non-dispersive rod would be given by $\bar{c} = 1$. It is seen that the experimental results closely agree with the predictions of longitudinal theory with lateral-inertia effects included.

2.7.5. *Some other results of longitudinal wave experiments*

Many investigations of longitudinal waves in rods are aimed at determining certain material properties of the rod. For example, by measuring the decay of pulse amplitude with repeated reflection and traverse of the rod, material loss characteristics and/or visco-elastic parameters can be determined. Goldsmith, Polivka, and Yang [15] have studied pulse propagation in concrete cylinders in order to determine a material model and for assessing

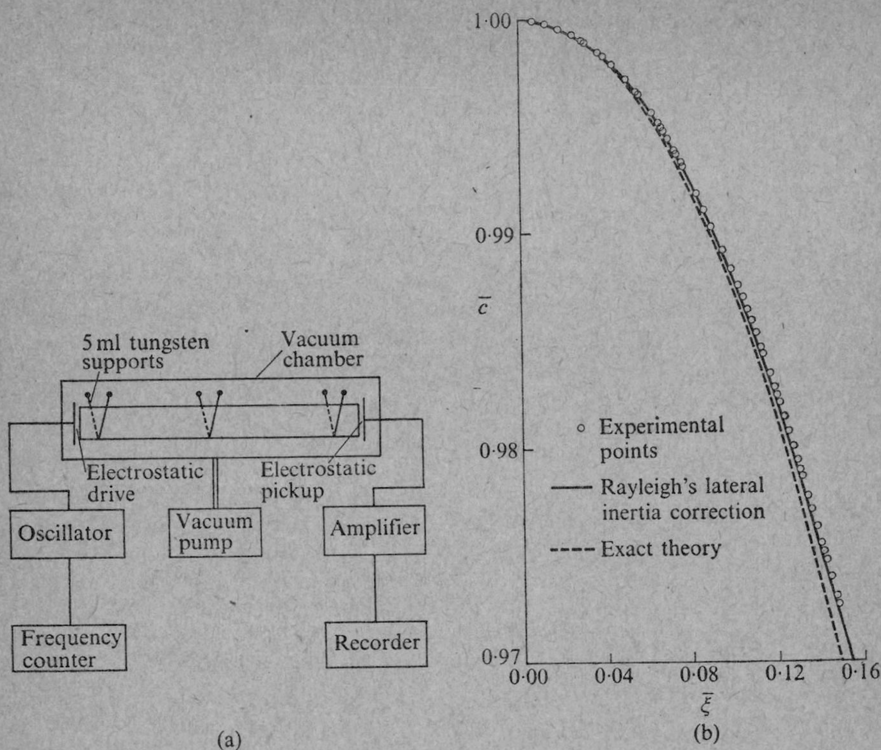

FIG. 2.35. (a) Apparatus used for determining the longitudinal modes of a rod, and (b) the dispersion curve for a limited wavenumber range, where $\bar{c} = c/c_0$, $\bar{\xi} = a\xi/2\pi$. (After Zemanek and Rudnicks [40], Figs. 1 and 5)

the effects of the highly inhomogeneous properties of concrete on pulse propagation. Similar studies were also carried out on rock cylinders by Goldsmith and Austin [16] and by Ricketts and Goldsmith [33]. The spallation phenomenon associated with the reflection of a compressive pulse from the free end of a rod has been used by Abbott and Cornick [1] to determine the tensile strength of brittle materials. Strain gauges mounted internally in the specimen bar have been used by Baker and Dove [2] to determine variations of stress distribution over the cross section. Lewis, Goldsmith, and Cunningham [21] have also used internally mounted gauges to study the wave propagation in cones. Brillhart and Dally [6] have used dynamic photo-elasticity to study waves in the conical geometry.

References

1. ABBOTT, B. W. and CORNISH, R. H. A stress-wave technique for determining the tensile strength of brittle materials. *Exp. Mech.* **22**, 148–53. (1965).
2. BAKER, W. E. and DOVE, R. C. Measurements of internal strains in a bar subjected to longitudinal impact. *Exp. Mech.* **19**, 307–11. (1962).

3. Barton, C. S., Volterra, E. G., and Citron, S. J. On elastic impacts of spheres on long rods. *Proc. 3rd U.S. natn. Cong. appl. Mech.* 89–94 (1958).
4. Becker, E. C. H. and Carl, H. Transient loading technique for mechanical impedance measurement. In *Experimental techniques in shock and vibration* (Ed. W. J. Worley). A.S.M.E., New York (1962).
5. Berlincourt, D. A., Curran, D. R., and Jaffe, H. Piezoelectric and Piezomagnetic materials and their function in transducers. In *Physical acoustics* (Ed. W. P. Mason) Chap. 3, Vol. 1, Academic Press, New York (1964).
6. Brillhart, L. V. and Dally, J. W. A dynamic photoelastic investigation of stress-wave propagation in cones. *Exp. Mech.* **25**, 1–9 (1968).
7. Davies, R. M. A critical study of the Hopkinson pressure bar. *Phil. Trans. R. Soc.* **A240**, 375–457 (1948).
8. Eisner, E. Design of sonic amplification transducers of high magnification. *J. acoust. Soc. Am.* **35**, 1367 (1963).
9. ——. Complete solutions of the 'Webster' horn equation. *J. acoust. Soc. Am.* **41**, 1126 (1967).
10. Eubanks, R. A., Muster, D., and Volterra, E. *An investigation of the dynamic properties of plastics and rubber-like materials.* Office of Nav. Res., Department of the Navy, Contract No. N7 ONR 32911, Tech. Rep. No. 1 (June 1952).
11. Feng, C. C. *Energy transfer in sonic impact coupling.* M.S. thesis, The Ohio State University (1969).
12. Fischer, H. C. Stress pulse in bar with neck or swell. *Appl. Scient. Res.* **A4**, 317–28 (1954).
13. Frederick, J. R. *Ultrasonic engineering.* John Wiley and Sons, New York (1965).
14. Goldsmith, W. *Impact: the theory and physical behaviour of colliding solids.* Edward Arnold, London (1960).
15. ——, Polivka, M., and Yang, T. Dynamic behavior of concrete. *Exp. Mech.* **23**, 65–79 (1966).
16. —— and Austin, C. F. Some dynamic characteristics of rocks. In *Stress Waves in Anelastic Solids* (Ed. H. Kolsky and W. Prager), pp. 277–303. Springer-Verlag, Berlin (1964).
17. Katz, H. W. (Ed.) *Solid state magnetic and dielectric devices.* John Wiley and Sons, New York (1959).
18. Kolsky, H. *Stress waves in solids.* Dover Publications, New York (1963).
19. ——. An investigation of the mechanical properties of materials at very high rates of loading. *Proc. phys. Soc.* **B62**, 676–700 (1949).
20. Langhaar, H. L. *Energy methods in applied mechanics.* John Wiley and Sons, New York (1962).
21. Lewis, J. L., Goldsmith, W., and Cunningham, D. M. Internal-strain measurements of longitudinal pulses in conical bars. *Exp. Mech.* **26**, 313–20 (1969).
22. Lindholm, U. S. Some experiments with the split Hopkinson pressure bar. *J. Mech. Phys. Solids* **12**, 317–35 (1964).
23. ——, Yeakley, L. M., and Bessey, R. L. *An investigation of the behavior of materials under high rates of deformation.* Tech. Rep. AFML-TR-68-194, Air Force Materials Laboratory. (1968).
24. Love, A. E. H. *A treatise on the mathematical theory of elasticity.* Dover Publications, New York (1944).

25. McLachlan, N. W. *Bessel functions for engineers.* Clarendon Press, Oxford (1961).
26. Merkulov, L. G. and Kharitonov, A. V. *Sov. Phys. Acoust.* **5**, 184 (1959).
27. Morse, P. M. *Vibration and sound.* McGraw-Hill, New York (1948).
28. —— and Feshbach, H. *Methods of theoretical physics.* Vols. I and II. McGraw-Hill, New York (1953).
29. Nicholas, T. *The mechanics of ballistic impact—A survey.* Tech. Rep. AFML-TR-67-208, Air Force Materials Laboratory. (1967).
30. ——. *An analytical study of the split Hopkinson bar technique for strain-rate dependent material behavior.* Tech. Rep. AFML-TR-71-155, Air Force Materials Laboratory (1971).
31. Pochhammer, L. Über die Fortpflanzungsgeschwindigkeiten kleiner Schwingungen in einem unbegrenzten istropen Kreiszylinder. *J. reine angew. Math.* **81**, 324–36 (1876).
32. Rayleigh, J. W. S. *The theory of sound,* Vols. I and II. Dover Publications, New York (1945).
33. Ricketts, T. E. and Goldsmith, W. Dynamic properties of rocks and composite structural materials. *Int. J. Rock Mech. Mining Sci.* **7**, 315–35 (1970).
34. Ripperger, E. A. The propagation of pulses in cylindrical bars—an experimental study. *Proc. 1st midwest. Conf. Solid Mech.* pp. 29–39 (1953).
35. —— and Abramson, H. N. Reflection and transmission of elastic pulses in a bar at a discontinuity in cross section. *Proc. 3rd midwest. Conf. Solid Mech.* p. 135 (1957).
36. St-Venant, B. D. and Flamant, M. Résistance vive ou dynamique des solides. Représentation graphique des lois du choc longitudinal. *C. r. hebd. Scéanc. Acad. Sci., Paris* **97**, 127, 214, 281, and 353 (1883).
37. Timoshenko, S. P. and Goodier, J. N. *Theory of elasticity* (3rd edn). McGraw-Hill, New York (1970).
38. ——. *Vibration problems in engineering.* Van Nostrand, New Jersey (1928).
39. Todhunter, I. and Pearson, K. *A history of the theory of elasticity,* Vol. I (1886), Vol. II, Parts 1 and 2 (1893). Dover Publications, New York (1960).
40. Zemanek, J. (Jr.) and Rudnick, I. Attenuation and dispersion of elastic waves in a cylindrical bar. *J. Acoust. Soc. Am.* **33**, 1283–8 (1961).

Problems

2.1. Derive the governing equation of motion for an inhomogeneous rod where the modulus varies as $E = E_0(1+\varepsilon x^2)$. Assume the density remains constant.

2.2. The effects of lateral inertia are neglected in the classical rod theory and uniaxial stress is assumed. Give a physical argument for the existence of radial shear stresses on the face of an element.

2.3. *Mechanical impedance.* Show the mechanical impedance of a semi-infinite rod is $Z = A\sqrt{(\rho E)}$. Determine the impedance of a mass, a spring, and a dashpot. To which of these three elements is the rod analogous?

2.4. *Effects of lateral constraint.* The lateral motion of a thin rod is unconstrained and a pressure pulse $p(t)$ applied to the end of a semi-infinite rod travels at the velocity c_0. Now instead of a semi-infinite rod, consider a semi-infinite solid or 'half-space', subjected over its entire surface to the normal pressure pulse $p(t)$. Show that the one-dimensional wave equation governs the longitudinal motion in such a media. Develop the expression for the propagation velocity. Is it faster or slower than c_0? Give a physical interpretation of the result.

2.5. *Effects of lateral constraint.* Consider a thin rod of circular cross-section imbedded in an elastic medium such that a lateral resistive pressure $f_r = -ku_r$ is developed, where u_r is the radial displacement of the surface. Derive the equation of motion for the system and sketch the general form of the frequency spectrum.

2.6. Consider the reflection–transmission expressions (2.2.12) in the form $\sigma_t = K_t\sigma_i$, $\sigma_r = K_r\sigma_i$, where K_t, K_r are appropriately defined transmission and reflection coefficients. Plot K_t and K_r as a function of Z_2/Z_1 for various ratios of A_1/A_2 ($\frac{1}{4}$, $\frac{1}{2}$, 1, 2).

2.7. Recall the discussion of the experimental procedure involving a 'time piece' of § 2.2. Consider a pulse propagating toward the end of a bar to which a time piece of length l and of identical properties and diameter has been attached with a grease layer. What must be the length of the time piece relative to the pulse length to completely 'trap' the pulse, leaving the bar at rest? Suppose a rectangular compressive pulse of magnitude σ_0 and pulse length L enters a time piece of length $L/2$. What will be the fly-off velocity of the piece? Suppose the incident pulse is triangular in shape, of amplitude σ_0 and of length L with the rising portion, or head of the pulse, being $L/3$ and the tail $2L/3$. Suppose the time piece is $L/3$ long. Determine the fly-off velocity.

2.8. The case of a rectangular pulse incident on an elastic boundary was analysed in § 1.2 and also considered in Problem 1.10. Such a boundary is 'lossless', ultimately returning all of the incident pulse energy in the reflected wave. Consider now a rectangular pulse incident on a bilinear spring boundary, as shown in Fig. P2.8(a). Loading occurs along $F = k_1\delta$ and unloading

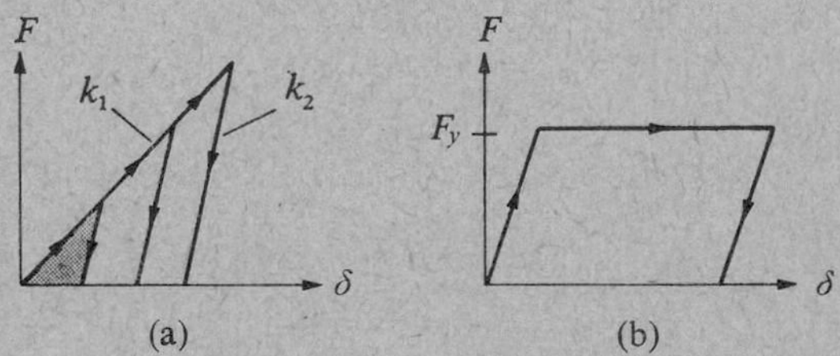

FIG. P2.8. (a) Bilinear spring; (b) elastic, perfectly plastic.

along one of the lines having slope k_2. The shaded area represents energy loss for unloading along a particular line. Such a model is a good approximation to a rock boundary. Predict the reflected wave. Consider an elastic, perfectly plastic boundary as in Fig. P2.8(b). Predict the reflected wave.

2.9. A rod of length l is fixed at one end and subjected to a compressive load P. The load is suddenly removed. Determine the resulting wave propagation in the bar. In particular, plot the displacement versus time for the end (does a sawtooth shape result?).

2.10. A rod of length l rests against a rigid base, but is not attached. A load P is applied to the rod and suddenly released (as in Problem 2.9). Determine the wave propagation in the rod. At some point, the rod will leave contact with the base. Determine the 'fly-off' velocity. Is the rod in uniform motion after fly-off?

2.11. Consider the free vibrations of a rod of length l, fixed at one end and constrained at the other by a spring of constant k. Derive the equation for the natural frequencies. Show that as $k \to 0, \infty$ that the fixed–free and fixed–fixed rod results are recovered.

2.12. The natural frequency of vibration of a simple spring–mass system is given by $\omega_n = \sqrt{(K/m)}$, where K is the spring constant and m the mass. Consider the longitudinal vibrations of an elastic rod, fixed at one end and with a mass attached at the other. Derive the frequency equation for this system. A result of the form $\alpha = \beta \tan \beta$ should be obtained, where α, β are parameters containing frequency and the properties of mass and rod. Suppose the mass of the rod is small in comparison with the attached mass. Show that the spring mass result is recovered if the approximation $\tan \beta = \beta$ is made. Show that the next order of approximation for $\tan \beta$ gives the result that adding one-third the mass of the rod to the end mass in the simple formula for ω_n predicts the natural frequency.

2.13. *Equivalent circuits.* Through analogies between mechanical and electrical quantities such as force and voltage and velocity and current, it is possible to develop electrical analogues to mechanical systems. The objective of this problem is to trace the steps for obtaining the electrical circuit for longitudinal rod vibration. Consider a rod as shown in Fig. P2.13(a), subjected to end

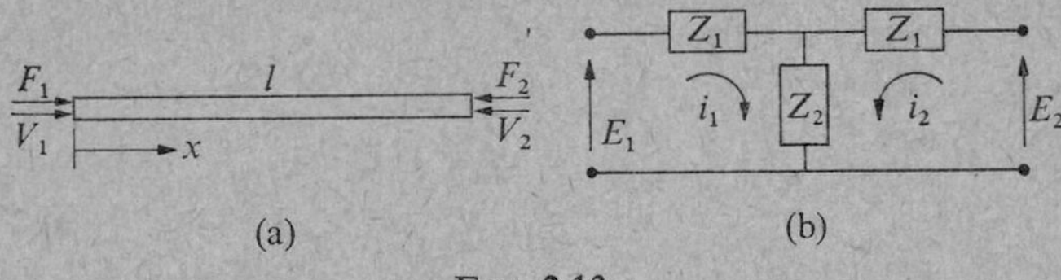

FIG. 2.13.

forces. The boundary conditions are specified by $\dot{u}(0, t) = V_1 \exp(i\omega t)$, $u(l, t) = -V_2 \exp(i\omega t)$, $F(0, t) = -F_1 \exp(i\omega t)$, and $F(l, t) = -F_2 \exp(i\omega t)$. Considering a solution $u(x, t) = U(x)\exp(i\omega t)$, obtain two equations for F_1, F_2 in terms of V_1, V_2. Now write the circuit equations for the Tee circuit shown in Fig. P2.13(b) expressing E_1, E_2 in terms of i_1, i_2. Comparing the two results, you should be able to show that $Z_1 = iZ_0 \tan(\gamma l/2)$, $Z_2 = Z_0/i \sin \gamma l$, where Z_0 is the rod impedance and $\gamma = \omega/c_0$.

Behaviour near resonance. Suppose $x = l$ is a free end. You should be able to reduce the electrical circuit to a single impedance given by $Z_4 = iZ_0 \sin \gamma l/\cos \gamma l$. The resonance of this circuit is at $\gamma l = \pi$. Express this near resonance as $\pi(\omega_0 + \delta\omega)/\omega_0$, where ω_0 is the resonance frequency. Near resonance, show that

$$Z_4 \simeq \mathrm{i}Z_0\left(\pi\frac{\delta\omega}{\omega_0}-\frac{\pi^3}{6}\frac{\delta\omega^3}{\omega_0^3}+\cdots\right).$$

Finally, expand the impedance of a series LC circuit near resonance. By comparison of the two results, show $L = \rho Al/2$, $C = 2l/\pi^2 AE$. For references here, see Katz [19, p. 170], Berlincourt, Curran, and Jaffe [5, pp. 220–49].

2.14. Consider the results leading to Fig. 2.13. Sketch the displacements predicted by (2.3.48) for $x = 3l/4, l/2, l/4, 0$.

2.15. A cylindrical rod of length l collides with a semi-infinite rod of the same outside diameter. The impact rod has a longitudinal cylindrical hole drilled in the impact end. The depth of the hole is $l/4$ and the diameter is one-half the rod diameter. Construct the characteristics plane representation of the wavefront propagation for this impact problem.

2.16. Hertz contact theory gives a non-linear relation between contact force and approach. Plot this relation for the given material-geometry parameters of (2.4.44). Approximate the curve with a linear relation $F = K_1\alpha$. Incorporate this relation in the impact analysis and develop the modified form of (2.4.42). Note the greatly simplified governing equation. Obtain the predicted stress pulse and compare to the results of Fig. 2.22. Comment on the need for the non-linear relationship. Now observe the approximate half sine-wave shape of the pulses of Fig. 2.22 and make the further simplification of omitting the $\dot{\alpha}$ term of the governing equation. Determine the rebound velocity (it should equal the impact velocity). Interpret the significance of omitting the equivalent 'damping' from the system.

2.17. Determine the impedance (in non-dimensional form) of the catenoidal horn.

2.18. Determine the impedance (in non-dimensional form) of the exponential horn. Note the governing equation has constant coefficients and that somewhat simpler solution-forms apply than for the linear and conical cases.

2.19. Refer to the design chart of Fig. 2.25. It is desired that a 33·02 cm (13 in) steel exponential horn be resonant at 10^4 Hz and have a small end diameter of 1·27 cm ($\frac{1}{2}$ in). What will be the diameter of the large end?

2.20. In the Davies analysis reviewed in § 2.5, verify the calculation of the residues (2.5.73) and (2.5.76). Show that the result (2.5.77) reduces to that obtained for classical rod theory if $H = \psi = 0$.

2.21. Draw the frequency spectrum corresponding to Love's theory for longitudinal waves.

2.22. Obtain the expression for the natural frequencies of a free–free rod of length l with lateral-inertia effects included. Consider a bar of steel 25·4 cm long and of circular cross-section. Take $c_0 = 5{\cdot}08\times10^3$ m s^{-1} and Poisson's ratio as 0·3. Calculate the first and third mode frequencies for bars of 0·635 cm, 2·54 cm, and 10·16 cm ($\frac{1}{4}$ in, 1 in, and 4 in) diameters. Compare results to that of classical theory.

3 Flexural waves in thin rods

OUR considerations now turn to the transverse motion of thin rods resulting from bending action. It will be found that the simplest governing theory for such motion, based on the Bernoulli–Euler theory of beams, yields a dispersive system, in contrast to the wave equation that results for simple strings and longitudinal and torsional rod motion. Following the pattern developed in earlier chapters, harmonic waves, the initial-value problem, and forced motion for infinite beams will be considered first. Free and forced motion of finite beams will follow. A section will be devoted to the effects of an elastic and viscous foundation on beam motion, since many interesting problems enter here. Then, analogous to the development of the Love theory for longitudinal rod motion, an improved theory for beams will be developed. Finally, the effects of rod curvature on wave propagation will be studied. The theory that will be developed will include longitudinal extensional effects, as well as flexural effects.

3.1. Propagation and reflection characteristics

The governing equation for transverse rod motion will be developed and the frequency spectrum and dispersion curve associated with harmonic wave propagation presented. The initial-value problem for two types of input disturbance will be considered. The forced motion of a beam will be considered, and the concept of local energy storage described. Finally, the reflection of harmonic waves from boundaries will be studied.

3.1.1. *The governing equation*

Consider a thin rod undergoing transverse motion, as shown in Fig. 3.1(a), and consider a differential element of the rod as isolated in Fig. 3.1(b). Bending moment M, shear force V, and variations of these quantities act on the beam element, as well as a distributed force $q(x, t)$. We invoke the basic hypothesis of the Bernoulli–Euler theory of beams: namely, that plane cross-sections initially perpendicular to the axis of the beam remain plane and perpendicular to the neutral axis during bending. This assumption implies that the longitudinal strains vary linearly across the depth of the beam and that, for elastic behaviour, the neutral axis of the beam passes through the centroid of the cross-section. Further, it results that the relationship between

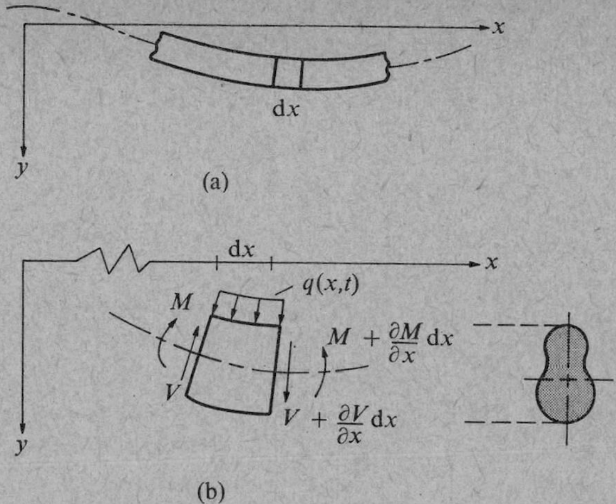

FIG. 3.1. (a) Thin rod undergoing transverse motion and (b) an element of rod subjected to various loads.

the bending moment and curvature is given by

$$\partial^2 y/\partial x^2 = -M/EI, \tag{3.1.1}$$

where y is the coordinate to the neutral surface of the beam. The result (3.1.1) carries the assumption that slopes and deflections of the beam are small.

Writing the equation of motion in the vertical direction for the element of Fig. 3.1(b), we have

$$-V+\left(V+\frac{\partial V}{\partial x}\,\mathrm{d}x\right)+q\,\mathrm{d}x = \rho A\,\mathrm{d}x\frac{\partial^2 y}{\partial t^2}, \tag{3.1.2}$$

where A is the cross-sectional area of the beam and ρ is the mass density per unit volume. This reduces to

$$\frac{\partial V}{\partial x}+q = \rho A\frac{\partial^2 y}{\partial t^2}. \tag{3.1.3}$$

Summation of moments is the second equation to be written. If we neglect the rotational-inertia effects of the element, the moment equation is, effectively, that of statics and gives

$$V = \frac{\partial M}{\partial x} \tag{3.1.4}$$

where the higher-order contributions of the loading q to the moment are neglected. Substituting (3.1.4) in (3.1.3) gives

$$\frac{\partial^2 M}{\partial x^2}+q = \rho A\frac{\partial^2 y}{\partial t^2}. \tag{3.1.5}$$

Finally, substituting (3.1.1) in (3.1.5) gives

$$\frac{\partial^2}{\partial x^2}\left(EI\frac{\partial^2 y}{\partial x^2}\right)+\rho A\frac{\partial^2 y}{\partial t^2} = q(x, t), \tag{3.1.6}$$

as the governing equation for the transverse motion of a thin rod or beam. If the loading is absent ($q = 0$), and material of the beam is homogeneous, so that E is constant and, furthermore, the cross-section is constant so that I is constant, then (3.1.6) reduces to the form

$$\frac{\partial^4 y}{\partial x^4}+\frac{1}{a^2}\frac{\partial^2 y}{\partial t^2} = 0, \qquad a^2 = \frac{EI}{\rho A}. \tag{3.1.7}$$

We immediately note this is not of the wave equation form and that a does not have the dimension of velocity.

Let us examine the basic restrictions of the theory. The restrictions on beam homogeneity and constant cross-section imposed in reducing (3.1.6) to (3.1.7) are not fundamental. In other words, beams not having these properties can be analysed within the framework of the theory, starting from (3.1.6), with only the cost of increased mathematical complexity entering. The assumption of small deflections has been specifically pointed out. Should this not be obeyed, the exact expression for curvature would have to be used in (3.1.1), instead of the second-derivative approximation. It is also assumed that the motion of the beam is in a single plane (the x,y plane). This implies that the beam has a symmetrical cross-section, with the plane of symmetry being in the x,y-plane. Any external loads must also act in this plane in order for such motion to occur. In order to relax this assumption, one must be prepared to consider the problem of coupled torsional–flexural motions. This was briefly alluded to in § 2.6.

We now consider the assumption wherein the effects of rotational inertia were neglected. To examine this assumption, we write general expressions for the translational and rotational kinetic energies of the element as

$$\mathrm{d}T_t = \tfrac{1}{2}\,\mathrm{d}m\left(\frac{\partial y^2}{\partial t^2}\right), \qquad \mathrm{d}T_r = \tfrac{1}{2}(k^2\,\mathrm{d}m)\dot{\theta}^2, \tag{3.1.8}$$

where $\mathrm{d}m$ is the mass of the element $\mathrm{d}x$,k^2 is its radius of gyration, and $\dot{\theta}$ refers to its rotational velocity. Neglecting rotary-inertia effects omits the contribution of $\mathrm{d}T_r$ to the system energy. At low frequencies, where $\dot{\theta}$ may not be large, this assumption is valid. As it turns out, however, for higher frequency motion this contribution must be included in the development. We note the similarity of this assumption to that occurring in rods, where radial-inertia effects were ignored.

The most important assumption, and hence limitation, to the theory pertains to the basic Bernoulli–Euler hypothesis that plane sections remain plane. As may be recalled from strength-of-materials theory, this assumption is valid only for pure bending. When shearing forces are present, the retention of the plane-section hypothesis in effect states that infinite shear rigidity is assumed or, equivalently, that shearing deformations are neglected. This assumption, as well as that regarding rotational inertia, will be re-examined in § 3.4 in the development of an improved theory.

3.1.2. *Propagation of harmonic waves*

We begin our study of waves and vibrations in beams in the usual fashion. Consider a beam, infinitely long and governed by the equation of motion (3.1.7). We establish conditions for the propagation of harmonic waves by assuming

$$y = Ae^{i(\gamma x-\omega t)} \tag{3.1.9}$$

and substituting in (3.1.7). The resulting relation between frequency and wavenumber is

$$\gamma^4-\omega^2/a^2 = 0 \tag{3.1.10}$$

or

$$\gamma = \pm\sqrt{\left(\frac{\omega}{a}\right)}, \quad \pm i\sqrt{\left(\frac{\omega}{a}\right)}. \tag{3.1.11}$$

The relationship between phase velocity and wavenumber is obtained by substituting $\omega = \gamma c$ in (3.1.11) or using a propagating wave of the form $\exp\{i\gamma(x-ct)\}$ in the original substitution. By either means, one obtains

$$c = \pm a\gamma. \tag{3.1.12}$$

The frequency spectrum, showing all branches of (3.1.11) and the dispersion curve, showing only the positive branch of (3.1.12) is given in Fig. 3.2.

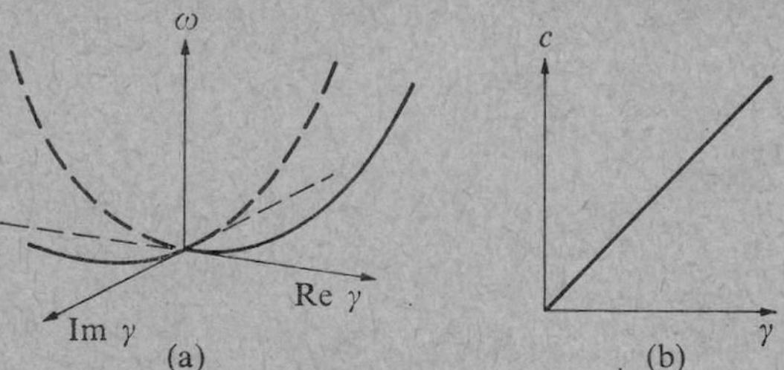

FIG. 3.2. (a) Frequency spectrum and (b) dispersion curve governing transverse harmonic waves in a rod.

Interpretation of these results is straightforward on the basis of our past work. Thus, referring to (3.1.11), we realize that the positive and negative real roots correspond to rightward- and leftward-propagating harmonic waves, while the imaginary wavenumbers give non-propagating, spatially varying vibrations. While not acceptable solutions for the case of propagating waves, we expect these solutions to play a role in forced and transient motion.

There is a striking anomaly in the results, particularly evident in the dispersion curve representation. It is seen that the phase velocity increases without limit for increasing wavenumber or shorter wavelength. This characteristic will yield some peculiar predictions in the transient response. Ultimately, it will be shown to be a consequence of neglecting rotary inertia and shear effects.

3.1.3. *The initial-value problem*

We now consider the problem of an infinite beam with an initial disturbance imposed on it of the form

$$y(x,0) = f(x), \qquad \frac{\partial y(x,0)}{\partial t} = g(x) = a\frac{d^2h(x)}{dx^2}. \tag{3.1.13}$$

The special form selected for the initial velocity is purely for later convenience. Performing the Laplace transform on (3.1.7) gives

$$a^2\frac{d^4\bar{y}}{dx^4}(x,s)+s^2\bar{y}(x,s) = sf(x)+g(x). \tag{3.1.14}$$

Taking the Fourier integral transform of the above gives

$$a^2\xi^4\bar{Y}(\xi,s)+s^2\bar{Y}(\xi,s) = sF(\xi)-\xi^2aH(\xi). \tag{3.1.15}$$

The transformed solution is thus

$$\bar{Y}(\xi,s) = \frac{sF(\xi)-\xi^2aH(\xi)}{s^2+a^2\xi^4}. \tag{3.1.16}$$

We first perform the Laplace inversion on the result. This is easily done if it is noted that

$$\mathscr{L}^{-1}\left(\frac{s}{s^2+a^2\xi^4}\right) = \cos\xi^2at, \qquad \mathscr{L}^{-1}\left(\frac{1}{s^2+a^2\xi^4}\right) = \frac{1}{\xi^2a}\sin\xi^2at. \tag{3.1.17}$$

Hence, we obtain

$$Y(\xi,t) = F(\xi)\cos\xi^2at-H(\xi)\sin\xi^2at. \tag{3.1.18}$$

The convolution theorem may be used to invert this last result. To do so, the Fourier inversions of $\cos\xi^2at$, $\sin\xi^2at$ are required. Using the basic result† that

$$\left(\frac{1}{2\pi}\right)^{\frac{1}{2}}\int_{-\infty}^{\infty}\exp(-\xi^2a-i\xi x)\,d\xi = \left(\frac{1}{2a}\right)^{\frac{1}{2}}\exp\left(\frac{-x^2}{4a}\right), \tag{3.1.19}$$

it is possible to obtain

$$F^{-1}\{\cos\xi^2at\} = \frac{1}{2\sqrt{(at)}}\left(\cos\frac{x^2}{4at}+\sin\frac{x^2}{4at}\right),$$

$$F^{-1}\{\sin\xi^2at\} = \frac{1}{2\sqrt{(at)}}\left(\cos\frac{x^2}{4at}-\sin\frac{x^2}{4at}\right). \tag{3.1.20}$$

† See Sneddon [22, p. 112].

From the convolution integral form

$$f * g = \frac{1}{\sqrt{(2\pi)}} \int_{-\infty}^{\infty} f(\zeta)g(x-\zeta)\,\mathrm{d}\zeta, \tag{3.1.21}$$

and using the results (3.1.20), we obtain for the formal solution of the problem

$$y(x,t) = \frac{1}{2\sqrt{(2\pi at)}} \int_{-\infty}^{\infty} f(x-\zeta)\left(\cos\frac{\zeta^2}{4at} + \sin\frac{\zeta^2}{4at}\right)\mathrm{d}\zeta -$$

$$-\frac{1}{2\sqrt{(2\pi at)}} \int_{-\infty}^{\infty} h(x-\zeta)\left(\cos\frac{\zeta^2}{4at} - \sin\frac{\zeta^2}{4at}\right)\mathrm{d}\zeta. \tag{3.1.22}$$

We consider a specific form for the input, given by

$$y(x,0) = f(x) = f_0\exp(-x^2/4b^2),\ \dot{y}(x,0) = 0. \tag{3.1.23}$$

This corresponds to a Gaussian distribution of displacement and, while giving a rather difficult expression to evaluate, corresponds to a physically acceptable displacement field. In developing the response to this input, Sneddon [22, p. 113] points out that it is frequently more advisable to work with the direct inverse transform of (3.1.18), given by

$$y(x,t) = \frac{1}{\sqrt{(2\pi)}} \int_{-\infty}^{\infty} \{F(\xi)\cos\xi^2 at - H(\xi)\sin\xi^2 at\}\exp(-\mathrm{i}\xi x)\,\mathrm{d}\xi, \tag{3.1.24}$$

than to work with the general result (3.1.22). Noting from tables that

$$F\{\exp(-x^2/4b^2)\} = \sqrt{2}b\exp(-\xi^2 b^2). \tag{3.1.25}$$

Then, with $H(\xi) = 0$, (3.1.24) reduces to

$$y(x,t) = \frac{f_0 b}{\sqrt{\pi}} \int_{-\infty}^{\infty} \exp(-\xi^2 b^2)\cos\xi^2 at\,\exp(-\mathrm{i}\xi x)\,\mathrm{d}\xi. \tag{3.1.26}$$

By writing $\cos\xi^2 at$ in exponential form and making use of the general result (3.1.25), one obtains

$$y(x,t) = \frac{f_0}{(1+a^2t^2/b^4)^{\frac{1}{4}}} \exp\left\{-\frac{x^2b^2}{4(b^4+a^2t^2)}\right\} \times$$

$$\times \cos\left\{\frac{atx^2}{4(b^4+a^2t^2)} - \tfrac{1}{2}\tan^{-1}\left(\frac{at}{b^2}\right)\right\}. \tag{3.1.27}$$

Fortunately, this rather complicated result has been presented by Morse [16, pp. 155–6] in a most interesting form, as shown in Fig. 3.3. The solid line represents the motion of the beam at various instants of time. The

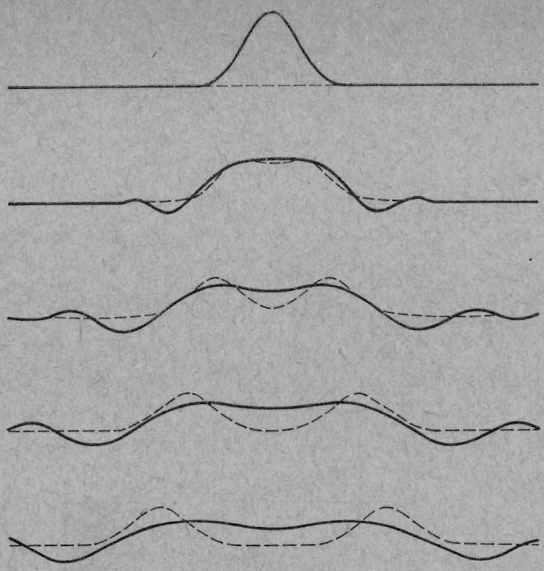

FIG. 3.3. Propagation of an initial disturbance in an infinite beam. (After Morse [16, Fig. 31].)

important item to note is the dispersion of the pulse shape at later times. Also presented in dashed lines is the non-distorted propagation of the Gaussian pulse in a string.

We now consider a more severe input to the system corresponding to an impulse in displacement. This will be specified by initial conditions given by

$$y(x, 0) = f(x) = \delta(x), \qquad \dot{y}(x, 0) = 0. \tag{3.1.28}$$

Such a displacement might be envisaged as a limiting case of the Gaussian input for smaller and smaller values of b. Using the general result (3.1.22), the solution may be written immediately as

$$y(x, t) = \frac{1}{2\sqrt{(2\pi at)}}\left(\cos\frac{x^2}{4at} + \sin\frac{x^2}{4at}\right) = \frac{1}{2\sqrt{(\pi at)}}\sin\left(\frac{x^2}{4at}+\frac{\pi}{4}\right). \tag{3.1.29}$$

The general form of this response is shown in Fig. 3.4 for a fixed location and variable time and for a fixed time at variable location. The first thing to be noted in either representation is that the high-frequency components appear at the front of the wave. For representation at $x = x_0$, this is indicated by the increased oscillation rate for smaller and smaller time, while for the representation at $t = t_0$, this is indicated by the more rapid oscillations at greater distance. This aspect is confirmed by the dispersion curve for the beam (Fig. 3.2(b)), where higher velocities are associated with higher frequencies. The second item to note is the singular behaviour of the oscillation

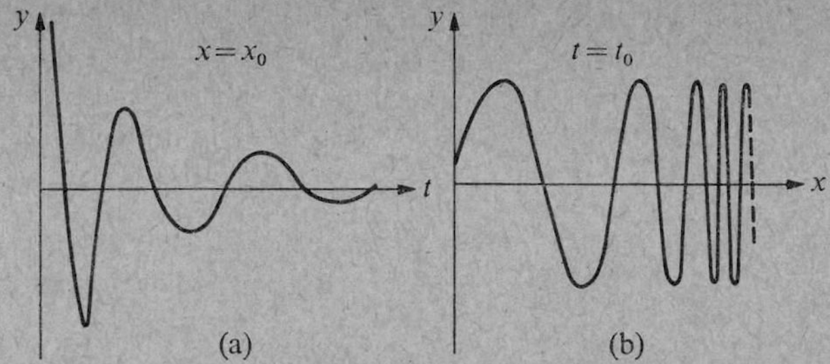

FIG. 3.4. (a) Waves at a given location x_0 in a beam for varying time and (b) at a given time t_0 for various x resulting from an initial impulse displacement field.

for small values of time. This is illustrated in the figure and is evident in the result (3.1.29). The peculiar aspect of the result is that at $t = 0+\varepsilon$, a disturbance of very high frequency is predicted instantaneously at remote locations. This is the manifestation of the infinite phase velocity anomaly pointed out in conjunction with the dispersion curve for the beam.†

A final remark on this problem is warranted. It might be postulated that the anomalous response is a consequence of the physically-unacceptable impulse initial displacement. Such a function can only be constructed by superimposing contributions from the entire wavelength (or wavenumber) spectrum, so that wavelengths approaching zero are indeed present in the initial waveform. However, the point is that it is the Bernoulli–Euler model of the beam that predicts that these components will travel at infinite velocity.

A slightly more physically realizable set of initial conditions are given by

$$y(x, 0) = 0, \qquad \dot{y}(x, 0) = \delta(x). \tag{3.1.30}$$

These conditions would approximate a sharp blow being struck at the origin of a beam initially undeformed. Applying the Laplace and then the Fourier transforms to (3.1.7) gives the transformed solution

$$\bar{Y}(\xi, s) = \frac{1}{\sqrt{(2\pi)}}\frac{1}{s^2+a^2\xi^4}. \tag{3.1.31}$$

The inverse Laplace transform of this function has already been given by (3.1.17), so that we have

$$Y(\xi, t) = \frac{1}{\sqrt{(2\pi a)}}\frac{\sin \xi^2 at}{\xi^2}. \tag{3.1.32}$$

Taking the inverse Fourier transform gives

$$y(x, t) = \frac{1}{2\pi a}\int_{-\infty}^{\infty}\frac{\sin a\xi^2 t}{\xi^2}e^{-i\xi x}\,d\xi. \tag{3.1.33}$$

† See Problem 3.7 regarding use of the stationary-phase method on this problem.

Since $(\sin a\xi^2 t)/\xi^2$ is an even function, (3.1.33) reduces to

$$y(x, t) = \frac{1}{2\pi a}\int_0^\infty \frac{\sin a\xi^2 t}{\xi^2}\cos \xi x \, d\xi, \tag{3.1.34}$$

which is, within a constant factor, the inverse Fourier cosine transform. This inverse transform is available from more comprehensive transform tables,† and is given by

$$y(x, t) = \frac{x}{4a}[S_2\{(2\pi at)^{-\frac{1}{2}}x\} - C_2\{(2\pi at)^{-\frac{1}{2}}x\}] + \\ +\frac{1}{2}\left(\frac{t}{\pi a}\right)^{\frac{1}{2}} \sin\left(\frac{x^2}{4at}+\frac{\pi}{4}\right), \tag{3.1.35}$$

where S_2 and C_2 are special function forms called the *Fresnel* integrals, defined by‡

$$C_2(v) = \frac{1}{\sqrt{(2\pi)}}\int_0^v \frac{\cos u}{u^{\frac{1}{2}}}\,du, \qquad S_2(v) = \frac{1}{\sqrt{(2\pi)}}\int_0^v \frac{\sin u}{u^{\frac{1}{2}}}\,du. \tag{3.1.36}$$

In order to determine the actual waveform numerical evaluation of (3.1.36) must be carried out using tabulated values of the Fresnel integrals.§ We note that for large x but small t that the high-frequency behaviour of the previous problem is still present. However, from the coefficient of the sine term it is seen that the amplitude of this 'instantaneous' high-frequency disturbance will be small.

3.1.4. *Forced motion of a beam*

We shall concern ourselves primarily with forced harmonic motion of a beam. Consider, as a first simple example, the case of a semi-infinite beam subjected to a harmonically varying end displacement. The governing equation is given by (3.1.7) for this problem. The boundary conditions are

$$y(0, t) = y_0 e^{-i\omega t}, \qquad \frac{\partial^2 y(0, t)}{\partial x^2} = 0. \tag{3.1.37}$$

The second condition results from the fact that the end of the beam is free to rotate during the motion, so that the end moment is zero. Then (3.1.1) leads to the condition of the second derivative. Considering a solution of the form

$$y(x, t) = Y(x)e^{-i\omega t}, \tag{3.1.38}$$

† Vol. I, p. 23 of Reference [6].
‡ p. 300 of Reference [1].
§ op. cit., pp. 321–2.

the governing equation reduces to

$$\frac{d^4Y}{dx^4}-\gamma^4Y = 0, \qquad \gamma^2 = \frac{\omega}{a}. \tag{3.1.39}$$

This has the solution

$$Y = Ae^{i\gamma x}+Be^{-i\gamma x}+Ce^{\gamma x}+De^{-\gamma x}. \tag{3.1.40}$$

In applying boundary conditions to determine the constants, some of the considerations first presented in § 1.2 apply. Specifically, the radiation condition requires that $B = 0$ since that term, in conjunction with the time variation for the problem, gives incoming waves. The second consideration bears on the third term of (3.1.40). For $x > 0$, this results in unbounded response for increasing x, so we set $C = 0$ on physical grounds. The remaining two constants are determined from the boundary conditions (3.1.37). These give

$$A+D = y_0, \qquad -A+D = 0, \tag{3.1.41}$$

resulting in $A = D = y_0/2$. The resulting motion is given by

$$y = \frac{y_0}{2}e^{i(\gamma x-\omega t)}+\frac{y_0}{2}e^{-\gamma x}e^{-i\omega t}. \tag{3.1.42}$$

The response is thus made up of a propagating and a non-propagating term. If we recall the problem of forced motion of a semi-infinite string on an elastic foundation (see Fig. 1.23), it was found for frequencies above a cutoff frequency that motion corresponding to the first term of (3.1.42) occurred, while below the cutoff frequency motion corresponding to the second term resulted. In the present problem, both occur simultaneously. In terms of energy, we may interpret the one term as continuously radiated energy and the other as *local stored energy*. This phenomenon will occur also in more complex problems. We conclude by again noting that the 'unacceptable' solutions for harmonic waves (the imaginary wavenumbers) play an important role in forced motion problems.

Let us consider a more general case of forced motion of a semi-infinite rod, as specified by

$$y(0, t) = V(t), \qquad \partial^2y(0, t)/\partial x^2 = 0, \tag{3.1.43}$$

with the beam being initially at rest. A double-transform approach will be used and a formal solution obtained. The main objective will be to demonstrate certain aspects of the Fourier cosine and sine transforms.

Apply the Laplace transform to the governing equation (3.1.7), giving

$$\frac{d^4\bar{y}(x, s)}{dx^4}+\frac{s^2}{a^2}\bar{y}(x, s) = 0. \tag{3.1.44}$$

We now consider application of the Fourier transform on the spatial variable. Because $0 < x < \infty$, either the Fourier cosine or sine transform must be used, and the question is—which one? This is, in fact, a common problem in transform applications and the answer is usually not obvious *a priori.* Consider using the cosine transform on (3.1.44). We must first evaluate the cosine transform of the fourth derivative term. Thus

$$F_c(\bar{y}^{iv}) = \sqrt{\left(\frac{2}{\pi}\right)} \int_0^\infty \frac{d^4\bar{y}}{dx^4} \cos \xi x \, dx. \tag{3.1.45}$$

Carrying out a repeated integration by parts gives

$$F_c(\bar{y}^{iv}) = \sqrt{\left(\frac{2}{\pi}\right)} [\bar{y}''' \cos \xi x + \bar{y}''\xi \sin \xi x - \bar{y}'\xi^2 \cos \xi x + \bar{y}\xi^3 \sin \xi x]_0^\infty - \\ -\xi^4 \sqrt{\left(\frac{2}{\pi}\right)} \int_0^\infty \bar{y} \cos \xi x \, dx. \tag{3.1.46}$$

We note the integral appearing in (3.1.46) is merely the cosine transform of $\bar{y}$. The resulting transformed equation is then

$$\left(\xi^4 - \frac{s^2}{a^2}\right) \bar{Y}_c = \sqrt{\left(\frac{2}{\pi}\right)} [\bar{y}''' \cos \xi x + \bar{y}''\xi \sin \xi x - \bar{y}'\xi^2 \cos \xi x + \bar{y}\xi^3 \sin \xi x]_0^\infty . \tag{3.1.47}$$

We consider the right-hand side of this result. Since the problem is one of transient motion, it is legitimate to assume the beam at rest so that

$$\bar{y} = \bar{y}' = \bar{y}'' = \bar{y}''' = 0$$

at infinity. For the lower limit, we have that $\sin \xi x = 0$ at $x = 0$. There remain the terms $\bar{y}'''$ and $\bar{y}'$. For this problem, these are unknowns to be determined and not specified boundary conditions. Evidently the choice of the cosine transform is improper for this problem since it does not 'ask' for the right boundary conditions.

If the Fourier sine transform is applied, we obtain for the fourth derivative

$$F_s(\bar{y}^{iv}) = \sqrt{\left(\frac{2}{\pi}\right)} \int_0^\infty \frac{d^4\bar{y}}{dx^4} \sin \xi x \, dx, \\ = \sqrt{\left(\frac{2}{\pi}\right)} [\bar{y}''' \sin \xi x - \bar{y}''\xi \cos \xi x - \bar{y}'\xi^2 \sin \xi x + \bar{y}\xi^3 \cos \xi x]_0^\infty + \\ + \xi^4 \sqrt{\left(\frac{2}{\pi}\right)} \int_0^\infty \bar{y} \sin \xi x \, dx. \tag{3.1.48}$$

Proceeding directly to inspect the bracketed term of the result, it is seen that the difficulty that arose with the cosine transform is now removed. The upper limits are zero, based on the same arguments as used in the cosine-transform attempt. Two of the lower limit terms are removed since $\sin \xi x = 0$. The two remaining terms involve $\bar{y}''(0, s)$ and $y(0, s)$. The first of these is zero and the second is specified by the Laplace transform of the boundary condition (2.1.43). Thus, the sine transform has 'asked' for the proper conditions and is the proper transform for this problem.

The resulting transformed solution is

$$\bar{Y}_s(\xi, s) = \sqrt{\left(\frac{2}{\pi}\right)}\frac{a^2\xi^3\bar{V}(s)}{s^2+a^2\xi^4}. \tag{3.1.49}$$

The major point of this example has now been made. The inversion of the result, first on the sine transform and then on the Laplace, using the convolution theorem in the latter step, yields the formal solution. It will be left as an exercise to obtain the result

$$y(x, t) = \frac{x}{4\pi}\sqrt{\left(\frac{2\pi}{a}\right)}\int_0^t \frac{V(\tau)}{(t-\tau)^{\frac{3}{2}}}\left\{\sin\frac{x^2}{4a(t-\tau)}+\cos\frac{x^2}{4a(t-\tau)}\right\}\mathrm{d}\tau. \tag{3.1.50}$$

As our last example of forced motion, we will revert to a simpler loading situation. Consider an infinite beam subjected to a harmonically varying, concentrated load placed at $x = \zeta$. The inhomogeneous equation

$$\frac{\partial^4 y}{\partial x^4}+\frac{1}{a^2}\frac{\partial^2 y}{\partial t^2} = \frac{1}{EI}\,\delta(x-\zeta)\mathrm{e}^{-\mathrm{i}\omega t} \tag{3.1.51}$$

now governs the motion. The specified problem is, of course, one of determining the Green's function for the system. Considering a solution of the type $y = Y(x)\exp(-\mathrm{i}\omega t)$, we obtain

$$\frac{\mathrm{d}^4 Y}{\mathrm{d}x^4}-\frac{\omega^2}{a^2}Y = \frac{1}{EI}\,\delta(x-\zeta). \tag{3.1.52}$$

Applying the exponential Fourier transform to (3.1.52) gives the transformed solution as

$$\bar{Y}(\xi) = \frac{1}{\sqrt{(2\pi)EI}}\frac{\mathrm{e}^{\mathrm{i}\xi\zeta}}{\xi^4-\xi_0^4}, \qquad \xi_0^2 = \frac{\omega}{a}. \tag{3.1.53}$$

The inverse Fourier transform gives

$$Y(x) = \frac{1}{2\pi EI}\int_{-\infty}^{\infty}\frac{\mathrm{e}^{-\mathrm{i}\xi(x-\zeta)}}{\xi^4-\xi_0^4}\,\mathrm{d}\xi. \tag{3.1.54}$$

This result is quite simple to evaluate by residue theory. Recalling the general arguments developed in the first chapter pertaining to Fig. 1.9, we see that for $x > \zeta$, we must close the semicircular contour in the lower half of the complex ξ-plane. There are four simple poles of the integrand given by

$$\xi = \pm\xi_0,\ \pm \mathrm{i}\xi_0. \tag{3.1.55}$$

Thus, two poles are on the real axis and two on the imaginary axis. The imaginary root in the upper half-plane is excluded by the contour closure. In so far as the poles on the real axis are concerned, we must recall the arguments developed in § 1.1 leading to Fig. 1.9. Thus, poles on the real axis must be included or excluded from the general contour by slight indentations as dictated by the radiation condition. Inspecting the exponential of (3.1.54) that will appear in the residues, it is seen that the pole at $\xi = -\xi_0$ in conjunction with the time behaviour $\exp(-\mathrm{i}\omega t)$ will give waves propagating to the right for $x > \zeta$. The pole at $\xi = +\xi_0$ will give improper radiation and must be excluded from the contour by an indentation below it. The resulting contour is shown in Fig. 3.5. The residues for the simple poles at $\xi = -\xi_0$,

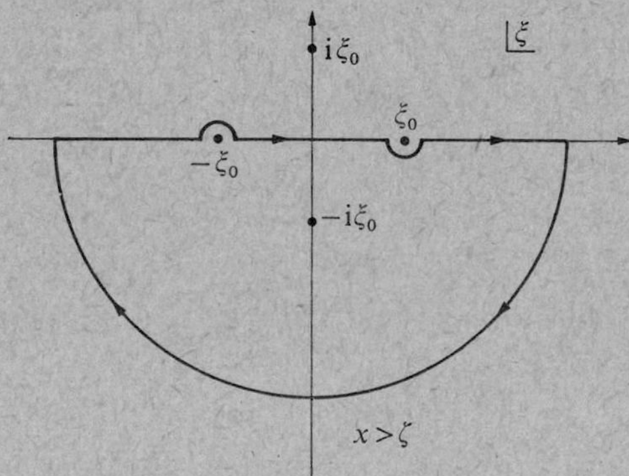

FIG. 3.5. Contour for the infinite beam subjected to a harmonically varying, concentrated load.

$-\mathrm{i}\xi_0$ are given, respectively, by

$$-\frac{\exp\{\mathrm{i}\xi_0(x-\zeta)\}}{4\xi_0^3},\qquad -\frac{\exp\{-\xi_0(x-\zeta)\}}{4\xi_0^3}. \tag{3.1.56}$$

From the residue theorem, we thus obtain for the inversion of (3.1.54), the result

$$y(0, t) = \frac{\mathrm{i}}{4\xi_0^3 EI}\exp[\mathrm{i}\{\xi_0(x-\zeta)-\omega t\}]- \\ -\frac{1}{4\xi_0^3 EI}\exp\{-\xi_0(x-\zeta)\}\exp(-\mathrm{i}\omega t), \tag{3.1.57}$$

where the time variation has been included. Superposition methods would be used to obtain the response to more general loadings. We again note the presence of propagating waves and local vibrations in the beam response.

3.1.5. *Reflection of harmonic waves*

As in our previous studies in the wave motion of strings and rods, we are interested in the interaction of propagating waves with boundaries. In approaching this problem, we see that it does not make sense to consider an incident pulse of specific shape because of the dispersive characteristics of the beam. Thus, pulse distortion due to dispersion and pulse distortion due to boundary interaction would both occur, and no general conclusions could be reached on the reflection characteristics of the boundary. Instead, we consider a steady train of harmonic waves to be incident, in the manner considered in § 1.2 for strings, and determine the frequency-dependent amplitude ratios of the reflected waves.

The various simple end conditions for beams are pinned, fixed, and free ends. Elastic boundary constraints may be incorporated in terms of deflection or torsion springs or both. These conditions must be given mathematical expression in terms of the deflection y, slope $\partial y/\partial x$, moment M and shear V where, for the last two quantities, we have

$$M = -EI\frac{\partial^2 y}{\partial x^2}, \qquad V = -EI\frac{\partial^3 y}{\partial x^3}. \tag{3.1.58}$$

End mass and dashpot constraints are also possible. Table 3.1 summarizes the various simple boundary conditions and those consisting of single elements such as a spring, dashpot, or mass.

In considering the reflective characteristics of various boundaries, we start with a solution of the governing equation (3.1.7) in the form

$$y = Ae^{-i(\gamma x+\omega t)}+Be^{i(\gamma x-\omega t)}+Ce^{-\gamma x}e^{-i\omega t}+De^{\gamma x}e^{-i\omega t}. \tag{3.1.59}$$

We presume that the incident harmonic wave, appearing as the first term of the solution, is specified in terms of amplitude A and frequency ω. It will have a corresponding wavenumber as given by (3.1.11). Next, we delete the last term of the solution, because of the unbounded response. This leaves the two amplitudes B and C to be determined by the boundary condition. As a simple first example, suppose the end of a semi-infinite beam $x > 0$ is pinned, so that the conditions, from Table 3.1, are

$$y(0, t) = \partial^2 y(0, t)/\partial x^2 = 0. \tag{3.1.60}$$

Substituting (3.1.59), with $D = 0$, in (3.1.60) gives

$$\begin{aligned} A+B+C &= 0, \\ -A-B+C &= 0. \end{aligned} \tag{3.1.61}$$

TABLE 3.1

Type	Diagram	Equation
Pinned		$y(0,t)=0$ $\dfrac{\partial^2 y(0,t)}{\partial x^2}=0$
Fixed		$y(0,t)=0$ $\dfrac{\partial y(0,t)}{\partial x}=0$
Free		$\dfrac{\partial^2 y(0,t)}{\partial x^2}=0$ $\dfrac{\partial^3 y(0,t)}{\partial x^3}=0$
Deflected spring	K_D	$\dfrac{\partial^2 y(0,t)}{\partial x^2}=0$ $-EI\dfrac{\partial^3 y(0,t)}{\partial x^3}=K_D\, y(0,t)$
Torsion spring	K_T	$y(0,t)=0$ $EI\dfrac{\partial^2 y(0,t)}{\partial x^2}=K_T\dfrac{\partial y(0,t)}{\partial x}$
Mass	m	$\dfrac{\partial^2 y(0,t)}{\partial x^2}=0$ $-EI\dfrac{\partial^3 y(0,t)}{\partial x^3}=m\dfrac{\partial^2 y(0,t)}{\partial t^2}$
Dashpot	c	$\dfrac{\partial^2 y(0,t)}{\partial x^2}=0$ $-EI\dfrac{\partial^3 y(0,t)}{\partial x^3}=c\dfrac{\partial y(0,t)}{\partial t}$

Solving these in terms of A gives $C = 0$, $B = -A$, so that the resulting disturbance is given by

$$y = Ae^{-i(\gamma x+\omega t)} - Ae^{i(\gamma x-\omega t)},$$
$$= -2iA \sin \gamma x e^{-i\omega t}. \qquad (3.1.62)$$

This corresponds to a standing-wave condition.

Consider the slightly more complicated case of a free end. The boundary conditions are

$$\partial^2 y(0, t)/\partial x^2 = \partial^3 y(0, t)/\partial x^3 = 0. \qquad (3.1.63)$$

Substituting (3.1.59) in the above, again with $D = 0$, gives

$$\begin{aligned} -A-B+C &= 0, \\ \mathrm{i}A-\mathrm{i}B-C &= 0. \end{aligned} \tag{3.1.64}$$

Solving this system gives

$$\frac{B}{A} = \frac{-1+\mathrm{i}}{1+\mathrm{i}} = \mathrm{i}, \qquad \frac{C}{A} = \frac{2\mathrm{i}}{1+\mathrm{i}} = 1+\mathrm{i}. \tag{3.1.65}$$

The fact that the ratios are complex numbers merely indicates phase shifting relative to the incident wave. Of particular interest here is the presence of the C term. Referring back to the solution (3.1.59), it is seen that this is the local effect previously noted in the forced vibration of beams. Such an effect is frequently referred to as *end resonance* and is also noted in more complex structures.

3.2. Free and forced vibrations of finite beams

In studying the free vibrations of beams, we are interested in the natural frequencies and normal modes for various constraint conditions, whether orthogonality of these modes exists, and in applying the modal solutions to the initial-value problem. Most of the methods used in problems of forced vibrations of beams are similar to those used in strings, such as the Green's function or transform approaches. These will be reviewed in the context of beam analysis and applied to several problems.

3.2.1. *Natural frequencies of finite beams*

Numerous combinations of boundary constraints of the type shown in Table 3.1 are possible for beams of finite length. If we confine our specific attention to combinations of the simple conditions, these consisting of the pinned (P), clamped (C), and free (F) ends, we see there are six possible combinations given by P–P, P–C, P–F, C–C, C–F, and F–F. To determine the natural frequencies and normal modes for these cases, we employ separation of variables. Thus we let

$$y = Y(x)T(t), \tag{3.2.1}$$

and substituting in (3.1.7) gives

$$a^2\frac{Y^{\mathrm{iv}}}{Y} = -\frac{T''}{T} = \omega^2. \tag{3.2.2}$$

Thus, for T we have

$$T = A\cos\omega t + B\sin\omega t \tag{3.2.3}$$

The solution for Y may be expressed in exponential form. A more useful form for our present purposes is given by

$$Y = C_1\sin\beta x + C_2\cos\beta x + C_3\sinh\beta x + C_4\cosh\beta x, \qquad \beta^4 = \omega^2/a^2. \tag{3.2.4}$$

An alternative form is given by

$$Y = D_1(\cos\beta x + \cosh\beta x) + D_2(\cos\beta x - \cosh\beta x) + \\ + D_3(\sin\beta x + \sinh\beta x) + D_4(\sin\beta x - \sinh\beta x). \qquad (3.2.5)$$

The various combinations of simple boundary conditions will now be considered.

1. *Pinned–pinned:* The boundary conditions, in terms of $Y(x)$, are given by

$$\begin{aligned} Y(0) &= \mathrm{d}^2 Y(0)/\mathrm{d}x^2 = 0, \\ Y(l) &= \mathrm{d}^2 Y(l)/\mathrm{d}x^2 = 0. \end{aligned} \qquad (3.2.6)$$

Using the solution form (3.2.4) in these boundary conditions gives

$$C_2 = C_3 = C_4 = 0$$

and the frequency equation

$$\sin\beta l = 0, \qquad \beta l = n\pi \qquad (n = 1, 2, 3...,). \qquad (3.2.7)$$

The radial and cyclic frequencies are, respectively,

$$\omega_n = a\left(\frac{n\pi}{l}\right)^2, \qquad f_n = \frac{a\pi}{2l^2}n^2 \qquad (n = 1, 2, 3,...). \qquad (3.2.8)$$

In terms of the beam parameters we have

$$f_n = \frac{n^2\pi}{2l^2}\sqrt{\left(\frac{EI}{\rho A}\right)}. \qquad (3.2.9)$$

The normal modes are then

$$Y_n = \sin\beta_n x, \qquad (3.2.10)$$

and a general solution is given by

$$y = \sum_{n=1}^{\infty}(A_n\cos\omega_n t + B_n\sin\omega_n t)\sin\beta_n x. \qquad (3.2.11)$$

2. *Free–free:* The boundary conditions are

$$\begin{aligned} \frac{\mathrm{d}^2 Y(0)}{\mathrm{d}x^2} &= \frac{\mathrm{d}^3 Y(0)}{\mathrm{d}x^3} = 0, \\ \frac{\mathrm{d}^2 Y(l)}{\mathrm{d}x^2} &= \frac{\mathrm{d}^3 Y(l)}{\mathrm{d}x^3} = 0. \end{aligned} \qquad (3.2.12)$$

Using the solution form (3.2.5) in the above quickly gives $D_2 = D_4 = 0$, with the remaining two conditions at $x = l$ being given by

$$\begin{pmatrix} (\cos\beta l - \cosh\beta l) & (\sin\beta l - \sinh\beta l) \\ (\sin\beta l + \sinh\beta l) & -(\cos\beta l - \cosh\beta l) \end{pmatrix}\begin{pmatrix} D_1 \\ D_3 \end{pmatrix} = 0. \qquad (3.2.13)$$

Setting the determinant of coefficients equal to zero gives the frequency equation

$$(\cos \beta l - \cosh \beta l)^2 + (\sin^2 \beta l - \sinh^2 \beta l) = 0, \tag{3.2.14}$$

which may be reduced to

$$\cos \beta l \cosh \beta l = 1. \tag{3.2.15}$$

The first six roots of this equation are given by

$$\begin{gathered} \beta_0 l = 0, \qquad \beta_1 l = 4{\cdot}730, \qquad \beta_2 l = 7{\cdot}853, \\ \beta_3 l = 10{\cdot}996, \qquad \beta_4 l = 14{\cdot}137, \qquad \beta_5 l = 17{\cdot}279. \end{gathered} \tag{3.2.16}$$

The cyclic frequencies are expressed by

$$f_n = \frac{(\beta_n l)^2}{2\pi l^2} \sqrt{\left(\frac{EI}{\rho A}\right)}. \tag{3.2.17}$$

The root $\beta_0 l = 0$ corresponds to the rigid-body motion term for this beam.

3. *Clamped–clamped:* The boundary conditions are

$$\begin{gathered} Y(0) = \mathrm{d}Y(0)/\mathrm{d}x = 0, \\ Y(l) = \mathrm{d}Y(l)/\mathrm{d}x = 0. \end{gathered} \tag{3.2.18}$$

There results $D_1 = D_3 = 0$ and

$$\begin{pmatrix} (\cos \beta l - \cosh \beta l) & (\sin \beta l - \sinh \beta l) \\ (\sin \beta l + \sinh \beta l) & -(\cos \beta l - \cosh \beta l) \end{pmatrix} \begin{pmatrix} D_2 \\ D_4 \end{pmatrix} = 0. \tag{3.2.19}$$

This is seen to be the same matrix of coefficients that resulted in the previous problem. The roots will be the same except that the zero root is excluded. Thus $\beta_1 l = 4{\cdot}730$, $\beta_2 l = 7{\cdot}853$, etc. The mode shapes are, of course, different.

4. *Clamped–free:* The boundary conditions are

$$\begin{gathered} Y(0) = \mathrm{d}Y(0)/\mathrm{d}x = 0, \\ \mathrm{d}^2 Y(l)/\mathrm{d}x^2 = \mathrm{d}^3 Y(l)/\mathrm{d}x^3 = 0. \end{gathered} \tag{3.2.20}$$

It is found that $D_1 = D_3 = 0$ with the frequency equation being given by

$$\cos \beta l \cosh \beta l = -1. \tag{3.2.21}$$

The first few roots are

$$\begin{gathered} \beta_1 l = 1{\cdot}875, \qquad \beta_2 l = 4{\cdot}694, \qquad \beta_3 l = 7{\cdot}855, \\ \beta_4 l = 10{\cdot}996, \qquad \beta_5 l = 14{\cdot}137, \qquad \beta_6 l = 17{\cdot}279. \end{gathered} \tag{3.2.22}$$

5. *Clamped–pinned:* The boundary conditions are

$$\begin{gathered} Y(0) = \mathrm{d}Y(0)/\mathrm{d}x = 0, \\ Y(l) = \mathrm{d}^2 Y(l)/\mathrm{d}x^2 = 0. \end{gathered} \tag{3.2.23}$$

The resulting frequency equation is

$$\tan \beta l = \tanh \beta l. \tag{3.2.24}$$

The first few roots are given by

$$\beta_1 l = 3{\cdot}927, \qquad \beta_2 l = 7{\cdot}069, \qquad \beta_3 l = 10{\cdot}210,$$
$$\beta_4 l = 13{\cdot}352, \qquad \beta_5 l = 16{\cdot}493. \tag{3.2.25}$$

6. *Pinned–free:* The boundary conditions are

$$Y(0) = \mathrm{d}^2 Y(0)/\mathrm{d}x^2 = 0, \tag{3.2.26}$$
$$\mathrm{d}^2 Y(l)/\mathrm{d}x^2 = \mathrm{d}^3 Y(l)/\mathrm{d}x^3 = 0.$$

The frequency equation turns out to be the same as for case 5 except that the zero root is an acceptable result for this case. It is ultimately interpretable in terms of rigid-body rotation.

The first few roots of the frequency equations are summarized in terms of the frequency parameter $\beta_n l$ in Table 3.2. The cyclic frequencies are given in

TABLE 3.2

Case	$\beta_0 l$	$\beta_1 l$	$\beta_2 l$	$\beta_3 l$	$\beta_4 l$	$\beta_5 l$
		1·875	4·694	7·855	10·996	14·137
		3·142	6·283	9·425	12·566	15·708
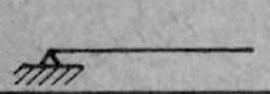	0	3·927	7·069	10·210	13·352	16·493
		3·927	7·069	10·210	13·352	16·493
		4·730	7·853	10·996	14·137	17·279
	0	4·730	7·853	10·996	14·137	17·279

terms of the frequency parameter by (3.2.17). It is to be noted that the frequencies are irregularly spaced for most cases for the first two or three modes. However, as the mode number increases, the difference between the frequency parameter for all cases approaches π. Thus, for the clamped–free beam, $\beta_5 l - \beta_4 l = 3{\cdot}141$, for the clamped–clamped case, $\beta_5 l - \beta_4 l = 3{\cdot}142$, and so on. The pinned–pinned case has all of the modes equally spaced. We may interpret this general result as indicating an insensitivity to end constraint at higher frequencies.

3.2.2. *Orthogonality*

We investigate possible orthogonality of the normal modes in a manner similar to that employed in the study of strings (§ 1.3). Thus consider two normal modes Y_n and Y_m, where each satisfies

$$Y_n^{\text{iv}} - \frac{\omega_n^2}{a^2} Y_n = 0,$$
$$Y_m^{\text{iv}} - \frac{\omega_m^2}{a^2} Y_m = 0. \tag{3.2.27}$$

Multiplying the first eqn (3.2.27) by Y_m and the second eqn by Y_n, forming the difference between the two systems, and integrating over the interval of the beam gives

$$\int_0^l (Y_m Y_n^{\text{iv}} - Y_n Y_m^{\text{iv}})\,\mathrm{d}x = -\left(\frac{\omega_m^2 - \omega_n^2}{a^2}\right) \int_0^l Y_m Y_n\,\mathrm{d}x. \tag{3.2.28}$$

Integrating the term $Y_m Y_n^{\text{iv}}$ by parts, we obtain

$$\int_0^l Y_m Y_n^{\text{iv}}\,\mathrm{d}x = [Y_m Y_n''' - Y_m' Y_n'' + Y_m'' Y_n' - Y_m''' Y_n]_0^l + \int_0^l Y_m^{\text{iv}} Y_n\,\mathrm{d}x. \tag{3.2.29}$$

Inserting this result in (3.2.28) gives

$$[Y_m Y_n''' - Y_m' Y_n'' + Y_m'' Y_n' - Y_m''' Y_n]_0^l = \left(\frac{\omega_n^2 - \omega_m^2}{a^2}\right) \int_0^l Y_m Y_n\,\mathrm{d}x. \tag{3.2.30}$$

We immediately note that combinations of the various simple boundary conditions such as clamped–free, pinned–pinned, and so on cause the left-hand side to vanish. Further, any set of homogeneous boundary conditions of the form

$$aY + bY' + cY'' + dY''' = 0, \tag{3.2.31}$$

where a, b, c, d are constants, will cause the left-hand side to vanish. A condition such as (3.2.31) could arise from a combination of deflection and torsion springs, for example. However, time-dependent boundary conditions, such as those resulting from mass or dashpot contributions, would not cause vanishing. So, for conditions of the form (3.2.31) we have that

$$\int_0^l Y_m Y_n\,\mathrm{d}x = 0 \qquad (m \neq n), \tag{3.2.32}$$

which establishes orthogonality.†

† op. cit., p. 41.

3.2.3. *The initial-value problem*

The initial value problem for the finite beam is specified by the homogeneous governing equation (3.1.7), the particular boundary conditions for the problem and, the initial conditions

$$y(x,0) = f(x), \qquad \partial y(x,0)/\partial t = g(x). \tag{3.2.33}$$

The solution is obtained by superimposing particular solutions to give

$$y(x,t) = \sum_{n=1}^{\infty} (A_n \cos \omega_n t + B_n \sin \omega_n t) Y_n(x), \tag{3.2.34}$$

where $Y_n(x)$ are the normal modes for the beam. If the modes are orthogonal, the constants A_n, B_n are determined after the manner of Fourier series investigations and give

$$A_n = \frac{1}{N} \int_0^l f(x) Y_n(x)\,\mathrm{d}x, \qquad B_n = \frac{1}{N\omega_n} \int_0^l g(x) Y_n(x)\,\mathrm{d}x, \tag{3.2.35}$$

where N is the normalizing factor for the interval. The general response is given by

$$y(x,t) = \sum_{n=1}^{\infty} \left\{ \cos \omega_n t \int_0^l f(x) Y_n(x)\,\mathrm{d}x + \frac{\sin \omega_n t}{\omega_n} \int_0^l g(x) Y_n(x)\,\mathrm{d}x \right\} \frac{Y_n(x)}{N}. \tag{3.2.36}$$

3.2.4. *Forced vibrations of beams—methods of analysis*

The methods of analysis for the forced motions of finite beams are quite similar to those presented for strings (§ 1.3) and include the Green's function approach and various transform methods. These will be reviewed in the context of the beam problem.

In the Green's function approach, a harmonically varying concentrated load will be analysed, so that the governing equation is

$$\frac{\partial^4 y}{\partial x^4} + \frac{1}{a^2} \frac{\partial^2 y}{\partial t^2} = \frac{1}{EI} \delta(x-\xi) \mathrm{e}^{-i\omega t}. \tag{3.2.37}$$

We let $y = Y(x)\exp(-i\omega t)$ and substitute in (3.3.73), giving

$$\frac{\mathrm{d}^4 Y}{\mathrm{d}x^4} - \beta^4 Y = \frac{1}{EI} \delta(x-\xi), \qquad \beta^4 = \frac{\omega^2}{a^2}. \tag{3.2.38}$$

Because of the properties of the Dirac delta function, we have

$$Y^{\mathrm{iv}} - \beta^4 Y = 0, \qquad x \neq \xi. \tag{3.2.39}$$

There will be two solutions to this equation, one for the region $x < \xi$, one for $x > \xi$. Thus

$$x < \xi; \quad Y_1(x) = A_1 \sin \beta x + B_1 \cos \beta x + C_1 \sinh \beta x + D_1 \cosh \beta x, \tag{3.2.40}$$

$$x > \xi; \quad Y_2(x) = A_2 \sin \beta x + B_2 \cos \beta x + C_2 \sinh \beta x + D_2 \cosh \beta x. \tag{3.2.41}$$

The application of two boundary conditions at $x = 0$ will enable two of the constants of the set A_1, B_1, C_1, D_1 to be eliminated, while application of two conditions at $x = l$ will allow the set A_2, B_2, C_2, D_2 to be reduced to two. Four conditions are required at $x = \xi$ to determine the problem. Three of the conditions are

$$\begin{aligned} Y_1(\xi-\varepsilon) &= Y_2(\xi+\varepsilon), \\ Y_1'(\xi-\varepsilon) &= Y_2'(\xi+\varepsilon), \\ Y_1''(\xi-\varepsilon) &= Y_2''(\xi+\varepsilon), \end{aligned} \tag{3.2.42}$$

where ε is an arbitrarily small quantity. These are continuity conditions on the deflection, slope, and curvature. The fourth relation is a jump condition on the shear and may be established by integrating (3.2.38) across $x = \xi$. Thus

$$\int_{\xi-\varepsilon}^{\xi+\varepsilon} Y^{\text{iv}}\,dx - \beta^4 \int_{\xi-\varepsilon}^{\xi+\varepsilon} Y\,dx = \frac{1}{EI} \int_{\xi-\varepsilon}^{\xi+\varepsilon} \delta(x-\xi)\,dx = \frac{1}{EI}. \tag{3.2.43}$$

Since Y is continuous across $x = \xi$, the second integral vanishes and we have

$$Y'''(x)\Big|_{\xi-\varepsilon}^{\xi+\varepsilon} = 1/EI, \tag{3.2.44}$$

giving

$$Y_2'''(\xi) - Y_1'''(\xi) = 1/EI. \tag{3.2.45}$$

This establishes the necessary fourth condition at $x = \xi$.

The final details of the solution depend on actually specifying the boundary conditions and solving for the constants $A_1, B_1, \ldots, C_2, D_2$. Without going into the details of this process, the results will be of the form

$$Y(x) = \begin{cases} G(x, \xi, \omega), & (0 < x < \xi) \\ G(\xi, x, \omega), & (\xi < x < l), \end{cases} \tag{3.2.46}$$

so that

$$y(x, t) = G(x, \xi, \omega)e^{-i\omega t}. \tag{3.2.47}$$

will give the system response. The principle of integral superposition must be applied to solve for more general loadings in both time and space.

In considering methods involving integral transforms, we have at our disposal the Laplace transform and the finite Fourier sine and cosine transforms. These methods may be applied to special loading types such as concentrated loads in space and/or harmonically varying loads in time, with extension to more general loads being done by integral superposition.

Alternatively, the case of arbitrary loading may be carried through in the solution with the final results, again in an integral superposition form, obtained by applying the convolution theorem. Obviously there are numerous approaches to the same end, with the question as to the best or most convenient method being governed by the conditions of the specific problem.

In the following, several approaches using the integral transform method will be given, attempting to retain, as in the last section, some generality as to the statement of boundary conditions.

1. *Finite Fourier transform*. Consider the inhomogeneous equation

$$\frac{\partial^4 y}{\partial x^4}+\frac{1}{a^2}\frac{\partial^2 y}{\partial t^2}=\frac{1}{EI}q(x,t), \tag{3.2.48}$$

where the initial conditions are taken as zero. Let $q(x,t)=Q(x)\exp(-i\omega t)$. Then, taking $y(x,t)=Y(x)\exp(-i\omega t)$, we have

$$Y^{\text{iv}}-\beta^4 Y=Q(x)/EI, \qquad \beta^4=\omega^2/a^2. \tag{3.2.49}$$

The finite Fourier transform will now be applied to the above. The question as to whether the sine or cosine transform is appropriate will be determined by the particular boundary conditions.† Recalling that these transforms are given by

$$\bar{F}_c(n)=\frac{1}{l}\int\limits_0^l F(x)\cos\frac{n\pi}{l}x\,dx, \qquad \bar{F}_s(n)=\frac{1}{l}\int\limits_0^l F(x)\sin\frac{n\pi}{l}x\,dx, \tag{3.2.50}$$

with the respective inverses

$$F(x)=\frac{\bar{F}_c(0)}{l}+2\sum_{n=1}^{\infty}\bar{F}_c(n)\cos\frac{n\pi}{l}x \tag{3.2.51}$$

and

$$F(x)=2\sum_{n=1}^{\infty}\bar{F}_s(n)\sin\frac{n\pi}{l}x. \tag{3.2.52}$$

The Fourier sine and cosine transformed equations are, respectively,

$$(\alpha_n^4-\beta^4)\bar{Y}_s(n)=-\frac{1}{l}[Y'''(x)\sin\alpha_n x-\alpha_n Y''(x)\cos\alpha_n x-$$
$$-\alpha_n^2 Y'(x)\sin\alpha_n x+\alpha_n^3 Y(x)\cos\alpha_n x]_0^l+\frac{\bar{Q}(n)}{EI}, \tag{3.2.53}$$

and

$$(\alpha_n^4-\beta^4)\bar{Y}_c(n)=-\frac{1}{l}[Y'''(x)\cos\alpha_n x+\alpha_n Y''(x)\sin\alpha_n x-$$
$$-\alpha_n^2 Y'(x)\cos\alpha_n x-\alpha_n^3 Y(x)\sin\alpha_n x]_0^l+\frac{\bar{Q}(n)}{EI}, \tag{3.2.54}$$

† Recall that a similar question arose in applying the sine and cosine transforms to the semi-infinite beam in § 3.1.

where $\alpha_n = n\pi/l$. Now it should be evident in the sine transformed solution $\bar{Y}_s(n)$ that the following quantities must be specified:

$$\bar{Y}_s(n): \quad x = 0,\ Y(0),\ Y''(0),$$
$$x = l,\ Y(l),\ Y''(l). \tag{3.2.55}$$

In the case of a beam simply supported at both ends, we see that

$$Y(0) = Y''(0) = Y(l) = Y''(l) = 0,$$

so that the sine transform would be appropriate for such a problem. Actually, a study of the bracketed expression in $\bar{Y}_s(n)$ shows that it will vanish or be specified if the linear combinations

$$Y''(l) - \alpha_n^2 Y(l), \qquad Y''(0) - \alpha_n^2 Y(0) \tag{3.2.56}$$

are zero or known, which suggests that certain other non-ideal boundary conditions might be possible.

A similar study of $\bar{Y}_c(n)$ shows that

$$\begin{aligned} x &= 0,\ Y'(0),\ Y'''(0) \\ x &= l,\ Y'(l),\ Y'''(l) \end{aligned} \tag{3.2.57}$$

must be given, or, more generally,

$$Y'''(l) - \alpha_n^2 Y'(l), \qquad Y'''(0) - \alpha_n^2 Y'(0) \tag{3.2.58}$$

must be known.

Assuming that the conditions are such that the bracket vanishes, and following through on the sine transform case, we have

$$\bar{Y}_s(n) = \frac{\bar{Q}_s(n)}{EI(\alpha_n^4 - \beta^4)}, \tag{3.2.59}$$

where

$$\bar{Q}_s(n) = \frac{1}{l}\int_0^l Q(x)\sin\frac{n\pi}{l}x\,dx. \tag{3.2.60}$$

Taking the inverse transform we have

$$Y(x) = \frac{2}{EI}\sum_{n=1}^{\infty}\frac{\bar{Q}_s(n)}{\alpha_n^4 - \beta^4}\sin\frac{n\pi}{l}x \tag{3.2.61}$$

or

$$Y(x) = \frac{2}{EIl}\sum_{n=1}^{\infty}\left[\sin\frac{n\pi}{l}x \Big/ (\alpha_n^4 - \beta^4)\right]\int_0^l Q(u)\sin\frac{n\pi}{l}u\,du. \tag{3.2.62}$$

2. *Expansion in normal modes.* A slightly different viewpoint of this problem is to consider eqn (3.2.49) and expand $Y(x)$, $Q(x)$ in the normal modes of

the given system. Thus assume

$$Y(x) = \sum_{n=1}^{\infty} a_n Y_n(x), \qquad Q(x) = \sum_{n=1}^{\infty} b_n Y_n(x), \tag{3.2.63}$$

where the $Y_n(x)$ satisfy

$$Y_n^{\text{iv}}(x) - \beta_n^4 Y_n(x) = 0. \tag{3.2.64}$$

The coefficient b_n is given by

$$b_n = \frac{2}{l} \int_0^l Y_n(x) Q(x)\, dx. \tag{3.2.65}$$

Substituting (3.2.63) in (3.2.49) gives

$$\sum_{n=1}^{\infty} (a_n Y_n^{\text{iv}} - \beta^4 a_n Y_n) = \frac{1}{EI} \sum_{n=1}^{\infty} b_n Y_n. \tag{3.2.66}$$

Using (3.2.64) this reduces to

$$\sum_{n=1}^{\infty} (\beta_n^4 - \beta^4) a_n Y_n = \sum_{n=1}^{\infty} b_n Y_n. \tag{3.2.67}$$

Comparing coefficients gives

$$a_n = \frac{b_n}{EI(\beta_n^4 - \beta^4)}, \tag{3.2.68}$$

so that the solution becomes

$$Y(x) = \frac{2}{EIl} \sum_{n=1}^{\infty} \frac{Y_n(x)}{\beta_n^4 - \beta^4} \int_0^l Y_n(u) Q(u)\, du. \tag{3.2.69}$$

3. *The Laplace transform.* As in the last section, we again assume a loading $q(x, t) = Q(x)\exp(-i\omega t)$ and thus still consider the non-homogeneous ordinary differential equation (3.2.49). Applying the Laplace transform gives

$$\bar{Y}(s) = \frac{1}{s^4 - \beta^4}\{s^3 Y(0) + s^2 Y'(0) + s Y''(0) + Y'''(0)\} + \frac{1}{EI} \frac{\bar{Q}(s)}{s^4 - \beta^4}. \tag{3.2.70}$$

To invert (3.2.70), the following Laplace inversions are required:

$$\begin{aligned}
\mathscr{L}^{-1}\left(\frac{1}{s^4 - \beta^4}\right) &= \frac{1}{\beta^3}\left(\frac{\sinh \beta x - \sin \beta x}{2}\right) = \frac{1}{\beta^3} L(\beta x), \\
\mathscr{L}^{-1}\left(\frac{s}{s^4 - \beta^4}\right) &= \frac{1}{\beta^2}\left(\frac{\cosh \beta x - \cos \beta x}{2}\right) = \frac{1}{\beta^2} M(\beta x), \\
\mathscr{L}^{-1}\left(\frac{s^2}{s^4 - \beta^4}\right) &= \frac{1}{\beta}\left(\frac{\sinh \beta x + \sin \beta x}{2}\right) = \frac{1}{\beta} N(\beta x), \\
\mathscr{L}^{-1}\left(\frac{s^3}{s^4 - \beta^4}\right) &= \left(\frac{\cosh \beta x + \cos \beta x}{2}\right) = P(\beta x).
\end{aligned} \tag{3.2.71}$$

Thus, (3.2.70) becomes

$$Y(x) = Y(0)P(\beta x)+\frac{Y'(0)N(\beta x)}{\beta}+\frac{Y''(0)M(\beta x)}{\beta^2}+\frac{Y'''(0)L(\beta x)}{\beta^3}+$$
$$+\frac{1}{EI\beta^3}\int_0^x Q(u)L\{\beta(x-u)\}\,du. \quad (3.2.72)$$

In the above, two of the constants of $Y(0)$, $Y'(0)$, $Y''(0)$, $Y'''(0)$ are zero from the conditions at $x = 0$. The other two must be found by applying the conditions at $x = l$.

We might elect to apply the Laplace transform with respect to time directly to the partial differential equation

$$\frac{\partial^4 y}{\partial x^4}+\frac{1}{a^2}\frac{\partial^2 y}{\partial t^2} = \frac{q(x, t)}{EI}, \quad (3.2.73)$$

giving

$$\bar{y}^{\text{iv}}(x, s)+\frac{s^2}{a^2}\bar{y}(x, s) = \frac{\bar{q}(x, s)}{EI}, \quad (3.2.74)$$

for the case of zero initial conditions. This still leaves us with a fourth-order equation to solve, the solution of which will contain the transform variable s in the arguments of sine, cosine, sinh, cosh functions in the form $\cos\sqrt{(sx)}$, $\sin\sqrt{(sx)}$, $\cosh\sqrt{(sx)}$, $\sinh\sqrt{(sx)}$. The determination of the inverse in such a case is somewhat complicated. This does not preclude the use of the Laplace transform with respect to time from the forced-vibration problem, but suggests it might be useful to combine it with a finite Fourier transform or an expansion in normal modes. We shall consider the latter case.

4. *Laplace transform—normal-mode expansion.* Apply the Laplace transform to the non-homogeneous equation to give

$$a^2\bar{y}^{\text{iv}}(x, s)+s^2\bar{y}(x, s) = \bar{q}(x, s)/\rho A, \quad (3.2.75)$$

where zero initial conditions have again been assumed. Now expand $\bar{y}(x, s)$, $\bar{q}(x, s)$ in a series of the normal modes $Y_n(x)$, given as

$$\bar{y}(x, s) = \sum_{n=1}^{\infty} a_n(s)Y_n(x), \qquad \bar{q}(x, s) = \sum_{n=1}^{\infty} b_n(s)Y_n(x), \quad (3.2.76)$$

where the $Y_n(x)$ satisfy (3.2.64) and the coefficients $b_n(s)$ are given by

$$b_n(s) = \frac{2}{l}\int_0^l \bar{q}(x, s)Y_n(x)\,dx. \quad (3.2.77)$$

Proceeding in the manner used to obtain (3.2.68), we obtain the result

$$a_n(s) = \frac{b_n(s)}{A\rho(a^2\beta_n^4+s^2)}. \tag{3.2.78}$$

Thus

$$\bar{y}(x, s) = \frac{2}{A\rho l}\sum_{n=1}^{\infty}\frac{Y_n(x)}{a^2\beta_n^4+s^2}\int_0^l \bar{q}(u, s)Y_n(u)\,du. \tag{3.2.79}$$

Recalling that

$$\mathscr{L}^{-1}\left(\frac{1}{s^2+a^2\beta_n^4}\right) = \frac{1}{a\beta_n^2}\sin a\beta_n^2 t, \tag{3.2.80}$$

we have, applying the convolution theorem,

$$y(x, t) = \frac{2}{A\rho l}\sum_{n=1}^{\infty}\frac{Y_n(x)}{a\beta_n^2}\int_0^l Y_n(u)\,du\int_0^t q(u, \tau)\sin a\beta_n^2(t-\tau)\,d\tau. \tag{3.2.81}$$

It might be noted that $a\beta_n^2 = \omega_n$, the natural frequency in the above.

5. *Solution by normal modes.* We have the basic equation

$$EI\frac{\partial^4 y}{\partial x^4}+\rho A\frac{\partial^2 y}{\partial t^2} = q(x, t). \tag{3.2.82}$$

Assume that $y(x, t)$ may be expanded in terms of the normal modes $Y_n(x)$ and general functions of time $q_n(t)$, so that

$$y(x, t) = \sum_{n=1}^{\infty} q_n(t)Y_n(x). \tag{3.2.83}$$

Substitution in the differential equation gives

$$\sum_{n=1}^{\infty}\left\{a^2 q_n(t)Y_n^{\text{iv}}(x)+\ddot{q}_n(t)Y_n(x)\right\} = \frac{q(x, t)}{\rho A}. \tag{3.2.84}$$

But $Y^{\text{iv}}(x) = \beta_n^4 Y_n(x)$, so that we have

$$\sum_{n=1}^{\infty}\{\ddot{q}_n(t)+a^2\beta_n^4 q_n(t)\}Y_n(x) = \frac{q(x, t)}{\rho A}. \tag{3.2.85}$$

Multiplying the above by $Y_m(x)$, integrating, and using the orthogonality property of the functions, we have

$$\ddot{q}_n(t)+a^2\beta_n^4 q_n(t) = \frac{2}{\rho A l}\int_0^l q(x, t)Y_n(x)\,dx = \frac{Q_n(t)}{\rho A} \quad (n = 1, 2,\ldots). \tag{3.2.86}$$

In the case of zero initial conditions, we know the solution of the above to be of the form

$$q_n(t) = -\frac{1}{\rho A\omega_n}\int_0^t Q_n(\tau)\sin\omega_n(t-\tau)\,d\tau, \tag{3.2.87}$$

where $\omega_n^2 = a^2\beta_n^4$. This determines the total solution.

This section has been devoted to a survey of methods of solution, avoiding consideration of special boundary conditions and considering special loadings only to the extent that these loadings enabled more general solutions to be found. In the next section, a number of special problems will be solved illustrating some of the techniques developed here.

3.2.5. *Some problems in forced vibrations of beams*

In this section, the solutions to some interesting problems in the forced vibrations of beams will be given. Several methods of analysis will be illustrated.

1. *Response of a beam to impact.* Consider the case of a simply supported beam of length l subjected to a short-duration impulse loading applied at $x = \xi$. We represent the load by

$$q(x, t) = P\delta(x-\xi)\delta(t). \tag{3.2.88}$$

From (3.2.81) the results of a Laplace-transform–normal-mode expansion solution to the vibrations of a beam with homogeneous initial conditions and under the general forcing $q(x, t)$ may be written as

$$y(x, t) = \frac{2}{\rho Al}\sum_{n=1}^{\infty}\frac{Y_n(x)}{\omega_n}\int_0^l Y_n(u)\,du\int_0^t q(u, \tau)\sin\omega_n(t-\tau)\,d\tau, \tag{3.2.89}$$

where $\omega_n = a\beta_n^2$. For the case at hand, the normal modes $Y_n(x)$ are

$$Y_n(x) = \sin\beta_n x, \tag{3.2.90}$$

where $\beta_n = n\pi/l$. Inserting the value for $q(x, t)$ we have

$$y(x, t) = \frac{2P}{\rho Al}\sum_{n=1}^{\infty}\frac{\sin\beta_n x}{\omega_n}\int_0^l \delta(u-\xi)\sin\beta_n u\,du\int_0^t \delta(\tau)\sin\omega_n(t-\tau)\,d\tau. \tag{3.2.91}$$

This gives directly

$$y(x, t) = \frac{2P}{\rho Al}\sum_{n=1}^{\infty}\frac{\sin\beta_n\xi\sin\beta_n x\sin\omega_n t}{\omega_n}. \tag{3.2.92}$$

For the case of $\xi = l/2$, $\beta_n\xi = n\pi/2$, so that

$$\sin\beta_n\xi = \sin\frac{n\pi}{2} = 1, 0, -1, 0,\ldots \qquad (n = 1, 2, 3, 4,\ldots,). \tag{3.2.93}$$

Thus we have

$$y(x,t) = \frac{2P}{\rho A l} \sum_{n=1,3,5}^{\infty} \frac{(-1)^{(n-1)/2} \sin \beta_n x \sin \omega_n t}{\omega_n} \tag{3.2.94}$$

as the solution to the given problem.

The solution is in a form simple enough to enable interpretation without an elaborate evaluation of the series. Noting that $\omega_n \propto n^2$, we may write

$$y(x,t) \propto \sum_{n=1,3,5}^{\infty} (-1)^{(n-1)/2} \frac{\sin \beta_n x \sin \omega_n t}{n^2}, \tag{3.2.95}$$

or

$$y(x,t) \propto \sin \beta_1 x \sin \omega_1 t - \frac{\sin \beta_3 x \sin \omega_3 t}{9} + \frac{\sin \beta_5 x \sin \omega_5 t}{25} - \dots \tag{3.2.96}$$

The dependence of the amplitudes on $1/n^2$ shows the dominance of the fundamental mode in the vibration. It is clear that the effect of the higher modes will be to superimpose 'ripples' on the fundamental mode. Although the theoretical solution predicts the presence of these higher frequencies in the motion for all time, observation of the motion would reveal that these components rapidly disappear after two or three oscillations, owing to damping, such as that arising from friction at the supports, internal friction in the beam, and interaction with the surrounding air.

The solution just obtained has been based on a loading impulsive in space and time. Physically, this loading is representative of the disturbance created by detonating a small explosive. A falling mass impacting on the beam, on the other hand, would actually represent a complicated interaction problem in which size of the falling mass in relation to the beam mass, vibrations of the impacting mass, and the degree to which the two bodies would 'stick' together due to plastic deformation would all be factors. The approximation of such an impact by an idealized impulse, nevertheless, provides an approximation of the response when the striking mass is somewhat less than the beam mass.

An approach to this forced-vibrations problem that brings in some of the mass–beam interaction aspects is to replace the non-homogeneous equation of forced vibrations with simple boundary conditions at $x = 0, l$ by a problem in the free vibrations of a beam where the impacting mass effects are brought in via added boundary conditions. Thus, consider†

$$\begin{aligned} EI\frac{\partial^4 y_1}{\partial x^4} + \rho A \frac{\partial^2 y_1}{\partial t^2} &= 0, \qquad y_1(0,t) = \frac{\partial^2 y_1(0,t)}{\partial x^2} = 0, \\ EI\frac{\partial^4 y_2}{\partial x^4} + \rho A \frac{\partial^2 y_2}{\partial t^2} &= 0, \qquad y_2(l,t) = \frac{\partial^2 y_2(l,t)}{\partial x^2} = 0. \end{aligned} \tag{3.2.97}$$

† See Goldsmith [7, pp. 59–60].

At $x = \xi$, continuity in deflection, slope, and curvature will give

$$y_1(\xi, t) = y_2(\xi, t), \quad \frac{\partial y_1(\xi, t)}{\partial x} = \frac{\partial y_2(\xi, t)}{\partial x}, \quad \frac{\partial^2 y_1(\xi, t)}{\partial x^2} = \frac{\partial^2 y_2(\xi, t)}{\partial x^2}. \tag{3.2.98}$$

There will be a discontinuity in the shear equal to the inertial effects of the striker, so that

$$EI\frac{\partial^3 y_2(\xi, t)}{\partial x^3} - EI\frac{\partial^3 y_1(\xi, t)}{\partial x^3} = m\frac{\partial^2 y(\xi, t)}{\partial t^2}, \tag{3.2.99}$$

where m is the striker mass. This last equation assumes that the striker remains in contact with the beam after impact. Finally, the initial conditions must be prescribed to this free-vibrations problem. If it is assumed that, at impact, a velocity equal to that of the falling mass is imparted to the beam at $x = \xi$, we have

$$y(x, 0) = 0, \qquad \partial y(x, 0)/\partial t = v_0\delta(x-\xi). \tag{3.2.100}$$

2. *Response to a moving load.* Consider a constant force moving across a beam of length l at constant velocity V, so that

$$q(x, t) = \begin{cases} P\delta(x-Vt), & 0 \leqslant Vt < l \\ 0, & l < Vt, \end{cases} \tag{3.2.101}$$

where simple support conditions are assumed at $x = 0,l$. Thus we have

$$EI\frac{\partial^4 y}{\partial x^4} + \rho A\frac{\partial^2 y}{\partial t^2} = P\delta(x-Vt) \tag{3.2.102}$$

and

$$y(x, 0) = \dot{y}(x, 0) = 0. \tag{3.2.103}$$

Now Timoshenko† considers this problem starting from the normal-mode expansion $\sum q_n(t) Y_n(x)$. However, the general solution used in the previous impact problem is easily applied to this case. Thus we have

$$y(x, t) = \frac{2P}{\rho Al}\sum_{n=1}^{\infty}\frac{\sin \beta_n x}{\omega_n}\int_0^t \sin \omega_n(t-\tau)\, d\tau \int_0^l \delta(u-V\tau)\sin \beta_n u\, du,$$

$$= \frac{2P}{\rho Al}\sum_{n=1}^{\infty}\frac{\sin \beta_n x}{\omega_n}\int_0^t \sin \beta_n V\tau \sin \omega_n(t-\tau)\, d\tau. \tag{3.2.104}$$

Performing the integration, we obtain

$$y(x, t) = \frac{2P}{\rho Al}\sum_{n=1}^{\infty}\frac{\sin \beta_n x}{\omega_n(\beta_n^2 V^2 - \omega_n^2)}(\beta_n V \sin \omega_n t - \omega_n \sin \beta_n V t). \tag{3.2.105}$$

† p. 351 of Reference [25].

This solution has several interesting features. We see there are a series of critical velocities, given by

$$V_c = a\beta_n, \tag{3.2.106}$$

at which resonance may occur. The time of passage T_f is

$$T_f = l/V_c = l/a\beta_n = l^2/an\pi, \tag{3.2.107}$$

which can be thought of as a forcing period. The period of beam vibration, on the other hand, is $T_v = 2l^2/an^2\pi$. Considering only the fundamental period $n = 1$, it is seen that this period is twice the time required for passage of the load, $T_v = 2T_f$. Other critical conditions occur when the forcing period is

$$\begin{aligned} T_f &= T_v, \qquad n = 2, \\ T_f &= \tfrac{3}{2}T_v, \qquad n = 3, \\ T_f &= 2T_v, \qquad n = 4, \text{ etc.} \end{aligned} \tag{3.2.108}$$

Inspection of the solution for any of the critical speeds reveals that an apparently indeterminate situation of 0/0 arises. Thus, as $\beta_n V \to \omega_n$, we have

$$y(x, t) \to \frac{2P}{\rho A l}\sum_{n=1}^{\infty}\frac{\sin \beta_n x}{\omega_n^2 - \omega_n^2}(\sin \omega_n t - \sin \omega_n t) \to \frac{0}{0}. \tag{3.2.109}$$

However, by the application of L'Hospital's rule, we obtain

$$\lim_{\beta_n V \to \omega_n} y(x, t) = \frac{P}{\rho A l}\sum_{n=1}^{\infty}\frac{\sin \beta_n x}{\omega_n^2}(\sin \omega_n t - \omega_n t \cos \omega_n t), \tag{3.2.110}$$

which, in view of the finite time required for passage of the load, is definitely bounded.

The second observation has to do with the amplitude of vibration at the critical velocities and can be tied in with the limit condition just obtained. Considering just the first term we have

$$\lim_{\beta_1 V \to \omega_1} y(x, t) = \frac{P}{\rho A l \omega_1^2}\sin \beta_1 x(\sin \omega_1 t - \omega_1 t \cos \omega_1 t). \tag{3.2.111}$$

It may be easily shown that this is a maximum for

$$t = \pi/\omega_1 = l/a\beta_1 = l/V_c. \tag{3.2.112}$$

In other words, the maximum deflection occurs just as the force is leaving the beam.

3.3. Foundation and prestress effects

As in the case of transverse string motion, the motion of beams may be influenced by elastic or viscous foundations. The beam may also be subjected to tensile forces although, in contrast to the string, these are not the fundamental elastic restoring mechanisms for the beam. Finally, in complete contrast to the string, axial compressive forces may be present in the beam. We will study wave propagation and vibrations in beams as influenced by these various factors.

3.3.1. *The governing equation*

We will derive a single governing equation including the effects of a visco-elastic foundation and prestress and then reduce the general equation to several special cases. So consider the beam shown in Fig. 3.6(a) and an isolated element as shown in Fig. 3.6(b). The visco-elastic foundation yields a resistive force $f(x, t)$, as shown in Fig. 3.6(b), where

$$f(x, t) = ky+c\frac{\partial y}{\partial t}. \tag{3.3.1}$$

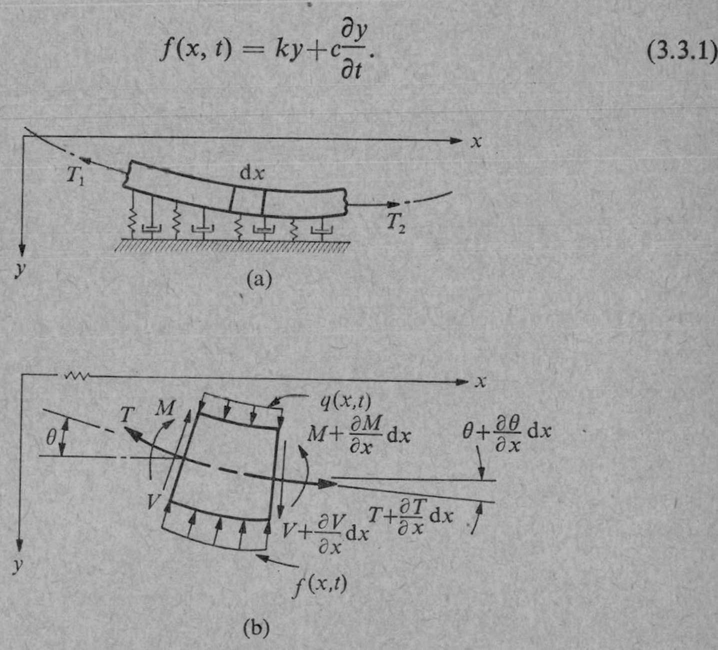

FIG. 3.6. (a) A beam under tension on a visco-elastic foundation and (b) an element of that beam.

The equation of motion in the vertical direction for the element is given by

$$-V+\left(V+\frac{\partial V}{\partial x}\,dx\right)-T\theta+\left(T+\frac{\partial T}{\partial x}\,dx\right)\left(\theta+\frac{\partial \theta}{\partial x}\,dx\right)-$$

$$-\left(ky+c\frac{\partial y}{\partial t}\right)dx+q\,dx = \rho A\,dx\frac{\partial^2 y}{\partial t^2}. \tag{3.3.2}$$

If the higher-order term in dx^2 appearing in conjunction with the tension term is neglected, this reduces to

$$\frac{\partial V}{\partial x}+\frac{\partial}{\partial x}(T\theta)-ky-c\frac{\partial y}{\partial t}+q=\rho A\frac{\partial^2 y}{\partial t^2}. \tag{3.3.3}$$

The equation for the axial motion gives

$$-T+\left(T+\frac{\partial T}{\partial x}\,\mathrm{d}x\right)+V\theta-\left(V+\frac{\partial V}{\partial x}\,\mathrm{d}x\right)\left(\theta+\frac{\partial\theta}{\partial x}\,\mathrm{d}x\right)=\rho A\,\mathrm{d}x\frac{\partial^2 u}{\partial t^2}. \tag{3.3.4}$$

In this last equation, we presume for the time being that axial-inertia effects are non-negligible. Again neglecting terms in dx^2, this last reduces to

$$\frac{\partial T}{\partial x}-\frac{\partial}{\partial x}(V\theta)=\rho A\frac{\partial^2 u}{\partial t^2}. \tag{3.3.5}$$

For the moment equation, we again neglect rotary-inertia effects. The moment effects due to the tension are of higher order, so that the results are the same as for the original beam development, being

$$V=\partial M/\partial x. \tag{3.3.6}$$

Using the relationship $\theta=\partial y/\partial x$ and the moment–curvature result

$$EI\,\partial^2 y/\partial x^2=-M$$

as well as (3.3.6) in eqns (3.3.3) and (3.3.4) gives

$$EI\frac{\partial^4 y}{\partial x^4}-\frac{\partial}{\partial x}\left(T\frac{\partial y}{\partial x}\right)+ky+c\frac{\partial y}{\partial t}+\rho A\frac{\partial^2 y}{\partial t^2}=q(x,t) \tag{3.3.7}$$

and

$$\frac{\partial T}{\partial x}+\frac{\partial}{\partial x}\left(EI\frac{\partial^3 y}{\partial x^3}\frac{\partial y}{\partial x}\right)=\rho A\frac{\partial^2 u}{\partial t^2}. \tag{3.3.8}$$

We now neglect the non-linear term of the last equation, reducing it to

$$\frac{\partial T}{\partial x}=\rho A\frac{\partial^2 u}{\partial t^2}. \tag{3.3.9}$$

From (3.3.7) and (3.3.9) we see that we have a potentially coupled system of equations. Writing the axial force as $T=EA\,\partial u/\partial x$, we would have the longitudinal displacements appearing in the transverse equation of motion. It is seldom that axial inertia effects are of importance in transverse-motion problems, however, so we presume that (3.3.9) may be reduced to

$$\partial T/\partial x=0. \tag{3.3.10}$$

Thus, the axial tension must be constant. The final form for the transverse equation of motion is thus

$$EI\frac{\partial^4 y}{\partial x^4}-T\frac{\partial^2 y}{\partial x^2}+ky+c\frac{\partial y}{\partial t}+\rho A\frac{\partial^2 y}{\partial t^2} = q(x, t). \tag{3.3.11}$$

The case of axial compression obtains merely by changing the sign of T in this result. We note in passing that a beam under tension could effectively become a string by reducing the stiffness EI to zero.

3.3.2. *The beam on an elastic foundation*

By requiring that $T = c = q = 0$, the case of a beam on a purely elastic foundation and free of external loading results. The equation is

$$\frac{\partial^4 y}{\partial x^4}+\frac{k}{EI}y+\frac{1}{a^2}\frac{\partial^2 y}{\partial t^2} = 0. \tag{3.3.12}$$

Let us consider the propagation of harmonic waves in an infinite beam by considering the solution

$$y = Ae^{\mathrm{i}(\gamma x-\omega t)}. \tag{3.3.13}$$

Substituting in (3.3.12) gives

$$\gamma^4 = \frac{\omega^2}{a^2}-\frac{k}{EI}. \tag{3.3.14}$$

This may be put in the dimensionless form

$$\bar{\gamma}^4 = \bar{\omega}^2-\bar{\omega}_0^2, \tag{3.3.15}$$

where

$$\bar{\gamma}^4 = I\gamma^4, \qquad \bar{\omega}^2 = \frac{\rho A}{E}\omega^2, \qquad \bar{\omega}_0^2 = \frac{\rho A}{E}\omega_0^2, \qquad \omega_0^2 = \frac{k}{\rho A}. \tag{3.3.16}$$

The frequency spectrum for this problem has a most interesting behaviour. We have that

$$\bar{\gamma} = \pm(\bar{\omega}^2-\bar{\omega}_0^2)^{\frac{1}{4}}, \pm\mathrm{i}(\bar{\omega}^2-\bar{\omega}_0^2)^{\frac{1}{4}}, \bar{\omega} > \bar{\omega}_0. \tag{3.3.17}$$

For $\bar{\omega} \to \bar{\omega}_0$ we observe a cutoff frequency, a phenomenon previously observed in strings. For $\bar{\omega} < \bar{\omega}_0$ we have that

$$\bar{\gamma} = \pm\frac{(1\pm\mathrm{i})}{\sqrt{2}}(\bar{\omega}_0^2-\bar{\omega}^2)^{\frac{1}{4}}. \tag{3.3.18}$$

We thus have complex branches to the frequency spectrum, as shown in Fig. 3.7. If we have a complex wavenumber of the general form

$$\gamma = \pm\gamma_{\mathrm{Re}}\pm\mathrm{i}\gamma_{\mathrm{Im}}, \tag{3.3.19}$$

the harmonic wave expression (3.3.13) will become

$$y = A\exp(\mp\gamma_{\mathrm{Im}}x)\exp\{\mathrm{i}(\pm\gamma_{\mathrm{Re}}x-\omega t)\}. \tag{3.3.20}$$

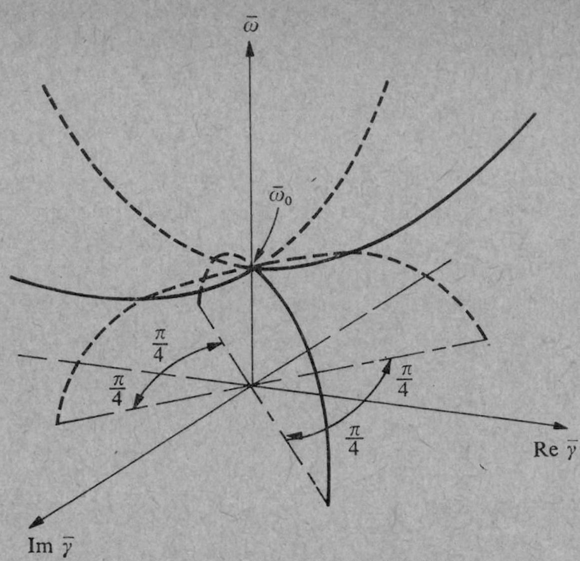

FIG. 3.7. Frequency spectrum for a beam on an elastic foundation.

The disturbance will thus be leftward or rightward propagating but also spatially varying. Again, in the context of the question on conditions for purely harmonic wave propagation, these are not acceptable solutions. Again, however, we expect these types of wavenumbers to play a role in transient and forced-motion problems.

This is not our first encounter with complex wavenumbers. They also arose in the study of harmonic waves in a damped string and were associated with the energy losses of the system. We now see that they can occur in a perfectly elastic system.

3.3.3. *The moving load on an elastically supported beam*

Problems of forced vibrations of infinite or semi-infinite beams on elastic foundations are left as exercises.† We now turn to a discussion of a most interesting effect associated with moving loads on elastically supported beams. In the areas of high-speed transportation or rocket-sledge technology, the response of rails and rail beds to high-speed moving loads is of interest. By considering the rail–rail-bed system as a beam on an elastic foundation subjected to a concentrated load moving at a constant velocity V_0, the following governing equation results:

$$EI\frac{\partial^4 y}{\partial x^4}+ky+\rho A\frac{\partial^2 y}{\partial t^2} = P_0\delta(x-V_0t). \tag{3.3.21}$$

† See Problem 3.13.

A separation-of-variables approach cannot be used on this problem owing to the inseparability of the space and time variables in the loading. The key to solution is to consider a coordinate system to be moving with the load and to realize that relative to the moving coordinate system, the beam is responding in an unchanging, steady-state manner. Thus, by introducing a new coordinate system x_1, y_1, where

$$x_1 = x - V_0 t, \qquad y_1 = y, \tag{3.3.22}$$

the governing equation (3.2.21) reduces to

$$EI\frac{d^4y_1}{dx_1^4} + \rho A V_0^2 \frac{d^2y_1}{dx_1^2} + ky_1 = P_0\delta(x_1). \tag{3.3.23}$$

Thus, under steady-state conditions and a moving coordinate system, the dynamic response problem becomes a static deformation problem.

The details of the analysis of this problem are too lengthy to present here.† However, a major result that appears is the presence of a critical velocity of motion at which an infinite response is predicted. The situation corresponds to when the moving-load velocity corresponds to the propagation velocity of disturbances in the beam. The energy thus does not radiate away from the moving load but builds up in the vicinity. The value of the critical velocity turns out to be

$$V_{cr} = \left(\frac{4kEI}{\rho^2 A^2}\right)^{\frac{1}{4}}. \tag{3.3.24}$$

Fig. 3.8(a) shows the system response for the case of zero velocity, one-half the critical velocity, and twice the critical velocity. The coordinates are in non-dimensional form. The response above the critical velocity is also of interest. Note that, at the loading point, the deflection is zero. Physically, this says that the inertia of the beam instantaneously is preventing motion. Yet there is disturbance ahead of the load owing to the transmission of moment from the disturbed region behind the load.

By including damping in the foundation, infinite response is found no longer to occur. For light damping, large amplitudes of response are found near the undamped critical velocity. Depending on the magnitude of damping, responses interpretable in terms of 'underdamped' and 'overdamped' response may be established. Fig. 3.8(b) shows three situations in this regard.

3.3.4. *The effects of prestress*

Now consider the beam under the effects of prestress alone, so that the general equation (3.3.11) reduces

$$\frac{\partial^4 y}{\partial x^4} - \frac{T}{EI}\frac{\partial^2 y}{\partial x^2} + \frac{1}{a^2}\frac{\partial^2 y}{\partial t^2} = 0. \tag{3.3.25}$$

† See Kenney [10] for complete analysis, including damping effects.

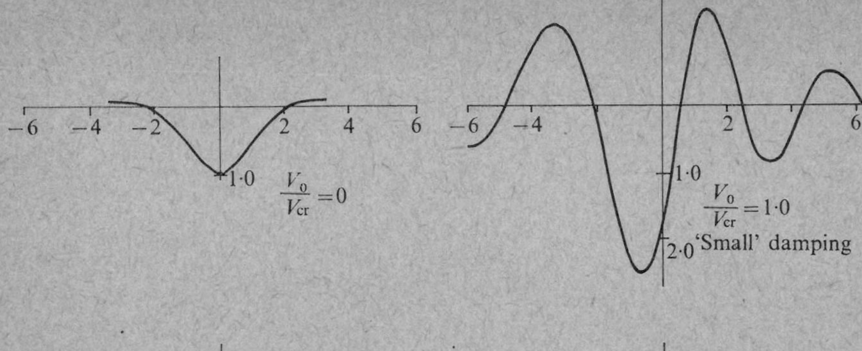

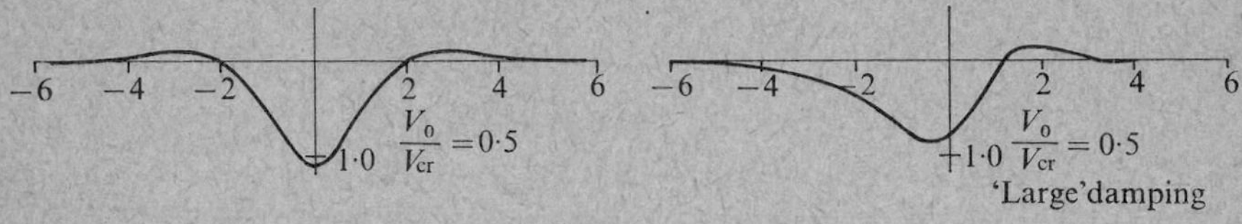

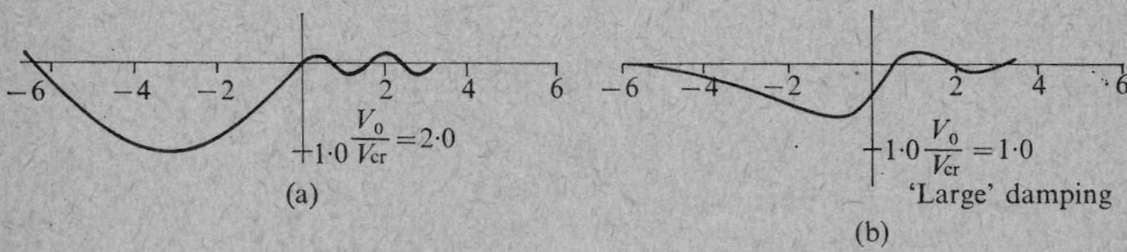

FIG. 3.8. (a) Undamped and (b) damped response of a beam to a load moving at various velocities. (Based on Kenney [10].)

Considering propagation of harmonic waves of the form $\exp\{i(\gamma x-\omega t)\}$ leads to the wavenumber–frequency relation,

$$\gamma^4+\frac{T}{EI}\gamma^2-\frac{\omega^2}{a^2}=0. \tag{3.3.26}$$

This has the roots

$$\gamma=\pm\{-\zeta\pm(\zeta^2+\omega^2/a^2)^{\frac{1}{2}}\}^{\frac{1}{2}}, \tag{3.3.27}$$

where $2\zeta = T/EI$. Now, for the case of tensile prestress, T and hence $\zeta > 0$ in (3.3.27). It should be evident under these conditions that the wavenumbers will be of the form

$$\gamma=\pm\alpha,\ \pm i\beta, \tag{3.3.28}$$

where

$$\alpha=\{-\zeta+(\zeta^2+\omega^2/a^2)^{\frac{1}{2}}\}^{\frac{1}{2}}, \qquad \beta=\{\zeta+(\zeta^2+\omega^2/a^2)^{\frac{1}{2}}\}^{\frac{1}{2}}. \tag{3.3.29}$$

If the direction of the prestress is reversed, $\zeta < 0$. The resulting wavenumbers are given by

$$\gamma=\pm\beta,\ \pm i\alpha. \tag{3.3.30}$$

We note in general that $\beta > \alpha$, so that for the wavelengths associated with these wavenumbers we have that $\lambda_\beta < \lambda_\alpha$. Thus, for a given frequency, pre-compression shortens the wavelength in comparison to pre-tension. In line with this, the propagation velocity is decreased.

Some of the more interesting effects of prestress are in conjunction with the vibrations of finite beams. Consider, for example, a pinned–pinned beam subjected to axial tension. Investigating this in the manner of a normal-mode study, we let

$$y = Y(x)e^{-i\omega t} \tag{3.3.31}$$

and substitute this in (3.3.25), to obtain

$$\frac{d^4Y}{dx^4} - \frac{T}{EI}\frac{d^2Y}{dx^2} - \frac{\omega^2}{a^2}Y = 0. \tag{3.3.32}$$

Using the notation of (3.3.29), we have for the solution

$$Y = A\cos\alpha x + B\sin\alpha x + C\cosh\beta x + D\sinh\beta x. \tag{3.3.33}$$

The boundary conditions for the problem are

$$Y(0) = Y''(0) = Y(l) = Y''(l) = 0. \tag{3.3.34}$$

Applying these to the solution gives $A = C = D = 0$ and

$$\sin\alpha l = 0, \qquad \alpha l = n\pi \qquad (n = 1, 2, \ldots). \tag{3.3.35}$$

The resulting frequencies are given by

$$\omega_n = \frac{n^2\pi^2}{l^2}\sqrt{\left(\frac{EI}{\rho A}\right)}\left(1 + \frac{Tl^2}{n^2\pi^2 EI}\right)^{\frac{1}{2}}. \tag{3.3.36}$$

If $T = 0$ in the above, the results for the pinned–pinned beam without prestress, previously given by (3.2.8), are recovered. We see that the effect of the tensile prestress is to increase the natural frequencies due to the stiffening effect.

If the force is reversed in direction, becoming compressive, the effect on the frequencies is directly obtained by changing the sign of T in (3.3.36). We see that a most interesting effect occurs. There results a critical load, for any value of n, such that $\omega_n \to 0$. These critical values are given by

$$T_{cr} = n^2\pi^2 EI/l^2 \tag{3.3.37}$$

and should be recognized as the Euler critical loads for a pin-ended column. Thus the instability is manifested dynamically by the vibrational frequencies approaching zero.

3.3.5. *Impulse loading of a finite, prestressed, visco-elastically supported beam*

Our objective here is to consider a single problem that includes several of the previously described effects of prestress, elastic foundation, and damping.

Several useful interpretations of the results are possible. Thus, consider the pulse loading of a simply supported beam resting on a viscous, elastic foundation and subjected to tension T on the ends, as shown in Fig. 3.9.

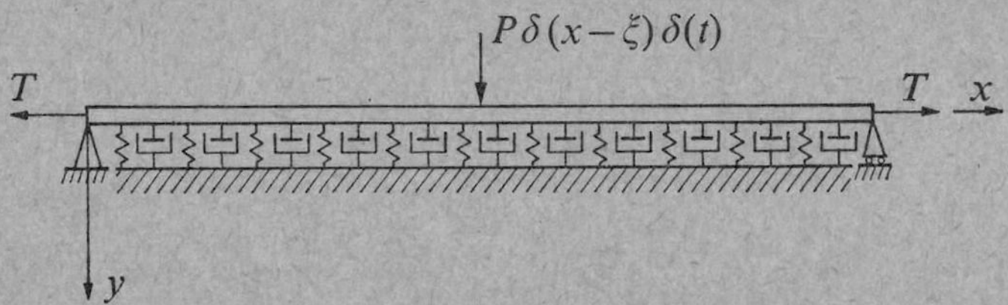

FIG. 3.9. Finite, prestressed beam on a visco-elastic foundation subjected to an impulsive load.

The governing equation for the beam is given by (3.3.11). The finite Fourier transform in conjunction with the Laplace transform will be applied. The finite Fourier sine transform is appropriate for these boundary conditions and gives

$$EI\alpha_n^4\bar{y}(n,t)+T\alpha_n^2\bar{y}(n,t)+k\bar{y}(n,t)+\rho A\ddot{\bar{y}}(n,t)+c\dot{\bar{y}}(n,t)=\bar{q}(n,t). \quad (3.3.38)$$

Applying the Laplace transform to the above yields

$$EI\alpha_n^4\bar{Y}(n,s)+T\alpha_n^2\bar{Y}(n,s)+k\bar{Y}(n,s)+s^2\rho A\bar{Y}(n,s)+sc\bar{Y}(n,s)=\bar{Q}(n,s), \quad (3.3.39)$$

where zero initial conditions have been assumed. This may be written as,

$$(s^2+2\zeta^2s+\Omega_n)\bar{Y}(n,s)=\frac{\bar{Q}(n,s)}{\rho A}, \quad (3.3.40)$$

where

$$\zeta^2=\frac{c}{2\rho A}, \qquad \Omega_n=\omega_n^2+\eta_n^2+\gamma_n^2 \quad (3.3.41)$$

and where

$$\omega_n^2=a^2\alpha_n^4, \qquad \eta_n^2=\frac{T}{\rho A}\alpha_n^2, \qquad \gamma_n^2=\frac{k}{\rho A}. \quad (3.3.42)$$

The frequencies ω_n are the natural frequencies of a simply supported beam without foundation or prestress effects. The transformed solution is then

$$\bar{Y}(n,s)=\frac{1}{\rho A}\frac{\bar{Q}(n,s)}{s^2+2\zeta^2s+\Omega_n}. \quad (3.3.43)$$

We first perform the Laplace inversion. Consider the denominator of the above. The roots are

$$s_{1,2}=-\zeta^2\pm(\zeta^4-\Omega_n)^{\frac{1}{2}}=-\zeta^2\pm i(\Omega_n-\zeta^4)^{\frac{1}{2}}. \quad (3.3.44)$$

Thus

$$s^2+2\zeta^2s+\Omega_n=(s+\alpha)(s+\beta), \quad (3.3.45)$$

where

$$\alpha=s_1, \qquad \beta=s_2. \quad (3.3.46)$$

By partial fractions we then have that

$$\frac{1}{s^2+2\zeta^2 s+\Omega_n}=\frac{1}{(s+\alpha)(s+\beta)}=\frac{1}{\beta-\alpha}\left(\frac{1}{s+\alpha}-\frac{1}{s+\beta}\right), \tag{3.3.47}$$

so that

$$\bar{Y}(n,s)=\frac{1}{\rho A(\beta-\alpha)}\left\{\frac{\bar{Q}(n,s)}{s+\alpha}-\frac{\bar{Q}(n,s)}{s+\beta}\right\}. \tag{3.3.48}$$

From tables we know

$$\mathscr{L}^{-1}\left(\frac{1}{s+\alpha}\right)=\mathrm{e}^{-\alpha t}, \tag{3.3.49}$$

so that using the convolution theorem enables us to write

$$\bar{y}(n,t)=\frac{1}{\rho A(\beta-\alpha)}\left\{\int_0^t \bar{q}(n,\tau)\mathrm{e}^{-\alpha(t-\tau)}\,\mathrm{d}\tau-\int_0^t \bar{q}(n,\tau)\mathrm{e}^{-\beta(t-\tau)}\,\mathrm{d}\tau\right\},$$

$$=\frac{1}{\rho A(\beta-\alpha)}\int_0^t \bar{q}(n,\tau)\{\mathrm{e}^{-\alpha(t-\tau)}-\mathrm{e}^{-\beta(t-\tau)}\}\,\mathrm{d}\tau. \tag{3.3.50}$$

We specify the load as $P\delta(x-\xi)\delta(t)$. Since

$$\bar{q}(n,t)=\frac{P\delta(t)}{l}\int_0^l \delta(x-\xi)\sin\alpha_n x\,\mathrm{d}x=\frac{P\delta(t)}{l}\sin\alpha_n\xi, \tag{3.3.51}$$

the result (3.3.50) becomes

$$\bar{y}(n,t)=\frac{P\sin\alpha_n\xi}{\rho Al(\beta-\alpha)}(\mathrm{e}^{-\alpha t}-\mathrm{e}^{-\beta t}). \tag{3.3.52}$$

From the definition of the Fourier inversion we have

$$y(x,t)=\frac{2P}{\rho Al}\sum_{n=1}^{\infty}\frac{\sin\alpha_n\xi}{\beta-\alpha}(\mathrm{e}^{-\alpha t}-\mathrm{e}^{-\beta t})\sin\alpha_n x. \tag{3.3.53}$$

We note the following:

$$\beta-\alpha=-2\mathrm{i}(\Omega_n-\zeta^4)^{\frac{1}{2}} \tag{3.3.54}$$

and

$$\exp(-\alpha t)-\exp(-\beta t)=-2\mathrm{i}\exp(-\zeta^2 t)\sin(\Omega_n-\zeta^4)^{\frac{1}{2}}t. \tag{3.3.55}$$

Also, if $\xi=l/2$, then

$$\sin\alpha_n\xi=(-1)^{(n-1)/2}\qquad(n=1,3,5,\ldots). \tag{3.3.56}$$

Hence our solution is

$$y(x,t)=\frac{2P}{\rho Al}\exp(-\zeta^2 t)\sum_{n=1,3,\ldots}^{\infty}\frac{(-1)^{(n-1)/2}\sin\alpha_n x}{(\Omega_n-\zeta^4)^{\frac{1}{2}}}\sin(\Omega_n\zeta^4)^{\frac{1}{2}}t. \tag{3.3.57}$$

A number of observations may be made about this result.

1. In the absence of damping, elasticity, or tension, that is, if

$$c = k = T = 0,$$

the above solution reduces to that previously obtained for an impulse load (3.2.94).

2. A study of the radical $(\Omega_n - \zeta^4)^{\frac{1}{2}}$ shows that the added stiffness due to k, T tends to increase the vibrational frequency, since they are additive to the basic term ω_n^2. This has been previously observed for the free-vibrations result.

3. Consider the special case of no foundation, so that $k = c = 0$; the solution becomes

$$y(x, t) = \frac{2P}{\rho Al} \sum_{n=1,3}^{\infty} \frac{(-1)^{(n-1)/2} \sin \alpha_n x}{(\omega_n^2 + \eta_n^2)^{\frac{1}{2}}} \sin(\omega_n^2 + \eta_n^2)^{\frac{1}{2}} t \tag{3.3.58}$$

where $\omega_n^2 = a^2 \alpha_n^4$, $n_n^2 = (T/\rho A)\alpha_n^2$. If we had the case $n_n^2 \gg \omega_n^2$, which would correspond to tensile forces dominating the stiffness term, the solution becomes that of the vibrating string, which is not surprising since the equation of string motion assumes no bending resistance.

4. Suppose T becomes compressive. It is only necessary to change its sign in the preceding results so that we now have $(\omega_n^2 - \eta_n^2)^{\frac{1}{2}}$. The possibility of an unstable motion now exists since if $\eta_n^2 > \omega_n^2$, we have sin → sinh and the vibration amplitudes increase without bounds as time passes.

5. Returning to the total solution (3.3.57) it is seen that critical values of ζ^2 may occur so that $\zeta^4 \gtreqless \Omega_n$. If $\zeta^4 < \Omega_n$, a damped oscillatory motion results. However, if $\zeta^4 = \Omega_n$ the case of critical damping arises, and if $\zeta^4 > \Omega_n$ the overdamped case occurs, since sin → sinh, as previously mentioned.

Of equal interest is to note that the foundation damping enters in as a simple, familiar $\exp(-\zeta^2 t)$ type term in front of the total solution. Thus, the distributed viscosity gives rise to a decay completely analogous to that existing in a lumped-parameter spring–mass–dashpot system.

3.4. Effects of shear and rotary inertia

It was pointed out in the development of the governing equation for thin beams that two major assumptions were made: first, that the effects of rotary inertia had been neglected and, secondly, that shear deformations were neglected. This latter assumption was actually stated in the form of the Bernoulli–Euler hypothesis that plane sections remain plane. The fact that this is equivalent to neglecting shear deformation is shown in the sequence of illustrations in Fig. 3.10. Thus, in Fig. 3.10(a), a typical element at a cross-section subjected to shearing force is shown. The shear stresses on the element

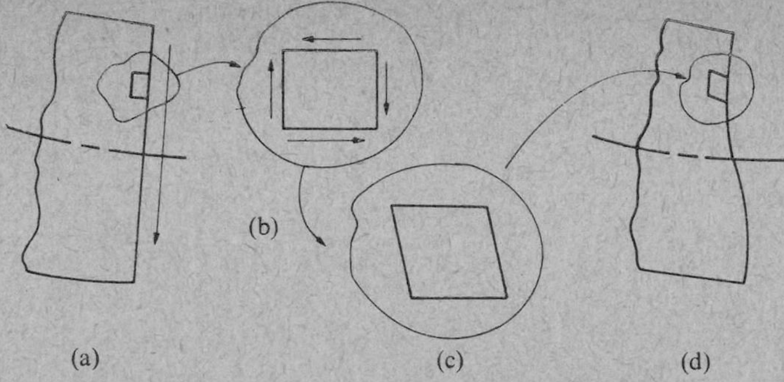

FIG. 3.10. Consequence of shearing force on the deformation of the cross-section of a beam.

are shown in (b), while in (c) the resulting shearing deformation of the element is shown. Because of variations in shear stress across the section, the various elements will be strained in differing amounts. Re-assembling these elements results in a section that is no longer perpendicular to the neutral axis and, in fact, will be 'warped' from the planar configuration.

The study of wave propagation in the Bernoulli–Euler beam showed that infinite phase velocities were predicted (Fig. 3.2(b)) and that 'instantaneous' far-field response was predicted in some problems (see Fig. 3.4), an anomaly resulting from infinite phase velocities. It was suggested at that stage that such behaviour was attributable to the rotary-inertia and shear-effect restrictions. The limitations of the theory and the probable cause were realized rather early. In 1894 Rayleigh† applied the correction for rotary inertia. Results obtained with this correction alone predicted finite propagation velocities. However, the upper bound was still greater than predicted by exact theory. In 1921 Timoshenko‡ included both effects of shear and rotary inertia and obtained results in accord with exact theory.

3.4.1. *The governing equations*

To start the development, we again consider an element of beam subjected to shear force, bending moment, and distributed load, as shown in Fig. 3.11(a). The displacement to the centroidal plane of the beam is still measured by y and the slope of the centroidal axis is still given by $\partial y/\partial x$. A new coordinate ψ is introduced to measure the slope of the cross-section due to bending. In the Bernoulli–Euler development, this is also the same as the slope of the centroidal axis $\partial y/\partial x$, so a special coordinate is not required. In Fig. 3.11(b) the essential features of the shear deformation development are shown. The slope of the centroidal axis is shown as $\partial y/\partial x$. This is now considered to be made up of two contributions. The first is ψ, due, as

† pp. 293–4 of Vol. I, Reference [18].
‡ Reference [24]; see also p. 329 of Reference [25].

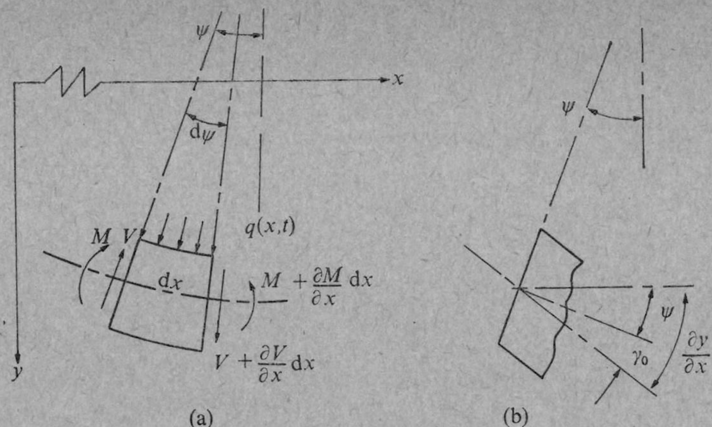

FIG. 3.11. (a) Differential element of beam subjected to load and (b) the kinematical details of additional shearing deformation.

mentioned, to the effects of bending. An additional contribution γ_0 due to shearing effects is now included. Thus we have

$$\partial y/\partial x = \psi + \gamma_0. \tag{3.4.1}$$

We should note that plane sections are still assumed to remain plane in this development, but no longer perpendicular to the centroidal plane. Thus, warping of the cross-section, as shown in Fig. 3.10(d), is still not permitted by these kinematics.

The problem now is to relate the above kinematical expressions to the loads. The assumption is made that the relationship between bending moment and curvature still holds. In terms of the parameters of the present problem this is expressed by

$$M/EI = -\partial\psi/\partial x. \tag{3.4.2}$$

This derives from the fact that $R\,d\psi = dx$, where R is the radius of curvature. Hence $1/R = d\psi/dx$. The expression (3.4.2) is the analogue of (3.4.1) for the Bernoulli–Euler development.

To determine γ_0, the essence of the Timoshenko argument is as follows. The shear force at the cross-section is given in terms of the shear stress τ or shear strain γ respectively as

$$V = \int_A \tau\,dA = G\int_A \gamma\,dA. \tag{3.4.3}$$

If γ_0 is the shear strain at the centroidal axis, then $G\gamma_0 A$ will give a shear force. However, it will not be equal to the value (3.4.3) obtained by integrating the variable stress distribution across the section. To bring the value into balance, an adjustment coefficient κ is introduced such that

$$V = G\int_A \gamma\,\mathrm{d}A = (G\gamma_0 A)\kappa. \tag{3.4.4}$$

The value of κ will depend on the shape of the cross-section and must be determined, usually by stress analysis means, for each cross-section. This parameter is usually designated as the (Timoshenko) shear coefficient. Substituting the expression for γ_0 obtained from (3.4.1) into (3.4.4) gives

$$V = AG\kappa\left(\frac{\partial y}{\partial x}-\psi\right). \tag{3.4.5}$$

With the preceding result in hand, development of the equations of motion is rather straightforward. Writing the equation of motion in the vertical direction for the element of Fig. 3.11(a), we obtain

$$-V+\left(V+\frac{\partial V}{\partial x}\,\mathrm{d}x\right)+q\,\mathrm{d}x = \rho A\,\mathrm{d}x\frac{\partial^2 y}{\partial t^2}, \tag{3.4.6}$$

or

$$\frac{\partial V}{\partial x}+q = \rho A\frac{\partial^2 y}{\partial t^2}. \tag{3.4.7}$$

Summing moments about an axis perpendicular to the x,y-plane and passing through the centre of the element, we obtain

$$M-\left(M+\frac{\partial M}{\partial x}\,\mathrm{d}x\right)+\frac{1}{2}V\,\mathrm{d}x+\frac{1}{2}\left(V+\frac{\partial V}{\partial x}\,\mathrm{d}x\right)\mathrm{d}x = J\frac{\partial^2\psi}{\partial t^2}, \tag{3.4.8}$$

where J is the polar inertia of the element. For an element of mass density ρ, length $\mathrm{d}x$, and having a cross-sectional-area moment of inertia about the moment axis of I, we have that

$$J = \rho I\,\mathrm{d}x. \tag{3.4.9}$$

Then (3.4.8) reduces to

$$V-\frac{\partial M}{\partial x} = \rho I\frac{\partial^2\psi}{\partial t^2}. \tag{3.4.10}$$

Substituting the expression for bending moment (3.4.2) and shear force (3.4.5) into the two governing equations (3.4.7) and (3.4.10) gives

$$GA\kappa\left(\frac{\partial\psi}{\partial x}-\frac{\partial^2 y}{\partial x^2}\right)+\rho A\frac{\partial^2 y}{\partial t^2} = q(x,t), \tag{3.4.11}$$

$$GA\kappa\left(\frac{\partial y}{\partial x}-\psi\right)+EI\frac{\partial^2\psi}{\partial x^2} = \rho I\frac{\partial^2\psi}{\partial t^2}. \tag{3.4.12}$$

The above results are the governing equations for the Timoshenko beam theory. There are, we see in this theory, two modes of deformation and these coupled governing equations represent the physical coupling that occurs between them. One mode of deformation is simply the transverse deflection of the beam as measured by $y(x, t)$. The other mode is the transverse shearing deformation γ_0, as measured by the difference $\partial y/\partial x - \psi$ (see (3.4.1)). This is our first, but far from last, encounter with coupled multi-mode elastic systems.

The effects of rotary inertia are carried solely by the inertia term of (3.4.12). Setting $I = 0$ thus removes this effect. The recovery of the Bernoulli–Euler theory by removing the shear effect can be accomplished by eliminating V between (3.4.7) and (3.4.8) and using the relationship (3.1.1).

3.4.2. *Harmonic waves*

Let us consider the propagation of harmonic waves in the infinite Timoshenko beam. Two approaches are possible. We may consider eqns (3.4.11) and (3.4.12) directly, with $q = 0$, or we may first reduce the two to a single equation. In most future investigations of this nature, one or the other approach will be used. Here, both will be presented. Considering the two equations, we assume solutions of the form

$$y = B_1 e^{i(\gamma x - \omega t)}, \qquad \psi = B_2 e^{i(\gamma x - \omega t)}. \tag{3.4.13}$$

Substituting in (3.4.11) and (3.4.12), the following two homogeneous equations in B_1, B_2 are obtained

$$\begin{aligned} (GA\kappa\gamma^2 - \rho A\omega^2)B_1 + iGA\kappa\gamma B_2 &= 0. \\ iGA\kappa\gamma B_1 - (GA\kappa + EI\gamma^2 - \rho I\omega^2)B_2 &= 0. \end{aligned} \tag{3.4.14}$$

These give the amplitude ratios

$$\frac{B_2}{B_1} = i\frac{(GA\kappa\gamma^2 - \rho A\omega^2)}{GA\kappa\gamma} = i\frac{GA\kappa\gamma}{(GA\kappa + EI\gamma^2 - \rho I\omega^2)}. \tag{3.4.15}$$

Equating the determinant of coefficients to zero gives the frequency equation

$$(GA\kappa\gamma^2 - \rho A\omega^2)(GA\kappa + EI\gamma^2 - \rho I\omega^2) - G^2A^2\kappa^2\gamma^2 = 0, \tag{3.4.16}$$

or simplifying,

$$\frac{EI}{\rho A}\gamma^4 - \frac{I}{A}\left(1 + \frac{E}{G\kappa}\right)\gamma^2\omega^2 - \omega^2 + \frac{\rho I}{GA\kappa}\omega^4 = 0. \tag{3.4.17}$$

This may be converted to the dispersion equation by using the identity $\omega = \gamma c$ in the above, giving

$$\frac{EI}{\rho A}\gamma^4 - \frac{I}{A}\left(1 + \frac{E}{G\kappa}\right)\gamma^4 c^2 - \gamma^2 c^2 + \frac{\rho I}{GA\kappa}\gamma^4 c^4 = 0. \tag{3.4.18}$$

To reduce the two governing equations to a single equation, differentiate (3.4.12) with respect to x. Then solve (3.4.11) for $\partial\psi/\partial x$, giving

$$\frac{\partial\psi}{\partial x}=\frac{\partial^2 y}{\partial x^2}-\frac{\rho}{G\kappa}\frac{\partial^2 y}{\partial t^2}. \tag{3.4.19}$$

By differentiating the above to give expressions for $\partial^3\psi/\partial x^3$, $\partial^3\psi/\partial x\,\partial t^2$ and substituting these in (3.4.12), one can obtain

$$\frac{EI}{\rho A}\frac{\partial^4 y}{\partial x^4}-\frac{I}{A}\left(1+\frac{E}{G\kappa}\right)\frac{\partial^4 y}{\partial x^2\,\partial t^2}+\frac{\partial^2 y}{\partial t^2}+\frac{\rho I}{GA\kappa}\frac{\partial^4 y}{\partial t^4}=0. \tag{3.4.20}$$

Considering a harmonic wave solution

$$y=Ce^{i(\gamma x-\omega t)} \tag{3.4.21}$$

leads directly to the result (3.4.18).

Before presenting specific numerical data on the dispersion curve we investigate the asymptotic behaviour of (3.4.18). In particular, consider the behaviour as the wavenumber becomes large. This can be easily done by factoring γ^4 from the equation and then letting $\gamma\to\infty$. The equation reduces to

$$\lim_{\gamma\to\infty}(3.4.18)=\frac{EI}{\rho A}-\frac{I}{A}\left(1+\frac{E}{G\kappa}\right)c^2+\frac{\rho I}{GA\kappa}c^4=0, \tag{3.4.22}$$

or

$$c^4-\frac{G\kappa}{\rho}\left(1+\frac{E}{G\kappa}\right)c^2+\frac{GE\kappa}{\rho^2}=0. \tag{3.4.23}$$

This may be expressed as

$$\bar{c}^4-\left(1+\frac{G\kappa}{E}\right)\bar{c}^2+\frac{G\kappa}{E}=0, \tag{3.4.24}$$

where $\bar{c}=c/c_0$ and c_0 is the bar velocity. This equation has the two roots

$$\bar{c}^2=1,\qquad \frac{G\kappa}{E}, \tag{3.4.25}$$

or

$$c=c_0,\qquad \sqrt{\left(\frac{G\kappa}{\rho}\right)}, \tag{3.4.26}$$

where the negative roots are ignored (giving only waves in the opposite direction) and the non-dimensionalization has been removed in the last expression. We thus have the important result that the wave velocities are bounded at large wavenumbers, in contrast to the Bernoulli–Euler behaviour. The fact that there are two limits is associated with the fact that there are two basic modes that are operative.

The long-wavelength limit ($\gamma\to 0$) should also be investigated for the possibility of cutoff frequencies. Considering (3.4.18) for this limit, we have

$$\lim_{\gamma\to 0}(3.4.18)=-\omega^2+\frac{\rho I}{GA\kappa}\omega^4=0, \tag{3.4.27}$$

which has the roots

$$\omega_c = 0, \qquad \sqrt{\left(\frac{GA\kappa}{\rho I}\right)}. \tag{3.4.28}$$

Thus, one of the modes has a finite cutoff frequency. If we consider (3.4.14), we see that as $\gamma = \varepsilon \to 0$, we have the general behaviour

$$\begin{aligned} -\rho A\omega_c^2 B_1 + \mathrm{i}O(\varepsilon)B_2 &= 0, \\ \mathrm{i}O(\varepsilon)B_1 - (GA\kappa - \rho I\omega_c^2)B_2 &= 0, \end{aligned} \tag{3.4.29}$$

where $O(\varepsilon)$ indicates a very small quantity. If $\omega_c \to 0$, we have $B_1 \neq 0$, $B_2 = 0$ as possibilities. If $\omega_c \to (GA\kappa/\rho I)^{\frac{1}{2}}$, we have $B_2 \neq 0$, $B_1 = 0$ as possibilities. For this latter behaviour, we have the motion given by

$$y = 0, \qquad \psi = B_2 \exp(-\mathrm{i}\omega_c t). \tag{3.4.30}$$

This corresponds to a shearing motion as shown in Fig. 3.12.

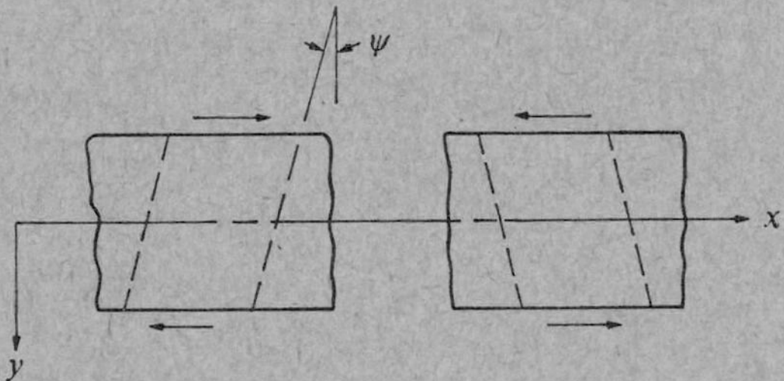

FIG. 3.12. Shear vibration at the cutoff frequency.

Before it is possible to present specific data on the dispersion curve or the frequency spectrum, it is necessary to specify the cross-section so that the shear coefficient can be determined. Values for rectangular and circular cross-sections have been given as 0·833 and $\frac{10}{9}$ respectively.

By considering a bar of circular cross-section, it is possible to compare the results for the Timoshenko beam with those from the exact theory of elasticity. These are shown in the dispersion curve of Fig. 3.13. Only the first branch of the dispersion curve for formula (3.4.17) is shown, but this is the one of greatest interest, since it is the primarily flexural mode. In addition the results for rotary-inertia effects alone (called the 'Rayleigh' theory) are shown as well as those for Bernoulli–Euler theory. The velocity and wave-number have been non-dimensionalized as

$$\bar{c} = \frac{c}{c_0}, \qquad \bar{\gamma} = \frac{a\gamma}{2\pi}, \tag{3.4.31}$$

where a is the radius of a circular bar. In addition to specifying the shear coefficient, Poisson's ratio must be given.† It is seen that the agreement

† See Problems 3.16, 3.17.

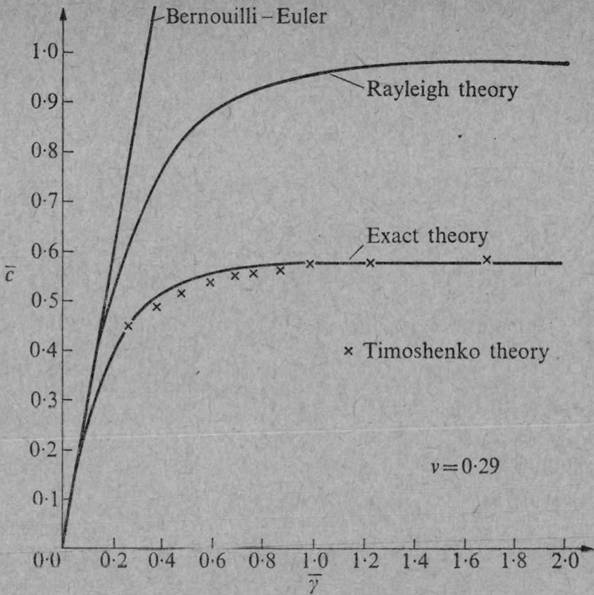

FIG. 3.13. Dispersion relations from Timoshenko, exact, Rayleigh, and Bernoulli–Euler beam theories. (After Kolsky [11, Fig. 16].)

between Timoshenko theory and exact theory is quite remarkable. As was remarked previously, the Rayleigh theory is seen to give a bounded but still too high phase velocity. The Bernoulli–Euler theory is seen to agree with Timoshenko and exact theory in only a very limited range of wavenumber (say $\bar{\gamma} \leq 0{\cdot}1$).

3.4.3. *Pulse propagation in a Timoshenko beam*

In determining the response of beams to sharp transients, it is almost necessary at the outset to use the Timoshenko beam theory in contrast to the Bernoulli–Euler theory, particularly if short-time response is desired. This is somewhat in distinction to longitudinal transients in rods, which may be adequately described by the rod wave equation even when the loading pulse is fairly broad-band.† Analysis in this area becomes rather complicated, however, and our attention must therefore be comparatively restricted because of the rather extensive analysis required.

In the following, the problem of transient loading of a semi-infinite Timoshenko beam will be reviewed in part. The review is based on the work of Boley and Chao [2]. The main objectives will be to outline the steps necessary to obtain the transformed solution to more complicated problems, to develop basic information on propagation of wavefronts by rather

† See Problem 3.18.

elementary means, to explore some of the subtleties in establishing the complete contour when branch cuts are necessary, and to present some results for a specific loading.

The governing equations for the problem are (3.4.11) and (3.4.12) with $q(x, t) = 0$. These equations may be put in non-dimensional form by introducing the dimensionless variables x_1, t_1, y_1, where

$$x_1 = x/r, \quad t_1 = c_0 t/r, \quad y_1 = y/r, \quad \gamma = E/G\kappa, \tag{3.4.32}$$

where r is the radius of gyration of the cross-section. The governing equations then reduce to

$$\psi'' + \frac{1}{\gamma}(y_1' - \psi) - \ddot{\psi} = 0, \tag{3.4.33}$$

$$\ddot{y}_1 - \frac{1}{\gamma}(y_1'' - \psi') = 0, \tag{3.4.34}$$

where the prime and dot notation refer to partial derivatives with respect to the dimensionless distance and time variables. Most of the results will be presented in terms of the shear force and bending moment. From (3.4.5) and (3.4.2) these are

$$\frac{V}{GA\kappa} = \frac{\partial y}{\partial x} - \psi = y_1' - \psi,$$

$$\frac{Mr}{EI} = -r\frac{\partial \psi}{\partial x} = -\psi'. \tag{3.4.35}$$

We apply the Laplace transform on the time variable to (3.4.33) and (3.4.34), giving

$$\bar{\psi}'' + \frac{1}{\gamma}(\bar{y}_1' - \bar{\psi}) - s^2\bar{\psi} = 0,$$
$$s^2\bar{y}_1 - \frac{1}{\gamma}(\bar{y}_1'' - \bar{\psi}') = 0, \tag{3.4.36}$$

where zero initial conditions have been assumed. These two equations are solved by eliminating one or the other of the dependent variables, giving a fourth-order equation. In terms of $\bar{y}_1$, the equation is

$$\bar{y}_1^{\text{iv}} - (1+\gamma)s^2\bar{y}_1'' + (1+\gamma s^2)s^2\bar{y}_1 = 0. \tag{3.4.37}$$

This is the Laplace transform of (3.4.20) with the non-dimensionalizations of the present problem incorporated. Considering a solution of the form $\bar{y}_1 = C\exp(\lambda x_1)$ gives the characteristic equation

$$\lambda^4 - (1+\gamma)s^2\lambda^2 + (1+\gamma s^2)s^2 = 0. \tag{3.4.38}$$

Solving this gives

$$\lambda^2 = \left(\frac{1+\gamma}{2}\right)s\left[s \pm \left\{s^2 - \frac{4(1+\gamma s^2)}{(1+\gamma)^2}\right\}^{\frac{1}{2}}\right]. \tag{3.4.39}$$

After some manipulation and again taking the square root, one obtains

$$\lambda = \pm Bs^{\frac{1}{2}}\{s \pm N(s^2-a^2)^{\frac{1}{2}}\}^{\frac{1}{2}}, \tag{3.4.40}$$

where

$$B = \left(\frac{\gamma+1}{2}\right)^{\frac{1}{2}}, \qquad N = \frac{\gamma-1}{\gamma+1}, \qquad a = \frac{2}{\gamma-1}. \tag{3.4.41}$$

We represent (3.4.40) in simplified form as

$$\lambda = \pm\lambda_1, \pm\lambda_2, \tag{3.4.42}$$

where λ_1 corresponds to the positive sign within the bracket of (3.4.40). The resulting solution for $\bar{y}_1$ is

$$\bar{y}_1 = C_1 \exp(-\lambda_1 x_1) + C_2 \exp(-\lambda_2 x_1) + C_3 \exp(\lambda_1 x_1) + C_4 \exp(\lambda_2 x_1). \tag{3.4.43}$$

A similar solution would hold for $\bar{\psi}$ with arbitrary coefficients $B_1,\ldots, B_4$ in place of $C_1,\ldots, C_4$. These would not be independent, but related through (3.4.36). Thus, substituting (3.4.43) and the solution for $\bar{\psi}$ in the second equation of (3.4.36) leads to the following relations:

$$\frac{B_1}{C_1} = -\frac{B_3}{C_3} = \frac{(\gamma s^2-\lambda_1^2)}{\lambda_1}, \tag{3.4.44}$$

$$\frac{B_2}{C_2} = -\frac{B_4}{C_4} = \frac{(\gamma s^2-\lambda_2^2)}{\lambda_2}. \tag{3.4.45}$$

The solution of $\bar{\psi}$ is then given by

$$\bar{\psi} = \frac{\lambda_1^2-\gamma s^2}{\lambda_1}\{C_3 \exp(\lambda_1 x_1) - C_1 \exp(-\lambda_1 x_1)\} + \\ + \frac{\lambda_2^2-\gamma s^2}{\lambda_2}\{C_4 \exp(\lambda_2 x_1) - C_2 \exp(-\lambda_2 x_1)\}. \tag{3.4.46}$$

Because only semi-infinite beams $x > 0$ will be considered here, it is required that $C_3 = C_4 = 0$.

Several types of boundary conditions may be considered within the present formulation. Several of them are:

(1) step end velocity with zero moment;
(2) step end moment with zero displacement;
(3) step angular velocity with zero force;
(4) step end force with zero rotation.

Attention will be directed toward case (1), although the methods are quite similar in all cases.† The boundary conditions are given by

$$\dot{y}_1(0, t) = v_0 H\langle t\rangle, \qquad \bar{\psi}'(0, t) = 0, \tag{3.4.47}$$

† Reference [2] presents in tabular form the basic results for all of the above cases.

and in transformed form as

$$\bar{y}_1(0, s) = \frac{v_0}{s^2}, \qquad \bar{\psi}'(0, s) = 0. \tag{3.4.48}$$

Substituting (3.4.43) and (3.4.46) with $C_3 = C_4 = 0$ in these boundary conditions gives

$$C_1 = \frac{v_0(\lambda_2^2-\gamma s^2)}{s^2(\lambda_2^2-\lambda_1^2)}, \qquad C_2 = \frac{-v_0(\lambda_1^2-\gamma s^2)}{s^2(\lambda_2^2-\lambda_1^2)}. \tag{3.4.49}$$

Using (3.4.40), the expression $(\lambda_2^2-\lambda_1^2)$ in (3.4.49) may be simplified. The resulting transformed solutions are

$$\bar{y}_1(x_1, s) = \frac{v_0 a}{2s^3(s^2-a^2)^{\frac{1}{2}}}\{(\gamma s^2-\lambda_2^2)\exp(-\lambda_1 x_1)-(\gamma s^2-\lambda_1^2)\exp(-\lambda_2 x_1)\}, \tag{3.4.50}$$

$$\bar{\psi}(x_1, s) = \frac{v_0 a}{2s(s^2-a^2)^{\frac{1}{2}}}\left\{\frac{1}{\lambda_1}\exp(-\lambda_1 x_1)-\frac{1}{\lambda_2}\exp(-\lambda_2 x_1)\right\}. \tag{3.4.51}$$

The transformed expression for the shear force is

$$\frac{\bar{V}}{GA\kappa} = \frac{v_0\gamma a}{2s(s^2-a^2)^{\frac{1}{2}}}\left\{-\frac{\gamma s^2-\lambda_2^2}{\lambda_1}\exp(-\lambda_1 x_1)+\frac{\gamma s^2-\lambda_1^2}{\lambda_2}\exp(-\lambda_2 x_1)\right\}. \tag{3.4.52}$$

In an effort to have some generality of discussion, we note that the results for $\bar{y}_1$, $\bar{\psi}$, and $\bar{V}$ all can have the general form

$$F(x_1, s) = F_1(s)\exp(-\lambda_1 x_1)+F_2(s)\exp(-\lambda_2 x_1), \tag{3.4.53}$$

where $F_1(s)$, $F_2(s)$ are obtained by inspection of the solutions. The Laplace inversion is then given by

$$f(x_1, t_1) = \frac{1}{2\pi i}\int_{c-i\infty}^{c+i\infty} F(x_1, s)\exp(st_1)\, ds = I_1+I_2, \tag{3.4.54}$$

where I_1 is the inversion of $F_1(s)\exp(-\lambda_1 x_1)$ and I_2 the inversion of

$$F_2(s)\exp(-\lambda_2 x_1).$$

We first deal with the matter of closure of the Bromwich contour. This yields most interesting information on the propagation velocity of wavefronts. Thus, for I_1 we have

$$I_1 = \frac{1}{2\pi i}\int_{c-i\infty}^{c+i\infty} F_1(s)\exp(st_1-\lambda_1 x_1)\, ds. \tag{3.4.55}$$

In closing the Bromwich contour, either to the right or left, we see that s will be of the form $R\exp(i\theta)$ along a semicircular path. For s large we have that

$$\lambda_1 = Bs\left\{1+N\left(1-\frac{a^2}{s^2}\right)^{\frac{1}{2}}\right\}^{\frac{1}{2}}\Bigg|_{s\to\infty} \to Bs(1+N)^{\frac{1}{2}}. \tag{3.4.56}$$

From the definitions of B and N, given by (3.4.41), this becomes

$$\lambda_1 \big|_{s\to\infty} \to \gamma^{\frac{1}{2}} s. \tag{3.4.57}$$

Then

$$\exp(st_1 - \lambda_1 x_1) \to \exp\{s(t_1 - \gamma^{\frac{1}{2}} x_1)\}. \tag{3.4.58}$$

Thus, if $t_1 < \gamma^{\frac{1}{2}} x_1$, the contour must be closed to the right, while for $t_1 > \gamma^{\frac{1}{2}} x_1$, the contour must be closed to the left. A similar type of argument for I_2 yields the result that

$$\exp(st_1 - \lambda_2 x_1) \to \exp\{s(t_1 - x_1)\}. \tag{3.4.59}$$

Thus, for $t_1 < x_1$, closure is rightward, while for $t_1 > x_1$, closure is leftward. The three types of closure are indicated in Fig. 3.14. The closure to the left

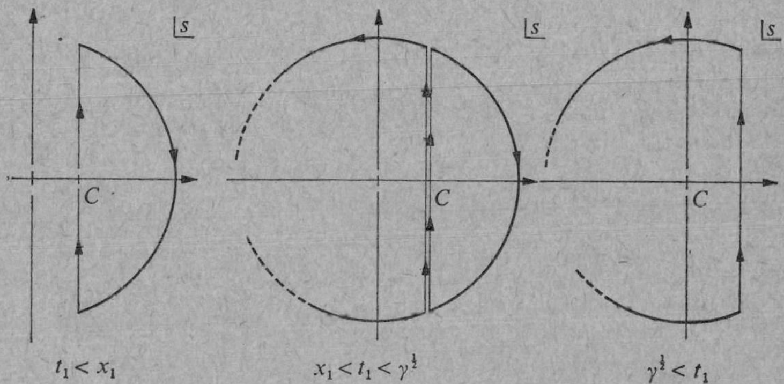

FIG. 3.14. Contour closure for various ranges of t_1.

is left purposely vague since considerable detail must be added in that region.

It does not greatly pre-empt later discussion to state here that no poles or branch points of the integrand exist in Re $s > c$. Hence, for closure to the right, we have $I_1 = I_2 = 0$. The significance of this is that it indicates signal arrival time. Thus, at a station x_1 no signal arrives until $t_1 = x_1$. In dimensional form this is given by $t = x/c_0$. Then, at $t_1 = \gamma^{\frac{1}{2}} x_1$, a second clearly distinguishable signal arrives. In dimensional form, this is at $t = (\rho/G\kappa)^{\frac{1}{2}} x$. Thus, two distinct wavefronts exist, travelling at the velocities c_0 (the faster) and $(G\kappa/\rho)^{\frac{1}{2}}$ (the slower). Referring back to (3.4.26), these are seen to be the large-wavenumber, high-frequency limits for the Timoshenko beam. As to the nature of the disturbance arriving at these times, we hope to establish more about this later.

We now consider the integral I_1 in somewhat greater detail. The complexities that arise in the evaluation of the inversion integral are in connection with the several branch points of the integrands. Specifically, consider the expression

$$I_1^{\psi} = \frac{1}{2\pi i}\int_{c-i\infty}^{c+i\infty} \frac{\exp(st_1-\lambda_1 x_1)}{s(s^2-a^2)^{\frac{1}{2}}\lambda_1}\,ds. \tag{3.4.60}$$

This corresponds to the I_1 part of the result (3.4.51) for the rotation. We have that

$$(s^2-a^2)^{\frac{1}{2}}\lambda_1 = Bs^{\frac{1}{2}}(s+a)^{\frac{1}{2}}(s-a)^{\frac{1}{2}}\{s+N(s^2-a^2)^{\frac{1}{2}}\}. \tag{3.4.61}$$

These quantities must be made single-valued by proper branch cuts in the s-plane. Using the representations

$$s-a = \rho_1\exp(i\theta_1), \qquad s = \rho\exp(i\theta), \qquad s+a = \rho_2\exp(i\theta_2), \tag{3.4.62}$$

we see that these functions may be made single-valued by restricting the arguments to the range

$$-\pi < \theta_1,\ \theta,\ \theta_2 < \pi. \tag{3.4.63}$$

The geometry of this situation in the complex plane is shown in Fig. 3.15,

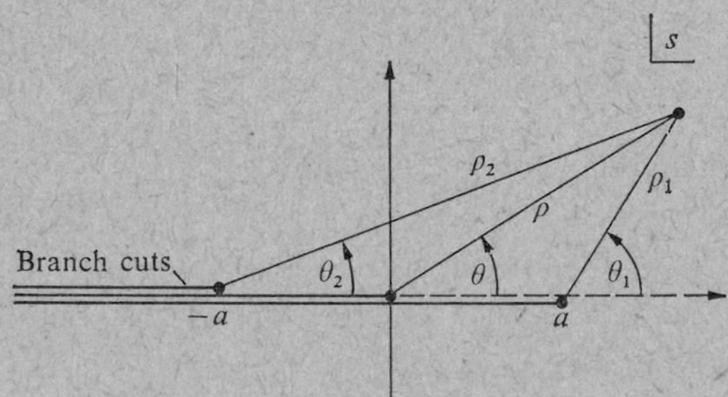

FIG. 3.15. Branch cut situation for the functions $s^{\frac{1}{2}}$, $(s+a)^{\frac{1}{2}}$, $(s-a)^{\frac{1}{2}}$.

as well as the branch cuts to the left along the real axis to establish this range. The remaining function of (3.4.61), $\{s+N(s^2-a^2)^{\frac{1}{2}}\}^{\frac{1}{2}}$, will also be single-valued if the argument of the square of this function is restricted to the range (3.4.63). However, the possibility that a branch cut might also be required for this function must be considered. This will be true if $s+N(s^2-a^2)^{\frac{1}{2}} = 0$. This will occur only if $s = \pm i/\gamma^{\frac{1}{2}}$. Considering the positive root, we write

$$s+N(s^2-a^2)^{\frac{1}{2}} = \frac{i}{\gamma^{\frac{1}{2}}}+N\left(\frac{i}{\gamma^{\frac{1}{2}}}+a\right)^{\frac{1}{2}}\left(\frac{i}{\gamma^{\frac{1}{2}}}-a\right)^{\frac{1}{2}}. \tag{3.4.64}$$

Using Fig. 3.15 as an aid to interpreting, it is seen that the real parts of the function will cancel but that the imaginary parts, being all positive, cannot be zero. Hence, $s = i/\gamma^{\frac{1}{2}}$ will not cause the function in question to be zero. A similar result holds for $s = -i/\gamma^{\frac{1}{2}}$, except that the imaginary parts are all negative. Thus, all of the branch points are accounted for.

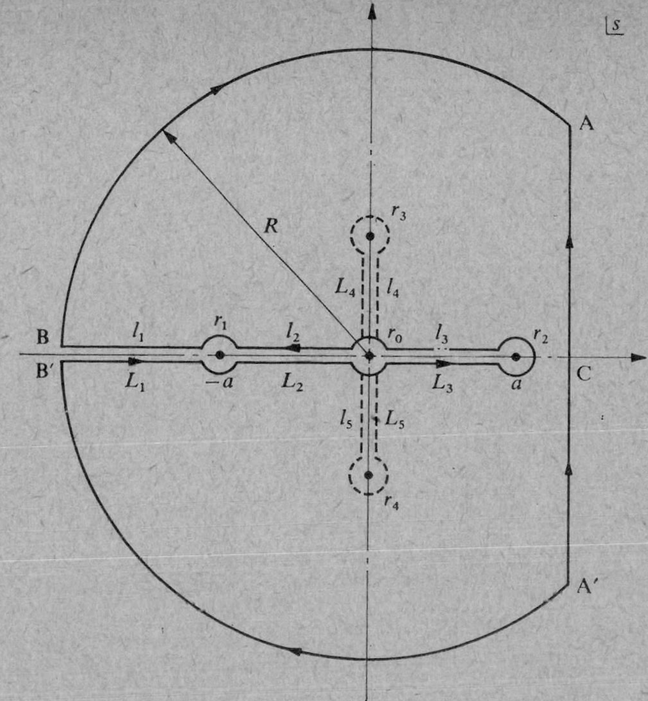

FIG. 3.16. Integration path for evaluating I_1-type integrals.

The resulting form when closed to the left, is shown in Fig. 3.16 as the solid-line contour. For this contour, the following facts hold:†

(1) the contributions from AB and A′B′ vanish as $R \to \infty$;

(2) integration along $l_1 + L_1$ gives a zero value;

(3) integration about the circular contours r_1, r_2 gives a zero result as the radii approach zero;

(4) integration about the circular contour r_0 gives zero for the case at hand.

Since there are no poles within the contour, the entire path integral vanishes. Then the expression for I_1^{ψ} may be written as

$$I_1^{\psi} = \frac{1}{2\text{i}} \int\limits_{L_2+L_3+l_3+l_2} \frac{\exp(st_1 - \lambda_1 x_1)}{s(s^2 - a^2)^{\frac{1}{2}}\lambda_1} \, \text{d}s. \tag{3.4.65}$$

The task of evaluating the result (3.4.60) thus resolves down to evaluation of four definite integrals having finite limits.

It is noted by Boley and Chao [2, p. 583] that statement (4) does not hold if the exponent of s in the denominator is greater than unity. This occurs in the problems at hand, for example, for $\bar{y}_1$. The complexity of the problem then increases because branch points of higher order arise. The authors present a

† Problem 3.20 requests the verification of these facts.

method of circumventing this difficulty by using various reciprocal relations existing among the dependent variables.

The main additional complexity that is present in the problem concerns the evaluation of the I_2 type integrals (see (3.4.54)). Specifically, the expression $\{s-N(s^2-a^2)^{\frac{1}{2}}\}^{\frac{1}{2}}$ is found to contribute additional branch points (recall the discussion of $\{s+N(s^2-a^2)^{\frac{1}{2}}\}^{\frac{1}{2}}$) within the contour. The location of these branch points and the modified contour necessary for the I_2 integrals are shown in Fig. 3.16 as the solid contour with the dashed line additions. Additional definite integrals are introduced by the paths along the additional branch cuts.

We terminate the general review of this problem with presentation of results. Fig. 3.17(a) shows the variation of shear force with time at two different

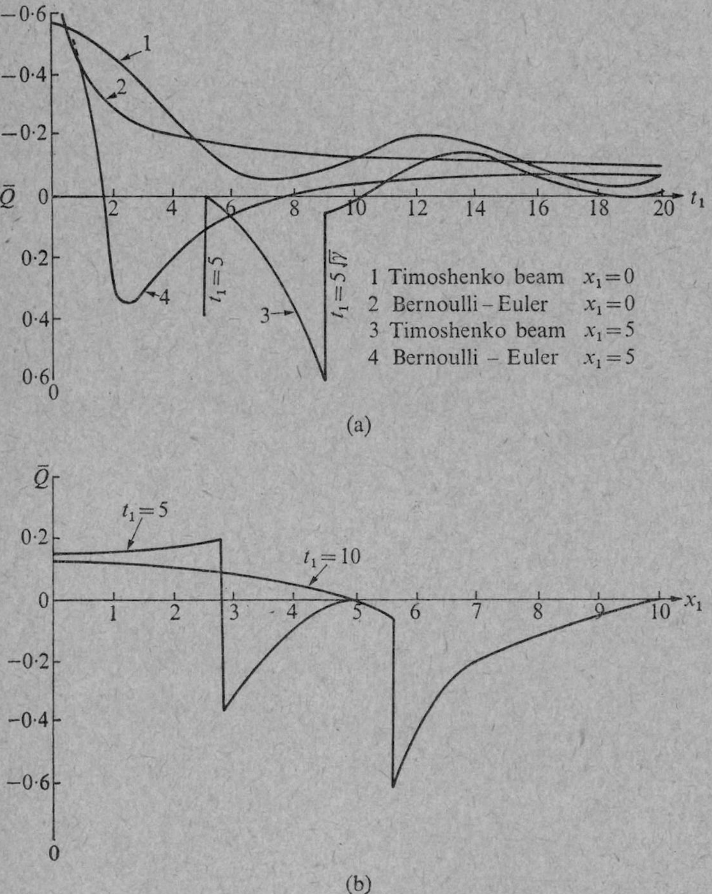

FIG. 3.17. (a) Variation in the shear force $\bar{Q}$, with time at various locations, and (b) the variation of $\bar{Q}$ with location at two times, where $\bar{Q} = Q/EAV_0$. (After Boley and Chao [2].)

locations. Also shown is the shear force as predicted by Bernoulli–Euler theory. Considering in particular the behaviour at $x_1 = 5$, it is seen that, as expected, the Bernoulli–Euler theory predicts instantaneous response. The beam is at rest, according to Timoshenko theory, until $t_1 = 5$, the arrival of the wavefront propagated at c_0. The shear increases until the arrival of the $c_0\sqrt{\gamma}$ wavefront. A discontinuity in shear occurs at this stage. Thus the step disturbance at the origin has created a shear discontinuity, and this propagates with the aforementioned limit velocity. Other results and discussion presented by the authors indicate that the velocity discontinuities propagate with this same limit velocity, while discontinuities in bending moment and angular velocity propagate at the limit velocity c_0. Fig. 3.17(b) shows the variation of shear force along the beam at two successive times. It is to be noted that the maximum value of shear force does not occur at the origin but at a later time and further location.

3.5. Wave propagation in rings

The addition of curvature to rods results in an infinite variety of shapes. The development of the governing equations for rods 'naturally curved' goes back to the 1800's (for example, to the work of Kelvin in 1859). The standard reference for the equations for rods of arbitrary curvature remains to be Love [13, Ch. 18, 21]. The dynamical equations of motion for a rod of circular curvatures are also presented by Love [13, pp. 451–4]. These basic equation forms are widely referred to. It is in the governing relations between the forces, moments, displacements, and rotations that a variety of views are set forth. A similar, but even more complicated, situation will be found to exist for shells. Our development will be restricted to rods of circular curvature.

3.5.1. *The governing equations*

Consider an element isolated from a curved rod, where the rod possesses a plane of symmetry, and the plane of curvature, symmetry, and the plane of all loads coincide, as shown in Fig. 3.18.

The tensile load is N, the shear force is V and the bending moment is M. Variations of these quantities are shown for a positive increment of angle $\mathrm{d}\theta$ and arc length $\mathrm{d}s$. The displacements of the centroidal axis in the radial and tangential directions are given by w and v respectively. The equations of motion in the w and v directions are

$$-V+\left(V+\frac{\partial V}{\partial \theta}\,\mathrm{d}\theta\right)-\left(N+\frac{\partial N}{\partial \theta}\,\mathrm{d}\theta\right)\mathrm{d}\theta = \rho AR\,\mathrm{d}\theta\frac{\partial^2 w}{\partial t^2}, \qquad (3.5.1)$$

$$-N+\left(N+\frac{\partial N}{\partial \theta}\,\mathrm{d}\theta\right)+\left(V+\frac{\partial V}{\partial \theta}\,\mathrm{d}\theta\right)\mathrm{d}\theta = \rho AR\,\mathrm{d}\theta\frac{\partial^2 v}{\partial t^2}. \qquad (3.5.2)$$

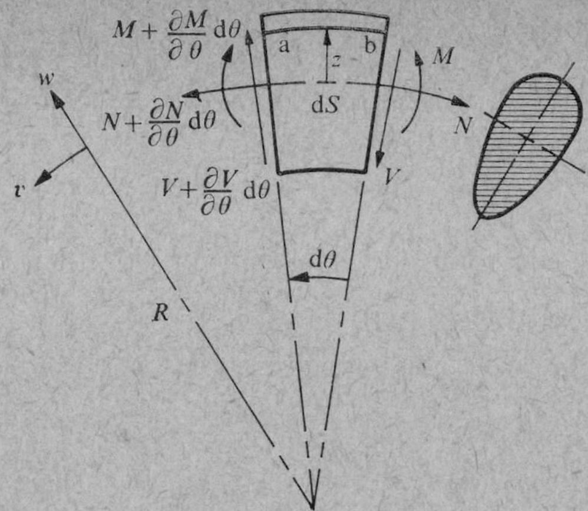

FIG. 3.18. Differential element from a curved rod.

The moment equation, if rotary-inertia effects are neglected, is given by

$$M-\left(M+\frac{\partial M}{\partial \theta}\,\mathrm{d}\theta\right)-\left(V+\frac{\partial V}{\partial \theta}\,\mathrm{d}\theta\right)R\,\mathrm{d}\theta = 0. \tag{3.5.3}$$

These reduce to

$$\frac{\partial V}{\partial \theta}-N = \rho RA\frac{\partial^2 w}{\partial t^2}, \tag{3.5.4}$$

$$\frac{\partial N}{\partial \theta}+V = \rho RA\frac{\partial^2 v}{\partial t^2}, \tag{3.5.5}$$

$$\frac{\partial M}{\partial \theta}+RV = 0. \tag{3.5.6}$$

If the shearing force is eliminated from the first two equations, the result is

$$-\frac{1}{R}\frac{\partial^2 M}{\partial \theta^2}-N = \rho RA\frac{\partial^2 w}{\partial t^2}, \tag{3.5.7}$$

$$\frac{\partial N}{\partial \theta}-\frac{1}{R}\frac{\partial M}{\partial \theta} = \rho RA\frac{\partial^2 v}{\partial t^2}. \tag{3.5.8}$$

Finally, these results could be expressed in terms of the arc length s, where $\mathrm{d}s = R\,\mathrm{d}\theta$. Using this, we have for the preceding equations

$$\begin{aligned} -\frac{\partial^2 M}{\partial s^2}-\frac{N}{R} &= \rho A\frac{\partial^2 w}{\partial t^2}, \\ \frac{\partial N}{\partial s}-\frac{1}{R}\frac{\partial M}{\partial s} &= \rho A\frac{\partial^2 v}{\partial t^2}. \end{aligned} \tag{3.5.9}$$

Although our interest will be in rings of circular curvature, the form (3.5.9) applies to arbitrarily (plane) curved rods where R is now interpreted as a variable radius of curvature.

We now must relate the ring forces and moments to the deformations and displacements. We have shown, in Fig. 3.19, a typical lamina (ab) of the ring, located a distance z from the centroidal axis. If the axial stress in that lamina is σ, then we have for the ring that

$$N = \int_A \sigma \, dA, \qquad M = -\int_A \sigma z \, dA, \tag{3.5.10}$$

where $\sigma = E\varepsilon$ and ε is the axial strain in the lamina. The strain will be given by

$$\varepsilon = (l_2 - l_1)/l_1, \tag{3.5.11}$$

where l_1, l_2 are the initial and final lengths of ab. We now assume that plane sections, initially perpendicular to the central axis, remain plane and perpendicular to the central axis after deformation. This is, of course, the Bernoulli–Euler hypothesis applied to the case of rings. Then we have that

$$l_1 = (R+z)\, d\theta, \qquad l_2 = (R'+z)\, d\theta', \tag{3.5.12}$$

where R', $d\theta'$ are the radius of curvature and subtended angle of the deformed element. We now establish these quantities in terms of the displacements.

Consider, in Fig. 3.19, the central axis of the element in the undeformed

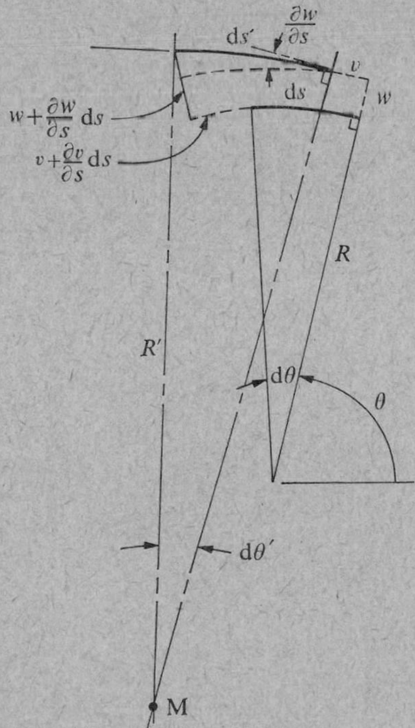

FIG. 3.19. Undeformed and deformed positions of the central axis of the rod.

and deformed positions. Point 0 undergoes the displacements v and w to the position 0′ while P undergoes the displacements $v+(\partial v/\partial s)\,ds$,

$$w+(\partial w/\partial s)\,ds$$

to P′. The length of the deformed element may be expressed as

$$ds' = (w+R)\,d\theta+\frac{\partial v}{\partial s}\,ds. \tag{3.5.13}$$

The contribution of $(\partial w/\partial s)\,ds$ to the change in arc length has been neglected. We now calculate $d\theta'$. This angle is given by the difference in angle between the rays MO′ and MP′. The angle to MO′ is given by $\theta+v/R-\partial w/\partial s$. To MP′ the angle will be $\theta+d\theta+\{v+(\partial v/\partial s)\,ds\}/R-\{\partial w/\partial s+(\partial^2 w/\partial s^2)\,ds\}$. Then for $d\theta'$ we have

$$\begin{aligned} d\theta' &= \left\{\theta+d\theta+\frac{1}{R}\left(v+\frac{\partial v}{\partial s}\,ds\right)-\left(\frac{\partial w}{\partial s}+\frac{\partial^2 w}{\partial s^2}\,ds\right)\right\}-\left(\theta+\frac{v}{R}-\frac{\partial w}{\partial s}\right) \\ &= d\theta+\frac{1}{R}\frac{\partial v}{\partial s}\,ds-\frac{\partial^2 w}{\partial s^2}\,ds. \end{aligned} \tag{3.5.14}$$

The results (3.5.13) and (3.5.14) may be expressed in terms of the angle $d\theta$. Thus

$$ds' = (w+R)\,d\theta+\frac{\partial v}{\partial \theta}\,d\theta, \qquad d\theta' = d\theta+\frac{1}{R}\frac{\partial v}{\partial \theta}\,d\theta-\frac{1}{R}\frac{\partial^2 w}{\partial \theta^2}\,d\theta. \tag{3.5.15}$$

We may now establish ε. Noting that $R'\,d\theta' = ds'$, we have that

$$l_2 = \left\{\left(w+R+\frac{\partial v}{\partial \theta}\right)+z\left(1+\frac{1}{R}\frac{\partial v}{\partial \theta}-\frac{1}{R}\frac{\partial^2 w}{\partial \theta^2}\right)\right\}\,d\theta. \tag{3.5.16}$$

Then we have from (3.5.11)

$$\varepsilon = \left\{w+\frac{\partial v}{\partial \theta}+\frac{z}{R}\left(\frac{\partial w}{\partial \theta}-\frac{\partial^2 w}{\partial \theta^2}\right)\right\}\Big/R\left(1+\frac{z}{R}\right). \tag{3.5.17}$$

If z/R is neglected with respect to unity in the denominator we have

$$\varepsilon = \frac{1}{R}\left\{w+\frac{\partial v}{\partial \theta}+\frac{z}{R}\frac{\partial}{\partial \theta}\left(v-\frac{\partial w}{\partial \theta}\right)\right\}. \tag{3.5.18}$$

Upon substituting this result in the expression (3.5.10) for N and performing the integration we obtain

$$N = \frac{EA}{R}\left(w+\frac{\partial v}{\partial \theta}\right). \tag{3.5.19}$$

Thus the z contribution of (3.5.18) does not enter since the axis is the centroidal axis. Substituting in the expression for M, we obtain

$$M = -\frac{EAk^2}{R^2}\frac{\partial}{\partial\theta}\left(v - \frac{\partial w}{\partial\theta}\right), \tag{3.5.20}$$

where k^2 is the radius of gyration of the cross-section.

With the development of the ring stress–displacement equations (3.5.19) and (3.5.20), the equations of motion (3.5.7) and (3.5.8) are

$$\frac{EAk^2}{R^3}\frac{\partial^3}{\partial\theta^3}\left(v - \frac{\partial w}{\partial\theta}\right) - \frac{EA}{R}\left(w + \frac{\partial v}{\partial\theta}\right) = \rho RA\frac{\partial^2 w}{\partial t^2}, \tag{3.5.21}$$

$$\frac{EAk^2}{R^3}\frac{\partial^2}{\partial\theta^2}\left(v - \frac{\partial w}{\partial\theta}\right) + \frac{EA}{R}\frac{\partial}{\partial\theta}\left(w + \frac{\partial v}{\partial\theta}\right) = \rho RA\frac{\partial^2 v}{\partial t^2}. \tag{3.5.22}$$

3.5.2. *Wave propagation*

The propagation characteristics of thin rings may be established by considering harmonic waves of the form

$$w = A_1 e^{i(\gamma R\theta - \omega t)}, \qquad v = A_2 e^{i(\gamma R\theta - \omega t)}. \tag{3.5.23}$$

Substitution of these into the governing equations (3.5.21), (3.5.22) gives

$$\begin{bmatrix} \left(\dfrac{\omega^2 R^2}{c_0^2} - 1 - \gamma^4 R^2 k^2\right) & -i(\gamma^3 Rk^2 + \gamma R) \\ i(\gamma^3 Rk^2 + \gamma R) & \left(\dfrac{\omega^2}{c_0^2}R^2 - \gamma^2 R^2 - \gamma^2 k^2\right) \end{bmatrix} \begin{bmatrix} A_1 \\ A_2 \end{bmatrix} = 0. \tag{3.5.24}$$

We introduce the non-dimensionalizations

$$\bar{k} = k/R, \qquad \bar{\gamma} = k\gamma, \qquad \bar{\omega} = \omega k/c_0, \qquad \bar{c} = c/c_0. \tag{3.5.25}$$

Then the frequency equation resulting from (3.5.24) is

$$(\bar{\omega}^2 - \bar{k}^2 - \bar{\gamma}^4)(\bar{\omega}^2 - \bar{\gamma}^2 - \bar{k}^2\bar{\gamma}^2) - \bar{k}^2\bar{\gamma}^2(\bar{\gamma}^2 + 1)^2 = 0, \tag{3.5.26}$$

and in expanded form is given by

$$\bar{\omega}^4 - \{\bar{\gamma}^4 + (1 + \bar{k}^2)\bar{\gamma}^2 + \bar{k}^2\}\bar{\omega}^2 + \bar{\gamma}^2(\bar{k}^2 - \bar{\gamma}^2)^2 = 0. \tag{3.5.27}$$

The dispersion relation is obtained by noting that $\bar{\omega} = \bar{\gamma}\bar{c}$ so that we obtain, from (3.5.27),

$$\bar{c}^4 - \{\bar{\gamma}^2 + (1 + \bar{k}^2) + \bar{k}^2/\bar{\gamma}^2\}\bar{c}^2 + \bar{\gamma}^2(1 - \bar{k}^2/\bar{\gamma}^2)^2 = 0. \tag{3.5.28}$$

Before presenting the general behaviour as predicted by (3.5.27) and (3.5.28), we note the behaviour at long wavelengths ($\bar{\gamma} \to 0$) and short wavelengths ($\bar{\gamma} \to \infty$). From (3.5.27) we have that, as $\bar{\gamma} \to 0$,

$$\lim_{\bar{\gamma} \to 0}(3.5.27) = \bar{\omega}^2(\bar{\omega}^2 - \bar{k}^2) = 0. \tag{3.5.29}$$

Thus, $\bar{\omega} = 0, \bar{k}$ are the limits. The latter value indicates a cutoff frequency of one of the modes. As $\bar{\gamma} \to \infty$, we have from (3.5.28) that

$$\lim_{\gamma\to\infty}(3.5.28) = \bar{\gamma}^2(\bar{c}^4/\bar{\gamma}^2 - \bar{c}^2 + 1) = 0. \tag{3.5.30}$$

If $\bar{c}$ remains finite in (3.5.30), we must have that $\bar{c} = 1$. This corresponds to the velocity of longitudinal waves in a thin straight rod. A solution to the general equation may be found for $\bar{c} = 0$. Thus (3.5.28) reduces to

$$\bar{\gamma}^2(1 - \bar{k}^2/\bar{\gamma}^2)^2 = 0,$$

from which we have $\bar{\gamma} = \bar{k}$. Another limit of interest is that obtained by allowing the radius of curvature to become large. When this occurs, we have that $\bar{k} \to 0$ as $R \to \infty$. We see that (3.5.28) reduces to

$$\lim_{\bar{k}\to 0}(3.5.28) = \bar{c}^4 - (\bar{\gamma}^2 + 1)\bar{c}^2 + \bar{\gamma}^2 = (\bar{c}^2 - \bar{\gamma}^2)(\bar{c}^2 - 1) = 0. \tag{3.5.31}$$

Thus $\bar{c} \to \bar{\gamma}, 1$. These are the classical limits for flexural waves in straight beams according to Bernoulli–Euler theory and for longitudinal waves in thin rods according to the wave equation. Thus, in dimensional form, we have

$$c \to \sqrt{\left(\frac{EI}{\rho A}\right)}\gamma,\ c_0. \tag{3.5.32}$$

The data for the frequency spectrum and dispersion curves of a curved rod must be presented in terms of the curvature parameter $\bar{k}$. If $\bar{k} = 0$, we have the case of a straight rod. The maximum value that $\bar{k}$ can attain for a rod of circular cross-section is $\frac{1}{2}$ (this gives a radius of curvature equal to the radius of the cross-section). However, restrictions similar to those for straight beams and rods hold regarding wavelength in comparison to thickness and, in this case, in comparison to radius of curvature. Consequently $\bar{k} \ll \frac{1}{2}$ must hold. The general behaviour of the real, positive branches of the frequency spectrum and dispersion curves for $\bar{k}^2 = 0{\cdot}05$ are shown in Fig. 3.20. The cutoff frequency occurring in the frequency spectrum at $\bar{\omega} = \bar{k}$ is shown. The dashed lines correspond to the case of $\bar{k} = 0$, which are the results for flexural and longitudinal waves in straight rods. The zero propagation velocity occurring at the special root of $\bar{\gamma} = \bar{k}$ corresponds to a wavelength equal to the circumference.

This concludes a rather brief treatment of waves in curved rods. There are, of course, many other aspects that could be considered. In the context of curved rings, theories including shear and rotary-inertia effects could be developed. Out-of-plane forces and motion could also be considered. The present development was based on both bending and extensional effects. In many developments, the latter effect is neglected. Love [13, p. 451] has presented the equations for out-of-plane motion of a circular ring with

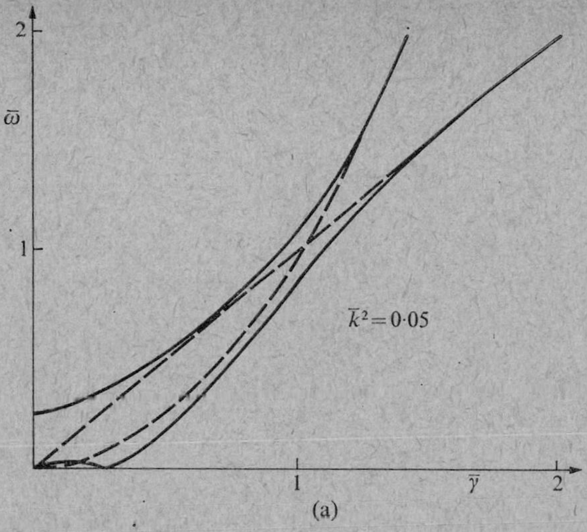

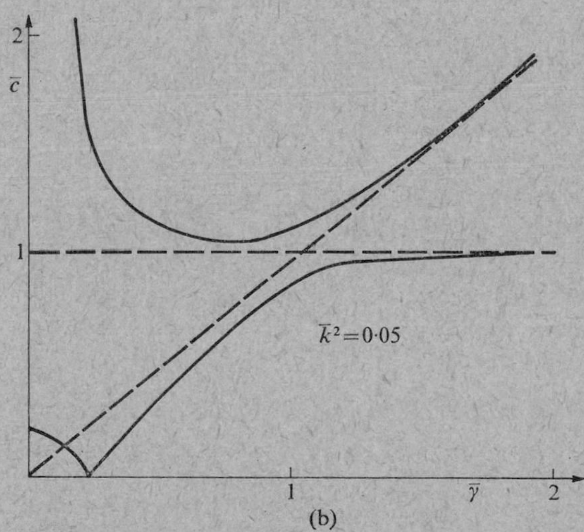

FIG. 3.20. (a) Frequency spectrum and (b) dispersion curves for a curved rod for which $\bar{k} = 0{\cdot}05$. The dashed lines correspond to the case of $\bar{k} = 0$.

extensional effects neglected. Philipson [17] has paralleled Love's development, but with extensional effects included. Morley [15] and Graff [8] have presented theories including shear effects and rotary inertia, with dispersion curves for various curvatures being given in the latter. The major portion of the technical literature on rings is devoted to the vibrations of complete rings or ring sectors, with extensional effects usually neglected.

3.6. Experimental studies on beams

A fairly large number of experimental studies have been conducted on waves and vibrations in beams, with the measurement of transient flexural waves probably receiving the greatest attention. Some of these studies, plus some results on Timoshenko beam theory and waves in curved rods, will be presented here.

3.6.1. *Propagation of transients in straight beams*

A number of studies have been made of the propagation of transient flexural disturbances in beams. Dohrenwend, Drucker, and Moore [5] presented results on waves in strings, beams, and plates. The experimental results were compared to theoretical solutions based on assumed initial velocity distributions of the form $v_0 \exp(-x^2/4b^2)$. Vigness [26] presented additional experimental data on the wave motion in a cantilever beam subjected to a step change in velocity at the built in end. Hoppmann [9] presented results for transient waves in multi-span beams. The work by Ripperger and Abramson [20], cited in § 2.7, also contained results on flexural waves in rods and followed an earlier work [19] giving results on the propagation of flexural waves in beams.

Cunningham and Goldsmith [4] reported on the oblique impact of a steel ball on a beam. Strain gauges were used to record the outer fibre strains in beams of rectangular cross-section subjected to the transverse impact. Fig. 3.21 shows the recorded waveform at various locations along the beam

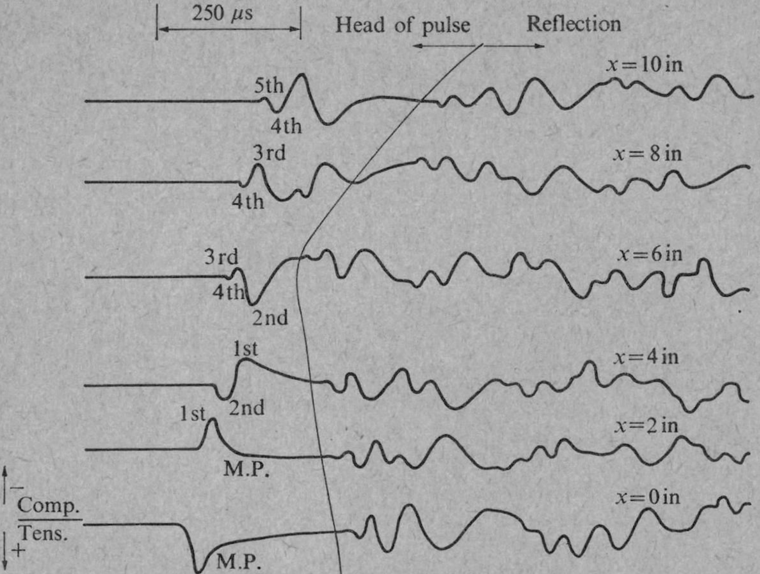

FIG. 3.21. Stress wave propagation in a $\frac{3}{8}$ in $\times \frac{1}{2}$ in $\times 22$ in clamped beam subjected to the transverse impact of a $\frac{1}{2}$ in diameter ball travelling at 30 ft s^{-1} and 7° to the vertical. (After Cunningham and Goldsmith [4, Fig. 2].)

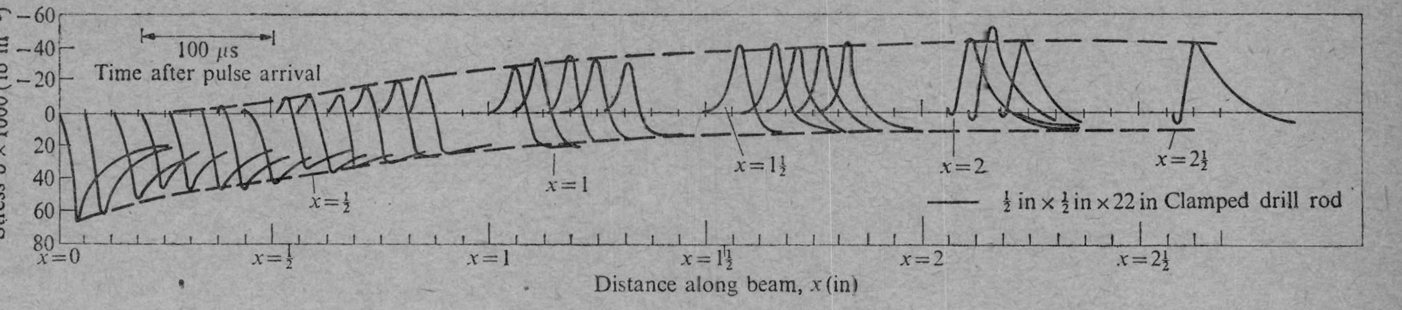

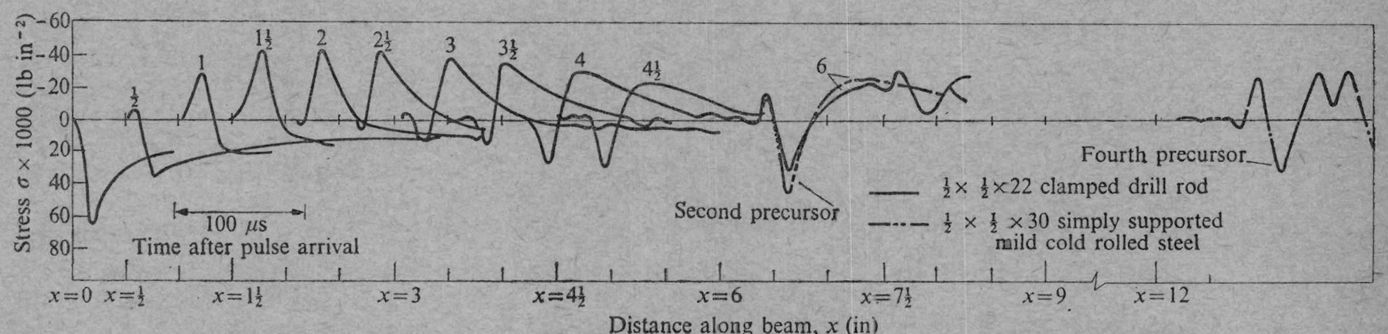

FIG. 3.22. Head-of-pulse distortion at successive points along a beam subjected to transverse impact. (After Cunningham and Goldsmith [4, Fig. 3].)

for a specific set of impact conditions. Reflections from the end of the beam comprise a substantial portion of the records and should be ignored. The details of the distortion occurring at the head of the pulse due to dispersion effects are shown in Fig. 3.22. It is seen that the peak amplitude undergoes inversion as it propagates along the beam. In addition, the presence of high-frequency wavelets becomes more noticeable with distance of propagation.

In a later study, Kuo [12] subjected a rod to the eccentric longitudinal impact of another rod, thus inducing flexural as well as longitudinal waves in the struck rod. The experimental arrangement is shown in Fig. 3.23(a) and

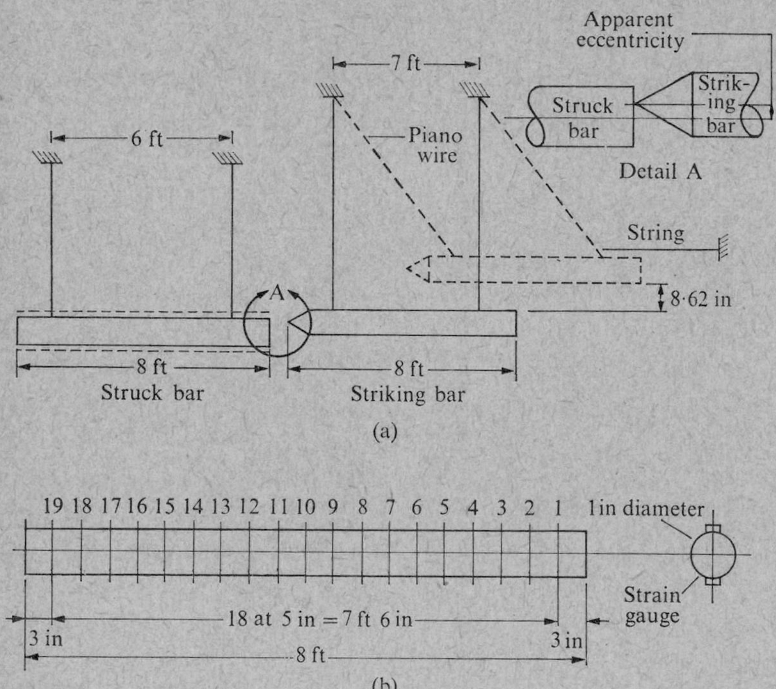

FIG. 3.23. (a) Experimental apparatus for eccentric longitudinal impact of two bars and (b) the location of strain gauges along the struck bar. (After Kuo [12, Figs. 1 and 2].)

the location of strain gauges on the struck bar shown in Fig. 3.23(b). Each pair of gauges was wired into a bridge circuit so as to eliminate the longitudinal strain signals. A record of oscilloscope traces from the various stations is shown in Fig. 3.24. Also shown are calibration records. It should be noted that the calibration of Station 16 is 400 μin per in per major vertical division, whereas it is 200 μin per in for all other stations. The time base of Station 3 is 500 μs per major division. Referring to Station 1, it is seen that the loading is practically that of a rectangular bending pulse showing a duration of about 960 μs. This time is consistent with the duration of loading expected for

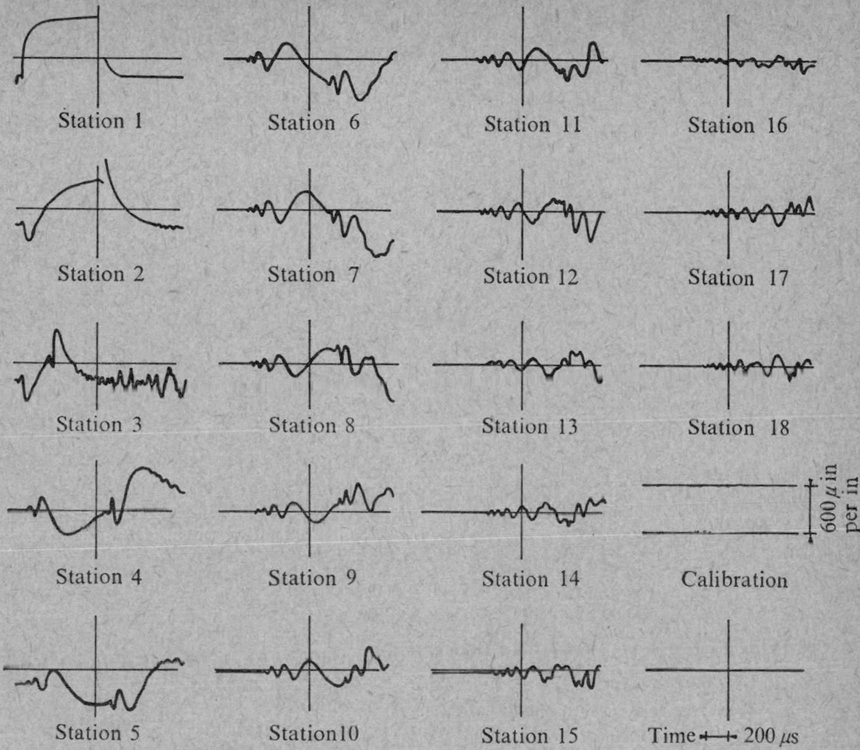

FIG. 3.24. Oscilloscope records of the outer fibre strains in a rod subjected to eccentric longitudinal impact. (After Kuo [12, Fig. 4].)

perfect longitudinal impact of two 8 ft steel rods. The degeneration of the step pulse into a variable frequency harmonic wave train is quite evident in these results.

Kuo also obtained theoretical solutions to the problem of a free–free beam subjected to an end moment. In one case, the Bernoulli–Euler model of the beam was used and a modal superposition was applied (the first 27 modes were used) to obtain the results. In the other theoretical case, the Timoshenko beam model was used, and the method of characteristics applied to obtain the solution. In Fig. 3.25 the comparison between the experimental results and the predictions of the Timoshenko beam theory are shown. Kuo also presents the comparison between the purely theoretical results of the two beam theories. The agreement of the results in the figure are generally quite good, with the main discrepancy occurring in the phase shifting.

Stephenson and Wilhoit [23] have also studied the propagation of bending transients in a rod. An ingenious scheme for producing a sudden end moment involving the rapid unloading due to fracture of a tensile loading piece was employed. A rod 30 ft in length was used with eight strain-gauge

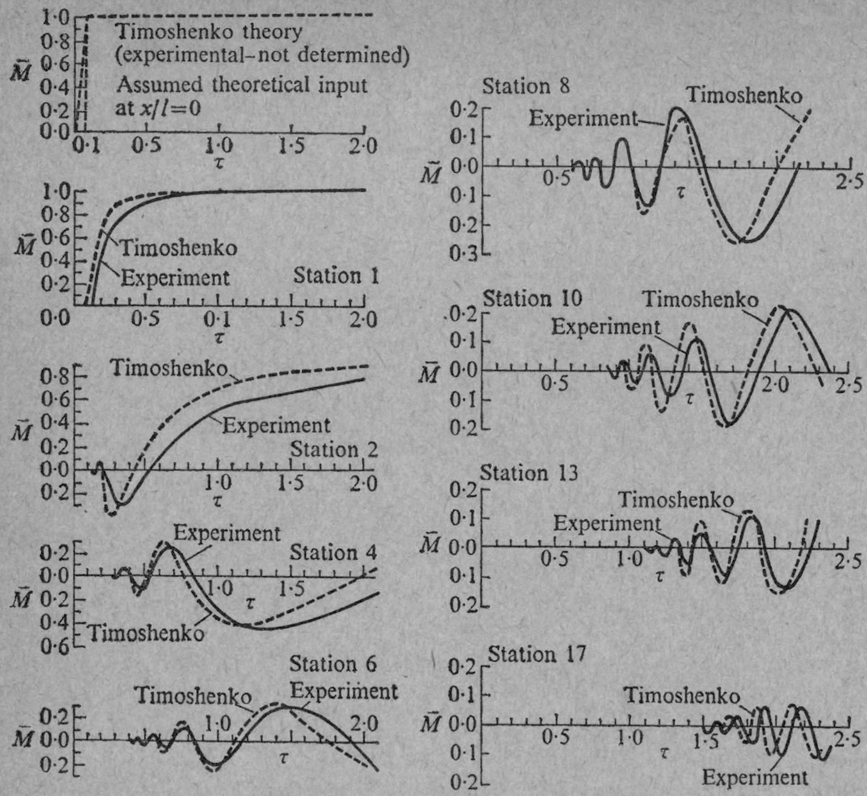

FIG. 3.25. Comparison of experimental results and the prediction of Timoshenko beam theory, where $\tau = c_0t/L$ and $\bar{M} = ML/EI$, where $\bar{M}$ is the dimensionless bending moment. (After Kuo [12, Fig. 8].)

stations in the first 21 ft recording the wave propagation. The results again showed the evolution of the pulse into a variable frequency harmonic wave train. The great length of the test specimen enabled the wavefront velocity to be established with great accuracy. Schweiger [21] has also studied the transverse impact of beams, obtaining data on the impact force and central bending strain. Photo-elastic-layer and strain-gauge data was obtained. Mori [14] obtained experimental data on the propagation of bending waves in longitudinally prestressed beams subjected to transverse impact. Finally, we note that in the previously cited work of Ripperger and Abramson [20] (§ 2.7) that experimental data on the reflection of a flexural pulse from a step discontinuity in rod cross-section was obtained.

3.6.2. *Beam vibration experiments*

Reference has already been made in the previous section to the work of Kuo [12] in comparing Timoshenko beam theory with experimental results for transient waves. Zemanek and Rudnick [28], previously cited in § 2.7 for their experimental results on longitudinal rod vibrations, have also obtained data on the transverse vibrations of beams. The experimental arrangement shown in Fig. 2.24(a) was used for the flexural wave study, except that the electrostatic drive was replaced by an electromagnetic drive unit. The first 306 resonant frequencies were excited and the resulting phase velocity computed from the formula

$$c = 2lf_n/(n+\tfrac{1}{2}). \tag{3.6.1}$$

The experimental data and the predictions of three different beam theories are shown in Fig. 3.26. The plot is one of non-dimensional phase velocity

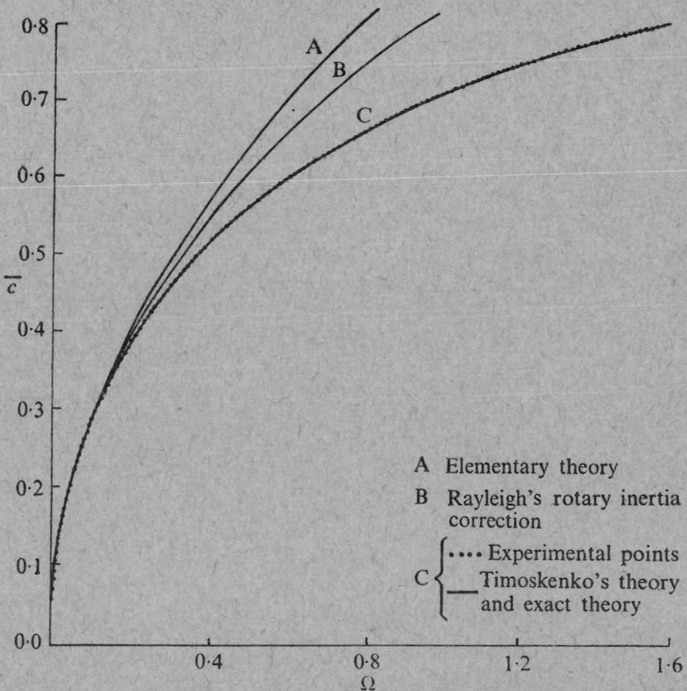

FIG. 3.26. Experimental and theoretical results for phase velocity versus frequency in the transverse motion of a beam. (After Zemanek and Rudnick [28, Fig. 6].)

versus frequency, where

$$\bar{c} = c/c_2, \qquad \Omega = \omega a/c_2, \qquad c_2 = \sqrt{(G/\rho)}, \tag{3.6.2}$$

and a is the radius of the rod. Curve A is the prediction of Bernoulli–Euler beam theory. Curve B is the prediction of a beam theory indicating rotary-inertia effects alone, and curve C is the Timoshenko and exact theory prediction. The excellent agreement between the experimental results and curve C need hardly be commented on.

3.6.3. *Waves in curved rings*

Only a few theoretical or experimental studies on wave propagation in rings have been made, with reference being made to some of the theoretical work in § 3.5. Britton and Langley [3] have conducted some noteworthy experimental studies on wave propagation in helical springs. The geometry of the test specimen is shown in Fig. 3.27(a), and the technique for inducing

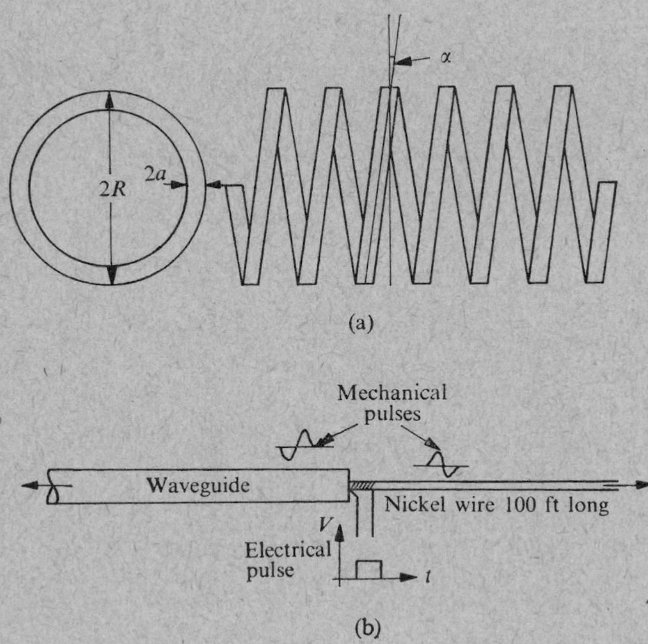

FIG. 3.27. (a) Helical ring test specimen and (b) the means for inducing stress pulses into the helix. (After Britton and Langley [3, Figs. 1 and 8].)

stress waves into the helix is shown in Fig. 3.27(b). The pulse is induced by using the strong magneto-strictive effect of nickel. The extreme length of nickel wire is merely to absorb the image pulse produced by the electrical pulse excitation. Flexural pulses may be excited by placing the nickel wire transverse to the waveguide.

The objective of the work was to compare the experimental results with those predicted by the theories put forth by Morley [15] and Wittrick [27]. In the former case, dispersion curves were obtained for a Timoshenko type of theory for the in-plane motions of a circular rod. In the latter case, out-of-plane motions were included in the development. The theoretical arrival-time curves for Morley's theory are shown in Fig. 3.28 as the solid lines for a particular value of curvature ratio ($a/R = 0{\cdot}106$). The parameters t and T_0 are time and x/c_0 respectively. T_p is the period of the arriving wave. Curves 1

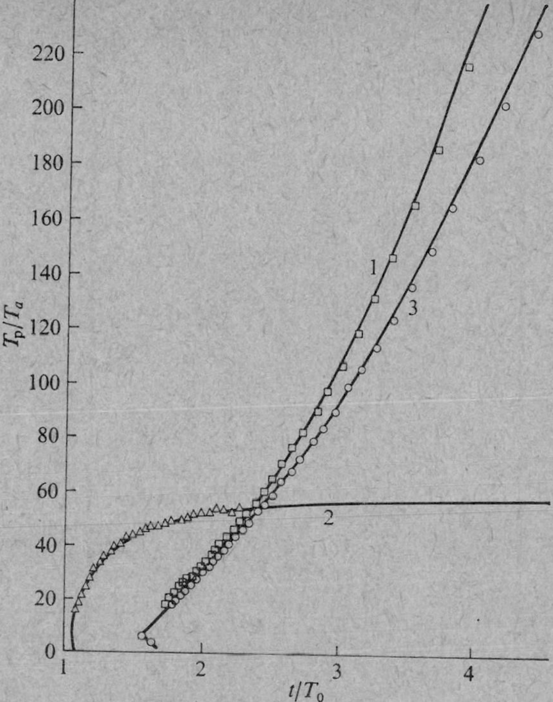

FIG. 3.28. Comparison of experimental data on waves in curved rings with the predictions of Morley's theory for $a/R = 0{\cdot}106$ (Curves 1 and 2). Curve 3 is the straight-rod case. (After Britton and Langley [3, Fig. 11].)

and 2 correspond to flexural and longitudinal modes in a curved rod, while curve 3 is the flexural mode for a straight Timoshenko beam.

The experimental technique was to induce a wide-band stress pulse by the method previously shown. The arrival time of the predominant period was measured. Data was obtained on modes 1 and 2 and for the straight rod case. The results are as shown in Fig. 3.28, with curve 3 corresponding to the straight-rod case. Agreement is seen to be excellent in all cases. Additional comparisons were made by the authors with Wittrick's theory.

References

1. ABRAMOWITZ, M. and STEGUN, I. A. *Handbook of mathematical functions: with formulas, graphs, and mathematical tables*. Dover Publications, New York (1965).
2. BOLEY, B. A. and CHAO, C. C. Some solutions of the Timoshenko beam equations. *J. appl. Mech.* **22**, 579–86 (1955).
3. BRITTON, W. G. B. and LANGLEY, G. O. Stress pulse dispersion in curved mechanical waveguides. *J. Sound Vib.* **7** (3), 417–30 (1968).

4. Cunningham, D. M. and Goldsmith, W. An experimental investigation of beam stresses produced by oblique impact of a steel sphere. *J. appl. Mech.* **23,** 606–11 (1956).
5. Dohrenwend, C. O., Drucker, D. C., and Moore, P. Tranverse impact Transients. *Exp. Stress Analysis* **1,** 1–10 (1944).
6. Erdélyi, A. (Ed.). *Tables of integral transforms.* (Bateman Manuscript Project). McGraw-Hill, New York (1954).
7. Goldsmith, W. *Impact: the theory and physical behaviour of colliding solids.* Edward Arnold, London (1960).
8. Graff, K. F. Elastic wave propagation in a curved sonic transmission line. *IEEE Trans., Sonics and Ultrasonics* **SU-17,** 1–6 (1970).
9. Hoppmann, W. H. (II) Impulsive loads on beams. *Proc. Soc. exp. Stress Analysis* **10,** 157–64 (1952).
10. Kenney, J. T. (Jr.). Steady-state vibrations of beam on elastic foundation for moving load. *J. appl. Mech.* **21,** 359–64 (1954).
11. Kolsky, H. *Stress waves in solids.* Dover Publications, New York (1963).
12. Kuo, S. S. Beam subjected to eccentric longitudinal impact. *Exp. Mech.* **18,** 102–8 (1961).
13. Love, A. E. H. *A treatise on the mathematical theory of elasticity.* Dover Publications, New York (1944).
14. Mori, D. Laterial impact of bars and plates. *Proc. Soc. exp. Stress Analysis* **15,** 171–8 (1957).
15. Morley, L. S. D. Elastic waves in a naturally curved rod. *Quart. Jl Mech. appl. Math.* **14,** 155–72 (1961).
16. Morse, P. M. *Vibration and sound.* McGraw-Hill, New York (1948).
17. Philipson, L. L. On the role of extension in the flexural vibrations of rings. *J. appl. Mech.* **23,** 364–6 (1956).
18. Rayleigh, J. W. S. *The theory of sound,* Vols. I and II. Dover Publications, New York (1945).
19. Ripperger, E. A. The propagation of pulses in cylindrical bars—an experimental study. *Proc. 1st midwest. Conf. Solid Mech.* pp. 29–39 (1953).
20. —— and Abramson, H. N. Reflection and transmission of elastic pulses in a bar at a discontinuity in cross section. *Proc. 3rd midwest. Conf. Solid Mech.* p. 135 (1957).
21. Schwieger, H. A simple calculation of the transverse impact on beams and its experimental verification. *Exp. Mech.* **22,** 378–84 (1965).
22. Sneddon, I. N. *Fourier transforms.* McGraw-Hill, New York (1951).
23. Stephenson, J. G. and Wilhoit, J. C. (Jr.). An experimental study of bending impact waves in beams. *Exp. Mech.* **22,** 16–21 (1965).
24. Timoshenko, S. P. On the correction for shear of the differential equation for transverse vibrations of prismatic bars. *Phil. Mag.*, Ser. 6, **41,** 744 (1921).
25. ——. *Vibration problems in engineering.* Van Nostrand, New Jersey (1928).
26. Vigness, I. Transverse waves in beams. *Exp. Stress Analysis* **8,** 69–82 (1951).
27. Wittrick, W. H. On elastic wave propagation in helical springs. *Int. J. Mech. Sci.* **8,** 25–47 (1966).
28. Zemanek, J. (Jr.) and Rudnick, I. Attenuation and dispersion of elastic waves in a cylindrical bar. *J. Acoust. Soc. Am.* **33,** 1283–8 (1961).

Problems

3.1. Draw the group velocity versus wavenumber curve for the Bernoulli-Euler beam.

3.2. Solve the problem of a concentrated, harmonic load applied at the origin of an infinite beam by solving the homogeneous governing equation for $x \neq 0$ and then applying proper boundary conditions at the origin.

3.3. Obtain the expression for the impedance of a semi-infinite beam subjected to the end force $F_0 \exp(-i\omega t)$ and free to rotate at the end.

3.4. Consider an infinite beam and two concentrated loads located at $x = \pm a$ and each given by $P \exp(-i\omega t)$. Solve for the steady wave propagation. Look for special cases of excitation frequency where constructive or destructive interference can occur in the region between the two loads.

3.5. Determine the amplitude ratio of harmonic waves in a semi-infinite beam incident on a fixed boundary, an elastic deflection spring boundary and a torsion spring boundary.

3.6. Consider two semi-infinite beams of differing stiffness EI (but same density) joined together at the origin. Consider harmonic waves travelling from left to right to be incident on the junction. Obtain the amplitude ratios of the reflected and transmitted waves.

3.7. Apply the method of stationary phase to analysis of the initial value problem starting with the initial conditions (3.1.28). You should obtain the same result as (3.1.29). To explain this peculiarity, go back to the stationary-phase development in § 1.6 and note the truncation of the expansion of $h(\omega)$ at the second derivative. Evaluate $h'''(\omega_0)$ for the present problem. Comment on the conditions under which the stationary-phase method can yield 'exact' results.

3.8. Obtain the normal modes $Y_n(x)$ for the cases of free–free, clamped–clamped, and clamped–free beams.

3.9. Obtain the frequency equation for a beam of length l, pinned at each end and with a torsion spring K_T at each end. Let $K_T \to 0, \infty$ and see if the pinned–pinned and clamped–clamped frequency equations are recovered. (Your general result should be in terms of the frequency parameter βl and the ratio $EI/K_T l$). Plot βl versus a properly-non-dimensionalized K_T for $3{\cdot}142 < \beta l < 4{\cdot}730$, with K_T increasing from zero. The range cited falls between the first natural frequency of a pinned–pinned and clamped–clamped beam. Is βl (frequency) sensitive to slight initial changes of K_T? Relate these results to the experimental problem of simulating pinned versus clamped boundary conditions.

3.10. It is possible to apply the Laplace transform to the problem of the natural frequencies of finite beams. Start by considering harmonic motion $y = Y \exp(-i\omega t)$ and then apply the Laplace transform on the spatial variable of the ordinary differential equation. The results given by (3.2.71) might be of help in this analysis.

3.11. Consider a beam of length l, pinned at both ends and having an intermediate deflection spring of constant K located at $x = l/2$. Determine the natural frequencies for various stiffness K. Some rather interesting results should arise in this problem. Let $K \to 0, \infty$: are the natural frequencies for a pinned–pinned beam recovered for $K \to 0$? Now let $K \to \infty$. At a certain value of K, there should be a point at which the first symmetrical mode of the beam becomes unstable and the beam switches to an antisymmetrical mode. This also occurs for the higher modes.

3.12. Draw the dispersion curve for the beam on an elastic foundation. Interpret the meaning of the double values for c and of the minimum that occurs in the curve. Interpret the behaviour as $\gamma \to 0$.

3.13. Solve the problem of forced harmonic motion of an infinite beam on an elastic foundation, where the load is described by $\delta(x-\zeta)\exp(-i\omega t)$. Use transform methods and residue theory or treat the homogeneous differential equation under proper boundary conditions.

3.14. Include slight damping in the case of an infinite beam subjected to a harmonic, concentrated load at the origin. Verify that the poles are displaced from the real axis in a manner consistent with the radiation condition (refer to Fig. 1.26 for the analogous string problem).

3.15. Determine the lowest Euler buckling load of a fixed–pinned column by the vibration method.

3.16. Calculate the second branch of the dispersion curve for the Timoshenko beam for the value of Poisson's ratio and range of wavenumber shown in Fig. 3.13.

3.17. Draw the frequency spectrum for the Timoshenko beam for a Poisson's ratio of $\nu = 0{\cdot}29$ Show both branches, and the imaginary portions, if any, of the curves. Non-dimensionalize the wavenumber, as in Fig. 3.13, and make the spectrum for $\bar{\gamma} \leq 2{\cdot}0$.

3.18. A dispersion curve for longitudinal waves according to Love's theory was shown in Fig. 2.27 and a region of validity was established in terms of frequencies. Do the same for the Timoshenko beam, using Fig. 3.13. Obtain a frequency bandwidth for a 1 in. diameter steel rod. Compare this with the bandwidth of longitudinal waves in the same rod.

3.19. Exclude the effects of rotary inertia from the Timoshenko beam results. Calculate a few points on the new dispersion curve. Results should suggest that shear effects predominate in bringing Bernoulli–Euler theory into accord with exact theory.

3.20. Establish the validity of the four 'facts' regarding the integral I_1 about the parts of the contour shown in Fig. 3.16.

3.21. Delete centre-line extensibility effects in the development of the governing equations for a curved rod. The results should be a purely flexural wave theory for the ring. Obtain the dispersion curve for this case.

3.22. Derive the governing equation for a ring having no bending resistance (that is, $M = 0$). What conditions are placed on the shear force and $\partial/\partial\theta$ variations? Using the resulting governing equation, derive the frequency equation for a complete ring. Sketch the nature of the vibrational mode.

4 Waves in membranes, thin plates, and shells

IN OUR study of wave propagation and vibrations of elastic bodies, we have previously restricted our attention to one-dimensional problems. That is, only one independent spatial variable was admitted, the length along the member. Within these confines, the transverse motion of strings, longitudinal waves in rods, and transverse waves in beams have been investigated. Such structural shapes could be classified as members, one of whose dimensions (length) was large in comparison to the other two (depth, breadth).

We now will study the propagation of elastic waves under more complicated conditions, involving two independent spatial variables. Two of the structural types, membranes and thin plates, may be classified as flat elements having two dimensions (length, breadth) large in comparison to the remaining one (depth). The membrane element may be thought of as the two-dimensional analogue of the string, while the thin plate is the two-dimensional analogue of the beam. The third structural shape will be the thin shell. Again, two of the characteristic dimensions (length, radius) will be large compared to the third (thickness). There will also be the considerable added complexity of curvature.

The coverage in these areas will be somewhat more restricted than in the earlier chapters. Part of the reason for this is that nearly all of the basic methods of analysis have been illustrated at this stage and do not require further repetition. A second reason is the fact that analysis of these geometrically more complicated systems becomes, at a minimum, more tedious and frequently more complicated. Attention will be focused on the main aspects of harmonic wave propagation, initial-value problems, reflection characteristics, and vibrations of finite elements.

4.1. Transverse motion in membranes

In speaking of the membrane as the two-dimensional analogue of the string, we are speaking of an element whose restoring forces arise from the in-plane tensile or stretching forces. There is no resistance to shear and bending in such an element. It will be the two-dimensional characteristics of waves in membranes (and plates) that most distinguish this work from the previous chapters. Of particular interest with reference to later, more complicated, elastic systems will be the concept of plane waves and the reflection of oblique waves from boundaries.

4.1.1. *The governing equation*

Consider a taut membrane under in-plane tensile force T, as shown in Fig. 4.1(a), and further consider a rectangular element of the membrane in a

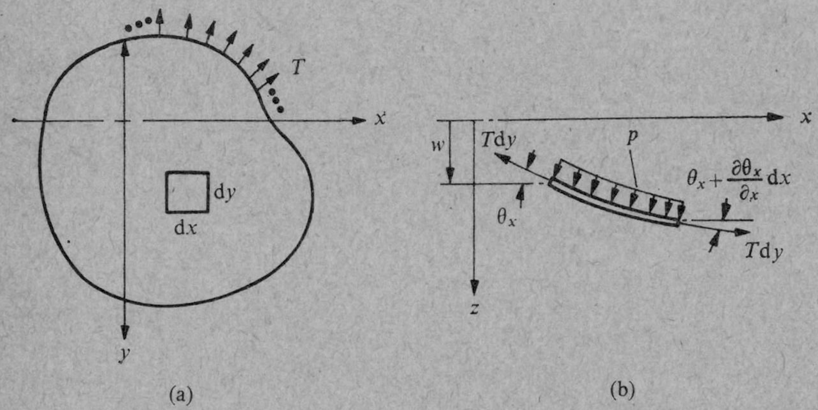

FIG. 4.1. (a) Taut membrane under tensile load, and (b) side view of a differential element of that membrane.

deflected configuration, as shown in Fig. 4.1(b). The coordinate w is used to measure the deflection of the membrane in the z direction. The equation of motion in the z-direction is given by

$$-T\,dy\theta_x + T\,dy\left(\theta_x + \frac{\partial \theta_x}{\partial x}dx\right) - T\,dx\theta_y + T\,dx\left(\theta_y + \frac{\partial \theta_y}{\partial y}dy\right) + p\,dx\,dy = \rho\,dx\,dy\frac{\partial^2 w}{\partial t^2}, \quad (4.1.1)$$

where ρ is the mass density per unit area of the membrane and the angles θ_x, θ_y are given by $\partial w/\partial x$, $\partial w/\partial y$. We note that small deflections have been assumed in making the approximations $\sin\theta_x \simeq \theta_x$, etc. in (4.1.1) and in approximating the area of the deflected element by $dx\,dy$. Equation (4.1.1) then rather directly reduces to

$$T\left(\frac{\partial^2 w}{\partial x^2} + \frac{\partial^2 w}{\partial y^2}\right) + p(x, y, t) = \rho\frac{\partial^2 w}{\partial t^2}. \quad (4.1.2)$$

Since the Laplacian operator in rectangular coordinates is defined by

$$\nabla^2 = \partial^2/\partial x^2 + \partial^2/\partial y^2,$$

we may write

$$T\nabla^2 w(x, y, t) + p(x, y, t) = \rho\frac{\partial^2 w(x, y, t)}{\partial t^2}, \quad (4.1.3)$$

as the governing equation for the membrane. This is the two-dimensional form of the wave equation.

Many wave-motion problems in membranes are best expressed in terms of polar coordinates due to axisymmetric loading, circular boundaries, or both. It is possible to re-derive the governing equation from equilibrium principles applied to a differential element in the polar coordinates r, θ,† or to employ a coordinate transformation on (4.1.3). Foregoing both, we merely present the results as

$$T\nabla^2 w(r,\theta,t)+p(r,\theta,t)=\rho\frac{\partial^2 w(r,\theta,t)}{\partial t^2}, \tag{4.1.4}$$

where ∇^2 is the Laplacian in polar coordinates, defined as

$$\nabla=\frac{1}{r}\frac{\partial}{\partial r}\left(r\frac{\partial}{\partial r}\right)+\frac{1}{r^2}\frac{\partial^2}{\partial\theta^2}=\frac{\partial^2}{\partial r^2}+\frac{1}{r}\frac{\partial}{\partial r}+\frac{1}{r^2}\frac{\partial^2}{\partial\theta^2}. \tag{4.1.5}$$

4.1.2. *Plane waves*

The study of the basic propagation characteristics of one-dimensional systems involved investigating the propagation of harmonic waves in the x direction. The analogue of this in two dimensions is to investigate the propagation of *plane waves*. Such waves are propagating disturbances in two or three dimensions, where the motion of every particle in the planes perpendicular to the direction of propagation is the same. A propagating two-dimensional plane disturbance is illustrated in Fig. 4.2. For such a disturbance,

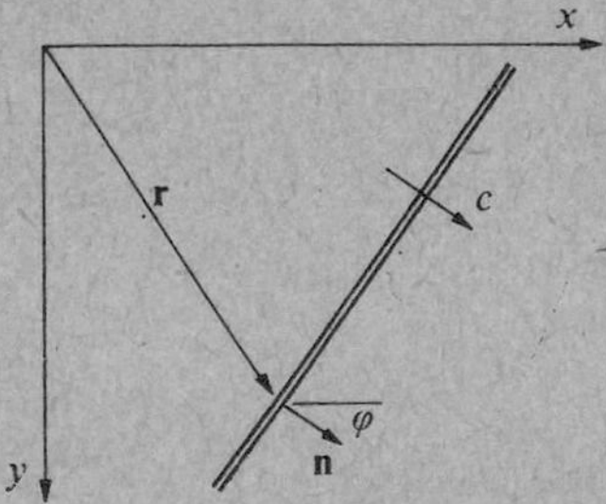

FIG. 4.2. A propagating plane disturbance in two dimensions.

the motion of every particle along the line ('plane') defined by

$$\mathbf{n}\cdot\mathbf{r}-ct=\text{constant} \tag{4.1.6}$$

will be the same. The propagation velocity of the plane is c and $\mathbf{n}$ is the normal to the plane. The position of an arbitrary point on the plane is defined by $\mathbf{r}$, where $\mathbf{n}$ and $\mathbf{r}$ are given by

$$\mathbf{n}=l\mathbf{i}+m\mathbf{j}=\cos\phi\mathbf{i}+\sin\phi\mathbf{j},\quad \mathbf{r}=x\mathbf{i}+y\mathbf{j}. \tag{4.1.7}$$

† See Problem 4.1.

Consider, then, the propagation of plane harmonic waves in a membrane. We ask 'under what conditions can waves of the type

$$w = Ae^{i\gamma(lx+my-ct)} \tag{4.1.8}$$

exist in the membrane?' We substitute (4.1.8) in the governing equation (4.1.3) with $p(x, y, t) = 0$ and obtain

$$T(-\gamma^2 l^2-\gamma^2 m^2)Ae^{i\gamma(lx+my-ct)} = -\rho\gamma^2 c^2 Ae^{i\gamma(lx+my-ct)}. \tag{4.1.9}$$

This reduces to

$$T\gamma^2(l^2+m^2) = \rho\gamma^2 c^2. \tag{4.1.10}$$

Since $l^2+m^2 = 1$, we have that

$$c^2 = T/\rho, \quad c = \sqrt{(T/\rho)}. \tag{4.1.11}$$

Thus we have that the propagation velocity of plane harmonic waves of any frequency is constant.

The preceding result may be generalized to a planar disturbance of arbitrary form, such as

$$w = f(\mathbf{n}\cdot\mathbf{r}-ct) = f(lx+my-ct). \tag{4.1.12}$$

Defining the argument of the function as ψ, we have

$$\begin{gathered}\frac{\partial w}{\partial x} = \frac{\partial w}{\partial \psi}\frac{\partial \psi}{\partial x} = lw', \\ \frac{\partial^2 w}{\partial x^2} = \frac{\partial}{\partial \psi}(lw')\frac{\partial \psi}{\partial x} = l^2 w'', \\ \frac{\partial^2 w}{\partial y^2} = m^2 w'', \qquad \frac{\partial^2 w}{\partial t^2} = c^2 w''.\end{gathered} \tag{4.1.13}$$

Thus from (4.1.3) with $p = 0$ we have

$$T(l^2+m^2)w'' = \rho c^2 w'', \tag{4.1.14}$$

which leads to the previous result that $c = \sqrt{(T/\rho)}$. Thus we conclude that it is possible for a plane disturbance of arbitrary shape to propagate without distortion in the membrane. These results are possibly not surprising in view of the effective one-dimensionalization that occurs in considering propagation in a single direction.

We now briefly consider the membrane equation in polar form (4.1.4), with $p = 0$. The natural question to raise is whether waves having a circular wave-front can exist in a membrane. Allowing polar symmetry, so that $\partial/\partial\theta = 0$, the equation to be considered is

$$\frac{\partial^2 w}{\partial r^2}+\frac{1}{r}\frac{\partial w}{\partial r} = \frac{1}{c_0^2}\frac{\partial^2 w}{\partial t^2}. \tag{4.1.15}$$

It may be quickly established that a circular wave of the form $\exp\{i(\gamma r-\omega t)\}$ will not satisfy this equation. This should not be surprising since a circular wave, moving either inward or outward, would be expected to have an amplitude that would depend on distance merely from conservation of energy considerations. However, it may be established that a solution of the form $f(r)\exp\{i(\gamma r-\omega t)\}$ will not work either. Evidently, a circular waveform will not maintain its shape in a membrane as a planar waveform does. This aspect will be remarked upon further in the next section.

4.1.3. *The initial-value problem*

We shall first consider the case of axisymmetric motion of a membrane, so that the governing equation is given by (4.4.15) and the initial conditions are

$$w(r,0)=f(r), \qquad \partial w(r,0)/\partial t = g(r). \tag{4.1.16}$$

Now, in problems involving polar or cylindrical coordinates, it is the Hankel transform that finds application. For the case at hand, we employ the zeroth-order transform given by†

$$\bar{w}(\xi,t)=\int_0^\infty rw(r,t)J_0(\xi r)\,dr. \tag{4.1.17}$$

The Hankel transform of the polar Laplacian yields a particularly simple form, giving

$$H\left(\frac{\partial^2 w}{\partial r^2}+\frac{1}{r}\frac{\partial w}{\partial r}\right)=-\xi^2\bar{w}(\xi,t). \tag{4.1.18}$$

Thus, the Hankel transform of (4.1.15) gives

$$\frac{d^2\bar{w}}{dt^2}+c_0^2\xi^2\bar{w}=0, \tag{4.1.19}$$

which has the solution

$$\bar{w}(\xi,t)=A\cos c_0\xi t+B\sin c_0\xi t. \tag{4.1.20}$$

The transformed initial conditions (4.1.16) are

$$\bar{w}(\xi,0)=\bar{f}(\xi), \qquad \frac{\partial\bar{w}(\xi,0)}{\partial t}=\bar{g}(\xi). \tag{4.1.21}$$

Applying the solution (4.1.20) to these conditions gives the result

$$\bar{w}(\xi,t)=\bar{f}(\xi)\cos c_0\xi t+\frac{\bar{g}(\xi)}{c_0\xi}\sin c_0\xi t. \tag{4.1.22}$$

† See Appendix B.4 for brief remarks. See Chapter 2 and pp. 125–8 of Reference [16] for treatment of this problem.

Taking the inverse Hankel transform, we have

$$w(r,t)=\int_0^\infty \xi \bar{f}(\xi)\cos c_0\xi t J_0(\xi r)\,\mathrm{d}\xi+\frac{1}{c_0}\int_0^\infty \bar{g}(\xi)\sin c_0\xi t J_0(\xi r)\,\mathrm{d}\xi. \quad (4.1.23)$$

It is possible to carry the solution one step further and use a convolution-type integral to express the result. However, the generality of such an expression is not always of help in solving a particular problem, so we shall leave the solution in the preceding form.

As an example, consider a problem where the initial velocity is zero and the displacement is defined by

$$w(r,0)=\begin{cases}1/\pi a^2, & r<a\\ 0, & r>a.\end{cases} \quad (4.1.24)$$

This results in a cylindrical membrane shape having a volume of unity. The Hankel transform of this expression is given by (see Appendix B.4)

$$\bar{w}(\xi,0)=\frac{1}{\pi a}\frac{J_1(a\xi)}{\xi}. \quad (4.1.25)$$

Now let $a\to 0$ in this result. We have for small values of argument that $J_1(z)\to z/2$, so that

$$\bar{w}(\xi,0)\big|_{a\to 0}=\frac{1}{2\pi}. \quad (4.1.26)$$

The resulting solution is given by

$$w(r,t)=\frac{1}{2\pi}\int_0^\infty \xi\cos c_0\xi t J_0(\xi r)\,\mathrm{d}\xi. \quad (4.1.27)$$

By expressing this in the form

$$w(r,t)=\frac{1}{2\pi c_0}\frac{\partial}{\partial t}\int_0^\infty \sin c_0\xi t J_0(\xi r)\,\mathrm{d}\xi \quad (4.1.28)$$

results available in tables of Hankel transforms are readily applied.† The results are

$$w(r,t)=\begin{cases}\dfrac{1}{2\pi c_0 r^{\frac{1}{2}}}\dfrac{\partial}{\partial t}\dfrac{1}{(c_0^2t^2-r^2)^{\frac{1}{2}}}, & 0<r<c_0t\\ 0, & c_0t<r<\infty.\end{cases} \quad (4.1.29)$$

Upon carrying out the differentiation, we obtain

$$w(r,t)=\begin{cases}-\dfrac{1}{2\pi}\dfrac{c_0t}{r^{\frac{1}{2}}(c_0^2t^2-r^2)^{\frac{3}{2}}}, & 0<r<c_0t\\ 0, & c_0t<r<\infty.\end{cases} \quad (4.1.30)$$

† p. 528 of Reference [16].

In interpreting this result, we see that a clearly defined wavefront exists, propagating at the velocity c_0. In this respect, the response is similar to that which would exist in a string. However, it is seen that after the wavefront has passed, the disturbance persists. This differs from the string response to the analogous impulse displacement. In that case, a sharp 'spike' would propagate outward at c_0, but the medium behind the wave would be at rest once the front passed. The membrane response exhibits what is frequently referred to as a *tail* or *wake* in the response. The response of the membrane at various instants of time is shown in Fig. 4.3. Also shown is the string response to the analogous

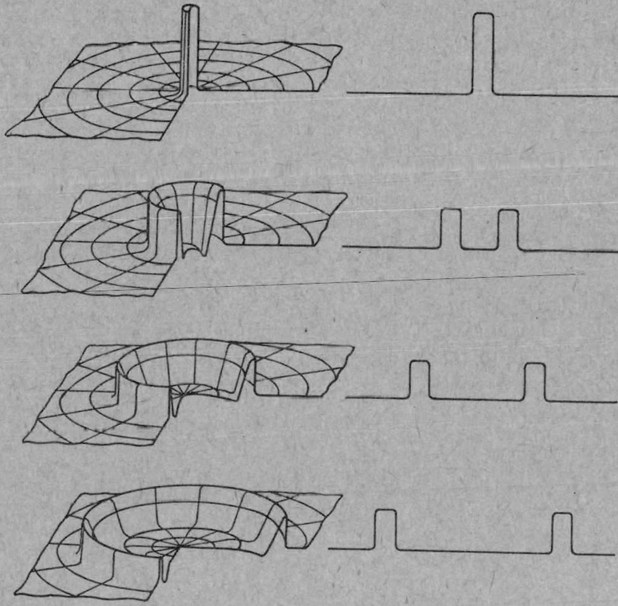

FIG. 4.3. Response of the membrane to an initially imposed displacement field and the string response to the analogous initial condition. (After Morse [12, Fig. 40].)

initial displacement.

Consider, as a next example, the case where the initial displacement is zero and the velocity is prescribed by

$$\frac{\partial w(r, 0)}{\partial t} = \begin{cases} 1/\pi a^2, & r < a \\ 0, & r > a. \end{cases} \tag{4.1.31}$$

This corresponds to a constant velocity imparted over a circular region. The Hankel transform of this expression has been given by (4.1.25) and is

$$\frac{\partial \bar{w}(r, 0)}{\partial t} = \frac{1}{\pi a} \frac{J_1(a\xi)}{\xi}. \tag{4.1.32}$$

As $a \to 0$, we again have that

$$\left.\frac{\partial \bar{w}(r, 0)}{\partial t}\right|_{a \to 0} = \frac{1}{2\pi}. \tag{4.1.33}$$

The solution (4.1.23) reduces to

$$w(r, t) = \frac{1}{2\pi c_0} \int_0^\infty \sin c_0 \xi t J_0(\xi r)\, d\xi. \tag{4.1.34}$$

The evaluation of this integral is contained in the result (4.1.29) and is

$$w(r, t) = \begin{cases} \dfrac{1}{2\pi c_0} \dfrac{1}{(c_0^2 t^2 - r^2)^{\frac{1}{2}}}, & 0 < r < c_0 t \\ 0, & c_0 t < r < \infty. \end{cases} \tag{4.1.35}$$

The response of the membrane to the velocity input is shown in Fig. 4.4. The

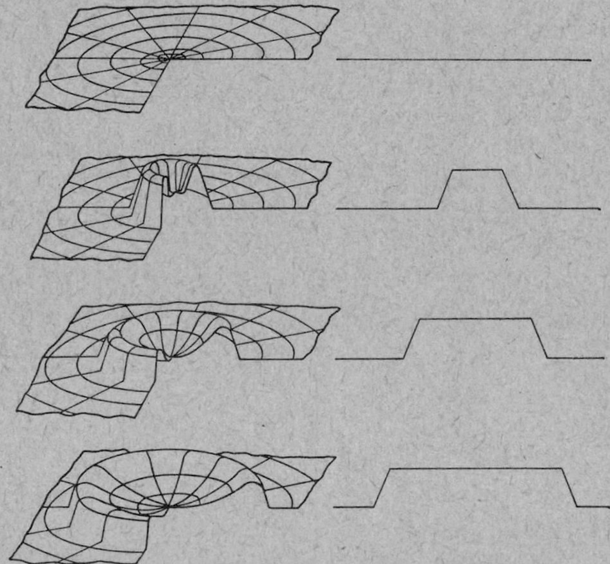

FIG. 4.4. Response of a membrane to a velocity impulse and of a string to the analogous input. (After Morse [12, Fig. 41].)

string response to the analogous input is again shown. The presence of a clearly defined wavefront and a wake to the disturbance are again to be noted in the membrane response.

4.1.4. *Forced vibration of a membrane*

Let us now consider the wave motion in a membrane resulting from a harmonically varying load acting within a circle of radius a at the origin. We may view this problem in terms of the inhomogeneous equation (4.1.4) with a prescribed loading or, alternatively, consider the homogeneous governing equation with a prescribed forcing function at $r = a$. Since our usual viewpoint in such problems has been the former, we shall adopt the latter procedure here for a change.

To establish the condition at $r = a$, we presume the load to be given by

$$p(r, t) = \begin{cases} p_0 e^{-i\omega t}, & r < a \\ 0, & r > a. \end{cases} \tag{4.1.36}$$

This will lead to a total force $\pi a^2 p_0 \exp(-i\omega t)$ acting on the circle $r < a$. This must be balanced by the vertical component of membrane force acting on the periphery of the circle $r = a$. The resulting force balance equation is given by

$$\pi a^2 p_0 e^{-i\omega t} = -2\pi a T \frac{\partial w(a, t)}{\partial r}. \tag{4.1.37}$$

Assuming a solution of the form $w(r, t) = W(r)\exp(-i\omega t)$, the boundary condition takes the form

$$dW(a)/dr = -p_0 a/2T, \tag{4.1.38}$$

and the governing equation is given by

$$\frac{d^2 W}{dr^2} + \frac{1}{r}\frac{dW}{dr} + \frac{\omega^2}{c_0^2} W = 0. \tag{4.1.39}$$

We recognize (4.1.39) as Bessel's equation having the solution

$$W(r) = AH_0^{(1)}(\beta r) + BH_0^{(2)}(\beta r), \qquad \beta = \omega/c_0. \tag{4.1.40}$$

We have encountered this equation and solution form previously in conjunction with longitudinal waves in tapered horns (§ 2.5). Using the arguments developed in that section on proper selection of the Hankel function to meet the radiation condition, we set $B = 0$. Applying the condition (4.1.38), and again using results presented in the section on horns in regard to differentiation of the Hankel function, we are led to the solution

$$w(r, t) = \frac{p_0 a}{2\beta T} \frac{H_0^{(1)}(\beta r)}{H_1^{(1)}(\beta a)} e^{-i\omega t}. \tag{4.1.41}$$

Far from the region of load application, we have the response given by

$$w(r, t) \sim \frac{p_0 a}{\sqrt{(2\pi)}\beta^{\frac{1}{2}} T H_1^{(1)}(\beta a)} \frac{1}{\sqrt{r}} e^{i(\beta r - \omega t - \pi/4)}. \tag{4.1.42}$$

We note that the $r^{-\frac{1}{2}}$ amplitude dependence is the same as observed in the analysis of the initial-value problem.

4.1.5. *Reflection of waves from membrane boundaries*

The reflection of waves from the boundaries of a membrane has a new element over that of wave reflection in one-dimensional systems. In the latter systems, the direction of the incident wave on a boundary was not a variable in the process. In a two-dimensional system, the direction is a variable, since the angle of the normal of the wavefront may take on any orientation relative to the boundary.

To illustrate the basic aspects of reflection, consider a semi-infinite membrane $y \geq 0$, that is fixed along the boundary $y = 0$. The boundary condition is thus

$$w(x, 0, t) = 0. \tag{4.1.43}$$

We now wish to consider harmonic plane waves propagating in the membrane. Thus, we seek harmonic plane-wave solutions to

$$\nabla^2 w(x, y, t) = \frac{1}{c_0^2}\frac{\partial^2 w}{\partial t^2}(x, y, t). \tag{4.1.44}$$

Although we could build our analysis from the expression (4.1.8) this matter of plane-wave solutions to the system governing equation arises frequently enough in future work to trace the steps in some detail here.

Considering a separation of variables solution to the homogeneous form of (4.1.2),

$$w = X(x)Y(y)e^{-i\omega t}, \tag{4.1.45}$$

we obtain

$$\left(\frac{X''}{X}+\frac{Y''}{Y}\right) = -\frac{\omega^2}{c_0^2} = -\beta^2. \tag{4.1.46}$$

Writing this as

$$\frac{X''}{X} = -\left(\frac{Y''}{Y}+\beta^2\right) = -\xi^2, \tag{4.1.47}$$

we obtain the solutions

$$X = A_1 e^{i\xi x}+A_2 e^{-i\xi x}, \qquad Y = B_1 e^{i\zeta y}+B_2 e^{-i\zeta y}, \tag{4.1.48}$$

where

$$\zeta^2 = \beta^2-\xi^2. \tag{4.1.49}$$

Upon multiplying the results in (4.1.48) together, substituting in (4.1.45), and defining new constants A, B, C, D we obtain four plane-wave solutions

$$w = Ae^{i(\xi x-\zeta y-\omega t)}+Be^{i(\xi x+\zeta y-\omega t)}+Ce^{-i(\xi x-\zeta y+\omega t)}+De^{-i(\xi x+\zeta y+\omega t)}. \tag{4.1.50}$$

Each of these expressions corresponds to a plane wave of particular orientation and direction of propagation as illustrated in Fig. 4.5. We then proceed somewhat in the manner of wave-reflection studies in one-dimension. An incident wave is specified. In the present case, we let this be the first plane wave of (4.1.50). We then set $C = D = 0$ because they correspond to waves having a leftward direction of propagation. Thus we are reduced to considering

$$w = Ae^{i(\xi x-\zeta y-\omega t)}+Be^{i(\xi x+\zeta y-\omega t)}. \tag{4.1.51}$$

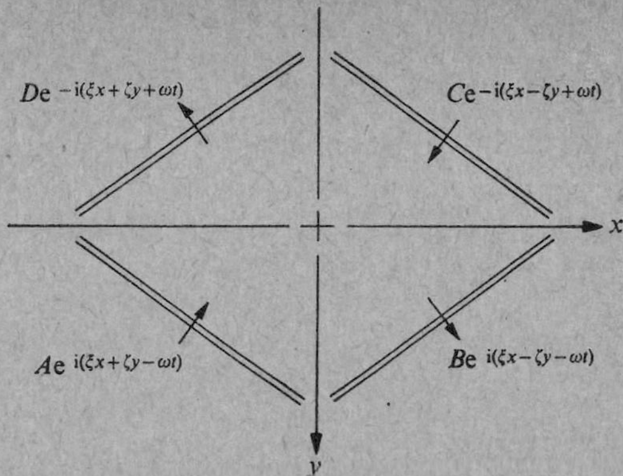

FIG. 4.5. Orientations and propagation directions of various plane waves.

Referring back to (4.1.8), we see that the plane wave was expressed in terms of the direction cosines and the propagation velocity. This can be done in the present case by defining

$$\xi = \gamma l = \gamma \cos \phi, \quad \zeta = \gamma m = \gamma \sin \phi, \tag{4.1.52}$$

where ϕ is the angle between the wave normal and the positive x-axis (see Fig. 4.2). Then (4.1.51) becomes

$$w = Ae^{i\gamma(lx-my-ct)} + Be^{i\gamma(lx+my-ct)}. \tag{4.1.53}$$

Alternatively, ξ and ζ are sometimes expressed in the form

$$\xi = \gamma l' = \gamma \sin \phi', \quad \zeta = \gamma m' = \gamma \cos \phi', \tag{4.1.54}$$

where ϕ' is the angle between the normal and the positive y-axis. The angle of incidence of a wave on an edge is then measured relative to the perpendicular, which is the usual convention in reflection–refraction studies.

To proceed to the reflection problem at hand, we now have solutions to the governing equation in the form (4.1.51) and the boundary conditions for the semi-infinite membrane given by (4.1.43). Substituting in the latter, we obtain

$$(A+B)e^{i(\xi x-\omega t)} = 0 \tag{4.1.55}$$

or

$$B/A = -1. \tag{4.1.56}$$

Thus the amplitude of the reflected wave is equal to that of the incident wave and out of phase by 180° relative to the incident wave. This aspect is shown in Fig. 4.6. The angle of incidence and reflection are, of course, equal. A second aspect of the reflection phenomenon for this problem is brought out by substituting (4.1.56) back in the solution (4.1.51), giving

$$w = A(e^{-i\zeta y} - e^{i\zeta y})e^{i(\xi x-\omega t)} = -2iA \sin \zeta y e^{i(\xi x-\omega t)}. \tag{4.1.57}$$

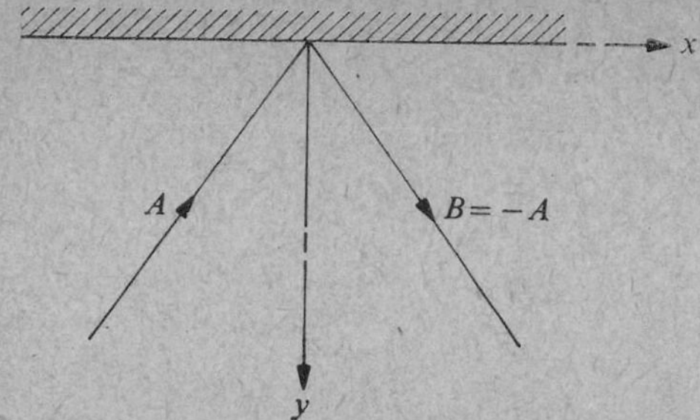

FIG. 4.6. Incident and reflected waves from a fixed membrane boundary.

The y variation in this result predicts a series of equally spaced, horizontal 'interference' bands. In between the bands, waves are propagating in the x direction.

It would be possible to speak at some length about wave reflection in membranes by considering a variety of boundary conditions. However, the fixed-edge membrane represents the most realistic situation. Furthermore, many of the considerations would tend to overlap those that will arise in Chapter 6 on plane waves in an elastic half-space.

4.1.6. *Waves in a membrane strip*

Consider now a membrane strip, bounded by parallel planes at $y = 0$ and $y = b$ and extending to infinity in the positive and negative x directions. We wish to consider the conditions for the propagation of harmonic waves in the x direction. The governing equation for the problem is again the homogeneous form of (4.1.3) with the boundary conditions

$$w(x, 0, t) = w(x, b, t) = 0. \tag{4.1.58}$$

Without repeating the separation of variables steps, we immediately consider a solution of the form

$$w(x, y, t) = Y(y)\mathrm{e}^{\mathrm{i}(\xi x-\omega t)}. \tag{4.1.59}$$

Substitution in the governing equation yields

$$\frac{\mathrm{d}^2Y}{\mathrm{d}y^2}+\zeta^2Y = 0, \qquad \zeta^2 = \beta^2-\xi^2, \tag{4.1.60}$$

which is the same form previously encountered in considering plane waves. We write the solution of (4.1.60) as

$$Y = A\sin\zeta y + B\cos\zeta y. \tag{4.1.61}$$

The boundary conditions (4.1.58) in terms of $Y(y)$ are simply that

$$Y(0) = Y(b) = 0.$$

This gives $B = 0$ and

$$\sin \zeta b = 0, \quad \zeta b = n\pi \qquad (n = 1, 2, \ldots). \tag{4.1.62}$$

In terms of the frequency and wavenumber parameters ω and ξ, this can be expressed as

$$\omega^2 = c_0^2(\xi^2 + n^2\pi^2/b^2), \qquad (n = 1, 2, \ldots). \tag{4.1.63}$$

The interpretation of this result is as follows: for a given frequency ω and integer n, (4.1.63) may be solved for the wavenumber ξ. The resulting wavelength λ and phase velocity c of the wave are given by $\lambda = 2\pi/\xi$, $c = \omega/\xi$. These establish the parameters of the propagating harmonic disturbance in the strip. The value of n determines the y variation of the motion. Figure 4.7

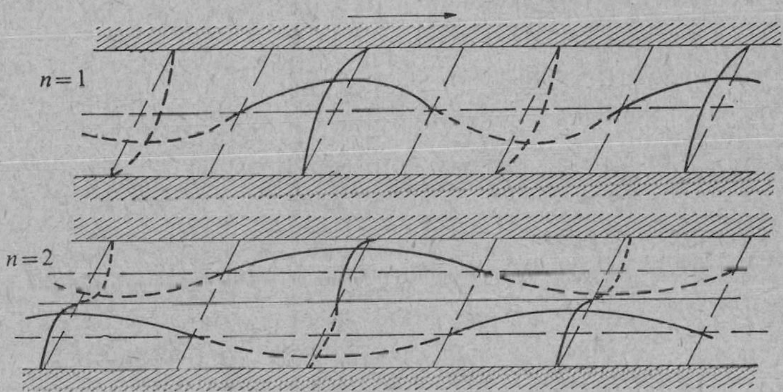

FIG. 4.7. Waves in a membrane strip for two values of n.

illustrates the situation for $n = 1, 2$. We note from (4.1.63) that, for a given frequency, the wavelength will be longer for larger values of n. This may best be seen by writing the result in the form

$$\xi^2 = \frac{\omega^2}{c_0^2} - \frac{n^2\pi^2}{b^2}. \tag{4.1.64}$$

This form also points out the fact that for a given value of n, there will be a frequency such that $\xi = 0$, and below which $\xi \to \pm i\xi$. The former will correspond to cutoff frequencies for a given mode of propagation and the latter will correspond to non-propagating behaviour.

Numerous other problems of waves in semi-infinite strips, transient motion of strips, and so on could be considered here. Again, these problems will have analogues in the area of waves in plates, and will be treated there.

4.1.7. *Vibrations of finite membranes*

Parallelling our considerations of wave motion in one-dimensional systems, we now consider the vibrations of membranes of finite size. While there is generally no difficulty in considering the vibrations of one-dimensional systems of arbitrary length, analysis of the vibrations of two-dimensional systems of arbitrary shape is generally not possible except by approximate means. Considerations must generally be restricted to simple membrane shapes conveniently described by coordinate surfaces. Hence we consider only rectangular and circular membrane shapes.

In the case of a rectangular membrane, we seek solutions to the homogeneous form of (4.1.3), subject to the boundary conditions

$$w(x, 0, t) = w(x, b, t) = w(0, y, t) = w(a, y, t) = 0. \tag{4.1.65}$$

This represents a membrane of length a, breadth b, and fixed along all edges. We consider a solution of the form

$$w = X(x)Y(y)(A \cos \omega t + B \sin \omega t). \tag{4.1.66}$$

We now express the solutions as

$$X = A_1 \sin \xi x + A_2 \cos \xi x, \tag{4.1.67}$$

$$Y = B_1 \sin \zeta y + B_2 \cos \zeta y,$$

where, as before,

$$\zeta^2 = \beta^2 - \xi^2, \qquad \beta^2 = \omega^2/c_0^2. \tag{4.1.68}$$

The boundary conditions (4.1.65) are equivalent to

$$Y(0) = Y(b) = X(0) = X(a) = 0.$$

These lead to $A_2 = B_2 = 0$ and

$$\sin \xi a = 0, \quad \sin \zeta b = 0, \tag{4.1.69}$$

or

$$\xi a = n\pi, \quad \xi_n = n\pi/a \quad (n = 1, 2, ...), \tag{4.1.70}$$

$$\zeta b = m\pi, \quad \zeta_m = m\pi/b \quad (m = 1, 2, ...). \tag{4.1.71}$$

For a given value of n, m, the vibrational frequency is given from (4.1.68) as

$$\omega_{mn}^2 = c_0^2(\xi_n^2 + \zeta_m^2) = \pi^2 c_0^2\left(\frac{n^2}{a^2} + \frac{m^2}{b^2}\right). \tag{4.1.72}$$

The general solution is then constructed from the particular solutions by superposition. Thus

$$w = \sum_{n=1}^{\infty} \sum_{m=1}^{\infty} (A_{mn} \cos \omega_{mn} t + B_{mn} \sin \omega_{mn} t) W_{mn}, \tag{4.1.73}$$

where W_{mn} are the normal modes, given here by

$$W_{mn} = \sin \xi_n x \sin \zeta_m y. \tag{4.1.74}$$

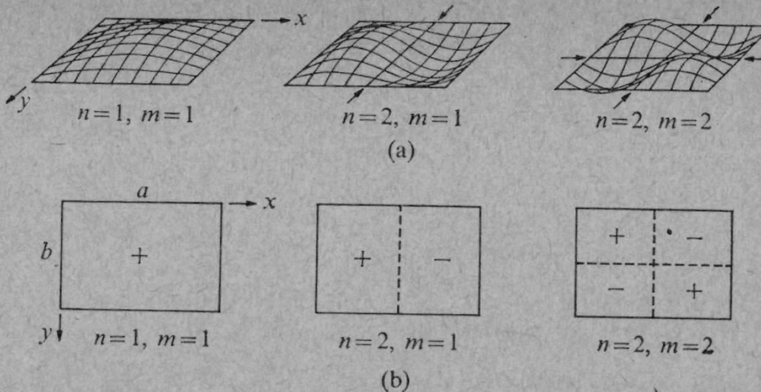

FIG. 4.8. (a) Graphic illustration of the normal modes of a membrane for $n = m = 1$, $n = 2, m = 1$, and $n = m = 2$ (based on Morse [12], Fig. 36); (b) schematic illustration of the same modes.

The mode shapes for $n = m = 1, n = 2, m = 1$, and $n = m = 2$ are shown in Fig. 4.8(a). This graphic illustration gives a clear picture of the deformation. A diagrammatic means of illustrating the same modes is shown in Fig. 4.8(b).

Let us determine the natural frequencies and normal modes of a circular membrane. The governing equation is (4.1.4), with $p(r, \theta, t) = 0$, and the boundary conditions are

$$w(a, \theta, t) = 0. \tag{4.1.75}$$

We consider a solution of the form

$$w(r, \theta, t) = R(r)\Theta(\theta)(A \cos \omega t + B \sin \omega t), \tag{4.1.76}$$

which leads to

$$\frac{R''}{R} + \frac{1}{r}\frac{R'}{R} + \beta^2 = -\frac{\Theta''}{\Theta} = \gamma^2, \qquad \beta^2 = \omega^2/c_0^2. \tag{4.1.77}$$

For Θ we have

$$\Theta = A_1 \cos \gamma\theta + A_2 \sin \gamma\theta. \tag{4.1.78}$$

Now, the condition of continuity of membrane displacement requires that $w(r, \theta, t) = w(r, \theta + 2\pi, t)$. This imposes a periodicity condition on (4.1.78) that can only be met by γ being an integer n.

The governing equation for R is now given by

$$R'' + \frac{1}{r}R' + \left(\beta^2 - \frac{n^2}{r^2}\right)R = 0. \tag{4.1.79}$$

This is Bessel's equation of order n having the solution

$$R = B_1 J_n(\beta r) + B_2 Y_n(\beta r), \tag{4.1.80}$$

where J_n, Y_n are the Bessel functions of first and second kind. Now the functions $Y_n(\beta r)$ approach infinity at the origin, so for a complete membrane, we must set $B_2 = 0$. The boundary condition (4.1.75) is given in terms of R as

$R(a) = 0$. From (4.1.80) this gives the resulting frequency equation

$$J_n(\beta a) = 0. \tag{4.1.81}$$

For a given value of the integer n, there will be a series of roots corresponding to the zeros of $J_0(\beta a)$, $J_1(\beta a)$, $J_2(\beta a)$, etc. Some of the results are†

$$\begin{aligned} n &= 0,\ J_0(\beta a) = 0: \\ &\beta a = 2{\cdot}405,\ 5{\cdot}520,\ 8{\cdot}654,\ 11{\cdot}792,\ 14{\cdot}931,\ \dots, \\ n &= 1,\ J_1(\beta a) = 0: \\ &\beta a = 3{\cdot}832,\ 7{\cdot}016,\ 10{\cdot}173,\ 13{\cdot}324,\ 16{\cdot}471,\ \dots, \\ n &= 2,\ J_2(\beta a) = 0: \\ &\beta a = 5{\cdot}136,\ 8{\cdot}417,\ 11{\cdot}620,\ 14{\cdot}796,\ 17{\cdot}960,\ \dots, \\ n &= 3,\ J_3(\beta a) = 0: \\ &\beta a = 6{\cdot}380,\ 9{\cdot}761,\ 13{\cdot}015,\ 16{\cdot}223,\ 19{\cdot}409,\ \dots . \end{aligned} \tag{4.1.82}$$

It should be noted that $\beta a = 0$ is a root for all Bessel functions of order $n \geq 1$. However, this leads to trivial solutions for w and is excluded. The resulting natural frequencies are expressed as

$$\omega_{nm} = \beta_{nm} c_0, \qquad (n = 0, 1, \dots, m = 1, 2, \dots), \tag{4.1.83}$$

where the β_{nm} are assigned as follows: For a given value of n, $m = 1$ corresponds to the first root of J_n, $m = 2$ is the second root, and so forth. As examples

$$\omega_{01} = 2{\cdot}405(c_0/a), \quad \omega_{12} = 7{\cdot}016(c_0/a), \quad \omega_{34} = 16{\cdot}233(c_0/a), \dots . \tag{4.1.84}$$

The resulting general form of the solution becomes rather complicated, since it combines various combinations of J_n, $\sin n\theta$, $\cos n\theta$, $\cos \omega_{nm}t$, $\sin \omega_{nm}t$. It is given by

$$w(r, \theta, t) = \sum_{m=1}^{\infty} \left\{ \sum_{n=0}^{\infty} W_{nm}(A_{nm} \cos \omega_{nm}t + B_{nm} \sin \omega_{nm}t) + \right.$$
$$\left. + \sum_{n=1}^{\infty} \tilde{W}_{nm}(\tilde{A}_{nm} \cos \omega_{nm}t + \tilde{B}_{nm} \sin \omega_{nm}t) \right\}, \tag{4.1.85}$$

where the normal modes are

$$W_{nm} = J_n(\beta_{nm}r)\cos n\theta, \quad \tilde{W}_{nm} = J_n(\beta_{nm}r)\sin n\theta. \tag{4.1.86}$$

For given values of n and m ($n \neq 0$) the normal modes W_{nm}, $\tilde{W}_{nm}$ have the same shape, differing from one another only by an angular rotation of 90°. Several of the modes W_{nm} are shown in Fig. 4.9 both in graphic and diagrammatic form for several values of n and m.

We shall not investigate orthogonality or free and forced motion problems of the finite membrane. These matters will be studied in the more general case

† p. 409 of Reference [1].

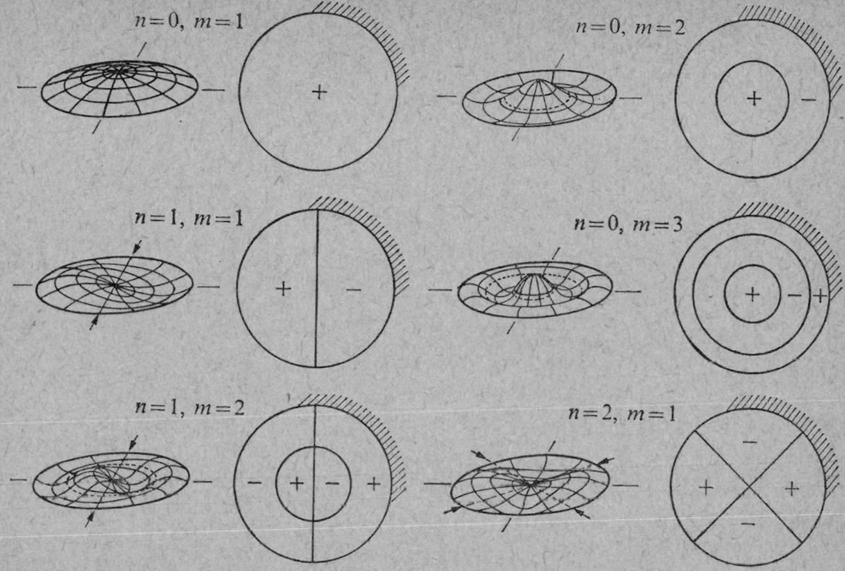

FIG. 4.9. First few normal modes of a circular membrane illustrated in graphic and schematic form. (Based, in part, on Morse [12, Fig. 42].)

of plate vibrations in the next section. Procedures developed for the plate case then easily may be modified to the simpler membrane case.

4.2. Flexural waves in thin plates

The plate is the two-dimensional analogue of the beam. We thus are considering the motion of a two-dimensional elastic system where bending moments and transverse shear forces are active, as they are in a beam. The basic kinematics of the classical theory of thin plates is the same as that of Bernoulli–Euler beams. Once the governing equations for the plate are established, the propagation of plane waves, the initial-value problem, a transient-loading problem, and wave reflection will be studied. Free and forced vibrations of finite plates will also be considered.

4.2.1. *The governing equations*

Consider a plate of thickness h and of infinite extent having its undeflected surface in the x, y-plane, as shown in Fig. 4.10(a). Consider also a differential element $h\,dx\,dy$ of the plate, also shown in Fig. 4.10(a) and in Fig. 4.10(b) where, in the latter figure, the various shear forces, bending and twisting moments, and external loads are shown acting. The bending moments per unit length M_x, M_y arise from distributions of normal stresses σ_x, σ_y, while the twisting moments per unit length M_{xy}, M_{yx} (shown as double-arrow vectors) arise from shearing stresses τ_{xy}, τ_{yx}. The shear forces per unit length Q_x, Q_y

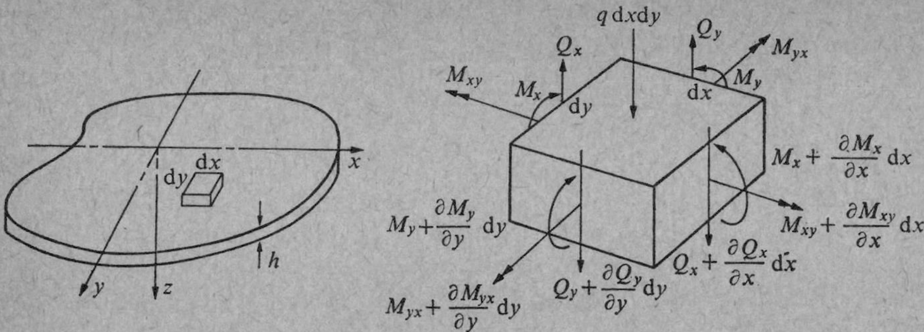

FIG. 4.10. (a) Region of a thin plate, and (b) an element of that plate subjected to forces and moments.

arise from shearing stresses τ_{xz}, τ_{yz}. There are three force equations of motion to be applied, but only that in the z direction is non-trivial. Of the three moment equations of motion, that about the z-axis is identically zero. The remaining three equations of motion give

$$-Q_x\,dy+\left(Q_x+\frac{\partial Q_x}{\partial x}\,dx\right)dy-Q_y\,dx+\left(Q_y+\frac{\partial Q_y}{\partial y}\,dy\right)dx+ \\ +q\,dx\,dy=\rho h\,dx\,dy\frac{\partial^2 w}{\partial t^2}, \quad (4.2.1)$$

$$\left(M_y+\frac{\partial M_y}{\partial y}\,dy\right)dx-M_y\,dx+M_{xy}\,dy-\left(M_{xy}+\frac{\partial M_{xy}}{\partial x}\,dx\right)dy- \\ -Q\;dx\,dy=0, \quad (4.2.2)$$

$$\left(M_x+\frac{\partial M_x}{\partial x}\,dx\right)dy-M_x\,dy+\left(M_{yx}+\frac{\partial M_{yx}}{\partial y}\,dy\right)dx-M_{yx}\,dx- \\ -Q_x\,dy\,dx=0 \quad (4.2.3)$$

The displacement $w(x, y, t)$ appearing in (4.2.1) measures the deflection of the middle plane of the plate. This will be brought out more clearly in describing the kinematics of the plate. It should be noted that rotary-inertia effects have been neglected in the moment equations (4.2.2) and (4.2.3). Higher-order contributions to the moments from the loading q have also been neglected in these equations. Cancelling terms, the equations of motion reduce to

$$\frac{\partial Q_x}{\partial x}+\frac{\partial Q_y}{\partial y}+q=\rho h\frac{\partial^2 w}{\partial t^2}, \quad (4.2.4)$$

$$\frac{\partial M_y}{\partial y}-\frac{\partial M_{xy}}{\partial x}-Q_y=0, \quad (4.2.5)$$

$$\frac{\partial M_x}{\partial x}+\frac{\partial M_{yx}}{\partial y}-Q_x=0. \quad (4.2.6)$$

Solving the last two equations for Q_x, Q_y and substituting in the first equation gives a single equation in terms of the various moments,

$$\frac{\partial^2 M_x}{\partial x^2}+\frac{\partial^2 M_{yx}}{\partial x\,\partial y}-\frac{\partial^2 M_{xy}}{\partial y\,\partial x}+\frac{\partial^2 M_y}{\partial x^2}+q=\rho h\frac{\partial^2 w}{\partial t^2}. \tag{4.2.7}$$

The relationships between the moments and the deflection must now be established.

As in the case of the beam, the kinematics of the deformation must now be introduced. Of course the situation is now more complicated owing to the two-dimensional aspects. In Fig. 4.11, the major kinematical aspects of plate

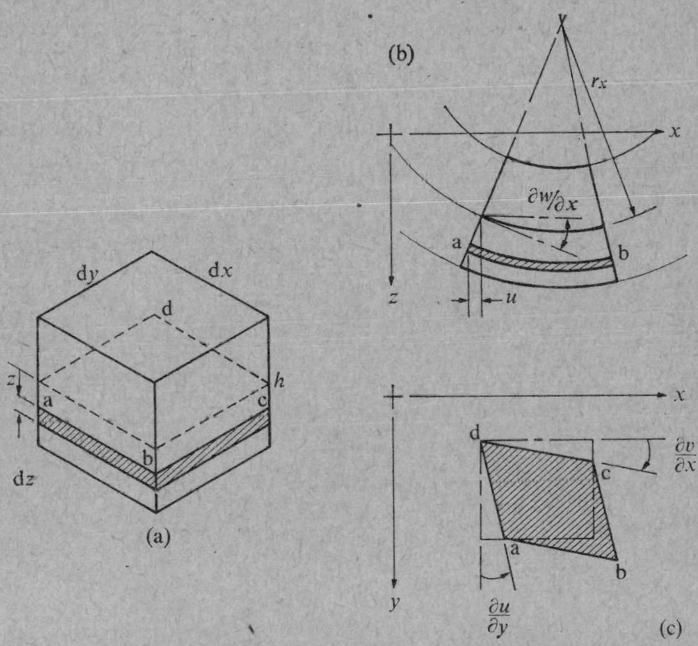

FIG. 4.11. (a) Differential element of plate with a typical lamina abcd shown shaded; (b) a side view of the element during bending; (c) a top view of the lamina showing shear deformation.

deformation that are required for our development are presented. A typical lamina (abcd) of a differential element of plate is shown in Fig. 4.11(a). The lamina is located at a distance z below the mid plane of the plate. When the element is subjected to pure bending, it is assumed to deform as shown in Fig. 4.11(b). It is assumed that plane sections remain plane and perpendicular to the mid plane, just as in the Bernoulli–Euler beam development. A behaviour similar to that shown in the above also holds in the y, z-plane. It follows that the normal strains in the lamina are given by

$$\varepsilon_x = z/r_x, \qquad \varepsilon_y = z/r_y, \tag{4.2.8}$$

where r_x, r_y are the radii of curvature in the x, z- and y, z-planes. If small deflections and slopes are assumed, the curvatures may be approximated by $-\partial^2 w/\partial x^2$, $-\partial^2 w/\partial y^2$, so that (4.2.8) becomes

$$\varepsilon_x = -z\frac{\partial^2 w}{\partial x^2}, \qquad \varepsilon_y = -z\frac{\partial^2 w}{\partial y^2}. \tag{4.2.9}$$

Now, in Fig. 4.11(c), the lamina is shown in a sheared configuration (extensional strains are not shown in this representation). The rotations of the sides are given by $\partial u/\partial y$ and $\partial v/\partial x$, where u and v are the displacement components of a particle in the x and y directions. The shear strain in the lamina is then given by†

$$\gamma_{xy} = \frac{\partial u}{\partial y}+\frac{\partial v}{\partial x}. \tag{4.2.10}$$

Referring back to Fig. 4.11(b), it is seen that the displacement component u is given by $u = -z\,\partial w/\partial x$. Similarly, $v = -z\,\partial w/\partial y$, so that γ_{xy} becomes

$$\gamma_{xy} = -2z\frac{\partial^2 w}{\partial x\,\partial y}. \tag{4.2.11}$$

The stresses are given from the general Hooke's law as

$$\sigma_x = \frac{E}{1-\nu^2}(\varepsilon_x+\nu\varepsilon_y) = -\frac{Ez}{1-\nu^2}\left(\frac{\partial^2 w}{\partial x^2}+\nu\frac{\partial^2 w}{\partial y^2}\right), \tag{4.2.12}$$

$$\sigma_y = \frac{E}{1-\nu^2}(\varepsilon_y+\nu\varepsilon_x) = -\frac{Ez}{1-\nu^2}\left(\frac{\partial^2 w}{\partial y^2}+\nu\frac{\partial^2 w}{\partial x^2}\right), \tag{4.2.13}$$

$$\tau_{xy} = G\gamma_{xy} = -2Gz\frac{\partial^2 w}{\partial x\,\partial y}. \tag{4.2.14}$$

The expressions for the bending and twisting moments may now be found. Thus, consider the face of the element in Fig. 4.10(a) defined by $h\,dy$. The bending moment on that face due to σ_x will be

$$M_x\,dy = \int_{-h/2}^{h/2} z\sigma_x\,dy\,dz, \tag{4.2.15}$$

or

$$M_x = \int_{-h/2}^{h/2} z\sigma_x\,dz. \tag{4.2.16}$$

Substituting (4.2.12) in (4.2.16) and carrying out the integration gives

$$M_x = -D\left(\frac{\partial^2 w}{\partial x^2}+\nu\frac{\partial^2 w}{\partial y^2}\right), \tag{4.2.17}$$

† The engineering definition of shear strain is used here. The mathematical elasticity definition of

$$\gamma_{xy} = \frac{1}{2}\left(\frac{\partial u}{\partial x}+\frac{\partial v}{\partial y}\right)$$

is used from Chapter 5 onward.

where

$$D = Eh^3/12(1-\nu^2). \tag{4.2.18}$$

Similarly, for M_y we obtain

$$M_y = -D\left(\frac{\partial^2 w}{\partial y^2}+\nu\frac{\partial^2 w}{\partial x^2}\right). \tag{4.2.19}$$

For M_{xy}, the integral is

$$M_{xy} = -\int_{-h/2}^{h/2} z\tau_{xy}\, dz. \tag{4.2.20}$$

The negative sign in (4.2.20) is to bring the resulting twisting moment caused by positive shear stress into accord with the convention displayed in Fig. 4.10(b). We obtain, upon substituting (4.2.14) into (4.2.20),

$$M_{xy} = D(1-\nu)\frac{\partial^2 w}{\partial x\,\partial y}. \tag{4.2.21}$$

Furthermore, we have that $M_{xy} = -M_{yx}$. Then, substituting (4.2.17), (4.2.19), and (4.2.21) in (4.2.7), we obtain

$$D\left(\frac{\partial^4 w}{\partial x^4}+2\frac{\partial^4 w}{\partial x^2\,\partial y^2}+\frac{\partial^4 w}{\partial y^4}\right)-q = -\rho h\frac{\partial^2 w}{\partial t^2}. \tag{4.2.22}$$

The expression in parenthesis may be written as

$$\frac{\partial^4 w}{\partial x^4}+2\frac{\partial^4 w}{\partial x^2\,\partial y^2}+\frac{\partial^4 w}{\partial y^4} = \left(\frac{\partial^2}{\partial x^2}+\frac{\partial^2}{\partial y^2}\right)\left(\frac{\partial^2 w}{\partial x^2}+\frac{\partial^2 w}{\partial y^2}\right) = \nabla^2\nabla^2 w. \tag{4.2.23}$$

The Laplacian of the Laplacian is designated as the biharmonic operator ∇^4. The governing equation for the motion of a thin plate is then

$$D\nabla^4 w(x, y, t)+\rho h\frac{\partial^2 w(x, y, t)}{\partial t^2} = q(x, y, t). \tag{4.2.24}$$

In terms of polar coordinates, this is given by

$$D\nabla^4 w(r, \theta, t)+\rho h\frac{\partial^2 w(r, \theta, t)}{\partial t^2} = q(r, \theta, t), \tag{4.2.25}$$

where $\nabla^4 w$ is again given by $\nabla^2\nabla^2 w$ and ∇^2 is the Laplacian in polar coordinates. The various bending and twisting moments are given, in polar coordinates, as

$$M_r = -D\left\{\frac{\partial^2 w}{\partial r^2}+\nu\left(\frac{1}{r}\frac{\partial w}{\partial r}+\frac{1}{r^2}\frac{\partial^2 w}{\partial \theta^2}\right)\right\}, \tag{4.2.26}$$

$$M_\theta = -D\left\{\frac{1}{r}\frac{\partial w}{\partial r}+\frac{1}{r^2}\frac{\partial^2 w}{\partial \theta^2}+\nu\frac{\partial^2 w}{\partial r^2}\right\}, \tag{4.2.27}$$

$$M_{r\theta} = (1-\nu)D\left(\frac{1}{r}\frac{\partial^2 w}{\partial r\,\partial\theta}-\frac{1}{r^2}\frac{\partial w}{\partial\theta}\right). \tag{4.2.28}$$

4.2.2. *Boundary conditions for a plate*

Although our immediate analyses will concern waves in infinite plates, it is relevant to consider the matter of boundary conditions at this stage. By analogy with beams, there are three simple types of plate boundaries; simply supported, fixed, and free. The mathematical statements for the first two conditions, in terms of rectangular coordinates and for an edge located at $x = x_0$, are as follows.

1. Edge simply supported at $x = x_0$. Then

$$w = M_x = 0, \tag{4.2.29}$$

or, in terms of deflections,

$$w = \frac{\partial^2 w}{\partial x^2} + \nu \frac{\partial^2 w}{\partial y^2} = 0. \tag{4.2.30}$$

2. Clamped edge at $x = x_0$. Then

$$w = \frac{\partial w}{\partial x} = 0. \tag{4.2.31}$$

The case of the free edge is not so straightforward. Since we have three plate stresses M_x, M_{xy}, Q_x to consider, it would seem that these three quantities must vanish, implying three conditions at the boundary. However, in 1850 it was shown by Kirchhoff that M_{xy}, Q_x combine to give a single condition. The development of the free edge condition can proceed by the following argument.† The equilibrium of the plate is not changed if the net twisting couple $M_{xy}\,dy$, shown in Fig. 4.12(a) is replaced by two forces, as shown in Fig. 4.12(b). There is a local perturbation in the stress field but this is assumed to rapidly decay out. If adjacent sections of the edge are considered, the situation is as shown in Fig. 4.12(c). Again replacing these couples by forces, the situation is as shown in Fig. 4.12(d). Summing forces on the shaded element, we have a net force of $(\partial M_{xy}/\partial y)\,dy$ in the upward direction. The free edge condition requires that the net vertical force be zero. Thus, introducing the quantity V_x, we have

$$V_x = Q_x - (\partial M_{xy}/\partial y) = 0. \tag{4.2.32}$$

Thus, at a free edge $x = x_0$, the boundary conditions are $V_x = M_x = 0$ or, in terms of displacements,

$$\frac{\partial^2 w}{\partial x^2} + \nu \frac{\partial^2 w}{\partial y^2} = \frac{\partial^3 w}{\partial x^3} + (2-\nu)\frac{\partial^3 w}{\partial x\,\partial y^2} = 0. \tag{4.2.33}$$

It is of interest to consider the source of this somewhat peculiar, and certainly not self-evident, condition of a free edge of a plate. The general state of stress that may exist at a point consists of the six stresses σ_x, σ_y, σ_z, τ_{xy}

† Timoshenko and Woinowsky-Krieger [17, pp. 83–4].

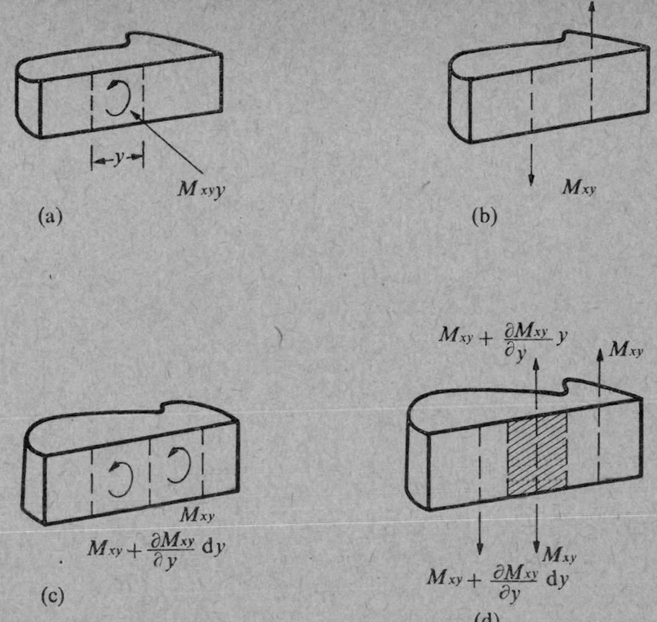

FIG. 4.12. The steps in developing the free edge boundary condition for a plate.

τ_{yz}, τ_{zx}. However, in thin plate theory it is assumed that $\sigma_z = 0$, while σ_x, σ_y, τ_{xy} are non-zero. However, τ_{zx}, τ_{zy} have not been brought into the analysis as yet, although it is obvious they must be non-zero so as to support vertical plate loads. It must be recalled, however, that plane sections have been assumed to remain plane. This implies that $\gamma_{zy}, \gamma_{zx} = 0$ on a typical element, since non-zero shearing strains here would yield warping of the section. Of course, this aspect has been discussed previously in conjunction with beam theory. But zero strains indicate an infinite shear rigidity. Thus, although shearing stresses are present, we are unable to determine the details of the stress distribution. The anomalous boundary condition thus has its source in a mathematical model accounting for only part of the total deformation a plate may undergo.

4.2.3. *Plane waves in an infinite plate*

It should be evident, upon drawing the parallel with simple beam theory, that waves will propagate dispersively. Let us investigate the conditions under which harmonic plane waves may propagate. Thus consider a plane wave of the form

$$w = Ae^{i\gamma(\mathbf{n}\cdot\mathbf{r}-ct)}, \tag{4.2.34}$$

where r is the position vector to a point on the plane of the wave and n is the normal to that plane and, as in the membrane investigation of the same problem,

$$\mathbf{r} = x\mathbf{i}+y\mathbf{j}, \qquad \mathbf{n} = l\mathbf{i}+m\mathbf{j}. \tag{4.2.35}$$

Letting the external load q be zero and substituting in the differential equation, we obtain for the various terms

$$\nabla^2 w = -A(l^2+m^2)\gamma^2 e^{i\gamma(\mathbf{n}.\mathbf{r}-ct)},$$
$$= -A\gamma^2 e^{i\gamma(\mathbf{n}.\mathbf{r}-ct)}, \tag{4.2.36}$$

$$\nabla^4 w = A\gamma^4 e^{i\gamma(\mathbf{n}.\mathbf{r}-ct)}, \tag{4.2.37}$$

$$\frac{\partial^2 w}{\partial t^2} = -A\gamma^2 c^2 e^{i\gamma(\mathbf{n}.\mathbf{r}-ct)}. \tag{4.2.38}$$

The resulting dispersion relation is given by

$$D\gamma^2-\rho hc^2 = 0, \qquad c = \sqrt{\left(\frac{D}{\rho h}\right)}\gamma. \tag{4.2.39}$$

This linear relationship between phase velocity and wavenumber is similar to that of Bernoulli–Euler beam theory. It predicts unbounded wave velocity for very short-wavelength, high-frequency conditions. This physically unacceptable situation is, as in beams, a consequence of an imperfect mathematical model in which effects of shear and rotary inertia have been neglected; just as in beam theory there are available higher-order theories of plate vibration which incorporate these effects. Finally, we note the frequency–wavenumber expression follows directly from (4.2.39) through the relation $\omega = \gamma c$, and is given by

$$\omega = \sqrt{\left(\frac{D}{\rho h}\right)}\gamma^2. \tag{4.2.40}$$

4.2.4. *An initial-value problem*

An initial-value problem in plate vibrations will be considered first, in which the case of axisymmetric vibrations will be discussed. The biharmonic equation in polar coordinates will be the governing equation, with $\partial^2/\partial\theta^2 = 0$ in the Laplacian. Then, in the absence of external loads, we have

$$D\left(\frac{\partial^2}{\partial r^2}+\frac{1}{r}\frac{\partial}{\partial r}\right)^2 w+\rho h\frac{\partial^2 w}{\partial t^2} = 0. \tag{4.2.41}$$

Assume the initial conditions

$$w(r,0) = f(r), \qquad \dot{w}(r,0) = 0. \tag{4.2.42}$$

To apply integral transforms to the present problem, the Hankel transform, which was used in the preceding section on axisymmetric membrane problems will again be used here. The zero-order Hankel transform

$$\bar{w}(\xi) = \int_0^\infty rw(r)J_0(\xi r)\,\mathrm{d}r, \tag{4.2.43}$$

with inverse

$$w(r) = \int_0^\infty \xi\bar{w}(\xi)J_0(\xi r)\,\mathrm{d}\xi, \tag{4.2.44}$$

will be relevant. In applying this transform to the biharmonic operator ∇^4 in polar coordinates, we recall the particularly simple result arising from the transform of the Laplacian in the previous membrane studies. In the case of the biharmonic, the result is†

$$H(\nabla^4 w) = \xi^4\bar{w}(\xi, t). \tag{4.2.45}$$

Then, upon taking the Hankel transform of (4.2.41), we obtain

$$D\xi^4\bar{w}+\rho h\frac{\partial^2\bar{w}}{\partial t^2} = 0. \tag{4.2.46}$$

Defining $b^2 = D/\rho h$, we thus have the transformed ordinary differential equation

$$\frac{\partial^2\bar{w}}{\partial t^2}+b^2\xi^4\bar{w} = 0. \tag{4.2.47}$$

This has the solution

$$\bar{w}(\xi, t) = A\cos b\xi^2 t+B\sin b\xi^2 t. \tag{4.2.48}$$

The Hankel transforms of the initial conditions (4.2.42) are

$$\bar{w}(\xi, 0) = \bar{f}(\xi), \qquad \partial\bar{w}(\xi, 0)/\partial t = 0. \tag{4.2.49}$$

Applying the initial conditions to the solution gives

$$A = \bar{f}(\xi), \qquad B = 0. \tag{4.2.50}$$

The transformed solution may thus be expressed in the form

$$\bar{w}(\xi, t) = \cos b\xi^2 t\int_0^\infty uf(u)J_0(\xi u)\,\mathrm{d}u, \tag{4.2.51}$$

where the integral representation of $\bar{f}(\xi)$ has been used and the dummy variable u employed.

By the Hankel inversion theorem, we have

$$\begin{aligned} w(r, t) &= \int_0^\infty \xi\bar{w}(\xi, t)J_0(\xi r)\,\mathrm{d}\xi, \\ &= \int_0^\infty \xi J_0(\xi r)\cos b\xi^2 t\,\mathrm{d}\xi\int_0^\infty uf(u)J_0(u\xi)\,\mathrm{d}u, \end{aligned} \tag{4.2.52}$$

† See Appendix B.4.

or, interchanging the order of integration,

$$w(r, t) = \int_0^\infty uf(u)\,du \int_0^\infty \xi J_0(\xi r)J_0(\xi u)\cos b\xi^2 t\,d\xi. \tag{4.2.53}$$

In order to complete the evaluation of this problem, a particular integral, known as 'Weber's second exponential integral' must be used. This is the known result that†

$$\int_0^\infty \xi J_0(\xi u)J_0(\xi r)\exp(-p\xi^2)\,d\xi = \frac{1}{2p}\exp\left\{-\frac{u^2+r^2}{4p}\right\}I_0\left(\frac{ur}{2p}\right), \tag{4.2.54}$$

where I_0 is the modified Bessel function of the first kind defined as

$$I_0(z) = J_0(\mathrm{i}z). \tag{4.2.55}$$

Letting $p = -ibt$ in the above and equating the real parts gives

$$\int_0^\infty \xi J_0(\xi u)J_0(\xi r)\cos b\xi^2 t\,d\xi = \frac{1}{2bt}J_0\left(\frac{ur}{2bt}\right)\sin\left(\frac{u^2+r^2}{4bt}\right). \tag{4.2.56}$$

Hence our solution is

$$w(r, t) = \frac{1}{2bt}\int_0^\infty uf(u)J_0\left(\frac{ur}{2bt}\right)\sin\left(\frac{u^2+r^2}{4bt}\right)du. \tag{4.2.57}$$

Consider the specific initial waveform

$$f(r) = f_0\exp(-r^2/a^2), \tag{4.2.58}$$

where f_0 is a constant. Instead of using the above result directly, we reconsider the transformed solution (4.2.51) and write

$$\bar{w}(\xi, t) = f_0\cos b\xi^2 t\int_0^\infty u\exp(-u^2/a^2)J_0(\xi u)\,du. \tag{4.2.59}$$

The integral in the above has the value‡

$$\frac{a^2}{2}\exp\left(-\frac{\xi^2 a^2}{4}\right), \tag{4.2.60}$$

so that

$$\bar{w}(\xi, t) = \frac{f_0 a^2}{2}\cos b\xi^2 t\exp\left(-\frac{\xi^2 a^2}{4}\right). \tag{4.2.61}$$

† p. 393 of Reference [19].
‡ See Appendix B.5.

Hence, applying the Hankel inversion to the above gives

$$w(r, t) = \frac{f_0 a^2}{2} \int_0^\infty \xi \exp\left(-\frac{\xi^2 a^2}{4}\right) \cos b\xi^2 t J_0(\xi r)\, d\xi. \tag{4.2.62}$$

Fortunately, this integral form has also been evaluated. It is known as the confluent hypergeometric function,† and yields the result

$$w(r, t) = \frac{f_0}{1+\tau^2} \exp\left(-\frac{\rho^2}{1+\tau^2}\right)\left\{\cos\left(\frac{\rho^2 \tau}{1+\tau^2}\right) + \tau \sin\left(\frac{\rho^2 \tau}{1+\tau^2}\right)\right\}, \tag{4.2.63}$$

where

$$\tau = 4bt/a^2, \qquad \rho = r/a. \tag{4.2.64}$$

A plot of w/f_0 for various values of non-dimensionalized time is shown in Fig. 4.13.

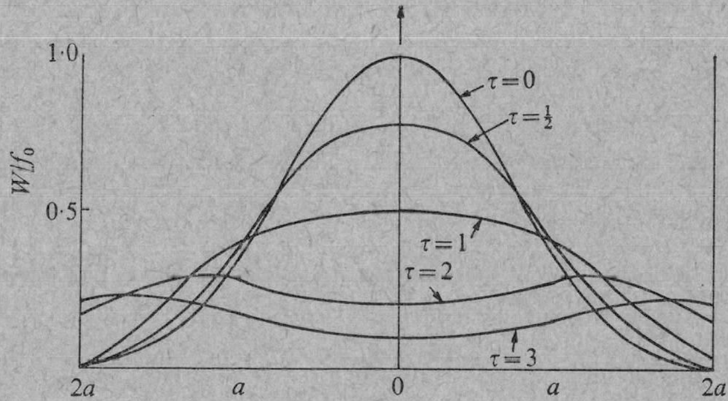

FIG. 4.13. Wave motion in a plate released from an initial displacement. (After Sneddon [16, Fig. 14].)

We will not investigate the plate motion under more severe initial conditions, such as impulse displacements or velocities. Drawing on our experience in beam theory, we would expect certain anomalies in the results, such as instantaneous response at remote locations.

4.2.5. *Forced motion of an infinite plate*

We now wish to consider an infinite plate subjected to a transient loading. Axisymmetric conditions will again be assumed. The analysis is based on the work of Medick [10].‡ The governing equation of motion for the problem is

† pp. 513–14 of Reference [16].

‡ Reference [10] derives a portion of its analytical basis from the treatment by Sneddon [16, pp. 139–47]. It contains equally important experimental studies which will be cited later in this chapter.

given by

$$D\nabla^4 w(r, t) + \rho h \frac{\partial^2 w(r, t)}{\partial t^2} = q(r, t), \tag{4.2.65}$$

with the homogeneous initial conditions

$$w(r, 0) = \dot{w}(r, 0) = 0 \tag{4.2.66}$$

being assumed. If we define the loading in the rather general form

$$q(r, t) = 8b\rho h f(r)\psi'(t), \tag{4.2.67}$$

where $b^2 = D/\rho h$ and $f(r)$ and $\psi'(t)$ describe the spatial and time variation of the loading respectively, then the equation of motion may be written as

$$b^2\nabla^4 w + \frac{\partial^2 w}{\partial t^2} = 8bf(r)\psi'(t). \tag{4.2.68}$$

The Hankel and Laplace transforms will be used. Applying the former, we obtain

$$\frac{\partial^2 \bar{w}(\xi, t)}{\partial t^2} + b^2\xi^4 \bar{w}(\xi, t) = 8b\bar{f}(\xi)\psi'(t). \tag{4.2.69}$$

The Laplace transformation gives

$$s^2\overline{W}(\xi, s) + b^2\xi^4\overline{W}(\xi, s) = 8bs\bar{f}(\xi)\bar{\psi}(s), \tag{4.2.70}$$

so that the transformed solution is given by

$$\overline{W}(\xi, s) = \frac{8bs\bar{f}(\xi)\bar{\psi}(s)}{s^2 + b^2\xi^4}. \tag{4.2.71}$$

We first apply the Laplace inversion to (4.2.71). Noting that

$$\mathscr{L}^{-1}\left(\frac{s}{s^2 + b^2\xi^4}\right) = \cos b\xi^2 t, \tag{4.2.72}$$

then the Laplace inversion is

$$\bar{w}(\xi, t) = 8b\bar{f}(\xi)\int_0^t \psi(u)\cos b\xi^2(t-u)\,du. \tag{4.2.73}$$

Taking the Hankel inversion, we have

$$w(r, t) = 8b\int_0^\infty \xi J_0(\xi r)\bar{f}(\xi)\int_0^t \psi(u)\cos b\xi^2(t-u)\,du\,d\xi. \tag{4.2.74}$$

Rearranging terms slightly gives us the formal solution for $w(r, t)$ in terms of arbitrary $f(r)$, $\psi(t)$. Thus

$$w(r, t) = 8b\int_0^t \psi(u)\,du\int_0^\infty \xi\bar{f}(\xi)J_0(\xi r)\cos b\xi^2(t-u)\,d\xi. \tag{4.2.75}$$

The above solution may be further refined by putting it in the form

$$w(r, t) = 8b \int_0^t \psi(u)\, du \int_0^\infty vf(v)\, dv \int_0^\infty \xi J_0(\xi r) J_0(\xi v) \cos b\xi^2(t-u)\, d\xi, \quad (4.2.76)$$

where $\bar{f}(\xi)$ has been expressed as

$$\bar{f}(\xi) = \int_0^\infty vf(v) J_0(\xi v)\, dv, \quad (4.2.77)$$

and the terms rearranged slightly. Using Weber's second exponential integral (see (4.2.54)), we have that

$$\int_0^\infty \xi J_0(\xi r) J_0(\xi v) \cos b\xi^2(t-u)\, d\xi$$

$$= \frac{1}{2b(t-u)} J_0\left(\frac{vr}{2b(t-u)}\right) \sin \frac{v^2+r^2}{4b(t-u)}. \quad (4.2.78)$$

Then the solution becomes

$$w(r, t) = 4 \int_0^t \frac{\psi(u)}{t-u}\, du \int_0^\infty vf(v) J_0\left(\frac{vr}{2b(t-u)}\right) \sin\left\{\frac{v^2+r^2}{4b(t-u)}\right\} dv. \quad (4.2.79)$$

The total magnitude of the force acting at the origin will be considered as $8b\rho h$. The form of $f(r)$ so that the load is at the origin is determined by noting that $f(r) = 0$, $r \neq 0$, and that

$$\int_0^\infty 2\pi r f(r)\, dr = 1. \quad (4.2.80)$$

Thus $f(r) = \delta(r)/2\pi r$ will give the case of a concentrated force at the origin. The solution (4.2.79) then reduces to

$$w(r, t) = \frac{2}{\pi} \int_0^t \frac{\psi(u)}{t-u} \sin\left\{\frac{r^2}{4b(t-u)}\right\} du. \quad (4.2.81)$$

Although we are ultimately interested in the plate response to a pulse load acting at the origin, by considering a slightly different case the desired results can be more efficiently obtained. Let

$$\psi'(t) = H\langle t\rangle, \quad (4.2.82)$$

which is the Heaviside function. Then $\psi(t) = tH\langle t\rangle$, and the solution is then expressible as

$$w(r, t) = \frac{2}{\pi} \int_0^t \frac{u}{t-u} \sin\left\{\frac{r^2}{4b(t-u)}\right\} du. \quad (4.2.83)$$

To evaluate this integral, we introduce the change of variable

$$z = r^2/4b(t-u). \tag{4.2.84}$$

Noting that

$$u = 0, \qquad z = r^2/4bt; \qquad u = t,\ z = \infty, \tag{4.2.85}$$

the solution may be written as

$$w(r, t) = \frac{2}{\pi}\int\limits_{r^2/4bt}^{\infty}\left(t-\frac{r^2}{4bz}\right)\frac{\sin z}{z}\,dz. \tag{4.2.86}$$

We now introduce a second change of variables, given by $x = r^2/4bt$. Then (4.2.86) may be written as

$$w(r, t) = \frac{2}{\pi}\int\limits_{x}^{\infty}\left(t-\frac{xt}{z}\right)\frac{\sin z}{z}\,dz = \frac{2}{\pi}I, \tag{4.2.87}$$

where I is defined as

$$I = t\int\limits_{x}^{\infty}\frac{\sin z}{z}\,dz - xt\int\limits_{x}^{\infty}\frac{\sin z}{z^2}\,dz. \tag{4.2.88}$$

We now introduce the sine and cosine integrals defined as†

$$\mathrm{Si}(x) = \int\limits_{0}^{x}\frac{\sin z}{z}\,dz, \qquad \mathrm{Ci}(x) = \int\limits_{\infty}^{x}\frac{\cos z}{z}\,dz. \tag{4.2.89}$$

Then I may be written as

$$I = t\left(\int\limits_{0}^{\infty}\frac{\sin z}{z}\,dz - \int\limits_{0}^{x}\frac{\sin z}{z}\,dz\right) - xt\left(-\frac{\sin z}{z}\bigg|_{x}^{\infty} + \int\limits_{x}^{\infty}\frac{\cos z}{z}\,dz\right). \tag{4.2.90}$$

Now‡

$$\int\limits_{0}^{\infty}\frac{\sin z}{z}\,dz = \frac{\pi}{2} \tag{4.2.91}$$

so that I becomes

$$I = t\{\pi/2 - \mathrm{Si}(x) - \sin x + x\mathrm{Ci}(x)\} = tH(x), \tag{4.2.92}$$

where the definition of $H(x)$ is obvious. Then recalling that $x = r^2/4bt$, we have for $w(r, t)$

$$w(r, t) = \frac{2}{\pi}tH\left(\frac{r^2}{4bt}\right). \tag{4.2.93}$$

† pp. 231–3 of Reference [1].
‡ op. cit., p. 232.

Finally, we recall that $8b\rho h$ represents the total load, so that if P represents this value we have $P/4b\rho h = 2$, and $w(r, t)$ may be written as

$$w(r, t) = \frac{P}{4\pi b\rho h} tH\left(\frac{r^2}{4bt}\right), \tag{4.2.94}$$

where, from (4.2.92),

$$H\left(\frac{r^2}{4bt}\right) = \frac{\pi}{2} - \mathrm{Si}\left(\frac{r^2}{4bt}\right) - \sin\frac{r^2}{4bt} + \frac{r^2}{4bt}\,\mathrm{Ci}\left(\frac{r^2}{4bt}\right). \tag{4.2.95}$$

This, then, represents the response of the plate to a step load at the origin.

Other loadings may be found rather easily. Thus the response to a rectangular pulse of duration β is directly found by superposition. Thus

$$w(r, t) = \frac{P}{4\pi b\rho h}\left\{tH\left(\frac{r^2}{4bt}\right) - (t-\beta)H\left(\frac{r^2}{4b(t-\beta)}\right)\right\}. \tag{4.2.96}$$

The case of an impulse load may also be obtained. Although in theory the response to an impulse load may be found by differentiating the response to a step loading, the rather complicated form of the step solution makes it advantageous to reconsider the solution as given by (4.2.81). Thus, for an impulse loading,

$$\psi'(t) = \delta(t), \qquad \psi(t) = H\langle t\rangle, \tag{4.2.97}$$

so that

$$w(r, t) = \frac{2}{\pi}\int_0^t \frac{1}{t-u}\sin\left\{\frac{r^2}{4b(t-u)}\right\} du. \tag{4.2.98}$$

The previously used change of variables puts this in the form

$$w(r, t) = \frac{2}{\pi}\int_{r^2/4bt}^{\infty} \frac{1}{r^2/4bz}\,\frac{\sin z}{4bz^2/r^2}\,dz = \frac{2}{\pi}\int_{r^2/4bt}^{\infty}\frac{\sin z}{z}\,dz \tag{4.2.99}$$

or

$$w(r, t) = \frac{2}{\pi}\left(\int_0^{\infty}\frac{\sin z}{z}\,dz - \int_0^{r^2/4bt}\frac{\sin z}{z}\,dz\right). \tag{4.2.100}$$

Then

$$w(r, t) = \frac{P}{4\pi b\rho h}\left\{\frac{\pi}{2} - \mathrm{Si}\left(\frac{r^2}{4bt}\right)\right\} \tag{4.2.101}$$

represents the response to an impulse load.

Some of the theoretical results obtained by Medick for the motion of the plate are shown in Fig. 4.14. The displacement $w(r, t)$ has been non-dimensionalized as

$$\bar{w}(r, t) = \frac{w(r, t)}{(I/4\pi)\sqrt{(\rho h D)}}, \qquad I = P\beta, \tag{4.2.102}$$

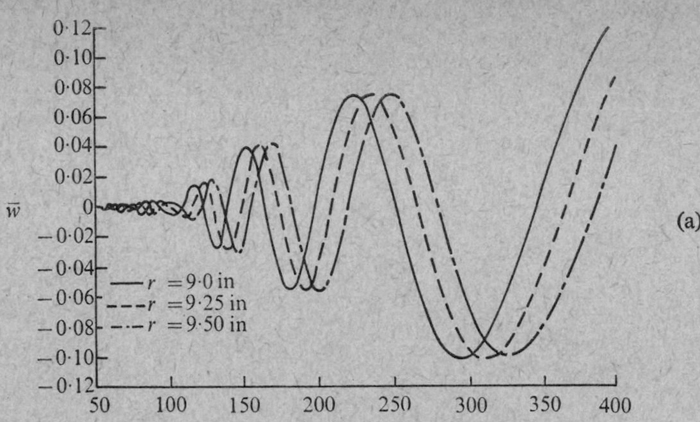

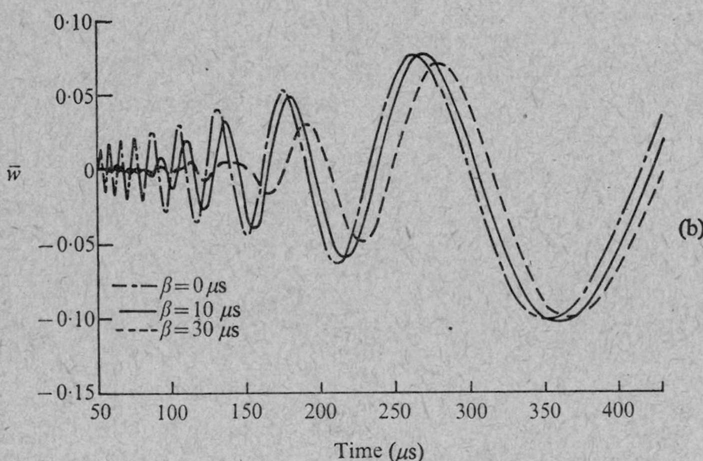

FIG. 4.14. (a) Displacement as a function of time at different locations for a given impulse, and (b) the response as a function of time at a given location for various impulse durations. (After Medick [10].)

where I is the total impulse transmitted to the plate. Precursors at every location are predicted for $t > 0$, but the scale of the drawings would not show significant amplitudes for most cases. However, in Fig. 4.14(b), the impulse response ($\beta = 0$) has been plotted, and this clearly shows high-frequency precursors of significant amplitude even for small time. It should be noted, again referring to Fig. 4.14(b), that for later times the response to impulses of varying duration do not significantly differ. Thus, as in the case of Bernoulli–Euler beam theory, classical plate theory gives poorest results for short time.

4.2.6. *Reflection of plane waves from boundaries*

We wish to study reflection phenomena in plates by considering plane waves to be incident on the straight boundary of a semi-infinite plate $y > 0$. Only plates as governed by the conditions of simply supported, clamped, and free edge boundaries will be considered. Our starting point is the homogeneous form of eqn (4.2.24). Without repeating the laborious separation of variables procedure presented for the analogous situation in membranes, we straightway consider a solution of the form

$$w = f(y)e^{i(\xi x-\omega t)}. \tag{4.2.103}$$

This represents a wave system moving in the positive x direction. Substituting in (4.2.24) gives

$$\xi^4 f(y)-2\xi^2\frac{d^2f(y)}{dy^2}+\frac{d^4f(y)}{dy^4}-\frac{\rho h}{D}\omega^2 f(y) = 0 \tag{4.2.104}$$

or

$$\frac{d^4f}{dy^4}-2\xi^2\frac{d^2f}{dy^2}-\left(\frac{\rho h}{D}\omega^2-\xi^4\right)f = 0. \tag{4.2.105}$$

Introducing the definitions

$$\beta^4 = \omega^2/a^2, \qquad a^2 = D/\rho h, \qquad \eta^4 = \beta^4-\xi^4, \tag{4.2.106}$$

we write (4.2.105) as

$$\frac{d^4f}{dy^4}-2\xi^2\frac{d^2f}{dy^2}-\eta^4 f = 0. \tag{4.2.107}$$

For a trial solution of the type $\exp(sy)$ we obtain the characteristic roots

$$s = \pm\zeta_1, \pm i\zeta_2, \tag{4.2.108}$$

where

$$\zeta_1 = (\xi^2+\beta^2)^{\frac{1}{2}}, \qquad \zeta_2 = (\beta^2-\xi^2)^{\frac{1}{2}}. \tag{4.2.109}$$

The result gives a wave system

$$\begin{aligned} w = {} & A\exp\{i(\xi x-\zeta_2 y-\omega t)\}+B\exp\{i(\xi x+\zeta_2 y-\omega t)\}+ \\ & +C\exp(-\zeta_1 y)\exp\{i(\xi x-\omega t)\}+D\exp(\zeta_1 y)\exp\{i(\xi x-\omega t)\}. \end{aligned} \tag{4.2.110}$$

Other results are possible. Thus suppose $\beta^2 > \xi^2$ in the expression (4.2.109) for ζ_2. Then $\zeta_2 \rightarrow i\zeta_2'$, where $\zeta_2'^2 = -\zeta_2^2$. The A and B terms in the solution (4.2.110) would then take on the appearance of the C and D terms. Another possibility is that $\beta^2 = \xi^2$, so that $\zeta_2 = 0$. This yields a result

$$\begin{aligned} w = {} & \{Ay\exp(-\zeta_1 y)+C\exp(-\zeta_1 y)+By\exp(\zeta_1 y)+D\exp(\zeta_1 y)\}\times \\ & \times\exp\{-i(\xi x-\omega t)\}. \end{aligned} \tag{4.2.111}$$

This also is not in the form of plane waves. The point is that only the form (4.2.110) permits propagating plane waves. If operative frequencies are such that either of the other possibilities mentioned arises, it is no longer possible to consider wave reflection.

Considering the solution (4.2.109) further, it is seen that the A and B terms are indeed plane harmonic waves. The A term is a wave propagating inward from the positive y direction toward the boundary at $y = 0$, while the B term is an outward propagating wave. We further see that, for a plate $y > 0$, that the D term must be discarded because it yields exponentially increasing waves.

As a first example, consider the simply supported boundary, described by

$$w(x, 0, t) = \partial^2 w(x, 0, t)/\partial y^2 = 0. \tag{4.2.112}$$

Substituting (4.2.109) with $D = 0$ in these conditions gives

$$\begin{aligned} A+B+C &= 0, \\ -\zeta_2^2 A - \zeta_2^2 B + \zeta_1^2 C &= 0. \end{aligned} \tag{4.2.113}$$

The resulting amplitude ratios are

$$B/A = -1, \qquad C = 0. \tag{4.2.114}$$

Thus a plane harmonic wave incident on a pinned boundary reflects as a plane wave with a phase shift. The behaviour is as shown in Fig. 4.15(a).

As a second example, consider a clamped boundary specified by

$$w(x, 0, t) = \partial w(x, 0, t)/\partial y = 0. \tag{4.2.115}$$

Substituting the solution (4.2.109), with $D = 0$, in the above conditions gives

$$\begin{aligned} A+B+C &= 0, \\ -i\zeta_2 A + i\zeta_2 B - \zeta_1 C &= 0, \end{aligned} \tag{4.2.116}$$

with the amplitude ratios

$$\frac{B}{A} = -\frac{\zeta_1 - i\zeta_2}{\zeta_1 + i\zeta_2}, \qquad \frac{C}{A} = -\frac{2i\zeta_2}{\zeta_1 + i\zeta_2}. \tag{4.2.117}$$

Thus, when a plane wave is incident on a fixed boundary, a plane wave is reflected. Also, an exponentially-attenuated wave is induced that propagates along the edge of the plate. The situation is shown in Fig. 4.15(b).

4.2.7. *Free vibrations of finite plates*

There is a vast amount of literature on the free vibrations of plates of various geometries. This has arisen, in the main, from the importance of the plate structure in aerospace applications. Only the briefest coverage can be given to the subject here.

1. *Vibrations of rectangular plates.* For our first topic, consider the free vibrations of rectangular plates. We again consider a separation-of-variable solution

$$w = X(x)Y(y)e^{-i\omega t}, \tag{4.2.118}$$

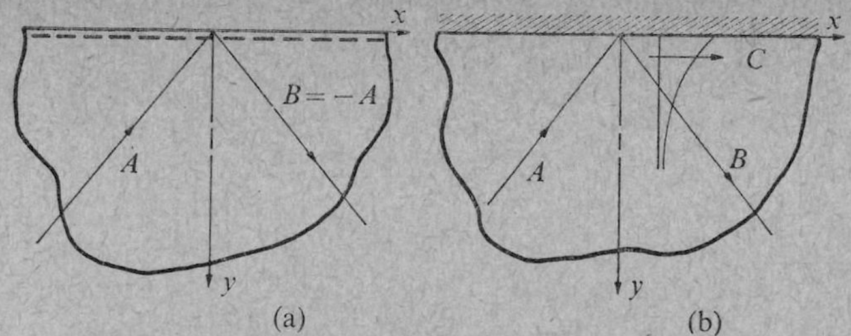

FIG. 4.15. Reflected waves from (a) a simply supported edge and (b) a clamped edge.

to the homogeneous governing equation (4.2.24). We leave boundary conditions unspecified at this stage. We obtain the resulting equation

$$X^{iv}Y+2X''Y''+XY^{iv}-\beta^4XY=0, \qquad \beta^4=\omega^2\rho h/D. \quad (4.2.119)$$

Now in order for the separation of variables to occur, we must have that

$$Y''=-\gamma^2Y, \qquad Y^{iv}=\gamma^4Y, \quad (4.2.120)$$

or

$$X''=-\alpha^2X, \qquad X^{iv}=\alpha^4X, \quad (4.2.121)$$

or both. Let us suppose the last case holds. The solution must be of the form

$$X=\sin\alpha x,\ \cos\alpha x. \quad (4.2.122)$$

If $\alpha^2<0$, hyperbolic sine and cosines could arise, but these will be excluded shortly on other grounds.

We now consider possible boundary conditions along the edges $x=0$ and $x=a$ of the plate. If we confine ourselves to the simple boundary conditions of simply supported, clamped, and free, we would have, for the various possibilities along $x=0$,

$$\begin{aligned}&\text{SS: } X(0)Y(y)=\{-\alpha^2Y(y)+\nu Y''(y)\}X(0)=0,\\&\text{C: } X(0)Y(y)=X'(0)Y(y)=0,\\&\text{F: } X(0)\{-\alpha^2Y(y)+\nu Y''(y)\}=X'(0)\{-\alpha^2Y(y)+(2-\nu)Y''(y)\}=0,\end{aligned} \quad (4.2.123)$$

with similar conditions holding on $x=a$. It should be readily apparent that the only set of boundary conditions satisfied by either one of the solutions (4.2.122) will be the case of simple support on both edges for which

$$X_n=\sin\alpha_nx, \qquad \alpha_n=n\pi/a \qquad (n=1,2,\ldots) \quad (4.2.124)$$

is a solution. Thus in order to apply separation of variables to the problem, we must restrict attention to the combinations of boundary conditions which have two opposite edges simply supported. There are six such combinations.

We now return to the y dependence. It may be that, in addition to X obeying simple support conditions, Y also will be so governed. Then

$$Y = \sin \gamma y, \cos \gamma y. \tag{4.2.125}$$

This is the simplest case and corresponds to the results obtained for X. Thus the edges $y = 0, b$ must be simply supported, and we have

$$Y_m = \sin \gamma_m y, \qquad \gamma_m = m\pi/b \qquad (m = 1, 2, \ldots). \tag{4.2.126}$$

This, in conjunction with (4.2.119), enables the natural frequencies of a plate simply supported on all edges to be found. Thus from (4.2.119) we have

$$(\alpha_n^4 + 2\alpha_n^2\gamma_m^2 + \gamma_m^4 - \beta^4)X_n Y_m = 0. \tag{4.2.127}$$

Solving for the frequency ω_{nm}, we obtain

$$\omega_{nm} = a(\alpha_n^2 + \gamma_m^2) \tag{4.2.128}$$

or

$$\omega_{nm} = \pi^2\left(\frac{n^2}{a^2} + \frac{m^2}{b^2}\right)\sqrt{\left(\frac{D}{h}\right)} \qquad (n, m = 1, 2, \ldots). \tag{4.2.129}$$

The mode shapes for this simple case will be given by

$$W_{nm} = \sin \alpha_n x \sin \gamma_m y. \tag{4.2.130}$$

The case of all edges simply supported is but one of the six combinations of boundary conditions for which two opposite edges are simply supported. For the remaining five cases, we must solve

$$Y^{\text{iv}} - 2\alpha_n^2 Y'' - (\beta^4 - \alpha_n^4)Y = 0. \tag{4.2.131}$$

The characteristic equation and resulting roots for this equation arose in the study of plane waves (see (4.2.108) and (4.2.109)). We recall that depending on whether $\beta^4 \gtreqless \alpha_n^4$, various types of solutions are possible. In the plane-wave study, only one type was admissible but, in the present problem, all are. The three cases and resulting solution forms are given in the following.

Case 1: $\beta^4 > \alpha_n^4$,

$$Y = A \sin \zeta_2 y + B \cos \zeta_2 y + C \sinh \zeta_1 y + D \cosh \zeta_1 y, \tag{4.2.132}$$

where ζ_1, ζ_2 are given by

$$\zeta_1 = (\beta^2 + \alpha_n^2)^{\frac{1}{2}}, \qquad \zeta_2 = (\beta^2 - \alpha_n^2)^{\frac{1}{2}} \tag{4.2.133}$$

and are of the form that previously arose in the plane-wave study.

Case 2: $\beta^4 = \alpha_n^4$.

$$Y = A \sinh \zeta_1 y + By \sinh \zeta_1 y + C \cosh \zeta_1 y + Dy \cosh \zeta_1 y. \tag{4.2.134}$$

Case 3: $\beta^4 < \alpha_n^4$,

$$Y = A \sinh \zeta_2' y + B \cosh \zeta_2' y + C \sinh \zeta_1 y + D \cosh \zeta_1 y, \quad (4.2.135)$$

where $\zeta_2'^2 = -\zeta_2^2$.

To complete the solution of any of the five remaining combinations of edge conditions on $y = 0, b$ the preceding results must be substituted into the boundary condition equations. There will result four homogeneous equations for A, B, C, D, the determinant of coefficients of which will yield a frequency equation. As an example, consider clamped edges at $y = 0, b$. Considering only the solution given by Case 1 and applying the boundary conditions

$$Y(0) = Y'(0) = Y(b) = Y'(b) = 0. \quad (4.2.136)$$

gives the equations

$$\begin{bmatrix} 0 & 1 & 0 & 1 \\ \zeta_2 & 0 & \zeta_1 & 0 \\ \sin \zeta_2 b & \cos \zeta_2 b & \sinh \zeta_1 b & \cosh \zeta_1 b \\ \zeta_2 \cos \zeta_2 b & -\zeta_2 \sin \zeta_2 b & \zeta_1 \cosh \zeta_1 b & \zeta_1 \sinh \zeta_1 b \end{bmatrix} \begin{bmatrix} A \\ B \\ C \\ D \end{bmatrix} = 0. \quad (4.2.137)$$

Equating the determinant of coefficients to zero gives the frequency equation

$$2\zeta_1\zeta_2(\cos \zeta_2 b \cosh \zeta_1 b - 1) - \alpha_n^2 \sin \zeta_2 b \sinh \zeta_2 b = 0. \quad (4.2.138)$$

For a given value of n there will be successive values of β, hence ω, which satisfy (4.2.138), and likewise for $n = 2, 3, \ldots$. Thus there will result a series of frequencies $\omega_{11}, \omega_{12}, \omega_{13}, \ldots, \omega_{21}, \omega_{22}, \ldots$. These values will, of course, depend on the aspect ratio a/b of the plate, the thickness, and the material. For completeness, the Case 2 and Case 3 solutions must be investigated. A proof that Case 3 yields no roots is rather recondite, while Case 2 gives a single root of $\omega = (D/\rho h)^{\frac{1}{2}} n^2\pi^2/a^2$. The modal curves for Case 1 are given by

$$Y_m = (\cosh \zeta_1 b - \cos \zeta_2 b)(\zeta_2 \sinh \zeta_1 y - \zeta_1 \sin \zeta_2 y) - $$
$$-(\zeta_2 \sinh \zeta_1 b - \zeta_1 \sin \zeta_2 b)(\cosh \zeta_1 y - \cos \zeta_2 y). \quad (4.2.139)$$

Thus, at a given frequency ω_{nm}, the mode shape is given by $W_{nm} = Y_m \sin \alpha_n x$.

In the following, the frequency equations and mode shapes will be summarized for all six combinations of boundary conditions. The results just discussed will be included for completeness.

SS–SS–SS–SS:

$$\sin \zeta_2 b = 0, \quad (4.2.140)$$

$$W_{nm} = \sin \alpha_n x \sin \gamma_m y. \quad (4.2.141)$$

SS–C–SS–C:

$$2\zeta_1\zeta_2(\cosh\zeta_1 b\cos\zeta_1 b-1)\zeta_2=\alpha_n^2\sin\zeta_2 b\sinh\zeta_2 b, \tag{4.2.142}$$

$$W_{nm}=\{(\cosh\zeta_1 b-\cos\zeta_2 b)(\zeta_2\sinh\zeta_1 y-\zeta_1\sin\zeta_2 y)-\\ -(\zeta_2\sinh\zeta_1 b-\zeta_1\sin\zeta_2 b)(\cosh\zeta_1 y-\cos\zeta_2 y)\}\sin\alpha_n x. \tag{4.2.143}$$

SS–C–SS–SS:

$$\zeta_1\cosh\zeta_1 b\sin\zeta_2 b=\zeta_2\sinh\zeta_1 b\cos\zeta_2 b, \tag{4.2.144}$$

$$W_{nm}=(\sin\zeta_2 b\sinh\zeta_1 y-\sinh\zeta_1 b\sin\zeta_2 y)\sin\alpha_n x. \tag{4.2.145}$$

SS–F–SS–F:

$$\sinh\zeta_1 b\sin\zeta_2 b[\zeta_1^2\{\beta^2-\alpha_n^2(1-\nu)\}^4-\zeta_2^2\{\beta^2+\alpha_n^2(1-\nu)\}^4]\\ =2\zeta_1\zeta_2\{\beta^4-\alpha_n^4(1-\nu)^2\}^2(\cosh\zeta_1 b\cos\zeta_2 b-1), \tag{4.2.146}$$

$$W_{nm}=(-(\cosh\zeta_1 b-\cos\zeta_2 b)\{\beta^4-\alpha_n^4(1-\nu)^2\}\times\\ \times[\zeta_2\{\beta^2+\alpha_n^2(1-\nu)\}\sinh\zeta_1 y+\zeta_1\{\beta^2-\alpha_n^2(1-\nu)\}\sin\zeta_2 y]+\\ +[\zeta_2\{\beta^2+\alpha_n^2(1-\nu)\}^2\sinh\zeta_1 b-\zeta_1\{\beta^2-\alpha_n^2(1-\nu)\}^2\sin\zeta_2 b]\times\\ \times[\{\beta^2-\alpha_n^2(1-\nu)\}\cosh\zeta_1 y+\{\beta^2+\alpha_n^2(1-\nu)\}\cos\zeta_2 y])\sin\alpha_n x. \tag{4.2.147}$$

SS–F–SS–SS:

$$\zeta_1\{\beta^2-\alpha_n(1-\nu)\}^2\cosh\zeta_1 b\sin\zeta_2 b\\ =\zeta_2\{\beta^2+\alpha_n^2(1-\nu)\}^2\sinh\zeta_1 b\cos\zeta_2 b, \tag{4.2.148}$$

$$W_{nm}=[\{\beta^2-\alpha_n^2(1-\nu)\}\sin\zeta_2 b\sinh\zeta_1 y+\{\beta^2+\alpha_n^2(1-\nu)\}\times\\ \times\sinh\zeta_1 b\sin\zeta_2 y]\sin\alpha_n x. \tag{4.2.149}$$

SS–F–SS–C:

$$\zeta_1\zeta_2\{\beta^4-\alpha_n^4(1-\nu)^2\}+\zeta_1\zeta_2\{\beta^4+\zeta_n^4(1-\nu)^2\}\cosh\zeta_1 b\cos\zeta_2 b+\\ +\alpha_n^2\{\beta^4(1-2\nu)-\alpha_n^4(1-\nu)^2\}\sinh\zeta_1 b\sin\zeta_2 b=0, \tag{4.2.150}$$

$$W_{nm}=([\{\beta^2+\alpha_n^2(1-\nu)\}\cosh\zeta_1 b+\{\beta^2-\alpha_n^2(1-\nu)\}\cos\zeta_1 b]\times\\ \times(\zeta_1\sin\zeta_2 y-\zeta_2\sinh\zeta_1 y)+[\zeta_2\{\beta^2+\alpha_n^2(1-\nu)\}\sinh\zeta_1 b+\\ +\zeta_1\{\beta^2-\alpha_n^2(1-\nu)\}\sin\zeta_2 b](\cosh\zeta_1 y-\cos\zeta_2 y))\sin\alpha_n x. \tag{4.2.151}$$

All of the preceding solutions are for Case 1. For Case 2, the single root $\omega=(D/\rho h)^{\frac{1}{2}}n^2\pi^2/a^2$ holds. For Case 3, it has been shown that the first three combinations of edge conditions have no roots. However, the last three combinations do have roots for this case, and these have been shown to be dependent on Poisson's ratio. A detailed discussion of these last three cases, however, is beyond the scope of the present work.

Because of the several parameters entering into the plate frequency equation, the data on the frequency parameters for plates must be based on the aspect ratio a/b. Only in the case of a plate simply supported on all edges (SS–SS–SS–SS) is frequency information and mode shape easily obtainable. Figure 4.16 shows diagrams of the modes from ω_{11} to ω_{43} for such a plate.

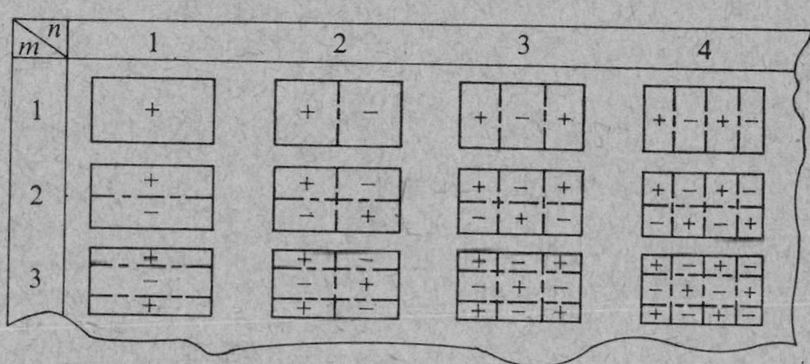

FIG. 4.16. Diagrams of the simply supported plate modes ω_{11} through ω_{43}.

2. *Vibrations of circular plates.* Let us now turn to the free vibrations of circular plates. We consider the governing eqn (4.2.25) with $q(r, \theta, t) = 0$ and assume a solution

$$w(r, \theta, t) = W(r, \theta)e^{-i\omega t}. \tag{4.2.152}$$

This leads to the result

$$\nabla^4 W(r, \theta) - \beta^4 W(r, \theta) = 0, \qquad \beta^4 = \omega^2 \rho h/D. \tag{4.2.153}$$

The solution to the above may be written as

$$W = W_1 + W_2, \tag{4.2.154}$$

where W_1, W_2 satisfy respectively

$$\nabla^2 W_1 + \beta^2 W_1 = 0, \qquad \nabla^2 W_2 - \beta^2 W_2 = 0. \tag{4.2.155}$$

Considering W_1 and assuming $W_1 = R_1\Theta_1$, we obtain

$$R_1''\Theta_1 + \frac{1}{r}R_1'\Theta_1 + \frac{1}{r^2}R_1\Theta_1'' + \beta^2 R_1\Theta_1 = 0. \tag{4.2.156}$$

Separation occurs if

$$\Theta_1'' = -\alpha^2\Theta_1. \tag{4.2.157}$$

That is,

$$\Theta_1 = \sin\alpha\theta, \cos\alpha\theta. \tag{4.2.158}$$

However, from continuity conditions that require

$$W(r, \theta) = W(r, \theta + 2\pi), \tag{4.2.159}$$

it is readily seen that $\alpha = n$, where n is an integer. Thus

$$\Theta_1 = \sin n\theta, \cos n\theta, \tag{4.2.160}$$

and

$$R_1''+\frac{1}{r}R_1'+\left(\beta^2-\frac{n^2}{r^2}\right)R_1 = 0. \tag{4.2.161}$$

This is Bessel's equation of order n, which has the solution

$$R_1 = AJ_n(\beta r)+BY_n(\beta r). \tag{4.2.162}$$

Thus

$$W_1 = \{AJ_n(\beta r)+BY_n(\beta r)\}\begin{bmatrix}\sin n\theta\\ \cos n\theta\end{bmatrix}. \tag{4.2.163}$$

For W_2 the same results are obtained for Θ_2 while, for R_2, the modified Bessel's equation holds,

$$R_2''+\frac{1}{r}R_2'-\left(\beta^2+\frac{n^2}{r^2}\right)R_2 = 0, \tag{4.2.164}$$

which has the solution

$$R_2 = CI_n(\beta r)+DK_n(\beta r). \tag{4.2.165}$$

In the above I_n, K_n are the modified Bessel functions of the first and second kind respectively, and are related to J_n, Y_n by

$$\mathrm{i}^n I_n(\beta r) = J_n(\mathrm{i}\beta r), \qquad K_n(\beta r) = Y_n(\mathrm{i}\beta r). \tag{4.2.166}$$

The total solution is thus

$$W(r,\theta) = \{AJ_n(\beta r)+BY_n(\beta r)+CI_n(\beta r)+DK_n(\beta r)\}\begin{bmatrix}\sin n\theta\\ \cos n\theta\end{bmatrix}. \tag{4.2.167}$$

If we restrict our attention to full circular plates, we must set $B = D = 0$ in the above since Y_n, K_n have singularities at $r = 0$. Thus we are reduced to

$$W(r,\theta) = \{AJ_n(\beta r)+CI_n(\beta r)\}\begin{bmatrix}\sin n\theta\\ \cos n\theta\end{bmatrix}. \tag{4.2.168}$$

There are three types of complete, circular plates having simple boundary conditions (that is, simply supported, clamped, or free on the circumference). Of the three, the clamped edge is the simplest. We have

$$W(a,\theta) = \partial W(a,\theta)/\partial r = 0. \tag{4.2.169}$$

Substituting (4.2.168) in these equations gives the following frequency equation for the clamped plate,

$$I_n(\beta a)J_n'(\beta a)-J_n(\beta a)I_n'(\beta a) = 0. \tag{4.2.170}$$

For each value of n, there will be an infinite number of roots to (4.2.172). We define the frequency parameter λ_{nm}, where

$$\lambda_{nm} = \beta_{nm}a, \tag{4.2.171}$$

n is the integer arising in (4.2.170), and m corresponds to the order of the root for a given n. Some of the first few values for λ_{nm} are

$$\begin{aligned} \lambda_{01}^2 &= 10.216, & \lambda_{02}^2 &= 39.771, & \lambda_{03}^2 &= 89.104, \\ \lambda_{11}^2 &= 21.26, & \lambda_{12}^2 &= 60.82, & \lambda_{13}^2 &= 120.08, \\ \lambda_{21}^2 &= 34.88, & \lambda_{22}^2 &= 84.58, & \lambda_{23}^2 &= 153.81. \end{aligned} \tag{4.2.172}$$

The normal modes are given by

$$W_{nm}(r,\theta) = \left\{J_n(\beta_{nm}r) - \frac{J_n(\beta_{nm}a)}{I_n(\beta_{nm}a)} I_n(\beta_{nm}r)\right\} \begin{bmatrix} \sin n\theta \\ \cos n\theta \end{bmatrix}. \tag{4.2.173}$$

A few of the mode shapes are shown in graphic form in Fig. 4.17.

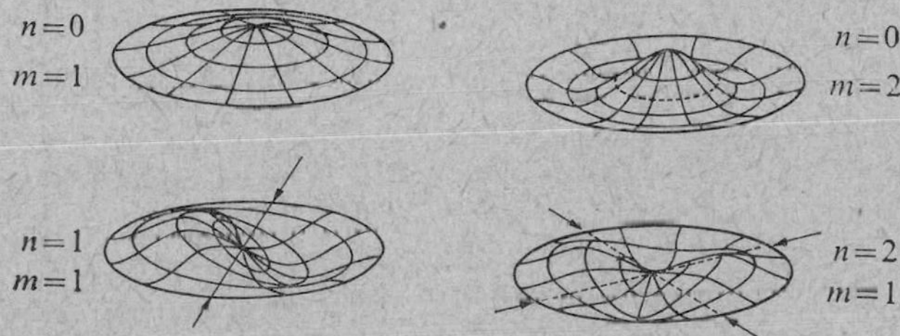

FIG. 4.17. Graphic illustration of the first few normal modes of a clamped circular plate. (After Morse [12].)

Consideration of a plate simply supported at $r = a$ yields a more complicated transcendental equation, as does the plate with a free edge. Plates with circular concentric holes may be included easily in the study. For such a case, all four terms of the solution are retained since the singular behaviour of Y_m, K_m at $r = 0$ no longer enters in. It is then necessary to specify two additional boundary conditions at the inner radius $r = b$, say.

3. *Orthogonality*. We now wish to develop the orthogonality property for the plate normal modes. We will use the rectangular plate modes for the development, although the arguments may be applied to other cases. Thus, consider the mode $W_{ij}(x, y)$ associated with the ω_{ij} natural frequency of the plate and the W_{kl} mode associated with ω_{kl}. Thus W_{ij}, W_{kl} satisfy

$$\nabla^4 W_{ij} - \beta_{ij}^4 W_{ij} = 0, \qquad \nabla^4 W_{kl} - \beta_{kl}^4 W_{kl} = 0. \tag{4.2.174}$$

Now to proceed in the usual manner to investigate whether orthogonality exists between the normal modes would require subtraction of the above two equations and integration over the region $0 \leq x \leq a$, $0 \leq y \leq b$. Considerable manipulation would be required to reach the desired results. This procedure can be circumvented if we take the following viewpoint. The equation

$$\nabla^4 W = \beta^4 W \tag{4.2.175}$$

can be considered as the equation for the deflection surface produced by the load $q = D\beta^4 W$ since, in static plate theory, the differential equation has the form

$$\nabla^4 W = q/D. \tag{4.2.176}$$

Thus, under the load $q_{ij} = D\beta_{ij}^4 W_{ij}(x, y)$, the plate assumes the deflected form $W_{ij}(x, y)$. Likewise for $q_{kl} = D\beta_{kl}^4 W_{kl}(x, y)$. We now wish to apply Betti's reciprocal theorem to this problem.

Reviewed in brief, the Betti reciprocal theorem considers an elastic body under two loads P_1 and P_2. Under P_1 alone, deflections δ_1 and δ_2 are produced, where δ_1 is in the direction of P_1 and δ_2 is in the direction of P_2, if it were acting. Under the action of P_2 alone, δ_1' and δ_2' are produced, with δ_1' being in the direction of P_1 if it were acting and δ_2' is in the direction of P_2. Then, according to the theorem, $P_1\delta_1' = P_2\delta_2$. In more formal terms, the theorem states that: *the work done by forces of the first state on the corresponding displacements of the second state is equal to the work done by the forces of the second state on the corresponding displacements of the first.*

The application of this theorem in the context of the present problem is as follows: the loading $q_{ij} = D\beta_{ij}^4 W_{ij}$ is analogous to P_1 while the deflection W_{kl} is analogous to δ_1' and $q_{kl} = D\beta_{kl}^4 W_{kl}$ is analogous to P_2 with W_{ij} corresponding to δ_2. To obtain a work expression, integration over the area of the plate is required. Thus

$$D\beta_{ij}^4 \int_0^b\int_0^a W_{ij}W_{kl}\,dx\,dy = D\beta_{kl}^4 \int_0^a\int_0^b W_{ij}W_{kl}\,dx\,dy. \tag{4.2.177}$$

This gives

$$(\beta_{ij}^4 - \beta_{kl}^4)\int_0^b\int_0^a W_{ij}W_{kl}\,dx\,dy = 0 \tag{4.2.178}$$

which, since $\beta_{ij} \neq \beta_{kl}$, establishes the orthogonality property

$$\int_0^a\int_0^b W_{ij}(x, y)W_{kl}(x, y)\,dx\,dy = 0. \tag{4.2.179}$$

It should be noted that this orthogonality condition in no way depends on the separability property $W = X(x)Y(y)$. The general motion of the plate is then conveniently expressed in the form

$$w(x, y, t) = \sum_{n=0}^{\infty}\sum_{m=1}^{\infty} q_{nm}(t)W_{nm}(x, y), \tag{4.2.180}$$

which is, of course, the logical extension of the normal-mode expansion method first encountered in string and beam problems. The initial-value problem in plate vibrations takes such a form. The orthogonality property of the normal modes enables the coefficients of the expansion to be determined, at least in theory. Of course the complicated nature of the modes and the two-dimensional nature of the expansion makes solution of even seemingly simple problems in this area quite tedious.

It was mentioned earlier that the literature on the vibrations of plates is vast. Only the briefest of results for two particular plate geometries (rectangular and circular), subject to only the simplest types of boundary constraints, have been presented. Little in the way of numerical data has been given. While this is the only practical way to proceed in a book devoted primarily to wave propagation, it should be noted that it is possible to resolve the bulk of the literature for the vibrations of homogeneous, isotropic plates into the major geometrical categories of *circular*, *elliptical*, *rectangular*, *parallelogram*, *trapezoidal*, and *triangular*, with the subject of rectangular plates receiving the greatest coverage. Reference should be made to a most useful compilation of data on plate frequencies reported by Leissa [8]. This reference presents the numerical results from several hundred papers and reports.

4.2.8. *Experimental results on waves in plates*

Several studies have been made on transient wave propagation in plates of which only a few will be mentioned here. One of the first studies was that by Dohrenwend, Drucker, and Moore [3], cited also in § 3.6 in the discussion of transient waves in beams. In that study, a large steel plate, $\frac{1}{2}$ in. thick was struck a blow with a heavy sledge hammer and the radial strain at various distances from the point of impact was measured using wire resistance strain gauges. The experimental results are shown in Fig. 4.18(a). The theoretical response of the plate was determined using an assumed initial velocity input of $v_0 \exp(-r^2/4b^2)$ and an analysis based on classical plate theory. The predicted response is shown in Fig. 4.18(b). The distance from point of impact is r and the plate thickness is h. It should be noted that this study represented one of the earlier applications of strain gauges to the measurement of sharp transients.

Press and Oliver [14] obtained results for flexural waves excited by a spark source. Their study was aimed at the broader aspects of air-coupled surface waves, with the concentrated load results being only one of several cases studied. A diagram of the experimental apparatus and the results obtained are shown in Fig. 4.19. The spark source is S and the detector, a piezoelectric device, is D. The plate was aluminium, $\frac{1}{32}$ in. (0·08 cm) thick and several feet in breadth. The baffle B was placed close to the source to prevent air-coupling over the distance d. It is seen that the response is quite similar to the far field response observed in beams.

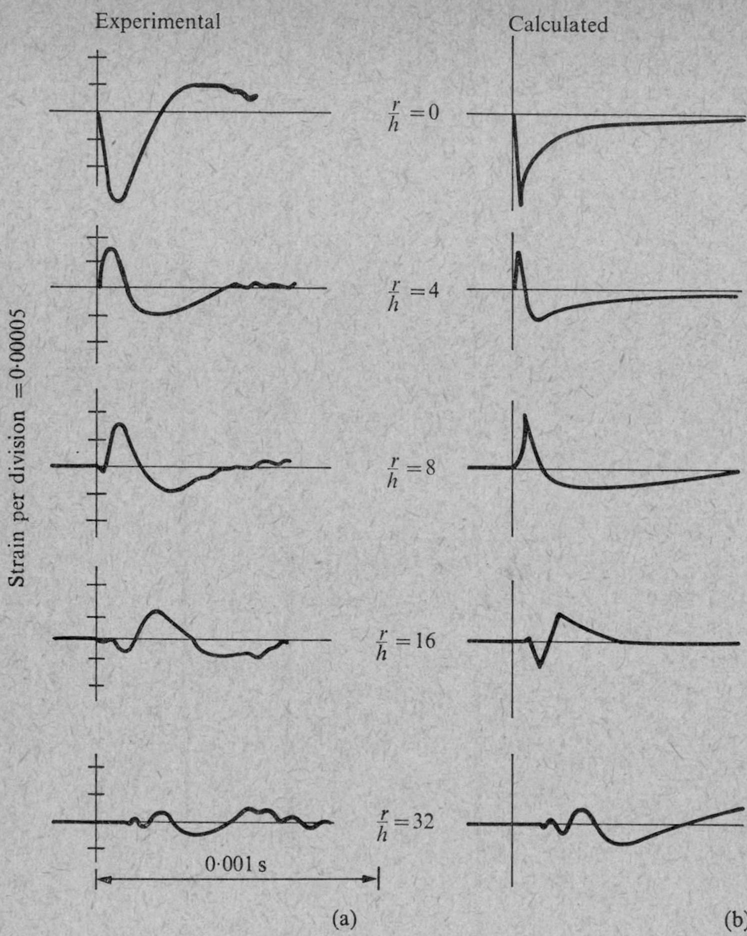

FIG. 4.18. (a) Experimental and (b) theoretical values of radial strain in a plate subjected to impact. (After Dohrenwend *et al.* [3, Fig. 10].)

The work of Medick [10] has been cited previously in this section (see, for example, Fig. 4.14) for the analysis of the transverse impact of plates. He also performed an experimental investigation of this problem using an experimental apparatus as shown in Fig. 4.20(a). Thus, a capacitance pick-up was used to measure the transient plate displacement. Typical displacement records are shown in Fig. 4.20(b). The experimental results were compared with theoretical predictions for $r = 2{\cdot}2$ in., 4·1 in., and 10·1 in. (5·59 cm, 10·91 cm, 25·65 cm) from the impact point. The results for the case of 10·1 in. is shown in Fig. 4.21. The agreement between the results is seen to be rather good. It should be recalled that the Medick analysis was based on classical plate theory. It is seen that the theoretical maxima exceed the experimental maxima

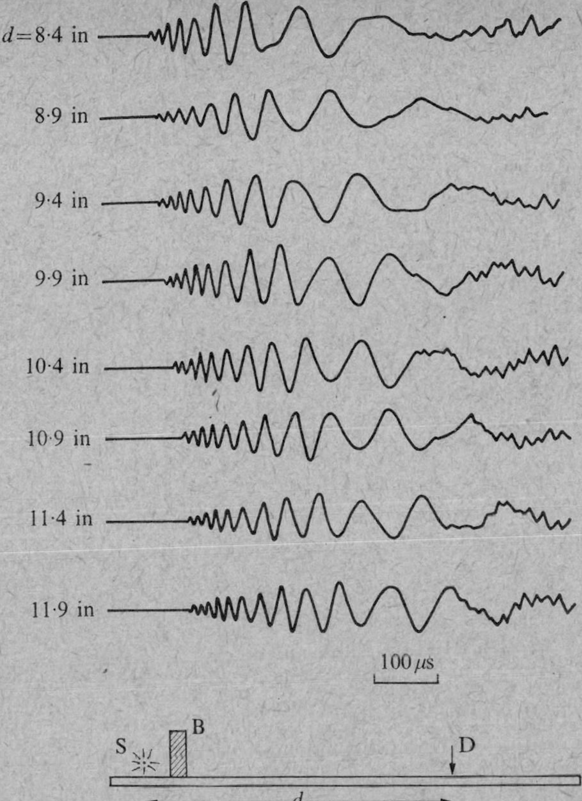

FIG. 4.19. Flexural waves excited in a thin plate by a spark source S. (After Press and Oliver [14, Fig. 1].)

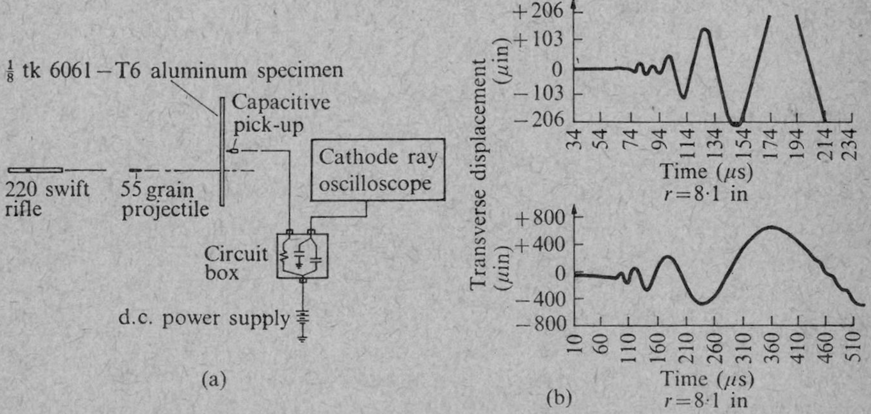

FIG. 4.20. (a) Experimental setup used to measure the transient displacement in a plate subjected to transverse impact and (b) typical displacement records. (After Medick [10, Figs. 3 and 4].)

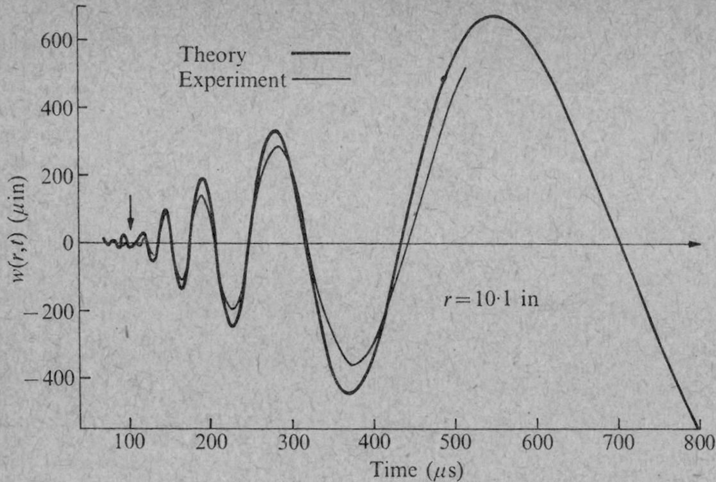

FIG. 4.21. Comparison of theoretical and experimental values of transient plate displacement for $r = 10{\cdot}1$ in. (25·65cm) (After Medick [10, Fig. 7].)

somewhat, while the phase agreement is very good. For the case of $r = 4{\cdot}1$ in. (not shown), experimental maxima slightly exceeded theoretical values and some phase shift was noted.

4.3. Waves in thin, cylindrical shells

In the investigations thus far, we have progressed from transverse waves in taut strings to the propagation of flexural waves in thin plates. Dimensionally, we have proceeded from one-dimensional to two-dimensional problems. Nearly all structural elements considered have been straight and flat, however. The situation may be further complicated by the addition of curvature, as was found in the case of rings. Thus rods and beams may become rings and plates may become shells. It is in this area that our considerations now lie.

With the additional element of curvature, the variety of elastic systems becomes unmanageably large. Thus, in the case of (uniform) rods and beams, one need only consider the length parameter of the system and its means of end-constraint, a fairly denumerable situation. For the case of plates, the shape of the plate enters as well as possible mixtures of constraint about the periphery, and the number of possibilities becomes unlimited. Even in the context of practical considerations, the number of plate geometries and constraints is quite large. It thus should be evident that adding curvature effects to the preceding situations easily creates a class of problems in elastic systems that must be brought into manageable proportions by brutal elimination. This is done in the present section by confining attention to the case of thin cylindrical shells. Fortunately, this matter of expediency covers the geometry of greatest practical importance.

The matter of the governing equations for shells should be remarked upon. Whereas the governing equations for longitudinal and flexural waves in rods and plates seem to be well agreed upon by the 'authorities', the situation is not so in the case of shells. One thus finds a large number of shell theories, usually being differentiated by slight differences in the kinematics of deformation, inertial contributions, or curvature approximations. The approach taken here to this problem will be to present the simplest shell equations, saving for a later time the more complicated theories that may be developed using procedures similar to those that will be presented for plates and rods.

The theory used in this section is known as the membrane shell theory. Under this development only forces, normal and shear, acting in the mid surface of the shell are considered. The transverse shear forces and the bending and twisting moments are assumed negligibly small. Thus the shell behaves as a curved membrane. If there is a shell analogue of the flat membrane, one expects, in analogy to the flat plate, a shell theory where moments and transverse shear forces act. The classical development in this area was put forth by Love.† Many slight modifications of this theory have appeared by Flügge [5], Vlasov [18], Donnell [4], Sanders [15], and others. One is referred to the text by Kraus [7] for extensive discussion and review of the theories, as well as numerous analyses in the statics and vibrations of shells. It is the proliferation of theories in this area that can lead to more confusion. It is characteristic of all the aforementioned developments that shear deformations are neglected, as in Bernoulli–Euler beam theory and classical plate theory. Developments of 'Timoshenko' shell theories are associated with Hildebrand *et al.* [6], Naghdi [13], and others.

With the extensive developments in shell theories, our restriction to membrane theory seems pale by comparison. There are two justifications for the present restriction, however. First, being the simplest theory, the essential features are easily presented and results obtained. More importantly, the more complicated theories associated with Love and others contain the essential weakness, from the standpoint of wave propagation and sharp transients, of neglecting shear effects. Drawing from the experience in beam analysis, one knows, practically *a priori*, that a shear theory will be required. One is justified, therefore, in considering such a theory almost immediately. These developments, which generally take the exact equations of elasticity as their starting point, are best presented in detail in Chapter 8. With this lengthy introduction, we now proceed to the study of waves in cylindrical membrane shells.

4.3.1. *Governing equations for a cylindrical membrane shell*

It is, of course, possible to develop governing equations for shells of arbitrary curvature and then to specialize the results to a particular geometry

† Chapter 23, 24, 24A of Reference [9].

such as cylindrical. If a variety of geometries are being considered, such an effort would be worthwhile. Since our attention will be confined to cylindrical membrane shells, it is much more expedient to develop the equations directly in terms of the cylindrical geometry.

Thus, in Fig. 4.22(a), a strip from a cylindrical shell, is shown indicating the

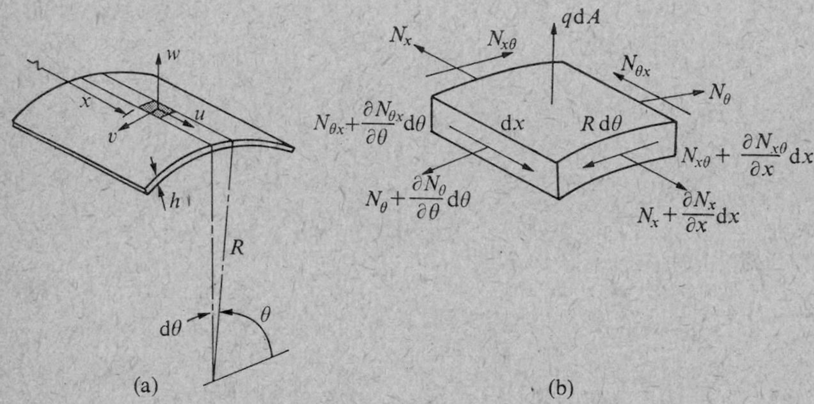

FIG. 4.22. (a) Section from a cylindrical membrane shell, and (b) a differential element of shell.

coordinates x (along the shell) and θ (the polar angle). The displacement components in the radial (w), longitudinal (u), and tangential (v) directions are shown on the shaded differential element. The forces per unit length on the element are shown in Fig. 4.22(b). Because only membrane action is being assumed, there are no bending moments or transverse shear forces. The equations of motion in the longitudinal, tangential, and radial directions are, respectively,

$$-N_x R\,d\theta+\left(N_x+\frac{\partial N_x}{\partial x}\,dx\right)R\,d\theta-N_{\theta x}\,dx+\left(N_{\theta x}+\frac{\partial N_{\theta x}}{\partial\theta}\,d\theta\right)dx$$

$$=\rho R\,d\theta\,dx h\frac{\partial^2 u}{\partial t^2}, \quad (4.3.1)$$

$$-N_\theta\,dx+\left(N_\theta+\frac{\partial N_\theta}{\partial\theta}\,d\theta\right)dx-N_{x\theta}R\,d\theta+\left(N_{x\theta}+\frac{\partial N_{x\theta}}{\partial x}\,dx\right)R\,d\theta$$

$$=\rho R\,d\theta\,dx h\frac{\partial^2 v}{\partial t^2}, \quad (4.3.2)$$

$$-N_\theta\frac{d\theta}{2}\,dx-\left(N_\theta+\frac{\partial N_\theta}{\partial\theta}\,d\theta\right)\frac{d\theta}{2}\,dx+qR\,d\theta\,dx=\rho R\,d\theta\,dx h\frac{\partial^2 w}{\partial t^2}. \quad (4.3.3)$$

These yield the equations of motion for a cylindrical membrane shell as

$$\frac{\partial N_x}{\partial x}+\frac{1}{R}\frac{\partial N_{\theta x}}{\partial \theta}=\rho h\frac{\partial^2 u}{\partial t^2}$$

$$\frac{1}{R}\frac{\partial N_\theta}{\partial \theta}+\frac{\partial N_{x\theta}}{\partial x}=\rho h\frac{\partial^2 v}{\partial t^2} \tag{4.3.4}$$

$$-\frac{N_\theta}{R}+q=\rho h\frac{\partial^2 w}{\partial t^2}.$$

The expressions for the membrane stresses N_x, N_θ, $N_{x\theta}$, $N_{\theta x}$ are obtained by integrating the usual stresses across the shell thickness. Thus we may write the general formula

$$N_x, N_\theta, N_{x\theta}, N_{\theta x}=\int_{-h/2}^{h/2}(\sigma_x, \sigma_\theta, \tau_{x\theta}, \tau_{\theta x})\,\mathrm{d}z, \tag{4.3.5}$$

where z is the distance measured outward from the mid surface of the shell. It is the same as the coordinate introduced in the curved-rod development (see Fig. 3.18). From Hooke's law, we have that

$$\sigma_x=\frac{E}{1-\nu^2}(\varepsilon_x+\nu\varepsilon_\theta), \qquad \sigma_\theta=\frac{E}{1-\nu^2}(\varepsilon_\theta+\nu\varepsilon_x), \qquad \tau_{x\theta}=\tau_{\theta x}=\gamma G, \tag{4.3.6}$$

where ε_x, ε_θ are the axial strains of the middle surface of the shell element and γ is the shear strain of the element with $\gamma=\gamma_{x\theta}=\gamma_{\theta x}$. Under the assumption of membrane-type stresses only, the stresses σ_x, σ_θ, $\tau_{x\theta}$, $\tau_{\theta x}$ are constant through the shell thickness, so that (4.3.5) becomes

$$N_x=\frac{Eh}{1-\nu^2}(\varepsilon_x+\nu\varepsilon_\theta), \qquad N_\theta=\frac{Eh}{1-\nu^2}(\varepsilon_\theta+\nu\varepsilon_x),$$

$$N_{x\theta}=N_{\theta x}=Gh\gamma=\frac{Eh}{2(1+\nu)}\gamma. \tag{4.3.7}$$

The kinematics of deformation must now be considered. Again, under the present conditions of membrane behaviour and cylindrical shape, these aspects are quite simple. In the axial direction, we have, exactly as in longitudinal rod theory, that

$$\varepsilon_x=\partial u/\partial x. \tag{4.3.8}$$

For ε_θ we have $\varepsilon_\theta=(\mathrm{d}s'-\mathrm{d}s)/\mathrm{d}s$, where $\mathrm{d}s=R\,\mathrm{d}\theta$ is the initial length of the arc segment. Now, an expression for $\mathrm{d}s'$, the length of an arc segment after deformation, was previously obtained in the analysis of waves in rings (see Fig. 3.19 and (3.5.13)), and this result is directly applicable here. Thus, we have that $ds' = (w+R)\,d\theta + (\partial v/\partial\theta)\,d\theta$. The result is that

$$\varepsilon_\theta = \frac{1}{R}\left(w+\frac{\partial v}{\partial\theta}\right). \tag{4.3.9}$$

The expression for the shear strain results directly from considering small changes in angle of the sides dx and $R\,d\theta$ of the element due to $\partial v/\partial x$ and $\partial u/\partial\theta$. We have that

$$\gamma = \frac{\partial v}{\partial x}+\frac{1}{R}\frac{\partial u}{\partial\theta}. \tag{4.3.10}$$

The membrane stresses are thus given by

$$\begin{aligned} N_x &= \frac{Eh}{1-\nu^2}\left\{\frac{\partial u}{\partial x}+\frac{\nu}{R}\left(w+\frac{\partial v}{\partial\theta}\right)\right\},\\ N_\theta &= \frac{Eh}{1-\nu^2}\left(\frac{w}{R}+\frac{1}{r}\frac{\partial v}{\partial\theta}+\nu\frac{\partial u}{\partial x}\right),\\ N_{x\theta} = N_{\theta x} &= \frac{Eh}{2(1+\nu)}\left(\frac{\partial v}{\partial x}+\frac{1}{R}\frac{\partial u}{\partial\theta}\right). \end{aligned} \tag{4.3.11}$$

The displacement equations of motion result from substituting (4.3.11) in (4.3.4). If we note that the coefficient of $N_{x\theta}$ may be written as

$$Eh(1-\nu)/2(1-\nu^2),$$

then we have

$$\left\{\frac{\partial^2 u}{\partial x^2}+\frac{\nu}{R}\left(\frac{\partial w}{\partial x}+\frac{\partial^2 v}{\partial x\,\partial\theta}\right)\right\}+\frac{(1-\nu)}{2R}\left(\frac{\partial^2 v}{\partial\theta\,\partial x}+\frac{1}{R}\frac{\partial^2 u}{\partial\theta^2}\right) = \frac{\rho(1-\nu^2)}{E}\frac{\partial^2 u}{\partial t^2}, \tag{4.3.12}$$

$$\frac{1}{R}\left(\frac{1}{R}\frac{\partial w}{\partial\theta}+\frac{1}{R}\frac{\partial^2 v}{\partial\theta^2}+\nu\frac{\partial^2 u}{\partial\theta\,\partial x}\right)+\frac{(1-\nu)}{2}\left(\frac{\partial^2 v}{\partial x^2}+\frac{1}{R}\frac{\partial^2 u}{\partial x\,\partial\theta}\right) = \frac{\rho(1-\nu^2)}{E}\frac{\partial^2 v}{\partial t^2}, \tag{4.3.13}$$

$$-\frac{1}{R}\left(\frac{w}{R}+\frac{1}{R}\frac{\partial v}{\partial\theta}+\nu\frac{\partial u}{\partial x}\right)+\frac{1-\nu^2}{Eh}q = \frac{\rho(1-\nu^2)}{E}\frac{\partial^2 w}{\partial t^2}. \tag{4.3.14}$$

We recall the remark that cylindrical membrane shells represent about the simplest theory for the simplest shell geometry. Yet even under these circumstances, coupled equations of some complexity arise.

The governing equations for a shell, including bending effects on the deformation and bending moments and shear forces in the equations of motion, yield considerably more complicated equations than the preceding. However, the Donnell formulation,† including these effects with, additionally, some slight simplifications related to the influence of transverse shearing force on tangential motion, and related to the expressions for curvature and twist, yields equations quite like (4.3.12)–(4.3.14). There is, in fact, only the additional term $(-h^2\nabla^4 w/12)$ on the left-hand side of (4.3.14).

† See pp. 200–4 of Reference [7].

4.3.2. *Wave propagation in the shell*

We wish to consider the propagation of harmonic waves in the membrane shell. We could immediately substitute harmonic wave expressions for u, v, w in eqns (4.3.12)-(4.3.14) and obtain a frequency equation. A rather complicated expression would result, however, and interpretation of the results would be difficult. A better approach is to consider various special modes of motion and study the simplified frequency equation.

One of the most important special cases results from considering motion independent of θ.† Thus, if $\partial/\partial\theta = 0$ (also set $q = 0$) in the displacement equations of motion we obtain

$$\frac{\partial^2 u}{\partial x^2}+\frac{\nu}{R}\frac{\partial w}{\partial x} = \frac{\rho(1-\nu^2)}{E}\frac{\partial^2 u}{\partial t^2}, \tag{4.3.15}$$

$$\frac{(1-\nu)}{2}\frac{\partial^2 v}{\partial x^2} = \frac{\rho(1-\nu^2)}{E}\frac{\partial^2 v}{\partial t^2}, \tag{4.3.16}$$

$$-\frac{w}{R^2}-\frac{\nu}{R}\frac{\partial u}{\partial x} = \frac{\rho(1-\nu^2)}{E}\frac{\partial^2 w}{\partial t^2}. \tag{4.3.17}$$

The first observation to make is that the equation for the tangential motion (4.3.16) has uncoupled from the remaining two equations. This equation may be written as

$$\frac{\partial^2 v}{\partial x^2} = \frac{2\rho(1+\nu)}{E}\frac{\partial^2 v}{\partial t^2}. \tag{4.3.18}$$

Since $G = E/2(1+\nu)$, we have the result

$$\frac{\partial^2 v}{\partial x^2} = \frac{1}{c_s^2}\frac{\partial^2 v}{\partial t^2}, \qquad c_s = \sqrt{\left(\frac{G}{\rho}\right)}. \tag{4.3.19}$$

This is the familiar wave equation, and it is governing the purely torsional motion of the shell. We note the propagation velocity of the torsional disturbance is $\sqrt{(G/\rho)}$, the same as found for such waves in a solid circular rod (see § 2.6).

Now consider the motion as governed by the remaining coupled equations in u and w. We let

$$u = A\mathrm{e}^{\mathrm{i}(\gamma x-\omega t)}, \qquad w = B\mathrm{e}^{\mathrm{i}(\gamma x-\omega t)}, \tag{4.3.20}$$

and substitute in (4.3.15) and (4.3.17). This gives

$$\begin{bmatrix} \left(\frac{\omega^2}{c_p^2}-\gamma^2\right) & \mathrm{i}\gamma\frac{\nu}{R} \\ -\mathrm{i}\gamma\frac{\nu}{R} & \left(\frac{\omega^2}{c_p^2}-\frac{1}{R^2}\right) \end{bmatrix} \begin{bmatrix} A \\ B \end{bmatrix} = 0, \tag{4.3.21}$$

† You are asked to consider x-independent motion in Problem 4.16.

where the 'thin-plate' velocity has been introduced, given by†

$$c_p = (E/(1-\nu^2)\rho)^{\frac{1}{2}}. \tag{4.3.22}$$

The determinant of coefficients of (4.3.21) gives the frequency equation

$$\omega^4 - c_p^2\left(\gamma^2+\frac{1}{R^2}\right)\omega^2+(1-\nu^2)\frac{c_p^4}{R^2}\gamma^2 = 0. \tag{4.3.23}$$

In terms of phase velocity and wavenumber, we have

$$c^4 - c_p^2\left(1+\frac{1}{R^2\gamma^2}\right)c^2+(1-\nu^2)\frac{c_p^4}{R^2\gamma^2} = 0. \tag{4.3.24}$$

Introducing the non-dimensionalized quantities

$$\bar{c} = c/c_p, \quad \bar{\gamma} = h\gamma, \quad \bar{h} = h/R, \quad \bar{\omega} = h\omega/c_p, \tag{4.3.25}$$

the above equations reduce to

$$\bar{\omega}^4-(\bar{h}^2+\bar{\gamma}^2)\bar{\omega}^2+(1-\nu^2)\bar{h}^2\bar{\gamma}^2 = 0, \tag{4.3.26}$$

and, using $\bar{\omega} = \bar{\gamma}\bar{c}$,

$$\bar{c}^4-(1+\bar{h}^2/\bar{\gamma}^2)\bar{c}^2+(1-\nu^2)\bar{h}^2/\bar{\gamma}^2 = 0. \tag{4.3.27}$$

The long- and short-wavelength limits are easily obtained. At long wavelengths, we have

$$\begin{aligned} \lim_{\bar{\gamma}\to 0}(4.3.26) &= \bar{\omega}^4-\bar{h}^2\bar{\omega}^2 = 0, \qquad \bar{\omega} = 0, \bar{h}, \\ \lim_{\bar{\gamma}\to 0}(4.3.27) &= \frac{1}{\bar{\gamma}^2}\left\{\bar{c}^4\bar{\gamma}^2-\bar{h}^2\bar{c}^2+(1-\nu^2)\bar{h}^2\right\} = 0. \end{aligned} \tag{4.3.28}$$

In the last case, if $\bar{c}^2$ is finite, we must have the result that $\bar{c}^2 = (1-\nu^2)$. If one inspects this result in its dimensional form, it gives $c(\gamma\to 0) = (E/\rho)^{\frac{1}{2}}$, which is the longitudinal bar velocity. Further, we have

$$\lim_{\bar{\gamma}\to\infty}(4.3.27) = \bar{c}^4-\bar{c}^2 = 0, \qquad \bar{c} = 0, 1. \tag{4.3.29}$$

We also note, as $R\to\infty$, that $\bar{h}\to 0$ and the result (4.3.29) is again recovered from (4.3.27). The complete dispersion curves are shown in Fig. 4.23 for two different curvature ratios $\bar{h}$ and for a material having a Poisson's ratio of 0·3.

To obtain more general results on the propagation characteristics of waves in the longitudinal direction, we consider solutions for u, v, w of the form $f(\theta)\exp\{i(\gamma x-\omega t)\}$. Conditions on continuity of the displacements for θ and $\theta+2\pi$, similar to those arising in the analysis of circular membranes and plates, requires that $f(\theta) = \sin n\theta, \cos n\theta$. In order for separation of variables to occur, inspection of the governing equations (4.3.12)–(4.3.14) shows that

† See Problem 4.13.

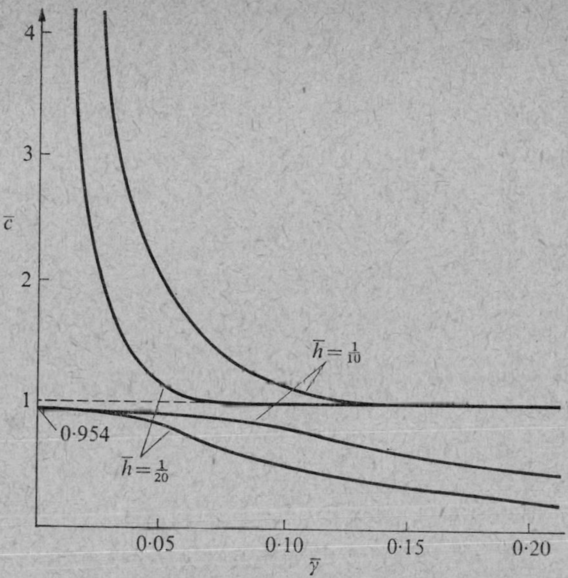

FIG. 4.23. Dispersion curves for a membrane shell for $\bar{h} = \frac{1}{10}$ and $\frac{1}{20}$

u, v, w must have the form

$$u = A\cos n\theta e^{i(\gamma x-\omega t)}, \qquad v = B\sin n\theta e^{i(\gamma x-\omega t)},$$
$$w = C\cos n\theta e^{i(\gamma x-\omega t)}. \tag{4.3.30}$$

A solution with the $\sin n\theta$, $\cos n\theta$ terms interchanged would also be valid. Proceeding to substitute (4.3.30) in the governing equations gives, after some simplification, rearrangement and the introduction of the previous non-dimensionalizations (4.3.25),

$$\begin{bmatrix} \left\{\bar{\omega}^2-\bar{\gamma}^2-\dfrac{(1-\nu)\bar{h}^2n^2}{2}\right\} & \dfrac{i(1+\nu)\bar{h}n\bar{\gamma}}{2} & i\nu\bar{h}\bar{\gamma} \\ \dfrac{i(1+\nu)}{2}\bar{h}n\bar{\gamma} & -\left\{\bar{\omega}^2+\bar{h}^2n^2-\dfrac{(1-\nu)}{2}\bar{\gamma}^2\right\} & \bar{h}^2n \\ i\nu\bar{h}\bar{\gamma} & n\bar{h}^2 & -(\bar{\omega}^2-\bar{h}^2) \end{bmatrix}\begin{bmatrix} A \\ B \\ C \end{bmatrix} = 0. \tag{4.3.31}$$

We first note that the case of $n = 0$ gives

$$\left\{\bar{\omega}^2-\frac{(1-\nu)}{2}\bar{\gamma}^2\right\}\left\{(\bar{\omega}^2-\bar{\gamma}^2)(\bar{\omega}^2-\bar{h}^2)-\nu^2\bar{h}^2\bar{\gamma}^2\right\} = 0. \tag{4.3.32}$$

The second bracketed term in the above is the previously-studied frequency eqn (4.3.25) for the axisymmetric longitudinal modes. The first bracketed term gives $\bar{\omega}^2 = (1-\nu)\bar{\gamma}^2/2$ or, in dimensional form,

$$\omega^2 = c_p^2 \frac{(1-\nu)}{2}\gamma^2 = \frac{G}{\rho}\gamma^2, \tag{4.3.33}$$

or, using $\omega = \gamma c$, we have that $c = c_s$. This is the result for the torsional mode. Of course, if $n = 0$ the torsional term in (4.3.30) vanishes. However, this would not be the case if the alternate solution involving the interchanged sines and cosines were used.

Investigation of the general result (4.3.31) for $n \neq 0$ becomes rather complex. The general motion of the membrane shell is transverse, such as in the transverse motion of a string. However, the deformation of the cross-section can be fairly complicated, depending on the value of n. While this aspect of analysis will not be further pursued, we remark that the study of waves in circular rods and shells according to the exact theory (Chapter 8) will have many similarities to the membrane-shell analysis.

4.3.3. *Longitudinal impact of a membrane shell*

The analysis of transient disturbances in the membrane shell is, of course, difficult, due to the complicated nature of the governing equations. Moreover, there does not appear to have been a great deal of analysis in this area. The coverage here will be restricted to a brief review and presentation of results obtained by Berkowitz [2] on the longitudinal impact of a semi-infinite cylindrical shell against a rigid surface. The basic situation is shown in Fig. 4.24 at the instant of impact of the shell, travelling to the left with velocity

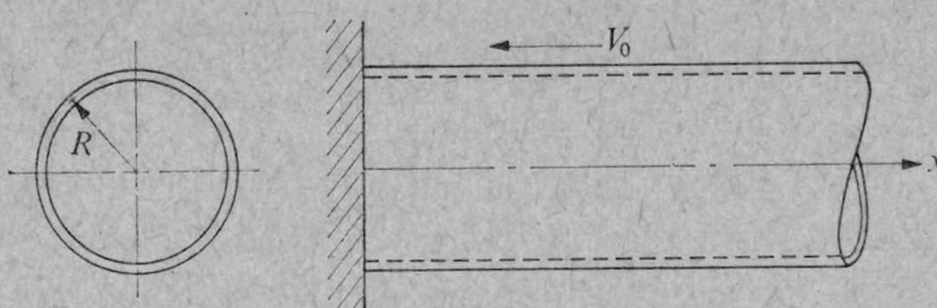

FIG. 4.24. Longitudinal impact of a cylindrical shell against a rigid barrier.

V_0, with the rigid surface.

Axisymmetric conditions pertain, so that the governing equations (4.3.15) and (4.3.17) describe the motion. The initial conditions of the problem are given by

$$u(x, 0) = w(x, 0) = \frac{\partial w(x, 0)}{\partial t} = 0, \qquad \frac{\partial u(x, 0)}{\partial t} = -V_0, \tag{4.3.34}$$

and the boundary conditions are

$$\partial u(0, t)/\partial t = 0, \qquad \partial u(\infty, t)/\partial t = -V_0. \tag{4.3.35}$$

Taking the Laplace transform of (4.3.15) and (4.3.17) gives

$$\frac{d^2\bar{u}}{dx^2}+\frac{\nu}{R}\frac{d\bar{w}}{dx} = \frac{s^2}{c_p^2}\bar{u}+\frac{V_0}{c_p^2},$$
$$-\frac{1}{R^2}\bar{w}-\frac{\nu}{R}\frac{d\bar{u}}{dx} = \frac{s^2}{c_p^2}\bar{w}, \tag{4.3.36}$$

where $\bar{u} = \bar{u}(x, s)$, $\bar{w} = \bar{w}(x, s)$, and the plate velocity c_p previously used has been introduced. Eliminating $\bar{w}$ in the first equation gives

$$\frac{d^2\bar{u}}{dx^2}-s^2\zeta^2\bar{u} = V_0\zeta^2, \tag{4.3.37}$$

where

$$\zeta^2 = \frac{s^2+c_p^2/R^2}{c_p^2(s^2+c_0^2/R^2)}, \qquad c_0^2 = \frac{E}{\rho}. \tag{4.3.38}$$

This has the solution

$$\bar{u} = Ae^{-s\zeta x}+Be^{s\zeta x}-\frac{V_0}{s^2}. \tag{4.3.39}$$

The transformed boundary conditions (4.3.35) are

$$\bar{u}(0, s) = 0, \quad \bar{u}(\infty, s) = -V_0/s^2. \tag{4.3.40}$$

These conditions give $B = 0$ and the resulting transformed solution

$$\bar{u} = -\frac{V_0}{s^2}+\frac{V_0}{s^2}e^{-s\zeta x}. \tag{4.3.41}$$

The solution for $\bar{w}$ is obtained by substituting the result for $\bar{u}$ in the second of (4.3.36), giving

$$\bar{w} = \frac{\nu V_0}{R}\frac{\zeta e^{-s\zeta x}}{s(s^2+c_p^2/R^2)}. \tag{4.3.42}$$

The transformed expression for the axial shell stress is

$$\bar{N}_x = \frac{Eh}{1-\nu^2}\left(\frac{d\bar{u}}{dx}+\frac{\nu}{R}\bar{w}\right). \tag{4.3.43}$$

Substituting the transformed solutions for $\bar{u}$, $\bar{w}$ in $\bar{N}_x$ gives

$$\bar{N}_x = \frac{-EhV_0}{(1-\nu^2)c_p^2}\frac{e^{-s\zeta x}}{s\zeta}. \tag{4.3.44}$$

We shall consider only the inversion of $\bar{N}_x$. We have

$$N_x(x, t) = \frac{-EhV_0}{(1-\nu^2)c_p^2}\frac{1}{2\pi i}\int_{c-i\infty}^{c+i\infty}\frac{e^{s(t-\zeta x)}}{s\zeta}\,ds. \tag{4.3.45}$$

Thus an evaluation of the integral I is sought, where

$$I = \int_{c-i\infty}^{c+i\infty} \frac{e^{s(t-\zeta x)}}{s\zeta} ds. \tag{4.3.46}$$

Applying the same arguments as used in the Timoshenko beam analysis (§ 3.4), it is seen that the Bromwich contour must be closed to the right for $t-\zeta x < 0$ and to the left for $t-\zeta x > 0$. For large s, inspection of the expression (4.3.38) for ζ shows that $\zeta \to 1/c_p$. Since (as it turns out) there are no poles for $\text{Re}\, s > c$, the result is that

$$I = 0, \qquad t < x/c_p. \tag{4.3.47}$$

This establishes the arrival time of the first possible disturbance. It corresponds to the previously-established short-wavelength limit velocity for the shell.

It is seen that the integrand of I has a simple pole at $s = 0$. Again considering ζ, we may write

$$\zeta = \frac{(s+ic_p/R)^{\frac{1}{2}}(s-ic_p/R)^{\frac{1}{2}}}{c_p(s+ic_0/R)^{\frac{1}{2}}(s-ic_0/R)^{\frac{1}{2}}}. \tag{4.3.48}$$

Thus branch points are located at $\pm ic_0/R$, $\pm ic_p/R$. Appropriate branch cuts are introduced to make the integrand single-valued. The resulting form of the contour, closed to the left and deformed about the branch cuts, is shown in Fig. 4.25. Now the integral along the arc AB may be shown to vanish.

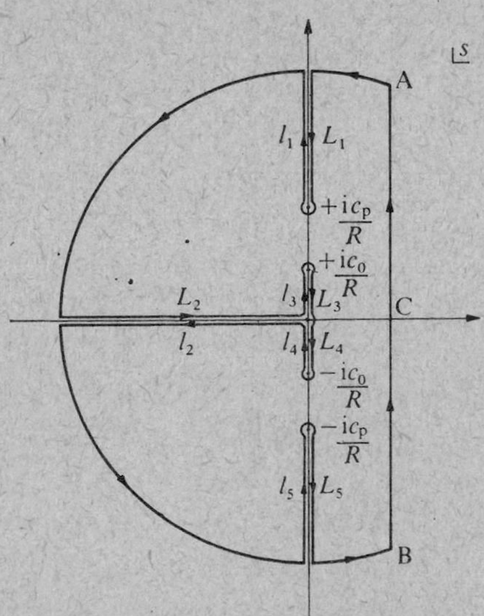

FIG. 4.25. Bromwich contour for evaluation of the integral I.

Furthermore, the integrals along L_2 and l_2 cancel. The remaining integrals contribute. Fortunately, they combine, giving the result that

$$I = I_1 + I_2, \tag{4.3.49}$$

where

$$I_1 = -\int_{c_p/R}^{\infty} \frac{F(s)}{s\zeta'}\,ds, \qquad I_2 = -\int_{0}^{c_0/R} \frac{F(s)}{s\zeta'}\,ds, \tag{4.3.50}$$

and where

$$F(s) = \sin(st+s\zeta'x) + \sin(st-s\zeta'x),$$
$$\zeta' = \frac{(c_p^2/R^2-s^2)^{\frac{1}{2}}}{c_p(c_0^2/R^2-s^2)^{\frac{1}{2}}}, \tag{4.3.51}$$

and where s is now real in the above expressions.

The result (4.3.49) represents the effective starting point of the analysis of Berkowitz [2]. The problem, of course, is to evaluate the integrals I_1 and I_2. The method of stationary phase is employed to obtain results for large time. The analysis is rather recondite and, while not necessarily beyond the scope of the present work, would prove quite lengthy to review here. The major result of the analysis is the predicted stress N_x for large values of time. This is shown in Fig. 4.26, where the dimensionless quantities

$$\hat{N}_x = N_x/DVh, \qquad \hat{x} = x/R, \qquad T = c_p t/R, \tag{4.3.52}$$

and

$$D = E/(1-\nu^2), \qquad V = V_0/c_p \tag{4.3.53}$$

have been introduced. The most interesting aspect of the result is the arrival time of the major part of the pulse. Although the first signal arrives at a given point according to the propagation velocity c_p, the main wavefront arrives according to the bar velocity c_0. The signal actually starts to rise slightly ahead

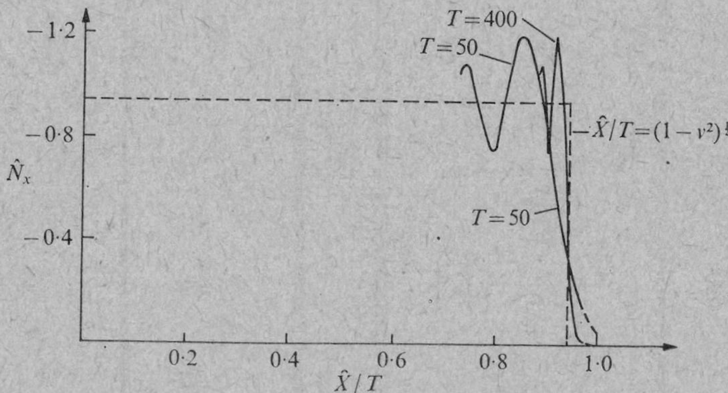

FIG. 4.26. Propagation of the N_x stress wave due to longitudinal impact. (After Berkowitz [2].)

of this time and peaks slightly after this time. The second aspect to note is the oscillatory character of the signal. The general behaviour of the oscillation is governed by the Airy integral. This type of response will be noted in several future analyses of step inputs to elastic systems. Some care must be used in interpreting the oscillatory behaviour for the values of $T = 50$ and 400. One might be tempted to conclude that the further the signal progressed, the more oscillatory it becomes. Exactly the opposite is true. To establish this, the width of the rising portion of the pulse should be calculated for the two values of time shown. The rise time at $T = 400$ is much slower, as it should be. It is the presentation of this data on the same scale that causes this illusion. No results are obtained for $\hat{x}/T < 0{\cdot}7$. However, the pulse quite likely decays to the dashed line. Finally, mention should be made as to other results not shown in the figure. The author's analysis showed a sharp spike pulse occurring at the c_p arrival time ($\hat{x}/T = 1$ in the figure). Evidently analysis by Miklowitz [11] of a somewhat similar problem in impact of rods also showed such a spike but this was discarded owing to considerations of the exact theory. The possibility exists that the spike stress arising in the analysis reviewed here should be similarly discarded but, as pointed out by Berkowitz, this awaits analysis of the shell-impact problem by exact theory.

References

1. Abramowitz, M. and Stegun, I. A. *Handbook of mathematical functions: with formulas, graphs, and mathematical tables*. Dover Publications, New York (1965).
2. Berkowitz, H. M. Longitudinal impact of a semi-infinite elastic cylindrical shell. *J. appl. Mech.* **30**, 347–54 (1963).
3. Dohrenwend, C. O., Drucker, D. C., and Moore, P. Transverse impact transients. *Exp. Stress Analysis* **1**, 1–10 (1944).
4. Donnell, L. H. *Stability of thin walled tubes under torsion*. NACA *Rep*. No. 479 (1933).
5. Flügge, W. *Statik und Dynamik der Schalen*. Springer-Verlag, Berlin (1934).
6. Hildebrand, F. B., Reissner, E., and Thomas, G. B. *Notes on the foundation of the theory of small displacements of orthotropic shells*. Tech. Notes natn. advis. Comm. Aeronaut., Wash. No. 1833, pp. 1–59 (1949).
7. Kraus, H. *Thin elastic shells*. John Wiley and Sons, New York (1967).
8. Leissa, A. W. *Vibrations of plates*. NASA S.P. 160 (1969).
9. Love, A. E. H. *A treatise on the mathematical theory of elasticity*. Dover Publications, New York (1944).
10. Medick, M. A. On classical plate theory and wave propagation. *J. appl. Mech.* **28**, 223–8 (1961)
11. Miklowitz, J. On the use of approximate theories of an elastic rod in problems of longitudinal impact. *Proc. 3rd U.S. natn. Congr. appl. Mech.* pp. 215–24. A.S.M.E. New York (1958).
12. Morse, P. M. *Vibration and sound*. McGraw-Hill, New York (1948).
13. Naghdi, P. M. On the theory of thin elastic shells. *Q. appl. Math.* **14**, 369–80 (1957).

14. PRESS, F. and OLIVER, J. Model study of air-coupled surface waves. *J. Acoust. Soc. Am.* **27**, 43–6 (1955).
15. SANDERS, J. L. An improved first approximation theory for thin shells. NASA tech. Rep. R24 (1959). Also see BUDIANSKY, B. and SANDERS, J. L. On the 'best' first order linear shell theory. *Progress in applied Mechanics*, Prager Anniversary Volume, p. 129. Macmillan, London (1963).
16. SNEDDON, I. N. *Fourier transforms*. McGraw-Hill, New York (1951).
17. TIMOSHENKO, S. and WOINOWSKY-KRIEGER, S. *Theory of plates and shells*. McGraw-Hill, New York (1959).
18. VLASOV, V. Z. *General theory of shells and its application to engineering*. Moscow-Leningrad (1949). NASA tech. Trans. 99 (1964).
19. WATSON, G. N. *A treatise on the theory of bessel functions* (2nd edn). Cambridge University Press (1966).

Problems

4.1. Derive the governing equation for the motion of a membrane in polar co-ordinates. Start from 'first principles', that is consider a polar element initially instead of a coordinate transformation.

4.2. Starting with a separation of variables solution to the membrane equation (4.1.3), with $p = 0$, develop the solution form (4.1.8).

4.3. Consider an infinite membrane resting on an elastic foundation. Obtain the dispersion curve governing propagation of plane waves in such a membrane.

4.4. Extending the considerations of Problem 4.3, consider a semi-infinite membrane $y > 0$, resting on an elastic foundation. Assuming fixed boundary conditions along $y = 0$, consider plane harmonic waves to be incident on the boundary. Determine the amplitude ratio of the reflected waves.

4.5. Consider the case of waves in a membrane strip defined by $x \geq 0, y = \pm b/2$. Consider the case of forced motion at the boundary $x = 0$, given by $w(0, y, t) = w_0 \cos py \exp(i\omega t)$, where $p = \pi/b$. Determine the resulting membrane response for frequencies above, at, and below the cutoff frequency.

4.6. Draw diagrams of the ω_{35} and ω_{42} modes of a rectangular membrane and the ω_{32} mode of a circular membrane.

4.7. Consider a circular membrane fixed along the outer radius b and having a rigid cylindrical mass of radius a attached in the centre. Derive the governing equation for the natural frequencies of this system.

4.8. Consider a membrane consisting of a circular sector fixed on all edges, where the sector radius is a and the angle is ϕ. Develop the equation for the natural frequencies.

4.9. Attempt to derive the governing equations and boundary conditions for a plate using energy considerations.

4.10. Attempt to derive the expression for the driving-point impedance (that is, the ratio of force to velocity) of a plate subjected to the harmonic pressure $p(r, \theta, t) = p_0 \exp(i\omega t)$, $r \leq a$.

4.11. Consider a semi-infinite plate having a free edge and consider plane harmonic waves to be impinging on the edge. Determine the reflected wave amplitude ratios B/A, C/A, where A is the amplitude of the incident wave.

4.12. Consider wave propagation in a plate strip of width $2a$, where the two edges of the strip are simply supported. Obtain the frequency equation governing the propagation of harmonic waves.

4.13. Consider longitudinal (instead of flexural) plane waves in a plate. Show that the propagation velocity of such waves is $c_p = \{E/\rho(1-\nu^2)\}^{\frac{1}{2}}$.

4.14. Derive the frequency equation for the natural frequencies of a clamped, circular plate.

4.15. Sketch the deformation mode of a cylindrical shell cross-section for the case of $n = 1$.

4.16. Consider the propagation of waves in membrane shells under the conditions $u = \partial/\partial x = 0$. Obtain the frequency equation governing the propagation. Compare the results to those obtained for waves in a curved ring. In what way does the model for the shell differ from that of the ring for this mode of propagation?

5 Waves in infinite media

WE NOW embark on a new phase of study of elastic wave propagation and vibrations. Our considerations will now be ruled by the exact equations and boundary conditions of infinitesimal isotropic elasticity theory. In our prior investigations of Chapters 1–4 the considerations were on strength-of-material theories for rods, plates, and shells. Inherent in all such theories were assumptions on the kinematics of deformation. Since the kinematics were generally only approximations of the true deformations, the resulting theories were approximate. Improvements in the theories were possible (for example, the Love rod theory and the Timoshenko beam theory), but only limited additional information was obtainable.

Thus, one objective in turning to the exact elasticity equations will be to develop exact theories for previously considered structural shapes such as rods, plates, and shells. Another objective, of equal importance, will be to consider classes of problems that have no counterparts in the elementary theories. In other words, problems that are inherently three-dimensional problems. These concern waves in extended media and the interaction of elastic waves with surfaces and boundaries.

As the first step in our investigation, we shall consider the class of problems for which boundary interactions are not possible, namely those involving infinite media. Fundamental insight will be obtained on the nature of elastic waves that may exist by considering special solutions to the equations of motion. Waves emanating from point disturbances will then be covered followed by the study of waves from various cavity sources.

5.1. Wave types

The basic elasticity equations will be presented, followed by resolution into scalar and vector potential equations. It will be shown that two basic types of wave, dilatational and distortional, can propagate in an infinite medium, with each being characterized by a specific velocity. Furthermore, these wave types can exist independent—or uncoupled—from one another. The propagation of plane waves will be studied, with the nature of the resulting displacement and stress fields being determined and shown graphically. Typical propagation velocities of dilatational and distortional waves are presented.

5.1.1. *The governing equations*

The equations for a homogeneous isotropic elastic solid may be summarized in Cartesian tensor notation as†

$$\begin{aligned} \tau_{ij,j}+\rho f_i &= \rho \ddot{u}_i \\ \tau_{ij} &= \lambda\varepsilon_{kk}\delta_{ij}+2\mu\varepsilon_{ij}, \\ \varepsilon_{ij} &= \tfrac{1}{2}(u_{i,j}+u_{j,i}), \\ \omega_{ij} &= \tfrac{1}{2}(u_{i,j}-u_{j,i}), \end{aligned} \tag{5.1.1}$$

where τ_{ij} is the stress tensor at a point and u_i is the displacement vector of a material point. The stress tensor is symmetric, so that $\tau_{ij} = \tau_{ji}$. The mass density per unit volume of the material is ρ and f_i is the body force per unit mass of material. The strain and rotation tensors are given by ε_{ij} and ω_{ij} respectively. It should he noted for the former that the factor of $\frac{1}{2}$ is now present in the shear strain, in contrast to the engineering definition of shear strain used in the earlier chapters. The elastic constants for the material are λ and μ, the Lamé constants. The latter is the usual shear modulus and both constants may be expressed in terms of the other elastic constants, such as Young's modulus, Poisson's ratio, and the bulk modulus.

The governing equations in terms of displacements are obtained by substituting the expression for strain into the stress–strain relation and that result into the stress equations of motion, giving Navier's equations for the media

$$(\lambda+\mu)u_{j,ji}+\mu u_{i,jj}+\rho f_i = \rho \ddot{u}_i. \tag{5.1.2}$$

The vector equivalent of this expression is

$$(\lambda+\mu)\nabla\nabla.\mathbf{u}+\mu\nabla^2\mathbf{u}+\rho\mathbf{f} = \rho\ddot{\mathbf{u}}. \tag{5.1.3}$$

In terms of rectangular scalar notation, this represents the three equations

$$\begin{aligned} (\lambda+\mu)\left(\frac{\partial^2 u}{\partial x^2}+\frac{\partial^2 v}{\partial x\,\partial y}+\frac{\partial^2 w}{\partial x\,\partial z}\right)+\mu\nabla^2 u+\rho f_x &= \rho\frac{\partial^2 u}{\partial t^2}, \\ (\lambda+\mu)\left(\frac{\partial^2 u}{\partial y\,\partial x}+\frac{\partial^2 v}{\partial y^2}+\frac{\partial^2 w}{\partial y\,\partial z}\right)+\mu\nabla^2 v+\rho f_y &= \rho\frac{\partial^2 v}{\partial t^2}, \\ (\lambda+\mu)\left(\frac{\partial^2 u}{\partial z\,\partial x}+\frac{\partial^2 v}{\partial z\,\partial y}+\frac{\partial^2 w}{\partial z^2}\right)+\mu\nabla^2 w+\rho f_z &= \rho\frac{\partial^2 w}{\partial t^2}, \end{aligned} \tag{5.1.4}$$

where u, v, w are the particle displacements in the x, y, z directions. Returning to the vector notation, we note that the dilatation of a material is defined by

$$\Delta = \nabla.\mathbf{u} = \varepsilon_x+\varepsilon_y+\varepsilon_z = \varepsilon_{kk}, \tag{5.1.5}$$

† See Appendix A for a review of the elasticity equations.

so that (5.1.3) may also be written as

$$(\lambda+\mu)\nabla\,\Delta+\mu\nabla^2\mathbf{u}+\rho\mathbf{f} = \rho\ddot{\mathbf{u}}. \tag{5.1.6}$$

The results (5.1.3) and (5.1.6) are the most commonly employed forms of the equations. An alternative form that also finds application is obtainable by using the vector identity

$$\nabla^2\mathbf{u} = \nabla\nabla.\mathbf{u}-\nabla\times\nabla\times\mathbf{u}. \tag{5.1.7}$$

Substituting the above result for $\nabla^2\mathbf{u}$ in (5.1.3) gives

$$(\lambda+2\mu)\nabla\nabla.\mathbf{u}-\mu\nabla\times\nabla\times\mathbf{u}+\rho\mathbf{f} = \rho\ddot{\mathbf{u}}. \tag{5.1.8}$$

Recalling that the rotation vector $\boldsymbol{\omega}$ is defined by

$$\boldsymbol{\omega} = \tfrac{1}{2}\nabla\times\mathbf{u}, \tag{5.1.9}$$

and again using the dilatation Δ, we may express the last result (5.1.8) as

$$(\lambda+2\mu)\nabla\,\Delta-2\mu\nabla\times\boldsymbol{\omega}+\rho\mathbf{f} = \rho\ddot{\mathbf{u}}. \tag{5.1.10}$$

One of the advantages of the last form is that it explicitly displays the dilatation and rotation. A greater advantage is that the result is valid in any curvilinear coordinate system, whereas the results (5.1.3) and (5.1.6) are valid only in rectangular coordinates.

We note the highly complex nature of the displacement equations of motion. It is possible to obtain a simpler set of equations by introducing the scalar and vector potentials Φ and $\mathbf{H}$ such that

$$\mathbf{u} = \nabla\Phi+\nabla\times\mathbf{H}, \qquad \nabla.\mathbf{H} = 0. \tag{5.1.11}$$

The resolution of a vector field into the gradient of a scalar and the curl of a zero-divergence vector is due to a theorem by Helmholtz.† The condition $\nabla.\mathbf{H} = 0$ provides the necessary additional condition to uniquely determine the three components of $\mathbf{u}$ from the four components of Φ, $\mathbf{H}$. We also express

$$\mathbf{f} = \nabla f+\nabla\times\mathbf{B}, \qquad \nabla.\mathbf{B} = 0. \tag{5.1.12}$$

Substituting (5.1.11) and (5.1.12) in (5.1.3) gives

$$(\lambda+\mu)\nabla\nabla.(\nabla\Phi+\nabla\times\mathbf{H})+\mu\nabla^2(\nabla\Phi+\nabla\times\mathbf{H})+\nabla f+\nabla\times\mathbf{B} = \rho(\nabla\ddot{\Phi}+\nabla\times\ddot{\mathbf{H}}). \tag{5.1.13}$$

These regroup to‡

$$\nabla\{(\lambda+2\mu)\nabla^2\Phi+\rho f-\rho\ddot{\Phi}\}+\nabla\times(\mu\nabla^2\mathbf{H}+\rho\mathbf{B}-\rho\ddot{\mathbf{H}}) = 0. \tag{5.1.14}$$

This equation will be satisfied if each bracketed term vanishes, thus giving

$$(\lambda+2\mu)\nabla^2\Phi+\rho f = \rho\ddot{\Phi}, \tag{5.1.15}$$

$$\mu\,\nabla^2\mathbf{H}+\rho\mathbf{B} = \rho\ddot{\mathbf{H}}. \tag{5.1.16}$$

† See Morse and Feshbach [16, pp. 52–3] for discussion and proof.

‡ One must use $\nabla.\nabla\Phi = \nabla^2\Phi$, the fact that $\nabla^2(\nabla\Phi) = \nabla(\nabla^2\Phi)$ and the fact that $\nabla.\nabla\times\mathbf{H} = 0$ to achieve the results.

An alternative form of the scalar and vector potential equations are obtained by substituting (5.1.11) into the general vector form (5.1.8). The result is

$$(\lambda+2\mu)\nabla^2\Phi+\rho f = \rho\ddot{\Phi}, \tag{5.1.17}$$

$$-\mu\,\nabla\times\nabla\times\mathbf{H}+\rho\mathbf{B} = \rho\ddot{\mathbf{H}}. \tag{5.1.18}$$

While it is evident that (5.1.14) will be satisfied if eqns (5.1.15) and (5.1.16) hold, it would also appear that values of Φ and $\mathbf{H}$ not satisfying these equations might still cause the original equation to be satisfied. This aspect, in fact, has been investigated by Sternberg [19] and Sternberg and Gintin [20], and it has been established that the complete solution is given by the solution of (5.1.15) and (5.1.16).

5.1.2. *Dilatational and distortional waves*

Consider the governing displacement equations in the absence of body forces, given by

$$(\lambda+\mu)\nabla\nabla.\mathbf{u}+\mu\,\nabla^2\mathbf{u} = \rho\ddot{\mathbf{u}}. \tag{5.1.19}$$

If the vector operation of divergence is performed on the above, we obtain

$$(\lambda+\mu)\nabla.(\nabla\nabla.\mathbf{u})+\mu\nabla.(\nabla^2\mathbf{u}) = \rho\nabla.\ddot{\mathbf{u}}. \tag{5.1.20}$$

Since $\nabla\cdot\nabla \sim \nabla^2$, $\nabla.(\nabla^2\mathbf{u}) = \nabla^2(\nabla.\mathbf{u})$, and $\nabla.\mathbf{u} = \Delta$, the dilatation, (5.1.20) reduces to

$$(\lambda+2\mu)\,\nabla^2\Delta = \rho\frac{\partial^2\Delta}{\partial t^2}. \tag{5.1.21}$$

This we recognize as the wave equation, expressible in the form

$$\nabla^2\Delta = \frac{1}{c_1^2}\frac{\partial^2\Delta}{\partial t^2}, \tag{5.1.22}$$

where the propagation velocity c_1 is given by†

$$c_1 = \left(\frac{\lambda+2\mu}{\rho}\right)^{\frac{1}{2}}. \tag{5.1.23}$$

We thus conclude that a change in volume, or dilatational disturbance, will propagate at the velocity c_1.

We now perform the operation of curl on the governing equation (5.1.20). Since the curl of the gradient of a scalar is zero, this gives

$$\mu\,\nabla^2\boldsymbol{\omega} = \rho\frac{\partial^2\boldsymbol{\omega}}{\partial t^2}, \tag{5.1.24}$$

† Alternative expressions in terms of E, k, ν are

$$c_1 = \left(\frac{E(1-\nu)}{\rho(1+\nu)(1-2\nu)}\right)^{\frac{1}{2}} = \left(\frac{3k(3k+E)}{\rho(9k-E)}\right)^{\frac{1}{2}} = \left(\frac{\mu(4\mu-E)}{\rho(3\mu-E)}\right)^{\frac{1}{2}}.$$

where $\boldsymbol{\omega} = \nabla \times \mathbf{u}/2$ is the previously-defined rotation vector. This result is in the form of the vector wave equation and may be expressed as

$$\nabla^2 \boldsymbol{\omega} = \frac{1}{c_2^2} \frac{\partial^2 \boldsymbol{\omega}}{\partial t^2}, \tag{5.1.25}$$

where the propagation velocity c_2 is given by

$$c_2 = \sqrt{(\mu/\rho)}. \tag{5.1.26}$$

Thus, rotational waves propagate with a velocity c_2 in the medium. This characteristic velocity has been previously encountered in Chapters 2 and 4 as the velocity of torsional waves in circular rods and membrane shells, and was indicated to be the propagation velocity of shear waves.

Reasoning slightly differently, suppose that the rotation $\boldsymbol{\omega}$ is zero. Then the displacement vector may be represented as the gradient of a scalar, namely, $\mathbf{u} = \nabla \psi$, so that (5.1.8) becomes, with $\mathbf{f} = 0$,

$$(\lambda + 2\mu) \nabla^2(\nabla \psi) = \rho \frac{\partial^2}{\partial t^2}(\nabla \psi). \tag{5.1.27}$$

This result also follows directly from (5.1.21). The interpretation here is that an irrotational disturbance propagates at the velocity c_1. In a similar manner, suppose that the dilatation Δ is zero. Then (5.1.6), with $\mathbf{f} = 0$, reduces directly to

$$\mu \nabla^2 \mathbf{u} = \rho \frac{\partial^2 \mathbf{u}}{\partial t^2}. \tag{5.1.28}$$

Here the velocity c_2 arises again. The interpretation of the result is that equivoluminal waves propagate at the velocity c_2.

Finally we refer to eqns (5.1.15) and (5.1.16), the equations that resulted from introducing the scalar and vector potentials Φ and $\mathbf{H}$. If the body forces are zero, we have $\mathbf{f} = \mathbf{B} = 0$, and the two equations again give the scalar and vector wave equations and contain the velocities c_1 and c_2. The significance of the Helmholtz resolution of $\mathbf{u}$ becomes even more apparent at this stage. The scalar potential is seen to be associated with the dilatational part of the disturbance, and the vector potential is associated with the rotational part.

We have thus found that waves may propagate in the interior of an elastic solid at two different speeds c_1 and c_2. Volumetric waves, involving no rotation, propagate at c_1 while rotational waves, involving no volume changes, propagate at c_2. The ratio of the two wave speeds may be expressed as

$$k = \frac{c_1}{c_2} = \left(\frac{\lambda + 2\mu}{\mu}\right)^{\frac{1}{2}} = \left(\frac{2 - 2\nu}{1 - 2\nu}\right)^{\frac{1}{2}}. \tag{5.1.29}$$

Since $0 \leq \nu \leq \frac{1}{2}$ always, we see that $c_1 > c_2$. Nominal values of the propagation velocities for several materials are given in Table 5.1.

TABLE 5.1
Propagation velocities c_1, c_2 for various materials†

	c_1		c_2	
Material	$\text{m s}^{-1}\times 10^{-3}$	$\text{in. s}^{-1}\times 10^{-4}$	$\text{m s}^{-1}\times 10^{-3}$	$\text{in. s}^{-1}\times 10^{-4}$
Aluminum	6·15	24·2	3·10	12·2
Brass	4·24	16·7	2·14	8·42
Copper	4·27	16·8	2·15	8·47
Gold	3·14	12·4	1·17	4·59
Iron	5·06	19·9	3·19	12·6
Lead	2·12	8·35	0·74	2·93
Magnesium	6·44	25·3	3·09	12·2
Nickel	5·59	22·0	2·93	11·6
Silver	3·45	13·6	1·57	6·17
Steel	5·71	22·5	3·16	12·4
Tin	2·96	11·6	1·49	5·87
Tungsten	4·78	18·8	2·64	10·4
Zinc	3·86	15·2	2·56	10·1

† Nominal values calculated from data on elastic constants and density.

A variety of terminology exists for the two wave-types. Dilatational waves are also called irrotational and primary (P) waves. The rotational waves are also called equi-voluminal, distortional, and secondary (S) waves. The P and S wave designations have arisen in seismology, where they are also occasionally picturesquely designated as the 'push' and 'shake' waves. Other respective designations frequently used are longitudinal and shear waves, although this aspect of their behaviour is yet to be investigated.

5.1.3. *Plane waves*

Let us now investigate the conditions under which plane waves may propagate in an infinite elastic solid. Our approach will be to generalize to three dimensions the approach taken in the study of plane waves in membranes (see, for example, Fig. 4.2 and eqn (4.1.8)). Thus, consider a plane wave, as shown in Fig. 5.1, and expressed by

$$\mathbf{u} = \mathbf{A}f(\mathbf{n}.\mathbf{r}-ct) \tag{5.1.30}$$

or, in index notation,

$$u_i = A_i f(n_k x_k - ct). \tag{5.1.31}$$

Thus, in (5.1.31), the vector A_i gives the particle displacement along the plane of the wave while n_i is the wave normal. We define the phase as ψ, where

$$\psi = n_k x_k - ct. \tag{5.1.32}$$

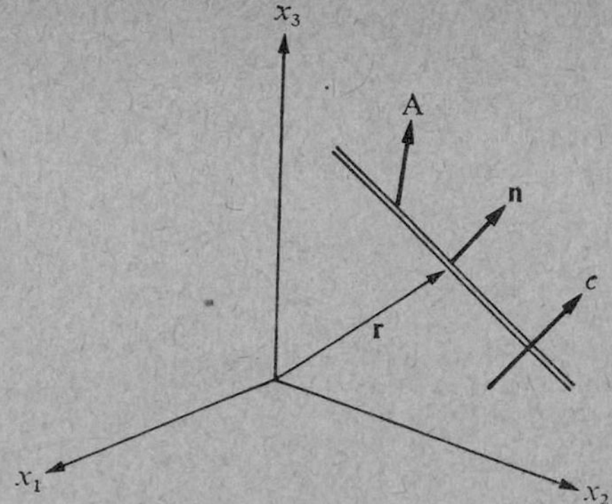

FIG. 5.1. Plane wave propagating in three dimensions.

In substituting (5.1.31) in the equations of motion (5.1.2) (with body forces zero), we must evaluate $u_{i,jj}$, $u_{j,ji}$, and $\ddot{u}_i$. We have that

$$u_{i,j} = A_i\frac{\partial f}{\partial x_j} = A_i\frac{\partial f}{\partial \psi}\frac{\partial \psi}{\partial x_j} = A_i f' n_j,$$
$$u_{i,jj} = A_i f'' n_j n_j = A_i f'', \qquad n_j n_j = 1, \tag{5.1.33}$$
$$u_{j,ji} = A_j f'' n_j n_i, \qquad \ddot{u}_i = c^2 A_i f''.$$

Thus the governing equations reduce to

$$(\lambda+\mu)A_j n_j n_i + \mu A_i = \rho c^2 A_i \qquad (i = 1, 2, 3). \tag{5.1.34}$$

This represents three homogeneous equations in the amplitude components A_1, A_2, A_3. Upon expanding the determinant of coefficients, there results

$$(\lambda+2\mu-\rho c^2)(\mu-\rho c^2)^2 = 0, \tag{5.1.35}$$

which gives the two roots

$$c_1 = [(\lambda+2\mu)/\rho]^{\frac{1}{2}}, \qquad c_2 = (\mu/\rho)^{\frac{1}{2}}, \tag{5.1.36}$$

which, again, are the velocities of dilatational and distortional waves. Thus, plane waves propagate at one or the other velocity in a media.

Let us now consider the nature of the displacements and tractions for plane waves. Without attempting a general development, we merely first postulate that u_i is parallel to n_i. If this is the case, we have that

$$A_j n_j = A, \qquad n_i = A_i/a, \tag{5.1.37}$$

so that (5.1.34) becomes

$$(\lambda+2\mu-\rho c^2)A_i = 0. \tag{5.1.38}$$

It may be further shown for this condition that $\nabla\times\mathbf{u} = 0$. The tractions are given by $t_i = \tau_{ij}n_j$. Using the stress–strain and the strain–displacement relations, this may be written as

$$t_i = \{\lambda u_{k,k}\,\delta_{ij}+\mu(u_{i,j}+u_{j,i})\}n_j. \tag{5.1.39}$$

Substituting expressions for $u_{i,j}$, $u_{k,k}$ derived as in (5.1.33) in the traction expression gives

$$t_i = \{(\lambda+\mu)A_k n_k n_i+\mu A_i\}f'. \tag{5.1.40}$$

Again, if u_i is parallel to n_i, using the result (5.1.37) in the above gives

$$t_i = (\lambda+2\mu)Af'n_i. \tag{5.1.41}$$

Thus, the tractions are parallel to the wave normal. Hence we have established that, if the displacements are in the direction of the wave normal, the propagation velocity of such a wave is c_1 and the stresses along the wave are normal to the front.

A second case is to consider the displacements to be perpendicular to the wave normal. Under these conditions, we have $A_j n_j = 0$, so that (5.1.34) reduces to

$$(\mu-\rho c^2)A_i = 0. \tag{5.1.42}$$

It may also be shown that $\nabla.\mathbf{u} = 0$ for this case. The traction expression (5.1.40) reduces immediately to

$$t_i = \mu A_i f'. \tag{5.1.43}$$

This indicates that the tractions are also perpendicular to the wavefront. Thus, for this case, the disturbance propagates at the velocity c_2 and only shearing stresses are acting along the wavefront.

All of the basic aspects of plane waves have now been demonstrated. At the risk of some redundancy, but for emphasis on the nature of the wave motion occurring, suppose that simple harmonic plane waves are propagating in the media. For simplicity, suppose they are propagating along a coordinate axis. Then, dropping the index notation, we write

$$u = A\mathrm{e}^{\mathrm{i}\gamma(x-ct)}, \qquad v = B\mathrm{e}^{\mathrm{i}\gamma(x-ct)}, \qquad w = C\mathrm{e}^{\mathrm{i}\gamma(x-ct)}, \tag{5.1.44}$$

where u, v, w are displacements in the x, y, z (or x_1, x_2, x_3) directions. Substitution in the governing eqn (5.1.4) gives

$$\gamma^2\{(\lambda+2\mu)-\rho c^2\}A = 0,$$
$$\gamma^2(\mu-\rho c^2)B = 0,$$
$$\gamma^2(\mu-\rho c^2)C = 0. \tag{5.1.45}$$

If $c = c_1$, which satisfies the first of (5.1.45), we see that $B = C = 0$ is required, whereas if $c = c_2$, satisfying the last two of (5.1.45), then $A = 0$ is required. In the first case, where $A \neq 0$, the motion is purely longitudinal, while in the last case, with $A = 0$, the motion is purely transverse. Also, in the last case, the transverse components B and C are independent of one another. For final emphasis, the basic nature of the particle motion for the two types of waves is shown in Fig. 5.2 for the present case of harmonic waves.

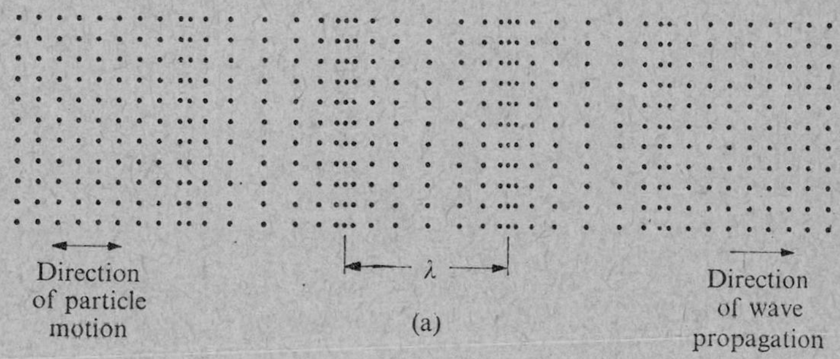

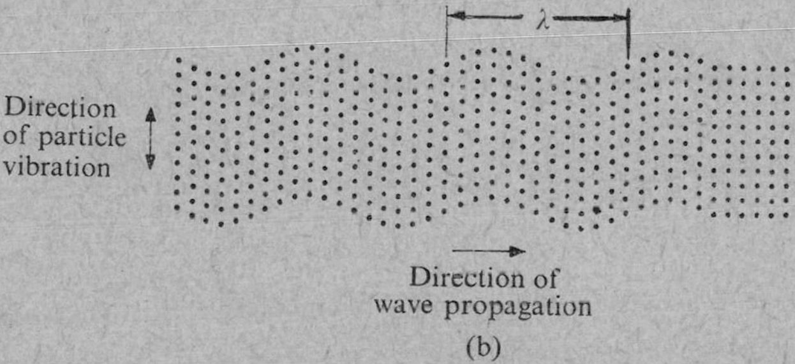

FIG. 5.2. Directions of particle motion for (a) dilatational and (b) transverse waves. (After Fredrick [14, Figs. 2.1, 2.3].)

5.2. Waves generated by body forces

Waves in a continuous and infinite elastic solid may result from imposing certain initial conditions of displacement and velocity on the media, with the disturbances propagating into the undisturbed media with increasing time. Mathematically, this requires consideration of the homogeneous equations of motion. Another source of waves results from time-varying body forces in the interior. This requires consideration of the non-homogeneous governing equations. Another wave source arises from time-varying forces on the walls of cavities embedded in the material, a type of problem that will be considered in the next section.

Solutions of body-force problems represented some of the earliest investigations of dynamical elasticity. Hence certain classical solutions contributed by Poisson, Kirchhoff, and others will be discussed briefly. Consideration will then be given to the analysis of two problems in wave propagation from body forces, one fairly simple and one not so simple.

5.2.1. *Certain classical solutions*

We have only considered various special solutions to the governing equations thus far, such as solutions demonstrating the existence of dilatational and rotational waves and the propagation of plane waves. In seeking solutions to the governing equations for arbitrary initial conditions and body forces, the equations in terms of the potentials Φ and $\mathbf{H}$ ((5.1.17) and (5.1.18)) are usually considered.

The classical initial-value problem, with body forces absent, was given the following formulation by Cauchy.

Given the values of a function $\Phi(x, y, z, t)$ and its time derivatives at $t = 0$,

$$\Phi(x, y, z, 0) = \Phi_0(x, y, z),$$
$$\left.\frac{\partial\Phi(x, y, z, t)}{\partial t}\right|_{t=0} = \Phi_1(x, y, z), \tag{5.2.1}$$

determine the function $\Phi(\bar{x}, \bar{y}, \bar{z}, t)$ which satisfies the given conditions and the wave equation $\nabla^2\Phi = \ddot{\Phi}/c^2$.

Since the formulation pertains only to a single scalar equation, it is in reality a problem in acoustics. However, since the governing equations in potential form are four scalar wave equations of similar form (in rectangular coordinates), solution of the Cauchy problem has application in elasticity.

Both Poisson (1820) and Kirchhoff (1883) contributed solutions to this problem. In addition to the original papers, refer to Love† for a review of these works. Rayleigh‡ also has contributed in this field. Kirchhoff presented the more general solution to the problem. While the intricacies of developing this classical solution will not be presented here, the results will be given.

Consider a volume V of material bounded by the surface S as shown in Fig. 5.3.

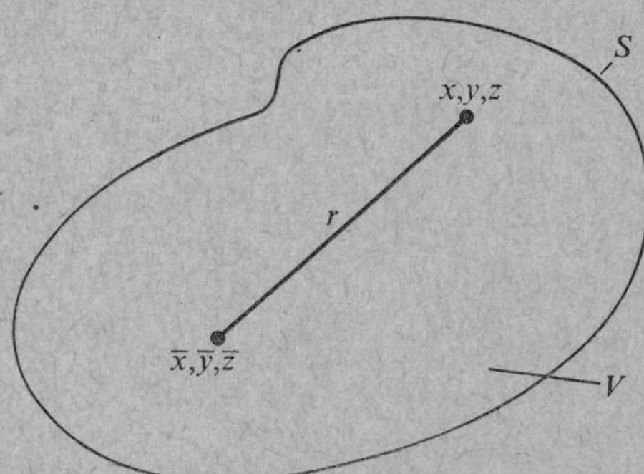

FIG. 5.3. A volume V of material bounded by the surface S.

† pp. 300–2 of Reference [12]. In addition, arbitrary initial conditions involving both dilatational and distortional disturbances are discussed on pp. 302–4 of that Reference.

‡Vol. 2 of Reference [17].

The Kirchhoff analysis considers a single scalar equation with body force included, given by

$$c^2\nabla^2\Phi+f = \partial^2\Phi/\partial t^2. \tag{5.2.2}$$

The solution to this, often called the retarded potential solution, is given by

$$\Phi(\bar{x}, \bar{y}, \bar{z}, t) = \frac{1}{4\pi c^2}\int_V \frac{1}{r}[f]\,\mathrm{d}V+\frac{1}{4\pi}\int_S \left(\frac{1}{r}\left[\frac{\partial\Phi}{\partial n}\right]-[\Phi]\frac{\partial r^{-1}}{\partial n}+\frac{1}{cr}\frac{\partial r}{\partial n}\left[\frac{\partial\Phi}{\partial t}\right]\right)\mathrm{d}S, \tag{5.2.3}$$

where $[f]$, $[\partial\Phi/\partial n]$, and other bracketed terms are given according to

$$[f] = f \quad\text{at}\quad t = t-r/c. \tag{5.2.4}$$

Thus, the solution at any given point and time $(\bar{x}, \bar{y}, \bar{z}, t)$ is found from the solution at an earlier (or 'retarded') time $t-r/c$. The result may be looked upon as embodying Huygen's principle, which states that every point on a wavefront acts as a source, emitting waves travelling at velocity c.

The solution to problems involving motion due to body forces are obtainable by proper application of the Kirchhoff results. In 1849 Stokes evidently used this method to solve the problem of a concentrated force acting at the origin in a media (the solution to this problem preceded solution to the static counterpart). By superposition of the results for a single force, the case of a centre of twist or dilatation can be obtained. Love† reviews the analyses in this field.

5.2.2. *The simple SH wave source*

For our first analysis of waves generated by body forces in an infinite media, we shall consider the 'SH' wave source. The designation is somewhat in anticipation of later studies of waves in a half-space. Basically, we assume that the following holds for displacements and body forces:

$$\begin{aligned} u_x = u_y = 0, &\qquad u_z = u_z(x, y, t),\\ f_x = f_y = 0, &\qquad f_z = f_z(x, y, t). \end{aligned} \tag{5.2.5}$$

Under these circumstances, the governing equations (5.1.4) reduce to

$$\mu\nabla^2 u_z+\rho f_z = \rho\ddot{u}_z, \qquad \nabla^2 = \frac{\partial^2}{\partial x^2}+\frac{\partial^2}{\partial y^2}. \tag{5.2.6}$$

The particle motions are polarized in a single direction and the resulting waves will be shear waves propagating at the velocity c_2. The SH designation pertains to 'horizontally polarized shear (or secondary) waves'. The governing equation, it should be noted, is the same as for the transverse motion of membranes. We shall consider several aspects of solution in the following.

† Pp. 304–6 of Reference [12].

As a first illustration, suppose the body force has a harmonic time variation given by

$$f_z = c_2^2 F(x, y)e^{-i\omega t}. \tag{5.2.7}$$

If we assume that $u_z = U(x, y)\exp(-i\omega t)$, then the governing equation (5.2.6) reduces to

$$\nabla^2 U + \beta^2 U = -F(x, y), \qquad \beta^2 = \omega^2/c_2^2. \tag{5.2.8}$$

We will use the double Fourier transform defined by

$$\bar{h}(\xi, \eta) = \frac{1}{2\pi}\int_{-\infty}^{\infty}\int_{-\infty}^{\infty} h(x, y)e^{-i(\xi x+\eta y)}\,dx\,dy. \tag{5.2.9}$$

Applying this transform to (5.2.8) gives the transformed solution

$$\bar{U}(\xi, \eta) = \frac{\bar{F}(\xi, \eta)}{\xi^2+\eta^2-\beta^2}, \tag{5.2.10}$$

with the inverse given by

$$U(x, y, \omega) = \frac{1}{2\pi}\int_{-\infty}^{\infty}\int_{-\infty}^{\infty} \frac{\bar{F}(\xi, \eta)}{\xi^2+\eta^2-\beta^2}e^{i(\xi x+\eta y)}\,d\xi\,d\eta. \tag{5.2.11}$$

Suppose the loading is given by the concentrated line load at x_0, y_0,

$$F(x, y) = \delta(x-x_0)\delta(y-y_0). \tag{5.2.12}$$

Then the solution (5.2.11) is the Green's function

$$G(\mathbf{r}, \mathbf{r}_0, \omega) = \frac{1}{2\pi}\int_{-\infty}^{\infty}\int_{-\infty}^{\infty} \frac{\exp\{i\xi(x-x_0)+i\eta(y-y_0)\}}{\xi^2+\eta^2-\beta^2}\,d\xi\,d\eta. \tag{5.2.13}$$

The above is a formal result. The axisymmetry existing about the axis x_0, y_0 enables an explicit solution form to be obtained. This may be better recognized with the aid of Fig. 5.4. Thus, we may write

$$\mathbf{l} = \xi\mathbf{i}+\eta\mathbf{j}, \qquad \mathbf{R} = (x-x_0)\mathbf{i}+(y-y_0)\mathbf{j}. \tag{5.2.14}$$

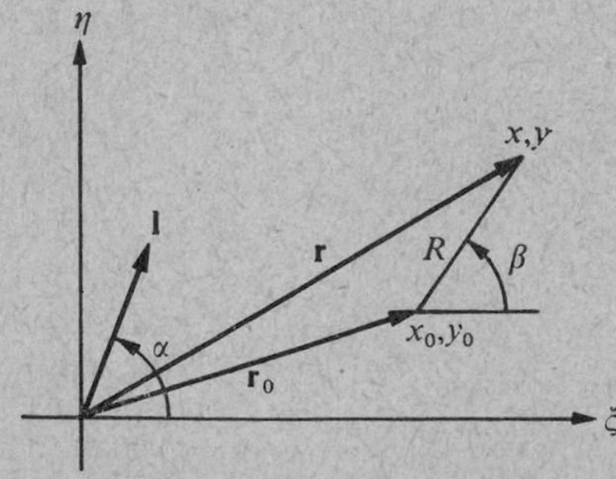

FIG. 5.4. ξ,η-plane representation of $\exp\{i\xi(x-x_0)+i\eta(y-y_0)\}$.

Then (5.2.13) may be expressed in the form

$$G(\mathbf{r}, \mathbf{r}_0, \omega) = \frac{1}{2\pi}\int_{-\infty}^{\infty}\int_{-\infty}^{\infty}\frac{\exp(\mathrm{i}\mathbf{l}\,.\,\mathbf{R})}{l^2-\beta^2}\,\mathrm{d}\xi\,\mathrm{d}\eta. \tag{5.2.15}$$

This may be converted to a polar-coordinate representation l, α if it is noted that $\mathrm{d}\xi\,\mathrm{d}\eta = l\,\mathrm{d}l\,\mathrm{d}\alpha$ and that $\mathbf{l}\,.\,\mathbf{R} = lR\cos(\alpha-\beta)$. Then (5.2.15) becomes

$$G(\mathbf{r}, \mathbf{r}_0, \omega) = \frac{1}{2\pi}\int_0^{\infty} l\,\mathrm{d}l\int_0^{2\pi}\frac{\exp\{\mathrm{i}lR\cos(\alpha-\beta)\}}{l^2-\beta^2}\,\mathrm{d}\alpha. \tag{5.2.16}$$

The integral with respect to α is in the form that defines the Bessel function† $2\pi J_0(lR)$. So we have

$$G(\mathbf{r}, \mathbf{r}_0, \omega) = \int_0^{\infty}\frac{J_0(lR)}{l^2-\beta^2}\,l\,\mathrm{d}l. \tag{5.2.17}$$

This integral also is of a known form. Thus it is known that

$$\int_0^{\infty}\frac{J_0(lR)}{l^2+\beta^2}\,l\,\mathrm{d}l = K_0(\beta R), \tag{5.2.18}$$

where $K_0(\beta R)$ is the modified Bessel function of the second kind. We also have that

$$K_0(z) = \frac{\pi\mathrm{i}}{2}H_0^{(1)}(\mathrm{i}z). \tag{5.2.19}$$

Thus we have that

$$\int_0^{\infty}\frac{J_0(lR)}{l^2-\beta^2}\,l\,\mathrm{d}l = \frac{\pi\mathrm{i}}{2}H_0^{(1)}(\beta R), \tag{5.2.20}$$

and

$$G(\mathbf{r}, \mathbf{r}_0, \omega) = \frac{\pi\mathrm{i}}{2}H_0^{(1)}(\beta R). \tag{5.2.21}$$

The objective here is to illustrate general analysis procedures. In the case of a concentrated, harmonic load acting at the origin, working in polar coordinates is most direct. Thus, the governing equation still has the form

$$\nabla^2 u_z - \frac{1}{c_2^2}\frac{\partial^2 u_z}{\partial t^2} = -F_z(r)\mathrm{e}^{-\mathrm{i}\omega t}, \tag{5.2.22}$$

where

$$\nabla^2 = \frac{\partial^2}{\partial r^2}+\frac{1}{r}\frac{\partial}{\partial r}. \tag{5.2.23}$$

† See pp. 1361–2 of Reference [16] for this result and other aspects of the present development.

Again letting $u_z(r, t) = U(r)\exp(-i\omega t)$ we have

$$\nabla^2 U + \beta^2 U = -F(r), \qquad \beta^2 = \omega^2/c_2^2. \tag{5.2.24}$$

Applying the Hankel transform† to this equation, we obtain the transformed solution

$$\bar{U} = \bar{F}(\xi)/(\xi^2 - \beta^2), \tag{5.2.25}$$

with the inverse given by

$$U(r) = \int_0^\infty \frac{\xi \bar{F}(\xi)}{\xi^2 - \beta^2} J_0(\xi r)\, dr. \tag{5.2.26}$$

For a concentrated line load, we let‡ $F(r) = \delta(r)/2\pi r$ so that $\bar{F}(\xi) = \frac{1}{2}\pi$. Then

$$U(r) = \frac{1}{2\pi} \int_0^\infty \frac{\xi J_0(\xi r)}{\xi^2 - \beta^2}\, d\xi. \tag{5.2.27}$$

The results for this integral have just been given by (5.2.20), so that we have

$$U(r) = \frac{i}{4} H_0^{(1)}(\beta r). \tag{5.2.28}$$

Instead of considering a harmonic load, it is possible to use the triple Fourier transform, defined by

$$\bar{h}(\xi, \eta, \omega) = \frac{1}{(2\pi)^{\frac{3}{2}}} \int_{-\infty}^{\infty} \int_{-\infty}^{\infty} \int_{-\infty}^{\infty} h(x, y, t) e^{-i(\xi x + \eta y - \omega t)}\, dx\, dy\, dt, \tag{5.2.29}$$

with the inverse given by

$$h(x, y, t) = \frac{1}{(2\pi)^{\frac{3}{2}}} \int_{-\infty}^{\infty} \int_{-\infty}^{\infty} \int_{-\infty}^{\infty} \bar{h}(\xi, \eta, \omega) e^{i(\xi x + \eta y - \omega t)}\, d\xi\, d\eta\, d\omega. \tag{5.2.30}$$

Applying this transform to the governing equation (5.2.6) gives the result

$$\bar{u}(\xi, \eta, \omega) = \frac{\bar{F}(\xi, \eta, \omega)}{(\xi^2 + \eta^2 - \omega^2)/c_2^2}, \tag{5.2.31}$$

where the body force has been taken to be $f(x, y, t) = c_2^2 F(x, y, t)$. The inverse is given by

$$u(x, y, t) = \frac{1}{(2\pi)^{\frac{3}{2}}} \int_{-\infty}^{\infty} \int_{-\infty}^{\infty} \int_{-\infty}^{\infty} \frac{\bar{F}(\xi, \eta, \omega)}{(\xi^2 + \eta^2 - \omega^2)/c_2^2} e^{i(\xi x + \eta y - \omega t)}\, d\xi\, d\eta\, d\omega. \tag{5.2.32}$$

† See Appendix B.4; also see §§ 4.1, 4.2 for previous applications.

‡ See § 4.2 for the basis for obtaining this result.

The result is particularly instructive to consider. The exponential term in the above should be recognized as corresponding to plane harmonic waves. The solution may thus be regarded as a superposition of plane waves. The previously obtained solution for the harmonic source may also be interpreted in this manner. The particular result (5.2.13), for example, may be regarded as the plane-wave representation of the Bessel function.

Let us now consider the case of an impulse source. Thus, suppose

$$f(x, y, t) = c_2^2\delta(x-x_0)\delta(y-y_0)\delta(t). \tag{5.2.33}$$

The solution to this problem will yield the Green's function $g(\mathbf{r}, \mathbf{r}_0, t)$. We could consider obtaining this result directly. However, since the result $G(\mathbf{r}, \mathbf{r}_0, \omega)$ has been obtained already, we shall use a basic relationship holding between the two Green's functions. Thus, it may be shown that the Laplace transform of $g(\mathbf{r}, \mathbf{r}_0, t)$ gives $G(\mathbf{r}, \mathbf{r}_0, \omega)$, namely,

$$\mathscr{L}\{g(\mathbf{r}, \mathbf{r}_0, t)\} = G(\mathbf{r}, \mathbf{r}_0, \omega). \tag{5.2.34}$$

The approach taken will be indirect and will illustrate, for the first time, an elegant means of inverting Laplace transforms that will be used in later studies. Returning to (5.2.17), we replace ω by is, thus giving

$$G(\mathbf{r}, \mathbf{r}_0, \mathrm{i}s) = \int_0^\infty \frac{J_0(lR)}{l^2+s^2/c_2^2}\, l\,\mathrm{d}l = K_0\left(\frac{sR}{c_2}\right). \tag{5.2.35}$$

The integral representation for K_0 may be rearranged† to the form

$$K_0\left(\frac{sR}{c_2}\right) = \int_1^\infty \frac{\exp(-sR\tau/c_2)}{(\tau^2-1)^{\frac{1}{2}}}\,\mathrm{d}\tau. \tag{5.2.36}$$

The form of the exponential is suggestive of the Laplace transform definition

$$\bar{f}(s) = \int_0^\infty f(t)\mathrm{e}^{-st}\,\mathrm{d}t. \tag{5.2.37}$$

We introduce the change of variables $t = R\tau/c_2$, so that (5.2.36) becomes

$$K_0\left(\frac{sR}{c_2}\right) = \int_{R/c_2}^\infty \frac{\mathrm{e}^{-st}\,\mathrm{d}t}{\{t^2-(R/c_2)^2\}^{\frac{1}{2}}}. \tag{5.2.38}$$

† See pp. 1363 of Reference [16].

This is nearly of the form of the Laplace transformation except for the lower limit. We introduce the step function $H\langle t-R/c_2\rangle$, so that (5.2.38) becomes

$$K_0\left(\frac{sR}{c_2}\right) = \int_0^\infty \frac{e^{-st}H\langle t-R/c_2\rangle}{\{t^2-(R/c_2)^2\}^{\frac{1}{2}}}\,dt = \mathscr{L}\left[\frac{H\langle t-R/c_2\rangle}{\{t-(R/c_2)^2\}^{\frac{1}{2}}}\right]. \tag{5.2.39}$$

Thus we have expressed the Green's function $G(\mathbf{r}, \mathbf{r}_0, \omega)$ in terms of a Laplace transformation. Referring to the basic relationship (5.2.34) we have, by inspection of the result (5.2.38), that

$$g(\mathbf{r}, \mathbf{r}_0, t) = H\langle t-R/c_2\rangle\{t^2-(R/c_2)^2\}^{-\frac{1}{2}}. \tag{5.2.40}$$

The result shows no disturbance prior to $t = R/c_2$. A sharp front arrives at that time and a wake exists behind the front. This is, of course, the result obtained in the analysis of the membrane initial-value problem.† This scheme for obtaining the inverse transformation of a function is known as Cagniard's method‡ and will find application in the analysis of the half-space problem and elsewhere.

5.2.3. *More general body forces*

We now will consider more general body-force loading than the SH wave source considered in the previous section. The analysis presented will basically follow a portion of the analysis by Eason, Fulton, and Sneddon [5]. Thus, consider again the displacement equations of motion (5.1.2). We introduce the four-dimensional Fourier transform, defined by

$$\bar{\phi}(\xi_1, \xi_2, \xi_3, \omega) = \frac{1}{4\pi^2}\int_{V_4} \phi(x_1, x_2, x_3, \tau)\exp\{i(\xi_p x_p+\omega\tau)\}\,dV_4 \quad (p = 1, 2, 3), \tag{5.2.41}$$

where $dV_4 = dx_1\,dx_2\,dx_3\,d\tau$ and V_4 denotes the entire $x_1x_2x_3t$ space. The inverse is simply

$$\phi(x_1, x_2, x_3, \tau) = \frac{1}{4\pi^2}\int_{\bar{V}_4} \bar{\phi}(\xi_1, \xi_2, \xi_3, \omega)\exp\{-i(\xi_p x_p+\omega\tau)\}\,d\bar{V}_4, \tag{5.2.42}$$

where $d\bar{V}_4 = d\xi_1\,d\xi_2\,d\xi_3\,d\omega$. The symbol τ corresponds to a spatial coordinate defined by $\tau = c_1 t$. Thus, the spatial coordinate is determined by the time.

† See § 4.1.
‡ See Reference [3].

We apply the transform (5.2.41) to the governing equations. Retaining the index notation, we obtain the transformed equations

$$(\lambda+\mu)\xi_p\xi_q\bar{u}_q+\mu\xi_q\xi_q\bar{u}_p-\rho c_1^2\omega^2\bar{u}_p = \rho\bar{f}_p, \tag{5.2.43}$$

where the time t has been replaced by τ/c_1 before transformation. The determinant of coefficients for this set of equations gives

$$D = \{(\lambda+2\mu)\gamma^2-\rho c_1^2\omega^2\}(\mu\gamma^2-\rho c_1^2\omega^2)^2, \tag{5.2.44}$$

where $\gamma^2 = \xi_1^2+\xi_2^2+\xi_3^2$. The solution for $\bar{u}_1$ is given by

$$\bar{u}_1 = (\mu\gamma^2-\rho c_1^2\omega^2)[\{(\lambda+2\mu)\gamma^2-\rho c_1^2\omega^2\}\rho\bar{f}_1-(\lambda+\mu)\xi_1(\rho\bar{f}_q\xi_q)]/D. \tag{5.2.45}$$

The solution for all $\bar{u}_p$ is obtained merely by replacing the unity subscripts of $\bar{f}_1$, ξ_1 by p. Introducing the definition

$$\beta^2 = (\lambda+2\mu)/\mu, \tag{5.2.46}$$

it is possible to write the transformed solution for $\bar{u}_p$ as

$$\bar{u}_p = \frac{\beta^2(\gamma^2-\omega^2)\bar{f}_p-(\beta^2-1)\xi_p\xi_q\bar{f}_q}{c_1^2(\gamma^2-\omega^2)(\gamma^2-\beta^2\omega^2)}. \tag{5.2.47}$$

Expressions for the transformed strains $\bar{\varepsilon}_{pq}$, dilatation $\bar{\Delta}$, stresses $\bar{\tau}_{pq}$, and principal stresses $\bar{\tau}_{pp}$ are also given by Eason *et al.* [5]. The inverted expressions for the displacements are

$$u_p = \frac{1}{4\pi^2}\int\limits_{V_4}\frac{\beta^2(\gamma^2-\omega^2)\bar{f}_p-(\beta^2-1)\xi_p\xi_q\bar{f}_q}{c_1^2(\gamma^2-\omega^2)(\gamma^2-\beta^2\omega^2)}\exp\{-i(\xi_r x_r+\omega\tau)\}\,dV_4. \tag{5.2.48}$$

Now, the analysis by Eason *et al.* is quite extensive and covers two-dimensional and three-dimensional axisymmetric problems under a variety of loading conditions (harmonic, impulse, step). A large portion of the work pertains to various moving-load problems. Even the results for a static loading are recovered as a special case. Only the two-dimensional problem of the displacements produced by harmonic and impulse loadings will be pursued here in detail.

To two-dimensionalize the results (5.2.48), we first note that $f_3 = 0$ and all quantities will be a function of x_1, x_2 only. The three-dimensional Fourier transform would be appropriate and would result in $u_\alpha(\alpha = 1, 2)$ being given by

$$u_\alpha = \frac{1}{(2\pi)^{\frac{3}{2}}}\int\limits_{\bar{V}_3}\frac{\beta^2(\gamma^2-\omega^2)\bar{f}_\alpha-(\beta^2-1)\xi_\alpha\xi_\eta\bar{f}_\eta}{c_1^2(\gamma^2-\omega^2)(\gamma^2-\beta^2\omega^2)}\exp\{-i(\xi_\eta x_\eta+\omega\tau)\}\,d\bar{V}_3, \tag{5.2.49}$$

where now $\gamma^2 = \xi_1^2+\xi_2^2$ and α, $\eta = 1, 2$. In the following, we shall revert to rectangular coordinate notation, where $x = x_1$, $y = x_2$, $u = u_1$, $v = u_2$. If we confine our attention to those problems where the body force $f_y = 0$, we have the two-dimensional displacement solutions given by

$$u = \frac{1}{c_1^2(2\pi)^{\frac{3}{2}}} \int\limits_{V_3} \frac{\{\beta^2(\xi^2+\eta^2-\omega^2)-(\beta^2-1)\xi^2\}}{(\xi^2+\eta^2-\omega^2)(\xi^2+\eta^2-\beta^2\omega^2)} \bar{f}_x e^{-i(\xi x+\eta y+\omega\tau)}\, dV_3, \quad (5.2.50)$$

$$v = \frac{-(\beta^2-1)}{c_1^2(2\pi)^{\frac{3}{2}}} \int\limits_{V_3} \frac{\xi\eta\bar{f}_x e^{-i(\xi x+\eta y+\omega\tau)}}{(\xi^2+\eta^2-\omega^2)(\xi^2+\eta^2-\beta^2\omega^2)}\, dV_3. \quad (5.2.51)$$

As a first type of loading, suppose that f_x is a harmonic force concentrated at the origin and given by

$$f_x = \frac{F}{p}\delta(x)\delta(y)e^{i\lambda\tau}, \qquad \lambda = p/c_1, \quad (5.2.52)$$

and p is the usual radial frequency. The three-dimensional transform of f_x is given by

$$\bar{f}_x = \frac{1}{(2\pi)^{\frac{3}{2}}} \int\limits_{V_3} f_x e^{i(\xi x+\eta y+\omega\tau)}\, dV_3. \quad (5.2.53)$$

Substituting (5.2.52) in the above gives†

$$\bar{f}_x = \frac{F}{\sqrt{(2\pi)}\,p}\delta(\omega+\lambda). \quad (5.2.54)$$

Before substituting $\bar{f}_x$ in the inversion integrals, we use partial fractions and rewrite (5.2.50) and (5.2.51) as

$$u = \frac{1}{c_1^2(2\pi)^{\frac{3}{2}}} \int\limits_{V_3} \frac{\bar{f}_x}{\xi^2+\eta^2} \left(\frac{\xi^2}{\xi^2+\eta^2-\omega^2} + \frac{\beta^2\eta^2}{\xi^2+\eta^2-\beta^2\omega^2}\right) e^{-i(\xi x+\eta y+\omega\tau)}\, dV_3, \quad (5.2.55)$$

$$v = \frac{1}{c_1^2(2\pi)^{\frac{3}{2}}} \int\limits_{V_3} \frac{\xi\eta\bar{f}_x}{\xi^2+\eta^2} \left(\frac{1}{\xi^2+\eta^2-\omega^2} - \frac{\beta^2}{\xi^2+\eta^2-\beta^2\omega^2}\right) e^{-i(\xi x+\eta y+\omega\tau)}\, dV_3. \quad (5.2.56)$$

When (5.2.54) is substituted into these last results for u and v, the integration with respect to ω follows immediately by virtue of the properties of the Dirac delta function. The results may be expressed in the relatively simple form

$$u = -\frac{Fe^{i\lambda\tau}}{4\pi^2\mu\beta^2}\left[\frac{\partial^2}{\partial x^2}I(x, y, \lambda)+\beta^2\frac{\partial^2}{\partial y^2}I(x, y, \beta\lambda)\right], \quad (5.2.57)$$

$$v = -\frac{Fe^{i\lambda\tau}}{4\pi^2\mu\beta^2}\left[\frac{\partial^2}{\partial x\,\partial y}\{I(x, y, \lambda)-\beta^2 I(x, y, \beta\lambda)\}\right], \quad (5.2.58)$$

† We have previously established the Fourier transform of a harmonic function by an inverse argument. Thus

$$\int\limits_{-\infty}^{\infty} \delta(\omega+\lambda)e^{-i\omega\tau}\, d\omega = e^{i\lambda\tau}.$$

where

$$I(x, y, \lambda) = \int_{-\infty}^{\infty}\int_{-\infty}^{\infty} \frac{e^{-i(\xi x+\eta y)}\, d\xi\, d\eta}{(\xi^2+\eta^2)(\xi^2+\eta^2-\lambda^2)}. \tag{5.2.59}$$

We now introduce a change of variables quite similar in form to that used on the SH wave source problem (see Fig. 5.4) previously analysed. Thus, let $\xi = \rho \cos \phi$, $\eta = \rho \sin \phi$, $x = r \cos \theta$, $y = r \sin \theta$. The integral I then is given by

$$I(r, \theta, \lambda) = \int_0^{2\pi}\int_0^{\infty} \frac{e^{-i\rho r \cos(\phi-\theta)}}{\rho(\rho^2-\lambda^2)}\, d\rho\, d\phi. \tag{5.2.60}$$

The integration with respect to ϕ makes use of the result that†

$$J_0(z) = \frac{1}{2\pi}\int_0^{2\pi} e^{\pm iz \sin \phi}\, d\phi. \tag{5.2.61}$$

We thus obtain

$$I(r, \lambda) = 2\pi \int_0^{\infty} \frac{J_0(\rho r)}{\rho(\rho^2-\lambda^2)}\, d\rho. \tag{5.2.62}$$

We now note that

$$\frac{\partial I}{\partial r} = -2\pi \int_0^{\infty} \frac{J_1(\rho r)}{\rho^2-\lambda^2}\, d\rho = \frac{2\pi}{\lambda^2}\int_0^{\infty}\left(1-\frac{\rho^2}{\rho^2-\lambda^2}\right)J_1(\rho r)\, d\rho. \tag{5.2.63}$$

The evaluation of this last integral form uses two special results on Bessel functions. The first is that‡

$$\int_0^{\infty} J_1(\rho r)\, d\rho = 1/r. \tag{5.2.64}$$

The second result is more recondite, and is given by Watson as §

$$\int_0^{\infty} \frac{\rho^2}{\rho^2-\lambda^2} J_1(\rho r)\, d\rho = \frac{\pi i \lambda}{2} H_1^{(1)}(\lambda r). \tag{5.2.65}$$

Thus, we have that

$$\frac{\partial I(r, \lambda)}{\partial r} = \frac{2\pi}{\lambda^2}\left\{\frac{1}{r} - \frac{\pi i \lambda}{2} H_1^{(1)}(\lambda r)\right\}. \tag{5.2.66}$$

† P. 190 of Reference [13].
‡ See, for example, McLachlan [13, p. 194, formula 68].
§ Watson [21, p. 424, eqn (1)].

The resulting expressions for the displacements are given by

$$u = \frac{iFe^{ipt}}{4\mu\beta^2 r}\left[\frac{1}{p}\left\{c_1 H_1^{(1)}\left(\frac{pr}{c_1}\right)+c_2 H_1^{(1)}\left(\frac{pr}{c_2}\right)\right\}-\frac{1}{r}\left\{x^2 H_2^{(1)}\left(\frac{pr}{c_1}\right)+\beta^2 y^2 H_2^{(1)}\left(\frac{pr}{c_2}\right)\right\}\right],$$

$$v = -\frac{iFe^{ipt}xy}{4\mu\beta^2 r^2}\left\{H_2^{(1)}\left(\frac{pr}{c_1}\right)-\beta^2 H_2^{(1)}\left(\frac{pr}{c_2}\right)\right\}. \tag{5.2.67}$$

Consider now the case of an impulse load where f_x is given by

$$f_x = \frac{F}{\rho}\delta(x)\delta(y)\delta(t). \tag{5.2.68}$$

The transformed body force is given by

$$\bar{f}_x = Fc_1/\rho(2\pi)^{\frac{3}{2}}, \tag{5.2.69}$$

where the fact that $\delta(t) = c_1\delta(\tau)$ has been used. The solutions for u and v follow again from (5.2.55) and (5.2.56), and may be expressed as

$$u = -\frac{Fc_1}{8\pi^3\mu\beta^2}\left(\frac{\partial^2 I_1}{\partial x^2}+\beta^2\frac{\partial^2 I_2}{\partial y^2}\right), \tag{5.2.70}$$

$$v = -\frac{Fc_1}{8\pi^3\mu\beta^2}\frac{\partial^2}{\partial x\,\partial y}(I_1-\beta^2 I_2), \tag{5.2.71}$$

where

$$I_1 = \int\limits_{V_3}\frac{e^{-i(\xi x+\eta y+\omega\tau)}}{(\xi^2+\eta^2)(\xi^2+\eta^2-\omega^2)}\,dV_3, \tag{5.2.72}$$

$$I_2 = \int\limits_{V_3}\frac{e^{-i(\xi x+\eta y+\omega\tau)}}{(\xi^2+\eta^2)(\xi^2+\eta^2-\beta^2\omega^2)}\,dV_3. \tag{5.2.73}$$

Again, it is found that $\partial I_1/\partial r$, $\partial I_2/\partial r$ are functions only of r. Thus

$$\frac{\partial I_2}{\partial r} = -\frac{4\pi^2}{\beta}\int\limits_0^\infty \frac{\sin(\rho\tau/\beta)}{\rho}J_1(\rho r)\,d\rho. \tag{5.2.74}$$

Again using a special result on the Bessel function, it is found that†

$$\frac{\partial I_2}{\partial r} = \begin{cases} -4\pi^2\tau/\beta^2 r, & \tau < \beta r \\ -4\pi^2\{\tau-(\tau^2-\beta^2 r^2)^{\frac{1}{2}}\}/\beta^2 r, & \tau > \beta r. \end{cases} \tag{5.2.75}$$

† Formula 73, p. 195, of Reference [13].

A similar result may be obtained for $\partial I_1/\partial r$ by letting $\beta = 1$ in (5.2.75). The resulting expressions for the displacements are given by

$$\frac{2\pi\mu\beta^2 u}{c_1 F} = \begin{cases} 0, & r > \tau \\ \dfrac{x^2}{r^2}(\tau^2-r^2)^{-\frac{1}{2}} + \dfrac{x^2-y^2}{r^4}(\tau^2-r^2)^{\frac{1}{2}}, & \tau' < r < \tau \\ \dfrac{x^2}{r^2}(\tau^2-r^2)^{-\frac{1}{2}} + \dfrac{\beta y^2}{r^2}(\tau'^2-r^2)^{-\frac{1}{2}} + & \\ \quad + \dfrac{x^2-y^2}{r^4}\{(\tau^2-r^2)^{\frac{1}{2}} - \beta(\tau'^2-r^2)^{\frac{1}{2}}\}, & r < \tau', \end{cases} \tag{5.2.76}$$

$$\frac{2\pi\mu\beta^2 v}{c_1 F} = \begin{cases} 0, & r > \tau \\ \dfrac{xy}{r^2}\left\{(\tau^2-r^2)^{-\frac{1}{2}} + \dfrac{2}{r^2}(\tau^2-r^2)^{\frac{1}{2}}\right\}, & \tau' < r < \tau \\ \dfrac{xy}{r^2}\Big[(\tau^2-r^2)^{-\frac{1}{2}} - \beta(\tau'^2-r^2)^{-\frac{1}{2}} + & \\ \quad + \dfrac{2}{r^2}\{(\tau^2-r^2)^{\frac{1}{2}} - \beta(\tau'^2-r^2)^{\frac{1}{2}}\}\Big], & r < \tau', \end{cases} \tag{5.2.77}$$

where $\tau = c_1 t$, $\tau' = c_2 t$. The various intervals in (5.2.76) and (5.2.77) correspond to the arrival of the dilatational and distortional waves. Thus, for $r > \tau(c_1 t)$, no disturbance is felt. At $r = \tau$, a sharp wavefront from the dilatational part arrives, and at $r = \tau'$, the distortional wave arrives. The radial displacement is shown for various orientations relative to the source in Fig. 5.5. It is to be noted that a discontinuity occurs in the radial displacement u_r for $\theta = 0°$ when the P wave arrives, but not when the S wave arrives. At

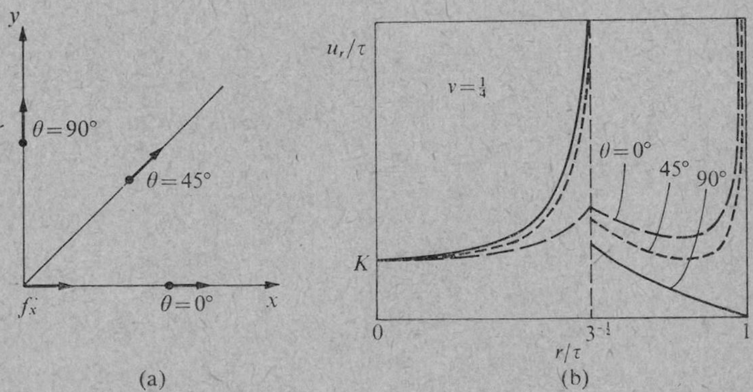

FIG. 5.5. Radial displacement parameter u_r/τ for three different orientations relative to the applied force ($K = c_1F/2\pi\beta^2\mu\tau^2$). (After Eason *et al.* [5].)

$\theta = 90°$, perpendicular to the direction of the applied force, a discontinuity exists for u_r on the arrival of the S wave, but not for the earlier P wave. At $\theta = 45°$, discontinuities exist for both wavefronts.

5.3. Cavity source problems

Let us now consider the case of cavities, spherical or cylindrical, buried in an infinite medium and subjected to internal pressures of one type or another. Because the resulting waves will emanate from the cavity and propagate outward, boundary effects are still avoided in this class of problems. Our considerations mainly will be with dilatational wave sources. That is, waves resulting from time-varying but uniformly-applied normal pressures on the walls of the cavity. Such problems are essentially those of acoustic wave propagation. Waves from more general loading will be briefly discussed.

5.3.1. *Harmonic dilatational waves from a spherical cavity*

Consider a spherical cavity of radius a subjected to internal pressure, as shown in Fig. 5.6. The loading will be presumed to have spherical symmetry in

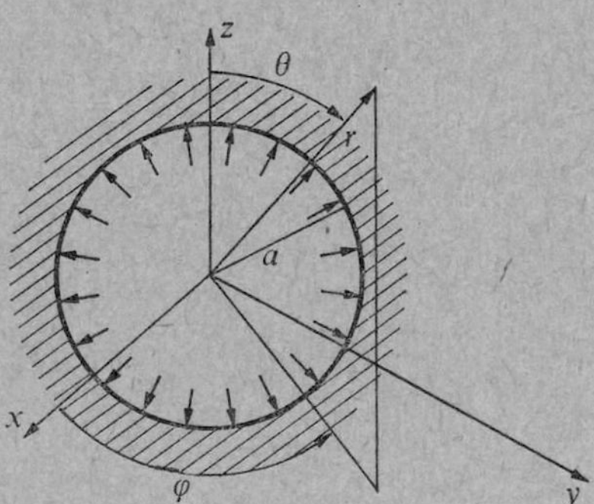

FIG. 5.6. Spherical cavity of radius a subjected to internal pressure.

the present analysis. Consequently the wave propagation will also have spherical symmetry, and will be described by

$$u_r = u(r,t),$$
$$u_\theta = u_\phi = \frac{\partial}{\partial\theta} = \frac{\partial}{\partial\phi} = 0. \tag{5.3.1}$$

Consider now the Helmholtz resolution of the displacement vector in terms of spherical coordinates. This is given in general by

$$\mathbf{u} = \left(\frac{\partial\Phi}{\partial r}\mathbf{e}_r + \frac{1}{r}\frac{\partial\Phi}{\partial\theta}\mathbf{e}_\theta + \frac{1}{r\sin\theta}\frac{\partial\Phi}{\partial\phi}\mathbf{e}_\phi\right) + \left(\frac{1}{r}\frac{\partial H_\phi}{\partial\theta} - \frac{1}{r\sin\phi}\frac{\partial H_\theta}{\partial\phi}\right)\mathbf{e}_r + $$
$$+\left(\frac{1}{r\sin\theta}\frac{\partial H_r}{\partial\phi} - \frac{\partial H_\phi}{\partial r}\right)\mathbf{e}_\theta + \left(\frac{\partial H_\theta}{\partial r} - \frac{1}{r}\frac{\partial H_r}{\partial\theta}\right)\mathbf{e}_\phi. \tag{5.3.2}$$

As a consequence of the assumed symmetry of the displacement field, (5.3.2) simply reduces to

$$\mathbf{u} = \frac{\partial \Phi}{\partial r}\mathbf{e}_r \tag{5.3.3}$$

With this considerable simplification, the potential equations reduce to

$$(\lambda+2\mu)\frac{1}{r^2}\frac{\partial}{\partial r}\left(r^2\frac{\partial \Phi}{\partial r}\right) = \rho\frac{\partial^2 \Phi}{\partial t^2} \tag{5.3.4}$$

or

$$\frac{\partial^2 \Phi}{\partial r^2}+\frac{2}{r}\frac{\partial \Phi}{\partial r} = \frac{1}{c_1^2}\frac{\partial^2 \Phi}{\partial t^2}. \tag{5.3.5}$$

Our immediate considerations will be with harmonic loading having the time variation $\exp(-i\omega t)$. Then, assuming a solution $\Phi = \Phi(r)\exp(-i\omega t)$, we have (5.3.5) reducing to

$$\frac{d^2\Phi(r)}{dr^2}+\frac{2}{r}\frac{d\Phi(r)}{dr}+\beta^2\Phi(r) = 0, \qquad \beta^2 = \omega^2/c_1^2. \tag{5.3.6}$$

This equation has been previously encountered in the analysis of longitudinal waves in conical horns and is known as the spherical Bessel's equation having the solution†

$$\Phi(r) = Ah_0^{(1)}(\beta r)+Bh_0^{(2)}(\beta r). \tag{5.3.7}$$

The condition of outgoing waves from the cavity dictates selection of $h_0^{(1)}$, since its asymptotic behaviour

$$h_n^{(1)}(\beta r) \sim \frac{i^{-n}}{i\beta r}e^{i\beta r} \tag{5.3.8}$$

in conjunction with the time dependence for this problem satisfies the radiation condition. We thus set $B = 0$ in (5.3.7).

The determination of A must come from the boundary conditions, given by

$$\tau_{rr}(a, \theta, \phi, t) = p_0 e^{-i\omega t}, \qquad \tau_{r\theta} = \tau_{r\phi} = 0. \tag{5.3.9}$$

For the condition of spherical symmetry, we have that

$$\tau_{rr} = \lambda\left(\frac{\partial u}{\partial r}+\frac{2}{r}u\right)+2\mu\frac{\partial u}{\partial r}. \tag{5.3.10}$$

Since $u = \partial\Phi/\partial r$, this last expression becomes

$$\tau_{rr} = \lambda\left(\frac{\partial^2 \Phi}{\partial r^2}+\frac{2}{r}\frac{\partial \Phi}{\partial r}\right)+2\mu\frac{\partial^2 \Phi}{\partial r^2}. \tag{5.3.11}$$

If we compare the terms in the above to the equation of motion (5.3.5), we see that we may write

$$\tau_{rr} = \frac{\lambda}{c_1^2}\frac{\partial^2 \Phi}{\partial t^2}+2\mu\left(\frac{1}{c_1^2}\frac{\partial^2 \Phi}{\partial t^2}-\frac{2}{r}\frac{\partial \Phi}{\partial r}\right). \tag{5.3.12}$$

† See eqns (2.5.24)–(2.5.27).

Recognizing the harmonic time dependence, we write this as

$$\tau_{rr} = -(\lambda+2\mu)\beta^2\Phi(r) - \frac{4\mu}{r}\frac{d\Phi(r)}{dr}. \tag{5.3.13}$$

Substituting the solution (5.3.7) in the boundary condition gives

$$p_0 = -A\mu\left\{k^2\beta^2 h_0(\beta r) + \frac{4}{r}\frac{dh_0(\beta r)}{dr}\right\}\bigg|_{r=a}, \tag{5.3.14}$$

where $k^2 = (\lambda+2\mu)/\mu$. Since $dh_0(\beta r)/dr = -\beta h_1(\beta r)$, we have

$$p_0 = -A\mu\left\{k^2\beta^2 h_0(\beta a) - \frac{4\beta}{a}h_1(\beta a)\right\}. \tag{5.3.15}$$

The resulting solution is given by

$$\Phi(r) = -\frac{p_0 a^2}{\mu M(\beta a)}h_0^{(1)}(\beta r), \tag{5.3.16}$$

where

$$M(\beta a) = k^2(\beta a)^2 h_0^{(1)}(\beta a) - 4\beta a h_1^{(1)}(\beta a). \tag{5.3.17}$$

The displacement field is given by

$$u(r) = \frac{p_0 a^2\beta}{\mu M(\beta a)}h_1^{(1)}(\beta r), \tag{5.3.18}$$

and the stress field by

$$\tau_{rr}(r) = \frac{p_0}{M(\beta a)}\left(\frac{a}{r}\right)^2\left\{k^2(\beta r)^2 h_0^{(1)}(\beta r) - 4\beta r h_1^{(1)}(\beta r)\right\}. \tag{5.3.19}$$

Equation (5.3.19), with the time factor $\exp(-i\omega t)$ inserted, represents the formal solution to the problem. As previously discussed,† the spherical Hankel functions may be represented by finite series. For $h_0^{(1)}$, $h_1^{(1)}$ we have

$$h_0^{(1)}(\beta r) = -\frac{ie^{i\beta r}}{\beta r}, \qquad h_1^{(1)}(\beta r) = \frac{e^{i\beta r}}{\beta r}\left(1+\frac{i}{\beta r}\right). \tag{5.3.20}$$

If these expressions are inserted in (5.3.19), we obtain

$$\tau_{rr}(r) = -\frac{p_0}{M(\beta a)}\left(\frac{a}{r}\right)^2\left\{ik^2\beta r + 4\left(1+\frac{i}{\beta r}\right)\right\}e^{i\beta r}. \tag{5.3.21}$$

It is of interest to consider the result as $a \to 0$, so that the cavity size becomes small in comparison with the wavelength at a given frequency. We first define the 'strength' of the source as

$$S_0 = 4\pi a^3 p_0/3, \tag{5.3.22}$$

† See (2.5.30).

and require that this quantity be constant. For $M(\beta a)$ we have

$$M(\beta a) = -\frac{1}{\beta a}\left\{k^2(\beta a)^2\mathrm{i}+4\beta a\left(1+\frac{\mathrm{i}}{\beta a}\right)\right\}\mathrm{e}^{\mathrm{i}\beta a}. \tag{5.3.23}$$

Then $\tau_{rr}(r)$ is given by

$$\tau_{rr}(r) = p_0 a^3\beta\frac{\{\mathrm{i}k^2\beta/r+4(1+\mathrm{i}/\beta r)/r^2\}\mathrm{e}^{\mathrm{i}\beta(r-a)}}{\{k^2(\beta a)^2\mathrm{i}+4\beta a(1+\mathrm{i}/\beta a)\}}. \tag{5.3.24}$$

As $a \to 0$, $\beta a \to 0$ and the denominator becomes $4\mathrm{i}$. For large r compared to the wavelength, the numerator is approximated by $\mathrm{i}k^2\beta/r$. The result, with the time dependence inserted, reduces to

$$\tau_{rr}(r, t) \to \frac{3S_0}{16\pi}\frac{k^2\beta^2}{r}\mathrm{e}^{\mathrm{i}(\beta r-\omega t)}. \tag{5.3.25}$$

This represents the far-field radiation for a 'point' source of dilatational waves.

5.3.2. *Dilatational waves from a step pulse*

We now consider the waves generated by a transient load applied to the surface of the cavity. Again, spherical symmetry will be assumed. Our considerations may start with eqn (5.3.5) which can be written in the form

$$\frac{1}{r^2}\frac{\partial}{\partial r}\left(r^2\frac{\partial\Phi}{\partial r}\right) = \frac{1}{c_1^2}\frac{\partial^2\Phi}{\partial t^2}. \tag{5.3.26}$$

This may be rewritten in the form

$$\frac{\partial^2(r\Phi)}{\partial r^2} = \frac{1}{c_1^2}\frac{\partial^2(r\Phi)}{\partial t^2}. \tag{5.3.27}$$

This is in the wave equation form in terms of $r\Phi$. The solution may be written immediately as

$$\Phi(r, t) = \frac{1}{r}f(r-c_1t)+\frac{1}{r}g(r+c_1t). \tag{5.3.28}$$

These represent outgoing and incoming spherical waves, propagating without distortion of shape, but changing only in amplitude. It should be emphasized that it is the potential Φ that is behaving in this manner. Since, in the present problem, we will have only outgoing waves, the solution $g(r+c_1t)$ will be discarded. To complete the prescription of the problem, consider the initial conditions to be homogeneous, so that

$$u(r, 0) = \partial u(r, 0)/\partial t = 0. \tag{5.3.29}$$

We shall assume a specific loading at this stage, prescribed by a step pressure pulse, given by

$$\tau_{rr}(a, t) = -p_0H\langle t\rangle, \qquad \tau_{r\theta} = \tau_{r\phi} = 0. \tag{5.3.30}$$

As a first step, express the solution (5.3.28) in the form

$$\Phi = \frac{1}{r}F(\tau), \qquad \tau = t - \frac{r-a}{c_1}, \tag{5.3.31}$$

where $\tau = 0$, for $t < (r-a)/c_1$ and where $c_1 t = r - a$ corresponds to the position of the wavefront for all time. The displacement is given by

$$u = \frac{\partial \Phi}{\partial r} = -\frac{1}{r^2}F(\tau) - \frac{1}{rc_1}F'(\tau). \tag{5.3.32}$$

For the stress, we have

$$\tau_{rr} = \lambda \nabla^2 \Phi + 2\mu \frac{\partial^2 \Phi}{\partial r^2} = \frac{\lambda + 2\mu}{c_1^2}\frac{F''(\tau)}{r} + 4\mu \frac{F(\tau)}{r^3} + \frac{4\mu}{c_1}\frac{F'(\tau)}{r^2}, \tag{5.3.33}$$

where the prime notation indicates differentiation with respect to τ. We now substitute τ_{rr} into the boundary condition (5.3.30), giving after a slight amount of manipulation

$$F''(t) + \frac{4c_2^2}{ac_1}F'(t) + \frac{4c_2^2}{a^2}F(t) = -\frac{ac_2^2}{\mu}p_0. \tag{5.3.34}$$

Thus, upon setting $r = a$, we see that τ reduces to t.

The solution to the governing equation for F is given by

$$F(t) = \mathrm{e}^{-\zeta t}(A \cos \omega t + B \sin \omega t) - a^3 p/4\mu, \tag{5.3.35}$$

where the last term is the particular solution and where

$$\zeta = 2c_2^2/ac_1, \qquad \omega = \zeta\{(c_1^2/c_2^2) - 1\}^{\frac{1}{2}}. \tag{5.3.36}$$

Applying the initial conditions to determine A and B, we obtain

$$F(t) = \frac{a^3 p}{4\mu}\left\{-1 + e^{-\zeta t}\left(\cos \omega t + \frac{\zeta}{\omega}\sin \omega t\right)\right\}. \tag{5.3.37}$$

For $r > a$, we merely replace t by τ to obtain the general solution. We note that $F(\tau) = 0$ for $\tau < 0$. The resulting expression for $u(r)$ is given by

$$u(r, t) = \begin{cases} 0, & \tau < 0 \\ \dfrac{a^3 p}{4\mu r^2}\left[1 - e^{-\zeta \tau}\left\{\left(\dfrac{2r}{a} - 1\right)\dfrac{\zeta}{\omega}\sin \omega\tau - \cos \omega\tau\right\}\right], & \tau > 0. \end{cases} \tag{5.3.38}$$

The displacement field at three different values of r/a is shown in Fig. 5.7. The first and obvious observation is that an oscillatory disturbance is produced from a step pulse. In view of the non-dispersive nature of the governing equation for $r\Phi$ (see (5.3.27)), this might have been unexpected. The reason, of course, is that, while $r\Phi$ propagates without distortion, the displacements

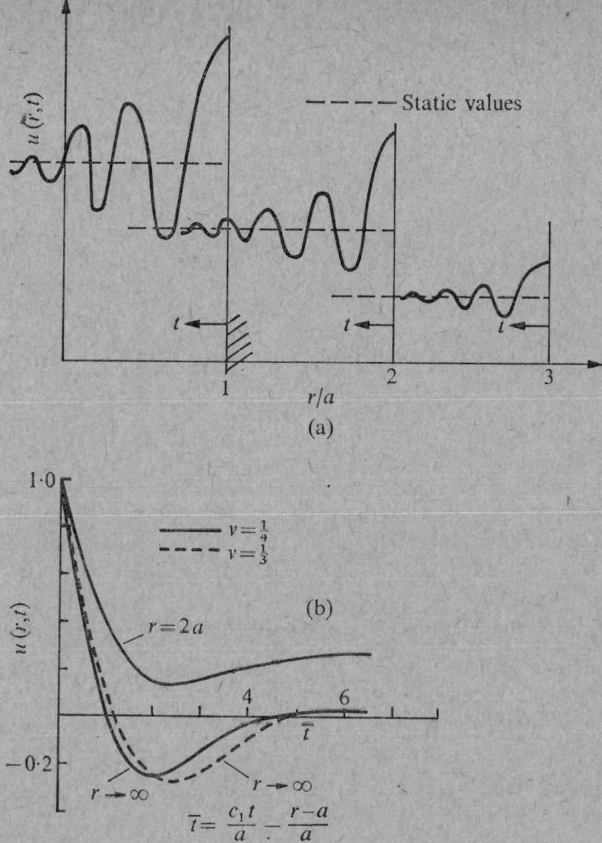

FIG. 5.7. (a) General form of the displacements resulting from a step pressure pulse applied at the surface ($r = a$) of a spherical cavity and (b) the radial stress obtained by Selberg [18] for a specific case.

and stresses (5.3.32) and (5.3.33) are derivatives or combinations of derivatives of Φ and may assume a different pulse shape. We note for $r \gg 1$, that

$$u(r, t) \to a^3p/4\mu r^2, \tag{5.3.39}$$

which corresponds to the static displacement field (shown by the dashed lines in the figure). A further interpretation of interest is to suppose ζ large so that ω is large and, for $\tau > 0$, $\zeta\tau$ is large. The result is that, at the head of the pulse, the oscillations become more rapid and decay more quickly. Of course, we must bear in mind that the exact nature of the oscillation is dependent on ζ and ω, which depends on the materials and cavity size. For realistic materials and cavity sizes on the order of several centimetres, the behaviour is much more highly damped than indicated in the figure. Figure 5.7(b) shows the results obtained by Selberg [18] for the radial stresses under an applied step loading. As mentioned, a highly damped behaviour is evident.

5.3.3. *General case of dilatational waves with spherical symmetry*

We now wish to generalize the analysis of the cavity-source problem to include arbitrary time variations in the pressure distributions in the cavity. However, by assuming the pressure to be uniformly distributed over the interior of the cavity and to be normal pressure only, as in the last section, the spherically symmetric nature of the problem will be retained. Only dilatational waves will be generated and the problem will still be effectively a one-space-dimension one. Many elements of the previous analysis will be retained. Specifically, we still have the potential Φ given by (5.3.31) and the homogeneous initial conditions (5.3.29). The boundary conditions are given by

$$\tau_{rr}(a,t) = -p(t), \quad t > 0, \tag{5.3.40}$$

where $p(t)$ is an arbitrary function of time.

The previously given expression for τ_{rr} (5.3.33) still holds. Applying this to the boundary condition (5.3.40) gives

$$F''(t)+\frac{4c_2^2}{ac_1}F'(t)+\frac{4c_2^2}{a^2}F(t) = \frac{-ac_2^2}{\mu}p(t). \tag{5.3.41}$$

We apply the Fourier transform to the above, giving the transformed solution

$$\bar{F}(\omega) = \frac{ac_2^2}{\mu}\bar{p}(\omega)\Big/\left(\omega^2-\frac{4c_2^2}{ac_1}\mathrm{i}\omega-\frac{4c_2^2}{a^2}\right). \tag{5.3.42}$$

Hence

$$F(t) = \frac{ac_2^2}{\mu\sqrt{(2\pi)}}\int_{-\infty}^{\infty}\bar{p}(\omega)\mathrm{e}^{-\mathrm{i}\omega t}\Big/\left(\omega^2-\frac{4c_2^2}{ac_1}\mathrm{i}\omega-\frac{4c_2^2}{a^2}\right)\,\mathrm{d}\omega. \tag{5.3.43}$$

We note several items. First, that $F(\tau)$ is given from the above by replacing t by τ. Second, that $\Phi(\tau)$ is given by $F(\tau)/r$. Third, we may incorporate the integral definition of $\bar{p}(\omega)$ directly in the result. Thus we may write

$$\Phi(\tau) = \frac{ac_2^2}{2\pi\mu}\frac{1}{r}\int_{-\infty}^{\infty}\int_{-\infty}^{\infty}p(t')\exp\{\mathrm{i}\omega(t'-\tau)\}\Big/\left(\omega^2-\frac{4c_2^2}{ac_1}\mathrm{i}\omega-\frac{4c_2^2}{a^2}\right)\,\mathrm{d}t'\,\mathrm{d}\omega, \tag{5.3.44}$$

where t' is a dummy variable. Indulging in one final modification, we let $\omega = c_1x/a$. Then we have that

$$\omega^2-\frac{4c_2^2}{ac_1}\mathrm{i}\omega-\frac{4c_2^2}{a^2} = \frac{c_1^2}{a^2}\left\{x^2-\frac{2(1-2\nu)}{(1-\nu)}(\mathrm{i}x+1)\right\}. \tag{5.3.45}$$

In deriving this, we have used the identity $(\lambda+2\mu)/\mu = (2-2\nu)/(1-2\nu)$. Then (5.3.44) may be written as

$$\Phi(\tau) = \frac{a^2}{2\pi\rho c_1}\frac{1}{r}\int_{-\infty}^{\infty}\int_{-\infty}^{\infty} p(t')\exp\left\{i\frac{c_1 x}{a}(t'-\tau)\right\}\bigg/\left\{x^2-\frac{2(1-2\nu)}{1-\nu}(ix+1)\right\}\,dt'\,dx. \tag{5.3.46}$$

The integration with respect to x is achieved by contour integration. Thus define

$$I = \int_{-\infty}^{\infty} \frac{\exp\{ic_1 x(t'-\tau)/a\}}{x^2-\kappa(ix+1)}\,dx, \tag{5.3.47}$$

where $\kappa = 2(1-2\nu)/(1-\nu)$. Considering x complex, we see that the poles are located at

$$x = \tfrac{1}{2}\{\kappa i \pm (4\kappa-\kappa^2)^{\frac{1}{2}}\}. \tag{5.3.48}$$

Typical values of κ are $1(\nu=\frac{1}{3})$, $1{\cdot}14(\nu=0{\cdot}3)$, and $2(\nu=\frac{1}{4})$, so that $4\kappa-\kappa^2>0$ for common materials. The poles will thus be located in the upper half-plane symmetric with respect to the imaginary axis. The appropriate contour will be along the real axis and closed in the upper or lower half-plane. For $t'<\tau$, the contour must be closed below the real axis and $I=0$. For $t'>\tau$, closure is above and the residues must be computed. It may easily be shown that the residues are respectively

$$\mathrm{Res}[\tfrac{1}{2}\{\kappa i\pm(4\kappa-\kappa^2)^{\frac{1}{2}}\}] = \pm\exp\left[\frac{ic_1(t'-\tau)}{2a}\{\kappa i\pm(4\kappa-\kappa^2)^{\frac{1}{2}}\}\right]\bigg/2(4\kappa-\kappa^2)^{\frac{1}{2}}. \tag{5.3.49}$$

Then we obtain that

$$-2\pi i\sum \mathrm{Res} = 4\pi\frac{\exp\{-c_1(t'-\tau)\kappa/2a\}}{(4\kappa-\kappa^2)^{\frac{1}{2}}}\sin\left\{\frac{c_1(t'-\tau)}{2a}(4\kappa-\kappa^2)^{\frac{1}{2}}\right\}. \tag{5.3.50}$$

Before substituting this in (5.3.46), we note that $(4\kappa-\kappa^2)^{\frac{1}{2}} = 2(1-2\nu)^{\frac{1}{2}}/(1-\nu)$. Then we obtain

$$\Phi(\tau) = \frac{a^2(1-\nu)}{\rho c_1(1-2\nu)^{\frac{1}{2}}}\frac{1}{r}\int_{\tau}^{\infty} p(t')\exp\left\{-\frac{1-2\nu}{1-\nu}\frac{c_1}{a}(t'-\tau)\right\}\times$$
$$\times\sin\left\{\frac{(1-2\nu)^{\frac{1}{2}}}{1-\nu}\frac{c_1}{a}(t'-\tau)\right\}\,dt'. \tag{5.3.51}$$

The lower limit has been changed to τ, since $\Phi(\tau)=0$ for $t'<\tau$.†

A number of results have appeared in the literature depicting waveforms resulting from various pressure pulses. The general form of the response to a

† See Hopkins [10] for analysis of the cavity problem, including numerous references to past work. This result (5.3.51) varies from the result of Hopkin's formula (5.31) in the limits of the integral. This appears to stem from a sign difference between the $i\omega$ term in the present work versus that of formula (5.25) of Hopkins. A considerable portion of Hopkins's work is devoted to anelastic waves from cavities.

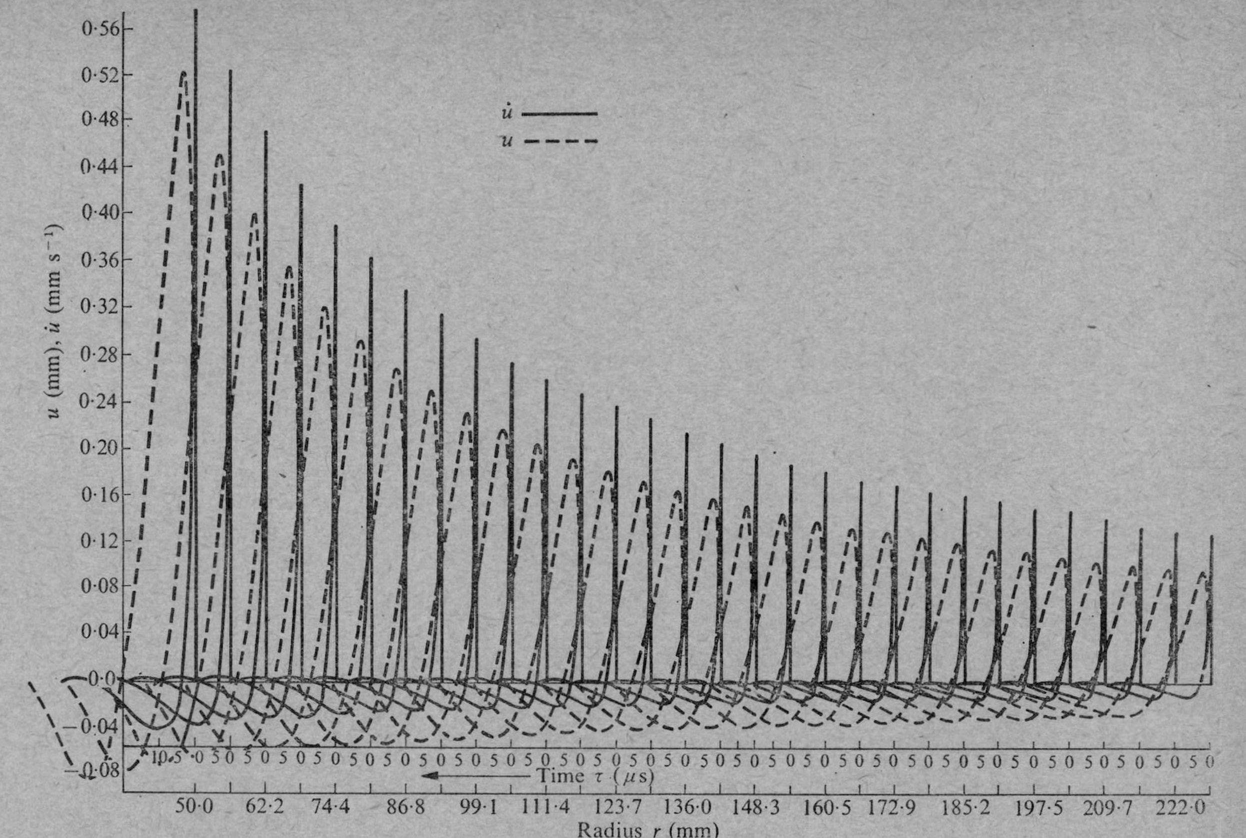

FIG. 5.8. Particle velocity and displacements as a function of radius a = 50 mm and a decay constant of $\alpha = 1\times10^{-6}$ s^{-1}. (After Goldsmith and Allan [9, Fig. 5].)

step pulse was given in the previous section, as well as the specific result by Selberg [18]. Goldsmith and Allen [9] have presented extensive results for the response to an input pulse given by

$$\tau_{rr}(a) = -p_0 e^{-\alpha t}. \tag{5.3.52}$$

The analysis of this problem was presented earlier by Blake [2]. This type of pulse approximates explosive loading. Figure 5.8 presents but one of a number of velocity and stress results presented by Goldsmith *et al.* [9] for a variety of cavity sizes and decay constants α. The figure is interpreted in the same manner as Fig. 5.7(a), with the time response at a given radius obtained for time increasing to the left. Other results are presented by Goldsmith *et al.* [9] for cavities of 20 mm, 1000 mm, with decay constants of $1\times10^{-6}\,\text{s}^{-1}$ and $2\times10^{-6}\,\text{s}^{-1}$.

The previous results have been for spherical symmetry, so that only dilatational waves are generated. If the pressure distribution is not symmetric or if shear stresses are present, shear waves also will be generated and, in general, the analysis will be more complicated. Das Gupta [4], Wright and Carpenter [22], Meyer [14], Achenbach and Sun [1], and others have contributed in this field. Eringen [6] has given the formal solution to the general problem, where the cavity wall is subjected to arbitrary normal and shear stresses. The results for the displacements and stresses are in terms of infinite series in Hankel functions and spherical harmonics. The means for reducing the general results for a number of special cases (ten in all) of loading, including concentrated loads and ring loads, are given. Specific results, however, are presented only for the displacements and stresses in the case of a spherically symmetric impulse loading.

5.3.4. *Harmonic waves from a cylindrical cavity*

Suppose now we have an infinite cylindrical cavity of radius a in an elastic media, with the axis of the cavity coinciding with the z-axis. If we presume all loads on the cavity surface to be z independent, the problem will be two dimensional in terms of x and y. Within this broad class, two simple cases of harmonic waves will be considered in this section.

The governing scalar and vector wave equations are

$$\nabla^2\Phi = \frac{1}{c_1^2}\frac{\partial^2\Phi}{\partial t^2}, \qquad \nabla^2\mathbf{H} = \frac{1}{c_2^2}\frac{\partial^2\mathbf{H}}{\partial t^2}, \tag{5.3.53}$$

where the scalar and vector Laplacians are given by

$$\nabla^2\Phi = \frac{1}{r}\frac{\partial}{\partial r}\left(r\frac{\partial\Phi}{\partial r}\right)+\frac{1}{r^2}\frac{\partial^2\Phi}{\partial\theta^2}+\frac{\partial^2\Phi}{\partial z^2}, \tag{5.3.54}$$

$$\nabla^2\mathbf{H} = \left(\nabla^2 H_r-\frac{H_r}{r^2}-\frac{2}{r^2}\frac{\partial H_\theta}{\partial\theta}\right)\mathbf{e}_r+\left(\nabla^2 H_\theta-\frac{H_\theta}{r^2}+\frac{2}{r^2}\frac{\partial H_r}{\partial\theta}\right)\mathbf{e}_\theta+\nabla^2 H_z\mathbf{e}_z, \tag{5.3.55}$$

and where

$$\mathbf{u} = \nabla\Phi + \nabla\times\mathbf{H}. \tag{5.3.56}$$

The stresses are given by

$$\tau_{ij} = \lambda\varepsilon_{kk}\delta_{ij} + 2\mu\varepsilon_{ij}, \tag{5.3.57}$$

where

$$e_{rr} = \frac{\partial u_r}{\partial r}, \qquad e_{\theta\theta} = \frac{1}{r}\frac{\partial u_\theta}{\partial \theta} + \frac{u_r}{r}, \qquad e_{zz} = \frac{\partial u_z}{\partial z},$$

$$e_{\theta z} = \frac{1}{2}\left(\frac{\partial u_\theta}{\partial z} + \frac{1}{r}\frac{\partial u_z}{\partial \theta}\right), \qquad e_{zr} = \frac{1}{2}\left(\frac{\partial u_r}{\partial z} + \frac{\partial u_z}{\partial r}\right), \tag{5.3.58}$$

$$e_{r\theta} = \frac{1}{2}\left(\frac{1}{r}\frac{\partial u_r}{\partial \theta} + \frac{\partial u_\theta}{\partial r} - \frac{u_\theta}{r}\right).$$

Consider first the case of dilatational waves, which will arise if

$$u_\theta = \frac{\partial}{\partial \theta} = u_z = \frac{\partial}{\partial z} = 0. \tag{5.3.59}$$

Then (5.3.56) reduces to

$$\mathbf{u} = \frac{\partial \Phi}{\partial r}\mathbf{e}_r, \tag{5.3.60}$$

where Φ is governed by

$$\frac{1}{r}\frac{\partial}{\partial r}\left(r\frac{\partial \Phi}{\partial r}\right) = \frac{1}{c_1^2}\frac{\partial^2 \Phi}{\partial t^2} \tag{5.3.61}$$

or

$$\frac{\partial^2 \Phi}{\partial r^2} + \frac{1}{r}\frac{\partial \Phi}{\partial r} = \frac{1}{c_1^2}\frac{\partial^2 \Phi}{\partial t^2}. \tag{5.3.62}$$

Suppose a uniform harmonically varying pressure is acting on the cavity surface $r = a$. Thus

$$\tau_{rr}(a) = -p_0 e^{-i\omega t}. \tag{5.3.63}$$

Then we may let $\Phi(r, t) = \Phi(r)\exp(-i\omega t)$, so that (5.3.62) becomes

$$\frac{d^2\Phi}{dr^2} + \frac{1}{r}\frac{d\Phi}{dr} + \beta^2\Phi = 0, \qquad \beta^2 = \omega^2/c_1^2. \tag{5.3.64}$$

This represents the third instance that the zeroth-order Bessel's equation has arisen in our study of wave motion.† We know immediately that the solution for the time behaviour in this problem must be given by

$$\Phi(r) = AH_0^{(1)}(\beta r). \tag{5.3.65}$$

The constant A is determined from the boundary condition at $r = a$. The stress is

$$\tau_{rr} = \lambda\left(\frac{\partial u_r}{\partial r} + \frac{u_r}{r}\right) + 2\mu\frac{\partial u_r}{\partial r},$$

$$= \lambda\left(\frac{\partial^2 \Phi}{\partial r^2} + \frac{1}{r}\frac{\partial \Phi}{\partial r}\right) + 2\mu\frac{\partial^2 \Phi}{\partial r^2}. \tag{5.3.66}$$

† Previously in the study of membranes (§ 4.1) and earlier yet in the case of longitudinal waves in tapered rods (§ 2.5). See these sections for discussion of $H_0^{(1)}$, $H_0^{(2)}$, and the asymptotic behaviour.

This may also be written as

$$\tau_{rr} = (\lambda+2\mu)\left(\frac{\partial^2\Phi}{\partial r^2}+\frac{1}{r}\frac{\partial\Phi}{\partial r}\right)-\frac{2\mu}{r}\frac{\partial\Phi}{\partial r}. \tag{5.3.67}$$

Using (5.3.64) in the above, re-organizing the harmonic time dependence, and factoring out μ gives

$$\tau_{rr} = -\mu\left(k^2\beta^2\Phi+\frac{2}{r}\frac{\mathrm{d}\Phi}{\mathrm{d}r}\right), \tag{5.3.68}$$

where $k^2 = (\lambda+2\mu)/\mu$. Applying this to the boundary condition (5.3.63) gives

$$\mu A\left\{k^2\beta^2H_0^{(1)}(\beta r)+\frac{2}{r}\frac{\mathrm{d}H_0^{(1)}(\beta r)}{\mathrm{d}r}\right\}\bigg|_{r=a} = p_0. \tag{5.3.69}$$

Using the relation $\mathrm{d}H_0^{(1)}(\beta r)/\mathrm{d}r = -\beta H_1^{(1)}(\beta r)$, A is easily found, with the result being given by

$$\Phi(r, t) = \frac{p_0}{\mu N(\beta a)}H_0^{(1)}(\beta r)\mathrm{e}^{-\mathrm{i}\omega t}, \tag{5.3.70}$$

where

$$N(\beta a) = k^2\beta^2H_0^{(1)}(\beta a)-2\frac{\beta}{a}H_1^{(1)}(\beta a). \tag{5.3.71}$$

The case of torsional waves is also easily obtained. We assume

$$\frac{\partial}{\partial\theta} = u_z = \frac{\partial}{\partial z} = 0. \tag{5.3.72}$$

Then (5.3.56) reduces to

$$\mathbf{u} = \frac{\partial\Phi}{\partial r}\mathbf{e}_r-\frac{\partial H_z}{\partial r}\mathbf{e}_\theta, \tag{5.3.73}$$

where Φ is given by (5.3.70), the same as in the study of dilatational waves, and H_z is given by

$$\nabla^2H_z = \frac{1}{c_2^2}\frac{\partial^2H_z}{\partial t^2}. \tag{5.3.74}$$

We note that $\mathbf{u}$ has two independent components u_r and u_θ. A purely dilatational disturbance similar to that just considered would be described by u_r if normal stresses were acting on the cavity surface. However, we will assume the boundary conditions to be purely shear, given by

$$\tau_{r\theta}(a, t) = \tau_0\mathrm{e}^{-\mathrm{i}\omega t}. \tag{5.3.75}$$

Thus only a shear wave will be produced. We have, for the symmetry conditions of the problem, that

$$\tau_{r\theta} = \mu\left(\frac{\partial u_\theta}{\partial r}-\frac{u_\theta}{r}\right), \tag{5.3.76}$$

where $u_\theta = -\partial H_z/\partial r$. Thus we may write

$$\tau_{r\theta} = -\mu\left(\frac{\partial^2H_z}{\partial r^2}-\frac{1}{r}\frac{\partial H_z}{\partial r}\right). \tag{5.3.77}$$

Following procedures similar to that used for dilatational waves, this may be written as

$$\tau_{rr} = \mu\left\{\beta^2 H(r) + \frac{2}{r}\frac{\partial H(r)}{\partial r}\right\}, \tag{5.3.78}$$

where $H_z(r, t) = H(r)\exp(-i\omega t)$ and $\beta^2 = \omega^2/c_2^2$. At this point the methods of analysis are quite similar to those for dilatational harmonic waves, and there is little to be gained by pursuing the problem further.

5.3.5. *Transient dilatational waves from a cylindrical cavity*

We now consider a transient disturbance applied to walls of a cylindrical cavity. Other than the nature of the loading, the displacements, stresses, and governing equation will be as given in the previous section on harmonic waves from a cylindrical cavity. Although this problem is the cylindrical analogue of the previously considered spherical cavity under a step pressure, the analysis is not correspondingly simple. Basically, this is because the scalar wave equation (5.3.62) in cylindrical coordinates does not admit a solution of the type $r^n f(r - c_1 t)$, such as applied in spherical coordinates ($n = -1$) and also in rectangular coordinates ($n = 0$). The analysis of this problem has been given by Selberg [18].† The following is based on his work.

Instead of using the potentials Φ and $\mathbf{H}$, we work directly with the dilatation Δ, given by

$$\Delta = \nabla . \mathbf{u} = \frac{1}{r}\frac{\partial(ru_r)}{\partial r}, \tag{5.3.79}$$

for the present symmetry conditions. As we found in our initial investigation of types of waves in an infinite media, the dilatation is also governed by the scalar wave equation

$$\nabla^2\Delta = \frac{1}{c_1^2}\frac{\partial^2\Delta}{\partial t^2}, \tag{5.3.80}$$

where, still,

$$\nabla^2 = \frac{r^{-1}\partial(r\partial/\partial r)}{\partial r}$$

for the axial symmetry and z-independence of the present problem.

We apply the Laplace transform to (5.3.80), giving

$$\frac{d^2\bar{\Delta}}{dr^2} + \frac{1}{r}\frac{d\bar{\Delta}}{dr} - \beta^2\bar{\Delta} = 0, \qquad \beta = s/c_2, \tag{5.3.81}$$

where $\bar{\Delta} = \bar{\Delta}(r, s)$ and homogeneous initial conditions have been assumed. This has the solution

$$\bar{\Delta} = AK_0(\beta r) + BI_0(\beta r), \tag{5.3.82}$$

† Selberg's paper covers both the spherical and cylindrical cavity problems. Figure 5.7(b) has presented some of his results for the former. The bulk of the paper is devoted to the cylindrical-cavity analysis.

where I_0, K_0 are modified Bessel functions of the first and second kinds of zero order.† These are related to the Bessel functions of the first kind and the Hankel functions by‡

$$K_\nu(z) = \frac{\pi \mathrm{i}}{2} \mathrm{e}^{\nu\pi \mathrm{i}/2} H_\nu^{(1)}(\mathrm{i}z), \qquad I_\nu(z) = \mathrm{e}^{-\nu\pi\mathrm{i}/2} J_\nu(\mathrm{i}z). \tag{5.3.83}$$

For increasing r, it is found that $I_0(\beta r)$ is unbounded, whereas $K_0(\beta r) \to 0$. We thus set $B = 0$ in (5.3.82).

Consider now the boundary conditions. We may write for the transformed stress

$$\bar{\tau}_{rr} = \lambda\bar{\Delta} + 2\mu \frac{\partial \bar{u}_r}{\partial r} = (\lambda+2\mu)\bar{\Delta} - 2\mu \frac{\bar{u}_r}{r}. \tag{5.3.84}$$

We note from (5.3.80) that we may write u_r as

$$\bar{u}_r = -\frac{1}{r} \int_r^\infty \eta\, \bar{\Delta}(\eta, s)\, \mathrm{d}\eta. \tag{5.3.85}$$

Now, we have that§

$$\frac{1}{\beta} \frac{\mathrm{d}}{\mathrm{d}r} \{rK_1(\beta r)\} = rK_0(\beta r), \tag{5.3.86}$$

so that

$$\bar{u}_r = \frac{A}{\beta} K_1(\beta r). \tag{5.3.87}$$

Then we have

$$\bar{\tau}_{rr}(r, s) = A\left\{(\lambda+2\mu)K_0(\beta r) - \frac{2\mu}{\beta r} K_1(\beta r)\right\}. \tag{5.3.88}$$

Let the boundary conditions be prescribed by

$$\tau_{rr}(a, t) = p(t), \qquad \bar{\tau}_{rr}(a, s) = \bar{p}(s). \tag{5.3.89}$$

Then A is easily found from (5.3.88) for $r = a$. The resulting solution, in inverted form, is given by

$$\tau_{rr}(r, t) = \frac{1}{2\pi \mathrm{i}} \int_{c-\mathrm{i}\infty}^{c+\mathrm{i}\infty} \frac{F(\beta r)}{F(\beta a)} \bar{p}(s) \mathrm{e}^{st}\, \mathrm{d}s, \tag{5.3.90}$$

where

$$F(\beta r) = (\lambda+2\mu)K_0(\beta r) - 2\mu K_1(\beta r)/\beta r. \tag{5.3.91}$$

Evaluation of the inversion integral requires knowledge of the zeros of $F(\beta a)$. Selberg establishes, through fairly sophisticated considerations on the properties of Bessel functions, that only one root exists and that it is located in

† P. 190 of Reference [13].
‡ Formula 161 and formula 206 of Reference [13].
§ Formula 32 of Reference [13].

the second quadrant of the s-plane. We label that root as s_0 and the corresponding value of β is labelled β_0.

Now consider the particular case of $p(t) = H\langle t\rangle$, so that $\bar{p}(s) = 1/s$. Then Selberg expresses his result in the following form

$$\tau_{rr} = \frac{1}{\pi}\,\mathrm{Im}\int\limits_0^{-\infty} \frac{F(\beta r)}{sF(\beta a)}\exp(st)\,\mathrm{d}s + 2\,\mathrm{Re}\,\frac{F(\beta_0 r)}{s_0 F'(\beta_0 a)}\exp(s_0 t) + \left(\frac{a_0}{r}\right)^2, \quad (5.3.92)$$

where Im, Re denote the imaginary and real parts of the respective expressions. Asymptotic expressions are obtainable for large values of r. Thus, using the approximate formula† for large z,

$$K_\nu(z) \sim \sqrt{\left(\frac{\pi}{2z}\right)}\mathrm{e}^{-z}. \quad (5.3.93)$$

Selberg obtains for $r/a \to \infty$

$$\sqrt{\left(\frac{r}{a}\right)}\tau_{rr} = \frac{\lambda+2\mu}{\sqrt{(2\pi)}}\,\mathrm{Im}\int\limits_0^{\infty} \frac{\exp\left\{\frac{c_2\xi}{a}\left(t-\frac{r}{c_2}\right)\right\}}{\xi^{\frac{3}{2}}F(\xi)}\,\mathrm{d}\xi + $$

$$+(\lambda+2\mu)\sqrt{(2\pi)}\,\mathrm{Re}\,\frac{\exp\left\{\frac{c_2\xi_0}{a}\left(t-\frac{r}{c_2}\right)\right\}}{\xi_0^{\frac{3}{2}}F'(\xi_0)}, \quad (5.3.94)$$

where $\xi = \beta a$, $\xi_0 = \beta_0 a$.

Results were determined for the case of $\nu = \frac{1}{4}$ (corresponding to $\lambda = \mu$). The resulting value of $\beta_0 a$ was found to be $\beta_0 a = -0{\cdot}442057 + 0{\cdot}447357\mathrm{i}$. Figure 5.9(a) shows the result for a step loading, where $\bar{\sigma}_r$, $\bar{t}$ are given by

$$\bar{\sigma}_r = \sqrt{\left(\frac{r}{a}\right)}\sigma_r, \qquad \bar{t} = t - \frac{r-a}{a}. \quad (5.3.95)$$

Results are also given, without further theoretical discussion, for the case of a pressure pulse of the form

$$\tau_{rr}(a,t) = \mathrm{e}^{-\kappa t}. \quad (5.3.96)$$

These cases are shown in Fig. 5.9(b) and (c). In (b), all curves are for $r/a \to \infty$, for various values of κ. In (c), $\kappa = 0{\cdot}25$, and differing positions are shown.

We close this section by commenting on the more general problem of the cylindrical cavity subjected to tractions τ_{rr} and $\tau_{r\theta}$, arbitrarily prescribed with respect to θ, but invariant with respect to z. As in the case of the spherical cavity, Eringen [7] has contributed a general formal solution to the problem, with discussions of several special cases. Miklowitz [15], Jordan [11], and others have also contributed in this area.

† Formula 204 of Reference [13].

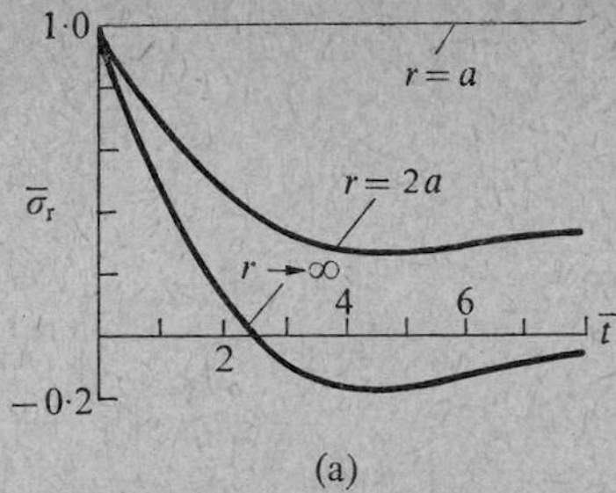

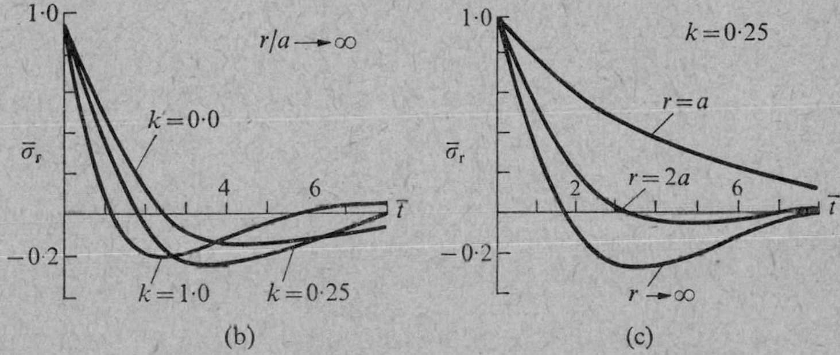

FIG. 5.9. Radial stress τ_{rr} resulting from a step pressure pulse in a cylindrical cavity (a), and from exponential decay pulses, (b) and (c). (After Selberg [18].)

References

1. ACHENBACH, J. D. and SUN, C. T. Propagation of waves from a spherical surface of time-dependent radius. *J. Acoust. Soc. Am.* **40,** 877–82 (1966).
2. BLAKE, F. G. Spherical wave propagation in solid media. *J. acoust. Soc. Am.* **24,** 211 (1952).
3. CAGNIARD, L. *Reflection et refraction des ondes seismiques progressive.* Gauthiers-Villars, Paris (1935).
4. DAS GUPTA, S. C. Waves and stresses produced in an elastic medium due to impulsive radial forces and twist on the surface of a spherical cavity. *Geofis. pura. Appl.* **27,** 3–8 (1954).
5. EASON, G., FULTON, J., and SNEDDON, I. N. The generation of waves in an infinite elastic solid by variable body forces. *Phil. Trans. R. Soc.* **A248,** 575–607 (1955–6).
6. ERINGEN, A. C. Elasto-dynamic problem concerning the spherical cavity. *Q. Jl Mech. appl. Math.* **10,** 257–70 (1957).
7. ——. Propagation of elastic waves generated by dynamical loads on a circular cavity. *J. appl. Mech.* **28,** 218–22 (1961).
8. FREDERICK, J. R. *Ultrasonic engineering.* John Wiley and Sons, New York (1965).
9. GOLDSMITH, W. and ALLEN, W. A. Graphical representation of the spherical propagation of explosive pulses in elastic media. *J. acoust. Soc. Am.* **27,** 47–55 (1955).

10. HOPKINS, H. G. Dynamic expansion of spherical cavities in metals. In *Progress in Solid Mechanics*, Vol. I, Chap. 3, (Ed. I. N. Sneddon and R. Hill) North Holland (1960).
11. JORDAN, D. W. The stress wave from a finite, cylindrical explosive source. *J. Math. Mech.* **11**, 503–51 (1962).
12. LOVE, A. E. H. *A treatise on the mathematical theory of elasticity*. Dover Publications, New York (1944).
13. MCLACHLAN, N. W. *Bessel functions for engineers*. Clarendon Press, Oxford (1961).
14. MEYER, M. L. On spherical near fields and far fields in elastic and viscoelastic solids. *J. Mech. Phys. Solids* **12**, 77–111 (1964).
15. MIKLOWITZ, J. Plane-stress unloading waves emanating from a suddenly punched hole in a stretched elastic plate. *J. appl. Mech.* **27**, 165–7 (1960).
16. MORSE, P. and FESHBACH, H. *Methods of theoretical physics* Vols. I and II. McGraw-Hill, New York (1953).
17. RAYLEIGH, J. W. S. *The theory of sound* Vols. I and II. Dover Publications, New York (1945).
18. SELBERG, H. L. Transient compression waves from spherical and cylindrical cavities. *Ark. Fys.* **5**, 97–108 (1952).
19. STERNBERG, E. On the integration of the equations of motion in the classical theory of elasticity. *Archs ration Mech. Analysis* **6**, 34 (1960).
20. —— and GINTIN, *Proc. 4th U.S. Congr. appl. Mech.* p. 793 (1962).
21. WATSON, G. N. *A treatise on the theory of Bessel functions* (2nd edn). Cambridge University Press (1966).
22. WRIGHT, J. K. and CARPENTER, E. W. The generation of horizontally polarized shear waves by underground explosions. *J. geophys. Res.* **67**, 1957–63 (1962).

Problems

5.1. Consider a plane harmonic dilatational wave to be propagating in an infinite medium. Determine the expression for the dilatation.

5.2. Consider two SH wave sources f_1, f_2, where $f_1 = c_2^2\,\delta(x-a)\delta(y)\exp(-i\omega t)$ and $f_2 = c_2^2\,\delta(x+a)\,\delta(y)\exp(-i\omega t)$. Using superposition of the simple SH wave source results, obtain an expression for $u_z(x, y, t)$. Assume the wavelength is large in comparison to $2a$. See if an approximate expression for u_z can be obtained for these circumstances.

5.3. Consider the problem of a spherical cavity subjected to a uniformly distributed pressure pulse $\tau_{rr}(a, t) = P_0\,\delta(t)$ and obtain the solution for the wave propagation. Sketch the waveform at various time intervals.

5.4. Consider a solid sphere of radius a. Determine the frequency equation governing the spherically symmetric 'expansion' modes of the sphere.

5.5. Consider the step pressure pulse solution (5.3.38). Discuss the consequences on the pulse shape for ζ becoming large. In the limit, does the wave begin to resemble a step pulse, with a sharp 'spike' disturbance at the wavefront?

5.6. Consider a cylindrical cavity, defined by $r = a$, in an infinite medium. Let the surface of the cavity be subjected to the prescribed displacements $u_r = u_z = 0$, $u_\theta(a, \theta, t) = u_0\exp(i\omega t)$. Determine the resulting wave propagation.

6 Waves in semi-infinite media

As the next step in the study of elastic waves, we consider the propagation and reflection of waves in a semi-infinite media. It is, of course, the inclusion of a boundary that distinguishes this problem from those of the last chapter. Waves in semi-infinite solids, either homogeneous or inhomogeneous, have been of long-standing interest in seismology. Problems in ultrasonics, delay lines, soil dynamics, blast, and impact have also led to analysis of waves in a half-space.

The first area of study will be the propagation of plane harmonic waves in a half-space. This study will establish the characteristics of mode conversion that occurs when waves encounter a free boundary and the existence of surface waves. Understanding of the behaviour of simple harmonic waves will provide insight into the interaction of waves with more complicated boundary shapes, will find application in the study of waves in plates and rods, and will aid in the analysis of transient-loading problems.

The analysis of waves from surface and buried sources will then be carried out. The technical literature in this area is quite extensive, and the methods of analysis are quite sophisticated. Here, it will only be possible to give rather limited coverage to this topic. As an introduction, the simplest case of SH wave sources will be considered. This problem will be used to develop the method of steepest descent, an analytical tool representing an extension of the stationary-phase method developed in Chapter 1.

Finally, consideration will be given to wave propagation in a layered media. This topic also is extremely broad, with a large amount of technical literature and entire books devoted to the subject. The reflection and refraction of plane waves between two media in contact will be covered, a new type of surface wave considered, and a limited number of results presented for pulse propagation.

6.1. Propagation and reflection of plane waves in a half-space

When an elastic wave encounters a boundary between two media, energy is reflected and transmitted from and across the boundary. This is, of course, no different to phenomena occurring in acoustics and optics. If the boundary is a free surface, a pure reflection process will occur. It will be found that a distinguishing characteristic of the wave–boundary interaction process for elastic waves in a solid is that mode conversion occurs. This describes the behaviour by which an incident wave, either pressure or shear, is converted into two waves on reflection. This behaviour, along with the fact that two types of waves may exist in an elastic solid, accounts for the relative complexity of elastic wave problems in solids compared to equivalent problems in acoustics and electromagnetics. It will also be established that surface waves may propagate in a half-space. These waves, of long-standing interest in seismology, have counterparts in hydrodynamics and electromagnetics.

6.1.1. *Governing equations*

Let us consider plane harmonic waves propagating in the half-space $y \geqslant 0$. No generality will be lost if we assume the wave normal $\mathbf{n}$ to lie in the x,y-plane. This will be called the 'vertical' plane and the x,z-plane, which is the surface of the half-space, will be called the 'horizontal' plane. On the basis of our studies of plane waves in infinite media, we should realize that the particle motion due to dilatational effects will be in the direction of the wave normal and will thus lie completely in the vertical plane. The transverse particle motion due to shear may have components in the vertical plane and, also, parallel to the horizontal plane. The general situation is shown in Fig. 6.1. The normal displacement component is u_n and the transverse

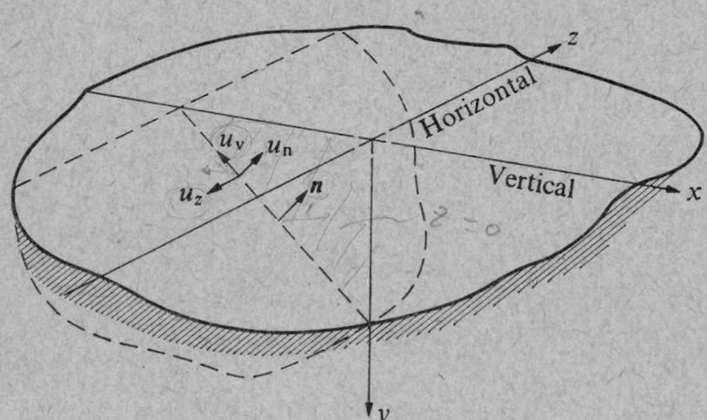

FIG. 6.1. Plane wave, with wave normal $\mathbf{n}$ in the x,y-(vertical) plane advancing toward a free surface.

components are u_v and u_z which are, respectively, in the vertical and horizontal planes. Finally, since every point along the plane of the wave is executing the same motion, we have that the motion is invariant with respect to z if the wave normal is in the vertical plane.

The governing equations for our investigation are

$$u_x = \frac{\partial \Phi}{\partial x} + \frac{\partial H_z}{\partial y}, \qquad u_y = \frac{\partial \Phi}{\partial y} - \frac{\partial H_z}{\partial x}, \tag{6.1.1}$$

$$u_z = -\frac{\partial H_x}{\partial y} + \frac{\partial H_y}{\partial x}, \qquad \frac{\partial H_x}{\partial x} + \frac{\partial H_y}{\partial y} = 0, \tag{6.1.2}$$

$$\nabla^2 \Phi = \frac{1}{c_1^2}\frac{\partial^2 \Phi}{\partial t^2}, \qquad \nabla^2 H_p = \frac{1}{c_2^2}\frac{\partial^2 H_p}{\partial t^2} \qquad (p = x, y, z). \tag{6.1.3}$$

where the z independence of all quantities has been used. The second equation of (6.1.2) results from $\nabla.\mathbf{H} = 0$. The stress–displacement expressions are given by

$$\tau_{xx} = (\lambda+2\mu)\left(\frac{\partial u_x}{\partial x}+\frac{\partial u_y}{\partial y}\right)-2\mu\frac{\partial u_y}{\partial y}, \tag{6.1.4}$$

$$\tau_{yy} = (\lambda+2\mu)\left(\frac{\partial u_x}{\partial x}+\frac{\partial u_y}{\partial y}\right)-2\mu\frac{\partial u_x}{\partial x}, \tag{6.1.5}$$

$$\tau_{zz} = \frac{\lambda}{2(\lambda+\mu)}(\tau_{xx}+\tau_{yy}), \tag{6.1.6}$$

$$\tau_{xy} = \mu\left(\frac{\partial u_x}{\partial y}+\frac{\partial u_y}{\partial x}\right), \tag{6.1.7}$$

$$\tau_{yz} = \mu\frac{\partial u_z}{\partial y}, \qquad \tau_{xz} = 0. \tag{6.1.8}$$

In terms of the potentials Φ, H_x, H_y, H_z, these are

$$\tau_{xx} = (\lambda+2\mu)\left(\frac{\partial^2\Phi}{\partial x^2}+\frac{\partial^2\Phi}{\partial y^2}\right)-2\mu\left(\frac{\partial^2\Phi}{\partial y^2}-\frac{\partial^2 H_z}{\partial y\,\partial x}\right), \tag{6.1.9}$$

$$\tau_{yy} = (\lambda+2\mu)\left(\frac{\partial^2\Phi}{\partial x^2}+\frac{\partial^2\Phi}{\partial y^2}\right)-2\mu\left(\frac{\partial^2\Phi}{\partial x^2}+\frac{\partial^2 H_z}{\partial x\,\partial y}\right), \tag{6.1.10}$$

$$\tau_{xy} = \mu\left(2\frac{\partial^2\Phi}{\partial x\,\partial y}+\frac{\partial^2 H_z}{\partial y^2}-\frac{\partial^2 H_z}{\partial x^2}\right), \tag{6.1.11}$$

$$\tau_{yz} = \mu\left(-\frac{\partial^2 H_x}{\partial y^2}+\frac{\partial^2 H_y}{\partial y\,\partial x}\right), \qquad \tau_{xz} = 0. \tag{6.1.12}$$

Finally, we have the boundary conditions given by

$$\tau_{yy} = \tau_{yx} = \tau_{yz} = 0, \qquad y = 0. \tag{6.1.13}$$

We make the observation, at this stage, that we are actually dealing with two uncoupled problems of wave motion. Thus, we see that u_x, u_y depend only on Φ and H_z, which are in turn governed by the independent scalar wave equations (6.1.3), where $p = z$ in the second of the two equations. Further, the stresses τ_{xx}, τ_{yy}, τ_{xy} depend only on u_x, u_y, and hence only on Φ and H_z. The component u_z depends on H_x, H_y which are governed by the second of (6.1.3), where $p = y,z$. Further, the stress τ_{yz} depends only on u_z, and hence only on H_x, H_y. This makes it possible to resolve the motion into two parts, where one is plane strain with $u_z = \partial/\partial z = 0$, u_x, $u_y \neq 0$ and the other is SH wave motion, where $\partial/\partial z = u_x = u_y = 0$, $u_z \neq 0$. If we did not recognize the uncoupling at this stage, it would still be brought out in the boundary condition equations (this will be shown in the analysis of waves in plates). Thus we have the following:

plane strain: $u_z = \partial/\partial z = 0$,

$$u_x = \frac{\partial \Phi}{\partial x} + \frac{\partial H_z}{\partial y}, \qquad u_y = \frac{\partial \Phi}{\partial y} - \frac{\partial H_z}{\partial x}, \tag{6.1.14}$$

$$\nabla^2 \Phi = \frac{1}{c_1^2}\frac{\partial^2 \Phi}{\partial t^2}, \qquad \nabla^2 H_z = \frac{1}{c_2^2}\frac{\partial^2 H_z}{\partial t^2}. \tag{6.1.15}$$

$\tau_{xx}, \tau_{yy}, \tau_{zz}, \tau_{xy}$: eqns (6.1.4)–(6.1.7), (6.1.9)–(6.1.11).

$$\tau_{yy} = \tau_{xy} = 0, \qquad y = 0. \tag{6.1.16}$$

SH waves: $u_x = u_y = \partial/\partial z = 0$,

$$u_z = -\frac{\partial H_x}{\partial y} + \frac{\partial H_y}{\partial x}, \qquad \frac{\partial H_x}{\partial x} + \frac{\partial H_y}{\partial y} = 0, \tag{6.1.17}$$

$$\nabla^2 H_x = \frac{1}{c_2^2}\frac{\partial^2 H_x}{\partial t^2}, \qquad \nabla^2 H_y = \frac{1}{c_2^2}\frac{\partial^2 H_y}{\partial t^2}, \tag{6.1.18}$$

τ_{yz}: eqns (6.1.8), (6.1.12),

$$\tau_{yz} = 0, \qquad y = 0. \tag{6.1.19}$$

We also note in the case of SH waves that we could directly consider the displacement equation of motion

$$\nabla^2 u_z = \frac{1}{c_2^2}\frac{\partial^2 u_z}{\partial t^2}. \tag{6.1.20}$$

Consider now the solution to the case of plane strain and let

$$\Phi = f(y)e^{i(\xi x - \omega t)}, \qquad H_z = h_z(y)e^{i(\zeta x - \omega t)}. \tag{6.1.21}$$

Substitution in the governing equations (6.1.3) gives

$$\frac{d^2 f}{dy^2} + \alpha^2 f = 0, \qquad \frac{d^2 h_z}{dy^2} + \beta^2 h = 0, \tag{6.1.22}$$

where

$$\alpha^2 = \frac{\omega^2}{c_1^2} - \xi^2, \qquad \beta^2 = \frac{\omega^2}{c_2^2} - \zeta^2. \tag{6.1.23}$$

The plane wave solutions for Φ and H_z are then given by

$$\Phi = A_1 e^{i(\xi x - \alpha y - \omega t)} + A_2 e^{i(\xi x + \alpha y - \omega t)}, \tag{6.1.24}$$

$$H_z = B_1 e^{i(\zeta x - \beta y - \omega t)} + B_2 e^{i(\zeta x + \beta y - \omega t)}. \tag{6.1.25}$$

If we define θ_1, θ_2 as the angles between the y-axis and the wave normal of the dilatational and shear waves, we may write

$$\xi = \gamma_1 \sin \theta_1, \qquad \alpha = \gamma_1 \cos \theta_1, \tag{6.1.26}$$

$$\zeta = \gamma_2 \sin \theta_2, \qquad \beta = \gamma_2 \cos \theta_2, \tag{6.1.27}$$

where γ_1, γ_2 are the wavenumbers along the respective waves. Then Φ and H_z may also be written as

$$\Phi = A_1 \exp\{i\gamma_1(\sin \theta_1 x - \cos \theta_1 y - c_1 t)\} + \\ + A_2 \exp\{i\gamma_1(\sin \theta_1 x + \cos \theta_1 y - c_1 t)\}, \tag{6.1.28}$$

$$H_z = B_1 \exp\{i\gamma_2(\sin \theta_2 x - \cos \theta_2 y - c_2 t)\} + \\ + B_2 \exp\{i\gamma_2(\sin \theta_2 x + \cos \theta_2 y - c_2 t)\}. \tag{6.1.29}$$

The resulting plane-wave situation is shown in Fig. 6.2 for the Φ wave.

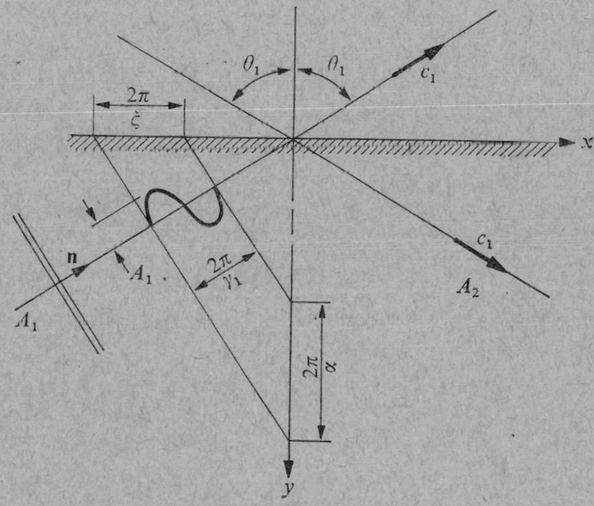

FIG. 6.2. Incident and reflected wave system for $\Phi(x, y, t)$.

Since γ_1 is the wavenumber in the wave direction, $2\pi/\gamma_1$ is the wavelength in the direction of travel. It is seen that ξ and α may be interpreted as the horizontal and vertical wavenumbers, with $2\pi/\xi$, $2\pi/\alpha$ being the horizontal and vertical wavelengths. The horizontal wavelength is of interest since this would be a quantity readily measured by surface transducers.

We now apply the solutions (6.1.28) and (6.1.29) to the plane-strain boundary conditions (6.1.16), obtaining

$$(\tau_{yy})_{y=0}: \quad \gamma_1^2(2 \sin^2\theta_1 - k^2)(A_1 + A_2)\exp\{i\gamma_1(\sin \theta_1 x - c_1 t)\} - \\ - \gamma_2^2 \sin 2\theta_2(B_1 - B_2)\exp\{i\gamma_2(\sin \theta_2 x - c_2 t)\} = 0, \tag{6.1.30}$$

$$(\tau_{xy})_{y=0}: \quad \gamma_1^2 \sin 2\theta_1(A_1 - A_2)\exp\{i\gamma_1(\sin \theta_1 x - c_1 t)\} - \\ - \gamma_2^2 \cos 2\theta_2(B_1 + B_2)\exp\{i\gamma_2(\sin \theta_2 x - c_2 t)\} = 0, \tag{6.1.31}$$

where we have again introduced the ratio of the wave velocities,

$$k^2 = c_1^2/c_2^2 = (\lambda+2\mu)/\mu.$$

Of course, we could immediately factor out $\exp(-\mathrm{i}\omega t)$ from the above. We now take note of the following argument. If the preceding results are to hold for arbitrary x, then we must be able to factor $\exp(\mathrm{i}\gamma_1 \sin\theta_1 x)$, $\exp(\mathrm{i}\gamma_2 \sin\theta_2 x)$ from the results. This can only occur if we have

$$\gamma_1 \sin\theta_1 = \gamma_2 \sin\theta_2. \tag{6.1.32}$$

Since $\omega = \gamma_1 c_1 = \gamma_2 c_2$, so that $\gamma_2/\gamma_1 = c_1/c_2 = k$, we may write the above also as

$$\gamma_2/\gamma_1 = \sin\theta_1/\sin\theta_2 = k. \tag{6.1.33}$$

This result may be interpreted as the form of Snell's law for elastic waves. With this, the boundary condition equations reduce to

$$\gamma_1^2(2\sin^2\theta_1 - k^2)(A_1+A_2) - \gamma_2^2 \sin 2\theta_2(B_1-B_2) = 0, \tag{6.1.34}$$

$$\gamma_2^2 \sin 2\theta_1(A_1-A_2) - \gamma_2^2 \cos 2\theta_2(B_1+B_2) = 0. \tag{6.1.35}$$

This governs the reflection of plane waves in a half-space. Various cases will be considered in the next section.

We now consider the solution for the SH wave case, and let

$$H_x = h_x(y)\mathrm{e}^{\mathrm{i}(\xi x-\omega t)}, \qquad H_y = h_y(y)\mathrm{e}^{\mathrm{i}(\xi x-\omega t)}. \tag{6.1.36}$$

Substitution in the governing equations (6.1.18) gives

$$\frac{\mathrm{d}^2 h_x}{\mathrm{d}y^2}+\eta^2 h_x = 0, \qquad \frac{\mathrm{d}^2 h_y}{\mathrm{d}y^2}+\eta^2 h_y = 0, \tag{6.1.37}$$

where

$$\eta^2 = \frac{\omega^2}{c_2^2}-\xi^2. \tag{6.1.38}$$

The solutions are

$$H_x = C_1\mathrm{e}^{\mathrm{i}(\xi x-\eta y-\omega t)}+C_2\mathrm{e}^{\mathrm{i}(\xi x+\eta y-\omega t)}, \tag{6.1.39}$$

$$H_y = D_1\mathrm{e}^{\mathrm{i}(\xi x-\eta y-\omega t)}+D_2\mathrm{e}^{\mathrm{i}(\xi x+\eta y-\omega t)}. \tag{6.1.40}$$

These results may also be expressed in terms of an incidence angle θ_3, as was previously done for Φ and H_z.

Not all of the above quantities are independent. This is a consequence of the $\nabla.\mathbf{H} = 0$ condition that attaches to the Helmholtz vector resolution. As mentioned in the previous chapter, this enables the three components of the displacement to be established from the four components of Φ and $\mathbf{H}$. In the present study of plane strain and SH waves, it was found that u_x and u_y depend only on the two quantities Φ and H_z and are thus uniquely determined. Not so for u_z, which depends on H_x and H_y. For the present case of z independence, the divergence condition is given by the second eqn (6.1.2).

Applying this condition to the results (6.1.39) and (6.1.40) gives

$$\mathrm{i}\xi(C_1\mathrm{e}^{-\mathrm{i}\eta y}+C_2\mathrm{e}^{\mathrm{i}\eta y})+\mathrm{i}\eta(-D_1\mathrm{e}^{-\mathrm{i}\eta y}+D_2\mathrm{e}^{\mathrm{i}\eta y})=0, \tag{6.1.41}$$

where $\exp\{\mathrm{i}(\xi x-\omega t)\}$ has been factored out. This re-groups to

$$(\xi C_1-\eta D_1)\mathrm{e}^{-\mathrm{i}\eta y}+(\xi C_2+\eta D_2)\mathrm{e}^{\mathrm{i}\eta y}=0. \tag{6.1.42}$$

In order for the above result to hold for all y, we must have C_1, D_1, C_2, D_2 related by

$$\xi C_1=\eta D_1, \qquad \xi C_2=-\eta D_2. \tag{6.1.43}$$

Thus, two of the constants of (6.1.39) and (6.1.40) may be eliminated. Arbitrarily choosing to eliminate D_1, D_2, we thus have

$$H_x=C_1\mathrm{e}^{\mathrm{i}(\xi x-\eta y-\omega t)}+C_2\mathrm{e}^{\mathrm{i}(\xi x+\eta y-\omega t)}, \tag{6.1.44}$$

$$H_y=\frac{\xi}{\eta}C_1\mathrm{e}^{\mathrm{i}(\xi x-\eta y-\omega t)}-\frac{\xi}{\eta}C_2\mathrm{e}^{\mathrm{i}(\xi x+\eta y-\omega t)}. \tag{6.1.45}$$

Substituting these results into the boundary condition $\tau_{yz}=0$, $y=0$ gives

$$(\tau_{yz}): \qquad \eta^2(C_1+C_2)+\xi^2(C_1+C_2)=0. \tag{6.1.46}$$

This result governs the reflection of SH waves in a half-space. Specific cases will be considered in the next section.

6.1.2. *Waves at oblique incidence*

We now wish to determine the reflection characteristics of various types of incoming waves. The order of investigation will be (1) P waves at oblique incidence, (2) SV waves at oblique incidence, (3) SH waves at oblique incidence, and (4) Pairs of incident waves. By oblique incidence, we mean that θ_1 or θ_2 of the incident wave may be in the range of $0 \leqslant \theta_1, \theta_2 < \pi/2$.

1. *Incident P waves.* Let us assume that the incident wave is compressional only. This results if $B_1=0$ in the wave expressions (6.1.28) and (6.1.29). Further, we presume that the angle θ_1, frequency ω, and amplitude A_1 of the wave are specified. The boundary condition equations (6.1.30), (6.1.31) become

$$\gamma_1^2(2\sin^2\theta_1-k^2)(A_1+A_2)+\gamma_2^2\sin 2\theta_2 B_2=0, \tag{6.1.47}$$

$$\gamma_1^2\sin 2\theta_1(A_1-A_2)-\gamma_2^2\cos 2\theta_2 B_2=0. \tag{6.1.48}$$

Solving, we obtain the amplitude ratios

$$\frac{A_2}{A_1}=\frac{\sin 2\theta_1\sin 2\theta_2-k^2\cos^2 2\theta_2}{\sin 2\theta_1\sin 2\theta_2+k^2\cos^2 2\theta_2}, \tag{6.1.49}$$

$$\frac{B_2}{A_1}=\frac{2\sin 2\theta_1\cos 2\theta_2}{\sin 2\theta_1\sin 2\theta_2+k^2\cos^2 2\theta_2}. \tag{6.1.50}$$

The reflection angle θ_2 and the wavenumber γ_2 are given by (6.1.33).

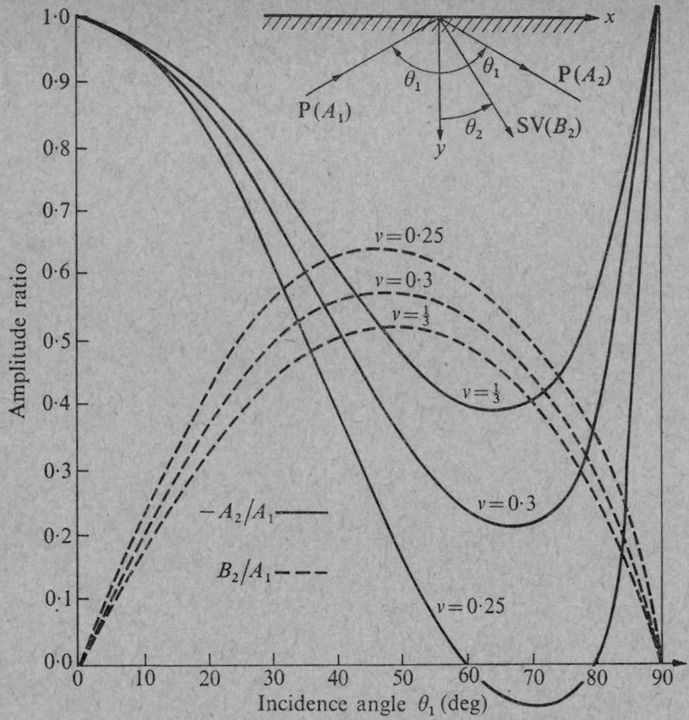

FIG. 6.3. Amplitude ratios A_2/A_1, B_2/A_1 for incident P waves, for various Poisson's ratios, with a ray representation of the reflection also shown.

One of the major features of this result is that, for a single P wave incident, two waves, P and SV, are reflected. This phenomenon is referred to as *mode conversion*. We recall that P and S waves propagate independently, or uncoupled, in a material. However, when a free surface is present, coupling of the two wave systems occurs through the boundary conditions.

The nature of the reflection is shown as part of Fig. 6.3, where a simple ray representation has been used to designate the various waves and directions of propagation. We note from (6.1.33) that $\gamma_2 = c_1\gamma_1/c_2 > \gamma_1$. Hence from $\sin\theta_2 = \gamma_1 \sin\theta_1/\gamma_2$ we conclude that $\theta_2 < \theta_1$ always. From (6.1.49) and (6.1.50), it is seen that the amplitude ratios A_2/A_1, B_2/A_1 depend only on the incidence angle and the Poisson's ratio of the material (since k^2 depends only on Poisson's ratio). These ratios are plotted in Fig. 6.3 for $\nu = \frac{1}{3}, 0{\cdot}3, \frac{1}{4}$. We note an apparent anomaly for B_2/A_1 when $\nu = \frac{1}{3}$. Thus, $B_2/A_1 > 1$ for $\theta \approx 50\,°$, possibly implying violation of energy conservation. However, energy transfer depends on propagation velocity as well as amplitude. The SV waves are slower than the P waves, so it is possible for amplitude ratios greater than unity to occur.

A special case of interest is that of normal incidence ($\theta_1 = 0°$). From (6.1.49) and (6.1.50) we obtain

$$A_2/A_1 = -1, \qquad B_2/A_1 = 0. \tag{6.1.51}$$

This corresponds to an incident compression wave reflecting as tension and tension reflecting as compression, a result first noted in the case of longitudinal waves in rods. A second special case occurs for $A_2/A_1 = 0$, implying no reflected P wave. This occurs if

$$\sin 2\theta_1 \sin 2\theta_2 - k^2 \cos^2\theta_2 = 0. \tag{6.1.52}$$

This equation can be satisfied only for selected ranges of ν. Thus, if $\nu = \frac{1}{4}$, we obtain $\theta_1 = 60°$, $77{\cdot}5°$ as critical values of incidence for which no P wave is reflected. These values also appear in Fig. 6.3.

2. *Incident SV waves.* This case is obtained by setting $A_1 = 0$ in (6.1.28) and the boundary condition equations (6.1.34) and (6.1.35). The resulting amplitude ratios are

$$\frac{B_2}{B_1} = \frac{\sin 2\theta_1 \sin 2\theta_2 - k^2 \cos^2 2\theta_2}{\sin 2\theta_1 \sin 2\theta_2 + k^2 \cos^2 2\theta_2}, \tag{6.1.53}$$

$$\frac{A_2}{B_1} = \frac{-2k^2 \sin 2\theta_2 \cos 2\theta_2}{\sin 2\theta_1 \sin 2\theta_2 + k^2 \cos^2 2\theta_2}. \tag{6.1.54}$$

As for incident P waves, mode conversion again occurs for incident SV waves. The ray representation of the wave reflection is shown in Fig. 6.4. The reflection angle θ_1 and wavenumber γ_1 are determined by (6.1.33). We see for both types of incident wave, P or SV, that the ray of the reflected P wave is 'outside' that of the SV wave. The amplitude ratios A_2/B_1, B_2/B_1 are shown in Fig. 6.4 for several values of Poisson's ratio.

Various special cases of wave reflection are easily found. The case of normal incidence is given by $\theta_2 = 0$. We have from (6.1.53) and (6.1.54) that

$$A_2/B_1 = 0, \qquad B_2/B_1 = -1. \tag{6.1.55}$$

The case of $\theta_2 = 45°$ gives $A_2/B_1 = 0$, $B_2/B_1 = 1$. This result finds application in plate theory. It is also possible to have an incident SV wave, with only a reflected P wave ($B_2 = 0$). This occurs for

$$\sin 2\theta_1 \sin 2\theta_2 = k^2 \cos^2 2\theta_2. \tag{6.1.56}$$

A special case of particular interest occurs for θ_2 beyond the *critical angle.* Thus, referring to Fig. 6.4, we note that for increasing θ_2 there will occur a value of θ_2 such that the reflected P wave will be tangental to the surface. The value of θ_2 for which this occurs will be given from (6.1.33) as

$$\sin \theta_1 = k \sin \theta_2 = 1, \tag{6.1.57}$$

where $k > 1$ always. For example, if $\nu = \frac{1}{3}$, we have that $k = 2$ and θ_2

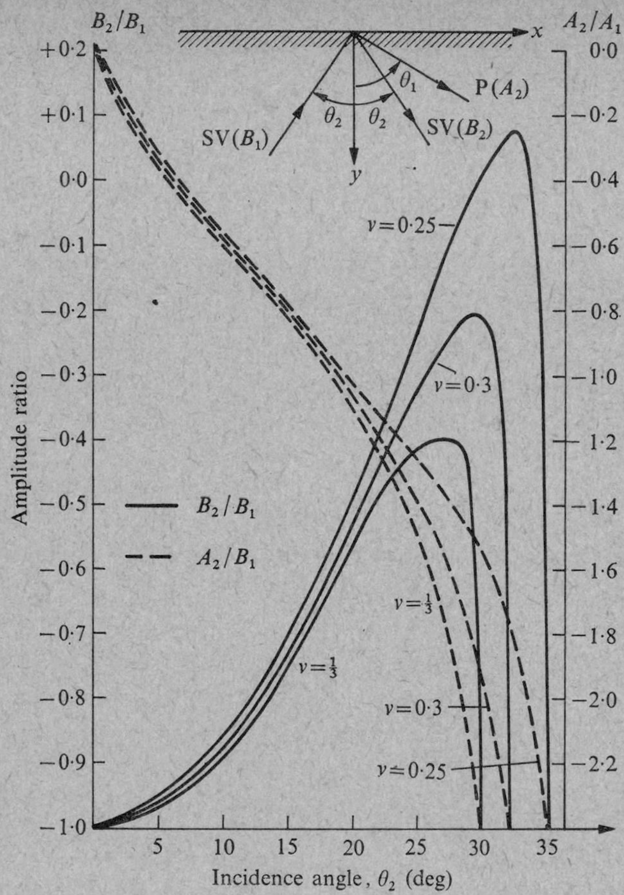

FIG. 6.4. Reflected wave amplitude ratios A_2/B_1, B_2/B_1 for incident SV waves and various Poisson's ratios, with the ray representation of the reflection also shown.

(critical) = 30 °. Now, since SV waves may be incident at any angle, values of θ_2 greater than the critical value are possible. But this would predict values of $\sin\theta_1 > 1$, an impossible situation. To understand the nature of the reflection phenomenon for this case, we must go back to the original differential equation determining Φ, specifically the first of (6.1.22), and note that $\alpha^2 > 0$ was assumed in arriving at the results (6.1.24) and (6.1.28). Now we may express α^2 as

$$\alpha^2 = \frac{\omega^2}{c_1^2} - \xi^2 = \frac{\omega^2}{c_1^2} - \gamma_1^2 \sin^2\theta_1. \tag{6.1.58}$$

Since $\gamma_1 \sin\theta_1 = \gamma_2 \sin\theta_2$ and $\omega = \gamma_1 c_1 = \gamma_2 c_2$, this may be put in the form

$$\alpha^2 = \frac{\gamma_2^2}{k^2}(1-k^2\sin^2\theta_2). \tag{6.1.59}$$

If (6.1.57) holds, $\alpha^2 = 0$, and $\alpha^2 < 0$ if $k^2 \sin^2\theta_2 > 1$. Although $\sin\theta_1 > 1$ is not possible, $\alpha^2 \leqslant 0$ is possible. Our approach then is to re-examine the governing equation for these cases. We have

$$\alpha^2 = 0, \qquad d^2f/dy^2 = 0, \qquad f = A_1y + A_2, \tag{6.1.60}$$

$$\Phi = (A_1y + A_2)e^{i(\xi x - \omega t)}. \tag{6.1.61}$$

The A_1 term must be discarded on physical grounds in the present half-space problem, leaving a plane wave of constant amplitude travelling parallel to the free surface. The behaviour is shown in Fig. 6.5(a). If

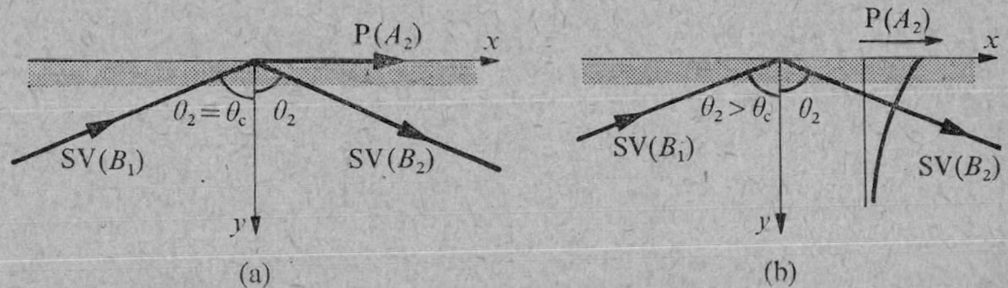

FIG. 6.5. (a) Incident SV waves at the critical angle and (b) greater than the critical angle θ_c.

$$\alpha^2 < 0, \qquad \frac{d^2f}{dy^2} - \bar{\alpha}^2 f = 0, \qquad \bar{\alpha}^2 = -\alpha^2, \tag{6.1.62}$$

$$\Phi = A_1e^{\bar{\alpha}y}e^{i(\xi x - \omega t)} + A_2e^{-\bar{\alpha}y}e^{i(\xi x - \omega t)}. \tag{6.1.63}$$

Again, we discard A_1 because of the unbounded wave amplitude for increasing y. The result is an exponentially decaying wave, as shown in Fig. 6.5(b).

3. *Incident SH waves.* This is the simplest case of wave reflection. Thus, from (6.1.46), we have

$$(\eta^2 + \xi^2)(C_1 + C_2) = 0, \qquad C_2 = -C_1, \tag{6.1.64}$$

and the reflection angle is equal to the incidence angle. Thus, the SH wave reflects as itself, with no mode conversion, quite analogous to acoustic wave reflection. Now, if a shear wave of arbitrary polarization impinges on a free surface, the SV portion of the wave will lose a portion of its energy to P waves, whereas the SH portion of the amplitude and energy will reflect with only change in phase.

4. *Reflections of pairs of waves.* Under special circumstances, P and SV waves may reflect as themselves. This can occur when pairs of P and SV waves with specific amplitude ratios are incident on the free boundary. The necessary conditions may be obtained directly from (6.1.34), (6.1.35). However, by first noting that $\gamma_2^2/\gamma_1^2 = k^2$ and $\sin\theta_1 = k\sin\theta_2$, we may reduce the

cited equations to

$$\cos 2\theta_2(A_1+A_2)+\sin 2\theta_2(B_1-B_2) = 0, \tag{6.1.65}$$

$$\sin 2\theta_1(A_1-A_2)-k^2\cos 2\theta_2(B_1+B_2) = 0. \tag{6.1.66}$$

These relations may be satisfied by either

$$A_1 = -A_2, \qquad B_1 = B_2, \qquad A_1/B_1 = k^2 \cos 2\theta_2 \cos 2\theta_1 \tag{6.1.67}$$

or

$$A_1 = A_2, \qquad B_1 = -B_2, \qquad A_1/B_1 = -\tan 2\theta_2. \tag{6.1.68}$$

The two resulting cases of wave reflection are shown in Fig. 6.6(a) and (b)

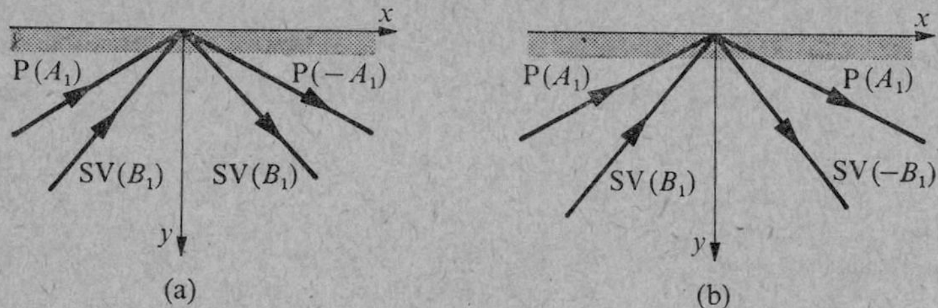

FIG. 6.6. (a) Reflections of pairs of waves, with $A_1 = -A_2$, $B_1 = B_2$, and (b) $A_1 = A_2$, $B_1 = -B_2$.

respectively. This behaviour finds application in the study of plates.

6.1.3. *Waves at grazing incidence*

A study of the previously-derived amplitude ratios for P and SV waves shows that for $\theta_1 \to 90°$ (in case of P waves) or $\theta_2 \to 90°$ (in case of SV waves) that no mode conversion occurs so that a P wave incoming at grazing incidence reflects as itself, and likewise for a grazing SV wave. This is also shown in the results of Figs. 6.3 and 6.4. However, it has been shown by a proper limiting process involving the amplitude ratios that other cases of reflection are possible.† In our discussion of this case, however, we shall follow the procedure used in investigating SV waves incident beyond the critical angle.

Thus, in obtaining (6.1.24) and (6.1.25) for Φ and H_z, it was assumed that $\alpha^2, \beta^2 > 0$ in (6.1.22) and (6.1.23). However, as we realize from the study of the special case of SV waves, as $\theta_1 \to 90°$, $\alpha \to 0$ and as $\theta_2 \to 90°$, $\beta \to 0$. We thus have for $\alpha \to 0$ (P waves grazing) that

$$\frac{d^2f}{dy^2}+\alpha^2 f = 0 \to \frac{d^2f}{dy^2} = 0, \qquad f = A_1+A_2y, \tag{6.1.69}$$

$$\Phi = (A_1+A_2y)e^{i(\xi x-\omega t)}, \tag{6.1.70}$$

† Goodier and Bishop [14].

and for $\beta \to 0$ (SV waves grazing) that

$$\frac{d^2h_z}{dy^2}+\beta^2h_z = 0 \to \frac{d^2h_z}{dy^2} = 0, \qquad h_z = B_1+B_2y, \tag{6.1.71}$$

$$H_z = (B_1+B_2y)e^{i(\xi x-\omega t)}, \tag{6.1.72}$$

$$\Phi = A_2e^{-\bar{\alpha}y}e^{i(\xi x-\omega t)}. \tag{6.1.73}$$

We note that for grazing SV waves, the critical angle has been excluded so that Φ is given by (6.1.63), as shown in the previous section.

For the case of grazing P waves, we set $B_1 = 0$ in (6.1.25) and, using (6.1.70), we have that

$$\Phi = (A_1+A_2y)e^{i(\xi x-\omega t)}, \tag{6.1.74}$$

$$H_z = B_2e^{i(\xi x+\beta y-\omega t)}. \tag{6.1.75}$$

The wave reflection situation is as shown in Fig. 6.7(a). For the case of grazing

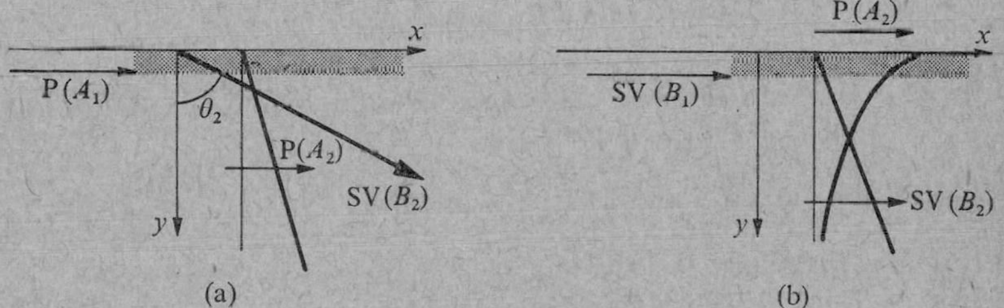

FIG. 6.7. Reflection of waves at grazing incidence with (a) P waves incident and (b) SV waves incident.

SV waves, we directly have (6.1.72) and (6.1.73) as describing the wave propagation. The wave system is as shown in Fig. 6.7(b).

The possibility of wave systems with linearly increasing amplitudes, as occur in the preceding solutions, certainly violates physical intuition, as have other mathematically correct solutions obtained in other studies. Goodier and Bishop suggested that SV wavefronts having some of the characteristics just illustrated are encountered in some cases of impact, although the continuations of these fronts into the interior was left open to question. In the context of the half-space problem, such waves are of little interest. However, it will be found that these waves have a role in the theory of vibrations of finite elastic plates as governed by the equations of elasticity.

6.1.4. *Surface waves*

We have shown in the work of Chapter 5 that in an unbounded elastic media two and only two types of waves can be propagated. In the preceding sections we have investigated the interaction of these waves with a boundary and have noted the mode conversion that occurs when P or SV waves impinge, also noting that at most only two waves of the P and SV type are produced. However, when there is a boundary, as in the half-space problem, a third type of wave may exist whose effects are confined closely to the surface. These waves were first investigated by Lord Rayleigh [37], who showed that their effect decreases rapidly with depth and that their velocity of propagation is smaller than that of body waves.

The discovery of this wave-type was closely related to seismology, where it was early observed that earthquake tremors consisted of two early, rather minor disturbances corresponding to P and SV wave arrivals, followed closely by a significant damage-causing tremor. Such a disturbance was not consistent with existing understanding of elastic wave theory. The first question was, therefore, whether another wave-type could exist. Further consideration strongly suggested that such a wave should be a surface wave. Thus, the relative insignificance of P and SV waves was considered to be a consequence of volumetric dispersion of their energy into the earth's interior. The significant energy associated with the third wave suggested that it dissipated its energy less rapidly than P and SV waves. This could only be accounted for by assuming it was essentially confined to the surface.

We start by again considering Φ and H_z to be given by (6.1.3) with, now, $f(y)$, $h_z(y)$ given by

$$\frac{d^2f}{dy^2}-\bar{\alpha}^2f=0, \qquad \frac{d^2h_z}{dy^2}-\bar{\beta}^2h_z=0, \tag{6.1.76}$$

where $\bar{\alpha}^2 = -\alpha^2$, $\bar{\beta}^2 = -\beta^2$, and α^2, β^2 are as previously defined by (6.1.23). We recognize the first of (6.1.76) as arising in the study of incident SV waves beyond the critical angle. The solutions give waves with exponentially increasing and decreasing parts. Discarding the increasing terms, we have

$$\Phi = Ae^{-\bar{\alpha}y}e^{i\xi(x-ct)}, \qquad H_z = Be^{-\bar{\beta}y}e^{i\xi(x-ct)}. \tag{6.1.77}$$

The expressions for the displacements and stresses are

$$u_x = (i\xi Ae^{-\bar{\alpha}y}-\bar{\beta}Be^{-\bar{\beta}y})e^{i\xi(x-ct)}, \tag{6.1.78}$$

$$u_y = -(\bar{\alpha}Ae^{-\bar{\alpha}y}+i\xi Be^{-\bar{\beta}y})e^{i\xi(x-ct)}, \tag{6.1.79}$$

$$\tau_{xx} = \mu\{(\bar{\beta}^2-\xi^2-2\bar{\alpha}^2)Ae^{-\bar{\alpha}y}-2i\bar{\beta}\xi Be^{-\bar{\beta}y}\}e^{i\xi(x-ct)}, \tag{6.1.80}$$

$$\tau_{yy} = \mu\{(\bar{\beta}^2+\xi^2)Ae^{-\bar{\alpha}y}+2i\bar{\beta}\xi Be^{-\bar{\beta}y}\}e^{i\xi(x-ct)}, \tag{6.1.81}$$

$$\tau_{xy} = \mu\{-2i\bar{\alpha}\xi Ae^{-\bar{\alpha}y}+(\xi^2+\bar{\beta}^2)Be^{-\bar{\beta}y}\}e^{i\xi(x-ct)}. \tag{6.1.82}$$

At the free surface we have $\tau_{yy} = \tau_{xy} = 0$. From (6.1.81) and (6.1.82) this gives

$$\begin{aligned} (\bar{\beta}^2+\xi^2)A+2i\bar{\beta}\xi B &= 0, \\ -2i\bar{\alpha}\xi A+(\bar{\beta}^2+\xi^2)B &= 0. \end{aligned} \tag{6.1.83}$$

These give the amplitude ratios

$$\frac{A}{B} = -\frac{2i\bar{\beta}\xi}{\bar{\beta}^2+\xi^2} = \frac{\bar{\beta}^2+\xi^2}{2i\bar{\alpha}\xi}, \tag{6.1.84}$$

and the frequency equation for surface waves

$$(\bar{\beta}^2+\xi^2)^2-4\bar{\alpha}\bar{\beta}\xi^2 = 0, \tag{6.1.85}$$

where $\bar{\alpha}^2 = \xi^2-\omega^2/c_1^2$, $\bar{\beta}^2 = \xi^2-\omega^2/c_2^2$. This result may be expressed in terms of wave velocity by noting that $\omega = \xi c$. The result is

$$(2-c^2/c_2^2)^2 = 4(1-c^2/c_1^2)^{\frac{1}{2}}(1-c^2/c_2^2)^{\frac{1}{2}}. \tag{6.1.86}$$

Finally, we may rationalize this last equation to give

$$\frac{c^2}{c_2^2}\left\{\left(\frac{c}{c_2}\right)^6-8\left(\frac{c}{c_2}\right)^4+(24-16k^{-2})\left(\frac{c}{c_2}\right)^2-16(1-k^{-2})\right\} = 0. \tag{6.1.87}$$

To investigate the roots of (6.1.87) we first note that it is a reduced cubic equation in $(c/c_2)^2$ and, secondly, that the roots are dependent on Poisson's ratio, since as we have shown earlier $k^2 = 2(1-\nu)/(1-2\nu)$. There will be three roots to the wave velocity equation. Previous studies have shown that the nature of roots (that is, real, imaginary, and complex) is dependent on the range of Poisson's ratio; thus

$$\begin{aligned} &\nu > 0{\cdot}263\ \ldots,\ 1 \text{ real, 2 complex conjugate roots,}\\ &\nu < 0{\cdot}263\ \ldots,\ 3 \text{ real roots.} \end{aligned} \tag{6.1.88}$$

However, any resulting complex roots will not be acceptable in the present situation, since this will yield behaviour of the type

$$\Phi,\ H_z \sim e^{-ay}e^{-bt}e^{i(\xi x+dy-et)}, \tag{6.1.89}$$

which is indicative of attenuation with respect to time, such as if damping were present, which is not the case in the present problem. Furthermore, we cannot have roots for which $c/c_2 > 1$, since $\bar{\beta}^2 > 0$ and this condition would be violated. It has been shown† that for all real media $(0 < \nu < 0{\cdot}5)$ there is only one real root meeting this last requirement. The resulting surface wave propagating with the velocity established from (6.1.87) is usually called the *Rayleigh surface wave*.

As an example, consider the surface wave for $\lambda = \mu$. This is a special case, known as 'Poisson's relation', and corresponds to $\nu = \frac{1}{4}$, a value often used for rock. The roots are

$$(c/c_2)^2 = 4,\ 2+2/\sqrt{3},\ 2-2/\sqrt{3}. \tag{6.1.90}$$

The question is: which corresponds to the Rayleigh velocity c_R? By putting

† According to Viktorov [43, p. 3].

the two largest values back into the expressions for $\bar{\alpha}^2, \bar{\beta}^2$, it is found that the requirement of $\bar{\alpha}^2, \bar{\beta}^2 > 0$ is violated. This leaves

$$(c/c_2)^2 = (2-2/\sqrt{3})^{\frac{1}{2}} = 0{\cdot}9194 \tag{6.1.91}$$

or

$$c_R = 0{\cdot}9194c_2. \tag{6.1.92}$$

A plot of c_R for all values of Poisson's ratio is shown in Fig. 6.8. The fact

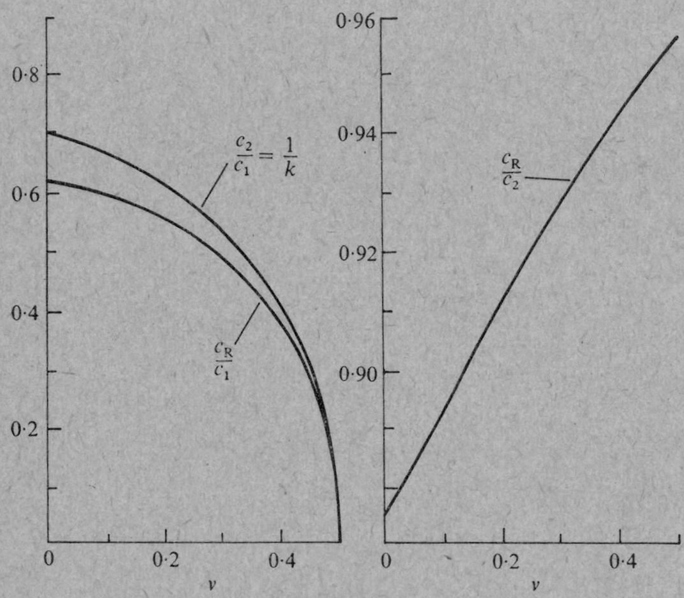

FIG. 6.8. The ratios of c_R/c_1, c_2/c_1, c_R/c_2 for various values of Poisson's ratio. (After Knopoff [21].)

that the propagation velocity is independent of frequency indicates that a surface pulse propagates non-dispersively, with a velocity somewhat less than the shear velocity. An approximate expression that has been developed for the Rayleigh velocity is†

$$c_R/c_2 = (0{\cdot}87+1{\cdot}12\nu)/(1+\nu). \tag{6.1.93}$$

The particle motion may be found from (6.1.78) and (6.1.79), using also the amplitude ratio (6.1.84). At $y = 0$, these become

$$\begin{aligned} u_x &= Ai\left(\gamma - \frac{\bar{\beta}^2+\gamma^2}{2\gamma}\right)e^{i\gamma(x-ct)}, \\ u_y &= A\left(-\bar{\alpha}+\frac{\bar{\beta}^2+\gamma^2}{2\bar{\beta}}\right)e^{i\gamma(x-ct)}. \end{aligned} \tag{6.1.94}$$

† op cit., p. 3.

Taking real parts, these give

$$u_x = a(\gamma)\sin \gamma(x-ct), \qquad u_y = b(\gamma)\cos \gamma(x-ct). \tag{6.1.95}$$

The particle motion is elliptical in nature and retrograde with respect to the direction of propagation (that is, it is counter clockwise for a wave travelling to the right) which is in contrast to the case of water waves. The vertical component of the displacement is greater than the horizontal component at the surface (for example, vertical = 1·5 × horizontal is typical). The motion decreases exponentially in amplitude away from the surface. However, at a slight depth (given as 0·192 wavelength), the direction of particle rotation reverses. A diagram of the particle motion is shown in Fig. 6.9(a). In Fig. 6.9(b), the displacement components at various locations at and below the free surface are shown. The displacements have been normalized with respect to the free surface displacement in the vertical direction u_{y_0}. The depth has been normalized with respect to the Rayleigh wave length λ_R,

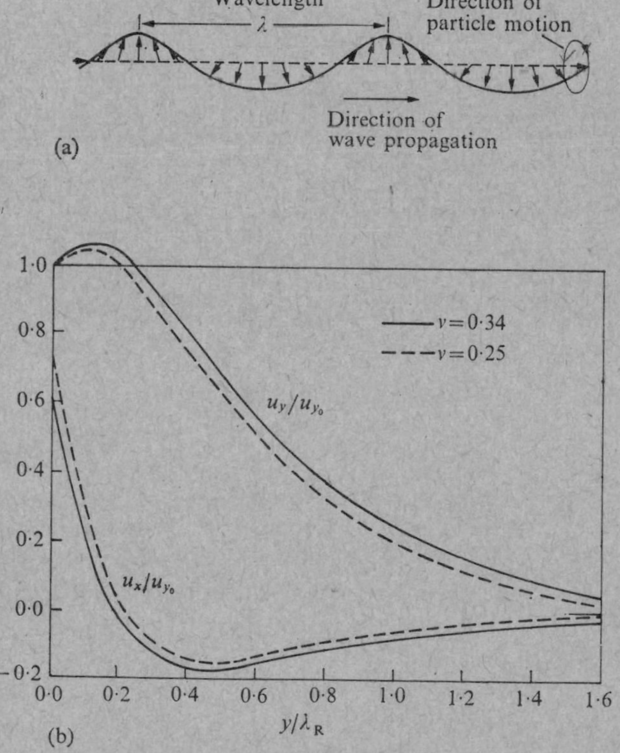

FIG. 6.9. (a) Particles motion during propagation of a Rayleigh surface wave. (Based on Frederick [12, Fig. 2.3]). (b) Normalized displacements under surface wave excitation. (After Viktorov [43, Fig. 2].)

given by $\lambda_R = c_R/f$. Note that the results have been plotted for two values of Poisson's ratio ($\nu = 0{\cdot}25$, $0{\cdot}34$). Although ν may theoretically take on values of $0 \leqslant \nu \leqslant 0{\cdot}5$, the values shown cover a range representative of many practical materials ($\nu = 0{\cdot}25 \sim$ rock; $\nu \leqslant 0{\cdot}34 \sim$ many metals).

Finally, we remark on the extraneous root of the surface wave equation. Only one of the three roots of (6.1.87) corresponds to Rayleigh surface waves and the question of the significance, if any, of the remaining roots remains. These are extraneous roots introduced by rationalizing the original wave velocity equation (6.1.86).

In fact, a meaningful interpretation attaches to the remaining roots, as pointed out by Ewing, Jardetsky, and Press [11, p. 33]. They correspond to previously discussed special cases of incident harmonic P and SV waves, corresponding to a P wave incident, an SV wave only reflected and to an incident SV wave, a P wave only reflected.

As inferred by early seismologists, surface, or Rayleigh, waves are essentially two dimensional. Hence, energy associated with these waves will not disperse as rapidly as the energy associated with the three-dimensional waves of dilatation and rotation. Such waves are of particular importance in seismology, since it is these waves that are most destructive in earthquakes.

6.1.5. *Wave reflection under mixed boundary conditions*

We close this section on waves in a half-space by briefly considering boundary conditions other than traction-free ones. Consider the case of mixed boundary conditions, given for the plane-strain case by

$$u_y = \tau_{xy} = 0, \qquad y = 0. \tag{6.1.96}$$

Such conditions could correspond to an elastic half-space constrained by a rigid, lubricated boundary. As previously given, the potential functions governing the waves are

$$\Phi = A_1 e^{i(\xi x - \alpha y - \omega t)} + A_2 e^{i(\xi x + \alpha y - \omega t)}, \tag{6.1.97}$$

$$H_z = B_1 e^{i(\xi x - \beta y - \omega t)} + B_2 e^{i(\xi x + \beta y - \omega t)}. \tag{6.1.98}$$

The displacements and stresses of interest are

$$u_y = -i\alpha(A_1 e^{-i\alpha y} - A_2 e^{i\alpha y})e^{i(\xi x - \omega t)} - i\xi(B_1 e^{-i\beta y} + B_2 e^{i\beta y})e^{i(\xi x - \omega t)}, \tag{6.1.99}$$

$$\tau_{xy} = \mu\{2\xi\alpha(A_1 e^{-i\alpha y} - A_2 e^{i\alpha y}) + (\xi^2 - \beta^2)(B_1 e^{-i\beta y} + B_2 e^{i\beta y})\}e^{i(\xi x - \omega t)}. \tag{6.1.100}$$

Applying the conditions $u_y = \tau_{xy} = 0$ at $y = 0$ gives

$$\begin{aligned} 2\xi\alpha(A_1 - A_2) + (\xi^2 - \beta^2)(B_1 + B_2) &= 0, \\ \alpha(A_1 - A_2) + \xi(B_1 + B_2) &= 0, \end{aligned} \tag{6.1.101}$$

which in turn may be written as

$$\begin{bmatrix} 2\xi\alpha & (\xi^2-\beta^2) \\ \alpha & \xi \end{bmatrix} \begin{bmatrix} (A_1-A_2) \\ (B_1+B_2) \end{bmatrix} = 0. \tag{6.1.102}$$

Thus

$$A_1 = A_2, \qquad B_1 = -B_2, \tag{6.1.103}$$

unless the determinant is zero. Investigating this possibility, we have

$$\alpha\{2\xi^2-(\xi^2-\beta^2)\} \overset{?}{=} 0. \tag{6.1.104}$$

Since $\beta^2 = \omega^2/c_2^2-\xi^2$, this reduces to $\alpha\omega^2 \overset{?}{=} 0$. But we cannot have $\omega = 0$, and if $\alpha = 0$, we will not have the plane wave case. Hence, we have that

$$A_2/A_1 = 1, \qquad B_2/B_1 = -1. \tag{6.1.105}$$

It is seen that no mode conversion occurs since, if $B_1 = 0$ (P wave in), $B_2 = 0$, and if $A_1 = 0$ (SV wave in), $A_2 = 0$.

The possibility of surface waves in such a half-space is also of interest. We use the solutions (6.4.77) directly in the boundary conditions for u_y, τ_{xy}, giving

$$\begin{aligned} \bar{\alpha}A+\mathrm{i}\xi B &= 0, \\ 2\mathrm{i}\bar{\alpha}\xi A+(\xi^2+\bar{\beta}^2)B &= 0. \end{aligned} \tag{6.1.106}$$

This gives the frequency equation

$$\bar{\alpha}\{(\xi^2+\bar{\beta}^2)-2\xi^2\} = 0, \tag{6.1.107}$$

where $\bar{\alpha}$, $\bar{\beta}$ are as previously defined. The solution $\bar{\alpha} = 0$ is not acceptable since this would require $\bar{\beta}^2 < 0$ and give plane waves instead of surface waves. The other root is $\omega^2/c_2^2 = 0$, or $c^2 = 0$, which is not acceptable since wave propagation would not occur. Hence, surface waves cannot exist in a half-space under such boundary conditions. This case of boundary constraint, while of less physical interest than the traction-free case, will play a role in certain plate studies.

6.2. SH wave source—method of steepest descent

We now consider the first of several problems involving waves from sources located on the surface of a half-space. The simplest case will be considered in this section—that of a harmonic SH wave source. Such a source is created by an applied shearing load, where the load is acting in, say, the z direction and variations in that direction are zero. The case of prescribed displacements may also be considered. The important facts about such a source, as was found in Chapter 5, are that pure shear waves in the displacement variable u_z are propagated and that a single scalar equation governs the motion. The situation is thus quite analogous to an acoustics problem.

The first portion of the section will be devoted to obtaining several general results for SH wave propagation. The second portion will be devoted to introducing the method of steepest descent, an analytical technique for obtaining approximate evaluations of integrals. This method represents a generalization of the stationary-phase technique introduced in the first chapter. It finds wide application in many problems of elastic wave analysis.

6.2.1. *The SH wave source—formal solution*

Let us consider the problem of waves generated by a distribution of load given, in general terms, by

$$\begin{aligned} \tau_{yz}(x, 0, z, t) &= \tau(x)e^{i\omega t}, \\ \tau_{yy}(x, 0, z, t) &= \tau_{yx}(x, 0, z, t) = 0. \end{aligned} \tag{6.2.1}$$

Such a loading will generate SH waves where the only displacement component is $u_z = u_z(x, y, t)$. Under these conditions, the displacement equations of motion reduce to

$$\nabla^2 u_z = \frac{1}{c_2^2}\frac{\partial^2 u_z}{\partial t^2}, \qquad \nabla^2 = \frac{\partial^2}{\partial x^2}+\frac{\partial^2}{\partial y^2}. \tag{6.2.2}$$

If we assume a harmonic time variation in u_z such that

$$u_z(x, y, t) = U(x, y)\exp(i\omega t),$$

then (6.2.2) reduces to

$$\nabla^2 U + \beta^2 U = 0, \qquad \beta^2 = \omega^2/c_2^2. \tag{6.2.3}$$

We apply the Fourier transform† to the last, giving

$$\frac{d^2\bar{U}}{dy^2}-(\xi^2-\beta^2)\bar{U} = 0. \tag{6.2.4}$$

This has the solution

$$\bar{U}(\xi, y, \omega) = Ae^{-\gamma y}+Be^{\gamma y}, \qquad \gamma^2 = \xi^2-\beta^2. \tag{6.2.5}$$

On the basis of finite response for increasing y, we set $B = 0$ in the last result. For the case of SH waves, as we found in the last section, the stress τ_{yz} is given by

$$\tau_{yz} = \mu\frac{\partial u_z}{\partial y} = \mu\frac{\partial U}{\partial y}e^{i\omega t}. \tag{6.2.6}$$

The first boundary condition of (6.2.1) then reduces to

$$\mu\frac{\partial U}{\partial y}\bigg|_{y=0} = \tau(x). \tag{6.2.7}$$

† We take as our transform definitions

$$\bar{f}(\xi) = \frac{1}{\sqrt{(2\pi)}}\int_{-\infty}^{\infty} f(x)e^{-i\xi x}\, dx, \qquad f(x) = \frac{1}{\sqrt{(2\pi)}}\int_{-\infty}^{\infty} \bar{f}(\xi)e^{i\xi x}\, d\xi.$$

The transformed condition is

$$\mu \frac{\mathrm{d}\bar{U}}{\mathrm{d}y}\bigg|_{y=0} = \bar{\tau}(\xi). \tag{6.2.8}$$

Substituting (6.2.5) with $B = 0$ in the last expression, we obtain for the transformed solution

$$\bar{U}(\xi, y) = -\frac{\bar{\tau}(\xi)}{\mu\gamma}\mathrm{e}^{-\gamma y}. \tag{6.2.9}$$

Finally, the formal inverted solution is

$$U(x, y) = -\frac{1}{\mu\sqrt{(2\pi)}}\int_{-\infty}^{\infty} \frac{\bar{\tau}(\xi)}{\gamma}\mathrm{e}^{-\gamma y}\mathrm{e}^{\mathrm{i}\xi x}\,\mathrm{d}\xi. \tag{6.2.10}$$

Several results for specific load distributions are easily obtained. Suppose $\tau(x)$ is of constant magnitude and is acting on a finite width strip such that

$$\tau(x) = \begin{cases} \tau_0, & |x| < a \\ 0, & |x| > a. \end{cases} \tag{6.2.11}$$

Applying the Fourier transform to this, we obtain

$$\bar{\tau}(\xi) = \frac{2\tau_0}{\sqrt{(2\pi)}}\frac{\sin \xi a}{\xi}. \tag{6.2.12}$$

Then we have

$$U(x, y) = -\frac{\tau_0}{\mu\pi}\int_{-\infty}^{\infty} \frac{\sin \xi a \mathrm{e}^{-\gamma y}\mathrm{e}^{\mathrm{i}\xi x}}{\gamma\xi}\,\mathrm{d}\xi. \tag{6.2.13}$$

If $a \to 0$ but the total load per unit length remains constant, the results for a line load are obtained. Thus, multiply and divide (6.2.13) by $2a$, let $2a\tau_0 = P$, and let $a \to 0$. Noting that $\sin \xi a/\xi a \to 1$ as $a \to 0$, we obtain the Green's function

$$G(\mathbf{r}, 0, \omega) = -\frac{P}{2\pi\mu}\int_{-\infty}^{\infty} \frac{\mathrm{e}^{-\gamma y}\mathrm{e}^{\mathrm{i}\xi x}}{\gamma}\,\mathrm{d}\xi. \tag{6.2.14}$$

The case of a line source located at $x = x_0$ is given by

$$G(\mathbf{r}, x_0, \omega) = -\frac{P}{2\pi\mu}\int_{-\infty}^{\infty} \frac{\exp(-\gamma y)\exp\{\mathrm{i}\xi(x-x_0)\}}{\gamma}\,\mathrm{d}\xi. \tag{6.2.15}$$

These last results could be obtained also by originally considering a loading

$$\tau_{yz}(x, 0, z, t) = P\delta(x-x_0)\mathrm{e}^{\mathrm{i}\omega t}, \tag{6.2.16}$$

so that

$$\bar{\tau}(\xi, 0) = \frac{P}{\sqrt{(2\pi)}}\exp(-\mathrm{i}\xi x_0). \tag{6.2.17}$$

6.2.2. *Direct evaluation of the integral*

As will soon be found, the various integral results for the SH source problem can be evaluated exactly by certain changes of variable. Before so doing we consider some of the aspects involved in directly carrying out the evaluation for a line load at the origin. A number of the considerations involving the contour integral are quite similar to those for more complicated half-space problems.

Consider, then, the result (6.2.14). It should be evident that a semicircular contour including the real ξ-axis would be appropriate. If $x > 0$, the contour should be closed in the upper half-ξ-plane, while for $x < 0$, closure is in the lower half-plane. The main difficulty in evaluation arises from the existence of branch points, and it is this aspect that we now consider. Thus, the function $\gamma = (\xi^2-\beta^2)^{\frac{1}{2}}$ has branch points at $\xi = \pm\beta$, which are on the real axis.

It will be useful to generalize slightly here and let $\beta^2 = \beta'^2$, where β' is complex, given by

$$\beta' = \alpha - \mathrm{i}\lambda, \qquad (\alpha, \lambda > 0). \tag{6.2.18}$$

This is similar to the inclusion of damping, as previously done in the analysis of strings. With β'^2 complex, it is seen that the branch points $\xi = \pm\beta'$ are now moved off the real axis into the second and fourth quadrants.

The necessary branch cuts will be selected according to the requirement that $\operatorname{Re}\gamma > 0$. This arises from $\exp(-\gamma y)$, where $y > 0$ always. If we let

$$\gamma = X+\mathrm{i}Y, \qquad \gamma^2 = X^2-Y^2+2\mathrm{i}XY, \tag{6.2.19}$$

then the cuts will be defined by $\operatorname{Re}\gamma = 0$, which in turn requires that

$$\operatorname{Re}\gamma^2 \leqslant 0, \qquad \operatorname{Im}\gamma^2 = 0. \tag{6.2.20}$$

Letting $\xi = \zeta+\mathrm{i}\eta$ and β' as given by (6.2.18), we write

$$\gamma^2 = \zeta^2-\eta^2+2\mathrm{i}\zeta\eta-\alpha^2+\lambda^2+2\mathrm{i}\alpha\lambda. \tag{6.2.21}$$

From (6.2.20), this leads to

$$\zeta^2-\eta^2-\alpha^2+\lambda^2 \leqslant 0, \qquad \zeta\eta+\alpha\lambda = 0. \tag{6.2.22}$$

The second condition yields the two hyperbolas (one for $\alpha, \lambda > 0$, the other for $\alpha, \lambda < 0$) passing through the branch points. The first conditions show which portion of the hyperbolas the cut must be along. The resulting branch points and branch cuts are shown in Fig. 6.10(a). Suppose now that β' is real, so that $\lambda \to 0$ in (6.2.22). This gives

$$\zeta^2-\eta^2+\alpha^2 \leqslant 0, \qquad \zeta\eta = 0. \tag{6.2.23}$$

If $\zeta = 0$, then $-\eta^2+\alpha^2 \leqslant 0$, so that $\eta^2 \leqslant \alpha^2$ and if $\eta = 0$, $-\zeta^2 \leqslant \alpha^2$. These combine to give the cuts shown in Fig. 6.10(b). These are the limiting cases of the hyperbolas for the presence of damping.

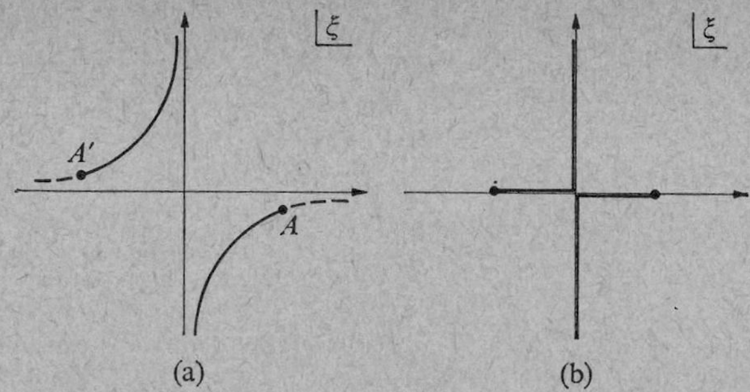

FIG. 6.10. (a) Branch cuts along hyperbolas and (b) the limiting case as $\lambda \to 0$.

On the basis of the branch cuts indicated, the contour used for evaluating (6.2.14) has the form shown in Fig. 6.11. We have

$$\int_{-R}^{R} + \int_{\Gamma_1+\Gamma_2} + \int_{\Gamma} = 0, \tag{6.2.24}$$

where no poles have been enclosed within the contour. The contributions along Γ_1, Γ_2 may be shown to go to zero as $R \to \infty$. The result is that

$$I = \int_{-\infty}^{\infty} \frac{e^{-\gamma y} e^{i\xi x}}{\gamma} d\xi = \lim_{R\to\infty} \int_{-R}^{R} \frac{e^{-\gamma y} e^{i\xi x}}{\gamma} d\xi = -\int_{\Gamma}. \tag{6.2.25}$$

Now, the integral around the branch cut may be broken into five parts along AO, OB, BO, ON, and a small circular path about the branch point at B. For the latter integral, it is found that the integrand is of $O(\varepsilon^{\frac{1}{2}})$, where ε is the radius of a small circle about the branch point. As $\varepsilon \to 0$, this contribution vanishes. If we let

$$\xi - \beta = \rho_1 \exp(i\theta_1), \qquad \xi + \beta = \rho_2 \exp(i\theta_2), \tag{6.2.26}$$

where θ_1, θ_2 are measured from the real ξ-axis, we find that the argument of

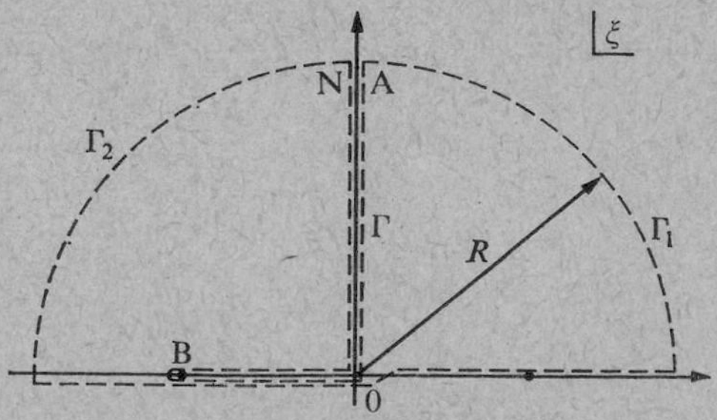

FIG. 6.11. Contour for evaluating SH wave response.

γ is $\pi/2$, $\pi/2$, $-\pi/2$, $-\pi/2$ along, respectively, AO, OB, BO, and ON. The resulting expression for $G(\mathbf{r}, 0, \omega)$ is given by

$$G(\mathbf{r}, 0, \omega) = \frac{P}{\pi\mu}\left\{\int_0^\infty \frac{e^{-\xi x}}{(\beta^2+\xi^2)^{\frac{1}{2}}} \cos(\beta^2+\xi^2)^{\frac{1}{2}} y \, d\xi - \right.$$

$$\left. -i\int_0^\infty \frac{e^{-i\xi x}}{(\beta^2-\xi^2)^{\frac{1}{2}}} \cos(\beta^2-\xi^2)^{\frac{1}{2}} y \, d\xi\right\}, \quad (6.2.27)$$

where ξ is a real quantity. The first integral results from combining the contributions of OA and ON, the second from OB, BO. We shall not pursue this evaluation further except to note that the task of evaluating these integrals would remain in a general problem. In this example, when the solution is known to be a Hankel function (this will be shown next), the integrals could be manipulated into the integral identities for the Hankel function. The main purpose here is to illustrate the contour integration along the single branch cut that arises for SH waves.

Rather than pursuing the integral results (6.2.27) further, we can obtain an explicit solution for the SH wave problem by certain changes of variables similar to those used in considering SH waves in an infinite media. To start, we express (6.2.10) as

$$U(x, y) = -\frac{1}{2\pi\mu}\int_{-\infty}^{\infty} \tau(x')\, dx' \int_{-\infty}^{\infty} \frac{\exp(-\gamma y)\exp\{i\xi(x-x')\}}{\gamma}\, d\xi. \quad (6.2.28)$$

We may express $\exp(-\gamma y)$ as an inverse Fourier transform through the following steps:

$$\mathscr{F}^{-1}\left(\frac{\gamma}{\gamma^2+\zeta^2}\right) = \frac{1}{2\pi}\int_{-\infty}^{\infty} \frac{\gamma}{\gamma^2+\zeta^2} e^{i\zeta y}\, d\zeta$$

$$= \frac{1}{\sqrt{(2\pi)}}\left\{\sqrt{\left(\frac{2}{\pi}\right)}\int_0^\infty \frac{\gamma}{\gamma^2+\zeta^2} \cos \zeta y \, dy\right\}$$

$$= \frac{1}{\sqrt{(2\pi)}}\mathscr{F}_c^{-1}\left(\frac{\gamma}{\gamma^2+\zeta^2}\right). \quad (6.2.29)$$

From tables we have

$$\mathscr{F}_c^{-1}\left(\frac{\gamma}{\gamma^2+\zeta^2}\right) = \sqrt{\left(\frac{\pi}{2}\right)} e^{-\gamma y}, \quad (6.2.30)$$

so that

$$e^{-\gamma y} = 2\mathscr{F}^{-1}\left(\frac{\gamma}{\gamma^2+\zeta^2}\right). \quad (6.2.31)$$

Then (6.2.28) becomes

$$U(x, y) = -\frac{1}{2\pi^2\mu}\int_{-\infty}^{\infty}\tau(x')\,dx'\int_{-\infty}^{\infty}\int_{-\infty}^{\infty}\frac{\exp[i\{\zeta y+\xi(x-x')\}]}{\gamma^2+\zeta^2}\,d\xi\,d\zeta. \quad (6.2.32)$$

At this stage, the double integral (call it q) is recognizable as similar to the one encountered for the SH source in an infinite medium. As before, we let

$$\mathbf{l} = \xi\mathbf{i}+\zeta\mathbf{j}, \qquad \mathbf{R} = (x-x')\mathbf{i}+y\mathbf{j}, \quad (6.2.33)$$

and convert the double integral q to polar coordinates, giving

$$q(R) = \int_0^{\infty} l\,dl\int_0^{2\pi}\frac{\exp(i\mathbf{l}.\mathbf{R})}{l^2-\beta^2}\,d\alpha = \pi^2 iH_0^{(1)}(\beta R), \quad (6.2.34)$$

where

$$R^2 = (x-x')^2+y^2. \quad (6.2.35)$$

Then

$$U(x, y) = -\frac{1}{2\pi^2\mu}\int_{-\infty}^{\infty}\tau(x')q(R)\,dx'. \quad (6.2.36)$$

For the special case of a point-loading $\tau(x') = P_0\delta(x')$, we obtain

$$G(\mathbf{r}, \omega) = -\frac{Pi}{2\mu}H_0^{(1)}(\beta R). \quad (6.2.37)$$

The first thing to note in this result is that it is identical (within constants) to the solution for an infinite medium. This is because the infinite-medium solution automatically satisfies the boundary conditions for a half-space on planes passed through the source (this may be intuitively evident, after the fact). However, a careful comparison of the coefficients would show that identical sources, S_0, placed in the infinite medium and on the surface of the half-space would yield twice the response in the latter case. This is interpreted as the result of half the source output being reflected back into the semi-infinite media, whereas the source effectively radiates into two semi-infinite media in the former case.

Because of the close analogy of SH waves to acoustic waves, the solution of source problems by using image-source techniques naturally suggests itself. This is quite applicable here. Thus, suppose we have a 'buried' SH wave source in a semi-infinite media. This problem may be solved by considering an infinite medium with a source and an image source placed such that the perpendicular plane bisecting the line between the two sources coincides with the boundary of the half-space. As the two sources approach the boundary, a source of double strength is obtained, which also explains twice the response of a surface source compared to a single source in an infinite medium.

6.2.3. *Method of steepest descent*

In the preceding section, we have obtained exact results for the SH wave source or obtained explicit integral forms to be evaluated. The exact evaluation was, of course, satisfying in terms of being explicit. However, the results were quite atypical, since most wave-propagation problems are usually too complex for this to occur and must be evaluated using various approximate techniques. Typically, the problem may be resolved into evaluation of a contour integral of the type

$$I = \int_C e^{Rf(\xi)} g(\xi)\, d\xi, \tag{6.2.38}$$

where a portion of the path is along the real axis (Fourier transforms) or along the Bromwich contour (Laplace transforms).

We have previously approximately evaluated integrals of the type

$$\int_a^b e^{ixh(\omega)} g(\omega)\, d\omega, \tag{6.2.39}$$

by the method of stationary phase. In such integrals, ω, $g(\omega)$, and $h(\omega)$ were real. It was shown for x large, that the major contribution to the integral was from a small region near a stationary point, given by $h'(\omega) = 0$. Away from such a point, the increasing rapid oscillations of the integrand were assumed to cancel by interference. In the following, we shall develop the method for approximately evaluating the contour integral of a complex variable ξ, for large values of R. This will represent a generalization of the stationary-phase method.

1. *General basis of the method.* The basic idea of the steepest-descent method is to deform the contour of integration to pass through a strategic point (or points) such that the major contribution to the integral comes from a short portion of path in the vicinity of that point. If we write

$$f(\xi) = f_1 + i f_2, \tag{6.2.40}$$

then

$$\exp(Rf) = \exp(Rf_1)\exp(iRf_2). \tag{6.2.41}$$

The objective will be to maximize the contribution of $\exp(Rf_1)$ at a point along the deformed contour. Away from the point, it is desired that this contribution rapidly decrease.

However, a potential weakness of this argument is that $\exp(iRf_2)$ is oscillatory and, for large R, these dense oscillations may negate the contributions of the real part. It would be desirable, therefore, to have a path such that f_2 is (relatively) constant.

2. *Saddle points.* The selection of critical points and paths will be aided by a brief review of topological aspects of analytic functions of a complex variable. Thus consider the real and imaginary parts of $f(\xi)$, given by

$$f_1 = f_1(\zeta, \eta), \qquad f_2 = f_2(\zeta, \eta), \tag{6.2.42}$$

The gradient of f_1 is given by

$$\nabla f_1 = \frac{\partial f_1}{\partial \zeta}\mathbf{i} + \frac{\partial f_1}{\partial \eta}\mathbf{j}. \tag{6.2.43}$$

This represents the direction of maximum variation of f_1. The unit vector in this direction could be $\mathbf{n}_1$ given by

$$\mathbf{n}_1 = \nabla f_1 / |\nabla f_1|. \tag{6.2.44}$$

Now, the direction of $\mathbf{n}_1$ is always at right angles to the contour lines of f_1 (the lines of constant f_1). This latter direction is $\mathbf{s}_1$, where

$$\mathbf{n}_1 . \mathbf{s}_1 = 0, \qquad \mathbf{s}_1 = \frac{1}{|\nabla f_1|}\left(-\frac{\partial f_1}{\partial \eta}\mathbf{i} + \frac{\partial f_1}{\partial \zeta}\mathbf{j}\right). \tag{6.2.45}$$

It may be easily shown that the direction of maximum variation of f_1 (that is, $\mathbf{n}_1$) is parallel to the direction of constant f_2. Thus we have

$$\nabla f_2 = \frac{\partial f_2}{\partial \zeta}\mathbf{i} + \frac{\partial f_2}{\partial \eta}\mathbf{j}, \tag{6.2.46}$$

and

$$\mathbf{n}_2 = \frac{\nabla f_2}{|\nabla f_2|}, \qquad \mathbf{s}_2 = \frac{1}{|\nabla f_2|}\left(-\frac{\partial f_2}{\partial \eta}\mathbf{i} + \frac{\partial f_2}{\partial \zeta}\mathbf{j}\right), \tag{6.2.47}$$

where $\mathbf{s}_2$ is the direction of f_2 constant. However, from the Cauchy–Riemann conditions

$$\frac{\partial f_1}{\partial \zeta} = \frac{\partial f_2}{\partial \eta}, \qquad \frac{\partial f_1}{\partial \eta} = -\frac{\partial f_2}{\partial \zeta}. \tag{6.2.48}$$

Hence

$$\mathbf{s}_2 = \frac{-1}{|\nabla f_2|}\left(\frac{\partial f_1}{\partial \zeta}\mathbf{i} + \frac{\partial f_1}{\partial \eta}\mathbf{j}\right). \tag{6.2.49}$$

Thus, $\mathbf{s}_2$ is parallel to $\mathbf{n}_1$. This aspect is of great importance in removing the possible problem of oscillations of $\exp(iRf_2)$ along the strategic path.

Now, extreme values of f_1 occur for $\nabla f_1 = 0$ or

$$\partial f_1/\partial \zeta = \partial f_2/\partial \eta = 0. \tag{6.2.50}$$

It also holds that the Cauchy–Riemann conditions are satisfied in any direction $\mathbf{n}$ and $\mathbf{s}$, so that, at an extreme, we have

$$\partial f_1/\partial n = \partial f_1/\partial s = 0. \tag{6.2.51}$$

Also, by the Cauchy–Riemann conditions, it immediately follows that f_2 is stationary, and, in general, $\mathrm{d}f/\mathrm{d}\xi = 0$.

The nature of the extremes of f_1 defined by (6.2.50) are of a particular type. By the maximum-modulus theorem of complex variables, f_1 (and f_2) cannot attain local maximum or minimum values within a contour C, but in fact attain the extreme values on C. The only way that f_1 can satisfy (6.2.50) and yet not violate the maximum-modulus theorem is to pass through a 'saddle point', as shown in Fig. 6.12(a). We see that at P_s, the slope is

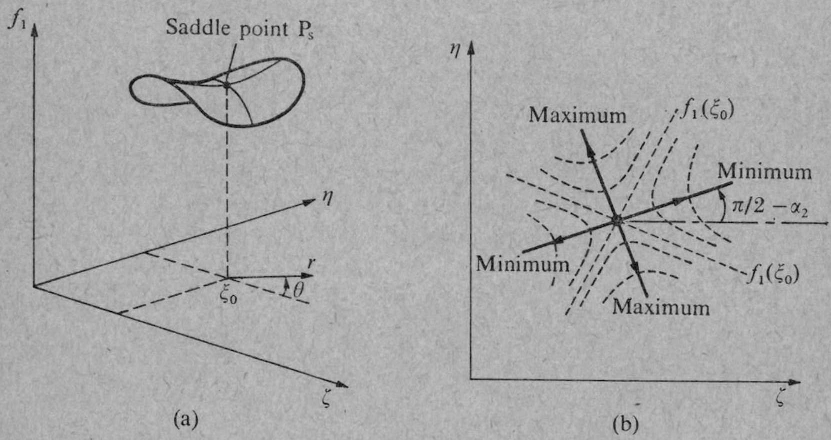

FIG. 6.12. (a) The surface $f_1(\beta, \eta)$ in the vicinity of a saddle point and (b) the topological behaviour of f_1 in the vicinity of the saddle point ξ_0.

locally zero. However, in passing through P_s in one direction, f_1 attains a local maximum while, in another direction, it reaches a local minimum.

The local topology of a saddle point may be better understood by expanding $f(\xi)$ about ξ_0 as

$$f(\xi) = f(\xi_0)+f'(\xi_0)(\xi-\xi_0)+\tfrac{1}{2}f''(\xi_0)(\xi-\xi_0)^2+\dots. \tag{6.2.52}$$

However, $f'(\xi_0) = 0$. We further assume, in this level of development of the theory, that $f''(\xi_0) \neq 0$, and let

$$\tfrac{1}{2}f''(\xi_0) = a_2 \exp(\mathrm{i}\alpha_2), \qquad \xi-\xi_0 = r\exp(\mathrm{i}\theta). \tag{6.2.53}$$

Then we have for $f(\xi)$ and $f_1(\xi)$ in the vicinity of ξ_0,

$$f(\xi) = f(\xi_0)+a_2r^2\exp\{\mathrm{i}(2\theta+\alpha_2)\}, \tag{6.2.54}$$

$$f_1(\xi_0) = \operatorname{Re} f(\xi_0)+a_2r^2\cos(2\theta+\alpha_2). \tag{6.2.55}$$

Noting the variation of $\cos(2\theta+\alpha_2)$, it is seen that f_1 will attain two maxima and two minima as θ varies from 0 to 2π about ξ_0. The directions are shown in Fig. 6.12(b). This behaviour is in accord with that shown qualitatively in Fig. 6.12(a).

The local contour lines of f_1 are given by $\cos(2\theta+\alpha_2) = 0$, so that $f_1 = \text{constant} = \operatorname{Re} f(\xi_0)$. There are two such lines, and they are at 45° with respect to the maximum and mininum directions. These are shown in Fig. 6.12, as are additional contours above and below $f_1(\xi_0)$. In the maximum direction these are contours of $f_1 > f_1(\xi_0)$, while in the minimum directions they are for $f_1 < f_1(\xi_0)$. Locally, they are families of hyperbolas.

Finally we have that

$$f_2 = \operatorname{Im} f(\xi_0) + a_2 r^2 \sin(2\theta + \alpha_2). \qquad (6.2.56)$$

Several analogous remarks regarding the behaviour of f_2 in the vicinity of the saddle point are possible, but the most important thing to note is that the directions of constant f_2 coincide with the maximum and minimum directions of f_1.

3. *The deformed contour*. The preceding has shown the detailed behaviour in the vicinity of a saddle point. We now assume that the original contour C may be deformed into a new one C' along the steepest descent path through the saddle point. The path C', we realize, is defined by the characteristic that $f_2 =$ constant (that is, it is a contour line of f_2). This may be used to determine the specific form of C' in a given problem. It is often important to know this form, since in deforming the original path to the new one, various poles and branch points may be passed. It then becomes necessary to account for these by adding the necessary residues or additional paths along branch cuts. We shall not immediately concern ourselves with such additions, however.

4. *Change in variables*. Along the deformed contour C', which passes through ξ, we realize that $f(\xi)$ may be written as

$$f(\xi) = f_1(\xi) + \mathrm{i} f_2(\xi_0), \qquad (6.2.57)$$

since f_2 is constant. It is possible to express f_1 in terms of its maximum value at ξ_0 as

$$f_1(\xi) = f_1(\xi_0) - m, \qquad (6.2.58)$$

where m is always positive. A graphical interpretation of this is shown in Fig. 6.13(a). Then for $f(\xi)$, we may write

$$f(\xi) = f_1(\xi_0) - m + \mathrm{i} f_2(\xi_0) = f(\xi_0) - m. \qquad (6.2.59)$$

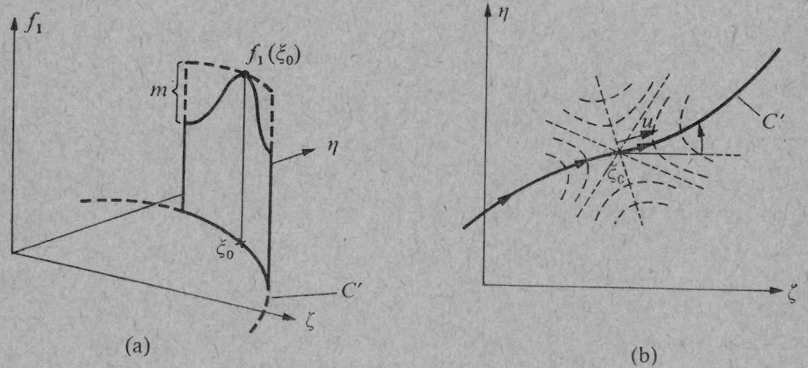

FIG. 6.13. (a) Representation of f_1 along the contour C' and (b) a particular path direction of C' through the saddle point at ξ_0.

It is convenient, from the standpoint of later developments, to let $m = u^2$, so that we have

$$f(\xi) = f(\xi_0) - u^2. \tag{6.2.60}$$

The original integral is then

$$I = \exp\{Rf(\xi_0)\} \int_{-\infty}^{\infty} \exp(-Ru^2) g\{\xi(u)\} \left(\frac{d\xi}{du}\right) du, \tag{6.2.61}$$

where the range of integration has been extended to $\pm\infty$, since negligible contributions are expected away from the saddle point.

We must now evaluate $d\xi/du$. Now in the vicinity of ξ_0 we have, from (6.2.52), that

$$f(\xi) - f(\xi_0) = \tfrac{1}{2} f''(\xi_0)(\xi - \xi_0)^2. \tag{6.2.62}$$

Comparing this to (6.2.55), we then have

$$u^2 = -f''(\xi_0)(\xi - \xi_0)^2. \tag{6.2.63}$$

Letting $\xi - \xi_0 = r \exp(i\theta)$, as before, we have

$$u^2 = -r^2 f''(\xi_0) e^{2i\theta}. \tag{6.2.64}$$

We write

$$f''(\xi_0) = |f''(\xi_0)| \, e^{i\beta}, \tag{6.2.65}$$

so that

$$u^2 = -r^2 |f''| \, e^{i(\beta + 2\theta)} = -r^2 |f''| \, e^{i\phi}. \tag{6.2.66}$$

In order for u^2 to be real and positive, we must have $\exp(i\phi)$ real and negative. This fixes $\phi = \pm\pi$. Then

$$u = r\,|f''|^{\frac{1}{2}} \, e^{i\phi/2} e^{\mp i/2}, \qquad \phi = \pm\pi, \tag{6.2.67}$$

so that

$$u = \pm r\,|f''|^{\frac{1}{2}}. \tag{6.2.68}$$

Then, substituting for r, we obtain

$$u = \pm(\xi - \xi_0) e^{-i\theta} \, |f''(\xi_0)|^{\frac{1}{2}}. \tag{6.2.69}$$

Differentiating this gives

$$\frac{du}{d\xi} = \pm e^{-i\theta} \, |f''(\xi_0)|^{\frac{1}{2}}. \tag{6.2.70}$$

The selection of the proper sign in (6.2.70) depends on the direction of the path through the saddle point. Suppose the deformed path passes through the saddle point as shown in Fig. 6.13(b). After passing through the saddle point, if u is to be positive, the positive sign must be selected.

Upon substituting (6.2.70) in (6.2.61), we have

$$I = \frac{\exp\{Rf(\xi_0)\} \exp(i\theta)}{|f''(\xi_0)|^{\frac{1}{2}}} \int_{-\infty}^{\infty} \exp(-Ru^2) g\{\xi(u)\} \, du. \tag{6.2.71}$$

5. *Watson's lemma.* A simplified form of Watson's lemma pertains to the existence of an asymptotic expression of the integral†

$$\bar{I} = \int_{-\infty}^{\infty} \exp(-\tfrac{1}{2}a^2z^2)f(z)\,dz. \tag{6.2.72}$$

Writing the series expansion for $f(z)$ as

$$f(z) = a_0 + a_1z + a_2z^2 + \dots \tag{6.2.73}$$

and noting that

$$\int_{-\infty}^{\infty} \exp(-\tfrac{1}{2}a^2z^2)z^{2n}\,dz = \sqrt{(2\pi)}\frac{(2n)!}{2^n n!\, a^{2n+1}}, \tag{6.2.74}$$

we have

$$\bar{I} \sim \sqrt{(2\pi)}\left(\frac{a_0}{a} + \frac{a_2}{a^3} + \frac{1.3}{a^5}a_4 + \dots\right), \tag{6.2.75}$$

with odd powers zero.

This result may be applied to the present integral, where we let $a = (2R)^{\frac{1}{2}}$. Letting $g\{\xi(u)\}$ be given by $G(u)$, we have

$$\int_{-\infty}^{\infty} \exp(-Ru^2)G(u)\,du = \sqrt{(2\pi)}\left\{\frac{G(0)}{(2R)^{\frac{1}{2}}} + \frac{1}{2!}\frac{G''(0)}{(2R)^{\frac{3}{2}}} + \dots\right\}. \tag{6.2.76}$$

Considering only the first term, we obtain as a final result

$$I = \frac{\sqrt{(\pi)}\exp(i\theta)\exp\{Rf(\xi_0)\}G(0)}{|Rf''(\xi_0)|^{\frac{1}{2}}}. \tag{6.2.77}$$

This completes our general development of the steepest-descent method. No consideration has been given to complications that may occur if poles lie on the steepest-descent path, or at a saddle point, or due to vanishing of higher derivatives in the expansion of $f(\xi)$.‡

6.2.4. *SH wave source solution by steepest descent*

Let us apply the method of steepest descent to determination of the far-field response of the line SH wave source acting at the origin. Specifically, we consider (6.2.14) or, writing just the integral,

$$I = \int_{-\infty}^{\infty} \frac{e^{-\gamma y}e^{i\xi x}}{\gamma}\,d\xi. \tag{6.2.78}$$

† Jeffreys and Jeffreys [20, pp. 501–6].

‡ Numerous developments of this appear in the literature of mathematics, physics, and engineering. Two most useful references are by Jeffreys and Jeffreys [20, pp. 473] and Carrier, Krook, and Pearson [2, pp. 257]. Ewing, Jardetsky, and Press [11] and Brekhvoskikh [1] also contain developments of the method.

We let $x = R\cos\theta$, $y = R\sin\theta$. Then

$$I = \int_{-\infty}^{\infty} \frac{e^{R(i\xi\cos\theta-\gamma\sin\theta)}}{\gamma}\,d\xi. \tag{6.2.79}$$

Comparing this expression to (6.2.38), we let

$$f(\xi) = i\xi\cos\theta-\gamma\sin\theta, \qquad g(\xi) = (\xi^2-\beta^2)^{-\frac{1}{2}}. \tag{6.2.80}$$

The saddle points are then given by

$$df/d\xi = -(\xi^2-\beta^2)^{-\frac{1}{2}}\xi\sin\theta+i\cos\theta = 0. \tag{6.2.81}$$

so that

$$\xi = \pm\beta\cos\theta. \tag{6.2.82}$$

Also

$$\frac{d^2f}{d\xi^2} = \frac{-\sin\theta}{(\xi^2-\beta^2)^{\frac{1}{2}}}+\frac{\xi^2\sin\theta}{(\xi^2-\beta^2)^{\frac{3}{2}}}. \tag{6.2.83}$$

We then have, at the saddle point $\xi = -\beta\cos\theta$,

$$f(\xi_0) = -i\beta, \qquad f''(\xi_0) = i\,\mathrm{cosec}^2\theta/\beta. \tag{6.2.84}$$

In addition, we must determine $G(0)$ or $g\{\xi(0)\}$. From (6.2.63) we have

$$-u^2 = f''(\xi_0)(\xi-\xi_0)^2 = \frac{i\,\mathrm{cosec}^2\theta}{\beta}(\xi+\beta\cos\theta)^2, \tag{6.2.85}$$

which gives for u

$$u = \frac{\mathrm{cosec}\,\theta}{\sqrt{\beta}}e^{-\pi i/4}(\xi+\beta\cos\theta), \qquad \frac{\mathrm{cosec}\,\theta}{\sqrt{\beta}}e^{3\pi i/4}(\xi+\beta\cos\theta). \tag{6.2.86}$$

Solving for ξ,

$$\xi = \sqrt{(\beta)}\sin\theta e^{\pi i/4}u-\beta\cos\theta, \qquad \sqrt{(\beta)}\sin\theta e^{-3\pi i/4}u-\beta\cos\theta. \tag{6.2.87}$$

For $u = 0$, we have

$$\xi(0) = -\beta\cos\theta, \tag{6.2.88}$$

so that

$$g\{\xi(0)\} = \frac{1}{(\beta^2\cos^2\theta-\beta^2)^{\frac{1}{2}}} = \frac{-i}{\beta\sin\theta}. \tag{6.2.89}$$

Finally, we must evaluate the term $\exp(i\theta)$. This will pertain to the direction of the path through the saddle point. Referring back to (6.2.53), we may write

$$\frac{f''(\xi_0)}{2} = a_2\exp(i\alpha_2) = \frac{i\,\mathrm{cosec}^2\theta}{2k} = \frac{\mathrm{cosec}^2\theta}{2k}\exp\left(\frac{\pi}{2}i\right), \tag{6.2.90}$$

$$\xi-\xi_0 = \xi+k\cos\theta = re^{i\theta}. \tag{6.2.91}$$

Then, following (6.2.54) and (6.2.55), we have

$$\begin{aligned} a_2r^2\cos(2\theta+\alpha_2) &= \frac{\mathrm{cosec}^2\theta r^2}{2k}\cos\left(2\theta+\frac{\pi}{2}\right), \\ &= \frac{\mathrm{cosec}^2\theta r^2}{2k}\cos\phi. \end{aligned} \tag{6.2.92}$$

The steepest-descent direction occurs for $\phi = \pi$. Then $2\theta+\pi/2 = \pi$, or $\theta = \pi/4$ so that $\exp(i\theta) = \exp(\pi i/4)$. Substituting the various quantities obtained in (6.2.71) we have

$$I = \frac{-\sqrt{(\pi)}\mathrm{i}e^{-\mathrm{i}\beta R}e^{\pi\mathrm{i}/4}}{\beta\sin\theta\left|\dfrac{\mathrm{i}\operatorname{cosec}^2\theta R}{\beta}\right|^{\frac{1}{2}}} = \frac{-\sqrt{(\pi)}e^{-\mathrm{i}\beta R}e^{3\pi\mathrm{i}/4}}{\sqrt{(\beta R)}}. \tag{6.2.93}$$

Then

$$G(\mathbf{r}, 0, \omega) = \frac{Pe^{-\mathrm{i}\beta R}e^{3\pi\mathrm{i}/4}}{2\mu\sqrt{(\pi\beta R)}}. \tag{6.2.94}$$

Previously, we had obtained (see (6.2.37))

$$G(\mathbf{r}, 0, \omega) = \frac{P\pi\mathrm{i}}{\mu}H_0^{(1)}(\beta R) \tag{6.2.95}$$

as the exact solution. This has the asymptotic form

$$G(\mathbf{r}, 0, \omega) \sim \frac{P}{\mu}\sqrt{\left(\frac{2\pi}{\beta R}\right)}e^{\mathrm{i}(\beta R-3\pi/4)}, \tag{6.2.96}$$

a result in agreement with the steepest-descent result.

This problem represents a fortunate circumstance—where the problem is rather simple, an exact solution is obtainable, and asymptotic results are already available. The steepest-descent method, it is found, yields the same asymptotic behaviour. In the more complicated problems to be considered, this asymptotic method is frequently the only means of evaluation.

6.3. Surface source problems

Our attention now turns to more general problems of waves from surface sources. Under general conditions of normal and shear loads applied to the surface of the half-space, both dilatational and shear waves are generated, with the resulting mathematical expressions for the wave propagation being considerably more complicated than those for the simple SH wave source of the last section.

The classical analysis in this area was done by Lamb [22] in 1904. He considered the half-space subjected to line and point loads on the surface and to buried sources. Harmonic loadings were considered, and superposition techniques were used to obtain results for pulse loadings. Since the early analysis of Lamb, a great many contributions have appeared pertaining to what is usually referred to as 'Lamb's' problem. Ewing, Jardetsky, and Press† have given a very thorough review of the analysis of this problem. Miklowitz‡ also thoroughly reviews the literature, including contributions by Mitra [33], Pekeris [34], Chao [3], Lang [23], and many others that appeared subsequent to the book by Ewing *et al.*

† Pp. 34–70 of Reference [11].
‡ Pp. 821–7 of Reference [29].

The large class of problems involving waves in a half-space from surface and buried sources makes it impossible to present analytical details of the various treatments. The approach taken will be to consider the case of a harmonic normal loading in the half-space in some detail, drawing on the work presented in Ewing *et al.* [11] and on the work of Miller and Pursey [30, 31]. Some consideration will then be given to the analysis of the transient-load problem. The main emphasis in the transient problem will be on presenting the results, in terms of displacement and stress waveforms, as obtained by a number of investigators. Included here will be the case of studies involving impact on a half-space and results obtained for buried sources.

6.3.1. *Waves from a harmonic, normal line force*

We consider a half-space subjected to a loading normal to the surface, applied parallel to the z-axis, and invariant with respect to z. The load is considered to act on the strip $|x| < a$ and to be of unity magnitude. The resulting situation is one of plane strain, where $u_z = \partial/\partial z = 0$.

1. *Basic equations.* Following Miller and Pursey [30], we use the displacement equations of motion (see (5.1.8) with $\mathbf{f} = 0$),

$$(\lambda+2\mu)\nabla\nabla\cdot\mathbf{u}-\mu\nabla\times\nabla\times\mathbf{u} = \rho\partial^2\mathbf{u}/\partial t^2. \tag{6.3.1}$$

For the conditions of plane strain, we have

$$\Delta = \nabla\cdot\mathbf{u} = \frac{\partial u_x}{\partial x}+\frac{\partial u_y}{\partial y}, \qquad W\mathbf{k} = \nabla\times\mathbf{u} = \left(\frac{\partial u_x}{\partial y}-\frac{\partial u_y}{\partial x}\right)\mathbf{k}. \tag{6.3.2}$$

We take note of the harmonic time variation of the loading $\exp(i\omega t)$ and write

$$u_x(x, y, t) = u_x(x, y)e^{i\omega t}, \qquad u_y(x, y, t) = u_y(x, y)e^{i\omega t}. \tag{6.3.3}$$

Then the vector equation (6.3.1) may be written as

$$(\lambda+2\mu)\frac{\partial\Delta}{\partial x}+\mu\frac{\partial W}{\partial y}+\rho\omega^2 u_x = 0, \tag{6.3.4}$$

$$(\lambda+2\mu)\frac{\partial\Delta}{\partial y}-\mu\frac{\partial W}{\partial x}+\rho\omega^2 u_y = 0. \tag{6.3.5}$$

Eliminating W and Δ successively from the preceding we obtain

$$\nabla^2\Delta+k_1^2\Delta = 0, \qquad \nabla^2 W+k_2^2 W = 0, \tag{6.3.6}$$

where $\nabla^2 = \partial^2/\partial x^2+\partial^2/\partial y^2$ and

$$k_1^2 = \omega^2/c_1^2, \qquad k_2^2 = \omega^2/c_2^2. \tag{6.3.7}$$

The stresses

$$\tau_{yy} = \lambda\Delta+2\mu\frac{\partial u_y}{\partial y}, \qquad \tau_{xy} = \mu\left(\frac{\partial u_y}{\partial x}+\frac{\partial u_x}{\partial y}\right), \tag{6.3.8}$$

with $\tau_{yz} = 0$, may be expressed in terms of Δ and W as

$$\tau_{yy} = \frac{\mu^2}{\rho\omega^2}\left\{2\frac{\partial^2 W}{\partial x\,\partial y} - k^2(k^2-2)\frac{\partial^2\Delta}{\partial x^2} - k^4\frac{\partial^2\Delta}{\partial y^2}\right\}, \tag{6.3.9}$$

$$\tau_{xy} = \frac{\mu^2}{\rho\omega^2}\left(\frac{\partial^2 W}{\partial x^2} - \frac{\partial^2 W}{\partial y^2} - 2k^2\frac{\partial^2\Delta}{\partial x\,\partial y}\right), \tag{6.3.10}$$

where $k^2 = (\lambda+2\mu)/\mu = k_2^2/k_1^2$.

2. *The formal solution.* The Fourier transform on the spatial variable x will be applied, where

$$\bar{f}(\zeta) = \int_{-\infty}^{\infty} f(x)\mathrm{e}^{-\mathrm{i}\zeta x}\,\mathrm{d}x, \qquad f(x) = \frac{1}{2\pi}\int_{-\infty}^{\infty} \bar{f}(\zeta)\mathrm{e}^{\mathrm{i}\zeta x}\,\mathrm{d}\zeta \tag{6.3.11}$$

are taken as the transform and inverse transform definitions, respectively. Applying the transform to (6.3.9) and (6.3.5) we obtain for the transformed displacements

$$\bar{u}_x = -\frac{1}{k_2^2}\left(\frac{\mathrm{d}\bar{W}}{\mathrm{d}y} - \mathrm{i}\zeta k^2\bar{\Delta}\right), \tag{6.3.12}$$

$$\bar{u}_y = -\frac{1}{k_2^2}\left(k^2\frac{\mathrm{d}\bar{\Delta}}{\mathrm{d}y} - \mathrm{i}\zeta\bar{W}\right). \tag{6.3.13}$$

The transformed wave equations (6.3.7) are

$$\frac{\mathrm{d}^2\bar{\Delta}}{\mathrm{d}y^2} - (\zeta^2 - k_1^2)\bar{\Delta} = 0, \qquad \frac{\mathrm{d}^2\bar{W}}{\mathrm{d}y^2} - (\zeta^2 - k_2^2)\bar{W} = 0, \tag{6.3.14}$$

and the transformed stresses (6.3.9) and (6.3.10) are

$$\bar{\tau}_{yy} = \frac{\mu^2}{\rho\omega^2}\left\{-k^4\frac{\mathrm{d}^2\bar{\Delta}}{\mathrm{d}y^2} + 2\mathrm{i}\zeta\frac{\mathrm{d}\bar{W}}{\mathrm{d}y} + k^2(k^2-2)\zeta^2\bar{\Delta}\right\}, \tag{6.3.15}$$

$$\bar{\tau}_{xy} = -\frac{\mu^2}{\rho\omega^2}\left(\frac{\mathrm{d}^2\bar{W}}{\mathrm{d}y^2} + 2\mathrm{i}\zeta k^2\frac{\mathrm{d}\bar{\Delta}}{\mathrm{d}y} + \zeta^2\bar{W}\right). \tag{6.3.16}$$

The boundary conditions for the problem are (omitting the time variation),

$$\tau_{yy}(x, 0) = \begin{cases}1, & |x| < a\\ 0, & |x| > a\end{cases} \qquad \tau_{xy}(x, 0) = 0 \tag{6.3.17}$$

The transformed boundary conditions are then

$$\bar{\tau}_{yy}(\zeta, 0) = 2\sin\zeta a/\zeta, \qquad \bar{\tau}_{xy}(\zeta, 0) = 0. \tag{6.3.18}$$

Now, the solutions of the governing equations (6.3.14) are given by

$$\bar{\Delta} = A\exp\{-(\zeta^2-k_1^2)^{\frac{1}{2}}y\}, \qquad \bar{W} = B\exp\{-(\zeta^2-k_2^2)^{\frac{1}{2}}y\}, \tag{6.3.19}$$

where the exponentially increasing terms have been discarded. When these solutions are substituted in the expression for $\bar{\tau}_{yy}$ and $\bar{\tau}_{xy}$ and the results into the boundary conditions (6.3.18), there results

$$\frac{\mu^2}{\rho\omega^2}\{-k^4(\zeta^2-k_1^2)A-2i\zeta(\zeta^2-k_2^2)^{\frac{1}{2}}B+k^2(k^2-2)\zeta^2A\} = \frac{2\sin\zeta a}{\zeta}, \quad (6.3.20)$$

$$\{(\zeta^2-k_2^2)B-2i\zeta k^2(\zeta^2-k_1^2)^{\frac{1}{2}}A+\zeta^2B\} = 0. \quad (6.3.21)$$

Solving these two equations for A and B and putting the results back into (6.3.19), we have

$$\bar{\Delta} = \frac{2\rho\omega^2(k_2^2-2\zeta^2)}{\mu^2k^2\zeta F(\zeta)}\sin\zeta a\exp\{-(\zeta^2-k_1^2)^{\frac{1}{2}}y\}, \quad (6.3.22)$$

$$\overline{W} = \frac{4i\rho\omega^2(\zeta^2-k_1^2)}{\mu^2F(\zeta)}\sin\zeta a\exp\{-(\zeta^2-k_2^2)^{\frac{1}{2}}y\}, \quad (6.3.23)$$

where

$$F(\zeta) = (2\zeta^2-k_2^2)^2-4\zeta^2(\zeta^2-k_1^2)^{\frac{1}{2}}(\zeta^2-k_2^2)^{\frac{1}{2}}. \quad (6.3.24)$$

The transformed displacements are given by

$$\bar{u}_x = \frac{2\sin\zeta a}{i\mu F(\zeta)}[2(\zeta^2-k_1^2)^{\frac{1}{2}}(\zeta^2-k_2^2)^{\frac{1}{2}}\exp\{-(\zeta^2-k_2^2)^{\frac{1}{2}}y\}+$$
$$+(k_2^2-2\zeta^2)\exp\{-(\zeta^2-k_1^2)^{\frac{1}{2}}y\}], \quad (6.3.25)$$

$$\bar{u}_y = \frac{2(\zeta^2-k_1^2)^{\frac{1}{2}}\sin\zeta a}{\mu\zeta F(\zeta)}[2\zeta^2\exp\{-(\zeta^2-k_2^2)^{\frac{1}{2}}y\}+(k_2^2-2\zeta^2)\exp\{-(\zeta^2-k_1^2)^{\frac{1}{2}}y\}]. \quad (6.3.26)$$

The displacement components u_x, u_y are obtained from the inversion integral, the second of (6.3.11). Before writing the results, we note that k_1, k_2 have the units of reciprocal length. We choose k_1 as a normalizing factor for all length parameters in the results. Then the displacements are

$$u_x(x, y) = \frac{1}{i\mu\pi}\int_{-\infty}^{\infty}\frac{\sin\zeta a}{F_0(\zeta)}[2(\zeta^2-1)^{\frac{1}{2}}(\zeta^2-k^2)^{\frac{1}{2}}\exp\{-(\zeta^2-k^2)^{\frac{1}{2}}y\}+$$
$$+(k^2-2\zeta^2)\exp\{-(\zeta^2-1)^{\frac{1}{2}}y\}]\exp(i\zeta x)\,d\zeta, \quad (6.3.27)$$

$$u_y(x, y) = \frac{1}{\mu\pi}\int_{-\infty}^{\infty}\frac{(\zeta^2-1)^{\frac{1}{2}}\sin\zeta a}{\zeta F_0(\zeta)}[2\zeta^2\exp\{-(\zeta^2-k^2)^{\frac{1}{2}}y\}+$$
$$+(k^2-2\zeta^2)\exp\{-(\zeta^2-1)^{\frac{1}{2}}y\}]\exp(i\zeta x)\,d\zeta, \quad (6.3.28)$$

where

$$F_0(\zeta) = (2\zeta^2-k^2)^2-4\zeta^2(\zeta^2-1)^{\frac{1}{2}}(\zeta^2-k^2)^{\frac{1}{2}}. \quad (6.3.29)$$

It should be understood that $x \sim k_1x$, $y \sim k_1y$, $\zeta \sim \zeta/k_1$ in the preceding.

The case of a line source (the first problem considered by Lamb) recovers from the results for u_x, u_y by letting $a \to 0$ but letting the total load per unit length $2a$ be a constant. Thus, in (6.3.27), $\sin \zeta a$ would be replaced by $a\zeta$ and $\sin \zeta a/\zeta$ in (6.3.28) would be replaced by a.

3. *Poles of the integrands.* We denote the integrands of $u_x(x, y)$ and $u_y(x, y)$ by $\Phi(\zeta), \Psi(\zeta)$ respectively. The poles of these functions are given by the zeros of $F_0(\zeta) = 0$. This equation is, in fact, the previously-encountered frequency equation for Rayleigh surface waves, as may be seen by comparing (6.3.29) to (6.1.86). A direct correspondence is obtained if the comparison is made between (6.3.24) and the earlier equation, where

$$\bar{\alpha}^2 = \xi^2 - \omega^2/c_1^2, \qquad \bar{\beta}^2 = \xi^2 - \omega^2/c_2^2$$

in the latter. Thus the equation governing the propagation of free surface waves has arisen in the course of analysing the forced motion of a half-space. The zeros of $F_0(\zeta)$ are given by $\zeta = \pm\zeta_R$, where ζ_R is a real number.† We have

$$\begin{aligned} \nu &= \tfrac{1}{4}, & \zeta_R &= \pm 1{\cdot}8839, \\ \nu &= \tfrac{1}{3}, & \zeta_R &= \pm 2{\cdot}1447. \end{aligned} \tag{6.3.30}$$

Recall that ζ_R is non-dimensionalized, so that the wave velocity would be found from the preceding by replacing ζ_R by ζ_R/k_1.

4. *Branch points and branch cuts.* We see that the functions $\Phi(\zeta)$, $\Psi(\zeta)$ will have branch points located at $\zeta = \pm 1, \pm k$, due to $(\zeta^2-1)^{\frac{1}{2}}$, $(\zeta^2-k^2)^{\frac{1}{2}}$. Now the considerations as to the appropriate branch necessary to make the integrands single valued about the contour follow quite closely those presented for the single set of branch points arising in the SH wave-source problem.‡ Thus, briefly, the functions $\alpha(\zeta) = (\zeta^2-1)^{\frac{1}{2}}$, $\beta(\zeta) = (\zeta^2-k^2)^{\frac{1}{2}}$ must have their real parts always greater than zero owing to the terms $\exp(-\alpha y)$ and $\exp(-\beta y)$ appearing in the solution. With small damping included in the system, the branch cuts lie along hyperbolas which then degenerate to cuts along the real and imaginary axes as the damping becomes zero. The resulting situation is shown in Fig. 6.14. The contour is closed in the upper half-plane on the assumption that $x > 0$. The entire contour integral is given by

$$\oint = \int_{\Gamma_1} + \int_{\Gamma_\alpha} + \int_{\Gamma_\beta} + \int_{\Gamma_2} + \int_{-R}^{R} = -2\pi i \sum \text{Res}. \tag{6.3.31}$$

† Recall in the discussion of surface waves that other, extraneous roots arose from solving the rationalized equation.

‡ See (6.2.18)–(6.2.23) and Fig. 6.17(a) and (b). See also Ewing *et al.* [11, pp. 45–54].

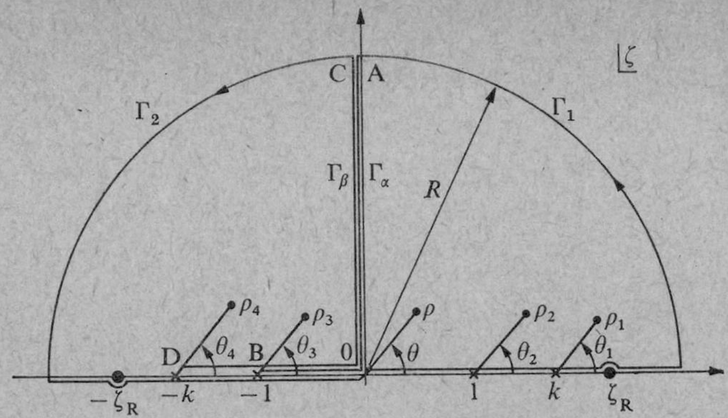

FIG. 6.14. Integration contour for $x > 0$.

The integrals along the branch cuts Γ_α, Γ_β are given by the segments

$$\Gamma_\alpha = \text{AO}+\text{OB}+\text{BO}+\text{OA},$$

$$\Gamma_\beta = \text{CO}+\text{OD}+\text{DO}+\text{OC}. \tag{6.3.32}$$

Furthermore, the poles at $\zeta = -\zeta_R$, $+\zeta_R$ are, respectively, included and excluded from the contour by slight indentations as dictated by the radiation condition.

To check that the branch cuts Γ_α, Γ_β do indeed yield the proper behaviour of $\alpha(\zeta)$, $\beta(\zeta)$, we introduce the polar coordinates ρ_1, θ_1, ρ_2, θ_2, ρ, θ, etc. as shown in Fig. 6.14. With these coordinates, we have that

$$\alpha(\zeta) = (\rho_2\rho_3)^{\frac{1}{2}} \exp\{i(\theta_2+\theta_3)/2\}, \qquad \beta(\zeta) = (\rho_1\rho_4)^{\frac{1}{2}} \exp\{i(\theta_1+\theta_4)/2\}. \tag{6.3.33}$$

The values of these functions along the various parts of Γ_α, Γ_β are given in Table 6.1. It is seen that Re α, Re $\beta \geqslant 0$ always. Thus the formal integral

TABLE 6.1
Value of α, β along Γ_α, Γ_β

Path	$\theta_2+\theta_3$	$\theta_1+\theta_4$	α	β	Re α	Im β	Re β	Im α
AO	π	π	$(1+\rho^2)^{\frac{1}{2}}i$	$(k^2+\rho^2)^{\frac{1}{2}}i$	0	>0	0	>0
OB	π	π	$(1+\rho^2)^{\frac{1}{2}}i$	$(k^2-\rho^2)^{\frac{1}{2}}i$	0	>0	0	>0
BO	$-\pi$	π	$-(1-\rho^2)^{\frac{1}{2}}i$	$(k^2-\rho^2)^{\frac{1}{2}}i$	0	<0	0	>0
OA	$-\pi$	π	$-(1+\rho^2)^{\frac{1}{2}}i$	$(k^2+\rho^2)^{\frac{1}{2}}i$	0	<0	0	>0
CO	Same as OA							
OB	Same as BO							
BD	0	π	$(\rho^2-1)^{\frac{1}{2}}$	$(k^2-\rho^2)^{\frac{1}{2}}i$	>0	0	0	>0
DB	0	$-\pi$	$(\rho^2-1)^{\frac{1}{2}}$	$-(k^2-\rho^2)^{\frac{1}{2}}i$	>0	0	0	<0
BO	$-\pi$	$-\pi$	$-(1-\rho^2)^{\frac{1}{2}}i$	$-(k^2-\rho^2)^{\frac{1}{2}}i$	0	<0	0	<0
OC	$-\pi$	$-\pi$	$-(1+\rho^2)^{\frac{1}{2}}i$	$-(k^2+\rho^2)^{\frac{1}{2}}i$	0	<0	0	<0

solutions (6.3.27) and (6.3.28) are determined from the residues at the poles and the evaluation of the integrals along the various portions of the contour. The contributions from Γ_1, Γ_2 vanish, so determination of the branch-cut integrals is the main task in obtaining an exact evaluation.

5. *Application of the steepest-descent method.* The task of evaluating the branch-cut integrals remains most formidable, so approximate results are sought. The method of steepest descent will be used to determine the field at infinity. We note that the integrals occurring in the displacement expressions (6.3.27) and (6.3.28) have the general form

$$I_1 = \int_{-\infty}^{\infty} \chi(\zeta)\exp\{i\zeta x-(\zeta^2-m^2)^{\frac{1}{2}}y\}\, d\zeta, \tag{6.3.34}$$

where $m = 1$ or k. We introduce the polar coordinates

$$x = R\sin\theta, \qquad y = R\cos\theta, \tag{6.3.35}$$

where θ is measured from the y-axis. Then I_1 may be written as

$$I_1 = \int_{-\infty}^{\infty} \chi(\zeta)e^{Rf(\zeta)}\, d\zeta, \tag{6.3.36}$$

where

$$f(\zeta) = i\zeta\sin\theta-(\zeta^2-m^2)^{\frac{1}{2}}\cos\theta. \tag{6.3.37}$$

We see that I_1 is now in the form (6.2.38), used in the development of the steepest-descent method.

We determine the saddle points of $\operatorname{Re} f(\zeta)$ from $df(\zeta)/d\zeta = 0$, and obtain

$$i\sin\theta = \frac{\zeta\cos\theta}{(\zeta^2-m^2)^{\frac{1}{2}}}, \qquad \zeta_0 = \pm m\sin\theta. \tag{6.3.38}$$

The point at $\zeta_0 = -m\sin\theta$ is the one of interest here; the point at $+m\sin\theta$ would be used for consideration on the negative real axis, in the range $-m \leqslant \zeta_0 \leqslant 0$. At the saddle point, we obtain that

$$f(\zeta_0) = -im, \qquad f''(\zeta_0) = i\sec^2\theta/m. \tag{6.3.39}$$

The contour of integration is now deformed to pass through the saddle point along the steepest-descent path. The general shape of the deformed contour will now be established. We know that near the saddle point that (see (6.2.62))

$$f(\zeta)-f(\zeta_0) = \tfrac{1}{2}(\zeta-\zeta_0)^2 f''(\zeta_0) \tag{6.3.40}$$

Also $f(\zeta)-f(\zeta_0) = -u^2$ (see (6.2.63)) along the path. Since $f''(\zeta_0)$ is given by the second of (6.3.39), we have from the preceding,

$$-u^2 = \tfrac{1}{2}(\zeta-\zeta_0)^2\frac{i\sec^2\theta}{m}, \tag{6.3.41}$$

from which we obtain

$$\zeta-\zeta_0 = \pm 2\sqrt{m}u\cos\theta e^{\pi i/4}. \tag{6.3.42}$$

The sign will be determined by the direction in which the contour passes through the saddle point. Thus, the positive sign represents a path at $+45°$, the negative sign a path at $-135°$, both with respect to the real ζ-axis.

To determine the path behaviour away from the saddle point, we note that the points at which the path crosses the real ζ-axis are given by

$$\operatorname{Im}\{f(\zeta)-f(\zeta_0)\} = 0, \qquad \zeta \sim \text{real}. \tag{6.3.43}$$

The first condition holds for all points along the steepest-descent path, the second condition gives the real-axis intersections. Substituting (6.3.40) and $f(\zeta_0) = -im$ in the preceding condition gives $\zeta_1 = -\text{m cosec } \theta$ as the only other crossover point (the branch point also being a crossover point).

The asymptotic behaviour of the path may be determined. Writing the first condition of (6.3.43) as $\operatorname{Im} f(\zeta) = \operatorname{Im} f(\zeta_0)$ we have

$$\operatorname{Im}\{i\zeta \sin\theta-(\zeta^2-m^2)^{\frac{1}{2}} \cos\theta\} = -m. \tag{6.3.44}$$

For large $|\zeta|$ we may neglect m in the radical above and obtain

$$\operatorname{Im}\{\zeta(\text{i} \sin\theta \mp \cos\theta\} = -m. \tag{6.3.45}$$

Letting $\zeta = \xi+\text{i}\eta$, we obtain

$$\xi \sin\theta \mp \eta \cos\theta = -m, \tag{6.3.46}$$

as the lines for the path asymptotes. We note that $0 < \theta < \pi/2$, so that $\sin\theta, \cos\theta > 0$. Also we note that both asymptotes pass through

$$\zeta = -m \operatorname{cosec}\theta.$$

The general form of the contour is shown in Fig. 6.15(a). On the basis of the direction of passage, we select the positive sign in (6.3.46).

We now consider the deformed contour relative to the pole and branch points along the negative real axis, located at $\zeta = -\zeta_R, -k, -1$, where $\zeta_R > k > 1$. Consider the case where $m = -k$. The saddle point will lie in the range $-k < \zeta_0 < 0$, and the branch point at $\zeta = -1$ is located within this range. For $-1 < \zeta_0 < 0$, the contour is as shown in Fig. 6.15(a). For $\theta > \text{cosec}^{-1}k$, $\zeta_0 < -1$ and the steepest-descent contour differs in its manner of circulating the branch point from that shown in the figure. Basically, a

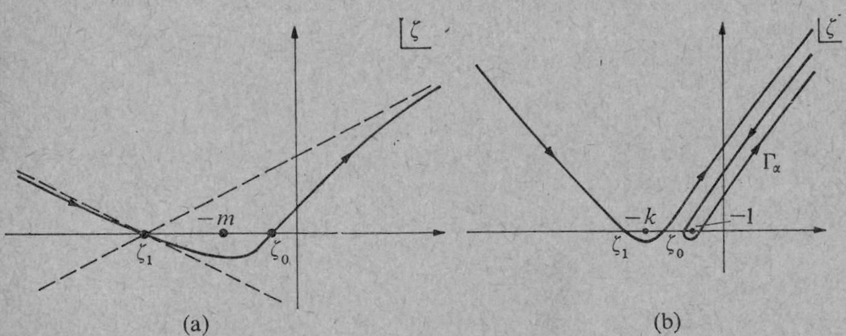

FIG. 6.15. (a) The steepest descent contour passing through ζ_0, and (b) modification of the steepest descent path to include a branch point.

'return loop' must be added that returns from infinity, passes about the branch point in the proper manner, and goes off again to infinity, as shown in Fig. 6.15(b). When $\zeta_0 = -1$, so that the steepest-descent path passes through the branch point, the path Γ_α is made to coincide with the steepest-descent path. When $m = -1$, there is no problem of the positive sloping portion of the path not properly passing the branch point at $\zeta = -k$. However, when $\theta > \operatorname{cosec}^{-1}k$, we have $\zeta_1 > -k$, so that the negative sloping portion is not properly circulating that branch point. A return loop is incorporated to account for $-k$ similar to that used in the previous case. If these additional loops yielded significant contributions, their exact evaluation would be necessary. However, Miller and Pursey state that contributions from these loops are asymptotically negligible.

There remains the matter of the pole $-\zeta_R$. If $\theta < \operatorname{cosec}^{-1}(\zeta_R/m)$, then the crossover point ζ_1 will be to the right of ζ_R and the pole will no longer be within the general contour. For $\theta > \operatorname{cosec}^{-1}(\zeta_R/m)$, the pole will be within the contour and must be accounted for by the additional residue term. Referring back to (6.3.36) and (6.3.37), we see that the resulting residue will contain the term

$$\exp\{-R(\zeta_R^2-m^2)^{\frac{1}{2}}\}\cos\theta. \tag{6.3.47}$$

For R large, this will result in a negligible contribution and may be neglected except when $\theta = \pi/2$. This circumstance will yield the surface wave contribution and will, in fact, be the dominant term. This will be given separate consideration.

With the saddle points established and the steepest-descent path determined, the resulting asymptotic value of the integral I_1 is given by

$$I_1 \sim \sqrt{\left(\frac{2\pi m}{R}\right)}\exp\left\{\mathrm{i}\left(\frac{\pi}{4}-mR\right)\right\}\cos\theta[\chi(-m\sin\theta)], \tag{6.3.48}$$

where $0 < \theta < \pi/2$.

6. *The far-field results.* Using the result (6.3.48) in the evaluation of the integrals (6.3.27) and (6.3.28), where we let $a \to 0$ and thus have the line source case, one obtains

$$u_x \sim \frac{a\mathrm{e}^{\pi\mathrm{i}/4}\cos\theta}{\mu}\left(\frac{2}{\pi R}\right)^{\frac{1}{2}}\left\{-\frac{k^{\frac{5}{2}}\sin 2\theta(k^2\sin^2\theta-1)^{\frac{1}{2}}}{F_0(k\sin\theta)}\mathrm{e}^{-\mathrm{i}kR}+\right.$$
$$\left.+\frac{\mathrm{i}\sin\theta(k^2-2\sin^2\theta)}{F_0(\sin\theta)}\mathrm{e}^{-\mathrm{i}R}\right\}, \tag{6.3.49}$$

$$u_y \sim \frac{a\mathrm{e}^{\pi\mathrm{i}/4}\cos\theta}{\mu}\left(\frac{2}{\pi R}\right)^{\frac{1}{2}}\left\{\frac{2k^{\frac{5}{2}}\sin^2\theta(k^2\sin^2\theta-1)^{\frac{1}{2}}}{F_0(k\sin\theta)}\mathrm{e}^{-\mathrm{i}kR}+\right.$$
$$\left.+\frac{\mathrm{i}\cos\theta(k^2-2\sin^2\theta)}{F_0(\sin\theta)}\mathrm{e}^{-\mathrm{i}R}\right\}. \tag{6.3.50}$$

To obtain the radial and tangential components of the field, we use the relations

$$u_{\mathrm{R}} = u_y \cos\theta + u_x \sin\theta,$$

$$u_\theta = u_x \cos\theta - u_y \sin\theta. \tag{6.3.51}$$

This gives

$$u_R \sim \frac{a\exp\left\{\mathrm{i}\left(\dfrac{3\pi}{4}-R\right)\right\}}{\mu}\left(\frac{2}{\pi R}\right)^{\frac{1}{2}}\frac{\cos\theta(k^2-2\sin^2\theta)}{F_0(\sin\theta)}, \tag{6.3.52}$$

$$u_\theta \sim \frac{a\exp\left\{\mathrm{i}\left(\dfrac{5\pi}{4}-kR\right)\right\}}{\mu}\left(\frac{2k^5}{\pi R}\right)^{\frac{1}{2}}\frac{\sin 2\theta(k^2\sin^2\theta-1)^{\frac{1}{2}}}{F_0(k\sin\theta)}. \tag{6.3.53}$$

The resulting displacement fields u_{R}, u_θ are shown as a function of θ $(0 \leq \theta < \pi/2)$ for Poisson's ratio of $\frac{1}{3}$ in Fig. 6.16.

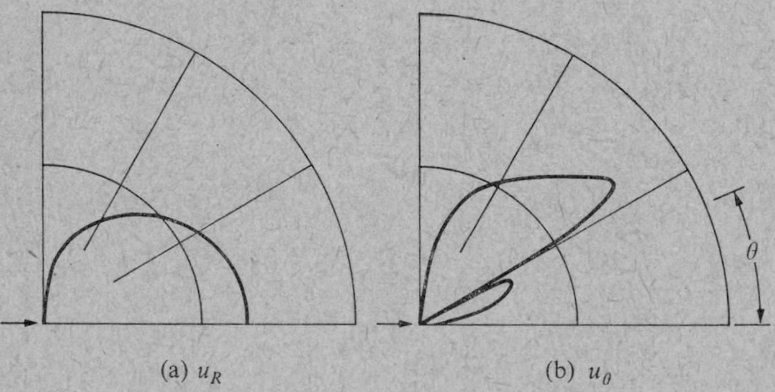

FIG. 6.16. Polar plots of (a) u_R, and (b) u_θ for Poisson's ratio of $\frac{1}{3}$. (After Miller and Pursey [30, Figs. 5 and 7].)

7. *Surface waves.* The case of surface waves from a line source is given by setting $y = 0$ in the results (6.3.27) and (6.3.28) for u_x, u_y and letting $a \to 0$ in the manner previously prescribed. We obtain

$$u_x(x, 0) = \frac{a}{\mathrm{i}\mu\pi}\int_{-\infty}^{\infty}\frac{\zeta}{F_0(\zeta)}\{2(\zeta^2-1)^{\frac{1}{2}}(\zeta^2-k^2)^{\frac{1}{2}}+(k^2-2\zeta^2)\}\mathrm{e}^{\mathrm{i}\zeta x}\,\mathrm{d}\zeta, \tag{6.3.54}$$

$$u_y(x, 0) = \frac{ak^2}{\mu\pi}\int_{-\infty}^{\infty}\frac{(\zeta^2-1)^{\frac{1}{2}}}{F_0(\zeta)}\mathrm{e}^{\mathrm{i}\zeta x}\,\mathrm{d}\zeta. \tag{6.3.55}$$

If, in performing the contour integration of Fig. 6.14, we consider only the residue contribution and neglect the contribution of the branch cut integrals Γ_α, Γ_β, we will obtain the surface-wave effect. Writing the general forms of the integrands of $u_x(x, 0)$, $u_y(x, 0)$ as

$$\chi(\zeta) = \psi(\zeta)/F_0(\zeta), \tag{6.3.56}$$

we have the residue at $\zeta = -\zeta_R$ given by

$$\text{Res} = \frac{\psi(-\zeta_R)\exp(-i\zeta_R x)}{F_0'(-\zeta_R)}. \tag{6.3.57}$$

Thus the general waveform will be given by

$$u_x(x, 0) \sim \exp\{-i(\zeta_R x-\omega t)\}, \qquad u_y(x, 0) \sim \exp\{i(\zeta_R x-\omega t)\}. \tag{6.3.58}$$

The propagation velocity will be c_R, that of Rayleigh surface waves. We note that the amplitudes are not affected by distance of propagation, whereas $u_x(x, y), u_y(x, y)$, or $u_R(R, \theta), u_\theta(R, \theta)$ go as $R^{-\frac{1}{2}}$. This, again, is a consequence of the waves propagating along the surface. We emphasize that this result is for the plane-strain, line-load case. If the loading were a point load, the Rayleigh wave amplitude would be attenuated with distance, but not as severely as the waves into the interior. Miller and Pursey give specific results for two values of Poisson's ratio. Thus

$\nu = \frac{1}{4}$:

$$u_x(x, 0) \sim 0{\cdot}250\frac{a}{\mu}\exp(-1{\cdot}884ix),$$

$$u_y(x, 0) \sim 0{\cdot}367\frac{ia}{\mu}\exp(-1{\cdot}884ix). \tag{6.3.59}$$

$\nu = \frac{1}{3}$:

$$u_x(x, 0) \sim 0{\cdot}198\frac{a}{\mu}\exp(-2{\cdot}145ix),$$

$$u_y(x, 0) \sim 0{\cdot}311\frac{ia}{\mu}\exp(-2{\cdot}145ix). \tag{6.3.60}$$

6.3.2. *Other results for harmonic sources*

Many analyses have been done on periodic loading of a half-space, of which the results presented in the previous section are somewhat representative. The previous analysis was concerned with a line normal load. The case of a line tangential loading, where the action of the load is perpendicular to the load line has also been considered by Lamb [22], Miller and Pursey [30], and, no doubt, others. Of greater practical interest is the case of a point normal load, or a normal load applied over a small (circular) region. The case of torsional loads applied at a point or over a small region have also been considered. The bases for interest in harmonic wave excitation are several fold. The first is that harmonic wave solutions provide a basis, through superposition techniques, of obtaining solutions to transient problems. There are several areas, however, where the results are of direct application. In ultrasonics, transducers transmit wave trains that are often very narrow-band and may be approximated as purely harmonic. Many problems involving foundation vibrations involve steady-state excitation of an extended medium.

The major additional results given here for harmonic loads are also from Miller and Pursey [30, 31]. Thus in [30] the problems of a tangential line load, a normal load applied to a circular region $r \leqslant a$, and the case of a torque applied about the y-axis were all analysed. Far-field radiation patterns for the tangential loading were also obtained, and are shown in Fig. 6.17.

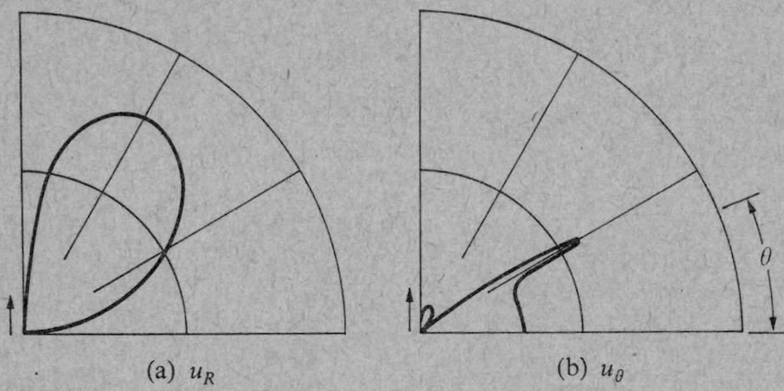

FIG. 6.17. The far-field displacements (a) u_R and (b) u_θ for a line tangential load applied at the origin for $0 \leqslant \theta < \pi/2$. Poisson's ratio $\nu = \frac{1}{4}$. (After Miller and Pursey [30, Figs. 9 and 11].)

The analytical expressions for these given by Miller and Pursey are

$$u_R \sim \frac{a\exp\left\{\mathrm{i}\left(\frac{3\pi}{4}-R\right)\right\}}{\mu}\left(\frac{2}{\pi R}\right)^{\frac{1}{2}}\frac{\sin 2\theta(k^2-\sin^2\theta)}{F_0(\sin\theta)}, \tag{6.3.61}$$

$$u_\theta \sim \frac{a\exp\left\{\mathrm{i}\left(\frac{3\pi}{4}-kR\right)\right\}}{\mu}\left(\frac{2k^7}{\pi R}\right)\frac{\cos\theta\cos 2\theta}{F_0(k\sin\theta)}. \tag{6.3.62}$$

As mentioned, Miller and Pursey also presented the analysis of a normal stress, applied to the circular area $r \leq a$, and varying harmonically with time. The analysis is in terms of the coordinates r, y, but the results for the displacements are also given in terms of u_R, u_θ. For the far field, where $0 \leqslant \theta < \pi/2$, these are

$$u_R \sim -\frac{a^2}{2\mu}\frac{\mathrm{e}^{-\mathrm{i}R}}{R}\frac{\cos\theta(k^2-2\sin^2\theta)}{F_0(\sin\theta)}, \tag{6.3.63}$$

$$u_\theta \sim \frac{\mathrm{i}a^2k^3}{2\mu}\frac{\mathrm{e}^{-\mathrm{i}kR}}{R}\frac{\sin 2\theta(k^2\sin^2\theta-1)}{F_0(k\sin\theta)}. \tag{6.3.64}$$

The surface wave results are also given. Thus, for $\nu = \frac{1}{4}$,

$$u_r(r, 0) \sim 0{\cdot}215\frac{a^2 \exp(\pi i/4)}{\mu\sqrt{r}} \exp(-1{\cdot}884ir), \tag{6.3.65}$$

$$u_y(r, 0) \sim -0{\cdot}316\frac{a^2 \exp(\pi i/4)}{\mu\sqrt{r}} \exp(-1{\cdot}884ir). \tag{6.3.66}$$

For $\nu = \frac{1}{3}$, replace 0·215, 0·316, and 1·884 by 0·182, 0·286, and 2·145 respectively. It should be noted that the surface wave now undergoes amplitude attention with distance as $R^{-\frac{1}{2}}$, while the body waves attenuate as R^{-1}, a more severe attenuation. Lord [25] has computed the far-field radiation diagrams for this case of loading. The results, in terms of stresses for a Poisson's ratio of 0·20 are shown in Fig. 6.18. The scale is arbitrary for the

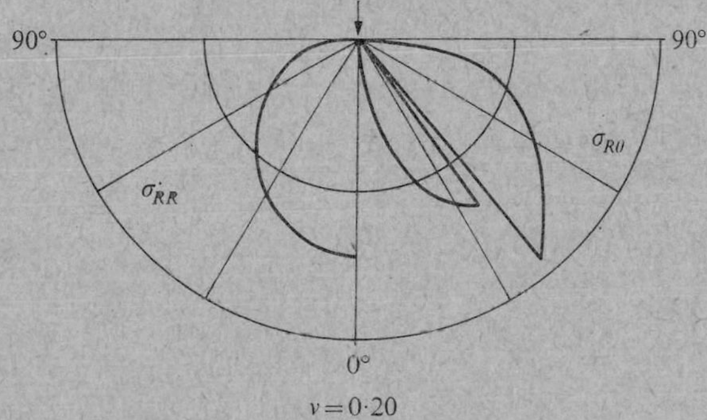

FIG. 6.18. Polar diagram for the stresses σ_{RR}, $\sigma_{R\theta}$ resulting from a point normal load at the origin for $\nu = 0{\cdot}20$. (After Lord [25, Figs. 7 and 8].)

plots, although both quadrants are to the same scale.

In another aspect of their work, Miller and Pursey [31] have computed the partition of energy among the dilatational, shear, and surface waves due to an oscillating normal point force. Woods [44] has presented this data in a most informative manner, as shown in Fig. 6.19. Thus the compressional and shear waves are shown spreading out in hemispherical wavefronts. The spacing of the wavefronts is in accord with their differing velocities. The relative amplitude of particle motion is shown. Also shown is the Rayleigh surface wave, with the vertical and horizontal displacement components shown on the leftward- and rightward-propagating parts of the wave. The various powers of r^{-n} ($n = 0{\cdot}5, 1, 2$) give the geometric attentuation of the displacement amplitudes with radial distance r. The shear window indicates the portion of the shear wave along which amplitudes are greatest. The partition of energy is shown in the table of Fig. 6.19. The predominance of the Rayleigh wave containing 67 per cent of the input energy and undergoing more gradual amplitude attentuation is clearly evident.

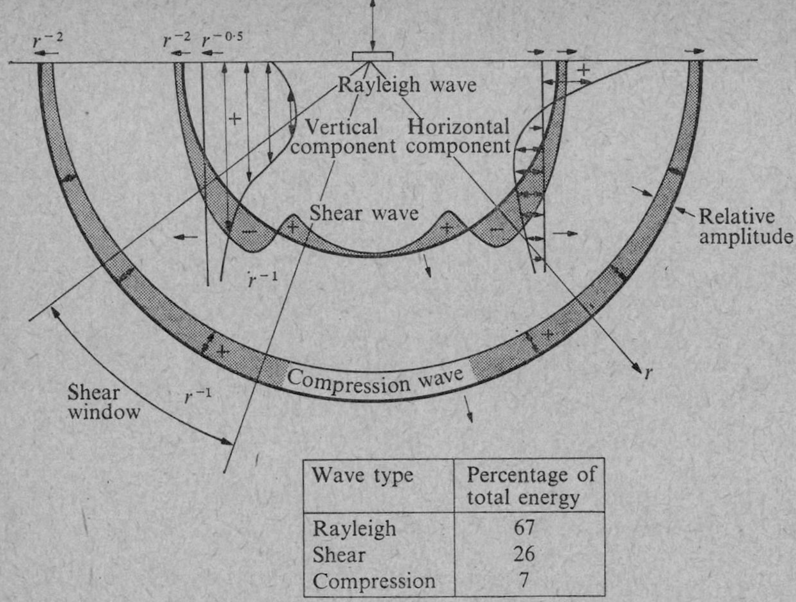

Wave type	Percentage of total energy
Rayleigh	67
Shear	26
Compression	7

FIG. 6.19. Distribution of displacement and energy in dilatational, shear, and surface waves from a harmonic normal load on a half-space for $\nu = \frac{1}{4}$. (After Woods [44, Fig. 1].)

6.3.3. *Transient normal loading on a half-space*

The original analysis by Lamb of the half-space problem employed Fourier superposition of harmonic waves to obtain the response to transient loading. Others have approached the problem directly by assuming zero initial conditions, and considering step or impulse loading. In the following, the case of a step normal loading, applied at the origin of the half-space will be formulated using integral transforms. The inversion of the results for two special cases will be partially carried out. The technique for performing the inversion, known as Cagniard's method, will be shown. The following section will be devoted to presenting several results of transient-surface or buried-source analyses.

1. *Governing equations and boundary conditions.* Consider the half-space $z \geqslant 0$ loaded by a concentrated, upward-directed force. Polar coordinates will be used, and consistency with the usual r, θ, z notation requires that the z-axis now be the vertical instead of the y-axis. Owing to the axisymmetry existing for this problem, the displacement component $u_\theta = 0$, so that

$$\mathbf{u}(r, z, t) = u_r\mathbf{e}_r + u_z\mathbf{e}_z. \tag{6.3.67}$$

In terms of the scalar and vector potentials Φ, $\mathbf{H}$, we have

$$\mathbf{u} = \nabla\Phi + \nabla\times(H_\theta\mathbf{e}_\theta). \tag{6.3.68}$$

The governing equations for Φ, H_θ are then

$$\nabla^2\Phi = \frac{1}{c_1^2}\frac{\partial^2\Phi}{\partial t^2}, \qquad \nabla^2 H_\theta - \frac{1}{r^2}H_\theta = \frac{1}{c_2^2}\frac{\partial^2 H_\theta}{\partial t^2}, \tag{6.3.69}$$

where $\nabla^2 = r^{-1}\,\partial(r\partial/\partial r)/\partial r + \partial^2/\partial z^2$. It is possible to reduce the second equation of (6.3.69) to the scalar wave equation by defining the function Ψ, where

$$H_\theta = -\partial\Psi/\partial r. \tag{6.3.70}$$

Then we obtain

$$\nabla^2\Psi = \frac{1}{c_2^2}\frac{\partial^2\Psi}{\partial t^2}. \tag{6.3.71}$$

The displacements and stresses are given by

$$u_r = \frac{\partial\Phi}{\partial r} + \frac{\partial^2\Psi}{\partial r\,\partial z}, \qquad u_\theta = 0,$$

$$u_z = \frac{\partial\Phi}{\partial z} + \frac{\partial^2\Psi}{\partial z^2} - \frac{1}{c_2^2}\ddot{\Psi}. \tag{6.3.72}$$

The stresses are

$$\tau_{rr} = \lambda\nabla^2\Phi + 2\mu\left(\frac{\partial^2\Phi}{\partial r^2} + \frac{\partial^3\Psi}{\partial r^2\,\partial z}\right),$$

$$\tau_{\theta\theta} = \lambda\nabla^2\Phi + \frac{2\mu}{r}\left(\frac{\partial\Phi}{\partial r} + \frac{\partial^2\Psi}{\partial r\,\partial z}\right),$$

$$\tau_{zz} = \lambda\nabla^2\Phi + 2\mu\frac{\partial}{\partial z}\left(\frac{\partial\Phi}{\partial z} + \frac{\partial^2\Psi}{\partial z^2} - \frac{1}{c_2^2}\ddot{\Psi}\right),$$

$$\tau_{rz} = \mu\frac{\partial}{\partial r}\left(2\frac{\partial\Phi}{\partial z} + 2\frac{\partial^2\Psi}{\partial z^2} - \frac{1}{c_2^2}\ddot{\Psi}\right),$$

$$\tau_{\theta z} = \tau_{r\theta} = 0. \tag{6.3.73}$$

The appearance of $\ddot{\Psi}$ terms in the above is a consequence of using the identity (6.3.71) when the appropriate combinations of spatial derivatives occur.

For the boundary conditions, we have

$$\tau_{zr} = 0, \qquad \tau_{zz} = F(r)H\langle t\rangle, \qquad z = 0, \tag{6.3.74}$$

where $F(r)$ is taken to be an arbitrary function for the moment. It may be represented as a Fourier–Bessel integral of the form

$$F(r) = \int_0^\infty \xi J_0(\xi r)\,\mathrm{d}\xi \int_0^\infty F(\sigma)\sigma J_0(\sigma\xi)\,\mathrm{d}\sigma. \tag{6.3.75}$$

This is, of course, the polar-coordinate analogue of the Fourier integral. In the present problem, we wish $F(r)$ to represent a point load. This is the case if

$$F(r)=\frac{\delta(r)}{2\pi r}Z, \tag{6.3.76}$$

where Z represents the magnitude of the applied force. Then (6.3.75) becomes

$$F(r)=\frac{Z}{2\pi}\int_0^\infty \xi J_0(\xi r)\,d\xi. \tag{6.3.77}$$

Finally, we note that homogeneous initial conditions are assumed.

2. *Transformed equations.* The Laplace and Hankel transforms will be applied to the present problem. The Laplace transform of various quantities will be indicated as

$$U_i(r,z,p)=\mathscr{L}\{u_i(r,z,t)\},\qquad T_{ij}(r,z,p)=\mathscr{L}\{\tau_{ij}(r,z,t)\},$$
$$\tilde{\Phi},\tilde{\Psi}=\mathscr{L}\{\Phi,\Psi\}. \tag{6.3.78}$$

The transformed governing equations are

$$\nabla^2\tilde{\Phi}-\frac{p^2}{c_1^2}\tilde{\Phi}=0,\qquad \nabla^2\tilde{\Psi}-\frac{p^2}{c_2^2}\tilde{\Psi}=0. \tag{6.3.79}$$

The transformed displacements and stresses are

$$U_r=\frac{\partial\tilde{\Phi}}{\partial r}+\frac{\partial^2\tilde{\Psi}}{\partial r\,\partial z},$$
$$U_z=\frac{\partial\tilde{\Phi}}{\partial z}+\frac{\partial^2\tilde{\Psi}}{\partial z^2}-\frac{p^2}{c_2^2}\tilde{\Psi}, \tag{6.3.80}$$

$$T_{rr}=\lambda\nabla^2\tilde{\Phi}+2\mu\left(\frac{\partial^2\tilde{\Phi}}{\partial r^2}+\frac{\partial^3\tilde{\Psi}}{\partial r^2\,\partial z}\right),$$
$$T_{\theta\theta}=\lambda\nabla^2\tilde{\Phi}+\frac{2\mu}{r}\left(\frac{\partial\tilde{\Phi}}{\partial r}+\frac{\partial^2\tilde{\Psi}}{\partial r\,\partial z}\right),$$
$$T_{zz}=\lambda\nabla^2\tilde{\Phi}+2\mu\frac{\partial}{\partial z}\left(\frac{\partial\tilde{\Phi}}{\partial z}+\frac{\partial^2\tilde{\Psi}}{\partial z^2}-\frac{p^2}{c_2^2}\tilde{\Psi}\right),$$
$$T_{rz}=\mu\frac{\partial}{\partial r}\left(2\frac{\partial\tilde{\Phi}}{\partial z}+2\frac{\partial^2\tilde{\Psi}}{\partial z^2}-\frac{p^2}{c_2^2}\tilde{\Psi}\right). \tag{6.3.81}$$

The transformed boundary conditions are

$$T_{zr}=0,\qquad T_{zz}=F(r)/p,\qquad z=0. \tag{6.3.82}$$

The procedure we could follow at this point would be to solve (6.3.79) explicitly subject to (6.3.82). This would lead directly to a transformed solution U_r, U_z. The problem of the Laplace inversion would then leave us with little choice but to tackle it head-on. An alternative procedure, used by Chao [3] will be used here. Thus, the Hankel transform will now be applied to the preceding Laplace-transformed equations. Defining

$$\bar{\phi}(\xi, z, p) = \int_0^\infty \xi J_0(\xi r)\tilde{\Phi}(r, z, p)\,\mathrm{d}r, \tag{6.3.83}$$

as the zero-order Hankel transform of $\tilde{\Phi}$, with similar definitions for $\bar{\psi}$, $\bar{U}_r$, etc., we have for the Hankel transform of (6.3.79)

$$\frac{\mathrm{d}^2\bar{\phi}}{\mathrm{d}z^2}-(\xi^2+h^2)\bar{\phi}=0, \qquad \frac{\mathrm{d}^2\bar{\psi}}{\mathrm{d}z^2}-(\xi^2+k^2)\bar{\psi}=0, \tag{6.3.84}$$

where

$$h^2 = p^2/c_1^2, \qquad k^2 = p^2/c_2^2 = (c_1^2/c_2^2)h^2. \tag{6.3.85}$$

We now apply the Hankel transform to U_r, U_z. However, because of the way the transform operates on derivatives with respect to r, the first-order transform is appropriate for U_r, while the zero-order transform is appropriate for U_z, giving

$$\bar{U}_r = \int_0^\infty rU_rJ_1(\xi r)\,\mathrm{d}r, \qquad \bar{U}_z = \int_0^\infty rU_zJ_0(\xi r)\,\mathrm{d}r. \tag{6.3.86}$$

This gives

$$\bar{U}_r = -\xi(\bar{\phi}+\bar{\psi}'),$$
$$\bar{U}_z = \bar{\phi}'+\bar{\psi}''-k^2\bar{\psi}, \tag{6.3.87}$$

where the primes indicate derivatives with respect to z. In a similar manner we transform the stresses according to

$$\bar{T}_{zz} = \int_0^\infty rT_{zz}J_0(\xi r)\,\mathrm{d}r, \qquad \bar{T}_{rz} = \int_0^\infty rT_{rz}J_1(\xi r)\,\mathrm{d}r, \tag{6.3.88}$$

giving

$$\bar{T}_{zz} = \lambda h^2\bar{\phi}+2\mu(\bar{\phi}''+\bar{\psi}'''-k^2\bar{\psi}'),$$
$$\bar{T}_{rz} = -\mu\xi(2\bar{\phi}'+2\bar{\psi}''-k^2\bar{\psi}). \tag{6.3.89}$$

The boundary conditions are thus

$$\lambda h^2\bar{\phi}+2\mu(\bar{\phi}''+\bar{\psi}''-k^2\bar{\psi}') = Z/2\pi p, \qquad z=0,$$
$$2\bar{\phi}'+2\bar{\psi}''-k^2\bar{\psi}=0, \qquad z=0. \tag{6.3.90}$$

3. *Transformed solutions and Hankel inversion.* We have for the solutions of the transformed equations (6.3.84),

$$\bar{\phi} = A_1\mathrm{e}^{-\alpha z}+B_1\mathrm{e}^{\alpha z}, \qquad \bar{\psi} = A_2\mathrm{e}^{-\beta z}+B_2\mathrm{e}^{\beta z}, \tag{6.3.91}$$

where

$$\alpha^2 = \xi^2+h^2, \qquad \beta^2 = \xi^2+k^2. \tag{6.3.92}$$

We discard the B_1, B_2 terms since they will lead to unbounded results, and substitute the remaining in the boundary conditions (6.3.90), giving

$$\begin{aligned}(\lambda h^2+2\mu\alpha^2)A_1-2\mu\beta(\beta^2-k^2)A_2 &= Z/2\pi p,\\ -2\alpha A_1+(2\beta^2-k^2)A_2 &= 0.\end{aligned} \tag{6.3.93}$$

Noting that

$$\lambda h^2+2\mu\alpha^2 = \mu(k^2+2\xi^2), \qquad \beta^2-k^2 = \xi^2, \qquad 2\beta^2-k^2 = 2\xi^2+k^2, \tag{6.3.94}$$

then (6.3.93) may be written as

$$\begin{bmatrix}(k^2+2\xi^2) & -2\beta\xi^2\\ -2\alpha & (2\xi^2+k^2)\end{bmatrix}\begin{bmatrix}A_1\\ A_2\end{bmatrix} = \begin{bmatrix}\dfrac{Z}{2\pi p\mu}\\ 0\end{bmatrix}. \tag{6.3.95}$$

Solving for A_1, A_2 we obtain

$$A_1 = \frac{Z}{2\pi\mu p}\frac{2\xi^2+k^2}{D}, \qquad A_2 = \frac{Z}{2\pi\mu p}\frac{2\alpha}{D},$$
$$D = (2\xi^2+k^2)^2-4\alpha\beta\xi^2. \tag{6.3.96}$$

With the coefficients in hand, we have the transformed solutions. Thus, from (6.3.87),

$$\begin{aligned}\bar{U}_r &= \frac{-Z}{2\pi\mu p}\frac{\xi\{(2\xi^2+k^2)e^{-\alpha z}-2\alpha\beta e^{-\beta z}\}}{D},\\ \bar{U}_z &= \frac{Z}{2\pi\mu p}\frac{\{-\alpha(2\xi^2+k^2)e^{-\alpha z}+2\alpha\xi^2 e^{-\beta z}\}}{D}.\end{aligned} \tag{6.3.97}$$

The preceding are the Laplace–Hankel transformed solutions. Performing the Hankel inversion, we have

$$U_r(r, z, p) = \frac{Z}{2\pi\mu p}\int_0^\infty \frac{\xi^2\{(2\xi^2+k^2)e^{-\alpha z}-2\alpha\beta e^{-\beta z}\}}{D}J_1(\xi r)\,d\xi, \tag{6.3.98}$$

$$U_z(r, z, p) = \frac{Z}{2\pi\mu p}\int_0^\infty \frac{\{-\alpha\xi(2\xi^2+k^2)e^{-\alpha z}+2\alpha\xi^3 e^{-\beta z}\}}{D}J_0(\xi r)\,d\xi. \tag{6.3.99}$$

We shall now seek to carry out the evaluation of the above, including the Laplace inversion aspect. Unfortunately, integrations of the above, valid for all r and z, are most difficult to obtain. Instead, only special cases have been evaluated, such as the values for $r = 0$ (directly under the load) or for $z = 0$ (along the surface). For these cases, the integrals are somewhat simplified. Fortunately, these special cases are also cases of considerable practical interest.

4. *Evaluation for $r = 0$.* The case of $r = 0$ is the simplest. From (6.3.98) we see that $U_r = 0$, since $J_1(0) = 0$, and that

$$U_z = \frac{Z}{2\pi\mu p}\int_0^\infty \frac{\{-\alpha\xi(2\xi^2+k^2)e^{-\alpha z}+2\alpha\xi^3 e^{-\beta z}\}}{D}\,d\xi, \tag{6.3.100}$$

where, we recall, α and β contain p, the Laplace transform parameter. We will apply Cagniard's method to this problem.† The essence of this method is as follows: Suppose we wish to Laplace invert $U(p)$ given as some integral

$$U(p) = \int_a^\infty g(t)e^{-f(p)t}\,dt. \tag{6.3.101}$$

The procedure is, by proper changes of variables, to manipulate the preceding into a form

$$U(p) = \int_0^\infty h(t)e^{-pt}\,dt = \mathscr{L}\{h(t)\}. \tag{6.3.102}$$

Then, by inspection,

$$u(t) = \mathscr{L}^{-1}\{U(p)\} = h(t). \tag{6.3.103}$$

The key to this technique is making the proper changes of variables to bring the integral into the desired form.

Proceeding, we break the integral into two parts and take the portion $\exp(-\alpha z)$. Let $\alpha z = pt$, which effectively treats α as an independent variable. Then

$$pt = (p/c_2)c_2t = kc_2t, \tag{6.3.104}$$

so that $\alpha = kc_2t/z = k\tau$, where $\tau = c_2t/z$. The consequences of the above change, which is meant to transform $\exp(-\alpha z)$ into $\exp(-pt)$ or the form of the Laplace transform, must now be incorporated in the remaining terms. Thus, from (6.3.92),

$$\alpha^2 = \xi^2+p^2/c_1^2 = k^2\tau^2. \tag{6.3.105}$$

Defining $\epsilon = (c_2/c_1)^2$, this gives

$$\xi^2 = k^2\tau^2-p^2/c_1^2 = k^2\tau^2-k^2\varepsilon = k^2(\tau^2-\varepsilon) \tag{6.3.106}$$

and

$$d\xi = \frac{p^2\tau}{c_2\xi z}\,dt. \tag{6.3.107}$$

Similarly, defining $\delta_1 = 1-\varepsilon$, $\delta_2 = 1-2\varepsilon$, we have

$$\beta^2 = k^2(\tau^2+\delta_1), \qquad 2\xi^2+k^2 = k^2(2\tau^2+\delta_2). \tag{6.3.108}$$

† Cagniard, L., *Reflexion et refraction des seismiques progressives*, Gauthiers–Villar, Paris (1935). Fung [13, pp. 218–25] gives a rather extensive presentation of the method as applied to Lamb's problem of the suddenly applied line load.

Manipulations on the second integral, containing $\exp(-\beta z)$ follow a similar pattern; thus let

$$\beta z = pt, \qquad \beta = k\tau, \qquad \xi^2 = k^2(\tau^2-1),$$

$$d\xi = \frac{p^2\tau}{c_2\xi z}\,dt, \qquad 2\xi^2+k^2 = k^2(2\tau^2-1), \qquad \alpha^2 = k^2(\tau^2-\delta_1). \tag{6.3.109}$$

The limits must now be considered. In particular, at $\xi = 0$, we have from (6.3.105)

$$\tau = p/c_1k = c_2/c_1 = c_2t/z, \qquad t = z/c_1, \tag{6.3.110}$$

while from (6.3.109) we have for $\xi = 0$, $t = z/c_2$ for the lower limit. The two integrals associated with U_z have thus taken the form

$$U_z \propto \int_{z/c_1}^{\infty} (\ldots)e^{-pt}\,dt + \int_{z/c_2}^{\infty} (\ldots)e^{-pt}\,dt. \tag{6.3.111}$$

We now introduce the step functions $H\langle t-z/c_1\rangle$ and $H\langle t-z/c_2\rangle$ inside the integrals. This enables the lower limits to be written as zero. Thus (6.3.100) becomes

$$U_z(0, z, p) = \frac{-Z}{2\pi\mu}\int_0^{\infty}\frac{\tau(2\tau^2+\delta_2)e^{-pt}H\langle t-z/c_1\rangle}{(2\tau^2+\delta_2)^2-4\tau(\tau^2+\delta_1)^{\frac{1}{2}}(\tau^2-\varepsilon)}\left(\frac{\tau}{z}\right)dt+$$

$$+\frac{Z}{2\pi\mu}\int_0^{\infty}\frac{2(\tau^2-\delta_1)^{\frac{1}{2}}(\tau^2-1)e^{-pt}H\langle t-z/c_2\rangle}{(2\tau^2-1)^2-4\tau(\tau^2-\delta_1)^{\frac{1}{2}}(\tau^2-1)}\left(\frac{\tau}{z}\right)dt. \tag{6.3.112}$$

The result is now in a form suitable for inversion by inspection and is

$$u_z(0, z, t) = \frac{Z}{2\pi\mu}\left\{\frac{-\tau^2(2\tau^2+\delta_2)H\langle t-z/c_1\rangle}{(2\tau+\delta_2^2)^2-4\tau(\tau^2-\varepsilon)(\tau^2+\delta_1)^{\frac{1}{2}}}+\right.$$

$$\left.+\frac{2\tau(\tau^2-1)(\tau^2-\delta_1)^{\frac{1}{2}}H\langle t-z/c_2\rangle}{(2\tau^2-1)-4\tau(\tau^2-1)(\tau^2-\delta_1)^{\frac{1}{2}}}\right\}, \tag{6.3.113}$$

where, we recall, $\tau = c_2t/z$.

5. *Evaluation for* $z = 0$. By letting $z = 0$, we will obtain the surface behaviour. The solutions (6.3.98) and (6.3.99) then become

$$U_r(r, 0, p) = \frac{Z}{2\pi\mu p}\int_0^{\infty}\frac{(2\xi^2+k^2-2\alpha\beta)}{D}\xi^2J_1(\xi r)\,d\xi,$$

$$U_z(r, 0, p) = \frac{-Z}{2\pi\mu p}\int_0^{\infty}\frac{\alpha\xi k^2}{D}J_0(\xi r)\,d\xi. \tag{6.3.114}$$

While considerably simplified over the original expressions, the presence of the Bessel functions makes the inversion process rather difficult. Only the inversion of $U_z(r, 0, p)$ will be partially outlined. The procedure follows that of Pekeris [34], where complete details may be found, as well as consideration of $U_r(r, 0, p)$.

We first introduce a change of variables; let $\xi = kx = px/c_2$. We now assume a specific value of Poisson's ratio $\nu = \frac{1}{4}$. Then

$$\alpha^2 = k^2(x^2+\tfrac{1}{3}), \qquad \beta^2 = k^2(x^2+1). \tag{6.3.115}$$

Then the second of (6.3.114) becomes

$$U_z(r, 0, p) = \frac{-Z}{2\pi\mu c_2}\int_0^\infty \frac{x(x^2+\frac{1}{3})^{\frac{1}{2}}J_0\left(\frac{p}{c_2}xr\right)\,\mathrm{d}x}{(2x^2+1)^2-4x^2(x^2+\frac{1}{3})^{\frac{1}{2}}(x^2+1)^{\frac{1}{2}}}. \tag{6.3.116}$$

We define

$$N(pr) = \int_0^\infty xm(x)J_0\left(\frac{prx}{c_2}\right)\,\mathrm{d}x, \tag{6.3.117}$$

where

$$m(x) = \frac{(x^2+\frac{1}{3})^{\frac{1}{2}}}{(2x^2+1)^2-4x^2(x^2+\frac{1}{3})^{\frac{1}{2}}(x^2+1)^{\frac{1}{2}}}. \tag{6.3.118}$$

Then we have that

$$U_z(r, 0, p) = -\left(\frac{Z}{2\pi\mu c_2}\right)N(pr). \tag{6.3.119}$$

We have in mind the application of Cagniard's method of inversion. However, as (6.3.116) is presently posed, the necessary ingredient of $\exp(-pt)$ is absent. In order to introduce this, we use the integral relation for the Bessel function, which is†

$$J_0(z) = \frac{2}{\pi}\int_0^\infty \sin(z\cosh\theta)\,\mathrm{d}\theta,$$

$$= \frac{1}{\pi\mathrm{i}}\int_0^\infty (\mathrm{e}^{\mathrm{i}z\cosh\theta}-\mathrm{e}^{-\mathrm{i}z\cosh\theta})\,\mathrm{d}\theta. \tag{6.3.120}$$

Then $N(pr)$ becomes

$$N(pr) = \frac{1}{\pi\mathrm{i}}\int_0^\infty xm(x)\int_0^\infty \exp\left(\frac{\mathrm{i}p}{c_2}rx\cosh\theta\right)\,\mathrm{d}\theta\,\mathrm{d}x -$$

$$-\frac{1}{\pi\mathrm{i}}\int_0^\infty xm(x)\int_0^\infty \exp\left(-\frac{\mathrm{i}p}{c_2}rx\cosh\theta\right)\,\mathrm{d}\theta\,\mathrm{d}x \tag{6.3.121}$$

† P. 56 of Reference [28].

or, defining the expressions N_1, N_2 in the obvious manner,

$$N(pr) = \frac{1}{\pi i}(N_1 - N_2). \tag{6.3.122}$$

We now wish to carry out the integration with respect to x in (6.3.121). The results will then be a single integral that may be treated by Cagniard's method. Integration in the complex plane will be used. To carry this out, we must determine locations of poles, take note of the branch points, and select a proper contour. For the poles, we consider

$$(2x^2+1)^2 - 4x^2(x^2+\tfrac{1}{3})^{\frac{1}{2}}(x^2+1)^{\frac{1}{2}} = 0, \tag{6.3.123}$$

which is the equivalent of the Rayleigh surface wave equation for this problem. Rationalizing the above gives

$$x^6 + \tfrac{7}{4}x^4 + \tfrac{3}{4}x^2 + \tfrac{3}{32} = 0, \tag{6.3.124}$$

which has roots

$$x^2 = -\frac{3+\sqrt{3}}{4}, \quad -\frac{3-\sqrt{3}}{4}, \quad -\frac{1}{4}. \tag{6.3.125}$$

The roots $x = \pm i(3-\sqrt{3})/2$, $\pm i/2$ are extraneous, arising from the rationalization. Thus, the poles of the integrand are those located at $x = \pm i(3+\sqrt{3})/2$. Branch points exist at $x = \pm i/\sqrt{3}$, $\pm i$, so appropriate branch cuts must be made to make the integrands single-valued.

The contours selected for the evaluation of N_1, N_2 are shown in Fig. 6.20. In the figure the upper contour must be associated with evaluating N_1

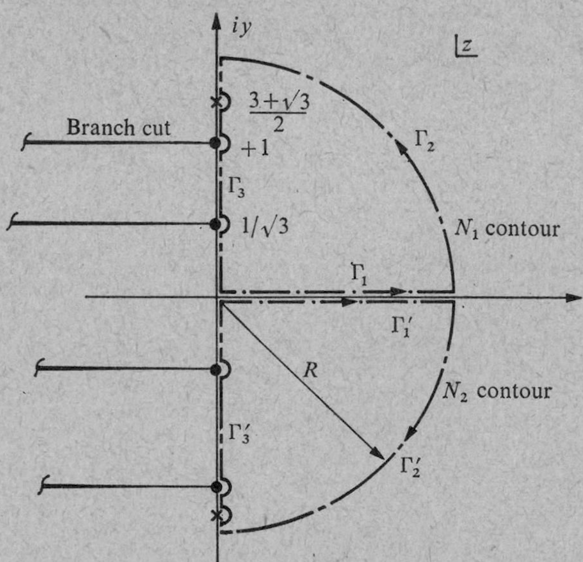

FIG. 6.20. Contours for evaluation of the integrals N_1 and N_2.

because of the positive sign of the exponential in (6.3.121) and vice versa for N_2. We thus have for N_1

$$\int_{\Gamma_1} + \int_{\Gamma_2} + \int_{\Gamma_3} = 0, \tag{6.3.126}$$

since no poles exist within the contour. As $R \to \infty$, the second integral goes to zero, and we have

$$\lim_{R\to\infty} \left(\int_0^R + \int_{iR}^0 \right) = 0. \tag{6.3.127}$$

The first integral is that which we are seeking to evaluate. The presence of the singularities on the path of integration for the second integral shows that this must be interpreted in the Cauchy principal-value sense. Similar considerations hold for integration about Γ_1', Γ_2', Γ_3'. In particular, integration about the poles at $\pm i(3+\sqrt{3})/2$ will yield contributions equal to one-half the residue at that point.

The resulting expressions for N_1, N_2 will then be given by

$$N_1 = -\fint_0^\infty ym(iy) \int_0^\infty \exp\left(\frac{-p}{c_2} ry \cosh\theta\right) d\theta\, dy + \pi i \text{Res}, \tag{6.3.128}$$

$$N_2 = -\fint_0^\infty ym(-iy) \int_0^\infty \exp\left(\frac{-p}{c_2} ry \cosh\theta\right) d\theta\, dy + \pi i \text{Res}, \tag{6.3.129}$$

where the slash mark on the integral sign indicates interpretation in the principal value sense. We combine N_1, N_2 according to (6.3.122), giving

$$N(pr) = \frac{i}{\pi} \fint_0^\infty iy\{m(iy) - m(-iy)\} \int_0^\infty \exp\left(\frac{-p}{c_2} ry \cosh\theta\right) d\theta\, dy, \tag{6.3.130}$$

where the residue expressions have cancelled. Finally, we note that $m(-iy)$ is the complex conjugate of $m(iy)$, so that

$$i\{m(iy) - m(-iy)\} = -2 \operatorname{Im} m(iy), \tag{6.3.131}$$

giving

$$N(pr) = -\frac{2}{\pi} \operatorname{Im} \fint_0^\infty ym(iy) \int_0^\infty \exp\left(-p\frac{ry}{c_2} \cosh\theta\right) d\theta\, dy. \tag{6.3.132}$$

The point of these operations now emerges. The θ-integral of (6.3.132) is coincident with the integral definition of the modified Bessel function of the second kind $K_0(pry)$, where

$$K_0(pry) = \int_0^\infty \exp\left(-\frac{pry}{c_2} \cosh\theta\right) d\theta. \tag{6.3.133}$$

Making the change of variable $(ry/c_2)\cosh\theta = t$, we have

$$\cosh\theta = \frac{c_2}{ry}t, \qquad \sinh\theta = \left\{\left(\frac{c_2}{ry}t\right)^2 - 1\right\}^{\frac{1}{2}}, \qquad d\theta = dt\bigg/\frac{ry}{c_2}\sinh\theta. \quad (6.3.134)$$

Then (6.3.133) becomes

$$K_0(pry) = \int_{ry/c_2}^{\infty} e^{-pt}\left[c_2\,dt\bigg/ry\left\{\left(\frac{c_2}{ry}t\right)^2-1\right\}^{\frac{1}{2}}\right]. \qquad (6.3.135)$$

Cagniard's method may now be used. Thus

$$\mathscr{L}^{-1}(K_0) = \frac{c_2}{ry\left\{\left(\frac{c_2}{ry}t\right)^2-1\right\}^{\frac{1}{2}}}H\langle t-ry/c_2\rangle, \qquad (6.3.136)$$

where

$$\tau = \frac{c_2}{r}t, \qquad (6.3.137)$$

so that

$$\mathscr{L}^{-1}\{K(pry)\} = \frac{c_2}{r(\tau^2-y^2)^{\frac{1}{2}}}H\langle\tau-y\rangle. \qquad (6.3.138)$$

Hence (6.3.132) is of the form

$$N(pr) = -\frac{2}{\pi}\,\mathrm{Im}\int_0^{\infty} ym(\mathrm{i}y)\,dy\,\mathscr{L}\{K(pry)\}, \qquad (6.3.139)$$

so that

$$\mathscr{L}^{-1}\{N(pr)\} = -\frac{2c_2}{r\pi}\,\mathrm{Im}\int_0^{\infty}\frac{ym(\mathrm{i}y)\,dy}{(\tau^2-y^2)^{\frac{1}{2}}}, \qquad (6.3.140)$$

$$m(\mathrm{i}y) = \frac{(\frac{1}{3}-y^2)^{\frac{1}{2}}}{(1-2y^2)^2+4y^2(\frac{1}{3}-y^2)^{\frac{1}{2}}(1-y^2)^{\frac{1}{2}}}. \qquad (6.3.141)$$

The treatment of the principal-value integral in the above is all that remains. We first observe that the imaginary part of $m(\mathrm{i}y)$ changes for various ranges of y; thus

$$y < \frac{1}{\sqrt{3}}; \quad \mathrm{Im}\,m(\mathrm{i}y) = 0,$$

$$\frac{1}{\sqrt{3}} < y < 1; \quad m(\mathrm{i}y) = \mathrm{i}(y^2+\tfrac{1}{3})^{\frac{1}{2}}\frac{\{(1-2y^2)^2-4\mathrm{i}y(y^2-\frac{1}{3})^{\frac{1}{2}}(1-y^2)^{\frac{1}{2}}\}}{1-8y^2+\frac{56}{3}y^4-\frac{32}{3}y^6},$$

$$1 < y; \quad m(\mathrm{i}y) = \mathrm{i}(y^2-\tfrac{1}{3})^{\frac{1}{2}}\frac{\{(1-2y^2)^2+4y^2(y^2-\frac{1}{3})^{\frac{1}{2}}(y^2-1)^{\frac{1}{2}}\}}{1-8y^2+\frac{56}{3}y^4-\frac{32}{3}y^6}. \qquad (6.3.142)$$

We then note that y varies with respect to τ in that $(\tau^2-y^2)^{\frac{1}{2}}$ may become imaginary for $y > \tau$. Hence, the solution for τ in the various regions given in (6.3.142) is (see Pekeris [34]),

$$u_z(r,0,t) = \begin{cases} 0, & (\tau < 1/\sqrt{3}) \\ \dfrac{3Z}{\pi^2\mu r}\displaystyle\int_{1/\sqrt{3}}^{\tau} \frac{y(y^2-\frac{1}{3})^{\frac{1}{2}}(1-2y^2)^2}{(\tau^2-y^2)^{\frac{1}{2}}F(y)}\,\mathrm{d}y, & (1/\sqrt{3} < \tau < 1), \\ \dfrac{3Z}{\pi^2\mu r}\displaystyle\int_{1}^{\tau} \frac{y(y^2-\frac{1}{3})^{\frac{1}{2}}\{(1-2y^2)^2+4y^2(y^2-\frac{1}{3})^{\frac{1}{2}}(y^2-1)^{\frac{1}{2}}\}}{(\tau^2-y^2)^{\frac{1}{2}}F(y)}\,\mathrm{d}y, & \\ & (1 < \tau), \end{cases} \quad (6.3.143)$$

where

$$F(y) = 3-24y^2+56y^4-32y^6 = \tfrac{1}{2}(1-4y^3)(4y^2-3+\sqrt{3})(4y^2-3-\sqrt{3}), \quad (6.3.144)$$

where the integral for $\tau > 1$ is in the principal-value sense because of the pole at $(3+\sqrt{3})/2$. Also recall $\tau = c_2t/r$.

Pekeris then carries out the evaluation of the integrals of the solution by a method involving partial fractions and obtains closed form results. Thus, for the integral appearing in (6.3.143),

$$G_1(\tau) = \int_{1/\sqrt{3}}^{\tau} \frac{y(y^2-\frac{1}{3})^{\frac{1}{2}}(1-2y^2)^2\,\mathrm{d}y}{(\tau^2-y^2)^{\frac{1}{2}}F(y)}, \quad (6.3.145)$$

the change of variables

$$y^2 = \tfrac{1}{3}+\omega^2\sin^2\theta, \qquad \omega^2 = \tau^2-\tfrac{1}{3}, \quad (6.3.146)$$

is made. The integral is thus transformed into

$$G_1(\tau) = \frac{1}{96}\int_0^{\pi/2}\left\{-12+\frac{1}{(\frac{1}{12}+\omega^2\sin^2\theta)}-\frac{B}{(-b+\omega^2\sin^2\theta)}-\frac{C}{(c+\omega^2\sin^2\theta)}\right\}\mathrm{d}\theta, \quad (6.3.147)$$

where

$$B = 3+5/\sqrt{3}, \quad b = 5/12+\sqrt{3}/4, \quad C = 3-5/\sqrt{3}, \quad c = 3/4-5/12. \quad (6.3.148)$$

Using the results that

$$\int_0^{\pi/2}\frac{\mathrm{d}\theta}{(\alpha^2+\omega^2\sin^2\theta)} = \frac{\pi}{2\alpha(\alpha^2+\omega^2)^{\frac{1}{2}}},$$

$$\int_0^{\pi/2}\frac{\mathrm{d}\theta}{(-\beta^2+\omega^2\sin^2\theta)} = \begin{cases} 0, & \beta < \omega \\ \dfrac{-\pi}{2\beta(\beta^2-\omega^2)^{\frac{1}{2}}}, & \beta > \omega \end{cases} \quad (6.3.149)$$

enables the integrals of (6.3.143) to be evaluated. The final results for the horizontal displacement field are

$$u_z(r,0,t) = \begin{cases} 0, & \tau < 1/\sqrt{3} \\ \dfrac{Z}{32\mu\pi r}\left\{6-\left(\dfrac{3}{\tau^2-\frac{1}{4}}\right)^{\frac{1}{2}}-\left(\dfrac{3\sqrt{3}+5}{\dfrac{3}{4}+\dfrac{\sqrt{3}}{4}-\tau^2}\right)^{\frac{1}{2}}+\left(\dfrac{3\sqrt{3}-5}{\tau^2+\dfrac{\sqrt{3}}{4}-\dfrac{3}{4}}\right)^{\frac{1}{2}}\right\}, & 1/\sqrt{3} < \tau < 1 \\ \dfrac{Z}{16\pi\mu r}\left\{6-\left(\dfrac{3\sqrt{3}+5}{\frac{3}{4}+\dfrac{\sqrt{3}}{4}-\tau^2}\right)^{\frac{1}{2}}\right\}, & 1 < \tau < \gamma \\ \dfrac{3Z}{8\pi\mu r}, & \tau > \gamma, \end{cases} \quad (6.3.150)$$

where $\gamma = (3+\sqrt{3})^{\frac{1}{2}}/2$. The various intervals are associated with the arrival of P, S, and surface waves. As will be shown in the next section, a singularity exists in the predicted response at the Rayleigh-wave arrival time.

6.3.4. *Results for transient loads on a half-space*

A number of transient-loading situations have been analysed by various investigators. The intent in this section will be to present the results, in terms of displacement and stress waveforms, of some of these studies.

Consider first the case of a transient, normal load applied at the origin. Near the conclusion of his extensive analysis of the half-space problem, Lamb [22] considered a line loading having the time variation

$$Z(t) = \frac{Z_0}{\pi}\frac{\tau}{t^2+\tau^2}, \quad (6.3.151)$$

where τ is a constant. For τ small, a sharp, impulse-line loading function is described. His results for the horizontal and vertical displacement components on the surface, far from the source, are shown in Fig. 6.21. Time and amplitude scales are not given, but the first disturbance is due to the arrival of the P wave, the second corresponds to the S wave, and the major response is from the arrival of the Rayleigh wave.

Pekeris [34], Lang [23], and Mitra [33] have also considered the half-space under a normal transient loading having a step behaviour in time. Some aspects of the Pekeris analysis have been under consideration in the previous section. His results for the horizontal and vertical displacements are shown in Fig. 6.22. Lang's analysis, although based on a different method than that of Pekeris, yielded essentially the same results. Mitra obtained the response

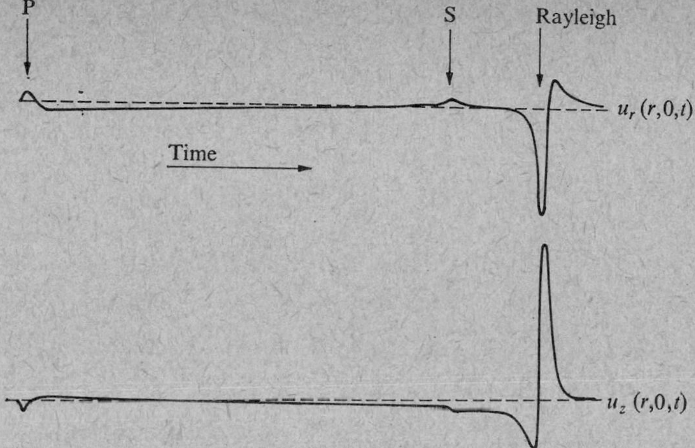

FIG. 6.21. Lamb's results for the horizontal and vertical surface displacements from an impulse-type point loading. (After Lamb [22, Fig. 10].)

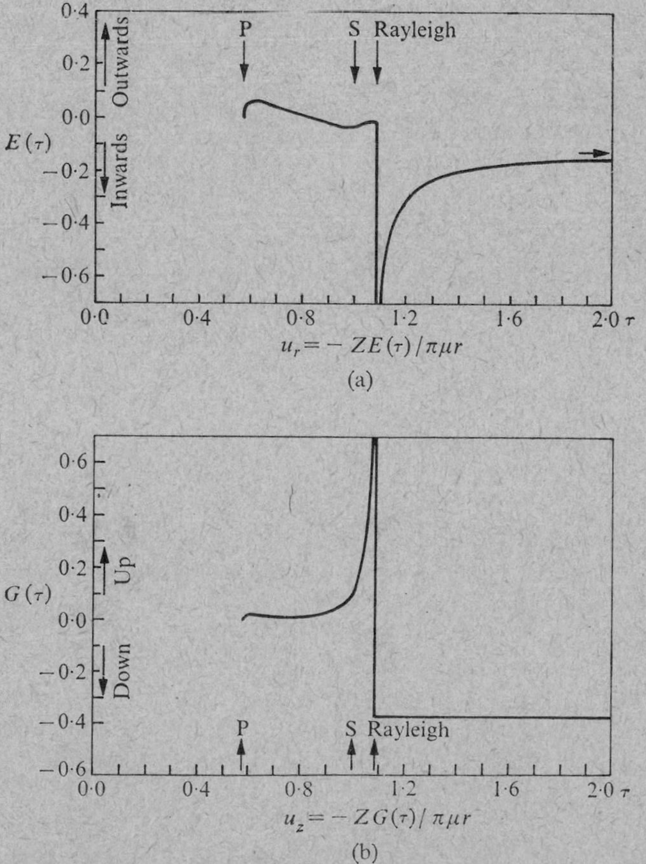

FIG. 6.22. (a) The vertical displacements $u_r(r, 0, t)$ and (b) the horizontal displacements $u_z(r, 0, t)$ resulting from a step loading. Note that $u_r = -ZE(\tau)/\pi\mu r$, $u_z = -ZG(\tau)/\pi\mu r$, where $\tau = c_2t/r$. (After Pekeris [34, Figs. 3 and 4].)

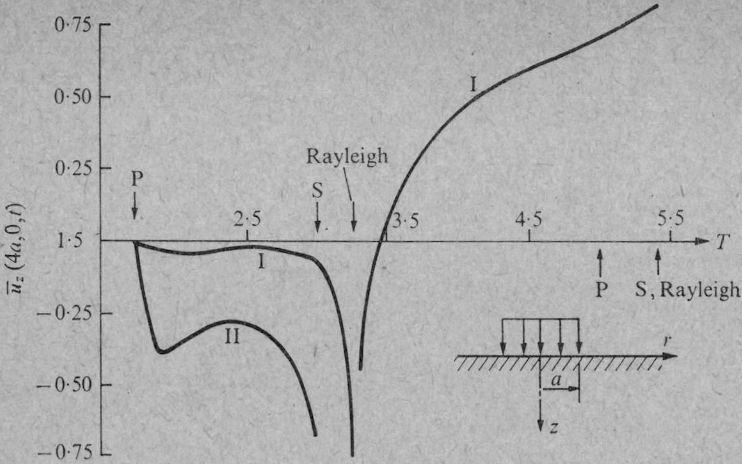

FIG. 6.23. Vertical displacement $\bar{u}_z(r, 0, t)$ at $r = 4a$ resulting from an impulse loading $P\delta(t)$ applied to a circular area $r \leqslant a$ on the surface of a half-space, where $\bar{u}_z = \pi^2\mu u_z/Pc_2$ and $T = c_2t/a$. (After Mitra [33, Fig. 3].)

to a normal load applied impulsively ($\delta(t)$ time behaviour) to a circular region $r \leqslant a$. His method of analysis was the Cagniard technique. The results for the vertical displacement $u_z(r, 0, t)$ are shown in Fig. 6.23 for $r = 4a$ as curve I. The response is more complicated owing to the finite source size. Thus, P wave contributions first start at $T = \sqrt{3}$ and continue until $T = 5$, when the first S wave contributions from the furthest point $r = 5a$ of the pressure area arrive. The first S waves arrive at $T = 3$ followed closely at $T = 6/(3+\sqrt{3})^{\frac{1}{2}}$ by the first Rayleigh wave contributions.

Another aspect of the response of the half-space may be brought out in conjunction with the earlier Fig. 6.19. Shown are the hemispherical P and S wavefronts followed by the Rayleigh surface wave. In addition, there is a wavefront known as the 'head wave' or *von Schmidt wave*, having a wavefront originating from the intersection point of the P wave with the free surface and being tangent to the SV wave surface. Fung [13, p. 225] points out that these waves can be understood on the basis of Huygen's principle, with the P wave acting as a continual wave source, generating both P and SV waves. Another possible explanation is that, near the surface, the wave system is that resulting from a P wave at grazing incidence (see Fig. 6.17).

The case of normal impact on a half-space has been analysed. Thus Hunter [19] has studied the case of a spherical ball impacting the surface of a half-space.† Using Hertz contact theory and a Fourier synthesis based on the results of Miller and Pursey [30], he determines the energy absorbed during the impact. It is found that the loss of impact energy to stress waves

† This problem is analogous to that considered in § 2.4 for the impact of a ball on a rod.

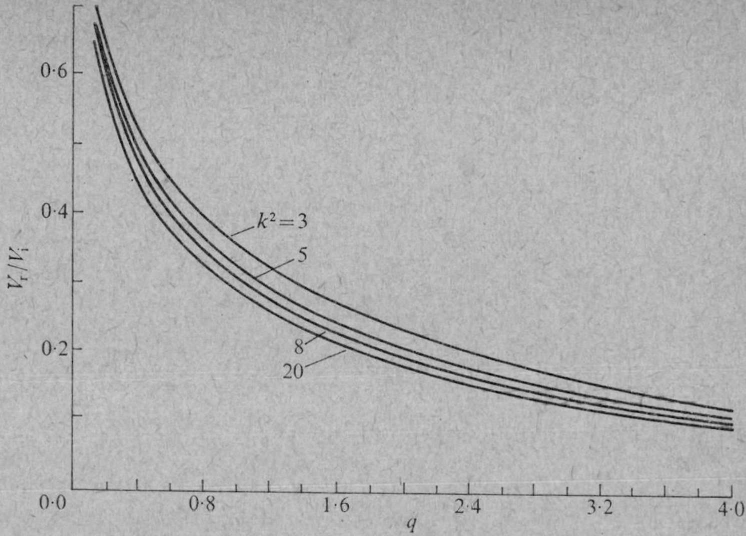

FIG. 6.24. Ratio of rebound to impact velocity, V_r/V_i, versus disc parameter $q = 2\rho_s r_0/\rho_d h$ for various k^2. (After Gutzwiller [17, Fig. 6].)

in an elastic collision process is very small (less than 1 per cent).† Gutzwiller [17] has considered the impact of a rigid, circular disc on a half-space. He introduces the concept of 'mode of vibration', whereby a transient in the coupled disc half-space can be described by a superposition of modes. His main results are for the ratio of rebound to impact velocity (V_r/V_i) for various discs impacting different elastic media and are shown in Fig. 6.24, where the parameter q is given by $q = 2\rho_s r_0/\rho_d h$. Here r_0, h, ρ_d are the radius, height, and density of the disc and ρ_s is the density of the elastic media. The parameter $k^2 = (\lambda+2\mu)/\mu$.

The analysis of a concentrated, tangential force, with step behaviour in time, has been carried out by Chao [3]. He obtained the response along $r = 0$ and on the surface $z = 0$. The problem possesses only x,z-plane symmetry, so that there are u_r, u_θ, and u_z displacements. Fig. 6.25(a)–(c) shows his results for the surface displacements $\bar{u}_r$, $\bar{u}_\theta$, $\bar{u}_z$, where

$$\bar{u}_r = \pi\mu r u_r/F\cos\theta, \quad \bar{u}_\theta = \pi\mu r u_\theta/F\sin\theta, \quad \bar{u}_z = \pi\mu r u_z/F\cos\theta, \qquad (6.3.152)$$

and F is the magnitude of the applied load. The non-dimensional time τ is $\tau = c_2 t/r$. Chao points out that, in directions perpendicular to the applied force ($\theta = \pm\pi/2$), $u_r = u_z = 0$ and u_θ decays rapidly with distance, so that no strong surface waves are noted in these directions.

Problems of torsional loads applied to the surface of the half-space have been considered by several investigators. As mentioned earlier, Miller and

† See § 6.5 on experimental results.

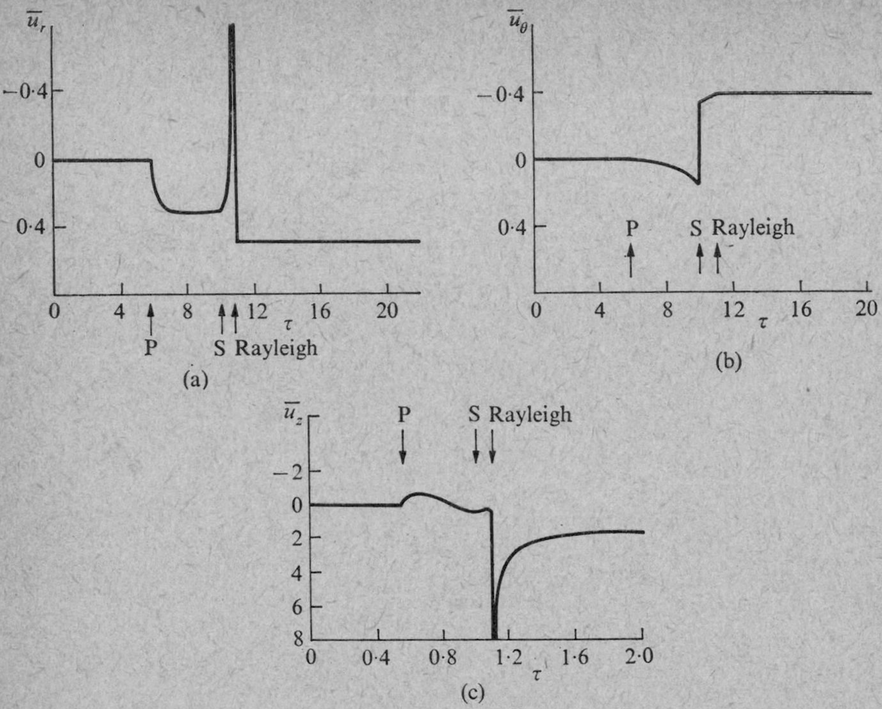

FIG. 6.25. The surface displacements (a) $\bar{u}_r$, (b) $\bar{u}_\theta$, (c) $\bar{u}_z$ versus τ, resulting from a tangential point load F suddenly applied at the origin, where $\bar{\tau} = c_2t/r$. (After Chao ([3, Figs. 3, 4, and 5].)

Pursey [30] considered a harmonic torsional loading. Mitra [32] has considered the case of an impulsive twisting moment applied to a rigid die attached to the half-space. Hill [18] solved the case of a rigid sphere imbedded in the surface of an elastic half-space, where an impulse torque is applied to the sphere. Eason [10] has considered an impulse torque applied to a half-space. Several distributions of stress yielding the resulting torque are considered. His Cases 1, 2, 3 are as follows:

$$\text{Case 1: } \tau_{r\theta} = \begin{cases} Qr, & r < a \\ 0, & r > a, \end{cases}$$

$$\text{Case 2: } \tau_{r\theta} = \begin{cases} Q/r, & r < a \\ 0, & r > a, \end{cases}$$

$$\text{Case 3: } \tau_{r\theta} = \begin{cases} Qr/(a^2-r^2)^{\frac{1}{2}}, & r < a \\ 0, & r > a, \end{cases} \tag{6.3.153}$$

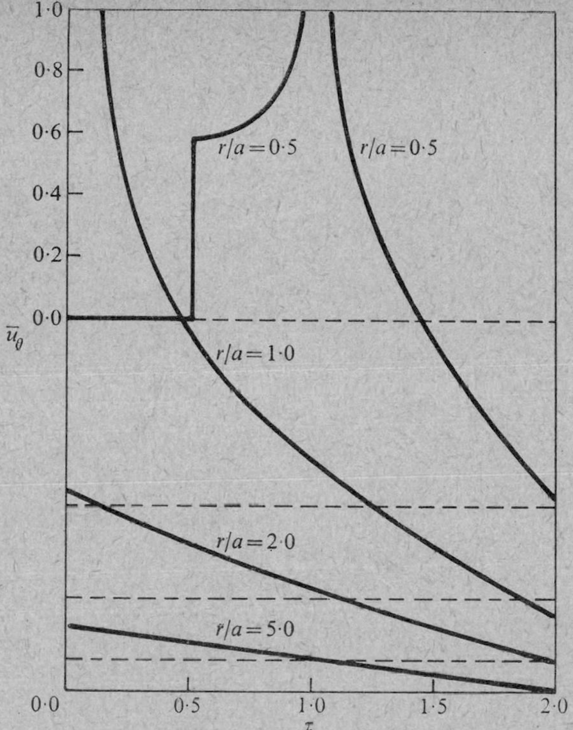

FIG. 6.26. Surface displacement $u_\theta(r, 0, t)$ resulting from a torsional impulse applied at the origin for the Case 3 stress distribution. (After Eason [10, Fig. 3].)

where Q is a constant. The time variation in all cases is that of the Dirac delta function. The first case was previously considered by Mitra. Eason's results for Case 3 are shown in Fig. 6.26. The results are given in terms of $\bar{u}_\theta$ versus τ, where

$$\bar{u}_\theta = -\mu u_\theta/Qa, \qquad \tau = (c_2t+a-r)/a. \tag{6.3.154}$$

In the figure the response is shown at $r/a = 0{\cdot}5$, $1{\cdot}0$, $2{\cdot}0$, and $5{\cdot}0$. All curves are to the same scale, but have been displaced vertically for clarity of presentation. The dashed lines in each case correspond to $\bar{u}_r = 0$. Note that $r/a = 0{\cdot}5$ is within the circle of the applied load.

All of the considerations thus far have been for the case of a surface source. Buried-source problems are of considerable interest and have been studied by many, including, initially, Lamb [22]. Results have been obtained for both line and point loadings. Ewing, Jardetsky, and Press [11] review many aspects of the analysis in this area. Although the analysis is quite complicated, it is of interest to consider certain results for the buried line source. Consider

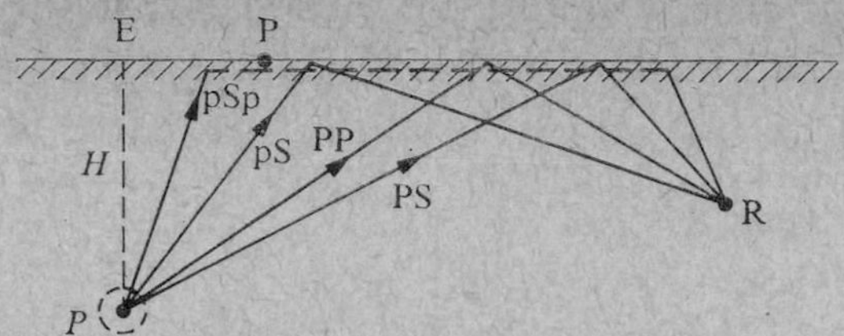

FIG. 6.27. Various propagation–reflection paths for P and S waves arriving at a receiver R as generated by a P wave source. (Based on Ewing, Jardetsky, and Press [11, Fig. 2.12].)

the case of a P wave source, as in Fig. 6.27, with a receiver R located some distance away and also below the surface. Analysis of the branch-cut integrals shows that the signal arriving at the receiver is in terms of P and S wave contributions arriving through various propagation, reflection paths. Thus, the first four arrival paths are shown, labelled as PP, PS, pS, pSp. The PP wave is formed from the initial source P wave and a P wave reflection. The PS wave is the initial P wave and an S wave reflection. The pS wave is also the initial P wave and an S wave reflection. The PS and pS cases differ in that the PS wave travels most of the path as a P wave, the pS wave travels mostly as an S wave. Finally, the pSp wave starts as a P wave, travels part way along the surface as an S wave, and then along the final portion as a P wave.

Another aspect of interest reviewed in Reference [11] concerns the first appearance of the Rayligh wave from a buried source, and results from a steepest descent analysis. Referring to Fig. 6.27, it is found that the minimum distance is EP, where $\mathrm{EP} = c_{\mathrm{R}}H/(c_1^2 - c_{\mathrm{R}}^2)^{\frac{1}{2}}$. This represents the location such that the time $\mathrm{EP}/c_{\mathrm{R}} = (H^2 + \mathrm{EP}^2)^{\frac{1}{2}}/c_1$.

Pekeris [35] has considered the case of a buried point load applied vertically and varying in a step fashion with time. In a later paper, Pekeris and Lifson [36] presented a number of results for this case. All results were obtained for the vertical and horizontal displacements at the surface due to the source at a depth H. Before considering these, it is useful to further consider the waves that may arrive at a point from a buried source. As shown in Fig. 6.28(a), an S wave arriving at a point r on the surface at less than the

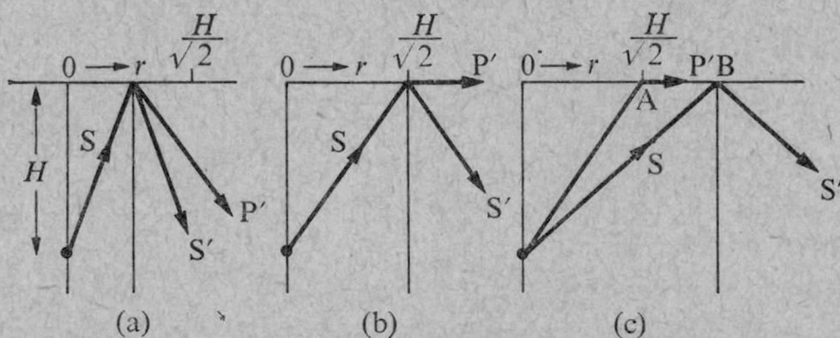

FIG. 6.28. Reflection of an S wave from the source at depth H, where S arrives at (a) less than, (b) equal to, and (c) greater than the critical angle. (After Pekeris and Lifson [36, Fig. 1].)

critical angle reflects as a P′ and S′ wave. At the critical angle given by (see (6.1.57)) $k \sin \theta_2 = 1$ the P wave is parallel to the surface, as shown in Fig. 6.28(b). For $\lambda = \mu$, the case considered by Pekeris and Lifson, $k = \sqrt{3}$ and the critical radius is $r = H/\sqrt{2}$. For values of r greater than the critical value, an S wave continues to arrive directly. However, an SP′ wave, where P′ is along the surface, can precede the S wave arrival. In addition to the S wave behaviour, a P wave arriving directly from the source represents the first signal. Much of this is similar to the behaviour presented in Fig. 6.27 for a buried source and a buried receiver.

The vertical and horizontal surface displacements are shown in Fig. 6.29(a)–(d) for various distances, r/H from the epicentre of the loading. The time base is given by τ, where $\tau = c_2 t/R$ and $R = (r^2+H^2)^{\frac{1}{2}}$. The normalized displacements $\bar{u}_z(r, 0, t)$, $\bar{u}_r(r, 0, t)$ are plotted, where

$$u_z(r, 0, t) = \frac{3Z}{\pi^2 \mu R} \bar{u}_z, \qquad u_r(r, 0, t) = -\frac{3Z}{\pi^2 \mu R} \bar{u}_r \tag{6.3.155}$$

and where Z is the applied force, acting in the downward direction at a depth H. The arrival of P, S, SP, and Rayleigh waves are marked on the displacement curves. The arrival of the P wave is unambiguous in the various cases. However, depending on location, the S or the SP wave may arrive first, as suggested by the previous discussion. It is to be noted that the Rayleigh wave does not appear when r is small, in accord with the 'minimum distance' discussion pertaining to Fig. 6.28. Also shown in Fig. 6.29(b) and (d) are the results for a surface source ($H = 0$).

6.4. Waves in layered media

The propagation and reflection of waves in a homogeneous, isotropic half-space represents a large class of problems of practical interest, particularly in the field of seismology. In many situations waves originate and propagate in media having a layered structure, where interfaces between dissimilar materials exist. Again, seismic waves in a layered earth are an example, but important applications in structures exist, such as waves in composite plates and shells. The large class of problems for a 'simple' half-space, such as reflection of plane waves and source problems, now have their more complicated and numerous counterparts in layered media problems. The very extent of the resulting class of problems precludes more than a cursory review in this presentation. One is referred to Ewing, Jardetsky, and Press [11] and Brekhovskikh [1] as source books devoted nearly in their entirety to this subject.

The simplest situation in this area consists of two semi-infinite media in contact. Such a situation, strictly speaking, is not a layered system since neither media possesses two parallel boundaries. Nevertheless, this natural extension of the single, semi-infinite media problem is a pre-requisite to the

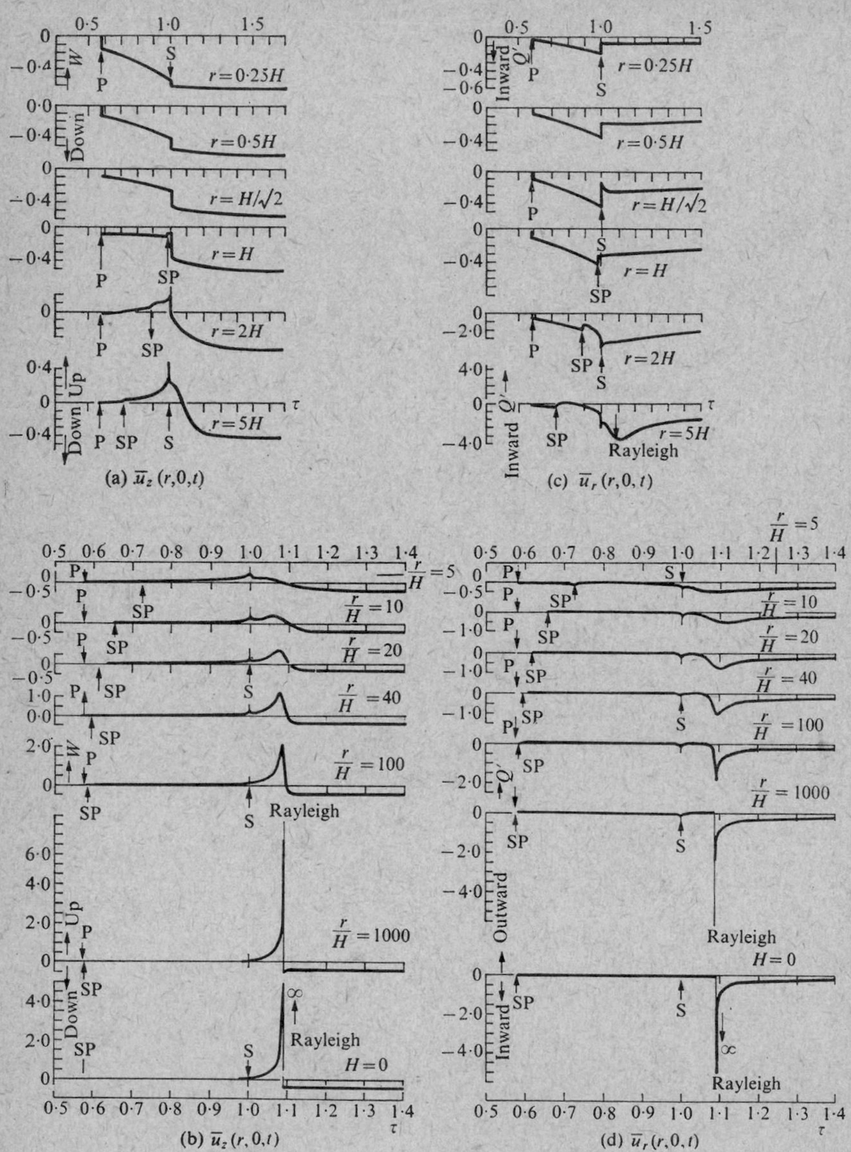

FIG. 6.29. (a) and (b) Vertical displacement components $\bar{u}_z$ and (c) and (d) horizontal displacements $\bar{u}_r$ for a concentrated force applied downward at a depth **H** with a step-function time behaviour. (After Pekeris and Lifson [36, Figs. 2–5].)

analysis of layered systems. The basic aspects of the propagation and transmission of plane waves across the interface between two semi-infinite media will be reviewed, including the various interface conditions that may exist. Certain results of waves from sources will be discussed. In the case of distinctly layered media, one situation will be analysed in some detail. This will be the case of SH waves in a layer overlaying a half-space. Such waves are also known as Love waves. Some discussion will be given to other situations.

6.4.1. *Two semi-infinite media in contact—plane waves*

When propagating waves encounter a boundary between two media, reflected waves occur, somewhat as in the case of encountering a free surface. In addition, energy is transmitted across the boundary in the form of refracted waves. The approach taken in the study of wave reflection–refraction in two semi-infinite media in contact is to consider propagating plane harmonic waves encountering the boundary.

Thus, consider two media in contact along the plane $y = 0$. The properties of the lower media are given by λ, μ, ρ and those of the upper media by λ', μ', ρ'. Proceeding in a manner quite analogous to the case of waves in a half-space, we have the governing equations for the lower media given by (6.1.1)–(6.1.12). For the upper media, we may reference the same equations, except that everywhere the quantities u_i, Φ, H_i, c_1, c_2, τ_{ij}, λ, μ, must be replaced by primed quantities. If we reduce our considerations to those of plane strain, eqns (6.1.14), (6.1.15) pertain, with the lower and upper media again being differentiated by unprimed and primed notation.

Considering now the case of plane harmonic waves, we parallel eqns (6.1.21)–(6.1.25). Thus for the lower media we still have the plane-wave expressions (6.1.24) and (6.1.25). For the upper media, we will have similar expressions except that Φ, A_1, A_2, H_z, B_1, B_2, α, β are replaced by primed quantities. Expression of all plane-wave results in terms of incidence, reflection, and refraction angles θ_1, θ_2, θ_1', θ_2', such as in (6.1.28) and (6.1.29) is also possible, but will not be used here. If we take the viewpoint that plane waves are propagating toward the boundary from the lower media, then all of the terms A_1, A_2, B_1, B_2 remain in the solutions. However, only two terms A_1', B_1' would remain in the primed solution, since the A_2', B_2' expressions would represent waves approaching the boundary from negative infinity. Thus, to summarize, the plane hamonic wave solutions are

$$\Phi = A_1 e^{i(\xi x - \alpha y - \omega t)} + A_2 e^{i(\xi x + \alpha y - \omega t)}, \tag{6.4.1}$$

$$H_z = B_1 e^{i(\xi x - \beta y - \omega t)} + B_2 e^{i(\xi x + \beta y - \omega t)}, \tag{6.4.2}$$

$$\Phi' = A_1' e^{i(\xi x - \alpha' y - \omega t)}, \qquad H_z' = B_1' e^{i(\xi x - \beta' y - \omega t)}, \tag{6.4.3}$$

where

$$\alpha^2 = \frac{\omega^2}{c_1^2} - \xi^2, \qquad \beta^2 = \frac{\omega^2}{c_2^2} - \xi^2, \tag{6.4.4}$$

$$\alpha'^2 = \frac{\omega^2}{c_1'^2} - \xi^2, \qquad \beta'^2 = \frac{\omega^2}{c_2'^2} - \xi^2. \tag{6.4.5}$$

The boundary conditions existing at the interface must now be specified. Two conditions are of particular interest in practical situations. The first is the case where the two media are bonded together. Under such conditions, continuity of displacement and stress across the interface is required. Thus, for a bonded interface, we have

$$u_x(x, 0, t) = u_x'(x, 0, t), \qquad u_y(x, 0, t) = u_y'(x, 0, t),$$

$$\tau_{yy}(x, 0, t) = \tau_{yy}'(x, 0, t), \qquad \tau_{xy}(x, 0, t) = \tau_{xy}'(x, 0, t). \tag{6.4.6}$$

The second condition is the case of a lubricated interface where transverse slip may occur. For this condition, we have

$$\begin{gathered} u_y(x, 0, t) = u_y'(x, 0, t), \qquad \tau_{yy}(x, 0, t) = \tau_{yy}'(x, 0, t), \\ \tau_{xy}(x, 0, t) = \tau_{xy}'(x, 0, t) = 0. \end{gathered} \tag{6.4.7}$$

This last case is of particular interest in ultrasonics, where transducers used to launch and receive waves into and from a solid are often coupled by an oil or grease film to the media.

Considering, then, the case of a bonded boundary, so that conditions (6.4.6) apply, we substitute the solutions (6.4.1)–(6.4.3) in the expressions for the displacements and stresses as given by (6.1.10), (6.1.11), and (6.1.14). Thus

$$u_x = u_x': \quad \xi(A_1+A_2)-\beta(B_1-B_2) = \xi A_1'-\beta' B_1', \tag{6.4.8}$$

$$u_y = u_y': \quad \alpha(A_1-A_2)+\xi(B_1+B_2) = \alpha' A_1'+\xi B_2', \tag{6.4.9}$$

$$\begin{aligned} \tau_{yy} = \tau_{yy}': \quad & \mu\{(\beta^2-\xi^2)(A_1+A_2)+2\xi\beta(B_1-B_2)\} \\ & = \mu'\{(\beta'^2-\xi^2)A_1'+2\xi\beta' B_1'\}, \end{aligned} \tag{6.4.10}$$

$$\begin{aligned} \tau_{xy} = \tau_{xy}': \quad & \mu\{2\xi\alpha(A_1-A_2)-(\beta^2-\xi^2)(B_1+B_2)\} \\ & = \mu'\{2\xi\alpha' A_1'-(\beta'^2-\xi^2)B_1'\}. \end{aligned} \tag{6.4.11}$$

The left-hand sides of (6.4.10) and (6.4.11) are identical to the boundary-condition equations (6.1.30) and (6.1.31), except for the multiplying parameter μ. Amplitude ratios immediately follow from the preceding equations. If we presume that we have an incident P wave, so that $B_1 = 0$, there follows the ratios A_2/A_1, B_2/A_1, A_1'/A_1, B_1'/A_1. If we presume an incident SV wave, so that $A_1 = 0$, the amplitude ratios A_2/B_1, B_2/B_1, A_1'/B_1, B_1'/B_1 follow. Thus, for an incident wave, either P or SV, there are generally two reflected and two refracted waves.

The angles of reflection, refraction may be readily obtained. We may write (6.4.1) and (6.4.2) in the forms (6.1.28) and (6.1.29), and for Φ', H_z' write

$$\Phi' = A_1' \exp\{i\gamma_1'(\sin\theta_1' x - \cos\theta_1' y - c_1' t)\}, \tag{6.4.12}$$

$$H_z' = B_1' \exp\{i\gamma_2'(\sin\theta_2' x - \cos\theta_2' y - c_2' t)\}, \tag{6.4.13}$$

where θ_1', θ_2' are the angles of the refracted wave normals relative to the vertical axis. We then have, from the requirement that the boundary conditions at the interface be independent of x and t, that

$$\gamma_1 \sin\theta_1 = \gamma_2 \sin\theta_2 = \gamma_1' \sin\theta_1' = \gamma_2' \sin\theta_2' \tag{6.4.14}$$

and also $\gamma_1 c_1 = \gamma_2 c_2 = \gamma_1' c_1' = \gamma_2' c_2' = \omega$. We presume that the frequency ω and incidence angle θ_1 or θ_2 of the incoming wave is specified. Thus, suppose the values ω, θ_1 are given. Then $\gamma_2, \gamma_1', \gamma_2'$ are found from $\gamma_2 = \omega/c_2, \gamma_1' = \omega/c_1'$, $\gamma_2' = \omega/c_2'$. The reflection and refraction angles follow from (6.4.14). The amplitude ratios follow from results obtained from (6.4.8) to (6.4.11). To obtain the parameters α, β, α', β', ξ we merely use

$$\alpha = \gamma_1 \cos\theta_1, \quad \beta = \gamma_2 \cos\theta_2, \quad \alpha' = \gamma_1' \cos\theta_1', \quad \beta' = \gamma_2' \cos\theta_2', \tag{6.4.15}$$

and the fact that $\xi = \gamma_1 \sin\theta_1 = \gamma_2 \sin\theta_2 = \gamma_1' \sin\theta_1' = \gamma_2' \sin\theta_2'$. Alternatively, the amplitude ratio expressions originally may be derived in terms of $\theta_1, \theta_2, \theta_1', \theta_2'$ as was done for the half-space. The resulting general reflection–refraction situation involving an incident wave, two reflected waves and two refracted waves, with known angles of incidence, reflection and refraction, is shown in Fig. 6.30 for the case of incident P and SV waves. There are a number of special circumstances of wave reflection–refraction that can occur,

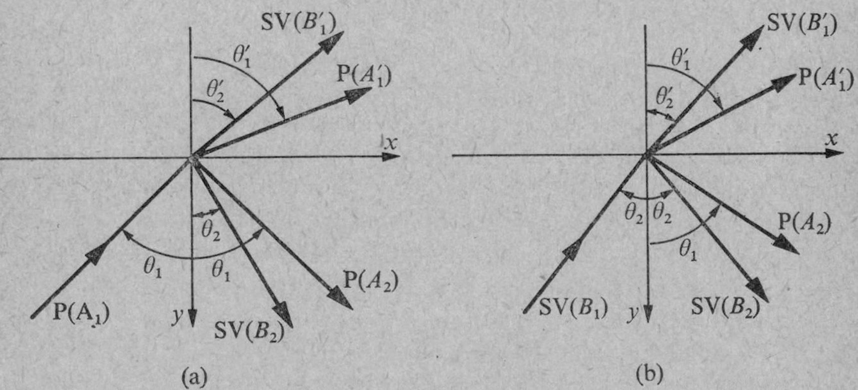

FIG. 6.30. Reflection–refraction of plane waves at the boundary of two media for incident; (a) P waves and (b) SV waves.

depending on the type of incident wave, the incidence angle, the material properties of the two media, and in which of the two media the incident wave is travelling. In particular, for incident SV waves, critical angles may exist beyond which the reflected P wave may disappear.

In addition to the wave-reflection problem, one might inquire whether the analogue of Rayleigh waves for a half-space can exist for two semi-infinite media in contact. Evidently Love [26] investigated the possibility and found that such waves could exist. Stonely [40] more thoroughly investigated this wave-type and found that the existence of such a wave required that the shear-wave velocities of the two media had to be nearly the same. This generalized Rayleigh wave is usually called the Stonely wave.

6.4.2. *Waves in layered media—Love waves*

Suppose we consider a homogeneous, isotropic semi-infinite media. Consider then a layer of some thickness h_1 and different material properties λ_1, μ_1, ρ_1 to be attached to the surface of the semi-infinite media. Consider the additional layers $h_2, h_3, \ldots$ of properties $\lambda_2, \mu_2, \rho_2, \lambda_3, \mu_3, \rho_3, \ldots$ to be added. Such a system constitutes the general layered media. The propagation of waves in such a system, with multiple reflections and refractions occurring at the interfaces according to the laws for a single interface are, of course, most complicated. In fact, the case of waves in a single layered system represents a more complicated situation than the waves in plates, an area to be considered in Chapter 8. References [1] and [11] again give an extensive treatment. One special case, easily analysed, of classic interest and having considerable practical application will now be considered.

In particular, we shall consider the propagation of SH waves in a half-space overlaid by a thin solid layer. As is the case for many problems in wave propagation the original impetus for study in this area came from seismology. One of the first established facts of seismology was the presence of large transverse (that is, horizontal) components of displacement in the main tremor of an earthquake. However, such displacements are not a feature of Rayleigh waves, which contain displacements only in the vertical plane. Furthermore, surface SH waves are not possible. It follows that the actual conditions in the earth must differ in some essential respect from those of an homogeneous, isotropic half-space. Love [26] suspected that such waves were a consequence of a layered construction of the earth, and that they consisted of SH waves trapped in a superficial layer and propagated by multiple reflections within the layer. The essential features of this analysis will be shown in the following.

Consider an isotropic half-space with an overlying layer of thickness T, bonded to the semi-infinite media at the interface $y = 0$. The situation is shown in Fig. 6.31. We use the prime notation to refer to the semi-infinite media having properties μ', c_2' and unprimed notation for the layer, having

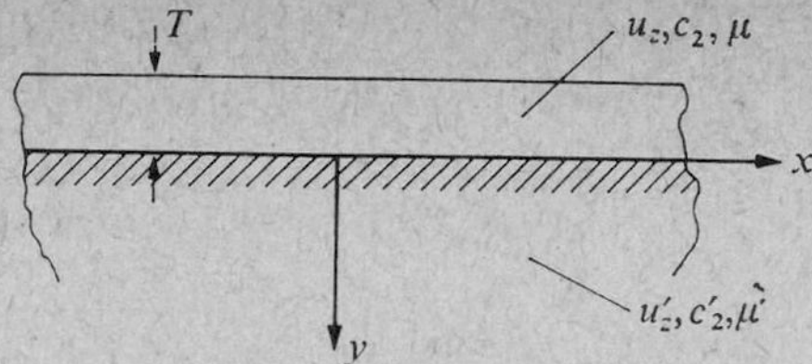

FIG. 6.31. A layer of thickness T over the semi-infinite media.

properties μ, c_2. We will consider only u'_z, u_z displacements so that

$$u_z = u_z(x, y, t), \qquad u_x = u_y = 0, \tag{6.4.16}$$

$$u'_z = u'_z(x, y, t), \qquad u'_x = u'_y = 0. \tag{6.4.17}$$

The governing equations may be written in terms of potential functions. However, as was found earlier for SH waves, it is possible and more direct to work with the displacement equations of motion, which reduce simply to

$$\nabla^2 u_z = \frac{1}{c_2^2}\frac{\partial^2 u_z}{\partial t^2}, \qquad \nabla^2 u'_z = \frac{1}{c_2'^2}\frac{\partial^2 u'_z}{\partial t^2}, \tag{6.4.18}$$

were $\nabla^2 = \partial^2/\partial x^2 + \partial^2/\partial y^2$. The non-trivial boundary conditions for the problem are

$$\begin{aligned} &\tau_{yz} = 0, \qquad y = -T, \\ &\tau_{yz} = \tau'_{yz}, \qquad u_z = u'_z, \qquad y = 0. \end{aligned} \tag{6.4.19}$$

For solutions to (6.4.18) we let

$$u_z = U(y)e^{i\xi(x-ct)}, \qquad u'_z = U'(y)e^{i\xi(x-ct)}, \tag{6.4.20}$$

and obtain

$$\frac{d^2U}{dy^2} + \beta^2 U = 0, \qquad \frac{d^2U'}{dy^2} - \beta'^2 U' = 0, \tag{6.4.21}$$

where

$$\beta^2 = \xi^2(c^2/c_2^2 - 1), \qquad \beta'^2 = \xi^2(1 - c^2/c_2'^2). \tag{6.4.22}$$

The resulting solutions are

$$u_z = A_1 e^{i(\xi x - \beta y - \omega t)} + A_2 e^{i(\xi x + \beta y - \omega t)}, \tag{6.4.23}$$

$$u'_z = B_1 e^{-\beta' y} e^{i(\xi x - \omega t)}. \tag{6.4.24}$$

The solution (6.4.23) represents plane waves propagating back and forth within the layer. The solution (6.4.24) (an $\exp(+\beta' y)$ term has been discarded) gives a wave that retains its energy close to the interface. A plane wave solution, based on $\beta'^2 < 0$, could be selected instead for u'_z. However, such a wave system would not be capable of giving the behaviour observed in seismology, since it would represent refracted waves carrying energy away from the layer. Such a wave system would quickly lose its energy and not be of significance at any distance. Thus the question is, are the solutions (6.4.23) and (6.4.24), capable of describing the physical phenomena, able to satisfy the boundary conditions.

We substitute the solutions in the boundary conditions (6.4.19) and obtain

$$\tau_{yz} = 0: \qquad e^{i\beta T}A_1 - e^{-i\beta T}A_2 = 0, \tag{6.4.25}$$

$$u_z = u_z': \qquad A_1 + A_2 - B_1 = 0, \tag{6.4.26}$$

$$\tau_{yz} = \tau_{yz}': \quad -i\mu A_1 + i\mu\beta A_2 - \mu'\beta' B_1 = 0. \tag{6.4.27}$$

The resulting determinant of coefficients gives

$$\mu'\beta' - \mu\beta \tan \beta T = 0. \tag{6.4.28}$$

Using (6.4.22) this may be put in the form

$$\mu'(1-(c/c_2')^2)^{\frac{1}{2}} - \mu((c/c_2)^2-1)^{\frac{1}{2}} \tan \xi T((c/c_2)^2-1)^{\frac{1}{2}} = 0. \tag{6.4.29}$$

By using the relation $\omega = \xi c$, this result may be expressed in terms of frequency and wavenumber.

The first observation is simply that Love waves, as SH waves in a layer are generally called, are dispersive. That is, the roots of (6.4.29) for successive values of ξ will result in $c = c(\xi)$ or in $\omega = \omega(\xi)$. The multiple branches of the tangent function also suggest that multiple roots will exist for any given ξ. Thus the dispersion curves and frequency spectrum should have multiple branches, corresponding to various modes of propagation. We note that, as $\gamma \to 0$ in (6.4.29), $c \to c_2'$. Thus, as the wavelength becomes large compared, say to the thickness T, the Love waves take on the velocity of the lower media.

In addition to applications in seismology, Love waves also find application in delay lines, as do Rayleigh waves. Thus, by depositing thin layers over substrates, another type of surface-wave delay line results.

6.5. Experimental studies on waves in semi-infinite media

Experimental investigations on waves in semi-infinite media are very wide in scope, ranging from ultrasonic excitation of high-frequency waves in small specimens to seismological studies of the earth. Only a most limited assortment of results will be given here, with the main attention being given to various aspects of surface waves.

6.5.1. *Waves into a half-space from a surface source*

Photo-elasticity has been used in a number of studies of waves propagated into a half-space from an impulsive surface source. One of the first was reported by Dally, Durelli, and Riley [5], where a low-modulus urethane rubber plate was dynamically loaded by a small explosive charge and the dynamic fringe propagation recorded by a high-speed (6000 frames per

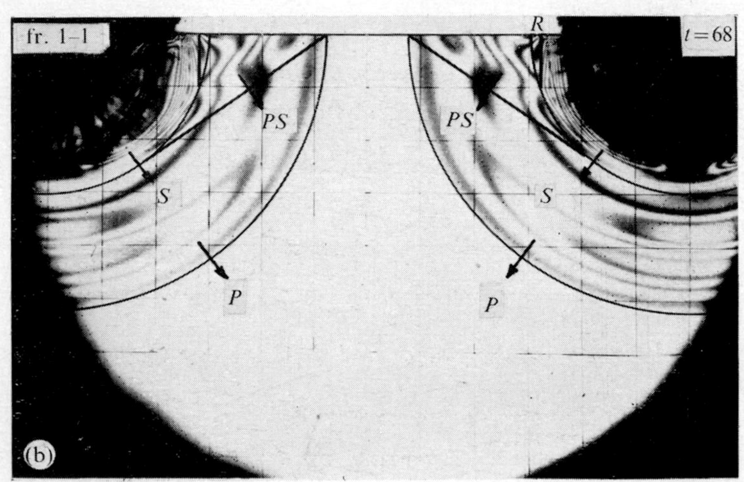

FIG. 6.32 (b)

second) camera. In a later photo-elastic study, Dally [4] considered a half-plane subjected to two loads placed some distance apart and obtained results on the development and interaction of the two waves. Before wave interaction occurs, the individual wave systems are the same as for the half-space under point loading, so it is of interest to study the results from that standpoint. It should be noted here that several of the later cited photo-elastic studies on waves in wedges or past discontinuities also present, for reference purposes, the results for a simple half-space.

The geometry of the plate and the placement of small charges of lead azide (PbN_6) are shown in Fig. 6.32(a). The charges were simultaneously

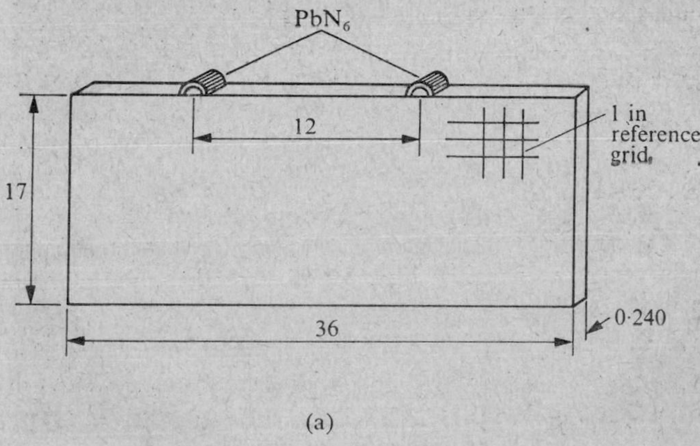

FIG. 6.32. (a) Photo-elastic plate and loading configuration employed in study of a double-loaded half-plane and (b: see separate plate) fringe pattern from a double-loaded half-plane before wave interaction has occurred. (After Dally [4, Fig. 1B, 6A].)

detonated and the dynamic fringe patterns recorded by a multiple-spark Cranz–Schardin camera operating at 127 000 frames per second. An early stage in the development of the wave system, before interaction has occurred, is shown in Fig. 6.32(b). Superimposed on the fringe system are solid lines showing positions of the various wavefronts. Thus, the cylindrical-fronted P and S wave systems are so indicated in the figure. The straight-crested PS wave is the von Schmidt head wave, arising from reflection of a grazing-incidence P wave. The Rayleigh surface wave is indicated by R. Because of the rather early stage of wave development at the instant shown, the Rayleigh wave has not yet clearly separated from the S wave. For the material constants of the CR-39 photo-elastic plate, the various wave velocities are $c_1 = 7{\cdot}63\times10^4$ in. s^{-1}, $c_2 = 4{\cdot}35\times10^4$ in. s^{-1}, and $c_R = 4{\cdot}0\times10^4$ in. s^{-1} (or $1{\cdot}94$, $1{\cdot}10$, and $1{\cdot}01\times10^3$ m s^{-1}, respectively). It is seen that the photo-elastic technique, with the capability of viewing the entire field, offers an excellent technique for qualitatively evaluating the stress field. Data on the stresses is easily obtainable along the boundary where one of the principal stresses is zero and the stress–optic law $\sigma_1 - \sigma_2 = Nf_\sigma/h$ reduces to $\sigma_1 = Nf_\sigma/h$.

The experimental conditions of edge-loading a plate used in photo-elastic studies do not exactly correspond to a line-loading of a half-space, since plane-strain conditions in the thickness direction do not prevail. In static photo-elastic studies, plane-stress conditions are assumed to hold in the plate thickness direction. Under dynamic loading conditions, wavelengths of the order of the plate thickness may occur, so that the plane-stress assumption is less valid. Dally and Riley [7] have attempted to circumvent this problem by using the embedded polariscope technique. This latter approach has enabled them to study directly the three-dimensional problem of a point load on a half-space using photo-elastic techniques.

In addition to the simple half-space, photo-elastic investigations have been done on waves in layered media. Thus Riley and Dally [39] have considered the case of a photo-elastic layer overlying an aluminium subgrade, while Daniel and Marino [9] have used a model consisting of two transparent photo-elastic layers. The geometry of the latter study was actually consistent with the case of two semi-infinite media in contact. A Moiré fringe technique was also used in the latter study to supplement the photo-elastic aspects.

6.5.2. *Surface waves on a half-space*

Measurement of surface strains and displacements in a half-space actually preceded entire-field measurements by photo-elastic means. Thus, Tatel [41] used a 'model seismogram' approach to compare the theoretical predictions of Lamb on surface motion to experimental measurements. A wave was induced on the surface of a large block of steel using a pulsed piezoelectric transducer. A detector placed several centimetres away measured the vertical component of displacement. The geometry of the apparatus is shown in Fig. 6.33(a), and the resulting vertical component displacement and velocity records are shown in (b) and (c). The basic waveform is seen to strongly

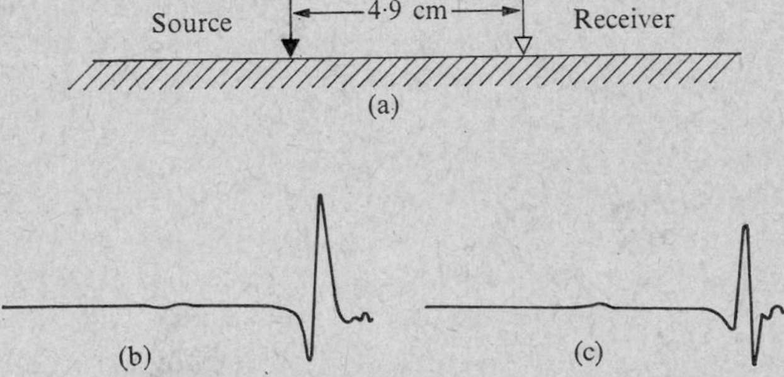

FIG. 6.33. (a) Experimental arrangement, and resulting (b) vertical component displacement and (c) velocity records obtained by Tatel [41].

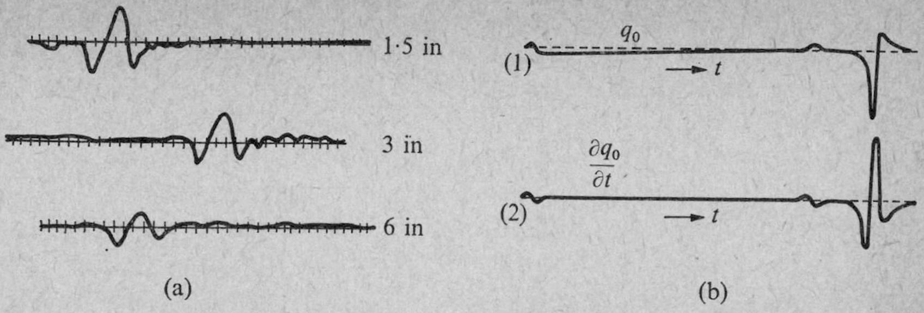

FIG. 6.34. (a) Strain–time records at three distances from the point of impact and (b) the radial displacement predicted by Lamb and the time derivative of that displacement. (After Goodier *et al.* [15, Figs. 1, 2].)

resemble that predicted by Lamb [22], shown in Fig. 6.21 and in the following Fig. 6.34. Barely perceptible in the figures is the arrival of the P wave.

Goodier, Jahsman, and Ripperger [15] studied the surface waves produced by the impact of a spherical ball on a half-space as a possible technique for recording the force–time curve oft he impact. The piezoelectric transducer used in the study recorded the sum of the principal strains ϵ_0, given by

$$\epsilon_0 = \partial q_0/\partial r + q_0/r,$$

where $q_0 = q_0(r, t)$ is the radial displacement at a given distance r. The resulting strain record at three different locations is shown in Fig. 6.34(a). The stress waves were caused by the impact of a $\frac{1}{16}$ in (0·16 cm) diameter ball. Goodier *et al.* were able to approximately compare the results to the theoretical predictions of Lamb [22]. Thus, Lamb's result for the radial displacement q_0, first shown in Fig. 6.34(a), is again shown in Fig. 6.34(b). By treating the disturbance as one-dimensional, the derivative $\partial q_0/\partial r$ has the same form as $\partial q_0/\partial t$, the latter which is also shown in Fig. 6.34(b). Since the contribution of q_0/r is small far from the source, the comparison of waveforms between Fig. 6.34(a) and Fig. 6.34(b) may be made and a strong similarity noted. Other aspects of the work by Goodier *et al.* dealt with obtaining the force–time curves of impact from the surface-wave measurements.

Dally and Thau [8] conducted a photo-elastic study of surface-wave propagation on a half-plane and compared results with theoretical predictions. General agreement was noted for effects due to the P wave but discrepancies were found between the theoretical and experimental results for the S and Rayleigh waves. The differences were ascribed to differences in the experimental loading situation and the loading considered in the mathematical analysis. In addition, three-dimensional effects due to the high-frequency content in the waves was believed contributory to the discrepancies. In a later paper, Thau and Dally [42] studied the subsurface characteristics of the

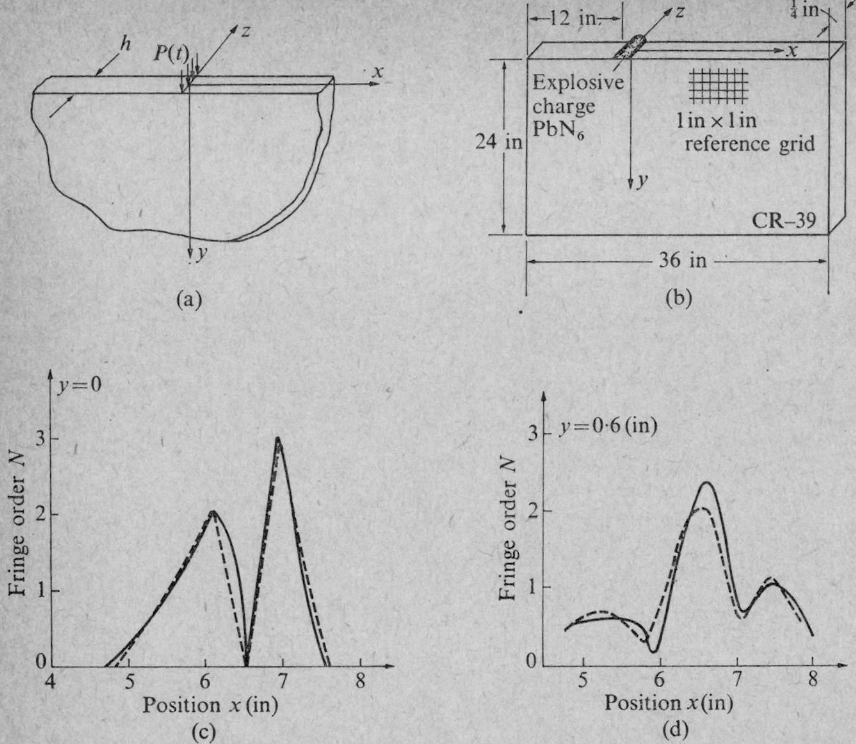

FIG. 6.35. (a) Mathematical model, (b) experimental model considered in study of Rayleigh waves, and (c), (d) comparisons of predicted and measured fringe-order versus propagation distance x for two values of y (at $t = 203$ μs after detonation). (After Thau and Dally [42, Figs. 1, 6].)

Rayleigh wave and obtained excellent agreement between theory and experiment. The theoretical model and experimental model used in the study are shown in Fig. 6.35(a), (b). The dynamic fringe pattern resulting from detonating the lead azide charge was recorded by the Cranz–Schardin camera operating at 68 000 frames per second. The general fringe field was as shown previously in Fig. 6.32(b). Theoretical predictions of the fringe order were made for various positions along the surface and at various depths. Fig. 6.35(c), (d) shows the comparison of results for a particular instant ($t = 203$ μs after detonation) at two different depths.

6.5.3. *Other studies on surface waves*

The previously-cited studies have pertained to surface waves in a half-space. Many other studies have been carried out aimed at determining the propagation of surface waves along curved boundaries or their interactions with surface irregularities. While such problems have not been covered theoretically in this book, they represent interesting extensions of such work.

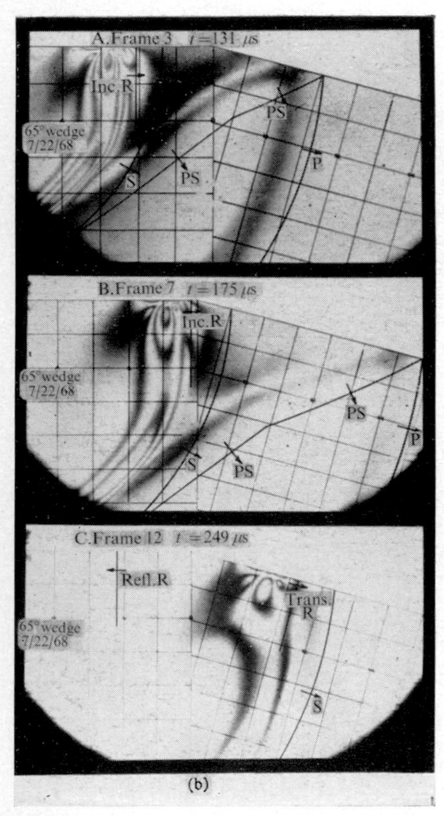

FIG. 6.36 (b)

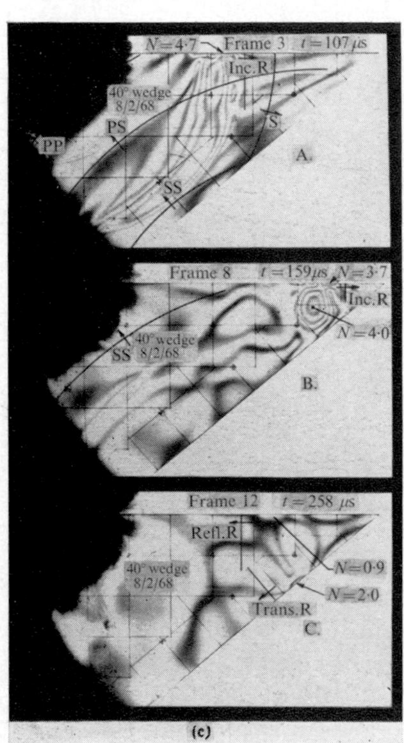

FIG. 6.36 (c)

The case of Rayleigh wave propagation along a curved surface has been studied using photo-elastic means by Marino and Dally [27]. Using techniques similar to those previously described for photo-elastic half-space studies, wave propagation along both concave and convex surfaces was measured. The main observations were (1) increased attenuation of the Rayleigh wave with a decrease in the radius of curvature for both convex and concave surfaces; (2) a decrease in surface wave amplitude with decreasing curvature for concave surfaces; (3) an increase in the compression portion of the surface wave with decreasing curvature of convex surfaces; and (4) the formulation of secondary Rayleigh pulses with both concave and convex surfaces of sharp curvatures. Viktorov [43, pp. 29–42] reports on surface-wave propagation along curved surfaces, including ultrasonic studies in this area.

The propagation of surface waves in wedges has also been investigated using both photo-elastic and ultrasonic techniques. Lewis and Dally [24] have reported on the former aspect. A typical specimen geometry is shown in Fig. 6.36(a). Fig. 6.36(b) shows three stages in the propagation of a wave

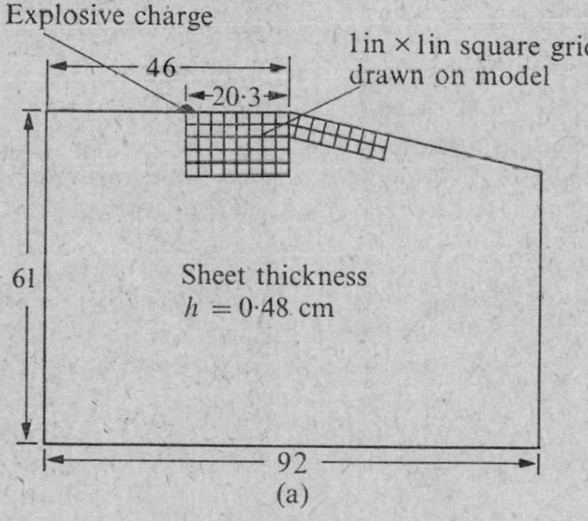

FIG. 6.36. (a) Typical specimen geometry for photo-elastic study of waves in a wedge (dimensions in centimetres), and transmission and reflection of waves in a (b: see separate plate) 165° wedge and (c: see seperate plate) 40° wedge. (After Lewis and Dally [24, Figs. 1A, 5, 7].)

from a point loading past a 165° wedge. The rather shallow wedge angle causes very little reflection of the Rayleigh wave. The propagation of waves in a very sharp (40° wedge angle) wedge is shown in Fig. 6.36(c). A more significant surface-wave reflection from the sharp corner is seen to occur. Some transmission of the Rayleigh wave is also noted. Viktorov [43, pp. 42–6] also reports on ultrasonic investigations of surface waves in wedges and rounded corners.

The propagation and reflection of surface waves from other surface discontinuities is also of interest. The effectiveness of trenches in screening

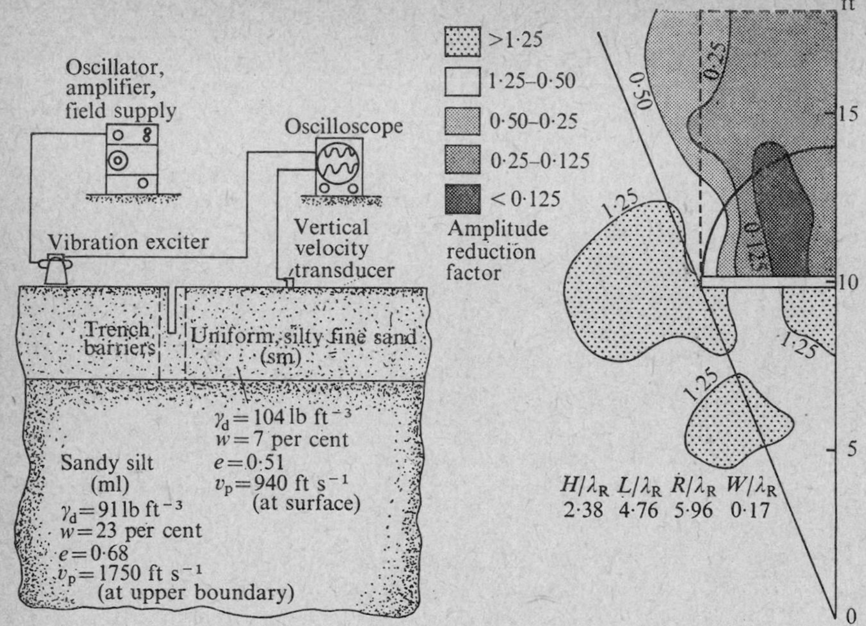

FIG. 6.37. (a) Experimental apparatus used for studying the influence of trenches on screening surface waves and (b) experimental data for a particular trench configuration. (After Woods [44, Figs. 5, 20].)

structural foundations from vibratory surface-wave energy has been studied by Woods [44]. A diagram of the field test apparatus is shown in Fig. 6.37(a). Trenches of various depths placed close to and far from the vibration source were considered. An example of the data obtained for a particular trench configuration is shown in Fig. 6.37(b). In the later figure, the trench depth was 4 ft (1·22 m), the trench length was 8 ft (2·44 m), and the trench width was 4 in. (10·16 cm). The vertical axis is the axis of symmetry of the system so that only half the test area is shown. The data is presented in terms of an 'amplitude reduction factor'. The vibration levels at various points in the test site were measured before the trench was dug. After the trench was prepared, vibration levels were again measured and the ratio of 'after' to 'before' measurements taken to obtain the reduction factor. Vibration frequencies of 200 Hz, 250 Hz, 300 Hz, and 350 Hz were used, with Fig. 6.37(b) being for 250 Hz. At this frequency it was established that the Rayleigh wave velocity was 420 ft s^{-1} (128 m s^{-1}) and that the wavelength was 1·68 ft (0·51 m). A wide variety of tests were reported by Woods with conclusions drawn as to effectiveness of various screening configurations.

A photo-elastic investigation on the reflection and transmission of surface waves from surface discontinuities have been carried out by Dally and Lewis

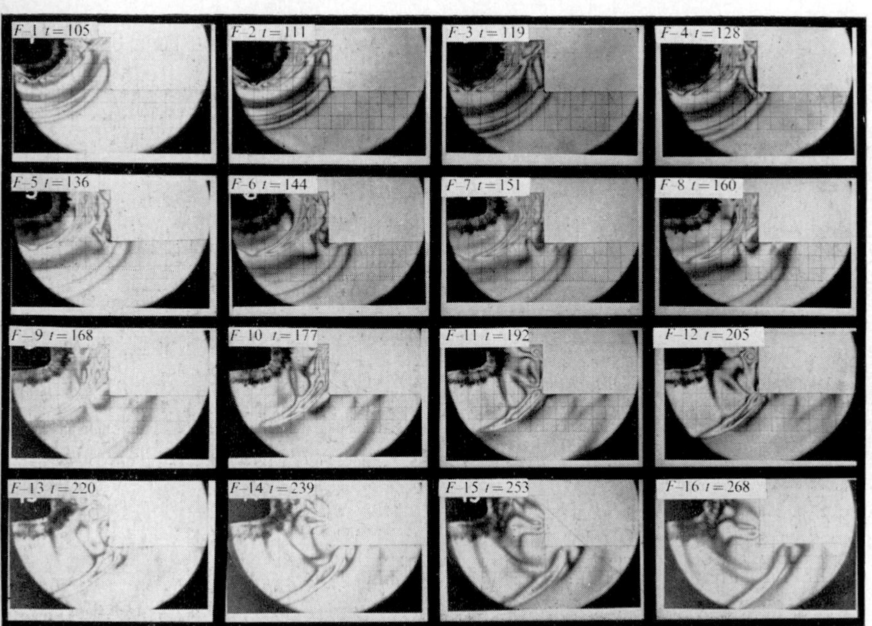
F–1 t=105
F–2 t=111
F–3 t=119
F–4 t=128
F–5 t=136
F–6 t=144
F–7 t=151
F–8 t=160
F–9 t=168
F–10 t=177
F–11 t=192
F–12 t=205
F–13 t=220
F–14 t=239
F–15 t=253
F–16 t=268

FIG. 6.38 (b)

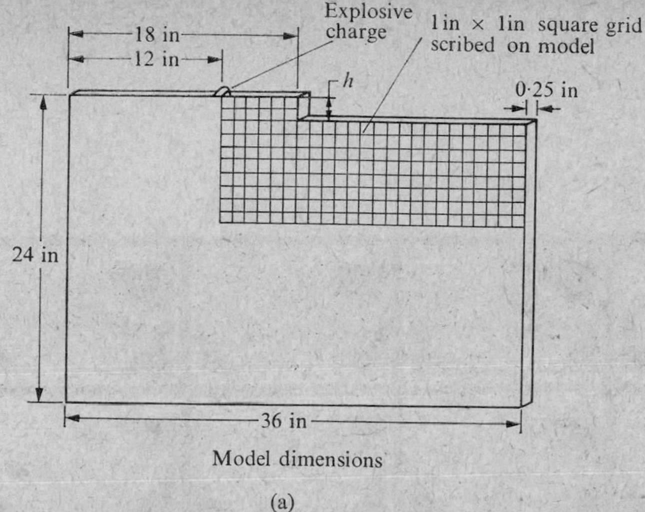

FIG. 6.38. (a) Geometry of the photo-elastic test model and (b: see separate plate) dynamic fringe pattern for wave propagation past a 4 in. step change in elevation. (After Dally and Lewis [6, Figs. 1,4].)

[6] and Reinhardt and Dally [38]. In the former study, the discontinuity was in the form of a step change in elevation in a half-space. The geometry of the photo-elastic model is shown in Fig. 6.38(a) and the dynamic fringe patterns recorded for the case of $h = 4$ in. (10·2 cm) shown in Fig. 6.38(b). Transmission and reflection coefficients for the Rayleigh wave were determined for several step changes in elevation. In the latter study by Reinhardt and Dally, the discontinuity was in the form of a vertical slot in a half-plane. Transmission and reflection coefficients for the Rayleigh wave were determined for various slot depths. A number of ultrasonic studies have been conducted on the influence of surface defects on Rayleigh waves and are reported by Viktorov [43, pp. 57–65].

References

1. BREKHOVSKIKH, LEONID M. *Waves in layered media.* Academic Press, New York (1960).
2. CARRIER, G. F., KROOK, M., and PEARSON, C. E. *Functions of a complex variable: theory and technique.* McGraw-Hill, New York (1966).
3. CHAO, C.-C. Dynamical response of an elastic half-space to tangential surface loadings. *J. appl. Mech.* **27**, 559–67 (1960).
4. DALLY, J. W. A dynamic photoelastic study of a doubly loaded half-plane. *Develop. Mech.* **4**, 649–64 (1968).
5. ——, DURRELLI, A. J., and RILEY, W. F. Photoelastic study of stress wave propagation in large plates. *Proc. Soc. exp. Stress Analysis* **17**, 33–50 (1960).

6. DALLY, J. W. and LEWIS, D. (III). A photoelastic analysis of propagation of Rayleigh waves past a step change in elevation. *Bull. seism. Soc. Am.* **58**, 539–63 (1968).
7. —— and RILEY, W. F. Initial studies in three-dimensional dynamic photoelasticity. *J. appl. Mech.* **34**, 405–10 (1967).
8. —— and THAU, S. A. Observations of stress wave propagation in a half-plane with boundary loading. *Int. J. Solids Struct.* **3**, 293–307 (1967).
9. DANIEL, I. M. and MARINO, R. L. Wave propagation in layered model due to point-source loading in low-impedance medium. *Exp. Mech.* **28**, 210–16 (1971).
10. EASON, G. On the torsional impulsive loading of an elastic half space. *Q. Jl. Mech. appl. Math.* **17**, 279–92 (1964).
11. EWING, W. M., JARDETZKY, W. S., and PRESS, F. *Elastic waves in layered media.* McGraw-Hill, New York (1957).
12. FREDERICK, J. R. *Ultrasonic engineering.* John Wiley and Sons, New York (1965).
13. FUNG, Y. C. *Foundations of solid mechanics.* Prentice-Hall, New Jersey (1965)
14. GOODIER, J. N. and BISHOP, R. E. D. On critical reflections of elastic waves at free surfaces. *J. appl. Phys.* **23**, 124–6 (1952).
15. ——, JAHSMAN, W. E., and RIPPERGER, E. A. An experimental surface-wave method for recording force-time curves in elastic impacts. *J. appl. Mech.* **26**, 3–7 (1959).
16. GUTENBERG, B. Energy ratio of reflected and refracted seismic waves. *Bull. seism. Soc. Am.* **34**, 85–102 (1944).
17. GUTZWILLER, M. C. The impact of a rigid circular cylinder on an elastic solid. *Proc. R. Soc.* **A255**, 153–91 (1962).
18. HILL, J. L. Torsional-wave propagation from a rigid sphere semi-embedded in an elastic half-space. *J. acoust. Soc. Am.* **40**, No. 2, 376–9 (1966).
19. HUNTER, S. C. Energy absorbed by elastic waves during impact. *J. Mech. Phys. Solids* **5**, 162–71 (1957).
20. JEFFREYS, H. and JEFFREYS, B. S. *Methods of mathematical physics.* Cambridge University Press (1946).
21. KNOPOFF, L. On Rayleigh wave velocities. *Bull. seism. Soc. Am.* **42**, 307–8 (1952).
22. LAMB, H. On the propagation of tremors over the surface of an elastic solid. *Phil. Trans. R. Soc.* **A203**, 1–42 (1904).
23. LANG, H. A. Surface displacements in an elastic half-space. *Z. angew Math. Mech.* **41**, 141–53 (1961).
24. LEWIS, D. and DALLY, J. W. Photoelastic analysis of Rayleigh wave propagation in wedges. *J. geophys. Res.* **75**, 3387–98 (1970).
25. LORD, A. E. (Jr.). Geometric diffraction loss in longitudinal and shear-wave attenuation measurements in an isotropic half-space. *J. acoust. Soc. Am.* **39**, 650–62 (1966).
26. LOVE, A. E. H. *Some problems of geodynamics.* Cambridge University Press (1911 and 1926).
27. MARINO, R. L. and DALLY, J. W. Rayleigh wave propagation along curved boundaries. *Develop. Mech.* **5**, 819–31 (1969).
28. MCLACHLAN, N. W. *Bessel functions for engineers.* Clarendon Press, Oxford (1961).

29. MIKLOWITZ, J. Elastic wave propagation. In *Applied mechanics surveys* (Ed. H. N. Abramson, H. Liebowitz, J. M. Crowley, and S. Juhasz). Spartan Books, Washington D.C. (1966).
30. MILLER, G. F. and PURSEY, H. The field and radiation impedance of mechanical radiators on the free surface of a semi-infinite isotropic solid. *Proc. R. Soc.* **A223,** 521–41 (1954).
31. —— and PURSEY, H. On the partition of energy between elastic waves in a semi-infinite solid. *Proc. R. Soc.* **A233,** 55–69 (1955).
32. MITRA, M. VON. Disturbance produced in an elastic half-space by an impulsive twisting moment applied to an attached rigid circular disc. *Z. angew Math. Mech.* **38,** 40–3 (1958).
33. ——. Disturbance produced in an elastic half-space by impulsive normal pressure. *Proc. Camb. phil. Soc. math. phys. Sci.* **60,** 683–96 (1961).
34. PEKERIS, C. L. The seismic surface pulse. *Proc. natn. Acad. Sci. U.S.A.* **41,** 469–80 (1955).
35. ——. The seismic buried pulse. *Proc. natn. Acad. Sci. U.S.A.* **41,** 629–38 (1955).
36. —— and LIFSON, H. Motion of the surface of a uniform elastic half-space produced by a buried pulse. *J. Acoust. Soc. Am.* **29,** 1233–8 (1957).
37. RAYLEIGH, J. W. S. On waves propagated along the plane surface of an elastic solid. *Proc. Lond. math. Soc.* **17,** 4–11 (1887).
38. REINHARDT, H. W. and DALLY, J. W. Some characteristics of Rayleigh wave interaction with surface flaws. *Mater. Eval.* **28,** 213–20 (1970).
39. RILEY, W. F. and DALLY, J. W. A photoelastic analysis of stress wave propagation in a layered model. *Geophysics* **31,** 881–99 (1966).
40. STONELEY, R. Elastic waves at the surface of separation of two solids. *Proc. R. Soc.* **A106,** 416–28 (1924).
41. TATEL, H. E. Note on the nature of a seismogram. II. *J. Geophys. Res.* **59,** 289–94 (1954).
42. THAU, S. A. and DALLY, J. W. Subsurface Characteristics of the Rayleigh Wave. *Int. J. Eng. Sci.* **7,** 37–52 (1969).
43. VIKTOROV, I. A. *Rayleigh and Lamb waves: physical theory and applications* Plenum Press, New York (1967).
44. WOODS, R. D. Screening of surface waves in soils. *J. Soil Mech. Founds Div. Am. Soc. civ. Engrs.* July **94,** 951–79 (1968).

Problems

6.1. Verify the statement made earlier (following (6.1.95)) that the extraneous roots of the Rayleigh wave equation correspond to the special cases of plane-wave reflection in a half-space (see, for example, (6.1.52), (6.1.56)).

6.2. Establish whether SH surface waves can exist in a traction-free half-space.

6.3. As indicated in the text, Goodier and Bishop [14] used a limiting process on wave amplitude ratios to obtain the results summarized by Fig. 6.7. From a review of the given reference, obtain the grazing SV wave results by the limiting process.

6.4. Consider the reflection of P, SV, and SH waves from a completely fixed boundary. Determine the amplitude ratios and investigate any special cases of reflection. Include the possibility of waves at grazing incidence.

6.5. Consider a semi-infinite media, $y \geq 0$, and the cases of incident plane harmonic P or SV waves. Let the boundary conditions be those of elastic restraint (that is, $\tau_{yy} = ku_y$, $\tau_{xy} = 0$ at $y = 0$) and obtain the results for the reflected wave amplitude ratios.

6.6. Consider the case of a semi-infinite medium with a slightly wavy boundary. Thus let the medium generally occupy the region $y > 0$, with the exact surface given by $y = \varepsilon f(x)$, where ε is a small parameter. First show that the unit normal vector **n** (directed into the media) has components

$$l = -\varepsilon f'(x)(1+\varepsilon^2 f'^2)^{-\frac{1}{2}}, \qquad m = (1+\varepsilon^2 f'^2)^{-\frac{1}{2}}.$$

Then show that traction-free boundary conditions on the free surface are given by $-\tau_{yy}\varepsilon f' + \tau_{xy} = 0$, $-\tau_{xy}\varepsilon f' + \tau_{yy} = 0$ on $y = \varepsilon f(x)$.

6.7. Consider two parallel line SH wave sources of equal strength, separated by the distance $2a$, in an infinite media. What conditions exist on the mid plane (that is, the plane perpendicular to the plane containing the sources and located midway between the sources) if the sources are (a) in phase and (b) 180° out of phase?

6.8. Consider a half-space excited by a strip surface SH wave source. That is, consider the half-space $y \geq 0$, with the prescribed displacements $u_z(x, 0, t) = 0$, $|x| > a$, and $u_x = u_y = 0$. Obtain the transformed solution and attempt inversion. Are the results for a line source recovered for distances several wavelengths from the source?

6.9. Attempt to verify the expression for u_x as given by (6.3.49). That is, as indicated in the text, apply the results (6.3.48) to (6.3.27).

6.10. Consider a half-space defined by $z \geq 0$, with a rigid hemisphere of radius a embedded at the origin. Let the hemisphere be undergoing torsional oscillations about the z-axis given by $\Omega_0 \exp(i\omega t)$, where Ω_0 is maximum angular displacement. Formulate the problem in terms of spherical coordinates. Note that only one of the displacement equations of motion survives. Solve for the resulting wave propagation.

6.11. Consider the case of two semi-infinite media in contact. Let the boundary conditions be of the transverse slip type. That is,

$$\tau_{yy} = \tau'_{yy}, \qquad \tau_{yx} = \tau_{yz} = \tau'_{yx} = \tau'_{yz} = 0.$$

Solve for reflection–refraction of incident plane harmonic P and SV waves.

6.12. Consider two semi-infinite media, having different material properties, bonded together. Develop the governing theory and equations for the reflection and transmission of SH waves across the boundary between the two media.

6.13. Consider a layered media as defined by Fig. 6.31. Consider the case of plane harmonic SH waves travelling in the lower media and impinging on the interface at some oblique angle. Solve for the resulting reflection–transmission expressions. Are there any special cases of interest involving critical incidence angles and/or material properties?

6.14. As an extension of the previous problem, obtain the reflection–transmission expressions for incident P and incident SV waves.

6.15. Again consider the case of two semi-infinite media in contact (see Fig. 6.30 for coordinate and media definitions). For the case of incident plane harmonic P and SV waves, several patterns of emerging waves are possible, depending on incoming wave-type, incidence angle, and whether $c_1 \gtrless c_1'$. Investigate the behaviour of the reflected–refracted wave system for incidence beyond the critical angle.

7 Scattering and diffraction of elastic waves

We now wish to study the interaction of elastic waves with discontinuities or boundaries of more complex shape than that of the half-space of the last chapter. Such problems might arise when waves propagating through an infinite medium encounter cavities, inclusions, or cracks. Such problems, generally denoted as scattering and diffraction problems, have been of long standing interest in acoustics and electro-magnetic theory. Problems of interest in these fields include sonar detection, architectural design, radar applications, and antenna design. Interest in the field of elasticity has been more recent, with problems in ultrasonic testing, dynamic stress concentrations, and blast effects on buried structures representing some areas of application.

The basic nature of the problem is the same for all fields. Namely, a propagating harmonic wave or a pulse (usually considered plane for either case) is considered to encounter a discontinuity, in the form of an inclusion (representing, say, a flaw in the material) or a slit or wedge (representative of a crack). As a consequence of reflection phenomena, such as discussed in Chapter 6 for the half-space, a scattering of elastic waves occurs. In addition, wave diffraction occurs near the edge of the discontinuity. The problem then is to determine the resultant stress and displacement fields with emphasis on near-fields (stress concentrations) or far-field effects (radiation patterns, total energy reflected and transmitted).

The increased complexity of the elastic-reflection phenomena, due to mode conversion effects, yields scattering problems in solids more complex than their acoustic or electro-magnetic counterparts. However, most tools of analysis for the simpler problems, some of which have been only recently developed, can also be applied to elastic scattering.

There is no section allocated for purely experimental studies on scattering and diffraction because of the relative scarcity of results in this area. Durelli and Riley [7] performed a photo-elastic study in which the stress distribution on the boundary of a circular hole in a large plate was determined under dynamic pulse loading. Shea [37] has measured the dynamic stress concentration factor of a circular hole in a plate under passage of a sharp pulse and noted a variation of this factor with frequency. The results were in qualitative agreement with those predicted by Pao [33]. Reference is also made to the experimental study by Wells and Post [49] and by Beebe [4], where photoelasticity was employed to determine the dynamic stress distribution about a running crack. Finally, it should be noted that a number of studies have been done on the reflection and transmission of ultrasonic waves by discontinuities from the standpoint of use in non-destructive testing.

In the following, the first section will be devoted to the cylindrical and spherical cavity problems. The second section will be devoted to a diffraction problem. Discussion of other methods of analysing problems in this area will be given.

7.1. Scattering of waves by cavities

The scattering of elastic waves by cavities or inclusions of simple geometry, such as cylindrical or spherical, represents our first consideration. The coordinate systems for such geometries enable separation of variables to be performed on the wave equation and solutions in terms of infinite series are possible. Solutions of this type are particularly attractive when the incident waves are simple harmonic in contrast, say, to sharp pulses.

7.1.1. *Scattering of SH waves by a cylindrical cavity*

One of the simplest cases of elastic scattering is that of SH waves impinging on a cylindrical cavity, where the plane of polarization is parallel to the cavity axis. If it is recalled that SH waves do not undergo mode conversion at a free surface under these circumstances, then the resultant displacement and stress fields will be governed by a single scalar equation. The problem becomes, consequently, identical to the equivalent acoustical problem.

1. *Governing equations.* Consider a plane harmonic SH wave system propagating in the positive z direction, and impinging on an infinite, cylindrical cavity of radius a as shown in Fig. 7.1. The displacement field for the SH wave system will be given by

$$u_x = u(y, z, t), \qquad u_y = u_z = 0. \tag{7.1.1}$$

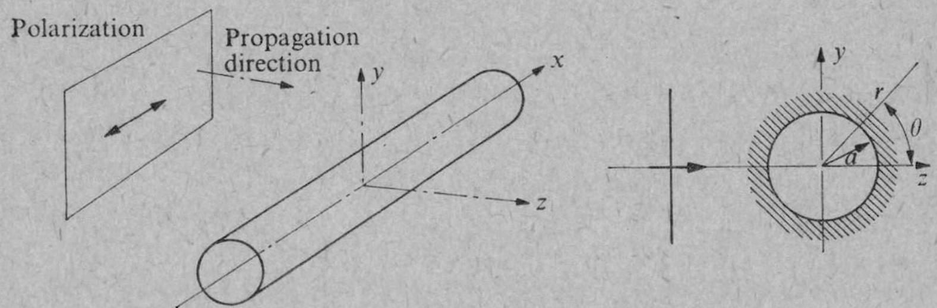

FIG. 7.1. SH waves incident on a cylindrical cavity.

The displacement equations of motion then reduce to

$$\nabla^2 u = \frac{1}{c_2^2}\frac{\partial^2 u}{\partial t^2}, \tag{7.1.2}$$

where ∇^2 is the Laplacian in polar coordinates. The traction-free cavity surface requires the boundary conditions

$$\tau_{rr} = \tau_{r\theta} = \tau_{rx} = 0, \qquad r = a, \tag{7.1.3}$$

where

$$\tau_{rr} = \lambda\left(\frac{\partial u_r}{\partial r}+\frac{1}{r}\frac{\partial u_\theta}{\partial \theta}+\frac{u_r}{r}+\frac{\partial u_x}{\partial x}\right)+2\mu\frac{\partial u_r}{\partial r},$$

$$\tau_{r\theta} = \mu\left(\frac{1}{r}\frac{\partial u_r}{\partial \theta}+\frac{\partial u_\theta}{\partial r}-\frac{u_\theta}{r}\right), \tag{7.1.4}$$

$$\tau_{rx} = \mu\left(\frac{\partial u_x}{\partial r}+\frac{\partial u_r}{\partial x}\right).$$

However, as a consequence of the characteristics of an SH field, we have that

$$u_r = u_\theta = 0, \qquad \frac{\partial}{\partial x} = 0, \tag{7.1.5}$$

so that the boundary conditions reduce to

$$\partial u/\partial r = 0, \qquad r = a. \tag{7.1.6}$$

An incident SH wave propagating in the positive z direction is given by

$$u_i = U_0 \exp\{\mathrm{i}(\omega t-\gamma z)\} = U_0 \exp\{\mathrm{i}\gamma(c_2 t-z)\}. \tag{7.1.7}$$

When the incident wave strikes the cavity, reflection will occur, setting up a scattered wavefield,

$$u_s = u_s(r, \theta, t). \tag{7.1.8}$$

The total displacement field will then be given as

$$u(r, \theta, t) = u_i+u_s, \tag{7.1.9}$$

where $u(r, \theta, t)$ must satisfy the governing equation and the boundary conditions.

2. *Expansion in infinite series.* The incident wavefield automatically satisfies the wave equation for $\gamma c_2 = \omega$. Let

$$u_s = R\Theta e^{\mathrm{i}\omega t} = U_s e^{\mathrm{i}\omega t}, \tag{7.1.10}$$

and substitute in (7.1.2), giving

$$R''\Theta+\frac{1}{r}R'\Theta+\frac{1}{r^2}R\Theta'' = -\gamma^2 R\Theta, \qquad \gamma^2 = \omega^2/c_2^2. \tag{7.1.11}$$

This separates to

$$\Theta''+k^2\Theta = 0, \tag{7.1.12}$$

$$R''+\frac{1}{r}R'+\left(\gamma^2-\frac{k^2}{r^2}\right)R = 0. \tag{7.1.13}$$

The solution of (7.1.12) is

$$\Theta = A\cos k\theta+B\sin k\theta. \tag{7.1.14}$$

Symmetry with respect to the x-axis requires $B = 0$ while the requirement that Θ be single-valued (that is, $\Theta(\theta) = \Theta(\theta+2\pi)$) indicates k is an integer, say n.

We recognize (7.1.13) as Bessel's equation of order n having the solutions

$$R = AH_n^{(2)}(\gamma r)+BH_n^{(1)}(\gamma r), \tag{7.1.15}$$

where the Hankel-function solution form has been chosen in anticipation of the convenient exponential representation of the asymptotic behaviour. We now impose the requirement that the scattered wavefield must be outward propagating. This condition will enable us to determine which Hankel function is appropriate. As we have shown previously, for large values of the argument, the Hankel functions have the following approximate expressions,

$z \gg 1$:

$$\begin{aligned} H_n^{(1)}(z) &\sim \left(\frac{2}{\pi z}\right)^{\frac{1}{2}}\exp\left\{i\left(z-\frac{\pi}{4}-\frac{n\pi}{2}\right)\right\}(1-\ldots), \\ H_n^{(2)}(z) &\sim \left(\frac{2}{\pi z}\right)^{\frac{1}{2}}\exp\left\{-i\left(z-\frac{\pi}{4}-\frac{n\pi}{2}\right)\right\}(1+\ldots). \end{aligned} \tag{7.1.16}$$

Recalling that the time dependence is $\exp(i\omega t)$, it is seen that an outward propagating wave must have the form $\exp\{i(\omega t-\gamma r)\}$, so that $H_n^{(2)}$ is appropriate in the present case. Hence let $B = 0$ in (7.1.15). The scattered field thus is given by

$$U_s(r, \theta) = \sum_{n=0}^{\infty} A_n H_n^{(2)}(\gamma r)\cos n\theta, \tag{7.1.17}$$

where A_n must be determined.

We now have solutions which satisfy the wave equation so that only substitution in the boundary condition remains. The form of $U_s(\theta)$ is ideally suited for this, but this is not the case for the incoming wave (7.1.7). What is required is a Bessel-function representation of the plane wave. Writing u_i as

$$u_i = U_i(r, \theta)e^{i\omega t} = U_0 e^{-i\gamma r\cos\theta}e^{i\omega t}, \tag{7.1.18}$$

it is found that†

$$U_i(r, \theta) = U_0\sum_{n=0}^{\infty}\varepsilon_n(-1)^n J_n(\gamma r)\cos n\theta \qquad (\varepsilon_0 = 1, \varepsilon_n = 2). \tag{7.1.19}$$

† Pp. 55–7 of Reference [23] or p. 96 of Reference [21].

With (7.1.17), (7.1.18) we have the incident and scattered wavefields similarly represented. Substitution in the boundary condition, where the time dependence has been omitted, gives

$$\frac{\partial U_{\mathrm{i}}}{\partial r}+\frac{\partial U_{\mathrm{s}}}{\partial r}=0, \qquad r=a. \tag{7.1.20}$$

Using (7.1.17) and (7.1.19), we obtain

$$\sum_{n=0}^{\infty}\left\{U_0\varepsilon_n(-1)^n\frac{\mathrm{d}J_n(\gamma r)}{\mathrm{d}r}+A_n\frac{\mathrm{d}H_n^{(2)}(\gamma r)}{\mathrm{d}r}\right\}\cos n\theta\,\bigg|_{r=a}=0. \tag{7.1.21}$$

Solving for A_n, we have

$$A_n=\frac{-\varepsilon_n(-1)^n U_0 J_n'(\gamma a)}{H_n^{(2)\prime}(\gamma a)}. \tag{7.1.22}$$

By use of recursion formula, we have

$$\begin{aligned}
J_n'(\gamma a)&=\frac{\gamma}{2}\{J_{n-1}(\gamma a)-J_{n+1}(\gamma a)\}, & J_0'(\gamma a)&=-\gamma J_1(\gamma a),\\
Y_n'(\gamma a)&=\frac{\gamma}{2}\{Y_{n-1}(\gamma a)-Y_{n+1}(\gamma a)\}, & Y_0'(\gamma a)&=-\gamma Y_1(\gamma a),\\
H_n^{(2)\prime}(\gamma a)&=\frac{\gamma}{2}\{H_{n-1}^{(2)}(\gamma a)-H_{n+1}^{(2)}(\gamma a)\}, & H_0^{(2)}(\gamma a)&=-\gamma H_1^{(2)}(\gamma a),
\end{aligned} \tag{7.1.23}$$

so that

$$\begin{aligned}
A_0&=-U_0\frac{J_1(\gamma a)}{H_1^{(2)}(\gamma a)},\\
A_n&=-2(-1)^n U_0\frac{J_{n+1}(\gamma a)-J_{n-1}(\gamma a)}{H_{n+1}^{(2)}(\gamma a)-H_{n-1}^{(2)}(\gamma a)}.
\end{aligned} \tag{7.1.24}$$

This may be expressed in somewhat simpler form by writing

$$A_0=U_0\frac{1}{1-\mathrm{i}(Y_1/J_1)}, \qquad A_n=-2(-1)^n U_0\bigg/\left(1-\mathrm{i}\frac{Y_{n+1}-Y_{n-1}}{J_{n+1}-J_{n-1}}\right), \tag{7.1.25}$$

which are of the general form

$$\frac{1}{1-\mathrm{i}q}=\frac{1}{1+q^2}+\frac{\mathrm{i}q}{1+q^2}. \tag{7.1.26}$$

Let $q=\cot\gamma$, so that

$$\frac{1}{1-\mathrm{i}q}=\sin\gamma(\sin\gamma+\mathrm{i}\cos\gamma)=\mathrm{i}\sin\gamma\mathrm{e}^{-\mathrm{i}\gamma}. \tag{7.1.27}$$

Then we may write for A_0, A_n

$$A_0=-U_0\mathrm{i}\sin\gamma_0\exp(-\mathrm{i}\gamma_0), \qquad A_n=2(-1)^{n+1}U_0\sin\gamma_n\exp(-\mathrm{i}\gamma_n), \tag{7.1.28}$$

where

$$\cot \gamma_0 = \frac{Y_1(\gamma a)}{J_1(\gamma a)}, \qquad \cot \gamma_n = \frac{Y_{n+1}(\gamma a) - Y_{n-1}(\gamma a)}{J_{n+1}(\gamma a) - J_{n-1}(\gamma a)}. \tag{7.1.29}$$

With this, the scattered solution takes the form

$$u_s(r, \theta, t) = U_0 e^{i\omega t}\Big\{-i \sin \gamma_0 \exp(-i\gamma_0) H_0^{(2)}(\gamma r) + \\ +2\sum_{n=1}^{\infty}(-i)^{n+1} \sin \gamma_n \exp(-i\gamma_n) H_n^{(2)}(\gamma r) \cos n\theta\Big\}. \tag{7.1.30}$$

We may study the scattered-field configuration by computing the above series. However, by considering the far field, for which $\gamma r \gg 1$, the result may be simplified by using the asymptotic forms (7.1.16). This gives

$\gamma r \gg 1$:

$$u_s(r, \theta, t) = U_0 \sqrt{\left(\frac{2}{\pi \gamma r}\right)} \exp\{i(\omega t - \gamma r)\}\Big[-i \sin \gamma_0 \exp\{-i(\gamma_0 - \pi/4)\} + \\ +2\sum_{n=1}^{\infty}(-i)^{n+1} \sin \gamma_n \exp\Big\{-i\Big(\gamma_n - \frac{2n+1}{4}\pi\Big)\Big\} \cos n\theta\Big] \\ = U_0 \sqrt{\left(\frac{2}{\pi \gamma r}\right)} \exp\{i(\omega t - \gamma r)\} \psi_s(\theta). \tag{7.1.31}$$

In the acoustic analogue of this problem, $u_s \sim p_s$, the scattered pressure field. Considerable interest is connected with the scattered power of the field, where†

$$P_s = \frac{2I_0}{\pi \gamma} \int_0^{2\pi} |\psi_s(\theta)|^2 \, d\theta, \tag{7.1.32}$$

and I_0 is a constant (in acoustics, the intensity of the incident wave). A plot of P_s versus γa gives the results shown in Fig. 7.2(a). Of equal interest is to consider the behaviour of $|\psi_s|^2$, appearing in the integrand of P_s. A plot of this versus θ indicates the directional characteristics of the scattering, and is shown in Fig. 7.2(b). The representations are in terms of the wavenumber parameter γa. Recalling that $\gamma = 2\pi/\lambda$, where λ is the wavelength, it is seen that, for $a \simeq \lambda(\gamma a = 1)$, most of scattered energy is back toward the incoming wave (hence 'back scattering'). The interaction of this field, primarily a result of reflection with the incoming wave will produce an irregular radiation field on the forward side of the cylinder. On the other hand, there is little scattered energy to the rear of the cylinder, so that the toal field there is quite

† See Lindsay [21, pp. 91–101] for complete coverage of this problem, including development of expressions for P_s.

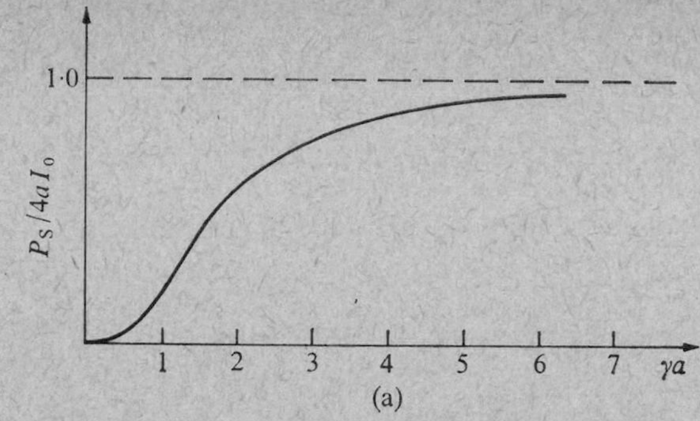

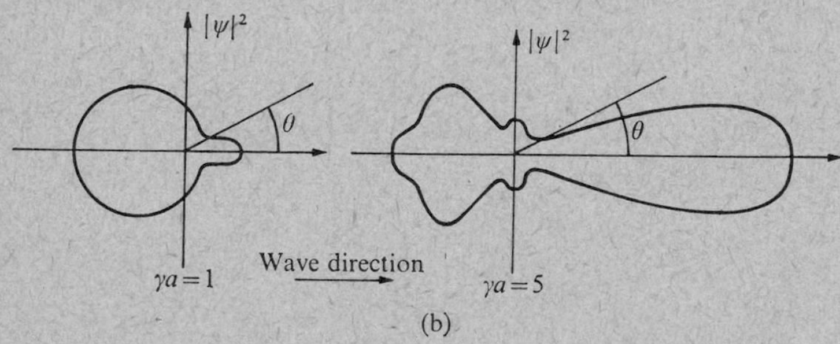

FIG. 7.2. (a) A plot of scattered power P_s versus wavenumber parameter and (b) the directional characteristics of the scattering for $\gamma a = 1, 5$. (After Lindsay [21, Figs. 3.8, 3.9].)

similar to the incident wavefield. The case of $a \gg \lambda(\gamma a = 5)$, or the short-wavelength case, indicates that a great deal of forward scattering has occurred. This field will interfere with the incident field to form a 'shadow zone'. For $\gamma a \gg 1$, we would expect the region behind the cylinder to be relatively undisturbed. However, we recall from optics that diffraction effects (interaction of radiation with the edges of objects) prevent objects from casting sharp shadows, regardless of wavelength. Thus, as γa becomes large, we would expect a shadow zone to be developed, but with indistinct edges. This would be borne out by calculations of $|\psi|^2$, for it would be found that its angular distribution would increase in complexity, containing many lobes and dips, and preventing complete annihilation of the incident field in the shadow region.

7.1.2. *Scattering of compressional waves by a spherical obstacle*

Let us now consider plane harmonic compressional waves impinging on a spherical obstacle. Such a problem is possibly more representative of actual situations of included flaws or 'stress raisers' in materials. The approach followed, however, will be similar to that of the previous section: that is, expansion of the wavefields in infinite series. The increased algebraic complexity of the present problem may be quickly surmised if it is realized that a total of five fields must be so expanded in the general case—the incident field, scattered compressional field, scattered shear field, refracted compression field, and refracted shear field. The latter two fields arise, of course, when the obstacle is taken as an elastic inclusion as opposed to an empty cavity. The coverage of this problem will be based on the work of Pao and Mow [34].

1. *Governing equations.* Consider a plane harmonic compression wave impinging on a spherical obstacle of radius a, as shown in Fig. 7.3. In this

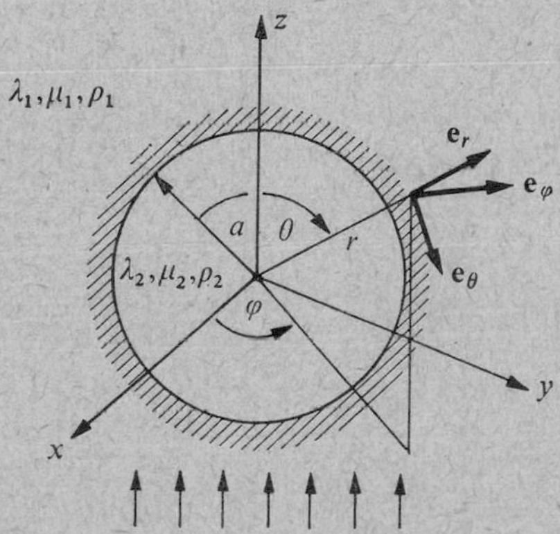

FIG. 7.3. Plane harmonic compressional wave incident on a spherical obstacle.

situation, subscripts 1 are used to identify the infinite medium, while subscripts 2 identify the properties of the spherical obstacle. Because of the axisymmetry of the present problem (this would not be the case if shear waves were impinging), we have that

$$\mathbf{u} = u_r\mathbf{e}_r + u_z\mathbf{e}_z. \tag{7.1.33}$$

In terms of potential functions, we follow the approach used in the half-space analysis (see § 6.3) and write

$$\mathbf{u} = \nabla\Phi + \nabla x\left(\frac{\partial \Psi}{\partial \theta}\mathbf{e}_\phi\right), \tag{7.1.34}$$

where Φ, Ψ satisfy

$$\nabla^2\Phi = \frac{1}{c_\alpha^2}\frac{\partial^2\Phi}{\partial t^2}, \qquad \nabla^2\Psi = \frac{1}{c_\beta^2}\frac{\partial^2\Psi}{\partial t^2}, \tag{7.1.35}$$

and where

$$c_\alpha^2 = (\lambda + 2\mu)/\rho, \qquad c_\beta^2 = \mu/\rho. \tag{7.1.36}$$

The stress–displacement equations are

$$\begin{aligned}
\tau_{rr} &= \lambda U + 2\mu \frac{\partial u_r}{\partial r}, \\
\tau_{\theta\theta} &= \lambda U + 2\mu\left(\frac{1}{r}\frac{\partial u_\theta}{\partial \theta} + \frac{u_r}{r}\right), \\
\tau_{\phi\phi} &= \lambda U + 2\mu\left(\frac{u_r}{r} + \frac{\cot\theta}{r} u_\theta\right), \\
\tau_{r\theta} &= \mu\left(\frac{1}{r}\frac{\partial u_r}{\partial \theta} + \frac{\partial u_\theta}{\partial r} - \frac{u_\theta}{r}\right),
\end{aligned} \tag{7.1.37}$$

where

$$U = \nabla\cdot\mathbf{u} = \frac{\partial u_r}{\partial r} + \frac{2}{r}u_r + \frac{1}{r}\frac{\partial u_\theta}{\partial \theta} + \frac{\cot\theta}{r}u_\theta. \tag{7.1.38}$$

2. *Incident, scattered, and refracted wavefields.* The incident compression wave propagating in the positive z direction is given by

$$\Phi^{(i)} = \Phi_0 \exp\{i(\alpha_1 z - \omega t)\}, \qquad \Psi^{(i)} = 0. \tag{7.1.39}$$

In order for $\Phi^{(i)}$ to satisfy the first of (7.1.35) we must have

$$\alpha_1^2 = \omega^2\rho_1/(\lambda_1 + 2\mu_1). \tag{7.1.40}$$

We recall in the simpler scattering problem of the previous section that it became necessary, when substituting in the boundary conditions, to expand the incoming plane wavefield in the 'natural' eigenfunctions of the coordinate system of the problem. In anticipation of this, we expand $\Phi^{(i)}$ in a similar fashion, giving†

$$\Phi^{(i)} = \Phi_0 \sum_{n=0}^{\infty} (2n+1) i^n j_n(\alpha_1 r) P_n(\cos\theta). \tag{7.1.41}$$

We have omitted the $\exp(-i\omega t)$ time dependence in this expression, and will do so in the following. The $j_n(\alpha_1 r)$ is the previously encountered spherical Bessel function given as

$$j_n(z) = \left(\frac{\pi}{2z}\right)^{\frac{1}{2}} J_{n+\frac{1}{2}}(z), \tag{7.1.42}$$

and $P_n(\cos\theta)$ are the Legendre polynomials.

Of course (7.1.41) represents but one of the solution forms to the Helmholtz equation, $\nabla^2\Phi + k^2\Phi = 0$, that arises in considering either of (7.1.35), with Φ or Ψ having harmonic time dependence and the spherical Laplacian being given by

$$\nabla^2 = \frac{1}{r^2}\frac{\partial}{\partial r}\left(r^2\frac{\partial}{\partial r}\right) + \frac{1}{r^2\sin\theta}\frac{\partial}{\partial\theta}\left(\sin\theta\frac{\partial}{\partial\theta}\right) + \frac{1}{r^2\sin^2\theta}\frac{\partial^2}{\partial\phi^2}. \tag{7.1.43}$$

† P. 1466 of Reference [27].

Separation of variables leads to

$$\left\{\frac{\partial}{\partial r}\left(r^2\frac{\mathrm{d}R}{\mathrm{d}r}\right)R^{-1}+\frac{1}{\sin\theta}\frac{\partial}{\partial\theta}\left(\sin\theta\frac{\mathrm{d}\Theta}{\mathrm{d}\theta}\right)\Theta^{-1}+k^2r^2\right\}\sin^2\theta=-\frac{\mathrm{d}^2\tilde{\phi}}{\mathrm{d}\phi^2}=\gamma^2, \quad (7.1.44)$$

where $\Phi = R(r)\,\Theta(\theta)\tilde{\phi}(\phi)$ and γ^2 is the first separation constant. Thus

$$\frac{\mathrm{d}^2\tilde{\phi}}{\mathrm{d}\phi^2}+\gamma^2\tilde{\phi}=0. \quad (7.1.45)$$

The requirement that $\tilde{\phi}$ be single-valued leads to $\gamma^2 = m^2$, where m is an integer. The second separation of (7.1.44) gives

$$\frac{1}{\sin\theta}\frac{\mathrm{d}}{\mathrm{d}\theta}\left(\sin\theta\frac{\mathrm{d}\Theta}{\mathrm{d}\theta}\right)+\left(l^2-\frac{m^2}{\sin^2\theta}\right)\Theta=0, \quad (7.1.46)$$

$$\frac{\mathrm{d}}{\mathrm{d}r}\left(r^2\frac{\mathrm{d}R}{\mathrm{d}r}\right)+\left(k^2-\frac{l^2}{r^2}\right)R=0. \quad (7.1.47)$$

Now the solutions of the preceding are the Legendre polynomials, where l^2 is constrained to be

$$l^2=n(n+1), \qquad n\sim\text{integer}, \quad (7.1.48)$$

and

$$\Theta_n=P_n(\cos\theta), \quad (7.1.49)$$

where the first few Legendre polynomials are given by

$$P_0(z)=1, \quad P_1(z)=z, \quad P_2(z)=\tfrac{1}{2}(3z^2-1),$$
$$P_3(z)=\tfrac{1}{2}(5z^3-3z), \quad P_4(z)=\tfrac{1}{8}(35z^4-30z^2+3),\ldots \quad (7.1.50)$$

Finally, (7.1.47) has the solutions

$$R(r)=A\sqrt{\left(\frac{\pi}{2kr}\right)}J_{n+\frac{1}{2}}(kr)+B\sqrt{\left(\frac{\pi}{2kr}\right)}Y_{n+\frac{1}{2}}(kr), \quad (7.1.51)$$

where $J_{n+\frac{1}{2}}$ and $Y_{n+\frac{1}{2}}$ are the half-order Bessel functions. The spherical Bessel and Hankel functions are thus

$$j_n(kr)=\sqrt{\left(\frac{\pi}{2kr}\right)}J_{n+\frac{1}{2}}(kr), \qquad n_n(kr)=\sqrt{\left(\frac{\pi}{2kr}\right)}Y_{n+\frac{1}{2}}(kr),$$
$$h_n^{(1)}(kr)=\sqrt{\left(\frac{\pi}{2kr}\right)}H_{n+\frac{1}{2}}^{(1)}(kr). \quad (7.1.52)$$

We recall that the spherical Hankel functions have the unique property of being representable by a finite sum; thus

$$h_n^{(1)}(kr)=\frac{\mathrm{e}^{\mathrm{i}kr}(-\mathrm{i})^{-n+1}}{kr}\sum_{l=0}^{n}\frac{(n+l)!}{l!(n-l)!}\left(\frac{\mathrm{i}}{2kr}\right)^l. \quad (7.1.53)$$

Hence (7.1.51) may also be written

$$R(r) = Ah_n^{(1)}(kr)+Bh_n^{(2)}(kr). \tag{7.1.54}$$

Continuing, the scattered wavefield, which will have dilatational and rotational components, will be given by

$$\Phi^{(s)} = \sum_{n=0}^{\infty} A_n h_n(\alpha_1 r)P_n(\cos\theta), \qquad \Psi^{(s)} = \sum_{n=0}^{\infty} B_n h_n(\beta_1 r)P_n(\cos\theta), \tag{7.1.55}$$

where $\beta_1^2 = \omega^2\rho_1/\mu_1$. In the above, $h_n = h_n^{(1)}$, where the spherical Hankel function of the first kind has been selected because it represents waves diverging from the obstacle. The impinging waves will set up the waves within the obstacle. Since this region will include the origin $r = 0$, the resulting solutions must be well behaved there. This leads to the selection of $j_n(z)$, so that

$$\begin{aligned} \Phi^{(r)} &= -\sum_{n=0}^{\infty} C_n j_n(\alpha_2 r)P_n(\cos\theta); \\ \Psi^{(r)} &= -\sum_{n=0}^{\infty} D_n j_n(\beta_2 r)P_n(\cos\theta), \end{aligned} \tag{7.1.56}$$

where the superscript identifies the refracted wave system. The minus sign is for later convenience in algebraic manipulations. The presence of the $r^{-\frac{1}{2}}$ in the definition of $j_n(kr)$ may raise the question of the behaviour of j_n at the origin. It turns out, however, that for small z

$$j_n(z) \to \frac{z^n}{1.3.5...(2n+1)}, \qquad n_n(z) \to \frac{1.1.3.5...(2n-1)}{z^{n+1}}, \tag{7.1.57}$$

so that $j_n(z)$ is still well behaved, while $n_n(z)$ is singular.

3. *Displacements and stresses.* Substitution into the boundary conditions requires the stresses in terms of the potential functions Φ, Ψ and in turn, in terms of the spherical Bessel functions. This data is compiled in the following:

Displacements

$$u_r = \frac{\partial\Phi}{\partial r}+\frac{1}{r}(D_\theta\Psi), \qquad u_\theta = \frac{1}{r}\frac{\partial\Phi}{\partial\theta}-\frac{\partial}{\partial\theta}(D_r\Psi), \tag{7.1.58}$$

where

$$D_r = \frac{1}{r}\frac{\partial}{\partial r}(r), \qquad D_\theta = \frac{1}{\sin\theta}\frac{\partial}{\partial\theta}\left(\sin\theta\frac{\partial}{\partial\theta}\right). \tag{7.1.59}$$

For the incident field, let

$$\Phi = \Phi^{(i)}, \qquad \Psi = 0. \tag{7.1.60}$$

For the scattered field, let

$$\Phi = \Phi^{(s)}, \qquad \Psi = \Psi^{(s)}. \tag{7.1.61}$$

For the refracted field, let

$$\Phi = \Phi^{(r)}, \qquad \Psi = \Psi^{(r)}. \tag{7.1.62}$$

Stresses

$$\tau_{rr} = 2\mu\left\{-\frac{\beta^2}{2}\Phi - \frac{2}{r}\frac{\partial\Phi}{\partial r} - \frac{1}{r^2}D_\theta\Phi + \frac{D_\theta}{r}\left(\frac{\partial\Psi}{\partial r} - \frac{\Psi}{r}\right)\right\}, \tag{7.1.63}$$

$$\tau_{\theta\theta} = 2\mu\left\{-\frac{(\beta^2-2\alpha^2)}{2}\Phi + \frac{1}{r}\frac{\partial\Phi}{\partial r} + \frac{1}{r^2}D_\theta\Phi - \frac{\cot\theta}{r^2}\frac{\partial\Phi}{\partial\theta}\right\} + $$
$$+2\mu\left\{\frac{\cot\theta}{r}\frac{\partial}{\partial\theta}D_r\Psi - \frac{1}{r}D_\theta\frac{\partial\Psi}{\partial r}\right\}, \tag{7.1.64}$$

$$\tau_{\phi\phi} = 2\mu\left\{-\frac{(\beta^2-2\alpha^2)}{2}\Phi + \frac{1}{r}\frac{\partial\Phi}{\partial r} + \frac{\cot\theta}{r^2}\frac{\partial\Phi}{\partial\theta} + \frac{D_\theta\Psi}{r^2} - \frac{\cot\theta}{r}\frac{\partial}{\partial\theta}D_r\Psi\right\}, \tag{7.1.65}$$

$$\tau_{r\theta} = \mu\frac{\partial}{\partial\theta}\left(\frac{2}{r}\frac{\partial\Phi}{\partial r} - \frac{2}{r^2}\Phi + \beta^2\Psi + \frac{2}{r}\frac{\partial\Psi}{\partial r} + \frac{2}{r^2}\Psi + \frac{2}{r^2}D_\theta\Psi\right), \tag{7.1.66}$$

where Φ, Ψ take on the superscripts appropriate to the particular field and $\alpha^2,\beta^2 = \alpha_1^2,\beta_1^2$ when the incident or scattered field is used and $\alpha^2,\beta^2 = \alpha_2^2,\beta_2^2$ for the refracted field.

Introducing the symbols ε_{ij}, which are linear combinations of the spherical harmonics defined later, we have for the displacements and stresses in medium 1;

$$\begin{aligned}
&\Phi_1 = \Phi^{(1)} + \Phi^{(s)}, \qquad \Psi_1 = \Psi^{(s)},\\
&u_{r_1} = \frac{1}{r}\sum_{n=0}^{\infty}(-\Phi_0\varepsilon_1 + A_n\varepsilon_{11} + B_n\varepsilon_{12})P_n,\\
&u_{\theta_1} = \frac{1}{r}\sum_{n=0}^{\infty}(-\Phi_0\varepsilon_2 + A_n\varepsilon_{21} + B_n\varepsilon_{22})\frac{dP_n}{d\theta},\\
&\tau_{rr_1} = \frac{2\mu_1}{r}\sum_{n=0}^{\infty}(-\Phi_0\varepsilon_3 + A_n\varepsilon_{31} + B_n\varepsilon_{32})P_n,\\
&\tau_{r\theta_1} = \frac{2\mu_1}{r}\sum_{n=0}^{\infty}(-\Phi_0\varepsilon_4 + A_n\varepsilon_{41} + B_n\varepsilon_{42})\frac{dP_n}{d\theta}.
\end{aligned} \tag{7.1.67}$$

For medium 2 we have

$$\begin{aligned}
&\Phi_2 = \Phi^{(r)}, \qquad \Psi_2 = \Psi^{(r)},\\
&u_{r_2} = -\frac{1}{r}\sum_{n=0}^{\infty}(C_n\varepsilon_{13} + D_n\varepsilon_{14})P_n,\\
&u_{\theta_2} = -\frac{1}{r}\sum_{n=0}^{\infty}(C_n\varepsilon_{23} + D_n\varepsilon_{24})\frac{dP_n}{d\theta},\\
&\tau_{rr_2} = -\frac{2\mu_2}{r}\sum_{n=0}^{\infty}(C_n\varepsilon_{33} + D_n\varepsilon_{34})P_n,\\
&\tau_{r\theta_2} = -\frac{2\mu_2}{r^2}\sum_{n=0}^{\infty}(C_n\varepsilon_{43} + D_n\varepsilon_{44})\frac{dP_n}{d\theta},
\end{aligned} \tag{7.1.68}$$

where $P_n = P_n(\cos\theta)$. The ε_j and ε_{ij} are defined as

$$
\begin{aligned}
\varepsilon_1 &= -\mathrm{i}^n(2n+1)\{nj_n(\alpha_1 r)-\alpha_1 r j_{n+1}(\alpha_1 r)\},\\
\varepsilon_2 &= -\mathrm{i}^n(2n+1)j_n(\alpha_1 r),\\
\varepsilon_3 &= -\mathrm{i}^n(2n+1)\{(n^2-n-\tfrac{1}{2}\beta_1^2 r^2)j_n(\alpha_1 r)+2\alpha_1 r j_{n+1}(\alpha_1 r)\},\\
\varepsilon_4 &= -\mathrm{i}^n(2n+1)\{(n-1)j_n(\alpha_1 r)-\alpha_1 r j_{n+1}(\alpha_1 r)\},\\
\varepsilon_{11} &= nh_n(\alpha_1 r)-\alpha_1 r h_{n+1}(\alpha_1 r),\\
\varepsilon_{21} &= h_n(\alpha_1 r),\\
\varepsilon_{31} &= (n^2-n-\tfrac{1}{2}\beta_1^2 r^2)h_n(\alpha_1 r)+2\alpha_1 r h_{n+1}(\alpha_1 r),\\
\varepsilon_{41} &= (n-1)h_n(\alpha_1 r)-\alpha_1 r h_{n+1}(\alpha_1 r),\\
\varepsilon_{12} &= -n(n+1)h_n(\beta_1 r),\\
\varepsilon_{22} &= -(n+1)h_n(\beta_1 r)+\beta_1 r h_{n+1}(\beta_1 r),\\
\varepsilon_{32} &= -n(n+1)\{(n-1)h_n(\beta_1 r)-\beta_1 r h_{n+1}(\beta_1 r)\},\\
\varepsilon_{42} &= -(n^2-1-\tfrac{1}{2}\beta_1^2 r^2)h_n(\beta_1 r)-\beta_1 r h_{n+1}(\beta_1 r),\\
\varepsilon_{13} &= nj_n(\alpha_2 r)-\alpha_2 r j_{n+1}(\alpha_2 r),\\
\varepsilon_{23} &= j_n(\alpha_2 r),\\
\varepsilon_{33} &= (n^2-n-\tfrac{1}{2}\beta_2^2 r^2)j_n(\alpha_2 r)+2\alpha_2 r j_{n+1}(\alpha_2 r),\\
\varepsilon_{43} &= (n-1)j_n(\alpha_2 r)-\alpha_2 r j_{n+1}(\alpha_2 r),\\
\varepsilon_{14} &= -n(n+1)j_n(\beta_2 r),\\
\varepsilon_{24} &= -(n+1)j_n(\beta_2 r)+\beta_2 r j_{n+1}(\beta_2 r),\\
\varepsilon_{34} &= -n(n+1)\{(n-1)j_n(\beta_2 r)-\beta_2 r j_{n+1}(\beta_2 r)\},\\
\varepsilon_{44} &= -(n^2-1-\tfrac{1}{2}\beta_2^2 r^2)j_n(\beta_2 r)-\beta_2 r j_{n+1}(\beta_2 r).
\end{aligned}
\tag{7.1.69}
$$

4. *Boundary conditions.* We shall consider the case of an elastic inclusion, considered to be bonded to the medium. Continuity of the displacement and stress fields gives

$$
\left.
\begin{aligned}
u_r^{(\mathrm{i})}+u_r^{(\mathrm{s})} &= u_r^{(\mathrm{r})},\\
u_\theta^{(\mathrm{i})}+u_\theta^{(\mathrm{s})} &= u_\theta^{(\mathrm{r})},\\
\tau_{rr}^{(\mathrm{i})}+\tau_{rr}^{(\mathrm{s})} &= \tau_{rr}^{(\mathrm{r})},\\
\tau_{r\theta}^{(\mathrm{i})}+\tau_{r\theta}^{(\mathrm{s})} &= \tau_{r\theta}^{(\mathrm{r})}.
\end{aligned}
\right\}\quad r=a
\tag{7.1.70}
$$

Taking u_r as an example, this gives

$$
\sum_{n=0}^{\infty}(-\Phi_0 E_1+A_n E_{11}+B_n E_{12}+C_n E_{13}+D_n E_{14})P_n = 0,
\tag{7.1.71}
$$

where we have let

$$E_i = \varepsilon_i\big|_{r=a}, \qquad E_{ij} = \epsilon_{ij}\big|_{r=a}. \tag{7.1.72}$$

Vanishing of each term of (7.1.71) gives

$$A_nE_{11}+B_nE_{12}+C_nE_{13}+D_nE_{14} = \Phi_0E_1. \tag{7.1.73}$$

The remaining three boundary conditions yield similar equations. The results, which are four equations in A_n, B_n, C_n, D_n, may be put in matrix form as

$$\begin{bmatrix} E_{11} & E_{12} & E_{13} & E_{14} \\ E_{21} & E_{22} & E_{23} & E_{24} \\ E_{31} & E_{32} & pE_{33} & pE_{34} \\ E_{41} & E_{42} & pE_{43} & pE_{44} \end{bmatrix} \begin{bmatrix} A_n \\ B_n \\ C_n \\ D_n \end{bmatrix} = \Phi_0 \begin{bmatrix} E_1 \\ E_2 \\ E_3 \\ E_4 \end{bmatrix}, \tag{7.1.74}$$

where $p = \mu_2/\mu_1$. Numerical evaluation of the coefficients presents no particular problem, except in the case of very long wavelengths (small arguments) or short wavelengths (large arguments). For those cases, replacement of the various spherical Bessel functions by their asymptotic limits may be necessary.

5. *Special cases.* The generality of the elastic inclusion problem enables a number of useful special cases to be derived, including the cases of a cavity, fluid inclusion, and rigid sphere, as well as these various types of scatterers in a fluid medium. However, except for the cavity case, the remaining cases must be deduced by limiting processes that contain not a few subtleties. Only results will be presented here.

Cavity: The boundary conditions are

$$\begin{aligned} \tau_{rr}^{(i)}+\tau_{rr}^{(s)} &= 0, \\ \tau_{r\theta}^{(i)}+\tau_{r\theta}^{(s)} &= 0, \end{aligned} \qquad r = a, \tag{7.1.75}$$

giving

$$\begin{bmatrix} E_{31} & E_{32} \\ E_{41} & E_{42} \end{bmatrix} \begin{bmatrix} A_n \\ B_n \end{bmatrix} = \Phi_0 \begin{bmatrix} E_3 \\ E_4 \end{bmatrix}. \tag{7.1.76}$$

Fluid inclusion: The boundary conditions are

$$\begin{aligned} u_r^{(i)}+u_r^{(s)} &= u_r^{(r)}, \\ \tau_{rr}^{(i)}+\tau_{rr}^{(s)} &= \tau_{rr}^{(r)}, \\ \tau_{r\theta}^{(i)}+\tau_{r\theta}^{(s)} &= 0, \end{aligned} \qquad r = a. \tag{7.1.77}$$

These conditions reflect the incapability of an inviscid fluid to transmit shear. Hence $\tau_{r\theta}$ must vanish at $r = a$ while the displacements u_θ may be discontinuous. The resulting equations for the coefficients are

$$\begin{bmatrix} E_{11} & E_{12} & E_{13} \\ E_{31} & E_{32} & E_{33}^{\mathrm{f}} \\ E_{41} & E_{42} & 0 \end{bmatrix} \begin{bmatrix} A_n \\ B_n \\ C_n \end{bmatrix} = \Phi_0 \begin{bmatrix} E_1 \\ E_2 \\ E_3 \end{bmatrix}, \tag{7.1.78}$$

where

$$E_{33}^{\mathrm{f}} = -\tfrac{1}{2}(\rho_2/\rho_1)\beta_1^2 r^2 j_n(\alpha_2 r). \qquad (7.1.79)$$

Rigid sphere: Under the action of the impinging waves, the sphere will translate as a rigid body, so that the boundary conditions become

$$\begin{aligned} u_r^{(\mathrm{i})}+u_r^{(\mathrm{s})} &= U_z \cos\theta, \\ u_\theta^{(\mathrm{i})}+u_\theta^{(\mathrm{s})} &= -U_z \sin\theta, \end{aligned} \qquad r = a, \qquad (7.1.80)$$

where

$$m\ddot{U}_z = \iint(\tau_{rr}\cos\theta-\tau_{r\theta}\sin\theta)a^2\sin\theta\,\mathrm{d}\theta\,\mathrm{d}\phi, \qquad (7.1.81)$$

and $m = 4\pi a^3\rho_2/3$. The coefficient matrix is given as

$$\begin{bmatrix} E_{11} & E_{12} \\ E_{21} & E_{22} \end{bmatrix}\begin{bmatrix} A_n \\ B_n \end{bmatrix} = \Phi_0\begin{bmatrix} E_1 \\ E_2 \end{bmatrix}, \qquad n \neq 1, \qquad (7.1.82)$$

while the E_{ij} take on slightly different values than given by (7.1.69) for $n = 1$.

The work of this section represents a formal solution to the stated problem. Unfortunately, numerical results for the various displacement and stress fields are rather scant. The dynamic stress concentration factor has been found by Pao [33] for the case of a hole in a plate, a problem with many similarities to the cylindrical cavity problem. Results tend to show only a 10–15 per cent increase in stress concentration at the most critical frequencies.

A number of other investigations have been carried out on scattering of harmonic waves by cylindrical and spherical obstacles. Ying and Truell [50] and Einspruch and Truell [8] have investigated the scattering of compressional waves by spherical obstacles and obtained results for the scattered field and the scattering cross-section. Knopoff [16] has also investigated this problem and that of shear wave scattering by obstacles [17] and obtained results for the far-field radiation patterns. The case of waves scattered by a hole in a plate has also been studied by McCoy [22]. Chieng [5] has investigated the scattering of elastic waves by multiple cylindrical cavities in a medium. The motion of a cylindrical rigid inclusion under harmonic P and SV waves has been investigated by Miles [26], while Mow [28, 29] has obtained results for the transient motion of a rigid spherical inclusion. Thau and Pao [45, 46, 47] have considered the case of wave scattering by parabolic cylindrical obstacles. Separation of variables and series expansions still pertain for this geometry, but, since the eigenfunctions of the problem are not orthogonal, large systems of equations must be solved simultaneously. Perturbation techniques are also applied in the references cited to supplement the expansion results in the low-frequency range. The investigations cited are only a partial list of the many studies that have been conducted in this area. Mow and Pao [30] have presented an extensive monograph on this subject. We close by noting, as in so many other areas of wave mechanics, that Rayleigh [35] made some of the earliest significant contributions.

7.2. Diffraction of plane waves

We now wish to consider the interaction of propagating plane waves with obstacles of more complex shape than the cylindrical and spherical obstacles of the last section. In particular, consider the presence of sharp edges in the radiation field. Such situations are also associated with diffraction effects in optics, wherein sharp shadows are precluded.

Now a characteristic of the problems of the last section was that the boundaries were such that coordinate systems for which the wave equation was separable were appropriate. There are, however, only eleven coordinate systems for which the scalar wave equation is separable† and when the vector wave equation governs (as in the general elasticity case) separation is possible in even fewer.‡ With the exception of some special axially symmetric problems, this accounts for the geometric shapes that can be treated by separation of variables. It is evident, therefore, that for those problems where the bounding surface is not separable, or 'not quite separable', some different mathematical tools must be used. This results in a certain degree of escalation in mathematical complexity, an unfortunate but unavoidable by-product of considering a wider class of problems.

For such problems, the use of integral-equation techniques offers powerful methods of solution. Included are the Green's function method and the Wiener–Hopf technique. The Green's function approach, which is widely used, will only be briefly discussed here. The Wiener–Hopf technique, also widely used, will be the method applied to the simplest diffraction problem. In addition to these methods, certain variational techniques also pertain.§

Finally, it should be noted that only scalar diffraction problems will be considered in the following. That is, only a single wave equation will be considered. Of course, this is completely descriptive of the acoustical situation or special elastic-wave cases (for example, SH waves impinging on certain boundaries), but is not adequate for the general elastic case, where a scalar and a vector wave equation govern. However, in many instances, the solution techniques developed for simpler problems can be extended to the more complex cases.

7.2.1. *Discussion of the Green's function approach*

The basic idea of the Green's function method is as follows. Suppose it is desired to calculate a field due to a source distribution; first calculate the effects of each elementary portion of source and call this result $G(\mathbf{r}/\mathbf{r}_0)$, where $\mathbf{r}_0$ represents the element at $\mathbf{r}_0$; then the total field at $\mathbf{r}$ due to the

† See Morse and Feshbach [27, pp. 494–523]. They are (1) rectangular, (2) circular cylindrical, (3) elliptic cylindrical, (4) parabolic cylindrical, (5) spherical, (6) conical, (7) parabolic, (8) prolate spheroidal, (9) oblate spheroidal, (10) ellipsoidal, and (11) paraboloidal.

‡ The first five listed in the preceding footnote.

§ See Morse and Feshbach [27, p. 1513–53] as a start in this field.

source distribution $\rho(\mathbf{r}_0)$ is the integral of $G\rho$ over the whole range of $\mathbf{r}_0$. The function $G(\mathbf{r}/\mathbf{r}_0)$ is the Green's function for the problem.

By considering the inhomogeneous Helmholtz equation as an illustration, these points may be brought out. Thus consider the Helmholtz equation

$$\nabla^2\psi+k^2\psi = -4\eta\rho(\mathbf{r}), \tag{7.2.1}$$

which results from the steady-state wave equation. Replace $\rho(\mathbf{r})$ by the loading or source,

$$\rho(\mathbf{r}) = \delta(\mathbf{r}-\mathbf{r}_0). \tag{7.2.2}$$

Then $G(\mathbf{r}/\mathbf{r}_0)$ will be the solution of

$$\nabla^2 G+k^2 G = -4\pi\delta(\mathbf{r}-\mathbf{r}_0). \tag{7.2.3}$$

Now by manipulating (7.2.1) and (7.2.3) and applying Gauss' theorem, the following integral equation results,†

$$\psi(\mathbf{r}) = \iiint \rho(\mathbf{r}_0)G(\mathbf{r}/\mathbf{r}_0)\,\mathrm{d}v+4\pi\iint \{G(\mathbf{r}/\mathbf{r}_0)\mathrm{grad}\;\psi^{\mathrm{s}}-\psi^{\mathrm{s}}\;\mathrm{grad}\;G(\mathbf{r}/\mathbf{r}_0)\}\,\mathrm{d}A. \tag{7.2.4}$$

Proper consideration of the surface integral in the above enables the boundary conditions appropriate to the given problem to be incorporated.

We will not attempt to go into further detail on this method. The point is, it is basically an integral-equation technique in which the determination of a special solution (the Green's function) enables a great number of additional solutions to be found. For examples of the application of this method to diffraction problems one is referred to Friedlander [10], Knopoff [15], and Thomas [48].

An alternative to the Green's function approach, called the Kirchhoff integral-equation method, has been used by Friedman and Shaw [11], Banaugh [2, 3], and others. As described by Ko and Karlsson [18], the method is based on integral representations of a potential which satisfies a wave equation. A solution for the scattered potential is then given in terms of the distributions of retarded values of the potential and its derivatives on a closed boundary surface together with volume distributions, in the field, of the sources which appear as inhomogeneous terms of the wave equation. Other applications of this technique have been by Fredricks [9] and Shaw [36].

7.2.2. *The Sommerfeld diffraction problem*

We shall now consider a specific diffraction problem as a vehicle for illustrating the general scope of the analysis that must be associated with waves impinging on irregular (that is, inseparable) surfaces. It shall also be used to illustrate a particular integral equation approach known as the Wiener–Hopf technique. This technique provides an extension to the range of problems that may be treated by integral transforms.

† Morse and Feshbach [27, pp. 804–6].

In the problem at hand, plane harmonic waves are considered to impinge on a rigid, half-plane barrier. In this situation, some of the incoming wavefield will reflect from the flat barrier surface, while some will miss the surface completely. Some of the incoming wavefield will strike near the edge of the barrier, and be diffracted into the shadow region behind the barrier. A rough illustration is given in Fig. 7.4. This is the classic Sommerfield diffraction

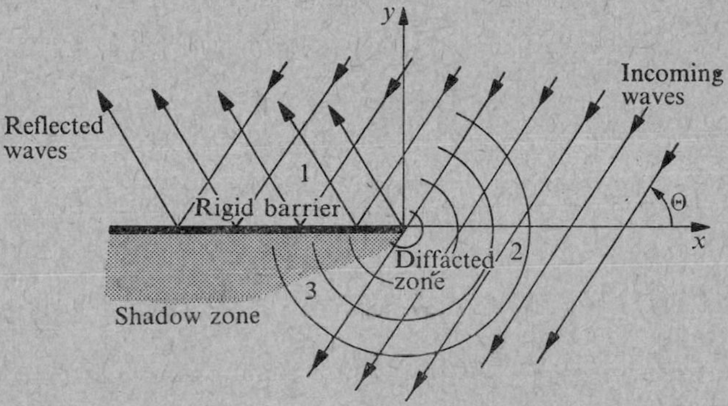

FIG. 7.4. Diffraction of waves by a rigid barrier.

problem, and has been solved by several methods.† The nature of the problem may be one of incident acoustic waves on a rigid barrier, or of incident SH waves on an interior crack. The following analysis of this problem, using the Wiener–Hopf method,‡ is rather involved and uses a number of concepts from complex variable theory. As far as possible, subsidiary discussion, meant to clarify certain points, will be given.

1. *Formulation.* Steady-state plane waves are considered to be propagating in from infinity and striking a rigid barrier. This incident wavefield is given as

$$\phi_i(x, y) = e^{-i(kx\cos\Theta + ky\sin\Theta)} \qquad (0 < \Theta < \pi), \tag{7.2.5}$$

where the time factor $\exp(-i\omega t)$ has been omitted in the preceding and all following expressions. Reflection and diffraction at the barrier will give rise to a diffracted–reflected field $\phi(x, y)$. The total field $\phi_t(x, y)$ will thus be

$$\phi_t(x, y) = \phi(x, y) + \phi_i(x, y), \tag{7.2.6}$$

where ϕ_t satisfies the Helmholtz equation

$$\nabla^2\phi_t + k^2\phi_t = 0, \qquad k^2 = \omega^2/c^2. \tag{7.2.7}$$

Since $\phi_i(x, y)$ satisfies the Helmholtz equation identically, the result (7.2.7) in effect reduces to

$$\nabla^2\phi + k^2\phi = 0. \tag{7.2.8}$$

† See, for example, Stoker [40, pp. 109, 141] or Morse and Feshbach [27, pp. 1383].
‡ See Noble [31] for this and many other diffraction problems solved using this technique.

The incident wave impinging on the barrier yields three regions of wave interaction, labelled 1, 2, and 3 in Fig. 7.4. They consist of the following:

region 1: incident, reflected, and diffracted waves;
region 2: incident and diffracted waves;
region 3: diffracted waves.

The primary boundary condition for the problem is

$$\partial\phi_t/\partial y = 0 \qquad (-\infty < x \leqslant 0, y = 0). \tag{7.2.9}$$

From (7.2.5) and (7.2.6) this gives

$$\partial\phi/\partial y = ik \sin \Theta e^{-ikx\cos\Theta} \qquad (y = 0, -\infty < x \leqslant 0). \tag{7.2.10}$$

(In terms of SH elastic waves, this would correspond to $\partial u/\partial y = 0$; that is, a stress-free boundary or slit.) In addition to this primary condition, which is the obvious one and serves to define the problem, a number of additional conditions, such as continuity or rate of decay, must be imposed on the field quantity ϕ. These conditions will be summarized in the following. The various roles these conditions play will be brought out as the analysis proceeds.

Continuity of ϕ_t, ϕ. We require that $\partial\phi_t/\partial y$ and therefore $\partial\phi/\partial y$ be continuous for $-\infty < x < \infty$ at $y = 0$. It is also required that ϕ_t, and therefore ϕ, be continuous for $0 < x < +\infty$. However, ϕ_t will be discontinuous at $y = 0$, $-\infty < x \leqslant 0$ (that is, on the barrier). This behaviour is illustrated in Fig. 7.5.

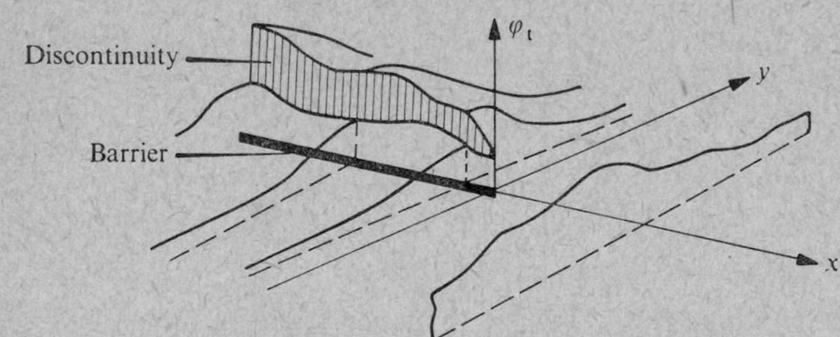

FIG. 7.5. Illustration of the discontinuity in ϕ_t that occurs at the barrier.

Bounds on ϕ. In determining the convergence of Fourier integrals that arise later, it is of value to put upper bounds on the diffracted field ϕ. Consider first regions 1 and 3 of Fig. 7.5. In region 1 as $x \to -\infty$ for any $y > 0$, the total field will be given by the reflected field. Hence, letting k be complex

$$k = k_1 + ik_2, \qquad k_1, k_2 > 0, \tag{7.2.11}$$

we have that $\phi_t \simeq \phi$, and that

$$|\phi| < C_1 \exp(k_2 x \cos \Theta), \qquad y > 0, x \to -\infty. \tag{7.2.12}$$

Similarly, in region 3, as $x \to -\infty$, $y < 0$, which is the shadow region, only a diffracted wave is present. But, as will be shown presently, this will be negligible at large values, so that

$$\phi = \phi_t - \phi_i \to \phi_i, \qquad x \to -\infty, y < 0. \qquad (7.2.13)$$

Hence

$$|\phi| < C_2 \exp(k_2 x \cos \Theta), \qquad y < 0, x \to -\infty. \qquad (7.2.14)$$

(The constants arising in the above and in the immediately following are arbitrary.)

As $x \to +\infty$, the diffracted field in terms of far-field effects may be considered to be produced by a source placed at the leading edge ($x = 0$) of the barrier. The approximate differential equation for this situation would be

$$\nabla^2\phi + k^2\phi = -4\pi\delta(x)\delta(y), \qquad (7.2.15)$$

which has the solution

$$\phi(x, y) = \pi i H_0^{(1)}(kr) \qquad r^2 = x^2 + y^2. \qquad (7.2.16)$$

The asymptotic behaviour of the Hankel function has been considered previously and is given by

$$\lim_{r \to \infty} H_0^{(1)}(kr) \sim C_3 r^{-\frac{1}{2}} \exp(-k_2 r)\exp(ik_1 r). \qquad (7.2.17)$$

Hence we may state

$$|\phi| < C_4 \exp\{-k_2(x^2+y^2)^{\frac{1}{2}}\}, \qquad y \lesseqgtr 0, x \to +\infty. \qquad (7.2.18)$$

Edge conditions. It would not be surprising if the solution had a singularity at the origin, where the barrier edge is located. Generally some type of physical arguments must be employed. The importance of these conditions, which are presented in the summary following, is in establishing the uniqueness of the final solution.

2. *Summary of equations and boundary conditions.*
(a) The total field ϕ_t is given by

$$\phi_t = \phi_i + \phi, \qquad (7.2.19)$$

where

$$\phi_i = e^{-i(kx \cos \Theta + ky \sin \Theta)}, \qquad k = k_1 + ik_2. \qquad (7.2.20)$$

Determine ϕ, which satisfies

$$\nabla^2\phi + k^2\phi = 0 \qquad (7.2.21)$$

and the following boundary conditions.
(b) $y = 0$, $-\infty < x \leqslant 0$,

$$\partial\phi_t/\partial y = 0, \qquad (7.2.22)$$

so that

$$\partial\phi/\partial y = ik \sin \Theta e^{-ikx\cos\Theta}. \tag{7.2.23}$$

Also, $\partial\phi_t/\partial y$, hence $\partial\phi/\partial y$, continuous for $y = 0$, $-\infty < x < \infty$.
(c) $y = 0$, $0 < x < \infty$, ϕ_t, ϕ continuous.
(d) For $y \gtrless 0$

$$\begin{aligned}&\text{(i) } x \to -\infty, \quad |\phi| < C_1 \exp(k_2 \cos\Theta),\\ &\text{(ii) } x \to +\infty, \quad |\phi| < C_2 \exp\{-k_2(x^2+y^2)^{\frac{1}{2}}\}.\end{aligned} \tag{7.2.24}$$

(e) At edge

$$\begin{aligned}\partial\phi_t/\partial y &\to C_3 x^{-\frac{1}{2}}, \quad && x \to +0,\ y = 0,\\ \phi_t &\to C_4, && x \to +0,\ y = 0,\\ \phi_t &\to C_5, && x \to -0,\ y = +0,\\ \phi_t &\to C_6, && x \to -0,\ y = -0.\end{aligned} \tag{7.2.25}$$

3. *Application of Fourier transform.* We seek to apply the Fourier transform, defined as

$$F(\alpha, y) = \frac{1}{\sqrt{(2\pi)}}\int_{-\infty}^{\infty} f(x, y)e^{i\alpha x}\, dx, \tag{7.2.26}$$

with inverse

$$f(x, y) = \frac{1}{\sqrt{(2\pi)}}\int_{-\infty}^{\infty} F(\alpha, y)e^{-i\alpha x}\, d\alpha, \tag{7.2.27}$$

where α is complex and given as $\alpha = \sigma + i\tau$. In the present problem, the semi-infinite nature of the barrier and consequent discontinuity in ϕ leads us to break up the Fourier transform as follows:

$$\Phi(\alpha, y) = \Phi_+(\alpha, y) + \Phi_-(\alpha, y) = \frac{1}{\sqrt{(2\pi)}}\int_{-\infty}^{\infty} \phi(x, y)e^{i\alpha x}\, dx, \tag{7.2.28}$$

where

$$\Phi_+(\alpha, y) = \frac{1}{\sqrt{(2\pi)}}\int_{0}^{\infty} \phi e^{i\alpha x}\, dx, \qquad \Phi_-(\alpha, y) = \frac{1}{\sqrt{(2\pi)}}\int_{-\infty}^{0} \phi e^{i\alpha x}\, dx. \tag{7.2.29}$$

It is important to know the region of regularity, or analyticity, of the transformed quantity Φ in the complex α-plane. From the bounds on Φ given in (7.2.24) it may be easily established that

$$\begin{aligned}&\Phi_+ \text{ analytic for } \tau > -k_2,\\ &\Phi_- \text{ analytic for } \tau < k_2 \cos\Theta.\end{aligned} \tag{7.2.30}$$

Thus, as shown in Fig. 7.6, the regions of analyticity of Φ_+, Φ_- overlap so that the entire function $\Phi(\alpha, y)$ is regular in the strip $-k_2 < \tau < k_2 \cos\Theta$.

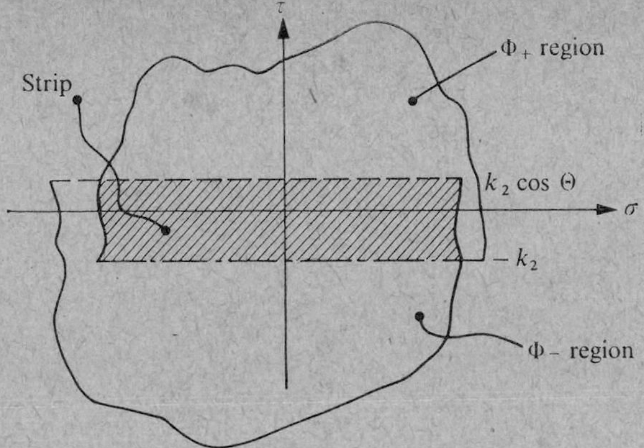

FIG. 7.6. Regions where Φ_+, Φ_- are analytic in the α-plane, and the strip where both are commonly analytic.

This discussion on regions of regularity of the Fourier transform is not peculiar to the Wiener–Hopf development, but pertains to any application of the transform. In the present case the regions are established as follows. Consider Φ_+ and $\alpha = \sigma + i\tau$. Then the first of (7.2.29) becomes

$$\Phi_+ = \int_0^\infty \phi e^{-\tau x}\, dx, \tag{7.2.31}$$

where the $e^{i\sigma x}$ has been dropped since it does not affect the convergence of the integral. As $x \to +\infty$, $|\phi| < \exp(-k_2 x)$, according to the boundary conditions. Hence

$$\Phi_+ \cong \int_0^\infty \exp\{-(\tau + k_2)x\}\, dx, \tag{7.2.32}$$

which exists as long as $\tau + k_2 > 0$, or $\tau > -k_2$. In other words, Φ_+ is analytic in the half-plane $\tau > -k_2$. The condition on Φ_- follows a similar development, except the boundary condition $|\phi| < \exp(-k_2 x \cos \Theta)$ as $x \to -\infty$ is used.

The Fourier transform of the Helmholtz equation then leads to

$$\frac{d^2\Phi(\alpha, y)}{dy^2} - \gamma^2\Phi(\alpha, y) = 0, \qquad \gamma^2 = \alpha^2 - k^2, \tag{7.2.33}$$

where Φ is defined in the sense of (7.2.28).

4. *Transformed solution—with some boundary conditions applied.* The differential equation (7.2.33) is easily solved. However, it must be recognized that $\phi(x, y)$, hence $\Phi(\alpha, y)$, is discontinuous across $y = 0$. Although this discontinuity is only for $x < 0$, we are forced at this point to admit two

solutions, for $y \geq 0$ and $y \leq 0$. Thus we have

$$\Phi(\alpha, y) = \begin{cases} A_1(\alpha)e^{-\gamma y} + B_1(\alpha)e^{\gamma y}, & y \geqslant 0 \\ A_2(\alpha)e^{-\gamma y} + B_2(\alpha)e^{\gamma y}, & y \leqslant 0. \end{cases} \tag{7.2.34}$$

First we will impose a radiation-type condition at infinity, where $y \to \pm\infty$. Thus we want ϕ to decay to zero far from the barrier. At first glance, it would appear that $y \to +\infty$ would require $B_1(\alpha) = 0$ and, as $y \to -\infty$, $A_2(\alpha) = 0$. Although these are the correct choices, the rational selection of the zero coefficients follows a more recondite line of reasoning.

Thus, selection of $B_1 = A_2 = 0$ in the preceding would imply that the real part of γ (which is complex) is greater than zero. This is not an obvious fact and requires closer consideration of γ. Now

$$\gamma = (\alpha^2 - k^2)^{\frac{1}{2}} = (\alpha + k)^{\frac{1}{2}}(\alpha - k)^{\frac{1}{2}}, \tag{7.2.35}$$

where γ is a multi-valued function with branch points at $\pm k$. In order to make these functions single-valued, branch cuts are incorporated in the complex plane. Although the appropriate cuts for the functions encountered in our analysis will be the subject of additional later discussion, it will suffice presently to indicate their selection, as shown in Fig. 7.7. In the figure, branch

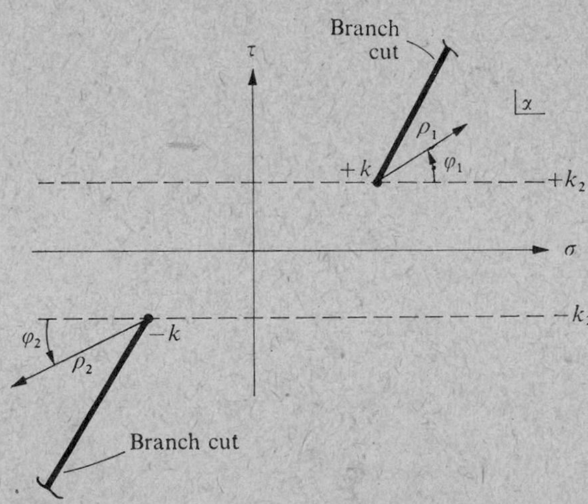

FIG. 7.7. Illustration of branch cuts in the α-plane necessary to make γ single valued.

points are at $\pm k$ and branch cuts extend from these points to $+\infty$ (from $+k$) and $-\infty$ (from $-k$). Using the coordinates $\rho_1, \rho_2, \phi_1, \phi_2$, we have

$$\alpha = k + \rho_1 \exp(i\phi_1), \qquad \alpha = -k + \rho_2 \exp(i\phi_2). \tag{7.2.36}$$

Thus

$$\gamma = \{\rho_1 \exp(i\phi_1)\}^{\frac{1}{2}}\{\rho_2 \exp(i\phi_2)\}^{\frac{1}{2}} = (\rho_1\rho_2)^{\frac{1}{2}} \exp\{\tfrac{1}{2}i(\phi_1 + \phi_2)\}. \tag{7.2.37}$$

Now the relevant statement for the present problem is that for α in the strip $-k_2 < \text{Im}(\alpha) < +k_2$, which encompasses the region of analyticity, then $\text{Re}(\gamma) > 0$. From (7.2.37) this implies $\cos(\phi_1+\phi_2)/2 > 0$. In the figure, $\pm k$ have been located at $\pm k_2$, the maximum permissible distances from the σ-axis. For these cases, with positive ϕ_1, ϕ_2 defined as shown, it should be evident that, as $\sigma \to \pm\infty$, $\cos(\phi_1+\phi_2)/2 \to 0$, and $\cos(\phi_1+\phi_2)/2 > 0$ for lesser values of σ.

With $\text{Re}\,\gamma > 0$ established, we are justified in reducing (7.2.34) to

$$\Phi(\alpha, y) = \begin{cases} A_1(\alpha)e^{-\gamma y}, & y \geqslant 0 \\ B_2(\alpha)e^{\gamma y}, & y \leqslant 0. \end{cases} \tag{7.2.38}$$

From boundary condition (b) regarding the continuity of $\partial\phi/\partial y$, hence $\partial\Phi/\partial y$, for $-\infty < x < \infty$, we have

$$\partial\Phi(\alpha, +0)/\partial y = \partial\Phi(\alpha, -0)/\partial y, \tag{7.2.39}$$

giving

$$-A_1(\alpha) = B_2(\alpha) = -A(\alpha). \tag{7.2.40}$$

Hence

$$\Phi(\alpha, y) = \begin{cases} A(\alpha)e^{-\gamma y}, & y \geqslant 0 \\ -A(\alpha)e^{\gamma y}, & y \leqslant 0. \end{cases} \tag{7.2.41}$$

5. *Introduction of* $\Phi_+(0)$, $\Phi_-(+0)$ *and the remaining boundary conditions.* Up to this point, we have essentially 'followed our nose' in the application of the Fourier transform to a problem with peculiar boundary conditions and, although the application of the Wiener–Hopf technique has been threatened, the analysis till now has not deviated from standard transform theory. However, the need for deviation has arisen in the following fashion. The discontinuity in $\phi(x, y)$ as x goes from > 0 to <0 has forced the definition of $\Phi(\alpha, y)$ in the Φ_+, Φ_- sense, as given by (7.2.29). Thus, having started with the transform and inverse transform defined on the infinite interval

$$(-\infty < x < \infty),$$

we have ended up with transform expressions defined on the semi-infinite intervals, $0 < x < \infty$, $-\infty < x < 0$. The basic idea of the Wiener–Hopf technique is to extend functions defined in one region ($-\infty < x < 0$, say) into a hitherto undefined region ($0 < x < \infty$, say), so that complete functions ($-\infty < x < \infty$) may result. Some of the characteristic means of analysis of implementing this simple concept constitute the apparatus of the Wiener–Hopf technique.

For brevity of notation in the following, we shall replace $\Phi(\alpha, y)$ by $\Phi(\alpha)$, or $\Phi(y)$ when there is no risk of confusion. Thus, for example,

$$\Phi_+(\alpha, 0) \to \Phi_+(0). \tag{7.2.42}$$

We now define

$$\Phi_-(\pm 0) = \lim_{y\to\pm 0} \frac{1}{\sqrt{(2\pi)}} \int_{-\infty}^{0} \phi e^{i\alpha x}\, dx,$$

$$\Phi_+(\pm 0) = \lim_{y\to\pm 0} \frac{1}{\sqrt{(2\pi)}} \int_{0}^{\infty} \phi e^{i\alpha x}\, dx, \qquad (7.2.43)$$

$$\Phi'_+(\alpha, y) = \frac{1}{\sqrt{(2\pi)}} \int_{0}^{\infty} \frac{\partial \phi}{\partial y} e^{i\alpha x}\, dx,$$

$$\Phi'_-(\alpha, y) = \frac{1}{\sqrt{(2\pi)}} \int_{-\infty}^{0} \frac{\partial \phi}{\partial y} e^{i\alpha x}\, dx. \qquad (7.2.44)$$

The definitions of $\Phi'_+(\pm 0)$, $\Phi'_-(\pm 0)$ are similar to those of (7.2.29).

Before applying the boundary conditions at $y = 0$, we make the following observation: continuity of $\phi(x, y)$, $\partial\phi/\partial y$ for $x > 0$ and continuity of $\partial\phi/\partial y$ for $x < 0$, all at $y = 0$, gives

$$\begin{aligned} \Phi_+(+0) &= \Phi_+(-0) = \Phi_+(0), \\ \Phi'_+(+0) &= \Phi_+(-0) = \Phi'_+(0), \\ \Phi'_-(+0) &= \Phi'_-(-0) = \Phi'_-(0). \end{aligned} \qquad (7.2.45)$$

We now enforce the conditions of continuity across $y = 0$ in the following essential statements:

$$\begin{aligned} \Phi_+(0) + \Phi_-(+0) &= A(\alpha), \\ \Phi_+(0) + \Phi_-(-0) &= -A(\alpha), \\ \Phi'_+(0) + \Phi'_-(0) &= -\gamma A(\alpha). \end{aligned} \qquad (7.2.46)$$

In interpreting these statements, we should focus attention on the third equation of (7.2.46). In applying the conditions on $\partial\phi/\partial y$ for $x < 0$ (see (b) of (2) summary of equations and boundary conditions), and hence on Φ', we see that only a portion of Φ' is known, namely $\Phi'_-(0)$. The Wiener–Hopf technique continues a function from its known domain ($x < 0$ here) to the entire domain ($x > 0$). This effectively introduces the unknown $\Phi'_+(0)$; the Wiener–Hopf method seeks to determine it by the process of analytic continuation. With $\Phi'_1(0)$ known, $A(\alpha)$ is known.

6. *Reduction to standard Wiener–Hopf equations.* We will be applying the process of analytic continuation to the various functions of (7.2.46). Hence, it will be desirable to work only with functions whose domain of regularity is known. Since $A(\alpha)$ is unknown in all respects, it will be eliminated from the above. Adding the first two equations of (7.2.46), we obtain

$$2\Phi_+(0) = -\Phi_-(+0) - \Phi_-(-0). \qquad (7.2.47)$$

Next, subtract the second from the first of (7.2.46) to yield an equation for $A(\alpha)$. Substitute this in the third of (7.2.46) to give

$$\Phi'_+(0)+\Phi'_-(0) = -\frac{\gamma}{2}\{\Phi_-(+0)-\Phi_-(-0)\}. \tag{7.2.48}$$

Now, as has been mentioned, $\Phi'_-(0)$ is known. Thus, from the boundary conditions,

$$\Phi'_-(0) = \frac{1}{\sqrt{(2\pi)}}\int_{-\infty}^{0} e^{i\alpha x}(ik \sin \Theta e^{-ikx\cos\Theta})\, dx,$$

$$= \frac{ik \sin \Theta}{\sqrt{(2\pi)}}\int_{-\infty}^{0} e^{ix(\alpha-k\cos\Theta)}\, dx. \tag{7.2.49}$$

This integral is readily found by contour integration† to give

$$\Phi'_-(0) = \frac{k \sin \Theta}{\sqrt{(2\pi)}(\alpha-k \cos \Theta)}. \tag{7.2.50}$$

Now, from (7.2.47) and (7.2.48) we have the sum and difference of two quantities $\Phi_-(+0)$ and $\Phi_-(-0)$. Define

$$2D_- = \Phi_-(+0)-\Phi_-(-0), \qquad 2S_- = \Phi_-(+0)+\Phi_-(-0). \tag{7.2.51}$$

With these definitions and (7.2.50), we obtain the two equations

$$\begin{aligned} \Phi_+(0) &= -S_-, \\ \Phi'_+(0)+\frac{k \sin \Theta}{\sqrt{(2\pi)}(\alpha-k \cos \Theta)} &= -\gamma D_-. \end{aligned} \tag{7.2.52}$$

These equations have been put in the 'standard' Weiner–Hopf form of

$$R(\alpha)\Phi_+(\alpha)+S(\alpha)\Psi_-(\alpha)+T(\alpha) = 0, \tag{7.2.53}$$

where R, S, T are known functions and Φ_+, Ψ_- are unknown functions, known only to be regular in the upper half-plane (Φ_+) and lower half-plane (Ψ_-), respectively. Thus, in the present case, we have from the first and second equations, respectively, of (7.2.52)

$$\begin{aligned} &R(\alpha) = 1, \quad S(\alpha) = 1, \quad T(\alpha) = 0, \\ &R(\alpha) = 1, \quad S(\alpha) = \gamma, \quad T(\alpha) = k \sin \Theta/\sqrt{(2\pi)}(\alpha-k \cos \Theta). \end{aligned} \tag{7.2.54}$$

In our case, S_-, D_- are unknown (as are Φ'_+, Φ_+), but regular in $\tau < k_2 \cos \Theta$.

† Thus, replace x by $z = x+iy$ and integrate around the contour $-\infty < x < 0$, $0 < iy < +\infty$, and a quarter-circle from $+i\infty$ to $-\infty$.

7. *Outline of the fundamental step.* We are now on the verge of applying the fundamental step of the Wiener–Hopf procedure. This is to find a function $K_+(\alpha)$, and $K_-(\alpha)$ such that

$$R(\alpha)/S(\alpha) = K_+(\alpha)/K_-(\alpha), \tag{7.2.55}$$

where $K_+(\alpha)$ is regular in $\tau > \tau_-$ ($-k_2$ in our case), and $K_-(\alpha)$ is regular in $\tau < \tau_+$ ($k_2 \cos \Theta$ in our case). Then (7.2.53) becomes

$$K_+(\alpha)\Phi_+(\alpha)+K_-(\alpha)\Psi_-(\alpha)+K_-(\alpha)T(\alpha)/S(\alpha) = 0. \tag{7.2.56}$$

Decompose K_-T/S into the form

$$K_-(\alpha)T(\alpha)/S(\alpha) = H_+(\alpha)+H_-(\alpha). \tag{7.2.57}$$

Then (7.2.56) may be written as

$$K_+(\alpha)\Phi_+(\alpha)+H_+(\alpha) = -K_-(\alpha)\Psi_-(\alpha)-H_-(\alpha) = J(\alpha). \tag{7.2.58}$$

By this rearrangement we have defined a new function $J(\alpha)$. Supposedly $J(\alpha)$ is regular only in the strip $\tau_- < \tau < \tau_+$ ($k_2 < \tau < k_2 \cos \Theta$ in our case). However, $K_+\Phi_+ + H_+$ is regular in the upper half-plane and $K_-\Psi_- + H_-$ is regular in the lower half-plane. Hence, by analytic continuation the function is regular over the whole α-plane.

The next step is to determine $J(\alpha)$, and this is done by applying boundary conditions (in our case, 2(e) (see p. 414)) and a form of Liouville's theorem from complex variables. Once $J(\alpha)$ is known solutions for Φ_+, Ψ_- follow from (7.2.58), so that, in principle, the problem is solved. Thus, in our present diffraction problem, steps 1–6 have been for the purpose of putting everything in the Wiener–Hopf form.

We note that the concept of analytic continuation of functions in the complex plane, referred to several times thus far, is discussed in any book on complex-variable theory.† Basically, the idea is the following: suppose a function $f_1(\alpha)$ is regular in region D_1 of the α-plane and $f_2(\alpha)$ is regular in region D_2 and that D_1, D_2 overlap; suppose $f_1 = f_2$ in the overlap region, then f_2 is said to be the analytic continuation of f_1 into D_2. A standard example illustrating this concept is the function

$$f_1(z) = 1+z+z^2 \ldots = \sum_{n=0}^{\infty} z^n, \qquad |z| < 1. \tag{7.2.59}$$

But, consider

$$f_2(z) = \frac{1}{1-z}, \qquad z \neq 1, \tag{7.2.60}$$

and note that

$$f_1(z) = f_2(z), \qquad |z| < 1. \tag{7.2.61}$$

Then $f_2(z)$ is the analytic continuation of $f_1(z)$ into the remainder of the complex plane $z \neq 1$.

† See, for example, Churchill [6, pp. 188–94] or Morse and Feshbach [27, pp. 389–98].

8. *Factorization of the Wiener–Hopf equations.* Consider the second of (7.2.52), and note that $\gamma = (\alpha-k)^{\frac{1}{2}}(\alpha+k)^{\frac{1}{2}}$, so that we may write

$$\frac{\Phi'_{+}(0)}{(\alpha+k)^{\frac{1}{2}}}+(\alpha-k)^{\frac{1}{2}}D_{-}+\frac{k\sin\Theta}{\sqrt{(2\pi)}(\alpha+k)^{\frac{1}{2}}(\alpha-k\cos\Theta)}=0. \qquad (7.2.62)$$

Now, in factoring γ in this way, we define the branches of the factors as follows:

$$\begin{aligned} \sigma &\to +\infty, \quad (\alpha-k)^{\frac{1}{2}} \to \alpha^{\frac{1}{2}}, \\ \sigma &\to -\infty, \quad (\alpha+k)^{\frac{1}{2}} \to \alpha^{\frac{1}{2}}. \end{aligned} \quad (-k_2 < \tau < k_2) \qquad (7.2.63)$$

Then the factor $(\alpha+k)^{\frac{1}{2}}$ is regular for $\tau > -k_2$, while $(\alpha-k)^{\frac{1}{2}}$ is regular for $\tau < +k_2$. Consequently, (7.2.62) has been brought to the general stage of the Wiener–Hopf procedure given by (7.2.56).

(*Remark.* Additional discussion on the branches of γ, referred to in the preceding and first referred to with reference to Fig. 7.7 is warranted. The liberty will be taken of reviewing the basic aspects of the subject as presented in complex variable theory.

Thus consider $f(\alpha) = \alpha^{\frac{1}{2}}$, and let $\alpha = \rho \exp(i\phi)$. This function is multi-valued, since $\rho \exp\{i(\phi+2n\pi)\} = \rho \exp(i\phi)$, so that

$$f(\alpha) = \rho^{\frac{1}{2}}e^{i\phi/2}, \qquad \rho^{\frac{1}{2}}e^{i(\phi/2+\pi)}, \ldots.$$

We may make $f(\alpha)$ single-valued by requiring $-\pi < \phi < \pi$, as shown in Fig. 7.8(a). With this restriction, the first branch of $f(\alpha)$ is generated in the $f(\alpha)$-plane (shaded region of Fig. 7.8(b)). This branch may be identified by the fact that $+p$ in the α-plane is taken to $+p^{\frac{1}{2}}$. The location of the branch cut is arbitrary, and the effects of other choices are shown in Fig. 7.8(c) and (d).

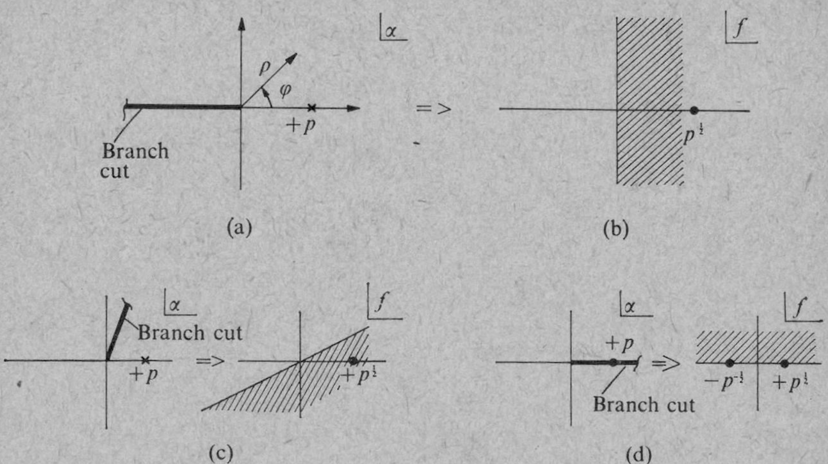

FIG. 7.8. (a), (b) Branch cut in the α-plane that makes $f = \alpha^{\frac{1}{2}}$ single-valued. (c), (d) The effects of other branch cuts.

Now, again referring to (a) in the preceding figure, the second branch of $f(\alpha)$ is obtained by restricting ϕ such that

$$\pi < \phi < 2\pi, \qquad -2\pi < \phi < -\pi,$$

This would generate the region $\tau < 0$ in Fig. 7.8(b) with similar restrictions on ϕ generating the other branches of Fig. 7.8(c) and (d).

To extend this, consider the two functions

$$\chi = (\alpha)^{\frac{1}{2}}, \qquad \psi = (-\alpha)^{\frac{1}{2}}.$$

Consider the first two branches of each of these functions, where the branch cut, common for both, has been taken in the upper half α-plane, as in Fig. 7.8(a). Select the branches so that

(1) if p = positive real number, $\chi = +p^{\frac{1}{2}}$;

(2) if $\alpha = -p$, $\psi = +p^{\frac{1}{2}}$.

This means selecting the first branch of χ and the second branch of ψ, as may be seen in the illustrations of Fig. 7.9(a) and (b). Thus the first branch

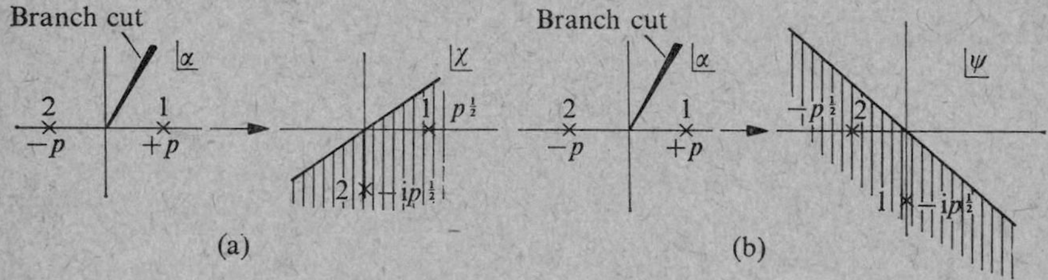

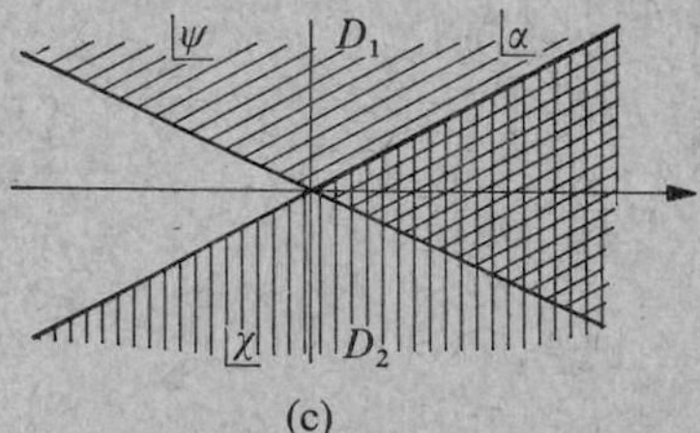

FIG. 7.9. (a), (b) Branches of χ, ψ. (c) The common zone of analyticity.

of χ takes $+p$ to $+p^{\frac{1}{2}}$, while the first branch of ψ takes $-p$ to $-p^{\frac{1}{2}}$. However, the second branch of ψ will take $-p$ to $+p^{\frac{1}{2}}$. We now observe that, along the real axis ($\tau = 0$), $\chi = \mathrm{i}\psi$. Thus, $+p$ gives

$$\chi = p^{\frac{1}{2}}, \qquad \psi = -\mathrm{i}p^{\frac{1}{2}}, \qquad \mathrm{i}\psi = +p^{\frac{1}{2}}.$$

The regions of analyticity of χ, ψ, with branches defined as given, are shown in Fig. 7.9(c). The double-cross-hatched region represents the common zone of of analyticity of χ and ψ. However, $\chi = i\psi$ along the real axis. Then, by a basic theorem of analytic continuation, χ is the continuation of ψ from D_2 to D_1 (and vice versa).

Although this review has been rather lengthy, it provides the necessary background for (7.2.63). Thus, we have factored γ as

$$\gamma = \chi_1\chi_2, \qquad \chi_1 = (\alpha-k)^{\frac{1}{2}}, \qquad \chi_2 = (\alpha+k)^{\frac{1}{2}}.$$

The cuts for χ_1, χ_2 have been shown previously in Fig. 7.7. With these definitions, it should be apparent that the first branches of χ_1, χ_2 are appropriate for (7.2.62).)

Hence, to continue, we see that (7.2.62) is in a form such that $\Phi'_+/(\alpha+k)^{\frac{1}{2}}$ is regular for $\tau > -k_2$, while $(\alpha-k)^{\frac{1}{2}}D_-$ is regular for $\tau < +k_2$.

We now consider the third term of the right-hand side of (7.2.62), with the idea of decomposing it to the form $H_+(\alpha)$, $H_-(\alpha)$ given in the Wiener–Hopf procedure outline step (7.2.57). In particular, we first note that this term, because of the pole at $\alpha = k \cos \Theta$ and the branch point of $(\alpha+k)^{\frac{1}{2}}$, is regular only in the strip $-k_2 < \tau < k_2 \cos \Theta$. But, following the previous procedure, we wish to resolve

$$\frac{k \sin \Theta}{\sqrt{(2\pi)}(\alpha+k)^{\frac{1}{2}}(\alpha-k \cos \Theta)} = H_+(\alpha)+H_-(\alpha). \qquad (7.2.64)$$

As in the case of much previous work in this section, the resolution relies on complex-variable theory.

The basic theorem on which the resolution relies is stated approximately as follows:

THEOREM *Let $f(\alpha)$ be analytic in the strip $\tau_- < \tau < \tau_+$ and bounded as $|\sigma| \to \infty$. Then for $\tau_- < c < \tau < d < \tau_+$, we have*

$$f(\alpha) = f_+(\alpha)+f_-(\alpha),$$

$$f_+(\alpha) = \frac{1}{2\pi i}\int_{-\infty+ic}^{-\infty+ic} \frac{f(\zeta)}{\zeta-\alpha}\, d\zeta, \qquad f_-(\alpha) = -\frac{1}{2\pi i}\int_{-\infty+id}^{+\infty+id} \frac{f(\zeta)}{\zeta-\alpha}\, d\zeta.$$

where $f_+(\alpha)$ is regular for all $\tau > \tau_-$, $f_-(\alpha)$ is regular for all $\tau < \tau_+$.

To implement the preceding theorem in the present case, we select contours and cuts as shown in Fig. 7.10. The point α is taken in the strip

$$-k_2 < \tau < k_2 \cos \Theta.$$

Consider the case of $f_+(\alpha)$.

$$\frac{1}{\sqrt{(2\pi)}}\int_{-\infty-ik_2}^{+\infty-ik_2} \frac{k \sin \Theta\, d\zeta}{(\zeta+k)^{\frac{1}{2}}(\zeta-k \cos \Theta)(\zeta-\alpha)} + \int_{\Gamma+} = 2\pi i \sum \text{Res.} \qquad (7.2.65)$$

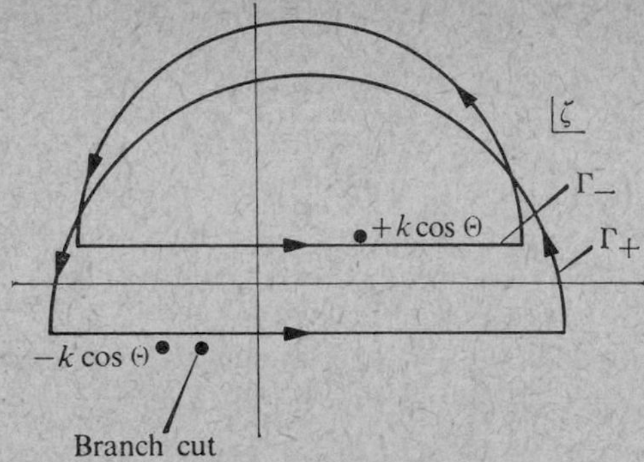

FIG. 7.10. Contours and cuts for H_+, H_-.

The integral about Γ_+ vanishes for the contour radius approaching infinity. Simple poles exist at $\zeta = \alpha$, $k\cos\Theta$, which have residues of

$$\text{Res} = \frac{k\sin\Theta}{(\alpha+k)^{\frac{1}{2}}(\alpha-k\cos\Theta)}, \frac{k\sin\Theta}{(k\cos\Theta+k)^{\frac{1}{2}}(k\cos\Theta-\alpha)}, \tag{7.2.66}$$

respectively. Then $H_+(\alpha)$ becomes

$$H_+(\alpha) = \frac{k\sin\Theta}{\sqrt{(2\pi)}(\alpha-k\cos\Theta)}\left\{\frac{1}{(\alpha+k)^{\frac{1}{2}}}-\frac{1}{(k+k\cos\Theta)^{\frac{1}{2}}}\right\}. \tag{7.2.67}$$

In a similar fashion $H_-(\alpha)$ may be evaluated, where only a singularity $\zeta = k\cos\Theta$ is contained in the integral. The results are

$$\begin{aligned}\frac{k\sin\Theta}{\sqrt{(2\pi)}(\alpha+k)^{\frac{1}{2}}(\alpha-k\cos\Theta)} &= \frac{k\sin\Theta}{\sqrt{(2\pi)}(\alpha-k\cos\Theta)}\left\{\frac{1}{(\alpha+k)^{\frac{1}{2}}}-\frac{1}{(k+k\cos\Theta)^{\frac{1}{2}}}\right\}+\\ &\quad+\frac{k\sin\Theta}{\sqrt{(2\pi)}(k+k\cos\Theta)^{\frac{1}{2}}(\alpha-k\cos\Theta)}\\ &= H_+(\alpha)+H_-(\alpha).\end{aligned} \tag{7.2.68}$$

With this resolution at hand, we now rearrange (7.2.62) according to the Wiener–Hopf form given in (7.2.58),

$$\frac{\Phi'_+(0)}{(\alpha+k)^{\frac{1}{2}}}+H_+(\alpha) = -(\alpha-k)^{\frac{1}{2}}D_- - H_-(\alpha) = J(\alpha). \tag{7.2.69}$$

9. *Determination of* $J(\alpha)$. The form (7.2.69) defines a function regular in $\tau > -k_2$, $\tau < k_2\cos\Theta$ and in the overlap strip—hence it is regular in the whole α-plane. Now the exact form of $J(\alpha)$ is found from an extended form of Liouville's theorem, which is approximately stated as follows: *If* $f(\alpha)$ *is a function such that* $|f(\alpha)| \leqslant M$ *for all* α, M *being a constant, then* $f(\alpha)$ *is a constant*. The extension of this theorem that pertains in the present case is as

follows: *If $f(\alpha)$ is a function such that $|f(\alpha)| \leqslant M|\alpha|^p$ as $|\alpha| \to \infty$, where M, p are constants, then $f(\alpha)$ is a polynomial of degree less than or equal to p.*

The application of this extended theorem in the present case used boundary condition (e) of the originally stated problem. These were conditions placed on the edge. Thus, having arrived at this stage of the analysis, it would be apparent that additional conditions of a particular type would need be invoked before the solution could proceed. This accounts for the rather peculiar form of these conditions.

The detailed application of these conditions will be foregone here, and the results stated. It can be shown that $J(\alpha)$ must be regular in the α-plane and tend to zero as $|\alpha| \to \infty$. Then, with this conclusion, the direct application of Liouville's theorem indicates that

$$J(\alpha) = 0. \tag{7.2.70}$$

10. *The Wiener–Hopf solution.* Having 'determined' $J(\alpha)$ in the last section, we now have from (4.2.69)

$$\begin{aligned} \Phi'_+(0) &= -(\alpha+k)^{\frac{1}{2}}H_+(\alpha), \\ D_- &= -(\alpha-k)^{\frac{1}{2}}H_-(\alpha). \end{aligned} \tag{7.2.71}$$

Then from the third eqn of (7.2.46) we have

$$\begin{aligned} A(\alpha) &= -\frac{1}{\gamma}\left\{\Phi'_+(0)+\frac{k \sin \Theta}{\sqrt{(2\pi)}(\alpha-k \cos \Theta)}\right\}, \\ &= -\frac{1}{\sqrt{(2\pi)}}\frac{k \sin \Theta}{(k+k \cos \Theta)^{\frac{1}{2}}(\alpha-k)^{\frac{1}{2}}(\alpha-k \cos \Theta)}. \end{aligned} \tag{7.2.72}$$

The Fourier inversion formula must now be applied to (7.2.43). The usual Fourier inversion is given as

$$f(x) = \frac{1}{\sqrt{(2\pi)}}\int_{-\infty}^{\infty} F(\alpha)e^{-i\alpha x}\, d\alpha. \tag{7.2.73}$$

However, for $F(\alpha)$ analytic in the strip $\tau_- < \tau < \tau_+$ we may, without loss of generality, shift the contour slightly above or below the $\tau = 0$ axis assumed in the above form, to give

$$f(x) = \frac{1}{\sqrt{(2\pi)}}\int_{i\tau-\infty}^{i\tau+\infty} F(\alpha)e^{-i\alpha x}\, d\alpha. \tag{7.2.74}$$

Using the above form of the Fourier inversion, the Weiner–Hopf solution for the total field is given by

$$\phi_+(x, y) = e^{-ik(x \cos \Theta+y \sin \Theta)} \mp \frac{1}{2\pi}(k-k \cos \Theta)^{\frac{1}{2}} \int_{-\infty+ia}^{+\infty+ia} \frac{e^{-i\alpha x \mp \gamma y}}{(\alpha-k)^{\frac{1}{2}}(\alpha-k \cos \Theta)}\, d\alpha, \tag{7.2.75}$$

where the upper sign is for $y \geqslant 0$, the lower sign for $y \leqslant 0$.

11. *The final solution.* The result (7.2.75) may be considered to be the Wiener–Hopf solution. It may appear somewhat of an anticlimax to have brought forth, after so much labour, such an apparently incomplete solution. However, this is not actually the case, since the integral resulting is 'well known'. Carrying out the details again requires complex-variable theory of a fairly heavy calibre, but the results are in terms of Fresnel integrals, defined as

$$F(v) = \int_v^\infty \exp(iu^2)\,du. \tag{7.2.76}$$

The properties of these integrals have been extensively tabulated.† The results are

$$\phi_t(x, y) = e^{-ik(x\cos\Theta + y\sin\Theta)} \mp \frac{I}{2\pi}, \tag{7.2.77}$$

where

$$I = 2\sqrt{\pi}e^{\pi i/4}[-e^{-ikr\cos(\theta-\Theta)}F\{\sqrt{(2kr)}\cos\tfrac{1}{2}(\theta-\Theta)\}+ \\ +e^{-ikr\cos(\theta+\Theta)}F\{\sqrt{(2kr)}\cos\tfrac{1}{2}(\theta+\Theta)\}], \qquad -\pi \leqslant \theta \leqslant \pi. \tag{7.2.78}$$

For details on completing the above integration, as well as for more detailed discussion of various points of the Wiener–Hopf procedure, the reader is referred to Noble [31].

12. *Discussion.* As an illustration of diffraction theory, where the boundary conditions are such as to remove separation of variables as an approach, the Sommerfeld diffraction problem has been considered. As an illustration of the method of solution, the Wiener–Hopf technique has been developed. We should first note that the problem considered was the simplest possible case. Complications due to additional edges or due to finite thicknesses could be added singly or in combination. Also, as has been pointed out, the simplest elastic-wave case, equivalent to the acoustic problem, was considered. Hence, if the analysis appeared formidable in the present problem, the difficulties inherent in more complex geometries are easily imagined.

As was mentioned before formal analysis was undertaken, an integral equation approach to such diffraction problems is appropriate. Possible approaches are the Green's function, Fourier transforms, or Fredholm integral equations. Although the Wiener–Hopf technique was presented in the context of the Fourier approach, the basic principles involving analytic continuation may be used in the other two methods.

In any event, the analysis of the present problem was rather intricate, and it is open to question whether the Green's function or Fredholm equation approach might not have been simpler. For example, Stoker‡ solves the

† See Abramowitz and Stegun [1].
‡ Pp. 109–33, 141–5 of Reference [40].

Sommerfeld problem by two techniques, one of them the Wiener–Hopf method. In summarizing the two approaches, he refers to the latter as having the air of a *tour de force* in function theory, amongst other things. In actuality, this method should be regarded as another tool of analysis, having limitations as well as points of strength. Many of the intricate points of analysing by this method have their analogues in the other approaches, for example.

We note that the technical literature of diffraction problems is quite voluminous and no effort is made to review the many contributions here. We note that Sih and coworkers [20, 38, 39] have considered P and S waves impinging on cracks of finite size and have employed or extended the Wiener–Hopf method in these studies. Thau and coworkers (see, for example, [41, 42, 43, and 44]) have investigated a large number of diffraction problems, including obstacles in a half-space and elastic obstacles. The Wiener–Hopf procedure arises in a number of these studies.

7.2.3. *Geometric acoustics*

Having established the formidability of elastic scattering and diffraction problems in the previous sections, the natural question arises whether new approaches can be developed to these problems that will generate useful information without some of the mathematical difficulties associated with present methods. Since a considerable amount of work has been done in acoustics and optics, it is logical to see if new methods have evolved in these areas for problems in scattering and diffraction, in the hope that they might be applied to elastic scattering.

As a matter of fact, it appears that certain methods have been devised in the field of acoustics for handling complex diffraction problems. These methods, which are approximate in nature, have been modelled on methods first developed in optics and are generally denoted geometrical acoustics. They represent extensions of geometrical optics.

As in the case of geometric optics, geometric acoustics is based on the postulate that fields propagate along rays. However, in optics it is well known that ray theory does not account for the 'bending' of light around corners, in other words diffraction regions. To circumvent this, the acoustic development introduces the concept of diffracted rays, in addition to the usual optic-type rays. These rays are capable of travelling in part on the surface of an object, hence enabling the diffraction effect to be produced. Furthermore, the theory assigns a field value at each point along the ray (including amplitude, phase, and polarization). The total field at a point is taken to be the sum of all rays passing through that point. Hence, by using the theory of geometrical acoustics, an explicit expression may be obtained for the field produced at any point when a wave hits a smooth, convex object.

The principal developments in this area have been made by J. B. Keller. References [12], [13], [14], and [19] represent only a very partial list of developments in this field by Keller and his co-workers. Other developments have been made by Zauderer [51, 52]. The book by Friedlander [10] is devoted to this aspect of considering diffraction problems. Miklowitz and coworkers [24, 25, 32] have applied this technique to elastic scattering problems.

References

1. ABRAMOWITZ, M. and STEGUN, I. A. *Handbook of mathematical functions: with formulas, graphs, and mathematical tables.* Dover Publications, New York (1965).
2. BANAUGH, R. P. *Scattering of acoustic and elastic waves by surfaces of arbitrary shape.* Univ. of Calif. Rad. Lab. Report No. UCRL-6779 (1962).
3. ——. Application of integral representations of displacement potentials in elastodynamics. *Bull. seism. Soc. Am.* **54,** 1073–86 (1964).
4. BEEBE, W. M. *An experimental investigation of dynamic crack propagation in plastic and metals.* Tech. Rep. AFML-TR-66-249, Air Force Material Laboratory (Nov. 1966).
5. CHIENG, S. L. Multiple scattering of elastic waves by parallel cylinders. *J. appl. Mech.* **36,** 523–7 (1969).
6. CHURCHILL, R. V. *Introduction to complex variables and applications.* McGraw-Hill, New York (1948).
7. DURELLI, A. J. and RILEY, W. F. Stress distribution on the boundary of a circular hole in a large plate during passage of a stress pulse of long duration. *J. appl. Mech.* **28,** 245–51 (1961).
8. EINSPRUCH, N. G. and TRUELL, R. Scattering of a plane longitudinal wave by a spherical fluid obstacle in an elastic medium. *J. acoust. Soc. Am.* **32,** 214–20 (1960).
9. FREDRICKS, R. W. Diffraction of an elastic pulse in a loaded half-space. *J. acoust. Soc. Am.* **33,** 17–22 (1961).
10. FRIEDLANDER, F. G. *Sound Pulses.* Cambridge University Press (1958).
11. FRIEDMAN, M. B. and SHAW, R. P. Diffraction of pulses by cylindrical obstacles of arbitrary cross section. *J. appl. Mech.* **29,** 40 (1962).
12. KELLER, J. B. Geometrical acoustics, I. The theory of weak shock waves. *J. appl. Phys.* **25,** 938–47 (1954).
13. ——. Geometrical theory of diffraction. *J. opt. Soc. Am.* **52,** 116–30 (1962).
14. —— and KARAL, F. C. (Jr.). Geometrical theory of elastic surface-wave excitation and propagation. *J. acoust. Soc. Am.* **36,** 32–40 (1964).
15. KNOPOFF, L. Diffraction of elastic waves. *J. acoust. Soc. Am.* **28,** 2, 217–29 (1956).
16. ——. Scattering of compression waves by spherical obstacles. *Geophysics* **24,** 30–9 (1959).
17. ——. Scattering of shear waves by spherical obstacles. *Geophysics,* **24,** 209–19 (1959).
18. Ko, W. L. and KARLSSON, T. Application of Kirchhoff's integral equation formulation to an elastic wave scattering problem. *J. appl. Mech.* **34,** 921–30 (1967).

19. LEVY, B. R. and KELLER, J. B. Diffraction by a smooth object. *Commun. pure appl. Math.* **12,** 159–209 (1959).
20. LOEBER, J. F. and SIH, G. C. Diffraction of antiplane shear waves by a finite crack. *J. acoust. Soc. Am.* **44,** 90–8 (1968).
21. LINDSAY, R. B. *Mechanical radiation.* McGraw-Hill, New York (1960).
22. McCOY, J. J. Effects of non-propagating plate waves on dynamical stress concentrations. *Int. J. Solids Struct.* **4,** 355–70 (1968).
23. McLACHLAN, N. W. *Bessel functions for engineers.* Clarendon Press, Oxford (1961).
24. MIKLOWITZ, J. Pulse propagation in a viscoelastic solid with geometric dispersion. In *Stress waves in anelastic solids*, pp. 255–76. Springer-Verlag, Berlin (1964).
25. ——. Scattering of a plane elastic compressional pulse by a cylindrical cavity. *Proc. XIth Int. Congr. appl. Mech.* Springer-Verlag, Berlin (1966).
26. MILES, J. W. Motion of a rigid cylinder due to a plane elastic wave. *J. acoust. Soc. Am.* **32,** 1656–9 (1960).
27. MORSE, P. and FESHBACH, H. *Methods of theoretical physics* Vols. 1 and 2. McGraw-Hill, New York (1953).
28. MOW, C. C. Transient response of a rigid spherical inclusion in an elastic medium. *J. appl. Mech.* **32,** 637 (1965).
29. ——. On the transient motion of a rigid spherical inclusion in an elastic medium and its inverse problem. *J. appl. Mech.* **33,** 807 (1966).
30. —— and PAO, Y. H. *The diffraction of elastic waves and dynamic stress concentrations.* RAND Rep. R-482-PR (April 1971).
31. NOBLE, B. *Methods based on the Wiener–Hopf technique.* Pergamon Press, New York (1958).
32. NORWOOD, F. R. and MIKLOWITZ, J. Diffraction of transient elastic waves by a spherical cavity. *J. appl. Mech.* **34,** 735–44 (1967).
33. PAO, Y. H. Dynamical stress concentration in an elastic plate. *J. appl. Mech.* **29,** 299–305 (1962).
34. —— and MOW, C. C. Scattering of plane compressional waves by a spherical obstacle. *J. appl. Phys.* **34,** 493–9 (1963).
35. RAYLEIGH, J. W. S. *The theory of sound* Vols. I and II. Dover Publications, New York (1945).
36. SHAW, R. P. Retarded potential approach to the scattering of elastic pulses by rigid obstacles of arbitrary shape. *J. acoust. Soc. Am.* **44,** 745–8 (1968).
37. SHEA, R. Dynamic stress-concentration Factors. *Exp. Mech.* **21,** 20–4 (1964).
38. SIH, G. C. and LOEBER, J. F. Torsional vibration of an elastic solid containing a penny-shaped crack. *J. acoust. Soc. Am.* **44,** 1237–45 (1968).
39. —— ——. Wave propagation in an elastic solid with a line of discontinuity or finite crack. *Q. appl. Math.* **27,** 193–213 (1969).
40. STOKER, J. J. *Water waves.* Wiley–Interscience, New York (1957).
41. THAU, S. A. Dynamic reactions along a rigid-smooth wall in an elastic half-space with a moving boundary load. *Int. J. Solids Struct.* **4,** 1–13 (1968).
42. ——. Motion of a finite rigid strip in an elastic half-space subjected to blast wave loading. *Int. J. Solids Struct.* **7,** 193–211 (1971).

43. THAU, S. A. and LU, T.-H. Dynamic stress concentration at a cylindrical inclusion in an elastic medium with an arbitrarily stiff bond. *Int. J. Mech. Sci.* **11**, 677–88 (1969).
44. —— ——. Diffraction of transient horizontal shear waves by a finite rigid ribbon. *Int. J. Eng. Sci.* **8**, 857–74 (1970).
45. —— and PAO, Y. H. Diffractions of horizontal shear waves by a parabolic cylinder and dynamic stress concentrations. *J. appl. Mech.* **33**, 785–92 (1966).
46. —— ——. Stress-intensification near a semi-infinite rigid-smooth strip due to diffraction of elastic waves. *J. appl. Mech.* **34**, 119–26 (1967).
47. —— ——. Wave function expansions and perturbation method for the diffraction of elastic waves by a parabolic cylinder. *J. appl. Mech.* **34**, 915–20 (1967).
48. THOMAS, D. P. Electromagnetic diffraction by two coaxial discs. *Proc. Camb. phil. Soc. Math. Phys. Sci.* **60**, 621–34 (1964).
49. WELLS, A. A. and POST, D. *The dynamic stress distribution surrounding a running crack—a photoelastic analysis*. Nav. Res. Laboratory, NRL-4935, Washington D.C. (April 1957).
50. YING, C. F. and TRUELL, R. Scattering of a plane longitudinal wave by a spherical obstacle in an isotropically elastic solid. *J. appl. Phys.* **27**, 1086–97 (1956).
51. ZAUDERER, E. Wave propagation around a convex cylinder. *J. Math. Mech.* **13**, 171–86 (1964).
52. ——. Wave propagation around a smooth object. *J. Math. Mech.* **13**, 187–200 (1964).

Problems

7.1. Formulate and solve the problem of scattering of plane harmonic SH waves incident on a rigid immovable cylinder. That is, let the boundary conditions be given by $u = 0$ at $r = a$.

7.2. Attempt a general formulation and solution of the problem of plane, harmonic SH waves incident on an elastic cylinder. Then, using a procedure similar to that illustrated in the text for the spherical scattering problem, attempt to recover various special cases such as the cavity, the rigid, immovable cylinder (see Problem 7.1), and the rigid cylinder capable of translation.

7.3. Consider the results for scattering of SH waves by a cylindrical cavity. Assume $\gamma a \gg 1$, and obtain an approximate expression for the scattered power for this case of Rayleigh scattering.

7.4. Consider the results given for scattering of waves by a spherical cavity (7.1.76). Verify the reduction of the general results (7.1.74) to the simpler form. Assume $\alpha_1 a \gg 1$ (Rayleigh scattering) and obtain approximate expressions for the coefficient matrix and the scattered wavefields.

7.5. Attempt to trace through the analysis of scattering of SH waves by a slit, where the edges of the slit are now considered to be clamped (that is, $u = 0$, $-\infty < x \leq 0$, $y = 0$) instead of traction-free as in the text.

8 Wave propagation in plates and rods

WE NOW consider the propagation of waves in plates and rods (and cylindrical shells) as governed by the exact equations of elasticity. This represents the first instance where geometries, previously studied using strength-of-material theories, are again considered. We recall that the simple theories, such as for longitudinal waves in rods or flexural waves in beams, were restricted to low frequencies owing to kinematical limitations. It is to be expected, therefore, that the exact theories of plates, rods, and shells will find greatest application at high frequencies and for transient loading conditions.

The frequency equations for waves in infinite rods and plates have been known for some time. Thus, Pochhammer (1876), and Chree (1889) developed the results for the rod and Rayleigh (1889) and Lamb (1889) presented the results for the plate. Very little additional work occurred in this area for many years, however. In 1948, Davies [11] studied, both theoretically and experimentally, a number of aspects of longitudinal waves in rods. As part of that study, the first few branches of the Pochhammer–Chree frequency equation for the rod were developed and the propagation characteristics of a transient according to the exact theory were considered. Since Davies' investigation, many aspects have been thoroughly investigated. Most attention has been given to understanding the complete frequency spectrum of the plate and the rod, to the analysis of transient disturbances, and to the development and application of approximate theories for plates, rods, and shells.

Our study of these geometries will be in the order just mentioned. Thus the propagation of waves in plates will be investigated first, with the development of the Rayleigh–Lamb frequency equation and the spectrum being the objective. The development of the Pochhammer–Chree equation for the rod will then follow, with the complete spectrum for that geometry also presented. The forced motion of plates and rods, both harmonic and transient, will be studied. Finally, the development of approximate theories for the various geometries will be considered.

8.1. Continuous waves in a plate

As previously mentioned, the early developments in wave propagation in plates were by Rayleigh and Lamb. The Rayleigh–Lamb theory pertains to the propagation of continuous, straight crested waves in a plate, infinite in extent and having traction-free surfaces. Plane-strain conditions apply. Our study will develop the frequency equation for this theory and present the complete frequency spectrum. The considerations here are somewhat complicated, however, and it will be advisable, before considering the Rayleigh–Lamb case, to study the propagation of SH waves in a plate. Recalling the simpler circumstances pertaining to this case in our previous studies in infinite and semi-infinite media and in wave scattering, we expect and will find a simpler theory governing these waves in a plate. Boundary conditions other than traction-free ones will also be considered.

8.1.1. *SH waves in a plate*

In considering waves in a plate, which has two boundary surfaces, two sources of complexity arise. First, multiple reflections of waves between the boundary surfaces occur. Secondly, mode conversion of P and SV waves occurs. By restricting to the SH wave case, the second complication is removed, and we may restrict our attention to the first area.

Consider, then, a plate of infinite extent in the z direction and of thickness $2b$, as shown in Fig. 8.1. The coordinate system is selected with the x, z-plane

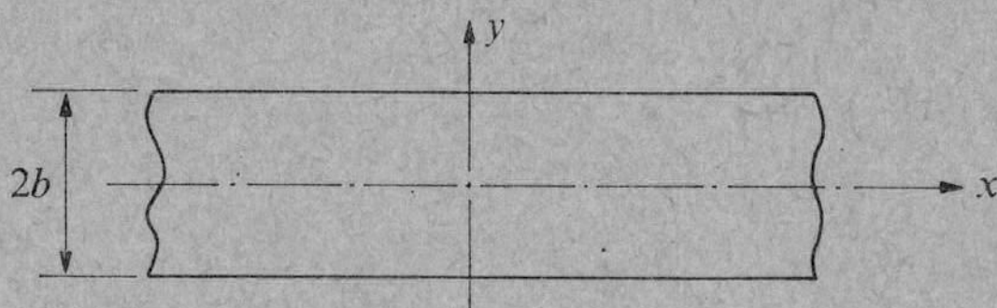

FIG. 8.1. Coordinate system for a plate of thickness $2b$.

coinciding with the middle surface of the plate, with y positive upward. For SH waves, we have the governing equations

$$\nabla^2 u_z = \frac{1}{c_2^2}\frac{\partial^2 u_z}{\partial t^2}, \tag{8.1.1}$$

where $u_z = u_z(x, y, t)$. We immediately consider solutions of the wave equation given by

$$u_z = h(y)e^{i(\xi x-\omega t)}. \tag{8.1.2}$$

Substitution in the wave equation gives

$$\frac{d^2h}{dy^2}+\beta^2 h = 0, \qquad \beta^2 = \frac{\omega^2}{c_2^2}-\xi^2, \tag{8.1.3}$$

which leads to

$$u_z = (A_1 \sin \beta y + A_2 \cos \beta y)e^{i(\xi x-\omega t)}. \tag{8.1.4}$$

This solution form is most convenient to the problem at hand. However, by way of interpretation, we note that an alternative solution form could as well be

$$u_z = A_1' e^{i(\xi x - \beta y - \omega t)} + A_2' e^{i(\xi x + \beta y - \omega t)}, \tag{8.1.5}$$

which explicitly brings out the plane-wave nature of the motion.

The boundary conditions for the problem are $\tau_{yy} = \tau_{xy} = \tau_{zy} = 0$ at $y = \pm b$. With the SH wave restriction, only the last condition on τ_{zy} is non-trivial, being given by

$$\partial u_z/\partial y = 0, \qquad y = \pm b. \tag{8.1.6}$$

Applying these conditions to the solution (8.1.4) gives

$$\begin{aligned} A_1 \cos \beta b - A_2 \sin \beta b &= 0, \\ A_1 \cos \beta b + A_2 \sin \beta b &= 0, \end{aligned} \tag{8.1.7}$$

from which results the frequency equation

$$\cos \beta b \sin \beta b = 0. \tag{8.1.8}$$

This equation is satisfied by

$$\beta b = n\pi/2 \qquad (n = 0, 1, 2, 3, 4, \ldots). \tag{8.1.9}$$

These results show that harmonic SH waves may propagate only under special conditions, as given by (8.1.9). Thus, given a frequency ω, the resulting wavenumber ξ will be given by $\xi = (\omega^2/c_2^2 - \beta^2)^{\frac{1}{2}}$, where β is given by (8.1.9).

Let us consider the motion in more detail. We first note that the displacement solution (8.1.4) involves a symmetric (A_2) and antisymmetric (A_1) motion with respect to the $y = 0$ mid surface. Now suppose that the frequency equation is satisfied by $\cos \beta b = 0$. From (8.1.7) we have that $A_2 = 0$ must hold so that the motion is antisymmetric, given by

$$u_z = A_1 \sin \beta_n y e^{i(\xi x - \omega t)}, \tag{8.1.10}$$

where, from $\cos \beta b = 0$, we have that $n = 1, 3, 5, \ldots$. Similarly, if $\sin \beta b = 0$ in (8.1.8), we have from (8.1.7) that $A_1 = 0$, and the resulting symmetric motion is given by

$$u_z = A_2 \cos \beta_n y e^{i(\xi x - \omega t)}, \tag{8.1.11}$$

where $n = 0, 2, 4, \ldots$. The resulting form of the y variation of displacement across the plate thickness is shown for the first few modes in Fig. 8.2(a) and (b).

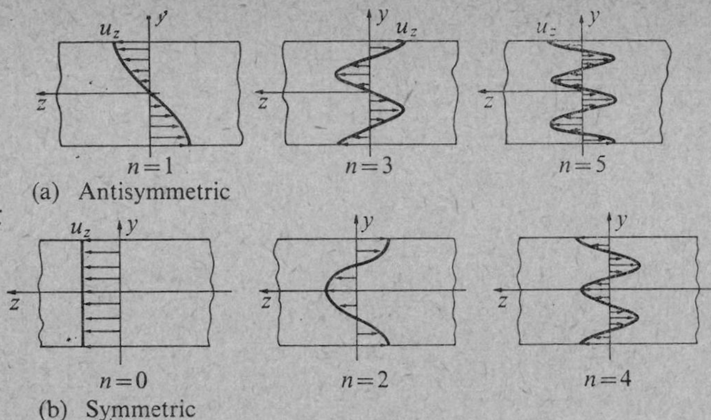

FIG. 8.2. The y-variation in displacement for the (a) first three antisymmetric, and (b) first three symmetric SH plate modes.

The frequency spectrum for SH waves results from (8.1.9). Thus we write $\beta^2 b^2 = (n\pi/2)^2$, and using the definition of β^2 obtain

$$\frac{\omega^2 b^2}{c_2^2} = \left(\frac{n\pi}{2}\right)^2 + \xi^2 b^2. \tag{8.1.12}$$

Letting

$$\Omega = 2b\omega/\pi c_2, \qquad \bar{\xi} = 2b\xi/\pi, \tag{8.1.13}$$

we have

$$\Omega^2 = n^2 + \bar{\xi}^2, \tag{8.1.14}$$

or

$$\bar{\xi} = \pm(\Omega^2 - n^2)^{\frac{1}{2}}, \tag{8.1.15}$$

where n odd gives the antisymmetric and n even the symmetric roots. Using $\omega = \xi c$ or, in non-dimensional form, $\Omega = \bar{\xi}\bar{c}$, where $\bar{c} = c/c_2$ we may obtain the dispersion curve equations. The group velocity, given by $c_g = \mathrm{d}\omega/\mathrm{d}\xi$ or, in non-dimensional form, by $\bar{c}_g = \mathrm{d}\Omega/\mathrm{d}\bar{\xi}$ also follows from (8.1.15).

Examining (8.1.15), we see that $n = 0$ gives the result that $\bar{\xi} = \Omega$ or, in dimensional form, $\omega = \xi c_2$. Thus we see that the first mode is non-dispersive, whereas all other modes propagate dispersively. Next, we see that, for $\Omega > n$, $\bar{\xi}$ is real and the spectrum consists of a family of hyperbolas ($n = 1, 2, 3, \ldots$). At $\bar{\xi} = 0$, $\Omega = n$ and the cutoff frequencies for the various modes result. For $\Omega < n$, $\bar{\xi}$ is imaginary and the spectrum consists of a family of circles ($n = 1, 2, 3 \ldots$). The resulting spectrum, showing just the positive real and positive imaginary branches for positive Ω is shown in Fig. 8.3. The solid lines correspond to the symmetric (n even) modes, the dashed lines are the antisymmetric modes (n odd). The interpretation of the imaginary wavenumbers,

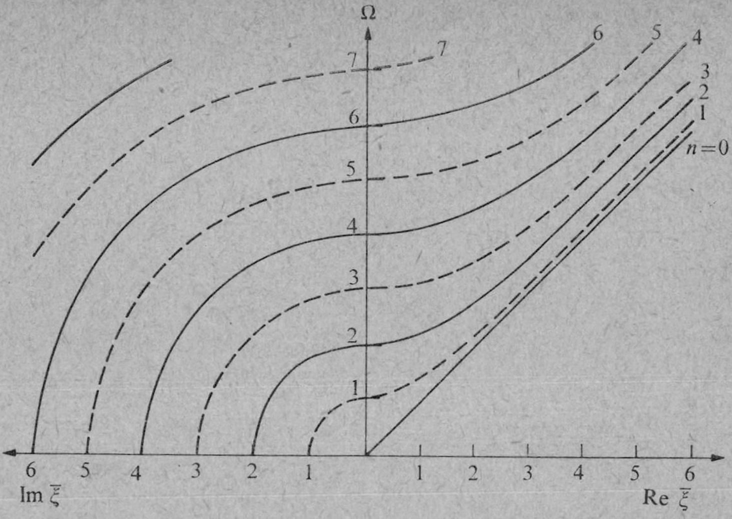

FIG. 8.3. Frequency spectrum for SH waves in a plate. Solid lines are the symmetric modes, dashed lines are the antisymmetric modes.

arising from (8.1.15) and shown in the figure, is quite familiar at this stage. Thus, for $\bar{\xi} = \pm i\bar{\xi}'$, we have

$$u_z = (A_1 \sin \beta y + A_2 \cos \beta y)\exp(\pm\bar{\xi}'x)\exp(-i\omega t), \qquad (8.1.16)$$

corresponding to a non-propagating, spatially varying disturbance. The importance of such solutions in forced-motion and wave-reflection problems has been well established from previous studies. Finally, we note that for a given frequency there are only a finite number of propagating SH modes (that is, the line Ω = constant cuts only a finite number of branches of the spectrum). This suggests it would not be possible to form an arbitrary stress distribution by a Fourier superposition of propagating modes. However, if the imaginary branches are included, an infinite mode set is obtained and the formation of an arbitrary stress distribution becomes possible.

8.1.2. *Waves in a plate with mixed boundary conditions*

As our next step on the road to the Rayleigh–Lamb equation for plates, we consider the case of a plate having mixed boundary conditions. In contrast to the previous section, we now admit P and SV waves in the plate and consider conditions of plane strain. The resulting wave behaviour, although more complicated than the SH wave case, will be less complicated than the case of traction-free surfaces. While the case of mixed boundary conditions is not of great practical importance, the results obtained here will be found to play a very important role in obtaining the Rayleigh–Lamb spectrum.

We again consider the plate geometry of Fig. 8.1. If conditions of plane strain hold in the z direction, we have that $u_z = \partial/\partial z = 0$ and

$$u_x = \frac{\partial\Phi}{\partial x}+\frac{\partial H_z}{\partial y}, \tag{8.1.17}$$

$$u_y = \frac{\partial\Phi}{\partial y}-\frac{\partial H_z}{\partial x}, \tag{8.1.18}$$

where $u_x = u_x(x, y, t)$, $u_y = u_y(x, y, t)$. Further, we have

$$\nabla^2\Phi = \frac{1}{c_1^2}\frac{\partial^2\Phi}{\partial t^2}, \qquad \nabla^2 H_z = \frac{1}{c_2^2}\frac{\partial^2 H_z}{\partial t^2}. \tag{8.1.19}$$

The case of mixed boundary conditions considered here is expressed by

$$u_y = \tau_{xy} = \tau_{zy} = 0, \qquad y = \pm b. \tag{8.1.20}$$

We consider solutions to (8.1.19) of the form

$$\Phi = f(y)e^{i(\xi x-\omega t)}, \qquad H_z = ih_z(y)e^{i(\xi x-\omega t)}, \tag{8.1.21}$$

where the factor i has been inserted in H_z for later convenience. Substitution in the wave equations gives for f, h_z

$$\frac{d^2 f}{dy^2}+\alpha^2 f = 0, \qquad \frac{d^2 h_z}{dy^2}+\beta^2 h_z = 0, \tag{8.1.22}$$

where

$$\alpha^2 = \omega^2/c_1^2-\xi^2, \qquad \beta^2 = \omega^2/c_2^2-\xi^2. \tag{8.1.23}$$

We obtain

$$f = A\sin\alpha y+B\cos\alpha y, \qquad h_z = C\sin\beta y+D\cos\beta y. \tag{8.1.24}$$

The resulting potentials and displacements are

$$\Phi = (A\sin\alpha y+B\cos\alpha y)e^{i(\xi x-\omega t)}, \tag{8.1.25}$$

$$H_z = i(C\sin\beta y+D\cos\beta y)e^{i(\xi x-\omega t)}, \tag{8.1.26}$$

$$u_x = i\{\xi(A\sin\alpha y+B\cos\alpha y)+\beta(C\cos\beta y-D\sin\beta y)\}e^{i(\xi x-\omega t)}, \tag{8.1.27}$$

$$u_y = \{\alpha(A\cos\alpha y-B\sin\alpha y)+\xi(C\sin\beta y+D\cos\beta y)\}e^{i(\xi x-\omega t)}. \tag{8.1.28}$$

The stresses in terms of the potentials have been previously given by (6.1.9)–(6.1.12) in the study of the half-space. Writing the stresses so that the Φ and H_z contributions are separated, we obtain

$$\tau_{xx} = \mu[\{2\alpha^2-k^2(\xi^2+\alpha^2)\}(A\sin\alpha y+B\cos\alpha y)- \\ -2\xi\beta(C\cos\beta y-D\sin\beta y)]e^{i(\xi x-\omega t)}, \tag{8.1.29}$$

$$\tau_{yy} = \mu[\{2\xi^2-k^2(\xi^2+\alpha^2)\}(A\sin\alpha y+B\cos\alpha y)+ \\ +2\beta\xi(C\cos\beta y-D\sin\beta y)]e^{i(\xi x-\omega t)}, \tag{8.1.30}$$

$$\tau_{xy} = i\mu\{2\alpha\xi(A\cos\alpha y-B\sin\alpha y)- \\ -(\beta^2-\xi^2)(C\sin\beta y+D\cos\beta y)\}e^{i(\xi x-\omega t)}. \tag{8.1.31}$$

For the plane-strain case at hand, τ_{zz} is obtainable from τ_{xx} and τ_{yy}, while $\tau_{zx} = \tau_{zy} = 0$.

We apply the solutions for u_y, τ_{xy} to the boundary conditions (8.1.20) and obtain

$$\begin{aligned}
\alpha(A\cos\alpha b - B\sin\alpha b)+\xi(C\sin\beta b + D\cos\beta b) &= 0,\\
\alpha(A\cos\alpha b + B\sin\alpha b)-\xi(C\sin\beta b - D\cos\beta b) &= 0,\\
2\alpha\xi(A\cos\alpha b - B\sin\alpha b)-(\beta^2-\xi^2)(C\sin\beta b + D\cos\beta b) &= 0,\\
2\alpha\xi(A\cos\alpha b + B\sin\alpha b)+(\beta^2-\xi^2)(C\sin\beta b - D\cos\beta b) &= 0.
\end{aligned} \tag{8.1.32}$$

Adding and subtracting the first two and the second two equations gives

$$\begin{aligned}
\alpha A\cos\alpha b + \xi D\cos\beta b &= 0,\\
\alpha B\sin\alpha b - \xi C\sin\beta b &= 0,\\
2\alpha\xi A\cos\alpha b - (\beta^2-\xi^2)D\cos\beta b &= 0,\\
2\alpha\xi B\sin\alpha b + (\beta^2-\xi^2)C\sin\beta b &= 0,
\end{aligned} \tag{8.1.33}$$

which re-group to

$$\begin{bmatrix} \alpha\cos\alpha b & \xi\cos\beta b \\ 2\alpha\xi\cos\alpha b & -(\beta^2-\xi^2)\cos\beta b \end{bmatrix}\begin{bmatrix} A \\ D \end{bmatrix} = 0, \tag{8.1.34}$$

$$\begin{bmatrix} \alpha\sin\alpha b & -\xi\sin\beta b \\ 2\alpha\xi\sin\alpha b & (\beta^2-\xi^2)\sin\beta b \end{bmatrix}\begin{bmatrix} B \\ C \end{bmatrix} = 0. \tag{8.1.35}$$

Before expanding the determinant of coefficients of the preceding results, we note that the displacements (8.1.27) and (8.1.28) contain symmetric and antisymmetric components. Thus, for u_x we see that the B and C terms give symmetric displacements with respect to $y = 0$, while the A and D terms give antisymmetric displacements. For u_y, the B and C terms and A and D terms again give symmetric and antisymmetric displacements, respectively. The general form of the various components are shown in Fig. 8.4.

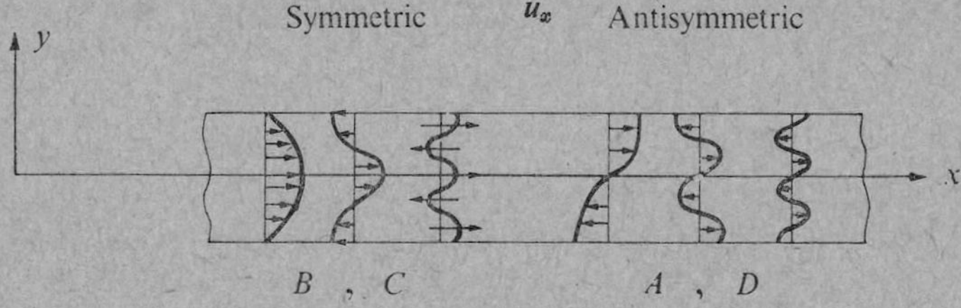

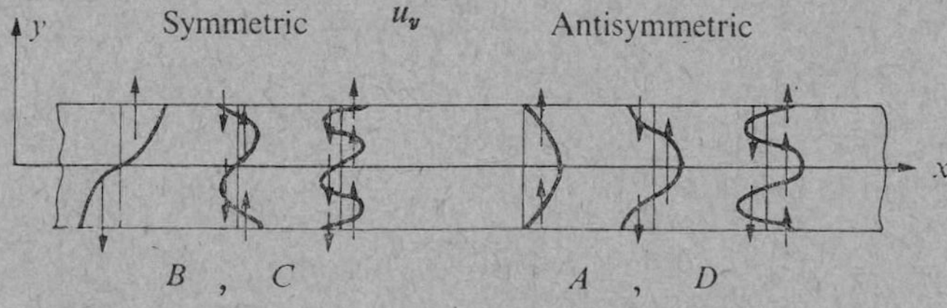

FIG. 8.4. Symmetric and antisymmetric components of the u_x, u_y displacements.

Continuing, we see that the result (8.1.34) corresponds to the antisymmetric modes. Thus, expanding the determinant, we obtain

$$\alpha(\beta^2+\xi^2)\cos\alpha b\cos\beta b=0. \tag{8.1.36}$$

This frequency equation will be satisfied by

$$\alpha=0,\quad \alpha b=m\pi/2,\quad \beta b=n\pi/2\quad (m,n=1,3,5,\ldots). \tag{8.1.37}$$

If $\alpha=0$ or $\alpha b=m\pi/2$, we have from (8.1.34) that $D=0$, so that

$$u_x=\mathrm{i}\xi A\sin\alpha_m y\mathrm{e}^{\mathrm{i}(\xi x-\omega t)},\qquad u_y=\alpha_m A\cos\alpha_m y\mathrm{e}^{\mathrm{i}(\xi x-\omega t)}. \tag{8.1.38}$$

If $\beta b=n\pi/2$, then $A=0$, and we have

$$u_x=-\mathrm{i}\beta D\sin\beta_n y\mathrm{e}^{\mathrm{i}(\xi x-\omega t)},\qquad u_y=\xi D\cos\beta_n y\mathrm{e}^{\mathrm{i}(\xi x-\omega t)}. \tag{8.1.39}$$

In the case of (8.1.38), we have antisymmetric modes resulting from the reflection of P waves within the plate, while (8.1.39) results from the reflection of SV waves. It is possible for these modes to be uncoupled from one another owing to the boundary conditions. Thus, recall in the study of the half-space that it was found that P and SV waves reflect without mode conversion from mixed boundary constraints of the present type.

In a similar way, we have that the result (8.1.35) governs symmetric modes in the plate. The frequency equation is

$$\alpha(\beta^2+\xi^2)\sin\alpha b\sin\beta b=0. \tag{8.1.40}$$

This will be satisfied by

$$\alpha=0,\quad \alpha b=m\pi,\quad \beta b=n\pi\quad (m=0,\quad m,n=1,2,3,\ldots). \tag{8.1.41}$$

For $\alpha b=m\pi$, we have that $C=0$, giving the symmetric P waves in the plate

$$u_x=\mathrm{i}\xi B\cos\alpha_m y\mathrm{e}^{\mathrm{i}(\xi x-\omega t)},\qquad u_y=-\alpha_m B\sin\alpha_m y\mathrm{e}^{\mathrm{i}(\xi x-\omega t)}. \tag{8.1.42}$$

For $m=0$, this reduces to

$$u_x=\mathrm{i}\xi B\mathrm{e}^{\mathrm{i}(\xi x-\omega t)},\qquad u_y=0. \tag{8.1.43}$$

For $\beta b=n\pi$, we have $B=0$, giving the symmetric SV waves in the plate

$$u_x=\mathrm{i}\beta_n C\cos\beta_n y\mathrm{e}^{\mathrm{i}(\xi x-\omega t)},\qquad u_y=\xi C\sin\beta_n y\mathrm{e}^{\mathrm{i}(\xi x-\omega t)}. \tag{8.1.44}$$

In obtaining the frequency spectrum for waves in a mixed boundary condition plate, we consider first that of the P waves. From (8.1.37) and (8.1.41), we have

$$\alpha b=m\pi/2\qquad (m=0,1,2,3,\ldots), \tag{8.1.45}$$

where m even governs the symmetric and m odd governs the antisymmetric waves. Using the first of (8.1.23), this may be put in the form

$$\Omega^2=k^2(m^2+\bar{\xi}^2)\qquad (m=0,1,2,\ldots), \tag{8.1.46}$$

where now

$$\Omega = 2b\omega/\pi c_2, \qquad \bar{\xi} = 2b\xi/\pi. \tag{8.1.47}$$

In a similar fashion, for the SV waves we have from (8.1.37) and (8.1.41)

$$\beta b = n\pi/2 \qquad (n = 1, 2, 3 \ldots), \tag{8.1.48}$$

where n even and odd governs, respectively, the symmetric and antisymmetric SV waves. Using the second of (8.1.23), this may be put in the form

$$\Omega^2 = (n^2+\bar{\xi}^2) \qquad (n = 1, 2, 3, \ldots). \tag{8.1.49}$$

In order to plot the spectrum, Poisson's ratio must be specified, since it enters into (8.1.46) through k^2.

The curves for the real branches of the spectrum are seen to be hyperbolas. The cutoff frequencies, given by $\bar{\xi} \to 0$, are $\Omega = km, n$ for the P and SV waves. For $\Omega < km$, the wavenumbers become imaginary. Replacing $\bar{\xi}$ by $i\bar{\xi}$ in (8.1.46), it is seen that the P wave branches of the spectrum are ellipses. For $\Omega < n$, the wavenumbers of the respective SV waves become imaginary and, it is seen from (8.1.49), in the form of circles. The resulting spectrum, plotted for $\nu = 0{\cdot}31$, so that $k^2 = 1{\cdot}91$, is shown in Fig. 8.5.

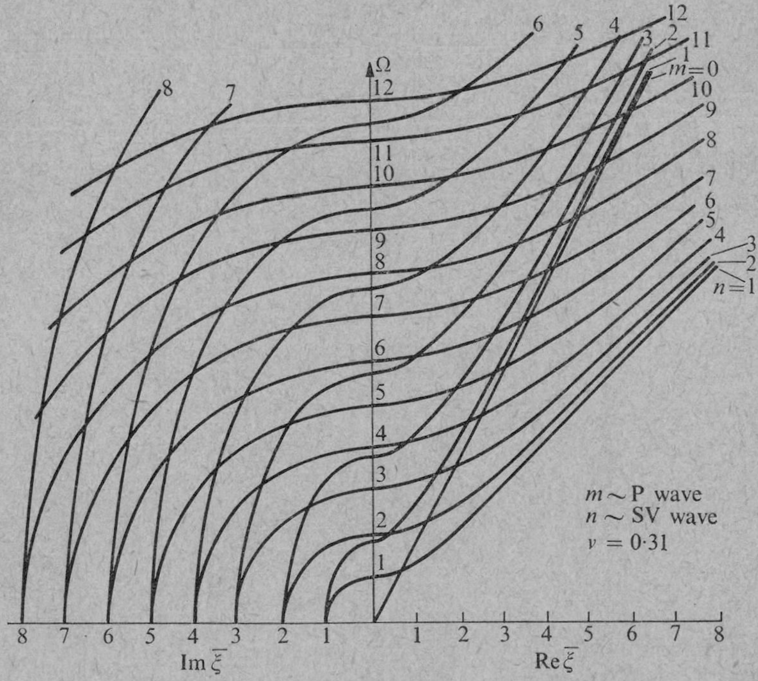

FIG. 8.5. Frequency spectrum for waves in a plate with mixed boundary conditions.

For the spectrum, we see that the first symmetric P wave ($m = 0$) is non-dispersive, whereas all other modes are dispersive. For large wavenumber ($\bar{\xi} \to \infty$), it is seen from (8.1.46) that P wave branches are asymptotic to $\Omega = k\bar{\xi}$. In dimensional form, this gives $\omega = \xi c_1$. Thus, at high frequency and short wavelength, the P wave modes propagate at the dilatational wave speed. Similarly, for the SV waves, $\bar{\xi} \to \infty$ gives the asymptote $\Omega = \bar{\xi}$ or $\omega = \xi c_2$. Thus the SV-wave modes propagate at the shear-wave velocity at high frequencies and short wavelengths. An illustration of the first few P and SV modes is shown in Fig. 8.6.

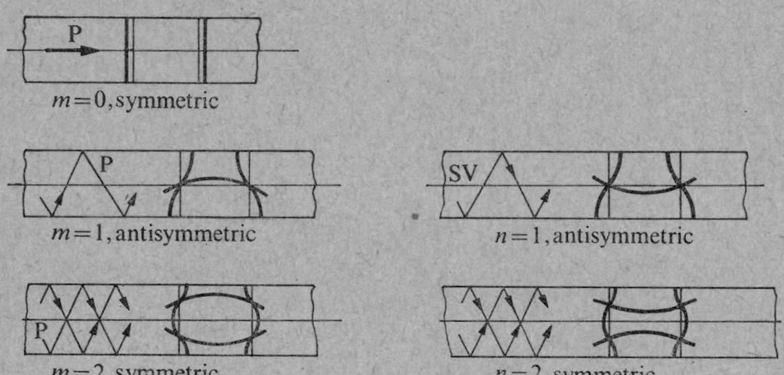

FIG. 8.6. First few P and SV modes in a mixed boundary condition plate. (After Mindlin [63, Fig. 17].)

8.1.3. *The Rayleigh–Lamb frequency equation for the plate*

We now consider the case of waves in a plate having traction-free boundaries. This is the case of greatest practical interest and is the classical case first studied by Rayleigh and Lamb. In our development, we can make direct use of many of the equations given in the previous study of waves in a mixed boundary-condition plate.

Thus, again consider waves of plane strain propagating in the x direction in a plate of thickness $2b$ (see Fig. 8.1) having traction-free boundaries. The governing equations for displacements, potential functions, and stresses, as given in the previous section by eqn (8.1.25)–(8.1.31), still hold. The boundary conditions are now given by

$$\tau_{yy} = \tau_{xy} = \tau_{zy} = 0, \quad y = \pm b, \tag{8.1.50}$$

where the last condition on τ_{zy} is satisfied identically. We now resolve our considerations into the cases of symmetric and antisymmetric waves.

Consider first the case of symmetric waves. From our previous considerations, we know the symmetric displacements to be given by

$$u_x = \mathrm{i}(B\xi \cos \alpha y + C\beta \cos \beta y)\mathrm{e}^{\mathrm{i}\varphi}, \tag{8.1.51}$$

$$u_y = (-B\alpha \sin \alpha y + C\xi \sin \beta y)\mathrm{e}^{\mathrm{i}\varphi}, \tag{8.1.52}$$

where we have let $A = D = 0$ in (8.1.27) and (8.1.28). The phase factor in the preceding equations is simply $\psi = \xi x - \omega t$. We apply the boundary conditions to eqns (8.1.30) and (8.1.31) for τ_{yy}, τ_{xy}, letting $A = D = 0$, and obtain

$$\begin{gathered}(\xi^2-\beta^2)B\cos\alpha b+2\xi\beta C\cos\beta b = 0,\\ \pm\mathrm{i}\{-2\xi\alpha B\sin\alpha b+(\xi^2-\beta^2)C\sin\beta b\} = 0.\end{gathered} \tag{8.1.53}$$

Thus the four boundary conditions on $y = \pm b$ reduce to two unique equations in B and C. Equating the determinant of coefficients to zero, we obtain from (8.1.53) the frequency equation

$$\frac{\tan\beta b}{\tan\alpha b} = -\frac{4\alpha\beta\xi^2}{(\xi^2-\beta^2)^2}. \tag{8.1.54}$$

This is the Rayleigh–Lamb frequency equation for the propagation of symmetric waves in a plate. From (8.1.53) we also obtain the amplitude ratios

$$\frac{B}{C} = -\frac{2\xi\beta\cos\beta b}{(\xi^2-\beta^2)\cos\alpha b} = \frac{(\xi^2-\beta^2)\sin\beta b}{2\xi\alpha\sin\alpha b}. \tag{8.1.55}$$

Now consider the case of the antisymmetric modes, given by the displacements

$$u_x = \mathrm{i}(\xi A\sin\alpha y-\beta D\sin\beta y)\mathrm{e}^{\mathrm{i}\psi}, \tag{8.1.56}$$

$$u_y = (\alpha A\cos\alpha y+\xi D\cos\beta y)\mathrm{e}^{\mathrm{i}\psi}. \tag{8.1.57}$$

Substituting the expressions for the stresses τ_{yy}, τ_{xy} in the boundary conditions, where $B = C = 0$ in (8.1.30) and (8.1.31), we obtain

$$\begin{gathered}\pm\{(\xi^2-\beta^2)A\sin\alpha b-2\beta\xi D\sin\beta b\} = 0,\\ 2\alpha\xi A\cos\alpha b-(\beta^2-\xi^2)D\cos\beta b = 0.\end{gathered} \tag{8.1.58}$$

This gives the Rayleigh–Lamb frequency equation for antisymmetric waves in a plate,

$$\frac{\tan\beta b}{\tan\alpha b} = -\frac{(\xi^2-\beta^2)^2}{4\alpha\beta\xi^2}, \tag{8.1.59}$$

and the amplitude ratios

$$\frac{A}{D} = \frac{2\xi\beta\sin\beta b}{(\xi^2-\beta^2)\sin\alpha b} = -\frac{(\xi^2-\beta^2)\cos\beta b}{2\xi\alpha\cos\alpha b}. \tag{8.1.60}$$

We may combine the frequency equations for symmetric and antisymmetric waves into a single equation given by

$$F(\alpha,\beta,\xi) = \frac{\tan\beta b}{\tan\alpha b}+\left\{\frac{4\alpha\beta\xi^2}{(\xi^2-\beta^2)^2}\right\}^{\pm 1} = 0, \qquad \begin{cases}+1 = \text{symmetric}\\ -1 = \text{antisymmetric}\end{cases} \tag{8.1.61}$$

where, we recall,

$$\alpha^2 = \omega^2/c_1^2-\xi^2, \qquad \beta^2 = \omega^2/c_2^2-\xi^2. \tag{8.1.62}$$

Hence the problem is: given the frequency ω, determine the wavenumbers satisfying the Rayleigh–Lamb equation and, from the relationship $\omega = \xi c$, establish the propagation velocity of the waves. Although the frequency equation was derived long ago and is fairly simple in appearance, a complete understanding of the spectrum, including the behaviour of the higher modes and complex branches, has come about only comparatively recently.

8.1.4. *The general frequency equation for a plate*

Our objective is to study in detail the Rayleigh–Lamb equation. Before doing so, a more general development of the frequency equations for the various types of waves in a plate will be presented. The analysis will recover the symmetric and antisymmetric waves of the Rayleigh–Lamb case as well as the previously-studied SH wave case. The results will show that it is not necessary to consider the various wave-types independently, but that they resolve themselves in the natural course of analysis. The work is based on that of Meeker and Meitzler [48].

Thus, again consider straight-crested waves propagating in a plate in the positive x direction, where the governing equations are

$$\mathbf{u} = \nabla\Phi + \nabla\times\mathbf{H}, \qquad \nabla.\mathbf{H} = 0,$$
$$\nabla^2\Phi = \frac{1}{c_1^2}\frac{\partial^2\Phi}{\partial t^2}, \qquad \nabla^2\mathbf{H} = \frac{1}{c_2^2}\frac{\partial^2\mathbf{H}}{\partial t^2}. \tag{8.1.63}$$

Since we wish to generalize somewhat from plane strain, all three components of the vector potential must be retained. The displacements are

$$u_x = \frac{\partial\Phi}{\partial x} + \frac{\partial H_z}{\partial y},$$
$$u_y = \frac{\partial\Phi}{\partial y} - \frac{\partial H_z}{\partial x}, \tag{8.1.64}$$
$$u_z = -\frac{\partial H_x}{\partial y} + \frac{\partial H_y}{\partial x},$$

where variations in the z direction have been excluded, so that $\partial/\partial z = 0$.

As before, we consider solutions of the general form

$$\Phi = f(y)e^{i(\xi x - \omega t)}, \qquad H_x = h_x(y)e^{i(\xi x - \omega t)},$$
$$H_y = h_y(y)e^{i(\xi x - \omega t)}, \qquad H_z = h_z(y)e^{i(\xi x - \omega t)}, \tag{8.1.65}$$

where, in following the notation of Reference [48], we have not introduced additional factors of i as was done previously in (8.1.21). Substitution in the differential eqns (8.1.63) gives

$$\begin{aligned}\Phi &= (A\cos\alpha y + B\sin\alpha y)e^{i(\xi x-\omega t)},\\ H_x &= (C\cos\beta y + D\sin\beta y)e^{i(\xi x-\omega t)},\\ H_y &= (E\cos\beta y + F\sin\beta y)e^{i(\xi x-\omega t)},\\ H_z &= (G\cos\beta y + H\sin\beta y)e^{i(\xi x-\omega t)}.\end{aligned} \tag{8.1.66}$$

The displacements are then given by

$$\begin{aligned}u_x &= \{i\xi(A\cos\alpha y + B\sin\alpha y) + \beta(-G\sin\beta y + H\cos\beta y)\}e^{i(\xi x-\omega t)},\\ u_y &= \{\alpha(-A\sin\alpha y + B\cos\alpha y) - i\xi(G\cos\beta y + H\sin\beta y)\}e^{i(\xi x-\omega t)},\\ u_z &= \{-\beta(-C\sin\beta y + D\cos\beta y) + i\xi(E\cos\beta y + F\sin\beta y)\}e^{i(\xi x-\omega t)}.\end{aligned} \tag{8.1.67}$$

The boundary conditions are as previously given by (8.1.50), where we write the stresses in the form

$$\begin{aligned}\tau_{yy} &= (\lambda+2\mu)\frac{\partial u_y}{\partial y} + \lambda\frac{\partial u_x}{\partial x},\\ \tau_{yx} &= \mu\left(\frac{\partial u_y}{\partial x} + \frac{\partial u_x}{\partial y}\right),\\ \tau_{yz} &= \mu\frac{\partial u_z}{\partial y}.\end{aligned} \tag{8.1.68}$$

The boundary conditions yield six equations in the eight unknown constants $A, B, \dots, H$. The remaining two equations result from the divergence condition on $\mathbf{H}$, given by

$$\frac{\partial H_x}{\partial x} + \frac{\partial H_y}{\partial y} = 0. \tag{8.1.69}$$

If the results for H_x, H_y are substituted in the above, and real and imaginary parts equated to zero, two equations result which would permit either C or D and E or F to be eliminated from the boundary condition equations. Proceeding in an alternative manner as in Reference [48], we evaluate (8.1.69) at $y = \pm b$ to generate two additional equations. The resulting boundary condition and divergence condition equations are

$$\begin{aligned}&\{(\lambda+2\mu)\alpha^2 + \lambda\xi^2\}(A\cos\alpha b + B\sin\alpha b) + 2i\mu\xi\beta(-G\sin\beta b + H\cos\beta b) = 0,\\ &\{(\lambda+2\mu)\alpha^2 + \lambda\xi^2\}(A\cos\alpha b - B\sin\alpha b) + 2i\mu\xi\beta(G\sin\beta b + H\cos\beta b) = 0,\\ &\beta^2(C\cos\beta b + D\sin\beta b) + i\xi\beta(-E\sin\beta b + F\cos\beta b) = 0,\\ &\beta^2(C\cos\beta b - D\sin\beta b) + i\xi\beta(E\sin\beta b + F\cos\beta b) = 0,\\ &2i\xi\alpha(-A\sin\alpha b + B\cos\alpha b) + (\xi^2-\beta^2)(G\cos\beta b + H\sin\beta b) = 0,\\ &2i\xi\alpha(A\sin\alpha b + B\cos\alpha b) + (\xi^2-\beta^2)(G\cos\beta b - H\sin\beta b) = 0,\\ &\beta(-E\sin\beta b + F\cos\beta b) + i\xi(C\cos\beta b + D\sin\beta b) = 0,\\ &\beta(E\sin\beta b + F\cos\beta b) + i\xi(C\cos\beta b - D\sin\beta b) = 0.\end{aligned} \tag{8.1.70}$$

This constitutes a system of eight homogeneous equations in the constants $A, B, \ldots, H$. A necessary and sufficient condition for the existence of a solution is that the determinant of coefficients must vanish. This determinant is given by

$$\begin{vmatrix} c\cos\alpha b & c\sin\alpha b & 0 & 0 & -f\sin\beta b & f\cos\beta b & 0 & 0 \\ c\cos\alpha b & -c\sin\alpha b & 0 & 0 & f\sin\beta b & f\cos\beta b & 0 & 0 \\ 0 & 0 & -h\sin\beta b & h\cos\beta b & 0 & 0 & \beta^2\cos\beta b & \beta^2\sin\beta b \\ 0 & 0 & h\sin\beta b & h\cos\beta b & 0 & 0 & \beta^2\cos\beta b & -\beta^2\sin\beta b \\ -d\sin\alpha b & d\cos\alpha b & 0 & 0 & g\cos\beta b & g\sin\beta b & 0 & 0 \\ d\sin\alpha b & d\cos\alpha b & 0 & 0 & g\cos\beta b & -g\sin\beta b & 0 & 0 \\ 0 & 0 & -\beta\sin\beta b & \beta\cos\beta b & 0 & 0 & \mathrm{i}\xi\cos\beta b & \mathrm{i}\xi\sin\beta b \\ 0 & 0 & \beta\sin\beta b & \beta\cos\beta b & 0 & 0 & \mathrm{i}\xi\cos\beta b & -\mathrm{i}\xi\sin\beta b \end{vmatrix} = 0, \tag{8.1.71}$$

where c, d, f, g, h are defined by

$$c = \{(\lambda+2\mu)\alpha^2+\lambda\xi^2\},$$
$$d = 2\mathrm{i}\xi\alpha, \quad f = 2\mathrm{i}\mu\xi\beta,$$
$$g = \xi^2-\beta^2, \quad h = \mathrm{i}\xi\beta. \tag{8.1.72}$$

The eight columns of the determinant are associated, respectively, with the constants A, B, E, F, G, H, C, D. By adding and subtracting rows and columns of the coefficient determinant, it is possible to recast it to the form

$$\begin{matrix} B & G & E & D & A & H & C & F \end{matrix}$$
$$\begin{vmatrix} - & - & 0 & 0 & 0 & 0 & 0 & 0 \\ - & - & 0 & 0 & 0 & 0 & 0 & 0 \\ 0 & 0 & - & - & 0 & 0 & 0 & 0 \\ 0 & 0 & - & - & 0 & 0 & 0 & 0 \\ 0 & 0 & 0 & 0 & - & - & 0 & 0 \\ 0 & 0 & 0 & 0 & - & - & 0 & 0 \\ 0 & 0 & 0 & 0 & 0 & 0 & - & - \\ 0 & 0 & 0 & 0 & 0 & 0 & - & - \end{vmatrix} = 0, \tag{8.1.73}$$

where the constants are positioned with the appropriate columns. A series of manipulations that takes (8.1.71) to the form (8.1.73) is as follows (use R and C to indicate 'row' and 'column,' with R1 being the top row, C1 being the left column):

(1) add R1 to R2, R3 to R4, R5 to R6, R7 to R8;
(2) subtract R2 from R1, R4 from R3, R6 from R5, R8 from R7;
(3) interchange R2, R6, R4, R7, leaving R1, R3, R5, R8 in place;
(4) interchange C2 to C1, C1 to C5, C5 to C2; interchange C4, C8; leave C3, C6, C7 in place.

The determinant (8.1.73) may be expanded to the product of four subdeterminants,

$$\begin{vmatrix} i\xi\cos\beta b & \beta\cos\beta b \\ \beta^2\cos\beta b & h\cos\beta b \end{vmatrix} \times \begin{vmatrix} -\beta\sin\beta b & i\xi\sin\beta b \\ h\sin\beta b & \beta^2\sin\beta b \end{vmatrix} \times \begin{vmatrix} c\cos\alpha b & f\cos\beta b \\ -d\sin\alpha b & g\sin\beta b \end{vmatrix} \times$$

$$\times \begin{vmatrix} g\cos\beta b & d\cos\alpha b \\ f\sin\beta b & c\sin\alpha b \end{vmatrix} = 0. \quad (8.1.74)$$

The coefficients associated with the subdeterminants are

$$|C, F| \times |E, D| \times |A, H| \times |B, G| = 0. \quad (8.1.75)$$

Various solutions to (8.1.74) are possible for various non-zero combinations of the constants. Thus

Solution I: $A, B, D, E, G, H = 0$, $C, F \neq 0$ gives

$$u_x = u_y = 0, \qquad (8.1.76)$$
$$u_z = (C\beta + iF\xi)\sin\beta y \exp\{i(\xi x - \omega t)\}.$$

Solution II: $A, B, C, F, G, H = 0$, $D, E \neq 0$ gives

$$u_x = u_y = 0, \qquad (8.1.77)$$
$$u_z = (-\beta D + i\xi E)\cos\beta y \exp\{i(\xi x - \omega t)\}.$$

Solution III: $B, C, D, E, F, G = 0$, $A, H \neq 0$ gives

$$u_x = (i\xi A\cos\alpha y + \beta H\cos\beta y)\exp\{i(\xi x - \omega t)\}, \qquad (8.1.78)$$
$$u_y = -(\alpha A\sin\alpha y + \xi H\sin\beta y)\exp\{i(\xi x - \omega t)\},$$
$$u_z = 0.$$

Solution IV: $A, C, D, E, F, H = 0$, $B, G \neq 0$ gives

$$u_x = (i\xi B\sin\alpha y - \beta G\sin\beta y)\exp\{i(\xi x - \omega t)\},$$
$$u_y = (\alpha B\cos\alpha y - i\xi G\cos\beta y)\exp\{i(\xi x - \omega t)\}, \qquad (8.1.79)$$
$$u_z = 0.$$

Allowing for difference in coefficient notation and the inclusion of i in basic definitions, it may be seen that (8.1.78) and (8.1.79) correspond to the previously derived Rayleigh–Lamb results (8.1.54) and (8.1.59). We have, in addition, obtained the cases of antisymmetric (8.1.76) and symmetric (8.1.77) SH modes in the more general derivation.

The frequency equations are obtained in the usual way, by expanding the various determinants. These give the following.

Solution I: $C, F \neq 0$. The determinant in question is

$$\begin{vmatrix} i\xi \cos \beta b & \beta \cos \beta b \\ \beta^2 \cos \beta b & i\xi\beta \cos \beta b \end{vmatrix} = 0, \tag{8.1.80}$$

giving

$$\beta(\xi^2+\beta^2)\cos^2 \beta b = 0. \tag{8.1.81}$$

Solution II: $D, E \neq 0$. We have

$$\begin{vmatrix} -\beta \sin \beta b & i\xi \sin \beta b \\ -i\xi\beta \sin \beta b & \beta^2 \sin \beta b \end{vmatrix} = 0, \tag{8.1.82}$$

giving

$$\beta(\xi^2+\beta^2)\sin^2 \beta b = 0. \tag{8.1.83}$$

Solutions III, IV: The results for these cases are precisely those derived previously for the Rayleigh–Lamb case.

8.1.5. *Analysis of the Rayleigh–Lamb equation*

In our investigation of SH waves in plates and P and SV waves in mixed boundary condition plates, we found the situation considerably simpler than for the Rayleigh–Lamb case. Thus, for SH waves, only a single wave-type could exist, and the frequency equation was quite simple and permitted analytical solution. For the case of mixed boundary conditions, two types of waves were possible, but they were uncoupled from one another. Further, the frequency equations were again quite simple and permitted analytical solution. For the Rayleigh–Lamb case, none of these situations hold. Both P and SV waves exist for any given mode owing to mode conversion at the traction-free surfaces. Further, the frequency equation does not permit simple analytical solution. We shall proceed through several steps in analysing this case.

1. *Physical interpretation of the Rayleigh–Lamb modes.* The displacements in the plate are given by (8.1.27) and (8.1.28). The nature of the symmetric and antisymmetric displacement components has been previously illustrated by Fig. 8.4. Now, representing $\sin \alpha y$, $\cos \alpha y$, $\sin \beta y$, and $\cos \beta y$ in exponential form, we see that it is possible to express the displacement u_x as

$$u_x = i\left[\frac{A\xi}{2i}\left\{\left(1+i\frac{B}{A}\right)e^{i(\xi x+\alpha y-\omega t)}+\left(1-i\frac{B}{A}\right)e^{i(\xi x-\alpha y-\omega t)}\right\}+\right.$$
$$\left.+\frac{C\beta}{2}\left\{\left(1+i\frac{D}{C}\right)e^{i(\xi x-\beta y-\omega t)}+\left(1-i\frac{D}{C}\right)e^{i(\xi x-\beta y-\omega t)}\right]\right\}, \tag{8.1.84}$$

with a similar expression holding for u_y. For a given frequency, the amplitude ratios B/A, D/C would be fixed. This explicitly shows the plane-wave nature of the disturbance.

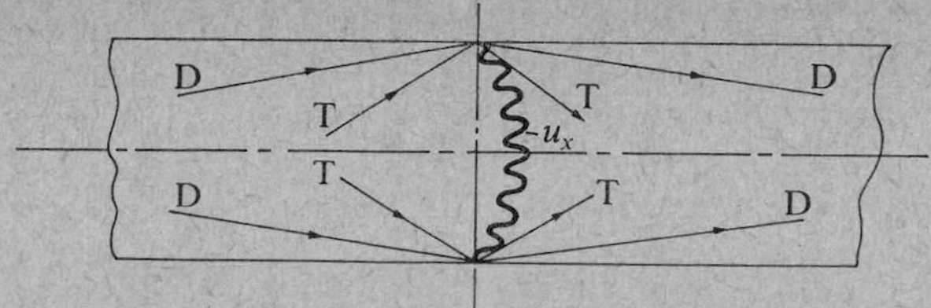

FIG. 8.7. Variation of the symmetric displacement u_x resulting from the reflection and interference of dilatational and shear waves. D = dilatational, T = transverse. (After Redwood [80, Fig. 5.1].)

Figure 8.7 shows how we may consider the modes of propagation in a plate using the plane-wave representation. Consider a pair of dilatational waves to be incident at such an angle that their reflection and interference produces u_x having a symmetric one-half cycle variation across y. Consider a pair of shear waves incident at a smaller angle. Since they are at the same frequency, their reflection and interference would produce a greater number of cyclic variations. The superposition of the two effects yields the results shown for u_x.

2. *Various regions of the Rayleigh–Lamb equation.* We recall that

$$\begin{aligned}\alpha^2 &= \omega^2/c_1^2-\xi^2 = \xi^2(c^2/c_1^2-1),\\ \beta^2 &= \omega^2/c_2^2-\xi^2 = \xi^2(c^2/c_2^2-1).\end{aligned} \tag{8.1.85}$$

Hence, depending on whether $\xi^2 \gtreqless \omega^2/c_1^2$, ω^2/c_2^2 or whether $c^2 \gtreqless c_1^2$, c_2^2, we may have α, β being real, zero, or imaginary. Then the frequency equation is correspondingly altered as follows.

Region I, $\xi > \omega/c_2$. It follows also that $\xi > \omega/c_1$ and that $c < c_2, c_1$. Then we replace α, β in the frequency equation by $i\alpha'$, $i\beta'$, where $\alpha'^2 = -\alpha^2$, $\beta'^2 = -\beta^2$, and obtain

$$\frac{\tanh \beta' b}{\tanh \alpha' b} = \left\{\frac{4\alpha'\beta'\xi^2}{(\xi^2-\beta'^2)^2}\right\}^{\pm 1}. \tag{8.1.86}$$

Region II, $\omega/c_2 > \xi > \omega/c_1$. It follows that $c_2 < c < c_1$, and we replace α by $i\alpha'$ in the frequency equation, giving

$$\frac{\tan \beta b}{\tanh \alpha' b} = \pm\left\{\frac{4\alpha'\beta\xi^2}{(\xi^2-\beta^2)^2}\right\}^{\pm 1}. \tag{8.1.87}$$

Region III, $\xi < \omega/c_1$. It follows that $c > c_1$, and the frequency equation has the previously derived form (8.1.61).

3. *Reduction to thin-plate results.* Let us consider the case when the transverse wavelength with respect to the thickness is quite large, so that $2\pi/\beta$, $2\pi/\alpha \gg b$. The analysis of regions I and II yield the results of interest.

Region I. Consider both symmetric and antisymmetric cases. For the former, there are no roots. For the antisymmetric case, we expand the hyperbolic tangent

$$\tanh x = x(1-\tfrac{1}{3}x^2+\ldots). \tag{8.1.88}$$

Retaining the first two terms, the frequency equation is reduced to

$$\frac{\beta'(1-\frac{1}{3}\beta'^2b^2)}{\alpha'(1-\frac{1}{3}\alpha'^2b^2)} = \frac{(\xi^2+\beta'^2)^2}{4\xi^2\alpha'\beta'}. \tag{8.1.89}$$

Put this in the form

$$-(\xi^2-\beta'^2) = \tfrac{4}{3}\xi^2\beta'^4b^2-\tfrac{1}{3}\alpha'^2b^2(\xi^2+\beta'^2)^2. \tag{8.1.90}$$

Discarding terms of higher order than $(c/c_2)^4$, we obtain

$$\frac{c}{c_2} = 2\xi b\left\{\frac{1}{3}\left(1-\frac{1}{k^2}\right)\right\}^{\frac{1}{2}}. \tag{8.1.91}$$

Using $c_1^2 = k^2c_2^2$, $k^2 = 2(1-\nu)/(1-2\nu)$, and $c_2^2 = \mu/\rho$, this becomes

$$c = \xi b\left\{\frac{E}{3\rho(1-\nu^2)}\right\}^{\frac{1}{2}}. \tag{8.1.92}$$

This result, with the linear dependence of c on ξ, agrees with that derived from classical plate theory.† It pertains, of course, to the flexural vibration case, and represents only a single vibrational mode in a limited frequency range in the over-all frequency spectrum.

Region II: The antisymmetric case has no roots. The symmetric case becomes

$$\frac{\beta}{\alpha'} = \frac{4\xi^2\alpha'\beta}{(\xi^2-\beta^2)^2}, \tag{8.1.93}$$

giving

$$\frac{c}{c_2} = 2\left(1-\frac{1}{k^2}\right)^{\frac{1}{2}}, \tag{8.1.94}$$

or

$$c = \left\{\frac{E}{\rho(1-\nu^2)}\right\}^{\frac{1}{2}}. \tag{8.1.95}$$

This is the thin-plate or plane-stress analogue of the bar velocity $c_0 = (E/\rho)^{\frac{1}{2}}$ of longitudinal rod theory.

4. *Lamé modes*. A special class of exact solutions, called the Lamé modes but evidently first identified by Lamb in 1917, can be obtained by considering the special case of $\xi = \beta$. Then from the definition of α^2 and β^2 we have that $\alpha^2 = \omega^2/c_1^2-\beta^2$, $2\xi^2 = \omega^2/c_2^2$. The roots for this case are in region II. The frequency equation reduces to:

symmetric: $\tan\beta b \to \infty$, $\quad \beta = n\pi/2b \quad (n = 1, 3, \ldots)$,
antisymmetric: $\tan\beta b = 0$, $\quad \beta = n\pi/2b \quad (n = 0, 2, 4, \ldots)$. (8.1.96)

† See Chapter 4, eqn (4.2.39).

The frequency is given by

$$\omega = \sqrt{2}\xi c_2 = \pi n c_2/\sqrt{2}b \qquad (n = 0, 1, 2, \ldots). \tag{8.1.97}$$

These modes will be examined in more detail in our analysis of bounded plates.

5. *Cutoff frequencies.* The cutoff frequencies for the various plate modes will be obtained by considering $\xi \to 0$. For this limiting value, the Rayleigh–Lamb equation reduces to:

$$\begin{aligned}&\text{symmetric: } \sin \beta b \cos \alpha b = 0,\\ &\text{antisymmetric: } \sin \alpha b \cos \beta b = 0.\end{aligned} \tag{8.1.98}$$

Symmetric case (thickness modes):

$$\begin{aligned}\cos \alpha b &= 0, \qquad \alpha b = \pi p/2 \qquad (p = 1, 3, 5, \ldots),\\ \sin \beta b &= 0, \qquad \beta b = \pi q/2 \qquad (q = 0, 2, 4, \ldots).\end{aligned} \tag{8.1.99}$$

From (8.1.51) and (8.1.52), we see that the displacements are now given by

$$u_x = i\beta C \cos \beta y e^{-i\omega t}, \qquad u_y = -\alpha B \sin \alpha y e^{-i\omega t}. \tag{8.1.100}$$

For the case of $\cos \alpha b = 0$, we see from the boundary condition eqns (8.1.53) that $C = 0$, so that

$$u_x = 0, \qquad u_y = -\alpha B \sin \alpha y e^{-i\omega t}, \qquad \alpha = \pi p/2b. \tag{8.1.101}$$

Such a mode is called a 'thickness-stretch' mode. For the case of $\sin \beta b = 0$, we have $B = 0$ and

$$u_x = i\beta C \cos \beta y e^{-i\omega t}, \qquad u_y = 0, \qquad \beta = \pi q/2b. \tag{8.1.102}$$

These are called the 'thickness-shear' modes.

Antisymmetric case: From (8.1.98) we have

$$\begin{aligned}\sin \alpha b &= 0, \qquad \alpha b = \pi p/2 \qquad (p = 0, 2, 4, \ldots),\\ \cos \beta b &= 0, \qquad \beta b = \pi q/2 \qquad (q = 2, 4, 6, \ldots).\end{aligned} \tag{8.1.103}$$

From (8.1.56) and (8.1.57) the displacements are

$$u_x = -i\beta D \sin \beta y e^{-i\omega t}, \qquad u_y = \alpha A \cos \alpha y e^{-i\omega t}, \tag{8.1.104}$$

with the boundary condition equations being given by (8.1.58). For $\sin \alpha\beta = 0$, we obtain $D = 0$ and

$$u_x = 0, \qquad u_y = \alpha A \cos \alpha y e^{-i\omega t}, \qquad \alpha = \pi p/2b. \tag{8.1.105}$$

For $\cos \beta b = 0$, we have $A = 0$ and

$$u_x = -i\beta D \sin \beta y e^{-i\omega t}, \qquad u_y = 0, \qquad \beta = \pi q/2b. \tag{8.1.106}$$

6. *The short-wavelength limit.* Some information on the asymptotic behaviour of the branches is obtainable by letting $\xi \to \infty$. For region I, we have

tanh $\beta' b$/tanh $\alpha' b \to 1$ as $\xi \to \infty$, so that the frequency equation reduces to

$$4\xi^2\alpha'\beta' = (\xi^2 + \beta'^2)^2, \tag{8.1.107}$$

for the symmetric and antisymmetric cases. This is merely the Rayleigh surface wave equation. The Rayleigh results enter here since, for such small wavelengths, the finite-thickness plate appears as a semi-infinite media. Hence vibrational energy is transmitted mainly along the surface of the plate.

For region II, we have, as $\xi \to \infty$, that

$$\frac{\{4(\alpha'/\xi)(\beta/\xi)\}^{\pm 1}}{(1-\beta^2/\xi^2)^2} \to 0. \tag{8.1.108}$$

Consider first the symmetric case (positive exponent) and note that

$$\frac{\alpha'}{\xi} = \left(1-\frac{c^2}{c_1^2}\right)^{\frac{1}{2}}, \quad \frac{\beta}{\xi} = \left(\frac{c^2}{c_2^2}-1\right)^{\frac{1}{2}}. \tag{8.1.109}$$

As $\xi \to \infty$, the product $(\alpha'/\xi)(\beta/\xi) \to 0$ and the question is whether $c \to c_1$ or c_2 to give this result. Since $1/c_1 < 1/c_2$, we conclude that β/ξ will approach zero the fastest. Hence, as $\xi \to \infty$, $c \to \sqrt{2}c_2$. The same results hold for the antisymmetric case (negative exponent), as can be shown by writing the right-hand side of (8.1.87) as

$$\frac{(2-c^2/c_2^2)^2}{(1-c^2/c_1^2)^{\frac{1}{2}}(c^2/c_2^2-1)^{\frac{1}{2}}} \to 0. \tag{8.1.110}$$

Finally, for region III, there are no roots in the short-wavelength limit.

7. *The grid of bounds.* The analysis of the Rayleigh–Lamb equation thus far has extracted some information on the behaviour of the branches of the frequency spectrum and dispersion curves for plate waves. This information is rather limited, however, and the details of the spectrum are far from complete. However, Mindlin† has developed a technique for constructing a grid of bounding curves which define the spectrum exactly at selected points and approximately (within the bounds) in the intervening regions. We proceed to develop the basic aspects of the technique.

We first recall the analysis of waves in a plate under mixed boundary conditions, presented in the previous section. The boundary conditions were given by $u_y = \tau_{xy} = 0$, $y = \pm b$. The frequency equations for this case were given by (8.1.36) and (8.1.40). The frequency spectrum was given by Fig. 8.6.

We now consider the case of a plate having *elastically restrained* boundaries. This is specified by the boundary conditions

$$\tau_{yy} = \mp e u_y, \qquad \tau_{xy} = 0, \qquad y = \pm b, \tag{8.1.111}$$

† Mindlin [63, pp. 210–14] gives a thorough exposition of the technique and interpretation of the spectrum.

where e is the elastic modulus of the foundation. By letting $e \to 0, \infty$ the cases of traction-free and mixed boundary conditions are recovered. From the previously given expressions for displacements and stresses in a plate (8.1.27), (8.1.28), (8.1.30), and (8.1.31), the preceding boundary conditions give:

Symmetric case ($A = D = 0$):

$$\mu\{B(\xi^2-\beta^2)\cos \alpha b+2C\xi\beta \cos \beta b\} = e(B\alpha \sin \alpha b-C\xi \sin \beta b),$$
$$2B\xi\alpha \sin \alpha b-C(\xi^2-\beta^2)\sin \beta b = 0. \tag{8.1.112}$$

Antisymmetric case ($B = C = 0$):

$$\mu\{A(\xi^2-\beta^2)\sin \alpha b-2D\xi\beta \sin \beta b\} = -e(A\alpha \cos \alpha b+D\xi \cos \beta b),$$
$$2A\xi\alpha \cos \alpha b+D(\xi^2-\beta^2)\cos \beta b = 0. \tag{8.1.113}$$

The frequency equations for symmetric and antisymmetric waves in an elastically restrained plate are obtainable from the determinants of coefficients.

Now, from the standpoint of complexity, the frequency equations resulting from (8.1.112) and (8.1.113) are considerably more complex than the traction-free Rayleigh–Lamb equation or the rigid-restraint case. However, it is to be expected that these equations would furnish a smooth transition of the frequency spectrum from the case of the rigid boundary ($e \to \infty$), for which the simple results (8.1.36) and (8.1.40) are available, to the traction-free case ($e \to 0$). While conceptually this may be obvious enough, the usefulness of this approach lies in certain special solutions to (8.1.112) and (8.1.113) and their relation to the mixed boundary condition case.

Consider, then, the frequency spectrum for the case of mixed boundary conditions, or rigid restraint, as given in Fig. 8.5. Isolate a portion of the spectrum where the branches of the P and SV waves intersect. A typical region is shown in Fig. 8.8(a). We recall that the m integers refer to the dilatational modes and the n integers refer to the equivoluminal modes. Furthermore, the even integers (both m and n) are symmetric modes and the odd integers are

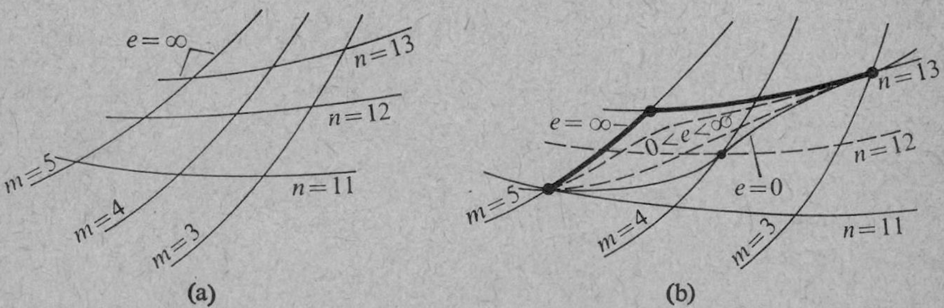

FIG. 8.8. (a) A portion of the frequency spectrum for the mixed boundary condition plate and (b) transition of a portion of the spectrum from $e = 0$ to $e \to \infty$ conditions. (Based on Mindlin [63, Fig. 20].)

antisymmetric modes. Also, the fact that these branches are for the rigid boundary is indicated by $e = \infty$.

The essential stages in determining the transition of the spectrum from rigid to traction-free conditions now arise. Considering first the antisymmetric case, we refer to (8.1.113) and note that these are satisfied by

$$\cos \alpha b = \cos \beta b = 0, \tag{8.1.114}$$

$$A/D = \pm 2\xi\beta/(\xi^2 - \beta^2). \tag{8.1.115}$$

Now (8.1.114) is identical to the antisymmetric mode case for mixed boundary conditions given by (8.1.36). For this type of condition we recall that $\cos \alpha b = 0$, $\alpha b = m\pi/2$ (m odd) represents the dilatational modes and $\cos \beta b = 0$, ($\beta b = n\pi/2$, n odd) represents the shear modes. The point here is that $\cos \alpha b = \cos \beta b = 0$ represents the intersection points of the branches $m = 1, 3, 5, 7, \ldots$ and $n = 1, 3, 5, 7, \ldots$. The significance of this is that, regardless of boundary constraint (that is, $0 < e < \infty$), certain common points of the frequency spectrum have been located. In the case of the limited region shown in Fig. 8.8(a), these would be the two points at $m = 5$, $n = 11$ and $m = 3$, $n = 13$.

The next factor that enables us to further structure the spectrum is the special case of $e = 0$. Thus, for this case, we see from (8.1.113) that

$$\sin \alpha b = \sin \beta b = 0, \tag{8.1.116}$$

$$A/D = \pm(\xi^2 - \beta^2)/2\xi\alpha, \tag{8.1.117}$$

represent solutions. Now (8.1.116) are the frequency equations for the previously encountered case of mixed boundary conditions, symmetric modes given by (8.1.40). These branches are the (m, n = even) curves of the spectrum of Fig. 8.5. Hence their simultaneous satisfaction by (8.1.116) represents the intersection points of the (m, n even)-curves. Referring to Fig. 8.8(a) this would be the point $m = 4$, $n = 12$ for the region shown.

With these results, we have the following information regarding the antisymmetric modes:

(1) $0 \leq e \leq \infty$; all curves of the spectrum pass through the intersection points of the (m, n = odd)-curves;

(2) $e = \infty$; the spectrum is represented by the (m, n = odd)-curves;

(3) $e = 0$ all curves of the spectrum pass through the (m, n = even)-intersection points, in addition to those points of (2) above.

The nature of a portion of the spectrum meeting these conditions is shown in Fig. 8.8(b). The location of a specific point in the transition from $e = \infty$ to $e = 0$, excepting those cited above, would have to be calculated numerically.

With the information available from the grid-of-bounds considerations plus that previously available on cutoff frequencies, Lame' modes, and high-frequency limits, a fairly detailed construction of the spectrum becomes

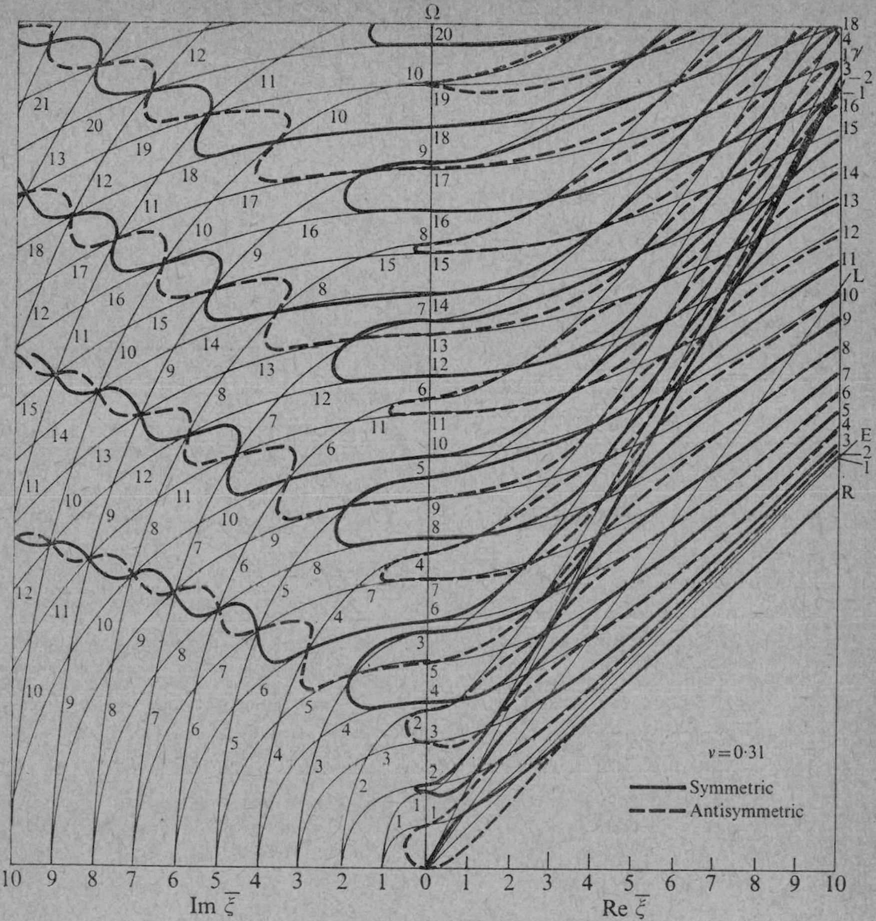

FIG. 8.9. Frequency spectrum for the Rayleigh–Lamb equation. (After Mindlin [63, Fig. 19].)

possible. Additional information on the curvature of the branches at the cutoff frequency (not developed here) is used. The resulting spectrum as given by Mindlin [63] for the case of Poisson's ratio of $\nu = 0{\cdot}31$ is shown in Fig. 8.9. The heavy solid lines of the spectrum correspond to the symmetric modes, the dashed lines to the antisymmetric modes. The thin solid lines are the grid of bounds provided by the frequency spectrum for the mixed boundary condition plate. The integers associated with the various modes are indicated in the imaginary plane. The normalizations of wavenumber and frequency are the same as used previously. Thus

$$\bar{\xi} = 2b\xi/\pi, \qquad \Omega = 2b\omega/\pi c_2. \tag{8.1.118}$$

The integers along the real Ω-axis indicate the mode number, with the integers on the left corresponding to $p = 1, 2, 3, \ldots$ (thickness stretch) and on the right corresponding to $q = 1, 2, 3, \ldots$ (thickness shear). Finally, we note the four rays OR, OE, OL, OD in the spectrum. The rays OE and OD represent the shear wave speed and dilatational wave speed lines, respectively, and divide regions I, II, and III. The line OR is the Rayleigh wave speed line, and OL is that of the Lamé modes.

8. *Discussion of the spectrum.* Following very closely Mindlin's discussion of the frequency spectrum, we start at zero wavenumber. The curvature of the branch and bound at $\bar{\xi} = 0$ determines whether a given branch starts out above or below its bound. Thereafter, a branch is confined between bounds, as described in the development of (7) *The grid of bounds*, crossing them only at successive intersections of bounds m even with n even and m odd with n odd. The antisymmetric modes are predominantly equivoluminal ($|A/D| < 1$) at the intersections m even, n even and predominantly dilatational ($|A/D| > 1$) at the intersections m odd, n odd. The converse holds for the symmetric modes.

For increasing real $\bar{\xi}$, every branch, except the lowest symmetric and antisymmetric ones, eventually crosses the ray OD. As mentioned, this is the dilatational wave speed line. This also corresponds to the situation when $\alpha = 0$, and gives rise to Goodier–Bishop type waves that were investigated for the half-space (see, for example, Fig. 6.12). Further, OD is the bound $m = 0$, so that the symmetric branches cross it at its intersections with the bounds n even. The slopes of all the symmetric branches are the same at these crossover points and are less than the slope of OD.

With further increase of $\bar{\xi}$, all the branches, except the lowest antisymmetric one, cross the ray OL at its intersections with the bounds $n = 1, 2, 3, \ldots$, to which the branches are tangent. At these points, the mode is purely equivoluminal and is composed of SV waves reflecting at 45° angles of incidence (these are the Lamé modes, to be discussed in more detail later). Since the modes of these points are purely equivoluminal, these are the only points that remain fixed as Poisson's ratio is varied.

After crossing OL, all the real branches except the lowest symmetric and antisymmetric ones approach the ray OE, representing the shear-wave velocity. This is in accord with the results obtained in (6) *The short-wavelength limit*. Only the lowest symmetric branch intersects OE, resulting in a Goodier–Bishop wave at that point. Thereafter, the lowest symmetric and antisymmetric branches approach the ray OR asymptotically, corresponding to the Rayleigh surface wave velocity.

9. *Complex branches.* Our considerations thus far have been for real, positive frequency and real or imaginary wavenumbers. It turns out that branches of the frequency spectrum having complex wavenumber also exist.

Referring to our basic definitions (8.1.23) for α, β we see if ξ is real, then α, β may be both real, both imaginary, or α imaginary and β real. If ξ is imaginary, α, β will be real, and if ξ is complex, in general, α, β will both be complex. The resulting spatial behaviour of the waves for some of these possibilities are as follows:

ξ real; α, β real:

$$e^{i(\xi x\pm\alpha y-\omega t)}, \qquad e^{i(\xi x\pm\beta y-\omega t)}. \tag{8.1.119}$$

ξ real; α, β imaginary:

$$e^{\pm\alpha y}e^{i(\xi x-\omega t)}, \qquad e^{\pm\beta y}e^{i(\xi x-\omega t)}. \tag{8.1.120}$$

ξ imaginary; α, β real:

$$e^{\pm\xi x}e^{i(\pm\alpha y-\omega t)}, \qquad e^{\pm\xi x}e^{i(\pm\beta y-\omega t)}. \tag{8.1.121}$$

ξ complex; α, β complex:

Let

$$\xi = a+ib, \qquad \alpha = c+id, \qquad \beta = e+if, \tag{8.1.122}$$

$$e^{\pm bx}e^{\pm dy}e^{i(bx+cy-\omega t)}, \qquad e^{\pm bx}e^{\pm fy}e^{i(bx+ey-\omega t)}. \tag{8.1.123}$$

We have encountered real and complex wavenumbers previously,† and realize that such wavenumbers play a role in forced vibration and reflection problems.

In considering complex branches of the spectrum, we confine our attention to the first three symmetric modes of the spectrum for which there is a single, complex branch. The representation of the spectrum in Fig. 8.9 is for positive real and positive imaginary wavenumber. The spectrum is actually symmetric with respect to the real and imaginary planes owing to the occurrence of the wavenumber as ξ^2. Figure 8.10 is a three-dimensional representation of a portion of the spectrum containing the first three symmetric modes. A complex branch is seen originating from a minimum point on the second longitudinal mode $L(2)$. Other complex branches originate from other such minima of the spectrum. From the complete spectrum of Fig. 8.9, it is seen that such minima occur rather rarely.

The portion of the $L(2)$ branch between the cutoff frequency and the minimum was an early puzzling feature of the spectrum, since a negative group velocity was indicated. The existence of complex branches, while of significance, particularly in regard to the question of Fourier synthesis of pulses, did not in itself resolve the question of negative group velocity. However, Folk [16] showed that the proper path of integration for a Fourier pulse analysis must be such that the slope $d\omega/d\xi$ (or $d\Omega/d\bar{\xi}$) is always of the same sign. This requires interpreting the spectrum in terms of just the solid or just the dashed lines in Fig. 8.12.

† See § 3.3 for the case of complex wavenumber.

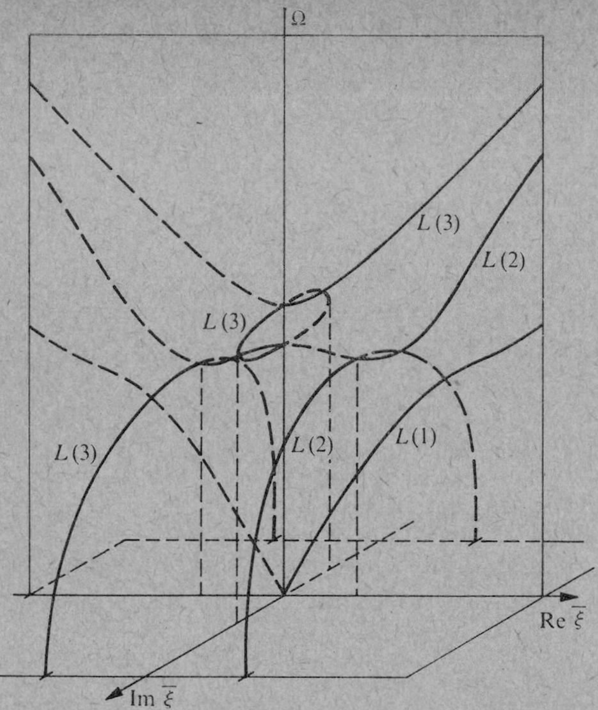

FIG. 8.10. Three-dimensional representation of a portion of the plate frequency spectrum for the first three longitudinal modes. (After Mindlin [63, Fig. 23].)

10. *Dispersion curves.* Information on the phase velocity is obtainable by directly considering the Rayleigh–Lamb equation in terms of c and ξ, or by computing the results from the roots of the frequency spectrum using the relation $\omega = \xi c$. The results for the first few modes are shown in Fig. 8.11 for a Poisson's ratio of $\nu = \frac{1}{3}$. The normalized phase velocity is given by $\bar{c} = c/c_2$. Again, the solid curves are the symmetric, the dashed curves are the antisymmetric modes. The light solid lines represent grid-of-bounds curves.

11. *Status.* We close this section on the Rayleigh–Lamb equation by quoting Mindlin's† evaluation of the understanding in this field.

Lamb [39] in 1917, studied the lowest symmetric and antisymmetric modes. He also identified the cut-off modes, the Lamé [40] modes and certain aspects of the high-frequency spectrum. Bounds α = constant, β = constant were employed by Holden [26], in 1951, to construct a portion of the spectrum of symmetric modes for real wavenumbers and this method was considerably elaborated and extended to include the antisymmetric modes and imaginary phase velocities by Onoe [74]. Analogous bounds were employed by Mindlin [60], in 1951, to construct the branches of a similar transcendental equation, which appears in the theory of

† P. 215 of Reference [63].

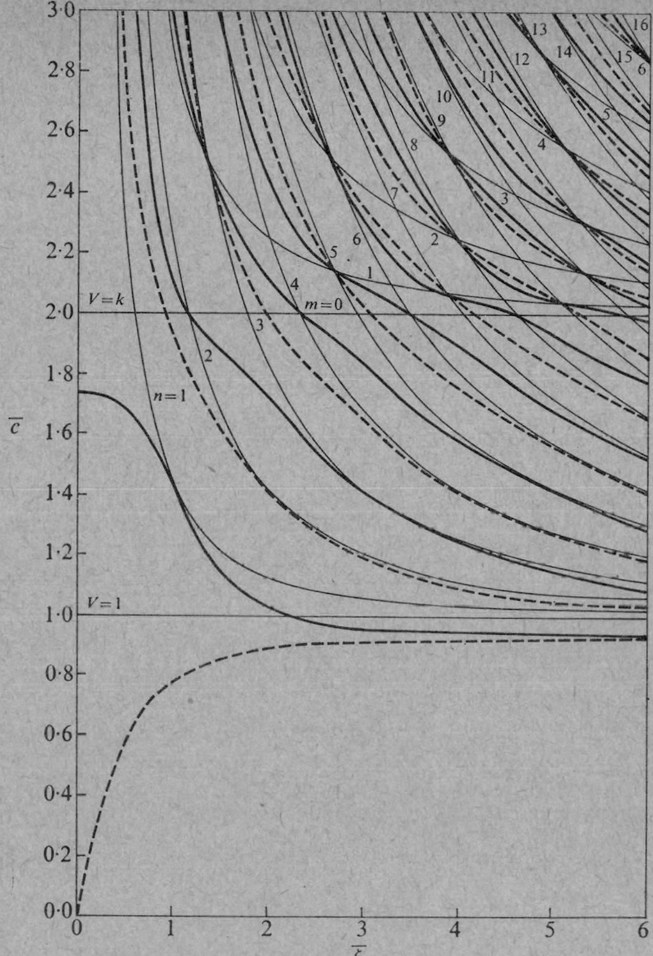

FIG. 8.11. Dispersion curves for a plate for Poisson's ratio of $\frac{1}{3}$. (After Mindlin [63, Fig. 18].)

vibrations of crystal plates, and this method was applied later to (8.1.61). The intricate behavior of the branches in the neighborhood of zero wavenumber and the important role of Poisson's ratio were studied by Onoe [74], Mindlin [36], and Mindlin and Onoe [67]. The imaginary loop that connects the second and third symmetric branches, in a certain range of Poisson's ratio, had been brought to light previously in computations by Aggarwal and Shaw [2], in 1954, and a computation of the family of imaginary branches has been performed by Lyon [44]. The existence of modes at the cut-off frequencies, other than the modes identified by Lamb, was established by Mindlin [62]. The phenomenon of the occasional appearance of phase and group velocities of opposite sign was encountered and explained by Tolstoy and Usdin [87], and the criteria for the existence of this anomaly in any branch were given by Mindlin [61]. The possibility of resolving the waves in the plate into pairs of reflecting P and SV waves was noticed by Harrison [24]. Complex wavenumbers and phase velocities associated with real frequencies were found by Mindlin and Medick [66] in an approximate theory of vibrations of plates. The existence and important aspects of the behaviour of the complex branches of (8.1.61) were established by Onoe [67, pp. 14–17]. At this writing, the understanding of the roots of the equation appears to be reasonably complete except for the behaviour of the higher complex branches when both the real and imaginary parts of the wavenumber are large.

8.1.6. *Circular crested waves in a plate*

We have now considered the case of straight-crested waves in a plate in some detail. However, problems of axisymmetric loading will result in circularly crested waves, and the immediate question is whether the frequency equation is different for such waves. Goodman [21] investigated this aspect and found that, in fact, the Rayleigh–Lamb equation is again generated. We will review briefly the basic aspects of his analysis.

We use cylindrical coordinates r, θ, z with the z coordinate measured perpendicular to the mid plane of the plate. We assume axisymmetric conditions hold, so that $u_\theta = \partial/\partial\theta = 0$. The plate is of thickness $2b$, with traction-free surfaces, so that

$$\tau_{zz} = \tau_{zr} = \tau_{z\theta} = 0, \qquad z = \pm b. \tag{8.1.124}$$

For the axisymmetric case, $\tau_{z\theta} = 0$ always. The resulting form of the displacement equations of motion for this situation is

$$(\lambda+\mu)\frac{\partial\Delta}{\partial r}+\mu\nabla^2 u_r-\mu\frac{u_r}{r^2} = \rho\frac{\partial^2 u_r}{\partial t^2}, \tag{8.1.125}$$

$$(\lambda+\mu)\frac{\partial\Delta}{\partial z}+\mu\nabla^2 u_z = \rho\frac{\partial^2 u_z}{\partial t^2}, \tag{8.1.126}$$

where Δ is the dilatation, given by

$$\Delta = \frac{\partial u_r}{\partial r}+\frac{u_r}{r}+\frac{\partial u_z}{\partial z}. \tag{8.1.127}$$

By analogy with the statical solution of the problem, assume a solution for the dilatation to be given by

$$\Delta = A\frac{\mu}{\lambda+\mu}J_0(\xi r)e^{i\omega t}\begin{cases}\cosh\alpha z\\ \sinh\alpha z\end{cases}, \tag{8.1.128}$$

where A, ξ, α are constants, The cosh, sinh yield, respectively, symmetrical and antisymmetrical motions relative to the mid plane. For a dilatational solution of the preceding form, and referring to (8.1.127), assume the displacements to be of the form

$$u_r = f_1(z)J_1(\xi r)e^{i\omega t}, \qquad u_z = f_2(z)J_0(\xi r)e^{i\omega t}. \tag{8.1.129}$$

Substituting these and (8.1.128) in the definition of the dilatation gives the requirement that

$$\xi f_1+\frac{\mathrm{d}f_2}{\mathrm{d}z} = A\frac{\mu}{\lambda+\mu}\begin{cases}\cosh \alpha z \\ \sinh \alpha z\end{cases}. \tag{8.1.130}$$

Substituting (8.1.128) and (8.1.129) in the equations of motion gives, for the symmetric case of $\cosh \alpha z$,

$$\begin{aligned}\frac{\mathrm{d}^2 f_1}{\mathrm{d}z^2}-\beta^2 f_1 &= A\xi \cosh \alpha z,\\ \frac{\mathrm{d}^2 f_2}{\mathrm{d}z^2}-\beta^2 f_2 &= -A\alpha \sinh \alpha z,\end{aligned} \tag{8.1.131}$$

where $\beta^2 = \xi^2-\omega^2/c_2^2$. For the antisymmetric case, where $\sinh \alpha z$ is used in (8.1.128), the $\cosh \alpha z$, $\sinh \alpha z$ terms are interchanged in (8.1.131). The solutions of (8.1.131), with constants adjusted so as to satisfy the conditions (8.1.130), give

$$\begin{aligned}u_r &= J_1(\xi r)\left\{B \sinh \beta z - B'\frac{\beta}{\xi}\cosh \beta z + A\frac{\xi}{\alpha^2-\beta^2}\cosh \alpha z\right\}e^{i\omega t},\\ u_z &= J_0(\xi r)\left\{B' \sinh \beta z - B\frac{\xi}{\beta}\cosh \beta z - A\frac{\alpha}{\alpha^2-\beta^2}\sinh \alpha z\right\}e^{i\omega t},\end{aligned} \tag{8.1.132}$$

where $\alpha^2 = \xi^2-\omega^2/c_1^2$. For the antisymmetric case, it is again only necessary to interchange $\sinh \alpha z$, $\cosh \alpha z$.

The stresses τ_{zz}, τ_{zr} are given for the symmetric case by

$$\tau_{zz} = \mu J_0(\xi r)\left\{2B'\beta \cosh \beta z - 2B\xi \sinh \beta z - A\frac{\xi^2+\beta^2}{\alpha^2-\beta^2}\cosh \alpha z\right\}e^{i\omega t}, \tag{8.1.133}$$

$$\tau_{rz} = \mu J_1(\xi r)\left\{\frac{2\alpha\xi}{\alpha^2-\beta^2}A \sinh \alpha z + B\frac{\xi^2+\beta^2}{\beta}\cosh \beta z - B'\frac{\xi^2+\beta^2}{\beta}\sinh \beta z\right\}e^{i\omega t}. \tag{8.1.134}$$

In order for the stresses to vanish on $y = \pm b$, the constant B and the determinant of coefficients resulting from (8.1.33) and (8.1.34) must vanish. The resulting frequency equation is

$$\frac{\tanh \beta b}{\tanh \alpha b} = \frac{4\alpha\beta\xi^2}{(\xi^2-\beta^2)^2}. \tag{8.1.135}$$

This we recognize as the Rayleigh–Lamb equation for symmetric waves in a plate in 'region I' of the spectrum.† Considering antisymmetric waves would similarly yield the antisymmetric Rayleigh–Lamb equation.

† See the previous section, eqns (8.1.85)–(8.1.87).

While the objective of reviewing a portion of the Goodman analysis has now been accomplished, namely showing that the Rayleigh–Lamb equation also governs circular-crested waves in a plate, we shall continue a little further. The displacements are now given by

$$\begin{aligned} u_r &= AJ_1(\xi r)\left(\frac{\xi}{\alpha^2-\beta^2}\right)\left(\cosh \alpha z-\frac{\xi^2+\beta^2}{2\xi^2}\frac{\cosh \alpha b}{\cosh \beta b}\cosh \beta z\right)e^{i\omega t}, \\ u_z &= -AJ_0(\xi r)\left(\frac{\alpha}{\alpha^2-\beta^2}\right)\left(\sinh \alpha z-\frac{2\xi^2}{\xi^2+\beta^2}\frac{\sinh \alpha b}{\sinh \beta b}\sinh \beta z\right)e^{i\omega t}, \end{aligned} \tag{8.1.136}$$

for the symmetric case. Thus, although the frequency–wavenumber relationship holds whether the waves are straight or circularly crested, the displacements (and stresses) vary according to Bessel functions rather than trigonometric functions, in so far as the radial coordinate is concerned. For large values of r, we have that†

$$J_0(\xi r) \to \frac{\sin \xi r + \cos \xi r}{\sqrt{(\pi \xi r)}}, \qquad J_1(\xi r) \to \frac{\sin \xi r - \cos \xi r}{\sqrt{(\pi \xi r)}}. \tag{8.1.137}$$

Thus far from the origin the motion becomes periodic in r. Actually, 'far' occurs rather rapidly, within four or five zeros of the Bessel function. As r becomes very large, the straight crested behaviour is the limit of circular-crested waves.

8.1.7. *Bounded plates—SH and Lamé modes*

Having considered the propagation of continuous waves in infinite plates, a natural next question is whether the natural frequencies of finite plates can be determined in analogy to the situation in simple plate theory. Generally, the answer to this is negative. Thus the problem of the natural frequencies of a rectangular parallelopiped plate of arbitrary dimensions, say $2a$, $2b$, $2c$, and having traction-free surfaces is presently intractable. Nevertheless, considerations of such problems are relevant and necessary in many practical situations. In this section we will review the simple case of SH modes and the Lamé modes first mentioned in the analysis of the Rayleigh–Lamb equation.

Consider first the case of SH modes, and consider a plate having x and y dimensions of $2a$ and $2b$, as shown in Fig. 8.12(a) and to be infinite in extent in the z direction. For SH waves we have the governing equation given by $\nabla^2 u_z = (\partial^2 u_z/\partial t^2)/c_2^2$, and the non-trivial boundary conditions given by

$$\begin{aligned} x &= \pm a, \qquad \tau_{xz} = \frac{\partial u_z}{\partial x} = 0, \\ y &= \pm b, \qquad \tau_{zy} = \frac{\partial u_z}{\partial y} = 0. \end{aligned} \tag{8.1.138}$$

† McLachlan [46].

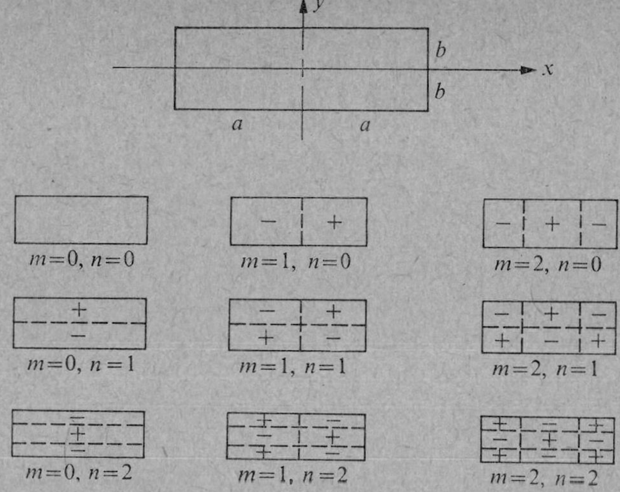

FIG. 8.12. (a) Plate finite in the x, y directions but of infinite extent in the z direction and (b) illustration of the first few SH modes.

The solution to this problem is quite simple, being quite like the case for vibrations of rectangular membranes, except that the present boundary conditions are on the derivative along the boundary. Thus, considering a solution of the form $u_z = X(x)Y(y)\exp(-i\omega t)$, we obtain

$$X_m = A_m \sin \xi_m x + B_m \cos \xi_m x, \qquad \xi_m = m\pi/2a,$$
$$Y_n = C_n \sin \alpha_n y + D_n \cos \alpha_n y, \qquad \alpha_n = n\pi/2b, \qquad (8.1.139)$$

where $m, n = 1, 2, 3 \ldots$ and $\alpha_n^2 = \omega_{mn}^2/c_2^2 - \xi_m^2$. The values $m, n = 0$ are also roots but give only rigid-body translation.

For the results (8.1.139) we have modes symmetric with respect to x given by $A_m = 0$, m even, antisymmetric in x by $B_m = 0$, m odd. Modes symmetric in y are given by $C_n = 0$, n even and antisymmetric in y by $D_n = 0$, n odd. The natural frequencies are given by

$$\omega_{mn} = \pi\left\{\left(\frac{m}{2a}\right)^2 + \left(\frac{n}{2b}\right)^2\right\}^{\frac{1}{2}}. \qquad (8.1.140)$$

The first few mode shapes are shown in Fig. 8.12(b). Now, our 'bounded' plate in this analysis is only partly so, being infinite in the z direction. The SH solutions satisfying traction-free boundary conditions on $x = \pm a$, $y = \pm b$ would not satisfy such conditions on any surface z = constant. However, if the dimensions of the finite plate were such that $2c \gg 2a$, $2b$ and SH wave type of excitation was given, the results from the present analysis would probably closely predict most modes. However, quite possibly extraneous modes due to the finiteness of the plate would be noted also.

We now consider the Lamé modes. Recall from the analysis of the Rayleigh–Lamb equation (p. 448) that the Lamé modes represented special solutions to the frequency equation given when $\xi = \beta$. It was found (see (8.1.96)) that $\beta = n\pi/2b$, where n odd was the symmetric case, n even was the antisymmetric case. The displacements and stresses are given by (8.1.27)–(8.1.31). Recall, in general, that for the symmetric modes in a plate, we have $A = D = 0$ in the displacement–stress expressions, while for the antisymmetric modes, we have $B = C = 0$. For the special case of the symmetric Lamé modes, we refer to (8.1.53), the boundary condition equations. For $\xi = \beta$ and $\tan \beta b = \infty$, so that $\cos \beta b = 0$, we have that $B = 0$ must occur. For the antisymmetric Lamé modes refer to (8.1.58), where again $\xi = \beta$ and $\sin \beta b = 0$, so that we must have $A = 0$. The resulting potentials, displacements, and stresses are:

Symmetric:

$$\Phi = 0, \qquad H_z = \mathrm{i}C \sin \beta y e^{\mathrm{i}\psi}, \tag{8.1.141}$$

$$u_x = \mathrm{i}\beta C \cos \beta y e^{\mathrm{i}\psi}, \qquad u_y = \xi C \sin \beta y e^{\mathrm{i}\psi}, \tag{8.1.142}$$

$$\begin{aligned} \tau_{xx} &= -2\mu\xi\beta C \cos \beta y e^{\mathrm{i}\psi}, \\ \tau_{yy} &= 2\mu\xi\beta C \cos \beta y e^{\mathrm{i}\psi}, \\ \tau_{xy} &= 0. \end{aligned} \tag{8.1.143}$$

Antisymmetric:

$$\Phi = 0, \qquad H_z = \mathrm{i}D \cos \beta y e^{\mathrm{i}\psi}, \tag{8.1.144}$$

$$u_x = -\mathrm{i}\beta D \sin \beta y e^{\mathrm{i}\psi}, \qquad u_y = \xi D \cos \beta y e^{\mathrm{i}\psi}, \tag{8.1.145}$$

$$\begin{aligned} \tau_{xx} &= 2\mu\xi\beta D \sin \beta y e^{\mathrm{i}\psi}, \\ \tau_{yy} &= 2\mu\xi\beta D \sin \beta y e^{\mathrm{i}\psi}, \\ \tau_{xy} &= 0, \end{aligned} \tag{8.1.146}$$

where $\psi = \xi x - \omega t$.

A quite meaningful physical interpretation of these results is possible by using exponential representations for $\sin \beta y$, $\cos \beta y$. Thus, for the symmetric u_x displacement, we may write

$$u_x = \mathrm{i}\frac{\beta C}{2}\{e^{\mathrm{i}(\xi x+\beta y-\omega t)} + e^{\mathrm{i}(\xi x-\beta y-\omega t)}\}. \tag{8.1.147}$$

Since $\beta = \xi$, it is seen that the result is in terms of plane waves at 45° with respect to the boundaries. We also note that dilatational effects are completely absent ($\Phi = 0$) in this mode and, finally, recall that the case of SV waves incident at 45° was found to be a special case of wave reflection, where no conversion occurs and only SV waves are reflected. We thus conclude that the Lamé modes result from a propagating train of SV waves at 45°. The general

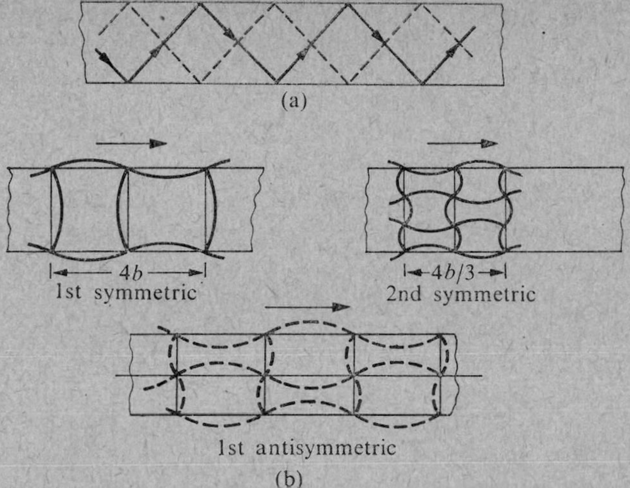

FIG. 8.13. Formation of (a) symmetric Lamé modes by SV waves at 45°, and (b) the first few Lamé modes.

situation for symmetric modes is shown in Fig. 8.13(a), while the first two symmetric modes and the first antisymmetric mode are shown in Fig. 8.13(b).

Our considerations thus far, while interesting, do not seem to relate to bounded plates. Now, a plate bounded by, say, $x = \pm a$ would have to satisfy conditions of $\tau_{xx} = \tau_{xy} = 0$ on these surfaces. We note that $\tau_{xy} = 0$ for the Lamé modes. Further, we note for, say, the symmetric case that $\text{Re}\,\tau_{xx} = 0$ for $\cos(\xi x - \omega t) = 0$. These represent propagating planes of zero τ_{xx} stress. To achieve the standing-wave case necessary for a bounded plate, merely add an oppositely propagating wave system. This would be obtained, for the symmetric case, directly from (8.1.27)–(8.1.31), where ψ is replaced by $\psi' = -\xi x - \omega t$. For the stress τ_{xx}, this would give

$$\begin{aligned}\tau_{xx} &= -2\mu\xi\beta C \cos\beta y e^{i(\xi x-\omega t)} - 2\mu\xi\beta C \cos\beta y e^{-i(\xi x+\omega t)} \\ &= -4\mu\xi\beta C \cos\beta y \cos\xi x e^{-i\omega t}.\end{aligned} \tag{8.1.148}$$

For the symmetric Lamé modes, $\beta = \xi = n\pi/2b$, n odd. From (8.1.148) we see that

$$\tau_{xx} = 0, \qquad \frac{n\pi x}{2b} = \frac{p\pi}{2}, \qquad p \text{ odd}, \tag{8.1.149}$$

so that $x = pb/n$ give locations of zero τ_{xx} stress. Since $\tau_{xy} = 0$ already, these establish the dimensions of bounded plates capable of free vibration in the Lamé modes. Again, as for the SH wave case, the z dimension of the plate would have to be large compared to the x and y dimensions in order for the Lamé modes to be excited. Mindlin [63, pp. 220–6] has given an extensive discussion of other bounded-plate cases, obtained for mixed boundary conditions and other special situations.

8.2. Waves in circular rods and cylindrical shells

We now extend our considerations to wave effects in solid, circular cylinders and cylindrical shells. The situation here is analogous to that in plates, in that these geometries have been previously studied in the context of strength-of-material theories. It was found that longitudinal and torsional waves were governed by the wave equation and only a single, non-dispersive mode of propagation was possible in each case. The propagation of flexural waves was governed by Bernoulli–Euler theory and such waves propagated dispersively although, again, only a single mode of propagation was possible. Refinements of these simple equations resulted, in the case of rods, by including lateral-inertia effects, and in the case of beams, by considering shear and rotary-inertia effects. Waves in shells were studied using only the membrane theory.

The coverage in this area will be rather brief compared to that of plates. There are many similarities between the two situations which justify briefer coverage. Thus, the SH and longitudinal modes of the plate have their analogues in torsional and longitudinal rod modes. The antisymmetric plate modes are analogous to the flexural rod modes. The major objective will be to present frequency-spectrum and dispersion-curve information.

It is possible, in studying torsional, longitudinal, and flexural waves in rods and shells, to consider each type of motion separately and derive frequency equations for each. This was done, for example, in the case of plates where SH and plane-strain modes were considered. However, as was also done in the case of plates, it is possible to develop a general frequency equation for the problem and to then resolve it into the various modes. This was done by Gazis [20] in the analysis of cylindrical shells, for example. Meeker and Meitzler [48], following the approach of Gazis, developed the Pochhammer–Chree equations for a solid cylinder in this manner. The approach taken in this section will follow that of the cited references.

8.2.1. *The frequency equation for the solid rod*

Consider a solid, circular, cylindrical rod as shown in Fig. 8.14. As in our previous treatment of plate problems, we shall formulate the displacements

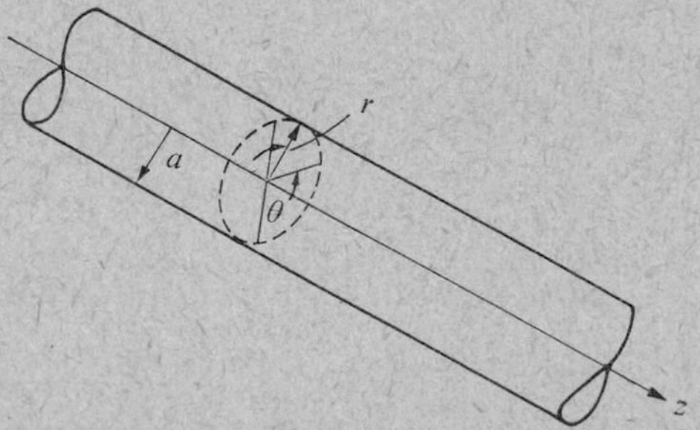

FIG. 8.14. Coordinates for a solid, cylindrical rod.

and stresses in terms of potential functions Φ and $\mathbf{H}$. Cylindrical coordinates are appropriate here, and we write for the displacements

$$\mathbf{u} = \nabla\Phi + \nabla\times\mathbf{H}, \qquad \nabla.\mathbf{H} = F(\mathbf{r}, t). \tag{8.2.1}$$

An alternate condition on the divergence has been chosen in (8.2.1), where $F(\mathbf{r}, t)$ is an arbitrary function. As pointed out by Gazis, the choice of $F(\mathbf{r}, t)$ is arbitrary due to the gauge invariance of the Helmholtz resolution.† The use of this condition will come somewhat later. The scalar components of $\mathbf{u}$ are given by

$$u_r = \frac{\partial\Phi}{\partial r} + \frac{1}{r}\frac{\partial H_z}{\partial\theta} - \frac{\partial H_\theta}{\partial z},$$
$$u_\theta = \frac{1}{r}\frac{\partial\Phi}{\partial\theta} + \frac{\partial H_r}{\partial z} - \frac{\partial H_z}{\partial r},$$
$$u_z = \frac{\partial\Phi}{\partial z} + \frac{1}{r}\frac{\partial}{\partial r}(rH_\theta) - \frac{1}{r}\frac{\partial H_r}{\partial\theta}. \tag{8.2.2}$$

The potentials Φ and $\mathbf{H}$ satisfy the scalar and vector wave equations,

$$\nabla^2\Phi = \frac{1}{c_1^2}\frac{\partial^2\Phi}{\partial t^2}, \qquad \nabla^2\mathbf{H} = \frac{1}{c_2^2}\frac{\partial^2\mathbf{H}}{\partial t^2}, \tag{8.2.3}$$

where

$$\nabla^2\Phi = \frac{\partial^2\Phi}{\partial r^2} + \frac{1}{r}\frac{\partial\Phi}{\partial r} + \frac{1}{r^2}\frac{\partial^2\Phi}{\partial\theta^2} + \frac{\partial^2\Phi}{\partial z^2}, \tag{8.2.4}$$

$$\nabla^2\mathbf{H} = \left(\nabla^2 H_r - \frac{H_r}{r^2} - \frac{2}{r^2}\frac{\partial H_\theta}{\partial\theta}\right)\mathbf{e}_r + \left(\nabla^2 H_\theta - \frac{H_\theta}{r^2} + \frac{2}{r^2}\frac{\partial H_r}{\partial\theta}\right)\mathbf{e}_\theta + \nabla^2 H_z\mathbf{e}_z. \tag{8.2.5}$$

The stresses are given by Hooke's law, $\tau_{ij} = \lambda\,\Delta\delta_{ij} + 2\mu e_{ij}$, where

$$e_{rr} = \frac{\partial u_r}{\partial r}, \qquad e_{\theta\theta} = \frac{1}{r}\frac{\partial u_\theta}{\partial\theta} + \frac{u_r}{r}, \qquad e_{zz} = \frac{\partial u_z}{\partial z},$$
$$e_{r\theta} = \frac{1}{2}\left(\frac{1}{r}\frac{\partial u_r}{\partial\theta} + \frac{\partial u_\theta}{\partial r} - \frac{u_\theta}{r}\right), \qquad e_{rz} = \frac{1}{2}\left(\frac{\partial u_z}{\partial r} + \frac{\partial u_r}{\partial z}\right), \tag{8.2.6}$$
$$e_{\theta z} = \frac{1}{2}\left(\frac{\partial u_\theta}{\partial z} + \frac{1}{r}\frac{\partial u_z}{\partial\theta}\right).$$

The boundary conditions for the problem will be given by

$$\tau_{rr} = \tau_{r\theta} = \tau_{rz} = 0, \quad r = a. \tag{8.2.7}$$

We now consider the conditions under which harmonic waves may propagate in a cylinder. Thus consider Φ, H_r, etc. to be of the general form

$$\Phi = f(r)\Theta_\phi(\theta)e^{i(\xi z-\omega t)}, \qquad H_r = h_r(r)\Theta_r(\theta)e^{i(\xi z-\omega t)},\ldots. \tag{8.2.8}$$

† See, for example, Morse and Feshbach [70, p. 207].

When these are substituted in the scalar and vector wave equations, sine and cosine solutions result for the θ-dependence. Thus, for Φ we have

$$f''\Theta_\phi+\frac{1}{r}f'\Theta_\phi+\frac{1}{r^2}f\Theta_\phi''-\xi^2 f\Theta_\phi = -\frac{\omega^2}{c_1^2}f\Theta_\phi, \tag{8.2.9}$$

giving

$$r^2\frac{f''}{f}+r\frac{f'}{f}-\left(\xi^2-\frac{\omega^2}{c_1^2}\right)r^2 = -\Theta_\phi''/\Theta_\phi = k^2. \tag{8.2.10}$$

Thus,

$$\Theta_\phi = A\sin k\theta+B\cos k\theta. \tag{8.2.11}$$

Single-valuedness requirements on Θ_ϕ make $k = n$, an integer. Similar solutions also hold for Θ_r, Θ_θ, Θ_z. Furthermore, later requirements on the nature of the θ dependence for the longitudinal, torsional, and flexural modes would lead us to discard either sine or cosine terms in the various Θ results. The resulting expressions for Φ, H_r, H_θ, H_z become

$$\begin{aligned}
\Phi &= f(r)\cos n\theta e^{i(\xi z-\omega t)},\\
H_r &= h_r(r)\sin n\theta e^{i(\xi z-\omega t)},\\
H_\theta &= h_\theta(r)\cos n\theta e^{i(\xi z-\omega t)},\\
H_z &= h_z(r)\sin n\theta e^{i(\xi z-\omega t)}.
\end{aligned} \tag{8.2.12}$$

We now proceed with the determination of the r dependence for the four functions. Starting with Φ, we have from (8.2.11) that

$$\frac{d^2f}{dr^2}+\frac{1}{r}\frac{df}{dr}+\left(\alpha^2-\frac{n^2}{r^2}\right)f = 0, \tag{8.2.13}$$

where $\alpha^2 = \omega^2/c_1^2-\xi^2$. This is Bessel's equation of order n having the solution

$$f(r) = AJ_n(\alpha r), \tag{8.2.14}$$

where the second solution $Y_n(\alpha r)$ has been discarded because of its singular behaviour at the origin. The equation that results for h_z is similar to (8.2.13) with α^2 replaced by β^2. The solution is

$$h_z(r) = B_3J_n(\beta r), \tag{8.2.15}$$

where $\beta^2 = \omega^2/c_2^2-\xi^2$. The remaining two equations in $h_r(r)$, $h_\theta(r)$ will be coupled, as study of the vector Laplacian (8.2.5) will reveal. The resulting equations are

$$\begin{aligned}
&\frac{d^2h_r}{dr^2}+\frac{1}{r}\frac{dh_r}{dr}+\frac{1}{r^2}(-n^2h_r+2nh_\theta-h_r)-\xi^2h_r+\frac{\omega^2}{c_2^2}h_r = 0,\\
&\frac{d^2h_\theta}{dr^2}+\frac{1}{r}\frac{dh_\theta}{dr}+\frac{1}{r^2}(-n^2h_\theta+2nh_r-h_\theta)-\xi^2h_\theta+\frac{\omega^2}{c_2^2}h_\theta = 0.
\end{aligned} \tag{8.2.16}$$

These equations may be solved simultaneously for h_r, h_θ. Thus subtract the first from the second to give

$$\left\{\frac{d^2}{dr^2}+\frac{1}{r}\frac{d}{dr}+\beta^2-\frac{(n+1)^2}{r^2}\right\}(h_r-h_\theta)=0. \tag{8.2.17}$$

This has the solution

$$h_r-h_\theta=2B_2J_{n+1}(\beta r). \tag{8.2.18}$$

Add the two equations of (8.2.16) to give

$$\left\{\frac{d^2}{dr^2}+\frac{1}{r}\frac{d}{dr}+\beta^2-\frac{(n-1)^2}{r^2}\right\}(h_r+h_\theta)=0. \tag{8.2.19}$$

This has the solution,

$$h_r+h_\theta=2B_1J_{n-1}(\beta r). \tag{8.2.20}$$

Adding and subtracting (8.2.18) and (8.2.20), we obtain

$$\begin{aligned} h_r &= B_1J_{n-1}(\beta r)+B_2J_{n+1}(\beta r),\\ h_\theta &= B_1J_{n-1}(\beta r)-B_2J_{n+1}(\beta r). \end{aligned} \tag{8.2.21}$$

There are four constants associated with the components of displacement, with three boundary conditions to be applied. The property of gauge invariance can now be used to eliminate one of the constants, without loss of generality. Setting $B_1=0$, which results in $h_r(r)=-h_\theta(r)$, the resulting displacements and some of the stresses are

$$\begin{aligned} u_r &= \{f'+(n/r)h_z+\xi h_r\}\cos n\theta e^{i(\xi z-\omega t)},\\ u_\theta &= \{-(n/r)f+\xi h_r-h_z'\}\sin n\theta e^{i(\xi z-\omega t)},\\ u_z &= \{-\xi f-h_r'-(n+1)h_r/r\}\cos n\theta e^{i(\xi z-\omega t)}, \end{aligned} \tag{8.2.22}$$

$$\begin{aligned} \tau_{rr} &= \left[-\lambda(\alpha^2+\xi^2)f+2\mu\left\{f''+\frac{n}{r}\left(h_z'-\frac{h_z}{r}\right)+\xi h_r'\right\}\right]\cos n\theta e^{i(\xi z-\omega t)},\\ \tau_{r\theta} &= \mu\left[-\frac{2n}{r}\left(f'-\frac{f}{r}\right)-(2h_z''-\beta^2h_z)-\xi\left(\frac{n+1}{r}h_r-h_r'\right)\right]\sin n\theta e^{i(\xi z-\omega t)},\\ \tau_{rz} &= \mu\left[-2\xi f'-\frac{n}{r}\left\{h_r'+\left(\frac{n+1}{r}-\beta^2+\xi^2\right)h_r\right\}-\frac{n\xi}{r}h_z\right]\cos n\theta e^{i(\xi z-\omega t)}. \end{aligned} \tag{8.2.23}$$

The procedure to obtain the frequency equation is to substitute the results for f, h_r, h_θ, h_z in (8.2.23) evaluated at $r=a$. The resulting determinant of coefficients, which yields the frequency equation, is

$$|a_{ij}|=0 \qquad (i,j=1,2,3), \tag{8.2.24}$$

where

$$\begin{aligned}
a_{11} &= \left\{\frac{\lambda(\alpha^2+\xi^2)(\alpha a)^2}{2\mu\alpha^2}+(\alpha a)^2-n^2\right\}J_n(\alpha a)+\alpha a J_n'(\alpha a),\\
a_{12} &= \{n^2-(\beta a)^2\}J_n(\beta a)-\beta a J_n'(\beta a),\\
a_{13} &= 2n\{\beta a J_n'(\beta a)-J_n(\beta a)\},\\
a_{21} &= n\{\alpha a J_n'(\alpha a)-J_n(\alpha a)\},\\
a_{22} &= -n\{\beta a J_n'(\beta a)-J_n(\beta a)\},\\
a_{23} &= -\{2n^2-(\beta a)^2\}J_n(\beta a)+2\beta a J_n'(\beta a),\\
a_{31} &= -\alpha a J_n'(\alpha a),\\
a_{32} &= -\frac{\beta^2-\xi^2}{2\xi^2}\beta a J_n'(\beta a),\\
a_{33} &= nJ_n(\beta a).
\end{aligned} \tag{8.2.25}$$

8.2.2. *Torsional, longitudinal, and flexural modes in a rod*

The result (8.2.24) is a general frequency equation in the same sense as (8.1.61), obtained for the plate. As in the case of the plate, various special modes, such as torsional, longitudinal, and flexural result from the general case.

1. *Torsional modes*. The family of torsional modes results when only the u_θ displacement is assumed to exist. Such a displacement field is obtained if only $H_z \neq 0$ is assumed, resulting in

$$H_z = B_3 J_0(\beta r)\mathrm{e}^{\mathrm{i}(\xi z-\omega t)}, \tag{8.2.26}$$

and

$$u_\theta = BJ_1(\beta r)\mathrm{e}^{\mathrm{i}(\xi z-\omega t)}. \tag{8.2.27}$$

We have replaced $-\beta B_3$ that results from differentiating $J_0(\beta r)$ by B in (8.2.27). The frequency equation for the torsional modes may be obtained by using the boundary condition $\tau_{r\theta} = 0$ and noting from (8.2.23) that this is merely

$$r\frac{\partial}{\partial r}\left(\frac{u_\theta}{r}\right) = 0, \qquad r = a, \tag{8.2.28}$$

or by setting $n = 0$ in (8.2.24). From the latter procedure, (8.2.24) reduces to the term a_{23} and its cofactor matrix. The remaining elements are zero. We thus have,

$$\begin{vmatrix} a_{11}' & a_{12}' \\ a_{31}' & a_{32}' \end{vmatrix} a_{23}' = 0, \tag{8.2.29}$$

where

$$\begin{aligned}
a_{11}' &= \left\{\frac{\lambda(\alpha^2+\xi^2)(\alpha a)^2}{2\mu\alpha^2}+(\alpha a)^2\right\}J_0(\alpha a)+\alpha a J_0'(\alpha a),\\
a_{12}' &= -(\beta a)^2 J_0(\beta a)-\beta a J_0'(\beta a),\\
a_{31}' &= -\alpha a J_0'(\alpha a), \qquad a_{32}' = -\frac{\beta^2-\xi^2}{2\xi^2}\beta a J_0'(\beta a),\\
a_{23}' &= (\beta a)^2 J_0(\beta a)+2\beta a J_0'(\beta a).
\end{aligned} \tag{8.2.30}$$

The present case of torsional waves is governed by $a'_{23} = 0$, giving

$$\beta a J_0(\beta a) = 2J_1(\beta a), \tag{8.2.31}$$

as the frequency equation for torsional waves. This frequency equation would result if (8.2.28) were applied directly. Some of the roots of the torsional wave frequency equation are

$$\beta_1 a = 5{\cdot}136, \quad \beta_2 a = 8{\cdot}417, \quad \beta_3 a = 11{\cdot}62, \ldots . \tag{8.2.32}$$

Given a root, say $\beta_p a$, the resulting frequency–wavenumber relation is

$$(\beta_p a)^2 = (\omega a/c_2)^2 - (\xi a)^2. \tag{8.2.33}$$

If this spectrum is plotted, it will be found to be quite similar to the SH modes of a plate (see Fig. 8.3). It is seen that the torsional modes governed by (8.2.33) propagate dispersively.

There is an additional solution of the frequency eqn (8.2.31) given by $\beta = 0$. Upon examining the governing equation for $h_z(r)$ (see comments leading to (8.2.15)), it is found that we have $\mathrm{d}^2h_z/\mathrm{d}r^2 + r^{-1}\,\mathrm{d}h_z/\mathrm{d}r = 0$, having a solution $h_z = A + B\ln r$. This does not yield an acceptable displacement field. However, if one examines the displacement equations of motion under the conditions of the present problem, where $u_\theta = u_\theta(r, z)$, $u_r = u_z = 0$, the only non-trivial equation is

$$\frac{\partial^2 u_\theta}{\partial r^2} + \frac{1}{r}\frac{\partial u_\theta}{\partial r} - \frac{u_\theta}{r^2} + \frac{\partial^2 u_\theta}{\partial z^2} = \frac{1}{c_2^2}\frac{\partial^2 u_\theta}{\partial t^2}. \tag{8.2.34}$$

Considering a solution $u_\theta = U(r)\exp\{\mathrm{i}(\xi z - \omega t)\}$ gives

$$\frac{\mathrm{d}^2 U}{\mathrm{d}r^2} + \frac{1}{r}\frac{\mathrm{d}U}{\mathrm{d}r} + \left(\beta^2 - \frac{1}{r^2}\right)U = 0. \tag{8.2.35}$$

For $\beta = 0$, the resulting solution is

$$U = \frac{A}{r} + Br. \tag{8.2.36}$$

The singular behaviour at $r = 0$ requires $A = 0$. Thus, for $\beta = 0$, we have a displacement field given by

$$u_\theta = Br\mathrm{e}^{\mathrm{i}(\xi z - \omega t)}, \tag{8.2.37}$$

where $\xi = \omega/c_2$. This is the lowest mode of propagation of torsional waves and it is this mode of propagation that is described by the 'strength-of-materials' approach. It represents the exceptional case where elasticity and strength of materials yield the same results. This mode propagates non-dispersively.

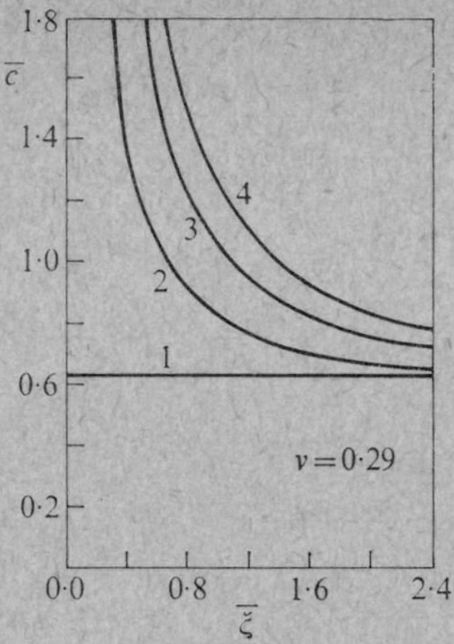

FIG. 8.15. Dispersion curves for torsional waves in a rod.

The dispersion curves for the first four torsional modes ($\beta a = 0$, 5·136, 8·417, 11·62) are plotted in Fig. 8.15, where

$$\bar{c} = c/c_1, \qquad \bar{\xi} = a\xi/2\pi. \tag{8.2.38}$$

As previously mentioned, the frequency spectrum has the same shape as for SH waves in a plate. In fact, the torsional modes for a rod are considered the analogue of the SH plate modes.

2. *The longitudinal modes*. The reduction of the general frequency equation for the case of $n = 0$ led to the result (8.2.29), for which the term $a'_{23} = 0$ yielded the torsional modes. It turns out that the frequency equation for the longitudinal modes is given by the cofactor matrix. We proceed to develop this case in more detail.

Consider the propagation when $u_\theta = \partial/\partial\theta = 0$. From (8.2.2) we have

$$u_r = \frac{\partial\Phi}{\partial r} - \frac{\partial H_\theta}{\partial z}, \qquad u_z = \frac{\partial\Phi}{\partial z} + \frac{1}{r}\frac{\partial}{\partial r}(rH_\theta), \tag{8.2.39}$$

so that determination of Φ and H_θ shall be sufficient to prescribe the motion. The solutions for Φ and H_θ have been given previously by (8.2.12), where $n = 0$ in the cos $n\theta$ dependence. We thus have that

$$\Phi = AJ_0(\alpha r)e^{i(\xi z - \omega t)}, \qquad H_\theta = -B_2 J_1(\beta r)e^{i(\xi z - \omega t)}. \tag{8.2.40}$$

Substitution of the above in the non-trivial boundary conditions, which are $\tau_{rr} = \tau_{rz} = 0$, $r = a$, yields the frequency equation. This was given in (8.2.29) as a cofactor matrix. It expands to give

$$\frac{2\alpha}{a}(\beta^2+\xi^2)J_1(\alpha a)J_1(\beta a) - (\beta^2-\xi^2)^2 J_0(\alpha a)J_1(\beta a) - \\ -4\xi^2\alpha\beta J_1(\alpha a)J_0(\beta a) = 0. \tag{8.2.41}$$

This result is referred to as the 'Pochhammer' frequency equation for the longitudinal modes. It was first published in 1876, but because of its complexity, detailed calculations of the roots did not appear until much later (the 1940s).

The displacements for this mode are given by

$$\begin{aligned} u_r &= B_2\left\{-\frac{A}{B_2}\alpha J_1(\alpha r)+\mathrm{i}\xi J_1(\beta r)\right\}\mathrm{e}^{\mathrm{i}(\xi z-\omega t)}, \\ u_z &= B_2\left\{\frac{A}{B_2}\mathrm{i}\xi J_0(\alpha r)-\beta J_0(\beta r)\right\}\mathrm{e}^{\mathrm{i}(\xi z-\omega t)}, \end{aligned} \tag{8.2.42}$$

where

$$\frac{A}{B_2} = -\left(\frac{\beta}{\alpha}\right)^2 \frac{\beta^2-\xi^2}{2\xi^2}\frac{J_1(\beta a)}{J_1(\alpha a)}. \tag{8.2.43}$$

The interpretation of the displacement fields as being a resultant of dilatational and shear waves that holds for plates also holds here. Thus, in the case of u_z the $J_0(\alpha r)$ term of (8.2.42) may be interpreted as the longitudinal component of a set of plane dilatational waves whose normals form a conical surface, where the axis of the cone is the z-axis. The $J_0(\beta r)$ term of (8.2.42) is the longitudinal component of a set of transverse waves. Figure 8.7, first drawn for the case of plates, also applies for this interpretation if the normals shown in that figure are interpreted as the normals of two sets of diametrically opposite waves. As before, it is the transverse component that produces the rapid variation of u_z.

A plot of the first three modes of the dispersion curve is shown in Fig. 8.16, where the dimensionless velocity and wavenumber are given by

$$\bar{c} = c/c_0, \qquad \bar{\xi} = a\xi/2\pi, \tag{8.2.44}$$

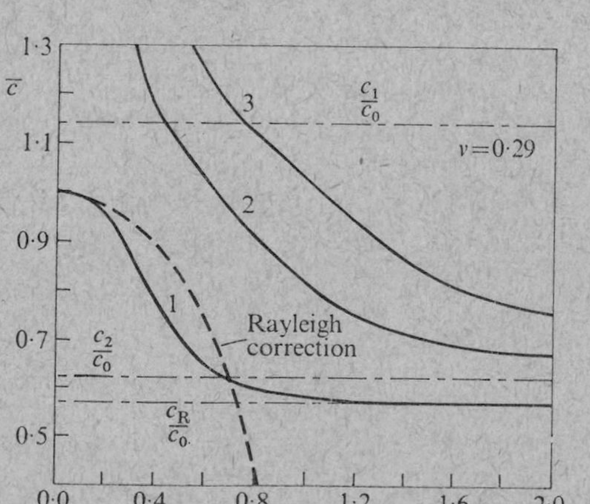

FIG. 8.16. Dispersion curves for the first three longitudinal modes in a rod.

and c_0 is the classical bar velocity, $c_0 = \sqrt{(E/\rho)}$. It is of interest to observe the behaviour of the first mode. As $\xi \to 0$, the phase velocity approaches the classical bar velocity. However, the deviation from c_0 increases for increasing ξ, emphasizing the diminishing accuracy of classical rod theory for high frequency. This aspect, of course, was also brought out in Chapter 2. As ξ increases to large values, we note that the wave velocity approaches that of Rayleigh waves. This phenomena, also encountered in plates, indicates that at higher and higher frequencies the disturbance is mainly confined to the surface.

Returning to the low-frequency behaviour of the first mode, some additional comments may be made. If J_0 and J_1 are expanded in a power series as

$$\begin{aligned} J_0(z) &= 1-\tfrac{1}{4}(z)^2+\tfrac{1}{64}(z^4)+\dots, \\ J_1(z) &= \tfrac{1}{2}(z)-\tfrac{1}{16}(z)^3+\dots, \end{aligned} \tag{8.2.45}$$

and $J_0(z) \simeq 1$, $J_1(z) \simeq z/2$ are used as approximations, then the insertion of (8.2.45) in (8.2.41) will yield the results $\omega^2/\xi^2 = E/\rho$, which is the bar velocity. If the next higher-order terms are retained in the expansion, a dispersive relationship is obtained and corresponds to the results obtained when lateral-inertia effects are included in the strength-of-materials approach. This was studied in Chapter 2 as the Love theory for longitudinal waves in rods. It is also designated as the Rayleigh correction, and is shown as the dashed line in the preceding figure.

The complete frequency spectrum for longitudinal waves in a rod has been obtained by Onoe, McNiven, and Mindlin [75]. The methods used closely follow those used for constructing the plate spectrum, such as establishing cutoff frequencies, asymptotic behaviour, and, most importantly, a grid of boundary curves. A three-dimensional illustration of the spectrum, showing real, imaginary, and complex branches, is shown in Fig. 8.17. Additional illustrations of just the real and imaginary branches, and the detailed behaviour of the lowest modes are also included in the paper by Onoe *et al.* The non-dimensional frequency and wavenumber parameters are given by

$$\Omega = \omega a/\delta c_2, \qquad \bar{\xi} = \xi a, \tag{8.2.46}$$

where δ is the lowest non-zero root of $J_1(\delta) = 0$.

A particularly interesting feature of the spectrum is the behaviour of the higher complex branches. We note that the lowest complex branch emanates from a minimum of the second longitudinal mode, just as in plate theory. Most of the higher complex branches, however, emanate from minima of the imaginary branches, interconnecting the various branches, or dropping to the $\Omega = 0$ plane. This behaviour was not shown for the plate spectrum, but it is quite reasonable to expect similar behaviour.

3. *The flexural modes.* The general characteristic eqn (8.2.24) was found to yield the torsional and longitudinal frequency equations for $n = 0$. For these

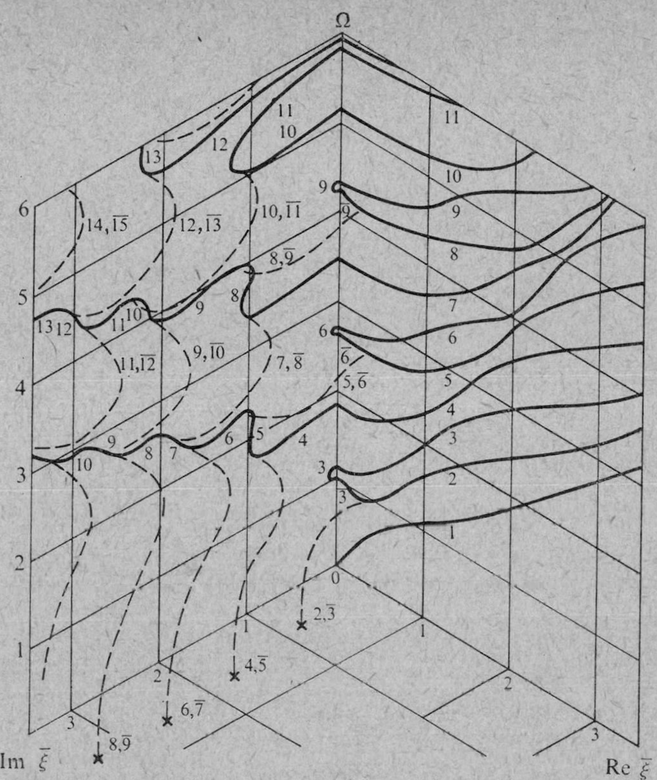

FIG. 8.17. Frequency spectrum for the longitudinal modes of a rod. (After Onoe *et al.* [75, Fig. 6].)

cases one or two of the displacement components were found to vanish. In order to investigate the propagation of flexural waves, all displacement components will exist. The case of $n = 1$ corresponds to the lowest-order family of flexural modes. The displacements are given from (8.2.22) and the frequency equations, more complicated than those for the longitudinal and torsional modes and even more so than the frequency equation for flexural modes in a plate, is obtained by expanding (8.2.24). Hudson [27] has carried out calculations for some of the lowest branches of flexural modes and Pao and Mindlin [76, 77] have investigated them in some detail. As given by Reference [77], the resulting Pochhammer frequency equation is

$$J_1(\bar{\alpha})J_1^2(\bar{\beta})(f_1\mathscr{J}_\beta^2+f_2\mathscr{J}_\alpha\mathscr{J}_\beta+f_3\mathscr{J}_\beta+f_4\mathscr{J}_\alpha+f_5) = 0, \tag{8.2.47}$$

where

$$\begin{aligned} &f_1 = 2(\bar{\beta}^2-\bar{\xi}^2)^2, \quad f_2 = 2\bar{\beta}^2(5\bar{\xi}^2+\bar{\beta}^2),\\ &f_3 = \bar{\beta}^6-10\bar{\beta}^4-2\bar{\beta}^4\bar{\xi}^2+2\bar{\beta}^2\bar{\xi}^2+\bar{\beta}^2\bar{\xi}^4-4\bar{\xi}^4,\\ &f_4 = 2\bar{\beta}^2(2\bar{\beta}^2\bar{\xi}^2-\bar{\beta}^2-9\bar{\xi}^2),\\ &f_5 = \bar{\beta}^2(-\bar{\beta}^4+8\bar{\beta}^2-2\bar{\beta}^2\bar{\xi}^2+8\bar{\xi}^2-\bar{\xi}^4), \end{aligned} \tag{8.2.48}$$

and where

$$\bar{\alpha} = \alpha a, \quad \bar{\beta} = \beta a, \qquad \bar{\xi} = \xi a, \quad \Omega = \omega a/c_2, \qquad\qquad (8.2.49)$$
$$\mathcal{J}_x = xJ_0(x)/J_1(x).$$

Using the techniques previously used for obtaining the plate spectrum and the spectrum for the longitudinal modes for a rod, Pao and Mindlin obtained a grid of boundary curves for the flexural modes. The considerations are somewhat more complicated in the flexural-mode case, since it is found that the boundary curves do not resolve into simple dilatational and shear modes. The resulting spectrum, showing the real and imaginary branches, is shown in Fig. 8.18. It is to be noted that some of the imaginary branches drop to the imaginary $\bar{\xi}$-axis. Complex branches interconnect the gaps in the imaginary branches or drop to the $\Omega = 0$ plane.

Higher-order flexural modes are generated by considering $n \geqslant 2$. Frequency spectra having the general appearance of Fig. 8.18 arise. Evidently, the possibility of coupling between certain higher-order flexural modes and the lowest (or lower) longitudinal modes exists, and is suggested by some of the branches of the individual spectra crossing.

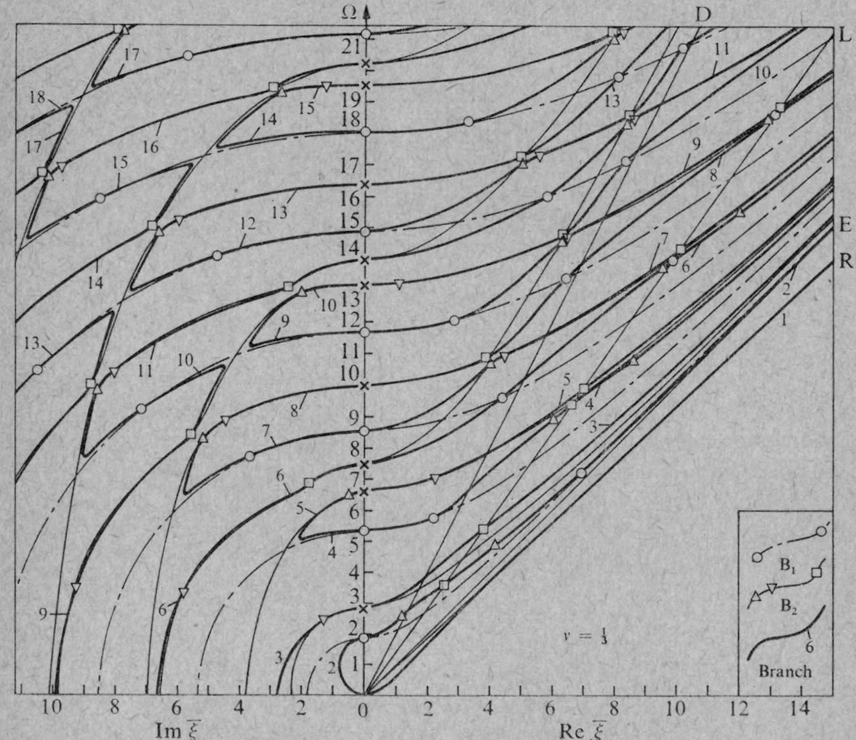

FIG. 8.18. Frequency spectrum for the $n = 1$ family of flexural modes. (After Pao [76, Fig. 4].)

8.2.3. *Waves in cylindrical shells*

The analysis of wave propagation in circular, cylindrical shells, according to elasticity theory, has been done by Gazis [19, 20]. We recall that the analysis of waves in rods was based on the procedure used by Gazis. Hence, the development of the frequency equations for shells may proceed quite straightforwardly. Somewhat greater complexity of expression results from the two sets of boundary conditions at inner and outer free surfaces. The analysis follows that of Gazis [20].

The cylindrical shell geometry has an inner radius a and outer radius b, with cylindrical coordinates as shown earlier in Fig. 8.14. The governing equations used for the rod study, (8.2.1)–(8.2.5) still hold. The boundary conditions are now given by

$$\tau_{rr} = \tau_{r\theta} = \tau_{rz} = 0, \qquad r = a, b, \tag{8.2.50}$$

where a and b are internal and external radii, respectively. The solution forms (8.2.12) still hold. However, Gazis uses a slightly different form, given by

$$\begin{aligned} \Phi &= f(r)\cos n\theta \cos(\omega t+\xi z), \\ H_r &= h_r(r)\sin n\theta \sin(\omega t+\xi z), \\ H_\theta &= h_\theta(r)\cos n\theta \sin(\omega t+\xi z), \\ H_z &= h_3(r)\sin n\theta \cos(\omega t+\xi z), \end{aligned} \tag{8.2.51}$$

where $h_3(r)$ replaces the previously used $h_z(r)$. Bessel equations of various order and argument again govern f, h_r, h_θ, h_3 and are given by (8.2.14) (which also holds for h_3 with α^2 replaced by β^2) and (8.2.21). The solutions are given by

$$\begin{aligned} f &= AZ_n(\alpha_1 r)+BW_n(\alpha_1 r), \\ h_3 &= A_3 Z_n(\beta_1 r)+B_3 W_n(\beta_1 r), \\ 2h_1 &= h_r - h_\theta = 2A_1 Z_{n+1}(\beta_1 r)+2B_1 W_{n+1}(\beta_1 r), \\ 2h_2 &= h_r + h_\theta = 2A_2 Z_{n-1}(\beta_1 r)+2B_2 W_{n-1}(\beta_1 r). \end{aligned} \tag{8.2.52}$$

To interpret this solution, we first note that the Bessel equations will have solutions J and Y if $\alpha^2, \beta^2 > 0$ and solutions I, K for $\alpha^2, \beta^2 < 0$, where I and K are the modified Bessel functions. Furthermore, both solutions to Bessel's equation apply in the present shell analysis, since singular behaviour at the origin (used to discard the solution Y_n in the rod analysis) is no longer a consideration. Thus, in (8.2.52) Z_n corresponds to J_n if α^2 or β^2 is greater than zero, and to I_n if they are less than zero. Similarly, W_n corresponds to Y_n or K_n. Also, $\alpha_1 = |\alpha|$, $\beta_1 = |\beta|$, where as before

$$\alpha^2 = \omega^2/c_1^2 - \xi^2, \qquad \beta^2 = \omega^2/c_2^2 - \xi^2. \tag{8.2.53}$$

The property of gauge invariance is used to eliminate two of the integration constants of (8.2.52). Owing to this property, any one of the three potentials h_1, h_2, h_3 may be set to zero without loss of generality. Setting $h_2 = 0$ gives

$h_r = -h_\theta = h_1$. The resulting displacements and stresses are then given by

$$\begin{aligned} u_r &= \{f'+(n/r)h_3+\xi h_1\}\cos n\theta\cos(\omega t+\xi z), \\ u_\theta &= \{-(n/r)f+\xi h_1-h_3'\}\sin n\theta\cos(\omega t+\xi z), \\ u_z &= \{-\xi f-h_1'-(n+1)h_1/r\}\cos n\theta\sin(\omega t+\xi z), \end{aligned} \tag{8.2.54}$$

$$\tau_{rr} = \left[-\lambda(\alpha^2+\xi^2)f+2\mu\left\{f''+\frac{n}{r}\left(h_3'-\frac{h_3}{r}\right)+\xi h_1'\right\}\right]\times$$
$$\times\cos n\theta\cos(\omega t+\xi z),$$

$$\tau_{r\theta} = \mu\left[-\frac{2n}{r}\left(f'-\frac{f}{r}\right)-(2h_3''-\beta^2h_3)-\xi\left(\frac{n+1}{r}h_1-h_1'\right)\right]\times \tag{8.2.55}$$
$$\times\sin n\theta\cos(\omega t+\xi z),$$

$$\tau_{rr} = \mu\left[-2\xi f'-\frac{n}{r}\left\{h_1'+\left(\frac{n+1}{r}-\beta^2+\xi^2\right)h_1\right\}-\frac{n\xi}{r}h_3\right]\times$$
$$\times\cos n\theta\sin(\omega t+\xi z).$$

The frequency equation results from substituting (8.2.55) in the boundary conditions (8.2.50). The six constants A, B, A_1, B_1, A_2, B_2 appear in each of the six boundary condition equations. The resulting determinant of coefficients is given by

$$|c_{ij}| = 0 \qquad (i, j = 1, \dots, 6). \tag{8.2.56}$$

The elements of the first three rows are given by

$$\begin{aligned} c_{11} &= \{2n(n-1)-(\beta^2-\xi^2)a^2\}Z_n(\alpha_1 a)+2\lambda_1\alpha_1 aZ_{n+1}(\alpha_1 a), \\ c_{12} &= 2\xi\beta_1 a^2Z_n(\beta_1 a)-2\xi a(n+1)Z_{n+1}(\beta_1 a), \\ c_{13} &= -2n(n-1)Z_n(\beta_1 a)+2\lambda_2 n\beta_1 aZ_{n+1}(\beta_1 a), \\ c_{14} &= \{2n(n-1)-(\beta^2-\xi^2)a^2\}W_n(\alpha_1 a)+2\alpha_1 aW_{n+1}(\alpha_1 a), \\ c_{15} &= 2\lambda_2\xi\beta_1 a^2W_n(\beta_1 a)-2(n+1)\xi aW_{n+1}(\beta_1 a), \\ c_{16} &= -2n(n-1)W_n(\beta_1 a)+2n\beta_1 aW_{n+1}(\beta_1 a), \\ c_{21} &= 2n(n-1)Z_n(\alpha_1 a)-2\lambda_1 n\alpha_1 aZ_{n+1}(\alpha_1 a), \\ c_{22} &= -\xi\beta_1 a^2Z_n(\beta_1 a)+2\xi a(n+1)Z_{n+1}(\beta_1 a), \\ c_{23} &= -\{2n(n-1)-\beta^2a^2\}Z_n(\beta_1 a)-2\lambda_2\beta_1 aZ_{n+1}(\beta_1 a), \\ c_{24} &= 2n(n-1)W_n(\alpha_1 a)-2n\alpha_1 aW_{n+1}(\alpha_1 a), \\ c_{25} &= -\lambda_2\xi\beta_1 a^2W_n(\beta_1 a)+2\xi a(n+1)W_{n+1}(\beta_1 a), \\ c_{26} &= -\{2n(n-1)-\beta^2a^2\}W_n(\beta_1 a)-2\beta_1 aW_{n+1}(\beta_1 a), \\ c_{31} &= 2n\xi\alpha_1 Z_n(\alpha_1 a)-2\lambda_1\xi\alpha_1 a^2Z_{n+1}(\alpha_1 a), \\ c_{32} &= n\beta_1 aZ_n(\beta_1 a)-(\beta^2-\xi^2)a^2Z_{n+1}(\beta_1 a), \\ c_{33} &= -n\xi aZ_n(\beta_1 a), \\ c_{34} &= 2n\xi aW_n(\alpha_1 a)-2\xi\alpha_1 a^2W_{n+1}(\alpha_1 a), \\ c_{35} &= \lambda_2 n\beta_1 aW_n(\beta_1 a)-(\beta^2-\xi^2)a^2W_{n+1}(\beta_1 a), \\ c_{36} &= -n\xi aW_n(\beta_1 a), \end{aligned} \tag{8.2.57}$$

with the remaining three rows obtained from the first three by replacing a by b. The parameters λ_1 and λ_2 are $+1$ if the Bessel functions J and Y are used and -1 when I and K are used. The frequency equation, of course, is most complicated. However, Gazis obtains a number of special cases of interest, as well as numerical results. Some of these are considered in the following.

1. *Motion independent of z.* Motion independent of z occurs when $\xi = 0$. This gives the cutoff frequencies for the shell. Under these conditions, the determinant (8.2.56) breaks into the product of subdeterminants,

$$D_1 D_2 = 0, \tag{8.2.58}$$

where

$$D_1 = \begin{vmatrix} c_{11} & c_{13} & c_{14} & c_{16} \\ c_{21} & c_{23} & c_{24} & c_{26} \\ c_{41} & c_{43} & c_{44} & c_{46} \\ c_{51} & c_{53} & c_{54} & c_{56} \end{vmatrix}, \qquad D_2 = \begin{vmatrix} c_{32} & c_{35} \\ c_{62} & c_{65} \end{vmatrix}, \tag{8.2.59}$$

and the c_{ij} are given by (8.2.57) with $\xi = 0$.

The case of $D_1 = 0$ corresponds to the case of plane-strain motion extensively analysed by Gazis in a separate paper [19]. In considering this case, suppose first that motion is also independent of θ. This is given by $n = 0$ in the solutions. It is found under these conditions of axially symmetric vibrations that the extensional and shear modes uncouple. The results presented by Gazis for this case are shown in Fig. 8.19(a) and (b). The parameter h is the

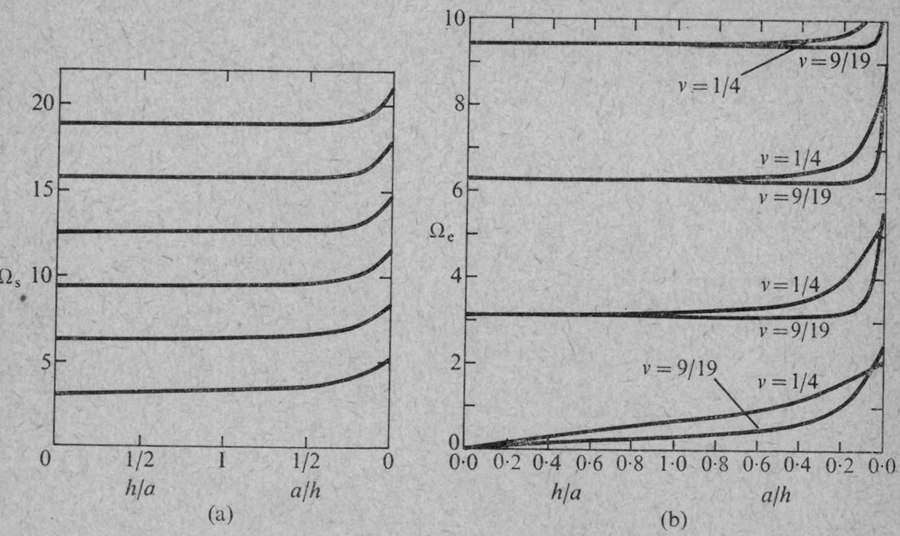

FIG. 8.19. (a) Shear and (b) extensional frequencies for motion independent of z (cutoff frequencies) and also axially symmetric. (After Gazis [19, Figs. 2, 3].)

thickness of the shell, $h = b-a$. The abscissae are divided into the two regions $0 \leq h/a \leq 1$ and $1 \geq a/h > 0$. For h/a small, the behaviour approaches that of a plate, while for a/h small, the behaviour approaches that of the solid cylinder. The non-dimensional frequencies are

$$\Omega_e = \omega h/c_1, \qquad \Omega_s = \omega h/c_2. \tag{8.2.60}$$

The extensional frequencies are seen to depend on Poisson's ratio. Continuing the case of plane-strain vibrations, consider now the non-axially symmetric case ($n \neq 0$). Shown in Fig. 8.20 are the results for $n = 2$ for $\nu = \frac{1}{3}$.

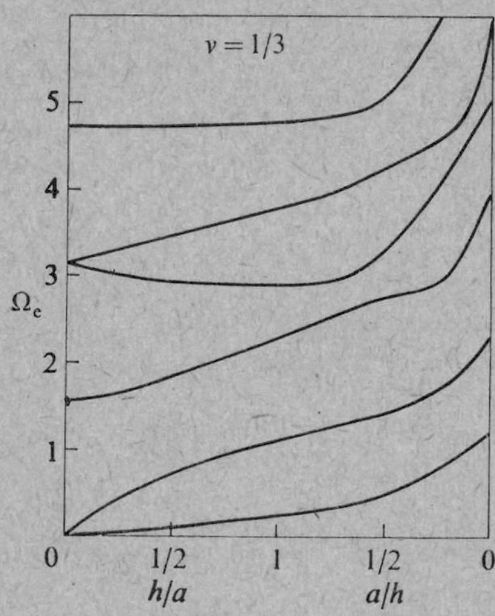

FIG. 8.20. Non-axially symmetric vibrations ($n = 2$) for motion independent of z. (After Gazis [19, Figs. 7, 8].)

Now consider the frequency equation (8.2.58) for z-independent motion to be satisfied by $D_2 = 0$. This motion corresponds to the case of longitudinal shear where only the u_z displacement occurs and is given by

$$u_z = \{A_1\beta J_n(\beta r)+B_1\beta Y_n(\beta r)\}\cos n\theta \sin \omega t. \tag{8.2.61}$$

The resulting form of the frequency equation is

$$J_n'(\beta a)Y_n'(\beta a)-J_n'(\beta b)Y_n'(\beta a) = 0, \tag{8.2.62}$$

and the amplitude ratio is given by

$$A_1/B_1 = -Y_1'(\beta a)/J_1'(\beta a). \tag{8.2.63}$$

2. *Motion independent of* θ. For this type of motion we have $n = 0$. The frequency equation degenerates to

$$D_3 D_4 = 0, \tag{8.2.64}$$

where

$$D_3 = \begin{vmatrix} c_{11} & c_{12} & c_{14} & c_{15} \\ c_{31} & c_{32} & c_{34} & c_{35} \\ c_{41} & c_{42} & c_{44} & c_{45} \\ c_{61} & c_{62} & c_{63} & c_{65} \end{vmatrix}, \qquad D_4 = \begin{vmatrix} c_{23} & c_{26} \\ c_{53} & c_{56} \end{vmatrix}. \tag{8.2.65}$$

Considering first $D_3 = 0$, this is found to represent the longitudinal modes involving only the displacements u_r, u_z. As is the case for plates and solid rods, these modes involve both dilatational and equivoluminal waves through the potentials f and h_1. A special class of solutions corresponding to equivoluminal Lamé-type modes is found to exist for the special case of

$$\beta^2 = \xi^2 > 0.$$

The case of torsional modes, where $f = h_1 = 0$, occurs for $D_4 = 0$. The resulting displacements involve only u_θ and the frequency equation is given by

$$J_2(\beta a)Y_2(\beta b) - J_2(\beta b)Y_2(\beta a) = 0. \tag{8.2.66}$$

This equation is the same that results for the axially symmetric shear modes in (1) *Motion independent of z* (p. 477). As in the case of the solid rod, the lowest torsional mode is non-dispersive.

3. *Additional numerical results.* In Reference [20], Gazis presents numerical results for a variety of cases of waves in cylinders. In Fig. 8.21 additional results for the cutoff frequencies are presented for the case of $n = 1$ (see

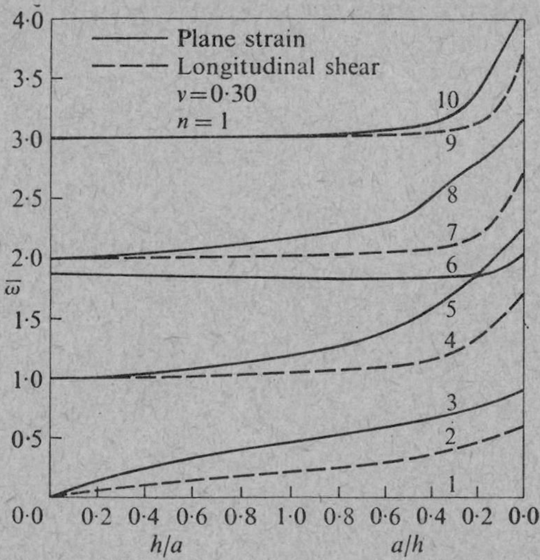

FIG. 8.21. Cutoff frequencies of the plane-strain and longitudinal-shear modes for $n = 1$. (After Gazis [20, Fig. 1].)

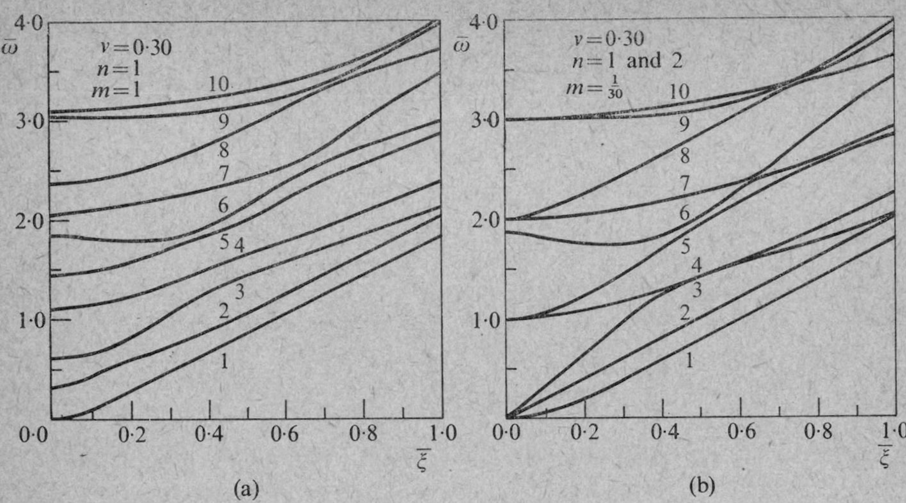

FIG. 8.22. Frequency spectrum for waves in a shell for $n = 1$ and (a) $m = 1$, (b) $m = \frac{1}{30}$, $n = 1$ and 2. (After Gazis [20, Figs. 3–6].)

Fig. 8.19 for the case of $n = 0$). The non-dimensional frequency $\bar{\omega}$ and wavenumber are now given by

$$\bar{\omega} = \omega h/\pi c_2, \qquad \bar{\xi} = h\xi/2\pi. \tag{8.2.67}$$

The relation of $\bar{\omega}$ to $\bar{\xi}$ depends, in the case of the shell, on the ratio of thickness to radius, as well as Poisson's ratio. Results are shown in Fig. 8.22 for the frequency spectrum for two different values of m, where

$$m = h/R, \tag{8.2.68}$$

and R is the mean radius. The case of $n = 1$ is that of the lowest flexural mode. For the case of a very thin shell, $m = 1/30$, the results for $n = 1$ and 2 are indistinguishable for the scale shown.

8.3. Approximate theories for waves in plates, rods, and shells

Let us review our knowledge of wave motion in plates, rods, and shells. As a result of our studies of §§ 8.1, 8.2, we realize these geometries are capable of infinitely many modes of vibration. This aspect was summarized in the multi-branched frequency spectra of the various geometries. The extensive analysis and results presented for the Rayleigh–Lamb and Pochhammer–Chree spectrum and results presented for the case of cylindrical shells suggests that the propagation of continuous waves according to the exact theory of elasticity is fairly well understood. However, the solution of free- and forced-vibration problems has become rather difficult since the cost of applying exact theory has been to escalate the complexity of the governing equations and boundary conditions. This is brought out by the relative sparseness of solutions for the free vibrations of finite solids or the difficulty of solving transient-loading problems for semi-infinite plates and rods.

At the other extreme, we have the strength-of-material theories of rods, plates, and shells, studied in the first few chapters. The simple wave equation described the longitudinal and torsional motion of rods, and the flexural motion of beams and plates was described by single, fourth-order partial differential equations. In the context of exact theory, these simpler theories contained only a single degree of freedom and approximated the lowest branch of the various exact spectra only over a limited range. However, the simple governing equations of the strength-of-material theories made solution of free- and forced-vibration problems comparatively easy, although the solutions were limited in frequency range.

The question is whether other theories can be developed, valid for higher frequencies than the simple theories, containing some of the features of exact theories and yet still yielding tractable governing equations. The Love and Timoshenko theories for rods represent instances of such developments. In the former, the basic kinematical assumptions of classical longitudinal rod theory were retained and only an additional lateral-inertia effect was considered. In the latter, the kinematical assumptions on the deformation of Bernoulli–Euler theory of beams were refined to include shear-deformation and rotary-inertia effects. Such developments, although *ad hoc* in nature, served to yield higher-order strength-of-material theories.

Over the years, many developments have occurred in this field, with various approaches used. Green [22] surveyed the development of dispersion relations for bars and divided the development of approximate theories into two classes. In one class, approximations are made in the equations of motion and Green listed contributions by Rayleigh [79], Love [43], Timoshenko [86], Prescott [78], Mindlin and Herrmann [64], Volterra [89], Bishop [6], and Kynch [37]. In the second class, solutions of the exact equations which only approximately satisfy the boundary conditions are considered and contributions by Chree [7], Morse [71], and Kynch and Green [38] were reviewed.

Although many and varied developments in approximate theories have occurred, the approach that has become prevalent was first applied to the case of plates by Mindlin [59] and to the case of rods by Mindlin and Herrman [64]. A large number of subsequent contributions by Mindlin and his coworkers and many others have placed the development of approximate theories for rods, plates, and shells on a very systematic basis. Much of the work in this area was based on the analysis of the vibration of piezoelectric plates used as elements in electronic systems. Thus, much of the literature pertains to coupled electro-mechanical or anisotropic elastic elements. The coverage here will be restricted to the isotropic, elastic case.

The approach will be as follows. First the basic early development by Mindlin [59] will be set forth, since it contains many of the basic ingredients of all later approximate theories, yet can be definitely related to the Timoshenko beam theory. The more modern work on plates, by Mindlin and Medick [66], will then be reviewed. The case of rods will be covered, and the work of Mindlin and Herrmann [64] and Mindlin and McNiven [65] reviewed, with these two papers serving as the rod counterparts of the two previously-cited plate papers. Finally, discussion of developments in the area of shell studies will cover work by Herrmann and Mirsky [25], McNiven, Shah, and Sackman [47], and others.

8.3.1. *An approximate theory for plate flexural waves*

The first development of an approximate theory will be for flexural waves in plates and will follow Mindlin's first contribution. The essential feature of this development and those that follow for other approximate theories is the integration of the exact equations of elasticity across the plate thickness. Other features include the restriction of deformation to finite degrees of freedom and the introduction of adjustment coefficients. These last are generalizations of the method used in the development of Timoshenko beam theory.

1. *Plate stresses and stress–strain relations.* Consider a differential element of plate of thickness h, having coordinates as shown in Fig. 8.23, and

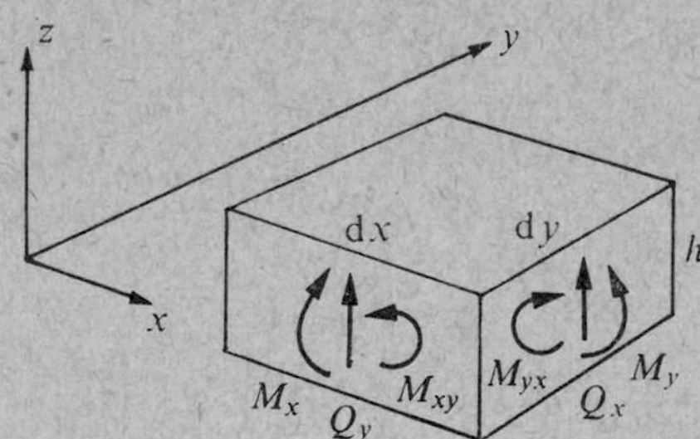

FIG. 8.23. An element of plate subjected to forces and moments.

subjected to bending and twisting moments and shear forces as shown.

The plate stresses M_x, M_y, M_{xy}, Q_x, Q_y are defined by

$$
\begin{aligned}
(M_x, M_y, M_{yx}) &= \int_{-h/2}^{h/2} (\tau_{xx}, \tau_{yy}, \tau_{xy}) z \, dz, \\
(Q_x, Q_y) &= \int_{-h/2}^{h/2} (\tau_{xz}, \tau_{yz}) \, dz,
\end{aligned}
\tag{8.3.1}
$$

which are the same as the definitions of classical plate theory.

The stress–strain equations of elasticity, given by the general Hooke's law are $\tau_{ij} = \lambda\, \Delta\delta_{ij} + 2\mu\varepsilon_{ij}$ where $\Delta = \varepsilon_{kk}$. The usual procedure in elasticity is to use the six stress–strain equations in conjunction with the strain–displacement relations to reduce the three equations of motion (in the six stress components) to equations in the displacement components. In the present case, there are only five plate-stress components, and these will be defined in terms of five plate strain components. Plate displacements will be introduced later. Start by writing the stress–strain equation for τ_{zz} in the form

$$\varepsilon_{zz} = -\frac{\lambda}{\lambda+2\mu}(\varepsilon_{xx}+\varepsilon_{yy}) + (\lambda+2\mu)^{-1}\tau_{zz}. \tag{8.3.2}$$

Now eliminate ε_{zz} from the stress–strain equations for ε_{xx}, ε_{yy}, giving the five equations

$$\begin{gathered}\tau_{xx} = \frac{4\mu(\lambda+\mu)}{\lambda+2\mu}\varepsilon_{xx} + \frac{2\mu\lambda}{\lambda+2\mu}\varepsilon_{yy} + \frac{\lambda}{\lambda+2\mu}\tau_{zz},\\ \tau_{yy} = \frac{2\mu\lambda}{\lambda+2\mu}\varepsilon_{xx} + \frac{4\mu(\lambda+\mu)}{\lambda+2\mu}\varepsilon_{yy} + \frac{\lambda}{\lambda+2\mu}\tau_{zz},\\ \tau_{xy} = 2\mu\varepsilon_{xy}, \qquad \tau_{yz} = 2\mu\varepsilon_{yz}, \qquad \tau_{zx} = 2\mu\varepsilon_{zx}.\end{gathered} \tag{8.3.3}$$

Using relations between the elastic constants, these may be rewritten as

$$\begin{gathered}\tau_{xx} = \frac{E}{1-\nu^2}(\varepsilon_{xx}+\nu\varepsilon_{yy}) + \frac{\nu}{1-\nu}\tau_{zz},\\ \tau_{yy} = \frac{E}{1-\nu^2}(\varepsilon_{yy}+\nu\varepsilon_{xx}) + \frac{\nu}{1-\nu}\tau_{zz},\\ \tau_{xy} = 2\mu\varepsilon_{xy}, \qquad \tau_{yz} = 2\mu\varepsilon_{yz}, \qquad \tau_{zx} = 2\mu\varepsilon_{zx}.\end{gathered} \tag{8.3.4}$$

The plate stress–strain equations are obtained by integrating the preceding over the thickness of the plate. Thus, for M_x we have

$$M_x = \int_{-h/2}^{h/2} \tau_{xx} z\, dz = \frac{E}{1-\nu^2}\int_{-h/2}^{h/2} (\varepsilon_{xx}+\nu\varepsilon_{yy})z\, dz + \frac{\nu}{1-\nu}\int_{-h/2}^{h/2} \tau_{zz} z\, dz. \tag{8.3.5}$$

The integral contribution of the stress τ_{zz} is now neglected. Upon defining the plate strain components

$$\begin{gathered}(\Gamma_x, \Gamma_y, \Gamma_{xy}) = \frac{12}{h^3}\int_{-h/2}^{h/2} (\varepsilon_{xx}, \varepsilon_{yy}, \varepsilon_{xy}) z\, dz,\\ (\Gamma_{xz}, \Gamma_{yz}) = \frac{1}{h}\int_{-h/2}^{h/2} (\varepsilon_{xz}, \varepsilon_{yz})\, dz,\end{gathered} \tag{8.3.6}$$

we obtain for M_x and M_y

$$M_x = D(\Gamma_x+\nu\Gamma_y), \qquad M_y = D(\Gamma_y+\nu\Gamma_x), \tag{8.3.7}$$

where D is the usual plate stiffness given as

$$D = \frac{Eh^3}{12(1-\nu^2)}. \tag{8.3.8}$$

For M_{xy}, we have

$$M_{xy} = 2\mu \int_{-h/2}^{h/2} \varepsilon_{xy} z \, dz = \frac{E}{1+\nu} \int_{-h/2}^{h/2} \varepsilon_{xy} z \, dz, \tag{8.3.9}$$

giving

$$M_{xy} = (1-\nu) D\Gamma_{xy}. \tag{8.3.10}$$

The plate shear forces are treated somewhat differently than in classical plate theory, which neglects shear effects. Here, a Timoshenko-like shear effect is introduced by writing

$$Q_x = 2\mu' \int \varepsilon_{xz} \, dz, \tag{8.3.11}$$

where $\mu' = \kappa^2\mu$. Thus

$$Q_x = \mu' h\Gamma_{xz}. \tag{8.3.12}$$

The motivation behind the introduction of the modified shear modulus μ' is similar to that of beam theory. Thus if we denote $\bar{\varepsilon}_{xz}$ as the exact shear strain, then the exact shear force $\bar{Q}_x$ is

$$\bar{Q}_x = 2\mu \int_{-h/2}^{h/2} \bar{\varepsilon}_{xz} \, dz. \tag{8.3.13}$$

However, as a consequence of neglecting certain stresses and because of kinematical assumptions that will be made, we have an inexact strain ε_{xz} that gives an inexact shear force Q_x, where $Q_x \neq \bar{Q}_x$. We introduce the shear coefficient κ^2, leading to the modified shear modulus μ' such that Q_x, $\bar{Q}_x$ are brought into agreement. We may then summarize our plate stress–strain relations as

$$\begin{aligned} M_x &= D(\Gamma_x+\nu\Gamma_y), \qquad M_y = D(\Gamma_y+\nu\Gamma_x), \\ M_{xy} &= (1-\nu)D\Gamma_{xy}, \\ Q_x &= \mu' h\Gamma_{xz}, \qquad Q_y = \mu' h\Gamma_{yz}. \end{aligned} \tag{8.3.14}$$

Two comments are in order. First, (8.3.14) could have been obtained by setting $\tau_{zz} = 0$ at the outset. However, adopting the present procedure reveals that a weighted average of τ_{zz} was neglected and not τ_{zz} itself. Second, the determination of κ^2 in the approximate plate theory will be handled quite differently than in previous beam or plate developments, which used elasticity analysis to establish the shear coefficient.

2. *Kinematics and plate stress–displacement relations.* We have the strain–displacement equations of elasticity given by $\varepsilon_{ij} = (u_{i,j}+u_{j,i})/2$. Then,

integrating the strains across the plate thickness as suggested by the plate strain definitions (8.3.6), gives

$$\int_{-h/2}^{h/2} (\varepsilon_{xx}, \varepsilon_{yy}, \varepsilon_{xy}) z\,dz = \int_{-h/2}^{h/2} \left(\frac{\partial u}{\partial x}, \frac{\partial v}{\partial y}, \frac{\partial u}{\partial y} + \frac{\partial v}{\partial x}\right) z\,dz,$$

$$\int_{-h/2}^{h/2} (\varepsilon_{xz}, \varepsilon_{yz})\,dz = \int_{-h/2}^{h/2} \left(\frac{\partial u}{\partial z} + \frac{\partial w}{\partial x}, \frac{\partial v}{\partial z} + \frac{\partial w}{\partial y}\right) dz. \tag{8.3.15}$$

This last expression explicitly brings into the development the displacements. The important assumptions on the kinematics of deformation are now made by considering u, v, w to be given by

$$u(x, y, z, t) = z\psi_x(x, y, t), \quad v(x, y, z, t) = z\psi_y(x, y, t),$$
$$w(x, y, z, t) = \bar{w}(x, y, t). \tag{8.3.16}$$

Several general remarks are in order here. First, the w displacements are independent of z, so that thickness modes (stretch and shear), possible in the exact theory, are ruled out in this approximation. Second, the assumed u, v, w displacement field represents the two-dimensional generalization of the Timoshenko assumptions. If shear deformations were to be neglected, as in Bernoulli–Euler beam theory or classical plate theory, we would have $\partial w/\partial x = -\psi_x$, $\partial w/\partial y = -\psi_y$, and

$$u(x, y, z, t) = -z\,\partial w/\partial x, \quad v(x, y, z, t) = -z\,\partial w/\partial y.$$

Further, if it were desired to develop a theory capable of predicting higher-order deformations, more refined kinematical assumptions would be required. A systematic way of doing this would be to expand u, v, w as power series in the thickness coordinate. Thus, using the general indicial form given below as a guide,

$$u_j(x, y, z, t) = \sum_{n=0}^{\infty} z^n u_j^{(n)}(x, y, t), \tag{8.3.17}$$

we would have

$$u = u^{(0)} + zu^{(1)} + z^2u^{(2)} + \dots,$$
$$v = v^{(0)} + zv^{(1)} + z^2v^{(2)} + \dots,$$
$$w = w^{(0)} + zw^{(1)} + z^2w^{(2)} + \dots. \tag{8.3.18}$$

Thus, in the present case, we have only retained the $u^{(1)}$, $v^{(1)}$, $w^{(0)}$ terms of the expansion. In neglecting the $u^{(0)}$, $v^{(0)}$ terms, we have, in effect, neglected extensional vibrations in the x, y directions. The remaining terms have been discarded as higher order in the present development, but could be retained in a more exact analysis. Other expansions could be used. In particular, an expansion in Legendre polynomials in the thickness coordinates will be shown later. Finally, it is seen how various vibrational modes may be selectively studied by suppressing or retaining various terms of the expansion.

Returning to the development, the assumed deformations (8.3.16) are inserted into the right-hand side of the strain–displacement integrals (8.3.15). For Γ_x, we have for the various steps

$$\Gamma_x = \frac{12}{h^3}\int_{-h/2}^{h/2} \varepsilon_x z\, dz = \frac{12}{h^3}\int_{-h/2}^{h/2} \frac{\partial u}{\partial x} z\, dz$$
$$= \frac{\partial \psi_x}{\partial x}\frac{12}{h^3}\int_{-h/2}^{h/2} z^2\, dz = \frac{\partial \psi_x}{\partial x}. \tag{8.3.19}$$

Similarly, for Γ_{xz},

$$\Gamma_{xz} = \frac{1}{h}\int_{-h/2}^{h/2} \varepsilon_{xz}\, dz = \frac{1}{h}\int_{-h/2}^{h/2} \left(\frac{\partial u}{\partial z}+\frac{\partial w}{\partial x}\right) dz$$
$$= \left(\psi_x+\frac{\partial \bar{w}}{\partial x}\right)\frac{1}{h}\int_{-h/2}^{h/2} dz = \psi_x+\frac{\partial \bar{w}}{\partial x}. \tag{8.3.20}$$

We thus have for the plate strain–displacement relations,

$$\Gamma_x = \frac{\partial \psi_x}{\partial x}, \quad \Gamma_y = \frac{\partial \psi_y}{\partial y}, \quad \Gamma_{xy} = \frac{\partial \psi_y}{\partial x}+\frac{\partial \psi_x}{\partial y},$$
$$\Gamma_{xz} = \psi_x+\frac{\partial \bar{w}}{\partial x}, \quad \Gamma_{yz} = \psi_y+\frac{\partial \bar{w}}{\partial y}. \tag{8.3.21}$$

The plate stress–displacement relations are

$$M_x = D\left(\frac{\partial \psi_x}{\partial x}+\nu\frac{\partial \psi_y}{\partial y}\right), \quad M_y = D\left(\frac{\partial \psi_y}{\partial y}+\nu\frac{\partial \psi_x}{\partial x}\right),$$
$$M_{xy} = \frac{1-\nu}{2}D\left(\frac{\partial \psi_y}{\partial x}+\frac{\partial \psi_x}{\partial y}\right), \tag{8.3.22}$$
$$Q_x = \kappa^2 Gh\left(\frac{\partial \bar{w}}{\partial x}+\psi_x\right), \quad Q_y = \kappa^2 Gh\left(\frac{\partial \bar{w}}{\partial y}+\psi_y\right).$$

The result for classical plate theory is recovered from the above by letting $\psi_x = -\partial\bar{w}/\partial x$, $\psi_y = -\partial\bar{w}/\partial y$. Then $M_x = -D(\partial^2\bar{w}/\partial x^2+\nu\partial^2\bar{w}/\partial y^2)$, the classical plate result, with M_y and M_{xy} following in a similar fashion. Of course, $Q_x = Q_y = 0$ then occurs in (8.3.32). This anomaly is the well-known result of neglecting shear deformations, yet retaining shear forces in the equilibrium equations. The shear forces are in fact determined from the equilibrium equations in classical theory.

3. *Equations of motion.* Consider now the stress equations of motion of three-dimensional elasticity theory, given as

$$\frac{\partial \tau_{xx}}{\partial x}+\frac{\partial \tau_{xy}}{\partial y}+\frac{\partial \tau_{xz}}{\partial z}=\rho\ddot{u},$$
$$\frac{\partial \tau_{yx}}{\partial x}+\frac{\partial \tau_{yy}}{\partial y}+\frac{\partial \tau_{yz}}{\partial z}=\rho\ddot{v}, \qquad (8.3.23)$$
$$\frac{\partial \tau_{zx}}{\partial x}+\frac{\partial \tau_{zy}}{\partial y}+\frac{\partial \tau_{zz}}{\partial z}=\rho\ddot{w}.$$

To convert these to the plate stress equations of motion first multiply the first two of (8.3.23) by z and integrate across the thickness. Exhibiting the operations only for the first case, we have

$$\frac{\partial}{\partial x}\int_{-h/2}^{h/2}\tau_{xx}z\,dz+\frac{\partial}{\partial y}\int_{-h/2}^{h/2}\tau_{xy}z\,dz+\int_{-h/2}^{h/2}\frac{\partial \tau_{xz}}{\partial z}z\,dz=\rho\int_{-h/2}^{h/2}\ddot{u}z\,dz. \qquad (8.3.24)$$

The first two integrals of the preceding are M_x, M_{xy} respectively. The third expression is integrated by parts, giving

$$\int_{-h/2}^{h/2}\frac{\partial \tau_{xz}}{\partial z}z\,dz=[z\tau_{xz}]_{-h/2}^{h/2}-\int_{-h/2}^{h/2}\tau_{xz}\,dz=-Q_x, \qquad (8.3.25)$$

where $z\tau_{xz}$ is zero at $\pm h/2$, since τ_{xz} vanishes on the boundaries. The right-hand side of (8.3.24) gives

$$\rho\int_{-h/2}^{h/2}\ddot{u}z\,dz=\rho\ddot{\psi}_x\int_{-h/2}^{h/2}z^2\,dz=\frac{\rho h^3\ddot{\psi}_x}{12}. \qquad (8.3.26)$$

The second of (8.3.23) is handled in the same way. The third equilibrium equation is integrated directly. Thus

$$\frac{\partial}{\partial x}\int_{-h/2}^{h/2}\tau_{zx}\,dz+\frac{\partial}{\partial y}\int_{-h/2}^{h/2}\tau_{zy}\,dz+\int_{-h/2}^{h/2}\frac{\partial \tau_{zz}}{\partial z}\,dz=\rho\int_{-h/2}^{h/2}\ddot{w}\,dz. \qquad (8.3.27)$$

The first two integrals yield Q_x and Q_y respectively. The third integral gives

$$\int_{-h/2}^{h/2}\frac{\partial \tau_{zz}}{\partial z}\,dz=[\tau_{zz}]_{-h/2}^{h/2}=-q_1-(-q_2)=q_2-q_1=q. \qquad (8.3.28)$$

The right-hand side of (8.3.28) represents the external loading on the plate

The plate stress equations of motion thus become

$$\frac{\partial M_x}{\partial x}+\frac{\partial M_{xy}}{\partial y}-Q_x = \frac{\rho h^3}{12}\frac{\partial^2 \psi_x}{\partial t^2},$$
$$\frac{\partial M_{xy}}{\partial x}+\frac{\partial M_y}{\partial y}-Q_y = \frac{\rho h^3}{12}\frac{\partial^2 \psi_y}{\partial t^2}, \tag{8.3.29}$$
$$\frac{\partial Q_x}{\partial x}+\frac{\partial Q_y}{\partial y}+q = \rho h\frac{\partial^2 \bar{w}}{\partial t^2}.$$

When the plate stress–displacement eqns (8.3.22) are substituted in the preceding, we obtain the equations of motion

$$\frac{D}{2}\left\{(1-\nu)\nabla^2\psi_x+(1+\nu)\frac{\partial \Phi}{\partial x}\right\}-\kappa^2\mu h\left(\psi_x+\frac{\partial \bar{w}}{\partial x}\right) = \frac{\rho h^3}{12}\frac{\partial^2 \psi_x}{\partial t^2},$$
$$\frac{D}{2}\left\{(1-\nu)\nabla^2\psi_y+(1+\nu)\frac{\partial \Phi}{\partial y}\right\}-\kappa^2\mu h\left(\psi_y+\frac{\partial \bar{w}}{\partial y}\right) = \frac{\rho h^3}{12}\frac{\partial^2 \psi_y}{\partial t^2}, \tag{8.3.30}$$
$$\kappa^2\mu h(\nabla^2\bar{w}+\Phi)+q = \rho h(\partial^2\bar{w}/\partial t^2),$$

where

$$\Phi = \frac{\partial \psi_x}{\partial x}+\frac{\partial \psi_y}{\partial y}. \tag{8.3.31}$$

4. *Kinetic and potential energy*. If our aim was only to derive the governing differential equations for a higher-order plate theory, the task would be complete with the results (8.3.30). Development of energy expressions for the plate is also necessary, since this quantity is an important parameter in its own right, and also lays down the groundwork for establishing the proper boundary conditions. Proceeding, we have the strain energy function of elasticity given by

$$\begin{aligned}2W &= \tau_{xx}\varepsilon_{xx}+\tau_{yy}\varepsilon_{yy}+\tau_{zz}\varepsilon_{zz}+\tau_{xy}\varepsilon_{xy}+\tau_{yz}\varepsilon_{yz}+\tau_{zx}\varepsilon_{zx}\\ &= \tau_{xx}\frac{\partial u}{\partial x}+\tau_{yy}\frac{\partial v}{\partial y}+\tau_{zz}\frac{\partial w}{\partial z}+\tau_{xy}\left(\frac{\partial v}{\partial x}+\frac{\partial u}{\partial y}\right)+\\ &\quad +\tau_{yz}\left(\frac{\partial w}{\partial y}+\frac{\partial v}{\partial z}\right)+\tau_{zx}\left(\frac{\partial w}{\partial x}+\frac{\partial u}{\partial z}\right).\end{aligned} \tag{8.3.32}$$

We substitute the expressions for u, v, w, given by (8.3.16) into (8.3.32) and integrate over the plate thickness to give

$$\begin{aligned}2\overline{W} &= M_x\frac{\partial \psi_x}{\partial x}+M_y\frac{\partial \psi_y}{\partial y}+M_{yx}\left(\frac{\partial \psi_y}{\partial x}+\frac{\partial \psi_x}{\partial y}\right)+\\ &\quad +Q_x\left(\frac{\partial \bar{w}}{\partial x}+\psi_x\right)+Q_y\left(\frac{\partial \bar{w}}{\partial y}+\psi_y\right)\\ &= M_x\Gamma_x+M_y\Gamma_y+M_{yx}\Gamma_{yx}+Q_x\Gamma_{xz}+Q_y\Gamma_{yz}.\end{aligned} \tag{8.3.33}$$

This represents the plate strain energy per unit area. Using the plate stress–strain relations (8.3.14) in the preceding, we obtain

$$4\overline{W} = D(1+\nu)(\Gamma_x+\Gamma_y)^2+D(1-\nu)\{(\Gamma_x-\Gamma_y)^2+\Gamma_{yx}^2\}+ \\ +2\kappa^2\mu h(\Gamma_{yz}^2+\Gamma_{xz}^2). \quad (8.3.34)$$

We note that $\overline{W}$ is positive definite if $E(1+\nu)$, $E(1-\nu)$ are required to be positive. Further, we note that

$$\frac{\partial \overline{W}}{\partial \Gamma_x} = M_x, \quad \frac{\partial \overline{W}}{\partial \Gamma_y} = M_y, \quad \frac{\partial \overline{W}}{\partial \Gamma_{yx}} = M_{yx}, \quad \frac{\partial \overline{W}}{\partial \Gamma_{zx}} = Q_x, \quad (8.3.35)$$
$$\partial \overline{W}/\partial \Gamma_{zy} = Q_y.$$

The kinetic energy per unit volume is given as $\rho(\dot{u}^2+\dot{v}^2+\dot{w}^2)/2$. Using (8.3.16) and integrating over the thickness gives

$$T = \frac{\rho h^3}{24}\left\{\left(\frac{\partial \psi_x}{\partial t}\right)^2+\left(\frac{\partial \psi_y}{\partial t}\right)^2\right\}+\frac{\rho h}{2}\left(\frac{\partial \bar{w}}{\partial t}\right)^2 \quad (8.3.36)$$

as the kinetic energy per unit area for the plate. The kinetic and potential energies in the plate at time t are given by

$$\bar{T} = \iint\left\{\frac{\rho h^3}{24}(\dot{\psi}_x^2+\dot{\psi}_y^2)+\frac{\rho h}{2}\dot{\bar{w}}^2\right\} \mathrm{d}x\, \mathrm{d}y, \qquad \bar{V} = \iint \overline{W}\, \mathrm{d}x\, \mathrm{d}y. \quad (8.3.37)$$

The total energy at time t is the sum of $\bar{T}$ and $\bar{V}$ and may be written as

$$\bar{T}+\bar{V} = \int_{t_0}^{t}\mathrm{d}t\iint \frac{\partial T}{\partial t}\, \mathrm{d}x\, \mathrm{d}y+\int_{t_0}^{t}\mathrm{d}t\iint \frac{\partial \overline{W}}{\partial t}\, \mathrm{d}x\, \mathrm{d}y+\bar{T}_0+\bar{V}_0, \quad (8.3.38)$$

where $\bar{T}_0$, $\bar{V}_0$ represent the values of $\bar{T}$, $\bar{V}$ at t_0.

The time derivatives of (8.3.36) and (8.3.33) are given by

$$\frac{\partial T}{\partial t} = \frac{\rho h^3}{12}(\dot{\psi}_x\ddot{\psi}_x+\dot{\psi}_y\ddot{\psi}_y)+\rho h\dot{\bar{w}}\ddot{\bar{w}}, \quad (8.3.39)$$

$$\frac{\partial \overline{W}}{\partial t} = \frac{\partial \overline{W}}{\partial \Gamma_x}\frac{\partial \Gamma_x}{\partial t}+\frac{\partial \overline{W}}{\partial \Gamma_y}\frac{\partial \Gamma_y}{\partial t}+\frac{\partial \overline{W}}{\partial \Gamma_{xy}}\frac{\partial \Gamma_{xy}}{\partial t}+\frac{\partial \overline{W}}{\partial \Gamma_{zx}}\frac{\partial \Gamma_{zx}}{\partial t}+\frac{\partial \overline{W}}{\partial \Gamma_{zy}}\frac{\partial \Gamma_{zy}}{\partial t}. \quad (8.3.40)$$

By using relations (8.3.35) and the expressions (8.3.21) in (8.3.40), we obtain

$$\frac{\partial \overline{W}}{\partial t} = \left(M_x\frac{\partial}{\partial x}+M_{yx}\frac{\partial}{\partial y}+Q_x\right)\frac{\partial \psi_x}{\partial t}+\left(M_{yx}\frac{\partial}{\partial x}+M_y\frac{\partial}{\partial y}+Q_y\right)\frac{\partial \psi_y}{\partial t}+ \\ +\left(Q_x\frac{\partial}{\partial x}+Q_y\frac{\partial}{\partial y}\right)\frac{\partial \overline{W}}{\partial t}. \quad (8.3.41)$$

By integrating (8.3.41) by parts, as contained in (8.3.38), the contributions of the external forces to the total energy may be found. As an example, we have

$$\iint\left(M_x\frac{\partial\dot\psi_x}{\partial x}+M_{yx}\frac{\partial\dot\psi_x}{\partial y}\right)\,dx\,dy=\iint\left\{\frac{\partial}{\partial x}(M_x\dot\psi_x)+\frac{\partial}{\partial y}(M_{yx}\dot\psi_x)\right\}\,dx\,dy-$$
$$-\iint\left(\frac{\partial M_x}{\partial x}+\frac{M_{yx}}{\partial y}\right)\dot\psi_x\,dx\,dy. \quad (8.3.42)$$

We apply Green's theorem in evaluating the first integral on the right-hand side of the above, to obtain

$$\iint\left(M_x\frac{\partial\dot\psi_x}{\partial x}+M_{yx}\frac{\partial\dot\psi_x}{\partial y}\right)\,dx\,dy=\oint\dot\psi_x(M_xl+M_{yx}m)\,ds-$$
$$-\iint\left(\frac{\partial M_x}{\partial x}+\frac{\partial M_{yx}}{\partial y}\right)\dot\psi_x\,dx\,dy, \quad (8.3.43)$$

where l, m are direction cosines of the normal to the boundary. We thus obtain

$$\iint\frac{\partial\overline{W}}{\partial t}\,dx\,dy=\oint\left\{\dot\psi_x(M_xl+M_{yx}m)+\dot\psi_y(M_{yx}l+M_ym)+\dot w(Q_xl+Q_ym)\right\}\,ds-$$
$$-\iint\left\{\dot\psi_x\left(\frac{\partial M_x}{\partial x}+\frac{\partial M_{yx}}{\partial y}-Q_x\right)+\right.$$
$$\left.+\dot\psi_y\left(\frac{\partial M_{yx}}{\partial x}+\frac{\partial M_y}{\partial y}-Q_y\right)+\dot w\left(\frac{\partial Q_x}{\partial x}+\frac{\partial Q_y}{\partial y}\right)\right\}\,dx\,dy. \quad (8.3.44)$$

in terms of coordinates $\bar\nu$ and s measured normal to and along the boundary, the line integral above becomes

$$\oint(\dot\psi_{\bar\nu}M_{\bar\nu}+\dot\psi_sM_{\bar\nu s}+\dot wQ_{\bar\nu})\,ds. \quad (8.3.45)$$

With these results, (8.3.38) becomes

$$\bar T+\bar V=\int_{t_0}^{t}dt\oint(\dot\psi_{\bar\nu}M_{\bar\nu}+\dot\psi_sM_{\bar\nu s}+\dot wQ_{\bar\nu})\,ds+$$
$$+\int_{t_0}^{t}dt\iint\left\{\dot\psi_x\left(\frac{\rho h^3}{12}\ddot\psi_x-\frac{\partial M_x}{\partial x}-\frac{\partial M_{yx}}{\partial y}+Q_x\right)+\right.$$
$$+\dot\psi_y\left(\frac{\rho h^3}{12}\ddot\psi_y-\frac{\partial M_{yx}}{\partial x}-\frac{\partial M_y}{\partial y}+Q_y\right)+$$
$$\left.+\dot w\left(\rho h\ddot w-\frac{\partial Q_x}{\partial x}-\frac{\partial Q_y}{\partial y}\right)\right\}\,dx\,dy+\bar T_0+\bar V_0. \quad (8.3.46)$$

The expressions in the parenthesis of the area integral are the plate equations of motion. We presume these are satisfied, so that the preceding reduces to

$$\bar{T}+\bar{V}=\int_{t_0}^{t}\mathrm{d}t\oint\left(\frac{\partial\psi_{\bar{\nu}}}{\partial t}M_{\bar{\nu}}+\frac{\partial\psi_s}{\partial t}M_{\bar{\nu}s}+\frac{\partial\bar{w}}{\partial t}Q_{\bar{\nu}}\right)\mathrm{d}s+ \\ +\int_{t_0}^{t}\mathrm{d}t\iint q\frac{\partial\bar{w}}{\partial t}\,\mathrm{d}x\,\mathrm{d}y+\bar{T}_0+\bar{V}_0. \quad (8.3.47)$$

This result is a statement that the total energy at time t is equal to the sum of the energy at time t_0 and the work done by the external forces along the edge of the plate and over the surface in the time interval $(t-t_0)$.

5. *Boundary conditions.* The establishment of boundary and initial conditions follows from uniqueness-of-solutions arguments. This argument is used in establishing boundary conditions for the general elasticity case, and it only needs slight rephrasing here to apply to the present form of the total energy. Thus, consider two sets of plate displacements and surface loads. If the components of each set satisfy the equations of motion so will their differences. Then the energies and the plate stress components calculated from the differences will satisfy an equation of the same form as (8.3.47). If the right-hand side of (8.3.47) vanishes, $\bar{T}$ and $\bar{V}$ vanish separately, since they are both positive. If $\bar{T}$ vanishes, the kinetic energy per unit volume vanishes, since it is positive, and hence plate velocities vanish. If $\bar{V}$ vanishes $\bar{W}$ vanishes, since it is positive, and if $\bar{W}$ vanishes so do the plate strain and stress components. Hence, if the right-hand side of (8.3.47) vanishes, the two systems must be identical, except possibly for a rigid-body displacement.

We now return to the single solution to establish the boundary conditions (those conditions necessary for vanishing of the right-hand side of (8.3.47)). It is required that one each of the three pairs of quantities

$$\dot{\psi}_{\bar{\nu}}M_{\bar{\nu}}, \qquad \dot{\psi}_s M_{\bar{\nu}s}, \qquad \dot{\bar{w}}Q_{\bar{\nu}} \quad (8.3.48)$$

be specified on the edge of the plate. Throughout the plate, either q or $\bar{w}$ must be given as must be the initial values of ψ_x, ψ_y, $\bar{w}$, and their time derivatives.

It is of interest to compare the boundary conditions (8.3.48) to those of classical plate theory. For illustration, consider the plate edge given by $x=$ constant. Thus we have

$$\dot{\psi}_x M_x, \qquad \dot{\psi}_y M_{xy}, \qquad \dot{\bar{w}}Q_x = 0. \quad (8.3.49)$$

Now, $\psi_y = Q_y/\kappa^2\mu h - \partial\bar{w}/\partial y$, from (8.3.22), and in classical theory this reduces to $\psi_y = -\partial\bar{w}/\partial y$. Thus

$$\dot{\psi}_y M_{xy} \to -\frac{\partial^2\bar{w}}{\partial t\,\partial y}M_{xy}. \quad (8.3.50)$$

However,

$$-\int \frac{\partial^2 \bar{w}}{\partial t\,\partial y} M_{xy}\,\mathrm{d}y = \int \frac{\partial \bar{w}}{\partial t}\frac{\partial M_{xy}}{\partial y}\,\mathrm{d}y. \tag{8.3.51}$$

Hence the boundary conditions reduce to

$$-\frac{\partial \dot{\bar{w}}}{\partial x} M_x, \qquad \frac{\partial \dot{\bar{w}}}{\partial t}\left(\frac{\partial M_{xy}}{\partial y} + Q_x\right) = 0, \tag{8.3.52}$$

which are the Kirchhoff conditions of classical plate theory.

5. *Propagation of harmonic waves.* The differential equations of motion may be reduced to a single equation for $\bar{w}$ by differentiating the first and second of (8.3.30) and adding the results to give

$$\left(D\nabla^2 - \mu' h - \frac{\rho h^3}{12}\frac{\partial^2}{\partial t^2}\right)\Phi = \mu' h \nabla^2 \bar{w}. \tag{8.3.53}$$

Next eliminate Φ between (8.3.53) and the third equation of (8.3.30), to give

$$\left(\nabla^2 - \frac{\rho}{\mu'}\frac{\partial^2}{\partial t^2}\right)\left(D\nabla^2 - \frac{\rho h^3}{12}\frac{\partial^2}{\partial t^2}\right)\bar{w} + \rho h \frac{\partial^2 \bar{w}}{\partial t^2} = \left(1 - \frac{D\nabla^2}{\mu' h} + \frac{\rho h^2}{12\mu'}\frac{\partial^2}{\partial t^2}\right) q. \tag{8.3.54}$$

We have already studied the dispersion relations for exact plate theory. Now consider the conditions under which straight-crested harmonic waves may propagate. It is sufficient to let

$$\bar{w} = \cos \xi(x - ct), \tag{8.3.55}$$

and substitute in (8.3.54) with $q = 0$. The resulting dispersion relation is

$$\frac{h^2\xi^2}{12}\left(1 - \frac{c^2}{\kappa^2 c_2^2}\right)\left(\frac{c_p^2}{c^2} - 1\right) = 1, \tag{8.3.56}$$

where c_2 is the shear-wave velocity and

$$c_p = \left(\frac{E}{\rho(1-\nu^2)}\right)^{\frac{1}{2}}, \tag{8.3.57}$$

which is the plate analogue of the bar velocity $(E/\rho)^{\frac{1}{2}}$. Equation (8.3.56) may be put in the form

$$\left(\frac{c^2}{c_2^2}\right)^2 - \left(\kappa^2 + \frac{c_p^2}{c_2^2} - \frac{12\kappa^2}{h^2\xi^2}\right)\left(\frac{c^2}{c_2^2}\right) + \kappa^2 \frac{c_p^2}{c_2^2} = 0. \tag{8.3.58}$$

There will thus be two roots for c^2. Now consider the behaviour as $\xi \to \infty$ (that is, high frequency). From the last we obtain $c^2 = \kappa^2 c_2^2$. However, according to exact theory, this velocity should approach the Rayleigh surface wave velocity (see Fig. 8.16, for example). This gives a method for adjusting

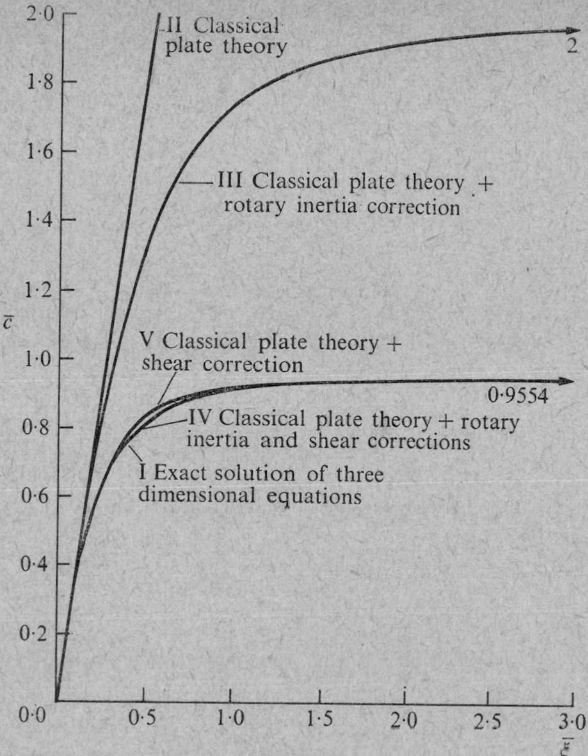

FIG. 8.24. The dispersion curve resulting from Mindlin's approximate theory for flexural waves in a plate (Curve IV) and results from other theories. (From Mindlin [59, Fig. 1].)

the constant κ^2. Thus, in order for $c \to c_R$ (the Rayleigh velocity) as ξ becomes large, we must have $\kappa = c_R/c_2$. This ratio has been plotted in Fig. 6.8 for various Poisson's ratio.

The resulting dispersion curve is shown as curve IV in Fig. 8.24 for the case of $\nu = \frac{1}{2}$, for which $\kappa = 0{\cdot}9554$. Also shown in the figure are the dispersion curves for the lowest flexure mode of exact theory (I), classical plate theory (II), classical theory with a rotary-inertia correction (III), and classical plate theory with shear correction only (V). The curves are quite similar to those previously displayed in the study of Timoshenko beam theory (see Fig. 3.13). For the first mode of vibration, it is not possible to distinguish the difference between I and IV. The dimensionless velocity and wavenumber of the figure are $\bar{c} = c/c_s$ and $\bar{\xi} = \xi h/2\pi$.

We may investigate the conditions under which pure thickness-shear vibrations may occur by letting

$$\psi_y = \bar{w} = 0, \qquad \psi_x = e^{i\omega t}. \tag{8.3.59}$$

By letting $\xi = 0$ we are, in effect, investigating the cutoff frequency. Substituting in the equations of motion (8.3.30) with $q = 0$ yields

$$\omega_c = 2\sqrt{3}(\kappa c_2/h). \tag{8.3.60}$$

From exact theory, the value for the cutoff frequency of the first antisymmetric mode of thickness-shear vibration is $\omega = \pi c_2/h$. To make these two results identical requires $\kappa^2 = \pi^2/12$. This value of κ^2 differs from the previously obtained value of $\kappa^2 = c_R^2/c_2^2$. The present value has been obtained by adjusting the low-frequency behaviour and the other the high-frequency behaviour of the approximate theory. Which technique is better may depend on the problem at hand in terms of frequency range or the primary vibration mode.

8.3.2. *An approximate theory for extensional waves in plates*

The development of another approximate theory for waves in plates that differs in several respects from the study of the previous section will now be presented. First, the description of a different type of motion, extensional (longitudinal) instead of flexural, will be considered. As discussed in the previous section, this is conveniently done in approximate theories by retaining and omitting various terms in the expansions for the displacements. Secondly, the energy equation will be used as the starting point, instead of directly integrating the equations of motion across the thickness. Thirdly, the displacements will be expanded in Legendre polynomials of the thickness coordinate instead of the thickness coordinate itself. In addition, the deformation kinematics are more elaborate than for the flexural theory previously considered, and a larger number of adjustment parameters enter. The procedures for determining these parameters are accordingly more intricate than before. The theory presented here is that developed by Mindlin and Medick [66].

1. *Expansion of the displacements.* To enable indicial notation to be used, let the plate coordinates be x_1, x_2, x_3, with x_2 being the thickness coordinate and the x_1, x_3-plane being the mid plane of the plate. The plate thickness is $2b$. Assume that the displacements u_1, u_2, u_3 may be expanded in terms of the Legendre polynomials P_n as

$$u_j = \sum_{n=0}^{\infty} P_n(\eta) u_j^{(n)}(x_1, x_3, t) \qquad (j = 1, 2, 3), \tag{8.3.61}$$

where $\eta = x_2/b$ and the first few polynomials are

$$P_0(\eta) = 1, \qquad P_1(\eta) = \eta, \qquad P_2(\eta) = (3\eta^2-1)/2, \qquad P_3(\eta) = (5\eta^3-3\eta)/2,$$

$$P_n(\eta) = \frac{1}{2^n n!} \frac{d^n(\eta^2-1)^n}{d\eta^n}. \tag{8.3.62}$$

The reason for expanding in $P(\eta)$ instead of η itself (as, for example, suggested in the discussion leading to (8.3.17)) was given by Mindlin and Medick as follows. Expansions in η of second and higher powers lead to awkward mathematical forms owing to lack of orthogonality of the terms of a power series. Although similarly awkward forms occur using the Legendre polynomials, they generally do not occur until third-order terms are reached. Since the present theory will be at most third order, this will not seriously affect the work.

2. *Stress equations of motion.* We start with the variational equations of motion as obtained from Hamilton's principle, given by

$$\int_V (\tau_{ij,i}-\rho\ddot{u}_j)\,\delta u_j\,\mathrm{d}V = 0. \tag{8.3.63}$$

Now

$$\begin{aligned} \ddot{u}_j &= \sum_{n=0}^{\infty} P_n(\eta)\ddot{u}_j^{(n)}(x_1, x_3, t), \\ \delta u_j &= \sum_{n=0}^{\infty} P_n(\eta)\,\delta u_j^{(n)}(x_1, x_3, t). \end{aligned} \tag{8.3.64}$$

Substitution of the above in the equations of motion gives two integrals to be evaluated:

$$\begin{aligned} I_1 &= \int_V \tau_{ij,i}\left(\sum_{n=0}^{\infty} P_n(\eta)\,\delta u_j^{(n)}\right)\mathrm{d}V, \\ I_2 &= \rho\int_V \left(\sum_{n=0}^{\infty} P_m(\eta)\ddot{u}_j^{(m)}\right)\left(\sum_{n=0}^{\infty} P_n(\eta)\,\delta u_j^{(n)}\right)\mathrm{d}V. \end{aligned} \tag{8.3.65}$$

Considering first I_1, we have

$$I_1 = b\int_A \mathrm{d}A\left\{\sum_{m=0}^{\infty} \delta u_j^{(n)}(x_1, x_3, t)\int_{-1}^{1} \tau_{ij,i}P_n(\eta)\,\mathrm{d}\eta\right\}. \tag{8.3.66}$$

Now, using conventional notation on the derivatives, it is evident that

$$\int_{-1}^{1} \frac{\partial\tau_{1j}}{\partial x_1}P_n(\eta)\,\mathrm{d}\eta = \frac{\partial}{\partial x_1}\int_{-1}^{1} \tau_{1j}P_n(\eta)\,\mathrm{d}\eta \tag{8.3.67}$$

and

$$\int_{-1}^{1} \frac{\partial\tau_{3j}}{\partial x_3}P_n(\eta)\,\mathrm{d}\eta = \frac{\partial}{\partial x_3}\int_{-1}^{1} \tau_{3j}P_n(\eta)\,\mathrm{d}\eta. \tag{8.3.68}$$

The integrals are analogous to the plate stresses that have arisen in earlier approximate theories. For the partial derivatives with respect to x_2, we have

$$\int_{-1}^{1} \frac{\partial \tau_{2j}}{\partial x_2} P_n(\eta)\,\mathrm{d}\eta = \int_{-1}^{1} \frac{\partial}{\partial x_2}(\tau_{2j}P_n(\eta))\,\mathrm{d}\eta - \int_{-1}^{1} \tau_{2j}\frac{\mathrm{d}P_n(\eta)}{\mathrm{d}x_2}\,\mathrm{d}\eta$$

$$= \left[\frac{1}{b}\tau_{2j}P_n(\eta)\right]_{-1}^{1} - \frac{1}{b}\int_{-1}^{1} \tau_{2j}\frac{\mathrm{d}P_n(\eta)}{\mathrm{d}\eta}\,\mathrm{d}\eta. \tag{8.3.69}$$

Now it is known that

$$\frac{\mathrm{d}P_n(\eta)}{\mathrm{d}\eta} = \sum_{m=1,3,\cdots}^{n} D_{mn}P_{n-m}(\eta), \qquad D_{mn} = 2(n-m)+1. \tag{8.3.70}$$

Thus

$$\int_{-1}^{1} \tau_{2j}\frac{\mathrm{d}P_n}{\mathrm{d}\eta}\,\mathrm{d}\eta = \sum_{m=1,3,\cdots}^{n} D_{mn}\int_{-1}^{1} \tau_{2j}P_{n-m}(\eta)\,\mathrm{d}\eta. \tag{8.3.71}$$

We now define the plate stresses as

$$\tau_{ij}^{(n)} = \int_{-1}^{1} \tau_{ij}P_n\,\mathrm{d}\eta. \tag{8.3.72}$$

The integral I_1 then becomes

$$\begin{aligned} I_1 = b\int_A \mathrm{d}A\Bigg(&\sum_{n=0}^{\infty}\delta u_1^{(n)}\left\{\frac{\partial\tau_{11}^{(n)}}{\partial x_1}+\frac{\partial\tau_{31}^{(n)}}{\partial x_3}-\frac{1}{b}\left(\sum_{m=1,3,\cdots}^{n} D_{mn}\tau_{21}^{(n-m)}\right)+\frac{1}{b}[\tau_{21}P_n(\eta)]_{-1}^{1}\right\}+\\ &+\sum_{n=0}^{\infty}\delta u_2^{(n)}\left\{\frac{\partial\tau_{12}^{(n)}}{\partial x_1}+\frac{\partial\tau_{32}^{(n)}}{\partial x_3}-\frac{1}{b}\left(\sum_{m=1,3,\cdots}^{\infty} D_{mn}\tau_{22}^{(n-m)}\right)+\frac{1}{b}[\tau_{22}P_n(\eta)]_{-1}^{1}\right\}+\\ &+\sum_{n=0}^{\infty}\delta u_3^{(n)}\left\{\frac{\partial\tau_{13}^{(n)}}{\partial x_1}+\frac{\partial\tau_{33}^{(n)}}{\partial x_3}-\frac{1}{b}\left(\sum_{m=1,3,\cdots}^{\infty} D_{mn}\tau_{23}^{(n-m)}\right)+\frac{1}{b}[\tau_{23}P_n(\eta)]_{-1}^{1}\right\}\Bigg). \end{aligned} \tag{8.3.73}$$

Now consider I_2. We have

$$I_2 = \rho b\int_A \mathrm{d}A\left\{\int_{-1}^{1}\left(\sum_{m=0}^{\infty}P_m(\eta)\ddot{u}_j^{(m)}\right)\left(\sum_{n=0}^{\infty}P_n(\eta)\,\delta u_j^{(n)}\right)\mathrm{d}\eta\right\},$$

$$= \rho b\int_A \mathrm{d}A\left\{\sum_{m=0}^{\infty}\sum_{n=0}^{\infty}\ddot{u}_j^{(m)}\,\delta u_j^{(n)}\int_{-1}^{1}P_m(\eta)P_n(\eta)\,\mathrm{d}\eta\right\}. \tag{8.3.74}$$

Now

$$\int_{-1}^{1} P_m(\eta)P_n(\eta)\,\mathrm{d}\eta = \begin{cases}0, & m\neq n\\ C_n, & m = n\end{cases}, \qquad C_n = 2/(2n+1). \tag{8.3.75}$$

Then

$$I_2 = \rho b \int_A \mathrm{d}A\left(\sum_{n=0}^{\infty} C_n \ddot{u}_j^{(n)}\, \delta u_j^{(n)}\right). \tag{8.3.76}$$

We now define

$$F_j^{(n)} = [\tau_{2j} P_n(\eta)]_{-1}^{1}. \tag{8.3.77}$$

Then I_1, I_2 combine to give

$$\begin{aligned} I_1 - I_2 &= \int_V (\tau_{ij,i} - \rho \ddot{u}_j)\, \delta u_j \,\mathrm{d}V \\ &= b\int_A \mathrm{d}A\Bigg[\sum_{n=0}^{\infty} \delta u_1^{(n)}\Bigg\{\frac{\partial \tau_{11}^{(n)}}{\partial x_1} + \frac{\partial \tau_{31}^{(n)}}{\partial x_3} - \frac{1}{b}\Bigg(\sum_{m=1,3,\cdots}^{n} D_{mn}\tau_{21}^{(n-m)}\Bigg) + \\ &\qquad + F_1^{(n)} - \rho C_n \ddot{u}_1^{(n)}\Bigg\} + \\ &\quad + \sum_{n=0}^{\infty} \delta u_2^{(n)}\Bigg\{\frac{\partial \tau_{12}^{(n)}}{\partial x_1} + \frac{\partial \tau_{32}^{(n)}}{\partial x_3} - \frac{1}{b}\Bigg(\sum_{m=1,3,\cdots}^{\infty} D_{mn}\tau_{22}^{(n-m)}\Bigg) + F_2^{(n)} - \rho C_n \ddot{u}_2^{(n)}\Bigg\} + \\ &\quad + \sum_{m=0}^{\infty} \delta u_3^{(m)}\{\ldots\}\Bigg] = 0. \end{aligned} \tag{8.3.78}$$

Using index notation this reduces to

$$I_1 - I_2 = \int_A \mathrm{d}A\left(\sum_{n=0}^{\infty} \delta u_j^{(n)}\left\{b\tau_{1j,1}^{(n)} + b\tau_{3j,3}^{(n)} - \sum_{m=1,3,\cdots}^{n} D_{mn}\tau_{2j}^{(n-m)} + \right.\right.$$

$$\left.\left. + F_j^{(n)} - \rho C_n \ddot{u}_j^{(n)}\right\}\right) = 0. \tag{8.3.79}$$

We thus arrive at the stress equations of motion

$$b\tau_{1j,1}^{(n)} + b\tau_{3j,3}^{(n)} - \sum_{m=1,3,\cdots}^{n} D_{mn}\tau_{2j}^{(n-m)} + F_j^{(n)} = \rho C_n \ddot{u}_j^{(n)} \qquad (j = 1, 2, 3)$$

$$(n = 0, 1, 2, \ldots). \tag{8.3.80}$$

3. *The plate strains.* The plate stress–strain relations must now be derived. Starting with the definition of infinitesimal strain $\varepsilon_{ij} = (u_{i,j} + u_{j,i})/2$, we obtain

$$2\varepsilon_{ij} = \sum_{n=0}^{\infty}\{P_n(\eta) u_i^{(n)}\}_{,j} + \sum_{n=0}^{\infty}\{P_n(\eta) u_j^{(n)}\}_{,i}. \tag{8.3.81}$$

Now

$$\begin{aligned} \sum_{n=0}^{\infty}\{P_n(\eta) u_i^{(n)}\}_{,1} &= \sum_{n=0}^{\infty} P_n(\eta) u_{i,1}^{(n)}, \\ \sum_{n=0}^{\infty}\{P_n(\eta) u_i^{(n)}\}_{,3} &= \sum_{n=0}^{\infty} P_n(\eta) u_{i,3}^{(n)}, \\ \sum_{n=0}^{\infty}\{P_n(\eta) u_i^{(n)}\}_{,2} = \sum_{n=0}^{\infty} \frac{\mathrm{d}P_n(\eta)}{\mathrm{d}x_2} u_i^{(n)} &= \frac{1}{b}\sum_{n=0}^{\infty}\left(\sum_{m=1,3}^{n} D_{mn} P_{n-m}(\eta)\right) u_i^{(n)}. \end{aligned} \tag{8.3.82}$$

Then the strains ε_{11}, ε_{33}, ε_{13} have the form

$$2\varepsilon_{ij}=\sum_{n=0}^{\infty}P_n(\eta)(u_{i,j}^{(n)}+u_{j,i}^{(n)}) \qquad (i,j\neq 2). \tag{8.3.83}$$

The strains ε_{12}, ε_{32} have the form

$$2\varepsilon_{i2}=\frac{1}{b}\sum_{n=0}^{\infty}\left\{\sum_{m=1,3}^{n}D_{mn}P_{n-m}(\eta)\right\}u_i^{(n)}+\sum_{n=0}^{\infty}P_n(\eta)u_{2,i}^{(n)} \qquad (i\neq 2). \tag{8.3.84}$$

The strain ε_{22} is given by

$$2\varepsilon_{22}=\frac{2}{b}\sum_{n=0}^{\infty}\left\{\sum_{m=1,3}^{\infty}D_{mn}P_{n-m}(\eta)\right\}u_2^{(n)}. \tag{8.3.85}$$

The general expression for ε_{ij} that combines the various aspects of (8.3.81)–(8.3.85) is then

$$2\varepsilon_{ij}=\sum_{n=0}^{\infty}\sum_{m=1,3}^{\infty}\{(u_{i,j}^{(n)}+u_{j,i}^{(n)})P_n+(\delta_{2j}u_i^{(n)}+\delta_{2i}u_j^{(n)})b^{-1}D_{mn}P_{n-m}\}. \tag{8.3.86}$$

We are seeking plate stress–strain relations, where plate stresses of some order n, $\tau_{ij}^{(n)}$ will be related to plate strains of similar order. Thus it is desired, effectively, to have ε_{ij} expanded in the form

$$\varepsilon_{ij}=\sum_{n=0}^{\infty}P_n(\eta)\varepsilon_{ij}^{(n)}. \tag{8.3.87}$$

Although the first bracketed term of (8.3.86) is of this form, some manipulation must be done to bring the entire expression into this form. According to Mindlin and Medick, considering the double sum as a triangular array and interchanging the order of summation of columns and rows brings about the desired result, with

$$2\varepsilon_{ij}^{(n)}=u_{i,j}^{(n)}+u_{j,i}^{(n)}+\frac{(2n+1)}{b}\sum_{m=1,3}^{\infty}(\delta_{2j}u_i^{(m+n)}+\delta_{2i}u_j^{(m+n)}). \tag{8.3.88}$$

4. *The plate stress–strain relations.* We now have the conventional stresses related to the plate strains by

$$\tau_{ij}=c_{ijkl}\varepsilon_{kl}=c_{ijkl}\sum_{n=0}^{\infty}P_n(\eta)\varepsilon_{kl}^{(n)}. \tag{8.3.89}$$

These may be substituted into the defining equation for the plate stresses (8.3.72) to give

$$\begin{aligned}\tau_{ij}^{(n)}&=\int_{-1}^{1}P_n(\eta)c_{ijkl}\sum_{m=0}^{\infty}P_m\varepsilon_{kl}^{(m)}\,d\eta\\&=c_{ijkl}\sum_{m=0}^{\infty}\varepsilon_{kl}^{(m)}\int_{-1}^{1}P_n(\eta)P_m(\eta)\,d\eta\\&=C_nc_{ijkl}\varepsilon_{kl}^{(n)},\end{aligned} \tag{8.3.90}$$

where the orthogonality condition (8.3.75) has been employed.

We use the reduced index notation given by

$$\tau_1 = \tau_{11}, \quad \tau_2 = \tau_{22}, \quad \tau_3 = \tau_{33}, \quad \tau_4 = \tau_{23}, \quad \tau_5 = \tau_{31}, \quad \tau_6 = \tau_{12},$$

$$\varepsilon_1 = \varepsilon_{11}, \quad \varepsilon_2 = \varepsilon_{22}, \quad \varepsilon_3 = \varepsilon_{33}, \quad \varepsilon_4 = 2\varepsilon_{23}, \quad \varepsilon_5 = 2\varepsilon_{31}, \quad \varepsilon_6 = 2\varepsilon_{12}. \tag{8.3.91}$$

Then

$$\tau_p^{(n)} = C_n c_{pq} \varepsilon_q^{(n)} \qquad (p, q = 1, 2), \tag{8.3.92}$$

5. *Strain energy.* To complete the definition of the important quantities of elastodynamics in terms of plate stresses and strains, consider the strain energy, given by

$$2U = c_{ijkl}\varepsilon_{ij}\varepsilon_{kl} = c_{pq}\varepsilon_p\varepsilon_q. \tag{8.3.93}$$

We define the plate strain energy density by

$$\bar{U} = \int_{-1}^{1} U \, d\eta. \tag{8.3.94}$$

Then

$$\bar{U} = \frac{1}{2}\int_{-1}^{1} c_{pq}\left(\sum_{n=0}^{\infty} P_n(\eta)\varepsilon_p^{(n)}\right)\left(\sum_{m=0}^{\infty} P_m(\eta)\varepsilon_q^{(m)}\right) d\eta,$$

$$= \tfrac{1}{2}c_{pq}\left(\sum_{n=0}^{\infty}\sum_{m=0}^{\infty} \varepsilon_p^{(n)}\varepsilon_q^{(m)} \int_{-1}^{1} P_n(\eta)P_m(\eta)\, d\eta\right),$$

$$= \tfrac{1}{2}c_{pq}\sum_{n=0}^{\infty} C_n \varepsilon_p^{(n)}\varepsilon_q^{(n)}. \tag{8.3.95}$$

Also this equals

$$\bar{U} = \tfrac{1}{2}\sum_{n=0}^{\infty} \tau_q^{(n)}\varepsilon_q^{(n)}. \tag{8.3.96}$$

Further, we see from (8.3.95) that $\partial\bar{U}/\partial\varepsilon_p^{(n)} = c_{pq}C_n\varepsilon_q^{(n)}$, so that

$$\tau_p^{(n)} = \partial\bar{U}/\partial\varepsilon_p^{(n)}. \tag{8.3.97}$$

Finally, we have the kinetic energy, given for exact theory by

$$K = \tfrac{1}{2}\rho\dot{u}_j\dot{u}_j. \tag{8.3.98}$$

For the plate we define $\bar{K}$ by

$$\bar{K} = \int_{-1}^{1} K \, d\eta = \frac{1}{2}\int_{-1}^{1} \rho\left(\sum_{m=0}^{\infty} P_m(\eta)\dot{u}_j^{(m)}\right)\left(\sum_{n=0}^{\infty} P_n(\eta)\dot{u}_j^{(n)}\right) d\eta,$$

$$= \tfrac{1}{2}\rho\sum_{n=0}^{\infty} C_n \dot{u}_j^{(n)}\dot{u}_j^{(n)}. \tag{8.3.99}$$

6. *The equations for extensional vibrations.* The developments thus far have been quite general. If considerations are now restricted only to extensional (that is, longitudinal or symmetric) motions of the plate, only certain terms of the expansion may be retained. Now the first few terms of u_1, u_2, u_3 are

$$u_1 = P_0 u_1^{(0)} + P_1 u_1^{(1)} + P_2 u_1^{(2)} + \ldots,$$

$$u_2 = P_0 u_2^{(0)} + P_1 u_2^{(1)} + P_2 u_2^{(2)} + \ldots,$$

$$u_3 = P_0 u_3^{(0)} + P_1 u_3^{(1)} + P_2 u_3^{(2)} + \ldots. \tag{8.3.100}$$

Observing the forms of $P_0, P_1, P_2, \ldots$, the forms of the thickness displacement variation for the first few modes are shown in Fig. 8.25. For $j = 1, 3$ the

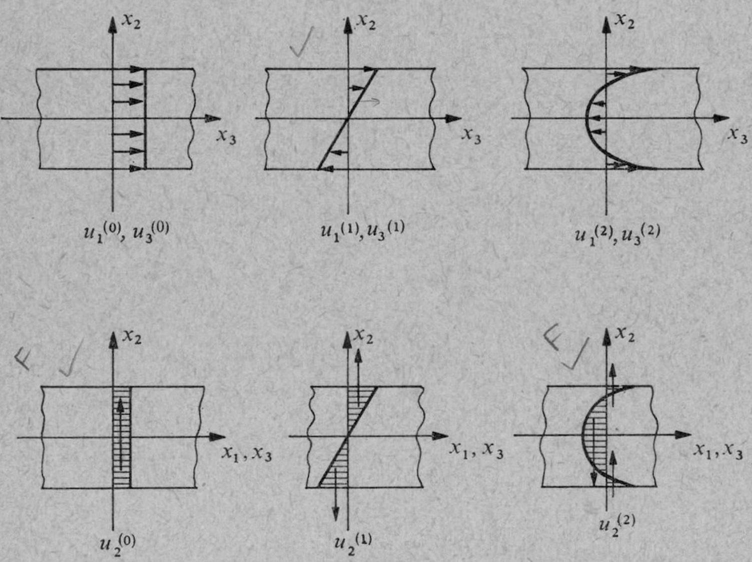

FIG. 8.25. Thickness variation of the first few displacement modes $u_j^{(n)}$.

symmetric modes of $u_j^{(n)}$ are $u_1^{(0)}$, $u_3^{(0)}$, $u_1^{(2)}$, $u_3^{(2)}$, $u_1^{(4)}$, $u_2^{(4)}$, ... For $j = 2$, the symmetric modes are $u_2^{(1)}$, $u_2^{(3)}$, $u_2^{(5)}$, ... Thus, only n = even terms are retained in $u_1^{(n)}$, $u_3^{(n)}$ and n = odd terms in $u_2^{(n)}$. A general rule covering the selection of the symmetric displacement modes is that $n+j$ = odd. The extension of this rule to cover the appropriate stresses $\tau_{ij}^{(n)}$ and strains $\varepsilon_{ij}^{(n)}$ is that $i+j+n$ = even. On this basis, the governing equations for extensional vibrations may be summarized. For the stress equations of motion, we have

$$\begin{aligned}
&\frac{\partial\tau_1^{(0)}}{\partial x_1}+\frac{\partial\tau_5^{(0)}}{\partial x_3}+\frac{F_1^{(0)}}{b}=2\rho\frac{\partial^2 u_1^{(0)}}{\partial t^2},\\
&\frac{\partial\tau_5^{(0)}}{\partial x_1}+\frac{\partial\tau_3^{(0)}}{\partial x_3}+\frac{F_3}{b}=2\rho\frac{\partial^2 u_3^{(0)}}{\partial t^2},\\
&\frac{\partial\tau_6^{(1)}}{\partial x_1}+\frac{\partial\tau_4^{(1)}}{\partial x_3}-\frac{\tau_2^{(0)}}{b}+\frac{F_2^{(1)}}{b}=\frac{2\rho}{3}\frac{\partial^2 u_2^{(1)}}{\partial t^2},\\
&\frac{\partial\tau_1^{(2)}}{\partial x_1}+\frac{\partial\tau_5^{(2)}}{\partial x_3}-\frac{3\tau_6^{(1)}}{b}+\frac{F_1^{(2)}}{b}=\frac{2\rho}{5}\frac{\partial^2 u_1^{(2)}}{\partial t^2},\\
&\frac{\partial\tau_5^{(2)}}{\partial x_1}+\frac{\partial\tau_3^{(2)}}{\partial x_3}-\frac{3\tau_4^{(1)}}{b}+\frac{F_3^{(2)}}{b}=\frac{2\rho}{5}\frac{\partial^2 u_3^{(2)}}{\partial t^2},\\
&\frac{\partial\tau_6^{(3)}}{\partial x_1}+\frac{\partial\tau_4^{(3)}}{\partial x_3}-\frac{5\tau_2^{(2)}}{b}-\frac{\tau_2^{(0)}}{b}+\frac{F_2^{(3)}}{b}=\frac{2\rho}{7}\frac{\partial^2 u_2^{(3)}}{\partial t^2}.
\end{aligned}\tag{8.3.101}$$

The strains are

$$\begin{aligned}
\varepsilon_1^{(0)}&=\partial u_1^{(0)}/\partial x_1,\\
\varepsilon_2^{(0)}&=(u_2^{(1)}+u_2^{(3)}+\ldots)/b,\\
\varepsilon_3^{(0)}&=\partial u_3^{(0)}/\partial x_3,\\
\varepsilon_5^{(0)}&=\partial u_3^{(0)}/\partial x_1+\partial u_1^{(0)}/\partial x_3,\\
\varepsilon_4^{(1)}&=\partial u_2^{(1)}/\partial x_3+3(u_3^{(2)}+u_3^{(4)}+\ldots)/b,\\
\varepsilon_6^{(1)}&=\partial u_2^{(1)}/\partial x_1+3(u_1^{(2)}+u_1^{(4)}+\ldots)/b,\\
\varepsilon_1^{(2)}&=\partial u_1^{(2)}/\partial x_1,\\
\varepsilon_2^{(2)}&=5(u_2^{(3)}+u_2^{(5)}+\ldots)/b,\\
\varepsilon_3^{(2)}&=\partial u_3^{(2)}/\partial x_3,\\
\varepsilon_5^{(2)}&=\partial u_3^{(2)}/\partial x_1+\partial u_1^{(2)}/\partial x_3,\\
\varepsilon_4^{(3)}&=\partial u_2^{(3)}/\partial x_3+7(u_3^{(4)}+u_3^{(6)}+\ldots)/b,\\
\varepsilon_6^{(3)}&=\partial u_2^{(3)}/\partial x_1+7(u_1^{(4)}+u_1^{(6)}+\ldots)/b.
\end{aligned}\tag{8.3.102}$$

The stress–strain relations are given by

$$
\begin{aligned}
\tau_1^{(0)} &= 2\{(\lambda+2\mu)\varepsilon_1^{(0)}+\lambda(\varepsilon_2^{(0)}+\varepsilon_3^{(0)})\},\\
\tau_2^{(0)} &= 2\{(\lambda+2\mu)\varepsilon_2^{(0)}+\lambda(\varepsilon_3^{(0)}+\varepsilon_1^{(0)})\},\\
\tau_3^{(0)} &= 2\{(\lambda+2\mu)\varepsilon_3^{(0)}+\lambda(\varepsilon_1^{(0)}+\varepsilon_2^{(0)})\},\\
\tau_5^{(0)} &= 2\mu\varepsilon_5^{(0)},\\
\tau_4^{(1)} &= 2\mu\varepsilon_4^{(1)}/3,\\
\tau_6^{(1)} &= 2\mu\varepsilon_6^{(1)}/3,\\
\tau_1^{(2)} &= 2\{(\lambda+2\mu)\varepsilon_1^{(2)}+\lambda(\varepsilon_2^{(2)}+\varepsilon_3^{(2)})\}/5,\\
\tau_2^{(2)} &= 2\{(\lambda+2\mu)\varepsilon_2^{(2)}+\lambda(\varepsilon^{(2)}+\varepsilon_1^{(2)})\}/5,\\
\tau_3^{(2)} &= 2\{(\lambda+2\mu)\varepsilon_3^{(2)}+\lambda(\varepsilon_1^{(2)}+\varepsilon_3^{(2)})\}/5,\\
\tau_5^{(2)} &= 2\mu\varepsilon_5^{(2)}/5,\\
\tau_4^{(3)} &= 2\mu\varepsilon_4^{(3)}/7,\\
\tau_6^{(3)} &= 2\mu\varepsilon_6^{(3)}/7.
\end{aligned}
\tag{8.3.103}
$$

The strain energy and kinetic energy densities are given by

$$
\begin{aligned}
2\bar{U} = {} & \tau_1^{(0)}\varepsilon_1^{(0)}+\tau_3^{(0)}\varepsilon_3^{(0)}+\tau_5^{(0)}\varepsilon_5^{(0)}+\tau_2^{(0)}\varepsilon_2^{(0)}+\tau_4^{(1)}\varepsilon_4^{(1)}+\tau_6^{(1)}\varepsilon_6^{(1)}+\\
& +\tau_1^{(2)}\varepsilon_1^{(2)}+\tau_3^{(2)}\varepsilon_3^{(2)}+\tau_5^{(2)}\varepsilon_5^{(2)}+\tau_2^{(2)}\varepsilon_2^{(2)}+\tau_4^{(3)}\varepsilon_4^{(3)}+\tau_6^{(3)}\varepsilon_6^{(3)}+\ldots,
\end{aligned}
\tag{8.3.104}
$$

$$
\bar{K} = \rho(\dot{u}_1^{(0)}\dot{u}_1^{(0)}+\dot{u}_3^{(0)}\dot{u}_3^{(0)}+\tfrac{1}{3}\dot{u}_2^{(1)}\dot{u}_2^{(1)}+\tfrac{1}{5}\dot{u}_1^{(2)}\dot{u}_1^{(2)}+\tfrac{1}{5}\dot{u}_3^{(2)}\dot{u}_3^{(2)}+\tfrac{1}{7}\dot{u}_2^{(3)}\dot{u}_2^{(3)}+\ldots).
\tag{8.3.105}
$$

7. *Truncation of the series.* We now retain only $u_1^{(0)}$, $u_1^{(2)}$, $u_3^{(0)}$, $u_3^{(2)}$, $u_2^{(1)}$, $u_2^{(3)}$. All other $u_j^{(n)}$ we set equal to zero. These modes have been shown in the previous illustrations. We are retaining two degrees of freedom in the form of the u_1, u_3 displacements and two degrees of freedom in the u_2 displacement. From Mindlin and Medick:

> The terms $u_1^{(0)}$, $u_3^{(0)}$ are the amplitudes of uniform distributions of displacements which occur in low-frequency extensional and shear motions in the plane of the plate: $u_2^{(1)}$ is the amplitude of a linear distribution of displacement which is an approximation to the exact sinusoidal distribution in the lowest, symmetric, thickness-stretch mode; $u_1^{(2)}$ and $u_3^{(2)}$ are the amplitudes of quadratic distributions of displacements which are approximations to the sinusoidal distributions in the lowest symmetric, thickness-shear mode, and the face-shear mode of the same order.

Some slight complications enter at this stage. We first note that $u_2^{(3)}$ has been retained, representing a third-order displacement term. However, we will only be interested in strains of order two, $\varepsilon_i^{(2)}$ or less. However, terms third-order in $u_2^{(n)}$ contribute to these strains (see $\varepsilon_2^{(2)}$ of (8.3.102)). Several stresses in turn contain $\varepsilon_2^{(2)}$. Thus, a second-order theory in strains may contain terms of yet higher order in displacement. The particular strain and stress expressions containing contributions from $u_2^{(3)}$ are

$$\varepsilon_2^{(0)} = (u_2^{(1)}+u_2^{(3)})/b, \qquad \varepsilon_2^{(2)} = 5u_2^{(3)}/b, \tag{8.3.106}$$

$$\begin{aligned} \tau_1^{(2)} &= 2\{(\lambda+2\mu)\varepsilon_1^{(2)}+\lambda(\varepsilon_2^{(2)}+\varepsilon_3^{(2)})\}/5, \\ \tau_2^{(2)} &= 2\{(\lambda+2\mu)\varepsilon_2^{(2)}+\lambda(\varepsilon_3^{(2)}+\varepsilon_1^{(2)})\}/5, \\ \tau_3^{(2)} &= 2\{(\lambda+2\mu)\varepsilon_3^{(2)}+\lambda(\varepsilon_1^{(2)}+\varepsilon_2^{(2)})\}/5. \end{aligned} \tag{8.3.107}$$

In addition, $\tau_2^{(0)}$ contains a contribution from $\varepsilon_2^{(0)}$. It should be noted that $u_2^{(3)}$ is not the sole contributor to this latter strain, whereas it is for the strain $\varepsilon_2^{(2)}$.

Now, it is recognized that $\varepsilon_2^{(2)}$ expansions may result from $\tau_1^{(2)}$, $\tau_3^{(2)}$ stresses due to the Poisson effect. As it now stands, however, coupling with the $u_2^{(3)}$ mode occurs as a result of such strains. The procedure taken is to neglect $\tau_2^{(2)}$, the stress associated with the designated expansion and contraction. With $\tau_2^{(2)} = 0$, we have from the second of (8.3.107) that

$$\varepsilon_2^{(2)} = -\frac{\lambda}{\lambda+2\mu}(\varepsilon_3^{(2)}+\varepsilon_1^{(2)}). \tag{8.3.108}$$

This relates the strain of interest to strains containing only the second-order displacement modes and replaces the definition of $\varepsilon_2^{(2)}$ in terms of $u_2^{(3)}$. The remaining stresses are

$$\begin{aligned} \tau_1^{(2)} &= 2E'(\varepsilon_1^{(2)}+\nu\varepsilon_3^{(2)})/5, \\ \tau_3^{(2)} &= 2E'(\varepsilon_3^{(2)}+\nu\varepsilon_1^{(2)})/5, \end{aligned} \tag{8.3.109}$$

where

$$\nu = \frac{\lambda}{2(\lambda+\mu)}, \qquad E' = \frac{4\mu(\lambda+\mu)}{\lambda+2\mu} = \frac{E}{1-\nu^2}. \tag{8.3.110}$$

Thus the contribution of a strain mode due, in reality, to a yet higher-order displacement mode is approximated by lower-order strain and displacement modes. Finally, the term $u_2^{(3)}$ is dropped from the strain $\varepsilon_2^{(0)}$ and thus from the stress $\tau_2^{(0)}$.

It is recognized, of course, that an approximate theory having limited degrees of freedom has been developed. Such a theory obviously cannot reproduce the higher branches of the exact frequency spectrum. In all probability, it will also not agree with the lowest branches in all detail, since the omission of higher polynomial terms will adversely affect the agreement of the lower modes as well as omit the higher modes. By introducing a number of parameters analogous to the Timoshenko shear coefficients, it is possible to retain some freedom of adjustment of the resulting dispersion curves. Mindlin and Medick state that the incorrect distributions of displacement affect the frequencies mainly through the thickness strains and velocities. They let

$$\begin{aligned} \varepsilon_2^{(0)} &= \kappa_1 \varepsilon_2^{(0)}, & \dot{u}_2^{(1)} &= \kappa_3 \dot{u}_2^{(1)}, \\ \varepsilon_4^{(1)} &= \kappa_2 \varepsilon_4^{(1)}, & \dot{u}_1^{(2)} &= \kappa_4 \dot{u}_1^{(2)}, \\ \varepsilon_6^{(1)} &= \kappa_2 \varepsilon_6^{(1)}, & \dot{u}_3^{(2)} &= \kappa_4 \dot{u}_3^{(2)}. \end{aligned} \tag{8.3.111}$$

Thus, four coefficients have been introduced and are available for later adjustment.

With the restriction to extensional motion, truncation of the series to include second-order effects, including the manipulations to remove coupling to $u_2^{(3)}$, and the introduction of the adjustment coefficients, the complete equations for the second-order approximate theory are now summarized. The kinetic and strain energy densities are now given by

$$K^{(2)} = \rho\{\dot{u}_1^{(0)}\dot{u}_1^{(0)} + \dot{u}_3^{(0)}\dot{u}_3^{(0)} + \tfrac{1}{3}\kappa_3^2 \dot{u}_2^{(1)}\dot{u}_2^{(1)} + \tfrac{1}{5}\kappa_4^2(\dot{u}_1^{(2)}\dot{u}_1^{(2)} + \dot{u}_3^{(2)}\dot{u}_3^{(2)})\}, \tag{8.3.112}$$

$$\begin{aligned} \bar{U}^{(2)} = {} & (\lambda+2\mu)(\varepsilon_1^{(0)}\varepsilon_1^{(0)} + \kappa_1^2 \varepsilon_2^{(0)}\varepsilon_2^{(0)} + \varepsilon_3^{(0)}\varepsilon_3^{(0)}) + \\ & + 2\lambda(\kappa_1 \varepsilon_2^{(0)}\varepsilon_3^{(0)} + \varepsilon_3^{(0)}\varepsilon_1^{(0)} + \kappa_1 \varepsilon_1^{(0)}\varepsilon_2^{(0)}) + \\ & + \mu \varepsilon_5^{(0)}\varepsilon_5^{(0)} + \tfrac{1}{3}\mu\kappa_2^2(\varepsilon_4^{(1)}\varepsilon_4^{(1)} + \varepsilon_6^{(1)}\varepsilon_6^{(1)}) + \\ & + \tfrac{1}{5}E'(\varepsilon_1^{(2)}\varepsilon_1^{(2)} + \varepsilon_3^{(2)}\varepsilon_3^{(2)} + 2\nu\varepsilon_1^{(2)}\varepsilon_3^{(2)}) + \tfrac{1}{5}\mu\varepsilon_5^{(2)}\varepsilon_5^{(2)}. \end{aligned} \tag{8.3.113}$$

The stress–strain relations are

$$\begin{aligned} \tau_1^{(0)} &= 2\{(\lambda+2\mu)\varepsilon_1^{(0)} + \lambda(\kappa_2 \varepsilon_2^{(0)} + \varepsilon_1^{(0)})\}, \\ \tau_2^{(0)} &= 2\{\kappa_1^2(\lambda+2\mu)\varepsilon_2^{(0)} + \lambda\kappa_1(\varepsilon_3^{(0)} + \varepsilon_1^{(0)})\}, \\ \tau_3^{(0)} &= 2\{(\lambda+2\mu)\varepsilon_3^{(0)} + \lambda(\varepsilon_1^{(0)} + \kappa_1 \varepsilon_2^{(0)})\}, \\ \tau_5^{(0)} &= 2\mu\varepsilon_5^{(0)}, \\ \tau_4^{(1)} &= \tfrac{2}{3}\mu\kappa_2^2 \varepsilon_4^{(1)}, \\ \tau_6^{(1)} &= \tfrac{2}{3}\mu\kappa_2^2 \varepsilon_6^{(1)}, \\ \tau_1^{(2)} &= \tfrac{2}{5}E'(\varepsilon_1^{(2)} + \nu\varepsilon_3^{(2)}), \\ \tau_3^{(2)} &= \tfrac{2}{5}E'(\varepsilon^{(2)} + \nu\varepsilon_1^{(2)}), \\ \tau_5^{(2)} &= \tfrac{2}{5}\mu\varepsilon_5^{(2)}. \end{aligned} \tag{8.3.114}$$

Strain displacements:

$$
\begin{aligned}
\varepsilon_1^{(0)} &= \frac{\partial u_1^{(0)}}{\partial x_1}, \\
\varepsilon_2^{(0)} &= \frac{u_2^{(1)}}{b}, \\
\varepsilon_3^{(0)} &= \frac{\partial u_3^{(0)}}{\partial x_3}, \\
\varepsilon_5^{(0)} &= \frac{\partial u_3^{(0)}}{\partial x_1}+\frac{\partial u_1^{(0)}}{\partial x_3}, \\
\varepsilon_4^{(1)} &= \frac{3u_3^{(2)}}{b}+\frac{\partial u_2^{(1)}}{\partial x_3}, \\
\varepsilon_6^{(1)} &= \frac{\partial u_2^{(1)}}{\partial x_1}+\frac{3u_1^{(2)}}{b}, \\
\varepsilon_1^{(2)} &= \frac{\partial u_1^{(2)}}{\partial x_1}, \\
\varepsilon_3^{(2)} &= \frac{\partial u_3^{(2)}}{\partial x_3}, \\
\varepsilon_5^{(2)} &= \frac{\partial u_3^{(2)}}{\partial x_1}+\frac{\partial u_1^{(2)}}{\partial x_3}.
\end{aligned}
\tag{8.3.115}
$$

Stress equations of motion:

$$
\begin{aligned}
\frac{\partial \tau_1^{(0)}}{\partial x_1}+\frac{\partial \tau_5^{(0)}}{\partial x_3}+\frac{F_1^{(0)}}{b} &= 2\rho\frac{\partial^2 u_1^{(0)}}{\partial t^2}, \\
\frac{\partial \tau_5^{(0)}}{\partial x_1}+\frac{\partial \tau_3^{(0)}}{\partial x_3}+\frac{F_3^{(0)}}{b} &= 2\rho\frac{\partial^2 u_3^{(0)}}{\partial t^2}, \\
\frac{\partial \tau_6^{(1)}}{\partial x_1}+\frac{\partial \tau_4^{(1)}}{\partial x_3}-\frac{\tau_2^{(0)}}{b}+\frac{F_2^{(1)}}{b} &= \frac{2\rho\kappa_3^2}{3}\frac{\partial^2 u_2^{(1)}}{\partial t^2}, \\
\frac{\partial \tau_1^{(2)}}{\partial x_1}+\frac{\partial \tau_5^{(2)}}{\partial x_3}-\frac{3\tau_6^{(1)}}{b}+\frac{F_1^{(2)}}{b} &= \frac{2\rho\kappa_4^2}{5}\frac{\partial^2 u_1^{(2)}}{\partial t^2}, \\
\frac{\partial \tau_5^{(2)}}{\partial x_1}+\frac{\partial \tau_3^{(2)}}{\partial x_3}-\frac{3\tau_4^{(1)}}{b}+\frac{F_3^{(2)}}{b} &= \frac{2\rho\kappa_4^2}{5}\frac{\partial^2 u_3^{(2)}}{\partial t^2}.
\end{aligned}
\tag{8.3.116}
$$

The displacement equations of motion are

$$\mu\,\nabla^2 u_1^{(0)}+(\lambda+\mu)\frac{\partial e_0}{\partial x_1}+\frac{\lambda\kappa_1}{b}\frac{\partial u_2^{(1)}}{\partial x_1}+\frac{F_1^{(0)}}{2b}=\rho\frac{\partial^2 u_1^{(0)}}{\partial t^2},$$

$$\mu\,\nabla^2 u_3^{(0)}+(\lambda+\mu)\frac{\partial e_0}{\partial x_3}+\frac{\lambda\kappa_1}{b}\frac{\partial u_2^{(1)}}{\partial x_3}+\frac{F_3^{(0)}}{2b}=\rho\frac{\partial^2 u_3^{(0)}}{\partial t^2},$$

$$\mu\kappa_2^2\,\nabla^2 u_2^{(1)}-\frac{3\lambda\kappa_1 e_0}{b}-\frac{3\kappa_1^2(\lambda+2\mu)u_2^{(1)}}{b^2}+\frac{3\mu\kappa_2^2 e_2}{b}+\frac{3F_2^{(1)}}{2b}=\rho\kappa_3^2\frac{\partial^2 u_2^{(1)}}{\partial t^2},\tag{8.3.117}$$

$$\frac{E'}{2}\left\{(1-\nu)\,\nabla^2 u_1^{(2)}+(1+\nu)\frac{\partial e_2}{\partial x_1}\right\}-\frac{5\mu\kappa_2^2}{b}\left(\frac{\partial u_2^{(1)}}{\partial x_1}+\frac{3u_1^{(2)}}{b}\right)+\frac{5F_1^{(2)}}{2b}=\rho\kappa_4^2\frac{\partial^2 u_1^{(2)}}{\partial t^2},$$

$$\frac{E'}{2}\left\{(1-\nu)\,\nabla^2 u_3^{(2)}+(1+\nu)\frac{\partial e_2}{\partial x_3}\right\}-\frac{5\mu\kappa_2^2}{b}\left(\frac{\partial u_2^{(1)}}{\partial x_3}+\frac{3u_3^{(2)}}{b}\right)+\frac{5F_3^{(2)}}{2b}=\rho\kappa_4^2\frac{\partial^2 u_3^{(2)}}{\partial t^2},$$

where

$$\nabla^2=\frac{\partial^2}{\partial x_1^2}+\frac{\partial^2}{\partial x_3^2},\qquad e_0=\frac{\partial u_1^{(0)}}{\partial x_1}+\frac{\partial u_3^{(0)}}{\partial x_3},\qquad e_2=\frac{\partial u_1^{(2)}}{\partial x_1}+\frac{\partial u_3^{(2)}}{\partial x_3}.\tag{8.3.118}$$

8. *Propagation of harmonic waves.* Consider straight-crested waves propagating in the x_1 direction, so that $\partial/\partial x_3=0$. The plate displacement equations of motion reduce to

$$\mu\frac{\partial^2 u_1^{(0)}}{\partial x_1^2}+(\lambda+\mu)\frac{\partial e_0}{\partial x_1}+\frac{\lambda\kappa_1}{b}\frac{\partial u_2^{(1)}}{\partial x_1}=\rho\ddot{u}_1^{(0)},$$

$$\mu\frac{\partial^2 u_3^{(0)}}{\partial x_1^2}=\rho\ddot{u}_3^{(0)},$$

$$\mu\kappa_2^2\frac{\partial^2 u_2^{(1)}}{\partial x_1^2}-\frac{3\lambda\kappa_1 e_0}{b}-\frac{3\kappa_1^2(\lambda+2\mu)}{b^2}u_2^{(1)}+\frac{3\mu\kappa_2^2 e_2}{b}=\rho\kappa_3^2\ddot{u}_2^{(1)},\tag{8.3.119}$$

$$\frac{E'}{2}\left\{(1-\nu)\frac{\partial^2 u_1^{(2)}}{\partial x_1^2}+(1+\nu)\frac{\partial e_2}{\partial x_1}\right\}-\frac{5\mu\kappa_2^2}{b}\left(\frac{\partial u_2^{(1)}}{\partial x_1}+\frac{3u_1^{(2)}}{b}\right)=\rho\kappa_4^2\ddot{u}_1^{(2)},$$

$$\frac{E'(1-\nu)}{2}\frac{\partial^2 u_3^{(2)}}{\partial x_1^2}-\frac{15\mu\kappa_2^2}{b^2}u_3^{(2)}=\rho\kappa_4^2\ddot{u}_3^{(2)},$$

where

$$e_0=\frac{\partial u_1^{(0)}}{\partial x_1},\qquad e_2=\frac{\partial u_1^{(2)}}{\partial x_1}.\tag{8.3.120}$$

The five equations may be represented symbolically as

$$
\begin{aligned}
f_1\{u_1^{(0)}, u_2^{(1)}\} &= \rho\ddot{u}_1^{(0)},\\
f_2\{u_3^{(0)}\} &= \rho\ddot{u}_3^{(0)},\\
f_3\{u_2^{(1)}, u_1^{(0)}, u_1^{(2)}\} &= \rho\ddot{u}_2^{(1)},\\
f_4\{u_1^{(2)}, u_2^{(1)}\} &= \rho\ddot{u}_1^{(2)},\\
f_5\{u_3^{(2)}\} &= \rho\ddot{u}_3^{(2)}.
\end{aligned}
\tag{8.3.121}
$$

We see that f_1, f_3, f_4 couple $u_1^{(0)}, u_1^{(2)}, u_2^{(1)}$, while f_2 and f_5 are independent in $u_3^{(0)}, u_3^{(2)}$ respectively. The latter two are identified with the face-shear modes.

Considering the three coupled equations, let

$$
\begin{aligned}
u_1^{(0)} &= A\sin\xi x_1 e^{i\omega t},\\
u_2^{(1)} &= B\cos\xi x_1 e^{i\omega t},\\
u_1^{(2)} &= C\sin\xi x_1 e^{i\omega t}.
\end{aligned}
\tag{8.3.122}
$$

Substitution in the first, third, and fourth of (8.3.121) gives the frequency equation

$$|a_{ij}| = 0 \qquad (i, j = 1, 2, 3), \tag{8.3.123}$$

where

$$
\begin{aligned}
a_{11} &= k^2z^2-\Omega^2,\\
a_{22} &= \kappa_2^2z^2/3+4\kappa_1^2k^2/\pi^2-\kappa_3^2\Omega^2/3,\\
a_{33} &= E'z^2/5\mu+12\kappa_2^2/\pi^2-\kappa_4^2\Omega^2/5,\\
a_{12} &= 2\kappa_1(k^2-2)z/\pi = a_{21},\\
a_{23} &= -2\kappa_2^2z/\pi = a_{32},\\
a_{13} &= a_{31} = 0,
\end{aligned}
\tag{8.3.124}
$$

and

$$
z = \frac{2\xi b}{\pi}, \qquad \Omega = \frac{\omega}{\omega_s}, \qquad \omega_s = \frac{\pi(\mu/\rho)^{\frac{1}{2}}}{2b},
$$
$$
k^2 = (\lambda+2\mu)/\mu = 2(1-\nu)/(1-2\nu). \tag{8.3.125}
$$

In addition, three amplitude ratios are obtained

$$A_i : B_i : C_i = 1 : a_i/z_i : a_i/b_i, \qquad i = 1, 2, 3, \tag{8.3.126}$$

where

$$
\begin{aligned}
a_i &= \pi(\Omega^2-k^2z_i^2)/2\kappa_1(k^2-2),\\
b_i &= \frac{3}{2\pi}\left(\frac{\pi\kappa_4^2\Omega^2}{15\kappa_2^2}-4\right)-\frac{2\pi(k^2-1)z_i^2}{5\kappa_2^2k^2}.
\end{aligned}
\tag{8.3.127}
$$

9. *Determination of the* κ_i. It should be recalled in the flexural wave theory of the previous section that the adjustment coefficient was obtained by

matching the short-wavelength behaviour ($\xi \to \infty$) to that of exact theory. An alternate procedure was to match the behaviour at the cutoff frequency ($\xi \to 0$). Mindlin and Medick describe the considerations in obtaining the κ_i and, in particular, the advantage in matching the approximate to the exact spectrum at $\xi = 0$ as follows.

The relation between Ω and z [in eqn (8.3.123)] should match, as closely as possible, the corresponding relation obtained from the three-dimensional equations. The match is improved, within the framework of the present approximation, by choosing appropriate values for the coefficients κ_i; but since the κ_i are constants, a perfect match can be made only at one value of z for each of them. Now, large enough z corresponds to frequencies high enough to enter the range of modes that have not been included in the approximate equations. In a plate vibrating at such high frequencies under practical (i.e., not mixed) edge conditions, the high modes would, in general, couple with the ones of lower order. Thus the applicability of the approximate equations to bounded plates is limited to frequencies below the lowest frequency of the lowest neglected mode. There is, then, little advantage to be gained in matching the approximate and exact solutions at short wavelengths (large z) at the expense of a good match at long wavelengths. In fact, we go to the extreme and do all of the matching in the neighborhood of $z = 0$ primarily because of the intricate behavior of the exact solution at long wavelengths and also because this choice results in a reasonably good match out to as short wavelengths as the frequency limitation permits.

For matching purposes, the cutoff frequencies are obtained as $\xi \to 0$ ($z \to 0$, where z is the non-dimensionalized wavenumber). The three modes at $z \to 0$ are extensional, thickness stretch, and thickness shear. Now two of the cutoff frequencies are

$$\Omega^2 = 12\kappa_1^2 k^2/\pi^2\kappa_3^2, \qquad 60\kappa_2^2/\pi^2\kappa_4^2. \tag{8.3.128}$$

By adjusting the ratios κ_1^2/κ_3^2, κ_2^2/κ_4^2, the intercepts may be brought into proper adjustment. By equating slopes of the second two branches at their cutoff frequencies, the other two relations to establish the coefficients are found. Exact agreement in magnitude and curvature of the frequency spectrum at the cutoff frequencies is obtained. This is at some sacrifice in accuracy of the face shear modes, however.

10. *The frequency spectrum.* The frequency equation relating Ω to z is a cubic in Ω^2. Application of Decartes' rule of signs shows that there are three real positive, two real positive and one negative or one real positive and two complex conjugate roots. It is also found that Poisson's ratio greatly influences the spectrum, with the critical ranges defined by $\nu \gtreqless \frac{1}{3}$. The case of $\nu < \frac{1}{3}$ will be discussed first, where reference is made to Fig. 8.26.

The three branches shown are the simple longitudinal $L(1)$, the thickness stretch $L(2)$ and the thickness shear $L(3)$. Consider Ω to take on the values indicated by the lines (1), (2), and so forth. (1) For $\Omega \geqslant 2$, the three positive real roots $L(1)$, $L(2)$, $L(3)$ result. However, since these roots result from z_1^2, z_2^2,

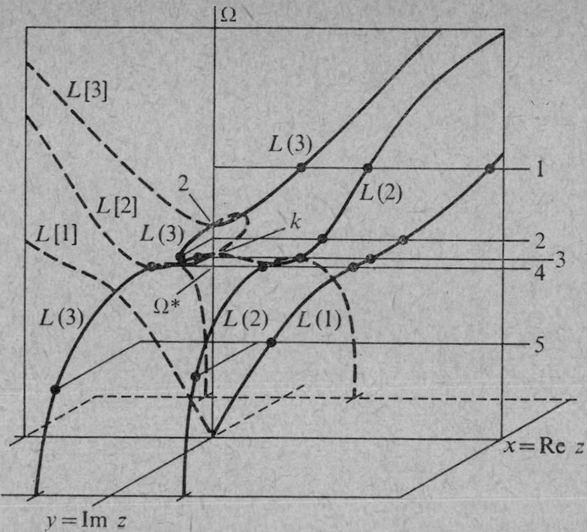

FIG. 8.26. The frequency spectrum ($\nu < \frac{1}{3}$) for the second-order extensional plate theory.

z_3^2, there are also roots $-L(1)$, $-L(2)$, $-L(3)$ in the negative x-plane. (2) For $k \leqslant \Omega < 2$, there are still two positive real roots $L(1)$, $L(2)$. However, $L(3)$ becomes imaginary. Reflections of the real and imaginary roots still occur. (3) For $\Omega^* < \Omega < k$, there are again three real roots. However, the root $L(3)$ has become negative, so that there are two real positive and one real negative. It is the branch $L[3]$, previously the reflection of $L(3)$, that becomes real and positive. (4) As $\Omega \to \Omega^*$, the roots $L[3]$, $L(2)$ approach a minimum. So, at the same time, do $L[2]$, $L(3)$ in the negative x-plane. (5) For $\Omega < \Omega^*$, the roots $L(2)$, $L[3]$ become complex conjugates of one another, given by $x \pm iy$. This also occurs for the branches $L[3]$, $L(2)$. There continues to be the real positive root $L(1)$, with its reflection $L[1]$.

For $\nu < \frac{1}{3}$, the thickness-shear mode has a higher frequency than the thickness-stretch mode. As $\nu \to \frac{1}{3}$, the cutoff frequencies approach one another and the imaginary loop shrinks to a point. For $\nu > \frac{1}{3}$, the two branches are interchanged. The spectrums for the cases $\nu \gtrless \frac{1}{3}$ are shown in Fig. 8.27. Also shown as dashed lines in the figures are the branches of the spectrum as obtained from exact theory. The agreement is seen to be remarkably close for the frequency range shown.

It should be noted that as ν continues to increase beyond $\nu = \frac{1}{3}$, the cutoff frequency of the thickness-stretch mode continues up the Ω-axis. However, there are restrictions on how high up we may go, since the second thickness-shear mode will be encountered at $\Omega = 4$. Even before this value is reached, coupling with this mode should be important. However, it is not included in the present approximate theory. Consequently, ν is limited to values less than

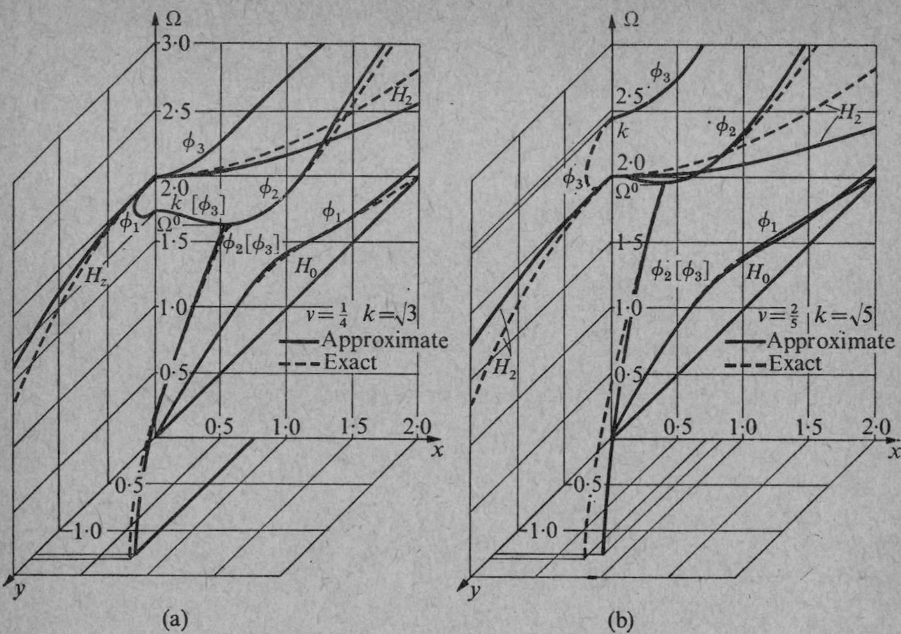

FIG. 8.27. The approximate frequency spectrum (solid lines) and exact frequency spectrum (dashed lines) for the cases of (a) $\nu < \frac{1}{3}$ and (b) $\nu > \frac{1}{3}$. (After Mindlin and Medick [66, Fig. 4].)

about $\frac{7}{16}$. Finally, as $z \to \infty$, the limiting phase velocities are found to be

$$c = \frac{\kappa_2}{\kappa_3}\left(\frac{\mu}{\rho}\right)^{\frac{1}{2}}, \quad \left(\frac{\lambda+2\mu}{\rho}\right)^{\frac{1}{2}}, \quad \frac{1}{\kappa_4}\left\{\frac{E}{\rho(1-\nu^2)}\right\}^{\frac{1}{2}}. \tag{8.3.129}$$

According to exact theory, the first of these should be the Rayleigh velocity, and the second and third the shear (equivoluminal) wave velocity.

8.3.3. *Approximate theories for longitudinal waves in rods*

A number of approximate theories for rods have appeared, as suggested in the survey by Green [22]. However, the developments presented here are again by Mindlin and his coworkers. The techniques are quite similar to those reviewed for plates, so the presentation will be rather brief. Both developments are for axially symmetric waves.

1. *Mindlin–Herrmann theory.* The development of an approximate theory for longitudinal waves in rods was presented by Mindlin and Herrmann [64] in 1950, appearing at about the same time as the work by Mindlin on an approximate theory for flexural waves in plates. Consider, then, a circular rod of radius a having a traction-free outer surface and having cylindrical coordinates as shown in Fig. 8.14. Starting from energy considerations, we have

that the change in internal energy in a volume V and in a time interval $t-t_0$ is given by

$$\Delta U = \int_{t_0}^{t} dt \int_{v} \frac{\partial}{\partial t}(T+V)\, dv, \tag{8.3.130}$$

where T and V are the kinetic and strain energy densities. For the former

$$T = \tfrac{1}{2}\rho(\dot{u}_r^2+\dot{u}_\theta^2+\dot{u}_z^2), \tag{8.3.131}$$

while for the latter we have that $V = V(\varepsilon_{rr}, \varepsilon_{\theta\theta}, \varepsilon_{zz}, \varepsilon_{r\theta}, \varepsilon_{rz}, \varepsilon_{\theta z})$, in general, and that

$$\partial V/\partial t = \tau_{rr}\dot{\varepsilon}_{rr}+\tau_{\theta\theta}\dot{\varepsilon}_{\theta\theta}+\ldots+\tau_{\theta z}\dot{\varepsilon}_{\theta z}. \tag{8.3.132}$$

The strains are related to the displacements in cylindrical coordinates by

$$\begin{gathered}
\varepsilon_{rr} = \frac{\partial u_r}{\partial r}, \qquad \varepsilon_{\theta\theta} = \frac{1}{r}\frac{\partial u_\theta}{\partial \theta}+\frac{u_r}{r}, \qquad \varepsilon_{zz} = \frac{\partial u_z}{\partial z}, \\
\varepsilon_{r\theta} = \left(\frac{1}{r}\frac{\partial u_r}{\partial \theta}+\frac{\partial u_\theta}{\partial r}-\frac{u_\theta}{r}\right), \qquad \varepsilon_{rz} = \left(\frac{\partial u_z}{\partial r}+\frac{\partial u_r}{\partial z}\right), \\
\varepsilon_{\theta z} = \left(\frac{\partial u_\theta}{\partial z}+\frac{1}{r}\frac{\partial u_z}{\partial \theta}\right).
\end{gathered} \tag{8.3.133}$$

The following kinematics of deformation are now assumed:

$$u_r = \frac{r}{a}u(z, t), \qquad u_\theta = 0, \qquad u_z = w(z, t). \tag{8.3.134}$$

Thus, two modes of deformation are admitted as illustrated in Fig. 8.28. With

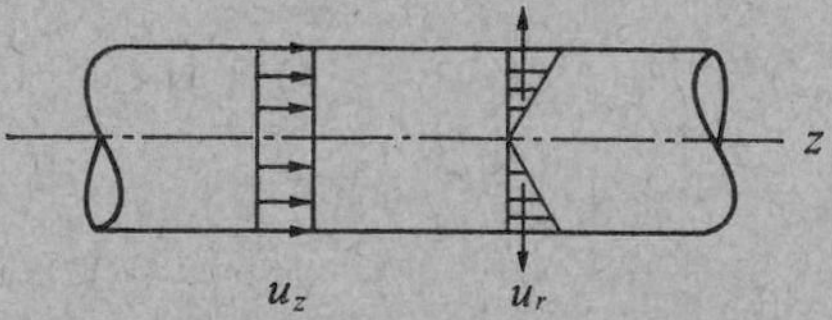

FIG. 8.28. Kinematics of the assumed deformations of u_r, u_z in a rod.

the assumed kinematics we have

$$\frac{\partial T}{\partial t} = \rho(\dot{u}_r\ddot{u}_r+\dot{u}_z\ddot{u}_z) = \rho\left(\frac{r^2}{a^2}\dot{u}\ddot{u}+\dot{w}\ddot{w}\right), \tag{8.3.135}$$

and

$$\frac{\partial V}{\partial t} = \frac{\tau_{rr}}{a}\dot{u}+\frac{\tau_{\theta\theta}}{a}\dot{u}+\tau_{zz}\frac{\partial \dot{w}}{\partial z}+\tau_{rz}\frac{r}{a}\frac{\partial \dot{u}}{\partial z}, \tag{8.3.136}$$

where $\varepsilon_{rr} = u/a$, $\varepsilon_{\theta\theta} = u/a$, $\varepsilon_{zz} = \partial w/\partial z$, $\varepsilon_{r\theta} = 0$, $\varepsilon_{rz} = (r/a)\partial u/\partial z$, $\varepsilon_{\theta z} = 0$.

Substituting these results in the volume integral of (8.3.130), simply called I, gives

$$I = 2\pi\int_b^c \mathrm{d}z\int_0^a\left\{\rho\left(\frac{r^2}{a^2}\dot{u}\ddot{u}+\dot{w}\ddot{w}\right)+\frac{\tau_{rr}}{a}\dot{u}+\frac{\tau_{\theta\theta}}{a}\dot{u}+\tau_{zz}\frac{\partial\dot{w}}{\partial z}+\tau_{rz}\frac{r}{a}\frac{\partial\dot{u}}{\partial z}\right\}r\,\mathrm{d}r. \quad (8.3.137)$$

Again noting that u, w are independent of r, we define the rod stresses

$$P_r = \int_0^a \tau_{rr}r\,\mathrm{d}r, \qquad P_\theta = \int_0^a \tau_{\theta\theta}r\,\mathrm{d}r,$$

$$P_z = \int_0^a \tau_{zz}r\,\mathrm{d}r, \qquad Q = \int_0^a \frac{\tau_{zr}r^2}{a}\,\mathrm{d}r. \quad (8.3.138)$$

Then the integral I becomes

$$I = 2\pi\int_b^c \mathrm{d}z\left\{\rho\left(\frac{a^2}{4}\dot{u}\ddot{u}+\frac{a^2}{2}\dot{w}\ddot{w}\right)+\frac{P_r}{a}\dot{u}+\frac{P_\theta}{a}\dot{u}+P_z\frac{\partial\dot{w}}{\partial z}+Q\frac{\partial\dot{u}}{\partial z}\right\}. \quad (8.3.139)$$

The last two terms of (8.3.139) may be integrated by parts. Carrying this out and re-grouping the various terms, the change in internal energy is then given by

$$\Delta U = 2\pi\int_{t_0}^t \mathrm{d}t\int_b^c\left\{\left(\rho\frac{a^2}{4}\ddot{u}+\frac{P_r+P_\theta}{a}-\frac{\partial Q}{\partial z}\right)\dot{u}+\left(\rho\frac{a^2}{2}\ddot{w}-\frac{\partial P_z}{\partial z}\right)\dot{w}\right\}\mathrm{d}z+$$

$$+2\pi\int_{t_0}^t \mathrm{d}t[Q\dot{u}+P_z\dot{w}]_b^c. \quad (8.3.140)$$

With this result in hand, consider now the stress equations of motion of elasticity, given by

$$\frac{\partial\tau_{rr}}{\partial r}+\frac{\partial\tau_{zr}}{\partial z}+\frac{\tau_{rr}-\tau_{\theta\theta}}{r} = \rho\frac{\partial^2 u_r}{\partial t^2},$$

$$\frac{\partial\tau_{zr}}{\partial r}+\frac{\partial\tau_{zz}}{\partial z}+\frac{1}{r}\tau_{zr} = \rho\frac{\partial^2 u_z}{\partial t^2} \quad (8.3.141)$$

for the present case of axial symmetry. To convert these to the rod equations, multiply the first by r^2, the second by r, and integrate over the cross-section. Thus, for the first case, we have

$$\int_0^a\left\{r^2\frac{\partial\tau_{rr}}{\partial r}+r^2\frac{\partial\tau_{zr}}{\partial z}+r(\tau_{rr}-\tau_{\theta\theta})\right\}\mathrm{d}r = \frac{\rho}{a}\int_0^a r^3\ddot{u}\,\mathrm{d}r. \quad (8.3.142)$$

Carrying out the integration gives

$$\frac{\partial Q}{\partial z}-\frac{P_\theta+P_r}{a}+aR=\rho\frac{a^2}{4}\frac{\partial^2 u}{\partial t^2}, \tag{8.3.143}$$

where $R=\tau_{rr}|_{r=a}$. For the second equation of motion, there results

$$\frac{\partial P_z}{\partial z}+aZ=\rho\frac{a^2}{2}\frac{\partial^2 w}{\partial t^2}, \tag{8.3.144}$$

where $Z=\tau_{zr}|_{r=a}$. These are the rod stress equations of motion.

The boundary conditions and initial conditions follow next. Thus using (8.3.143) and (8.3.144) in (8.3.140) gives

$$\Delta U=2\pi a\int_{t_0}^{t}\mathrm{d}t\int_{b}^{c}(R\dot{u}+Z\dot{w})\,\mathrm{d}z+2\pi\int_{t_0}^{t}(Q\dot{u}+P_z\dot{w})\,\mathrm{d}t. \tag{8.3.145}$$

This is simply the statement of work–energy which says that the change of internal energy is equal to the work done on the system in the time interval t_0 to t. By applying uniqueness-of-solutions considerations, similar to those used in the approximate plate development, the boundary and initial conditions follow:

(a) along the rod, one each of the pairs of quantities $R\dot{u}$, $Z\dot{w}$ must be given;
(b) at the ends of the rod, one each of the two pairs of quantities $Q\dot{u}$, $P_z\dot{w}$ must be given;
(c) the initial displacements and velocities must be given.

The rod stress–displacement relations are now required. These are obtained in the usual fashion, starting with the generalized Hooke's law. In cylindrical coordinates for axisymmetry, these are

$$\begin{aligned}\tau_{rr}&=\lambda\Delta+2\mu\varepsilon_{rr},\\ \tau_{\theta\theta}&=\lambda\Delta+2\mu\varepsilon_{\theta\theta},\\ \tau_{zz}&=\lambda\Delta+2\mu\varepsilon_{zz},\\ \tau_{zr}&=\mu\varepsilon_{zr},\\ \Delta&=\varepsilon_{rr}+\varepsilon_{\theta\theta}+\varepsilon_{zz}.\end{aligned} \tag{8.3.146}$$

Substituting the assumed displacements in the strain definitions, the resulting strains in Hooke's law, and the resulting stresses in the rod stresses, and carrying out the integrations gives the rod stress–displacement relations. To enable the approximate theory to be adjusted for better agreement with exact theory, the constants κ, κ_1 are introduced. The results are

$$P_r = P_\theta = \frac{\kappa_1^2}{2}\left\{2a(\lambda+\mu)u + a^2\lambda\frac{\partial w}{\partial z}\right\},$$

$$P_z = \frac{1}{2}\left\{2a\lambda u + a^2(\lambda+2\mu)\frac{\partial w}{\partial z}\right\}, \tag{8.3.147}$$

$$Q = \frac{\kappa^2 a^2 \mu}{4}\frac{\partial u}{\partial z}.$$

When these relations are substituted in the rod stress equations of motion, we obtain

$$a^2\kappa^2\mu\frac{\partial^2 u}{\partial z^2} - 8\kappa_1^2(\lambda+\mu)u - 4a\kappa_1^2\lambda\frac{\partial w}{\partial z} = \rho a^2\frac{\partial^2 u}{\partial t^2},$$

$$2a\lambda\frac{\partial u}{\partial z} + a^2(\lambda+2\mu)\frac{\partial^2 w}{\partial z^2} = \rho a^2\frac{\partial^2 w}{\partial t^2}. \tag{8.3.148}$$

The effects of body forces and surface loads have been omitted from the above equations. The first equation is mainly associated with radial shear and inertia. The second equation is similar to classical rod theory, except for the added $2a\lambda(\partial u/\partial z)$ term. Note also that the resulting wave velocity is that of dilatational waves instead of the bar velocity.

Now consider the propagation of harmonic waves, letting $R = Z = 0$ and

$$u = Ae^{i\xi(z-ct)}, \qquad w = Be^{i\xi(z-ct)}. \tag{8.3.149}$$

Substituting these expressions in the displacement equations of motion and evaluating the resulting determinant of coefficients gives the dispersion relation

$$\left\{\frac{\kappa^2\mu}{\rho} + \frac{8\kappa_1^2(\lambda+\mu)}{a^2\kappa^2\rho} - c^2\right\}\left(\frac{\lambda+2\mu}{\rho} - c^2\right) - \frac{8\kappa_1^2\lambda^2}{a^2\kappa^2\rho^2} = 0. \tag{8.3.150}$$

Consider now the long- and short-wavelength limits. As $\xi \to 0$, the limiting phase velocities are

$$c^2 = E/\rho = c_0^2; \qquad c^2 = \infty. \tag{8.3.151}$$

Both agree with exact results. The first, it is noted, is the classical bar velocity. As $\xi \to \infty$, the results are

$$c^2 = \kappa^2\frac{\mu}{\rho} = \kappa^2 c_2^2, \qquad c^2 = \frac{\lambda+2\mu}{\rho} = c_1^2. \tag{8.3.152}$$

In exact theory, the first of these is the Rayleigh velocity c_R^2. In order to bring the short-wavelength limit into agreement, it is necessary to select κ^2 as $\kappa^2 = c_R^2/c_2^2$. The second limit in the exact theory is $c_2^2 = \mu/\rho$. This discrepancy cannot be corrected in this present form of the theory. Selection of κ_1 to obtain better agreement of approximate and exact theory is based on certain

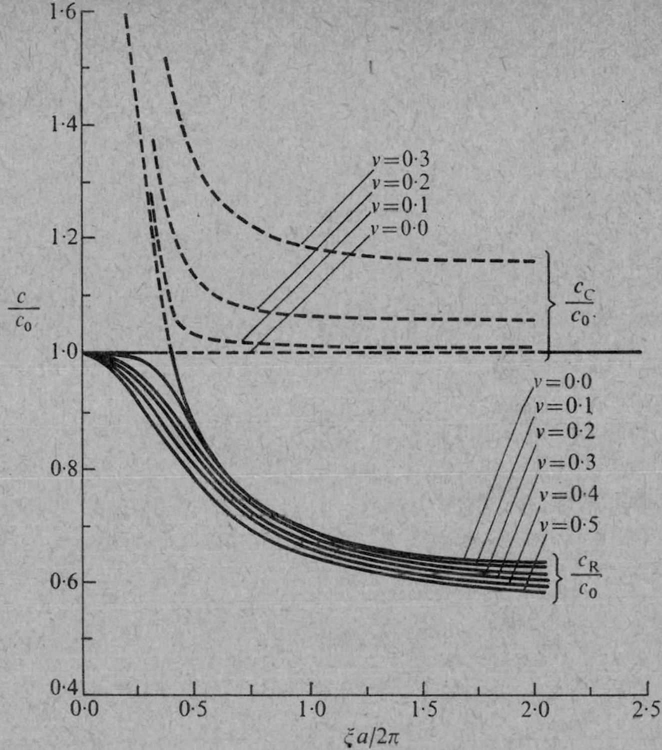

FIG. 8.29. Dispersion curves for Mindlin–Herrmann rod theory for various Poisson's ratio. (After Mindlin and Herrmann [64, Fig. 2].)

observations by Hudson [29] on the behaviour of the first-mode curves of exact theory for various values of Poisson's ratio. He observed that the curves are all tangent at a common point, given by $a/\lambda = 0{\cdot}293$, $c/c_2 = \sqrt{2}$. Adjusting the approximate theory curves for a similar point of tangency gives

$$\kappa_1^2 = 0{\cdot}422(2-\kappa^2) \qquad (8.3.153)$$

The resulting dispersion curves for the two-mode rod theory are shown in Fig. 8.29 for various values of Poisson's ratio. The value of κ^2 has been selected according to $\kappa^2 = c_R^2/c_2^2$, while κ_1^2 has been taken as unity. It should be noted that the modes uncouple for $\nu = 0$.

2. *Mindlin–McNiven theory*. Similar to the refinements that followed Mindlin's first theory for plates, additional refinements followed the work on rods by Mindlin and Herrmann. The theory presented by Mindlin and McNiven [65] will now be briefly considered. Recall that Mindlin–Herrmann theory (p. 510) was a two-mode theory. However, considering the exact frequency spectrum for the rod, it must be appreciated that the cutoff

frequencies of the second and third symmetric rod modes can interchange positions, depending on Poisson's ratio. This was brought out in detail by the Mindlin–Medick theory of plates. Thus, one of the objectives of the Mindlin–McNiven development was to include a third degree of freedom or mode. In addition the adjustment coefficients, determined from the high frequency behaviour and other arguments in the Mindlin–Herrmann development, were obtained in the refined rod theory in the manner used by Mindlin and Medick; that is by adjusting the long-wavelength behaviour to match the exact spectrum. Only the essential results of the theory will be presented here.

Again consider a rod as shown in Fig. 8.14. For axisymmetry, $u_\theta = \partial/\partial\theta =$ and $u_r = u_r(r, z, t)$, $u_z = u_z(r, z, t)$. Now, expand these displacements in terms of Jacobi polynomials in the radial coordinate

$$u_r = \sum_{n=0}^{\infty} \mathscr{U}_n(\alpha)u_n(z, t), \qquad u_z = \sum_{n=0}^{\infty} \mathscr{W}_n(\alpha)w_n(z, t), \tag{8.3.154}$$

where $\alpha = r/a$ and the Jacobi polynomials are given by†

$$\begin{gathered}
\mathscr{U}_0(\alpha) = \alpha, \qquad \mathscr{U}_1(\alpha) = \alpha - \tfrac{3}{2}\alpha^3, \ldots, \\
\mathscr{U}_n(\alpha) = \alpha + \sum_{k=1}^{n} (-1)^k \binom{n}{k} \frac{(n+2)_k}{(k+1)!} \alpha^{2k+1}, \\
\mathscr{W}_0(\alpha) = 1, \qquad \mathscr{W}_1(\alpha) = 1 - 2\alpha^2, \ldots, \\
\mathscr{W}_n(\alpha) = 1 + \sum_{k=1}^{n} (-1)^k \binom{n}{k} \frac{(n+1)_k}{k!} \alpha^{2k},
\end{gathered} \tag{8.3.155}$$

where

$$\binom{n}{k} = \frac{n(n-1)(n-2)\ldots(n-k+1)}{k!},$$

$$(\beta)_k = \beta(\beta+1)(\beta+2)\ldots(\beta+k-1). \tag{8.3.156}$$

Now, the objective of using Jacobi polynomials in the expansion instead of the radial coordinate itself is quite similar to that of using Legendre polynomials instead of the thickness coordinate in the Mindlin–Medick plate theory. That is, these polynomials possess convenient orthogonality properties that simplify many of the integrations to be performed. These properties are given by

$$\begin{gathered}
4(n+1)^3 \int_0^1 \alpha \mathscr{U}_m \mathscr{U}_n \, d\alpha = \begin{cases} 0, & m \neq n \\ 1, & m = n, \end{cases} \\
2(2n+1) \int_0^1 \alpha \mathscr{W}_m \mathscr{W}_n \, d\alpha = \begin{cases} 0, & m \neq n \\ 1, & m = n. \end{cases}
\end{gathered} \tag{8.3.157}$$

† See, for example, Reference [45].

The derivative property is

$$\frac{d\mathscr{W}_n}{d\alpha} = \sum_{k=0}^{n-1} C_{nk}\mathscr{U}_k, \qquad C_{nk} = 4(k+1)^2(-1)^{n+k}. \tag{8.3.158}$$

The rod stress equations of motion are obtained by substituting the assumed displacements into the variational equations of motion and integrating across the cross-section. The results are

$$\begin{aligned} &\frac{dQ_n}{dz} - \frac{P_n}{a} + \frac{(-1)^n}{n+1}\frac{R}{a} = \frac{\rho}{4(n+1)^3}\frac{\partial^2 u_n}{\partial t^2}, \\ &\frac{dF_n}{dz} - \sum_{k=0}^{n-1} C_{nk}\frac{Q_k}{a} + (-1)^n\frac{Z}{a} = \frac{\rho}{2(2n+1)}\frac{\partial^2 w_n}{\partial t^2}, \end{aligned} \tag{8.3.159}$$

where the rod stresses are given by

$$\begin{aligned} P_n &= \int_0^1 \left(\tau_{\theta\theta}\mathscr{U}_n + \tau_{rr}\alpha\frac{d\mathscr{U}_n}{d\alpha}\right) d\alpha, \\ Q_n &= \int_0^1 \tau_{rz}\mathscr{U}_n\alpha \, d\alpha, \\ F_n &= \int_0^1 \tau_{zz}\mathscr{W}_n\alpha \, d\alpha, \end{aligned} \tag{8.3.160}$$

and

$$R = \tau_{rr}\big|_{r=a}, \qquad Z = \tau_{rz}\big|_{r=a}. \tag{8.3.161}$$

The strains are given by

$$\begin{aligned} \varepsilon_{rr} &= \frac{\partial u_r}{\partial r} = \sum_{n=0}^{\infty} \frac{\partial \mathscr{U}_n}{\partial \alpha}\frac{u_n}{a}, \\ \varepsilon_{\theta\theta} &= \frac{u_r}{r} = \sum_{n=0}^{\infty} \frac{\mathscr{U}_n}{\alpha}\frac{u_n}{a}, \\ \varepsilon_{zz} &= \frac{\partial u_z}{\partial z} = \sum_{n=0}^{\infty} \mathscr{W}_n\frac{\partial w_n}{\partial z}, \\ \varepsilon_{rz} &= \frac{\partial u_r}{\partial z} + \frac{\partial u_z}{\partial r} = \sum_{n=0}^{\infty}\left(\mathscr{U}_n\frac{\partial u_n}{\partial z} + \frac{\partial \mathscr{W}_n}{\partial \alpha}\frac{w_n}{a}\right). \end{aligned} \tag{8.3.162}$$

The rod stress–strain relations are obtained by substituting (8.3.162) into the usual stress–strain relations

$$\begin{aligned}\tau_{rr} &= \partial U/\partial \varepsilon_{rr} = \lambda\Delta+2\mu\varepsilon_{rr},\\ \tau_{\theta\theta} &= \partial U/\partial \varepsilon_{\theta\theta} = \lambda\Delta+2\mu\varepsilon_{\theta\theta},\\ \tau_{zz} &= \partial U/\partial \varepsilon_{zz} = \lambda\Delta_{zz}+2\mu\varepsilon_{zz},\\ \tau_{rz} &= \partial U/\partial \varepsilon_{rz} = \mu\varepsilon_{rz},\end{aligned} \tag{8.3.163}$$

where $\Delta = \varepsilon_{rr}+\varepsilon_{\theta\theta}+\varepsilon_{zz}$ and U is the strain energy, and then substituting the resulting stresses into the definitions (8.3.160). A few of the terms are

$$\begin{aligned}P_0 &= 2(\lambda+\mu)\frac{u_0}{a}+\lambda\frac{\partial w_0}{\partial z}+\dots,\\ Q_0 &= \frac{\mu}{4}\left(\frac{\partial u_0}{\partial z}-\frac{4w_1}{a}\right)+\dots,\\ F_0 &= \frac{\lambda+2\mu}{2}\frac{\partial w_0}{\partial z}+\lambda\frac{u_0}{a}+\dots,\\ F_1 &= \frac{\lambda+2\mu}{6}\frac{\partial w_1}{\partial z}+\dots.\end{aligned} \tag{8.3.164}$$

A second-order approximate theory is desired. To this end, retain only the terms associated with the u_0, w_0, and w_1 displacements. With this restriction, the rod displacements, stresses, and strains are redefined as

$$u = u_0, \qquad w = w_0, \qquad \psi = w_1, \tag{8.3.165}$$

$$\begin{aligned}P_r &= P_0 = \int_0^1 (\tau_{rr}+\tau_{\theta\theta})\alpha\, d\alpha,\\ P_z &= P_0 = \int_0^1 \tau_{zz}\alpha\, d\alpha,\\ P_\psi &= F_1 = \int_0^1 \tau_{zz}(1-2\alpha^2)\alpha\, d\alpha,\\ P_{rz} &= Q_0 = \int_0^1 \tau_{rz}\alpha^2\, d\alpha,\end{aligned} \tag{8.3.166}$$

$$\begin{aligned}\Gamma_r &= u/a, & \Gamma_z &= \partial w/\partial z,\\ \Gamma_\psi &= \partial\psi/\partial z, & \Gamma_{rz} &= \partial u/\partial z-4\psi/a.\end{aligned} \tag{8.3.167}$$

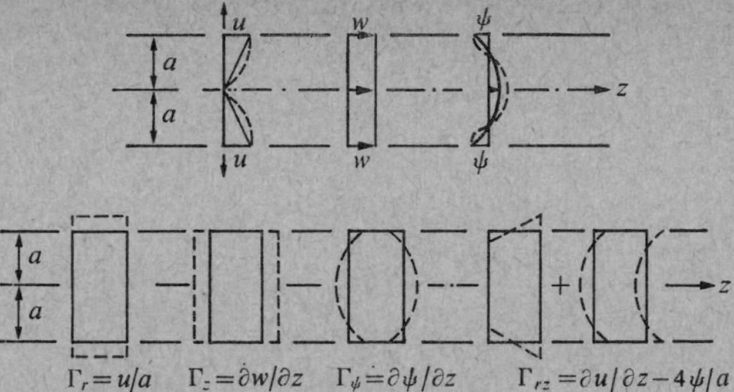

FIG. 8.30. Displacement and strain components for a second-order longitudinal rod theory. (After Mindlin and McNiven [65, Fig. 1].)

The displacement and strain components are shown in Fig. 8.30. In order to partially compensate for the effects of the omitted higher-order terms on the remaining modes, the adjustment coefficients κ_1, κ_2, κ_3, κ_4 are introduced, where Γ_r, Γ_{rz}, $\dot{u}$, ψ are replaced by $\kappa_1\Gamma_r$, $\kappa_2\Gamma_{rz}$, $\kappa_3\dot{u}$, and $\kappa_4\dot{\psi}$.

The resulting strain and kinetic energy densities for the second-order theory with the adjustment parameters incorporated are given by

$$\begin{aligned} U_2 &= \tfrac{1}{2}\{2(\lambda+\mu)\kappa_1^2\Gamma_r^2+\tfrac{1}{2}(\lambda+2\mu)\Gamma_z^2+2\lambda\kappa_1\Gamma_r\Gamma_z+ \\ &\quad +\tfrac{1}{4}\mu\kappa_2^2\Gamma_{rz}^2+\tfrac{1}{6}(\lambda+2\mu)\Gamma_\psi^2\}, \\ K_2 &= \frac{\rho}{2}(\tfrac{1}{4}\kappa_3^2\dot{u}^2+\tfrac{1}{2}\dot{w}^2+\tfrac{1}{6}\kappa_4^2\dot{\psi}^2). \end{aligned} \tag{8.3.168}$$

The second-order stress–strain–displacement relations are given by

$$\begin{aligned} P_r &= \partial U_2/\partial\Gamma_r = 2(\lambda+\mu)\kappa_1^2\Gamma_r+\lambda\kappa_1\Gamma_z, \\ &= \{2(\lambda+\mu)\kappa_1^2u+\lambda\kappa_1 w'\}a^{-1}, \\ P_z &= \partial U_2/\partial\Gamma_z = \tfrac{1}{2}(\lambda+2\mu)\Gamma_z+\lambda\kappa_1\Gamma_r, \\ &= \{\tfrac{1}{2}(\lambda+2\mu)w'+\lambda\kappa_1 u\}a^{-1}, \\ P_{rz} &= \partial U_2/\partial\Gamma_{rz} = \tfrac{1}{4}\mu\kappa_2^2\Gamma_{rz}, \\ &= \tfrac{1}{4}\mu\kappa_2^2(u'-4\psi)a^{-1}, \\ P_\psi &= \partial U_2/\partial\Gamma_\psi = \tfrac{1}{6}(\lambda+2\mu)\Gamma_\psi, \\ &= \tfrac{1}{6}(\lambda+2\mu)\psi' a^{-1} \end{aligned} \tag{8.3.169}$$

The stress equations of motion are given by

$$\frac{\partial P_{rz}}{\partial z}-P_r+R = \tfrac{1}{4}\rho a\kappa_3^2\ddot{u},$$

$$\frac{\partial P_z}{\partial z}+Z = \tfrac{1}{2}\rho a\ddot{w}, \tag{8.3.170}$$

$$\frac{\partial P_\psi}{\partial z}+4P_{rz}-Z = \tfrac{1}{6}\rho a\kappa_4^2\ddot{\psi}.$$

Finally, the displacement equations of motion are

$$(u''-4\psi')-8(\lambda+\mu)\kappa_1^2u-4\lambda\kappa_1w'+4aR = \rho a^2\kappa_3^2\ddot{u},$$

$$(\lambda+2\mu)w''+2\lambda\kappa_1u'+2aZ = \rho a^2\ddot{w}, \tag{8.3.171}$$

$$(\lambda+2\mu)\psi''+6\mu\kappa_2^2(u'-4\psi)-6aZ = \rho a^2\kappa_4^2\ddot{\psi}.$$

For propagation of harmonic waves, let

$$u = A\cos\gamma z e^{i\omega t}, \qquad w = B\sin\gamma z e^{i\omega t}, \qquad \psi = C\sin\gamma z e^{i\omega t} \tag{8.3.172}$$

and substitute in the displacement equations of motion (8.3.171) with $R = Z = 0$. The frequency equation is obtained from the resulting determinant of coefficients, given by

$$\begin{vmatrix} a_{11} & a_{12} & a_{13} \\ a_{12} & a_{22} & 0 \\ a_{13} & 0 & a_{33} \end{vmatrix} = 0, \tag{8.3.173}$$

where

$$a_{11} = \kappa_2^2\delta^2\zeta^2+8(k^2-1)\kappa_1^2-\kappa_3^2\delta^2\Omega^2,$$

$$a_{22} = 2\delta^2(k^2\zeta^2-\Omega^2),$$

$$a_{33} = 6(k^2\delta^2\zeta^2+24\kappa_2^2-\kappa_4^2\delta^2\Omega^2), \tag{8.3.174}$$

$$a_{12} = 4(k^2-2)\kappa_1\delta\zeta,$$

$$a_{13} = 12\kappa_2^2\,\delta\zeta,$$

and where

$$\Omega = \omega/\omega_s, \qquad \omega_s = \delta c_2/a, \qquad \zeta = \gamma a/\delta,$$

$$k^2 = c_1^2/c_2^2,$$

and where δ is the lowest non-zero root of $J_1(\delta) = 0$. The adjustment coefficients are obtained by matching the approximate spectrum to the exact spectrum at $\zeta = 0$. The procedures given by Mindlin–McNiven result in the ordinates, slopes, and curvatures of the three branches of the approximate spectrum being identical to those of the exact spectrum at $\zeta = 0$. The resulting branches are very similar to the first three branches of Fig. 8.17 for $\bar{\xi} < 2$. The deviations between approximate and exact theories is slight and occurs only at smaller wavelengths. As Poisson's ratio is increased, the cutoff frequencies of the second and third branches, corresponding to the radial mode and axial shear mode, approach one another, becoming equal at $\nu = 0{\cdot}2833$. For larger values of Poisson's ratio, the radial mode is above the axial shear mode. The behaviour is quite similar to that shown in Fig. 8.27 for plates.

8.3.4. *Approximate theories for waves in shells*

An extensive discussion was previously given on the many and varied approximate theories for vibrations of shells.† The lowest-order theory, membrane theory, was used in the analysis of waves in a cylindrical shell in the earlier chapter. Bending theories, such as by Love [43] and others represent a higher-order shell theory that has found wide application in shell vibration problems. Rather little has appeared on using these theories in transient wave-propagation problems, however. Quite possibly this is due to the inherent limitations imposed by the shear-rigidity assumption, limitations that were also noted in the case of Bernoulli–Euler beam theory and classical plate theory. A number of developments in yet-higher-order shell theories, containing shear deformations, rotary inertia and other deformations, have appeared, and it is to this area that our attention will be directed, with only cylindrical shells being considered.

Several developments in higher-order shell theories appeared within a short period of time. Mirsky and Herrmann [69] included shear effects in both the axial and circumferential direction and rotary-inertia effects in the study of non-axially symmetric waves in a cylindrical shell. This work was preceded by the study of axially symmetric motions [68], including shear effects and transverse normal stress, and a yet earlier study by Herrmann and Mirsky [25] for the axially symmetric case with shear effects included. Cooper and Naghdi [9] presented a theory including shear effects and rotary inertia for non-axially symmetric motions. They showed reduction of their equations to those of Love and Donnell upon selectively omitting various higher-order effects. This work was preceded by the study of the axially symmetric case by Naghdi and Cooper [72]. Lin and Morgan [42] also developed the equations for axially symmetric motions including shear and rotary-inertia effects.

† Chapter 4, § 4.3.

Yu [90] reduced the Herrmann–Mirsky results to Donnell-type equations. A most useful survey of these developments, including comparison of the dispersion curves and frequency spectra of the theories was given by Greenspon [23]. Also included was discussion and comparison of results for bending and membrane theories. McNiven, Shah, and Sackman [47] have presented a theory for axially symmetric waves that includes the first radial mode, as well as longitudinal and shear modes. The development is quite similar to that of Mindlin and McNiven [65] for rods.

In the following, the basic aspects of the Mirsky–Herrmann and Cooper–Naghdi theories will be presented, with the main emphasis on giving dispersion curves and frequency spectra. The comparisons of the various theories by Greenspon will be reviewed followed by the results from McNiven *et al.*

1. *Mirsky–Herrmann theory* [68]. Consider an infinite, cylindrical shell of mean radius R and thickness h. Let x be the axial coordinate, θ be the polar angle, and z be the radial distance from the middle surface of the shell, measured positively outwards. The displacement kinematics are assumed to be given by

$$\begin{aligned} \bar{u}_x(x, \theta, z, t) &= u(x, \theta, t) + z\psi_x(x, \theta, t), \\ \bar{u}_\theta(x, \theta, z, t) &= v(x, \theta, t) + z\psi_\theta(x, \theta, t), \\ \bar{u}_z(x, \theta, z, t) &= w(x, \theta, t). \end{aligned} \tag{8.3.175}$$

It is seen that the ψ_z, ψ_θ terms bring in the axial and circumferential shear effects.

The basic steps of the theory involve, first, integration of the strain energy density expression across the shell thickness. This leads to the shell stress expressions

$$\begin{aligned} N_{xx} &= \int_{-h/2}^{h/2} \sigma_{xx}(1+z/R)\,dz, & M_{x\theta} &= \int_{-h/2}^{h/2} \sigma_{x\theta}(1+z/R)\,dz, \\ M_{xx} &= \int_{-h/2}^{h/2} \sigma_{xx}(1+z/R)z\,dz, & N_{\theta x} &= \int_{-h/2}^{h/2} \sigma_{x\theta}\,dz, \\ N_{\theta\theta} &= \int_{-h/2}^{h/2} \sigma_{\theta\theta}\,dz, & M_{\theta x} &= \int_{-h/2}^{h/2} \sigma_{x\theta}z\,dz, \\ M_{\theta\theta} &= \int_{-h/2}^{h/2} \sigma_{\theta\theta}z\,dz, & Q_x &= \int_{-h/2}^{h/2} \sigma_{xz}(1+z/R)\,dz, \\ N_{x\theta} &= \int_{-h/2}^{h/2} \sigma_{x\theta}(1+z/R)\,dz, & Q_\theta &= \int_{-h/2}^{h/2} \sigma_{z\theta}\,dz. \end{aligned} \tag{8.3.176}$$

The kinetic energy expression is then developed. Using the two energy expressions in conjunction with Hamilton's principle leads to the shell stress equations of motion. The shell stress–strain–displacements are developed from Hooke's law. Somewhat paralleling the method used by Mindlin [59] in obtaining the approximate plate theory, the effects of the stress σ_{zz} are dropped. Furthermore, the adjustment coefficients κ_x, κ_θ are introduced in conjunction with the strains ε_{xz}, $\varepsilon_{\theta z}$. The resulting stress-displacement equations are given by

$$N_{xx} = E_p\frac{\partial u}{\partial x}+\left(\frac{D}{R}\right)\frac{\partial \psi_x}{\partial x}+\left(\frac{\nu E_p}{R}\right)\left(w+\frac{\partial v}{\partial \theta}\right),$$

$$N_{\theta x} = Gh\frac{\partial v}{\partial x}+\left(\frac{Gh}{R}\right)\left(1+\frac{Gh}{R}\right)\frac{\partial u}{\partial \theta}-\left(\frac{GI}{R^2}\right)\frac{\partial \psi_x}{\partial \theta},$$

$$M_{xx} = \left(\frac{D}{R}\right)\left(\frac{\partial u}{\partial x}+R\frac{\partial \psi_x}{\partial x}+\nu\frac{\partial \psi_\theta}{\partial \theta}\right),$$

$$M_{\theta x} = GI\left(\frac{\partial \psi_\theta}{\partial x}+R^{-2}\frac{\partial u}{\partial \theta}+R^{-1}\frac{\partial \psi_x}{\partial \theta}\right),$$

$$N_{x\theta} = G\left(h\frac{\partial v}{\partial x}+\left(\frac{I}{R}\right)\frac{\partial \psi_\theta}{\partial x}+\left(\frac{h}{R}\right)\frac{\partial u}{\partial \theta}\right),$$

$$N_{\theta\theta} = \left(\frac{E_p}{R}+\frac{D}{R^3}\right)\left(w+\frac{\partial v}{\partial \theta}\right)-\left(\frac{D}{R^2}\right)\frac{\partial \psi_\theta}{\partial \theta}+\nu E_p\frac{\partial u}{\partial x},$$

$$M_{x\theta} = \left(\frac{GI}{R}\right)\left(\frac{\partial v}{\partial x}+R\frac{\partial \psi_\theta}{\partial x}+\frac{\partial \psi_x}{\partial \theta}\right),$$

$$M_{\theta\theta} = \left(\frac{D}{R}\right)\frac{\partial \psi_\theta}{\partial \theta}-\left(\frac{D}{R^2}\right)\left(w+\frac{\partial v}{\partial \theta}\right)+D\nu\frac{\partial \psi_x}{\partial x},$$

$$Q_x = \kappa_x^2 Gh\left(\psi_x+\frac{\partial w}{\partial x}\right),$$

$$Q_\theta = \left(\kappa_\theta^2\frac{Gh}{R}\right)\left(1+\frac{h^2}{12R^2}\right)\left(\frac{\partial w}{\partial \theta}-v+R\psi_\theta\right), \tag{8.3.177}$$

where G is the shear modulus, $E_p = Eh/(1-\nu^2)$, $I = h^3/12$, and

$$D = Eh^3/12(1-\nu^2).$$

The resulting five displacement equations of motion, where body forces are omitted, are given by

$$\left\{E_p\frac{\partial^2}{\partial x^2}+\left(\frac{Gh}{R^2}\right)\left(1+\frac{I}{hR^2}\right)\frac{\partial^2}{\partial\theta^2}-\rho h\frac{\partial^2}{\partial t^2}\right\}u+$$
$$+\left\{\left(\frac{D}{R}\right)\frac{\partial^2}{\partial x^2}-\left(\frac{GI}{R^3}\right)\frac{\partial^2}{\partial\theta^2}-\left(\frac{\rho I}{R}\right)\frac{\partial^2}{\partial t^2}\right\}\psi_x+$$
$$+\left\{\left(\frac{E_p(1+\nu)}{2R}\right)\frac{\partial^2}{\partial x\,\partial\theta}\right\}v+\left\{\left(\frac{\nu E_p}{R}\right)\frac{\partial}{\partial x}\right\}w=0,$$

$$\left\{\left(\frac{D}{R}\right)\frac{\partial^2}{\partial x^2}-\left(\frac{GI}{R^3}\right)\frac{\partial^2}{\partial\theta^2}-\left(\frac{\rho I}{R}\right)\frac{\partial^2}{\partial t^2}\right\}u+$$
$$+\left\{D\frac{\partial^2}{\partial x^2}+\left(\frac{GI}{R^2}\right)\frac{\partial^2}{\partial\theta^2}-\kappa_x^2Gh-\rho I\frac{\partial^2}{\partial t^2}\right\}\psi_x+$$
$$+\left\{\left(\frac{D(1+\nu)}{2R}\right)\frac{\partial^2}{\partial x\,\partial\theta}\right\}\psi_\theta+\left(-\kappa_x^2Gh\frac{\partial}{\partial x}\right)w=0,$$

$$\left\{\left(\frac{E_p(1+\nu)}{2R}\right)\frac{\partial^2}{\partial x\,\partial\theta}\right\}u+$$
$$+\left\{Gh\frac{\partial^2}{\partial x^2}+\left(\frac{E_p}{R^2}+\frac{D}{R^4}\right)\frac{\partial^2}{\partial\theta^2}-\left(\kappa_\theta^2\frac{G}{R^2}\right)\left(h+\frac{I}{R^2}\right)-\rho h\frac{\partial^2}{\partial t^2}\right\}v+$$
$$+\left\{\left(\frac{GI}{R}\right)\frac{\partial^2}{\partial x^2}-\left(\frac{D}{R^3}\right)\frac{\partial^2}{\partial\theta^2}+\left(\kappa_\theta^2\frac{G}{R}\right)\left(h+\frac{I}{R^2}\right)-\left(\frac{\rho I}{R}\right)\frac{\partial^2}{\partial t^2}\right\}\psi_\theta+$$
$$+\left\{\frac{E_p}{R^2}+\frac{D}{R^4}+\left(\kappa_\theta^2\frac{G}{R^2}\right)\left(h+\frac{I}{R^2}\right)\right\}\frac{\partial w}{\partial\theta}=0,$$

$$\left\{\left(\frac{D(1+\nu)}{2R}\right)\frac{\partial^2}{\partial x\,\partial\theta}\right\}\psi_x+$$
$$+\left\{\left(\frac{GI}{R}\right)\frac{\partial^2}{\partial x^2}-\left(\frac{D}{R^3}\right)\frac{\partial^2}{\partial\theta^2}+\left(\kappa_\theta^2\frac{G}{R}\right)\left(h+\frac{I}{R^2}\right)-\left(\frac{\rho I}{R}\right)\frac{\partial^2}{\partial t^2}\right\}v+$$
$$+\left\{GI\frac{\partial^2}{\partial x^2}+\left(\frac{D}{R^2}\right)\frac{\partial^2}{\partial\theta^2}-\kappa_\theta^2G\left(h+\frac{I}{R^2}\right)-\rho I\frac{\partial^2}{\partial t^2}\right\}\psi_\theta+$$
$$+\left\{-\frac{D}{R^3}-\left(\kappa_\theta^2\frac{G}{R}\right)\left(h+\frac{I}{R^2}\right)\right\}\frac{\partial w}{\partial\theta}=0,$$

$$\left\{-\left(\frac{E_p\nu}{R}\right)\frac{\partial}{\partial x}\right\}u+\left\{\kappa_x^2Gh\frac{\partial}{\partial x}\right\}\psi_x+\left\{-\left(\kappa_\theta^2\frac{G}{R^2}\right)\left(h+\frac{I}{R^2}\right)-\left(\frac{E_p}{R^2}+\frac{D}{R^4}\right)\right\}\frac{\partial v}{\partial\theta}+$$
$$+\left\{\frac{D}{R^3}+\left(\kappa_\theta^2\frac{G}{R}\right)\left(h+\frac{I}{R^2}\right)\right\}\frac{\partial\psi_\theta}{\partial\theta}+$$
$$+\left\{\kappa_x^2Gh\frac{\partial^2}{\partial x^2}+\left(\kappa_\theta^2\frac{G}{R^2}\right)\left(h+\frac{I}{R^2}\right)\frac{\partial^2}{\partial\theta^2}-\left(\frac{E_p}{R^2}+\frac{D}{R^4}\right)-\rho h\frac{\partial^2}{\partial t^2}\right\}w=0. \quad (8.3.178)$$

Wave propagation is studied by considering solutions

$$\begin{aligned} u(x,\theta,t) &= U e^{i(\omega t-\alpha x)}\cos n\theta,\\ \psi_x(x,\theta,t) &= \psi e^{i(\omega t-\alpha x)}\cos n\theta,\\ v(x,\theta,t) &= V e^{i(\omega t-\alpha x)}\sin n\theta,\\ \psi_\theta(x,\theta,t) &= \Phi e^{i(\omega t-\alpha x)}\sin n\theta,\\ w(x,\theta,t) &= W e^{i(\omega t-\alpha x)}\cos n\theta. \end{aligned} \qquad (8.3.179)$$

Substitution in the equations of motion gives the frequency-equation determinant

$$\begin{vmatrix} A & B & C & 0 & D\\ B & E & 0 & F & G\\ C & 0 & H & J & K\\ 0 & F & J & L & M\\ D & G & K & M & W \end{vmatrix} = 0, \qquad (8.3.180)$$

where

$$\begin{aligned} A &= 4\pi^2\delta^2(s^2-2N)-m^2n^2(1+\tfrac{1}{12}m^2),\\ B &= \tfrac{1}{3}m\pi^2\delta^2(s^2-2N)+\tfrac{1}{12}m^3n^2,\\ C &= 2N\pi mn\delta(1+\nu)i,\\ D &= 4N\pi\nu m\delta i,\\ E &= \tfrac{1}{3}\pi^2\delta^2(s^2-2N)-\tfrac{1}{12}m^2n^2-\kappa_x^2,\\ F &= \tfrac{1}{6}Nmn\pi\delta(1+\nu)i,\\ G &= -2\kappa_x^2\pi\delta i,\\ H &= m^2(\kappa_\theta^2+2Nn^2)(1+\tfrac{1}{12}m^2)-4\pi^2\delta^2(s^2-1),\\ J &= -\tfrac{1}{3}m\pi^2\delta^2(s^2-1)-\kappa_\theta^2 m(1+\tfrac{1}{12}m^2)-\tfrac{1}{6}Nm^2n^2,\\ K &= m^2n(1+\tfrac{1}{12}m^2)(\kappa_\theta^2+2N),\\ L &= \kappa_\theta^2(1+\tfrac{1}{12}m^2)+\tfrac{1}{6}Nm^2n^2-\tfrac{1}{3}\pi^2\delta^2(s^2-1),\\ M &= -\kappa_\theta^2 mn(1+\tfrac{1}{12}m^2)-\tfrac{1}{6}Nm^3n,\\ W &= -4\pi^2\delta^2(s^2-\kappa_x^2)+m^2(1+\tfrac{1}{12}m^2)(\kappa_\theta^2 n^2+2N), \end{aligned} \qquad (8.3.181)$$

where

$$m = h/R,\quad N = 1/(1-\nu),\quad s = c/c_2,\quad \delta = h/L, \qquad (8.3.182)$$

and L is the wavelength, given by $2\pi/\alpha$. For the special case of axial symmetry, it is shown by the authors that the determinant degenerates into the product of two subdeterminants corresponding to pure torsional modes and to longitudinal modes. The adjustment coefficients κ_x, κ_θ are obtained by comparing the cutoff frequencies of the thickness shear modes in the axial and circumferential directions to those of exact theory.

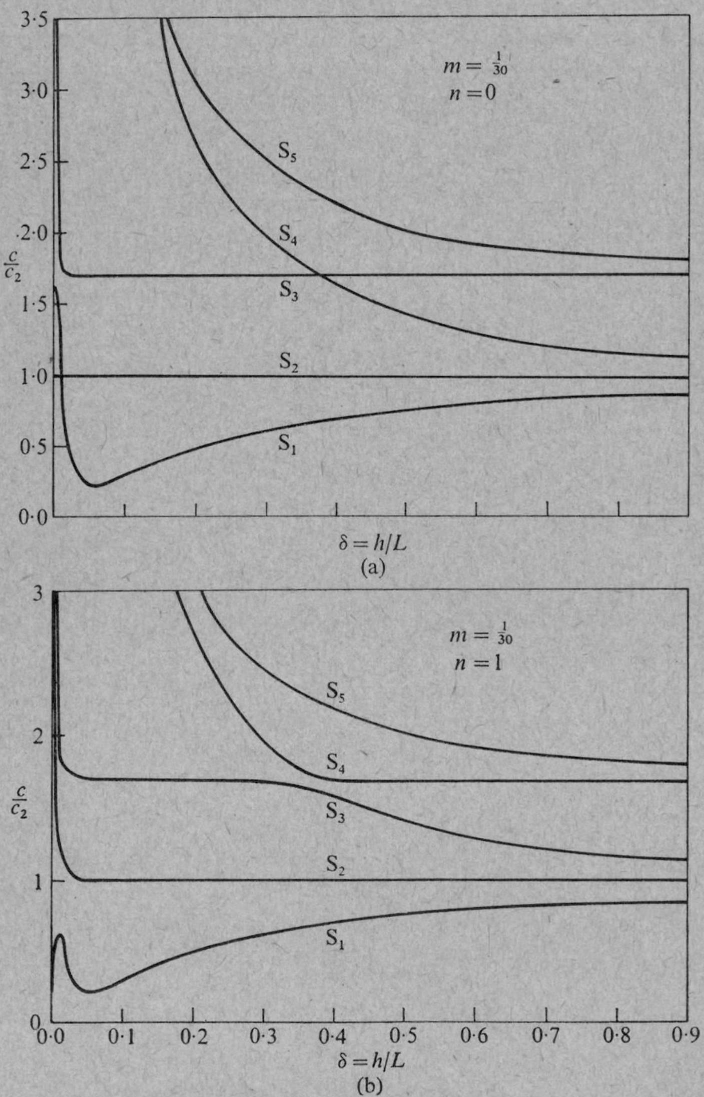

FIG. 8.31. Data on phase velocity versus wavenumber in a shell according to Mirsky–Herrmann theory for (a) $m = h/R = \frac{1}{30}$, $n = 0$; (b) $m = h/R = \frac{1}{30}$, $n = 1$. (After Herrmann and Mirsky [68, Figs. 1, 2].)

Results are presented by Mirsky and Herrmann for the axial phase velocity versus wavenumber for a number of situations, of which only two are shown in Fig. 8.31. The phase velocity is non-dimensionalized by the shear velocity c_2, while the wavenumber parameters δ is that defined by (8.3.182). Poisson's ratio is $\nu = 0{\cdot}3$ in all cases. In Fig. 8.31(a), the axisymmetric case ($n = 0$) is shown for a rather thin shell ($h/R = \frac{1}{30}$). The non-dispersive S_2 mode is associated with purely torsional motion, S_4 is the second torsional mode. The mode S_1 is longitudinal. Flexural motion ($n = 1$) is described by Fig. 8.31(b). All of the modes are now coupled.

2. *Naghdi–Cooper theory* [9, 72]. Again consider a cylindrical shell of thickness h and axial coordinate x. In this development, the circumferential coordinate is s, measured at the mid surface of the shell (this would be given by $s = R\theta$ in the Mirsky–Herrmann theory) and ζ is the coordinate directed radially outward from the mid surface (corresponding to z in the Mirsky–Herrmann development). The displacement kinematics are assumed to be

$$U_x = u_x(x, s, t) + \zeta\beta_x(x, s, t),$$
$$U_s = u_s(x, s, t) + \zeta\beta_s(x, s, t), \qquad (8.3.183)$$
$$U_\zeta = w(x, s, t),$$

which are the same form as (8.3.175).

Cooper and Naghdi have developed the governing equations based on a variational theorem by Reissner [81]. The resulting stress equations of motion are found to be

$$\frac{\partial N_x}{\partial x} + \frac{\partial N_{sx}}{\partial s} = \rho h \frac{\partial^2 u_x}{\partial t^2} + \frac{\rho h^3}{12a}\frac{\partial^2 \beta_x}{\partial t^2},$$

$$\frac{\partial N_{xs}}{\partial x} + \frac{\partial N_s}{\partial s} + \frac{V_s}{a} = \rho h \frac{\partial^2 u_s}{\partial t^2} + \frac{\rho h^3}{12a}\frac{\partial^2 \beta_s}{\partial t^2},$$

$$\frac{\partial V_x}{\partial x} + \frac{\partial V_s}{\partial s} - \frac{N_s}{a} = \rho h \frac{\partial^2 w}{\partial t^2}, \qquad (8.3.184)$$

$$\frac{\partial M_x}{\partial x} + \frac{\partial M_{sx}}{\partial s} - V_x = \rho \frac{h^3}{12}\left(\frac{\partial^2 \beta_x}{\partial t^2} + \frac{1}{a}\frac{\partial^2 u_x}{\partial t^2}\right),$$

$$\frac{\partial M_{xs}}{\partial x} + \frac{\partial M_s}{\partial s} - V_s = \rho \frac{h^3}{12}\left(\frac{\partial^2 \beta_s}{\partial t^2} + \frac{1}{a}\frac{\partial^2 u_s}{\partial t^2}\right),$$

where the shell stress–displacement equations are given by

$$
\begin{aligned}
N_x &= C\left[\left\{\frac{\partial u_x}{\partial x}+\nu\left(\frac{\partial u_s}{\partial s}+\frac{w}{a}\right)\right\}+\frac{h^2}{12a}\frac{\partial \beta_x}{\partial x}\right],\\
N_s &= C\left[\left\{\left(\frac{\partial u_s}{\partial s}+\frac{w}{a}\right)+\nu\frac{\partial u_x}{\partial x}\right\}-\frac{h^2}{12a}\frac{\partial \beta_s}{\partial s}\right],\\
N_{xs} &= \frac{(1-\nu)}{2}C\left\{\left(\frac{\partial u_x}{\partial s}+\frac{\partial u_s}{\partial x}\right)+\frac{h^2}{12a}\frac{\partial \beta_s}{\partial x}\right\},\\
N_{sx} &= \frac{(1-\nu)}{2}C\left\{\left(\frac{\partial u_x}{\partial s}+\frac{\partial u_s}{\partial x}\right)+\frac{h^2}{12a}\left(\frac{1}{a}\frac{\partial u_x}{\partial s}-\frac{\partial \beta_x}{\partial s}\right)\right\},\\
M_x &= D\left\{\left(\frac{\partial \beta_x}{\partial x}+\nu\frac{\partial \beta_s}{\partial s}\right)+\frac{1}{a}\frac{\partial u_x}{\partial x}\right\},\\
M_s &= D\left\{\left(\frac{\partial \beta_s}{\partial s}+\nu\frac{\partial \beta_x}{\partial x}\right)-\frac{1}{a}\left(\frac{\partial u_s}{\partial s}+\frac{w}{a}\right)\right\},\\
M_{xs} &= \frac{(1-\nu)}{2}D\left\{\left(\frac{\partial \beta_x}{\partial s}+\frac{\partial \beta_s}{\partial x}\right)+\frac{1}{a}\frac{\partial u_s}{\partial x}\right\},\\
M_{sx} &= \frac{(1-\nu)}{2}D\left\{\left(\frac{\partial \beta_x}{\partial s}+\frac{\partial \beta_s}{\partial x}\right)-\frac{1}{a}\frac{\partial u_x}{\partial s}\right\},\\
V_x &= \kappa Gh\left(\frac{\partial w}{\partial x}+\beta_x\right),\\
V_s &= \kappa Gh\left\{\frac{\partial w}{\partial s}-\left(\frac{u_s}{a}-\beta_s\right)\right\},
\end{aligned}
\tag{8.3.185}
$$

where a is the mean radius of the shell, ρ, E, G, ν are the material constants, $D = Eh^3/12(1-\nu^2)$ and $C = Eh/(1-\nu^2)$. Only a single adjustment coefficient is present in the theory. The resulting displacement equations of motion, referred to as System (I) by the authors, are given by

$$
\begin{aligned}
&\frac{\partial^2 u_x}{\partial x^2}+\frac{(1-\nu)}{2}\left(1+\frac{h^2}{12a^2}\right)\frac{\partial^2 u_x}{\partial s^2}+\frac{(1+\nu)}{2}\frac{\partial^2 u_s}{\partial x\,\partial s}+\frac{\nu}{a}\frac{\partial w}{\partial x}+\\
&\qquad+\frac{h^2}{12a}\left\{\frac{\partial^2 \beta_x}{\partial x^2}-\frac{(1-\nu)}{2}\frac{\partial^2 \beta_x}{\partial s^2}\right\}-\gamma^2\frac{\partial^2}{\partial t^2}\left(u_x+\frac{h^2}{12a}\beta_x\right)=0,\\
&\frac{\partial^2 u_s}{\partial s^2}+\frac{(1-\nu)}{2}\frac{\partial^2 u_s}{\partial x^2}+\frac{(1+\nu)}{2}\frac{\partial^2 u_x}{\partial x\,\partial s}+\frac{1}{a}\frac{\partial w}{\partial s}+\frac{\kappa_1}{a}\left(\beta_s-\frac{u_s}{a}+\frac{\partial w}{\partial s}\right)-\\
&\qquad-\frac{h^2}{12a}\left\{\frac{\partial^2 \beta_s}{\partial s^2}-\frac{(1-\nu)}{2}\frac{\partial^2 \beta_s}{\partial x^2}\right\}-\gamma^2\frac{\partial^2}{\partial t^2}\left(u_s+\frac{h^2}{12a}\beta_s\right)=0,\\
&\kappa_1\left(\nabla^2 w+\frac{\partial \beta_x}{\partial x}+\frac{\partial \beta_s}{\partial s}-\frac{1}{a}\frac{\partial u_s}{\partial s}\right)-\frac{1}{a}\left(\frac{\partial u_s}{\partial s}+\frac{w}{a}+\nu\frac{\partial u_x}{\partial x}\right)+\frac{h^2}{12a^2}\frac{\partial \beta_s}{\partial s}-\gamma^2\frac{\partial^2 w}{\partial t^2}=0,
\end{aligned}
\tag{8.3.186}
$$

$$\frac{h^2}{12}\left\{\frac{\partial^2\beta_x}{\partial x^2}+\frac{(1-\nu)}{2}\frac{\partial^2\beta_x}{\partial s^2}+\frac{(1+\nu)}{2}\frac{\partial^2\beta_s}{\partial x\,\partial s}\right\}-$$

$$-\kappa_1\left(\frac{\partial w}{\partial x}+\beta_x\right)+\frac{h^2}{12a}\left\{\frac{\partial^2 u_x}{\partial x^2}-\frac{(1-\nu)}{2}\frac{\partial^2 u_x}{\partial s^2}\right\}-\gamma^2\frac{h^2}{12}\frac{\partial^2}{\partial t^2}\left(\beta_x+\frac{u_x}{a}\right)=0,$$

$$\frac{h^2}{12}\left\{\frac{\partial^2\beta_s}{\partial s^2}+\frac{(1-\nu)}{2}\frac{\partial^2\beta_s}{\partial x^2}+\frac{(1+\nu)}{2}\frac{\partial^2\beta_x}{\partial x\,\partial s}\right\}-\kappa_1\left(\frac{\partial w}{\partial s}+\beta_s-\frac{u_s}{a}\right)-$$

$$-\frac{h^2}{12a}\left\{\frac{\partial^2 u_s}{\partial s^2}-\frac{(1-\nu)}{2}\frac{\partial^2 u_s}{\partial x^2}+\frac{1}{a}\frac{\partial w}{\partial s}\right\}-\gamma^2\frac{h^2}{12}\frac{\partial^2}{\partial t^2}\left(\beta_s+\frac{u_s}{a}\right)=0,$$

where

$$\nabla^2=\frac{\partial^2}{\partial x^2}+\frac{\partial^2}{\partial s^2},\qquad \gamma^2=\frac{(1-\nu^2)\rho}{E},\qquad \kappa_1=\frac{(1-\nu)\kappa}{2}. \tag{8.3.187}$$

When the effects of shear deformation and rotary inertia are neglected in the development of the System (I) equations, Love's equations for the shell are recovered.

An alternate set of shell equations is then presented by the authors, called System (II), with the intent that, when shear effects and rotary inertia are neglected, the more convenient shell equations of Donnell will be recovered. The simplification procedure involves neglecting certain displacement contributions, certain middle surface strains, and certain terms in h^2/a. The resulting shell stress–displacement equations are

$$N_x=C\left\{\frac{\partial u_x}{\partial x}+\nu\left(\frac{\partial u_s}{\partial s}+\frac{w}{a}\right)\right\},\qquad N_s=C\left\{\left(\frac{\partial u_s}{\partial s}+\frac{w}{a}\right)+\nu\frac{\partial u_x}{\partial x}\right\},$$

$$N_{xs}=N_{sx}=Gh\left(\frac{\partial u_x}{\partial s}+\frac{\partial u_s}{\partial x}\right),$$

$$M_x=D\left(\frac{\partial\beta_x}{\partial x}+\nu\frac{\partial\beta_s}{\partial s}\right),\qquad M_s=D\left(\frac{\partial\beta_s}{\partial s}+\nu\frac{\partial\beta_x}{\partial x}\right), \tag{8.3.188}$$

$$M_{xs}=M_{sx}=\frac{(1-\nu)}{2}D\left(\frac{\partial\beta_x}{\partial s}+\frac{\partial\beta_s}{\partial x}\right),$$

$$V_x=\kappa Gh\left(\frac{\partial w}{\partial x}+\beta x\right),\qquad V_s=\kappa Gh\left(\frac{\partial w}{\partial s}+\beta_s\right).$$

Certain additional minor adjustments are made in the displacement equations of motion (8.3.186) before substituting the preceding to give the System (II) equations

$$\frac{\partial^2 u_x}{\partial x^2}+\frac{(1-\nu)}{2}\frac{\partial^2 u_x}{\partial s^2}+\frac{(1+\nu)}{2}\frac{\partial^2 u_s}{\partial x\,\partial s}+\frac{\nu}{a}\frac{\partial w}{\partial x}-\gamma^2\frac{\partial^2 u_x}{\partial t^2}=0,$$

$$\frac{\partial^2 u_s}{\partial s^2}+\frac{(1-\nu)}{2}\frac{\partial^2 u_s}{\partial x^2}+\frac{(1+\nu)}{2}\frac{\partial^2 u_x}{\partial x\,\partial s}+\frac{1}{a}\frac{\partial w}{\partial s}-\gamma^2\frac{\partial^2 u_s}{\partial t^2}=0,$$

$$\kappa_1\left(\nabla^2 w+\frac{\partial \beta_x}{\partial x}+\frac{\partial \beta_s}{\partial s}\right)-\frac{1}{a}\left(\frac{\partial u_s}{\partial s}+\frac{w}{a}+\nu\frac{\partial u_x}{\partial x}\right)-\gamma^2\frac{\partial^2 w}{\partial t^2}=0, \tag{8.3.189}$$

$$\frac{h^2}{12}\left\{\frac{\partial^2 \beta_x}{\partial x^2}+\frac{(1-\nu)}{2}\frac{\partial^2 \beta_x}{\partial s^2}+\frac{(1+\nu)}{2}\frac{\partial^2 \beta_s}{\partial x\,\partial s}\right\}-\kappa_1\left(\frac{\partial w}{\partial x}+\beta_x\right)-\gamma^2\frac{h^2}{12}\frac{\partial^2 \beta_x}{\partial t^2}=0,$$

$$\frac{h^2}{12}\left\{\frac{\partial^2 \beta_s}{\partial s^2}+\frac{(1-\nu)}{2}\frac{\partial^2 \beta_s}{\partial x^2}+\frac{(1+\nu)}{2}\frac{\partial^2 \beta_x}{\partial x\,\partial s}\right\}-\kappa_1\left(\frac{\partial w}{\partial s}+\beta_s\right)-\gamma^2\frac{h^2}{12}\frac{\partial^2 \beta_s}{\partial t^2}=0.$$

The case of axially symmetric torsion-free wave propagation is considered in Reference [72]. Dispersion relations are obtained by considering propagating harmonic waves

$$\begin{bmatrix} u_x \\ \beta_x \\ w \end{bmatrix}=\begin{bmatrix} A' \\ B' \\ C' \end{bmatrix}\exp\{i(mx-pt)\}, \tag{8.3.190}$$

and substituting in the various equations of motion, appropriately simplified by letting $u_s=\beta_s=\partial/\partial s=0$. Dispersion equations are obtained for the System (I), System (II), and the Donnell equations, called System (III). The value of the adjustment coefficient is $\kappa_1=\frac{5}{6}$ and is, according to Naghdi and Cooper, 'a natural consequence of the consistent assumptions for the stresses and displacements employed in Reissner's variational theorem'. The resulting dispersion curves for the axially symmetric motion as given by the three systems of equations mentioned are shown in Fig. 8.32 for a Poisson's ratio of $\nu = 0{\cdot}3$ and a single value of the ratio h/a. The non-dimensional velocity is given by c/c_p, where c_p is the longitudinal thin plate velocity,

$$c_p=\{E/\rho(1-\nu^2)^{\frac{1}{2}}\}.$$

The wavelength is λ. Using the System (I) and (II) equations, Cooper and Naghdi [9] also studied the propagation of torsional waves and of non-axially symmetric waves.

3. *Greenspon's comparisons.* As previously mentioned, Greenspon [23] made a comparison of the results for several theories of waves in cylindrical shells. The theories included not only those just reviewed, but results from exact theory, membrane theory, and several bending theories. The discussion pertains to theories and contribution by Rayleigh [79] and Baron and

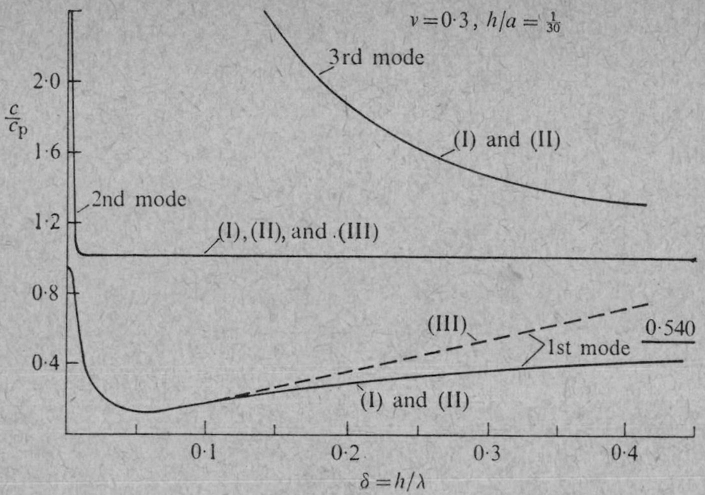

FIG. 8.32. Dispersion curves for axially symmetric waves in a shell according to Naghdi–Cooper theory for $h/a = \frac{1}{30}$. (After Naghdi and Cooper [72, Fig. 1(a)].)

Bleich [4] in the field of membrane shells, Love [43], Flugge [15], Arnold and Warburton [3], and Kennard [34] in the field of shell-bending theories, and the works of Mirsky and Herrmann [68], [69], Lin and Morgan [42], Yu [90], and Cooper and Naghdi [9, 72] for thick-shell (shear-deformation) theories.

The results of the comparisons are presented as dispersion curves and frequency spectra for various values of n, for a Poisson's ratio of $\nu = 0{\cdot}3$. The dimensionless velocity, frequency, and wavenumbers are respectively

$$\bar{c} = c/c_2, \qquad \Omega = \omega a_0/c_p, \qquad \beta = 2\pi a_0/\lambda, \tag{8.3.191}$$

where a_0 is the outside radius of the shell and λ is the wavelength. Also defined is the thickness ratio α, where

$$\alpha = a_i/a_0, \tag{8.3.192}$$

and a_i is the inner radius of the shell. A portion of the results of the comparison are given in Fig. 8.33. The rather elaborate code for identifying the various theories and contributions is given in conjunction with the figure.

4. *The theory of McNiven et al.* [47]. The thick-shell theories put forth by Mirsky and Herrmann, Naghdi and Cooper, and others contain shear-deformation effects. By invoking more elaborate assumptions on the deformation kinematics, higher-order shell theories are obtainable. McNiven *et al.* have presented a higher-order approximate theory for axisymmetric motions in cylindrical shells. The development is quite similar in spirit to that of Mindlin and Medick [66] for plates and Mindlin and McNiven [65] for rods. It contains the first three axisymmetric modes,

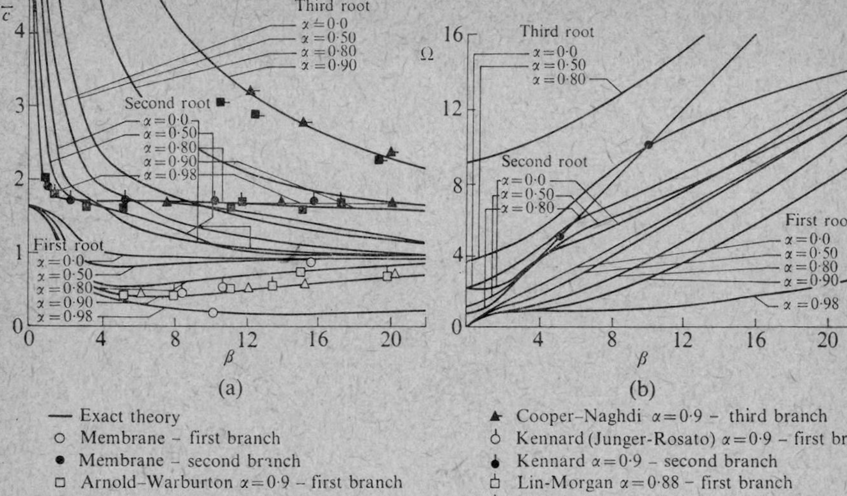

FIG. 8.33. Comparison of (a) dispersion curves and (b) frequency spectra for waves in shells according to various theories for $n = 0$ (axially symmetric case). (After Greenspon [23, Fig. 1].)

comprising the longitudinal, first radial, and first axial shear modes. Adjustment coefficients (four in number) are introduced and evaluated by matching the frequency spectrum of the approximate theory to that of the exact theory at the cutoff frequencies.

The real branches of the resulting frequency spectrum are shown in Fig. 8.34 for various cases. The non-dimensional frequency Ω and wavenumber ζ are given by

$$\Omega = \omega h/\pi c_2, \qquad \zeta = h\xi/2\pi, \tag{8.3.193}$$

where h is the shell thickness. The parameter a^* is the ratio of outer to inner radius, $a^* = b/a$. Thus the results are for various thickness–curvature ratios and for two values of Poisson's ratio. The approximate theory is indicated by the dashed lines. The first three modes of exact theory are shown by the solid lines, the fourth mode of exact theory by dot–dashed line. The behaviour of the imaginary and complex branches were also determined by McNiven *et al.* [47].

8.4. Forced motion of plates and rods

The objective in this section is to consider a limited number of problems in the forced motion of elastic plates and rods. The exact analysis of a simple problem in SH waves in plates and a qualitative analysis of longitudinal waves

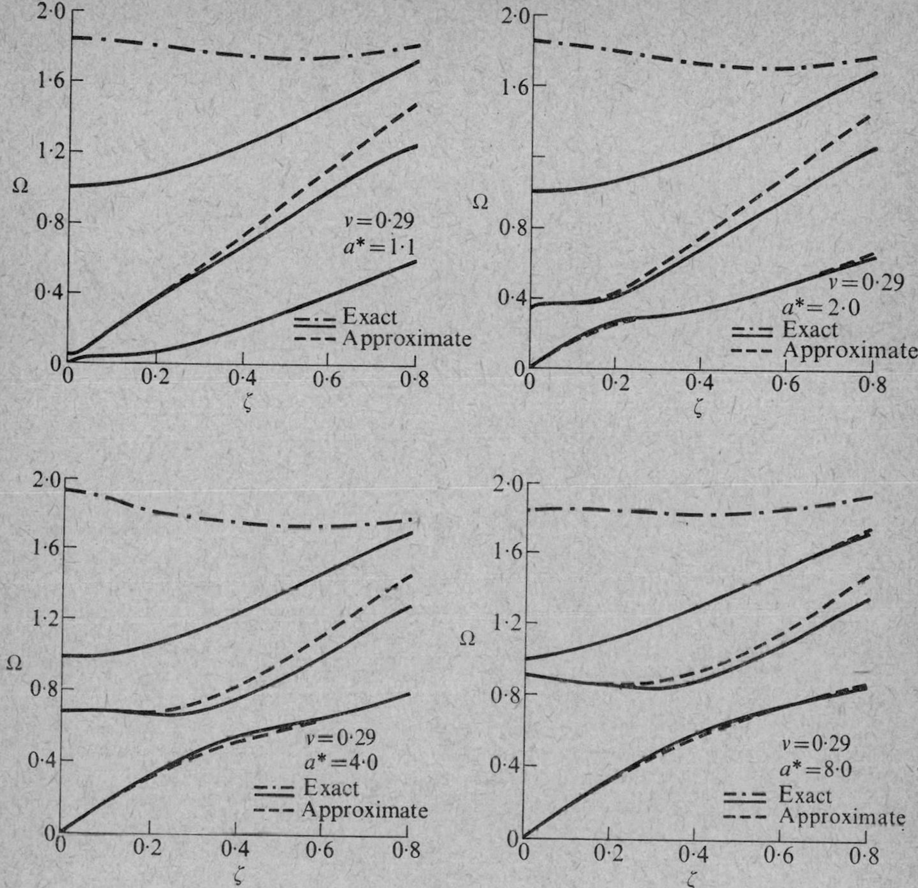

FIG. 8.34. Frequency spectra for axially symmetric waves in a shell according to the theory of McNiven *et al.* for various curvatures and Poisson's ratio = 0·29. (After McNiven *et al.* [47, Part I, Fig. 3].)

in rods will enable a general understanding of wave propagation in these structures to be obtained. The rather large class of problems involving the mathematical analysis of transient pulse propagation in plates and rods will then be discussed. However, analysis in this area, generally involving extensions of the saddle-point method presented in an earlier chapter, is rather complex. Attention will be confined mainly to presenting the results, in terms of stress waveforms, obtained by many contributors in this area.

8.4.1. *SH waves in a plate*

The case of SH waves has served well in several past situations to illustrate basic aspects of propagation or analysis, unobscured by the complicating effects due to mode conversion occurring from P and SV wave interactions with a surface. This will again be the case. Thus, consider a semi-infinite plate, defined by $y = \pm b$, $x \geqslant 0$, traction-free on the surfaces $y = \pm b$ and subjected to the end stress $\tau_{zx}(0, y, t)$. Such a loading will excite only SH waves in this geometry. Two basic problems will be considered, one involving harmonic loading and the second involving transient loading and homogeneous initial conditions.

1. *Harmonic SH waves.* The case of pure SH waves, polarized in the z direction, we know to be governed by the scalar wave equation in the u_z displacement

$$\nabla^2 u_z(x, y, t) = \frac{1}{c_2^2}\frac{\partial^2 u_z(x, y, t)}{\partial t^2}. \tag{8.4.1}$$

The boundary conditions for the problem are

$$\tau_{yz} = 0, \qquad y = \pm b, \qquad \tau_{xz}(0, y, t) = \tau(y)\mathrm{e}^{-\mathrm{i}\omega t}. \tag{8.4.2}$$

Also $\tau_{yy} = \tau_{xy} = 0$ on $y = \pm b$, but these are identically satisfied for SH waves.

Consider a solution

$$u_z(x, y, t) = U(x, y)\mathrm{e}^{-\mathrm{i}\omega t}, \tag{8.4.3}$$

and obtain, upon substituting in (8.4.1),

$$\nabla^2 U + k^2 U = 0, \qquad k^2 = \omega^2/c_2^2. \tag{8.4.4}$$

A separation of variables $U = X(x)Y(y)$ used in the preceding gives

$$\mathrm{d}X^2/\mathrm{d}x^2 + k^2 XY = -\mathrm{d}^2 Y/\mathrm{d}y^2 = \alpha^2. \tag{8.4.5}$$

For the y variable there results

$$Y = A \sin \alpha y + B \cos \alpha y. \tag{8.4.6}$$

The first boundary condition of (8.4.2) reduces simply to $\mathrm{d}Y/\mathrm{d}y = 0$, $y = \pm b$. The solution (8.4.6) thus becomes

$$Y_n = A_n \sin \alpha_n y + B_n \cos \alpha_n y, \quad \alpha_n = n\pi/2b \qquad (n = 0, 1, 2, \ldots). \tag{8.4.7}$$

The x variation becomes

$$\mathrm{d}^2 X_n/\mathrm{d}x^2 + \xi_n^2 X_n = 0, \qquad \xi_n^2 = k^2 - \alpha_n^2, \tag{8.4.8}$$

which has the solution, for $\xi_n^2 > 0$, of

$$X_n = C_n \exp(\mathrm{i}\xi_n x) + D_n \exp(-\mathrm{i}\xi_n x). \tag{8.4.9}$$

For $\xi_n^2 < 0$, we have

$$X_n = C_n' \exp(-\xi_n' x) + D_n' \exp(\xi_n' x). \tag{8.4.10}$$

We set $D_n = D_n' = 0$ since the D_n term violates the radiation condition for

$\xi_n^2 > 0$ and D'_n gives exponentially increasing displacements for $\xi_n^2 < 0$. The complete solution may then be written as

$$u_z(x, y, t) = \frac{B_0}{2}\exp\{i(\xi_0 x - \omega t)\} + \\ + \sum_{n=1}^{N}(A_n \sin \alpha_n y + B_n \cos \alpha_n y)\exp\{i(\xi_n x - \omega t)\} + \\ + \sum_{N+1}^{\infty}(A'_n \sin \alpha_n y + B'_n \cos \alpha_n y)\exp(-\xi'_n x)\exp(-i\omega t), \quad (8.4.11)$$

where

$$n < N, \quad \xi_n^2 > 0, \\ n \geq N, \quad \xi_n^2 < 0. \quad (8.4.12)$$

The A_n, B_n, A'_n, B'_n are determined from the boundary conditions at $x = 0$, given by the second of (8.4.2). Thus, we have that $\tau_{xz}(x, y, t) = (\mu/2)\partial u_z/\partial x$, leading to

$$\tau(y) = \frac{\mu}{2}\left\{i\frac{B_0\xi_0}{2} + i\sum_{n=1}^{N}\xi_n(A_n \sin \alpha_n y + B_n \cos \alpha_n y) - \\ - \sum_{N+1}^{\infty}\xi'_n(A'_n \sin \alpha_n y + B'_n \cos \alpha_n y)\right\}. \quad (8.4.13)$$

Multiplying both sides of (8.4.13) by $\sin \alpha_n y$ or $\cos \alpha_n y$ and integrating over the interval $-b \leqslant y \leqslant b$ gives

$$A_n = \frac{2}{i\mu b\xi_n}\int_{-b}^{b}\tau(y)\sin \alpha_n y \, dy, \\ A'_n = -\frac{2}{\mu b\xi'_n}\int_{-b}^{b}\tau(y)\sin \alpha_n y \, dy, \\ B_n = \frac{2}{i\mu b\xi_n}\int_{-b}^{b}\tau(y)\cos \alpha_n y \, dy, \\ B'_n = -\frac{2}{\mu b\xi'_n}\int_{-b}^{b}\tau(y)\cos \alpha_n y \, dy. \quad (8.4.14)$$

Let us now interpret the solution (8.4.13), with coefficients given by (8.4.14). This can best be done by also referring to the frequency spectrum for SH waves in a plate, given by Fig. 8.3. Each branch of the spectrum corresponds to a specific mode of propagation. Suppose that the driving frequency ω is such that

$$3 < \Omega < 4. \tag{8.4.15}$$

We recall that $\Omega = 2b\omega/\pi c_2$ is the non-dimensional frequency used in the figure. It is seen for this frequency range that four propagating modes ($n = 0, 1, 2, 3$) are capable of being exciting. All of the non-propagating modes (those with imaginary wavenumber) for $n \geqslant 4$ are capable of being excited. In the solution (8.4.13), the A_n, B_n are associated with the propagating modes, the A'_n, B'_n with the non-propagating modes. The degree to which a given mode is excited will depend on the amplitude coefficients which will in turn depend on the stress distribution $\tau(y)$. We note that the A'_n, B'_n are spatially decaying modes, so that, far from the end of the plate, their effect would not be felt† and only the propagating modes would contribute.

Suppose, as a simple example, that

$$\tau(0, y, t) = \tau_0 e^{-i\omega t}. \tag{8.4.16}$$

Then $A_n = B_n = A'_n = B'_n = 0$, $n \neq 0$ and we have $B_0 = 2\tau_0/i\mu b\xi_0$, so that

$$u_z(x, y, t) = \frac{\tau_0}{i\mu b\xi_0} \exp\{i(\xi_0 x - \omega t)\}, \tag{8.4.17}$$

where $\xi_0^2 = \omega^2/c_2^2$. For this particular example, only the lowest mode, which happens to be non-dispersive, is excited.

As a second simple example, suppose that

$$\tau_{xz}(0, y, t) = \tau(y)e^{-i\omega t}, \tag{8.4.18}$$

where $\tau(y)$ is symmetric with respect to y and ω is such that $2 < \Omega < 3$. Owing to the symmetry, $A_n = A'_n = 0$. Furthermore, only B_0, B_2 will be propagating for the given frequency range. Thus

$$u_z(x, y, t) = \frac{B_0}{2} \exp\{i(\xi_0 x - \omega t)\} + B_2 \cos \alpha_2 y \exp\{i(\xi_2 x - \omega t)\} +$$
$$+ \sum_{n=4,6,\ldots}^{\infty} B'_n \cos \alpha_n y \exp(-\xi'_n x)\exp(-i\omega t). \tag{8.4.19}$$

2. *Transient SH waves*. Suppose now that a transient disturbance is applied to the end of the plate such that

$$\tau_{xz}(0, y, t) = g(y)h(t),$$
$$u_z(x, y, 0) = \partial u_z(x, y, 0)/\partial t = 0. \tag{8.4.20}$$

Applying the Laplace transform to the governing eqn (8.4.1) gives

$$\nabla^2 \bar{u}_z(x, y, s) - \frac{s^2}{c_2^2}\bar{u}_z(x, y, s) = 0. \tag{8.4.21}$$

† This is somewhat too general a statement. Thus, if $\Omega \to 4$ (for example), the decay constant becomes quite small ($\xi'_n \sim 0$) and the decay distance can become appreciable. See, for example, Torvik [88].

Again using separation of variables $\bar{u}_z = \bar{X}(x, s)Y(y)$ gives

$$Y_n(y) = A_n \sin \alpha_n y + B_n \cos \alpha_n y, \quad \alpha_n = n\pi/2b, \tag{8.4.22}$$

and, for the governing equation for $\bar{X}(x, s)$,

$$\frac{d^2\bar{X}}{dx^2} - \xi_n^2 \bar{X} = 0, \qquad \xi_n^2 = \frac{s^2}{c_2^2} + \alpha_n^2. \tag{8.4.23}$$

This has the solution

$$\bar{X} = C \exp(\xi_n x) + D \exp(-\xi_n x). \tag{8.4.24}$$

We require $C = 0$ on the basis of the increasing exponential behaviour associated with that term. The solution may now be written as

$$\bar{u}_z(x, y, s) = \frac{B_0}{2} \exp(-\xi_0 x) + \sum_{n=1}^{\infty} (A_n \sin \alpha_n y + B_n \cos \alpha_n y) \exp(-\xi_n x). \tag{8.4.25}$$

The solution coefficients may be determined from the boundary conditions of (8.4.20). Thus we have

$$\bar{\tau}_{xz}(0, y, s) = \frac{\mu}{2} \frac{\partial \bar{u}_z(0, y, s)}{\partial x} = g(y)\bar{h}(s). \tag{8.4.26}$$

Substituting (8.4.25) in the last gives

$$g(y)\bar{h}(s) = -\frac{\mu}{2}\left\{\frac{\xi_0 B_0}{2} + \sum_{n=1}^{\infty} \xi_n (A_n \sin \alpha_n y + B_n \cos \alpha_n y)\right\}. \tag{8.4.27}$$

From this, the coefficients A_n, B_n are found to be

$$A_n = -\frac{2\bar{h}(s)}{\mu \xi_n} \int_{-b}^{b} g(y) \sin \alpha_n y \, dy,$$

$$B_n = -\frac{2\bar{h}(s)}{\mu \xi_n} \int_{-b}^{b} g(y) \cos \alpha_n y \, dy. \tag{8.4.28}$$

Designating the integrals as

$$a_n = \int_{-b}^{b} g(y) \sin \alpha_n y \, dy, \qquad b_n = \int_{-b}^{b} g(y) \cos \alpha_n y \, dy, \tag{8.4.29}$$

we have the transformed solution given by

$$\bar{u}_z(x, y, s) = -\frac{2\bar{h}(s)}{\mu}\left\{\frac{b_0 \exp(-\xi_0 x)}{2\xi_0} + \sum_{n=1}^{\infty} (a_n \sin \alpha_n y + b_n \cos \alpha_n y) \frac{\exp(-\xi_n x)}{\xi_n}\right\}. \tag{8.4.30}$$

The Laplace inversion is obtained from the typical term

$$\mathscr{L}^{-1}\left\{\frac{\bar{h}(s)\exp(-\xi_n x)}{\xi_n}\right\}. \tag{8.4.31}$$

We note from Laplace transform tables† that

$$f_n(t) = \mathscr{L}^{-1}\left\{\frac{\exp(-\xi_n x)}{\xi_n}\right\} = \begin{cases} 0, & 0 < t < x/c_2 \\ c_2 J_0\{\alpha_n c_2(t^2 - x^2/c_2^2)^{\frac{1}{2}}\}, & x/c_2 < t < \infty. \end{cases} \tag{8.4.32}$$

For an arbitrary time variation $h(t)$, the final inversion would have to be expressed in terms of the convolution integral. Thus

$$u_z(x, y, t) = -\frac{2}{\mu}\left\{\frac{b_0}{2}\int\limits_0^t h(t-\tau)f_0(\tau)\,d\tau + \right.$$

$$\left. + \sum_{n=1}^{\infty}(a_n \sin\alpha_n y + b_n \cos\alpha_n y)\int\limits_0^t h(t-\tau)f_n(\tau)\,d\tau\right\}. \tag{8.4.33}$$

A simple evaluation of this integral is possible only for special values of $h(t)$. Thus, suppose $h(t) = \delta(t)$. Then we have

$$u_z(x, y, t) = -\frac{2}{\mu}\left\{\frac{b_0}{2}f_0(t) + \sum_{n=1}^{\infty}(a_n \sin\alpha_n y + b_n \cos\alpha_n y)f_n(t)\right\}. \tag{8.4.34}$$

The main objective in this analysis of SH wave propagation is to show how the nature of the propagation in a plate or rod can be affected by two aspects of the input: first, the spatial distribution of the exciting stress determines the degree to which various modes may or may not be excited and, second, the time variation of the excitation determines which of the excited modes may be propagating and which non-propagating.

8.4.2. *Pulse propagation in an infinite rod*

While the theoretical analysis of pulse propagation in rods and plates is generally quite complicated, by using stationary-phase and group-velocity concepts, it is possible to obtain a qualitative understanding of the action. We now consider the case of an initial pulse applied to an infinitely long rod, and closely follow the original arguments of Davies [11] for this case.

1. *Basic stationary-phase argument.* Assuming that at $t = 0$ the initial pulse consists of a Fourier superposition of continuous harmonic waves then, for $t > 0$, the dispersion of the various frequency components will distort the

† See, for example, Churchill [8, Appendix 3].

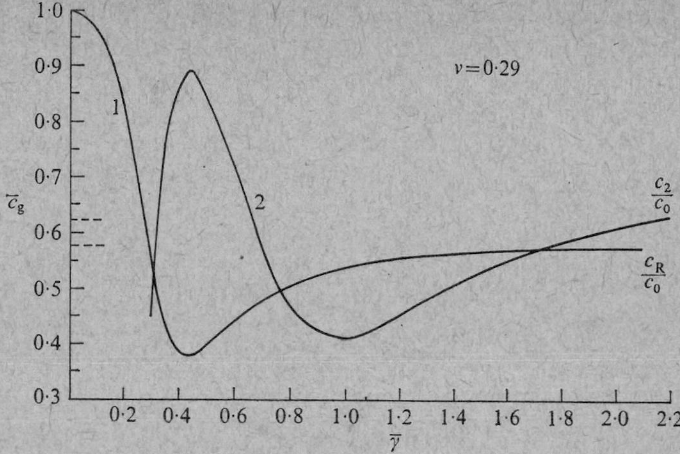

FIG. 8.35. Group velocity versus wavenumber for the first two longitudinal modes of a circular rod. (After Davies [11, Fig. 13].)

pulse, as has been discussed in earlier sections. According to stationary-phase arguments, the dominant components of the disturbance at a point x and time t will satisfy the condition that the phase ϕ is stationary, where

$$\phi = \gamma x - \omega t. \tag{8.4.35}$$

By differentiating, this may be shown to be equivalent to† $c_g(\omega) = x/t$. Thus for a given value of x and at a given time t, the frequency of the disturbance will be such that $c_g(\omega) = x/t$.

2. *Construction of period, c_g curves.* In order to determine the variation in the disturbance with time at a given location, it is useful to plot the period of the disturbance as a function of x/t. The procedure for obtaining this plot will be as follows:

(a) for a given $t/x = 1/c_g$, determine the value of γ corresponding to c_g;
(b) determine the value of phase velocity c, corresponding to γ;
(c) the period T, will be given by $T = 2\pi/\gamma c$.

Now, the dispersion curves for the first three rod modes were given earlier by Fig. 8.16. The group-velocity curves for the first two modes are given in Fig. 8.35. The non-dimensional velocities and wavenumbers are given by

$$\bar{c}_g = c_g/c_0, \qquad \bar{c} = c/c_0, \qquad \bar{\gamma} = a\gamma/2\pi, \tag{8.4.36}$$

† See Chapter 1, § 6.

where c_0 is the bar velocity, $c_0 = (E/\rho)^{\frac{1}{2}}$. Further, we introduce the non-dimensional distance $\bar{x}$, time $\bar{t}$, and period $\bar{T}$, where

$$\bar{x} = x/a, \qquad \bar{t} = t/T_a, \qquad \bar{T} = T/T_a, \tag{8.4.37}$$

where a is the bar radius and $T_a = a/c_0$. With these, the basic relationship between group velocity, distance, and time becomes

$$\bar{c}_g = \bar{x}/\bar{t}. \tag{8.4.38}$$

Considering the first mode, it is seen that $0{\cdot}38 < \bar{c}_g < 1{\cdot}0$. It follows that $1{\cdot}0 < \bar{t}/\bar{x} < 2{\cdot}64$. The wavenumber $\bar{\gamma}$ is zero at $\bar{c}_g = 1{\cdot}0$, which gives a period of infinity. As $\bar{c}_g$ decreases from 1·0, the wavenumber increases while the phase velocity $\bar{c}$ decreases. The period thus decreases from infinity. This and other aspects yet to be discussed are presented in Fig. 8.36 as a plot of $\bar{T}$ versus $\bar{t}/\bar{x}$.

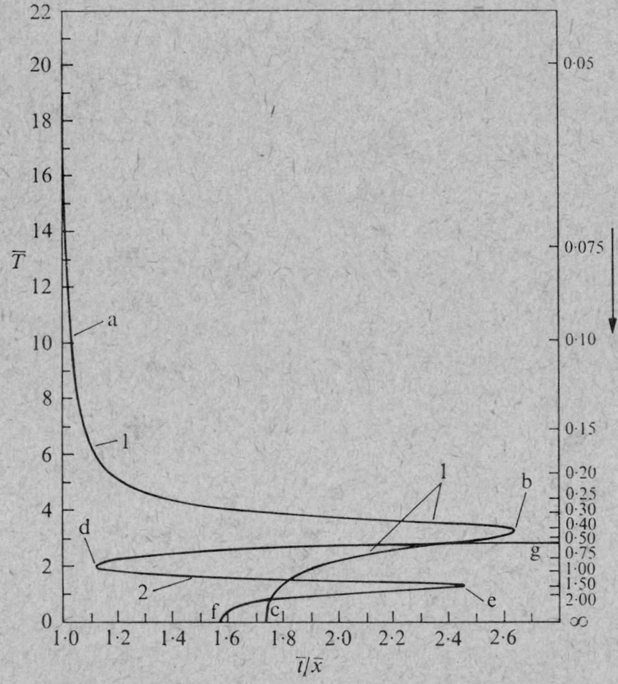

FIG. 8.36. Period $\bar{T}$ of the dominant group in a bar at a distance $\bar{x}$ and time $\bar{t}$. (After Davies [11, Fig. 15].)

Thus the aspect of the period decreasing from infinity is indicated by *a* of curve 1. Continuing, the group velocity of the first mode decreases to a minimum, given by $\bar{c}_g = 0{\cdot}38$ at $\bar{\gamma} = 0{\cdot}43$. This yields a period value of $\bar{T} = 3{\cdot}2$ and a maximum value of $\bar{t}/\bar{x} = 2{\cdot}64$ (point (b) of Fig. 8.36). Referring back to the group-velocity curve, it is seen that as $\bar{\gamma}$ increases beyond the minimum point ($\bar{\gamma} = 0{\cdot}43$), that the group velocity approaches a limiting value of c_R/c_0, where c_R is the Rayleigh velocity. Since $\bar{\gamma} \to \infty$ in this limit, the period approaches zero, as given by point (c) in Fig. 8.36.

Now consider the second mode. As seen from Fig. 8.35, the $\bar{c}_g$ curve has a maximum value at $\bar{c}_g = 0{\cdot}89$ (where $\bar{\gamma} = 0{\cdot}44$), a local minimum at $\bar{c}_g = 0{\cdot}42$ (where $\bar{\gamma} = 1{\cdot}0$) and approaches a limiting value of c_2/c_0. Although not completely drawn in, the $\bar{c}_g$ curve is approaching zero in the vicinity of $\bar{\gamma} = 0{\cdot}2$. This corresponds to the local minimum of the second branch of the frequency spectrum for the rod. In Fig. 8.35, the maximum point of the $\bar{c}_g$ curve gives point d on curve 2, the local minimum gives point (e). The limiting value as $\bar{\gamma} \to \infty$ is given by point (f). Finally, as $\bar{c}_g \to 0$, the wave-number and phase velocity approach definite limits, giving a limiting value to the period, indicated by point (g) of Fig. 8.36.

3. *Propagation of a sharp pulse*. Let us now use Fig. 8.35 to describe, in general terms, the disturbance at a point x due to a disturbance at the origin at $t = 0$. Suppose the disturbance is in the form of an infinite magnitude, infinitely short-duration pulse (a Dirac delta function). The Fourier spectrum of such a pulse has equal amplitudes for all Fourier components. If dispersion were absent, the c_g versus γ and c versus γ curves would simply be horizontal straight lines. The resulting T versus t/x, or $\bar{T}$ versus $\bar{t}/\bar{x}$ curve would be a vertical straight line located at $\bar{t} = 1$. This would indicate that waves of all periods would arrive simultaneously at a point, thereby reconstructing the delta pulse.

Consider initially only the time response in the first mode at a point x. The first disturbance is felt at $\bar{t}/\bar{x} = 1$ (that is, $t = x/c_0$) and consists of long-period waves travelling at the bar velocity c_0. With increasing time $\bar{t}$, the period of the disturbance decreases, indicating an increase in frequency. This change in frequency is at first rapid, since movement is along the nearly vertical portion of the curve, and then less rapid, as the $\bar{T}$ versus $\bar{t}/\bar{x}$ curve flattens out.

For $\bar{t}/\bar{x} \geqslant 1{\cdot}73$ it is seen that $\bar{T}$ versus $\bar{t}$ is double-valued. Thus, at $\bar{t} = 1{\cdot}73$ the nature of the signal arriving at x becomes more complex. Since the lower branch of the $\bar{T}$ curve approaches $\bar{t} = 1{\cdot}73$ nearly vertically, this indicates that nearly all of the waves having a period of $\bar{T} < 0{\cdot}5$ arrive simultaneously, thus superposing a high-frequency pulse on the lower-frequency upper-branch contribution. As $\bar{t}$ increases beyond $1{\cdot}73$, the signal contains two frequency contributions which, at first, are quite different but, as $\bar{t}/\bar{x}$ increases toward $2{\cdot}64$, approach the same frequency. At $\bar{t}/\bar{x} = 2{\cdot}64$, the disturbance due to the first mode suddenly ceases, with the period of the terminating signal given by $\bar{T} = 3{\cdot}2$. Thus, the total duration of the signal (due to the first-mode contribution) is $\bar{t}/\bar{x} = 1{\cdot}64$. In terms of absolute time, $t = \bar{t}x/c_0$. Hence, for larger values of x, it is seen that the total duration increases.

An attempt has been made to sketch the approximate character of the vibration in Fig. 8.37. The contributions from the upper and lower branches of the first mode are shown separately and superimposed to represent the total signal. The main aspect to be noted is the frequency behaviour, since amplitude contributions are uncertain. The main points to be observed are the arrival of the high-frequency contribution at $\bar{t}/\bar{x} = 1{\cdot}73$ and, as $\bar{t}/\bar{x} \to 2{\cdot}64$, the appearance of a 'beating'-type disturbance as the frequencies of the two branches approach the same value.

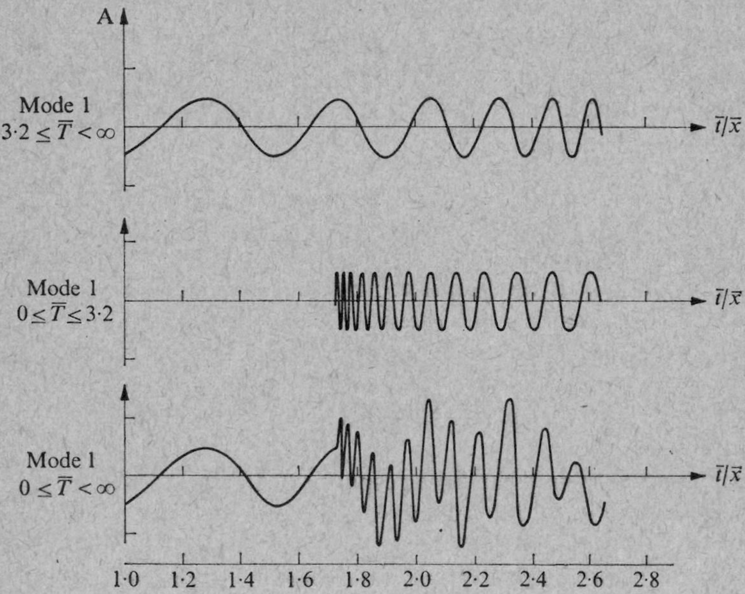

FIG. 8.37. Nature of the first mode signal arriving at a given location x for changing time.

Conceptually, there is no difficulty in adding the second-mode contribution to the above. The contribution would start at $\bar{t}/\bar{x} = 1{\cdot}12$ with the disturbance having a period $\bar{T} = 2$. For $\bar{t} > 1{\cdot}12$, the second mode would have, initially, two frequency components. At $\bar{t}/\bar{x} = 1{\cdot}57$ (point f) the third branch of the second mode enters in, so that, for $\bar{t} > 1{\cdot}57$, three frequency components contribute. As $\bar{t} \to 2{\cdot}44$ (point e) two of the components converge and terminate, but, unlike the first mode, signals from the second mode continues to arrive owing to the branch of the second mode that approaches the limiting value $\bar{T} = 2{\cdot}8$. This, we recall, was a result of the zero group velocity occurring for this mode. No effort is made here to sketch the signal behaviour. Obviously, the combined signal from the first and second modes would be quite complicated.

8.4.3. *Transient compressional waves in semi-infinite rods and plates*

Over the years, the problem of a transient load applied to the end of a semi-infinite rod has been extensively analysed. The geometry and loading situation is of considerable practical interest in experimental investigations of dynamic material properties and in measuring impact forces. Furthermore, geometry and loading are sufficiently simple to make theoretical analysis of the wave propagation, while complicated, still possible. Usually, the end of the rod or plate is considered to be subjected to a step loading in stress or to a step change in velocity. The solution to this problem according to elementary rod theory is well known; that is, the step pulse propagates undistorted with the bar velocity c_0. On theoretical grounds and by experimental observation, distortion of the step pulse with distance travelled is expected and has been observed for such a severe transient. The problem, then, is the theoretical analysis of the situation.

The usual procedure has been to apply integral transforms to the exact equations of elasticity. Usually, the inversion integrals have been evaluated by the saddle-point method, so that the results were valid only for the far field. Complications usually arise in this phase of the analysis owing to the coincidence of the saddle points with poles of the integrand under certain conditions. In many cases, only the contributions of the first mode were included in the inversion. The integral-transform technique has also been applied to various approximate rod theories, with inversion being performed by the saddle-point method. Numerical methods have been used in select cases to obtain near-field data. The results from a number of investigators will be reviewed briefly in the following.

1. *Skalak's solution for impact of two semi-infinite rods.* The case of longitudinal impact of two semi-infinite rods was first considered by Skalak [85], using the situation shown in Fig. 8.38. The approach used was both

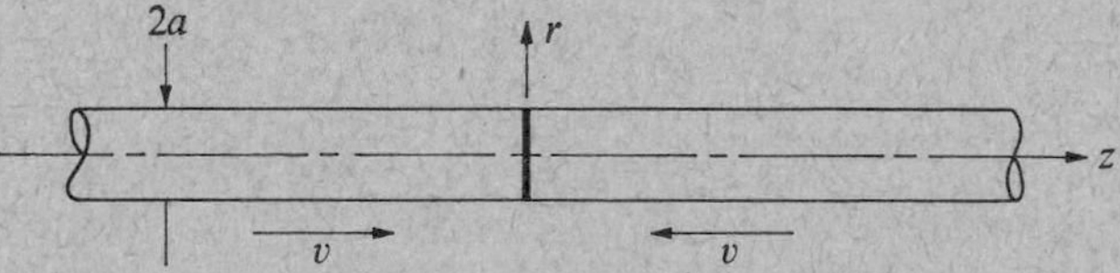

FIG. 8.38. Longitudinal impact of two semi-infinite rods.

unusual and ingenious and involved the superposition of two solutions. The first involves the impact of two semi-infinite rods, as shown in Fig. 8.38, but which are also completely constrained against lateral motion. Such a situation is quite like that of two semi-infinite media impacting, where plane-strain conditions prevail in the radial direction. Such an impact yields a displacement wave situation given by

$$u_z(z, t) = \begin{cases} -vt, & z > c_1 t \\ -\dfrac{z}{c_1}v, & 0 \leqslant z < c_1 t, \end{cases} \tag{8.4.39}$$

where $z > 0$. Such a wave, due to the radial constraint, leads to radial stresses of

$$\tau_{rr}(a, z, t) = \lambda\, \partial u_z/\partial z. \tag{8.4.40}$$

The second part consists of solving the problem of an infinite rod, initially at rest, but subjected to a traction on the surface of the bar. The traction consists of the radial stress (8.4.40), but opposite in sign. Thus, at time $t = 0$, a radial stress, directed radially outward, begins propagating from the origin in the z direction. This system of surface tractions, when superimposed on those of (8.4.40), given by the first part of the problem, exactly cancel and produce the traction-free lateral surfaces of the two colliding semi-infinite rods.

Solution of the second part is, of course, the difficult part. The problem is specified by the displacement equations of motion

$$\begin{aligned} (\lambda+2\mu)\frac{\partial \Delta}{\partial r} + 2\mu\frac{\partial \Omega}{\partial z} &= \rho\frac{\partial^2 u_r}{\partial t^2}, \\ (\lambda+2\mu)\frac{\partial \Delta}{\partial z} - \frac{2\mu}{r}\frac{\partial}{\partial r}(r\Omega) &= \rho\frac{\partial^2 u_z}{\partial t^2}, \end{aligned} \tag{8.4.41}$$

where

$$\Delta = \frac{1}{r}\frac{\partial(ru_r)}{\partial r} + \frac{\partial u_z}{\partial z}, \qquad \Omega = \frac{1}{2}\left(\frac{\partial u_r}{\partial z} - \frac{\partial u_z}{\partial r}\right), \tag{8.4.42}$$

and the boundary conditions

$$\tau_{rr}\big|_{r=a} = R(z, t) = \begin{cases} \dfrac{\lambda v}{c_1}, & -c_1 t < z < c_1 t \\ 0, & |z| > c_1 t \end{cases}, \qquad \tau_{rz}\big|_{r=a} = 0. \tag{8.4.43}$$

Skalak uses a Fourier–Laplace transform pair defined by

$$\bar{g}(\gamma, p) = \frac{1}{4\pi^2}\int_{-\infty}^{\infty} \mathrm{e}^{-\mathrm{i}\gamma z}\,\mathrm{d}z \int_{0}^{\infty} g(z, t)\mathrm{e}^{-\mathrm{i}pt}\,\mathrm{d}t, \tag{8.4.44}$$

with inverse

$$g(z, t) = \int_{-\infty}^{\infty} \mathrm{e}^{\mathrm{i}\gamma z}\,\mathrm{d}\gamma \int_{-\infty-\mathrm{i}\alpha}^{\infty-\mathrm{i}\alpha} \bar{g}(\gamma, p)\mathrm{e}^{\mathrm{i}pt}\,\mathrm{d}p. \tag{8.4.45}$$

Applying the transforms to the governing eqns (8.4.41) and (8.4.42) and eliminating $\bar{u}_r$, $\bar{u}_z$ gives two equations in $\bar{\Delta}$, $\bar{\Omega}$

$$\frac{\partial^2\bar{\Delta}}{\partial r^2}+\frac{1}{r}\frac{\partial\bar{\Delta}}{\partial r}+h^2\bar{\Delta} = 0,$$
$$\frac{\partial^2\bar{\Omega}}{\partial r^2}+\frac{1}{r}\frac{\partial\bar{\Omega}}{\partial r}+\left(k^2-\frac{1}{r^2}\right)\bar{\Omega} = 0, \tag{8.4.46}$$

where

$$h^2 = \frac{\rho p^2}{\lambda+2\mu}-\gamma^2, \qquad k^2 = \frac{\rho p^2}{\mu}-\gamma^2. \tag{8.4.47}$$

The solutions to (8.4.46) are then

$$\bar{\Delta} = BJ_0(hr), \qquad \bar{\Omega} = DJ_1(kr). \tag{8.4.48}$$

These last solutions are substituted for $\bar{\Delta}$, $\bar{\Omega}$ in the transformed equations of motion, and the results solved for $\bar{u}_r$, $\bar{u}_z$, giving

$$\bar{u}_r = A\frac{\partial}{\partial r}J_0(hr)+C\gamma J_1(kr),$$
$$\bar{u}_z = \mathrm{i}\gamma AJ_0(hr)+\frac{\mathrm{i}C}{r}\frac{\partial}{\partial r}\{rJ_1(kr)\}. \tag{8.4.49}$$

The transformed stresses are then obtained, using (8.4.49) and substituted in the transformed boundary conditions and the resulting two equations solved for A and C, with the results

$$A = \frac{\bar{R}}{F}\left(2\gamma^2-\frac{\rho p^2}{\mu}\right)J_1(ka), \qquad C = -\frac{2\bar{R}\gamma}{F}\frac{\partial J_0(ha)}{\partial a}, \tag{8.4.50}$$

where $\bar{R}$ is the transform of the load function and

$$F = \left\{2\mu\frac{\partial^2 J_0(ha)}{\partial a^2}-\frac{p^2\rho\lambda}{\lambda+2\mu}J_0(ha)\right\}\left(2\gamma^2-\rho\frac{p^2}{\mu}\right)J_1(ka)-2\mu\gamma\frac{\partial J_1(ka)}{\partial a}2\gamma\frac{\partial J_0(ha)}{\partial a}. \tag{8.4.51}$$

This last is the Pochhammer frequency equation for axially symmetric waves in an infinite rod. Applying the inversion gives for $\partial u_z/\partial z$

$$\frac{\partial u_z(r, z, t)}{\partial z} = -\int_{-\infty}^{\infty}\int_{-\infty-\mathrm{i}\alpha}^{\infty-\mathrm{i}\alpha}\bar{R}\{\gamma^2(2\gamma^2-\rho p^2/\mu)J_1(ka)J_0(hr)+$$
$$+2\gamma^2hkJ_1(ha)J_0(kr)\}\frac{\mathrm{e}^{\mathrm{i}(\gamma z+pt)}}{F}\,\mathrm{d}\gamma\,\mathrm{d}p, \tag{8.4.52}$$

where, for the present case,

$$\bar{R} = \frac{\lambda v}{2\pi c_1^2(\gamma^2-p^2/c_1^2)}. \tag{8.4.53}$$

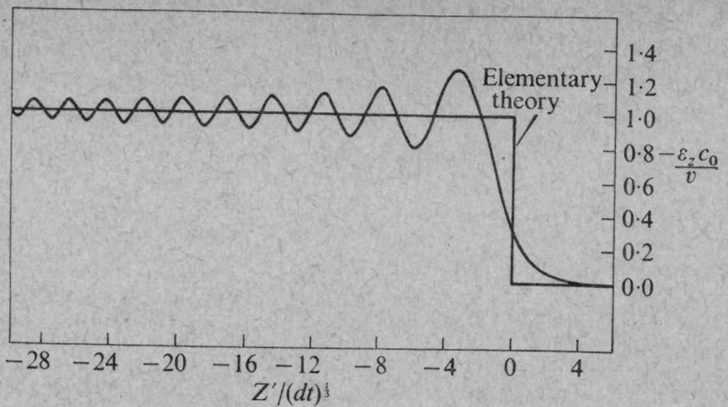

FIG. 8.39. Predicted strain wave $\varepsilon_z = \partial u_z/\partial z$ resulting from the impact of two semi-infinite rods. (After Skalak [85, Fig. 5].)

$z' = z - c_0 t = 0$ corresponds to the arrival time of the pulse according to classical theory. The Skalak analysis shows the rise of the pulse to begin at an earlier time, but with maximum amplitude not being attained until a later time than predicted by simple rod theory. As will be shown in § 8.5, the first few oscillations of the predicted pulse are in excellent agreement with experimental observations.

As pointed out by Skalak, the information essential to the preceding theoretical development is the first two terms of the expansion of the phase velocity for the first mode about $\gamma = 0$. Consequently, it is to be expected that approximate rod theories which duplicate the first mode near $\gamma = 0$ will yield results identical to the analysis that stems from exact elasticity and the Pochhammer equation. The Love theory for the rod, which incorporates lateral-inertia effects into the classical rod theory, does closely approximate the first mode for a limited region (see Fig. 2.27). Davies' analysis of a step pulse using Love's theory predicted oscillatory behaviour of the pulse (see Fig. 2.29) and, as checked by Skalak, the results of Fig. 2.29 and Fig. 8.39 agree quite closely when appropriate scale adjustments are made. The conclusion reached is that, despite the fact that many higher-order stress effects are present in the exact theory of waves in rods, the predominant effect causing deviation of the far-field pulse shape from that predicted by elementary theory is that of lateral inertia.

2. *Analysis by Folk et al. of the step pressure pulse on a rod.* As previously mentioned, many investigations have appeared on transient waves in rods, of which that of Skalak was the first to use exact theory in the analysis. The case of a step pressure pulse applied to the end of a rod was analysed by Folk, Fox, Shook, and Curtis [17], with other contributions on the flexural pulse case and experimental results being given by Fox and Curtis [18], DeVault and Curtis [12], and Curtis [10]. The method of analysis used in all cases was the direct

conditions is that, while the condition on τ_{zz} is realistic, that on the radial displacement is not in accord with the physical conditions of most experiments. It turns out that this approximation does not seriously affect the predicted far-field response.

Application of the proper transforms gives as the transformed solution

$$E^{\mathrm{SF}} = \overset{\mathrm{SF}}{\varepsilon}_{\theta\theta} + \overset{\mathrm{SF}}{\varepsilon}_{zz} = \frac{\overset{\mathrm{SF}}{u}_r}{r} - \gamma \overset{\mathrm{CF}}{u}_z$$

$$= \frac{(\lambda+2\mu)A}{\rho\omega^2}\left\{\frac{hJ_1(hr)}{r} + \gamma^2 J_0(hr)\right\} + \frac{2\mu\gamma B}{\rho\omega^2}\left\{\frac{J_1(kr)}{r} - kJ_0(kr)\right\} + \frac{\mathrm{i}P_0\gamma}{(\lambda+2\mu)\omega h^2}, \tag{8.4.63}$$

where

$$A(\gamma, \omega) = \frac{\mathrm{i}P_0\rho\lambda\gamma(k^2-\gamma^2)\omega J_1(ka)}{(\lambda+2\mu)^2\mu h^2\Phi(\gamma, \omega)},$$

$$B(\gamma, \omega) = \frac{\mathrm{i}P_0\rho\lambda\gamma^2\omega J_1(ha)}{(\lambda+2\mu)\mu^2 h\Phi(\gamma, \omega)}, \tag{8.4.64}$$

and

$$\Phi(\gamma, \omega) = \frac{2h}{a}(k^2+\gamma^2)J_1(ha)J_1(ka) -$$
$$-(k^2-\gamma^2)^2 J_0(ha)J_1(ka) - 4\gamma^2 hkJ_1(ha)J_0(ka). \tag{8.4.65}$$

The function $\Phi(\gamma, \omega) = 0$ is the Pochhammer equation. The particular form of the solution (8.4.63) was chosen so that the results could be compared directly with experimentally measured parameters.

The inverse sine transformation with respect to the wavenumber γ is first carried out. Since E^{SF} is an odd function in γ, the inverse transform is given by

$$E^{\mathrm{F}} = -\frac{\mathrm{i}}{\pi}\int_{-\infty}^{\infty} E^{\mathrm{SF}} \mathrm{e}^{\,\mathrm{i}\gamma z}\,\mathrm{d}\gamma. \tag{8.4.66}$$

This integral is evaluated by the Cauchy residue theorem by using a contour along the real γ-axis and a semicircle in the upper half-plane. The latter contribution vanishes for a circle radius approaching infinity, so that the integral (8.4.66) is given by $2\pi\mathrm{i}\sum$ Res of the poles enclosed by the contour.

It is at this stage that Folk *et al.* developed the arguments for including or excluding poles from the contour that directly relates to the interpretation of the portions of the branches of the frequency spectrum for rods (and plates) that indicate negative group velocity.† Thus, the position of a pole in the γ-plane depends on ω and is given by $\gamma_q = \gamma_q(\omega)$. This symbolic relationship represents nothing more than the branches of the Pochhammer–Chree

† For example, the region to the left of the local minimum or the second symmetrical branch of Fig. 8.9 and Fig. 8.10 for the plate case.

frequency spectrum, as shown in Fig. 8.17. Thus, for a given value ω_0 (or Ω_0 for the figure), an $\omega = \omega_0$ plane would be pierced at an infinite number of points by the branches of the spectrum, each representing a pole location for $\omega = \omega_0$. Many of the poles would be along the real and imaginary γ-axes, but some would be complex, owing to the complex branches of the spectrum.

Consider the poles on the real γ-axis. The question is: which poles should be included and which poles should be excluded from the contour. The answer to this is given by anticipating the inverse Fourier transform on the frequency ω. The path used in that transform will not be along the real ω-axis, but along an axis arbitrarily close to and parallel with the real axis, but still slightly above it. Then the ω used in calculating the poles of γ should have a small but positive imaginary component $\mathrm{i}\alpha$. Expanding $\gamma_q(\omega)$ about a frequency ω_0 gives

$$\gamma_q(\omega) = \gamma_q(\omega_0) + \frac{\mathrm{d}\gamma_q}{\mathrm{d}\omega}\Delta\omega + \dots. \tag{8.4.67}$$

Substitution of $\mathrm{i}\alpha$ for $\Delta\omega$ shows that γ_q will have a small but non-zero imaginary component whose sign is positive if $\mathrm{d}\gamma_q/\mathrm{d}\omega$ is positive. Hence only those poles on the real axis are included which meet this criterion. With this, the inverse sine transformed result is given by

$$E^{\mathrm{F}} = \frac{\mathrm{i}P_0(1-\nu)}{E}\sum_q F(r, \gamma_q, \omega)\exp(\mathrm{i}\gamma_q z), \tag{8.4.68}$$

where

$$F(r, \gamma_q, \omega) = \left(\frac{4\nu(1+\nu)}{(1-\nu)^2}\frac{\gamma}{\omega h}\left[\frac{(k^2-\gamma^2)J_1(ka)}{h}\left\{\frac{hJ_1(hr)}{r} + \gamma^2 J_0(hr)\right\} + \right.\right.$$
$$\left.\left. + 2\gamma^2 J_1(ha)\left\{\frac{J_1(kr)}{r} - kJ_0(kr)\right\}\right]\frac{1}{\partial\Phi/\partial\gamma}\right)_{\gamma=\gamma_q(\omega)}. \tag{8.4.69}$$

The inverse transform of E^{F} then gives

$$E(z, r, t) = \frac{1}{2\pi}\int_{-\infty+\mathrm{i}\alpha}^{\infty+\mathrm{i}\alpha} E^{\mathrm{F}}\mathrm{e}^{-\mathrm{i}\omega t}\,\mathrm{d}\omega$$
$$= -\frac{P_0(1-\nu)}{E}\sum_q \frac{1}{2\pi\mathrm{i}}\int_{-\infty+\mathrm{i}\alpha}^{\infty+\mathrm{i}\alpha} F(r, \gamma_q, \omega)\exp\{\mathrm{i}(\gamma_q z - \omega t)\}\,\mathrm{d}\omega. \tag{8.4.70}$$

Each integral in the result (8.4.70) corresponds to the contribution of an individual mode of the Pochhammer spectrum for the axisymmetric case.

The saddle-point method is used to evaluate the integrals appearing in (8.4.70) for locations far from the end of the rod. Referring back to the development of this method in Chapter 6 (§ 2), we see that the saddle points will be obtained from $\mathrm{d}f(\omega)/\mathrm{d}\omega = 0$, where we write for the exponential in (8.4.70)

$$\exp\{\mathrm{i}(\gamma_q z - \omega t)\} = \exp\{zf(\omega)\}, \qquad f(\omega) = \mathrm{i}\left(\frac{\gamma_q}{z} - \frac{\omega}{z}t\right). \tag{8.4.71}$$

Expansion about the saddle point $\bar{\omega}$ gives

$$F(r, \gamma_q, \omega) \cong F(r, \bar{\gamma}_q, \bar{\omega}),$$

$$\gamma_q z - \omega t \cong \gamma_q z - \bar{\omega} t + \frac{z}{2}\frac{\mathrm{d}^2\gamma_q}{\mathrm{d}\omega^2}(\omega - \bar{\omega})^2, \tag{8.4.72}$$

which holds as long as no poles or zeros are located near $\bar{\omega}$. The results are given by

$$E(z, r, t) = -\frac{P_0(1-\nu)}{E}\left\{1 + \sum_q A_q \sin\left(\bar{\gamma}_q z - \bar{\omega} t \pm \frac{\pi}{4}\right)\right\}, \tag{8.4.73}$$

where

$$A_q = 2F(r, \bar{\gamma}_q, \bar{\omega})\left(2\pi z \left|\frac{\mathrm{d}^2\gamma_q}{\mathrm{d}\omega^2}\right|\right)^{-\frac{1}{2}}. \tag{8.4.74}$$

This expression predicts that near a time $t = z/c_g$, there should appear oscillations having a period $2\pi/\bar{\omega}$, a wavelength $2\pi/\bar{\gamma}_q$ and an amplitude A_q.

The approximation used in obtaining the results (8.4.73) breaks down when $\mathrm{d}^2\gamma_q/\mathrm{d}\omega^2 \to 0$, or when there are poles and zeros of $F(r, \gamma_q, \omega)$ near $\bar{\omega}$. Furthermore, for the first mode, F has a pole coinciding with the saddle point at $\bar{\omega} = 0$ at the maximum group velocity. It becomes necessary to use a modification of the usual saddle-point method, where a third-order term is included. This technique is applied to the evaluation of the first-mode contribution near maximum group velocity. This gives the head of the pulse behaviour as

$$E(r, z, t) \cong \frac{P_0(1-\nu)}{F}\left\{\frac{1}{3} + \int_0^B (\mathrm{Ai})(-B)\,\mathrm{d}B\right\}, \tag{8.4.75}$$

where

$$B = \left(t - \frac{z}{c_0}\right)\left(\frac{4c_0^3}{3\nu^2 a^2 z}\right)^{\frac{1}{3}}, \tag{8.4.76}$$

and where $(\mathrm{Ai})(x)$ is the Airy integral. Now, at $t = z/c_0$, the integral of (8.4.75) is zero, so that the pulse has reached $\frac{1}{3}$ of its final value. The behaviour of the pulse is oscillatory and is the same as shown in Fig. 8.39 for Skalak's results. A 27 per cent overshoot occurs on the first oscillation.

The case of a step pressure pulse applied on a semicircular area of the end of the rod has been analysed by DeVault and Curtis [12]. Such a loading produces flexural as well as longitudinal disturbances. While the analysis is more complicated than for the uniform pressure pulse, the analysis follows generally the same steps just outlined.

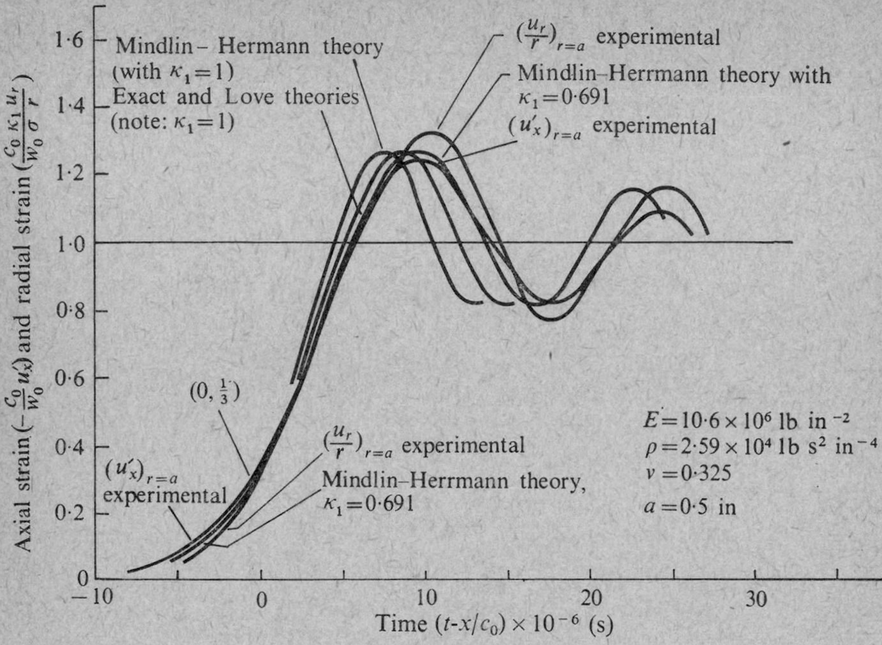

FIG. 8.40. Head-of-the-pulse behaviour as predicted by Mindlin–Herrmann, Love, and exact theories. (After Miklowitz [53, Fig. 4].)

3. *Other results for compressional waves in a rod.* A number of other results have been obtained for compressional waves in a rod. In several cases, approximate equations of motion for the rod have been used. Miklowitz [51] used the Mindlin–Herrmann theory for the rod and considered the case of a step pressure pulse loading and obtained a formal solution. The integral solution was numerically evaluated by Miklowitz [52] for the near-field response for various Poisson's ratio. Anomalous stress discontinuities were noted for arrival times given by x/c_1, corresponding to major wave contributions travelling at the dilatational velocity.† In a later contribution, Miklowitz [53] used the stationary-phase method, also partially covered in Reference [52], in conjunction with Mindlin–Herrmann theory to obtain the far-field response. Results were obtained for two values of the correction factor κ_1 appearing in the Mindlin–Herrmann theory and are shown in Fig. 8.40. Also shown are the results from the Skalak analysis using exact theory and the Davies analysis using Love's theory. Experimental results are also shown.

Kaul and McCoy [33] applied the approximate equations for the rod developed by Mindlin and McNiven [65] to the case of a step pressure pulse

† This aspect was previously commented on in the analysis of longitudinal waves in membrane shells in § 4.3.

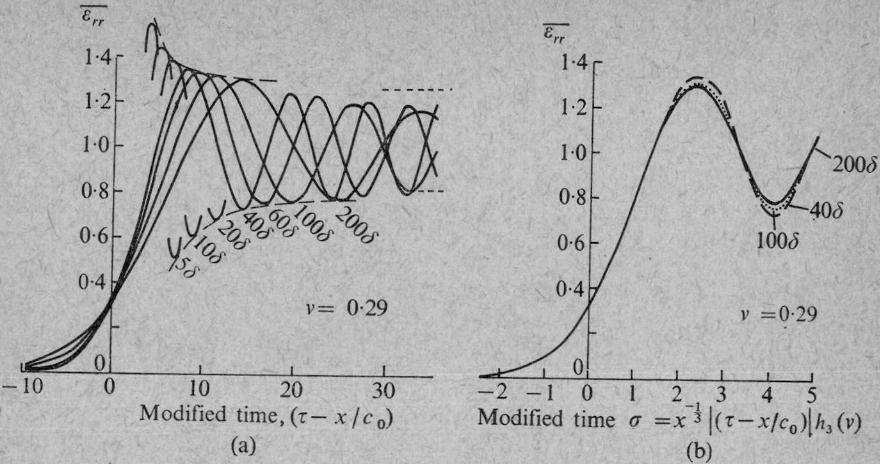

FIG. 8.41. Radial strain $\bar{\varepsilon}_{rr}$ as a function of the modified time (a) $\tau - x/c_0$ and (b) of the modified time σ. (After Kaul and McCoy [33, Figs. 4, 5].)

applied to a semi-infinite rod. Integral-transform methods were used and the steepest-descent or saddle-point method applied to obtain the far-field, head-of-the-pulse response. The solution is in terms of the Airy function. Results are shown in Fig. 8.41 for the radial strain as a function of time, where

$$\varepsilon_{rr} = \frac{u(x, \tau)}{a}, \qquad \bar{\varepsilon}_{rr} = \frac{k_1 E}{\nu P_0}\varepsilon_{rr}, \tag{8.4.77}$$

and $u(x, t)$ is the displacement function associated with the kinematical assumptions of the theory. Thus

$$\begin{aligned} u_x(r, x, \tau) &= w(x, \tau) + (1 - 2r^2/a^2)\psi(x, \tau), \\ u_r(r, x, \tau) &= (r/a)u(x, \tau). \end{aligned} \tag{8.4.78}$$

The parameters x and τ are non-dimensional distance along the rod and time, defined by

$$x = \delta(z/a), \quad \tau = (\delta t/a)c_2, \quad J_1(\delta) = 0, \quad \delta = 3{\cdot}8317. \tag{8.4.79}$$

The parameter k_1 in (8.4.77) is an adjustment coefficient of the approximate theory. For $\nu = 0{\cdot}29$, $k_1^2 = 0{\cdot}7739$. The amplitude of the applied stress is $P_0/2$. In Fig. 8.41(a), the evolution of the head of the pulse at various distances from the end is shown. In Fig. 8.41(b), the modified time is

$$\sigma = \frac{\{(\tau - x/c_0)\}h_3(\nu)}{x^{\frac{1}{3}}}, \qquad h_3(\nu) = c_0\left(\frac{2k_1}{\sqrt{3\nu\delta k_3}}\right)^{\frac{2}{3}}, \qquad k_3^2 = 0{\cdot}9754, \tag{8.4.80}$$

which is similar to the base used to present the data of Skalak. As pointed out by Kaul and McCoy and earlier by Fox and Curtis [18], it becomes evident from the representation of Fig. 8.41(b) that for different values of x, the initial portion of the curve is the same. This leads to the prediction that the time of the initial rise should vary inversely as the cube of the distance of travel.

Returning to results obtained by analysis using the exact equations of elasticity, Jones and Norwood [32] considered the semi-infinite rod subjected to both pressure step and velocity transient loads. The saddle-point technique was used to obtain the far-field response. A unique aspect of the work was that cross-section warping effects on the first-mode contribution were retained. The basic Airy integral solution obtained by previous investigations is contained in the result, with the warping effects adding second-order corrections that are of decreasing significance for increasing distances of travel. A comparison of the results of the pressure step and velocity impact showed less than 1 per cent difference in the solutions at a distance of 20 diameters from the end of the rod.

In all of the analyses reviewed thus far, asymptotic methods were used to obtain far-field, head-of-the-pulse information. Bertholf [5] obtained numerical solutions to the exact elasticity equations for the case of axisymmetric waves in semi-infinite and finite rods. The case of a step pulse was considered, with the case of free-end and rigid-lubricated conditions existing at the opposite end being considered. Results are shown in Fig. 8.42 for the axial strain in a one-diameter long cylindrical bar at various times for the free-end case.

To interpret the data of the figure, first note that the abscissa coordinate z/d is distance along the rod, where d is the rod diameter and z is the axial

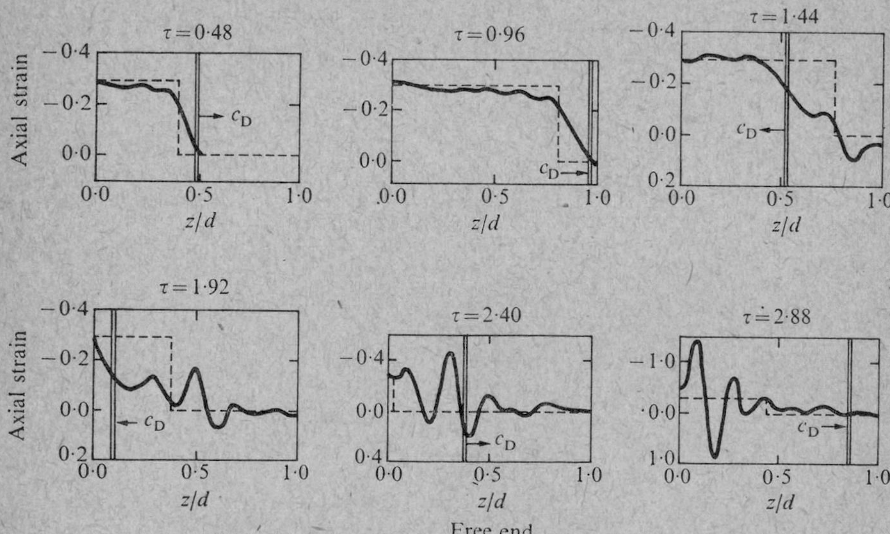

Fig. 8.42. Axial strain in a one-diameter long bar subjected to a step pressure pulse for various values of non-dimensional time τ. (After Bertholf [5, Figs. 12, 13].)

coordinate. The loaded end is at $z/d = 0$. The non-dimensional time τ is given by

$$\tau = tc_1/d. \tag{8.4.81}$$

The results were computed for a specific rod material (24S-T aluminum) for a specific impact stress. For our considerations, it is sufficient to consider the axial-strain ordinate as some relative value. Finally, the dashed line in the figures represents the wave system that would exist according to simple, one-dimensional rod theory. The vertical line $c_D (c_D = c_1)$ represents the position of a dilatational wavefront initiated at the instant of impact. As would be expected, the strain wave behaviour is considerably more intricate than the predictions of simple theory. Other results are given by Bertholf for the case of a two-diameter length rod, and the pulse behaviour in a semi-infinite rod.

Returning to the case of the semi-infinite rod, Kennedy and Jones [35] presented results having several features of interest. In all analyses reviewed thus far, the velocity or pressure step pulses applied to the end of the rod have been assumed to be uniformly distributed over the end. Kennedy and Jones considered the case of radial variation in the applied step pressure pulse, as shown in Fig. 8.43. The stress applied to the end of the rod is prescribed by

$$\tau_{zz}(0, r, t) = P(r)H\langle t\rangle, \tag{8.4.82}$$

where

$$P(r) = P_0(p+1)\{1-(r/a)^2\}^p, \quad p \geq 0. \tag{8.4.83}$$

Thus, the parameter p defines the nature of the radial, axisymmetric stress distribution. The value of $p = 0$ gives the case of a uniform pressure distribution considered in all previous studies. The second feature of interest in the

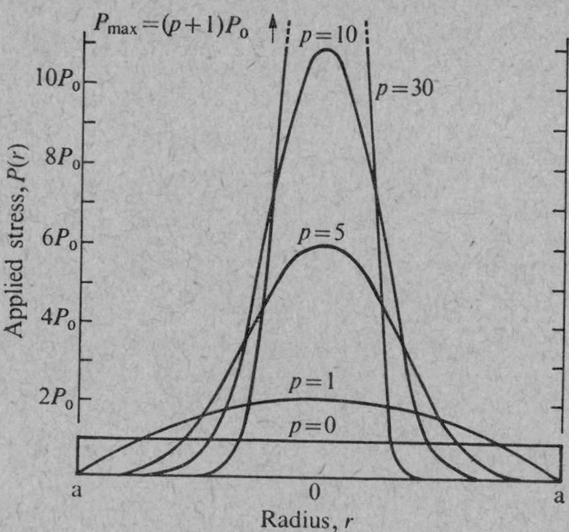

FIG. 8.43. Radial variation in the step pressure pulse applied to the end of a semi-infinite rod. (After Kennedy and Jones [35, Fig. 1].)

Kennedy–Jones analysis is that both near-field and far-field results are obtained. The numerical techniques developed by Berthoff [5] are applied to the near-field analysis, while the saddle-point asymptotic method is used for the far-field analysis.

Results were obtained for the specific impact situation of a steel bar of radius $a = 1{\cdot}27$ cm subjected to an end loading for which $P_0 = 1{\cdot}0$ kbar (1 bar $\cong$ 14·4 lb in^{-2}). The behaviour of the strain $E = \varepsilon_{zz} + \varepsilon_{\theta\theta}$ at the surface of the bar is shown in Fig. 8.44. It is sufficient here to interpret the strain ordinate scale arbitrarily. The abscissa z/a corresponds to various positions along the rod. The results are for three values of the loading parameter $p = 0$, 10, 30. The solid lines in the plots are the results from numerical analysis, the dashed lines are the results from asymptotic analysis. A first observation to be made for the far field, $z/a = 40$, is that numerical and analytical results are in fair agreement and, furthermore, that there is very

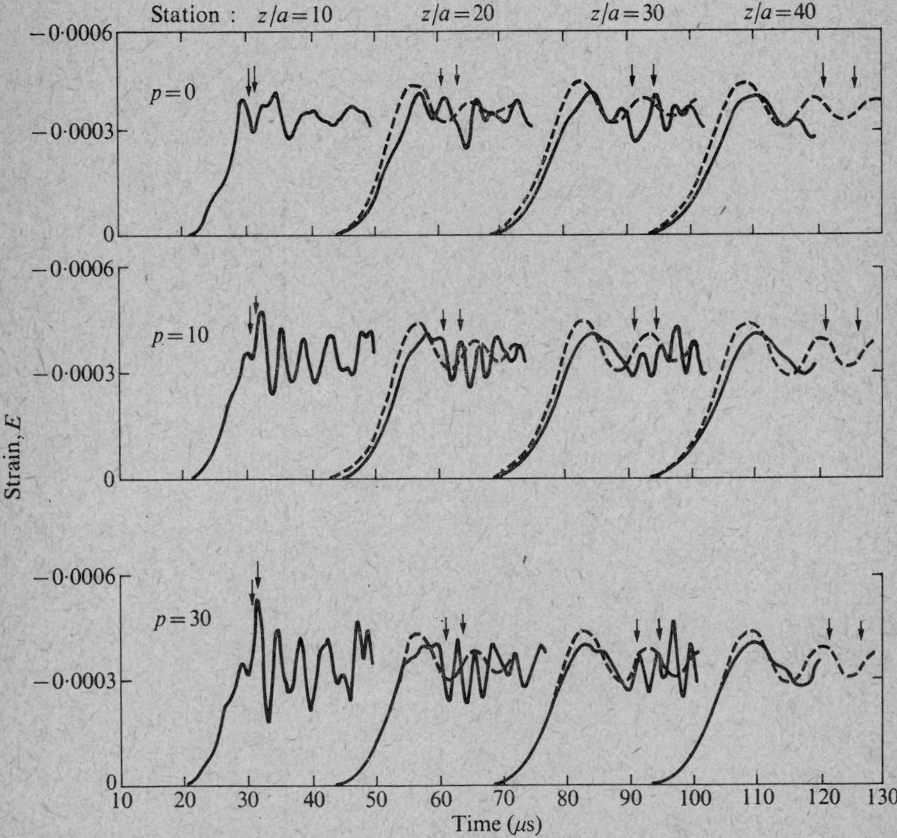

FIG. 8.44. The strain $E = \varepsilon_{zz} + \varepsilon_{\theta\theta}$ at various locations along the bar for three values of the loading parameter p. (After Kennedy and Jones [35, Fig. 4].)

little difference in the response for $p = 0, 10, 30$. This last merely indicates a type of dynamic St. Venant's principle, where the response far from the load is insensitive to variations in the load distribution. Now consider the very near-field response ($z/a = 10$) and the differences between the $p = 0, 10, 30$ behaviour. For the more severely concentrated load ($p = 30$), it is to be expected that higher rod modes will be more strongly excited than for a uniform distribution ($p = 0$). This is indicated by the greater presence of high-frequency signal for $p = 30$ compared to $p = 0$, with the case of $p = 10$ being intermediate. The small vertical arrows in the figure indicate the arrival time of second- and third-mode contributions. Numerous other results were given by Kennedy and Jones, including the behaviour of E along the axis, along a radius of $r/a = 0{\cdot}5$ and the stress behaviour.

4. *Transient waves in plates.* A number of analyses have appeared on transient waves in plates as governed by the exact equations of elasticity or higher-order plate theories. In the main, methods of analysis are quite similar to those employed in analysis of rod problems. Thus, integral-transform techniques are employed and far-field results obtained by asymptotic methods. Because of the many similarities of the techniques reviewed in the last few sections, the coverage here of this rather large subject will be rather brief.

The case of a semi-infinite rectangular bar subjected to a longitudinal step pulse has been considered by Jones and Ellis [30, 31]. The situation is the plate analogue of the semi-infinite rod problem extensively discussed in the last few sections. The bar is defined by $y = \pm a, z = \pm b, x \geqslant 0$ where $b \ll a$. Loading occurs at the $x = 0$ face. Plane-stress conditions were assumed to prevail in the z direction, with the exact elasticity equations being applied to the x, y coordinates. The case of plane-strain conditions in the z direction is easily obtained, of course, by changing the elastic constants. The method of analysis closely follows that first used by Folk *et al.* [17], except that higher-order cross-section warping effects are retained in the far-field evaluation. This aspect has been previously mentioned in conjunction with the rod analysis of Jones and Norwood [32] and derived from the work of Jones and Ellis. In addition, second-mode contributions are included in the results. The results obtained by Jones and Ellis for a specific impact situation at a location along the axis of the bar is shown in Fig. 8.45. The ordinate is the strain

$$E(\varepsilon_{xx}+\varepsilon_{yy})/P_0,$$

where E is Young's modulus and P_0 is the applied pressure. The influence of the various modes and correction terms is shown by the various curves.

Several contributions on compressional and flexural waves in plates have been made by Miklowitz and his coworkers. Thus Miklowitz [56] considered an elastic plate subjected to a pair of concentrated loads, as shown in

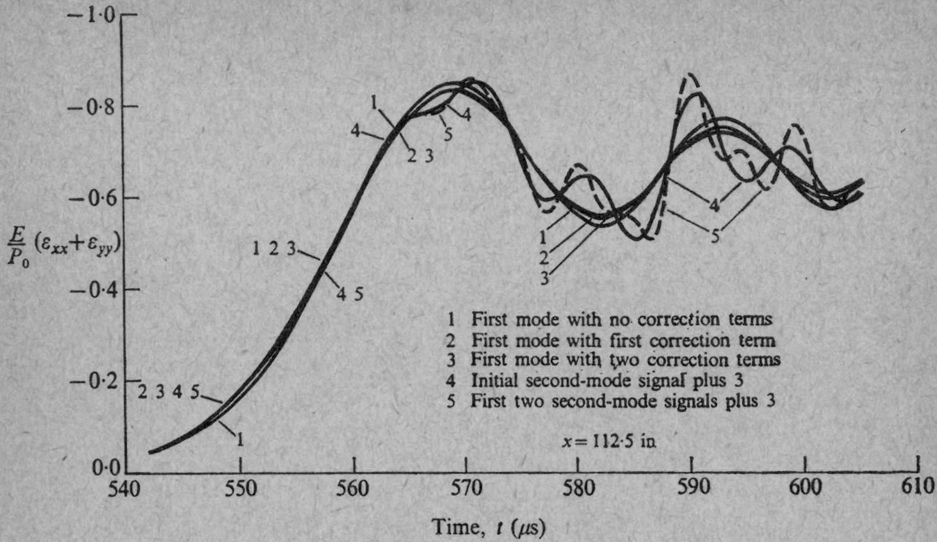

FIG. 8.45. The strain $E\,(\varepsilon_{xx}+\varepsilon_{yy})/P_0$ versus time at a specific location along the axis of a rectangular bar subjected to a step pressure pulse. (After Jones and Ellis [31, Fig. 9].)

Fig. 8.46(a). The symmetry of the loading with respect to the mid surface of the plate enables the problem to be reduced to the situation shown in Fig. 8.46(b) of a plate on a rigid, lubricated half-space. The method of stationary phase is used to obtain the far-field horizontal and vertical displacements. The results are shown in Fig. 8.47 for the former component, where

$$\bar{u}_\rho = \frac{\pi\mu}{2P_0} u_\rho(\rho, \xi, \tau) \times 10^{-3}, \tag{8.4.84}$$

and where ρ, ξ, τ are dimensionless radial, axial, and time coordinates, given by

$$\rho = r/H, \quad \xi = z/H, \quad \tau = c_2 t/H, \tag{8.4.85}$$

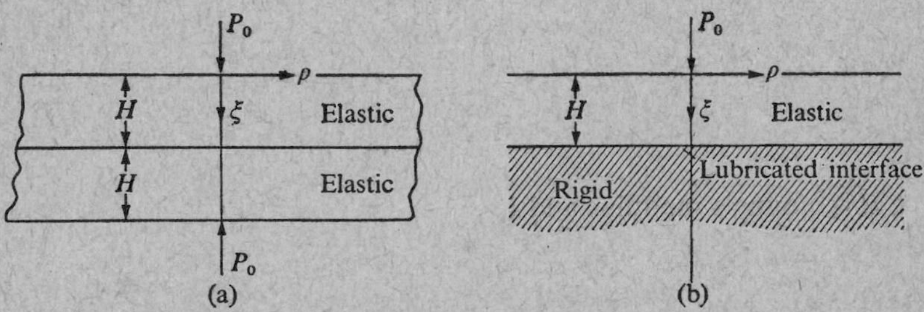

FIG. 8.46. (a) An elastic plate of thickness $2H$ subjected to a pair of concentrated loads and (b) the equivalent case of a plate on a rigid half-space. (After Miklowitz [56, Figs. 1, 2].)

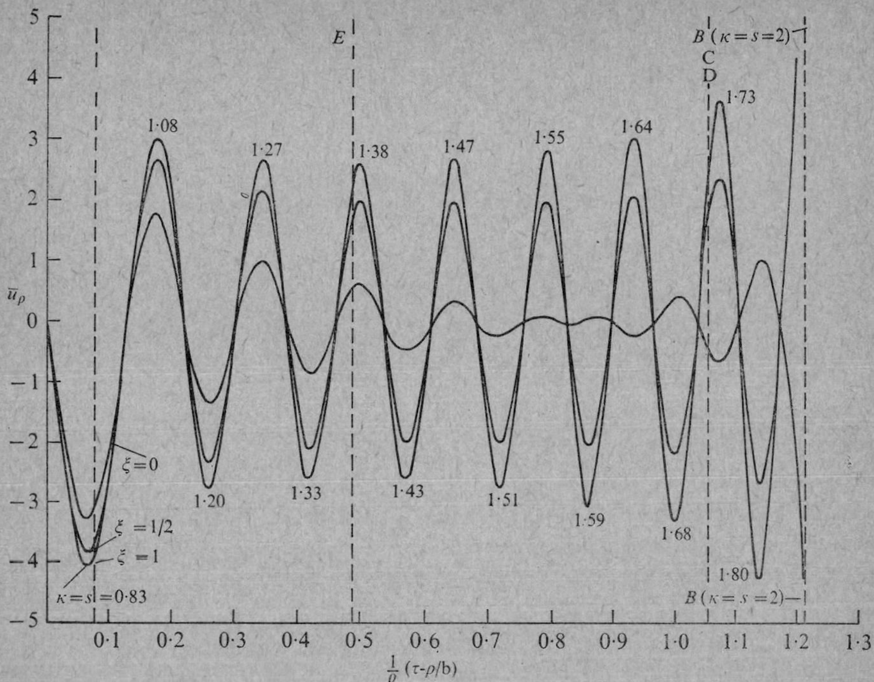

FIG. 8.47. Horizontal displacement $\bar{u}_\rho$ at the station $\rho = 20$ and $\xi = 0, \frac{1}{2}, 1$ as a result of a step load applied to the plate. (After Miklowitz [56, Fig. 4].)

and b is the velocity ratio

$$b = c_p/c_2 = \{E/\rho(1-\nu^2)\}^{\frac{1}{2}}/c_2. \tag{8.4.86}$$

The displacements are shown for three values of depth, $\xi = 0, \frac{1}{2}, 1$ at the station $\rho = 20$. Only the first plate-mode contribution is included in the analysis. The highly oscillatory nature of the response is to be noted. Also, the apparent increasing amplitude with the passage of time is to be noted. However, considerations related to arrival time of other mode contributions suggests that only the region from zero to the dashed line at E is sufficiently accurate.

Miklowitz [54] gave the solution to the case of a hole punched in a stretched elastic plate. However, only the plane-stress plate equations were used. In a later work, Scott and Miklowitz [82] considered the case of a radial step displacement applied to the wall of a circular, cylindrical cavity. The case of a radial step pressure pulse was considered in a later contribution by the same authors [83]. The Laplace and extended Hankel transforms were applied to the exact elasticity equations, and the method of stationary phase used to obtain the far-field response. The time behaviour of the radial and vertical

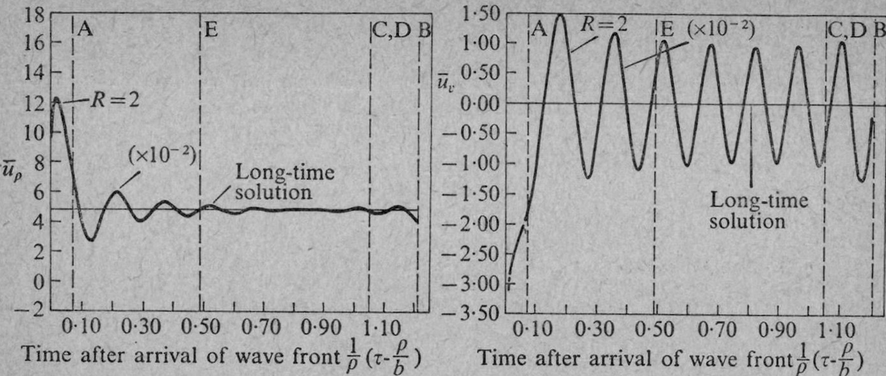

FIG. 8.48. Horizontal and vertical displacement components $\bar{u}_\rho$, $\bar{u}_v$ in a plate containing a circular hole subjected to a step radial displacement for $R = 2{\cdot}0$ at a station $\rho = 20$, $\xi = 1$. (After Scott and Miklowitz [82, Fig. 2].)

displacement components is shown in Fig. 8.48 for the step displacement case for a particular ratio of hole radius to plate half-thickness. The various parameters appearing in the figure are defined as follows:

$$\bar{u}_\rho = \frac{\pi(1-2\nu)}{8\nu u_0} u_\rho, \qquad \bar{u}_v = \frac{\pi(1-2\nu)}{8\nu u_0} u_v, \qquad R = \frac{a}{H}, \tag{8.4.87}$$

where $u_\rho = u_\rho(\rho, \tau, \xi)$, $u_v = u_v(\rho, \tau, \xi)$ are the radial and vertical displacements in terms of the dimensionless variables defined by (8.4.87). The time after arrival of the wavefront $(\tau - \rho/b)/\rho$ is the same as for Fig. 8.47. The observation point is at $\rho = 20$ and $\xi = 1$, corresponding to a point on the surface of the plate.

As in the case of the work in Reference [56], it is not possible to obtain head-of-the-pulse data from the approximate solution. This behaviour is associated with the group-velocity minimum. The difficulty is that the integrals which arise in extending the stationary phase to the point of a group-velocity minimum have not been computed. This is in contrast to the case of the rod and plate subjected to longitudinal impact, where the Airy integral results. Other considerations put forth by Scott and Miklowitz, based on period-arrival time considerations of the second and third modes and on the higher-frequency components of the first mode suggest that region 0–E is the strongest part of the results.

The analysis of flexural waves in a plate governed by the Mindlin plate equations was put forth by Miklowitz [55]. The case of a concentrated step-function load was considered using Laplace transform theory. The contours in the complex plane involved in the inversion are quite similar to those shown in Chapter 3 (Fig. 3.17) for the Timoshenko beam analysis. Results were presented for the moment and shear responses $M_r(r, t)$, $M_\theta(r, t)$, and $Q_r(r, t)$

for step and rectangular pulse function input at various stations. Scott and Miklowitz [84] have presented formal solutions, using Laplace and finite Fourier transforms of a general class of non-axisymmetric, transient plate wave-propagation problems. A particular case of a normal, half-ring load has been evaluated. Finally, Miklowitz [57] has presented a very extensive review of transient wave analysis in plates. A discussion of various methods of solution is given.

8.5. Experimental studies on waves in rods and plates

The main objective of this section will be to present experimental results illustrating the dispersive characteristics of rods and plates. This will include results illustrating multiple reflection of pulses and dispersion of sharp pulses as well as some studies on mode coupling.

8.5.1. *Multiple reflections within a waveguide*

It is known, of course, that dispersion is caused by the multiple reflections and mode conversions within a waveguide. It is of interest to present some of the results explicitly showing the early stages of this process. In a study by Kolsky [36], a sharp pulse was initiated on one side of a short, cylindrical slab of steel and a wave detector placed on the opposite side, as shown in Fig. 8.49(a). The initial portion of the wave system sensed by the detector is shown in Fig. 8.49(b). It is possible to relate the general character of the disturbance to waves travelling specific paths. Thus, in Fig. 8.49(b), disturbance 1 arrives by the direct path 1 and travels at the dilatational wave speed. The next signal arrival (2) arrives by path 2 and is a P–P wave. Signal 3 arriving by path 3 is a P–S wave. Signals 4, 5, and 6 are, respectively P–P–P, S–S, and P–P–S waves. The increased number of reflections makes the signal increasingly difficult to decipher after that.

A portion of a study by Evans, Hadley, Eisler, and Silverman [13] also provides insight into the early stages of wave development. A diagram of the experimental arrangement used for making the measurements is shown in Fig. 8.50(a). The model was a 2·15 in. (5·46 cm) thick specimen of plastic. The nature of the pulses received at six locations on the surface (each 1 cm apart) are shown in Fig. 8.50(b). The first signal that arrives at the detector is L, the directly travelling longitudinal wave. The next arrival sensed by the detector used by Evans *et al.* is called S and is the surface wave. The next arrival is the strong signal R_1 caused by a P–P wave reflected from the bottom of the plate. For the more distant receiver locations this signal actually precedes the surface wave arrival. The next signal C_1 results from both P–S and S–P waves reflected from the bottom of the plate. The signal peak R_2 results from a P–P–P–P wave system while C_2 results from a combination of P–P–P–S, P–P–S–P, P–S–P–P, and S–P–P–P wave systems.

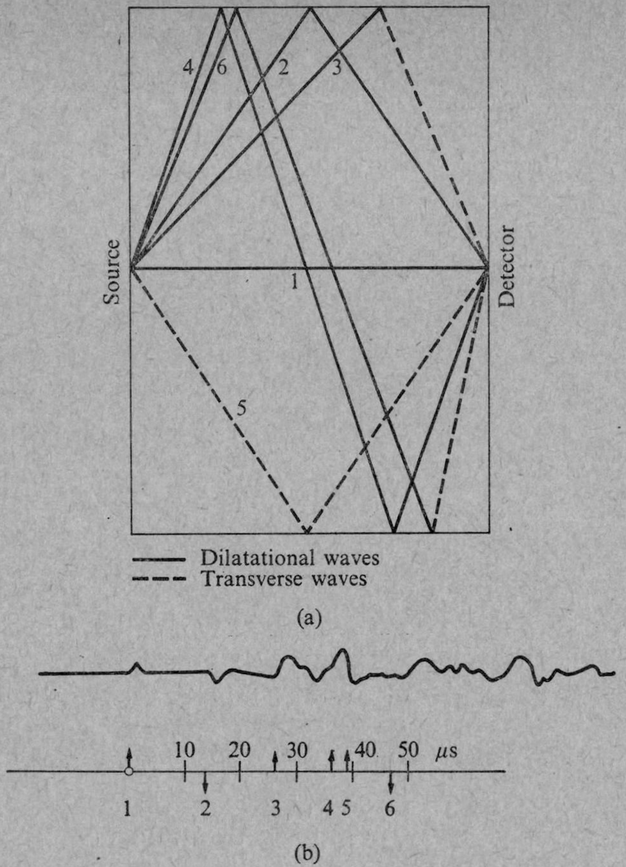

FIG. 8.49. (a) Source–detector arrangement for studying the early stages of wave reflection in a slab, and (b) the resulting signal at the detector. (After Kolsky [36].)

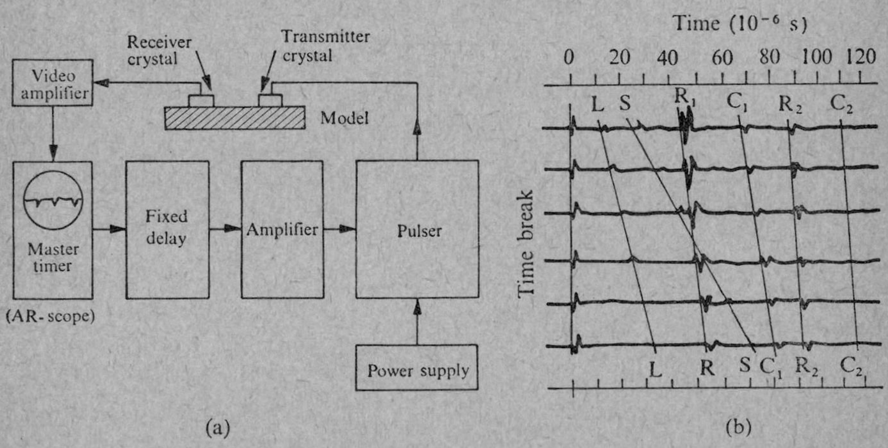

FIG. 8.50. (a) Experimental arrangement for observing pulse reflections in a plate, and (b) pulse forms observed at six stations. (After Evans *et al.* [13, Figs. 1, 3].)

8.5.2. *Dispersion of a sharp pulse in a cylindrical rod*

Experiments were conducted by Oliver [73] on the dispersion of sharp pulses in an elastic rod. An electrically pulsed piezoelectric transducer was used to induce a short duration (about 20 μs) pulse into a 19 ft, (5.8 m), 1 in. (2·54 cm) diameter steel rod. A second transducer, placed at various locations along the rod, including the end, was used to detect the propagating waves. Figure 8.51(a) is a block diagram of the experimental apparatus.

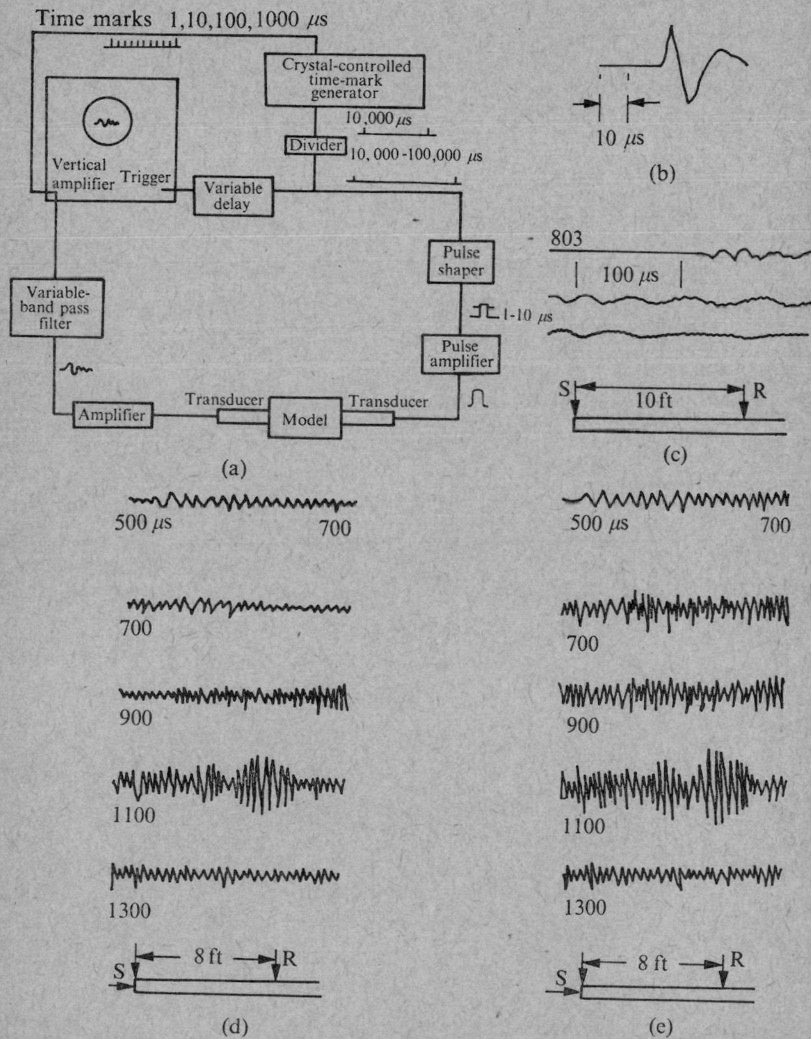

FIG. 8.51. (a) Block diagram of apparatus used in wide-band pulse studies on waves in rods; (b) acoustic pulse applied to the rod; (c) flexural disturbance induced by transversely pulsing the rod; (d) dispersed first longitudinal mode in a rod; (e) first and second longitudinal modes. (After Oliver [73, Figs. 2, 3, 5, 7, 9].)

Shown in Fig. 8.51(b) is the waveform of the acoustic pulse induced into the rod. By changing the orientation of the driving transducer, it was possible to induce antisymmetric or symmetric waves into the rod. For example, Fig. 8.51(c) shows the detected waveform 10 ft. (3·05 m) from the source when the pulse was imparted transversely to the rod, and represents a flexural disturbance similar in its early stages to those presented in § 3.6 on flexural waves. By longitudinally pulsing the rod, symmetrical waves could be induced. Two examples of the response are shown in Fig. 8.51(d) and (e). In the case of (d), the band pass of the filter was set to optimally detect the first longitudinal mode while in (e) the high-frequency cutoff was raised to include the second symmetric mode.

A very qualitative discussion on the dispersion of a sharp pulse, considering only the first mode, was given in § 8.4. It was pointed out that the initial signal would be of low frequency, with frequency increasing and an abrupt arrival of high-frequency components. Referring to Fig. 8.51(d) and following the discussion of Oliver, it is seen that at about 490 μs the train of long-period waves begins, with the signal frequency increasing to about 760 μs. The low-frequency waves arriving at about 750 μs are pointed out by Oliver as due to some antisymmetrical contributions. The short-period waves, resulting from the lower branch of the first-mode period-arrival time curve of Fig. 8.36 (and shown qualitatively in Fig. 8.37), arrive at about 760 μs. From this time on the disturbance consists of two parts, one a wave of increasing period, one of decreasing period. At about 900 μs, one period is about twice the other and at 1000 μs one is $\frac{3}{2}$ times the other. As time increases the two signals approach the same frequency and a distinct beating action is noted, as from about 1150 μs to 1250 μs. At the time corresponding to a minimum group velocity, the largest contribution occurs (at about 1250 μs). This is usually designated the 'Airy' phase. Theoretically, the first-mode contribution should sharply terminate at this point. The continuing signal noted in the detector output is explained by Oliver as resulting from a continued leakage of energy down the rod from an end resonance mode. In the case of Fig. 8.51(e), both first- and second-mode contributions are present. The second-mode contribution is initially noted at about 580 μs.

Hsieh and Kolsky [28] have considered the dispersion of a sharp pulse (about 2 μs) both theoretically and experimentally. The applied pulse was represented, for analytical purposes, by an error function of the noted duration. A Fourier superposition of 64 harmonics was used to predict the response, where the propagation velocity of each frequency component was determined from the Pochhammer–Chree frequency spectrum. The experimentally obtained response of the end of the bar was measured using a capacitance gauge. The results are shown in Fig. 8.52. The dashed line represents the end displacement that would have resulted from the error function pulse if dispersion were absent. The solid line is the result predicted by the

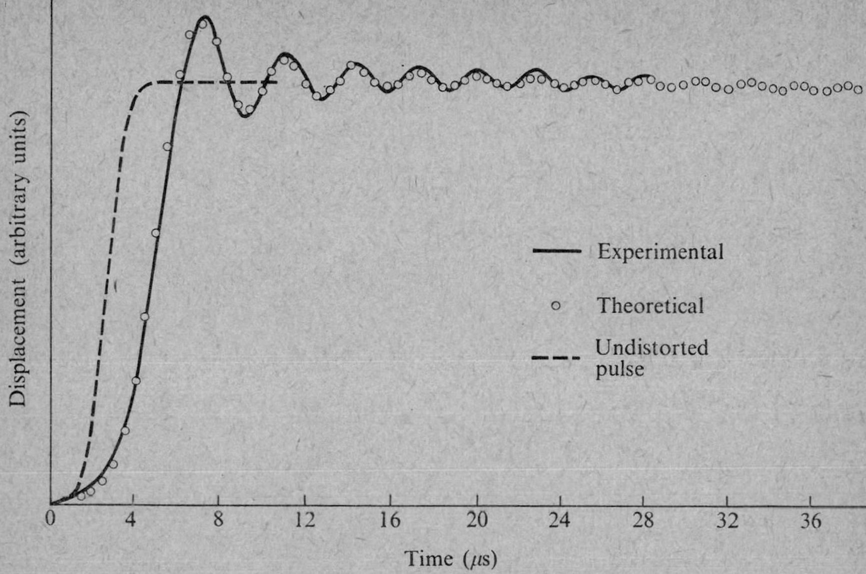

FIG. 8.52. The end displacement of a rod resulting from a sharp (2 μs) error-function pulse as predicted by Fourier superposition, simple theory, and as measured by experiment. (After Hsieh and Kolsky [28].)

Fourier superposition and the small circles give the experimentally measured displacements.

8.5.3. *Experimental results for step pulses*

A number of experimental investigations have been conducted in which a longitudinal step load was applied to the end of a rod or plate and the subsequent propagation measured. Miklowitz and Nisewanger [58] in 1956 used a shock tube to produce a 300 lb in^{-2} ($20{\cdot}7\times10^5$ N m^{-2}) step pressure pulse in a 1 in. (2·54 cm) diameter aluminum rod. Condenser microphone and strain-gauge transucers were used to measure the wave propagation at various locations along the rod. The microphone transducer was sensitive to the radial displacement of the rod surface while the strain gauges were oriented to be sensitive to the axial strain. The resulting displacement and strain records are shown in Fig. 8.53(a) and (b). It should be noted that the experimental boundary conditions are given by a step longitudinal stress and zero end shear stress. The mathematical boundary conditions for this problem, it will be recalled, are step longitudinal stress and zero radial displacement.

Intrepreting the records, it is apparent that the response at any station is quite different from the applied step function. For the locations close to the loaded end, it is to be noted that there is a considerable amount of high-frequency activity, particularly in the strain records. This is evidence of the

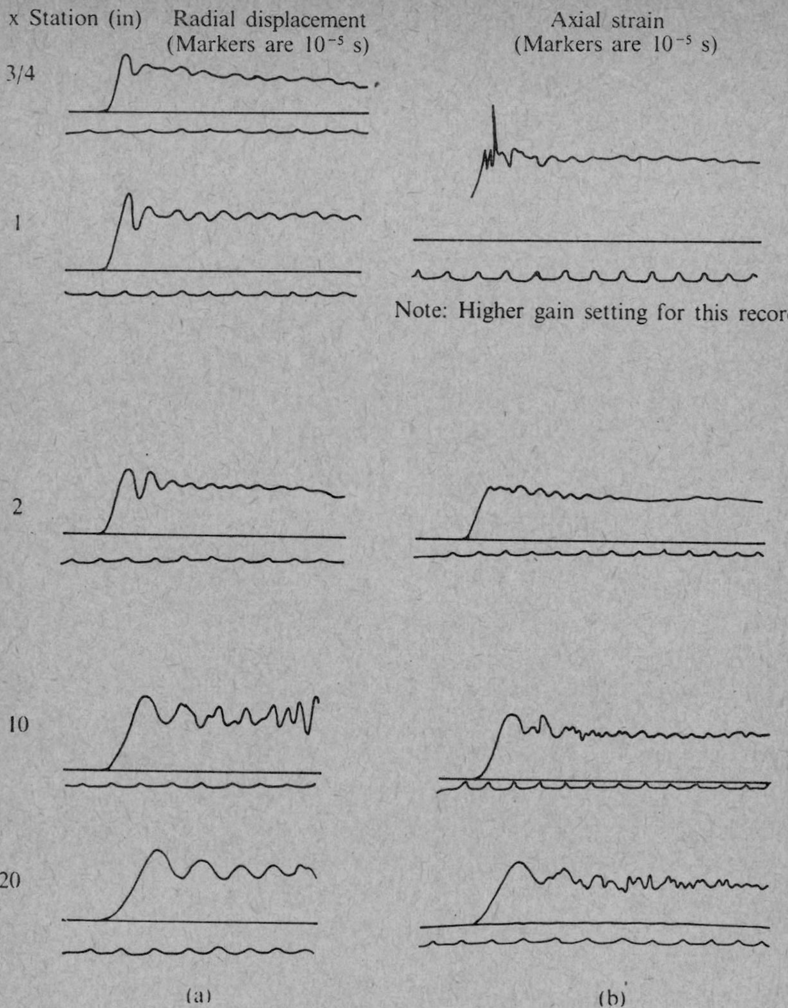

FIG. 8.53. (a) Radial displacement and (b) axial strain records at various locations along a 1 in. diameter bar subjected to a longitudinal step pressure pulse. (After Miklowitz and Nisewanger [58, Fig. 1].)

presence of higher-mode activity in the pulse. Considering the records from the more remote locations ($x = 20$ in. $= 51$ cm, say), it is seen that the head-of-the-pulse consists of the low-frequency, Airy function response predicted by exact theory and the various approximate theories for the rod such as the Love theory or the Mindlin–Herrmann theory.

Fox and Curtis [18, 10] have presented experimental results on longitudinal and bending waves in a rod subjected to step loading. A shock tube apparatus was used to produce the pressure pulse in a 1·5 in. (3·81 cm) diameter

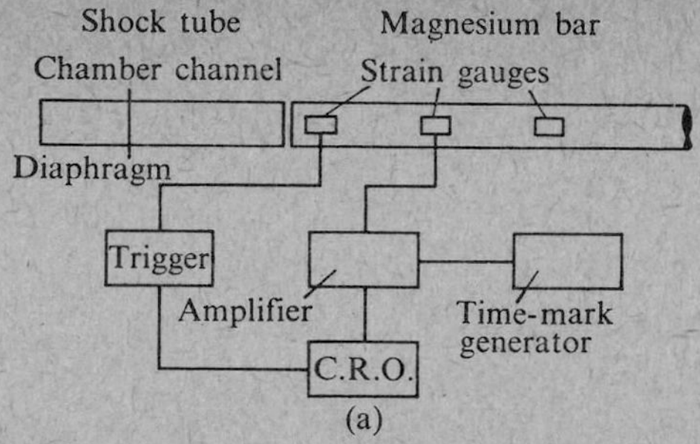

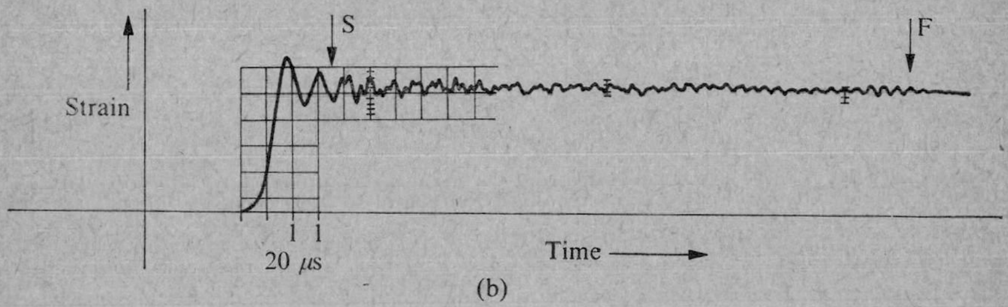

FIG. 8.54. (a) Apparatus used for the production and detection of stress waves, and (b) strain record at a distance of $z = 1{\cdot}51$ m from the end of a rod subjected to a longitudinal step pressure load. (After Fox and Curtis [18, Figs. 1, 2].)

magnesium bar. Piezoelectric strain gauges were used to detect the surface strains at several locations along the bar. The general experimental arrangement is shown in Fig. 8.54(a). The shock tube produced a 45 lb in^{-2} ($3{\cdot}14\times10^5$ N m^{-2}) step pulse in the bar that had less than a 1 μs rise time. A typical strain record for a longitudinal step pulse loading is shown in Fig. 8.54(b).

It is seen that the head-of-the-pulse has the Airy function behaviour predicted analytically for the far-field response. After the first one or two oscillations, the pulse becomes quite irregular in shape, as marked by the arrow S in the figure. On the basis of period-arrival time considerations, such as predicted in the Davies analysis of § 8.4, this behaviour is clearly associated with the arrival of second-mode contributions. As time passes, these contributions become of less importance and the signal becomes more regular. As the signal approaches the arrow F, the amplitude actually increases somewhat, and a type of beating action is perceptible. This again corresponds to the group-velocity minimum of the first mode and represents what was identified as the Airy phase in the review of Oliver's work earlier in this section. It should be noted that the signal terminates rather abruptly at this point.

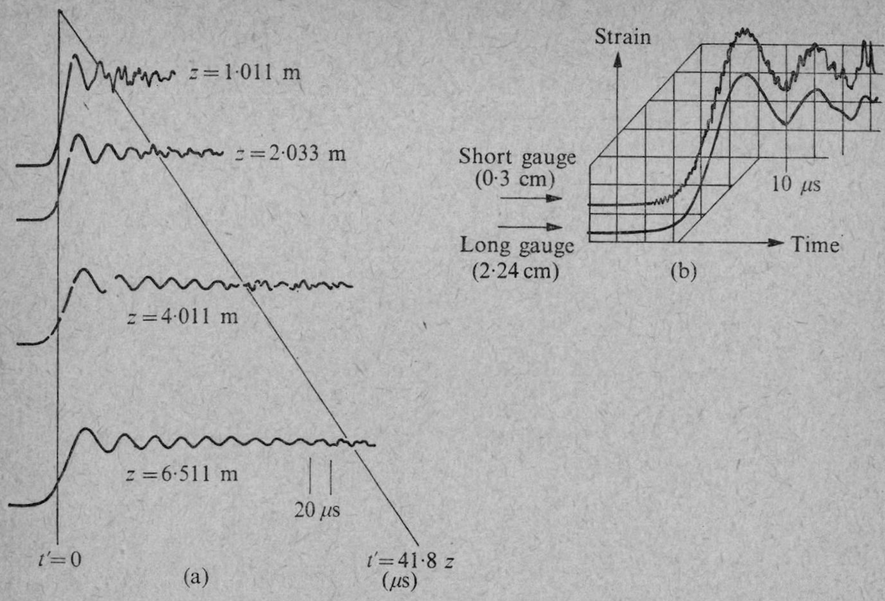

FIG. 8.55. (a) Onset of second mode contributions at various locations; (b) difference in strain signals as detected by short and long strain gauges. (After Curtis [10, Figs. 8, 9].)

Several other measurements of interest are presented in the work of Fox and Curtis. The strain record at various locations along the bar is shown in Fig. 8.55(a), showing the onset of the second-mode vibrations. A particularly interesting result is shown in Fig. 8.55(b) which brings out the influence of gauge size on the strain measurements. Using the short strain gauge, a large amount of high frequency is indicated that does not show on the records from larger gauges at the same location. By constructing frequency–arrival-time charts for the first six bar modes, Curtis showed on a qualitative basis that these higher modes appeared to account for the high-frequency activity.

Finally, mention should be made of the tests reported by Curtis [10] in which both longitudinal and flexural waves were induced in the rod using the shock tube. The technique used was to mask off the end of the rod so that the step pulse acted only on a semicircular end region, yielding a net moment on the rod as well as a net longitudunal force. Figure 8.56(a) shows the combined longitudinal–flexural response for a particular gauge location. The time scale of the record is greatly compressed over that of Fig. 8.54(b), so that about one-third of the longitudinal pulse of Fig. 8.54(b) is compressed into the first 200 μs shown in Fig. 8.56(a). The initiation of the flexural portion of the disturbance is marked by the arrow in the latter figure. The general behaviour of the flexural wave is seen to be quite similar to that previously shown in § 3.6 for the far-field response to impulsive moments. Figure 8.56(b) is a frequency

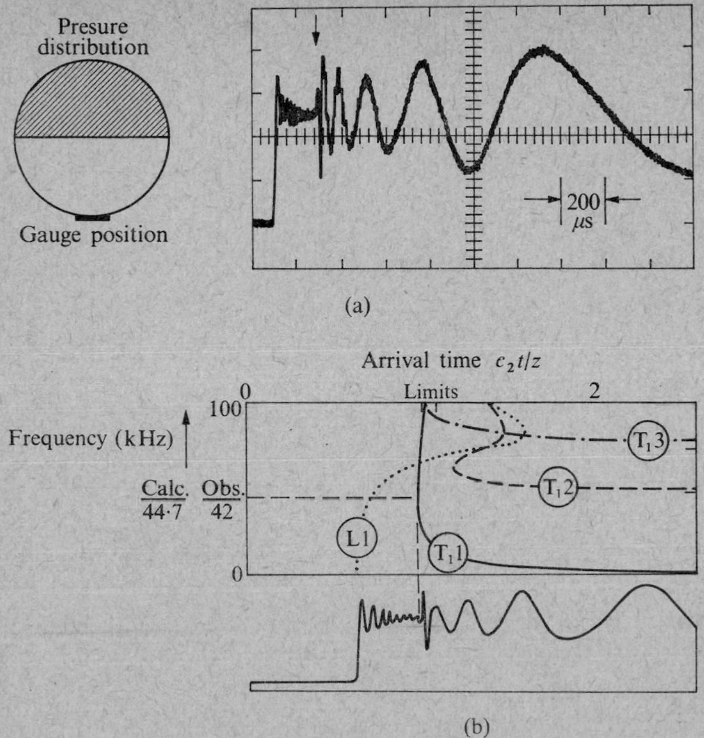

FIG. 8.56. (a) Combined longitudinal–flexural response at a gauge location of $z = 164$ cm from the end subjected to a step pressure pulse over a semicircular region; (b) frequency–arrival-time plot showing the flexural disturbance to be associated with the first transverse mode. (After Curtis [10, Figs. 11, 12].)

arrival-time plot showing the onset of the disturbance is clearly associated with the first antisymmetric, or flexural, mode.

In addition to the work described here, mention should be made of the results by Jones and Ellis [31], who were interested in the measurement of longitudinal waves propagating in a long, rectangular strip. A shock tube was used to step-pulse load the end of the strip quite in the manner shown for the circular rod in Fig. 8.54(a). The strips were of aluminum, 130 in. (3·3 m) in length, had a nominal depth of 1·5 in. (3·81 cm), and were of three different thicknesses, 0·064 in., 0·126 in., 0·252 in. (0·163 cm, 0·320 cm, 0·640 cm). Both condenser-microphone and strain-gauge records were taken at two different locations along the bar. Figure 8.57 shows the response from the microphone and strain-gauge pick-ups at the two locations for the three strip thicknesses. The microphone response at $x = 112·5$ in. $= 2·86$ m has the familiar Airy function form. A considerable amount of high-frequency

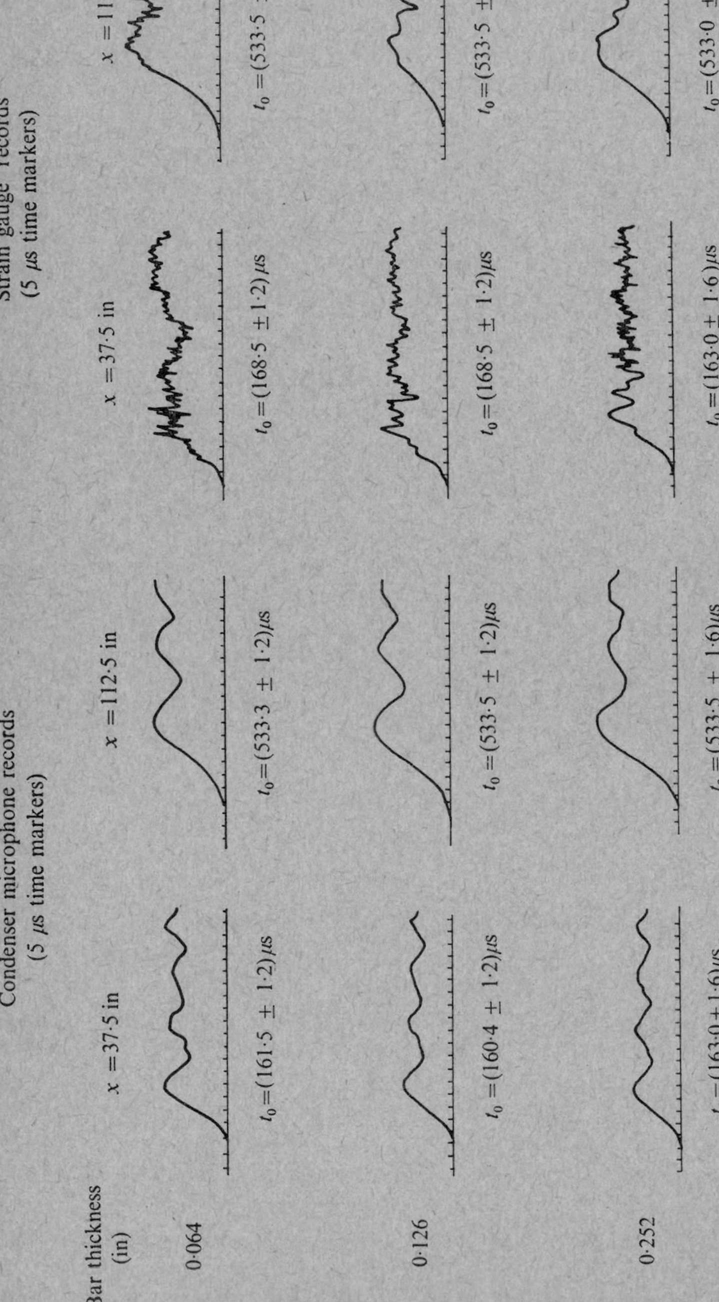

FIG. 8.57. Condenser microphone and strain-gauge records of the response at two different locations along aluminum strips of different thicknesses to a step pressure pulse. (After Jones and Ellis [31, Fig. 4].)

activity is to be noted in the strain-gauge responses, particularly at the closer location ($x = 37{\cdot}5$ in. $= 0{\cdot}95$ m) and for the thinner strips.

8.5.4. *Other studies of waves in cylindrical rods and shells*

Meitzler [49] has reported on the interesting phenomenon of mode coupling that can occur in longitudinal wave propagation in wires at critical frequencies. The basic aspects of the experimental equipment used in the investigation is shown in Fig. 8.58(a). A narrow-band acoustic pulse was applied to the end of

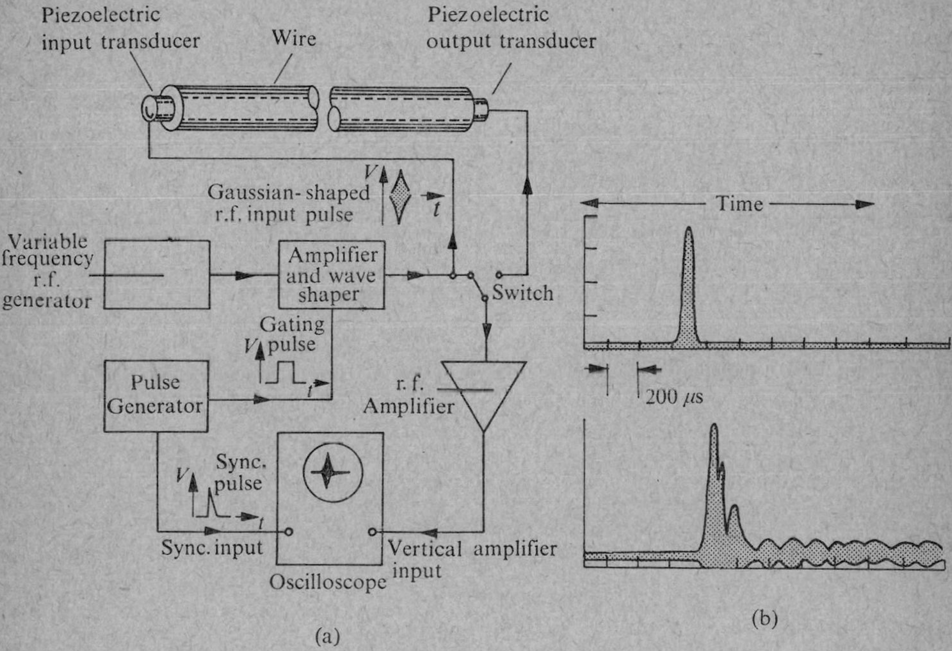

FIG. 8.58. (a) Schematic of apparatus used to apply a narrow-band pulse to a wire; (b) resulting wave transmission in an aluminum wire having a 0·178 cm diameter and a 365·8 cm length. Input pulse duration, 50 μs. Top figure is output at $f = 1{\cdot}280$ MHz, lower figure is output at $f = 1{\cdot}404$ MHz. (After Meitzler [49, Figs. 1, 2].)

the wire by a piezoelectric transducer and detected by the same means at the other end. The carrier frequency of the pulse was varied from 0·5 MHz to 4·0 MHz and a Gaussian pulse modulation was used having a duration of about 50 μs. A typical set of observations is shown in Fig. 8.58(b).

Using the apparatus described, a first-mode longitudinal pulse was initiated in the wire. The expected behaviour was for the modulated pulse to propagate at the group velocity of the carrier frequency, maintaining its Gaussian shape. In general, this is what occurred and the upper figure of Fig.8 .58(b) is typical of the output (and input) pulse at most frequencies. However, at certain critical frequencies the output was considerably distorted, such as in the lower figure of Fig. 8.58(b). Other examples are presented by Meitzler. It was found that the extent of the pulse distortion was dependent on the wire material and wire length. Critical frequencies for pulse distortion were also noted for other modes. The explanation given by Meitzler for the observed distortion was the phenomenon of mode coupling. By this was meant that, at critical frequencies, the initial energy launched into the wire in one mode would, during propagation, excite another rod mode. The resulting partition of the propagating energy into two modes considerably distorted the pulse. The explanation for the occurrence of this phenomenon was the presence of surface imperfections of the wire. Meeker and Meitzler [48] briefly review this phenomenon. Lange [41] has also contributed in this area, showing that the conversion of energy from the first longitudinal to first flexural mode can be observed in the long-wavelength limit.

Meitzler [50] has also reported on the phenomenon of backward wave transmission in rods and plates. The theoretical basis for this phenomenon is associated with a small region of the frequency spectrum having group and phase velocity of opposite signs. Referring to Fig. 8.10, such a region occurs, for positive real wavenumber, between the minimum of the $L(2)$ mode and the cutoff frequency, and is the dashed segment of the $L(2)$ branch. A similar segment exists for negative real wavenumber, where the group velocity is positive and the phase velocity is negative. The experimental arrangement used for investigating this phenomenon is the same as shown in Fig. 8.58(a). Figure 8.59(a) shows experimental results for the change in pulse delay for various carrier frequencies of the input Gaussian pulse. What occurs is that an input pulse excites several modes of the 212 cm, 0·144 cm diameter, isoelastic wire. As the carrier frequency is varied, the delay time of the various modes change or are expected to change, in accord with the predictions of Pochhammer–Chree theory. A theoretical plot of group velocity versus frequency for the first few rod modes is shown by the solid lines of Fig. 8.59(b). The modes $L(0, 1)$, $L(0, 2)$, $L(0, 3)$ refer to the first three, longitudinal modes while $F(1, 1)$, identified in Fig. 8.59(a), is the lowest flexural mode. Shown on Fig. 8.59(a) as solid lines are the theoretical frequency–delay-time curves predicted by Pochhammer–Chree theory. Thus the various peaks in the experimental response are fairly clearly associated with specific modes.

In interpreting Fig. 8.59(a), it is first noted that the first flexural mode $F(1, 1)$ is excited to a slight extent, as is evident in the top four photographs. The first longitudinal mode $L(0, 1)$ is strongly evident in all photographs. Consider now the $L(0, 2)$ and $L(0, 3)$ modes, which are identified as the $L(2)$ and $L(3)$ modes in the frequency spectrum of Fig. 8.10. Starting with the $L(0, 2)$ mode of Fig. 8.59(a) at high frequency (the bottom photograph) and decreasing frequency, it is seen that the group velocity becomes lower for increasing frequency. This is seen to be consistent with the $L(2)$ mode of the

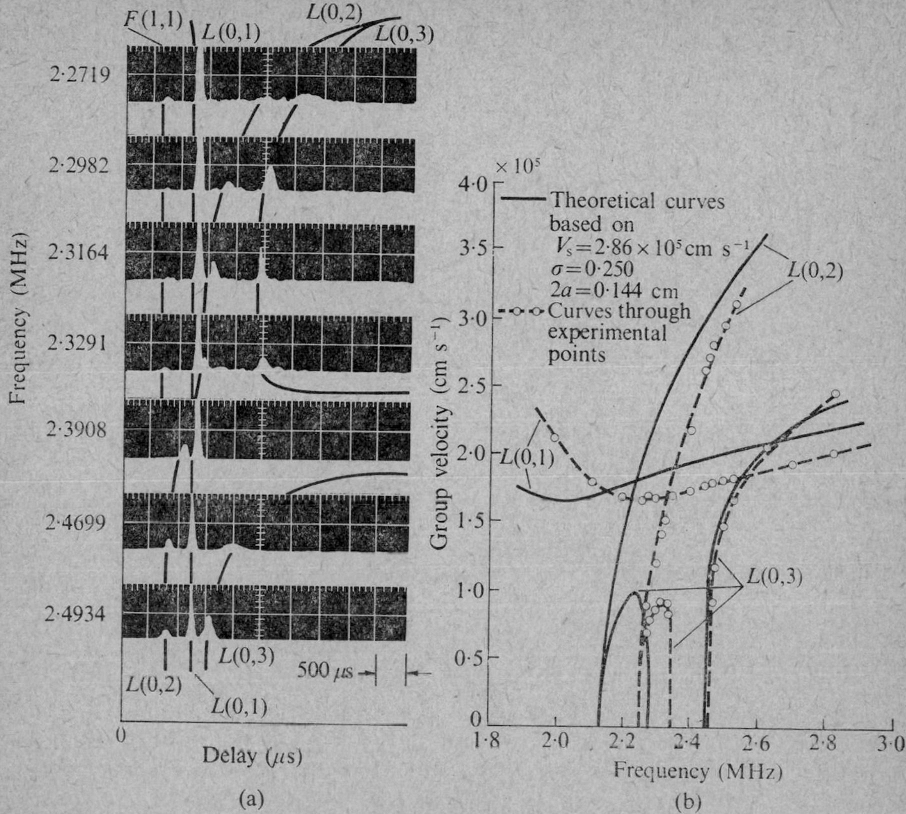

FIG. 8.59. (a) Variations in delay of the various modes excited by a single, narrow-band Gaussian pulse in an elastic wire; (b) theoretical and experimental curves of group velocity versus frequency. (After Meitzler [50, Figs. 4, 5].)

frequency spectrum. As frequency is decreased, the $L(2)$ mode approaches a local minimum, at which a cutoff frequency occurs. For the material and geometry used in the experiment, this is about at 2·2 MHz, or slightly above that of the top photograph of Fig. 8.59(a). It is seen in the latter figure that the $L(0, 2)$ pulse shape is becoming quite spread out at higher frequency, consistent with the increased dispersiveness as the minimum of the $L(2)$ mode is approached.

Considering now the $L(0, 3)$ mode of Fig. 8.59(a), it is seen for decreasing frequency in the lower two photographs that the delay is increasing, as is the amount of dispersion. At a frequency of 2·3908 MHz, the mode is completely absent. This behaviour is consistent with the $L(3)$ mode of the dispersion curve as it approaches its cutoff frequency. Now, for a further decrease in frequency, the $L(0, 3)$ mode is again present (top four photographs) with variation in delay and, again, increasing dispersiveness as frequency decreases to 2·2719 MHz. This behaviour is consistent with the $L(3)$ mode of the dispersion curve in the region of negative real wavenumber, where group velocity is positive but phase velocity negative. Again, it corresponds, in Fig. 8.10, to the short portion of the $L(3)$ branch occurring between $\xi = 0$ and the local minimum occurring at a negative value of ξ, and is the region of so-called backward wave transmission. Using the experimental results, Meitzler developed the group-velocity–frequency plots shown by the dashed lines in Fig. 8.59(b). Some difference existed between the experimental and theoretical

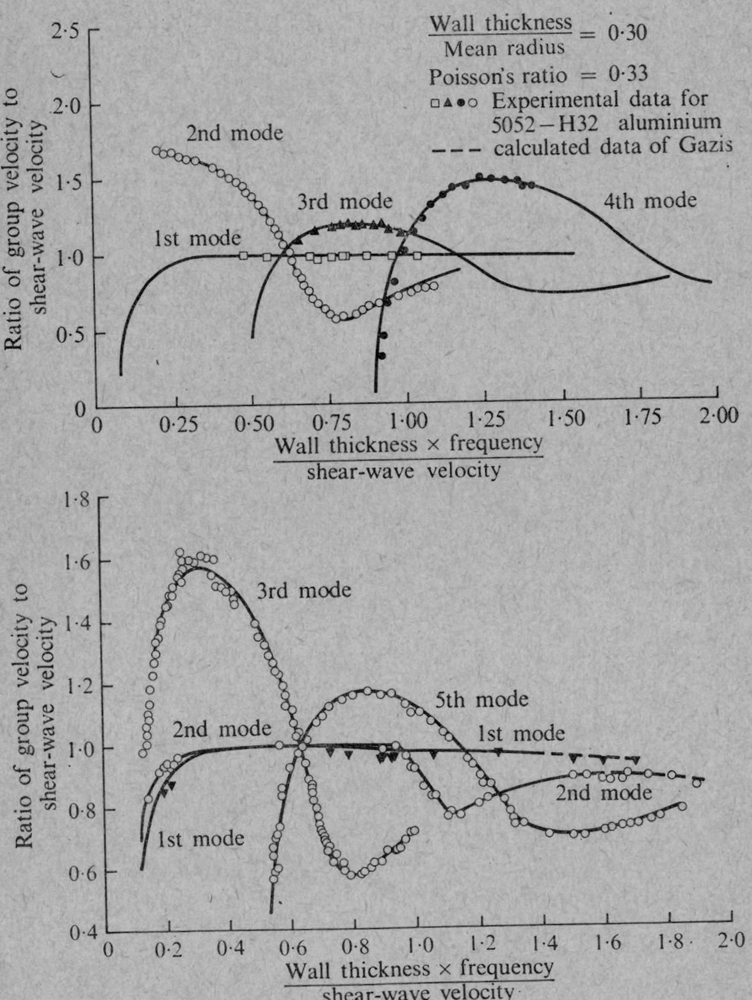

FIG. 8.60. Comparison of experimental results with Gazis' theory for waves in a cylindrical shell for (a) the first, second, third, and fourth longitudinal modes and (b) the first, second, third, and fifth non-axially symmetric modes. (After Fitch [14, Figs. 3, 5].)

results, as may be seen. Meitzler hypothesized, and put forth supporting arguments to show, that elastic anisotropy of the material was a cause of these discrepancies.

Experimental studies on the propagation of waves in cylindrical shells have been reported by Fitch [14]. The apparatus used for these tests was again essentially that shown in Fig. 8.54(a), except that a ring-shaped transducer was used to initiate the pulse into the cylindrical test specimen. The test specimen was a 6 ft (1·83 m) long hollow cylinder of 5052-H32 aluminum alloy. The outer diameter was $\frac{3}{8}$ in. (0·95 cm) and the wall thickness was 0·050 in. (1·27 mm). Narrow-band pulses were propagated in the shell and the group velocity of various modes were measured. The experimental results were compared to the theoretical predictions of the theory put forth by Gazis [20]. The results for the first few symmetric and non-symmetric modes are shown in Fig. 8.60. The comparison between theory and experiment was found to be extremely close. A comparison was also made by Fitch between the theoretical and experimental results for the second longitudinal mode in the shell and the theoretical results for the second longitudinal mode in a strip, with again excellent agreement being found.

References

1. ABRAMOWITZ, M. and STEGUN, I. A. *Handbook of mathematical functions: with formulas, graphs, and mathematical tables.* Dover Publications, New York (1965).
2. AGGRAWAL, R. R. and SHAW, E. A. G. Axially symmetric vibrations of a finite isotropic disk-IV. *J. acoust. Soc. Am.* **26,** 341 (1954).
3. ARNOLD, R. N. and WARBURTON, G. B. Flexural vibrations of the walls of thin cylindrical shells having freely supported ends. *Proc. R. Soc.* **A197,** 238–56 (1949).
4. BARON, M. L. and BLEICH, H. H. Tables of frequencies and modes of free vibration of infinitely long thin cylindrical shells. *J. appl. Mech.* **21,** 178–84 (1954).
5. BERTHOLF, L. D. Numerical solution for two-dimensional elastic wave propagation in finite bars. *J. appl. Mech.* **34,** 725–34 (1967).
6. BISHOP, R. E. D. Longitudinal waves in Beams. *Aeronant. Q.* **3,** 280 (1952).
7. CHREE, C. The equations of an isotropic elastic solid in polar and cylindrical coordinates, their solutions and applications. *Trans. Camb. phil. Soc. Math. Phys. Sci.* **14,** 250 (1889).
8. CHURCHILL, R. V. *Operational mathematics.* McGraw-Hill, New York (1958).
9. COOPER, R. M. and NAGHDI, P. M. Propagation of nonaxially symmetric waves in elastic cylindrical shells. *J. acoust. Soc. Am.* **29,** 1365–72 (1957).
10. CURTIS, C. W. Propagation of an elastic strain pulse in a semi-infinite bar, in *Stress wave propagation in materials,* (Ed. N. Davids) p. 15–43. Interscience, New York (1960).
11. DAVIES, R. M. A critical study of the Hopkinson pressure bar. *Phil. Trans. R. Soc.* **A240,** 375–457 (1948).

12. DeVault, G. P. and Curtis, C. W. Elastic cylinder with free lateral surface and mixed time-dependent end conditions. *J. acoust. Soc. Am.* **34,** 421–32 (1962).
13. Evans, J. F., Hadley, C. F., Eisler, J. D., and Silverman, D. A three-dimensional seismic wave model with both electrical and visual observation of waves. *Geophysics* **19,** 220–36 (1954).
14. Fitch, A. H. Observation of elastic-pulse propagation in axially symmetric and nonaxially symmetric longitudinal modes of hollow cylinders. *J. acoust. Soc. Am.* **35,** 706–8 (1962).
15. Flügge, W. *Statik und Dynamik der Schalen*, pp. 115 and 230. Springer-Verlag, Berlin (1934).
16. Folk, R. T. *Time dependent boundary value problems in elasticity.* Ph.D. Dissertation, Lehigh University, Bethlehem, Pennsylvania (1958).
17. ——, Fox, G., Shook, C. A., and Curtis, C. W. Elastic strain produced by sudden application of pressure to one end of a cylindrical bar—I. Theory. *J. acoust. Soc. Am.* **30,** 552–58 (1958).
18. Fox, G. and Curtis, C. W. Elastic strain produced by sudden application of pressure to one end of a cylindrical bar—II. Experimental observations. *J. acoust. Soc. Am.* **30,** 559–63 (1958).
19. Gazis, D. C. Exact analysis of the plane-strain vibrations of thick-walled hollow cylinders. *J. acoust. Soc. Am.* **30,** 786–94 (1958).
20. ——. Three-dimensional investigation of the propagation of waves in hollow circular cylinders—I. Analytical foundation II. Numerical results. *J. acoust. Soc. Am.* **31,** 568–78 (1959).
21. Goodman, L. E. Circular-crested vibrations of an elastic solid bounded by two parallel planes. *Proc. Ist Natn. Congr. appl. Mech.* pp. 65–73. ASME, New York (1952).
22. Green, W. A. Dispersion relations for elastic waves in bars, in *Progress in Solid Mechanics*, Vol. I, (Eds. I. N. Sneddon and R. Hill), Chap. 5. North-Holland Publishing Company, Amsterdam (1960).
23. Greenspon, J. E. Vibrations of a thick-walled cylindrical shell—comparison of the exact theory with approximate theories. *J. acoust. Soc. Am.* **32,** 571–8 (1960).
24. Harrison, M. *The propagation of elastic waves in a plate.* Report No. 872, the David W. Taylor model basin (1954).
25. Herrmann, G. and Mirsky, I. Three-dimensional and shell-theory analysis of axially symmetric motions of cylinders. *J. appl. Mech.* **23,** 563–8 (1956).
26. Holden, A. N. Longitudinal modes of elastic waves in isotropic cylinders and slabs. *Bell Sys. tech. J.* **30,** 956–69 (1951).
27. Hudson, G. E. Dispersion of elastic waves in solid circular cylinders. *Phys. Rev.* **63,** 46–51 (1943).
28. Hsieh, D. Y. and Kolsky, H. An experimental study of pulse propagation in elastic cylinders. *Proc. phys. Soc.* **71,** 608–12 (1958).
29. Hudson, G. E. Dispersion of elastic waves in solid circular cylinders. *Phys. Rev.* **63,** 46 (1943).
30. Jones, O. E. and Ellis, A. T. Longitudinal strain pulse propagation in wide rectangular bars, Part I—Theoretical considerations. *J. appl. Mech.* **30,** 51–60 (1963).

31. JONES, O. E. and ELLIS, A. T. Longitudinal strain pulse propagation in wide rectangular bars, Part II—Experimental observations and comparisons with theory. *J. appl. Mech.* **30**, 61–9 (1963).
32. —— and NORWOOD, F. R. Axially symmetric cross-sectional strain and stress distributions in suddenly loaded cylindrical elastic bars. *J. appl. Mech.* **34**, 718–24 (1967).
33. KAUL, R. K. and MCCOY, J. J. Propagation of axisymmetric waves in a circular semi-infinite elastic rod. *J. acoust. Soc. Am.* **36**, 653–60 (1964).
34. KENNARD, E. H. The new approach to shell theory: circular cylinders. *J. appl. Mech.* **75**, 33–40 (1953).
35. KENNEDY, L. W. and JONES, O. E. Longitudinal wave propagation in a circular bar loaded suddenly by a radially distributed end stress. *J. appl. Mech.* **36**, 470–8 (1969).
36. KOLSKY, H. The propagation of longitudinal elastic waves along cylindrical bars. *Phil. Mag.* **45**, 712–26 (1954).
37. KYNCH, G. J. *Br. J. appl. Phys.* **8**, 64 (1957).
38. —— and GREEN, W. A. *Q. Jl. Mech. appl. Math.* **10**, 63 (1957).
39. LAMB, H. On waves in an elastic plate. *Proc. R. Soc.* **A93**, 114 (1917).
40. LAMÉ, G. *Leçons sur la théorie mathématique de l'elasticité des corps solides* (2nd edn). Gauthier-Villars, Paris (1866).
41. LANGE, J. N Mode conversion in the long-wavelength limit. *J. acoust. Soc. Am.* **41**, 1449–52 (1967).
42. LIN, T. C. and MORGAN, G. W. A study of axisymmetric vibrations of cylindrical shells as affected by rotatory inertia and transverse shear. *J. appl. Mech.* **23**, 255–61 (1956).
43. LOVE, A. E. H. *A treatise on the mathematical theory of elasticity*. Dover Publications, New York (1944).
44. LYON, R. H. Response of an elastic plate to localized driving forces. *J. acoust. Soc. Am.* **27**, 259 (1955).
45. MAGNUS, W. and OBERHETTINGER, F. *Special functions of mathematical physics*. Chelsea Publishing Company, New York (1949).
46. MCLACHLAN, N. W. *Bessel functions for engineers*. Clarendon Press, Oxford (1961).
47. MCNIVEN, H. D., SHAH, A. H., and SACKMAN, J. L. Axially symmetric waves in hollow, elastic rods. Parts I and II. *J. acoust. Soc. Am.* **40**, 784–92 and 1073–6 (1966).
48. MEEKER, T. R. and MEITZLER, A. H. Guided wave propagation in elongated cylinders and plates, in *Physical acoustics*, (Ed. W. P. Mason) Vol. 1, Part A, Chap. 2. Academic Press, New York (1964).
49. MEITZLER, A. H. Mode coupling occurring in the propagation of elastic pulses in wires. *J. acoust. Soc. Am.* **33**, 435–45 (1961).
50. ——. Backward-wave transmission of stress pulses in elastic cylinders and plates. *J. acoust. Soc. Am.* **38**, 835–42 (1965).
51. MIKLOWITZ, J. Travelling compressional waves in an elastic rod according to the more exact one-dimensional theory. *Proc. IInd U.S. natn. Congr. appl. Mech.* pp. 179–186. ASME, New York (1955).

52. MIKLOWITZ, J. The propagation of compressional waves in a dispersive elastic rod, Part I—Results from the theory. *J. appl. Mech.* **24**, 231–9 (1957).
53. ——. On the use of approximate theories of an elastic rod in problems of longitudinal impact. *Proc. IIIrd U.S. natn. Congr. appl. Mech.* pp. 215–24. ASME, New York (1958).
54. ——. Plane-stress unloading waves emanating from a suddenly punched hole in a stretched elastic plate. *J. appl. Mech.* **27**, 165–7 (1960).
55. ——. Flexural stress waves in an infinite elastic plate due to a suddenly applied concentrated transverse load. *J. appl. Mech.* **27**, 681–9 (1960).
56. ——. Transient compressional waves in an infinite elastic plate or elastic layer overlying a rigid half-space. *J. appl. Mech.* **29**, 53–60 (1962).
57. ——. Transient wave propagation in elastic rods and plates. *J. geophys. Res.* **68**, 1190–2 (1963).
58. —— and NISEWANGER, C. R. The propagation of compressional waves in a dispersive elastic rod, Part II—Experimental results and comparison with theory. *J. appl. Mech.* **24**, 240–4 (1957).
59. MINDLIN, R. D. Influence of rotatory inertia and shear on flexural motions of isotropic, elastic plates. *J. appl. Mech.* **18**, 31 (1951).
60. ——. The thickness shear and flexural vibrations of crystal plates. *J. appl. Phys.* **22**, 316 (1951).
61. ——. *An introduction to the mathematical theory of vibrations of elastic plates.* U.S. Army Signal Corps Engineering Laboratories, Fort Monmouth, New Jersey (1955).
62. ——. Vibrations of an infinite elastic plate at its cut-off frequencies. *Proc. IIIrd U.S. natn. Congr. appl. Mech.* p. 225 (1958).
63. ——. Waves and vibrations in isotropic, elastic plates. In *Structural Mechanics* (Eds. J. N. Goodier and N. Hoff). pp. 199–232 (1960).
64. —— and HERRMANN, G. A one-dimensional theory of compressional waves in an elastic rod. *Proc. Ist U.S. natn. Congr. appl. Mech.* pp. 187–91 (1950).
65. —— and MCNIVEN, H. D. Axially symmetric waves in elastic rods. *J. appl. Mech.* **27**, 145–51 (1960).
66. —— and MEDICK, M. A. Extensional vibrations of elastic plates. *J. appl. Mech.* **26**, 561–9 (1959).
67. —— and ONOE, M. Mathematical theory of vibrations of elastic plates. *Proceedings of the XIth Annual Symposium on Frequency Control* pp. 17–40. U. S. Army Signal Corps Engineering Laboratories, Fort Monmouth, New Jersey (1957).
68. MIRSKY, I. and HERRMANN, G. Nonaxially symmetric motions of cylindrical shells. *J. acoust. Soc. Am.* **29**, 1116–23 (1957).
69. —— ——. Axially symmetric motions of thick cylindrical shells. *J. appl. Mech.* **25**, 97–102 (1958).
70. MORSE, P. and FESHBACH, H. *Methods of theoretical physics* Vol. I and II. McGraw-Hill, New York (1953).
71. MORSE, R. W. Velocity of compressional waves in rods of rectangular cross-section. *J. acoust. Soc. Am.* **22**, 219 (1950).
72. NAGHDI, P. M. and COOPER, R. M. Propagation of elastic waves in cylindrical shells, including the effects of transverse shear and rotatory inertia. *J. acoust. Soc. Am.* **28**, 56–63 (1956).

73. OLIVER, J. Elastic wave dispersion in a cylindrical rod by a wide-band short-duration pulse technique. *J. acoust. Soc. Am.* **29**, 189–94 (1957).
74. ONOE, M. A study of the branches of the velocity-dispersion equations of elastic plates and rods. *Report Joint Commitee on Ultrasonics of the Institute of Electrical Communication Engineers and the Acoustical Society of Japan* (1955).
75. ——, MCNIVEN, H. D., and MINDLIN, R. D. Dispersion of axially symmetric waves in elastic rods. *J. appl. Mech.* **29**, 729–34 (1962).
76. PAO, Y.-H. The dispersion of flexural waves in an elastic circular cylinder, Part II. *J. appl. Mech.* **29**, 61–4 (1962).
77. —— and MINDLIN, R. D. Dispersion of flexural waves in an elastic, circular cylinder. *J. appl. Mech.* **27**, 513–20 (1960).
78. PRESCOTT, J. Elastic waves and vibrations of thin rods. *Phil. Mag.* **33**, 703 (1942).
79. RAYLEIGH, J. W. S. *The theory of sound*, Vol. I and II. Dover Publications, New York (1945).
80. REDWOOD, M. *Mechanical Waveguides*. Pergamon Press, New York (1960).
81. REISSNER, E. *J. math. Phys.* **29**, 90–5 (1950).
82. SCOTT, R. A. and MIKLOWITZ, J. Transient compressional waves in an infinite elastic plate with a circular cylindrical cavity. *J. appl. Mech.* **31**, 627–34 (1964).
83. —— ——. Transient compressional waves in an infinite elastic plate generated by a time-dependent radial body force. *J. appl. Mech.* **32**, 706–8 (1965).
84. —— ——. Transient non-axisymmetric wave propagation in an infinite isotropic elastic plate. *Int. J. Solids Struct.* **5**, 65–79 (1969).
85. SKALAK, R. Longitudinal impact of a semi-infinite circular elastic bar. *J. appl. Mech.* **34**, 59–64 (1957).
86. TIMOSHENKO, S. P. On the correction for shear of the differential equation for transverse vibrations of prismatic bars. *Phil. Mag.* Ser. 6, **41**, 744 (1921).
87. TOLSTOY, I. and USDIN, E. Wave propagation in elastic plates: low and high mode dispersion. *J. acoust. Soc. Am.* **29**, 37–42 (1957).
88. TORVIK, J. Reflection of wave trains in semi-infinite plates. *J. acoust. Soc. Am.* **41**, 346–53 (1967).
89. VOLTERRA, E. A one-dimensional theory of wave-propagation in elastic rods based on the 'method of internal constraints'. *Ing.-Arch.* **23**, 410 (1955).
90. YU, Y.-Y. Vibrations of thin cylindrical shells analysed by means of Donnell-type equations. *J. Aerospace Sci.* **25**, 699–715 (1958).

Problems

8.1. Sketch the group velocity curves for the SH wave modes of a plate.

8.2. In addition to the frequency spectrum (ω versus ξ) and dispersion curves (c versus ξ), wave propagation data is sometimes presented in terms of c versus ω. Sketch this set of curves for the SH wave modes in a plate.

8.3. Consider the propagation of SH waves in a plate of thickness $2b$, where fixed boundary conditions govern at $y = \pm b$. Obtain the frequency equation and compare the resulting frequency spectrum to that of SH waves in a traction-free plate.

8.4. Consider the case of SH waves propagating in a plate with elastically restrained boundaries. Thus, at $y = \pm b$, we have $\tau_{yz} = ku_z$. Sketch the frequency spectrum. Illustrate the transition between fixed boundaries (see Problem 8.3) and free boundaries (Fig. 8.3) as k varies from infinity to zero.

8.5. Consider the propagation of SH waves in a symmetrical, three-layered plate. Using coordinates of Fig. 8.1, let the plate be defined by the mid layer $y = \pm b$, with attached layers at $y = +b$ and $y = -b$ each of thickness a. Assume the layers are of the same material and have a shear velocity less than the mid layer. Derive the frequency equation for propagation of waves in the positive x direction. Determine what simplifications occur in the frequency equation when $\gamma b \gg 1$ or $\gamma b \ll 1$.

8.6. Wave propagation in plates has been presented in terms of plane-strain conditions. Express the governing equations and solution forms for plane stress conditions. Thus, referring to Fig. 8.1, assume the thickness of the plate in the z direction to be finite ($z = \pm a$) and small compared to longitudinal wavelengths. Only changes in elastic constants should be necessary. What restrictions will be placed on the number of modes of the Rayleigh–Lamb spectrum that can be considered in describing wave propagation in such a system?

8.7. Using the basic relationship that $d\omega/d\gamma = c_g$, sketch the approximate form of the group-velocity curves for the first six modes shown for the plate in Fig. 8.9 for Re$\xi < 3$. Note regions of negative group velocity for certain of the modes, and recall the discussion given to this aspect in conjunction with Fig. 8.10.

8.8. Consider a semi-infinite plate having traction-free lateral surfaces on $y = \pm b$ and having a stress-free edge at $x = 0$. Investigate the reflection of incident longitudinal plane waves from the boundary. Thus, obtain reflection coefficient ratios for the various wave components.

8.9. Consider the vibrations of a bounded plate, where the dimensions are $2a$ and $2b$ in the x, y directions, respectively, while plane-strain conditions prevail in the z direction. Establish sets of mixed boundary conditions on $x = \pm a$, $y = \pm b$ that enable the problem of the free vibrations of such a plate to be solved.

8.10. Attempt to discover if the analogue of the Lamé mode in plates also exists for circular rods. Thus, do special solutions to the Pochhammer–Chree equation exist for $\xi = \beta$?

8.11. Starting with the Pochhammer–Chree equation, attempt to recover the 'thin rod' results by assuming that $2\pi/\beta$, $2\pi/\alpha \gg a$. Thus, see if results analogous to 8.1.92, 8.1.95 for the plate can be obtained for the rod.

8.12. Suppose one has a thin, cylindrical rod of diameter d, length l, such that the longitudinal resonance is adequately described by simple classical rod theory. Give a qualitative sketch of the expected change in resonant frequency that would occur if (a) the length is held constant and the diameter is increased and (b) the diameter is held constant and the length is increased.

8.13. Consider the propagation of pure torsional waves in the hollow cylinder described by the boundary conditions (8.2.50). Using the displacement equations of motion directly, obtain the frequency equation for the propagation of torsional waves. The result should, of course, agree with (8.2.66) obtained by the general, potential function approach.

8.14. Attempt to derive the frequency equation for pure torsional waves in a composite rod. The rod is defined by an inner cylinder of radius a attached to an outer shell of inner radius a, outer radius b. Assume the shear-wave velocity of the inner cylinder is greater than that of the shell.

8.15. Consider the development of an approximate theory for longitudinal waves in a plate, assuming displacements of the form

$$u(x, y, t) = u^{(0)}(x, t) + y^2 u^{(2)}(x, t)$$

$$v(x, y, t) = y v^{(1)}(x, t) + y^3 v^{(3)}(x, t)$$

which restrict the motion to symmetric only. Sketch the various displacement modes for these displacements. Derive the plate stress equations of motion and boundary conditions for the assumed displacement forms. Derive the plate stress–displacement relations. Simplify the development by letting

$$u^{(2)} = v^{(3)} = 0,$$

and give the resulting stress equations of motion, stress–displacement relations, and boundary conditions. Obtain the plate displacement equations of motion. Obtain the frequency equation and draw the frequency spectrum, using the non-dimensionalized frequency and wavenumbers $\Omega = 2b\omega/\pi c_2$, $\bar{\xi} = 2b\xi/\pi$. Determine the cutoff frequencies of the plate, comparing the values obtained with those of exact theory for $\nu = 0{\cdot}31$.

8.16. Consider the Mindlin approximate plate equations, given by (8.3.30) and the problem of reflection of flexural waves from the edge of a semiinfinite plate, $z = \pm h/2$, $y \geqslant 0$. First consider plane harmonic waves to be at normal incidence to the boundary $y = 0$ and obtain the reflected wave amplitude ratios. Now suppose plane waves arrive at oblique incidence. Determine the reflected wave system, including expressions for amplitude ratios.

8.17. Consider the case of longitudinal waves in a stepped rod, as governed by Mindlin–Herrmann theory. Let the rod be defined by $r = a$, $z \leqslant 0$, $r = b$, $z > 0$, where $b > a$. The material properties are the same on either side of the step at $z = 0$. Consider a harmonic, longitudinal wave to be propagating toward the step in the smaller rod. Determine the expressions for the reflected–transmitted wave systems, including amplitude ratios, if possible. Can any statements be made regarding the magnitude of the discontinuity relative to wavelength and/or rod radii? Are comparisons to the reflection–transmission results for the classical rod, given in Chapter 1, possible?

8.18. Consider the propagation of torsional waves in a semi-infinite cylinder of radius a. First consider the displacement $u_\theta(r, \theta, 0, t) = U_0 \exp(i\omega t)$ applied at $z = 0$, and attempt to solve for the wave propagation. What would be the nature of the radial distribution of displacement necessary to excite and propagate only the first torsional mode? Now attempt to solve the case of an applied displacement $u_0 H\langle t\rangle$ applied at $z = 0$. The Laplace transform is suggested. In all of the above work, it is suggested that the displacement equations of motion be used directly.

Appendix A: The elasticity equations

THE objective here is to review briefly the basic equations for an elastic continuum, including the concepts of strain and stress and the development of the constitutive relations. All equations will be referred to Cartesian coordinates, enabling the intricacies of tensor calculus to be avoided. The results for cylindrical and spherical coordinates will merely be summarized.

A.1. Notation

The use of index notation, summation conventions, and certain symbols enables the equations of a continuum to be developed and displayed with remarkable brevity. We first delineate all variables by numerical indices instead of by individual letters or alphabetic subscripts. Thus x_1, x_2, x_3 instead of x, y, z or x_x, x_y, x_z. Using index notation, we may write the equation

$$u = a_1x_1+a_2x_2+a_3x_3. \tag{A.1.1}$$

Using a conventional summation symbol, this may be written as

$$u = \sum_{i=1}^{3} a_ix_i. \tag{A.1.2}$$

We now introduce the summation convention wherein a repeated index denotes summation over the range of the index. Thus, (A.1.1) simply reduces to

$$u = a_ix_i \qquad (i = 1, 2, 3). \tag{A.1.3}$$

A repeated index may be changed to a different repeating index. Thus

$$a_ix_i = a_jx_j. \tag{A.1.4}$$

More than one double index may appear. Thus the equation

$$\begin{aligned} v = {} & a_{11}x_1x_1+a_{12}x_1x_2+a_{13}x_1x_3+ \\ & +a_{21}x_2x_1+a_{22}x_2x_2+a_{23}x_2x_3+ \\ & +a_{31}x_3x_1+a_{32}x_3x_2+a_{33}x_3x_3 \end{aligned} \tag{A.1.5}$$

becomes

$$v = a_{ij}x_ix_j \qquad (i, j = 1, 2, 3). \tag{A.1.6}$$

One indicial equation may represent several equations in extended notation. Thus

$$w_i = a_{ij}x_j \qquad (i, j = 1, 2, 3). \tag{A.1.7}$$

is equivalent to

$$\begin{aligned} w_1 &= a_{11}x_1 + a_{12}x_2 + a_{13}x_3, \\ w_2 &= a_{21}x_1 + a_{22}x_2 + a_{23}x_3, \\ w_3 &= a_{31}x_1 + a_{32}x_2 + a_{33}x_3. \end{aligned} \tag{A.1.8}$$

Two special symbols find wide use in indicial representation of equations. The first is the Kronecker delta defined as

$$\delta_{ij} = \begin{cases} +1, & i = j \\ 0, & i \neq j. \end{cases} \tag{A.1.9}$$

The second is the permutation symbol defined as

$$e_{ijk} = \begin{cases} +1, & ijk \text{ even permutation of } 1, 2, 3 \\ -1, & ijk \text{ odd permutation of } 1, 2, 3 \\ 0, & \text{any two indices equal.} \end{cases} \tag{A.1.10}$$

Thus we have $\delta_{11} = \delta_{22} = \delta_{33} = 1$, $\delta_{12} = 0$, $\delta_{23} = 0$, etc., and

$$e_{123} = e_{231} = e_{312} = 1, \qquad e_{213} = e_{321} = e_{132} = -1,$$
$$e_{112} = 0, \qquad e_{223} = 0, \text{ etc.}$$

Finally, we note the derivative notation where differentiation with respect to a variable will be indicated by a comma followed by an index. Thus

$$u_{,j} = \frac{\partial u}{\partial x_j}, \qquad v_{i,j} = \frac{\partial v_i}{\partial x_j}. \tag{A.1.11}$$

A number of the common vector operations may be easily written in index notation. A few of these are summarized in the following with their corresponding index notation form given alongside.

$$\begin{aligned} \mathbf{a} \cdot \mathbf{b} &\sim a_i b_i, \\ \mathbf{a} \times \mathbf{b} &\sim e_{ijk} a_k b_j, \\ \nabla\phi &\sim \phi_{,i}, \\ \nabla \cdot \mathbf{A} &\sim A_{i,i}, \\ \nabla \times \mathbf{A} &\sim e_{ijk} A_{k,j}, \\ \nabla \cdot \nabla\phi = \nabla^2\phi &\sim \phi_{,ii}. \end{aligned} \tag{A.1.12}$$

A.2. Strain

Consider a continuous medium of volume V and surface S that undergoes deformation. Before deformation, point P_0 is located by the position vector

X_i and P_1, a neighbouring point of P_0 is located by the vector dX_i from P_0. After deformation, P_0 goes into P_0' and is located by the vector x_i and P_1 goes into P_1' and is located by the vector dx_i relative to P_0'. The displacement of P_0 to P_0' is measured by the vector u_i. The displacement of P_1 to P_1' is measured by $\hat{u}_i$. The final volume and surface of the deformed body is V' and S' respectively. These various quantities are shown in Fig. A.1.

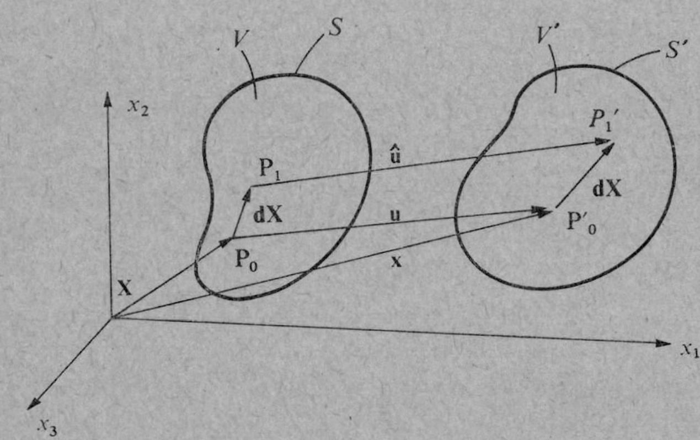

FIG. A.1. Deformation of a continuum of volume V into the volume V'.

The relationships between the various vector quantities are

$$x_i = X_i + u_i, \qquad u_i + dx_i = \hat{u}_i + dX_i. \tag{A.2.1}$$

But, from the first equation we have that $dx_i = dX_i + du_i$. Substituting in the second equation we have

$$\hat{u}_i = u_i + du_i. \tag{A.2.2}$$

To first order, we may express du_i as

$$du_i = u_{i,j}\, dx_j, \tag{A.2.3}$$

which may be put in the form

$$du_i = \tfrac{1}{2}(u_{j,i} + u_{j,i})\, dx_i + \tfrac{1}{2}(u_{i,j} - u_{j,i})\, dx_i. \tag{A.2.4}$$

We then define the infinitesimal strain and rotation tensors respectively as

$$e_{ij} = \tfrac{1}{2}(u_{i,j} + u_{j,i}), \qquad \omega_{ij} = \tfrac{1}{2}(u_{i,j} - u_{j,i}). \tag{A.2.5}$$

The result (A.2.4) emphasizes that the kinematics of an arbitrary neighbouring point of P_0 is governed by the local strain-gradient field $u_{i,j}$ and that the motion is a combination of local distortion effects e_{ij} and also local rigid-body rotation effects ω_{ij}.

A.3. Stress

Consider a continuum of volume V and surface S that is acted upon by various forces as shown in Fig. A.2(a). As a result of these forces, tractive

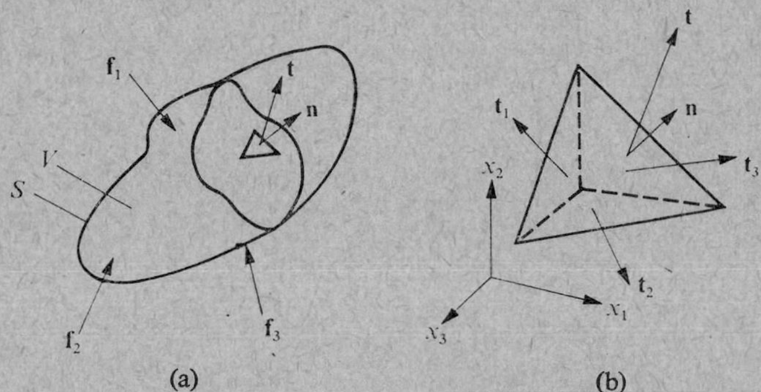

FIG. A.2. (a) A continuum subjected to forces, and (b) a trihedral element of that continuum.

forces will act on an arbitrary surface element within the body, as shown in Fig. A.2(b). The traction vector is given by

$$\mathbf{t} = t_j \mathbf{i}_j, \tag{A.3.1}$$

where the traction components t_j serve to define the stress tensor τ_{ij} by

$$t_i = \tau_{ij} \mathrm{n}_j. \tag{A.3.2}$$

In Cartesian extended notation these equations take the form

$$\begin{aligned} t_x &= \tau_{xx} l + \tau_{xy} m + \tau_{xz} n, \\ t_y &= \tau_{yx} l + \tau_{yy} m + \tau_{yz} n, \\ t_z &= \tau_{zx} l + \tau_{zy} m + \tau_{zz} n. \end{aligned} \tag{A.3.3}$$

A.4. Conservation equations

Certain fundamental axioms are essential to the construction of a continuum theory. Although the goal of this brief review is limited to the equations of infinitesimal, isotropic elasticity, development along certain fundamental lines is helpful in appreciating the basic unity of the theory and for observing the means by which effects of electrical or thermal phenomena may be included.

The axioms accepted as true on the basis of our experience in the physical world are:

conservation of mass, conservation of momentum, conservation of moment of momentum, and conservation of energy.

Should the inclusion of electrical or thermal effects be sought, axioms pertaining to the principle of entropy, conservation of charge, Faraday's law, and Ampere's law would need be appended. Our concern will only be with the mechanical effects, however. The mathematical statements of the foregoing principles will now be given.

A.4.1. *Conservation of mass*

Consider the volume V of surface S. At any instant, the total mass is given by

$$m = \int_V \rho \, \mathrm{d}V. \tag{A.4.1}$$

The principle, or axiom, of the conservation of mass states that time rate of change of this mass is zero or $\mathrm{D}m/\mathrm{D}t = 0$. Thus

$$\frac{\mathrm{D}}{\mathrm{D}t} \int_V \rho \, \mathrm{d}V = 0, \tag{A.4.2}$$

where ρ is the mass density. A statement of the last form is sometimes referred to as global conservation of mass.

(*Remark.* A few words on the nature of the time derivative are warranted. Consider the time variation of the quantity $F(x_1, x_2, x_3, t)$ with time. We may take two viewpoints: (1) focusing our attention on a point in space and determine the time rate of change of F at that point; (2) focusing our attention on a material point, following this point as time passes, and determining the time rate of change of F at this material point. Regardless of viewpoint, however, we have that

$$\frac{\mathrm{D}F}{\mathrm{D}t} = \left.\frac{\partial F}{\partial t}\right|_{x_i = \text{constant}} + \left.\frac{\partial F}{\partial x_i}\right|_{t = \text{constant}} \dot{x}_i. \tag{A.4.3}$$

Now, by viewpoint (1), $\dot{x}_i = 0$ in the above so that

$$\mathrm{D}F/\mathrm{D}t = \partial F/\partial t. \tag{A.4.4}$$

This is known as the spatial or Eulerian description. From viewpoint (2), however, the extended derivative (A.4.3) must be used and such a form is called the material or Lagrangian description. In our treatment of elasticity, the former will generally be used, so that distinction between total and partial derivatives disappears.)

The differential equation form of (A.4.2), sometimes referred to as the local conservation of mass equation, is obtained by taking the derivative inside the integral. Thus

$$\int_V \frac{\mathrm{D}\rho}{\mathrm{D}t} \, \mathrm{d}V = \int_V \left(\frac{\mathrm{D}\rho}{\mathrm{D}t} + \rho \frac{\mathrm{D}(\mathrm{d}V)}{\mathrm{D}t} \right)$$

$$= \int_V \left(\frac{\mathrm{D}\rho}{\mathrm{D}t} + \rho \frac{\partial \dot{x}_i}{\partial x_i} \right) \mathrm{d}V = 0. \tag{A.4.5}$$

Taken in the Lagrangian sense, we note that $\frac{D\rho}{Dt} = \frac{\partial \rho}{\partial t} + \frac{\partial \rho}{\partial x_j}\frac{\partial x_j}{\partial t}$, so that (A.4.5) becomes

$$\int_V \left\{\frac{\partial \rho}{\partial t} + \frac{\partial}{\partial x_i}(\rho \dot{x}_i)\right\} dV = 0; \tag{A.4.6}$$

or, since this must hold for arbitrary V,

$$\frac{\partial \rho}{\partial t} + (\rho v_{i,i}) = 0. \tag{A.4.7}$$

This latter form of the conservation of mass, or continuity equation, finds application most frequently in fluid dynamics.

A.4.2. *Conservation of momentum*

Consider the volume V of surface S. Associated with every point of V will be a velocity v_i, while acting on the body will be surface tractions t_i and body forces f_i. Conservation of momentum states that the time rate of change of momentum is equal to the total force acting on the body. Taken in the global sense, this statement has the form

$$\frac{D}{Dt}\int_V v_i \rho \, dV = \int_S t_i \, dS + \int_V f_i \rho \, dV. \tag{A.4.8}$$

This expression may also be put in differential equation, or local form, by using Gauss's theorem.

Green–Gauss theorem: In vector form, this is

$$\int_V \nabla . \mathbf{u} \, dV = \int_S \mathbf{u} . \mathbf{n} \, dS,$$

or, in Cartesian tensor form,

$$\int_V u_{j,j} \, dV = \int_S u_j n_j \, dS.$$

Thus upon letting $t_i = \tau_{ji} n_j$, (A.4.8) becomes

$$\int_V (\rho \ddot{u}_i - \tau_{ji,j} - \rho f_i) \, dV = 0 \tag{A.4.9}$$

or, since V is arbitrary, $\qquad \tau_{ji,j} + \rho f_i = \rho \ddot{u}_i. \qquad$ (A.4.10)

A.4.3. *Conservation of moment of momentum*

This principle states that the time rate of change of moment of momentum is equal to the sum of moments on the body. In the global sense, and using vector form, this is

$$\frac{\mathrm{D}}{\mathrm{D}t}\int_V \mathbf{r}\times\mathbf{v}\rho\,\mathrm{d}V=\int_S \mathbf{r}\times\mathbf{t}\,\mathrm{d}S+\int_V \mathbf{r}\times\mathbf{f}\rho\,\mathrm{d}V. \tag{A.4.11}$$

In tensor form, this is

$$\int_V e_{ijk}\ddot{u}_k x_j\rho\,\mathrm{d}V=\int_S e_{ijk}t_k x_j\,\mathrm{d}S+\int_V e_{ijk}f_k x_j\rho\,\mathrm{d}V. \tag{A.4.12}$$

This may be put in differential form, or the local sense, by using Gauss's theorem. Thus

$$\begin{aligned}\int_S e_{ijk}t_k x_j\,\mathrm{d}S&=\int_S e_{ijk}x_j(\tau_{lk}n_l)\,\mathrm{d}S\\&=\int_V (e_{ijk}x_j\tau_{lk,l})\,\mathrm{d}V.\end{aligned} \tag{A.4.13}$$

Carrying out the differentiations gives

$$\int_S e_{ijk}t_k x_j\,\mathrm{d}S=\int_V (e_{ijk}\tau_{jk}+e_{ijk}x_j\tau_{lk,l})\,\mathrm{d}V. \tag{A.4.14}$$

Inserting (A.4.14) in (A.4.12), and using the conservation of momentum results, gives

$$\int_V (e_{ijk}\tau_{jk})\,\mathrm{d}V=0 \tag{A.4.15}$$

or

$$e_{ijk}\tau_{jk}=0. \tag{A.4.16}$$

This is equivalent to

$$\tau_{ij}=\tau_{ji},\qquad i\neq j. \tag{A.4.17}$$

Thus symmetry of the stress tensor results from balance of moment of momentum. Thus reduces the unknown stresses from nine to six.

A.4.4. *Conservation of energy*

Conservation of energy states that the time rate of change of kinetic energy and internal energy is equal to the work done upon the body by the external forces per unit time and the sum of all other energies per unit time.

The kinetic $\mathscr{K}$ is defined as

$$\mathscr{K}=\frac{1}{2}\int_V v_i v_i\rho\,\mathrm{d}V. \tag{A.4.18}$$

The internal energy $\mathscr{E}$ is defined as

$$\mathscr{E}=\int_V \varepsilon\rho\,\mathrm{d}V. \tag{A.4.19}$$

where ε is the internal energy per unit mass. The work done by the external forces is

$$W=\int_S t_i v_i\,\mathrm{d}S+\int_V f_i v_i\rho\,\mathrm{d}V, \tag{A.4.20}$$

so that conservation of energy takes the form

$$\dot{\mathscr{K}}+\dot{\mathscr{E}}=W, \tag{A.4.21}$$

or

$$\frac{\mathrm{D}}{\mathrm{D}t}\int_V(\tfrac{1}{2}v_iv_i+\varepsilon)\rho\,\mathrm{d}V=\int_S t_iv_i\,\mathrm{d}S+\int_V f_iv_i\rho\,\mathrm{d}V. \tag{A.4.22}$$

Eqn (A.4.22) may be put in differential form by converting the surface integral to a volume integral as follows:

$$\int_V(\dot{u}_i\ddot{u}_i+\dot{\varepsilon})\rho\,\mathrm{d}V=\int_V(\tau_{ji}\dot{u}_{i,j})\,\mathrm{d}V+\int_V f_i\dot{u}_i\rho\,\mathrm{d}V, \tag{A.4.23}$$

or

$$\int_V\{(\rho\ddot{u}_i-\tau_{ji,j}-\rho f_i)\dot{u}_i+(\rho\dot{\varepsilon}-\tau_{ji}\dot{u}_{i,j})\}\,\mathrm{d}V=0. \tag{A.4.24}$$

The first parenthesis is the momentum equation (A.4.10). Hence the above reduces to

$$\rho\dot{\varepsilon}=\tau_{ji}\dot{u}_{i,j}. \tag{A.4.25}$$

Finally noting that

$$\dot{u}_{i,j}=\dot{\varepsilon}_{ji}+\dot{\omega}_{ij} \tag{A.4.26}$$

and that the product of a symmetric tensor (τ_{ji}) and an antisymmetric tensor (ω_{ij}) is zero, we have

$$\rho\dot{\varepsilon}=\tau_{ji}\dot{\varepsilon}_{ji}. \tag{A.4.27}$$

To summarize, the fundamental conservation equations have given

$$\left.\begin{array}{ll}\text{mass:} & \partial\rho/\partial t+(\rho\dot{u}_{i,i})=0,\\ \text{momentum} & \tau_{ji,j}+\rho f_i=\rho\ddot{u}_i,\\ \text{moment of momentum} & \tau_{ij}=\tau_{ji}, \qquad (i\neq j),\\ \text{energy} & \rho\dot{\varepsilon}=\tau_{ji}\dot{\varepsilon}_{ij}.\end{array}\right\} \tag{A.4.28}$$

The above is a system of eight equations in thirteen unknowns ($\rho=1$, $u_i=3$, $\tau_{ij}=9$), while f_i is assumed given and ε_{ij} is expressible in terms of u_i. The nature of the medium is determined by ε. Clearly the eight equations are inadequate for a unique determination of the thirteen unknowns.

Hence, the foregoing must be supplemented by additional equations. The need for added equations is also clear from purely physical considerations; the preceding equations are valid for any type of media, so that no differentiation has been made between, say, fluids, and solids. However, two different material bodies having the same geometry and mass distribution and subjected to identical external forces respond differently. This difference is a function of their intrinsic material properties, and it is these properties that must be incorporated into the continuum model.

A.5. Constitutive equations

The function of constitutive equations is to relate states of deformation with states of traction. In the case of ideally elastic bodies, two methods were developed, one by Green (1841) and one by Cauchy (1829). Brief presentations of both will be given.

A.5.1. *Green's method*

The essence of the formulation is that the body is perfectly elastic, so that there are no dissipative mechanisms, and the constitutive equations must be derivable from an internal energy function, which is a function of the strain. Thus define $U = \rho\varepsilon$, so that

$$U = U(\varepsilon_{ij}). \tag{A.5.1}$$

Then

$$\dot{U} = \frac{\partial U}{\partial \varepsilon_{ij}}\dot{\varepsilon}_{ij}, \tag{A.5.2}$$

so that from (A.4.27) we have

$$\tau_{ij} = \partial U/\partial \varepsilon_{ij}. \tag{A.5.3}$$

The precise functional form of $U(\varepsilon_{ij})$ is now the question. By expanding U in a power series of ε_{ij}, and retaining only the quadratic terms, we have

$$U \cong a_{ijkl}\varepsilon_{ij}\varepsilon_{kl}. \tag{A.5.4}$$

Discarding the linear terms of the expansion effectively postulates zero initial stress, while discarding the higher powers is in line with the assumption of small strains. From (A.5.3) we thus have

$$\tau_{ij} = a_{ijkl}\varepsilon_{kl}. \tag{A.5.5}$$

A.5.2. *Cauchy's method*

The essence of Cauchy's method is the assumption of a direct functional relationship between stress and strain of the form

$$\tau_{ij} = \tau_{ij}(\varepsilon_{ij}). \tag{A.5.6}$$

Expanding $\tau_{ij}(\varepsilon_{ij})$ in a power series and discarding the constant term (no initial stress) and the higher-order terms (infinitesimal elasticity) gives

$$\tau_{ij} = a_{ijkl}\varepsilon_{kl}. \tag{A.5.7}$$

Apparently, both Green's and Cauchy's method have led to the same results for τ_{ij}. However, such is not the case. To show this the 81 constants a_{ijkl} appearing in either result may be reduced to 36 by observing the symmetry with respect to ij and kl.† Thus both results may be put temporarily in the form

$$\tau_i = c_{ij}\varepsilon_j, \tag{A.5.8}$$

† See, for example, Sokolnikoff [52, pp. 59–60].

where

$$\tau_1 = \tau_{11}, \qquad \tau_2 = \tau_{22}, \qquad \tau_3 = \tau_{33},$$

$$\tau_4 = \tau_{23}, \qquad \tau_5 = \tau_{31}, \qquad \tau_6 = \tau_{12}, \tag{A.5.9}$$

and similarly for the ε_{ij}. However, from (A.5.3) and (A.5.4) of Green's method, which now take the form

$$\tau_i = \partial U/\partial \varepsilon_i, \qquad U = c_{ij}\varepsilon_i\varepsilon_j, \tag{A.5.10}$$

we are led to conclude that $c_{ij} = c_{ji}$, thereby reducing the elastic constants from 36 to 21. No such conclusion may be drawn, without further restrictive assumptions, in Cauchy's method. To reduce Cauchy's results to Green's, we assume the existence of a strain energy function, taking the form

$$U = \tfrac{1}{2}c_{ij}\varepsilon_i\varepsilon_j, \tag{A.5.11}$$

with the property that

$$\tau_i = \partial U/\partial \varepsilon_i. \tag{A.5.12}$$

This reduces the number of constants for the general anisotropic linear case to 21, in agreement with Green's results.

A.5.3. *Isotropic elastic solid*

By assuming homogeneity and isotropy, the number of constants reduces from 21 to 2.† Reverting to double subscript notation for the stresses, this takes the form

$$\tau_{ij} = \lambda\varepsilon_{kk}\delta_{ij} + 2\mu\varepsilon_{ij}, \tag{A.5.13}$$

where λ, μ are known as the Lamé constants. The latter is the material shear modulus. Under special loadings, such as simple tension or pure shear, the resulting relations between stress and strain are of such form as to make it convenient to define additional elastic constants, such as Young's modulus, Poisson's ratio, and the bulk modulus. These are merely combinations of λ and μ. Thus

$$\begin{aligned} E &= \mu(3\lambda+2\mu)/(\lambda+\mu) = \text{Young's modulus}, \\ \nu &= \tfrac{1}{2}\lambda/(\lambda+\mu) = \text{Poisson's ratio}, \\ K &= \lambda+\tfrac{2}{3}\mu = \text{bulk modulus}. \end{aligned} \tag{A.5.14}$$

The inverse strain–stress equations are

$$\varepsilon_{ij} = \frac{(1+\nu)}{E}\tau_{ij} - \frac{\nu}{E}\Theta\delta_{ij}, \qquad \Theta = \tau_{11}+\tau_{22}+\tau_{33}. \tag{A.5.15}$$

If we go back to the system of conservation equations (A.4.27), we see that the addition of eqns (A.5.13), for the isotropic case, make the equations

† See, for example, Sokolnikoff [52, pp. 62–6].

of a continuum determinate. Thus we have

(1) mass and momentum give four equations in ten unknowns (ρ, u_i, $\tau_{ij} = 10$). The moment of momentum results have already reduced the stresses from nine to six;

(2) the energy equation has generated the stress–strain results, giving six equations;

(3) generally, density is taken as specified, so that the conservation of mass equation may be omitted, giving a total of nine equations in nine unknowns.

Of couse, it should be apparent that the resulting constitutive equations have introduced constants (ranging from 2 in number for the isotropic case to 21 for the general anisotropic case). It is here that the vital role of experiment becomes apparent, whereby critical tests are performed, the results related to theoretical models, and the constants determined.

A.6. Solution uniqueness and boundary conditions

The equations for the case of linear, isotropic elasticity are

$$\begin{aligned} \tau_{ij,j}+\rho f_i &= \rho \ddot{u}_i, \\ \tau_{ij} &= \lambda \varepsilon_{kk}\delta_{ij}+2\mu\varepsilon_{ij}, \\ \varepsilon_{ij} &= \tfrac{1}{2}(u_{i,j}+u_{j,i}), \\ \omega_{ij} &= \tfrac{1}{2}(u_{i,j}-u_{j,i}). \end{aligned} \tag{A.6.1}$$

The momentum equation (the first of (A.6.1)) may be expressed in terms of displacements by utilizing the stress–strain and strain–displacement relations of (A.6.1) giving

$$(\lambda+\mu)u_{j,ji}+\mu u_{i,jj}+\rho f_i = \rho \ddot{u}_i, \tag{A.6.2}$$

or, in vector form

$$(\lambda+\mu)\nabla\nabla \cdot \mathbf{u}+\mu\nabla^2\mathbf{u}+\rho\mathbf{f} = \rho\ddot{\mathbf{u}}. \tag{A.6.3}$$

A fundamental question pertaining to the preceding is whether a solution that satisfies the equations as well as certain boundary and initial conditions is a unique solution. Phrased somewhat differently, we may ask 'what boundary and initial conditions must be imposed on the above equations to insure that a resulting solution, satisfying equations and conditions, is a unique solution?' Thus the questions of proper boundary conditions and uniqueness of solutions are inseparable.

A.6.1. *Uniqueness*

The question of uniqueness is approached by supposing two solutions to the same problem may exist and then showing that such an assumption leads to a contradiction.

Consider two unique solutions exist, given by u_i', u_i'', τ_{ij}', τ_{ij}'', ε_{ij}', ε_{ij}''. If these are indeed solutions, then the linear combination formed by taking the difference of the two solutions is also a solution. We thus form the difference system, defined as

$$\begin{aligned} u_i &= u_i'-u_i'', \qquad \tau_{ij} = \tau_{ij}'-\tau_{ij}'', \\ \varepsilon_{ij} &= \varepsilon_{ij}'-\varepsilon_{ij}'', \qquad f_i = f_i'-f_i'', \qquad t_i = t_i'-t_i''. \end{aligned} \tag{A.6.4}$$

Conservation of energy still holds for the difference system so from (A.4.22), we have

$$\frac{\mathrm{D}}{\mathrm{D}t}\int_V (\tfrac{1}{2}\rho\dot{u}_i\dot{u}_i+U)\,\mathrm{d}V = \int_S t_i\dot{u}_i\,\mathrm{d}S+\int_V f_i\dot{u}_i\rho\,\mathrm{d}V. \tag{A.6.5}$$

This, we recall, is a statement that the time rate of change of kinetic and potential energy equals the work done per unit time. Carrying out an integration with respect to time on the preceding gives

$$\int_V [\tfrac{1}{2}\rho\dot{u}_i\dot{u}_i+U]_{t_0}^{t}\,\mathrm{d}V = \int_{t_0}^{t}\mathrm{d}t\int_S t_i\dot{u}_i\,\mathrm{d}S + \int_{t_0}^{t}\mathrm{d}t\int_V f_i\dot{u}_i\,\mathrm{d}V. \tag{A.6.6}$$

It is seen that the first integral of the right-hand side contains the surface tractions t_i and time derivatives of displacements with the specification of these values at an initial time t_0 implied by the lower limit of integration. Likewise, the second integral contains body forces f_i and velocities $\dot{u}_i$.

Now, the conditions on the boundary S are prescribed by combinations of t_i and u_i, while interior forces are given by f_i. The point is that starting from identical conditions on S and in V, two different solutions have arisen. If conditions are the same, it follows that the right-hand side must be zero, since $t_i = t_i'-t_i''$, $f_i = f_i'-f_i''$ and both t_i', t_i'', etc. are constrained to be the same. Consequently

$$\int_V [\tfrac{1}{2}\rho\dot{u}_i\dot{u}_i+U]_{t_0}^{t}\,\mathrm{d}V = 0. \tag{A.6.7}$$

Using definitions (A.4.18), (A.4.19), this is of the form

$$\mathscr{K}+\mathscr{E} = \mathscr{K}_0+\mathscr{E}_0. \tag{A.6.8}$$

However, $\mathscr{K}_0$, $\mathscr{E}_0$ are based on the initial velocities $\dot{u}_i$ and displacements u_i of the difference system, and these are zero. Hence

$$\mathscr{K}+\mathscr{E} = 0. \tag{A.6.9}$$

Furthermore, both $\mathscr{K}$ and $\mathscr{E}$ are positive definite†, indicating that

$$\mathscr{K} = \mathscr{E} = 0. \tag{A.6.10}$$

Hence, the two supposedly different solutions must, in fact, be identical, so that only one solution exists.

† The positive definiteness of the strain energy can be used to place theoretical restrictions on the range of the elastic constants. For example, it may be shown that $\mu > 0$, $3\lambda+2\mu > 0$ must hold for the elastic case.

A.6.2. *Boundary conditions*

Additional remarks are now warranted on the boundary and initial conditions. Return now to the single solution u_i, τ_{ij}, ε_{ij}, etc. and note the previously appearing integrals

$$\int_{t_0}^{t} \mathrm{d}t \int_S t_i \dot{u}_i \,\mathrm{d}S, \qquad \int_{t_0}^{t} \mathrm{d}t \int_V f_i \dot{u}_i \rho \,\mathrm{d}V. \tag{A.6.11}$$

Consider the first integral, and the surface shown in Fig. A.3. Then

$$\begin{aligned} t_i u_i &= t_n u_n + t_s u_s + t_t u_t \\ &= \tau_{nn} u_n + \tau_{ns} u_s + \tau_{nb} u_b. \end{aligned} \tag{A.6.12}$$

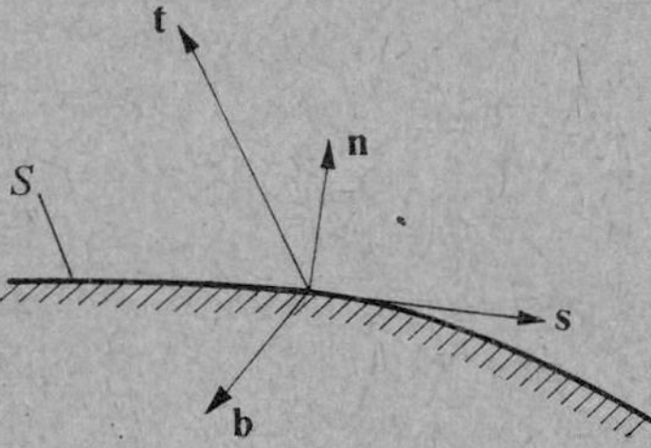

FIG. A.3. Base-vector triad at the surface of a continuum.

The disappearance of the above surface integral in the previous proof was based on specifying surface conditions and from (A.6.12), we see these conditions on S must be

$$\tau_{nn}, \qquad \tau_{ns}, \qquad \tau_{nb} \quad \text{or} \quad u_i, \tag{A.6.13}$$

or a proper mix of τ_{ij}, u_i. In addition, the specification of τ_{ij} or u_i at $t = t_0$ is required.

In the case of the second integral of (A.6.11), we see the specification of f_i is required, and the values of u_i, $\dot{u}_i$ at $t = t_0$. Thus we must have

(1) in V, at each point f_i and initial values of u_i and $\dot{u}_i$;

(2) on S, one member of each of the three products

$$\tau_{nn} u_n, \qquad \tau_{ns} u_s, \qquad \tau_{nb} u_b$$

as well as initial values of these quantities.

Thus the boundary conditions have resulted as sufficient conditions for uniqueness of solution.

A.7. Other continua

The fundamental unity of the study of continua, such as solids, liquids, and gases, is emphasized by the applicable equations of balance. The constitutive equations are then the distinguishing characteristics between various materials. In our work, we shall be concerned mainly with homogeneous isotropic solids, characterized by (A.6.1). It is of interest to remark on some other directions of study in solid and fluid mechanics, keeping in mind the universal applicability of the equations of balance, and noting the way in which constitutive relations are introduced.

1. *Anisotropy*. Elastic materials that are fundamentally anisotropic are crystals. Eqn (A.5.5) would still hold. However, depending on the degree of anisotropy, the number of elastic constants could range from 3 to 21.

2. *Piezoelectric effects*: It is well known that certain crystals and poled ceramics develop an electrical charge when strained and vice versa. This coupled electro-mechanical effect considerably complicates formulation of the continuum equations. Equations of mass, momentum, and moment of mementum would not be affected, however.

We would find the energy equation changed, since the work done by electric fields on charges would have to be incorporated in this balance equation. In addition, as was mentioned in § A.4, the number of fundamental axioms would have to be broadened to conservation of charge, Faraday's law, and Ampere's law. These axioms uncoupled from solid mechanics would lead to the well-known Maxwell equations, a set of field equations nearly as complicated as those of elasticity. The electro-mechanical coupling thus creates problems which, in general, are exceptionally difficult.

3. *Thermal effects*: Heat effects may be included in the energy balance equation. However, an axiom regarding entropy must also be added to the four equations of balance. Although heat effects will be neglected in our work, severe temperature gradients can cause interaction effects between heat and mechanical vibration, leading to thermoelastic waves.

4. *Fluids* (*gases and liquids*). Study of hydrodynamics, gasdynamics, supersonic, and hypersonic flow, etc. are all studies of continua characterized by particular constitutive equations. Depending on compressibility, viscosity, and heat, these equations take on varying degrees of complexity, just as do their solid analogues.

For example, the constitutive equation of incompressible, inviscid liquids, or of ideal gases, are simpler than those of isotropic solids. In all three cases, these represent the simplest models of a type of continua. As additional effects are added to solids, liquids, and gases, the resulting constitutive equations take their most complex form in the case of solids. As a consequence, considerable progress has been made in, say, the study of the propagation of shock waves in fluids, whereas less work has taken place in this area of solids.

5. *Viscoelastic effects*. In the case of solids, it is often found that stresses are significantly affected by strain rates as well as by the strains alone. The

resulting constitutive equation may then take a form $\tau = \tau(\varepsilon, \dot{\varepsilon}, \ddot{\varepsilon},\ldots)$, with corresponding complexity in subsequent analysis.

6. *Plasticity effects.* Again using solids as an example, it is observed, at sufficient strain amplitudes, that stresses and strains are no longer related in a linear, reversible fashion. The resulting non-linear continuum problem is, of course, exceedingly complex. Nevertheless, plastic wave propagation is an area of mechanics which is being actively studied. It sometimes occurs that experimental results are not adequately explained by amplitude effects (that is, plasticity) alone, but that strain rates also play a role. Thus a visco-plastic theory must be devised.

7. *Microstructure effects.* Continuum models are based on smoothly varying properties, such as density and moduli. However, at smaller and smaller dimensions, approaching grain sizes in metals, the fundamentally heterogeneous nature of solids begins to be of significance. Such might be the case if extremely high-frequency vibrations are occuring. In an effort to incorporate microstructure effects into a continuum theory, much work has been done in the fields of microelasticity, couple-stress theory and multipole continuum mechanics.

8. *Non-linear effects.* The effects of large strains in generating a non-linear set of equations was mentioned in the case of plasticity. In the case of all the foregoing effects, there is usually a linearized set of equations. However these equations have usually resulted from imposing restrictions on an original, fundamentally non-linear set of equations (for example, in isotropic elasticity, small deformations are assumed). Hence, in all cases, at sufficiently severe temperatures or electric fields or strain rates, the various problems can become non-linear.

A.8. Additional energy considerations

We now wish to review the application of work–energy concepts in contrast to equilibrium concepts, to elastodynamics. Interest in energy concepts may be justified on at least three counts. First, the energy stored in a body is an important quantity in its own right. Certain material failure theories, for example, are based on the idea of failure occurring when the strain energy reaches a critical value. Fracture theories also have critical energy levels as their basis. Thus, the Griffith fracture criteria is based on the relation between strain energy and free surface energy during crack growth. Secondly, methods have been developed for determining the deflection of elastic bodies that are based on energy aspects (for example, Castigliano's theorem). Thirdly, numerous methods have been developed for approximate solution of elasto-dynamics problems that are based on energy concepts. In fact, activity and emphasis in this regard has often been so great as to suggest that the only reason for energy consideration was to generate approximate solutions. However, the first considerations are also of considerable importance.

In many of our applications, we will use energy principles to develop approximate theories governing the motion of rods and plates (in contrast to approximate solutions). Developments starting from the law of conservation of energy stated as 'the rate of increase of energy in a body is equal to the rate at which work is done by the external forces' start with

$$\int_V (\dot{T}+\dot{V})\,\mathrm{d}V = \int_S t_i\dot{u}_i\,\mathrm{d}S + \int_V \rho f_i\dot{u}_i\,\mathrm{d}V, \qquad \text{(A.8.1)}$$

where

$$T = \tfrac{1}{2}\rho\dot{u}_i\dot{u}_i, \qquad V = V(e_{ij}). \qquad \text{(A.8.2)}$$

Then

$$\dot{T} = \rho\ddot{u}_i\dot{u}_i, \qquad \dot{V} = \frac{\partial V}{\partial e_{ij}}\dot{e}_{ij} = \tfrac{1}{2}\tau_{ij}(\dot{u}_{i,j}+\dot{u}_{j,i}). \qquad \text{(A.8.3)}$$

Now

$$\begin{aligned}\int_V \dot{V}\,\mathrm{d}V &= \tfrac{1}{2}\int_V \tau_{ij}(\dot{u}_{i,j}+\dot{u}_{j,i})\,\mathrm{d}V\\ &= \tfrac{1}{2}\int_V (\tau_{ij}\dot{u}_i)_{,j}\,\mathrm{d}V - \tfrac{1}{2}\int_V \tau_{ij,j}\dot{u}_i\,\mathrm{d}V +\\ &\quad + \tfrac{1}{2}\int_V (\tau_{ij}\dot{u}_j)_{,i}\,\mathrm{d}V - \tfrac{1}{2}\int_V \tau_{ij,i}\dot{u}_j\,\mathrm{d}V. \end{aligned} \qquad \text{(A.8.4)}$$

By the divergence theorem,

$$\int_V (\tau_{ij}\dot{u}_{i,j})\,\mathrm{d}V = \int_S \tau_{ij}\dot{u}_i n_j\,\mathrm{d}S, \qquad \int_V (\tau_{ij}\dot{u}_{j,i})\,\mathrm{d}V = \int_S \tau_{ij}\dot{u}_j n_i\,\mathrm{d}S. \qquad \text{(A.8.5)}$$

Then (A.8.4) becomes

$$\begin{aligned}\int_V \dot{V}\,\mathrm{d}V &= \tfrac{1}{2}\int_S (\tau_{ij}\dot{u}_i n_j+\tau_{ij}\dot{u}_j n_i)\,\mathrm{d}S - \tfrac{1}{2}\int_V (\tau_{ij,j}\dot{u}_i+\tau_{ij,i}\dot{u}_j)\,\mathrm{d}V\\ &= \int_S \tau_{ij}\dot{u}_i n_j\,\mathrm{d}S - \int_V \tau_{ij,j}\dot{u}_i\,\mathrm{d}V. \end{aligned} \qquad \text{(A.8.6)}$$

Since $t_i = \tau_{ij}n_j$, the above reduces to

$$\int_V \dot{V}\,\mathrm{d}V = \int_S t_i\dot{u}_i\,\mathrm{d}S - \int_V \tau_{ij,j}\dot{u}_i\,\mathrm{d}V. \qquad \text{(A.8.7)}$$

We thus have (A.8.1), reducing to

$$\int_V (\rho\ddot{u}_i - \tau_{ij,j} - \rho f_i)\dot{u}_i\,\mathrm{d}V = 0. \qquad \text{(A.8.8)}$$

Many of the developments will stem from *Hamilton's principle*. By way of background, Langhaar [35, pp. 234–5] points out that Newton's equations of motion refer only to a single mass particle. The analysis of the motion of a finite body by Newtonian methods involves subjecting the individual particles to Newton's laws and integrating the effects over the entire body. The Lagrange equations of motion are a generalization of this process and determine the motion of a body with finite degrees of freedom. Which ever equations are used, the general dynamical problem involves specifying the system location and velocity at some time t_0 and solving for the subsequent motion.

Hamilton (1805–65) formulated the problem of dynamics in a somewhat different way by considering the location of the system to be specified at two different times t_0 and t_1, with the intervening motion to be determined. Using the principle of virtual work, D'Alembert's principle, and applying variational calculus, Hamilton derived a general formulation of the equations of mechanics that determines the motion of a system with finite or infinite degrees of freedom. The mathematical statement of his principle is

$$\delta \int_{t_0}^{t_1} (\mathscr{E}+W)\, \mathrm{d}t = 0, \tag{A.8.9}$$

where $\mathscr{E}$ is the total energy of the system, W is the total work (exclusive of work done by inertial forces), and δ is in the sense of the calculus of variations. The above equation states that the motion of a system from t_0 to t_1 is such that the total of the system kinetic energy and system work is an extremum.

In our applications, (A.8.9) takes the somewhat more specific form†

$$\delta \int_{t_0}^{t_1} (\tilde{T}-\tilde{V})\, \mathrm{d}t + \int_{t_0}^{t} \delta W \, \mathrm{d}t = 0, \tag{A.8.10}$$

where

$$\tilde{T} = \int_V T \, \mathrm{d}V, \qquad \tilde{V} = \int_V V \, \mathrm{d}V \tag{A.8.11}$$

and

$$\delta W = \int_S t_i \, \delta u_i \, \mathrm{d}S + \int_V \rho f_i \delta u_i \, \mathrm{d}V, \tag{A.8.12}$$

and T and V have been previously defined by (A.8.2). Carrying out the variation on the kinetic energy we obtain

$$\delta \int_{t_0}^{t_1} \tilde{T}\, \mathrm{d}t = \int_{t_0}^{t_1} \mathrm{d}t \int_V \frac{\partial T}{\partial \dot{u}_i}\, \delta \dot{u}_i \, \mathrm{d}V. \tag{A.8.13}$$

Now

$$\delta \dot{u}_i = \frac{\partial}{\partial t}(\delta u_i), \qquad \delta u_{i,j} = (\delta u_i)_{,j}. \tag{A.8.14}$$

† P. 166 of Reference [36].

So we have

$$\delta\int_t \tilde{T}\,\mathrm{d}t = \int_V\left[\int_t \frac{\partial T}{\partial \dot{u}_i}\frac{\partial}{\partial t}(\delta u_i)\,\mathrm{d}t\right]\mathrm{d}V$$

$$= \left[\int_V \frac{\partial T}{\partial \dot{u}_i}\,\delta u_i\,\mathrm{d}V\right]_{t_0}^{t_1} - \int_t \mathrm{d}t\left\{\int_V \frac{\mathrm{d}}{\mathrm{d}t}\left(\frac{\partial T}{\partial \dot{u}_i}\right)\delta u_i\,\mathrm{d}V\right\}. \tag{A.8.15}$$

For the strain energy term we have that

$$\delta\int_{t_0}^{t_1} \tilde{V}\,\mathrm{d}t = \int_{t_0}^{t_1}\mathrm{d}t\int_V \frac{\partial V}{\partial \varepsilon_{ij}}\,\delta\varepsilon_{ij}\,\mathrm{d}V. \tag{A.8.16}$$

Now

$$\delta\varepsilon_{ij} = \tfrac{1}{2}\delta(u_{i,j}+u_{j,i}) = \left(\frac{\delta u_i}{2}\right)_{,j}+\left(\frac{\delta u_j}{2}\right)_{,i}. \tag{A.8.17}$$

Hence

$$\delta\int_{t_0}^{t_1} \tilde{V}\,\mathrm{d}t = \int_t \mathrm{d}t\int_V \frac{1}{2}\frac{\partial V}{\partial \varepsilon_{ij}}\{(\delta u_i)_{,j}+(\delta u_j)_{,i}\}\,\mathrm{d}V$$

$$= \int_t \mathrm{d}t\left[\frac{1}{2}\int_V\left\{\left(\frac{\partial V}{\partial \varepsilon_{ij}}\,\delta u_i\right)_{,j}+\left(\frac{\partial V}{\partial \varepsilon_{ij}}\,\delta u_j\right)_{,i}\right\}\mathrm{d}V - \right.$$

$$\left. -\frac{1}{2}\int_V\left\{\left(\frac{\partial V}{\partial \varepsilon_{ij}}\right)_{,j}\delta u_i+\left(\frac{\partial V}{\partial \varepsilon_{ij}}\right)_{,i}\delta u_j\right\}\mathrm{d}V\right] \tag{A.8.18}$$

We apply the divergence theorem to the first integral, giving

$$\delta\int_{t_0}^{t_1} \tilde{V}\,\mathrm{d}t = \int_t \mathrm{d}t\left[\frac{1}{2}\int\left(\frac{\partial V}{\partial \varepsilon_{ij}}\,\delta u_i n_j+\frac{\partial V}{\partial \varepsilon_{ij}}\,\delta u_j n_i\right)\mathrm{d}S - \right.$$

$$\left. -\frac{1}{2}\int_V\left\{\left(\frac{\partial V}{\partial \varepsilon_{ij}}\right)_{,j}\delta u_i+\left(\frac{\partial V}{\partial \varepsilon_{ij}}\right)_{,i}\delta u_j\right\}\mathrm{d}V\right]. \tag{A.8.19}$$

For the second integral of (A.8.10), we have

$$\int_{t_0}^{t_1}\delta W\,\mathrm{d}t = \int_{t_0}^{t_1}\mathrm{d}t\left\{\int_S t_i\delta u_i\,\mathrm{d}S + \int_V \rho f_i\delta u_i\,\mathrm{d}V\right\}. \tag{A.8.20}$$

Thus Hamilton's principle gives

$$\int_{t_0}^{t_1}\mathrm{d}t\int_V\left\{-\frac{d}{\mathrm{d}t}\left(\frac{\partial T}{\partial \dot{u}_i}\right)+\frac{1}{2}\left(\frac{\partial V}{\partial \varepsilon_{ij}}\right)_{,j}+\frac{1}{2}\left(\frac{\partial V}{\partial \varepsilon_{ji}}\right)_{,j}+\rho f_i\right\}\delta u_i\,\mathrm{d}V -$$

$$-\int_{t_0}^{t_1}\mathrm{d}t\int_S\left(\frac{1}{2}\frac{\partial V}{\partial \varepsilon_{ij}}n_j+\frac{1}{2}\frac{\partial V}{\partial \varepsilon_{ji}}n_j-t_i\right)\delta u_i\,\mathrm{d}S-\left[\int_V \frac{\partial T}{\partial \dot{u}_i}\,\delta u_i\,\mathrm{d}V\right]_{t_0}^{t_1} \equiv 0. \tag{A.8.21}$$

This is the general result. If we recognize

$$\tau_{ij} = \frac{\partial V}{\partial \varepsilon_{ij}}, \qquad \tau_{ij} = \tau_{ji}, \qquad \frac{\partial T}{\partial \dot{u}_i} = \rho \dot{u}_i, \tag{A.8.22}$$

then we obtain

$$\int_{t_0}^{t_1} \mathrm{d}t \int_V (-\rho\ddot{u}_i + \tau_{ij,j} + \rho f_i)\delta u_i \,\mathrm{d}V - \int_{t_0}^{t} \mathrm{d}t \int_S (\tau_{ij}n_j - t_i)\delta u_i \,\mathrm{d}S - \left[\int_V \rho\dot{u}_i\delta u_i \,\mathrm{d}V\right]_{t_0}^{t_1} = 0. \tag{A.8.23}$$

Since $\tau_{ij}n_j = t_i$, the surface integral vanishes identically. At t_0, t_1, $\delta u_i = 0$ so that the last integral vanishes. We thus obtain

$$\int_{t_0}^{t} \mathrm{d}t \int_V (\tau_{ij,j} + \rho f_i - \rho\ddot{u}_i)\,\delta u_i \,\mathrm{d}V \equiv 0. \tag{A.8.24}$$

A.9. Elasticity equations in curvilinear coordinates

The elasticity equations for rectangular Cartesian coordinates have been summarized in indicial form by (A.6.1), with the displacement equations presented by (A.6.2). These equations, as well as various mathematical operators such as gradient and divergence, are required in terms of cylindrical and spherical coordinates in several places of the book. These are summarized in the following.

A.9.1. *Cylindrical coordinates*

A cylindrical coordinate system r, θ, z is shown in Fig. A.4. The elasticity equations are as follows:

$$\begin{gathered} e_{rr} = \frac{\partial u_r}{\partial r}, \qquad e_{\theta\theta} = \frac{1}{r}\frac{\partial u_\theta}{\partial \theta} + \frac{u_r}{r}, \\ e_{zz} = \frac{\partial u_z}{\partial z}, \qquad e_{r\theta} = \frac{1}{2}\left(\frac{1}{r}\frac{\partial u_r}{\partial \theta} + \frac{\partial u_\theta}{\partial r} - \frac{u_\theta}{r}\right), \\ e_{rz} = \frac{1}{2}\left(\frac{\partial u_z}{\partial r} + \frac{\partial u_r}{\partial z}\right), \qquad e_{\theta z} = \frac{1}{2}\left(\frac{\partial u_\theta}{\partial z} + \frac{1}{r}\frac{\partial u_z}{\partial \theta}\right), \end{gathered} \tag{A.9.1}$$

$$\begin{gathered} \frac{\partial \tau_{rr}}{\partial r} + \frac{1}{r}\frac{\partial \tau_{r\theta}}{\partial \theta} + \frac{\partial \tau_{rz}}{\partial z} + \frac{\tau_{rr} - \tau_{\theta\theta}}{r} + \rho f_r = \rho\ddot{u}_r, \\ \frac{\partial \tau_{r\theta}}{\partial r} + \frac{1}{r}\frac{\partial \tau_{\theta\theta}}{\partial \theta} + \frac{\partial \tau_{\theta z}}{\partial z} + \frac{2}{r}\tau_{r\theta} + \rho f_\theta = \rho\ddot{u}_\theta, \\ \frac{\partial \tau_{rz}}{\partial r} + \frac{1}{r}\frac{\partial \tau_{\theta z}}{\partial \theta} + \frac{\partial \tau_{zz}}{\partial z} + \frac{1}{r}\tau_{rz} + \rho f_z = \rho\ddot{u}_z. \end{gathered} \tag{A.9.2}$$

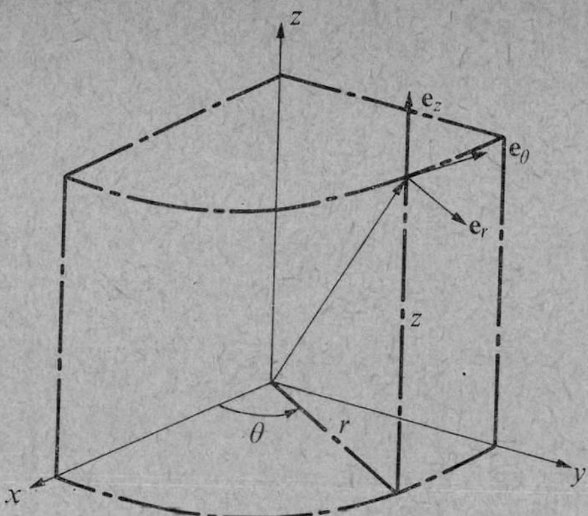

FIG. A.4. Cylindrical coordinate system.

The common operations on scalar and vector fields are the following:

$$\text{grad}\,\phi = \frac{\partial\phi}{\partial r}\mathbf{e}_r+\frac{1}{r}\frac{\partial\phi}{\partial\theta}\mathbf{e}_\theta+\frac{\partial\phi}{\partial z}\mathbf{e}_z,$$

$$\text{div}\,\mathbf{A} = \frac{1}{r}\frac{\partial}{\partial r}(rA_r)+\frac{1}{r}\frac{\partial A_\theta}{\partial\theta}+\frac{\partial A_z}{\partial z},$$

$$\text{curl}\,\mathbf{A} = \left(\frac{1}{r}\frac{\partial A_z}{\partial\theta}-\frac{\partial A_\theta}{\partial z}\right)\mathbf{e}_r+\left(\frac{\partial A_r}{\partial z}-\frac{\partial A_z}{\partial r}\right)\mathbf{e}_\theta+\left\{\frac{1}{r}\frac{\partial}{\partial r}(rA_\theta)-\frac{1}{r}\frac{\partial A_r}{\partial\theta}\right\}\mathbf{e}_z, \quad (A.9.3)$$

$$\nabla^2\phi = \frac{\partial^2\phi}{\partial r^2}+\frac{1}{r}\frac{\partial\phi}{\partial r}+\frac{1}{r^2}\frac{\partial^2\phi}{\partial\theta^2}+\frac{\partial^2\phi}{\partial z^2},$$

$$\nabla^2\mathbf{A} = \left(\nabla^2 A_r-\frac{A_r}{r^2}-\frac{2}{r^2}\frac{\partial A_\theta}{\partial\theta}\right)\mathbf{e}_r+\left(\nabla^2 A_\theta-\frac{A_\theta}{r^2}+\frac{2}{r^2}\frac{\partial A_r}{\partial\theta}\right)\mathbf{e}_\theta+\nabla^2 A_z\mathbf{e}_z.$$

A.9.2. *Spherical coordinates*

A spherical coordinate system is shown in Fig. A.5. The elasticity equations

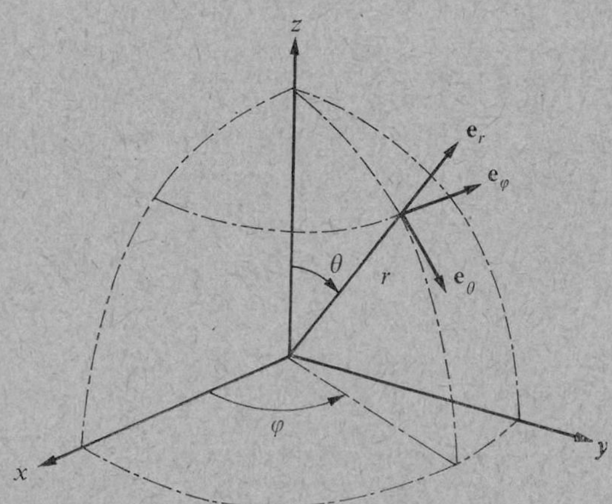

FIG. A.5. Spherical coordinate system.

are as follows:

$$e_{rr} = \frac{\partial u_r}{\partial r}, \qquad e_{\theta\theta} = \frac{1}{r}\frac{\partial u_\theta}{\partial \theta} + \frac{u_r}{r},$$

$$e_{\phi\phi} = \frac{1}{r \sin\theta}\frac{\partial u_\phi}{\partial \phi} + \frac{u_r}{r} + u_\theta \frac{\cot\theta}{r},$$

$$e_{r\phi} = \frac{1}{2}\left(\frac{1}{r\sin\theta}\frac{\partial u_r}{\partial\phi} - \frac{u_\phi}{r} + \frac{\partial u_\phi}{\partial r}\right), \tag{A.9.4}$$

$$e_{r\theta} = \frac{1}{2}\left(\frac{1}{r}\frac{\partial u_r}{\partial\theta} - \frac{u_\theta}{r} + \frac{\partial u_\theta}{\partial r}\right),$$

$$e_{\phi\theta} = \frac{1}{2}\left(\frac{1}{r}\frac{\partial u_\phi}{\partial\theta} - \frac{u_\phi \cot\theta}{r} + \frac{1}{r\sin\theta}\frac{\partial u_\theta}{\partial\phi}\right),$$

$$\frac{\partial \tau_{rr}}{\partial r} + \frac{1}{r\sin\theta}\frac{\partial \tau_{r\phi}}{\partial\phi} + \frac{1}{r}\frac{\partial\tau_{r\theta}}{\partial\theta} + \frac{(2\tau_{rr} - \tau_{\phi\phi} - \tau_{\theta\theta} + \tau_{r\theta}\cot\theta)}{r} + \rho f_r = \rho \ddot{u}_r,$$

$$\frac{\partial \tau_{r\phi}}{\partial r} + \frac{1}{r\sin\theta}\frac{\partial \tau_{\phi\phi}}{\partial\phi} + \frac{1}{r}\frac{\partial\tau_{\phi\theta}}{\partial\theta} + \frac{(3\tau_{r\phi} + 2\tau_{\phi\theta}\cot\theta)}{r} + \rho f_\phi = \rho \ddot{u}_\phi, \tag{A.9.5}$$

$$\frac{\partial \tau_{r\phi}}{\partial r} + \frac{1}{r\sin\theta}\frac{\partial \tau_{\phi\theta}}{\partial\phi} + \frac{1}{r}\frac{\partial\tau_{\theta\theta}}{\partial\theta} + \frac{\{3\tau_{r\theta} + (\tau_{\theta\theta} - \tau_{\phi\phi})\cot\theta\}}{r} + \rho f_\theta = \rho \ddot{u}_\theta.$$

The common operations on scalar and vector fields are

$$\text{grad}\,\Phi = \frac{\partial\Phi}{\partial r}\mathbf{e}_r + \frac{1}{r}\frac{\partial\Phi}{\partial\theta}\mathbf{e}_\theta + \frac{1}{r\sin\theta}\frac{\partial\Phi}{\partial\phi}\mathbf{e}_\phi,$$

$$\text{div}\,\mathbf{A} = \frac{1}{r^2}\frac{\partial}{\partial r}(r^2 A_r) + \frac{1}{r\sin\theta}\frac{\partial}{\partial\theta}(A_\theta \sin\theta) + \frac{1}{r\sin\theta}\frac{\partial A_\phi}{\partial\phi},$$

$$\text{curl}\,\mathbf{A} = \frac{1}{r\sin\theta}\left\{\frac{\partial}{\partial\theta}(A_\phi\sin\theta) - \frac{\partial A_\theta}{\partial\phi}\right\}\mathbf{e}_r + \\ + \left\{\frac{1}{r\sin\theta}\frac{\partial A_r}{\partial\phi} - \frac{1}{r}\frac{\partial}{\partial r}(rA_\phi)\right\}\mathbf{e}_\theta + \frac{1}{r}\left\{\frac{\partial}{\partial r}(rA_\theta) - \frac{\partial A_r}{\partial\theta}\right\}\mathbf{e}_\phi,$$

$$\nabla^2\Phi = \frac{1}{r^2}\frac{\partial}{\partial r}\left(r^2\frac{\partial\Phi}{\partial r}\right) + \frac{1}{r^2\sin\theta}\frac{\partial}{\partial\theta}\left(\sin\theta\frac{\partial\Phi}{\partial\theta}\right) + \frac{1}{r^2\sin^2\theta}\frac{\partial^2\Phi}{\partial\phi^2},$$

$$\nabla^2\mathbf{A} = \left\{\nabla^2 A_r - \frac{2}{r^2}A_r - \frac{2}{r^2\sin\theta}\frac{\partial}{\partial\theta}(\sin\theta A_\theta) - \frac{2}{r^2\sin\theta}\frac{\partial A_\phi}{\partial\phi}\right\}\mathbf{e}_r + \\ + \left\{\nabla^2 A_\theta - \frac{A_\theta}{r^2\sin^2\theta} + \frac{2}{r^2}\frac{\partial A_r}{\partial\theta} - \frac{2}{r^2}\frac{\cos\theta}{\sin^2\theta}\frac{\partial A_\phi}{\partial\phi}\right\}\mathbf{e}_\theta + \\ + \left\{\nabla^2 A_\phi - \frac{A_\phi}{r^2\sin^2\theta} + \frac{2}{r^2\sin\theta}\frac{\partial A_r}{\partial\phi} + \frac{2}{r^2}\frac{\cos\theta}{\sin^2\theta}\frac{\partial A_\theta}{\partial\phi}\right\}\mathbf{e}_\phi. \tag{A.9.6}$$

Appendix B. Integral transforms

B.1. General

In mathematics, the concept of a transformation is quite general, and most of the familiar mathematical operations such as multiplication, differentiation and integration can be thought of as transformations of functions under some set of rules. For example, the operation of differentiation is a transformation of the functions $F(t)$ to the functions $F'(t)$ where the transformation operator is represented by D, and

$$\mathrm{D}\{F(t)\} = F'(t). \qquad \text{(B.1.1)}$$

If we think of some function space as associated with $F(t)$, and another space associated with $F'(t)$, then the transformation D takes points from one space to another as illustrated schematically in Fig. 8.1. It could be said that p' is the 'image' of point p in $F(t)$ space. Now a transformation that returns p' back to p would be spoken of as an inverse transformation. In terms of D as a derivative, we see that integration would be such an inverse transformation.

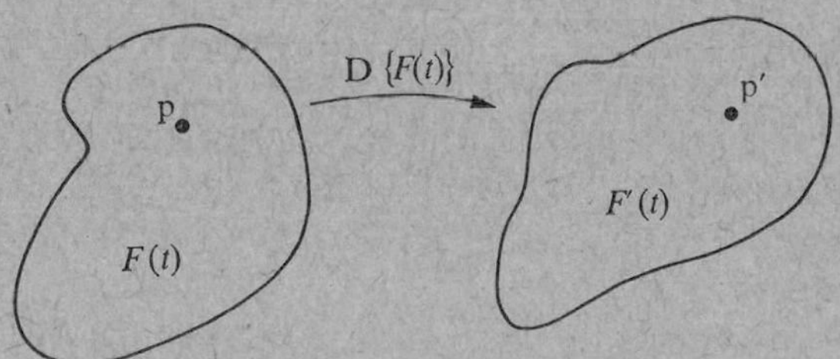

FIG. B.1. Illustration of the transformation of $F(t)$ by D.

In our study of Laplace, Fourier, or other integral transforms, we shall be concerned with transformations of the type $T\{F(t)\}$, where

$$T\{F(t)\} = \int_a^b K(t, s)F(t)\,\mathrm{d}t. \qquad \text{(B.1.2)}$$

The function $K(t, s)$ will be called the kernel of the transformation and $T\{F(t)\}$ will be an integral transformation of the function $F(t)$ with respect to the kernel $K(t, s)$. The various integral transforms will be characterized by their kernels and their limits a and b.

It will be found that, with certain kernels, the application of integral transforms to ordinary differential equations will yield algebraic expressions in the transformed variable. Partial differential equations will also undergo simplification. By treating the transformed problem, solutions may be found a great deal more easily. However, these solutions are in the transformed space, and the problem of inverting these solutions remains. Obtaining the inverse transformation will usually turn out to be the most formidable part of the entire problem.

B.2. Laplace transforms

B.2.1. *Definition*

If a function $F(t)$, defined for all positive values of the variable t, is multiplied by $\exp(-st)$ and integrated with respect to t from zero to infinity, a new function $f(s)$ of the parameter s is obtained. Thus

$$f(s) = \int_0^\infty e^{-st} F(t) \, dt. \tag{B.2.1}$$

The new function $f(s)$ is called the Laplace transform of $F(t)$. In the context of our previous discussion, we see that $\exp(-st)$ is the kernel of the transformation and $f(s)$ is the image of $F(t)$. We will abbreviate this operation with the notation $\mathscr{L}\{F\}$, where

$$\mathscr{L}\{F(t)\} = \int_0^\infty e^{-st} F(t) \, dt. \tag{B.2.2}$$

Although we shall not make use of this property immediately, it should be noted that s may be a complex quantity. Some simple examples of Laplace transforms of functions follow:

(1) $F(t) = 1$, $t > 0$.

$$\mathscr{L}(1) = \int_0^\infty e^{-st} \, dt = \left[-\frac{1}{s} e^{-st} \right]_0^\infty. \tag{B.2.3}$$

If $s > 0$, then

$$\mathscr{L}(1) = 1/s. \tag{B.2.4}$$

(2) $F(t) = e^{kt}$, $t > 0$, k constant.

$$\mathscr{L}(e^{kt}) = \left[\frac{1}{k-s} e^{-(s-k)t} \right]_0^\infty = \frac{1}{s-k}, \qquad s > k. \tag{B.2.5}$$

(3) $F(t) = t$

$$\mathscr{L}(t) = 1/s^2. \tag{B.2.6}$$

B.2.2. *Transforms of derivatives*

The transform of $F'(t)$ may be found through integration by parts. Thus

$$\mathscr{L}\{F'(t)\} = \int_0^\infty e^{-st}F'(t)\,dt$$

$$= [e^{-st}F(t)]_0^\infty + s\int_0^\infty e^{-st}F(t)\,dt. \qquad \text{(B.2.7)}$$

If $F(t)$ is of order $\exp(\alpha t)$ or less as t becomes large and if $s > \alpha$, it follows that

$$\mathscr{L}\{F'(t)\} = sf(s) - F(0). \qquad \text{(B.2.8)}$$

In a similar fashion we may show that

$$\mathscr{L}\{F''(t)\} = s^2f(s) - sF(0) - F'(0), \qquad \text{(B.2.9)}$$

or, in general,

$$\mathscr{L}\{F^{(n)}(t)\} = s^nf(s) - s^{n-1}F(0) - s^{n-2}F'(0) -$$

$$- \ldots - F^{(n-1)}(0). \qquad \text{(B.2.10)}$$

We see that the Laplace transform reduces $F^{(n)}(t)$ to an algebraic expression in s and includes the initial conditions of the problem (if t represents time) directly in the transformed expression.

B.2.3. *The inverse transform*

The problem of inverting a transformed solution is one of determining a function $F(t)$, given $f(s)$. Assuming that an inversion can be carried out, we indicate the process by the symbol $\mathscr{L}^{-1}$, where

$$\mathscr{L}^{-1}\{f(s)\} = F(t). \qquad \text{(B.2.11)}$$

Thus, $\mathscr{L}^{-1}\{f(s)\}$ denotes a function $F(t)$ whose Laplace transform is $f(s)$. As an example, suppose it is determined that

$$f(s) = 1/(s-k). \qquad \text{(B.2.12)}$$

But, we have already shown that

$$\mathscr{L}(e^{kt}) = 1/(s-k), \qquad \text{(B.2.13)}$$

so that

$$\mathscr{L}^{-1}\{f(s)\} = e^{kt}. \qquad \text{(B.2.14)}$$

As another example, it may be readily shown that, if $F(t) = \sin kt$, then

$$\mathscr{L}(\sin kt) = k/(s^2+k^2). \qquad \text{(B.2.15)}$$

Hence, if a solution in transformed space yields the result

$$f(s) = 1/(s^2+k^2), \qquad \text{(B.2.16)}$$

we then know that,

$$\mathscr{L}^{-1}\left(\frac{1}{s^2+k^2}\right) = \frac{1}{k}\sin kt = F(t). \tag{B.2.17}$$

A brief table of Laplace transforms, for reference purposes, is included at the end of this Appendix. More extensive tables are included in Churchill [7]. The Bateman manuscript project [15] has exhaustive listings of Laplace and other integral transforms. However, the solutions of problems often yield results not in the tables, and the inversion of such cases may require other considerations.

B.2.4. *Partial fractions*

As was stated in the last section, transformed solutions often yield results not tabulated. However, before we resort to extremely complicated inversion processes, every effort should be made to reset the transformed solution into combinations of already tabulated functions. As an example of this, it is often found that transformed solutions are in the form of quotients of polynomials. By the use of partial fractions, these may be decomposed into simpler fractions. For instance, suppose

$$f(s) = \frac{s+1}{s(s+2)}. \tag{B.2.18}$$

From the theory of partial fractions we know this may be expressed as

$$f(s) = \frac{A}{s}+\frac{B}{s+2}, \tag{B.2.19}$$

from which it is found that $A = B = \frac{1}{2}$. Hence

$$f(s) = \frac{1}{2s}+\frac{1}{2(s+2)}. \tag{B.2.20}$$

Then

$$\begin{aligned}\mathscr{L}^{-1}\{f(s)\} &= \mathscr{L}^{-1}\left\{\frac{1}{2s}+\frac{1}{2(s+2)}\right\} \\ &= \tfrac{1}{2}\mathscr{L}^{-1}\left\{\frac{1}{s}\right\}+\tfrac{1}{2}\mathscr{L}^{-1}\left\{\frac{1}{(s+2)}\right\}.\end{aligned} \tag{B.2.21}$$

Now, $\mathscr{L}^{-1}(1/s)$, $\mathscr{L}^{-1}\{1/(s+2)\}$ may be easily found from tables, giving

$$\mathscr{L}^{-1}\{f(s)\} = \tfrac{1}{2}+\tfrac{1}{2}e^{-2t}. \tag{B.2.22}$$

Reference should be made to any basic calculus or algebra book for the details of partial-fraction theory and the techniques of handling more difficult cases.

B.2.5. *Solutions of ordinary differential equations*

The use of Laplace transforms in solving ordinary differential equations with constant coefficients will be illustrated with a simple example. Consider the familiar differential equation

$$\frac{d^2y(t)}{dt^2}+k^2y(t) = 0, \tag{B.2.23}$$

where the initial conditions are

$$y(0) = y_0, \qquad \dot{y}(0) = \dot{y}_0. \tag{B.2.24}$$

Applying the Laplace transform we have,

$$\mathscr{L}\{\ddot{y}(t)\}+k^2\mathscr{L}\{y(t)\} = 0. \tag{B.2.25}$$

We recall that

$$\mathscr{L}\{\ddot{y}(t)\} = s^2\bar{y}(s)-sy(0)-\dot{y}(0), \tag{B.2.26}$$

where we have used $\bar{y}$ to denote the transformed dependent variable. Then, from the initial conditions, we have for the transformed equation

$$s^2\bar{y}(s)-sy_0-\dot{y}_0+k^2\bar{y}(s) = 0. \tag{B.2.27}$$

We solve this simple algebraic equation for $\bar{y}(s)$,

$$\bar{y}(s) = y_0\frac{s}{s^2+k^2}+\frac{\dot{y}_0}{k}\frac{k}{s^2+k^2}, \tag{B.2.28}$$

and see that $\mathscr{L}^{-1}\{\bar{y}(s)\}$ will give $y(t)$, the solution to the problem. From tables, we may find directly that

$$y(t) = \mathscr{L}^{-1}\{\bar{y}(s)\} = y_0 \cos kt+\frac{\dot{y}_0}{k} \sin kt. \tag{B.2.29}$$

As a second example, consider the simultaneous differential equations and initial conditions

$$\frac{d^2Y(t)}{dt^2}-\frac{d^2Z(t)}{dt^2}+\frac{dZ(t)}{dt}-Y(t) = e^t-2,$$

$$2\frac{d^2Y(t)}{dt^2}-\frac{d^2Z(t)}{dt}-2\frac{dY(t)}{dt}+Z(t) = -t, \tag{B.2.30}$$

$$Y(0) = \dot{Y}(0) = Z(0) = \dot{Z}(0) = 0. \tag{B.2.31}$$

Taking the Laplace transform of (B.2.30) we have

$$s^2\bar{y}(s)-s^2\bar{z}(s)+s\bar{z}(s)-\bar{y}(s) = \frac{1}{s-1}-\frac{2}{s},$$

$$2s^2\bar{y}(s)-s^2\bar{z}(s)-2s\bar{y}(s)+\bar{z}(s) = -1/s^2. \tag{B.2.32}$$

Eliminating $\bar{z}(s)$ from the above, we obtain

$$(s^2-2s-1)\bar{y}(s) = \frac{s^2-2s-1}{s(s-1)^2}. \tag{B.2.33}$$

By the use of partial fractions, we find

$$\bar{y}(s) = \frac{1}{s(s-1)^2} = \frac{a_1}{s}+\frac{a_2}{s-1}+\frac{a_3}{(s-1)^2}$$

$$= \frac{1}{s}-\frac{1}{s-1}+\frac{1}{(s-1)^2}. \tag{B.2.34}$$

From tables, the inverse transforms are found to be

$$y(t) = 1-e^t+te^t. \tag{B.2.35}$$

In a similar manner $\bar{z}(s)$ is found to be

$$\bar{z}(s) = \frac{2s-1}{s^2(s-1)^2} = -\frac{1}{s^2}+\frac{1}{(s-1)^2}, \tag{B.2.36}$$

with the inverse given by

$$z(t) = -t+te^t. \tag{B.2.37}$$

B.2.6. *Convolution*

Another very useful method of inverting certain types of transformed solutions will now be shown. Suppose $F(t)$, $G(t)$ are two functions whose transforms are $f(s)$ and $g(s)$. That is

$$f(s) = \mathscr{L}\{F(t)\}, \qquad g(s) = \mathscr{L}\{G(t)\}. \tag{B.2.38}$$

Before we can obtain our desired result, we need a preliminary development called the translation theorem (also called the shift theorem).

THEOREM: *If* $f(s) = \mathscr{L}\{F(t)\}$, *then*

$$e^{-bs}f(s) = \mathscr{L}\{F_b(t)\}, \tag{B.2.39}$$

where

$$F_b(t) = \begin{cases} 0, & 0 < t < b \\ F(t-b), & t > b. \end{cases} \tag{B.2.40}$$

This is easily shown. Thus

$$f(s) = \int_0^\infty e^{-st}F(t)\,dt, \tag{B.2.41}$$

$$e^{-bs}f(s) = \int_0^\infty e^{-s(t+b)}F(t)\,dt, \tag{B.2.42}$$

where b is a constant, assumed greater than zero. Let $t+b = \tau$, so that the last integral becomes

$$e^{-bs}f(s) = \int_b^\infty e^{-s\tau}F(\tau-b)\,d\tau$$

$$= \int_0^\infty e^{-s\tau}F(\tau-b)\,d\tau, \tag{B.2.43}$$

since $t > 0$ is assumed. Hence, if we define $F_b(t)$ as indicated in the theorem, we have proved the desired preliminary result.

Continuing, we apply the translation theorem to $g(s)$, changing notation slightly. Thus

$$e^{-s\tau}g(s) = \mathscr{L}\{G(t-\tau)\}$$

$$= \int_0^\infty e^{-st}G(t-\tau)\,dt, \tag{B.2.44}$$

where it is understood that $G(t) = 0$, $t < 0$. Then we may write

$$f(s)g(s) = g(s)\int_0^\infty F(\tau)e^{-s\tau}\,d\tau$$

$$= \int_0^\infty F(\tau)e^{-s\tau}g(s)\,d\tau. \tag{B.2.45}$$

Incorporating the integral representation of $g(s)$ in the above, we obtain

$$f(s)g(s) = \int_0^\infty F(\tau)\int_0^\infty e^{-st}G(t-\tau)\,dt\,d\tau. \tag{B.2.46}$$

This may be expressed as the limit

$$f(s)g(s) = \lim_{T\to\infty}\int_0^T\int_0^\infty F(\tau)e^{-st}G(t-\tau)\,dt\,d\tau$$

$$= \lim_{T\to\infty}\int_0^\infty e^{-st}\int_0^T F(\tau)G(t-\tau)\,d\tau\,dt. \tag{B.2.47}$$

The above is written as

$$f(s)g(s) = \lim_{T\to\infty}\{I_1(T)+I_2(T)\}, \tag{B.2.48}$$

where

$$I_1(T) = \int_0^T e^{-st}\int_0^T F(\tau)G(t-\tau)\,d\tau\,dt \tag{B.2.49}$$

and

$$I_2(T) = \int_T^\infty e^{-st}\int_0^T F(\tau)G(t-\tau)\,d\tau\,dt. \tag{B.2.50}$$

As $T \to \infty$, $I_2(T) \to 0$. We also recall that $G(t-\tau) = 0$ for $\tau > t$, so that the upper limit of the integration with respect to τ in (B.2.49), and (B.2.50) is replaced by t. Then we have

$$f(s)g(s) = \int_0^\infty e^{-st} \int_0^t F(\tau)G(t-\tau)\,d\tau\,dt. \tag{B.2.51}$$

Defining

$$F(t) * G(t) = \int_0^t F(\tau)G(t-\tau)\,d\tau, \tag{B.2.52}$$

we have

$$f(s)g(s) = \mathscr{L}\{F(t) * G(t)\} \tag{B.2.53}$$

or

$$F(t) * G(t) = \mathscr{L}^{-1}\{f(s)g(s)\}. \tag{B.2.54}$$

This is the convolution theorem (sometimes called the '*Faltung* theorem'). We see that the operation gives the inverse transform of the product of two transforms directly in terms of the original functions. As an example,

$$\mathscr{L}^{-1}\left(\frac{1}{s^2}\frac{1}{s-a}\right) = t * e^{at} = \int_0^t \tau e^{a(t-\tau)}\,d\tau$$

$$= e^{at}\int_0^t \tau e^{-a\tau}\,d\tau = \frac{1}{a^2}(e^{at}-at-1). \tag{B.2.55}$$

B.2.7. *The inversion integral*

The transformed solutions of many problems may yield results not contained in tables of Laplace transforms. What is needed, therefore, is a so-called 'first-principle' method of inverting a transformed solution that can be applied regardless of the availability of tabulated values. To develop the needed inversion process, we must extend our theory of the Laplace transformation by letting s represent a complex variable. An extension of the Cauchy integral formula provides the desired result.

From complex variables Cauchy's integral formula states that if $f(z)$ is an analytic function inside the closed curve C and if z_0 is a point within C, then

$$f(z_0) = \frac{1}{2\pi i}\int_C \frac{f(z)\,dz}{z-z_0}. \tag{B.2.56}$$

An extension of this formula is needed for the present work.

THEOREM. *Let $f(z)$ be analytic for* $\text{Re}(z) \geq \gamma$, *where γ is a real constant greater than zero. Then, if* $\text{Re}(z_0) > \gamma$,

$$f(z_0) = +\frac{1}{2\pi i}\lim_{\beta\to\infty}\int_{\gamma-i\beta}^{\gamma+i\beta}\frac{f(z)\,dz}{z-z_0}. \tag{B.2.57}$$

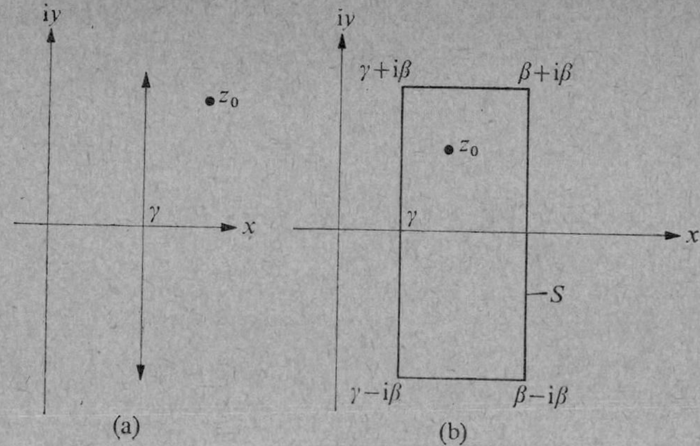

FIG. B.2. (a) The point z_0 in the complex plane located to the right of Re γ, (b) contour enclosing z_0.

This may be illustrated as shown in Fig. B.2(a). The proof of this theorem is somewhat involved, but it consists essentially of choosing a rectangular contour C that encloses z_0, as shown in Fig. B.2(b) and letting $\beta \to \infty$. By certain limiting arguments and inequalities, it is shown that the contribution from the path S vanishes, where S consists of the horizontal and right-hand vertical portions of the path.

We replace z by s in the previous theorem, so that

$$f(s) = \frac{1}{2\pi i} \lim_{\beta\to\infty} \int_{\gamma-i\beta}^{\gamma+i\beta} \frac{f(z)\,dz}{s-z}, \tag{B.2.58}$$

where s is complex and given by $s = x+iy$. Recall $f(s)$ is assumed analytic in the half-plane $\text{Re}(s) > \gamma$. We now formally apply the inverse Laplace transform to the functions on either side of this equation, giving

$$F(t) = \mathscr{L}^{-1}\{f(s)\} = \frac{1}{2\pi i}\mathscr{L}^{-1}\left\{\lim_{\beta\to\infty} \int_{\gamma-i\beta}^{\gamma+i\beta} \frac{f(z)}{s-z}\,dz\right\}$$

$$= \frac{1}{2\pi i} \lim_{\beta\to\infty} \int_{\gamma-i\beta}^{\gamma+i\beta} f(z)\mathscr{L}^{-1}\left(\frac{1}{s-z}\right) dz. \tag{B.2.59}$$

But

$$\mathscr{L}^{-1}\{1/(s-z)\} = e^{zt}, \tag{B.2.60}$$

so that

$$F(t) = \frac{1}{2\pi i} \lim_{\beta\to\infty} \int_{\gamma-i\beta}^{\gamma+i\beta} e^{st} f(s)\,ds, \tag{B.2.61}$$

where, in the above, the dummy variable z has been replaced by s. This is the inversion integral of the Laplace transform. The path of integration is often called the 'Bromwich contour', since Bromwich first devised this method of handling certain integrals that arose in operational mathematics.

The basic concept that will underlie the actual evaluation of inverse Laplace transforms by use of the inversion integral is the application of contour integration in the complex plane. The details of the calculation will depend on the nature of the transformed function $f(s)$. It is usually found that $f(s)$ is either: (1) a single-valued function of s with a finite or an infinite number of poles in the complex s-plane, or (2) a function of s having a number of branch points in the s-plane, as well as a number of poles. In the case of (1) a complete contour is formed from the Bromwich integral by adding a circle of radius R, as shown in Fig. B.3. Enclosed within the entire

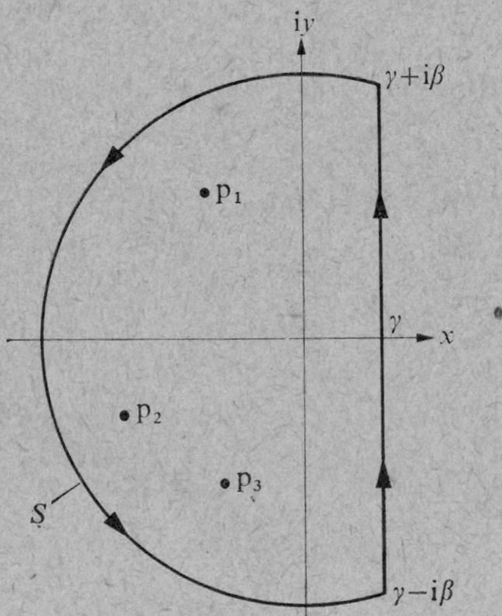

FIG. B.3. Poles enclosed by the Bromwich contour closed in the left-hand plane.

contour C will be a number of poles. From the theory of residues, we know that

$$\int_C f(z)\,dz = 2\pi i \sum_1^n (\text{Res}), \tag{B.2.62}$$

so that in our case we have

$$\frac{1}{2\pi i}\int_S e^{st}f(s)\,ds + \frac{1}{2\pi i}\int_{\gamma-i\beta}^{\gamma+i\beta} e^{st}f(s)\,ds = \sum_1^n (\text{Res}). \tag{B.2.63}$$

The essential point of the method is to then show by proper application of inequalities and limits that

$$\lim_{R\to\infty} \int_S e^{st} f(s)\, ds \to 0. \tag{B.2.64}$$

We are then left only with the Bromwich integral which is the inverse Laplace transform, so that we have

$$\mathscr{L}^{-1}\{f(s)\} = \sum_1^n (\text{Res}). \tag{B.2.65}$$

Ideas similar to those outlined above also apply in the case of (2). However, the function $f(s)$ is no longer single-valued because of the existence of branch points, so that closing the contour as shown in the previous figure would lead to difficulties. The procedure is still to complete the contour, but to deform the contour so as to envelop the branch cuts that are made to make $f(s)$ a single-valued function.

As an example, suppose

$$f(s) = e^{-\sqrt{s}}/s. \tag{B.2.66}$$

Now $\sqrt{s}$ is not single-valued, and a branch point exists at the origin, in this case. The branch cut necessary to make $\sqrt{s}$ single-valued may be, in theory, of arbitrary orientation. However, a convenient selection is along the negative real axis. We thus have the situation shown in Fig. B.4(a). The contour is completed as shown in Fig. B.4(b). We then have

$$\int_{\gamma-i\beta}^{\gamma+i\beta} + \int_{S_1} + \int_{\Gamma_1} + \int_{\Gamma_2} + \int_{\Gamma_3} + \int_{S_2} = 0, \tag{B.2.67}$$

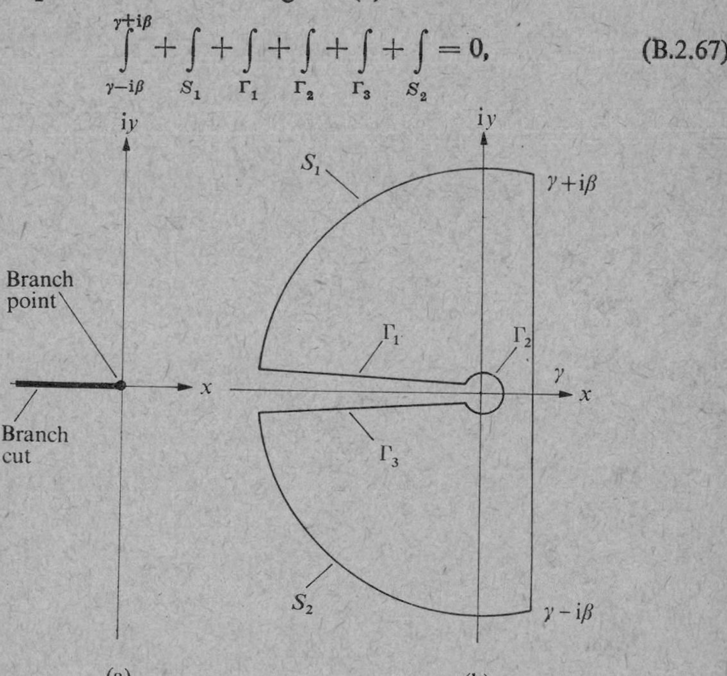

FIG. B.4. (a) Branch point located at the origin; (b) keyhole contour enclosing the branch point.

where it is assumed that no other poles have been enclosed within the contour. Then, again by proper application of inequalities and limits, it must be shown that

$$\int_{S_1} = \int_{S_2} = 0. \tag{B.2.68}$$

It remains then to evaluate $\int_{\Gamma_1}, \int_{\Gamma_2}, \int_{\Gamma_3}$. The second integral will be found to give essentially the residue at the origin, while the first and last integrals will be real integrals (integration is along the real axis). Thus the problem of finding the inverse transform will be reduced to evaluating

$$\mathscr{L}^{-1}\{f(s)\} = -\int_{\Gamma_1} - \int_{\Gamma_2} - \int_{\Gamma_3}. \tag{B.2.69}$$

B.3. Fourier transforms

B.3.1. *Definition*

The Fourier transform of a function $F(t)$, defined for all t, is given by

$$f(\gamma) = \frac{1}{\sqrt{(2\pi)}} \int_{-\infty}^{\infty} e^{i\gamma t} F(t)\, dt, \tag{B.3.1}$$

where $\exp(i\gamma t)$ is the kernel of the transformation. The above is sometimes referred to as the *exponential Fourier transform.* If $F(t)$ is an odd function, the above reduces to

$$f(\gamma) = \sqrt{\left(\frac{2}{\pi}\right)} \int_{0}^{\infty} \sin t\gamma F(t)\, dt, \tag{B.3.2}$$

which is the Fourier *sine transform.* Likewise, if $F(t)$ is an even function, the exponential transform reduces to the Fourier *cosine transform*

$$f(\gamma) = \sqrt{\left(\frac{2}{\pi}\right)} \int_{0}^{\infty} \cos t\gamma F(t)\, dt. \tag{B.3.3}$$

It might be noted that, as in the case of Fourier series, there is not unanimity in the selection of the normalizing constant. It is $1/\sqrt{(2\pi)}$ in our case, but it is sometimes $1/2\pi$, or even as a constant included in the arguments of the exponential.

B.3.2. *Transforms of derivatives*

Using integration by parts, we have for the Fourier transform of dF/dt,

$$\begin{aligned}\mathscr{F}(F') &= \frac{1}{\sqrt{(2\pi)}} \int_{-\infty}^{\infty} e^{i\gamma t} F'(t)\, dt \\ &= \left[\frac{1}{\sqrt{(2\pi)}} e^{i\gamma t} F(t)\right]_{-\infty}^{\infty} - \frac{i\gamma}{\sqrt{(2\pi)}} \int_{-\infty}^{\infty} e^{i\gamma t} F(t)\, dt \\ &= -i\gamma f(\gamma)\end{aligned} \tag{B.3.4}$$

We note that $e^{i\gamma t}F(t) \to 0$, as $t \to \pm\infty$ has been assumed, which places restrictions on the behaviour of $F(t)$ for large t. In general, we may show that

$$\mathscr{F}\{F^{(n)}(t)\} = (-i\gamma)^n f(\gamma). \tag{B.3.5}$$

The Fourier transform of derivatives places conditions on the function at $\pm\infty$, whereas the Laplace transform places one of the conditions at zero, the other at ∞. In either case, certain boundary conditions have been effectively placed on the function. The Fourier sine and cosine transforms have zero as their lower limits, we recall, and should incorporate the initial conditions in a manner similar to the Laplace transform. Thus we have

$$f_c^{(n)}(\gamma) = \sqrt{\left(\frac{2}{\pi}\right)} \int_0^\infty \cos t\gamma F^{(n)}(t)\,dt, \tag{B.3.6}$$

$$f_s^{(n)}(\gamma) = \sqrt{\left(\frac{2}{\pi}\right)} \int_0^\infty \sin t\gamma F^{(n)}(t)\,dt, \tag{B.3.7}$$

as the cosine and sine transforms of d^nF/dt^n. Integration by parts of $f_c^{(n)}(\gamma)$ gives

$$f_c^{(n)} = \sqrt{\left(\frac{2}{\pi}\right)} [F^{(n-1)}(t)\cos t\gamma]_0^\infty + \gamma\sqrt{\left(\frac{2}{\pi}\right)} \int_0^\infty \sin t\gamma F^{(n-1)}(t)\,dt. \tag{B.3.8}$$

We assume

$$\lim_{t\to 0} \sqrt{\left(\frac{2}{\pi}\right)} F^{(n-1)}(t) = a_{n-1}, \qquad \lim_{t\to\infty} F^{(n-1)}(t) = 0, \tag{B.3.9}$$

so that

$$f_c^{(n)} = -a_{n-1} + \gamma f_s^{(n-1)}. \tag{B.3.10}$$

However, integrating $f_s^{(n)}(\gamma)$ by parts, we obtain

$$f_s^{(n)} = -\gamma f_c^{(n-1)}. \tag{B.3.11}$$

From this and the previous equation we have

$$f_c^{(n)} = -a_{n-1} - \gamma^2 f_c^{(n-2)}. \tag{B.3.12}$$

By using these results as a type of recursion formula, we obtain

$$f_c^{(2n)} = -\sum_{r=0}^{n-1} (-1)^r a_{2n-2r-1}\gamma^{2r} + (-1)^n \gamma^{2n} f_c(\gamma), \tag{B.3.13}$$

$$f_c^{(2n+1)} = -\sum_{r=0}^{n} (-1)^r a_{2n-2r}\gamma^{2r} + (-1)^n \gamma^{2n+1} f_s(\gamma). \tag{B.3.14}$$

Similarly, for the sine transforms of derivatives, we obtain

$$f_s^{(2n)} = -\sum_{r=1}^{n} (-1)^r \gamma^{2r-1} a_{2n-2r} + (-1)^{n+1} \gamma^{2n} f_s, \tag{B.3.15}$$

$$f_c^{(2n+1)} = -\sum_{r=1}^{n} (-1)^r \gamma^{2r-1} a_{2n-2r+1} + (-1)^{n+1} \gamma^{2n+1} f_c. \tag{B.3.16}$$

B.3.3. *The inverse transform*

Given a function $f(\gamma)$, the inverse transformation will give the function $F(t)$. Thus we indicate this symbolically by

$$\mathscr{F}^{-1}\{f(\gamma)\} = F(t). \tag{B.3.17}$$

The problem is particularly simple if $f(\gamma)$ is recognized as the transform of a known function $F(t)$. The procedure for handling this case, including the use of partial fractions, has been covered in the section on Laplace transforms. Tables of Fourier transforms are available for such use.

The case frequently arises, however, in which $f(\gamma)$ is not tabulated or cannot be broken into simpler functions which are tabulated. In such cases, a formal inversion process must be used. Even an abbreviated version of the process for Fourier transforms, such as was given for the Laplace transforms, will not be given here. Instead, we merely present a formal definition of the inverse transformation.

Inverse exponential transforms: If $f(\gamma)$ is the Fourier transform of $F(t)$ given by

$$f(\gamma) = \frac{1}{\sqrt{(2\pi)}}\int_{-\infty}^{\infty} e^{i\gamma t}F(t)\,dt, \tag{B.3.18}$$

then $F(t)$ is given by

$$F(t) = \frac{1}{\sqrt{(2\pi)}}\int_{-\infty}^{\infty} e^{-i\gamma t}f(\gamma)\,d\gamma. \tag{B.3.19}$$

Inverse sine, cosine transforms: If $f_s(\gamma)$ is the sine transform

$$f_s(\gamma) = \sqrt{\left(\frac{2}{\pi}\right)}\int_{0}^{\infty} \sin t\gamma F(t)\,dt, \tag{B.3.20}$$

then

$$F(t) = \sqrt{\left(\frac{2}{\pi}\right)}\int_{0}^{\infty} \sin t\gamma f(\gamma)\,d\gamma. \tag{B.3.21}$$

Similarly, if $f_c(\gamma)$ is the cosine transform

$$f_c(\gamma) = \sqrt{\left(\frac{2}{\pi}\right)}\int_{0}^{\infty} \cos t\gamma F(t)\,dt, \tag{B.3.22}$$

then

$$F(t) = \sqrt{\left(\frac{2}{\pi}\right)}\int_{0}^{\infty} \cos t\gamma f(\gamma)\,d\gamma. \tag{B.3.23}$$

A transform whose inverse is identical in form, such as the sine and cosine transforms, is said to be symmetrical. The exponential transform, it is seen, is not quite symmetrical. As in the case of Laplace transforms, γ may be a complex variable, so that the inverse transform may involve contour integration in the complex plane.

B.3.4. *Convolution*

Consider $f(\gamma)$, $g(\gamma)$ to be the Fourier transformations of $F(t)$, $G(t)$ respectively. Then, as in the case of the Laplace transform, there is a convolution theorem which enables the inverse transform of the product $f(\gamma)g(\gamma)$ to be expressed as a convolution-type integral. That is,

$$\mathscr{F}^{-1}\{f(\gamma)g(\gamma)\} = F(t) * G(t). \tag{B.3.24}$$

The actual form of the integral is found as follows:

$$\begin{aligned}\mathscr{F}^{-1}\{f(\gamma)g(\gamma)\} &= \frac{1}{\sqrt{(2\pi)}}\int_{-\infty}^{\infty} f(\gamma)g(\gamma)e^{-i\gamma t}\,d\gamma \\ &= \frac{1}{2\pi}\int_{-\infty}^{\infty} f(\gamma)e^{-i\gamma t}\,d\gamma \int_{-\infty}^{\infty} G(\eta)e^{i\eta\gamma}\,d\eta \\ &= \frac{1}{2\pi}\int_{-\infty}^{\infty} G(\eta)\,d\eta \int_{-\infty}^{\infty} f(\gamma)e^{-i\gamma(t-\eta)}\,d\gamma.\end{aligned} \tag{B.3.25}$$

But

$$F(t-\eta) = \frac{1}{\sqrt{(2\pi)}}\int_{-\infty}^{\infty} f(\gamma)e^{-i\gamma(t-\eta)}\,d\gamma, \tag{B.3.26}$$

so that

$$\begin{aligned}\mathscr{F}^{-1}\{f(\gamma)g(\gamma)\} &= \frac{1}{\sqrt{(2\pi)}}\int_{-\infty}^{\infty} G(\eta)F(t-\eta)\,d\eta \\ &= F * G.\end{aligned} \tag{B.3.27}$$

Thus

$$F * G = \frac{1}{\sqrt{(2\pi)}}\int_{-\infty}^{\infty} G(\eta)F(t-\eta)\,d\eta, \tag{B.3.28}$$

is the convolution, or *Faltung* integral form for the Fourier transform.

B.3.5. *Finite Fourier transforms*

The Fourier-integral transform concepts for extended intervals may be used in problems involving a finite interval. The development starts with Fourier series considerations. The Fourier-series representation of a function periodic in the interval $-l < x < l$ is

$$F(x) = \frac{a_0}{2} + \sum_{n=1}^{\infty}\left(a_n \cos\frac{n\pi}{l}x + b_n \sin\frac{n\pi}{l}x\right), \tag{B.3.29}$$

where

$$a_n = \frac{1}{l}\int_{-l}^{l} F(u)\cos\frac{n\pi}{l}u\, du, \tag{B.3.30}$$

$$b_n = \frac{1}{l}\int_{-l}^{l} F(u)\sin\frac{n\pi}{l}u\, du. \tag{B.3.31}$$

We recall that if $F(x)$ is periodic in $0 < x < l$, or odd in $-l < x < l$, then the representation is

$$F(x) = \frac{2}{l}\sum_{n=1}^{\infty} \sin\frac{n\pi}{l}x \int_{0}^{l} F(u)\sin\frac{n\pi}{l}u\, du. \tag{B.3.32}$$

If $F(x)$ is periodic in $0 < x < l$ or even in $-l < x < l$, then

$$F(x) = \frac{1}{l}\int_{0}^{l} F(u)\, du + \frac{2}{l}\sum_{n=1}^{\infty} \cos\frac{n\pi x}{l}\int_{0}^{l} F(u)\cos\frac{n\pi}{l}u\, du. \tag{B.3.33}$$

We introduce the idea of a *finite Fourier transform* by defining

$$f_c(n) = \frac{1}{l}\int_{0}^{l} F(x)\cos\frac{n\pi}{l}x\, dx, \tag{B.3.34}$$

$$f_s(n) = \frac{1}{l}\int_{0}^{l} F(x)\sin\frac{n\pi}{l}x\, dx, \tag{B.3.35}$$

as the finite Fourier cosine and sine transforms respectively, where $F(x)$ is defined on the interval $0 < x < l$. Then we define the following inversions:

Finite inverse transform: If $f_c(n)$ is the finite Fourier cosine transform of $F(x)$ in $0 < x < l$, then

$$F(x) = \frac{f_c(0)}{l} + 2\sum_{n=1}^{\infty} f_c(n)\cos\frac{n\pi}{l}x. \tag{B.3.36}$$

If $f_s(n)$ is the finite Fourier sine transform of $F(x)$, then

$$F(x) = 2\sum_{n=1}^{\infty} f_s(n)\sin\frac{n\pi}{l}x. \tag{B.3.37}$$

In the above, the series representation plays the role of the inverse transform. Now, the use of finite Fourier transforms does not solve problems which are incapable of solution by the direct application of Fourier series. However, there will be occasion when this approach to a problem will have advantages over the direct series expansions of the various functions.

B.3.6. *The Fourier integral*

Again consider the Fourier series representation of $F(x)$, defined in $-l < x < l$ as

$$F(x) = \frac{a_0}{2} + \sum_{n=1}^{\infty}\left(a_n \cos\frac{n\pi}{l}x + b_n \sin\frac{n\pi}{l}x\right), \tag{B.3.38}$$

where a_n, b_n have been previously defined by (B.3.30) and (B.3.31). If the a_n, b_n definitions are introduced directly into the above, we have

$$\begin{aligned} F(x) &= \frac{1}{2l}\int_{-l}^{l} F(u)\,du + \\ &\quad + \frac{1}{l}\sum_{n=1}^{\infty}\left\{\int_{-l}^{l} F(u)\cos\frac{n\pi}{l}u \cos\frac{n\pi}{l}x\,dx + \int_{-l}^{l} F(u)\sin\frac{n\pi}{l}u \sin\frac{n\pi}{l}x\,dx\right. \\ &= \frac{1}{2l}\int_{-l}^{l} F(u)\,du + \frac{1}{l}\sum_{n=1}^{\infty}\int_{-l}^{l} F(u)\cos\frac{n\pi}{l}(u-x)\,du. \end{aligned} \tag{B.3.39}$$

Denote the ratio $n\pi/l$ as α. As $l \to \infty$ (so that $\pi/l \to \delta\alpha$) the first term becomes zero and the series becomes

$$\begin{aligned} F(x) &= \frac{1}{\pi}\sum_{n=1}^{\infty}\delta\alpha\int_{-\pi/\delta\alpha}^{\pi/\delta\alpha} F(u)\cos\{n\delta\alpha(u-x)\}\,du \\ &= \frac{1}{\pi}\int_{-\pi/\delta\alpha}^{\pi/\delta\alpha} F(u)\,du\sum_{n=1}^{\infty}\cos\{(u-x)n\delta\alpha\}\,\delta\alpha. \end{aligned} \tag{B.3.40}$$

The limiting value of a series is an integral under the proper conditions, so that

$$\sum_{i=1}^{\infty} F(x_i)\,\delta x_i \to \int_0^{\infty} F(x)\,dx. \tag{B.3.41}$$

Now $n\delta\alpha$ is analogous to x_i and $\delta\alpha$ to δx_i, so that we have for $F(x)$,

$$F(x) = \frac{1}{\pi}\int_{-\infty}^{\infty} F(u)\,\mathrm{d}u \int_{0}^{\infty} \cos\{(u-x)\alpha\}\,\mathrm{d}\alpha. \tag{B.3.42}$$

Hence the *Fourier integral* representation of the function $F(x)$ is

$$F(x) = \frac{1}{\pi}\int_{0}^{\infty} \mathrm{d}\alpha \int_{-\infty}^{\infty} F(u)\cos\{(u-x)\alpha\}\,\mathrm{d}u. \tag{B.3.43}$$

It may be easily shown that if $F(x)$ is defined in $0 < x < \infty$, then

$$F(x) = \frac{2}{\pi}\int_{0}^{\infty} \mathrm{d}\alpha \int_{0}^{\infty} F(u)\cos x\alpha \cos u\alpha\,\mathrm{d}u. \tag{B.3.44}$$

B.4. Hankel transforms

B.4.1. *Definitions*

The Hankel transform of order ν of the function $f(x)$ is defined as

$$\bar{f}(\xi) = \int_{0}^{\infty} xf(x)J_\nu(\xi x)\,\mathrm{d}x. \tag{B.4.1}$$

The inverse transform is given by

$$f(x) = \int_{0}^{\infty} \xi\bar{f}(\xi)J_\nu(x\xi)\,\mathrm{d}\xi. \tag{B.4.2}$$

Thus complete symmetry exists in the Hankel transform and its inverse.

As a simple example of a Hankel transform, suppose

$$f(x) = \begin{cases} 1, & 0 < x < a \\ 0, & x > a. \end{cases} \tag{B.4.3}$$

Using the zero-order Hankel transform gives

$$\bar{f}(\xi) = \int_{0}^{a} xJ_0(\xi x)\,\mathrm{d}x. \tag{B.4.4}$$

From the relation

$$\frac{\mathrm{d}}{\mathrm{d}z}\{z^n J_n(z)\} = z^n J_{n-1}(z), \tag{B.4.5}$$

one obtains

$$\bar{f}(\xi) = \frac{1}{\xi}\int_0^a \frac{d}{dx}\{xJ_1(\xi x)\}\,dx = \left[\frac{x}{\xi}J_1(\xi x)\right]_0^a$$

$$= \frac{a}{\xi}J_1(\xi a). \qquad \text{(B.4.6)}$$

B.4.2. *Transforms of derivatives and Parseval's theorem*

The Hankel transform of the derivative df/dx is given by

$$\bar{f}'_\nu(\xi) = \int_0^\infty x\frac{df}{dx}J_\nu(\xi x)\,dx. \qquad \text{(B.4.7)}$$

Using integration by parts and the derivative and recursion formula for Bessel functions, one obtains

$$\bar{f}'_\nu(\xi) = -\xi\left\{\frac{\nu+1}{2\nu}\bar{f}_{\nu-1}(\xi) - \frac{\nu-1}{2\nu}\bar{f}_{\nu+1}(\xi)\right\}. \qquad \text{(B.4.8)}$$

Formulas for higher derivatives are obtained by repeated application of (B.4.8).

The Hankel transform finds particular application to problems involving polar and cylindrical coordinate systems. Considerable simplification occurs, for example, to the operator $f''+f'/r-\nu^2f/r^2$. Thus it may be shown that

$$\int_0^\infty r\left(\frac{d^2f}{dr^2}+\frac{1}{r}\frac{df}{dr}-\frac{\nu^2}{r^2}f\right)J_\nu(\xi r)\,dr = -\xi^2\bar{f}_\nu(\xi). \qquad \text{(B.4.9)}$$

Finally, it should be noted that a simple convolution theorem does not exist for Hankel transforms. This is because there is no simple expression for the product $J_\nu(\xi x)J_\nu(\xi y)$ as there is, say, for $\exp(i\xi x)\exp(i\xi y)$ that arises in Fourier transforms. However, there is a simple Parseval theorem which states that

$$\int_0^\infty xf(x)g(x)\,dx = \int_0^\infty \xi\bar{f}(\xi)\bar{g}(\xi)\,d\xi, \qquad \text{(B.4.10)}$$

where $\bar{f}(\xi)$, $\bar{g}(\xi)$ are the Hankel transforms of $f(x)$, $g(x)$.

B.5. Tables of transforms

A few brief tables of Laplace and Fourier transforms are included here for use in analyses and problems presented in the book. More extensive tables are presented in the textbooks by Churchill [7] and Sneddon [51]. The tables in Erdelyi [15] represent some of the most complete listings.

TABLE B.1
Laplace transforms

$$F(t) = \frac{1}{2\pi i} \lim_{\beta\to\infty} \int_{\gamma-i\beta}^{\gamma+i\beta} f(s)e^{st}\,ds, \qquad f(s) = \int_0^\infty F(t)e^{-st}\,dt$$

	$F(t)$	$f(s)$
1.	$\int_0^t F_1(t-\tau)F_2(\tau)\,d\tau$	$f_1(s)f_2(s)$
2.	$F^{(n)}(t)$	$s^n f(s) - s^{n-1}F(0) - \ldots - F^{(n-1)}(0)$
3.	$e^{at}F(t)$	$f(s-a)$
4.	1	$\frac{1}{s}$
5.	$\frac{t^{n-1}}{(n-1)!}$	$\frac{1}{s^n}$ $(n = 1, 2, \ldots)$
6.	$\frac{1}{\sqrt{(\pi t)}}$	$\frac{1}{\sqrt{s}}$
7.	e^{at}	$\frac{1}{s-a}$
8.	$\frac{1}{(n-1)!} t^{n-1}e^{at}$	$\frac{1}{(s-a)^n}$ $(n = 1, 2, \ldots)$
9.	$\frac{1}{a-b}(e^{at} - e^{bt})$	$\frac{1}{(s-a)(s-b)}$
10.	$\frac{1}{a-b}(ae^{at} - be^{bt})$	$\frac{s}{(s-a)(s-b)}$
11.	$\frac{1}{a}\sin at$	$\frac{1}{s^2+a^2}$
12.	$\cos at$	$\frac{s}{s^2+a^2}$
13.	$\frac{1}{a}\sinh at$	$\frac{1}{s^2-a^2}$
14.	$\cosh at$	$\frac{s}{s^2-a^2}$
15.	$\frac{1}{b}e^{at}\sin bt$	$\frac{1}{(s-a)^2+b^2}$
16.	$e^{at}\cos bt$	$\frac{s-a}{(s-a)^2+b^2}$
17.	$J_0(at)$	$\frac{1}{\sqrt{(s^2+a^2)}}$
18.	$H\langle t-k\rangle$	$\frac{e^{-ks}}{s}$

TABLE B.2
Fourier transforms

$$f(x)=\frac{1}{\surd(2\pi)}\int_{-\infty}^{\infty}F(\xi)\mathrm{e}^{-\mathrm{i}\xi x}\,\mathrm{d}\xi,\qquad F(\xi)=\frac{1}{\surd(2\pi)}\int_{-\infty}^{\infty}f(x)\mathrm{e}^{\mathrm{i}\xi x}\,\mathrm{d}x.$$

$f(x)$	$F(\xi)$
$\dfrac{\sin(\alpha x)}{x}$	$\begin{cases}\left(\dfrac{\pi}{2}\right)^{\frac{1}{2}} & \lvert\xi\rvert<a\\ 0 & \lvert\xi\rvert>a\end{cases}$
$\left.\begin{matrix}\mathrm{e}^{\mathrm{i}\omega x} & p<x<q\\ 0 & x<p,\quad x>q\end{matrix}\right\}$	$\dfrac{\mathrm{i}}{(2\pi)^{\frac{1}{2}}}\dfrac{\mathrm{e}^{\mathrm{i}p(\omega+\xi)}-\mathrm{e}^{\mathrm{i}q(\omega+\xi)}}{\xi}$
$\left.\begin{matrix}\mathrm{e}^{-cx+\mathrm{i}\omega x} & x>0\\ 0 & x<0\end{matrix}\right\}$	$\dfrac{\mathrm{i}}{(2\pi)^{\frac{1}{2}}(\omega+\xi+\mathrm{i}c)}$
$\exp(-px^2),\quad R(p)>0$	$(2p)^{-\frac{1}{2}}\exp(-\xi^2/4p)$
$\cos(px^2)$	$(2p)^{-\frac{1}{2}}\cos\left(\dfrac{\xi^2}{4p}-\frac{1}{4}\pi\right)$
$\sin(px^2)$	$(2p)^{-\frac{1}{2}}\sin\left(\dfrac{\xi^2}{4p}+\frac{1}{4}\pi\right)$
$\dfrac{1}{\lvert x\rvert}$	$\dfrac{1}{\lvert\xi\rvert}$
$\dfrac{\mathrm{e}^{-a\lvert x\rvert}}{\lvert x\rvert^{\frac{1}{2}}}$	$\dfrac{\{(a^2+\xi^2)^{\frac{1}{2}}+a\}^{\frac{1}{2}}}{(a^2+\xi^2)^{\frac{1}{2}}}$
$\left.\begin{matrix}(a^2-x^2)^{-\frac{1}{2}} & \lvert x\rvert<a\\ 0 & \lvert x\rvert>a\end{matrix}\right\}$	$(\frac{1}{2}\pi)^{\frac{1}{2}}J_0(a\xi)$
$\dfrac{\sin\{b(a^2+x^2)^{\frac{1}{2}}\}}{(a^2+x^2)^{\frac{1}{2}}}$	$\begin{cases}0 & \lvert\xi\rvert>b\\ (\frac{1}{2}\pi)^{\frac{1}{2}}J_0\{a(b^2-\xi^2)^{\frac{1}{2}}\} & \lvert\xi\rvert<b\end{cases}$

TABLE B.3

Fourier cosine transforms

$$f(x) = \sqrt{\left(\frac{2}{\pi}\right)}\int_0^\infty F_c(\xi)\cos \xi x \, d\xi, \qquad F_c(\xi) = \sqrt{\left(\frac{2}{\pi}\right)}\int_0^\infty f(x)\cos \xi x \, dx$$

$f(x)$	$F_c(\xi)$
$\left.\begin{matrix} 1, & 0 < x < a \\ 0, & x > a \end{matrix}\right\}$	$\left(\frac{2}{\pi}\right)^{\frac{1}{2}} \frac{\sin(\xi a)}{\xi}$
e^{-x}	$\left(\frac{2}{\pi}\right)^{\frac{1}{2}} \frac{1}{1+\xi^2}$
$\operatorname{sech}(\pi x)$	$\frac{1}{1+\xi^4}$
$\exp(-x^2)$	$\exp(-\xi^2)$
$\cos(\frac{1}{2}x^2)$	$\frac{1}{\sqrt{2}}\{\cos(\frac{1}{2}\xi^2)+\sin(\frac{1}{2}\xi^2)\}$
$\sin(\frac{1}{2}x^2)$	$\frac{1}{\sqrt{2}}\{\cos(\frac{1}{2}\xi^2)-\sin(\frac{1}{2}\xi^2)\}$

TABLE B.4

Fourier sine transforms

$$f(x) = \sqrt{\left(\frac{2}{\pi}\right)}\int_0^\infty F_s(\xi)\sin \xi x \, d\xi, \qquad F_c(\xi) = \sqrt{\left(\frac{2}{\pi}\right)}\int_0^\infty f(x)\sin \xi x \, dx$$

$f(x)$	$F_s(\xi)$
e^{-x}	$\left(\frac{2}{\pi}\right)^{\frac{1}{2}} \frac{1}{1+\xi^2}$
$x \exp(-x^2/2)$	$\exp(-\xi^2/2)$
$x^n e^{-px}$	$\frac{2^{n+\frac{1}{2}}p^n n!\,\xi}{\pi^{\frac{1}{2}}(p^2+\xi^2)^{n+1}}$
$\cos(ax^2)$	$-a^{-\frac{1}{2}}\left\{\cos\left(\frac{\xi^2}{4a}\right)\operatorname{Si}\left(\frac{\xi}{\sqrt{(2\pi a)}}\right) - -\sin\left(\frac{\xi^2}{4a}\right)\operatorname{Ci}\left(\frac{\xi}{\sqrt{(2\pi a)}}\right)\right\}$
$x^{-\frac{1}{2}} \exp(-ax^{\frac{1}{2}})$	$\xi^{-\frac{1}{2}}\{\cos(2a\xi)^{\frac{1}{2}} - \sin(2a\xi)^{\frac{1}{2}}\}$
$\left.\begin{matrix} 0, & 0 < x < a \\ (x^2-a^2)^{-\frac{1}{2}}, & x > a \end{matrix}\right\}$	$\left(\frac{\pi}{2}\right)^{\frac{1}{2}} J_0(a\xi)$

TABLE B.5

Finite Fourier cosine transforms

$$f(x) = \frac{1}{a} f_c(0) + \frac{2}{a} \sum_{n=1}^{\infty} f_c(n) \cos \frac{n\pi x}{a}, \qquad f_c(n) = \int_0^a f(x) \cos \frac{n\pi x}{a} \, dx$$

$f(x)$	$f_c(n)$
1	$\begin{cases} a, & n = 0 \\ 0, & n = 1, 2, 3, \ldots \end{cases}$
$\begin{rcases} 1, & 0 < x < \frac{1}{2}a \\ -1, & \frac{1}{2}a < x < a \end{rcases}$	$\begin{cases} 0, & n = 0 \\ \frac{2a}{\pi n} \sin(\frac{1}{2}n\pi) & n = 1, 2, \ldots \end{cases}$
x	$\begin{cases} \frac{1}{2}a^2, & n = 0 \\ \left(\frac{a}{\pi n}\right)^2 \{(-1)^n - 1\}, & n = 1, 2, \ldots \end{cases}$
x^2	$\begin{cases} \frac{1}{3}a^3, & n = 0 \\ \frac{2a^3}{\pi^2 n^2} (-1)^n, & n = 1, 2, \ldots \end{cases}$
$\left(1 - \frac{x}{a}\right)^2$	$\begin{cases} \frac{1}{3}a, & n = 0 \\ \frac{2a}{\pi^2 n^2}, & n = 1, 2, \ldots \end{cases}$

TABLE B.6

Finite Fourier sine transforms

$$f(x) = \frac{2}{a} \sum_{n=1}^{\infty} f_s(n) \sin \frac{n\pi x}{a}, \qquad f_s(n) = \int_0^a f(x) \sin \frac{n\pi x}{a} \, dx$$

$f(x)$	$f_s(n)$
1	$\frac{a}{\pi n} \{1 + (-1)^{n+1}\}$
x	$(-1)^{n+1} \frac{a^2}{\pi n}$
$1 - \frac{x}{a}$	$\frac{a}{\pi n}$
$\begin{rcases} x, & 0 \le x \le \frac{1}{2}a \\ a - x, & \frac{1}{2}a \le x \le a \end{rcases}$	$\frac{2a^2}{\pi^2 n^2} \sin(\frac{1}{2}n\pi)$
x^2	$\frac{a^3(-1)^{n-1}}{\pi n} - \frac{2a^3\{1 - (-1)^n\}}{\pi^3 n^3}$
x^3	$(-1)^n \frac{a^4}{\pi^3}\left(\frac{6}{n^3} - \frac{\pi^2}{n}\right)$
$x(a^2 - x^2)$	$(-1)^{n+1} \frac{6a^4}{\pi^3 n^3}$

TABLE B.7
Hankel transforms

$$f(x) = \int_0^\infty \xi \bar{f}(\xi) J_\nu(\xi x)\, d\xi, \qquad \bar{f}(\xi) = \int_0^\infty x f(x) J_\nu(\xi x)\, dx$$

$f(x)$	ν	$\bar{f}(\xi)$
$\begin{cases} x^\nu, & 0 < x < a \\ 0, & x > a \end{cases}$	> -1	$\frac{a^{\nu+1}}{\xi} J_{\nu+1}(\xi a)$
$\begin{cases} 1, & 0 < x < a \\ 0, & x > a \end{cases}$	0	$\frac{a}{\xi} J_1(a\xi)$
$\begin{cases} (a^2-x^2), & 0 < x < a, \\ 0, & x > a \end{cases}$	0	$\frac{4a}{\xi^3} J_1(\xi a) - \frac{2a^2}{\xi^2} J_0(\xi a)$
$x^\nu \exp(-px^2)$	> -1	$\frac{\xi}{(2p)^{\nu+1}} \exp(-\xi^2/4p)$
$\frac{e^{-px}}{x}$	0	$(\xi^2+p^2)^{-\frac{1}{2}}$
e^{-px}	0	$p(\xi^2+p^2)^{-\frac{3}{2}}$
$x^{-2}e^{-px}$	1	$\frac{(\xi^2+p^2)^{\frac{1}{2}}-p}{\xi}$
$\frac{e^{-px}}{x}$	1	$\frac{1}{\xi} - \frac{p}{\xi(\xi^2+p^2)^{\frac{1}{2}}}$
e^{-px}	1	$\xi(\xi^2+p^2)^{-\frac{3}{2}}$
$\frac{a}{(a^2+x^2)^{\frac{3}{2}}}$	0	$e^{-a\xi}$
$\frac{\sin(ax)}{x}$	0	$\begin{cases} 0, & \xi > a \\ (a^2-\xi^2)^{-\frac{1}{2}}, & 0 < \xi < a \end{cases}$
$\frac{\sin(ax)}{x}$	1	$\begin{cases} \frac{a}{\xi(\xi^2-a^2)^{\frac{1}{2}}}, & \xi > a \\ 0 & \xi < a \end{cases}$
$\frac{\sin(x)}{x^2}$	0	$\begin{cases} \sin^{-1}\left(\frac{1}{\xi}\right), & \xi > 1 \\ \frac{1}{2}\pi, & \xi < 1 \end{cases}$

TABLE B.8
Fourier spectra of pulses

Description	$p(t)$		Spectrum	$\overline{f}_c(\omega)$†
Rectangular pulse	$A,\ \lvert t\rvert<\frac{\tau}{2}$ $0,\ \lvert t\rvert>\frac{\tau}{2}$	p, A, $-\tau/2$, $\tau/2$, t	$\frac{\tau}{2\pi}$, ω, $\frac{2\pi}{\tau}$ $\frac{4\pi}{\tau}$ $\frac{6\pi}{\tau}\ldots\left(\frac{2n\pi}{\tau}\right)$	$\dfrac{\sin\omega\tau/2}{\pi\omega}$
Triangle	$-\frac{2A}{\tau}t+A, 0<t<\frac{\tau}{2}$ $\frac{2A}{\tau}t+A, -\frac{\tau}{2}<t<0$ $0, \lvert t\rvert>\frac{\tau}{2}$	p, A, $-\tau/2$, $\tau/2$, t	$\frac{4\pi}{\tau}$ $\frac{8\pi}{\tau}\ldots\left(\frac{4n\pi}{\tau}\right)$ ω	$\dfrac{2}{\pi\tau\omega^2}\ (1-\cos\omega\tau/2)$
Half sine	$A\cos\pi t/\tau, \lvert t\rvert<\frac{\tau}{2}$ $0, \lvert t\rvert>\frac{\tau}{2}$	p, A, $-\tau/2$, $\tau/2$, t	$\frac{\tau}{\pi^2}$, $0{\cdot}79\tau/\pi^2$, $0{\cdot}33\tau/\pi^2$, $\cdots(2n-1)\frac{\pi}{\tau}$, $\frac{\pi}{\tau}$ $\frac{2\pi}{\tau}$ $\frac{3\pi}{\tau}$ $\frac{5\pi}{\tau}$ ω	$\dfrac{\cos\omega\tau/2}{\tau\left(\frac{\pi^2}{\tau^2}-\omega^2\right)}$
Sine²	$A\cos^2\frac{\pi t}{\tau}, \lvert t\rvert>\frac{\tau}{2}$ $0, \lvert t\rvert>\frac{\tau}{2}$	p, A, $-\tau/2$, $\tau/2$, t	$\frac{\tau}{4\pi}$, $0{\cdot}21\tau/\pi$, $\frac{\tau}{8\pi}$, $\ldots\frac{2n\pi}{\tau}$, $\frac{\pi}{\tau}$ $\frac{2\pi}{\tau}$ $\frac{4\pi}{\tau}$ $\frac{6\pi}{\tau}$ ω	$\dfrac{2\pi}{\tau^2\omega\left(\frac{4\pi^2}{\tau^2}-\omega^2\right)}\sin\dfrac{\omega\tau}{2}$
Gaussian	$A\exp(-4t^2/\tau^2)$	p, A, A/e, $-\tau/2$, $\tau/2$, t	$\frac{\tau}{4\sqrt{\pi}}$, $\frac{\tau}{4\sqrt{\pi}e}$, $4/\tau$, ω	$\dfrac{\tau}{4\sqrt{\pi}}\exp(-\omega^2\tau^2/16)$
Modulated sine	$h(t)\cos\omega_0\tau$ $h(t)\sim$even	p, t, τ	f_c, $\frac{1}{2}h_c(\omega+\omega_0)$, $\frac{1}{2}h_c(\omega+\omega_0)$, $-\omega_0$, ω_0, ω	$f_c(\omega)=(\sqrt{\frac{2}{\pi}})\int_0^\infty h\cos\omega_0 t$ $\times\cos\omega t\,dt$ $=\frac{1}{2}h_c(\omega+\omega_0)-$ $-\frac{1}{2}h_c(\omega-\omega_0)$
Exponential decay	$A\exp(-t/\tau)t>0$ $0, t<0$	p, A, $1/A$, τ, t	$\frac{\tau}{2\pi}$, $\lvert f/A\rvert$, $0{\cdot}707\left(\frac{\tau}{2\pi}\right)$, $1/\tau$, ω	$f(\omega)/A=\dfrac{1}{2\pi(1/\tau-i\omega)}$ Note phase dependence.
Rule of thumb		p, A, $A/2$, $\Delta\tau$, t	H, $H/2$, $\Delta\omega$, ω	$\Delta\tau\,\Delta\omega\cong 2\pi$ or $\Delta\tau\,\Delta f\cong 1$

† $\overline{f}_c(\omega)=\sqrt{(2\pi)}f_c(\omega)/A$

B.7. Fourier spectra of pulses

A mechanical pulse applied to a system is prescribed by its spatial and time distributions. The time variation is frequently replaced by a frequency description in the form of the Fourier spectrum or frequency spectrum of the pulse. The frequency characterization may arise in the course of mathematical analysis due to Fourier transform operations, or merely through a preference for frequency domain instead of time-domain pulse characterization.

The Fourier spectra of a number of common pulse shapes are shown in Table B.8. They are obtained simply by taking the Fourier transform of the pulse $p(t)$. Thus

$$f(\omega) = \frac{1}{\sqrt{(2\pi)}} \int_{-\infty}^{\infty} p(t) \mathrm{e}^{\mathrm{i}\omega t} \, \mathrm{d}t. \tag{B.7.1}$$

If $p(t)$ is an even function, as most of the tabulated cases are, the Fourier cosine transform is appropriate,

$$f_c(\omega) = \sqrt{\left(\frac{2}{\pi}\right)} \int_{0}^{\infty} p(t) \cos \omega t \, \mathrm{d}t. \tag{B.7.2}$$

Appendix C: Experimental methods in stress waves

THE object here is to survey a number of the common methods for producing and detecting stress waves and vibrations in structures and elements. The material is meant to provide an elementary background to references made to experimental work in the various chapters of the book. Two topics are considered, the first being a survey of methods for producing transient motion in a solid, the second pertaining to methods for detecting stress waves in a solid. Methods of recording transient and steady signals are only briefly discussed, and no attempt is made to consider the system characteristics of the many detection–recording schemes.

For those interested in the detailed aspects of experimental mechanics, there are many useful references. The *Handbook of experimental stress analysis* by Hetenyi [21] provides a broad coverage of many techniques in both static and dynamic measurements. More recent texts in the area are those of Dove and Adams [13] and Dally and Riley [10]. Both cover photo-elastic methods and strain-gauge techniques, with the former also giving coverage of motion measurement. The *Handbook of shock and vibration*, edited by Harris and Crede [20], has a number of chapters devoted to experimental methods. The characteristics of measurement systems, particularly those used in acoustics and steady vibrations of structures are considered in the texts by Keast [26], Magrab and Bloomquist [37], and Doeblin [12]. Several of the manufacturers of vibration equipment publish short monographs on selected topics in vibration measurement.

A number of survey papers on experimental methods in stress waves and vibrations have appeared. In the area of stress waves, Kolsky has prepared several articles [29, 30, 33]. Hillier [22, 23] has surveyed techniques for determining dynamic material properties. Proceedings of symposia on dynamic experimental methods have also appeared [54, 57]. The texts by Kolsky [32] and Goldsmith [19] also contain portions on experimental methods. Technical articles covering experimental work appear, of course, in many technical journals, but the journal *Experimental Mechanics* is exclusively devoted to this topic.

C.1. Methods for producing stress waves

The simplest and most common method of producing stress waves is by the mechanical impact of one solid against another. The early investigations of

Hopkinson [25] used a falling weight to dynamically load a wire. A swinging pendulum has been used in many instances (see, for example, Frocht [17]) to dynamically load a structure. A difficulty associated with these schemes is that the stress waveform imparted to the structure is not easily characterized by simple mathematical functions, and thus leads to more complex problems in comparing theoretical and experimental results.

In the case of studies involving longitudinal stress waves in rods, the longitudinal, collinear impact of a striker bar, produces 'predictable' stress waves. As shown in the analyses of Chapter 2, if the striker bar and impact bar are of the same material and cross-section, simple rod theory predicts a rectangular pulse, having a pulse length of twice the length of the striker bar. In practice, the waveform produced departs somewhat from this shape. If the impact is indeed collinear and the impact bars are perfectly flat, the stress wave has oscillatory characteristics, as shown in some of the results of Chapter 8. The oscillating results from excitation of the higher modes of the bar. In order to avoid pulse oscillations, the contact surfaces of the bars are slightly rounded. This yields a pulse having no overshoot, but with a more gradual rise time, as shown in some of the results of Chapter 2.

A spherical ball is used as the impacting object in many stress-wave studies. In the case of longitudinal stress-wave studies in rods, the pulse shape is quite simple, as shown in some of the results of Chapter 2, and is analysable on the basis of a combined Hertzian contact and simple rod theory, also as shown in Chapter 2. A number of studies on the transverse impact of beams and plates and impact on a half-space have used the spherical ball as the impact geometry. The impact situation is not so easily analysed for these configurations, however.

A wide variety of techniques is used to propel the impacting objects into collision with a load. Gravity is, of course, the simplest means and has been used in experiments involving falling weights, swinging pendulums, and dropping balls. In the case of longitudinal rod impact experiments, the striker rod must be suspended by two sets of thin strings or wires to maintain alignment at impact. The experimental apparatus used by Becker [1] and Kuo [34] are typical of arrangements of this type. Compressed air, hydraulic pistons, elastic springs, and slingshot-type arrangements have also been used to propel bars into impact. Explosives and the impact of a swinging pendulum have also been used to initiate the motion of a striker bar. The use of solenoids to accelerate ferromagnetic rods into impact has also been reported.

Electromechanical phenomena are used to produce stress pulses in solids, particularly in applications where high stress levels are not necessary. The piezoelectric effect, whereby certain materials exhibit mechanical strain when subjected to an electrical field and the inverse effect, is widely used. Piezoelectric materials include many natural materials, such as quartz and Rochelle salt, man-made crystals, such as ammonium dihydrogen phosphate (ADP) and lithium sulphate, and a number of ceramics, such as barium titanate and lead zirconate titanate. The characteristics of the stress pulse produced in a material by a piezoelectric transducer depends on several things, including the geometry of the transducer, the means of coupling the transducer to the solid, and the waveform of the applied electrical signal. It is dependent also on the nature of the mechanical response to the electrical signal. Thus particular cuts of crystals or polarized ceramics may vibrate in thickness expansion, shear, or torsional modes to the applied electrical signal. Useful references on the behaviour of piezoelectric materials and transducers are Mason [39, 40] and Berlincourt, Curran, and Jaffe [4]. Redwood [48, 49, 50] has presented several articles on the nature of the mechanical or electrical outputs of transducers to, respectively, electrical or mechanical inputs. A survey by Bradfield [5] on types of ultrasonic transducers is also most helpful. White [56] describes a class of thin-layer transducers that use the piezoelectric effect.

The magneto-strictive effect, whereby a mechanical pulse is produced in a ferromagnetic material subjected to a transient magnetic field, is also used to produce stress pulses in a material. May [41, Section VII] reviews some of the considerations related to these devices. This technique of pulse production was used in the study by Britton and Langley [6] reported on in Chapter 3.

Explosives of various types are frequently used to initiate stress pulses in materials. Lead azide is the solid explosive most commonly used in laboratory-scale studies of stress waves. Kolsky [27, 31] and Dally [8, 9] have used this technique for launching pulses in rods and slabs and in photo-elastic specimens. Many other applications are reported in the literature. Kolsky [28] has reported on certain difficulties associated with the electro-magnetic pulse generated by the chemical disassociation in the explosion. The use of sprayed silver acetylide–silver nitrate to initiate a laboratory-scale explosive pulse over a broad area has been reported by Neville and Hoese [43], and Hoese, Langner, and Baker [24]. The explosion of gaseous mixtures has been used for pulse production by Davies [11]. The sharp acoustic shock-front produced by a spark-gap discharge may also be used to initiate low-amplitude stress waves in solids, and was the technique used by Press and Oliver [47], reviewed in Chapter 8.

Exploding wires and foils are also used to produce stress pulses directly or to provide the energy for launching projectiles into impact with solids. The explosion actually results from the nearly instantaneous vaporization arising from the discharge of electrical energy from a capacitor bank through the wire or foil. The use of exploding wire to radially load a cylinder has been reported by Fyfe [18]. An extensive documentation of this phenomenon has been given by Moore and Chase [42]. The use of exploding foil in launching thin striker or flyer plates into planar impact for anelastic wave-propagation studies has been reported by several investigators, including Berkowitz and Cohen [3] and Dueweke [14].

The use of a shock tube for producing very uniform step pressure pulses has been reported by Fox and Curtis [16] and is reviewed in Chapter 8. The rapid unloading produced by fracture is often used, directly or indirectly, to initiate stress waves. Thus, in crack propagation studies such as reported by Wells and Post [55] and Beebe [2], the stress waves produced by the propagating crack are the phenomena of interest. In other cases, the rapid unloading due to fracture of an axially loaded bar is used to produce an impulsive moment in a beam, such as reported by Stephenson and Wilhoit [53] or an impulsive torque in a rod, such as reported by Nicholas and Campbell [44]. Stress pulses have also been produced by the rapid deposition of heat energy into a solid. Thus, Percival and Cheney [45] have used this principle in a scheme involving the deposition of luminous energy from a *Q*-switched laser into a coloured glass rod. The rapid heating of the rod then initiates a pulse into a metallic rod.

C.2. Methods for detecting stress waves

Prior to the development of sensitive transducing and recording devices, experimental investigations of stress-wave phenomena were hampered by the lack of techniques for measuring the propagated waveform. The pressure bar developed by B. Hopkinson in 1914 used 'momentum traps' in the form of small pellets loosely coupled to a rod to study the characteristics of longitudinal stress pulses. The general principle of this method has been described in Chapter 2. The same principle has found more recent application in measuring intense shock waves in solids and is described by Goldsmith [19].

The electrical-resistance strain gauge has probably been more widely used than any other device in the study of stress-wave propagation. The principle of the gauge is based on the fact that a slight change in length of a metallic wire is accompanied by a slight change in the electrical resistance of the wire. By forming extremely fine wire or foil into a compact grid, or gauge, and cementing it to a specimen, static or dynamic strains in the specimen result in changes in electrical resistance of the gauge. Connecting the gauge into a potentiometric or Wheatstone-bridge circuit enables resistance changes to be determined in terms of voltage changes. Proper calibration enables the mechanical strains to be established. Strain gauges are also made from piezoelectrically active materials. Such gauges are much more sensitive to strain, but also more fragile than wire and foil gauges. Thorough expositions on the various types of strain gauges, strain-gauge circuitry, and recording techniques are contained in the earlier cited texts by Dove and Adams [13] and Dally and Reilly [10]. Reference is also made to the work of Perry and Lissner [46].

The capacitance and inductance effects are also used to detect stress waves, with the former finding more numerous applications. The principle employed in capacitance transducers is that a slight change in distance between two charged surfaces results in a voltage change between the surfaces due to the change in capacitance. The capacitance device will effectively average the displacement over the area of the capacitor plate, so that contributions from stress-wave components having wavelengths of the order of the transducer size or smaller may be absent from the records. The inductance effect has probably found less use in the detection of stress waves. Malvern [38] employed this principle to measure elastic–plastic waves in rods. In this application, fine copper wires were wrapped around an aluminum rod. The stress-wave induced motion of the wire loops in a magnetic field yielded a voltage signal proportional to the particle velocity at that point in the rod.

The piezoelectric effect is used to detect stress waves as well as induce stress waves. Thus, a mechanical stress wave impinging on a piezoelectric crystal or ceramic element will produce an electrical signal across the poles of the element. A simple piezoelectric disc bonded to the surface of a structure can serve in this capacity. Usually the construction is more elaborate, with various types of backings used in order to prevent resonances of the element from obscuring the basic signal of the stress wave. In other applications, piezoelectric elements are sandwiched between cylindrical rods to monitor the passage of a stress pulse or are interposed between a striking element, such as a rod or spherical ball, and the target in order to measure the applied force.

Photo-elasticity has been widely used in the detection of stress waves. This technique is based on the principle that many transparent materials have the property of birefringence. This is the property whereby the electric-field vector of a beam of polarized light, upon entering a stressed, transparent specimen, is resolved into two components along the axes of principal stress. The two light components are retarded by differing amounts during passage through the specimen and, upon recombining outside the specimen, will form interference patterns, or fringes, owing to the difference in retardation of each of the light-vector components. When monochromatic light is used as an illumination source, the interference patterns are simply a series of light and dark fringes. When white light is employed, the patterns are quite picturesque, but less useful, multi-coloured bands of light. The basic law governing interpretation of photo-elastic data is the stress–optic law, given by $\sigma_1 - \sigma_2 = nf_\sigma/h$, where σ_1, σ_2 are the principal stresses, n is the fringe order, h is the specimen thickness, and f_σ is the fringe constant of the material and is dependent on the photo-elastic properties of the material and the wavelength of the light source.

One of the main advantages of photo-elasticity is that data on the entire stress field in a specimen may be obtained, whereas devices such as strain gauges and piezoelectric and capacitance transducers give the behaviour only in a very small region. The only technique for recording such entire-field data is by photography, so that various high-speed photographic recording techniques play an important role here. High-speed framing cameras are used, as are multiple-flash, multiple-lens devices. Illumination techniques vary from continuous illumination used for framing cameras to spark-gap or Q-spoiled laser sources for the intermittent illumination used in the multiple source–image systems. Other techniques for recording dynamic photo-elastic data include streak photography and the use of photocells to record light intensity. Both of these record only point information, however, so that the entire-field advantages of photo-elasticity are, to a large extent, lost.

Many other techniques are used for detecting stress waves, including interferometric techniques, Moiré fringes, and diffraction gratings. This last, for example, has found extensive use in measuring elastic–plastic waves in rods. Holography has found application in detecting the steady vibrations of structures. However, from the standpoint of the experimental studies reviewed in this book, the basic detection techniques reviewed in the foregoing describe the most common methods used.

References to Appendices A, B, C.

1. Becker, E. C.H. Transient loading technique for mechanical impedance measurement. In *Experimental techniques in shock and vibration* (Ed. W. J. Worley). ASME, New York (1962).
2. Beebe, W. M. *An experimental investigation of dynamic crack propagation in plastics and metals*. Tech. Rep. AFML-TR-66-249 Air Force Materials Laboratory (1966).
3. Berkowitz, H. M. and Cohen, L. J. *A study of plate-slap technology*, Part I. A critical evaluation of plate-slap technology. Tech. Rep. AFML-TR-69-106 Air Force Material Laboratories (1969).
4. Berlincourt, D. A., Curran, D. R., and Jaffe, H. Piezoelectric and Piezomagnetic materials and their function in transducers. In *Physical acoustics* (Ed. W. P. Mason), Vol. 1, Part A. Chap. 3. Academic Press, New York (1964).
5. Bradfield, G. Ultrasonic transducers. In *Ultrasonics*, Part A, pp. 112–23, Part B pp. 177–89 (1970).
6. Britton, W. G. B. and Langley, G. O. Stress pulse dispersion in curved mechanical waveguides. *J. Sound Vib.* **7**, 417–30 (1968).
7. Churchill, R. V. *Operational mathematics*. McGraw-Hill, New York (1958).
8. Dally, J. W. A dynamic photoelastic study of a doubly loaded half-plane. *Develop. Mech.* **4**, 645–64 (1968).
9. —— and Lewis, D. (III). A photoelastic analysis of propagation of rayleigh waves past a step change in elevation. *Bull. seism. Soc. Am.* **58**, 539–63 (1968).
10. —— and Riley, W. F. *Experimental stress analysis*. McGraw-Hill, New York (1965).
11. Davies, R. M. A critical study of the Hopkinson pressure bar. *Phil. Trans. R. Soc.* **A240**, 375–457 (1948).
12. Doebelin, E. O. *Measurement systems: application and design*. McGraw-Hill, New York (1966).
13. Dove, R. C. and Adams, P. H. *Experimental stress analysis and motion measurement*. Charles Merrill Books, Columbus, Ohio (1964).
14. Dueweke, P. W. A technique for launching intermediate velocity thin plastic sheets. *Rev. scient. Instrum.* **41**, 539–41 (1970).

15. Erdelyi, A. (Ed.) *Tables of Integral Transforms* (Bateman Manuscript Project). McGraw-Hill, New York (1954).

16. Fox, G. and Curtis, C. W. Elastic strain produced by sudden application of pressure to one end of a cylindrical bar—II. Experimental observations. *J. acoust. Soc. Am.* **30,** 559–63 (1958).

17. Frocht, M. M. Studies in dynamic photoelasticity with special emphasis on the stress-optic law, in *Stress Wave Propagation in Materials* (Ed. N. Davids). Interscience, New York (1960).

18. Fyfe, I. M. Plane-strain plastic wave propagation in a dynamically loaded hollow cylinder. *Symposium on the mechanical behavior of materials under dynamic loads*, San Antonio, Texas. Sponsored by U.S. Army Research Office and Southwest Research Institute (1967).

19. Goldsmith, W. *Impact: the theory and physical behaviour of colliding solids* Edward Arnold, London (1960).

20. Harris, C. M. and Crede, E. *Shock and vibration handbook* Vols. I, II, and III. McGraw-Hill, New York (1961).

21. Hetenyi, M. (Ed.) *Handbook of experimental stress analysis.* John Wiley and Sons, New York (1950).

22. Hillier, K. W. A review of the progress in the measurement of dynamic elastic properties, in *Stress wave propagation in materials* (Ed. N. Davids), pp. 183–98 Interscience, New York (1960).

23. ——. The measurement of dynamic elastic properties, in *Progress in Solid Mechanics*,(Eds. I. N. Sneddon and R. Hill), Vol. II. North-Holland Publishing Company, Amsterdam (1961).

24. Hoese, F. O., Langner, C. G., and Baker, W. E. Simultaneous initiation over large areas of a spray-deposited explosive. *Exp. Mech.* **25**, 392–7 (1968).

25. Hopkinson, N. *Collected scientific papers*, Vol. ii. (1872).

26. Keast, D. N. *Measurements in mechanical dynamics.* McGraw-Hill, New York (1967).

27. Kolsky, H. An investigation of the mechanical properties of materials at very high rates of loading. *Proc. phys. Soc., Lond.* **B62,** 676–700 (1949).

28. ——. Electromagnetic waves emitted on detonation of explosives. *Nature, Lond.* **173,** 77 (1954).

29. ——. The propagation of stress waves in viscoelastic solids. *Appl. Mech. Rev.* **2,** 465 (1958).

30. ——. Experimental wave-propagation in solids, in *Structural Mechanics* (Eds. J. N. Goodier and N. Hoff), pp. 233–62. Pergamon Press, Oxford (1960).

31. ——. Viscoelastic waves, in *Stress wave propagation in materials* (Ed. N. Davids), pp. 59–60. Interscience, New York (1960).

32. ——. *Stress waves in solids.* Dover Publications, New York (1963).

33. ——. Experimental studies in stress wave propagation. *Proc. Vth U.S. natn. Congr. appl. Mech.* pp. 21–36 (1965).

34. Kuo, S. S. Beam subjected to eccentric longitudinal impact, *Exp. Mech.* **18,** 102–8 (1961).

35. Langhaar, H. L. *Energy methods in applied mechanics.* John Wiley and Sons, New York (1962).

36. Love, A. E. H. *A treatise on the mathematical theory of elasticity*. Dover Publications, New York (1944).
37. Magrab, E. B. and Blomquist, D. S. *The measurement of time-varying phenomena*. Wiley–Interscience, New York (1971).
38. Malvern, L. E. Experiment studies of strain-rate effects and plastic-wave propagation in annealed aluminum. In *Behavior of materials under dynamic loading*, (Ed. N. J. Huffington (Jr.)), pp. 81–92. ASME, New York (1965).
39. Mason, W. P. *Electromechanical transducers and wave filters* (2nd edn). Van Nostrand Company, New York (1948).
40. ——. *Piezoelectric crystals and their application to ultrasonics*. Van Nostrand Company, New York (1950).
41. May, J. E. (Jr.) Guided wave ultrasonic delay lines. In *Physical acoustics* (Ed. W. P. Mason), Vol. 1, Part A, Chap. 6. Academic Press, New York (1964).
42. Moore, H. K. and Chace, W. G. (Eds.) *Exploding wires* Vol. 3. Plenum Press, New York (1964).
43. Neville, G. E. (Jr.) and Hoese, F. O. Impulsive loading using sprayed silver acetylide–silver nitrate, *Exp. Mech.* **5**, 294–8 (1965).
44. Nicholas, T. and Campbell, J. D. *The development and use of a torsional split Hopkinson bar for experiments in dynamic plasticity*. Tech. Rep. AFML-TR-71-32, Air Force Materials Laboratory (May 1971).
45. Percival, C. M. and Cheney, J. A. Thermally generated stress waves in a dispersive elastic rod. *Exp. Mech.* **26**, 49–57 (1969).
46. Perry, C. C. and Lissner, H. R. *The strain gage primer*. McGraw-Hill, New York (1955).
47. Press, F. and Oliver, J. Model study of air-coupled surface waves. *J. acoust. Soc. Am.* **27**, 43–6 (1955).
48. Redwood, M. Transient performance of a piezoelectric transducer. *J. acoust. Soc. Am.* **33**, 527–36 (1961).
49. ——. Piezoelectric generation of an electrical impulse. *J. acoust. Soc. Am.* **33**, 1386–90 (1961).
50. ——. Experiments with the electrical analog of a piezoelectric transducer. *J. acoust. Soc. Am.* **36**, 1872–80 (1964).
51. Sneddon, I. N. *Fourier transforms*. McGraw-Hill, New York (1951).
52. Sokolnikoff, I. S. *Mathematical theory of elasticity*. McGraw-Hill, New York (1956).
53. Stephenson, J. G. and Wilhoit, J. C. (Jr.) An experimental study of bending impact waves in beams. *Exp. Mech.* **22**, 16–21 (1965).
54. *Symposium on advanced experimental techniques in the mechanics of materials*, San Antonio, Texas. Sponsored by Air Force Office of Scientific Research and Southwest Research Institute (1970).
55. Wells, A. A. and Post, D. *The dynamic stress distribution surrounding a running crack—a photoelastic analysis*. Nav. Res. Laboratory, NRL-4935, Washington, D.C. (1957).
56. White, D. L. The depletion layer and other high-frequency transducers using fundamental modes, in *Physical acoustics* (Ed. W. P. Mason), Vol. I, Part B, Chap. 13. Academic Press, New York (1964).
57. Worely, W. J. (Ed.) *Experimental techniques in shock and vibration*. ASME. New York (1962).

Author index

Subject index

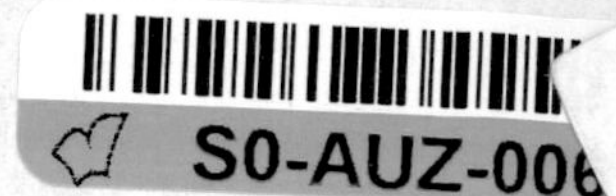

ORACLE7™ SERVER ADMINISTRATOR'S GUIDE

Part Number 6694-70-1292
December 1992

ORACLE®

Cooperative Server Technology for Transparent Data Sharing

ORACLE7 Server Administrator's Guide

Part Number 6694-70-1292
December 1992

Contributing Authors: Steven Bobrowski, with Eric Armstrong, Cynthia Closkey, Brian Linden

Contributors: Richard Allen, Dave Anderson, Lori Asher, Andre Bakker, Bill Bridge, Atif Chaudry, Gray Clossman, Jeff Cohen, Dave Ensor, Stephan Faris, John Frazzini, Gloria Gatlin, Anurag Gupta, Gary Hallmark, Chris Harmon, Michael Hartstein, Terry Hayes, Brian Hirano, Ken Jacobs, Sandeep Jain, Robert Jenkins, Jr., Kevin Jernigan, Derry Kabcenell, Michael Kennedy, Jonathan Klein, R. Kleinro, Robert Kooi, Andy Laursen, Lefty Leverenz, Walter Lindsay, Juan Loaiza, Brom Mahbod, William Maimone, Andrew Mendelsohn, Mark Moore, Edward Peeler, Mark Porter, Maria Pratt, Darryl Presley, Tuomas Pystynen, Brian Quigley, Patrick Ritto, Mark Sinykin, Gordon Smith, Leng Leng Tan, Mustafa Vahanvaty, Joyo Wijaya, Beth Winslow, Kevin Wharton

PREFACE

This Guide describes how to manage the ORACLE7 Server, a relational database management system (RDBMS).

Information in this Guide applies to the ORACLE7 Server, running on all operating systems. It provides information about the base ORACLE Server product and its special options, including the following:

- procedural option
- distributed option
- Parallel Server option

Any chapter of this Guide that applies only to a particular option is clearly indicated on the first page of the chapter.

Audience

This Guide is written for those responsible for administering the operation of an ORACLE database system. These persons, referred to as database administrators (DBAs), are assumed to be responsible for ensuring the smooth operation of an ORACLE database system and for monitoring its use. The responsibilities of database administrators are described in Chapter 1.

Knowledge Assumed of the Reader

Readers of this Guide are assumed to be familiar with relational database concepts. They are also assumed to be familiar with the operating system environment under which they are running ORACLE.

As a prerequisite, **all readers should read the first chapter of the *ORACLE7 Server Concepts Manual*,** "A Technical Introduction to the ORACLE Server." This chapter is a comprehensive introduction to the concepts and terminology used throughout this Guide.

Readers Interested in Installation and Migration Information

Administrators are frequently involved in installing the ORACLE Server software and migrating existing ORACLE databases to newer formats (for example, Version 6 databases to ORACLE7 format). This Guide is not an installation or migration manual. If your primary interest is installation, refer to the installation or user's guide for your particular operating system. If your primary interest is database or application migration, refer to the *ORACLE7 Server Migration Guide*.

Readers Interested in Application Design Information

In addition to administrators, experienced users of ORACLE and advanced database application designers might also find information in this Guide useful. However, database application developers should also refer to the *ORACLE7 Server Application Developer's Guide* and to the documentation for the tool or language product they are using to develop ORACLE database applications.

How This Guide Is Organized

This Guide is divided into parts and chapters, as described below.

Part I
Basic Database Administration

Chapter 1: Understanding Database Administration
This chapter outlines the responsibilities and concerns of the database administrator and describes the default ORACLE administrator accounts that can be used to administer a database.

Chapter 2: Creating a Database
This chapter describes the steps for creating a database in preparation for its use. (This information is intended to supplement, not substitute for, information in the installation or user's guides.)

Chapter 3: Starting Up and Shutting Down
This chapter describes how to control the accessibility of an ORACLE database system. It also describes how to initialize parameter settings.

Part II
ORACLE Server Configuration

Chapter 4: Managing ORACLE Processes
This chapter describes how to manage the processes that make up an ORACLE instance, including how to set up the different process configurations available for ORACLE.

Chapter 5: Managing the Online Redo Log
This chapter explains how to maintain the online redo log, including managing mirrored redo log groups and their members.

Chapter 6: Managing Control Files
This chapter explains how to create, mirror, replace, and drop control files for a database.

Part III
Database Storage

Chapter 7: Managing the Size and Files of the Database
This chapter discusses how to manage the physical storage space in an ORACLE database by managing tablespaces and data files. This includes adding and dropping tablespaces and data files, and taking tablespaces and data files on and off line.

Chapter 8: Managing Schema Objects
This chapter discusses how to manage the objects that contain data (tables, views, numeric sequences, and synonyms, as well as indexes and clusters). This includes controlling how data is stored and how storage space is allocated for and consumed by objects within an ORACLE database. It explains how to create, alter, and drop these objects, and how to perform other standard administrative functions on them.

Chapter 9: Managing Rollback Segments
This chapter discusses how to create, alter, manage, and drop rollback segments in the database, and offers guidelines for their management.

Part IV
Database Security

Chapter 10: Establishing Security Policies
This chapter discusses how to create a security policy that uses the security features of the ORACLE Server.

Chapter 11: Managing Users and Resources
This chapter describes how to manage database users and limit the use of system resources.

Chapter 12: Controlling User Privileges and Roles
This chapter discusses how to administer system and object security.

Chapter 13: Auditing Database Use
This chapter discusses how to monitor database activity using the auditing feature of the ORACLE Server.

Part V
Distributed Processing and Distributed Databases

Chapter 14: Administering Client-Server Systems
This chapter discusses setting up distributed processing environments that include the ORACLE Server.

Chapter 15: Managing Distributed Databases
This chapter explains how to administer a distributed database system, including setting up global names, using database links, and resolving in-doubt distributed transactions.

Chapter 16: Managing Table Snapshots
This chapter discusses how to replicate data among nodes of a distributed database, and how to refresh such snapshots.

Part VI
Database Backup and Recovery

Chapter 17: Archiving Redo Information
This chapter explains how to archive the redo log files for a database, and how to manage the archived files.

Chapter 18: Backing Up a Database
This chapter discusses how to protect an ORACLE database from possible failures.

Chapter 19: Recovering a Database
This chapter explains how to recover a database from failure using backups of the database.

Part VII
Database and Instance Tuning

Chapter 20: Understanding the Tuning Process
This chapter outlines the steps of the database tuning process. It tells you how to follow the steps described in subsequent chapters, and introduces issues discussed in each step.

Chapter 21: Tuning Memory Allocation
This chapter helps you allocate memory to ORACLE data structures most efficiently. These structures include SQL and PL/SQL areas and the buffer cache.

Chapter 22: Tuning I/O
This chapter discusses how to avoid I/O bottlenecks that can reduce performance. In this chapter, you learn to reduce disk contention, allocate space in data blocks, and avoid having ORACLE manage space dynamically.

Chapter 23: Tuning Contention
This chapter discusses the problems caused by contention and helps you recognize when these problems occur. In this chapter, you learn to reduce contention for rollback segments and redo log buffer latches.

Chapter 24: Additional Tuning Considerations
This chapter discusses specific performance-related aspects of the ORACLE Server, including sorts, free lists, and checkpoints.

Reference

Appendix A: Initialization Parameter Files
This appendix is a reference to the parameter files and individual parameters that are used to initialize various settings when an ORACLE database system is started.

Appendix B: Data Dictionary Reference
This appendix is a reference to the many data dictionary views of an ORACLE database.

Appendix C: National Language Support
This appendix explains how to configure ORACLE to handle data and interface with users using various languages.

Appendix D: Database Limits
This appendix is a quick reference to many limits of values associated with various database functions and objects.

Appendix E: Operating System Specific Information
This appendix is a summary of all the operating system specific references contained within this Guide.

How to Use This Guide

Every reader of this Guide **must** read Chapter 1 of the *ORACLE7 Server Concepts Manual,* "A Technical Introduction to the ORACLE Server." This overview of the concepts and terminology related to ORACLE provides a foundation for the more detailed information in this Guide. The rest of the *ORACLE7 Server Concepts Manual* explains the ORACLE architecture and features and how they operate in more detail.

Conventions Used in This Guide

The following sections explain the conventions used in this Guide.

Text of the Guide

The following section explains the conventions used within the text of this Guide:

UPPERCASE WORDS — Uppercase text is used to call attention to command keywords, object names, parameters, filenames, and so on. For example:

If you create a private rollback segment, the name of the rollback segment must be included in the ROLLBACK_SEGMENTS parameter of the parameter file

Italicized Words — Italicized words within text are used to indicate the first occurrence and definition of a term, as in the following example:

A *database* is a collection of data to be treated as a unit. The general purpose of a database is to store and retrieve related information, as needed.

Italicized words are also used to indicate book titles and to highlight names of performance statistics.

Bold Words — Bolding within text is used to call special attention to important information. For example:

In summary, remember that this procedure provides a reasonable **estimate** of a table's size, not an exact number of blocks or bytes.

Examples of the SQL*DBA Interface

Throughout this Guide, examples of the dialog boxes and menus of SQL*DBA, your primary utility for managing an ORACLE database, are provided. Illustrations of the character mode SQL*DBA screen are provided; however, the actual appearance of your screen may differ, depending on your system's user interface. (SQL*DBA is documented fully in the *ORACLE7 Server Utilities User's Guide*.)

Examples of Commands and Statements

SQL, SQL*DBA, and SQL*Plus commands and statements appear separated from the text of paragraphs in a fixed-width font:

```
ALTER TABLESPACE users
   ADD DATAFILE 'users2.ora' SIZE 50K;
```

Punctuation `, ' "`	Example statements may include punctuation such as commas or quotation marks. All punctuation given in example statements is required. All example statements are terminated with a semicolon. Depending on the application being used, a semi-colon or other terminator may or may not be required to end a statement.
Uppercase Words `INSERT, SIZE`	Uppercase words in example statements are used to indicate the keywords within ORACLE SQL. However, note that when issuing statements, keywords are not case-sensitive.
Lowercase Words `emp, users2.ora`	Lowercase words in example statements are used to indicate words supplied only for the context of the example. For example, lowercase words may indicate the name of a table, column, or file. Some operating systems are case sensitive, so refer to your installation or user's guide to determine whether you must pay attention to case.

Special Icons

Two special icons are provided to alert you to particular information within the body of this Guide and other manuals:

- The lightbulb highlights suggestions and practical tips that could save time, make procedures easier, and so on.
- The warning symbol highlights text that warns you of actions that could be particularly damaging or fatal to your system.

Related Publications

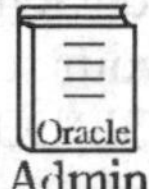

Admin

The *ORACLE7 Server Administrator's Guide* is one of many books used to explain various parts of an ORACLE database system.

In many sections of this Guide, the information is general because the Guide is written to apply to ORACLE working under any operating system and configuration. Therefore, you will also find many references in this book to important information in the related publications. To clearly indicate an area in this Guide that may be supported by information in a related book, a corresponding icon is placed in the margin of the page, adjacent to the text referring to the supporting book. The related books (and corresponding icons) referred to in this Guide are included below.

Concepts

- For general information about the ORACLE7 Server and how it works, see the *ORACLE7 Server Concepts Manual*, Part No. 6693-70.

AppDev

- For information about developing database applications within the ORACLE7 Server, see the *ORACLE7 Server Application Developer's Manual*, Part No. 6695-70.

Migrate

- For the procedures for migrating a previous version of ORACLE to ORACLE7, see the *ORACLE7 Server Migration Guide*, Part No. 6617-70.

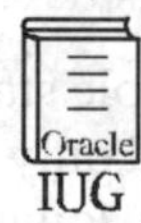

IUG

- For information specific to the ORACLE Server working on your host operating system, refer to your installation or user's guide (specific book titles vary by operating system) and system release bulletins, if available.

SQL

- For reference information on ORACLE's SQL commands and functions, refer to the *ORACLE7 Server SQL Language Reference Manual*, Part No. 778-70.

PL/SQL

- For information about ORACLE's procedural language extension to SQL, PL/SQL, refer to the *PL/SQL User's Guide and Reference*, Part No. 800-20.

OCI

- For information about programming applications that use the ORACLE Call Interfaces, see the *ORACLE Call Interfaces Programmer's Guide*, Part No. 5411-70.

Utilities

- For information about the utilities bundled with the ORACLE Server, including SQL*DBA, Export, Import, and SQL*Loader, refer to the *ORACLE7 Server Utilities User's Guide*, Part No. 3602-70.

- For information specific to administering the ORACLE Parallel Server, refer to the *ORACLE7 Parallel Server Administrator's Guide*, Part No. 5990-70.
- For information specific to administering ORACLE's multilevel secure database management system product, Trusted ORACLE, refer to the *Trusted ORACLE7 Server Administrator's Guide*, Part No. 6610-70.

- For more information about ORACLE messages and codes, refer to the *ORACLE7 Server Messages and Codes Manual*, Part No. 3605-70.

- For information about SQL*Net, see the SQL*Net documentation, which includes the *SQL*Net V2 Administrator's Guide*, Part No. 6545-20; the *MultiProtocol Interchange Administrator's Guide*, Part No. 6544-10; and the *Oracle Network Products Messages Manual*, Part No. 6543-00.

Oracle Corporation also publishes a file commonly named README.DOC. This file is available on your distribution media and describes differences between minor releases of Oracle software that are not accompanied by new manuals. The exact name and location of this file might vary, depending on your operating system. Read this file to learn about changes to the software that are not described in the regular manuals.

Your Comments Are Welcome

We value and appreciate your comments as an ORACLE user and reader of the manuals. As we write, revise, and evaluate, your opinions are the most important input we receive. At the back of this Guide is a Reader's Comment Form, which we encourage you to use to tell us what you like and dislike about this Guide or other ORACLE manuals. If the form has been used or you would like to contact us, please use the following address or FAX number, or call us at (415) 506-7000.

ORACLE7 Server Documentation Manager
Oracle Corporation
500 Oracle Parkway
Redwood Shores, CA 94065

FAX: (415) 506-7200

CONTENTS

PART II **ORACLE SERVER CONFIGURATION**

PART IV DATABASE SECURITY

Chapter 10

PART V

DISTRIBUTED PROCESSING AND DISTRIBUTED DATABASES

PART

I

BASIC DATABASE ADMINISTRATION

CHAPTER

1 ADMINISTERING ORACLE DATABASES

This chapter discusses the responsibilities of the person who administers the ORACLE Server, the database administrator.

This chapter covers the following topics:

- database administrator responsibilities
- the administrator's operating system account and the DBA role
- initial administrator usernames of an ORACLE database
- administrator tools and utilities
- database administrator priorities
- how to identify releases of ORACLE

Database Administrator Responsibilities

Because an ORACLE database system can be quite large and have many users, someone or some group of people must manage this system. The database administrator (or DBA) is this manager.

Every database requires at least one person to perform administrative duties; if a database is large, these administrative duties can be divided among multiple administrators.

As a database administrator, your responsibilities can include:

- installing and upgrading the ORACLE Server and application tools
- allocating system storage and planning future storage requirements for the database system
- creating primary database storage structures (tablespaces) once application developers have designed an application
- creating primary objects (tables, views, indexes) once application developers have designed an application
- modifying the database structure, as necessary, from information given by application developers
- enrolling users and maintaining system security
- ensuring compliance with your ORACLE license agreement
- controlling and monitoring user access to the database
- monitoring and optimizing the performance of the database
- planning for backup and recovery of database information
- maintaining archived data on tape
- backing up and restoring the database
- contacting Oracle Corporation for technical support

Security Officers

In some cases, a database might also have one or more security officers. A *security officer* is primarily concerned with enrolling users, controlling and monitoring user access to the database, and maintaining system security. You might not be responsible for these duties if your site has a separate security officer.

Responsibilities of Other Types of Users

Other types of ORACLE users have responsibilities, as well.

Application Developers

An application developer's responsibilities include:

- designing and developing the database application
- designing the database structure for an application
- estimating storage requirements for an application
- specifying modifications of the database structure for an application
- relaying the above information to a database administrator
- tuning the application during development
- establishing an application's security measures during development

Database Users

A typical user's responsibilities include:

- entering, modifying, and deleting data, where permitted
- generating reports of data

Database Administrator Security and Privileges

To accomplish administrative tasks in ORACLE, you need extra privileges both within the database and possibly in the operating system of the server on which the database runs. This section describes the privileges you need and database security facilities of which you should be aware.

Note: Access to a database administrator's account should be tightly controlled. See "Administrator Security" on page 10-6 for security guidelines for administrative personnel.

The Database Administrator's Operating System Account

To perform many of the administrative duties for a database, you must be able to execute operating system commands. Depending on the operating system that executes ORACLE, you might need an operating system account or ID to gain access to the operating system. If this is the case, your operating system account might require more operating system privileges or access rights than normal database users require (for example, to perform ORACLE software installation). Although you do not need the ORACLE files to be stored in your account, you should have access to them.

IUG

In addition, the SQL*DBA program requires that your operating system account or ID be distinguished in some way to allow you to use *operating system privileged* SQL*DBA commands. The method of distinguishing a database administrator's account is operating system specific; see your installation and user's guide for information.

Connecting as INTERNAL

Database startup and shutdown are powerful administrative capabilities. To protect their use, only those who connect to ORACLE as INTERNAL can execute them. Depending on your operating system, you must fulfill one of the following requirements to connect to ORACLE as INTERNAL:

- Your operating system account has the operating system privileges that allow you to connect as INTERNAL.
- You are authorized to connect as INTERNAL.
- Your database has a password for INTERNAL connections, and you know the password.

In addition, you must use a dedicated server when you connect as INTERNAL. You cannot CONNECT INTERNAL through a dispatcher and shared servers.

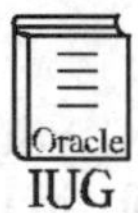

IUG

These requirements provide an extra layer of security to prevent unauthorized users from starting up or shutting down ORACLE databases. (See your installation or user's guide for details on how to set a user's privileges for connections as INTERNAL on your system.)

Systems with passwords for INTERNAL have additional considerations, which are described in the following sections.

Using a Password for INTERNAL

Some operating systems allow you to set a password for INTERNAL connections; some even require such a password.

IUG

You can set the INTERNAL password during ORACLE Server installation, and Oracle provides a utility for managing the password (creating, changing, and removing it) with the ORACLE release. The utility is operating system specific; see your installation and users guide for details.

INTERNAL and Non-Secure Connections

If you fulfill the requirements for connecting as INTERNAL and are using a secure connection (such as a single-task connection, available on some systems), you can always connect as INTERNAL.

However, if you are using a non-secure connection (such as most network connections), you *must* use the INTERNAL password to connect as INTERNAL; this requirement implies that your system must have an INTERNAL password to use non-secure connections for INTERNAL.

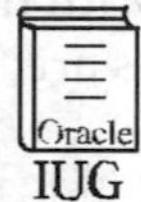

On some operating systems, you can enable and disable CONNECT INTERNAL over non-secure connections entirely. You make this choice during ORACLE installation, and can change the setting later. How this option is set is operating system specific; see your installation and user's guide for details.

Note: Some operating systems always prohibit all non-secure INTERNAL connections, even those for which you supply a password.

Alternatives to INTERNAL: OSOPER and OSDBA

Two special roles are used to control database operations that are executed when a database is not mounted: OSOPER and OSDBA. By granting these roles to DBAs rather than granting them the privileges for connecting as INTERNAL, you can protect use of INTERNAL.

OSOPER	permits the user to perform STARTUP, SHUTDOWN, ALTER DATABASE OPEN/MOUNT, ALTER DATABASE BACKUP, ARCHIVE LOG, and RECOVER, and includes the RESTRICTED SESSION privilege
OSDBA	contains all system privileges with ADMIN OPTION, and the OSOPER role; permits CREATE DATABASE and time-based recovery

OSOPER and OSDBA can have different names and functionality, depending on your operating system.

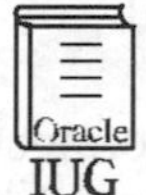

The OSOPER and OSDBA roles can only be granted to a user through the operating system; they cannot be granted through a GRANT statement, nor can they be revoked or dropped. When a user logs on as INTERNAL, ORACLE communicates with the operating system and attempts to enable first OSDBA and then, if unsuccessful, OSOPER. If both attempts fail, the connection fails. How you grant these privileges through the operating system is operating system specific; see your installation and user's guide for information.

Note: For operating systems that do not support operating system roles, you must specify a password with INTERNAL. If the password is valid, either OSDBA or OSOPER is enabled; each has a separate password. (See "Using a Password for INTERNAL" on page 1-4.)

The DBA Role

A pre-defined role named "DBA" is automatically created with every ORACLE database. This role contains all database system privileges.

Therefore, it is very powerful and should only be granted to fully functional database administrators.

Database Administrator Usernames

Two user accounts are automatically created with the database and granted the DBA role. These two user accounts are:

- SYS (initial password: CHANGE_ON_INSTALL)
- SYSTEM (initial password: MANAGER)

These two usernames are described in the following sections.

Note: To prevent inappropriate access to the data dictionary tables, you must change the passwords for the SYS and SYSTEM usernames immediately after creating an ORACLE database. See "Altering Users" on page 11-11.

You will probably want to create at least one additional administrator username, to use when performing daily administrative tasks. The section "Administrator Security" on page 10-6 discusses how to establish and maintain privileges for administrative users.

SYS

When any database is created, the user SYS, identified by the password CHANGE_ON_INSTALL, is automatically created and granted the DBA role.

All of the base tables and views for the database's data dictionary are stored in the schema SYS. These base tables and views are critical for the operation of ORACLE. To maintain the integrity of the data dictionary, tables in the SYS schema are manipulated only by ORACLE; they should never be modified by any user or database administrator, and no one should create any tables in the schema of the user SYS. (However, you can change the storage parameters of the data dictionary settings if necessary; see "Changing Storage Parameters for the Data Dictionary" on page 8-79.)

Most database users should never be able to connect using the SYS account. You can connect to the database using this account but should do so only when instructed by Oracle personnel or documentation.

SYSTEM

Also when a database is created, the user SYSTEM, identified by the password MANAGER, is automatically created and granted all system privileges for the database.

Additional tables and views that display administrative information, and internal tables and views used by ORACLE tools, are created using the SYSTEM username. Never create tables of interest to individual users in the SYSTEM schema.

Database Administrator Utilities

Several utilities are available to help you maintain and control the ORACLE Server.

SQL*DBA

SQL*DBA allows you to monitor and control an ORACLE database. All administrative operations discussed in this book are executed using SQL*DBA.

SQL*DBA uses a superset of ANSI/ISO standard SQL commands. These commands are executed by the SQL*DBA menu-driven interface. This interface provides an intuitive approach to administering a database. The most common administrative commands are available from SQL*DBA's menu; less-often-used commands can be typed into the SQL*DBA input window and executed. You select menu commands using a pointing device (such as a mouse) or cursor keys.

Utilities

SQL*DBA is documented in the *ORACLE7 Server Utilities User's Guide.*

SQL*Loader

Utilities

SQL*Loader is used by both database administrators and users of ORACLE. It loads data from standard operating system files (files in text or C data format) into ORACLE database tables. SQL*Loader's use and commands are detailed in the *ORACLE7 Server Utilities User's Guide*.

Export and Import Utilities

The Export and Import utilities allow you to move existing data in ORACLE format to and from ORACLE databases. For example, export files can be used to archive database data, or move data among different ORACLE databases that run on the same or different operating systems. The Export and Import utilities are covered briefly in Chapter 18, and detailed in the *ORACLE7 Server Utilities User's Guide*.

Utilities

Initial Priorities of a Database Administrator

In general, you must perform a series of steps to get the database system up and running, and then maintain it. This section lists the procedures required to configure an ORACLE Server and database on any type of computer system.

1. Install the ORACLE software.
2. Evaluate the hardware of the database server.
3. Plan the database.
4. Create and start the database.
5. Implement the database design.
6. Backup the database.
7. Enroll system users.
8. Tune database performance.

The following sections explain each step in further detail.

Install the ORACLE Software

As the database administrator, you must install the ORACLE Server software and any front-end tools and database applications used to access the database. In some distributed processing installations, the database is controlled by a central computer and the database tools and applications are executed on remote machines; in this case, you must also install the ORACLE SQL*Net drivers necessary to connect the remote machines to the computer that executes ORACLE.

IUG

Note: For information about identifying versions of ORACLE software, see "Identifying ORACLE Software Versions" on page 1-11.

SQL*Net

Reference: Refer to the respective installation or user's guide of your ORACLE Server, front-end tool, or SQL*Net driver for specific requirements and instructions for the installation of that product.

Evaluate the Database Server Hardware

After installation, evaluate how ORACLE and its applications can best use the available computer resources. This evaluation should reveal information such as:

- how many disk drives are available to ORACLE and its databases
- how many, if any, dedicated tape drives are available to ORACLE and its databases
- how much memory is available to the instances of ORACLE you will run

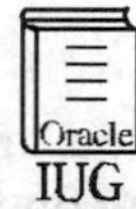

Reference: Refer to your system's configuration documentation (for example, the system log or user guide).

Plan the Database

As the database administrator, you must plan:

- the database's logical storage structure
- the overall database design
- a backup strategy for the database

It is important to plan how the logical storage structure of the database will affect system performance and various database management operations. For example, before creating any tablespaces for your database, you should know how many data files will make up the tablespace, where the data files will be physically stored (on which disk drives), and what type of information will be stored in each tablespace. When planning the database's overall logical storage structure, take into account the effects that this structure will have when the database is actually created and running. Such considerations include how the database's logical storage structure will affect the following items:

- the performance of the computer executing ORACLE
- the performance of the database during data access operations
- the efficiency of backup and recovery procedures for the database

Plan the relational design of the database's objects and the storage characteristics for each of these objects. By planning relationships between objects and the physical storage of each object before creating it, you can directly impact the performance of the database as a unit. Be sure to plan for the growth of the database as well.

In distributed database environments, this planning stage is extremely important. The physical location of highly accessed data can dramatically affect application performance.

During the above planning phases, also plan a backup strategy for the database. After developing this strategy, you might find that you want to alter the database's planned logical storage structure or database design to improve backup efficiency.

Reference: It is beyond the scope of this book to discuss relational and distributed database design; if you are not familiar with such design issues, refer to accepted industry-standard books that explain these studies. See Chapters 7 through 9 for specific information on creating logical storage structures, objects, and integrity constraints for your database.

Create and Open the Database

Once you have finalized the database design, you can create the database and open it for normal use. Depending on your operating system, a database may already have been created during the installation procedure for ORACLE. If this is the case, all you need to do is start an instance, and mount and open the initial database.

Reference: To determine if your operating system creates an initial database during the installation of ORACLE, check your installation or user's guide. If no database is created during installation or you want to create an additional database, see Chapter 2 for this procedure. See Chapter 3 for database and instance startup and shutdown procedures.

Implement the Database Design

Once you have created and started the database, you can create the database's planned logical structure by creating all necessary rollback segments and tablespaces. Once this is built, you can create the objects for your database.

Reference: See Chapters 7 through 9 for instructions on creating logical storage structures and objects for your database.

Back up the Database

After you have created the database structure, carry out the planned backup strategy for your database by creating any additional redo log files, taking the first full database backup (online or offline), and scheduling future database backups at regular intervals.

Reference: See Chapters 17 through 19 for instructions on customizing your backup operations and performing recovery procedures.

Enroll System Users

Once you have backed up the database structure, you can begin to enroll the users of the database in accordance with your ORACLE license agreement, create roles for these users, and grant appropriate roles to them.

Reference: See Chapters 10 through 12 for the procedures to create user accounts and roles, and information on complying with your license agreement.

Tune Database Performance

Optimizing the database system's performance is one of your ongoing responsibilities.

Reference: "Initial Tuning Guidelines" on page 2-12 describes steps you can take to start tuning your database immediately after creation. See Chapters 21 through 25 for more information about tuning ORACLE.

Identifying ORACLE Software Releases

Because Oracle products are always undergoing development and change, several releases of the products can be in use at any one time. To identify a software product fully, as many as five numbers may be required. For example, an ORACLE Server distribution tape might be labelled "Release 7.0.4.1." The following sections translate this number.

Version Number

The version number, such as **7**, is the most general identifier. A *version* is a major new edition of the software, which usually contains significant new functionality.

Maintenance Release Number

The maintenance release number signifies different releases of the general version, starting with 0, as in version 7.**0**. The maintenance release number increases when bug fixes or new features to existing programs are made available.

Patch Release Number

The patch release number identifies a specific level of the object code, such as 7.0.**4**. A patch release contains fixes for serious bugs that cannot wait until the next maintenance release. The first distribution of a maintenance release always has a patch number of 0.

Port-Specific Patch Release Number

A fourth number (and sometimes a fifth number) can be used to identify a particular emergency patch release of a software product on that operating system, such as 7.0.4.**1**. or 7.0.4.**1.3**. An emergency patch is not usually intended for wide distribution; it usually fixes or works around a particular, critical problem.

Examples of Release Numbers

The following examples show possible release numbers for ORACLE7:

7.0.0	the first distribution of ORACLE7 (technically a maintenance release)
7.2.0	the second maintenance release (the third release in all) of ORACLE7
7.2.2	the second patch release after the second maintenance release

Versions of Other Oracle Software

As Oracle Corporation introduces new products and enhances existing ones, the version numbers of the individual products increment independently. Thus, you might have an ORACLE7 Server Release 7.0.12.2 system working with SQL*Forms Version 4.0.3, SQL*Plus Version 3.1.9, and Pro*FORTRAN Version 1.5.2. (These numbers are used only for illustration.)

Checking Your Current Release Number

To see which release of ORACLE and its components you are using, query the data dictionary view V$VERSION, as below:

```
SQLDBA> SELECT * FROM v$version
BANNER
----------------------------------------------------------------
ORACLE7 Server Release 7.0.20.1 - Production
PL/SQL Release 2.0.15 - Production
CORE V2.2.5.9.0 - Production
TNS for VMS: Version 2.0.11.1.0 - Developer's Release
4 rows selected.
```

This information is useful if you need to call Oracle Support.

CHAPTER

2 Creating a Database

This chapter lists the steps necessary to create an ORACLE database. Topics include:

- preparing to create an ORACLE database
- creating an ORACLE database
- tuning the database initially
- creating the data dictionary
- adding structures after database creation

Trusted

If you are using Trusted ORACLE, see the *Trusted ORACLE7 Server Administrator's Guide* for additional information about creating databases in that environment.

Preparing to Create a Database

Database creation prepares several operating system files so they can work together as an ORACLE database. A database need be created only once, regardless of how many data files it has or how many instances access it. Database creation can also be used to erase information in an existing database and create a new database with the same name and physical structure.

Database creation includes the following operations:

- creating new data files or erasing data that existed in previous data files
- creating structures that ORACLE requires to access and use the database (the data dictionary)
- creating and initializing the control files and redo log files for the database

A database is created by issuing a statement that includes the SQL command CREATE DATABASE; however, before you can execute this statement, consider the following issues:

- Plan your database tables and indexes, and estimate how much space they will require. More information on tables, indexes, and space management is given in Chapters 7 and 8.
- Plan how to protect your new database, including the configuration of its online and archived redo log (and how much space it will require), and a backup strategy. For more information on the online and archive redo logs, see Chapters 5 and 17, respectively; for information on database backup and recovery, see Chapters 18, and 19.
- Select the database character set. You must specify the database character set when you create the database, and you cannot change it later without re-creating the database. All character data, including data in the data dictionary, is stored in the database character set. If users access the database using a different character set, the database character set should be the same as or a superset of all character sets they use. (For more information on National Language Support issues, see Appendix C.)

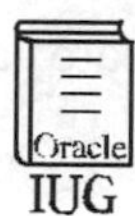

This chapter provides general information about database creation on all operating systems; it is relatively general. The installation or user's guide for your operating system is another important source of information about installing ORACLE and creating databases for that system. When creating a database for your database system, consistently refer to your installation or user's guide.

In addition, become familiar with information in Chapter 3, "Starting Up and Shutting Down," so that you understand the principles and options of starting up and shutting down an instance, mounting and opening a database, and using parameter files.

When creating a database using Trusted ORACLE, see the *Trusted ORACLE7 Server Administrator's Guide* for additional steps and considerations.

Creation Prerequisites

To create a new database, you must have the following items:

- the operating system privileges associated with a fully operational database administrator (See "Connecting as INTERNAL" on page 1-4.)
- sufficient memory to start the ORACLE instance
- sufficient disk storage space for the planned database on the computer that executes ORACLE

Using an Initial Database

Depending on your operating system, a database might have automatically been created as part of the installation procedure for ORACLE. You can use this initial database and customize it to meet your information management requirements, or discard it and create one or more new databases to replace it.

Migrating an Older Version of the Database

If you are using a previous release of ORACLE, database creation is required only if you want an entirely new database. Otherwise, you can migrate your existing ORACLE databases managed by a previous version of ORACLE and use it with the new version of the ORACLE software. (See the *ORACLE7 Server Migration Guide* and your installation or user's guide.)

Oracle
Trusted

For instructions about migrating to Trusted ORACLE, see the *Trusted ORACLE7 Server Administrator's Guide.*

Creating an ORACLE Database

Carry out the following steps in sequence to create each new database and make it available for system use:

1. Back up any existing databases.
2. Create parameter files.
3. Edit new parameter files.
4. Check the instance identifier for your system.
5. Start SQL*DBA and connect to ORACLE as INTERNAL.
6. Start an instance.
7. Create the database.
8. Back up the database.

The following sections describe each step.

Step 1: Back Up Existing Databases

Oracle Corporation strongly recommends that you make complete backups of all existing databases before creating a new database, in case database creation accidentally affects some existing files. Backup should include parameter files, data files, redo log files, and control files. For specific information on backing up ORACLE databases, refer to Chapter 18.

Step 2: Create Parameter Files

The instance (SGA and background processes) for any ORACLE database is started using a parameter file. (See "Using Parameter Files" on page 3-13.)

Each database on your system should have at least one customized parameter file that corresponds only to that database; do not use the same file for several databases.

IUG

To create a parameter file for the database you are about to make, use your operating system to make a copy of the parameter file that Oracle provided on the distribution media. Give this copy a new filename; you can then edit and customize this new file for the new database. (Refer to your installation or user's guide for more information about copying this file.)

In distributed processing environments, SQL*DBA is often executed from a client machine of the network. If a client machine is being used to execute SQL*DBA and create a new database, you need to copy the new parameter file (currently located on the computer executing

ORACLE) to your client workstation. This procedure is operating system dependent; see your installation or user's guide for more information about copying files among the computers of your network.

Step 3: Edit New Parameter Files

To create a new database, inspect and edit at least the following parameters of the new parameter file: DB_NAME, DB_DOMAIN, CONTROL_FILES, DB_BLOCK_SIZE, DB_BLOCK_BUFFERS, PROCESSES, and ROLLBACK_SEGMENTS.

In most cases, also edit either LICENSE_MAX_SESSIONS and LICENSE_SESSION_WARNING, or LICENSE_MAX_USERS.

Each parameter's significance is explained below. (Also see "Using Parameter Files" on page 3-13.)

DB_NAME and DB_DOMAIN

A database's *global database name* (name and location within a network structure) is created by setting both the DB_NAME and DB_DOMAIN parameters before database creation; after creation, the database's name cannot be easily changed. The DB_NAME parameter determines the local name component of the database's name, while the DB_DOMAIN parameter indicates the domain (logical location) within a network structure. The combination of the settings for these two parameters should form a database name that is unique within a network. For example, to create a database with a global database name of TEST.US.ACME.COM, edit the parameters of the new parameter file as follows:

```
DB_NAME = TEST
DB_DOMAIN = US.ACME.COM
```

DB_NAME must be set to a text string of no more than eight characters. During database creation, the name provided for DB_NAME is recorded in the data files, redo log files, and control file of the database. If during database instance startup the value of the DB_NAME parameter (of the parameter file) and the database name in the control file are not the same, the database does not start.

DB_DOMAIN is a text string that specifies the network domain where the database is created; this is typically the name of the organization that owns the database. If the database you are about to create will ever be part of a distributed database system, pay special attention to this initialization parameter before database creation. For more information, see "Managing Global Database Names" on page 15-3.

CONTROL_FILES

Include the CONTROL_FILES parameter in your new parameter file and set its value to a list of control filenames to use for the new database. If you want ORACLE to create new operating system files when creating your database's control files, make sure that the filenames listed in the CONTROL_FILES parameter do not match any filenames that currently exist on your system. If you want ORACLE to reuse or overwrite existing files when creating your database's control files, make sure that the filenames listed in the CONTROL_FILES parameter match the filenames that currently exist. **Use extreme caution when setting this option. If you inadvertently specify a file that you did not intend and execute the CREATE DATABASE statement, the previous contents of that file will be overwritten.**

IUG

If no filenames are listed for the CONTROL_FILES parameter, ORACLE uses a default filename. This name is operating system dependent; see your installation and user's guide for details.

Oracle Corporation strongly recommends you use at least two control files stored on separate physical disk drives for each database. Therefore, when specifying the CONTROL_FILES parameter of the new parameter file, follow these guidelines:

- List at least two filenames for the CONTROL_FILES parameter.
- Place each control file on a separate physical disk drives by fully specifying filenames that refer to different disk drives for each filename.

Note: The file specification for control files is operating system dependent. Regardless of your operating system, *always* fully specify filenames for your control files.

When you execute the CREATE DATABASE statement (in Step 8), the control files listed in the CONTROL_FILES parameter of the parameter file will be created.

DB_BLOCK_SIZE

IUG

The default data block size for every ORACLE Server is operating system specific; see your installation or user's guide. The ORACLE data block size is typically either 2K or 4K. In most cases, the default data block size should not be altered. In some cases, however, a larger data block size provides greater efficiency in disk and memory I/O (access and storage of data). Such cases include:

- ORACLE is on a large computer system with a large amount of memory and fast disk drives. For example, databases controlled by mainframe computers with vast hardware resources typically use a data block size of 4K or greater.
- The operating system that runs ORACLE uses a small operating system block size. For example, if the operating system block size is 1K and the data block size matches this,

ORACLE may be performing an excessive amount of disk I/O during normal operation. To correct for this, all databases created should have a data block size that is larger than the operating system block size.

Each database's block size is set during database creation by the initialization parameter DB_BLOCK_SIZE. The block size **cannot** be changed after database creation except by re-creating the database. If a database's block size is different from the operating system block size, make the data block size a multiple of the operating system's block size.

For example, if your operating system's block size is 2K (2048 bytes), the following setting for the DB_BLOCK_SIZE initialization parameter would be valid:

```
DB_BLOCK_SIZE=4096
```

DB_BLOCK_SIZE also determines the size of the database buffers in the buffer cache of the System Global Area (SGA).

DB_BLOCK_BUFFERS

This parameter determines the number of buffers in the buffer cache in the System Global Area (SGA). The number of buffers affects the performance of the cache. Larger cache sizes reduce the number of disk writes of modified data. However, a large cache may take up too much memory and induce memory paging or swapping.

Estimate the number of data blocks that your application accesses most frequently, including tables, indexes, and rollback segments. This estimate is a rough approximation of the minimum number of buffers the cache should have.

For more information on tuning the buffer cache, see the section "Tuning the Buffer Cache" beginning on page 21-17.

PROCESSES

This parameter determines the maximum number of operating system processes that can be connected to ORACLE concurrently. The value of this parameter must include 5 for the background processes and 1 for each user process. For example, if you plan to have 50 concurrent users, set this parameter to at least 55.

ROLLBACK_SEGMENTS

This parameter is a list of the rollback segments an ORACLE instance acquires at database startup. List your rollback segments as the value of this parameter. To determine how many rollback segments you need, see Table 23-1 on page 23-3.

After installation, you must create at least one rollback segment in the SYSTEM tablespace in addition to the SYSTEM rollback segment before you can create any schema objects.

LICENSE_MAX_SESSIONS, LICENSE_SESSION_WARNING, and LICENSE_MAX_USERS

ORACLE helps you ensure that your site complies with its ORACLE license agreement. If your site is licensed by concurrent usage, you can track and limit the number of sessions concurrently connected to an instance; if your site is licensed by named users, you can limit the number of named users created in a database. To use this facility, you need to know which type of licensing agreement your site has and what the maximum number of sessions or named users is. Your site might use either type of licensing (session licensing or named user licensing), but not both.

The following sections explain how you initially set the session and user limits. See "Using Session and User Licensing" on page 11-2 for more information about this facility, as well as instructions for managing licensing.

Setting Concurrent Usage Limits You can set a limit on the number of concurrent sessions that can connect to a database on the specified computer. To set the maximum number of concurrent sessions for an instance, set the parameter LICENSE_MAX_SESSIONS in the parameter file used to start the instance. For example:

```
LICENSE_MAX_SESSIONS = 80
```

In addition to setting a maximum, you can set a warning limit on the number of concurrent sessions. Once this limit is reached, additional users can continue to connect (up to the maximum limit), but ORACLE sends a warning for each connecting user. To set the warning limit for an instance, set the parameter LICENSE_SESSIONS_WARNING. Set the warning limit to a value lower than LICENSE_MAX_SESSIONS.

Parallel

For instances running with the Parallel Server, each instance can have its own concurrent usage limit and warning limit. However, the sum of the instances' limits must not exceed the site's session license. See the *ORACLE7 Parallel Server Administrator's Guide* for more information about setting these limits in that environment.

Using Named User Limits You can set a limit on the number of users created in the database. Once this limit is reached, you cannot create more users.

Note: This mechanism assumes that each person accessing the database has a unique user name and that no people share a user name. Therefore, so that named user licensing can help you ensure compliance with your ORACLE license agreement, do not allow multiple users to log in using the same user name.

To limit the number of users created in a database, set the LICENSE_MAX_USERS parameter in the database's parameter file. For example:

```
LICENSE_MAX_USERS = 200
```

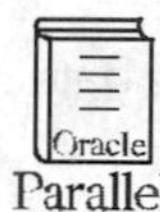

Parallel

For instances running with the Parallel Server, all instances connected to the same database should have the same named user limit. See the *ORACLE7 Parallel Server Administrator's Guide* for more information on setting this limit in that environment.

Step 4: Check the Instance Identifier

IUG

If you have other databases, check the ORACLE instance identifier. This procedure is operating system specific; see your installation or user's guide. The ORACLE instance identifier should match the name of the database (the value of DB_NAME) to avoid confusion with other ORACLE instances that are running concurrently on your system.

Step 5: Start SQL*DBA and Connect as INTERNAL

Starting SQL*DBA is operating system specific; see your installation or user's guide.

IUG

Once SQL*DBA is running, connect to the database as INTERNAL. (See "Connecting as INTERNAL" on page 1-4, as well as your installation or user's guide.)

Step 6: Start an Instance

To start an instance (SGA and background processes) to be used with the new database, use the Start Up Instance dialog box of SQL*DBA. In the Start Up Instance dialog box, make sure that the Nomount check box is selected, the database name is specified in the Database Name entry field, and the parameter file is specified in the Parameter File entry field. If you are not familiar with the Start Up Instance dialog box, see page 3-6 for an example.

After the Start Up Instance dialog box is executed, the instance is started. At this point, there is no database. Only an SGA and background processes are started in preparation for the creation of a new database.

Step 7: Create the Database

To create the new database, use the SQL command CREATE DATABASE, optionally setting parameters within the statement to name the database, establish maximum numbers of files, name files and set their sizes, and so on. When executed, a CREATE DATABASE statement performs the following operations:

- creates the data files for the database

- creates the control files for the database
- creates the redo log files for the database
- creates the SYSTEM tablespace and the SYSTEM rollback segment
- creates the data dictionary
- creates the users SYS and SYSTEM
- specifies the character set used to store data in the database
- mounts and opens the database for use

It might take a long time to allocate the specified data and redo log files and create the data dictionary.

Note: Make sure that the data files and redo log files that you specify do not conflict with files of another database. For complete information about the CREATE DATABASE command, refer to the *ORACLE7 Server SQL Language Reference Manual*. Also, for more information about character sets and database creation, see Appendix C.

Example of the CREATE DATABASE Command

The following statement is an example of a CREATE DATABASE statement:

```
CREATE DATABASE test
    LICENSE_MAX_USERS 64
    LOGFILE GROUP 1 ('test_log1a', 'test_log1b') SIZE 500K,
            GROUP 2 ('test_log2a', 'test_log2b') SIZE 500K
    DATAFILE 'test_system' SIZE 10M;
```

The values of the MAXLOGFILES, MAXLOGMEMBERS, MAXDATAFILES, MAXLOGHISTORY, and MAXINSTANCES options in this example assume the default values, which are operating system dependent. The database is mounted in the default modes NOARCHIVELOG and EXCLUSIVE and then opened.

The items and information in the example statement above result in creating a database with the following characteristics:

- The new database is named TEST.
- The SYSTEM tablespace of the new database is comprised of one 10MB data file named TEST_SYSTEM.
- The new database has two online redo log groups, each containing two 500KB members.
- The new database **does not** overwrite any existing files to create the control files specified in the parameter file.

Note: You can set several limits during database creation. Some of these limits are also subject to superseding limits of the operating system and can affect each other. For example, if you set

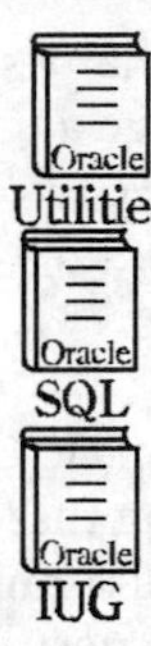

MAXDATAFILES, ORACLE allocates enough space in the control file to store MAXDATAFILES filenames, even if the database has only one data file initially; because the maximum control file size is limited and operating system-dependent, you might not be able to set all CREATE DATABASE parameters at their theoretical maximums. See the *ORACLE7 Server Utilities User's Guide* and the *ORACLE7 Server SQL Language Reference Manual* for more information on setting limits during database creation; see your installation or user's guide for information about operating system limits.

Step 8: Back Up the Database

You should make a full backup of the database to ensure that you have a complete set of files from which to recover if a media failure occurs. Se Chapter 18.

Troubleshooting Database Creation

If for any reason database creation does not succeed, complete the following steps before attempting to create it once again:

1. Shut down the instance.
2. Delete any files created by the CREATE DATABASE statement.

After completing these two steps and correcting the error that caused the failure of the database creation, continue from Step 6.

After Database Creation

After a database is created, the instance is left running and the database is open and available for normal database use. To subsequently start and stop the database, use SQL*DBA. If more than one database exists in your database system, specify the parameter file to use with any subsequent database startup. Refer to the *ORACLE7 Server Utilities User's Guide* for information about the Parameter File entry field of the Start Up Instance dialog box.

If you plan to install other ORACLE products to work with this database, refer to the installation instructions for those products; some products require you to create additional data dictionary tables. Refer to the installation or user's guide and additional documentation for the additional products. Usually, command files are provided to create and load these tables into the database's data dictionary.

The ORACLE Server distribution media can include various SQL files that let you experiment with the system, learn SQL, or create additional tables, views, or synonyms.

A newly created database has only two users, SYS and SYSTEM. The passwords for these two usernames should be changed soon after the database is created; see "Database Administrator Usernames" on page 1-6 for more information about these usernames, and "Altering Users" on page 11-11 for the procedure to change a user's password.

Initial Tuning Guidelines

You can make a few significant tuning alterations to ORACLE immediately following installation. By following these instructions, you can reduce the need to tune ORACLE when it is running. This section gives recommendations for these installation issues:

- allocating rollback segments
- distributing I/O across disks

Allocating Rollback Segments

Proper allocation of rollback segments makes for optimal database performance. The size and number of rollback segments required for optimal performance depends on your application. Table 23-1 on page 23-3 shows some general guidelines for choosing how many rollback segments to allocate based on the number of concurrent transactions on your ORACLE Server. These guidelines are appropriate for most application mixes.

To create rollback segments, use the CREATE ROLLBACK SEGMENT command. For more information on this command, see the *ORACLE7 Server SQL Language Reference Manual.*

Choosing Sizes for Rollback Segments

The size of your rollback segment can also affect performance. Rollback segment size is determined by the storage parameters in the CREATE ROLLBACK SEGMENT statement. Your rollback segments must be large enough to hold the rollback entries for your transactions. For information on choosing sizes for your rollback segments, see the section "Reducing Contention for Rollback Segments" beginning on page 23-2.

Distributing I/O

Proper distribution of I/O can improve database performance dramatically. I/O can be distributed during installation of ORACLE. Distributing I/O during installation can reduce the need to distribute I/O later when ORACLE is running.

There are several ways to distribute I/O when you install ORACLE:

- redo log file placement
- data file placement
- separation of tables and indexes

- density of data (rows per data block)

For complete information on each of these issues, see the section "Distributing I/O" beginning on page 22-4.

Creating the Data Dictionary

The data dictionary is automatically created when a database is created. Thereafter, whenever the database is in operation, ORACLE updates the data dictionary in response to every DDL statement.

The data dictionary base tables must be the first objects created in any database, because they must be present to store information about all other user-defined objects to be created. During database creation, the initialization parameter INIT_SQL_FILES is read to find the names of script files that should be run immediately following database creation, to create the data dictionary and other important structures. The default filenames for this parameter vary by operating system (see your installation or user's guide).

In general, these initial SQL files do the following tasks:

1. Define the SYSTEM tablespace and SYSTEM rollback segment.
2. Define the data dictionary base tables in the SYSTEM tablespace. (The data dictionary is created in and must remain in the SYSTEM tablespace.) For every table and column in a base table, a comment is also loaded to provide online documentation.
3. Load data into some data dictionary tables.

Table 2-1 lists the scripts that are required for the ORACLE Server with the indicated options. The appropriate scripts for your ORACLE Server options are run automatically when you create a database. They are described here because you might need to run them again, when upgrading to a new release of ORACLE; your release notes indicate when this is necessary. The names and locations of these scripts are operating system-dependent; see your installation or user's guide. To run these scripts, you should be connected as the user SYS. The scripts whose names start with DBMS are documented more fully in the *ORACLE7 Server Application Developer's Guide*, and in comments in the scripts themselves.

TABLE 2-1 Required SQL Scripts

Script Name	Requires Options	Description
CATALOG.SQL	none	Creates the data dictionary and public synonyms for many of its views, and grants PUBLIC access to the synonyms; also calls the scripts CATAUDIT.SQL, CATEXP.SQL, and CATLDR.SQL
CATAUDIT.SQL	none	Creates the database audit trail and views (This is run automatically by CATALOG.SQL; it can be removed by running CATNOAUD.SQL.)
CATEXP.SQL	none	Creates data dictionary tables for Import/ Export (This is run automatically by CATALOG.SQL.)
CATLDR.SQL	none	Creates views for using SQL*Loader (This is run automatically by CATALOG.SQL.)
CATPARR.SQL	Parallel Server	Creates data dictionary views on Parallel Server information
CATTRUST.SQL	Trusted ORACLE	Defines structures needed for the Trusted ORACLE Server
CATPROC.SQL	procedural	Runs all scripts required for or used within the procedural option: CATPRC.SQL, CATSNAP.SQL, CATRPC.SQL, STANDARD.SQL, DBMSSTDX.SQL, PIPDL.SQL, PIDIAN.SQL, DIUTIL.SQL, PISTUB.SQL, DBMSUTIL.SQL, DBMSSNAP.SQL, DBMSLOCK.SQL, DBMSPIPE.SQL, DBMSALRT.SQL, DBMSOTPT.SQL, DBMSDESC.SQL
CATPRC.SQL	procedural	Creates data dictionary views for stored procedures, packages, and database triggers (This is run automatically by CATPROC.SQL.)
CATSNAP.SQL	procedural, distributed	Creates data dictionary structures for storing and maintaining snapshots (This is run automatically by CATPROC.SQL; it requires CATPRC.SQL.)
CATRPC.SQL	procedural, distributed	Creates data dictionary views on distributed database information (This is run automatically by CATPROC.SQL; it requires CATPRC.SQL.)
STANDARD.SQL	procedural	Creates PL/SQL packages for the procedural option (This is run automatically by CATPROC.SQL; it requires CATPRC.SQL.)
DBMSSTDX.SQL	procedural	Includes extensions to the package standard (This is run automatically by CATPROC.SQL; it requires STANDARD.SQL.)
PIPIDL.SQL	procedural	Creates PL/SQL packages for the procedural option (This is run automatically by CATPROC.SQL; it requires DBMSSTDX.SQL.)

Script Name	Requires Options	Description
PIDIAN.SQL	procedural	Creates PL/SQL packages for the procedural option (This is run automatically by CATPROC.SQL; it requires DBMSSTDX.SQL.)
DIUTIL.SQL	procedural	Creates PL/SQL packages for the procedural option (This is run automatically by CATPROC.SQL; it requires PIDIAN.SQL.)
PISTUB.SQL	procedural	Creates PL/SQL packages for the procedural option (This is run automatically by CATPROC.SQL; it requires DIUTIL.SQL.)
DBMSUTIL.SQL	procedural	Creates utilities that can be called from within procedures (This is run automatically by CATPROC.SQL; it requires PISTUB.SQL.)
DBMSSNAP.SQL	procedural, distributed	Creates procedures for administering snapshots (This is run automatically by CATPROC.SQL; it requires CATSNAP.SQL, and you must run it on both the snapshot and master table nodes.)
DBMSALRT.SQL	procedural	Allows users and applications to use event alerters (This is run automatically by CATPROC.SQL; it requires PISTUB.SQL.)
DBMSLOCK.SQL	procedural	Allows users and applications to use the lock package (This is run automatically by CATPROC.SQL; it requires PISTUB.SQL.)
DBMSMAIL.SQL	procedural	Allows users and applications to send Oracle*Mail messages (This is run automatically by CATPROC.SQL; it requires PISTUB.SQL. You must run it on the sending database, and run UTLMAIL.SQL on the receiving Oracle*Mail database)
DBMSOTPT.SQL	procedural	Allows application developers to receive I/O from procedures (This is run automatically by CATPROC.SQL; it requires PISTUB.SQL.)
DBMSPIPE.SQL	procedural	Allows sessions in the same instance to communicate with each other (This is run automatically by CATPROC.SQL; it requires PISTUB.SQL.)
DBMSDESC.SQL	procedural	Creates a package that allows you to describe the arguments and return values of program units (This is run automatically by CATPROC.SQL; it requires PISTUB.SQL.)

The parameter INIT_SQL_FILES can also be used to specify other files to be run during database creation, after the data dictionary is created, to create site-specific tables. For example, you could add names of your files **after** the default filenames:

```
INIT_SQL_FILES = (CATALOG.SQL, CATPROC.SQL ACME_DBA.SQL)
```

In this example, ACME_DBA.SQL is an additional file to run during database creation.

Creating Additional Data Dictionary Structures

Oracle supplies a number of other scripts with the ORACLE Server that create additional structures you can use in managing your database and creating database applications. These scripts are listed below; for more information on them, see Appendix B. The exact names and locations of these scripts are operating system dependent; see your installation or user's guide for more details.

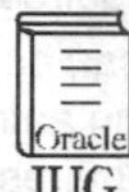
IUG

TABLE 2-2 Additional SQL Scripts

Script Name	Options Required	Run By	Description
CATALOG6.SQL	none	SYS	Creates Version 6 data dictionary views
CATBLOCK.SQL	none	SYS	Creates the view BLOCKING_LOCKS, which shows which locks are blocking the system
CATDBSYN.SQL	none	user with access to data dictionary tables	Creates private synonyms for DBA_ views in the data dictionary
CATEXP6.SQL	none	SYS	Creates views for using the Version 6 Export utility with ORACLE7
CATNOAUD.SQL	none	SYS	Removes the database audit trail created by CATAUDIT.SQL, including its data and views
CATNOPRC.SQL	none	SYS	Removes data dictionary structures that were created by CATPRC.SQL
CATSTAT.SQL	none	SYS	Executes the ANALYZE command on structures in the data dictionary, to allow cost-based optimization of internal SQL statements; should be run periodically to update the statistics (intended for sites that do not have the procedural option; procedural option sites can instead call ANALYZE_SCHEMA())
UTLBSTAT.SQL	none	any user	Begins collecting performance tuning statistics (end with UTLESTAT.SQL.)
UTLCHAIN.SQL	none	any user	Creates tables for storing the output of the ANALYZE command with CHAINED ROWS option

Script Name	Options Required	Run By	Description
UTLDTREE.SQL	procedural	any user	Creates tables and views that show dependencies between objects
UTLESTAT.SQL	none	any user	Ends collecting of performance tuning statistics started by UTLBSTAT.SQL
UTLEXCPT.SQL	none	any user	Creates the default table (EXCEPTIONS) for storing exceptions from enabling constraints
UTLEXP6.SQL	none	SYS	Returns a list of objects not exported by SQL*Net export of a Version 6 database
UTLDIDXS.SQL	none	any user	Displays the results of running the scripts UTLIDXSS.SQL and UTLIDXSO.SQL
UTLOIDXS.SQL	none	any user	Runs UTLIDXSS.SQL on multiple columns
UTLLOCKT.SQL	none	SYS	Displays a lock wait-for graph, in tree structure format
UTLMAIL.SQL	none	SYS	Allows Oracle*Mail database to receive messages from procedures (run on Oracle*Mail database; requires that you run DBMSMAIL.SQL on the database that will send messages)
UTLMONTR.SQL	none	SYS	Grants access to all performance tables used by SQL*DBA Monitors to PUBLIC group, including access to Monitors
UTLSAMPL.SQL	none	any user	Creates sample tables (such as EMP and DEPT) and users (such as SCOTT)
UTLSIDXS.SQL	none	any user	Computes the selectivity of a column, and tests whether an index created on the column would be appropriate
UTLXPLAN.SQL	none	any user	Creates the table PLAN_TABLE, which holds output from the EXPLAIN PLAN command

CHAPTER

3

STARTING UP AND SHUTTING DOWN

This chapter explains the procedures involved in starting and stopping an ORACLE database. Topics include:

- starting an instance and database
- changing the availability of a database
- shutting down an instance and database
- using parameter files

Trusted

If you are using Trusted ORACLE, see the *Trusted ORACLE7 Server Administrator's Guide* for information on starting up and shutting down in that environment.

General Startup Procedures

To startup a database or instance, use either the Start Up Instance dialog box or the STARTUP command (after you connect to ORACLE as INTERNAL). You can start an instance and database in a variety of ways:

- start the instance without mounting a database
- start the instance and mount the database, but leave it closed
- start the instance, and mount and open the database in:
    - unrestricted mode (accessible to all users)
    - RESTRICTED mode (accessible to DBAs only)

In addition, you can force the instance to start, or start the instance and have complete media recovery begin immediately. If your operating system supports the ORACLE Parallel Server, you may start an instance and mount the database in either exclusive or shared mode.

The following sections give instructions for each type of startup. Examples of starting databases and instances are provided in "Examples of Database and Instance Startup" on page 3-6.

Trusted

Note: You cannot start a database instance if you are connected to the database via a multi-threaded server process. (See Chapter 4 for more information about multi-threaded server processes.) Also, special conditions of database startup apply when using Trusted ORACLE; see the *Trusted ORACLE7 Server Administrator's Guide* for this information.

Preparing to Start an Instance

Before you can start an instance, you must connect as INTERNAL; you might also want to indicate for which database you are starting an instance and specify a parameter file.

Starting SQL*DBA and Connecting as INTERNAL

To start up a database or instance, you must start SQL*DBA. See the *ORACLE7 Server Utilities User's Guide* for instructions.

Utilities

You must also be connected as INTERNAL. This condition applies whether you are using SQL*DBA's graphical interface or SQL commands. (See "Connecting as INTERNAL" on page 1-4.)

Specifying a Database Name

When starting a database instance, specify the name of the database that will be mounted to the instance by either:

- using the Start Up Instance dialog box, entering the database name in the Database Name entry field
- using the STARTUP command and specifying the database name

Specifying a Parameter Filename

When starting a database instance, choose a parameter file to initialize the instance's settings by either:

- using the Start Up Instance dialog box and entering a filename in the Parameter File entry field
- using the STARTUP command with the PFILE option and a fully specified filename

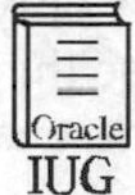

The specification of filenames is operating system specific; see your installation or user's guide. If no filename is entered, ORACLE uses the default filename.

Starting an Instance Without Mounting a Database

You might want to start an instance without mounting a database; this is usually the case only during database creation. To do this, use one of the following options of SQL*DBA:

- the Start Up Instance dialog box, selecting the Nomount radio button
- the STARTUP command with the NOMOUNT option

Starting an Instance and Mounting a Database

You might want to start an instance and mount a database, but not open the database, to perform specific maintenance operations. For example, the database must be mounted but not open during the following tasks:

- renaming data files
- adding, dropping, or renaming redo log files
- enabling and disabling redo log archiving options
- performing full database recovery

Start an instance and mount the database but leave it closed using one of the following options of SQL*DBA:

- the Start Up Instance dialog box, selecting the Mount radio button
- the STARTUP command with the MOUNT option

Starting an Instance, and Mounting and Opening a Database

Normal database operation means that an instance is started and the database is mounted and open. This stage allows any valid user to connect to the database and perform typical data access operations.

Start an instance, and mount and open the database, using one of the following options of SQL*DBA:

- the Start Up Instance dialog box, selecting the Open radio button
- the STARTUP command with the OPEN option

Restricting Access to a Database at Startup

You might want to start an instance, and mount and open a database in restricted mode so that the database is available only to administrative personnel and not to typical database users. Use this mode of database startup when you need to accomplish one of these tasks:

- perform structure maintenance, such as rebuilding indexes
- perform an export or import of database data
- perform a data load (with SQL*Loader)
- temporarily prevent typical users from using data

Normally, all users with the CREATE SESSION system privilege can connect to an open database. Opening a database in restricted mode allows database access only to users with both the CREATE SESSION and RESTRICTED SESSION system privilege; only database administrators should have the RESTRICTED SESSION system privilege.

Start an instance (and, optionally, mount and open the database) in restricted mode using one of the following options of SQL*DBA:

- the Start Up Instance dialog box, selecting the Restrict to DBAs check box
- the STARTUP command with the RESTRICT option

Note: Subsequently, you can make the database accessible to users without the RESTRICTED SESSION system privilege; see "Restricting Access to an Open Database" on page 3-9 for more information.

Forcing an Instance to Start

In unusual circumstances, you might experience problems when attempting to start a database instance. A database instance should not be forced to start unless:

- The current instance cannot be successfully shut down using either the Normal or Immediate options of the Shut Down menu (or an equivalent SHUTDOWN statement).
- You experience problems when starting an instance.

Note: Aborting the current instance has particular side effects; see "Aborting an Instance" on page 3-11.

If such a situation arises, you can usually solve the problem by starting a new instance (and optionally mounting and opening the database) using either of the following options of SQL*DBA:

- the Start Up Instance dialog box with the Force check box
- the STARTUP command with the FORCE option

These options of the Start Up Instance dialog box and the STARTUP command effectively shut down the current instance and then start a new instance (optionally mounting and opening the database).

Starting an Instance, Mounting a Database, and Starting Complete Media Recovery

If you know that media recovery is required, you can start an instance, mount a database to the instance, and have the recovery process automatically start by using one of the following options of SQL*DBA:

- the Start Up Instance dialog box with the Recover check box
- the STARTUP command with the RECOVER option

ORACLE might need archived redo log files to perform the automatic recovery. See Chapter 19 for more information about database recovery.

Starting in Exclusive or Parallel Mode

Parallel

If your ORACLE Server allows multiple instances to access a single database concurrently, you must choose whether to mount the database exclusively or in parallel. See the *ORACLE7 Parallel Server Administrator's Guide* for more information.

Miscellaneous Startup Topics

IUG

The following topics are unique options of database and instance startup that vary depending on your operating system. See your installation or user's guide for more information about each topic.

Automatic Database Startup at Operating System Start

Many sites use procedures to enable automatic startup of one or more ORACLE instances and databases immediately following a system start. The procedures for doing this are specific to each operating system.

Starting Remote Instances

If your local ORACLE Server is part of a distributed database, you might need to start a remote instance and database. Procedures for starting and stopping remote instances vary widely depending on communication protocol and operating system.

Examples of Database and Instance Startup

This section gives several examples of instance startup using the menu interface and commands of SQL*DBA. In each example, the DBA is already connected as INTERNAL.

The Startup Instance Dialog

The Startup Instance dialog allows you to start an instance and optionally mount and open a database. For example, Figure 3-1 shows the Startup Instance dialog.

FIGURE 3-1
The Start up Instance Dialog

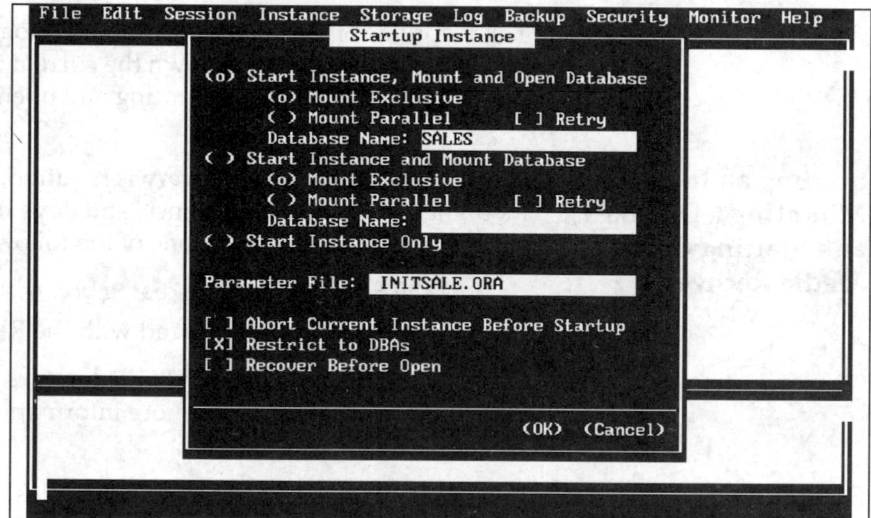

Utilities

This example results in starting an instance using the parameter file INITSALE.ORA, mounting and opening the database named SALES in exclusive mode, and restricting access to administrative personnel. (For more information about the Start Up Instance dialog, see the *ORACLE7 Server Utilities User's Guide.*)

The STARTUP Command

The command equivalent of using the Start Up Instance dialog is the SQL*DBA command STARTUP. The following statement is the command equivalent of the Start Up Instance dialog illustrated in Figure 3-1:

```
STARTUP OPEN sales PFILE=INITSALE.ORA EXCLUSIVE RESTRICT;
```

There are several restrictions to combining options of the STARTUP command. See the *ORACLE7 Server Utilities User's Guide* for more information.

Troubleshooting Startup

Sometimes you might have problems starting up an instance. For example, control files, database files, or redo log files might not be available. This section describes how to tell when this is the case and how to deal with the problem.

Unavailable Control Files

When you attempt to mount a database, if one or more of the files specified by the CONTROL_FILES parameter do not exist or cannot be opened, ORACLE returns a warning message and does not mount the database. For information about database recovery, see Chapter 19.

Unavailable Database or Redo Log Files

When attempting to open a database, if one or more of the data files or redo log files is not available or cannot be opened, ORACLE returns a warning message and does not open the database. For information about database recovery, see Chapter 19.

Altering Database Availability

You can make a database partially available to users. For example, you can open a previously mounted but closed database, so that database users can connect to and use the database.

The following sections explain how to change a database's availability. All procedures are accomplished using options of the Instance menu of SQL*DBA or the SQL command ALTER DATABASE. For complete information about SQL*DBA menu options, see the *ORACLE7 Server Utilities Guide*; for complete information about the ALTER DATABASE command, see the *ORACLE7 Server SQL Language Reference Manual.* To accomplish any of the following procedures, you must have the ALTER DATABASE system privilege.

Mounting a Database to an Instance

When you need to perform specific administrative operations, the database must be started and mounted to an instance, but closed. This can be accomplished by starting the instance and mounting the database in one or two steps.

Note: For a list of operations that require the database to be mounted and closed and for the procedures to start an instance and mount a database in one step, see "Starting an Instance and Mounting a Database" on page 3-3.

When mounting the database, you can indicate whether to mount the database exclusively to only this instance or mount the database so that it can be mounted concurrently by other instances.

To mount a database to a previously started instance, use either of the following options:

- the Mount Database menu of SQL*DBA
- the SQL command ALTER DATABASE with the MOUNT option

The Mount Database Menu

The Mount Database menu allows you to mount a database to a previously started instance. You can mount the database in either exclusive mode or parallel mode. Figure 3-2 shows the Mount Database menu.

FIGURE 3-2
The Mount Database Menu

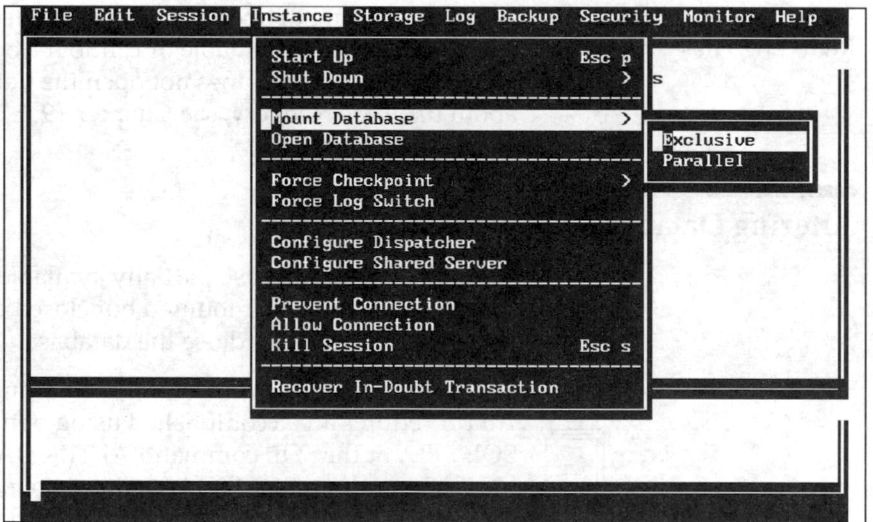

This example mounts a database in exclusive mode.

The command equivalent of using the Mount Database menu is the SQL command ALTER DATABASE, with the MOUNT option. (You can also select either the EXCLUSIVE or PARALLEL option if you are using the Parallel Server.) For example, the following statement is the command equivalent of the Mount Database menu illustrated in Figure 3-2:

```
ALTER DATABASE MOUNT;
```

Opening a Closed Database

You make a mounted but closed database available for general use by opening the database. To open a mounted database, use either of the following options:

- the Open option of the Instance menu of SQL*DBA
- the SQL command ALTER DATABASE with the OPEN option

For example, the following statement opens a mounted database:

```
ALTER DATABASE OPEN;
```

Once you have executed this command, any valid ORACLE user with the CREATE SESSION system privilege can connect to the database.

Restricting Access to an Open Database

Under normal conditions, all users with the CREATE SESSION system privilege can connect to an instance. However, you can take an instance in and out of restricted mode. When an instance is in restricted mode, only users who have both the CREATE SESSION and RESTRICTED SESSION system privileges can connect to the instance. Typically, only administrators have the RESTRICTED SESSION system privilege. Restricted mode is useful when you need to perform these tasks:

- perform structure maintenance, such as rebuilding indexes
- perform an export or import of database data
- perform a data load (with SQL*Loader)
- temporarily prevent non-administrator users from using data

To place an instance in restricted mode, use the Prevent Connections option of the Instance menu of SQL*DBA or the SQL command ALTER SYSTEM with the ENABLE RESTRICTED SESSION option. After placing an instance in restricted mode, you might also want to kill all current user sessions before performing any administrative tasks. (See "Killing Sessions" on page 4-13.)

To lift an instance from restricted mode, use the Allow Connections option of the Instance menu of SQL*DBA or the SQL command ALTER SYSTEM with the DISABLE RESTRICTED SESSION option.

Note: Alternatively, you can start a database instance, and mount and open the database in restricted mode. See "Restricting Access to a Database at Startup" on page 3-4.

Shutting Down a Database

To initiate database shutdown, use either the Shut Down menu or the SHUTDOWN command of SQL*DBA. Control is not returned to the session that initiates a database shutdown until shutdown is complete. Users who attempt connections while a shutdown is in progress receive a message similar to the following message:

```
ORA-01090: shutdown in progress - connection is not permitted
```

The following sections explain how to shut down a database. Examples of the Shut Down menu and the SHUTDOWN command are provided in "Examples of Database Shutdown" on page 3-12.

Trusted

Note: You cannot shut down a database if you are connected to the database via a multi-threaded server process. See Chapter 4 for more information about multi-threaded server processes. Also, several special options and conditions of database shutdown that apply when using Trusted ORACLE in OS MAC mode are not discussed in this section; for more information, see the *Trusted ORACLE7 Server Administrator's Guide*.

Connecting as INTERNAL

To shut down a database and instance, you must first be connected as INTERNAL. This condition applies whether you are using SQL*DBA's graphical interface or SQL commands. (See "Connecting as INTERNAL" on page 1-4.)

Shutting Down a Database Under Normal Conditions

Normal database shutdown proceeds as follows:

- No new connections are allowed after the statement is issued.
- Before the database is shut down, ORACLE waits for all currently connected users to disconnect from the database.
- The next startup of the database will not require any instance recovery procedures.

To shut down a database in normal situations, use either of the following options of SQL*DBA:

- the Normal option of the Shut Down menu
- the SHUTDOWN command with the NORMAL option

Shutting Down a Database Immediately

In emergency situations, you can immediately shut down a database; use immediate database shutdown only in situations such as:

- A power shutdown is going to occur soon.
- The database or one of its applications is functioning irregularly.

Immediate database shutdown proceeds with the following conditions:

- Current client SQL statements being processed by ORACLE are terminated immediately.
- Any uncommitted transactions are rolled back. (If long uncommitted transactions exist, this method of shutdown might not complete quickly, despite its name.)
- ORACLE does not wait for users currently connected to the database to disconnect; ORACLE implicitly rolls back active transactions and disconnects all connected users.
- The next startup of the database might require instance recovery (which is automatically performed by ORACLE).

To shut down a database immediately, use either of the following options of SQL*DBA:

- the Immediate option of the Shut Down menu
- the SHUTDOWN command with the IMMEDIATE option

Aborting an Instance

You can shutdown a database instantaneously by aborting the database's instance. Avoid this type of shutdown; use it only in the following situations:

- The database or one of its applications is functioning irregularly **and** neither of the other types of shutdown work.
- You need to shut down the database instantaneously (for example, if you know a power shutdown is going to occur in one minute).
- You experience problems when starting a database instance.

Aborting an instance shuts down a database as follows:

- Current client SQL statements being processed by ORACLE are immediately terminated.
- Uncommitted transactions are not rolled back.
- ORACLE does not wait for users currently connected to the database to disconnect; ORACLE implicitly disconnects all connected users.
- The next STARTUP of the database will require instance recovery procedures; however, instance recovery will be automatically performed during database startup.

If the normal and immediate shutdown options **both** do not work, abort the current database instance immediately by using either of the following options of SQL*DBA:

- the Abort Instance option of the Shut Down menu
- the SHUTDOWN command with the ABORT option

Examples of Database Shutdown

This section gives examples of database and instance shutdown using the menu interface and commands of SQL*DBA. In all of the examples, the DBA has already connected as INTERNAL.

Utilities

For more information about the Shut Down menu or the SHUTDOWN command, see the *ORACLE7 Server Utilities User's Guide.*

The Shut Down Menu

The Shut Down menu shuts down a database. For example, Figure 3-3 shows the Shut Down menu.

FIGURE 3-3
The Shut Down Menu

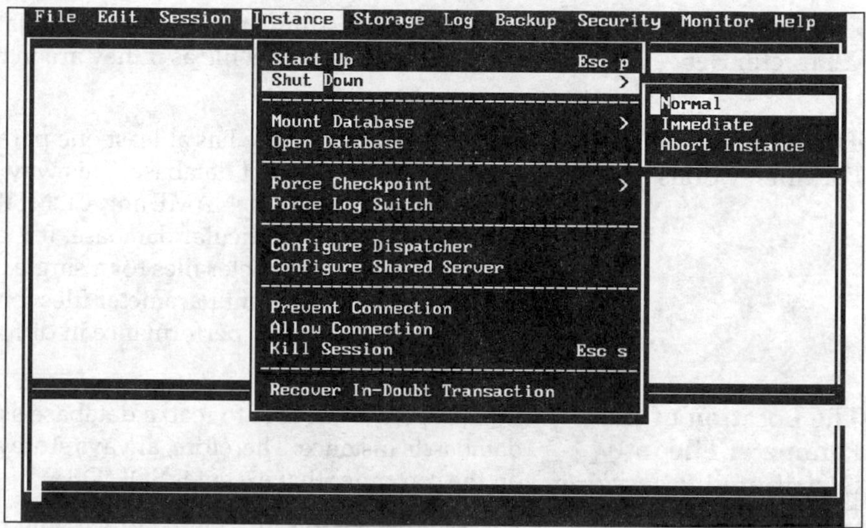

The option selected shuts down the database under normal conditions.

The SHUTDOWN Command

The command equivalent of using the Shut Down menu is the SQL*DBA command SHUTDOWN. For example, the following statement is the command equivalent of the Shut Down menu illustrated in Figure 3-3 of the previous section:

```
SHUTDOWN NORMAL;
```

Using Parameter Files

To start an instance, ORACLE must read a *parameter file*. Often, although not always, this file is named INIT.ORA or INIT*sid*.ORA, where *sid* is operating system specific. See your installation or user's guide for more information about this file.

The Sample Parameter File

A sample parameter file (INIT.ORA or INIT*sid*.ORA) is included in the ORACLE distribution set. This sample file's parameters are adequate for initial installations of an ORACLE database. After your system is operating and you have some experience with ORACLE, you will probably want to change some parameter values; see Chapters 20 through 24 for information about optimizing a database's performance using the parameter file.

Parameter File Character Set

ORACLE treats string literals defined for National Language Support (NLS) parameters in the file as if they are in the database character set.

The Number of Parameter Files

Each ORACLE database has at least one parameter file that corresponds only to that database. This way, database-specific parameters (such as DB_NAME and CONTROL_FILES) in a given file always pertain to a particular database. It is also possible to have several different parameter files for a single database. For example, you can have several different parameter files for a single database to optimize the database's performance in different situations.

The Location of the Parameter File in Distributed Processing Environments

SQL*DBA must be able to read a database's parameter file to start a database's instance. Therefore, always store a database's parameter file on the computer that executes SQL*DBA.

For example, in non-distributed processing installations, the same computer executes ORACLE and SQL*DBA; therefore, this computer has the parameter file stored on one of its disk drives.

However, in distributed processing installations, local client workstations can execute SQL*DBA to administer a database stored on a remote machine. In this type of configuration, the local client machines must each store a copy of the parameter file for the corresponding databases.

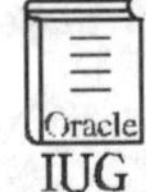

IUG

Some subjects concerning the setup and implementation of SQL*DBA are operating system dependent; see your installation or user's guide.

Editing Parameter Files

Methods of editing parameter files are operating system specific. The standard way to change the parameter values in a parameter file is to edit the file with a basic text editor.

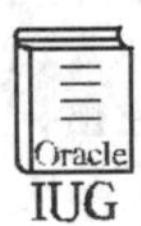

IUG

PART

II

ORACLE SERVER CONFIGURATION

CHAPTER

4 MANAGING ORACLE PROCESSES

This chapter explains how to manage the processes of an ORACLE instance. Topics include:

- starting single-process and multiple-process ORACLE instances
- configuring and starting ORACLE with multi-threaded servers
- connecting to an instance
- monitoring ORACLE processes
- killing user processes

Starting Single-Process and Multiple-Process Instances

On most operating systems, you can start an ORACLE instance in either single-process or multiple-process mode, regardless of how ORACLE was installed or last started. If the computer that executes the ORACLE Server supports multiple processes, database instances are normally started using multiple process mode so that multiple users can concurrently access a shared database; single-process instances support only one user at a time. However, in some testing situations, you might find it useful to start an instance using a single process.

Some operating systems (such as MS-DOS) do not support multiple processes or shared memory, so a single-process instance is the only option.

Setting the Process Mode

The initialization parameter SINGLE_PROCESS determines which type of instance is started. To start a single process instance, set the initialization parameter SINGLE_PROCESS to TRUE; to start a multiple process instance, set SINGLE_PROCESS to FALSE. If the SINGLE_PROCESS parameter is not included, its default value is FALSE.

If your system can only run single-task ORACLE, ORACLE is automatically installed for this configuration; you have no choice but to run ORACLE in a single-task configuration.

Starting ORACLE with Only Dedicated Servers

If your system must run with dedicated server processes, ORACLE is automatically installed for this configuration. However, if your operating system can support ORACLE in this configuration, it may also support the multi-threaded server (described in the next section).

To start an instance in a dedicated server configuration, set the initialization parameters MTS_SERVICE, MTS_DISPATCHERS, MTS_SERVERS, and MTS_LISTENER_ADDRESS in a database's parameter file to null or omit them from the file altogether. (Refer to Appendix A for more information about these parameters and parameter files.)

Starting ORACLE with Multi-Threaded Servers

To set up your system in a multi-threaded server configuration, start a network listener process and set several initialization parameters:

- SHARED_POOL_SIZE
- MTS_LISTENER_ADDRESS
- MTS_SERVICE
- MTS_DISPATCHERS
- MTS_MAX_DISPATCHERS
- MTS_SERVERS
- MTS_MAX_SERVERS

You can then restart the instance, which will use the multi-threaded server configuration.

SQL*Net

Directions for managing the network listener process are given in your SQL*NET documentation; instructions for setting each parameter are given in the following sections.

Note: User processes that want to use the multi-threaded server must connect through SQL*Net, even if they are on the same machine as the ORACLE instance.

Allocating Additional Space in the Shared Pool for Shared Server

When users connect through the multi-threaded server, ORACLE needs to allocate additional space in the shared pool for storing information about the connections between the user processes, dispatchers, and servers. For each user who will connect using the multi-threaded server, add 1K to the setting of the parameter SHARED_POOL_SIZE. (For more information on this parameter, see Appendix A; also see Chapter 23 for more information on tuning.)

Setting the Listener Process Address (MTS_LISTENER_-ADDRESS)

Within the database's parameter file, set the initialization parameter MTS_LISTENER_ADDRESS for each port to which the database will connect. The parameter supports the following syntax:

```
MTS_LISTENER_ADDRESS = "(addr)"
```

In this example, *addr* is an address to which the listener will listen for connection requests for a specific protocol. The file may contain several such addresses:

```
MTS_LISTENER_ADDRESS = "(ADDRESS=(PROTOCOL=tcp)(PORT=5000)\
                       (HOST=ZEUS)"

MTS_LISTENER_ADDRESS = "(ADDRESS=(PROTOCOL=decnet)(OBJECT=OUTA)\
                       (NODE=ZEUS)"
```

Note: This syntax differs slightly from that of the SQL*Net listener parameter: MTS_LISTENER_ADDRESS can contain only one address per line (ADDRESS_LIST is not supported), while the SQL*Net parameter can list multiple addresses. Otherwise, the address syntax is the same.

Each address specified in the database's parameter file must also be specified in the corresponding listener's configuration file. Addresses are specified differently for various network protocols. For more information about specifying addresses for the network listener process, refer to your installation or user's guide and SQL*Net documentation.

Specifying Service Names for Dispatchers (MTS_SERVICE)

Specify the name of the service associated with dispatchers using the parameter MTS_SERVICE. A user requests the multi-threaded server by specifying this service name in the connect string. A service name must be unique; if possible, use the instance's SID. If you do not set this parameter, it defaults to the DB_NAME parameter. (If DB_NAME is also not set, ORACLE returns the error ORA-00114, "missing value for system parameter mts_service," when you start the database.) To see your SID, type SHOW LOGICAL ORA_SID in SQL*DBA.

For example, if the dispatcher's service name is TEST_DB, the parameter would be set as in the following example:

```
MTS_SERVICE = "test_db"
```

Furthermore, a connect string for connecting to this dispatcher might look like the following example:

```
SQLPLUS scott/tiger@\
  (DESCRIPTION=(ADDRESS=(PROTOCOL=decnet)(NODE=hq)\
                          OBJECT=mts7))\
               (CONNECT_DATA=(SID=test_db)))
```

Refer to your installation or user's guide or SQL*Net documentation for more information about connect strings used with the multi-threaded server configuration.

Setting the Initial Number of Dispatchers

The number of dispatcher processes started at instance startup is controlled by the parameter MTS_DISPATCHERS. Estimate the number of dispatchers to start for each network protocol before instance startup.

The appropriate number of dispatcher processes for each instance depends upon the performance you want from your database and the host operating system's limit on the number of connections per process, which is operating system dependent, and the number of connections required per network protocol. (See your installation or user's guide for the operating system limit.) The instance must be able to provide as many connections as there are concurrent users on the database system; the more dispatchers you have, the better potential database performance users will see, since they will not have to wait as long for dispatcher service.

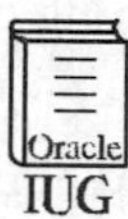

Once you know the number of possible connections per process for your operating system, calculate the initial number of dispatcher processes to create during instance startup, per network protocol, using the following formula:

```
  number                    maximum number of concurrent sessions
     of       = CEIL (─────────────────────────────────────────────)
dispatchers                     connections per dispatcher
```

Here, *connections/dispatcher* is operating system dependent. For example, assume that your system typically has 80 users concurrently connected via TCP/IP and 40 users connected via DECNet. In this case, the MTS_DISPATCHERS parameter should be set as follows:

```
MTS_DISPATCHERS = "TCPIP, 3"
MTS_DISPATCHERS = "DECNET, 3"
```

When setting the MTS_DISPATCHERS parameter, you can only include protocols specified in a MTS_LISTENER_ADDRESS parameter.

After instance startup, you can start more dispatcher processes if needed; however, you can only start dispatchers that use protocols mentioned in the database's parameter file. For example, if the parameter file starts dispatchers for protocol_A and protocol_B, you cannot later start dispatchers for protocol_C without changing the parameter file and restarting the instance. (See "Adding and Removing Dispatcher Processes" on page 4-7 for more information.)

Setting the Maximum Number of Dispatchers

The parameter MTS_MAX_DISPATCHERS sets the maximum number of dispatcher processes (of all network protocols combined) that can be started for the duration of an instance. To estimate the maximum number of dispatcher processes an instance will require, use the following formula:

```
                        maximum number of concurrent sessions
MTS_MAX_DISPATCHERS = ─────────────────────────────────────────
                             connections per dispatcher
```

You can create as many dispatcher processes as you need, but the total number of processes, including dispatchers, cannot exceed the host operating system's limit on the number of running processes.

Setting the Initial Number of Shared Server Processes

A number of shared server processes are started at instance startup, as determined by the parameter MTS_SERVERS. The appropriate number of initial shared server processes for a database system depends on how many users are typically connected and how much processing each user requires. If each user makes relatively few requests over a period of time, then each associated user process is idle for a large percentage of time. In that case, one shared server process can serve 10 to 20 users. If each user requires a significant amount of processing, a higher ratio of server processes to user processes is needed to handle requests.

If you want ORACLE to use shared servers, you must set MTS_SERVERS to at least 1. If you omit the parameter or set it to 0, ORACLE does not start any shared servers at all. However, you can later set MTS_SERVERS to a number greater than 0 while the instance is running; see "Changing the Minimum Number of Shared Server Processes" on page 4-6.

It is best to estimate fewer initial shared server processes. Additional shared servers are started automatically when needed and deallocated automatically if they remain idle for too long. However, the initial servers always remain allocated, even if they are idle. If you set the initial number of servers high, your system might incur unnecessary overhead. Experiment with the number of initial shared server processes and monitor shared servers until you find the ideal system performance for typical database activity.

Setting the Maximum Number of Shared Server Processes

The maximum number of shared server processes that can be started for the duration of an instance is established during instance startup by the parameter MTS_MAX_SERVERS. In general, set this parameter to allow an appropriate number of shared server processes at times of highest activity. Experiment with this limit and monitor shared servers to determine an ideal setting for this parameter.

Changing the Minimum Number of Shared Server Processes

Once the instance has started, you can change the minimum number of shared server processes with either the Configure Servers dialog box of SQL*DBA or the SQL command ALTER SYSTEM. Figure 4-1 shows the Configure Multi-Threaded Server dialog.

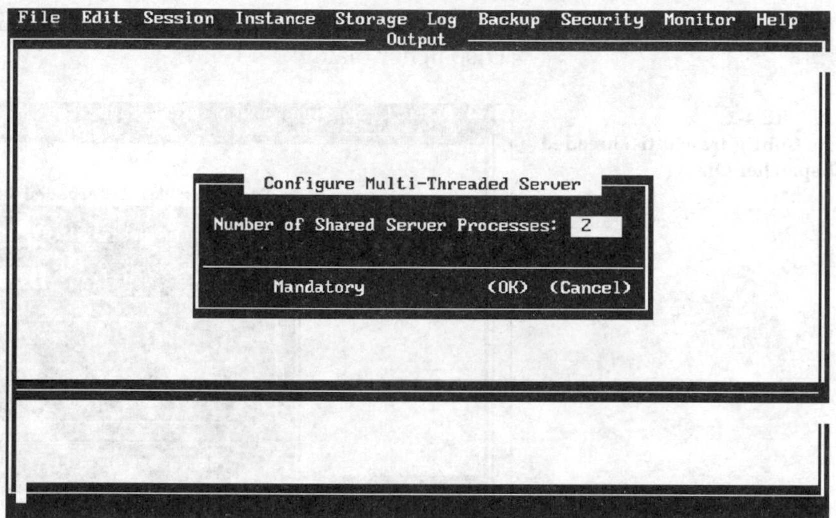

FIGURE 4-1
The Configure Multi-Threaded Server Dialog

This example sets the number of shared server processes to two. (ORACLE eventually kills dispatchers and servers that are idle for too long, to the minimum limit you specify.) The following statement is the command equivalent of the Configure Multi-Threaded Servers dialog box in Figure 4-1:

```
ALTER SYSTEM SET MTS_SERVERS = 2
```

If you set MTS_SERVERS to 0, ORACLE will terminate all current servers when they become idle and will not start any new servers until you increase MTS_SERVERS. Thus, setting MTS_SERVERS to 0 effectively disables the multi-threaded server temporarily.

Privileges Required to Change the Minimum Number of Shared Servers

To control the minimum number of shared server processes, you must have the ALTER SYSTEM privilege.

Adding and Removing Dispatcher Processes

You can control the number of dispatcher processes in the instance. If the V$QUEUE and V$DISPATCHER views indicate that the load on the dispatcher processes is consistently high, start additional dispatcher processes to route user requests without waiting; you may start new dispatchers until the number of dispatchers equals MTS_MAX_DISPATCHER. In contrast, if the load on dispatchers is consistently low, reduce the number of dispatchers. (See Chapter 23 for more information on tuning the multi-threaded server.)

To change the number of dispatcher processes, use the Configure Multi-Threaded Dispatchers dialog box of SQL*DBA or the ALTER

SYSTEM command. Figure 4-2 shows the Configure Multi-Threaded Dispatcher dialog:

FIGURE 4-2
The Configure Multi-Threaded Dispatcher Dialog

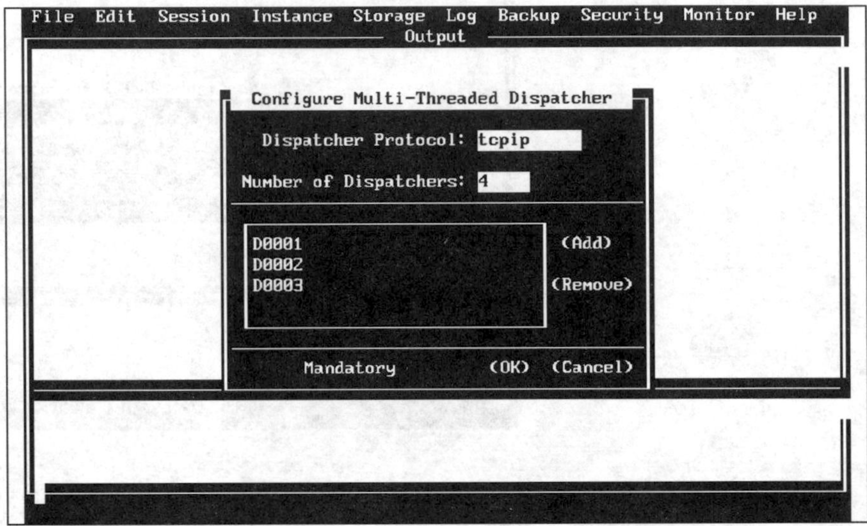

If the number of dispatchers was previously three, this example adds a dispatcher process. The following statement is the command equivalent of the Configure Multi-Threaded Dispatcher dialog in Figure 4-2:

```
ALTER SYSTEM
  SET MTS_DISPATCHERS = 'TCPIP,4';
```

You can start new dispatcher processes for protocols specified in the MTS_LISTENER_ADDRESS parameter and in the MTS_DISPATCHERS parameter. Therefore, you can add dispatchers only for protocols for which there are dispatchers; to start dispatchers for protocols for which there are currently no dispatchers, shutdown the database, change the parameter file, and restart the database.

If you reduce the number of dispatchers for a particular protocol, the dispatchers are not immediately removed. Rather, ORACLE eventually kills dispatchers that are idle for too long, down to the limit you specify in MTS_DISPATCHERS.

Changing the number of dispatchers for a specific protocol has no effect on dispatchers for other protocols. (For a complete description of the ALTER SYSTEM command, refer to the *ORACLE7 Server SQL Language Reference Manual.*)

Privileges Required to Change the Number of Dispatcher Processes

To control the number of dispatcher processes, you must have the ALTER SYSTEM privilege.

Deciding When to Connect to a Dedicated Server Process

If possible, users should connect to an instance via a dispatcher, to keep the number of processes required for the running instance low. In the following situations, however, users and administrators should explicitly connect to an instance using a dedicated server process:

- to submit a batch job (that is, the job can allow little or no idle time for the server process)
- to use SQL*DBA to start up, shut down, or perform media recovery on a database

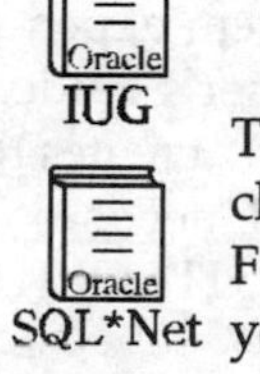

To request a dedicated server connection, a user must include the clause (SRVR=DEDICATED) in his or her SQL*Net TNS connect string. For a complete description of SQL*Net connect string syntax, refer to your installation or user's guide and SQL*Net documentation.

Managing ORACLE Processes

An ORACLE instance can have many background processes, which you need to track. This section explains how to identify and manage these processes.

Note: See Chapter 23 for more information on tuning ORACLE processes.

Monitoring the Processes of an ORACLE Instance

Use the Monitor feature of SQL*DBA to display current information about the processes of an ORACLE database. The following monitors of SQL*DBA are of interest:

PROCESS — The Process monitor summarizes information about all ORACLE processes, including client-server, user, server, and background processes, currently accessing the database via the current database instance.

SESSION — The Session monitor shows the session ID and status of each connected ORACLE session.

Viewing and Monitoring Locks

ORACLE also provides two facilities to display locking information for ongoing transactions within an instance:

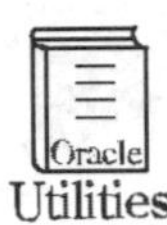	SQL*DBA Monitors (Lock and Latch Monitors)	The Monitor feature of SQL*DBA provides two monitors for displaying lock information of an instance. See the *ORACLE7 Server Utilities User's Guide* for complete information about the SQL*DBA monitors.
	UTLLOCKT.SQL	The UTLLOCKT.SQL script displays a simple character lock wait-for graph in tree structured fashion. Using any ad hoc query tool (such as SQL*DBA or SQL*Plus), the script prints the sessions in the system that are waiting for locks and the corresponding blocking locks. The location of this script file is operating system dependent; see your installation or user's guide. (A second script, CATBLOCK.SQL, creates the lock views that UTLLOCKT.SQL needs, so you must run it before running UTLLOCKT.SQL.)

Using Dynamic Performance Tables

Several performance tables are useful in monitoring the processes of an ORACLE instance, including:

- V$CIRCUIT
- V$QUEUE
- V$DISPATCHER
- V$SHARED_SERVER
- V$SQLAREA
- V$SESS_IO
- V$LATCH
- V$SYSSTAT

For example, the following query displays the processing load on each dispatcher process in the system:

```
SELECT (busy/(busy + idle))* 100 "% OF TIME BUSY"
   FROM v$dispatcher;
```

Refer to Appendix B for more information about performance tables.

Identifying ORACLE Background Processes from the Operating System

Because you might want to run many ORACLE databases concurrently on one computer, ORACLE provides a mechanism for naming the processes of an instance. The background process names are prefixed by an instance identifier to distinguish the set of processes for each instance.

For example, an instance named TEST might have background processes named:

- ORA_TEST_DBWR
- ORA_TEST_LGWR
- ORA_TEST_SMON
- ORA_TEST_PMON
- ORA_TEST_RECO
- ORA_TEST_LCK0
- ORA_TEST_ARCH
- ORA_TEST_D000
- ORA_TEST_S000
- ORA_TEST_S001

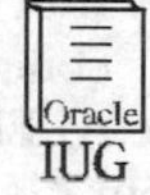

IUG

The instance identifier and the format of the ORACLE process names are operating system dependent; see your installation or user's manual.

Trace Files, the ALERT File, and Background Processes

Each server and background process can write to an associated *trace file*. When an internal error is detected by a process, it dumps information about the error to its trace file. Some of the information written to a trace file is intended for you as the database administrator, while other information is for Oracle support. Trace file information can also often be used in tuning applications and instances. (For more information about errors and messages, refer to the *ORACLE7 Server Messages and Codes Manual*.)

Message

One special trace file is the *ALERT* file. The ALERT file of a database is a chronological log of messages and errors, including:

- all internal errors (ORA-600), block corruption errors (ORA-1578), and deadlock errors (ORA-60) that occur
- administrative operations, such as CREATE/ALTER/DROP DATABASE/TABLESPACE/ROLLBACK SEGMENT SQL statements and STARTUP, SHUTDOWN, ARCHIVE LOG, and RECOVER SQL*DBA statements
- several messages and errors relating to the functions of shared server and dispatcher processes
- errors during the automatic refresh of a snapshot
- the values of all initialization parameters when the database and instance start

ORACLE uses the ALERT file to keep a log of these special operations as an alternative to displaying such information on an operator's console (although many systems display information on the console). If an operation is successful, a message is written in the ALERT file as "completed" along with a timestamp.

Using the Trace Files

You can periodically check the ALERT file and other trace files of an instance to see if the background processes have encountered errors. For example, when the Log Writer process (LGWR) cannot write to a member of a group, an error message is written to the LGWR trace file and the database's ALERT file to indicate the problem. If you see such error messages, a media or I/O problem has occurred that you should correct immediately.

Also, ORACLE writes values of initialization parameters to the ALERT file, as well as other statistics of importance. For example, when you shutdown an instance normally or immediately (but not abort), ORACLE writes the highest number of sessions concurrently connected to the instance, since the instance started, to the ALERT file; you can use this number to see whether you need to upgrade your ORACLE session license. (See "Using Session and User Licensing" on page 11-2 for details.)

Specifying the Location of Trace Files

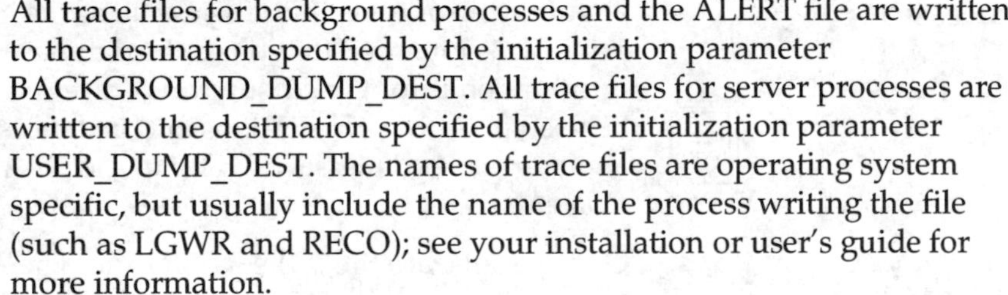

All trace files for background processes and the ALERT file are written to the destination specified by the initialization parameter BACKGROUND_DUMP_DEST. All trace files for server processes are written to the destination specified by the initialization parameter USER_DUMP_DEST. The names of trace files are operating system specific, but usually include the name of the process writing the file (such as LGWR and RECO); see your installation or user's guide for more information.

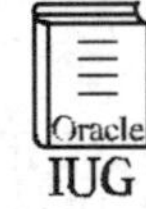

Controlling the Size of Trace Files

The maximum size of all trace files (excluding the ALERT file) can be controlled using the initialization parameter MAX_DUMP_FILE_SIZE. This limit is set as a number of operating system blocks. To control the size of an ALERT file, you must manually delete the file when you no longer need it; otherwise ORACLE continues to append to the file. (You can safely delete the ALERT file while the instance is running, although you might want to make an archived copy of it first.)

Controlling When ORACLE Writes to Trace Files

Background processes always write to a trace file when appropriate. However, trace files are written on behalf of server processes (in addition to being written to during internal errors) only if the initialization parameter SQL_TRACE is set to TRUE.

However, regardless of the current value for this parameter, each session can enable or disable trace logging on behalf of the associated server process by using the SQL command ALTER SESSION with the SET SQL_TRACE parameter. For example, the following statement enables writing to a trace file for the session:

```
ALTER SESSION SET SQL_TRACE TRUE;
```

For the multi-threaded server, because each session using a dispatcher is routed to a shared server process, trace information is written to the server's trace file only if the session has enabled tracing (or if an error is encountered). Therefore, to track tracing for a specific session that connects using a dispatcher, you might have to explore several shared server's trace files. Because the SQL trace facility for server processes can cause significant system overhead, enable this feature only when collecting statistics.

SQL

For complete information about the ALTER SESSION command, see the *ORACLE7 Server SQL Language Reference Manual.*

Starting the Checkpoint Process

If the Checkpoint process (CKPT) is not present , the Log Writer process (LGWR) is responsible for updating the headers of all control files and data files to reflect the latest checkpoint. To reduce the time necessary to complete a checkpoint, especially when a database is comprised of many data files, enable the CKPT background process.

To do so, set the CHECKPOINT_PROCESS parameter in the database's parameter file to TRUE. (Its default is FALSE.)

Killing Sessions

In some situations, you might want to kill current user sessions. For example, you might need to perform an administrative operation and need to kill all non-administrative sessions.

Kill a current session using either the Kill User Session dialog box of SQL*DBA or the SQL command ALTER SYSTEM with the KILL SESSION parameter. Figure 4-3 shows the Kill User Session dialog.

FIGURE 4-3
The Kill User Session Dialog

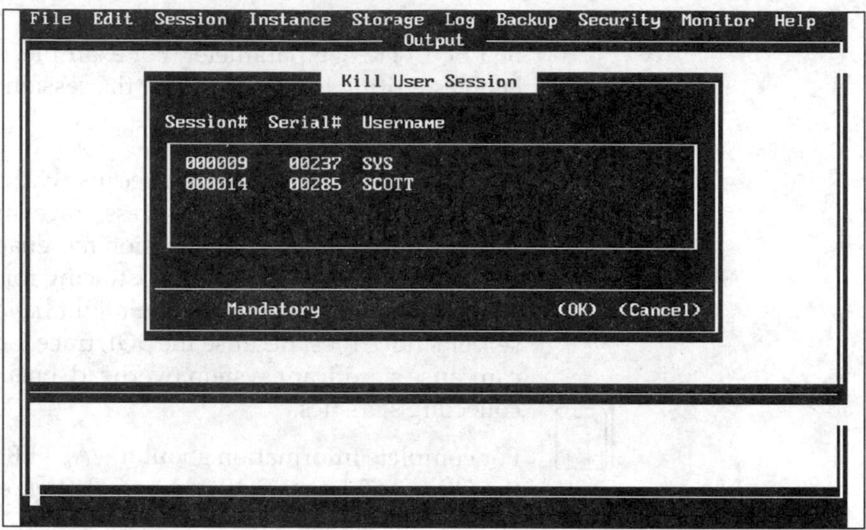

The following statement is the command equivalent of the Kill User Session dialog in Figure 4-3:

```
ALTER SYSTEM KILL SESSION '7,15';
```

To identify which session to kill, specify the session's index number and serial number. To identify the index (SID) and serial numbers of a session, query the V$SESSION dynamic performance table. For example, the following query identifies all sessions for the user JWARD:

```
SELECT sid, serial#
  FROM v$session
 WHERE username = 'JWARD';

SID       SERIAL#
--------- ----------
        7         15
```

When a session is killed, resources (such as locks and memory areas) held by the session are immediately released and available to other sessions.

If the user session is making a SQL call to ORACLE (is "active") when it is killed, the transaction is rolled back and the user immediately receives the following message:

```
ORA-00028: your session has been killed
```

If the session is not making a SQL call to ORACLE (is "inactive") when it is killed, the above message is not returned immediately, but when the user subsequently attempts to use the killed session.

If after receiving the ORA-00028 message a user submits additional statements before reconnecting to the database, ORACLE returns the following message:

```
ORA-01012: not logged on
```

The view V$SESSION also shows the STATUS of current sessions. The row for a killed session is removed from V$SESSION when the user receives the ORA-00028 message.

The following example shows a DBA killing an inactive session:

```
SELECT sid, serial#, status, server
  FROM v$session
WHERE username = 'JWARD';

SID        SERIAL# STATUS   SERVER
---------- ------- -------- ---------
         7      15 INACTIVE DEDICATED

ALTER SYSTEM KILL SESSION '7,15';

SELECT sid, serial#, status, server
  FROM v$session
 WHERE username = 'JWARD';

SID        SERIAL# STATUS   SERVER
---------- ------- -------- ---------
         7      15 KILLED   PSEUDO
```

If an active session cannot be interrupted (for example, it is performing network I/O or rolling back a transaction), the session cannot be killed until the operation completes. In this case, the session holds all resources until it is killed. Additionally, the session that issues the ALTER SYSTEM statement to kill a session waits up to 60 seconds for the session to be killed; if the operation that cannot be interrupted continues past one minute, the issuer of the ALTER SYSTEM statement receives a message indicating that the session has been "marked" to be killed. A session marked to be killed is indicated in V$SESSION with a status of "KILLED" and a server that is something other than "PSEUDO".

CHAPTER

5

MANAGING THE ONLINE REDO LOG

This chapter explains how to manage the online redo log. Topics include:

- policies for managing the online redo log
- creating redo log groups and members
- renaming and relocating redo log members
- dropping redo log groups and members
- forcing a redo log switch
- setting checkpoint intervals
- getting information about the online redo log

For information about managing the online redo logs of the instances when using the ORACLE Parallel Server, see the *ORACLE7 Parallel Server Administrator's Guide*.

For information about archiving the redo log, see Chapter 17.

Establishing Policies for the Online Redo Log

Consider the following guidelines when configuring a database instance's online redo log.

Mirror the Online Redo Log

The online redo log of a database instance should consist of mirrored groups of online redo log files. Furthermore, members in the same group should be stored on separate disks so that no single disk failure can cause LGWR and the database instance to fail.

Although the ORACLE Server allows mirrored groups to contain different numbers of members, this state should only be temporary, as the result of an abnormal situation such as a disk failure damaging a member of a group; if any group contains only one member, the failure of the disk containing that member could cause ORACLE to halt.

While mirrored groups require extra storage space, the cost of this space is usually insignificant compared to the potential cost of lost data if a disk failure were to destroy a non-mirrored online redo log.

Appropriately Place Online Redo Log Members

With a mirrored online redo log, place members of a group on different disks. This way, if a single disk fails, only one member of a group becomes unavailable to LGWR and other members remain accessible to LGWR, so the instance can continue to function.

If you are archiving the redo log, spread online redo log members across disks to eliminate contention between the LGWR and ARCH background processes. For example, if you have two groups of duplexed online redo log members, place each member on a different disk and set your archiving destination to a fifth disk. This way, there is never contention between LGWR (writing to the members) and ARCH (reading the members).

Data files and online redo log files should also be on different disks to reduce contention in writing data blocks and redo entries.

Appropriately Set the Size of Online Redo Log Members

Consider two issues when setting the size of online redo log files: the general size of online redo log files for an instance, and the size of a specific online redo log file compared to other online redo log files of the same database instance.

Online redo log files should be relatively small. If large online redo log files are used and checkpoints only occur at log switches, instance recovery takes a long time because of the large number of redo log entries that must be applied. In most cases, the default size of an online

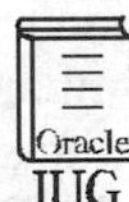

redo log file is sufficient; the default size of online redo log files is operating system dependent; see your installation or user's guide.

When setting the size of online redo log files, also consider if you will be archiving the redo log. The size of online redo log files should be such that a filled group can be archived to a single unit of offline storage media (such as a tape or disk), with the least amount of space on the medium left unused. For example, suppose only one filled online redo log group can fit per tape and 49% of the tape's storage capacity remains unused. In this case, it would be better to decrease the size of the online redo log files slightly, so that two log groups could be archived per tape.

With mirrored groups of online redo logs, all members of the same group must be the same size. Members of different groups can have different sizes; however, there is no advantage in varying file size between groups. If checkpoints are not set to occur between log switches, make all groups the same size to guarantee that checkpoints occur at regular intervals.

Choose the Number of Online Log Files

The best way to determine the appropriate number of online redo log files for a database instance is to test different configurations. The optimum configuration has the fewest groups possible without hampering LGWR's writing redo log information.

In some cases, a database instance may require only two groups; in other situations, a database instance may require additional groups to guarantee that a recycled group is always available to LGWR. During testing, the easiest way to determine if the current online redo log configuration is satisfactory is to examine the contents of the LGWR trace file and the database's ALERT file. If messages indicate that LGWR frequently has to wait for a group because a checkpoint has not completed or a group has not been archived, add groups.

Three parameters limit the number of online redo log files that you can add to a database:

- The MAXLOGFILES parameter used in the CREATE DATABASE statement that created the database determines the maximum number of groups of online redo log files per database; group values can range from 1 to MAXLOGFILES. The only way to override this upper limit is to re-create the database or its control file; therefore, it is important to consider this limit before creating a database. If MAXLOGFILES is not specified for the CREATE DATABASE statement, ORACLE uses an operating system default value.

- The LOG_FILES parameter of the parameter file can temporarily decrease the maximum number of groups of online redo log files for the duration of the current instance. However, LOG_FILES cannot override MAXLOGFILES to increase the limit. If LOG_FILES is not set in the database's parameter file, ORACLE uses an operating system specific default value.
- The MAXLOGMEMBERS parameter used in the CREATE DATABASE statement that created the database determines the maximum number of members per group. As with MAXLOGFILES, the only way to override this upper limit is to re-create the database or control file; therefore, it is important to consider this limit before creating a database. If no MAXLOGMEMBERS parameter is specified for the CREATE DATABASE statement, ORACLE uses an operating system default value.

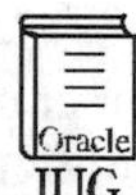

Consider the parameters that can limit the number of online redo log files before setting up or altering the configuration of an instance's online redo log. See your installation or user's guide for the default and legal values for the MAXLOGFILES and MAXLOGMEMBERS parameters of the CREATE DATABASE statement and the LOG_FILES initialization parameter.

Creating Online Redo Log Groups

You can create groups of online redo log files both as part of database creation and after a database has been created. If you can, plan the online redo log of a database and create all required groups of online redo log files during database creation; see Chapter 2 for information about database creation.

In some cases, you might need to create additional groups of online redo log files. For example, adding groups to an online redo log can correct redo log group availability problems. A database can have up to MAXLOGFILES groups.

To create a new group of online redo log files, use either the Add Online Redo Log Group dialog of SQL*DBA, or the SQL command ALTER DATABASE with the ADD LOGFILE parameter. Figure 5-1 shows the Add Online Redo Log Group dialog.

FIGURE 5-1
The Add Online Redo Log Group Dialog

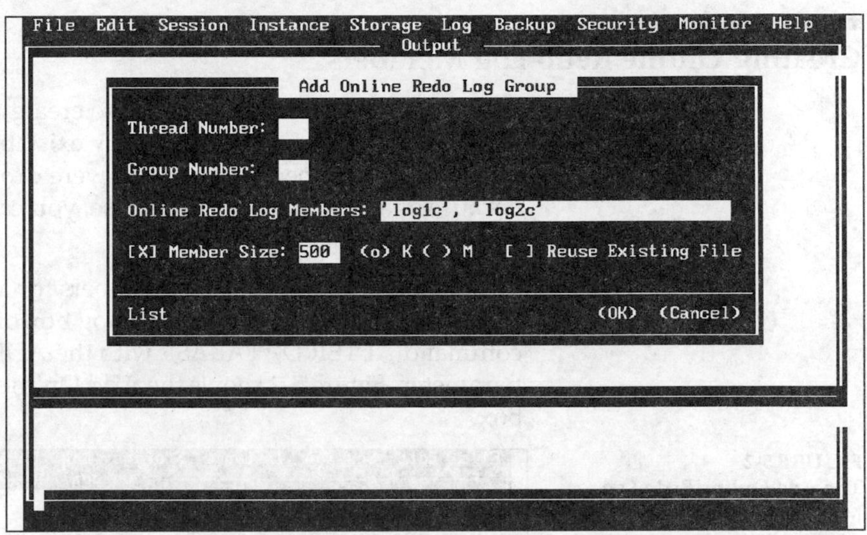

The following statement is the command equivalent of the Add Online Redo Log Group dialog in Figure 5-1:

```
ALTER DATABASE
    ADD LOGFILE ('log1c', 'log2c') SIZE 500K;
```

Note: Fully specify filenames of new log members to indicate where the operating system file should be created; otherwise, the file is created in the default directory of the database server, which is operating system dependent. If you want to reuse an existing operating system file, you do not have to indicate the file size.

In an ALTER DATABASE statement with the ADD LOGFILE option, you can specify the number that identifies the group with the GROUP option:

```
ALTER DATABASE
    ADD LOGFILE GROUP 10 ('log1c', 'log2c') SIZE 500K;
```

Using group numbers can make administering redo log groups easier. However, the group number must be between 1 and MAXLOGFILES; do not skip redo log file group numbers (that is, do not number your groups 10, 20, 30, and so on), or you will consume unnecessary space in the control files of the database.

Privileges Required to Create Online Redo Log Groups

To create new online redo log groups, you must have the ALTER DATABASE system privilege.

Creating Online Redo Log Members

In some cases, you might not need to create a complete group of online redo log files; the group may already exist, but not be complete because one or more members of the group were dropped (for example, because of a disk failure). In this case, you can add new members to an existing group.

To create new online redo log members for an existing group, use the Add Online Redo Log Member dialog box of SQL*DBA or the SQL command ALTER DATABASE with the ADD LOG MEMBER parameter. Figure 5-2 shows the Add Online Redo Log Member dialog box.

FIGURE 5-2
The Add Online Redo Log Member Dialog

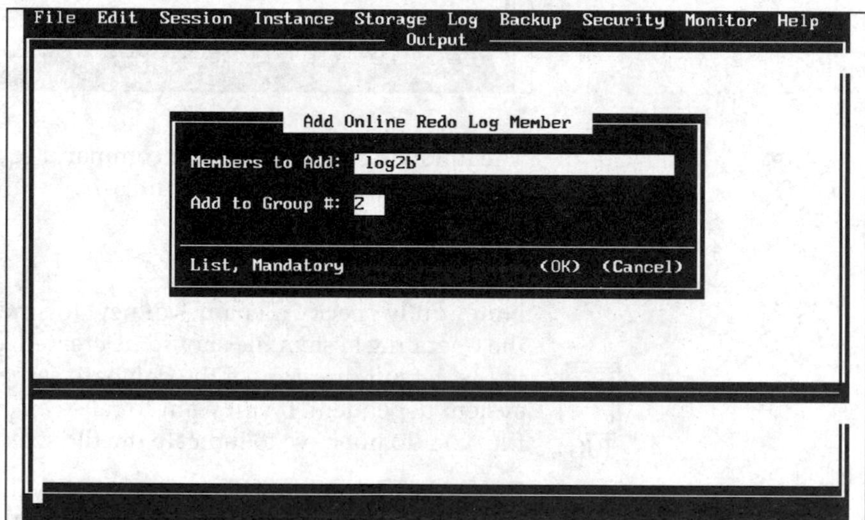

The following statement is the command equivalent of the Add Online Redo Log Member dialog box in Figure 5-2:

```
ALTER DATABASE
    ADD LOGFILE MEMBER 'log2b' TO GROUP 2;
```

Notice that filenames must be specified, but sizes need not be; the size of the new members is determined from the size of the existing members of the group.

When using the ALTER DATABASE command, you can alternatively identify the target group by specifying all of the other members of the group in the TO parameter. For example:

```
ALTER DATABASE
    ADD LOGFILE MEMBER 'log2c' TO ('log2a', 'log2b');
```

Note: Fully specify the filenames of new log members to indicate where the operating system files should be created; otherwise, the files will be created in the default directory of the database server.

Renaming and Relocating Online Redo Log Members

You can rename online redo log members to change their locations. This procedure is necessary, for example, if the disk currently used for some online redo log files is going to be removed, or if data files and a number of online redo log files are stored on the same disk and should be separated to reduce contention.

Before renaming any online redo log members, ensure that the new online redo log files already exist. The steps given below only modify the internal file pointers in a database's control files; they do not physically rename or create any operating system files. Use the operating system of your computer to copy the existing online redo log files to the new location.

Rename online redo log members with the Rename Online Redo Log Member dialog box of SQL*DBA, or the SQL command ALTER DATABASE with the RENAME FILE parameter. Figure 5-3 shows the Rename Online Redo Log Member dialog box.

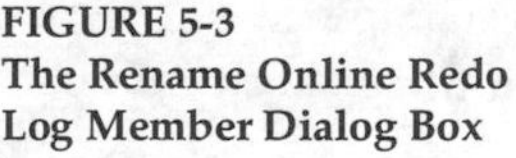

FIGURE 5-3
The Rename Online Redo Log Member Dialog Box

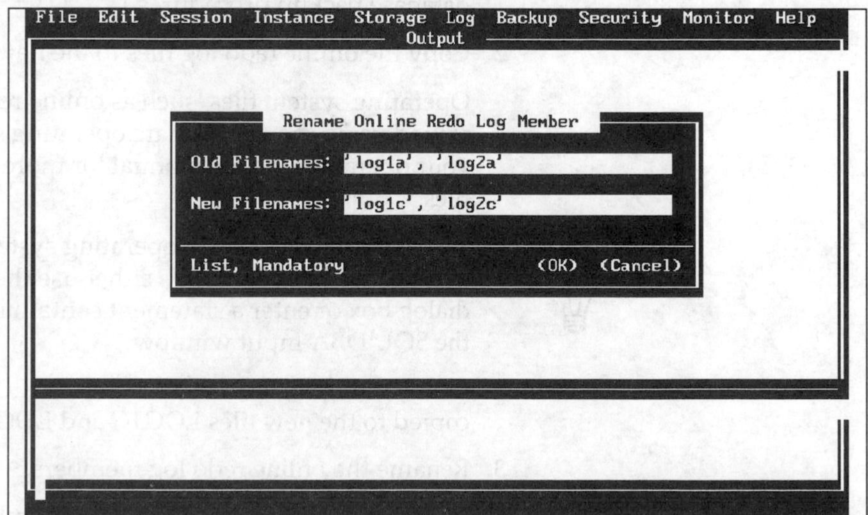

The following statement is the command equivalent of the Rename Online Redo Log Member dialog box in Figure 5-3:

```
ALTER DATABASE
  RENAME FILE 'log1a', 'log2a'
           TO 'log1c', 'log2c';
```

Example Assume the following conditions:

- The database is currently mounted by, but closed to, the instance.
- The online redo log is duplexed: one group consists of the members LOG1A and LOG1B, and the second group consists of the members LOG2A and LOG2B. The files LOG1A and LOG2A are both stored on Disk A, while LOG1B and LOG2B are stored on Disk B.
- The online redo log files located on Disk A must be relocated to Disk C. The new filenames will reflect the new location: LOG1C and LOG2C.

To complete this operation, the following steps are necessary:

1. Back up the database.

   Before making any structural changes to a database, such as renaming or relocating online redo log members, completely back up the database (including the control file) in case you experience any problems while performing this operation. (See Chapter 18 for database backup procedures.)

2. Copy the online redo log files to the new location.

   Operating system files, such as online redo log members, must be copied using the appropriate operating system commands. See your operating system manual for more information about copying files.

   Tip: You can execute an operating system command to copy a file without exiting SQL*DBA: either use the Enter System Command dialog box or enter a statement containing the HOST command in the SQL*DBA Input window.

   In this example, the files LOG1A and LOG2A on Disk A must be copied to the new files LOG1C and LOG2C on Disk C.

3. Rename the online redo log members.

   Use the Rename Online Redo Log Member dialog box or the ALTER DATABASE command with the RENAME FILE clause to rename the online redo log files used by the database.

4. Open the database for normal operation.

   The online redo log alterations take effect the next time that the database is opened. Opening the database may require shutting down the current instance (if the database was previously opened by the current instance) or just opening the database using the current instance.

5. Back up the control file.

   After renaming or relocating a set of online redo log files, immediately back up the database's control file in case any problems occur from this point forward.

Privileges Required to Rename or Relocate Online Redo Log Members

To rename online redo log members, you must have the ALTER DATABASE system privilege. Additionally, you might also need operating system privileges to copy files to the desired location and privileges to open and back up the database.

Dropping Online Redo Log Groups

In some cases, you might want to drop an entire group of online redo log members. For example, you might want to reduce the number of groups in an instance's online redo log.

Before dropping an online redo log group, consider the following restrictions and precautions:

- An instance requires at least two groups of online redo log files, regardless of the number of members in the groups. (A group is one or more members.)
- You can drop an online redo log group only if it is not the active group. If you need to drop the active group, first force a log switch to occur; see "Forcing A Log Switch" on page 5-14.
- Make sure an online redo log group is archived (if archiving is enabled) before dropping it. To see whether or not this has happened, use SQL*DBA's List Archive Status menu option (in the Log menu) or the ARCHIVE LOG command with the LIST parameter.

Drop an online redo log group with either the Drop Online Redo Log Group dialog box of SQL*DBA, or the SQL command ALTER DATABASE with the DROP LOGFILE clause. Figure 5-4 shows the Drop Online Redo Log Group dialog box:

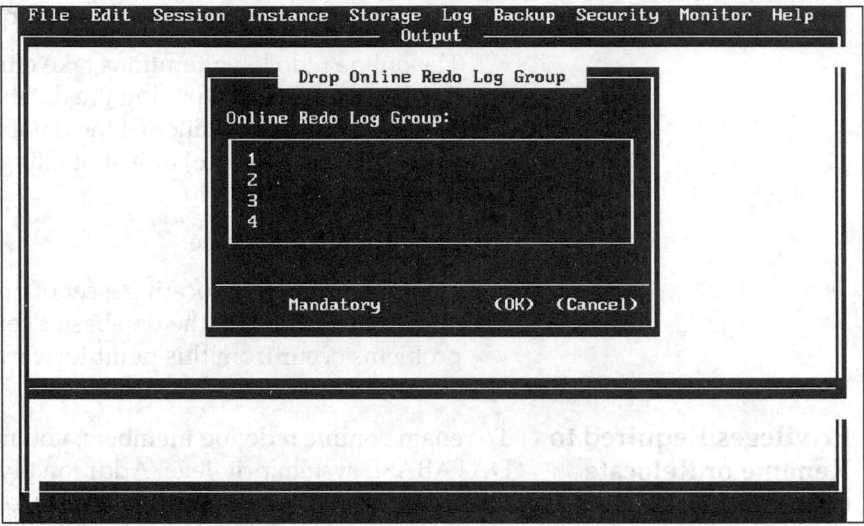

FIGURE 5-4
The Drop Online Redo Log Group Dialog

The following statement is the command equivalent of the Drop Online Redo Log Group dialog box in Figure 5-4:

```
ALTER DATABASE DROP LOGFILE GROUP 3;
```

When an online redo log group is dropped from the database, the operating system files are not deleted from disk. Rather, the control files of the associated database are updated to drop the members of the group from the database structure. After dropping an online redo log group, make sure that the drop completed successfully, and then use the appropriate operating system command to delete the dropped online redo log files.

Privileges Required to Drop Online Redo Log Groups

To drop an online redo log group, you must have the ALTER DATABASE system privilege.

Dropping Online Redo Log Members

In some cases, you might want to drop one or more specific online redo log members. For example, if a disk failure occurs, you might need to drop all the online redo log files on the failed disk so that ORACLE does not try to write to the inaccessible files. In other situations, particular online redo log files become unnecessary; for example, a file might be stored in an inappropriate location.

Consider the following restrictions and precautions when dropping individual online redo log members:

- It is OK to drop online redo log files so that a mirrored online redo log becomes temporarily unsymmetrical. For example, if you are using duplexed groups of online redo log files, you can drop one member of one group, even though all other groups have two members each. However, you should rectify this situation immediately so that all groups have at least two members, and thereby eliminate the single point of failure possible for the online redo log.
- An instance always requires at least two valid groups of online redo log files, regardless of the number of members in the groups. (A group is one or more members.) If the member you want to drop is the last valid member of the group, you cannot drop the member until the other members become valid; to see a redo log file's status, use the V$LOGFILE table. (A redo log file becomes INVALID if ORACLE cannot access it. It becomes STALE if ORACLE suspects that it is not complete or correct; a stale log file becomes valid again the next time its group is made the active group.)
- You can drop an online redo log member only if it is not part of an active group. If you want to drop a member of an active group, first force a log switch to occur; see "Forcing a Log Switch" on page 5-14.
- Make sure the group to which an online redo log member belongs is archived (if archiving is enabled) before dropping the member. To see whether this has happened, use SQL*DBA's List Archive Status menu option or the ARCHIVE LOG command with the LIST parameter.

To drop specific inactive online redo log members, use either the Drop Online Redo Log Member dialog box, or the SQL command ALTER DATABASE command with the DROP LOGFILE MEMBER clause. Figure 5-5 shows the Drop Online Redo Log Member dialog box.

FIGURE 5-5
The Drop Online Redo Log Member Dialog

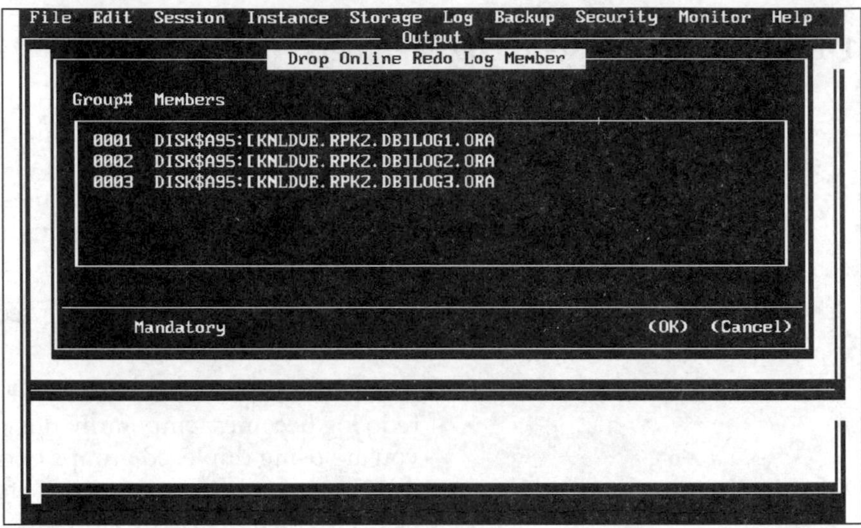

The following statement is the command equivalent of the Drop Online Redo Log Member dialog box in Figure 5-5:

```
ALTER DATABASE
  DROP LOGFILE MEMBER 'log3c';
```

When an online redo log member is dropped from the database, the operating system file is not deleted from disk. Rather, the control files of the associated database are updated to drop the member from the database structure. After dropping an online redo log file, make sure that the drop completed successfully, and then use the appropriate operating system command to delete the dropped online redo log file.

Privileges Required to Drop Online Redo Log Members

To drop an online redo log member, you must have the ALTER DATABASE system privilege.

Controlling Checkpoints and Log Switches

A checkpoint is the event during which the Database Writer process (DBWR) writes all modified database buffers in the SGA to the appropriate data files. A log switch is the event during which LGWR stops writing to one online redo log group and starts writing to another. The two events are often connected: an instance takes a checkpoint at each log switch by default. A log switch, by default, takes place automatically when the current online redo log file group fills.

Sometimes, however, you might want checkpoints to be taken more often than only at log switches, or you might want a checkpoint to take place ahead of schedule, without a log switch. You might also want a log switch and checkpoint to take place ahead of schedule, or you might just want a log switch to take place without an accompanying checkpoint. The following sections explain why and how to cause these events.

Setting Database Checkpoint Intervals

When your database uses large online redo log files, you might want additional database checkpoints to take place automatically at predetermined intervals, between the checkpoints that automatically occur at log switches. When more database checkpoints are taken, the time necessary to recover from an instance failure decreases. However, the performance of the ORACLE Server can also decrease as a checkpoint proceeds due to the extra I/O necessary for the checkpoint to complete.

Generally, unless your database consistently requires instance recovery on startup, set database checkpoint intervals so that checkpoints occur only at log switches. If you use small online redo log files, checkpoints already occur at frequent intervals (at each log switch). (For more information about tuning ORACLE with regard to checkpoints, see Chapter 24.)

The frequency of automatic database checkpoints is controlled by the values of the LOG_CHECKPOINT_INTERVAL and LOG_CHECKPOINT_TIMEOUT parameters.

Setting LOG_CHECK-POINT_INTERVAL

To have database checkpoints only occur at log switches (the default), set the value for the LOG_CHECKPOINT_INTERVAL parameter higher than the size of the online redo log files in use. Alternatively, to force additional checkpoints to occur at intervals between two log switches, set the value for the LOG_CHECKPOINT_INTERVAL parameter lower than the size of the online redo log files in use.

The value of the LOG_CHECKPOINT_INTERVAL is a number of operating system blocks, not ORACLE data blocks. Therefore, you must know the size, in bytes, of your operating system's blocks. Once you know this, calculate the number of operating system blocks per online redo log file. See your operating system documentation to determine the operating system block size.

Example

For example, assume the following conditions:

- All online redo log files of the database instance are 512K.
- The operating system block size is 512 bytes.
- Checkpoints should occur when an online redo log file is half full.

Using this information, you can compute the number of blocks per redo log file as in the following equation:

```
512K/redo log file
------------------- = approximately 1000 blocks/redo log file
512 bytes/OS block
```

Now that the approximate number of blocks per online redo log file (1000) is known, the LOG_CHECKPOINT_INTERVAL parameter can be set accordingly in the instance's parameter file.

```
LOG_CHECKPOINT_INTERVAL=500
```

Setting LOG_CHECKPOINT_TIMEOUT

To have database checkpoints only occur at log switches (the default), set the value for the LOG_CHECKPOINT_TIMEOUT parameter to zero. Alternatively, to force additional checkpoints to occur at intervals between two log switches, set the value for the LOG_CHECKPOINT_TIMEOUT parameter to a time interval (in seconds) less than the average time it takes to fill an online redo log file. To determine the average time it takes to fill online redo log files, examine the LGWR trace file for messages that indicate the times of log switches.

Note: See the *ORACLE7 Parallel Server Administrator's Guide* for more information about the LOG_CHECKPOINT_TIMEOUT parameter when using the ORACLE Parallel Server. Also, setting this parameter is particularly important when using Trusted ORACLE7 in OS MAC mode; see the *Trusted ORACLE7 Server Administrator's Guide* for more information.

Forcing a Log Switch

You might want to force a log switch to make the currently active group inactive and available for online redo log maintenance operations. For example, you might want to drop the currently active group, but not be able to do so until the group is inactive. You might also want to force a log switch if the currently active group needs to be archived at a specific time before the members of the group are completely filled; this option is often useful in configurations with large online redo log files that take a long time to fill.

To force a log switch, use either the Force Log Switch option of the Instance menu of SQL*DBA, or the SQL command ALTER SYSTEM with the SWITCH LOGFILE option. The following statement is the command equivalent of selecting the Force Log Switch option of the Instance menu of SQL*DBA:

```
ALTER SYSTEM SWITCH LOGFILE;
```

Privileges Required to Force a Log Switch

To force a log switch, you must have the ALTER SYSTEM system privilege.

Forcing a Fast Database Checkpoint Without a Log Switch

In some cases, you might want to force a fast database checkpoint. A fast checkpoint is one which does not involve a log switch; LGWR continues to write to the current online redo log file. A fast checkpoint allows DBWR to write more modified database buffers to disk per I/O on behalf of a checkpoint. Therefore, fewer I/Os (thus less time) are required to complete a fast checkpoint.Force a fast database checkpoint with either the Force Checkpoint option of the Instance menu of SQL*DBA or the SQL command ALTER SYSTEM with the CHECKPOINT option. The following statement is the command equivalent of the Force Checkpoint menu option:

```
ALTER SYSTEM CHECKPOINT;
```

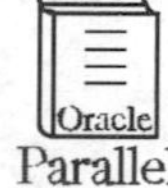

Parallel

Omitting the GLOBAL option allows you to force a checkpoint for only the connected instance, while including it forces a checkpoint for all instances of the database. Forcing a checkpoint for only the local instance is useful only with the ORACLE Parallel Server; see the *ORACLE7 Parallel Server Administrator's Guide* for more information. In a non-Parallel Server configuration, global and local checkpoints are identical.

Privileges Required to Force a Checkpoint

To force a database checkpoint, you must have the ALTER SYSTEM system privilege.

Listing Information about the Online Redo Log

Use the VLOG, VLOGFILE, and V$THREAD views to see information about the online redo log of a database; the V$THREAD view is of particular interest for Parallel Server administrators.

For example, the following query returns information about the online redo log of a database used without the Parallel Server:

```
SELECT group#, bytes, members
  FROM sys.v$log;

GROUP#     BYTES      MEMBERS
---------- ---------- ----------
         1      81920          2
         2      81920          2
```

To see the names of all of the member of a group, use a query like that below:

```
SELECT *
  FROM sys.v$logfile
 WHERE group# = 2;

GROUP#     STATUS     MEMBER
---------- ---------- --------------
         2            LOG2A
         2 STALE      LOG2B
         2            LOG2C
```

If STATUS is blank for a member, the file is in use.

CHAPTER

6 Managing Control Files

This chapter explains how to create and maintain the control files for your database. Topics include:

- guidelines for managing control files
- initially creating control files
- adding, renaming, and relocating control files
- dropping control files

Guidelines for Control Files

Consider the following guidelines when managing the control files for a database.

Name Control Files

The CONTROL_FILES parameter in the parameter file of a database indicates one or more names for the control files. The instance startup procedure recognizes and opens all the listed files; the instance maintains all listed control files during database operation.

All files listed for the CONTROL_FILES parameter are written to, as necessary, by the ORACLE Server during database operation.

Mirror Control Files on Different Disks

Every ORACLE database should have at least two control files, each stored on a different disk. If a control file is damaged due to a disk failure, the associated instance must be shut down. Once the disk drive is repaired, the damaged control file can be restored using an intact copy of the control file and the instance can be restarted; no media recovery is required. By using mirrored control files, you avoid unnecessary problems if a disk failure occurs on the database server.

The following list describes the behavior of mirrored control files:

- Two or more filenames are listed for the initialization parameter CONTROL_FILES in the database's parameter file.
- The first file listed in the CONTROL_FILES parameter is the only file read by the ORACLE Server during database operation.
- If any of the control files become unavailable during database operation, the instance becomes inoperable and should be aborted.

The only disadvantage of having multiple control files is that all operations that update the control files (such as adding a data file or checkpointing the database) can take slightly longer. However, this difference is usually insignificant (especially for operating systems that can perform multiple, concurrent writes) and does not justify using only a single control file.

Oracle Corporation strongly recommends that your database has a **minimum of two control files on different disks**.

Place Control Files Appropriately

Each copy of a control file should be stored on a different disk drive. Furthermore, a control file copy should be stored on every disk drive that stores members of online redo log groups, if the online redo log is mirrored. By storing control files in these locations, you minimize the risk that all control files and all groups of the online redo log will be lost in a single disk failure.

Manage Control File Size

IUG

Typical control files are small. The main determinants of a control file's size are the values set for the MAXDATAFILES, MAXLOGFILES, MAXLOGMEMBERS, MAXLOGHISTORY, and MAXINSTANCES parameters of the CREATE DATABASE statement that created the associated database. Increasing the values of these parameters increases the size of a control file of the associated database. The maximum control file size is operating system specific; see your installation or user's guide.

Creating Control Files

The control file of an ORACLE database is created at the same time as the database. By default, at least one copy of the control file must be created during database creation. On some operating systems, multiple copies are created. However, you should create two or more copies of the control file during database creation. You might also need to create control files later, if you lose control files or want to change particular settings in the control files. The ways to create control files are explained below.

Creating Initial Control Files

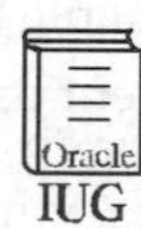

IUG

You create the initial control files of an ORACLE database by specifying one or more control file names in the CONTROL_FILES parameter in the parameter file used during database creation. The filenames specified in CONTROL_FILES should be fully specified; filename specification is operating system specific. If files with the specified names currently exist at the time of database creation, you must specify the CONTROLFILE REUSE parameter in the CREATE DATABASE command, or else an error occurs. (Also, if the size of the old control file differs from that of the new one, you cannot use the REUSE option. The size of the control file changes between some release of new version of ORACLE, as well as when the number of files specified in the control file changes; configuration parameters such as MAXLOGFILES, MAXLOGMEMBERS, MAXLOGHISTORY, MAXDATAFILES, and MAXINSTANCES affect control file size.) If no files are specified for CONTROL_FILES before database creation, a default filename is used; the default name is also operating system specific.

You can later change the value of the CONTROL_FILES parameter to add more control files or to change the names or locations of existing control files; see the next section for details.

Creating Additional Copies of the Control File, and Renaming and Relocating Control Files

You add a new control file by copying an existing file to a new location and adding the file's name to the list of control files. Similarly, you rename an existing control file by copying the file to its new name or location, and changing the file's name in the control file list. In both cases, to guarantee that control files do not change during the procedure, shut down the instance before copying the control file.

To mirror additional copies of the current control file for a database, or to move a control file, use the following steps:

1. Shut down the database.
2. Exit SQL*DBA.
3. Copy an existing control file to a different location, using operating system commands.
4. Edit the CONTROLFILES parameter in the database's parameter file to add the new control file's name, or to change the existing control file name.
5. Restart SQL*DBA.
6. Restart the database.

Creating a New Control File

You can create a new control file for a database using the CREATE CONTROLFILE command. This is useful in the following situations:

- All control files for the database have been permanently damaged and you do not have a control file backup.
- You want to change one of the permanent database settings originally specified in the CREATE DATABASE statement, including the database's name, MAXLOGFILES, MAXLOGMEMBERS, MAXLOGHISTORY, MAXDATAFILES, and MAXINSTANCES. (For example, you might need to change a database's name if it conflicts with another database's name in a distributed database. As another example, you might need to change one of the previously mentioned parameters if the original setting is too low.)

You create a new control file using the CREATE CONTROLFILE command. Use the following procedure to create a new control file.

Note: The CREATE CONTROLFILE command can potentially damage specified data files and online redo log files; omitting a filename can cause you to lose the data in that file, or even to lose access to the entire database. Use caution when using this command and be sure to use the steps in the following procedure:

1. Make a list of all data files and online redo log files of the database (see "Listing Database Files Before Backup" on page 18-6). If you followed the recommendations for database backups, you should already have a list of data files and online redo log files that reflect the current structure of the database. If you have no such lists and your control file has been damaged so that the database cannot be opened, then do your best to locate all of the data files and online redo log files that constitute the database. (Any files not specified in Step 5 are not recoverable once a new control file has been created; moreover, if you omit any of the files that make up the SYSTEM tablespace, you might not be able to recover the database.)
2. If the database is open, shutdown the database with normal priority, if possible. Use the immediate or abort options only as a last resort.
3. Backup all data files and online redo log files of the database using the procedure described in "Performing Full Backups" on page 18-7.
4. Start up an new instance, but do not mount or open the database.
5. Create a new control file for the database using the CREATE CONTROLFILE command. For example, the following statement creates a new control file for the PROD database (formerly a database that used a different database name):

```
CREATE CONTROLFILE
        SET DATABASE prod
        LOGFILE  GROUP 1 ('logfile1A', 'logfile1B') SIZE 50K,
                 GROUP 2 ('logfile2A', 'logfile2B') SIZE 50K
        NORESETLOGS
        DATAFILE 'datafile1' SIZE 3M, 'datafile2 SIZE 5M'
        MAXLOGFILES 50
        MAXLOGMEMBERS 3
        MAXDATAFILES 200
        MAXINSTANCES 6
        ARCHIVELOG;
```

   In creating the new control file, select the RESETLOGS option if you have lost any online redo log groups in addition to the control files.

In this case, you will need to recover from the loss of the redo logs in step 8.

Otherwise, select the NORESETLOGS option.

6. Store a backup of the new control file on an offline storage device.
7. Edit the parameter files of the database to indicate all of the control files created in Steps 5 and 6 (not including the backup control file) in the CONTROL_FILES parameter.
8. If you are creating the control file as part of recovery, recover the database. If the new control file was created using the NORESETLOGS option (in step 5), you can recover the database with complete, closed database recovery (see page 19-18). However, if the new control file was created using the RESETLOGS option, you must specify USING BACKUP CONTROL FILE (see page 19-23); if you have lost online or archived redo logs or data files, use the procedures for recovering those files (see "Loss of Online Redo Log Files" on page 19-29 and "Loss of Data Files" on page 19-28).
9. Open the database using one of the following methods:
   - **If you did not perform recovery**, open the database normally.
   - **If you performed complete, closed database recovery in Step 8**, use the Open Database option of the Instance menu of SQL*DBA.
   - **If you specified RESETLOGS when creating the control file**, use the ALTER DATABASE command, indicating RESETLOGS.

The database is now open and available for use.

Checking for Missing or Extra Files

After creating a new control file and using it to open the database, check the ALERT file to see if ORACLE has detected inconsistencies between the data dictionary and the control file, such as data files that the control file lists but the data dictionary does not include.

If a data file listed in the data dictionary is not mentioned in the new control file, ORACLE adds the file to the control file and renames it to MISSING*nnnn* in the data dictionary; you should rename this file to a new, appropriate name. In contrast, if a data file indicated in the control file is not present in the data dictionary, ORACLE removes references to it from the new control file. In both cases, ORACLE includes an explanatory message in the ALERT file to let you know what it found.

Handling Errors During CREATE CONTROLFILE

If ORACLE sends you an error (usually error ORA-01173, ORA-01176, ORA-01177, ORA-01215, or ORA-01216) when you attempt to mount and open the database after creating a new control file, the most likely cause is that you omitted a file from the CREATE CONTROLFILE statement or included one that should not have been listed. In this case, you should restore the files you backed up in step 3 and repeat the procedure from step 4, using the correct file names.

Note: See the *ORACLE7 Server SQL Language Reference Manual* for additional information about the CREATE CONTROLFILE command.

Dropping Control Files

You can drop control files from the database; for example, you might want to do this if the location of a control file is inappropriate. However, the database must always have at least two control files at all times.

To drop a control file from database use, do as follows:

1. Shut down the database.
2. Exit SQL*DBA.
3. Edit the CONTROLFILES parameter in the database's parameter file to delete the old control file's name.
4. Restart SQL*DBA.
5. Restart the database.

The operation above does not physically delete the unwanted control file from the disk; use operating system commands to delete the unnecessary file once you have completed the steps above. (See your installation or user's guide.)

PART

III DATABASE STORAGE

CHAPTER

7

MANAGING THE SIZE AND FILES OF THE DATABASE

This chapter explains how to control the amount of space in your database through managing tablespace and data files. Topics include:

- policies for managing tablespaces and data files
- creating tablespaces and data files
- setting storage parameters for tablespaces
- altering tablespace and data file availability
- renaming and relocating data files
- dropping tablespaces and data files
- viewing information on tablespaces and data files

Data files can also be created as part of database recovery from a media failure. Refer to Chapter 19 for information.

Trusted

If you are using Trusted ORACLE in DBMS MAC mode or OS MAC mode, see the *Trusted ORACLE7 Server Administrator's Guide* for additional information on tablespaces and data files.

Policies for Managing Tablespaces and Data Files

Before working with the tablespaces and data files of an ORACLE database, consider the information in the following sections.

Use Multiple Tablespaces

Using multiple tablespaces allows you more flexibility in performing database operations. For example, when a database has multiple tablespaces, you can perform the following tasks:

- Separate user data from data dictionary data.
- Separate one application's data from another's.
- Store different tablespaces' data files on separate disk drives to reduce I/O contention.
- Separate rollback segment data from user data, preventing a single disk failure from causing the permanent loss of data.
- Take individual tablespaces offline while others remain online.
- Reserve a tablespace for a particular type of database use, such as high update activity, read-only activity, or temporary segment storage.
- Back up individual tablespaces, leaving the rest available to users.

However, some operating systems set a limit on the number of files that can be simultaneously open; these limits indirectly affect the number of tablespaces that can be simultaneously online. To avoid exceeding this limit, plan your tablespaces efficiently. Create only enough tablespaces to fill your needs, and create these tablespaces with as few files as possible. If you need to increase the size of a tablespace, add one or two large data files rather than many small data files.

Review your data in light of these advantages and decide how many tablespaces you will need for your database design.

Number of Data Files

At least one data file is required for the SYSTEM tablespace of a database; a small system might have just a single data file. In general, few large files are better than many small files, because large files mean that fewer files need to be open at the same time.

You can add data files to tablespaces later, subject to several operating system specific data file limits (see your installation or user's guide):

operating system limit	Each operating system sets a limit on the maximum number of files per process. Regardless of all other limits, more data files cannot be created if the operating system limit of open files has been reached.
ORACLE system limit	ORACLE imposes a maximum limit on the number of data files for any ORACLE database opened by any instance.
control file upper bound	At database creation, you must indicate the maximum number of data files expected for the database so that an adequate amount of space can be reserved in the database's control file. You set this limit with the MAXDATAFILES parameter in the CREATE DATABASE statement. This maximum cannot exceed the ORACLE system limit or any operating system limit. If you are not sure how to set this parameter, use a high number to avoid unnecessary limitation. The default value is operating system specific.
instance or SGA upper bound	When starting an ORACLE instance, the database's parameter file indicates the amount of SGA space to reserve for data file information; the maximum number of data files is controlled by the DB_FILES parameter. This limit applies only for the life of the instance. DB_FILES can temporarily reduce the control file upper bound, but cannot raise it. The default value is the value of the control file upper bound.

Note: With the ORACLE Parallel Server, all instances must set the instance data file upper bound to the same value. Refer to the *ORACLE7 Parallel Server Administrator's Guide* for more information.

The use of DB_FILES and MAXDATAFILES is optional. If neither is used, the default maximum number of data files is the operating system dependent ORACLE system limit.

Set the Size of Data Files

The first data file (in the original SYSTEM tablespace) must be at least 2M, to contain the initial data dictionary and rollback segment. If you install other ORACLE products, they may require additional space in the SYSTEM tablespace (for online help, for example); refer to the installation instructions for other products you plan to install.

Place Data Files for Maximum Performance

Tablespace location is determined by the physical location of the data files that constitute that tablespace. Use the hardware resources of your computer appropriately.

For example, if several disk drives are available to store the database, it might be helpful to store table data in a tablespace on one disk drive, and index data in a tablespace on another disk drive. This way, when users query table information, both disk drives can work simultaneously, retrieving table and index data at the same time.

Store Data Files Separately From Redo Log Files

Data files should not be stored on the same disk drive that stores the database's redo log files. If the data files and redo log files are stored on the same disk drive and that disk drive fails, the files can be used in your database recovery procedures.

If you mirror your redo log files, then the likelihood of your losing all of your redo log files is low, so you can store data files on the same drive as some redo log file.

Specify Tablespace Storage Parameters

When you create a new tablespace, you can specify default storage parameters for objects that will be created in the tablespace. Storage parameters specified when an object is created override the default storage parameters of the tablespace containing the object, but if you do not specify storage parameters when creating an object, the object's segment automatically uses the default storage parameters for the tablespace.

Set the default storage parameters for a tablespace to account for the size of a typical object that the tablespace will contain. You can specify different storage parameters for an unusual or exceptional object when creating that object.

To follow this recommendation, you need to estimate the size of the typical object of the tablespace. See Chapter 8 for formulas for estimating the sizes of objects.

Note: If you do not specify the default storage parameters for a new tablespace, the default storage parameters of ORACLE become the tablespace's default storage parameters.

Assign Tablespace Quotas to Users

Grant to users who will be creating tables, clusters, snapshots, indexes, and so on, the privileges (abilities or rights) to create the object and a quota (space allowance or limit) in the tablespace intended to hold the object's segment. The security administrator is responsible for granting the required privileges to create objects to database users and is also responsible for assigning tablespace quotas, as necessary, to database users. To learn more about assigning tablespace quotas to database users, refer to Chapter 11.

Initially Creating Tablespaces and Data Files

The steps for creating data files vary by operating system. On most operating systems, you indicate the size and fully specified filenames for data files when creating a database, creating a new tablespace, or altering a tablespace by adding additional data files; in each situation, ORACLE automatically allocates and formats the data files as specified. However, on some operating systems, you must create the data files before installation. Check your installation or user's guide for the steps appropriate for your system.

IUG

The first tablespace in any database is always the SYSTEM tablespace. Therefore, the first data files of any database are automatically allocated for the SYSTEM tablespace during database creation.

Creating Additional Tablespaces

You can create a new tablespace for any of the following reasons:

- You want to allocate more disk storage space for the associated database, enlarging the database.
- You need to create a logical storage structure in which to store a specific type of data separate from other database data.

Note that to increase the total size of the database you can alternatively add a data file to an existing tablespace, rather than adding a new tablespace. See "Adding Data Files to a Tablespace" on page 7-7.

Note: No data can be inserted into any tablespace until the current instance has acquired at least two rollback segments (including the SYSTEM rollback segment). Query the data dictionary to determine how many rollback segments currently exist in a database; see page 9-16 for more information.

To create a new tablespace, use either the Create Tablespace dialog box of SQL*DBA or the SQL command CREATE TABLESPACE. Figure 7-1 shows the Create Tablespace dialog box.

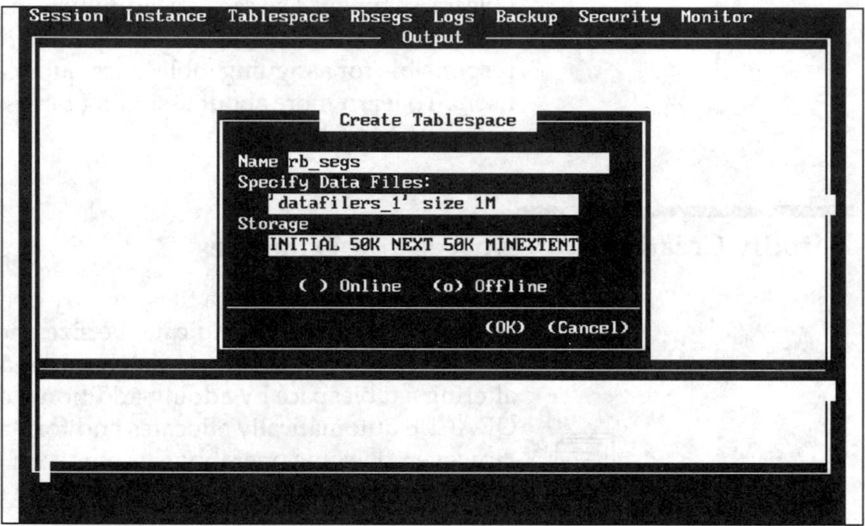

FIGURE 7-1
The Create Tablespace Dialog

This example creates a new tablespace named RB_SEGS (to hold rollback segments for the database) with the following options:

- The data of the new tablespace is to be contained in a single data file, 1M in size.
- The default storage parameters for any segments created in this tablespace are explicitly set.
- After the tablespace is created, it is left offline.

The following statement is the command equivalent of the Create Tablespace dialog box in Figure 7-1:

```
CREATE TABLESPACE rb_segs
  DATAFILE 'datafilers_1' SIZE 50M
  DEFAULT STORAGE (
    INITIAL 50K
    NEXT 50K
    MINEXTENTS 2
    MAXEXTENTS 50
    PCTINCREASE 0)
  OFFLINE;
```

If you do not fully specify filenames when creating tablespaces, the corresponding data files are created in the current directory of the database server.

Privileges Required to Create Tablespaces

To create a tablespace, you must have the CREATE TABLESPACE system privilege.

Adding Data Files to a Tablespace

You can create and add data files to a tablespace to increase the total amount of disk space allocated for the tablespace, and consequently the database.

Add data files to a tablespace with either SQL*DBA's Add Data Files to Tablespace dialog or the SQL command ALTER TABLESPACE. Figure 7-2 shows the Add Data File to Tablespace dialog box of SQL*DBA.

FIGURE 7-2
The Add Data File to Tablespace Dialog

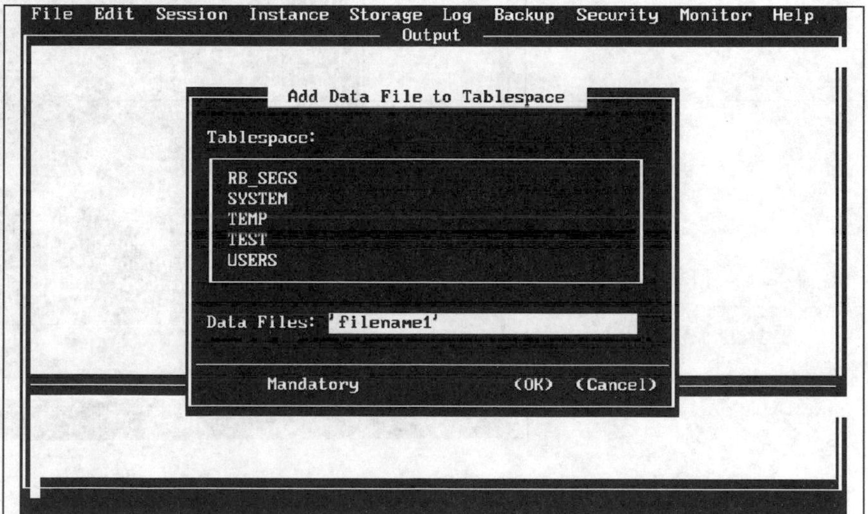

The example in Figure 7-2 creates a new data file for the RB_SEGS tablespace.

The following statement is the command equivalent of the Add Data File to Tablespace dialog box in Figure 7-2:

```
ALTER TABLESPACE rb_segs
  ADD DATAFILE 'filename1' SIZE 1M;
```

If you add new data files to a tablespace and do not fully specify the filenames, ORACLE creates the data files in the default directory of the database server. Unless you want to reuse existing files, make sure the new filenames do not conflict with other files; the old files will be overwritten.

Privileges Required to Add Data Files

To add data files to a tablespace, you must have the ALTER TABLESPACE system privilege.

Altering Storage Settings for Tablespaces

You can change the default storage parameters of a tablespace to change the default specifications for **future** objects created in the tablespace. To do so, use the Alter Default Segment Storage dialog box of SQL*DBA. Figure 7-3 shows the Alter Default Segment Storage dialog box.

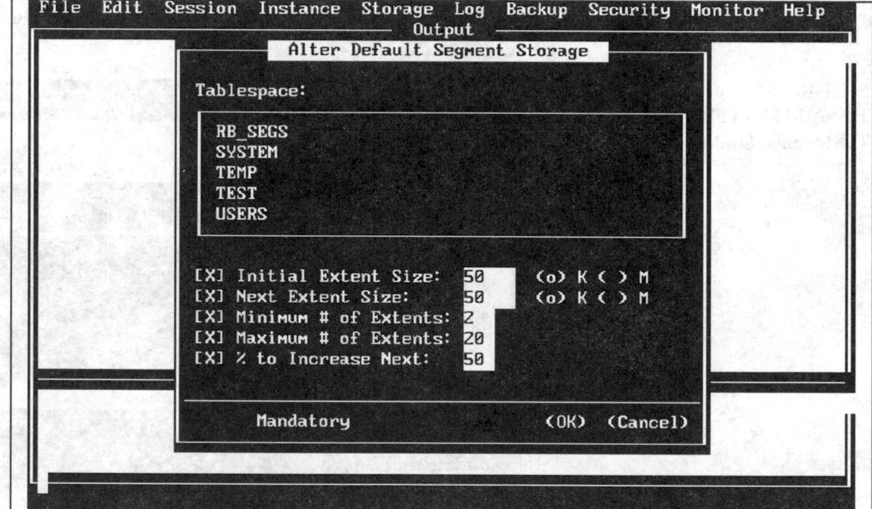

FIGURE 7-3
The Alter Default Segment Storage Dialog

The following statement is the command equivalent of the Alter Default Segment Storage dialog box in Figure 7-3:

```
ALTER TABLESPACE users
    DEFAULT STORAGE (
            INITIAL 50K
            NEXT 50K
            MINEXTENTS 2
            MAXEXTENTS 20
            PCTINCREASE 50);
```

New values for the default storage parameters of a tablespace affect only future extents allocated for the segments within the tablespace.

Privileges Required to Alter Tablespace Storage Settings

To alter the default storage parameters of a tablespace, you must have the ALTER TABLESPACE system privilege.

Altering Tablespace Availability

You can bring an offline tablespace online to make the schema objects within the tablespace available to database users. Alternatively, you can take an online tablespace offline while the database is open, so that this portion of the database is temporarily unavailable for general use but the rest is open and available. The following sections explain how to do this.

Bringing Tablespaces Online

Bring an offline tablespace online while the database is open using either the Set Tablespace Online dialog box of SQL*DBA or the SQL command ALTER TABLESPACE. Figure 7-4 shows the Set Tablespace Online dialog box.

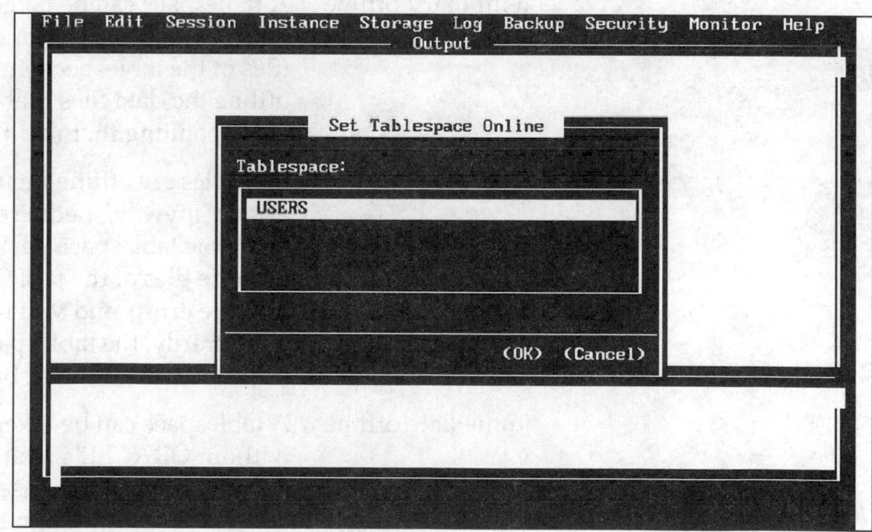

FIGURE 7-4
The Set Tablespace Online Dialog

The Set Tablespace Online dialog box in Figure 7-4 brings the USERS tablespace online.

The following statement is the command equivalent of the Set Tablespace Online dialog box in Figure 7-4:

```
ALTER TABLESPACE users ONLINE;
```

Note: If a tablespace to be brought online was not taken offline "cleanly" (that is, using the NORMAL option of the ALTER TABLESPACE OFFLINE command), you must first perform media recovery on the tablespace before bringing it online. Otherwise, ORACLE returns an error and the tablespace remains offline.

Privileges Required to Bring Tablespaces Online

To bring a tablespace online, you must have the MANAGE TABLESPACE system privilege.

Taking Tablespaces Offline

You can take a tablespace offline with any of the following three priorities:

normal offline — A tablespace can be taken offline *normally* if no error conditions exist for any of the data files of the tablespace; no data file in the tablespace can be currently offline as the result of a write error. In this case, ORACLE takes a checkpoint for all data files of the tablespace as it takes them offline.

temporary offline — A tablespace can be taken offline *temporarily*, even if error conditions are indicated for one or more files of the tablespace. In this case, ORACLE takes offline the data files that are not already offline, checkpointing them as it does so.

If no files are offline but you use the temporary option anyway, media recovery is not required to bring the tablespace back online. However, if one or more files of the tablespace are offline because of write errors and you take the tablespace offline temporarily, the tablespace will require recovery before you can bring it back online.

immediate offline — A tablespace can be taken offline *immediately*, without ORACLE's taking a checkpoint on any of the data files. In this case, media recovery for the tablespace is required before the tablespace can be brought online. You cannot take a tablespace offline immediately if the database is running in NOARCHIVELOG mode.

If you must take a tablespace offline, use the normal option (the default) if possible; this guarantees that the tablespace will not require recovery to come back online, even if you reset the redo log sequence (using an ALTER DATABASE OPEN RESETLOGS statement after incomplete media recovery) before bringing the tablespace back online.

Take a tablespace offline temporarily only when you cannot take it offline normally; in this case, only the files taken offline because of errors need to be recovered before the tablespace can be brought online. Take a tablespace offline immediately only after trying both the normal and temporary options.

Note: Before taking an online tablespace offline, verify that the tablespace contains no active rollback segments. See "Taking Rollback Segments Offline" on page 9-12.

Take an online tablespace offline while the database is open with either the Set Tablespace Offline dialog box of SQL*DBA or the SQL command ALTER TABLESPACE. Figure 7-5 shows the Set Tablespace Offline dialog box.

FIGURE 7-5
The Set Tablespace Offline Dialog

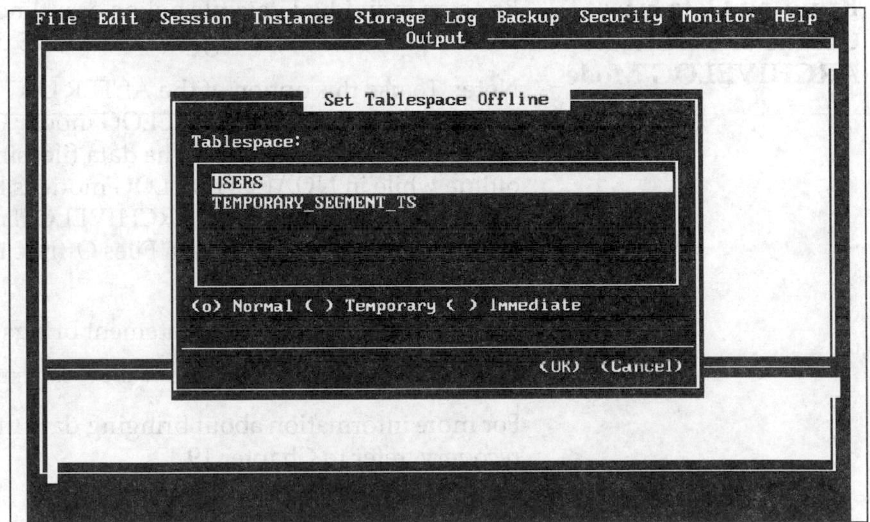

The example in Figure 7-5 takes the USERS tablespace offline normally. The Normal, Temporary, and Immediate radio buttons determine the priority with which to take the specified tablespace offline.

The following statement is the command equivalent of the Set Tablespace Offline dialog box in Figure 7-5:

```
ALTER TABLESPACE users OFFLINE NORMAL;
```

Privileges Required to Take Tablespaces Offline

To take a tablespace offline, you must have the MANAGE TABLESPACE system privilege.

Bringing Data Files Online and Offline

In very rare situations, you might need to bring specific data files online (make them available) or take specific files offline (make them unavailable). For example, when ORACLE has problems writing to a data file, it can automatically take the data file offline. You might need to take the damaged data file offline or bring it online manually.

Note: You can make all data files in a tablespace, other than the files in the SYSTEM tablespace, temporarily unavailable by taking the tablespace offline. You *must* leave these files in the tablespace to bring the tablespace back online.

Bringing Data Files Online or Offline in ARCHIVELOG Mode

Bring an individual data file online or offline with the SQL command ALTER DATABASE, using the DATAFILE parameter.

Note: To use this option of the ALTER DATABASE command, the database must be in ARCHIVELOG mode. This requirement prevents you from accidentally losing the data file, since taking the data file offline while in NOARCHIVELOG mode is likely to result in losing the file. If the database is in NOARCHIVELOG mode and you do want to drop the file, see "Taking Data Files Offline in NOARCHIVELOG Mode," below.

For example, the following statement brings a data file online:

```
ALTER DATABASE DATAFILE 'filename' ONLINE;
```

For more information about bringing data files online during media recovery, refer to Chapter 19.

Taking Data Files Offline in NOARCHIVELOG Mode

To take a data file offline when the database is in NOARCHIVELOG mode, use the ALTER DATABASE command with the DATAFILE parameter and the OFFLINE DROP option. This allows you to take the data file offline and drop it immediately. It is useful, for example, if the data file contains only data from temporary segments and has not been backed up, and the database is in NOARCHIVELOG mode.

For example, the following statement brings the specified data file offline:

```
ALTER DATABASE DATAFILE 'filename' OFFLINE DROP;
```

Privileges Required to Take a Data File On- or Offline

To bring a data file online or take it offline, in either archiving mode, you must have the ALTER DATABASE system privilege. You can perform these operations only when the database is open in exclusive mode.

Renaming and Relocating Data Files

You can rename data files to change either their names or locations. ORACLE provides options to make the following changes:

- Rename and relocate data files in a single offline tablespace (for example, FILENAME1 and FILENAME2 in TBSPACE1) while the rest of the database is open.
- Rename and relocate data files in several tablespaces simultaneously (for example, FILE1 in TBSP1 and FILE2 in TBSP2) while the database is mounted but closed.

The following sections explain each option in detail.

Note: To rename or relocate data files of the SYSTEM tablespace, you must use the second option, because you cannot take the SYSTEM tablespace offline.

Renaming and relocating data files with these procedures only change the pointers to the data files, as recorded in the database's control file; it does not physically rename any operating system files, nor does it copy files at the operating system level. Therefore, renaming and relocating data files involve several steps. Read the steps and examples carefully before performing these procedures.

Renaming and Relocating Data Files for a Single Tablespace

Rename or relocate data files from a single tablespace with the following steps:

1. Take the non-SYSTEM tablespace that contains the data files. offline
2. Copy the data files to the new location or new names using the operating system.
3. Make sure that the new, fully specified filenames are different from the old filenames.
4. Use either the Rename Data File dialog of SQL*DBA or the SQL command ALTER TABLESPACE with the RENAME DATAFILE option to change the filenames within the database.

Figure 7-6 shows the Rename Data File dialog box.

FIGURE 7-6
The Rename Data File Dialog

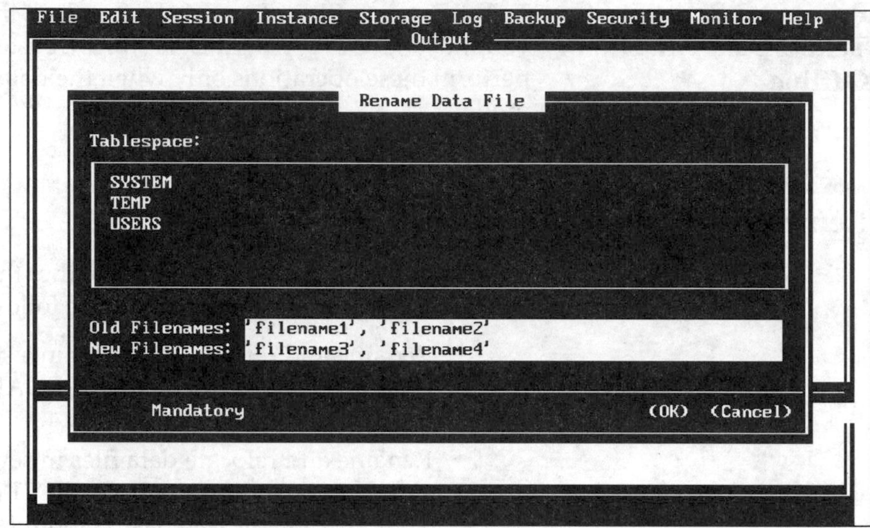

The example in Figure 7-6 renames the data files FILENAME1 and FILENAME2 to FILENAME3 and FILENAME4, respectively.

The following statement is the command equivalent of the Rename Data File dialog box in Figure 7-6:

```
ALTER TABLESPACE users
   RENAME DATAFILE 'filename1', 'filename2'
                TO 'filename3', 'filename4';
```

With either option, the new file must already exist; this command does not create a file. Also, always provide complete filenames (including their paths) to properly identify the old and new data files. In particular, specify the old filename exactly as it appears in the DBA_DATA_FILE view of the data dictionary.

Privileges Required to Rename Data Files of a Single Tablespace

To rename data files of a single tablespace, you must have the ALTER TABLESPACE system privilege.

Renaming and Relocating Data Files for Multiple Tablespaces

You can rename and relocate data files of one or more tablespaces with the SQL command ALTER DATABASE with the RENAME FILE option. This option is the only choice if you want to rename or relocate data files of several tablespaces in one operation, or rename or relocate data files of the SYSTEM tablespace. If the database must remain open, consider instead the procedure outlined in the previous section.

Rename or relocate data files for multiple tablespaces with the following steps:

1. Ensure that the database is mounted but closed.
2. Copy the data files to be renamed to their new locations and new names, using the operating system.
3. Make sure the new copies of the data files have different fully specified filenames from the data files currently in use.
4. Use the SQL command ALTER DATABASE to rename the file pointers in the database's control file. For example, the following statement renames the data files FILENAME 1 and FILENAME2 to FILENAME3 and FILENAME4, respectively:

```
ALTER DATABASE
   RENAME FILE 'filename1', 'filename2'
   TO 'filename3', 'filename4';
```

Note: Always provide complete filenames (with paths), so the RENAME FILE option properly identifies the old and new data files.

Privileges Required to Rename Data Files of Multiple Tablespaces

To rename data files of several tablespaces in one operation or to rename data files of the SYSTEM tablespace, you must have the ALTER DATABASE system privilege.

Example of Relocating a Data File

Assume the following conditions:

- An open database has a tablespace named USERS that is comprised of data files located on the same disk of a computer.
- The data files of the USERS tablespace are to be relocated to a different disk drive.
- You are currently connected to the open database as INTERNAL while using SQL*DBA. (See "Connecting as INTERNAL" on page 1-4.)

To complete this operation, the following steps are necessary:

1. Identify the data filenames of interest.

   If you are not sure of the filenames for the data files that constitute a tablespace, query the data dictionary view DBA_DATA_FILES. For example, the following query lists the data filenames and respective sizes (in bytes) of the USERS tablespace:

```
SELECT file_name, bytes FROM sys.dba_data_files
 WHERE tablespace_name = 'USERS';

FILE_NAME          BYTES
---------------------------
FILENAME1        102400000
FILENAME2        102400000
```

Here, FILENAME1 and FILENAME2 are two fully specified filenames, each 1MB in size. Refer to Appendix B for more information about the DBA_DATA_FILES data dictionary view.

2. Back up the database.

   Before making any structural changes to a database, such as renaming and relocating the data files of one or more tablespaces, always completely back up the database. (See Chapter 18 for database backup procedures.)

3. Take the tablespace offline, or shut down the database and restart and mount it, leaving it closed.

   Either option closes the data files that constitute the USERS tablespace. (See "Taking Tablespaces Offline" on page 7-10 for information about taking a tablespace offline, and Chapter 3 for information about mounting a database without opening it.)

4. Copy the data files.

   Once the USERS tablespace is offline, or the database is mounted and closed, use operating system commands to make copies of the current data files at the new location. For this example, the existing files FILENAME1 and FILENAME2 are copied to FILENAME3 and FILENAME4. (See your operating system documentation for information on how to copy files.)

Tip: You can execute an operating system command to copy a file without exiting SQL*DBA by using the Enter System Command dialog box or the HOST command in the SQL*DBA input window.

5. Rename the data files within ORACLE.

   The data file pointers for the files that comprise the USERS tablespace, recorded in the control file of the associated database, must now be changed from FILENAME1 and FILENAME2 to FILENAME3 and FILENAME4, respectively.

- If the USERS tablespace is offline but the database is open, use the Rename Data Files of Tablespace dialog box or ALTER TABLESPACE . . . RENAME DATAFILE command.
- If the database is mounted but closed, use the ALTER DATABASE . . . RENAME FILE command.

6. Bring the tablespace online, or shut down and restart the database.

   If the USERS tablespace is offline and the database is open, bring the tablespace back online. (See "Bringing Tablespaces Online" on page 7-9.)

   If the database is mounted but closed, open the database.

7. Back up the database.

   After making any structural changes to a database, always back up the database immediately and completely.

Dropping Tablespaces and Data Files

You can drop a tablespace and its contents (the segments contained in the tablespace) from the database if the tablespace and its contents are no longer required. Any tablespace in an ORACLE database, except the SYSTEM tablespace, can be dropped.

Once a tablespace has been dropped, the tablespace's data is not recoverable. Therefore, make sure that all data contained in a tablespace to be dropped will not be required in the future. Also, immediately before and after dropping a tablespace from a database, back up the database completely. This is **strongly recommended** so that you can recover the database if you mistakenly drop a tablespace, or if the database experiences a problem in the future after the tablespace has been dropped.

When you drop a tablespace, only the file pointers in the control files of the associated database are dropped; the data files that constituted the dropped tablespace continue to exist. To free previously used disk space, delete the data files of the dropped tablespace using the appropriate commands of your operating system after completing this procedure.

You cannot drop a tablespace that contains any active segments. For example, if a table in the tablespace is currently being used or the tablespace contains an active rollback segment, you cannot drop the tablespace. For simplicity, take the tablespace offline before dropping it. (See "Taking Tablespaces Offline" on page 7-10.)

After a tablespace is dropped, the tablespace's entry remains in the data dictionary (in the DBA_TABLESPACES view), but the tablespace's status is changed to INVALID.

Drop a tablespace using either the Drop Tablespace dialog box of SQL*DBA or the SQL command DROP TABLESPACE. Figure 7-7 shows the Drop Tablespace dialog box.

FIGURE 7-7
The Drop Tablespace Dialog

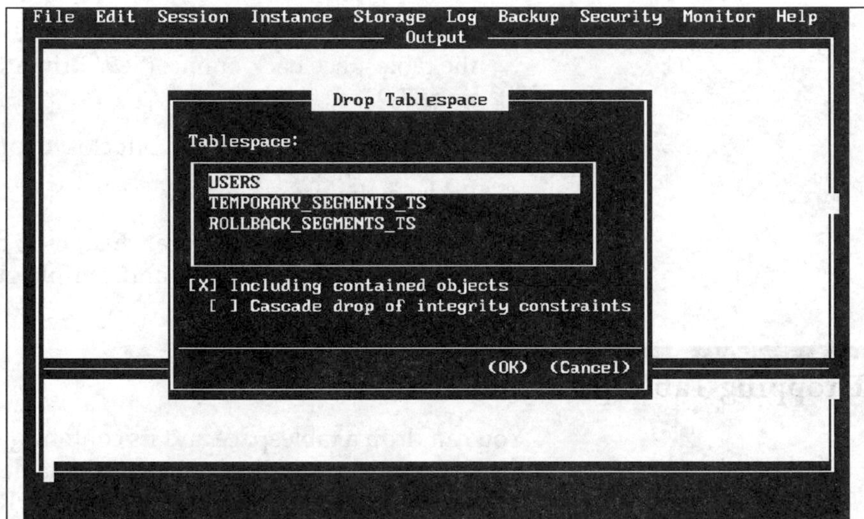

The example in Figure 7-7 drops the USERS tablespace, including the segments in the tablespace.

If the tablespace is empty (does not contain any tables, views, or other structures), you do not need to check the Including Contained Objects checkbox. If the tablespace contains any tables with primary or unique keys referenced by foreign keys of tables in other tablespaces and you want to cascade the drop of the FOREIGN KEY constraints of the child tables, select the Cascade Drop of Integrity Constraints checkbox to drop the tablespace.

The following statement is the command equivalent of the Drop Tablespace dialog box in Figure 7-7:

```
DROP TABLESPACE users INCLUDING CONTENTS;
```

Use the CASCADE CONSTRAINTS option to cascade the drop of the FOREIGN KEY constraints in the child tables.

Privileges Required to Drop Tablespaces

To drop a tablespace, you must have the DROP TABLESPACE system privilege.

Viewing Information About Tablespaces and Data Files

The following data dictionary views provide useful information about the tablespaces and data files of a database:

- USER_EXTENTS, DBA_EXTENTS (See Chapter 8.)
- USER_SEGMENTS, DBA_SEGMENTS (See Chapter 8.)
- USER_FREE_SPACE, DBA_FREE_SPACE
- DBA_USERS (See Chapter 11.)
- DBA_TS_QUOTAS (See Chapter 11.)
- USER_TABLESPACES, DBA_TABLESPACES
- DBA_DATA_FILES
- V$DATAFILE

The following examples illustrate how to use the views not already illustrated in other chapters of this Guide. They assume you are using a database that contains two tablespaces, SYSTEM and USERS. USERS is made up of two files, FILE1 (100MB) and FILE2 (200MB); the tablespace has been taken offline normally.

Example 1 Listing Tablespaces and Default Storage Parameters

To list the names and default storage parameters of all tablespaces in a database, use the following query on the DBA_TABLESPACES view:

```
SELECT tablespace_name "TABLESPACE",
       initial_extent "INITIAL_EXT",
       next_extent "NEXT_EXT",
       min_extents "MIN_EXT",
       max_extents "MAX_EXT",
       pct_increase
  FROM sys.dba_tablespaces;

TABLESPACE INITIAL_EXT NEXT_EXT MIN_EXT MAX_EXT PCT_INCREASE
---------- ----------- -------- ------- ------- ------------
SYSTEM        10240000 10240000       1      99           50
USERS         10240000 10240000       1      99           50
```

Example 2 Listing the Data Files and Associated Tablespaces of a Database

To list the names, sizes, and associated tablespaces of a database, enter the following query on the DBA_DATA_FILES view:

```
SELECT  file_name, bytes, tablespace_name
   FROM sys.dba_data_files;

FILE_NAME     BYTES        TABLESPACE_NAME
------------ ----------- -------------------
filename1     10240000     SYSTEM
filename2     10240000     USERS
filename3     20480000     USERS
```

Example 3 Listing the Free Space (Extents) of Each Tablespace

To see the amount of space available in the free extents of each tablespace in the database, enter the following query:

```
SELECT tablespace_name, file_id,
       COUNT(*)     "PIECES",
       MAX(blocks) "MAXIMUM",
       MIN(blocks) "MINIMUM",
       AVG(blocks) "AVERAGE",
       SUM(blocks) "TOTAL"
  FROM sys.dba_free_space
 WHERE tablespace_name = 'SYSTEM'
 GROUP BY tablespace_name, file_id;

TABLESPACE FILE_ID PIECES MAXIMUM MINIMUM AVERAGE     SUM
---------- ------- ------ ------- ------- ------- -------
SYSTEM           1      2    2928     115  1521.5    3043
```

SUM shows the amount of free space in each tablespace, PIECES shows the amount of fragmentation in the data files of the tablespace, and MAXIMUM shows the largest contiguous area of space. This query is useful when you are going to create a new object or you know that a segment is about to extend, and you want to make sure that there is enough space in the containing tablespace.

Example 4 Listing Status Information About Data Files

The view V$DATAFILE contains status information about data files of a database. For example:

```
SELECT name,
       file#,
       status,
       checkpoint_change# "CHECKPOINT"
  FROM v$datafile;

NAME                                 FILE#  STATUS   CHECKPOINT
------------------------------------ -----  -------  ----------
filename1                                1  SYSTEM         3839
filename2                                2  OFFLINE        3782
filename3                                3  OFFLINE        3782
```

FILE# lists the file number of each data file; the first data file in the SYSTEM tablespace, created with the database, is always file 1. STATUS lists other information about a data file. If a data file is part of the SYSTEM tablespace, its status is SYSTEM (unless it requires recovery). If a data file in a non-SYSTEM tablespace is online, its status is ONLINE. If a data file in a non-SYSTEM tablespace is offline, its status can be either OFFLINE or RECOVER. CHECKPOINT lists the final SCN written for a data file's most recent checkpoint.

CHAPTER

8 MANAGING SCHEMA OBJECTS

This chapter explains how to manage schema objects: tables, indexes, views, clusters, hash clusters, synonyms, sequences, stored procedures, packages, and database triggers. The following topics are included:

- estimating the size of, setting storage parameters for, and creating schema objects
- altering and dropping schema objects

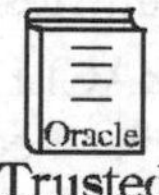

Trusted

Note: If you are using Trusted ORACLE, see the *Trusted ORACLE7 Server Administrator's Guide* for additional information on managing schema objects in that environment.

Guidelines for Managing Schema Objects

This section provides guidelines for the following aspects of schema object management:

- managing how the space of data blocks is used
- setting storage parameters of object segments
- understanding the space requirements of the various datatypes

Managing the Space Usage of Data Blocks

The following sections explain how to use the PCTFREE and PCTUSED parameters to make the following changes:

- increase the performance of writing and retrieving data
- decrease the amount of unused space in data blocks
- decrease the amount of row chaining between data blocks

Specifying PCTFREE

The default for PCTFREE is 10 percent; you may use any integer between 0 and 99, inclusive, as long as the sum of PCTFREE and PCTUSED does not exceed 100. (If you set PCTFREE to 99, ORACLE will put at least one row in each block, regardless of the row's size. If rows are very small and blocks very large, even more than one row may fit.)

A lower PCTFREE has the following effects:

- reserves less room for updates to existing table rows
- allows inserts to fill the block more completely
- may save space, because the total data for a table or index is stored in fewer blocks (more rows or entries per block)
- increases processing costs because ORACLE must frequently reorganize blocks as their free space area becomes filled with new or updated data
- potentially increases processing costs and space required if updates to rows or index entries cause rows to grow and span blocks

A low PCTFREE might be suitable, for example, for a segment that is rarely changed.

A higher PCTFREE has the following effects:

- reserves more room for future updates to existing table rows
- may require more blocks for the same amount of inserted data (inserting fewer rows per block)

- lessens processing costs because blocks infrequently need reorganization of their free space area
- may improve update performance, because ORACLE does not need to chain row pieces as frequently, if ever

A high PCTFREE is suitable, for example, for segments that are frequently INSERTed.

In setting PCTFREE, understand the nature of the table or index data. Updates can cause rows to grow. New values might not be the same size as values they replace. If there are many updates in which data values get longer, PCTFREE should be increased; if updates to rows do not affect the total row width, PCTFREE can be low. Your goal is to find a satisfactory tradeoff between densely packed data and good update performance.

PCTFREE also affects the performance of queries on tables with uncommitted transactions belonging to other users. Assuring read consistency may cause frequent reorganization of the free space area in a block if the free area is small.

PCTFREE for Non-Clustered Tables If the data in the rows of a non-clustered table is likely to increase in size over time, reserve some space for these updates. Otherwise, updated rows are likely to be chained among blocks.

PCTFREE for Clustered Tables The discussion for non-clustered tables also applies to clustered tables. However, if PCTFREE is reached, new rows from **any** table contained in the same cluster key go into a new data block that is chained to the existing cluster key.

PCTFREE for Indexes Indexes infrequently require the use of free space for updates to index data. Therefore, you can usually set PCTFREE for index segments very low (for example, 5 or lower).

Specifying PCTUSED

Once the free space in a data block reaches PCTFREE, no new rows are inserted in that block until the percentage of space used falls below PCTUSED. ORACLE tries to keep a data block at least PCTUSED full. The percent is of block space available for data after overhead is subtracted from total space.

The default for PCTUSED is 40 percent; you may specify any integer between 0 and 99, inclusive, as long as the sum of PCTUSED and PCTFREE does not exceed 100.

A lower PCTUSED has the following effects:

- on the average, keeps blocks less full than a higher PCTUSED

- reduces processing costs incurred during UPDATE and DELETE statements for moving a block to the free list when it has fallen below that percentage of usage
- increases the unused space in a database

A higher PCTUSED has the following effects:

- on the average keeps blocks fuller than a lower PCTUSED
- improves space efficiency
- increases processing cost during INSERTs and UPDATEs

Choosing Associated PCTUSED and PCTFREE Values

If you decide not to use the default values for PCTFREE or PCTUSED, keep the following guidelines in mind:

- The sum of PCTFREE and PCTUSED must be equal to or less than 100.
- If the sum is less than 100, then the ideal compromise of space utilization and I/O performance is a sum of PCTFREE and PCTUSED that differs from 100 by the percentage of space in the available block that an average row occupies. For example, assume that the data block size is 2048 bytes, minus 100 bytes of overhead, leaving 1948 bytes available for data. If an average row requires 195 bytes, or 10% of 1948, then an appropriate combination of PCTUSED and PCTFREE that sums to 90% would make the best use of database space.
- If the sum equals 100, then ORACLE attempts to keep no more than PCTFREE free space, and the processing costs are highest.
- Fixed block overhead is not included in the computation of PCTUSED or PCTFREE.
- The smaller the difference between 100 and the sum of PCTFREE and PCTUSED (as in PCTUSED of 75, PCTFREE of 20), the more efficient space usage is, at some performance cost.

Examples of Choosing PCTFREE and PCTUSED Values

The following examples illustrate specifying values for PCTFREE and PCTUSED in given scenarios.

Example 1

Scenario: Common activity includes UPDATE statements that increase the size of the rows.

Settings: PCTFREE = 20
PCTUSED = 40

Explanation: PCTFREE is set to 20 to allow enough room for rows that increase in size as a result of updates. PCTUSED is set to 40 so that less processing is done during high update activity, thus improving performance.

Example 2

Scenario: Most activity includes INSERT and DELETE statements, and UPDATE statements that do not increase the size of affected rows.

Settings: PCTFREE = 5
PCTUSED = 60

Explanation: PCTFREE is set to 5 because most UPDATE statements do not increase row sizes. PCTUSED is set to 60 so that space freed by DELETE statements is used soon, yet processing is minimized.

Example 3

Scenario: The table is very large; therefore, storage is a primary concern. Most activity includes read-only transactions.

Settings: PCTFREE = 5
PCTUSED = 90

Explanation: PCTFREE is set to 5 because UPDATE statements are rarely issued. PCTUSED is set to 90 so that more space per block is used to store table data. This setting for PCTUSED reduces the number of data blocks required to store the table's data, decreases the average number of data blocks to scan for queries, thereby increasing the performance of queries.

Setting Storage Parameters

You can set storage parameters for the following types of logical storage structures:

- tablespaces (any segment in the tablespace)
- tables, clusters, snapshots, and snapshot logs (data segments)
- indexes (index segments)
- rollback segments

Every database has default values for storage parameters. You can specify defaults for a tablespace, which override the system defaults to become the defaults for objects created in that tablespace only; furthermore, you can specify storage settings for each individual object. The storage parameters you can set are listed below, along with their system defaults. (Some defaults are operating system specific; see your installation or user's guide.)

INITIAL

The size, in bytes, of the first extent allocated when a segment is created.

Default: 5 data blocks
Minimum: 2 data blocks
Maximum: operating system specific

Although the default system value is given in data blocks, use bytes to set a value for this parameter. You can use the abbreviations K and M to indicate kilobytes and megabytes. The value is rounded **up** to the next multiple of the data block size, as determined by the parameter DB_BLOCK_SIZE.

Oracle IUG

For example, if the data block size of a database is 2048 bytes, then the system default for the INITIAL storage parameter of tablespaces is 10240 bytes. If you create a tablespace in this database and specify its default storage parameter INITIAL as 20000 (bytes), ORACLE automatically rounds this value up to 20480 (10 data blocks).

NEXT

The size, in bytes, of the next incremental extent to be allocated for a segment. The second extent is equal to the original setting for NEXT. From there forward, NEXT is set to the previous size of NEXT multiplied by (1 + PCTINCREASE/100).

Default: 5 data blocks
Minimum: 1 data block
Maximum: operating system specific

As with INITIAL, although the default system value is given in data blocks, use bytes to set a value for this parameter. You can use the abbreviations K and M to indicate kilobytes and megabytes. The value is rounded **up** to the next multiple of the data block size, as determined by the parameter DB_BLOCK_SIZE.

MAXEXTENTS

The total number of extents, including the first, that can ever be allocated for the segment.

Default: dependent on the data block size and operating system
Minimum: 1 (extent)
Maximum: operating system specific

MINEXTENTS	The total number of extents to be allocated when the segment is created. This allows for a large allocation of space at creation time, even if contiguous space is not available. **Default:** 1 (extent) **Minimum:** 1 (extent) **Maximum:** operating system specific If MINEXTENTS is greater than 1, then the specified number of incremental extents are allocated at creation time using the values INITIAL, NEXT, and PCTINCREASE. **Note:** The default and minimum values of MINEXTENTS for a rollback segment are always 2. You might want to increase the value for MINEXTENTS when you are creating a rollback segment or when your database is fragmented and you want to guarantee that you have enough space to load all the data for one table.
PCTINCREASE	The percent by which each incremental extent grows over the last incremental extent allocated for a segment. If PCTINCREASE is 0, then all incremental extents are the same size. If PCTINCREASE is greater than zero, then each time NEXT is calculated, it grows by PCTINCREASE. PCTINCREASE cannot be negative. The new NEXT equals 1 + PCTINCREASE/100, multiplied by the size of the last incremental extent (the old NEXT) and rounded **up** to the next multiple of a block size. **Default:** 50 (%) **Minimum:** 0 (%) **Maximum:** operating system specific **Note:** PCTINCREASE is always 0 for rollback segments. PCTINCREASE cannot be specified for rollback segments. By using PCTINCREASE correctly, you can reduce the fragmentation of a segment by enlarging incremental extents and reducing the number of extents that need to be allocated for the segment.

The segment contains a few large extents, rather than many smaller extents.

If you change PCTINCREASE for a segment, the current value of NEXT for that segment does not change; only future values of NEXT are affected.

INITRANS — Reserves a pre-allocated amount of space for an initial number of transaction entries to access rows in the data block concurrently. Space is reserved in the headers of all data blocks in the associated data or index segment. The default value is 1 for tables (because 1 * 23 bytes = 23 bytes) and 2 for clusters and indexes.

MAXTRANS — As multiple transactions concurrently access the rows of the same data block, space is allocated for each transaction's entry in the block. Once the space reserved by INITRANS is depleted, space for additional transaction entries is allocated out of the free space in a block, if available. Once allocated, this space effectively becomes a permanent part of the block header. The MAXTRANS parameter is used to limit the number of transaction entries that can concurrently use data in a data block. Therefore, you can limit the amount of free space that can be allocated for transaction entries in a data block using MAXTRANS. The default value is an operating system specific function of block size, not exceeding 255; see your installation or user's guide for information.

If MAXTRANS is too low, transactions blocked by this limit must wait until other transactions complete and free transaction entry space. For example, if MAXTRANS is 3 and a fourth concurrent transaction attempts to access a block already being accessed by three active transactions, the statement in the fourth transaction does not continue until one of the previous three transactions commits or rolls back.

Setting INITRANS and MAXTRANS

Transaction entry settings for the data blocks allocated for a table, cluster, or index should be set individually for each object based on the following criteria:

- the space you would like to reserve for transaction entries compared to the space you would like for database data
- the number of concurrent transactions that are likely to touch the same data blocks at any given time

For example, if a table is very large and only a small number of users simultaneously access the table, the chances of multiple concurrent transactions requiring access to the same data block is low. Therefore, both INITRANS and MAXTRANS can be set low, especially if space is at a premium in the database.

Alternatively, assume that a table is usually accessed by many users at the same time. In this case, you might consider pre-allocating transaction entry space by using a high INITRANS (to eliminate the overhead of having to allocate transaction entry space, as required when the object is in use) and allowing a higher MAXTRANS so that no user has to wait to access any necessary data blocks.

Setting Default Storage Parameters for Segments in a Tablespace

Default storage parameters can be set for each tablespace of a database. These default options are used when a segment is created in a tablespace and no storage parameters are explicitly set for the extents of the new segment. See "Creating Additional Tablespaces" on page 7-5.

Setting Storage Parameters for Data Segments

You can set the storage parameters for the data segment of a non-clustered table, snapshot, or snapshot log, using the STORAGE clause of the CREATE or ALTER statement for tables, snapshots, or snapshot logs.

In contrast, you set the storage parameters for the data segments of a cluster using the STORAGE clause of the CREATE CLUSTER or ALTER CLUSTER command, rather than the individual CREATE or ALTER commands that put tables and snapshots into the cluster. Storage parameters specified when creating or altering a **clustered** table or snapshot are ignored; the storage parameters set for the cluster override the table's storage parameters.

Setting Storage Parameters for Index Segments

Storage parameters for an index segment created for a table index can be set using the STORAGE clause of the CREATE INDEX or ALTER INDEX command. Storage parameters of an index segment created for the index used to enforce a primary key or unique key constraint can be set in the ENABLE clause of the CREATE TABLE or ALTER TABLE commands or the STORAGE clause of the ALTER INDEX command.

A PCTFREE setting for an index only has an effect when the index is created, and only if the index's table already contains rows when the index is created.

Changing Values for Storage Parameters

You can alter default storage parameters for tablespaces and specific storage parameters for individual segments if the current settings are incorrect. All default storage parameters can be reset for a tablespace. However, changes affect only new objects created in the tablespace.

The INITIAL and MINEXTENTS storage parameters cannot be altered for an existing table, cluster, index, or rollback segment. If only NEXT is altered for a segment, the next incremental extent is the size of the new NEXT, and subsequent extents can grow by PCTINCREASE as usual. If only PCTINCREASE is altered, the current value of NEXT is recomputed using the formula:

```
NEXT = NEXT * (1 + new PCTINCREASE/100)
```

If both NEXT and PCTINCREASE are altered for a segment, the next extent is the new value of NEXT, and from that point forward, NEXT is calculated using PCTINCREASE as usual.

Understanding Precedence in Storage Parameters

The storage parameters in effect at a given time are determined by the following types of SQL statements, listed in order of precedence:

1. an ALTER TABLE/CLUSTER/SNAPSHOT/SNAPSHOT LOG/INDEX/ROLLBACK SEGMENT statement
2. a CREATE TABLE/CLUSTER/SNAPSHOT/SNAPSHOT LOG/ROLLBACK SEGMENT statement.
3. an ALTER TABLESPACE statement.
4. a CREATE TABLESPACE statement.

Any storage parameter specified at the object level overrides the corresponding option set at the tablespace level. When storage parameters are not explicitly set at the object level, they default to those at the tablespace level. When storage parameters are not set at the tablespace level, ORACLE system defaults apply. If storage parameters are altered, the new options apply only to the extents not yet allocated.

Note: The storage parameters for temporary segments always use the default storage parameters set for the associated tablespace.

Storage Parameter Example

Assume the following statement has been executed:

```
CREATE TABLE test_storage
           ( . . . )
           STORAGE (INITIAL 100K   NEXT 100K
                    MINEXTENTS 2   MAXEXTENTS 5
                    PCTINCREASE 50);
```

Also assume that the initialization parameter DB_BLOCK_SIZE is set to 2K. The following table shows how extents are allocated for the TEST_STORAGE table. Also shown is the value for the incremental extent, as can be seen in the NEXT column of the USER_SEGMENTS or DBA_SEGMENTS data dictionary views:

Extent #	Extent Size	Value for NEXT
1	100K or 50 blocks	100K
2	100K or 50 blocks	CEIL(100K*1.5) = 150K
3	150K or 75 blocks	ceil(150K*1.5) = 228K
4	228K or 114 blocks	ceil(228K*1.5) = 342K
5	342K or 171 blocks	ceil(342K*1.5) = 516K

If you change the NEXT or PCTINCREASE storage parameters with an ALTER statement (such as ALTER TABLE), the specified value replaces the current value stored in the data dictionary. For example, the following statement modifies the NEXT storage parameter of the TEST_STORAGE table before the third extent is allocated for the table:

```
ALTER TABLE test_storage STORAGE (NEXT 500K);
```

As a result, the third extent is 500K when allocated, the fourth is (500K*1.5)=750K, and so on.

Understanding Space Use of Datatypes

In creating tables and other structures, you need to know how much space they will require. Each datatype has different space requirements, as explained in the following sections.

Character Datatypes

The CHAR and VARCHAR2 datatypes store alphanumeric data in strings of ASCII (American Standard Code for Information Interchange) or EBCDIC (Extended Binary Coded Decimal Interchange Code) values, depending on the character set used by the hardware that runs ORACLE. Character datatypes can also store data using character sets supported by the National Language Support (NLS) feature of ORACLE. (See Appendix C for more information about NLS and support for different character sets.)

The CHAR datatype stores fixed length character strings. When a table is created with a CHAR column, a column length (in bytes, not characters) between 1 and 255 is specified for the CHAR column; the default is 1 byte.

The VARCHAR2 datatype stores variable-length character strings. When a table is created with a VARCHAR2 column, a maximum column length (in bytes, not characters) between 1 and 2000 is specified for the VARCHAR2 column. For each row, each value in the column is stored as a variable-length field; extra blanks are not used to fill remaining space in the column.

NUMBER Datatype

The NUMBER datatype stores fixed and floating point numbers; Positive numbers in the range 1×10^{-130} to $9.99...9 \times 10^{125}$(with up to 38 significant digits), negative numbers in the range -1×10^{-130} to $-9.99..9 \times 10^{125}$ (with up to 38 significant digits), and zero. You can optionally specify a *precision* (total number of digits) and *scale* (number of digits to the right of the decimal point) when defining a NUMBER column. If precision is not specified, the column stores values as given. If no scale is specified, the scale defaults to zero.

ORACLE guarantees portability of numbers with a precision equal to or less than 38 digits. You can specify a scale and no precision:

```
column_name NUMBER (*, scale)
```

In this case, the precision is 38 and the specified scale is maintained.

DATE Datatype

The DATE datatype stores point-in-time values, such as dates and time. Date data is stored in fixed-length fields of seven bytes each.

LONG Datatype

Columns defined as LONG store variable-length character data containing up to two gigabytes of information. LONG data is text data, and is appropriately converted when moved between different character sets.

RAW and LONG RAW Datatypes

RAW is equivalent to VARCHAR2, and LONG RAW to LONG, except that SQL*Net (which connects users' sessions to the database instance) and the Export and Import utilities do not perform character conversion when transmitting RAW or LONG RAW data. In contrast, SQL*Net and Export/Import automatically convert CHAR, VARCHAR2, and LONG data between the database character set and the user session character set (set by the NLS_LANGUAGE parameter of the ALTER SESSION command) if the two character sets are different.

LONG RAW data cannot be indexed, while RAW data can be indexed.

ROWIDs and the ROWID Datatype

Every row in a non-clustered table of an ORACLE database is assigned a unique *ROWID* that corresponds to the physical address of a row's row piece (or the initial row piece if the row is chained among multiple row pieces). In the case of clustered tables, rows in different tables that are in the same data block can have the same ROWID.

Each table in an ORACLE database internally has a *pseudo-column* named ROWID; this pseudo-column is not evident when listing the structure of a table by executing a SELECT statement, or a DESCRIBE statement using SQL*Plus, but can be retrieved with a SQL query using the reserved word ROWID as a column name.

ROWIDs use a binary representation of the physical address for each row selected. A ROWID's VARCHAR2/hexadecimal representation is divided into three pieces: *block.row.file*. Here, *block* is the data block that contains the row, relative to its data file; *row* is the row in the block; and *file* is the data file that contains the row. A row's assigned ROWID remains unchanged in most cases; exceptions are when the row is exported and imported (using the IMPORT and EXPORT utilities) and, for clustered tables only, when values in the cluster key columns of a row change (although ORACLE maintains a marker at the old ROWID, pointing to the row's new location). When a row is deleted from a table (and the encompassing transaction is committed), the deleted row's associated ROWID can be assigned to a row inserted in a subsequent transaction.

You cannot set values of the pseudo-column ROWID; they are used internally by ORACLE for various operations. Although you can reference them, ROWIDs in this pseudo-column are not stored in the database, nor are they database data.

MLSLABEL Datatype

Trusted ORACLE provides one special datatype, called MLSLABEL. You can declare columns of this datatype in standard ORACLE, as well as Trusted ORACLE, for compatibility with Trusted ORACLE applications.

The MLSLABEL datatype stores a variable length tag (one to five bytes) that represents a binary label in the data dictionary. The ALL_LABELS data dictionary view lists all of the labels ever stored in the database. For more information, see the *Trusted ORACLE7 Server Administrator's Guide*.

Trusted

Summary of ORACLE Datatypes

Table 8-1 summarizes important information about each ORACLE datatype.

TABLE 8-1 Summary of ORACLE Datatype Information

Datatype	Description	Column Length (bytes)
CHAR (*size*)	Fixed length character data of length *size*.	Fixed for every row in the table (with trailing spaces); maximum size is 255 bytes per row, default size is one byte per row. Consider the character set that is used before setting *size.* (Are you using a one or two byte character set?)
VARCHAR2 (*size*)	Variable length character data. A maximum *size* must be specified.	Variable for each row, up to 2000 bytes per row. Consider the character set that is used before setting *size.* (Are you using a one or two byte character set?)
NUMBER (*p*, *s*)	Variable length numeric data. Maximum precision *p* and/or scale *s* is 38.	Variable for each row. The maximum space required for a given column is 21 bytes per row.
DATE	Fixed length date and time data, ranging from January 1, 4712 B.C. to December 31, 4712 A.D. Default format : DD-MON-YY.	Fixed at seven bytes for each row in the table.
LONG	Variable length character data.	Variable for each row in the table, up to 2^{31} * 1 bytes, or two gigabytes, per row.
RAW (*size*)	Variable length raw binary data. A maximum *size* must be specified.	Variable for each row in the table, up to 2000 bytes per row.
LONG RAW	Variable length raw binary data.	Variable for each row in the table, up to 2^{31} * 1 bytes, or two gigabytes, per row.
ROWID	Binary data representing row addresses.	Fixed at six bytes for each row in the table.
MLSLABEL	Variable length binary data representing OS labels.	Variable for each row in the table, ranging from two to five bytes per row.

Managing Tables

This section explains how to plan, create, alter, and drop tables.

Guidelines for Managing Tables

Use the following guidelines to make managing tables as easy as possible.

Design Tables Before Creation

Usually, the application developer is responsible for designing the elements of an application, including the tables. A DBA is responsible for setting storage parameters and defining clusters for tables, based on information from the application developer about how the application works and the types of data expected.

Working with your application developer, carefully plan each table so that:

- Tables are normalized.
- Each column is of the proper datatype.
- Columns that allow nulls are defined last, to conserve storage space.
- Tables are clustered whenever appropriate, to conserve storage space and optimize performance of SQL statements.

Specify How Data Block Space Is to Be Used

By specifying the PCTFREE and PCTUSED parameters during the creation of each table, you can affect the efficiency of space utilization and amount of space reserved for updates to the current data in the data blocks of a table's data segment. (See "Managing the Space Usage of Data Blocks" on page 8-2.)

Specify Transaction Entry Parameters

By specifying the INITRANS and MAXTRANS parameters during the creation of each table, you can affect how much space is initially and can ever be allocated for transaction entries in the data blocks of a table's data segment. (See "Setting Storage Parameters" on page 8-5.)

Specify the Location of Each Table

If you have the proper privileges and tablespace quota, you can create a new table in any tablespace that is currently online. Therefore, you should specify the TABLESPACE option in a CREATE TABLE statement to identify the tablespace that will store the new table.

If you do not specify a tablespace in a CREATE TABLE statement, the table is created in your default tablespace. (See "Assigning Tablespace Quotas" on page 11-9.)

When specifying the tablespace to contain a new table, make sure that you understand implications of your selection. By properly specifying a tablespace during the creation of each table, you can:

- increase the performance of the database system
- decrease the time needed for database administration

The following examples show how incorrect storage locations of schema objects can affect a database:

- If users' objects are created in the SYSTEM tablespace, the performance of ORACLE can be reduced, since both data dictionary objects and user objects must contend for the same data files.
- If an application's associated tables are arbitrarily stored in various tablespaces, the time necessary to complete administrative operations (such as backup and recovery) for that application's data can be increased.

Estimate Table Size and Set Storage Parameters

Estimating the sizes of tables before creating them is useful for the following reasons:

- You can use the combined estimated size of tables, along with estimates for indexes, rollback segments, and redo log files, to determine the amount of disk space that is required to hold an intended database. From these estimates, you can make correct hardware purchases and other decisions.
- You can use the estimated size of an individual table to better manage the disk space that the table will use. When a table is created, you can set appropriate storage parameters and improve I/O performance of applications that use the table.

  For example, assume that you estimate the maximum size of a table before creating it. If you then set the storage parameters when you create the table, fewer extents will be allocated for the table's data segment, and all of the table's data will be stored in a relatively contiguous section of disk space; this decreases the time necessary for disk I/O operations involving this table.

The following section explains in detail how to estimate the size of tables. Whether or not you estimate table size before creation, you can explicitly set storage parameters when creating each non-clustered table. (Clustered tables automatically use the storage parameters of the cluster.) Any storage parameter that you do not explicitly set when creating or subsequently altering a table automatically uses the corresponding default storage parameter set for the tablespace in which the table resides.

If you explicitly set the storage parameters for the extents of a table's data segment, try to store the table's data in a small number of large extents rather than a large number of small extents.

Plan for Very Large Tables

Large tables (such as those with millions of rows and requiring millions of bytes of space) require special planning and attention. If you have such tables in your database, consider the following recommendations:

Limit the Number of Extents in the Table The number of extents in any one segment is limited by the operating system and the database's block size. (See your installation or user's guide for information.) For example, in most databases with a block size of 2K, a segment can have at most 121 extents. Therefore, if a table is going to grow very large, you must ensure that its extents are large enough so that the segment does not have too many extents.

IUG

Note: If a segment is allocated the maximum number of extents and still needs more space, you must export, drop, and re-create (or truncate) the object, increasing its storage parameters, and re-import the data into the object. For an extremely large table, this can take as much as 14 hours, or more.

Separate the Table from Its Indexes Place indexes in separate tablespaces from other objects, and on separate disks if possible. If you ever need to drop and re-create an index on a very large table (such as when disabling and enabling a constraint, or re-creating the table), indexes isolated into separate tablespaces can often find contiguous space more easily than those in tablespaces that contain other objects.

Allocate Sufficient Temporary Space If applications that access the data in a very large table perform large sorts, ensure that enough space is available for large temporary segments and that users have access to this space. (Note that temporary segments always use the default STORAGE settings for their tablespaces.)

Calculating Space Required by Non-Clustered Tables

The following procedure shows how to estimate the initial amount of space required by a non-clustered table in an ORACLE database. For the steps for estimating the size of clustered tables, see "Calculating Space Required by Clusters" on page 8-43.

Several calculations are required to obtain a final estimate, and several of the constants (indicated by *) provided are operating system specific. Your estimates should not significantly differ from actual values. See

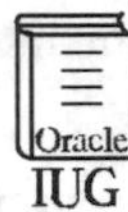

IUG

your installation or user's guide for any substantial deviations from the constants provided in the following procedure.

This procedure estimates the initial amount of space required for a table in an ORACLE database. When using these estimates, keep in mind the following points that can affect the accuracy of the estimations:

- The space used by transaction entries and deleted records does not become free immediately after completion due to delayed cleanout.
- Trailing nulls and length bytes are not stored.
- Inserts of, updates to, and deletes of rows, as well as columns larger than a single data block, can cause fragmentation and chained row pieces. Therefore, the following estimates will tend to be lower that the actual space required if significant fragmentation occurs.

Once you calculate a table's size using the following procedure, add about 10 percent additional space to calculate the initial extent size for a working table.

The steps to estimate a table's size are as follows:

1. Calculate the total block header size.
2. Calculate the available data space per data block.
3. Calculate the combined column lengths of the average row.
4. Calculate the total average row size.
5. Calculate the average number of rows that can fit in a data block.
6. Calculate the number of blocks and bytes required for the table.

Each step is explained below.

Step 1: Calculate Total Block Header Size

The space required by the data block header is the sum given by the formulas:

```
block header, part A = fixed header + variable transaction header
```

Here:

fixed header*	57 bytes
variable transaction header*	23**I* *I* is the value of INITRANS for the table.

```
block header, part B = table directory + row directory
```

Here:

table directory*	4
row directory	2*R *R* is the number of rows in the block (to be calculated in Step 5).

The block header size is broken up into two separate formulas because Part A is applicable to PCTFREE space, while Part B is not; we will need both the total block header size and Part A of the block header size in Step 2 of this procedure.

```
total block header = block header, part A + block header, part B
```

If INITRANS =1, we can partially solve the previous formulas:

```
total block header = (57 + 23) + (4 + 2R) bytes
                   = 80 + (4 + 2R) bytes
```

Step 2: Calculate Available Data Space Per Data Block

The space reserved in each data block for data, as specified by PCTFREE, is calculated as a percentage of the block size minus the block header:

```
available
  data     = (block size - total block header) -
  space      ((block size - block header, part A)*(PCTFREE/100))
```

The block size of a database is set during database creation; you can view it using the SQL*DBA command SHOW:

```
SHOW PARAMETERS db_block_size;
```

Utilities

Note: For more information about the SQL*DBA command SHOW, see the *ORACLE7 Server Utilities User's Guide.*

Assuming a data block size of 2K and PCTFREE=10 for a given non-clustered table, the total space for new data in data blocks allocated for the table is:

```
available
data       = (2048 - (80 + (4 + 2R)) -
space        ((2048 - 80) * (10/100) bytes
           = (1964 - 2R) - (1968 * 0.1) bytes
           = (1964 - 2R - 196) bytes
           = (1768 - 2R) bytes
```

Step 3: Calculate Combined Data Space

Calculate the space required by the values of an average row using the following information:

- the number of columns in the table definition
- the datatypes used for each column
- the average value size for variable length columns

If a test environment similar to the proposed production database is available, you can use SQL to calculate the combined data space for an average row in a table using the following query:

```
SELECT AVG(NVL(VSIZE(col1), 0)) +
       AVG(NVL(VSIZE(col2), 0)) +
       . . . +
       AVG(NVL(VSIZE(coln), 0)) "SPACE OF AVG ROW"
       FROM test_table_name;
```

Here, *col1*, *col2*, . . ., *coln* are the column names of the table, and *test_table_name* is the name of the test table being evaluated. This formula assumes that columns containing nulls are not trailing columns, so a column length of 1 is assumed. (The column length of a null in a trailing column is 0.)

For example, assume that you have a test table named T created with the following statement:

```
CREATE TABLE t (
  a   CHAR(10),
  b   DATE,
  c   NUMBER(10, 2));
```

To determine the space required by the average row in table T, issue the following query:

```
SELECT  AVG(NVL(VSIZE(A),0)) +
        AVG(NVL(VSIZE(B),0)) +
        AVG(NVL(VSIZE(C),0)) "SPACE OF AVG ROW"
        FROM t;
```

Alternatively, if a test database is not present, you can estimate the combined data space for an average row in a table. This is done by examining the datatype of each column in a table. If the column is of a fixed-length datatype, the value for the column in each row of the table is fixed. For variable-length columns, you must determine the average column value and determine how much space is required to hold this typical value. Table 8-1 provides a summary of datatype information to reference for this procedure.

For example, suppose you would like to calculate the combined column lengths of an average row in the table T. The column lengths of the first two columns are simple to determine because each column is of a fixed-length datatype. Each row in table T requires 10 bytes for values in column A (assuming a single byte character set is being used), and 7 bytes for values in column B.

The space required by values in the third column, C, can vary for each row in the table because the NUMBER datatype is a variable-length datatype. By estimating your proposed data, you might determine that the typical value in this column would have a precision of 8 (scale is irrelevant), and is a positive value. The typical value in column C requires approximately:

```
average length column C = (average p/2 + 1) bytes
                        = (8/2 + 1) bytes
                        = 5 bytes
```

In summary, the combined space required for the columns of an average row in table T is:

```
D (data space/average row) = (A + B + C)
                           = (10 + 7 + 5)bytes
                           = 22 bytes
```

Step 4: Calculate Total Average Row Size

You can calculate the minimum amount of space required by a row in a non-clustered table with the following equation:

```
bytes/row = row header + F + V + D
```

where:

row header*	3 bytes per row of a non-clustered table.
F	Total length bytes of all columns that store 250 bytes or less. The number of length bytes required by each column of this type is 1 byte.
V	Total length bytes of all columns that store more than 250 bytes. The number of length bytes required by each column of this type is 3 bytes.
D	Combined data space of all columns in average row (from Step 3).

For example, the total average row size of table T used in Step 3 is:

```
avg. row size, table T = (3 + (1 * 3) + (3 * 0) + 22) bytes
                       = 28 bytes
```

The absolute minimum row size of a non-clustered row is 9 bytes*. Therefore, if your calculated value for a table's total average row size is less than these absolute minimum row sizes, use the minimum value as the average row size in subsequent calculations.

Step 5: Calculate Average Rows Per Block

After the average row size is determined, you can calculate the average number of rows that can fit into a data block:

```
R (avg. # of rows/block) = available space / average row size
```

The available space was calculated in Step 2 and the average row size was calculated in Step 4. Continuing the example of the previous steps, the average number of rows in table T (a non-clustered table) that can fit into a data block is:

```
R rows/block = (1768 bytes - 2R bytes * rows/block)/28 bytes
28R bytes * rows/block = 1768 bytes - 2R bytes•rows/block
30R bytes * rows/block = 1768 bytes
R = 58 rows/block
```

Step 6: Calculate Number of Blocks and Bytes

Once you know the number of rows that can fit inside the available space of a data block, you can calculate the number of blocks required to hold the proposed table:

```
# blocks for table = # rows / R rows/block
```

For example, if you estimate that table T will have 10000 rows:

```
# blocks for table T = 10000 rows / 58 rows/block
                     = 173 blocks
```

To calculate the same space value in bytes, multiply the above result by the data block size of the corresponding database. For example, the block size in this database is 2048 bytes:

```
# bytes for table = # blocks for table * 2048 bytes/block
```

Continuing with the example of table T:

```
# bytes for table T = 173 blocks * 2048 bytes/block
                    = 354304 bytes (346K)
```

In summary, remember that this procedure provides a reasonable **estimate** of a table's size, not an exact number of blocks or bytes. Once you have estimated the size of a table, you can use this information when specifying the INITIAL storage parameter (size of the table's initial extent) in your corresponding CREATE TABLE statement.

Space Requirements for Tables in Use

Once a table is created and in use, the space required by the table is usually higher than the estimate given by the previous section. More space is required due to the method by which ORACLE manages free space in the database.

Creating Tables

Create tables using the SQL command CREATE TABLE. For example, if the user SCOTT issues the following statement, he creates a non-clustered table named EMP in his schema and stores it in the USERS tablespace:

```
CREATE TABLE emp (
    empno          NUMBER(5) PRIMARY KEY,
    ename          VARCHAR2(15) NOT NULL,
    job            VARCHAR2(10),
    mgr            NUMBER(5),
    hiredate       DATE DEFAULT (sysdate),
    sal            NUMBER(7,2),
    comm           NUMBER(7,2),
    deptno         NUMBER(3) NOT NULL
                   CONSTRAINT dept_fkey REFERENCES dept)
    PCTFREE 10
    PCTUSED 40
    TABLESPACE users
    STORAGE (      INITIAL 50K
                   NEXT 50K
                   MAXEXTENTS 10
                   PCTINCREASE 25 );
```

Notice that integrity constraints are defined on several columns of the table and that several storage settings are explicitly specified for the table.

Privileges Required to Create a Table

To create a new table in your schema, you must have the CREATE TABLE system privilege. To create a table in another user's schema, you must have the CREATE ANY TABLE system privilege. Additionally, the owner of the table must have a quota for the tablespace that contains the table, or the UNLIMITED TABLESPACE system privilege. (See Chapter 12 for more information about system privileges and Chapter 11 for more information about tablespace quotas.)

Altering Tables

A table in an ORACLE database can be altered for the following reasons:

- to add one or more new columns to the table
- to add one or more integrity constraints to a table
- to modify an existing column's definition (datatype, length, default value, and NOT NULL integrity constraint)
- to modify data block space usage parameters (PCTFREE, PCTUSED)
- to modify transaction entry settings (INITRANS, MAXTRANS)
- to modify storage parameters (NEXT, PCTINCREASE, etc.)

- to enable or disable integrity constraints or triggers associated with the table
- to drop integrity constraints associated with the table

You can increase the length of an existing column; you cannot decrease it, unless there are no rows in the table. Furthermore, if you are modifying a table to increase the length of a column of datatype CHAR, realize that this may be a time consuming operation and may require substantial additional storage, especially if the table contains many rows. This is because the CHAR value in each row must be blank-padded to satisfy the new column length.

When altering the data block space usage parameters (PCTFREE and PCTUSED) of a table, note that new settings apply to all data blocks used by the table, including blocks already allocated and subsequently allocated for the table. However, the blocks already allocated for the table are not immediately reorganized when space usage parameters are altered, but as necessary after the change.

When altering the transaction entry settings (INITRANS, MAXTRANS) of a table, note that a new setting for INITRANS only applies to data blocks subsequently allocated for the table, while a new setting for MAXTRANS applies to all blocks (already and subsequently allocated blocks) of a table.

The storage parameters INITIAL and MINEXTENTS cannot be altered. All new settings for the other storage parameters (e.g., NEXT, PCTINCREASE) affect only extents subsequently allocated for the table. The size of the next extent allocated is determined by the current values of NEXT and PCTINCREASE, and is not based on previous values of these parameters.

Alter a table using the SQL command ALTER TABLE. For example, the following statement alters the EMP table:

```
ALTER TABLE emp
    PCTFREE 30
    PCTUSED 60;
```

You should understand the following implications of altering a table:

- If a new column is added to a table, the column is initially null. You can add a column with a NOT NULL constraint to a table only if the table does not contain any rows.
- If a view or PL/SQL program unit depends on a base table, the alteration of the base table may affect the dependent object. See page 8-75 for information about how ORACLE manages such dependencies.

Privileges Required to Alter a Table

To alter a table, the table must be contained in your schema, or you must have either the ALTER object privilege for the table or the ALTER ANY TABLE system privilege.

Manually Allocating Storage for a Table

ORACLE dynamically allocates additional extents for the data segment of a table, as required. However, you might want to allocate an additional extent for a table explicitly. For example, when using the ORACLE Parallel Server, an extent of a table can be allocated explicitly for a specific instance.

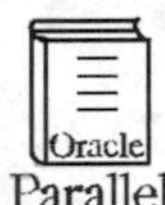

Parallel

A new extent can be allocated for a table using the SQL command ALTER TABLE with the ALLOCATE EXTENT option. For more information about this parameter of the ALTER TABLE command, see the *ORACLE7 Parallel Server Administrator's Guide*.

Dropping Tables

To drop a table that is no longer needed, use the SQL command DROP TABLE. For example, the following statement drops the EMP table:

```
DROP TABLE emp;
```

If the table to be dropped contains any primary or unique keys referenced by foreign keys of other tables and you intend to drop the FOREIGN KEY constraints of the child tables, include the CASCADE option in the DROP TABLE command, as below:

```
DROP TABLE emp CASCADE CONSTRAINTS;
```

Before dropping a table, consider the following effects:

- Dropping a table removes the table definition from the data dictionary. All rows of the table are no longer accessible.
- All indexes and triggers associated with a table are dropped.
- All views and PL/SQL program units dependent on a dropped table remain, yet become invalid (not usable). See page 8-75 for information about how ORACLE manages such dependencies.
- All synonyms for a dropped table remain, but return an error when used.
- All extents allocated for a non-clustered table that is dropped are returned to the free space of the tablespace and can be used by any other object requiring new extents.
- All rows corresponding to a clustered table are deleted from the blocks of the cluster.

Privileges Required to Drop a Table

To drop a table, the table must be contained in your schema or you must have the DROP ANY TABLE system privilege to drop the table.

Managing Views

The following sections explain how to create, replace, and drop views using several SQL commands.

Creating Views

You can create views using the SQL command CREATE VIEW. Each view is defined by a query that references tables, snapshots, or other views; the query that defines a view cannot contain the ORDER BY or FOR UPDATE clauses. For example, the following statement creates a view on a subset of data in the EMP table:

```
CREATE VIEW sales_staff AS
    SELECT empno, ename, deptno
    FROM emp
    WHERE deptno = 10
    WITH CHECK OPTION CONSTRAINT sales_staff_cnst;
```

The query that defines the SALES_STAFF view references only rows in department 10. Furthermore, the CHECK OPTION creates the view with the constraint that INSERT and UPDATE statements issued against the view cannot result in rows that the view cannot select. For example, the following INSERT statement successfully inserts a row into the EMP table via the SALES_STAFF view, which contains all rows with department number 10:

```
INSERT INTO sales_staff VALUES (7584, 'OSTER', 10);
```

However, the following INSERT statement is rolled back and returns an error because it attempts to insert a row for department number 30, which could not be selected using the SALES_STAFF view:

```
INSERT INTO sales_staff VALUES (7591, 'WILLIAMS', 30);
```

The following statement creates a view that joins data from the EMP and DEPT tables:

```
CREATE VIEW division1_staff AS
    SELECT ename, empno, job, dname
    FROM emp, dept
    WHERE emp.deptno IN (10, 30)
    AND emp.deptno = dept.deptno;
```

The DIVISION1_STAFF view joins information from the EMP and DEPT tables. The CHECK OPTION is not specified in the CREATE VIEW statement for this view; because rows cannot be inserted into or updated in a view defined with a query that contains a join, the CHECK OPTION is not meaningful for the DIVISION1_STAFF view.

Expansion of Defining Queries at View Creation Time

In accordance with the ANSI/ISO standard, ORACLE expands any wildcard in a top-level view query into a column list when a view is created and stores the resulting query in the data dictionary; any subqueries are left intact. The column names in an expanded column list are enclosed in quotation marks in case the columns of the base object were originally entered with quotation marks and require them for the query to be syntactically correct. Quotation marks are always included because the data dictionary does not store whether the user used quotation marks to specify the identifier in the original DDL statement that created the column and because it cannot reliably deduce from the column name itself whether or not the quotes are required. Although the quotation marks are unnecessary when a column name contains only numbers and capital letters and starts with a capital letter, they are harmless in these cases.

As an example, assume that the DEPT view is created as follows:

```
CREATE VIEW dept AS SELECT * FROM scott.dept;
```

ORACLE stores the defining query of the DEPT view as:

```
SELECT "DEPTNO", "DNAME", "LOC" FROM scott.dept
```

Note: ORACLE does not expand wildcards in views created with errors (see the next section). When the view is eventually compiled without errors, ORACLE expands wildcards in the defining query.

Creating Views with Errors

If there are no syntax errors in a CREATE VIEW statement, ORACLE can create the view even if the defining query of the view cannot be executed; the view is considered "created with errors." For example, when a view is created that refers to a non-existent table or an invalid column of an existing table, or when the view owner does not have the required privileges, the view can be created anyway and entered into the data dictionary. However, the view is not yet usable.

To create a view with errors, you must include the FORCE option of the CREATE VIEW command:

```
CREATE FORCE VIEW AS ....;
```

By default, views are not created with errors. When a view is created with errors, ORACLE returns a message indicating the view was created with errors. The status of a view created with errors is INVALID. If conditions later change so that the query of an invalid view can be executed, the view can be recompiled and become valid (usable). See "Managing Object Dependencies" on page 8-75.

Privileges Required to Create a View

To create a view, you must fulfill the requirements listed below:

- To create a view in your schema, you must have the CREATE VIEW privilege; to create a view in another user's schema, you must have the CREATE ANY VIEW system privilege. You may acquire these privileges explicitly or via a role.
- The **owner** of the view (whether it is you or another user) must have been explicitly granted privileges to access all objects referenced in the view definition; the owner **cannot** have obtained these privileges through roles. Also, the functionality of the view is dependent on the privileges of the view's owner. For example, if the owner of the view has only the INSERT privilege for Scott's EMP table, the view can only be used to insert new rows into the EMP table, not to SELECT, UPDATE, or DELETE rows from it.
- If the owner of the view intends to grant access to the view to other users, the owner must have received the object privileges to the base objects with the GRANT OPTION or the system privileges with the ADMIN OPTION.

Replacing Views

If the definition of a view must change, the view must be replaced; you cannot alter the definition of a view. You can replace views in the following ways:

- You can drop and re-create the view. When a view is dropped, all grants of corresponding object privileges are revoked from roles and users. After the view is re-created, privileges must be regranted.
- You can redefine the view with a CREATE VIEW statement that contains the OR REPLACE option. The OR REPLACE option replaces the current definition of a view and preserves the current security authorizations. For example, assume that you create the SALES_STAFF view as given in the previous example, and grant several object privileges to roles and other users. However, now you need to redefine the SALES_STAFF view to change the department number specified in the WHERE clause. You can replace the current version of the SALES_STAFF view with the following statement:

```
CREATE OR REPLACE VIEW sales_staff AS
    SELECT empno, ename, deptno
    FROM emp
    WHERE deptno = 30
    WITH CHECK OPTION CONSTRAINT sales_staff_cnst;
```

Before replacing a view, consider the following effects:

- Replacing a view replaces the view's definition in the data dictionary. All underlying objects referenced by the view are not affected.
- If a constraint in the CHECK OPTION was previously defined but not included in the new view definition, the constraint is dropped.
- All views and PL/SQL program units dependent on a replaced view become invalid (not usable). See page 8-75 for more information on how ORACLE manages such dependencies.

Privileges Required to Replace a View

To replace a view, you must have all the privileges required to drop and create a view.

Dropping Views

Drop a view using the SQL command DROP VIEW. For example, the following statement drops a view named SALES_STAFF:

```
DROP VIEW sales_staff;
```

Privileges Required to Drop a View

You can drop any view contained in your schema. To drop a view in another user's schema, you must have the DROP ANY VIEW system privilege.

Managing Sequences

The following sections explain how to create, alter, and drop sequences using SQL commands.

Creating Sequences

Create a sequence using the SQL command CREATE SEQUENCE. For example, the following statement creates a sequence used to generate employee numbers for the EMPNO column of the EMP table:

```
CREATE SEQUENCE emp_sequence
    INCREMENT BY 1
    START WITH 1
    NOMAXVALUE
    NOCYCLE
    CACHE 10;
```

The CACHE option pre-allocates a set of sequence numbers and keeps them in memory so that sequence numbers can be accessed faster. When the last of the sequence numbers in the cache has been used, ORACLE reads another set of numbers into the cache.

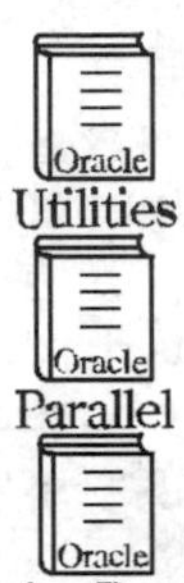

ORACLE might skip sequence numbers if you choose to cache a set of sequence numbers. For example, when an instance abnormally shuts down (for example, when an instance failure occurs or a SHUTDOWN ABORT statement is issued), sequence numbers that have been cached but not used are lost. ORACLE might also skip cached sequence numbers after an export and import; see the *ORACLE7 Server Utilities User's Guide* for details.

The ORACLE Parallel Server has additional effects on cached sequence numbers; see the *ORACLE7 Parallel Server Administrator's Guide* for more information. For performance information on caching sequence numbers, see the *ORACLE7 Server Application Developer's Guide.*

Privileges Required to Create a Sequence

To create a sequence in your schema, you must have the CREATE SEQUENCE system privilege; to create a sequence in another user's schema, you must have the CREATE ANY SEQUENCE privilege.

Altering Sequences

You can alter a sequence to change any of the parameters that define how it generates sequence numbers except the sequence's starting number. To change the starting point of a sequence, drop the sequence and then re-create it.

Alter a sequence using the SQL command ALTER SEQUENCE. For example, the following statement alters the EMP_SEQUENCE:

```
ALTER SEQUENCE emp_sequence
    INCREMENT BY 10
    MAXVALUE 10000
    CYCLE
    CACHE 20;
```

Privileges Required to Alter a Sequence

To alter a sequence, your schema must contain the sequence, or you must have the ALTER ANY SEQUENCE system privilege.

Initialization Parameters Affecting Sequences

The initialization parameter SEQUENCE_CACHE_ENTRIES sets the number of sequences that may be cached at any time. If auditing is enabled for your system, allow one additional sequence for the sequence to identify audit session numbers.

If the value for SEQUENCE_CACHE_ENTRIES is too low, ORACLE might skip sequence values, as in the following scenario: assume you are using five cached sequences, the cache is full, and SEQUENCE_-CACHE_ENTRIES = 4. If four sequences are currently cached, then a fifth sequence replaces the least recently used sequence in the cache and all remaining values (up to the last sequence number cached) in the displaced sequence are lost.

Dropping Sequences

If a sequence is no longer required, you can drop the sequence using the SQL command DROP SEQUENCE. For example, the following statement drops the ORDER_SEQ sequence:

```
DROP SEQUENCE order_seq;
```

When a sequence is dropped, its definition is removed from the data dictionary. Any synonyms for the sequence remain, but return an error when referenced.

Privileges Required to Drop a Sequence

You can drop any sequence in your schema. To drop a sequence in another schema, you must have the DROP ANY SEQUENCE system privilege.

Managing Synonyms

You can create both public and private synonyms. A *public* synonym is owned by the special user group named PUBLIC and is accessible to every user in a database. A *private* synonym is contained in the schema of a specific user and available only to the user and the user's grantees.

The following sections explain how to create and drop synonyms using SQL commands.

Creating Synonyms

Create a synonym using the SQL command CREATE SYNONYM. For example, the following statement creates a public synonym named PUBLIC_EMP on the EMP table contained in the schema of JWARD:

```
CREATE PUBLIC SYNONYM public_emp FOR jward.emp;
```

Privileges Required to Create a Synonym

To create a private synonym in your own schema, you must have the CREATE SYNONYM privilege; to create a private synonym in another user's schema, you must have the CREATE ANY SYNONYM privilege.

To create a public synonym, you must have the CREATE PUBLIC SYNONYM system privilege.

Dropping Synonyms

Drop a synonym that is no longer required using the SQL command DROP SYNONYM. To drop a private synonym, omit the PUBLIC keyword; to drop a public synonym, include the PUBLIC keyword.

For example, the following statement drops the private synonym named EMP:

```
DROP SYNONYM emp;
```

The following statement drops the public synonym named PUBLIC_EMP:

```
DROP PUBLIC SYNONYM public_emp;
```

When you drop a synonym, its definition is removed from the data dictionary. All objects that reference a dropped synonym remain; however, they become invalid (not usable). See "Managing Object Dependencies" on page 8-75.

Privileges Required to Drop a Synonym

You can drop any private synonym in your own schema. To drop a private synonym in another user's schema, you must have the DROP ANY SYNONYM system privilege. To drop a public synonym, you must have the DROP PUBLIC SYNONYM system privilege.

Managing Indexes

The following sections explain how to create, alter, and drop indexes using SQL commands, and provide guidelines on working with indexes.

Guidelines for Managing Indexes

The following sections give some guidelines to follow when managing indexes.

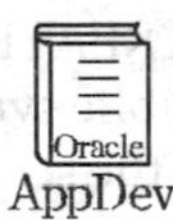

See the *ORACLE7 Server Application Developer's Guide* for performance implications of index creation.

Create Indexes After Inserting Table Data

For an index for a table, you should create the index after data has been inserted or loaded (by SQL*Loader or Import) into the table. It is more efficient to insert rows of data into a table that has no indexes and then create the indexes for subsequent access. If you create indexes before table data is loaded, every index must be updated every time a row is inserted into the table.

For an index for a cluster, you must create a cluster's index before any data can be inserted into the cluster.

When an index is created on a table that already has data, ORACLE must use sort space to create the index. ORACLE uses the sort space in memory allocated for the creator of the index (the amount per user is determined by the initialization parameter SORT_AREA_SIZE), but must also swap sort information to and from temporary segments allocated on behalf of the index creation.

If the index is extremely large, it may be beneficial to perform the following steps:

1. Create a new temporary segment tablespace.
2. Alter the index creator's temporary segment tablespace.
3. Create the index.
4. Remove the temporary segment tablespace and respecify the creator's temporary segment tablespace, if desired.

Utilities

Note: Under certain conditions, data can be loaded into a table with SQL*Loader's "direct path load" and an index can be created as data is loaded; see the *ORACLE7 Server Utilities User's Guide* for more information.

Index the Correct Tables and Columns

LONG and LONG RAW columns cannot be indexed. Also, the size of a single index entry cannot exceed roughly one-third the data block size. See "Calculating Space for Indexes" on page 8-35 to determine if an index violates this limit.

Limit the Number of Indexes per Table

A table can have any number of indexes. However, the more indexes there are, the more overhead is incurred as the table is altered. Specifically, when rows are inserted or deleted, all indexes on the table must be updated as well. Also, when a column is updated, all indexes that contain the column must be updated.

Thus, there is a tradeoff between speed of retrieving data from a table and speed of updating the table. For example, if a table is primarily read-only, having more indexes can be useful, but if a table is heavily updated, having fewer indexes can be preferable.

Specify Transaction Entry Parameters

By specifying the INITRANS and MAXTRANS parameters during the creation of each index, you can affect how much space is initially and can ever be allocated for transaction entries in the data blocks of an index's segment. For more information about setting these parameters, see "Setting Storage Parameters" on page 8-5.

Specify Data Block Space Use

When an index is created for a table, data blocks of the index are filled with the existing values in the table up to PCTFREE. The space reserved by PCTFREE for an index block is only used when a new row is inserted into the table and the corresponding index entry must be placed in the correct index block (that is, between preceding and following index entries); if no more space is available in the appropriate index block, the indexed value is placed in another index block, which is chained to the head block for the index leaf. Therefore, if you plan on inserting many rows into an indexed table, PCTFREE should be high to accommodate the new index values; if the table is relatively static without many inserts, PCTFREE for an associated index can be low so that fewer blocks are required to hold the index data.

Note: PCTUSED cannot be specified for indexes. See "Managing the Space Usage of Data Blocks" on page 8-2 for information about the PCTFREE parameter.

Specify the Tablespace for Each Index

Indexes can be created in any tablespace. An index can be created in the same or different tablespace as the table it indexes.

If you use the same tablespace for a table and its index, then database maintenance may be more convenient (such as tablespace or file backup and application availability or update) and all the related data will always be online together.

Using different tablespaces (on different disks) for a table and its index produces better performance than storing the table and index in the same tablespace, due to reduced disk contention.

If you use different tablespaces for a table and its index and one tablespace is offline (containing either data or index), then the statements referencing that table are not guaranteed to work.

Estimate Index Size and Set Storage Parameters

The reasons for estimating an index's size before creation are identical to those for estimating table size. See "Estimate Table Size and Set Storage Parameters" on page 8-16 if you are not familiar with this justification. "Calculating Space for Indexes" on page 8-35 explains how to estimate the size of indexes.

As with tables, you can explicitly set storage parameters when creating an index. If you explicitly set the storage parameters for an index, try to store the index's data in a small number of large extents rather than a large number of small extents.

Any storage parameter not explicitly set for an index automatically uses the corresponding default storage parameter set for the containing tablespace. If you do not specify storage parameters when creating an index, ORACLE allocates extents to index segments based on the total size of the index:

- If the table being indexed contains no rows when the index is created, extent sizes are allocated according to the default storage parameters of the containing tablespace.

- An index smaller than or equal to 25 blocks is allocated in one extent by default.
- For indexes larger than 25 blocks, the default sizes of the initial and incremental extents are one-fifth of the total index size.

For specific information about storage parameters, see "Set Storage Parameters" on page 8-5.

Consider Indexes Before Disabling or Dropping Constraints

Because unique and primary keys have associated indexes, you should factor in the cost of dropping and creating indexes when considering whether or not to disable or drop a UNIQUE or PRIMARY KEY constraint. If the associated index for a UNIQUE key or PRIMARY KEY constraint is extremely large, you may save time by leaving the constraint enabled rather than dropping and re-creating the large index.

Calculating Space for Indexes

The following procedure demonstrates how to estimate the initial amount of space required by an index. Several calculations are required to obtain a final estimate. Also, several of the constants (indicated by *) provided are operating system specific, yet should provide reasonable results that will not differ significantly from actual values. See your installation or user's guide for any dramatic deviations from the constants provided in the following procedure.

IUG

The calculations in the procedure rely on average column lengths of the columns that constitute an index; therefore, if column lengths in each row of a table are relatively constant with respect to the indexed columns, the estimates calculated by the following procedure are more accurate.

The steps to estimate an index's size are as follows:

1. Calculate the total block header size.
2. Calculate the available data space per data block.
3. Calculate the combined column lengths of an average index value.
4. Calculate the total average index value size.
5. Calculate the number of blocks and bytes required for the index.

Each step is explained below.

Step 1: Calculate the Total Block Header Size

The space required by the data block header of a block to contain index data is given by the formula:

```
block header size = fixed header + variable transaction header
```

where:

fixed header*	113 bytes
variable transaction header*	23*I I is the value of INITRANS for the index.

If INITRANS =2 (the default for indexes), the previous formulas can be simplified:

```
block header = 113 + (23*2) bytes
             = 159 bytes
```

Step 2: Calculate Available Data Space Per Data Block

The space reserved in each data block for index data, as specified by PCTFREE, is calculated as a percentage of the block size minus the block header:

```
available
   data     = (block size - block header) -
   space      ((block size - block header)*(PCTFREE/100))
```

The block size of a database is set during database creation and can be determined using the SQL*DBA command SHOW, if necessary:

```
SHOW PARAMETERS db_block_size;
```

Utilities

Note: For more information about the SQL*DBA command SHOW, see the *ORACLE7 Server Utilities User's Guide.*

If the data block size is 2K and PCTFREE=10 for a given index, the total space for new data in data blocks allocated for the index is:

```
available
data       = (2048 bytes - 159 bytes) -
space        ((2048 bytes - 159 bytes)*(10/100))
           = (1889 bytes) - (1889 bytes * 0.1)
           = 1889 bytes - 188.9 bytes
           = 1700.1 bytes
```

Step 3: Calculate Combined Column Lengths of an Index Value

The space required by the average value of an index must be calculated before you can complete Step 4, calculating the total row size. This step is identical to Step 3 in the procedure for calculating table size (page 8-19), except you only need to calculate the average combined column lengths of the columns in the index.

Step 4: Calculate Total Average Index Value Size

Once you have calculated the combined column length of an average index entry, you can calculate the total average entry size according to the following formula:

```
bytes/entry = entry header + ROWID length + F + V + D
```

where:

entry header	2 bytes
ROWID length	6 bytes
F	Total length bytes of all columns that store 128 bytes or less. The number of length bytes required by each column of this type is 1 byte.
V	Total length bytes of all columns that store more than 128 bytes. The number of length bytes required by each column of this type is 3 bytes.
D	Combined data space of all index columns (from Step 3).

For example, given that *D* is calculated to be 22 bytes and that the index is comprised of three CHAR(10) columns, the total average entry size of the index is:

```
avg. entry size = 1 + 6 + (1 * 3) + (3 * 0) + 22 bytes
                = 32 bytes
```

Step 5: Calculate Number of Blocks and Bytes

Calculate the number of blocks required to store the index using the following formula:

```
# blocks for index =

                    # not null rows * avg. entry size
1.05 * ──────────────────────────────────────────────────────
       (FLOOR(avail. data space/avg. entry size))*(avg. entry size)
```

Note: The additional 5% added to this result (via the multiplication factor of 1.05) accounts for the extra space required for branch blocks of the index.

For example, continuing with the previous example, and assuming you estimate that indexed table will have 10000 rows that contain non-null values in the columns that constitute the index:

```
# blocks for index =

                    10000 * 32 bytes
1.05 * ──────────────────────────────────────────
         (FLOOR(1700 bytes/32 bytes))*(32 bytes)
```

This results in 198 blocks. The number of bytes can be calculated by multiplying the number of blocks by the data block size.

Remember that this procedure provides a reasonable **estimate** of an index's size, not an exact number of blocks or bytes. Once you have estimated the size of a index, you can use this information when specifying the INITIAL storage parameter (size of the index's initial extent) in your corresponding CREATE INDEX statement.

Temporary Space Required for Index Creation

When creating an index for a loaded table, temporary segments are created to sort the index. The amount of space required to sort an index varies, but can be up to 110% of the size of the index.

Note: Temporary space is not required if the NOSORT option is included in the CREATE INDEX command. However, you cannot specify this option when creating a cluster index.

Creating Indexes

An index can be created for a table to improve the performance of queries issued against the corresponding table. An index can also be created for a cluster.

ORACLE enforces a UNIQUE key or PRIMARY KEY integrity constraint by creating a unique index on the unique key or primary key. This index is automatically created by ORACLE when the constraint is enabled; no action is required by the issuer of the CREATE TABLE or ALTER TABLE statement to create the index. This includes both when a constraint is defined and enabled, and when a defined but disabled constraint is enabled.

Note: In general, it is better to create constraints to enforce uniqueness than it is to use the CREATE UNIQUE INDEX syntax. A constraint's associated index always assumes the name of the constraint; you cannot specify a specific name for a constraint index.

In both types of index creation, if you do not specify the storage options for an index, they are automatically set to the default storage options of the containing tablespace.

Creating an Index Associated with a Constraint

Similarly to the above example, you can set the storage options for the indexes associated with UNIQUE key and PRIMARY KEY constraints using the ENABLE clause with the USING INDEX option. For example, the following statement defines a PRIMARY KEY constraint and specifies the associated index's storage option:

```
CREATE TABLE emp (
    empno NUMBER(5) PRIMARY KEY, . . . )
    ENABLE PRIMARY KEY USING INDEX
            TABLESPACE users
            PCTFREE 0;
```

Creating an Index Explicitly

Indexes are created explicitly (outside of integrity constraints) using the SQL command CREATE INDEX. For example, the following statement creates an index named EMP_ENAME for the ENAME column of the EMP table:

```
CREATE INDEX emp_ename ON emp(ename)
    TABLESPACE users
    STORAGE (INITIAL 20K
            NEXT 20k
            PCTINCREASE 75)
    PCTFREE 0;
```

Notice that several storage settings are explicitly specified for the index.

Privileges Required to Create an Index

To create a new index you must own or have the INDEX object privilege for the corresponding table. The schema that contains the index must also have a quota for the tablespace intended to contain the index, or the UNLIMITED TABLESPACE system privilege. To create an index in another user's schema, you must have the CREATE ANY INDEX system privilege.

To enable a UNIQUE key or PRIMARY KEY (which creates an associated index), the owner of the table needs a quota for the tablespace intended to contain the index, or the UNLIMITED TABLESPACE system privilege.

Altering an Index

You can alter an index only to change the transaction entry parameters or to change the storage parameters; you cannot change its column structure.

Alter the storage parameters of any index, including those created by ORACLE to enforce primary and unique key integrity constraints, using the SQL command ALTER INDEX. For example, the following statement alters the EMP_ENAME index:

```
ALTER INDEX emp_ename
    INITRANS 5
    MAXTRANS 10
    STORAGE (PCTINCREASE 50);
```

When you alter the transaction entry settings (INITRANS, MAXTRANS) of an index, a new setting for INITRANS only applies to data blocks subsequently allocated, while a new setting for MAXTRANS applies to all blocks (already and subsequently allocated blocks) of an index.

The storage parameters INITIAL and MINEXTENTS cannot be altered. All new settings for the other storage parameters affect only extents subsequently allocated for the index.

For indexes that implement integrity constraints, you can also adjust storage parameters by issuing an ALTER TABLE statement that includes the ENABLE clause with the USING INDEX option. For example, the following statement changes the storage options of the index defined in the previous section:

```
ALTER TABLE emp
    ENABLE PRIMARY KEY USING INDEX
    PCTFREE 5;
```

Privileges Required to Alter an Index

To alter an index, your schema must contain the index or you must have the ALTER ANY INDEX system privilege.

Monitoring Space Use of Indexes

If key values in an index are inserted, updated, and deleted frequently, the index may or may not use its acquired space efficiently over time. Monitor an index's efficiency of space usage at regular intervals by first validating the index's structure (see "Analyzing Tables, Indexes, and Clusters" on page 8-62) and then querying the INDEX_STATS view:

```
SELECT pct_used FROM sys.index_stats WHERE name = 'indexname';
```

The percentage of an index's space usage will vary according to how often index keys are inserted, updated, or deleted. Develop a history of an index's average efficiency of space usage by performing the following sequence of operations several times: validating the index, checking PCT_USED, and dropping and re-creating the index. When you find that an index's space usage drops below its average, you can condense the index's space by dropping the index and re-creating it.

Dropping Indexes

You might want to drop an index for any of the following reasons:

- The index is no longer required.
- The index is not providing anticipated performance improvements for queries issued against the associated table. (For example, the table might be very small, or there might be many rows in the table but very few index entries.)
- Applications do not use the index to query the data.

- The index has become invalid and must be dropped before being rebuilt. (See "Analyzing Tables, Indexes, and Clusters" on page 8-62.)
- The index has become too fragmented and must be dropped before being rebuilt.

When you drop an index, all extents of the index's segment are returned to the containing tablespace and become available for other objects in the tablespace.

How you drop an index depends on whether you created the index explicitly with a CREATE INDEX statement, or implicitly by defining a key constraint on a table. The following sections explain how to drop both kinds of indexes.

Note: If a table is dropped, all associated indexes are dropped automatically.

Dropping an Index Associated with an Integrity Constraint

You cannot drop only the index associated with an enabled UNIQUE key or PRIMARY KEY constraint. To drop a constraint's associated index, you must disable or drop the constraint itself. See "Managing Integrity Constraints" on page 8-70.

Dropping an Index Created Explicitly

Drop an index with the SQL command DROP INDEX. For example, to drop the EMP_ENAME index, enter the following statement:

```
DROP INDEX emp_ename;
```

Privileges Required to Drop An Index

To drop an index, the index must be contained in your schema or you must have the DROP ANY INDEX system privilege.

Managing Clusters, Clustered Tables, and Cluster Indexes

The following sections explain how to create, alter, and drop clusters, clustered tables, and cluster indexes. For additional information on managing hash clusters, see "Managing Hash Clusters and Clustered Tables" on page 8-54.

Guidelines for Managing Clusters

The following sections give some guidelines for creating clusters.

Choose Appropriate Tables to Cluster

Use clusters to store one or more tables that are primarily queried (not predominantly inserted into or updated) and for which the queries often join data of multiple tables in the cluster or retrieve related data from a single table.

Choose Appropriate Columns for the Cluster Key

Choose cluster key columns carefully. If multiple columns are used in queries that join the tables, make the cluster key a composite key. In general, the characteristics that indicate a good cluster index are the same as those for any index; see "Index the Correct Tables and Columns" on page 8-33 for these guidelines.

A good cluster key has enough unique values so that the group of rows corresponding to each key value fills approximately one data block. Having too few rows per cluster key value can waste space and result in negligible performance gains. Cluster keys that are so specific that only a few rows share a common value can cause wasted space in blocks, unless a small SIZE was specified at cluster creation time (see below).

Too many rows per cluster key value can cause extra searching to find rows for that key. Cluster keys on values that are too general (for example, MALE and FEMALE) result in excessive searching and can result in worse performance than with no clustering.

A cluster index cannot be unique or include a column defined as LONG.

Specify How Data Block Space Is to Be Used

By specifying the PCTFREE and PCTUSED parameters during the creation of a cluster, you can affect the space utilization and amount of space reserved for updates to the current rows in the data blocks of a cluster's data segment. Note that PCTFREE and PCTUSED parameters set for tables created in a cluster are ignored; clustered tables automatically use the settings set for the cluster. See "Managing the Space Usage of Data Blocks" on page 8-2 for more information and guidelines for setting PCTFREE and PCTUSED parameters.

Specify the Space Required by an Average Cluster Key and Its Associated Rows

The CREATE CLUSTER command has an optional argument, SIZE, which is the estimated number of bytes required by an average cluster key and its associated rows. ORACLE uses the SIZE parameter in performing the following tasks:

- estimating the number of cluster keys (and associated rows) that can fit in a clustered data block
- limiting the number of cluster keys placed in a clustered data block; this maximizes the storage efficiency of keys within a cluster

SIZE does not limit the space that can be used by a given cluster key. For example, if SIZE is set such that two cluster keys can fit in one data block, any amount of the available data block space can still be used by either of the cluster keys.

By default, ORACLE stores only one cluster key and its associated rows in each data block of the cluster's data segment. Although block size can vary from one operating system to the next, the rule of one key per block is maintained as clustered tables are imported to other databases on other machines.

Use the procedure in "Calculating Space Required by Clusters" on page 8-43 to calculate SIZE for a cluster.

If all the rows for a given cluster key value cannot fit in one block, the blocks are chained together to speed access to all the values with the given key. The cluster index points to the beginning of the chain of blocks, each of which contains the cluster key value and associated rows. If the cluster SIZE is such that more than one key fits in a block, blocks can belong to more than one chain.

Specify the Location of Each Cluster and Cluster Index

If you have the proper privileges and tablespace quota, you can create a new cluster and the associated cluster index in any tablespace that is currently online. Always specify the TABLESPACE option in a CREATE CLUSTER/INDEX statement to identify the tablespace to store the new cluster or index.

The cluster and its cluster index can be created in different tablespaces. In fact, creating a cluster and its index in different tablespaces that are stored on different storage devices allows table data and index data to be retrieved simultaneously with minimal disk contention.

Estimate Cluster Size and Set Storage Parameters

The reasons for estimating a cluster's size before creation are identical to those for estimating table size. See "Estimate Table Size and Set Storage Parameters" on page 8-16.

Use the procedure in the following section to calculate the space required by a cluster.

Calculating Space Required by Clusters

The following procedure demonstrates how to estimate the initial amount of space required by a set of tables in a cluster. Several calculations are required to obtain a final estimate, and several of the constants (indicated by *) provided are operating system specific. Your estimates should not significantly differ from actual values. See your installation or user's guide for any substantial deviations from the constants provided in the following procedure.

Note that this procedure estimates only the initial amount of space required for a cluster. When using these estimates, keep in mind the following points that can affect the accuracy of the estimations:

- The space used by transaction entries and deleted records does not become free immediately after completion due to delayed cleanout.
- Trailing nulls are not stored, nor is a length byte.
- Inserts of, updates to, and deletes of rows, as well as tables containing columns larger than a single data block can cause fragmentation and chained row pieces. Therefore, the following estimates may tend to be lower that the actual space required if significant fragmentation occurs.

Once you calculate a table's size using the following procedure, you should add about 10 to 20 percent additional space to calculate the initial extent size for a working table.

The steps to estimate a cluster's size are as follows:

1. Calculate the total block header size.
2. Calculate the available data space per data block.
3. Calculate the combined column lengths of the average rows per cluster key.
4. Calculate the average row size of all clustered tables.
5. Calculate the average cluster block size.
6. Calculate the total number of blocks required for the cluster.

Each step is explained below.

Step 1: Calculate Total Block Header Size

The following formula returns the amount of space required by the data block header:

```
block header = fixed header + variable transaction header
             + table directory + row directory
```

where:

fixed header*	57 bytes
variable transaction header*	23*I I is the value of INITRANS for the table.
table directory*	4*N + 1 N is the number of tables in the data segment.

row directory* $2*R$

R is the number of rows in the block. R will be estimated and the space required to hold the row directory information included in Step 5.

IF INITRANS = 2, the previous formula can be partially solved:

```
block header = 57 + 46 + (4N + 1) + 2R bytes
             = 104 + 4N + 2R bytes
```

Step 2: Calculate Available Data Space Per Data Block

The space reserved in each data block for data, as specified by PCTFREE, is calculated as the block size minus the block header:

```
available
data         = (block size - total block header)
space
```

The block size of a database is set during database creation and can be determined using the SQL*DBA command SHOW:

```
SHOW PARAMETERS db_block_size;
```

Utilities

Note: For more information about the SQL*DBA command SHOW, see the *ORACLE7 Server Utilities User's Guide.*

Assuming a data block size of 2K, the total space for new data in data blocks allocated for the cluster is as follows:

```
available
data         = (2048 - (104 + 4N + 2R)
space
             = (1944 - 4N - 2R) bytes
             = (1944 - 4N - 2R) bytes
```

Assuming there are two tables in the clusters (that is, N = 2), the formula simplifies to:

```
available
data         = 1944 - (4*2) - 2R  bytes
space
             = 19362 - 2R  bytes
```

Step 3: Calculate Space Required by a Row

Use Step 3 in the procedure discussed in "Calculating Space Required by Non-Clustered Tables" on page 8-19 to calculate this number. Make note of the following caveats:

- Calculate the data space required by an average row for each table in the cluster. For example, in a cluster that contains tables T1 and T2, calculate the average row size for both tables.

- Do not include the space required by the cluster key in any of the above calculations. However, make note of the space required to store an average cluster key value for Step 5. For example, calculate the data space required by an average row in table T1, not including the space required to store the cluster key.
- Do not include any space required by the row header (that is, the length bytes for each column); this space is accounted for in the next step.

For example, assume two clustered tables are created with the following statements:

```
CREATE TABLE t1 (a CHAR(10), b DATE, c NUMBER(10,2))
        CLUSTER t1_t2 (c);

CREATE TABLE t2 (c NUMBER(10,2), d CHAR(10))
        CLUSTER t1_t2 (c);
```

Notice that the cluster key is column C in each table.

Considering these example tables, the space required for an average row (D_1) of table T1 and the space required for an average row (D_2) of table T2 is:

```
D1 (space/average row) = (a + b)
                       = (10 + 7) bytes
                       = 17 bytes

D2 (space/average row) = (d)
                       = 10 bytes
```

Step 4: Calculate Total Average Row Size

You can calculate the minimum amount of space required by a row in a clustered table according to the following equation:

```
Sn bytes/row = row header + Fn + Vn + Dn
```

where:

row header*	4 bytes per row of a clustered table.
F_n	Total length bytes of all columns in table *n* that store 250 bytes or less. The number of length bytes required by each column of this type is 1 byte.
V_n	Total length bytes of all columns in table *n* that store more than 250 bytes. The number of length bytes required by each column of this type is 3 bytes.
D_n	Combined data space of all columns in table *n* (from Step 3).

Note: Do not include the column length for the cluster key in variables F or V for any table in the cluster. This space is accounted for in Step 5.

For example, the total average row size of the clustered tables T1 and T2 are:

```
S1 = (4 + (1 * 2) + (3 * 0) + 17) bytes
   = 23 bytes

S2 = (4 + (1 * 1) + (3 * 0) + 10) bytes
   = 15 bytes
```

Note: The absolute minimum row size of a clustered row is 10 bytes, and is operating system specific. Therefore, if your calculated value for a table's total average row size is less than these absolute minimum row sizes, use the minimum value as the average row size in subsequent calculations.

Step 5: Calculate Average Cluster Block Size

To calculate the average cluster block size, first estimate the average number of rows (for all tables) per cluster key. Once this is known, use the following formula to calculate average cluster block size:

```
avg. cluster block size (bytes)=
((R1*S1) + (R2*S2) + .. + (Rn*Sn)) + key header + Ck + Sk + 2Rt
```

where:

R_n	The average number of rows in table *n* associated with a cluster key.
S_n	The average row size in table *n* (see Step 4).
key header*	19
C_k	Column length for the cluster key.

S_k	Space required to store average cluster key value.
R_t	Total number of rows associated with an average cluster key ($R_1 + R_2 + ... + R_n$). This accounts for the space required in the data block header for each row in the block.

For example, consider the cluster that contains tables T1 and T2. An average cluster key has one row per table T1 and 20 rows per table T2. Also, the cluster key is of datatype NUMBER (column length is 1 byte), and the average number is 4 digits (3 bytes). Considering this information and the previous results, the average cluster key size is:

```
SIZE = ((1 * 23) + (20 * 15) + 19 + 1 + 3 + (2 * 21)) bytes
     = 388 bytes
```

Specify the estimated SIZE in the SIZE option when you create the cluster with the CREATE CLUSTER command. This specifies the space required to hold an average cluster key and its associated rows; ORACLE uses the value of SIZE to limit the number of cluster keys that can be assigned to any given data block. After estimating an average cluster key SIZE, choose a SIZE somewhat larger than the average expected size to account for the space required for cluster keys on the high side of the estimate.

To estimate the number of cluster keys that will fit in a database block, use the following formula, which uses the value you calculated in Step 2 for available data space, the number of rows associated with an average cluster key (R_t), and SIZE:

```
# cluster keys = FLOOR(available data space + 2R /
  per block               SIZE + 2Rt)
```

For example, with SIZE previously calculated as 400 bytes (calculated as 388 earlier in this step and rounded up), R_t estimated at 21, and available space per data block (from Step 2) calculated as 1742 - 2*R* bytes, the result is as follows:

```
# cluster keys = FLOOR((1936 - 2R + 2R)/
  per block               (400 + 2 * 21))
               = FLOOR(1936 / 442)
               = FLOOR(4.4)
               = 4
```

Step 6: Calculate Total Number of Blocks

To calculate the total number of blocks for the cluster, you must estimate the number of cluster keys in the cluster. Once this is estimated, use the following formula to calculate the total number of blocks required for the cluster:

```
# blocks = CEIL(# cluster keys / # cluster keys per block)
```

Note: If you have a test database, you can use statistics generated by the ANALYZE command to determine the number of key values in a cluster key. See "Analyzing Tables, Indexes, and Clusters" on page 8-62.

For example, assume that there is approximately 500 cluster keys in the T1_T2 cluster.

```
# blocks T1_T2 = CEIL(500/3)
               = CEIL(166.7)
               = 167
```

To convert the number of blocks to bytes, multiply the number of blocks by the data block size.

This procedure provides a reasonable **estimation** of a cluster's size, but not an exact number of blocks or bytes. Once you have estimated the space for a cluster, you can use this information when specifying the INITIAL storage parameter (size of the cluster's initial extent) in your corresponding CREATE CLUSTER statement.

Space Requirements for Clustered Tables in Use

Once clustered tables are created and in use, the space required by the tables is usually higher than the estimate given by the previous section. More space is required due to the method ORACLE uses to manage free space in the database.

Creating Clusters, Clustered Tables, and Cluster Indexes

A cluster is used to store one or more tables that are frequently joined together in queries. A cluster should not be used to cluster tables that are frequently accessed individually.

Once a cluster is created, tables can be created in the cluster. However, before any rows can be inserted into the clustered tables, a cluster index must be created. The use of clusters does not affect the creation of additional indexes on the clustered tables; they can be created and dropped as usual.

Create a cluster using the SQL command CREATE CLUSTER. For example, the following statement creates a cluster named EMP_DEPT, which stores the EMP and DEPT tables, clustered by the DEPTNO column:

```
CREATE CLUSTER emp_dept (deptno NUMBER(3))
    PCTUSED 80
    PCTFREE 5
    SIZE 600
    TABLESPACE users
    STORAGE (INITIAL 200k
             NEXT 300K
             MINEXTENTS 2
             MAXEXTENTS 20
             PCTINCREASE 33);
```

A table is created in a cluster using the SQL command CREATE TABLE with the CLUSTER option. For example, the EMP and DEPT tables can be created in the EMP_DEPT cluster using the following statements:

```
CREATE TABLE dept (
    deptno NUMBER(3) PRIMARY KEY, . . . )
    CLUSTER emp_dept (deptno);

CREATE TABLE emp (
    empno NUMBER(5) PRIMARY KEY,
    ename VARCHAR2(15) NOT NULL,
    . . .
    deptno NUMBER(3) REFERENCES dept)
    CLUSTER emp_dept (deptno);
```

Note: You can specify the schema for a clustered table is specified in the CREATE TABLE statement; a clustered table can be in a different schema than that which contains the cluster.

A cluster index must be created before any rows can be inserted into any clustered table. For example, the following statement creates a cluster index for the EMP_DEPT cluster:

```
CREATE INDEX emp_dept_index
    ON CLUSTER emp_dept
    INITRANS 2
    MAXTRANS 5
    TABLESPACE users
    STORAGE (INITIAL 50K
             NEXT 50K
             MINEXTENTS 2
             MAXEXTENTS 10
             PCTINCREASE 33)
    PCTFREE 5;
```

The cluster key establishes the relationship of the tables in the cluster. Several storage settings are explicitly specified for the cluster and cluster index.

Privileges Required to Create a Cluster, Clustered Table, and Cluster Index

To create a cluster in your schema, you must have the CREATE CLUSTER system privilege and a quota for the tablespace intended to contain the cluster or the UNLIMITED TABLESPACE system privilege. To create a cluster in another user's schema, you must have the CREATE ANY CLUSTER system privilege and the owner must have a quota for the tablespace intended to contain the cluster or the UNLIMITED TABLESPACE system privilege.

To create a table in a cluster, you must have either the CREATE TABLE or CREATE ANY TABLE system privilege. You do not need a tablespace quota or the UNLIMITED TABLESPACE system privilege to create a table in a cluster.

To create a cluster index, one of the following conditions must be true:

- Your schema contains the cluster and you have the CREATE INDEX system privilege.
- You have the CREATE ANY INDEX system privilege.

In either case, you must also have either a quota for the tablespace intended to contain the cluster index, or the UNLIMITED TABLESPACE system privilege.

See Chapter 12 for more information about system privileges and Chapter 11 about tablespace quotas.

Altering Clusters

You can alter an existing cluster to change the following settings:

- data block space usage parameters (PCTFREE, PCTUSED)
- the average cluster key size (SIZE)
- transaction entry settings (INITRANS, MAXTRANS)
- storage parameters (NEXT, PCTINCREASE, etc.)

Note: See "Managing Tables" and "Managing Clusters, Cluster Tables, and Cluster Indexes" on pages 8-15 and 8-41, respectively, for guidelines on these options.

When you alter data block space usage parameters (PCTFREE and PCTUSED) or the cluster size parameter (SIZE) of a cluster, the new settings apply to all data blocks used by the cluster, including blocks already allocated and blocks subsequently allocated for the cluster. Blocks already allocated for the table are reorganized when necessary (not immediately).

When you alter transaction entry settings (INITRANS, MAXTRANS) of a cluster, a new setting for INITRANS applies only to data blocks subsequently allocated for the cluster, while a new setting for

MAXTRANS applies to all blocks (already and subsequently allocated blocks) of a cluster.

The storage parameters INITIAL and MINEXTENTS cannot be altered. All new settings for the other storage parameters affect only extents subsequently allocated for the cluster.

To alter a cluster, use the SQL command ALTER CLUSTER. For example, the following statement alters the EMP_DEPT cluster:

```
ALTER CLUSTER emp_dept
    PCTFREE 30
    PCTUSED 60;
```

Privileges Required to Alter a Cluster

To alter a cluster, your schema must contain the cluster or you must have the ALTER ANY CLUSTER system privilege.

Altering Clustered Tables and Cluster Indexes

You can alter clustered tables using the SQL command ALTER TABLE. However, any data block space parameters, transaction entry parameters, or storage parameters you set in an ALTER TABLE statement for a clustered table are ignored; ORACLE uses the parameters of the cluster for all clustered tables. Therefore, you can use the ALTER TABLE command only to add or modify columns, or add, drop, enable, or disable integrity constraints or triggers for a clustered table. See "Altering Tables" on page 8-23.

You alter cluster indexes exactly as you do other indexes. See "Altering an Index" on page 8-39.

Manually Allocating Storage for a Cluster

ORACLE dynamically allocates additional extents for the data segment of a cluster, as required. In some circumstances, however, you might want to allocate an additional extent for a cluster explicitly. For example, when using the ORACLE Parallel Server, you can allocate an extent of a cluster explicitly for a specific instance.

Parallel

You allocate a new extent for a cluster using the SQL command ALTER CLUSTER with the ALLOCATE EXTENT option. For more information about this parameter of the ALTER CLUSTER command, see the *ORACLE7 Parallel Server Administrator's Guide.*

Dropping Clusters, Clustered Tables, and Cluster Indexes

A cluster can be dropped if the tables within the cluster are no longer necessary. When a cluster is dropped, so are the tables within the cluster and the corresponding cluster index; all extents belonging to both the cluster's data segment and the index segment of the cluster index are returned to the containing tablespace and become available for other segments within the tablespace.

Clustered tables can be dropped individually without affecting the table's cluster, other clustered tables, or the cluster index. A clustered table is dropped just as a non-clustered table is dropped—with the SQL command DROP TABLE; see "Dropping Tables" on page 8-25.

Note: When you drop a single table from a cluster, ORACLE deletes each row of the table individually. To maximize efficiency when you intend to drop an entire cluster, drop the cluster including all tables by using the DROP CLUSTER command with the INCLUDING TABLES option. Drop an individual table from a cluster (using the DROP TABLE command) only if you want the rest of the cluster to remain.

A cluster index can be dropped without affecting the cluster or its clustered tables. However, clustered tables cannot be used if there is no cluster index; you must re-create the cluster index to allow access to the cluster. Cluster indexes are sometimes dropped as part of the procedure to rebuild a fragmented cluster index. See "Dropping Indexes" on page 8-40.

To drop a cluster that contains no tables, and its cluster index, use the SQL command DROP CLUSTER. For example, the following statement drops the empty cluster named EMP_DEPT:

```
DROP CLUSTER emp_dept;
```

If the cluster contains one or more clustered tables and you intend to drop the tables as well, add the INCLUDING TABLES option of the DROP CLUSTER command, as in:

```
DROP CLUSTER emp_dept INCLUDING TABLES;
```

If the INCLUDING TABLES option is not included and the cluster contains tables, an error is returned.

If one or more tables in a cluster contain primary or unique keys that are referenced by FOREIGN KEY constraints of tables outside the cluster, the cluster cannot be dropped unless the dependent FOREIGN KEY constraints are also dropped. This can be easily done using the CASCADE CONSTRAINTS option of the DROP CLUSTER command. For example:

```
DROP CLUSTER emp_dept INCLUDING TABLES CASCADE CONSTRAINTS;
```

ORACLE returns an error if you do not use the CASCADE CONSTRAINTS option and constraints exist.

Privileges Required to Drop a Cluster

To drop a cluster, your schema must contain the cluster or you must have the DROP ANY CLUSTER system privilege. You do not have to have additional privileges to drop a cluster that contains tables, even if the clustered tables are not owned by the owner of the cluster.

Managing Hash Clusters and Clustered Tables

The following sections explain how to create, alter, and drop hash clusters and clustered tables using SQL commands. Several examples of these commands are given.

Deciding When to Use Hashing

Storing a table in a hash cluster is an alternative to storing the same table with an index. Hashing is useful in the following situations:

- Most queries are equality queries on the cluster key. For example:

  ```
  SELECT . . . WHERE cluster_key = . . . ;
  ```

  In such cases, the cluster key in the equality condition is hashed, and the corresponding hash key is usually found with a single read. In comparison, for an indexed table the key value must first be found in the index (usually several reads), and then the row is read from the table (another read).

- The tables in the hash cluster are primarily static in size so that you can determine the number of rows and amount of space required for the tables in the cluster. If tables in a hash cluster require more space than the initial allocation for the cluster, performance degradation can be substantial because overflow blocks are required.

Hashing is not advantageous in the following situations:

- Most queries on the table retrieve rows over a range of cluster key values. For example, in full table scans, or queries such as:

  ```
  SELECT . . . WHERE cluster_key < . . . ;
  ```

  In such cases, a hash function cannot be used to determine the location of specific hash keys; instead, the equivalent of a full table scan must be done to fetch the rows for the query. With an index, key values are ordered in the index, so cluster key values that satisfy the WHERE clause of a query can be found with relatively few I/Os.

- The table is not static and continually growing. If a table grows without limit, the space required over the life of the table (thus, its cluster) cannot be predetermined.
- Applications frequently perform full-table scans on the table and the table is sparsely populated. A full-table scan in this situation takes longer under hashing.
- You cannot afford to pre-allocate the space that the hash cluster will eventually need.

In most cases, you should decide (based on the above information) whether to use hashing or indexing. If you decide to use indexing, you should consider whether to store a table individually or as part of a cluster; see "Choose Appropriate Tables to Cluster" on page 8-41.

Note: Even if you decide to use hashing, a table can still have separate indexes on any columns, including the cluster key. See the *ORACLE7 Server Application Developer's Guide* for additional recommendations.

Calculating Space Required by Hash Clusters

As with index clusters, it is important to estimate the storage required for the data in a hash cluster. Use the procedure explained in "Calculating Space Required by Clusters" on page 8-43, with the following additional notes:

- A sub-goal of the procedure is to determine the SIZE of each cluster key. However, for hash clusters, the corresponding sub-goal is to determine the SIZE of each hash key. Therefore, you must consider not only the number of rows per cluster key value, but also the distribution of cluster keys over the hash keys in the cluster.
- In Step 3, make sure to include the space required by the cluster key value. Unlike an index cluster, the cluster key value is stored with each row placed in a hash cluster.
- In Step 5, you are calculating the average hash key size, not cluster key size. Therefore, take into account how many cluster keys map to each hash value. Also, disregard the addition of the space required by the cluster key value, C_k. This value has already been accounted for in Step 3 (see previous item).

ORACLE guarantees that the initial allocation of space is sufficient to store the hash table according to the settings SIZE and HASHKEYS. If settings for the storage parameters INITIAL, NEXT, and MINEXTENTS do not account for the hash table size, incremental (additional) extents are allocated until at least SIZE*HASHKEYS is reached. For example, assume that the data block size is 2K, the available data space per block is approximately 1900 bytes (data block size minus overhead), and that the STORAGE and HASH parameters are specified in the CREATE CLUSTER command as follows:

```
STORAGE (INITIAL 100K
         NEXT 150K
         MINEXTENTS 1
         PCTINCREASE 0)
SIZE 1500
HASHKEYS 100
```

In this example, only one hash key can be assigned per data block. Therefore, the initial space required for the hash cluster is at least 100*2K or 200K. The settings for the storage parameters do not account for this requirement. Therefore, an initial extent of 100K and a second extent of 150K are allocated to the hash cluster.

Alternatively, assume the HASH parameters are specified as:

```
SIZE 500 HASHKEYS 100
```

In this case, three hash keys are assigned to each data block. Therefore, the initial space required for the hash cluster is at least 34*2K or 68K. The settings for the storage parameters account for this requirement (an initial extent of 100K is allocated to the hash cluster).

Creating Hash Clusters and Clustered Tables

A hash cluster is used to store individual tables or a group of clustered tables that are static and often queried by equality queries. Once a hash cluster is created, tables can be created in the cluster.

A hash cluster is created using the SQL command CREATE CLUSTER. For example, the following statement creates a cluster named TRIAL_CLUSTER that is used to store the TRIAL table, clustered by the TRIALNO column:

```
CREATE CLUSTER trial_cluster (trialno NUMBER(5,0))
  PCTUSED 80
  PCTFREE 5
  TABLESPACE users
  STORAGE (INITIAL 250K   NEXT 50K
           MINEXTENTS 1   MAXEXTENTS 3
           PCTINCREASE 0)
  SIZE 2K
  HASH IS trialno HASHKEYS 150;

CREATE TABLE trial (
    trialno      NUMBER(5,0) PRIMARY KEY,
    ...)
    CLUSTER trial_cluster (trialno);
```

The following sections explain setting the parameters of the CREATE CLUSTER command specific to hash clusters. For additional information about creating tables in a cluster, guidelines for setting other parameters of the CREATE CLUSTER command, and the privileges required to create a hash cluster, see "Creating Clusters, Clustered Tables, and Cluster Indexes" on page 8-49.

Controlling Space Use Within a Hash Cluster

When creating a hash cluster, it is important to choose the cluster key correctly and set the HASH IS, SIZE, and HASHKEYS parameters so that performance and space use are optimal. The following sections provide guidance as well as examples of setting these parameters.

Choosing the Key Choosing the correct cluster key is dependent on the most common types of queries issued against the clustered tables. For example, consider the EMP table in a hash cluster. If queries often select rows by employee number, the EMPNO column should be the cluster key; if queries often select rows by department number, the DEPTNO column should be the cluster key. For hash clusters that contain a single table, the cluster key is typically the entire primary key of the contained table.

The key of a hash cluster (like that of an index cluster) can be a single column or a composite key (multiple column key). A hash cluster with a composite key must use ORACLE's internal hash function.

Setting HASH IS Only specify the HASH IS parameter if the cluster key is a single column of the NUMBER datatype, and contains uniformly distributed integers. If the above conditions apply, you can distribute rows in the cluster so that each unique cluster key value hashes to a unique hash value (with no collisions); also see the following sections for information on setting SIZE and HASHKEYS. If the above conditions do not apply, omit this option so that you use the internal hash function.

Setting SIZE SIZE should be set to the average amount of space required to hold all rows for any given hash key. Therefore, to properly determine SIZE, you must be aware of the characteristics of your data.

- If the hash cluster is to contain only a single table and the hash key values of the rows in that table are unique (one row per value), SIZE can be set to the average row size in the cluster.
- If the hash cluster is to contain multiple tables, SIZE can be set to the average amount of space required to hold all rows associated with a representative hash value.

To calculate a preliminary value for SIZE, follow the procedures given in "Calculating Space Required by Hash Clusters" on page 8-55. If the preliminary value for SIZE is small (more than four hash keys can be assigned per data block), you can use this value for SIZE in the CREATE CLUSTER command. However, if the value of SIZE is large (fewer than five hash keys can be assigned per data block), you should also consider the expected frequency of collisions and whether performance of data retrieval or efficiency of space usage is more important to you:

- If the hash cluster does not use the internal hash function (if you specified HASH IS) and you expect little or no collisions, you can set SIZE as calculated above; no collisions occur and space is used as efficiently as possible.
- If you expect frequent collisions on inserts, the likelihood of overflow blocks being allocated to store rows is high. To reduce the possibility of overflow blocks and maximize performance when collisions are frequent, you should increase SIZE according to the following chart:

Available Space per Block/Calc'd SIZE	Setting for SIZE
1	Calc'd SIZE
2	Calc'd SIZE + 15%
3	Calc'd SIZE + 12%
4	Calc'd SIZE + 8%
> 4	Calc'd SIZE

Overestimating the value of SIZE increases the amount of unused space in the cluster. If space efficiency is more important than the performance of data retrieval, disregard the above adjustments and use the calculated value for SIZE.

Setting HASHKEYS HASHKEYS should always be set to the number of unique cluster key values rounded up to the next prime number (assuming the guidance in the previous two sections is used). For maximum distribution of rows in a hash cluster, HASHKEYS should always be a prime number.

For example, suppose you cluster the EMP table by DEPTNO, and there are 100 DEPTNOs, with values 10, 20, . . ., 1000. Assuming you bypass the internal hash function and you create a cluster with HASHKEYS of 100, then department 10 will hash to 10, department 20 to 20, . . ., department 110 to 10 (110 mod 100), department 120 to 20, and so on. Notice that there are 10 entries for hash values of 10, 20, . . ., but none for 1, 2, . . ., and so on. As a result, there is a lot of wasted space and possibly a lot of overflow blocks because of collisions. Alternatively, if HASHKEYS is set to 101, then each department number hashes to a unique hash key value.

Examples of Choosing the Key and Setting HASH IS, SIZE, and HASHKEYS The following examples show how to correctly choose the cluster key and set the HASH IS, SIZE, and HASHKEYS parameters. For all examples, assume that the data block size is 2K and that on average, 1950 bytes of each block is available data space (block size minus overhead).

Example 1 You decide to load the EMP table into a hash cluster. Most queries retrieve employee records by their employee number. You estimate that the maximum number of rows in the EMP table at any given time is 10000 and that the average row size is 55 bytes.

In this case, EMPNO should be the cluster key. Since this column contains integers that are unique, the internal hash function can be bypassed. SIZE can be set to the average row size, 55 bytes; note that 34 hash keys are assigned per data block. HASHKEYS can be set to the number of rows in the table, 10000, rounded up to the next highest prime number, 10001:

```
CREATE CLUSTER emp_cluster (empno NUMBER)
. . .
SIZE 55
HASH IS empno HASHKEYS 10001;
```

Example 2 Conditions similar to the previous example exist. In this case, however, rows are usually retrieved by department number. At most, there are 1000 departments with an average of 10 employees per department. Note that department numbers increment by 10 (0, 10, 20, 30, . . .).

In this case, DEPTNO should be the cluster key. Since this column contains integers that are uniformly distributed, the internal hash function can be bypassed. A precalculated SIZE (the average amount of space required to hold all rows per department) is 55 bytes * 10, or 550 bytes. Using this value for SIZE, only three hash keys can be assigned per data block. If you expect some collisions and want maximum performance of data retrieval, slightly alter your calculated SIZE to prevent collisions from requiring overflow blocks. By adjusting SIZE by 12%, to 620 bytes (see previous section about setting SIZE for clarification), only three hash keys are assigned per data block, leaving more space for rows from expected collisions.

HASHKEYS can be set to the number of unique department numbers, 1000, rounded up to the next highest prime number, 1009.

```
CREATE CLUSTER emp_cluster (deptno NUMBER)
. . .
SIZE 620
HASH IS deptno HASHKEYS 1009;
```

Altering Hash Clusters

You alter a hash cluster with the SQL command ALTER CLUSTER:

```
ALTER CLUSTER emp_dept . . . ;
```

The implications for altering a hash cluster are identical for altering an index cluster. However, note that the SIZE, HASHKEYS, and HASH IS parameters cannot be specified in an ALTER CLUSTER statement. You must re-create the cluster to change these parameters and then copy the data from the original cluster. See "Altering Clusters" on page 8-51.

Dropping Hash Clusters

A hash cluster is dropped using the SQL command DROP CLUSTER:

```
DROP CLUSTER emp_dept;
```

A table in a hash cluster is dropped using the SQL command DROP TABLE. The implications of dropping hash clusters and tables in hash clusters are the same for index clusters. See "Dropping Clusters, Clustered Tables, and Cluster Indexes" on page 8-52.

Miscellaneous Management for Schema Objects

The following sections explain miscellaneous topics regarding the management of the various schema objects discussed in this chapter.

Creating Multiple Tables and Views in One Operation

You can create several tables and views and grant privileges in one operation using the SQL command CREATE SCHEMA. The CREATE SCHEMA command is useful if you want to guarantee the creation of several tables and views and grants in one operation; if an individual table or view creation fails or a grant fails, the entire statement is rolled back and none of the objects are created or the privileges granted. For example, the following statement creates two tables and a view that joins data from the two tables:

```
CREATE SCHEMA AUTHORIZATION scott
  CREATE TABLE dept (
    deptno    NUMBER(3,0) PRIMARY KEY,
    dname     VARCHAR2(15),
    loc       VARCHAR2(25)
  CREATE TABLE emp (
    empno     NUMBER(5,0) PRIMARY KEY,
    ename     VARCHAR2(15) NOT NULL,
    job       VARCHAR2(10),
    mgr       NUMBER(5,0),
    hiredate  DATE DEFAULT (sysdate),
    sal       NUMBER(7,2),
    comm      NUMBER(7,2),
    deptno    NUMBER(3,0) NOT NULL
    CONSTRAINT dept_fkey REFERENCES dept)
  CREATE VIEW sales_staff AS
    SELECT empno, ename, sal, comm
      FROM emp
     WHERE deptno = 30
    WITH CHECK OPTION CONSTRAINT sales_staff_cnst
  GRANT SELECT ON sales_staff TO human_resources;
```

The CREATE SCHEMA command does not support ORACLE extensions to the ANSI CREATE TABLE and CREATE VIEW commands; this includes the STORAGE clause.

Privileges Required to Create Multiple Schema Objects

To create schema objects using the CREATE SCHEMA command, you must have the required privileges for any included operation. For example, to create multiple tables using the CREATE SCHEMA command, you must have the privileges required to create tables.

Renaming Schema Objects

You can rename schema objects using two different methods: drop and re-create the object, or rename the object using the SQL command RENAME. If you drop an object and re-create it, all privilege grants for the object are lost. Privileges must be regranted when the object is recreated. Alternatively, a table, view, sequence, or a private synonym of a table, view, or sequence can be renamed using the RENAME command. When using the RENAME command, grants made for the object are carried forward for the new name. For example, the following statement renames the SALES_STAFF view:

```
RENAME sales_staff TO dept_30;
```

Note: You cannot rename a stored PL/SQL program unit, public synonym, index, or cluster. To rename such an object, you must drop and re-create it.

Before renaming a schema object, you should understand the following effects:

- All views and PL/SQL program units dependent on a renamed object become invalid (must be recompiled before next use). See page 8-75 for more information about how ORACLE manages such dependencies.
- All synonyms for a renamed object return an error when used.

Privileges Required to Rename an Object

To rename an object, you must own the object.

Analyzing Tables, Indexes, and Clusters

You can analyze a table (non-clustered or clustered), index, or cluster to gather data about it or to verify the validity of its storage format.

- A table, index, or cluster can be analyzed to collect or update statistics about the object. When a DML statement is issued, the statistics for the referenced objects are used to determine the most efficient execution plan for the statement; such optimization is called "cost-based optimization." The statistics are stored in the data dictionary. (For more information about analyzing tables, indexes, and clusters for performance statistics and the optimizer, see the *ORACLE7 Server Application Developer's Guide*.)

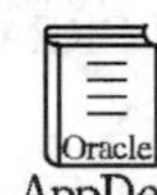

AppDev

- A table, index, or cluster can be analyzed to *validate* (confirm the integrity of) the structure of the object. For example, in rare cases (due to hardware or other system failures) an index can become corrupted and not perform its job correctly; when validating the index, you can confirm that every entry in the index points to the correct row of the associated table. If a schema object is corrupt, you can drop and re-create it.
- A table or cluster can be analyzed to collect information about chained rows of the table or cluster. This result is useful in determining whether you have enough room for updates to rows; for example, it can show whether PCTFREE is set appropriately for the table or cluster.

Updating and Deleting Statistics for Tables, Indexes, and Clusters

Statistics about the physical storage characteristics of a table, index, or cluster can be gathered and stored in the data dictionary using the SQL command ANALYZE with the STATISTICS option. Such statistics can be used by ORACLE when cost-based optimization is used to choose the most efficient execution plan for SQL statements that access analyzed objects. The database administrator or application developer can also use statistics generated by this command to write efficient SQL statements that access analyzed objects.

Statistics can be computed or estimated when using the ANALYZE command, as specified by the COMPUTE STATISTICS or ESTIMATE STATISTICS options, respectively:

- When computing statistics, an entire object is scanned to gather data about the object. The data is then used by ORACLE to compute exact statistics about the object. Therefore, slight variances throughout the object are accounted for in computed statistics. Because an entire object is scanned to gather information for computed statistics, the larger the size of an object, the more work that is required to gather the necessary information.
- When estimating statistics, ORACLE gathers representative information from portions of an object. This subset of information is used to provide reasonable, estimated statistics about the object. Therefore, the accuracy of estimated statistics depend on the representativeness of the sampling used by ORACLE. Because only parts of an object are scanned to gather information for estimated statistics, an object can be analyzed quickly. You can optionally specify the number or percentage of rows that ORACLE should use in making the estimate.

Whether statistics for an object are computed or estimated, the statistics are stored in the data dictionary. The statistics can be queried using the following data dictionary views:

- USER_INDEXES, ALL_INDEXES, DBA_INDEXES
- USER_TABLES, ALL_TABLES, DBA_TABLES
- USER_TAB_COLUMNS, ALL_TAB_COLUMNS, DBA_TAB_COLUMNS

Note: These tables contain entries (rows) only for indexes, tables, and clusters for which you have gathered statistics. The entries are updated for an object each time you ANALYZE the object.

You can gather the following statistics on a table:

- number of rows
- number of blocks that have been used (computed only)
- number of blocks never used
- average available free space
- number of chained rows
- average row length

- number of distinct values per column
- the second smallest value per column (computed only)
- the second largest value per column (computed only)

Note: Statistics for all indexes associated with a table are automatically gathered when the table is analyzed for statistics.

You can gather the following statistics on an index:

- index level (computed only)
- number of leaf blocks
- number of distinct keys
- average number of leaf blocks/key
- average number of data blocks/key
- clustering factor
- minimum key value (computed only)
- maximum key value (computed only)

The only statistic that can be gathered for a cluster is the average cluster key chain length; this statistic can be estimated or computed. Statistics for tables in a cluster and all indexes associated with the cluster's tables (including the cluster key index) are automatically gathered when the cluster is analyzed for statistics.

Note: If the data dictionary currently contains statistics for the specified object when an ANALYZE statement is issued, the new statistics replace the old statistics in the data dictionary.

Computing Statistics The following statement computes statistics for the EMP table:

```
ANALYZE TABLE emp COMPUTE STATISTICS;
```

Estimating Statistics for a Schema Object The following query estimates statistics on the EMP table, using the default statistical sample of 1064 rows:

```
ANALYZE TABLE emp ESTIMATE STATISTICS;
```

To specify the statistical sample that ORACLE should use, include the SAMPLE option with the ESTIMATE STATISTICS option. You can specify an integer that indicates either a number of rows or index values, or a percentage of the rows or index values in the table. The following statements show examples of each option:

```
ANALYZE TABLE emp
  ESTIMATE STATISTICS
    SAMPLE 2000 ROWS;
```

```
ANALYZE TABLE emp
  ESTIMATE STATISTICS
    SAMPLE 33 PERCENT;
```

In either case, if you specify a percentage greater than 50, or a number of rows or index values that is greater than 50% of those in the object, ORACLE computes the exact statistics, rather than estimating.

Removing Statistics for a Schema Object Statistics for a table, index, or cluster can be removed from the data dictionary using the DELETE STATISTICS option of the ANALYZE command. For example, you might want to delete statistics for an object if you do not want cost-based optimization to be used for statements regarding the object. For example, the following statement deletes statistics for the EMP table from the data dictionary:

```
ANALYZE TABLE emp DELETE STATISTICS;
```

Shared SQL and Analyzing Statistics Analyzing a table, cluster, or index can affect current shared SQL statements (those statements currently in the shared pool). Whenever an object is analyzed to update or delete statistics, all shared SQL statements that reference the analyzed object are flushed from memory so that the next execution of the statement can take advantage of the new statistics.

Analyzing Statistics for the Data Dictionary To use cost-based optimization on internal and recursive SQL calls, you have to ensure that ORACLE has gathered statistics on the data dictionary, and that these statistics are up-to-date. If no statistics are gathered on the data dictionary, ORACLE uses rule-based optimization on these calls.

If your site has ORACLE with the procedural option, you can call the following procedures:

DBMS_UTILITY.- ANALYZE_SCHEMA()	This procedure takes two arguments, the name of a schema and an analyzation method ('COMPUTE', 'ESTIMATE', or 'DELETE'), and gathers statistics on all of the objects in the schema.
DBMS_DDL.- ANALYZE_OBJECT()	This procedure takes four arguments, the type of an object ('CLUSTER', 'TABLE', or 'INDEX'), the schema of the object, the name of the object, and an analyzation method ('COMPUTE', 'ESTIMATE', or 'DELETE'), and gathers statistics on the object.

You should call these procedures periodically to update the statistics.

Whether or not your site has the procedural option, you can alternatively run the script CATSTAT.SQL, which gathers statistics for the objects in the data dictionary. As with the procedures described above, you should run this script periodically to update the statistics. See "Creating Additional Data Dictionary Structures" on page 2-16 for more information.

Validating Tables, Indexes, and Clusters

To verify the integrity of the structure of a table, index, cluster, or snapshot, use the VALIDATE STRUCTURE option of the ANALYZE command. If the structure is valid, no error is returned. However, if the structure is corrupt, an error message is returned. (If a table, index, or cluster is corrupt, you should drop it and re-create it. If a snapshot is corrupt, perform a complete refresh and check if that rectifies the problem; if it does not, drop and re-create the snapshot.)

For example, the following statement analyzes the EMP table:

```
ANALYZE TABLE emp VALIDATE STRUCTURE;
```

You can validate an object and all related objects by including the CASCADE option. For example, the following statement validates the EMP table and all associated indexes:

```
ANALYZE TABLE emp VALIDATE STRUCTURE CASCADE;
```

Listing Chained Rows of Tables and Clusters

The chained rows (and migrated rows) of a table or cluster can be easily detected using the LIST CHAINED ROWS parameter of the ANALYZE command. The results of this command are stored in a specified table that is created explicitly to accept the information returned by this option of the ANALYZE command.

To create an appropriate table to accept data returned by an ANALYZE... LIST CHAINED ROWS statement, use the UTLCHAIN.SQL script that is provided with ORACLE. The UTLCHAIN.SQL script creates a table named CHAINED_ROWS in the schema of the user that submits the script. The name and location of the UTLCHAIN.SQL script are operating system dependent; see your installation or user's guide.

IUG

After a CHAINED_ROWS table is created, you can specify it when using the ANALYZE command. For example, the following statement inserts rows (containing information about the chained rows in the EMP_DEPT cluster) into the CHAINED_ROWS table:

```
ANALYZE CLUSTER emp_dept LIST CHAINED ROWS INTO chained_rows;
```

AppDev

For more information about reducing the number of chained and migrated rows in a table or cluster, see the *ORACLE7 Server Application Developer's Guide.*

Privileges Required to Analyze a Table, Index, or Cluster

To analyze a table, cluster, or index, you must own the table, cluster, or index or have the ANALYZE ANY system privilege.

Truncating Tables and Clusters

You might want to delete all rows of a table or all rows in a group of clustered tables so that the table (or cluster) still exists, but is completely empty. For example, you may have a table that contains monthly data, and at the end of each month, you need to empty it (delete all rows) after archiving its data.

To delete all rows from a table, you have three options:

- You can delete the rows of a table using the DELETE command. For example, the following statement deletes all rows from the EMP table:

```
DELETE FROM emp;
```

- You can drop a table and then re-create the table. For example, the following statements drop and then recreate the EMP table:

```
DROP TABLE emp;
CREATE TABLE emp ( . . . );
```

- You can delete all rows of the table using the SQL command TRUNCATE. For example, the following statement truncates the EMP table:

```
TRUNCATE TABLE emp;
```

The first option, the DELETE command, has several characteristics, which may or may not be desired. If many rows are present in a table (or cluster), significant system resources are consumed as the rows are deleted (for example, CPU time, redo log space, and rollback segment space) from the table and any associated indexes. Also, as each row is deleted, triggers can be fired. The space previously allocated to the resulting (empty) table or cluster remains associated with that object.

The second option, dropping and recreating a table or cluster, also has several characteristics to consider. For example, all associated indexes, integrity constraints, and triggers are also dropped, all objects that depend on the dropped table (or clustered table) are invalidated, and all grants for the dropped table (or clustered table) are dropped.

In contrast, the TRUNCATE command provides a fast, efficient method for deleting all rows from a table or cluster. A TRUNCATE statement does not generate any rollback information and it commits immediately; it is a DDL statement and cannot be rolled back. A TRUNCATE statement does not affect any structures associated with the table being truncated (constraints and triggers) or authorizations (grants). A TRUNCATE statement also specifies whether or not space currently allocated for the table is returned to the containing tablespace after truncation.

As a TRUNCATE statement deletes rows from a table (or clustered table), triggers associated with the table are not fired. Also, a TRUNCATE statement does not generate any audit information corresponding to DELETE statements if auditing is enabled. Instead, a single audit record is generated for the TRUNCATE statement being issued. (See Chapter 13 for more information about auditing.)

A hash cluster cannot be truncated. Also, tables within a hash or index cluster cannot be individually truncated; truncation of an index cluster deletes all rows from all tables in the cluster. If all the rows must be deleted from an individual clustered table, the DELETE command can be used or the table must be dropped and re-created.

The REUSE STORAGE or DROP STORAGE options of the TRUNCATE command control whether or not space currently allocated for a table or cluster is returned to the containing tablespace after truncation. The default option, DROP STORAGE, reduces the number of extents allocated to the resulting table to the original setting for MINEXTENTS; freed extents are then returned to the system and can be used by other objects. Alternatively, the REUSE STORAGE option specifies that all space currently allocated for the table or cluster remains allocated to it. For example, the following statement truncates the EMP_DEPT cluster, leaving all extents previously allocated for the cluster available for subsequent inserts and deletes:

```
TRUNCATE CLUSTER emp_dept REUSE STORAGE;
```

The REUSE or DROP STORAGE option also applies to any associated indexes; when a table or cluster is truncated, all associated indexes are also truncated. Also note that the storage parameters for a truncated table or cluster (or associated indexes) are not changed as a result of the truncation.

Privileges and Prerequisites Required to Truncate a Table or Cluster

A user can truncate any table or cluster in the user's associated schema. Also, any user that has the DELETE ANY TABLE system privilege can truncate a table or cluster in any schema.

Before truncating a table (or cluster that contains a table) that contains a parent key, all referencing foreign keys in different tables must be disabled; a self-referential constraint does not have to be disabled.

Enabling and Disabling Triggers

A trigger can be in either of two distinct modes:

enabled — An enabled trigger executes its trigger body if a triggering statement is issued and the trigger restriction (if any) evaluates to TRUE.

disabled — A disabled trigger does not execute its trigger body, even if a triggering statement is issued and the trigger restriction (if any) evaluates to TRUE.

Disabling Triggers

You may want to temporarily disable a trigger if one of the following conditions is true:

- An object that the trigger references is not available.
- You have to perform a large data load and want it to proceed quickly without firing triggers.
- You are loading data into the table to which the trigger applies.

By default, triggers are enabled when first created. You disable a trigger using the ALTER TRIGGER command with the DISABLE option. For example, to disable the trigger REORDER on the INVENTORY table, enter the following statement:

```
ALTER TRIGGER reorder DISABLE;
```

You can disable all triggers associated with a table at the same time using the ALTER TABLE command with the DISABLE clause and the ALL TRIGGERS option. For example, to disable all triggers defined for the INVENTORY table, enter the following statement:

```
ALTER TABLE inventory
    DISABLE ALL TRIGGERS;
```

Enabling Triggers

Once you have completed the task that required the trigger to be disabled, you can reenable the trigger so that it fires when appropriate.

You enable a disabled trigger using the ALTER TRIGGER command with the ENABLE option. For example, to enable the disabled trigger named REORDER of the INVENTORY table, enter the following statement:

```
ALTER TRIGGER reorder ENABLE;
```

To enable all triggers defined for a specific table, use the ALTER TABLE command with the ENABLE clause with the ALL TRIGGERS option.

For example, to enable all triggers defined for the INVENTORY table, enter the following statement:

```
ALTER TABLE inventory
    ENABLE ALL TRIGGERS;
```

Privileges Required to Enable and Disable Triggers

To enable or disable triggers using the ALTER TABLE command, you must own the table, have the ALTER object privilege for the table, or have the ALTER ANY TABLE system privilege. To enable or disable an individual trigger using the ALTER TRIGGER command, you must own the trigger or have the ALTER ANY TRIGGER system privilege.

Managing Integrity Constraints

This section explains the mechanisms and procedures for manually enabling and disabling integrity constraint, and dropping constraints.

An integrity constraint defined on a table can be in either of two modes:

enabled — When a constraint is enabled, the rule defined by the constraint is enforced on the data values in the columns that define the constraint. The definition of the constraint is stored in the data dictionary.

disabled — When a constraint is disabled, the rule defined by the constraint is not enforced on the data values in the columns included in the constraint; however, the definition of the constraint is retained in the data dictionary.

An integrity constraint can be thought of as a statement about the data in a database. This statement is always not false when the constraint is enabled. However, the statement may or may not be true when the constraint is disabled because data in violation of the integrity constraint can be in the database.

To enforce the rules defined by integrity constraints, the constraints should always be enabled. In certain situations, however, it is desirable to temporarily disable the integrity constraints of a table for performance reasons. For example:

- when loading large amounts of data into a table using SQL*Loader
- when performing batch operations that make massive changes to a table (for example, changing every employee's number by adding 1000 to the existing number)
- when importing or exporting one table at a time

In all three cases, temporarily turning off integrity constraints can improve the performance of the operation.

While a constraint is enabled, no row that would violate the constraint can be inserted into the table. While the constraint is disabled, though, such a row can be inserted; this row is known as an *exception* to the constraint. While exceptions to a constraint exist in a table, **the constraint cannot be enabled**. The rows that violate the constraint must be either updated or deleted in order for the constraint to be enabled.

You can identify exceptions to a specific integrity constraint while attempting to enable the constraint. See "Reporting Constraint Exceptions" on page 8-73.

Understanding Indexes Associated with Constraints

An index associated with a UNIQUE key or PRIMARY KEY constraint is automatically created by ORACLE when the constraint is enabled, and dropped when the constraint is disabled or dropped; no action is required by the user in either case to manage the index. These associated indexes affect how you manage UNIQUE key and PRIMARY KEY constraints.

When disabling or dropping UNIQUE key and PRIMARY KEY integrity constraints, consider the following issues:

- The constraint's associated index will be dropped when the constraint is dropped or disabled.
- While enabled foreign keys reference a primary or unique key, you cannot disable or drop the primary or unique key constraint.

If the constraint is subsequently enabled or redefined, ORACLE creates another index for the constraint.

Because unique and primary keys have associated indexes, you should factor in the cost of dropping and creating indexes when considering whether or not to disable or drop a UNIQUE or PRIMARY KEY constraint. If the associated index for a UNIQUE key or PRIMARY KEY constraint is extremely large, you may save time by leaving the constraint enabled rather than dropping and re-creating the large index.

Enabling and Disabling Integrity Constraints Upon Definition

When an integrity constraint is defined in a CREATE TABLE or ALTER TABLE statement, it can be enabled by including the ENABLE clause in the constraint's definition or disabled by including the DISABLE clause in the constraint's definition. If neither the ENABLE nor the DISABLE clause is included in a constraint's definition, ORACLE automatically enables the constraint.

Enabling Constraints on Definition The following CREATE TABLE and ALTER TABLE statements both define and enable integrity constraints:

```
CREATE TABLE emp (
   empno NUMBER(5) PRIMARY KEY,  . . . ;
ALTER TABLE emp
   ADD PRIMARY KEY (empno);
```

An ALTER TABLE statement that defines and attempts to enable an integrity constraint may fail because rows of the table may violate the integrity constraint. In this case, the statement is rolled back and the constraint definition is not stored and not enabled. (See "Reporting Constraint Exceptions" on page 8-73.)

To enable a UNIQUE key or PRIMARY KEY (which creates an associated index), the owner of the table also needs a quota for the tablespace intended to contain the index, or the UNLIMITED TABLESPACE system privilege.

Disabling Constraints on Definition The following CREATE TABLE and ALTER TABLE statements both define and disable integrity constraints:

```
CREATE TABLE emp (
   empno NUMBER(5) PRIMARY KEY DISABLE,  . . . ;

ALTER TABLE emp
   ADD PRIMARY KEY (empno) DISABLE;
```

An ALTER TABLE statement that defines and disables an integrity constraints never fails because of rows of the table that violate the integrity constraint. The definition of the constraint is allowed because its rule is not enforced.

Enabling and Disabling Existing Integrity Constraints

The ALTER TABLE command can be used to:

- enable a disabled constraint, using the ENABLE clause
- disable an enabled constraint, using the DISABLE clause

Enabling Disabled Constraints The following statements enable disabled integrity constraints:

```
ALTER TABLE dept
   ENABLE CONSTRAINT dname_ukey;
ALTER TABLE dept
   ENABLE PRIMARY KEY,
   ENABLE UNIQUE (dname, loc);
```

An ALTER TABLE statement that attempts to enable an integrity constraint may fail because rows of the table may violate the integrity constraint. In this case, the statement is rolled back and the constraint is not enabled. (See "Reporting Constraint Exceptions" on page 8-73.)

To enable a UNIQUE key or PRIMARY KEY (which creates an associated index), the owner of the table also needs a quota for the tablespace intended to contain the index, or the UNLIMITED TABLESPACE system privilege.

Disabling Enabled Constraints The following statements disable integrity constraints:

```
ALTER TABLE dept
    DISABLE CONSTRAINT dname_ukey;
ALTER TABLE dept
    DISABLE PRIMARY KEY,
    DISABLE UNIQUE (dname, loc);
```

To disable or drop a UNIQUE key or PRIMARY KEY constraint and all dependent FOREIGN KEY constraints in a single step, use the CASCADE option of the DISABLE or DROP clauses. For example, the following statement disables a PRIMARY KEY constraint and any FOREIGN KEY constraints that depend on it:

```
ALTER TABLE dept
    DISABLE PRIMARY KEY CASCADE;
```

Dropping Integrity Constraints

You can drop an integrity constraint if the rule that it enforces is no longer true or if the constraint is no longer needed. Drop the constraint using the ALTER TABLE command with the DROP clause. For example, the following statements both drop integrity constraints:

```
ALTER TABLE dept
    DROP UNIQUE (dname, loc);
ALTER TABLE emp
    DROP PRIMARY KEY,
    DROP CONSTRAINT dept_fkey;
```

Dropping UNIQUE Key and PRIMARY KEY Constraints Dropping UNIQUE key and PRIMARY KEY constraints drops the associated indexes. Also, if FOREIGN KEYs reference a UNIQUE or PRIMARY KEY, you must include the CASCADE CONSTRAINTS clause in the DROP statement, or you cannot drop the constraint.

Reporting Constraint Exceptions

If no exceptions are present when a CREATE TABLE. . . ENABLE. . . or ALTER TABLE. . . ENABLE. . . statement is issued, the integrity constraint is enabled and all subsequent DML statements are subject to the enabled integrity constraints.

If exceptions exist when a constraint is enabled, an error is returned and the integrity constraint remains disabled. When a statement is not successfully executed because integrity constraint exceptions exist, the statement is rolled back. If exceptions exist, you cannot enable the constraint until all exceptions to the constraint are either updated or deleted.

To determine which rows violate the integrity constraint, include the EXCEPTIONS option in the ENABLE clause of a CREATE TABLE or ALTER TABLE statement. The EXCEPTIONS option places the ROWID, table owner, table name, and constraint name of all exception rows into a specified table. For example, the following statement attempts to enable the primary key of the DEPT table, and if exceptions exist, information is inserted into a table named EXCEPTIONS:

```
ALTER TABLE dept ENABLE PRIMARY KEY EXCEPTIONS INTO exceptions;
```

IUG

Note: You must create an appropriate exceptions report table to accept information from the EXCEPTIONS option of the ENABLE clause before enabling the constraint. An exception table can be created by submitting the script UTLEXCPT.SQL. (The exact name and location of the UTLEXCPT.SQL script are operating system specific; see your installation or user's guide.) The script creates a table named EXCEPTIONS. You can create additional exceptions tables with different names by modifying and resubmitting the script.

If duplicate primary key values exist in the DEPT table and the name of the PRIMARY KEY constraint on DEPT is SYS_C00301, the following rows might be placed in the table EXCEPTIONS by the previous statement:

```
SELECT * FROM exceptions;

 ROWID                OWNER      TABLE_NAME       CONSTRAINT
 ------------------   ---------  --------------   -----------
 000003A5.000C.0001   SCOTT      DEPT             SYS_C00301
 000003A5.000D.0001   SCOTT      DEPT             SYS_C00301
```

A more informative query would be to join the rows in an exception report table and the master table to list the actual rows that violate a specific constraint. For example:

```
SELECT deptno, dname, loc FROM dept, exceptions
    WHERE exceptions.constraint = 'SYS_C00301'
    AND dept.rowid = exceptions.row_id;

DEPTNO     DNAME           LOC
---------- --------------  -------------
        10 ACCOUNTING      NEW YORK
        10 RESEARCH        DALLAS
```

All rows that violate a constraint must be either updated or deleted from the table that contains the constraint. If updating exceptions, you must change the value that violates the constraint to a value consistent with the constraint or a null (if allowed). After the row in the master table is updated or deleted, the corresponding rows for the exception in the exception report table should be deleted to avoid confusion with later exception reports. The statements that update the master table and the exception report table should be in the same transaction to ensure transaction consistency.

For example, to correct the exceptions in the previous examples, the following transaction might be issued:

```
UPDATE dept SET deptno = 20 WHERE dname = 'RESEARCH';
DELETE FROM exceptions WHERE constraint = 'SYS_C00301';
COMMIT;
```

The goal, when managing exceptions, is to eliminate all exceptions in your exception report table.

Note: While you are correcting current exceptions for a table with the constraint disabled, other users may issue statements creating new exceptions.

Managing Object Dependencies

The following table shows how objects are affected by changes in other objects on which they depend.

TABLE 8-1 Operations that Affect Object Status

Operation	Resulting Status of Object	Resulting Status of Dependent Objects
CREATE table, sequence, synonym	VALID if there are no errors	No change*
ALTER table [ADD column |MODIFY column] RENAME table, sequence, synonym, view	VALID if there are no errors	INVALID
DROP table, sequence, synonym, view, procedure, function, package	None; the object is dropped	INVALID
CREATE view, procedure**	VALID if there are no errors; INVALID if there are syntax or authorization errors	no change*
CREATE OR REPLACE *viewor procedure***	VALID if there are no errors; INVALID if there are syntax or authorization errors	INVALID
REVOKE *object privilege**** ON *object* TO/FROM *user*	No change	All objects of *user* that depend on *object* are INVALID***
REVOKE *object privilege**** ON *object* TO/FROM PUBLIC	No change	All objects in the database that depend on *object* are INVALID***
REVOKE *system privilege***** TO/FROM *user*	No change	All objects of *user* are INVALID****
REVOKE *system privilege***** TO/FROM PUBLIC	No change	All objects in the database are INVALID****

* May cause dependent objects to be made INVALID, if object did not exist earlier.

** Stand-alone procedures and functions, packages, and triggers.

*** Only DML object privileges, including SELECT, INSERT, UPDATE, DELETE, and EXECUTE; revalidation does not require recompiling.

**** Only DML system privileges, including SELECT/INSERT/UPDATE/DELETE ANY TABLE, EXECUTE ANY PROCEDURE; revalidation does not require recompiling.

ORACLE automatically recompiles an invalid view or PL/SQL program unit the next time it is used. In addition, a user can force ORACLE to recompile a view or program unit using the appropriate SQL command with the COMPILE parameter. Forced compilations are most often used to test for errors when a dependent view or program unit is invalid, but is not currently being used; in such a case, automatic recompilation would not otherwise occur until the view or program unit was executed. (To identify invalid dependent objects, query the views USER_ / ALL_ / DBA_OBJECTS.)

Manually Recompiling Views

To recompile a view, use the ALTER VIEW command with the COMPILE parameter. For example, the following statement recompiles the view EMP_DEPT contained in your schema:

```
ALTER VIEW emp_dept COMPILE;
```

Privileges Required to Manually Recompile a View To recompile a view manually, the view must be contained in your schema or you must have the ALTER ANY TABLE system privilege.

Manually Recompiling Procedures and Functions

To recompile a stand-alone procedure or function, use the ALTER PROCEDURE/FUNCTION command with the COMPILE parameter. For example, the following statement recompiles the stored procedure UPDATE_SALARY contained in your schema:

```
ALTER PROCEDURE update_salary COMPILE;
```

Privileges Required to Manually Recompile a Procedure or Function To recompile a procedure manually, the procedure must be contained in your schema or you must have the ALTER ANY PROCEDURE system privilege.

Manually Recompiling Packages

To recompile either a package body or both a package specification and body, use the ALTER PACKAGE command with the COMPILE parameter. For example, the following statements recompile just the body, and the body and specification of the package ACCT_MGMT, respectively:

```
ALTER PACKAGE acct_mgmt COMPILE BODY;
ALTER PACKAGE acct_mgmt COMPILE PACKAGE;
```

Privileges Required to Manually Recompile a Package To recompile a package manually, the package must be contained in your schema or you must have the ALTER ANY PROCEDURE system privilege.

Manually Recompiling Triggers

Manually recompile an existing trigger, whether it is currently enabled or disabled, using the ALTER TRIGGER command. For example, to force the compilation of the trigger named REORDER, enter the following statement:

```
ALTER TRIGGER reorder COMPILE;
```

Privileges Required to Manually Recompile a Trigger To recompile a trigger manually, you must own the trigger or have the ALTER ANY TRIGGER system privilege.

Managing Object Name Resolution

Object names referenced in SQL statements can consist of several pieces, separated by periods. ORACLE resolves an object name using the following algorithm:

1. ORACLE attempts to qualify the first piece of the name referenced in the SQL statement; for example, in SCOTT.EMP, SCOTT is the first piece. If there is only one piece, the one piece is considered the first piece.

   a. In the current schema, ORACLE searches for an object whose name matches the first piece of the object name. If it does not find such an object, it continues with Step 1b.

   b. If no schema object is found in the current schema, ORACLE searches for a public synonym that matches the first piece of the name. If it does not find one, it continues with Step 1c.

   c. If no public synonym is found, ORACLE searches for a schema whose name matches the first piece of the object name. If it finds one, it returns to Step 1a, now using the second piece of the name as the object to find in the qualified schema. If the second piece does not correspond to a object in the previously qualified schema or there is not a second piece, ORACLE returns an error.

   If no schema is found in Step 1c, the object cannot be qualified and ORACLE returns an error.

2. A schema object has been qualified. Any remaining pieces of the name must match a valid part of the found object. For example, if SCOTT.EMP.DEPTNO is the name, SCOTT is qualified as a schema, EMP is qualified as a table, and DEPTNO must correspond to a column (because EMP is a table). If EMP is qualified as a package, DEPTNO must correspond to a public constant, variable, procedure, or function of that package.

When global object names are used in a distributed database (either explicitly or indirectly within a synonym), the local ORACLE resolves the reference locally; for example, it resolves a synonym to a remote table's global object name. The partially resolved statement is shipped to the remote database, and the remote ORACLE completes the resolution of the object as above.

Changing Storage Parameters for the Data Dictionary

If your database is very large or contains an unusually large number of objects, columns in tables, constraint definitions, users, or other definitions, the tables that make up the data dictionary might at some point not be able to acquire additional extents (for example, if a data dictionary table needs an additional extent, but there is not enough contiguous space in the SYSTEM tablespace). If this happens, you cannot create new objects, even though the tablespace intended to hold the objects seems to have sufficient space. To remedy this situation, you can change the storage parameters of the underlying data dictionary tables to allow them to be allocated more extents, in the same way that you can change the storage settings for user-created segments (for example, by adjusting the values of NEXT or PCTINCREASE for the data dictionary table).

Note: Be very careful when you change the storage settings for the data dictionary objects. If you choose inappropriate settings, you could damage the structure of the data dictionary and be forced to re-create your entire database. For example, if you set PCTINCREASE for the data dictionary table USER$ to 0 and NEXT to 2K, that table will quickly reach the maximum number of extents for a segment, and you will not be able to create any more users or roles without exporting, recreating, and importing the entire database.

Structures in the Data Dictionary

The following tables and clusters contain the definitions of all the user-created objects in the database:

SEG$	segments defined in the database (including temporary segments)
OBJ$	user-defined objects in the database (including clustered tables); indexed by I_OBJ1 and I_OBJ2
UNDO$	rollback segments defined in the database; indexed by I_UNDO1
FET$	available free extents not allocated to any segment
UET$	extents allocated to segments
TS$	tablespaces defined in the database
FILE$	files that make up the database; indexed by I_FILE1
TAB$	tables defined in the database (includes clustered tables); indexed by I_TAB1
CLU$	clusters defined in the database
IND$	indexes defined in the database; indexed by I_IND1

ICOL$	columns that have indexes defined on them (includes individual entries for each column in a composite index); indexed by I_ICOL1
COL$	columns defined in tables in the database; indexed by I_COL1 and I_COL2
CON$	constraints defined in the database (includes information on constraint owner); indexed by I_CON1 and I_CON2
CDEF$	definitions of constraints in CON$; indexed by I_CDEF1, I_CDEF2, and I_CDEF3
CCOL$	columns that have constraints defined on them (includes individual entries for each column in a composite key); indexed by I_CCOL1
USER$	users and roles defined in the database; indexed by I_USER1
TSQ$	tablespace quotas for users (contains one entry for each tablespace quota defined for each user)
C_OBJ#	cluster containing TAB$, CLU$, ICOL$, IND$, and COL$: indexed by I_OBJ#
C_TS#	cluster containing FET$, TS$, and FILE$; indexed by I_TS#
C_FILE#_BLOCK#	cluster containing SEG$ and UET$; indexed by I_FILE#_BLOCK#
C_USER#	cluster containing USER and TSQ$$; indexed by I_USER#
C_COBJ#	cluster containing CDEF$ and CCOL$; indexed by I_COBJ#

Of all of the data dictionary segments, you are most likely to need to change are the following segments:

- if the free space in your database is very fragmented, C_TS#
- if you have many indexes or many columns in your tables, C_OBJ#
- if you use integrity constraints heavily, CON$ and C_COBJ#
- if you have a lot of users defined in your database, C_USER#

For the clustered tables, you must change the storage settings for the cluster, not for the table.

Errors that Require Changing Data Dictionary Storage

ORACLE returns an error if a user tries to create a new object that requires ORACLE to allocate an additional extent to the data dictionary, but ORACLE cannot allocate the extent. The error message ORA-1547 ("failed to allocate extent of size *num* in tablespace *'name'*") indicates this kind of problem.

If you receive this error message and the segment you were trying to change (such as a table or rollback segment) has not reached the limits specified for it in its definition, check the storage settings for the object that contains its definition.

For example, if you received an ORA-1547 while trying to define a new PRIMARY KEY constraint on a table and there is sufficient space for the index that ORACLE must create for the key, check if CON$ or C_COBJ# cannot be allocated another extent; to do this, query DBA_SEGMENTS (see "Displaying Segments That Cannot Allocate Additional Extents" on page 8-84) and consider changing the storage parameters for CON$or C_COBJ#.

Displaying Information About Schema Objects

The data dictionary provides many views that provide information about the schema objects described in this chapter. The following list summarizes the views associated with schema objects:

- ALL_OBJECTS, USER_OBJECTS, DBA_OBJECTS
- ALL_CATALOG, USER_CATALOG, DBA_CATALOG
- ALL_TABLES, USER_TABLES, DBA_TABLES
- ALL_TAB_COLUMNS, USER_TAB_COLUMNS, DBA_TAB_COLUMNS
- ALL_TAB_COMMENTS, USER_TAB_COMMENTS
- ALL_COL_COMMENTS, USER_COL_COMMENTS, DBA_COL_COMMENTS
- ALL_VIEWS, USER_VIEWS, DBA_VIEWS
- ALL_INDEXES, USER_INDEXES, DBA_INDEXES
- ALL_IND_COLUMNS, USER_IND_COLUMNS, DBA_IND_COLUMNS
- USER_CLUSTERS, DBA_CLUSTERS
- USER_CLU_COLUMNS, DBA_CLU_COLUMNS
- ALL_SEQUENCES, USER_SEQUENCES, DBA_SEQUENCES
- ALL_SYNONYMS, USER_SYNONYMS, DBA_SYNONYMS
- ALL_DEPENDENCIES, USER_DEPENDENCIES, DBA_DEPENDENCIES

The following data dictionary views contain information about the segments of a database:

- USER_SEGMENTS
- DBA_SEGMENTS

Information about a database's extents is contained in the following data dictionary views:

- USER_EXTENTS
- DBA_EXTENTS
- USER_FREE_SPACE
- DBA_FREE_SPACE

The following sections provide examples of using some of the above views.

Example 1 Displaying Schema Objects By Type

The following query lists all of the objects owned by the user issuing the query:

```
SELECT object_name, object_type FROM user_objects;

OBJECT_NAME                OBJECT_TYPE
-------------------------  -------------------
EMP_DEPT                   CLUSTER
EMP                        TABLE
DEPT                       TABLE
EMP_DEPT_INDEX             INDEX
PUBLIC_EMP                 SYNONYM
EMP_MGR                    VIEW
```

Example 2 Displaying Column Information

Column information, such as name, datatype, length, precision, scale, and default data values can be listed using one of the views ending with the _COLUMNS suffix. For example, the following query lists all of the default column values for the EMP and DEPT tables:

```
SELECT table_name, column_name, data_default
    FROM user_tab_columns
    WHERE table_name = 'DEPT' OR table_name = 'EMP';

TABLE_NAME  COLUMN_NAME     DATA_DEFAULT
----------  --------------- --------------------
DEPT        DEPTNO
DEPT        DNAME
DEPT        LOC             'NEW YORK'
EMP         EMPNO
EMP         ENAME
EMP         JOB
EMP         MGR
EMP         HIREDATE        SYSDATE
EMP         SAL
EMP         COMM
EMP         DEPTNO
```

Notice that not all columns have user-specified defaults. These columns automatically have NULL as the default.

Example 3 Displaying Dependencies of Views and Synonyms

When you create a view or a synonym, the view or synonym is based on its underlying base object. The ALL/USER/DBA_DEPENDENCIES data dictionary views can be used to reveal the dependencies for a view and the ALL/USER/DBA_SYNONYMS data dictionary views can be used to list the base object of a synonym. For example, the following query lists the base objects for the synonyms created by the user JWARD:

```
SELECT table_owner, table_name, synonym_name
  FROM sys.dba_synonyms
 WHERE owner = 'JWARD';

TABLE_OWNER                 TABLE_NAME    SYNONYM_NAME
--------------------------- ------------- ----------------
SCOTT                       DEPT          DEPT
SCOTT                       EMP           EMP
```

Example 4 Displaying General Segment Information

The following query returns the name of each rollback segment, the tablespace that contains each, and the size of each rollback segment:

```
SELECT segment_name, tablespace_name, bytes, blocks, extents
   FROM sys.dba_segments
   WHERE segment_type = 'ROLLBACK';

SEGMENT_NAME TABLESPACE_NAME      BYTES     BLOCKS    EXTENTS
------------ --------------- ---------- ---------- ----------
RS1          SYSTEM               20480         10          2
RS2          TS1                  40960         20          3
SYSTEM       SYSTEM              184320         90          3
```

Example 5
Displaying General Extent Information

General information about the currently allocated extents in a database is stored in the DBA_EXTENTS data dictionary view. For example, the following query identifies the extents associated with rollback segments and the size of each of those extents:

```
SELECT segment_name, bytes, blocks
   FROM sys.dba_extents
   WHERE segment_type = 'ROLLBACK';

SEGMENT_NAME         BYTES     BLOCKS
--------------- ---------- ----------
RS1                  10240          5
RS1                  10240          5
SYSTEM               51200         25
SYSTEM               51200         25
SYSTEM               51200         25
```

Notice that the RS1 rollback segment is comprised of two extents, both 10K, while the SYSTEM rollback segment is comprised of three equally sized extents of 50K.

Example 6
Displaying the Free Space (Extents) of a Database

Information about the free extents (extents not allocated to any segment) in a database is stored in the DBA_FREE_SPACE data dictionary view. For example, the following query reveals the amount of free space available via free extents in each tablespace:

```
SELECT tablespace_name, file_id, bytes, blocks
   FROM sys.dba_free_space;

TABLESPACE_NAME          FILE_ID      BYTES     BLOCKS
------------------- ---------- ---------- ----------
SYSTEM                         1    8120320       3965
SYSTEM                         1      10240          5
TS1                            2   10432512       5094
```

Example 7
Displaying Segments That Cannot Allocate Additional Extents

You can also use DBA_FREE_SPACE, in combination with the views DBA_SEGMENTS, DBA_TABLES, DBA_CLUSTERS, DBA_INDEXES, and DBA_ROLLBACK_SEGS, to determine if any other segment is unable to allocate additional extents. A segment might not be able to be allocated an extent for any of the following reasons:

- The tablespace containing the segment does not have enough room for the next extent.
- The segment has the maximum number of extents, as recorded in the data dictionary (in SEG.MAX_EXTENTS).
- The segment has the maximum number of extents allowed by the data block size (which is operating system specific).

The following query returns the names, owners, and tablespaces of all segments that fit any of the above criteria:

```
SELECT seg.owner, seg.segment_name,
       seg.segment_type, seg.tablespace_name,
       DECODE(seg.segment_type,
              'TABLE', t.next_extent,
              'CLUSTER', c.next_extent,
              'INDEX', i.next_extent,
              'ROLLBACK', r.next_extent)
FROM sys.dba_segments seg,
     sys.dba_tables t,
     sys.dba_clusters c,
     sys.dba_indexes i,
     sys.dba_rollback_segs r
WHERE ((seg.segment_type = 'TABLE'
        AND seg.segment_name = t.table_name
        AND seg.owner = t.owner
        AND NOT EXISTS (SELECT tablespace_name
                        FROM dba_free_space free
                        WHERE free.tablespace_name =
                              t.tablespace_name
                        AND free.bytes >= t.next_extent))
OR     (seg.segment_type = 'CLUSTER'
        AND seg.segment_name = c.cluster_name
        AND seg.owner = c.owner
        AND NOT EXISTS (SELECT tablespace_name
                        FROM dba_free_space free
                        WHERE free.tablespace_name =
                              c.tablespace_name
                        AND free.bytes >= c.next_extent))
OR     (seg.segment_type = 'INDEX'
        AND seg.segment_name = i.index_name
        AND seg.owner = i.owner
        AND NOT EXISTS (SELECT tablespace_name
                        FROM dba_free_space free
                        WHERE free.tablespace_name =
                              i.tablespace_name
                        AND free.bytes >= i.next_extent))
```

```
OR      (seg.segment_type = 'ROLLBACK'
         AND seg.segment_name = r.segment_name
         AND seg.owner = r.owner
         AND NOT EXISTS (SELECT tablespace_name
                         FROM dba_free_space free
                         WHERE free.tablespace_name =
                               r.tablespace_name
                         AND free.bytes >= r.next_extent)))
OR seg.extents = seg.max_extents
OR seg.extents = data_block_size;
```

Note: When you use this query, replace *data_block_size* with the data block size for your system.

Once you have identified a segment that cannot allocate additional extents, you can solve the problem in either of two ways, depending on its cause:

- If the tablespace is full, add data files to the tablespace. (See Chapter 7.)
- If the segment has too many extents and you cannot increase MAXEXTENTS for the segment, perform the following steps: first, export the data in the segment; second, drop and recreate the segment, giving it a larger INITIAL setting so that it does not need to allocate so many extents; and third, import the data back into the segment.

CHAPTER 9

MANAGING ROLLBACK SEGMENTS

This chapter explains how to manage rollback segments. The following topics are included:

- guidelines for managing rollback segments
- creating and setting storage parameters for rollback segments
- altering rollback segments
- taking rollback segments on and off line
- assigning a transaction explicitly to a rollback segment
- dropping a rollback segment
- monitoring rollback segments

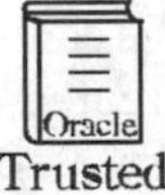

Trusted

If you are using Trusted ORACLE in DBMS MAC mode, see the *Trusted ORACLE7 Server Administrator's Guide* for additional information on managing rollback segments in that environment.

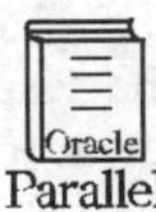

Parallel

If you are using ORACLE with the Parallel Server option, see the *ORACLE7 Parallel Server Administrator's Guide* for additional information on managing rollback segments in that environment.

Guidelines for Managing Rollback Segments

Here are some guidelines to keep in mind when creating or managing the rollback segments of your databases.

Use Multiple Rollback Segments

Using multiple rollback segments distributes rollback segment contention across many segments and improves system performance. Multiple rollback segments are required in the following situations:

- When a database is created, a single rollback segment named SYSTEM is created in the SYSTEM tablespace. If a database is to have other tablespaces, it **must** have two or more rollback segments in the SYSTEM tablespace. You cannot create any objects in non-SYSTEM tablespaces (not even rollback segments) until you have created and brought online at least one additional rollback segment in the SYSTEM tablespace.
- With the ORACLE Parallel Server, each instance requires access to its own rollback segment (in addition to the SYSTEM rollback segment) in order to start. For additional details, see the *ORACLE7 Parallel Server Administrator's Guide.*

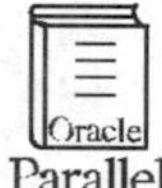

Parallel

- When many transactions are concurrently proceeding, more rollback information is generated at the same time. You can indicate the number of concurrent transactions you expect for the instance with the parameter TRANSACTIONS, and the number of transactions you expect each rollback segment to have to handle with the parameter TRANSACTIONS_PER_-ROLLBACK_SEGMENT. Then, when an instance opens a database, it attempts to acquire at least TRANSACTIONS/TRANSACTIONS_PER_ROLLBACK_SEGMENT rollback segments to handle the maximum amount of transactions. Therefore, after setting the parameters, create TRANSACTIONS/TRANSACTIONS_PER_ROLLBACK_SEGMENT rollback segments.

Add a Rollback Segment to the SYSTEM Tablespace

An initial rollback segment called SYSTEM is created when a database is created. The SYSTEM rollback segment is created in the SYSTEM tablespace using the default storage parameters associated with that tablespace. You cannot drop this rollback segment.

An instance always acquires the SYSTEM rollback segment in addition to any other rollback segments it needs. However, if there are multiple rollback segments, ORACLE tries to use the SYSTEM rollback segment only for special system transactions and distributes user transactions among other rollback segments; if there are too many transactions for the non-SYSTEM rollback segments, ORACLE uses the SYSTEM segment. Therefore, after database creation, create at least one additional rollback segment in the SYSTEM tablespace.

Choose Between Public and Private Rollback Segments

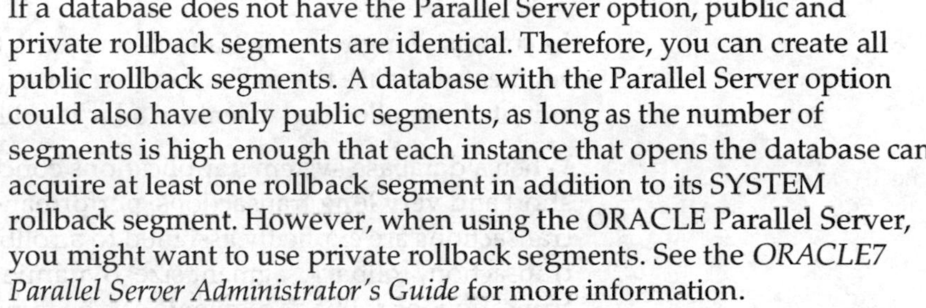

If a database does not have the Parallel Server option, public and private rollback segments are identical. Therefore, you can create all public rollback segments. A database with the Parallel Server option could also have only public segments, as long as the number of segments is high enough that each instance that opens the database can acquire at least one rollback segment in addition to its SYSTEM rollback segment. However, when using the ORACLE Parallel Server, you might want to use private rollback segments. See the *ORACLE7 Parallel Server Administrator's Guide* for more information.

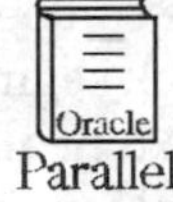

Parallel

Specify Rollback Segments to Acquire Automatically

By default, when an instance starts, it acquires TRANSACTIONS/ TRANSACTIONS_PER_ROLLBACK_SEGMENT rollback segments. If you want to ensure that the instance acquires particular rollback segments (of particular sizes or in particular tablespaces, for example, or specific to an instance in the case of the Parallel Server), specify the rollback segments by name in the parameter ROLLBACK_SEGMENTS in the instance's parameter file.

The instance acquires all the rollback segments listed in this parameter, even if more than TRANSACTIONS/TRANSACTIONS_PER_ROLL-BACK_SEGMENT segments are specified. The rollback segments can be either private or public.

Set Rollback Segment Sizes Appropriately

Total rollback segment size should be set based on the size of the most common transactions issued against a database. In general, short transactions experience better performance when the database has many smaller rollback segments, while long running transactions (such as batch jobs) perform better with larger rollback segments. In most cases, rollback segments can handle transactions of any size easily; however, in extreme cases when a transactions is either very short or very long, a user might want to use an appropriately sized rollback segment.

If a system is running only short transactions, rollback segments should be small so that they are always cached in main memory. If the rollback segments are small enough, they are more likely to be cached in the SGA according to the LRU algorithm and database performance is improved because less disk I/O is necessary. The main disadvantage of small rollback segments is the increased likelihood of the error "snapshot too old" when running a long query involving records that are frequently updated by other transactions. This error occurs because the rollback entries needed for read consistency are overwritten as other update entries wrap around the rollback segment; consider this issue when designing an application's transactions and make them short atomic units of work so that such problems are avoided.

In contrast, long running transactions work better with larger rollback segments because the rollback entries for a long running transaction can fit in pre-allocated extents of a large rollback segment.

When a database system's applications concurrently issue a mix of very short and very long transactions, performance can be optimized if transactions are explicitly assigned to a rollback segment based on the transaction / rollback segment size; dynamic extent allocation and truncation for rollback segments can be minimized. (This is not required for most systems and is intended for extremely large or small transactions.) To optimize for such situations, perform the following steps:

1. Make a number of rollback segments of appropriate size for each type of transaction (such as small, medium, and large). Most rollback segments should correspond to the typical transactions, with a fewer number of rollback segments for the atypical transactions. Set OPTIMAL for each such rollback segment so that the rollback segment returns to its intended size if it has to grow.
2. Tell the application developers or users about the different sets of rollback segments that correspond to the different types of transactions. In many cases, it is **not** beneficial to assign a transaction explicitly to a specific rollback segment; however, you can assign an atypical transaction to an appropriate rollback segment created for such transactions. For example, you can assign a transaction that contains a large batch job to a large rollback segment.

When a mix of transactions is not prevalent, each rollback segment should be 10% of the size of the database's largest table because most SQL statements affect 10% or less of a table; therefore, a rollback segment of this size should be sufficient to store the actions performed by most SQL statements.

Generally speaking, you should set a high MAXEXTENTS for rollback segments; this allows a rollback segment to allocate subsequent extents as it needs them.

Create Rollback Segments with Many Extents of Equal Size

Each rollback segment's total allocated space should be divided among many equally sized extents. In general, optimal rollback I/O performance is observed if each rollback segment for an instance has 10 to 20 equally sized extents.

After determining the desired total initial size of a rollback segment and the number of initial extents for the segment, use the following formula to calculate the size of each extent of the rollback segment:

```
T / n = s
```

where:

T	= total initial rollback segment size, in bytes
n	= number of extents initially allocate
s	= calculated size, in bytes, of each extent initially allocated

After *s* is calculated, create the rollback segment and specify the storage parameters INITIAL and NEXT as *s* and MINEXTENTS to *n*. Note that PCTINCREASE cannot be specified for rollback segments and defaults to 0. Also note that if the size *s* of an extent is not an exact multiple of the data block size, it is rounded up to the next multiple.

Set an Optimal Number of Extents for Each Rollback Segment

The OPTIMAL parameter for each rollback segment should be carefully chosen according to the kind of transactions that the system runs. For a system that executes long-running transactions frequently, OPTIMAL should be large so that ORACLE does not have to shrink and allocate extents frequently. For a system that executes long queries on active data, OPTIMAL should also be large in order to avoid "snapshot too old" errors. OPTIMAL should be smaller for a system that mainly executes short transactions and short queries so that the rollback segments remain small enough to be cached in memory, thus improving system performance.

To obtain estimates and to monitor the effectiveness of the OPTIMAL settings for rollback segments, use the MONITOR ROLLBACK feature of SQL*DBA. In this monitor, the following statistics are given for each rollback segment:

Sizes, High Water	the most space ever allocated for the rollback segment, in bytes
Sizes, Optimal	the OPTIMAL size of the rollback segment, in bytes
Occurrences, Wraps	the cumulative number of times a transaction continues writing from one extent in a rollback segment to another existing extent

Occurrences, Extends	the cumulative number of times a new extent is allocated for a rollback segment
Shrinks	the cumulative number of times ORACLE has truncated extents from the rollback segment
Average Sizes, Shrunk	the average size of the space ORACLE truncated from the rollback segment, in bytes
Average Sizes, Active	the average number of bytes in active extents in the rollback segment, measured over time

Assuming that an instance has equally sized rollback segments with comparably sized extents, the OPTIMAL parameter for a given rollback segment should be set slightly higher than *Average Sizes, Active.*

Table 9-1 provides additional information on how to interpret the statistics given in this monitor.

TABLE 9-1
Analyzing the Effectiveness of Current OPTIMAL Settings

Shrinks	***Average Sizes, Shrunk***	**Analysis and Recommendation**
Low	Low	If *Average Sizes, Active* is close to *Sizes, Optimal*, then the OPTIMAL setting is correct. Otherwise, OPTIMAL is too large (not many shrinks are being performed).
Low	High	Excellent—a good setting for OPTIMAL.
High	Low	OPTIMAL is too small—too many shrinks are being performed.
High	High	Periodic long transactions are probably causing these statistics. Set the OPTIMAL parameter higher until *Shrinks* is low.

Set the Storage Location for Rollback Segments

If possible, create one tablespace specifically to hold all rollback segments, other than the two required in the SYSTEM tablespace. This way, all rollback segment data is stored separately from other types of data. This rule will provide the following benefits:

- A tablespace holding rollback segments can always be kept online, thus maximizing the combined storage capacity of rollback segments at all times. (If some rollback segments are not available, the overall database operation can be affected.)
- Because tablespaces with active rollback segments cannot be taken offline, designating a tablespace to hold all rollback segments of a database ensures that the data stored in other

tablespaces can be taken offline without concern over the database's rollback segments.

- A tablespace's free extents are likely to be more fragmented if the tablespace contains rollback segments that frequently allocate and deallocate extents.

Creating Rollback Segments

To create additional rollback segments for a database, use either the Create Rollback Segment dialog box of SQL*DBA or the SQL command CREATE ROLLBACK SEGMENT. The tablespace to contain the new rollback segment must be online.

The Create Rollback Segment dialog box allows you to create a new rollback segment. Figure 9-1 shows the Create Rollback Segment dialog box.

FIGURE 9-1
The Create Rollback Segment Dialog

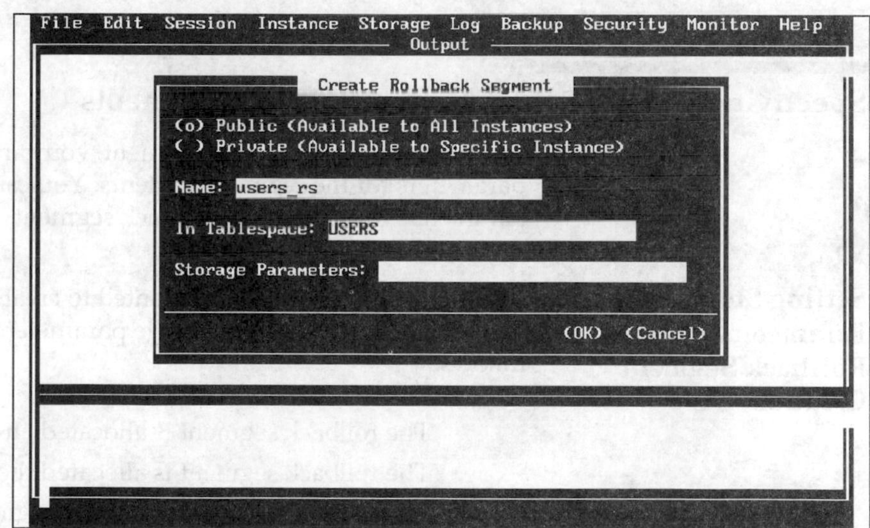

This example creates a public rollback segment named USERS_RS in the USERS tablespace, using the default storage parameters of the USERS tablespace.

The following statement is the command equivalent of the Create Rollback Segment dialog box in Figure 9-1:

```
CREATE PUBLIC ROLLBACK SEGMENT users_rs
  TABLESPACE users;
```

Privileges Required to Create Rollback Segments

To create rollback segments, you must have the CREATE ROLLBACK SEGMENT system privilege.

Bringing New Rollback Segments Online

Once a rollback segment is created, it is not available for use by transactions of any instance until it is brought online. See "Taking Rollback Segments Online and Offline" on page 9-10 for more information.

If you create a private rollback segment, you should add the name of the new rollback segment to the ROLLBACK_SEGMENTS parameter in the parameter file for the database. Doing so causes the private rollback segment to be captured by the instance at instance startup. For example, if two new private rollback segments are created and named RS1 and RS2, the ROLLBACK_SEGMENTS parameter of the parameter file should be similar to the following example:

```
ROLLBACK SEGMENTS= (RS1, RS2)
```

Specifying Storage Parameters for Rollback Segments

When you create a rollback segment, you can optionally specify storage parameters for the segment's extents. You can also change storage parameters for an existing rollback segment.

Setting Storage Parameters During Rollback Segment Creation

As an example, suppose you wanted to create a public rollback segment DATA1_RS with storage parameters and optimal size set as follows:

- The rollback segment is allocated an initial extent of 50K.
- The rollback segment is allocated the second extent of 50K.
- The optimal size of the rollback segment is 750K.
- The minimum number of extents and the number of extents initially allocated when the segment is created is 15.
- The maximum number of extents that the rollback segment can allocate, including the initial extent, is 100.

The following statement creates a rollback segment with these characteristics:

```
CREATE PUBLIC ROLLBACK SEGMENT data1_rs
  TABLESPACE users
  STORAGE (
```

```
INITIAL 50K
NEXT 50K
OPTIMAL 750K
MINEXTENTS 15
MAXEXTENTS 100);
```

You can also use SQL*DBA's Create Rollback Segment dialog to set the rollback segment's storage parameters.

Changing Rollback Segment Storage Parameters

You can change a rollback segment's storage parameters after creating it. However, you cannot alter the size of any extent currently allocated to a rollback segment; you can only affect future extents .

Alter a rollback segment's storage parameters using either the Alter Rollback Segment Storage dialog box of SQL*DBA or the SQL command ALTER ROLLBACK SEGMENT. Figure 9-2 shows the Alter Rollback Segment Storage dialog box that alters the maximum number of extents that the DATA1_RS rollback segment can allocate.

FIGURE 9-2
The Alter Rollback Segment Storage Dialog

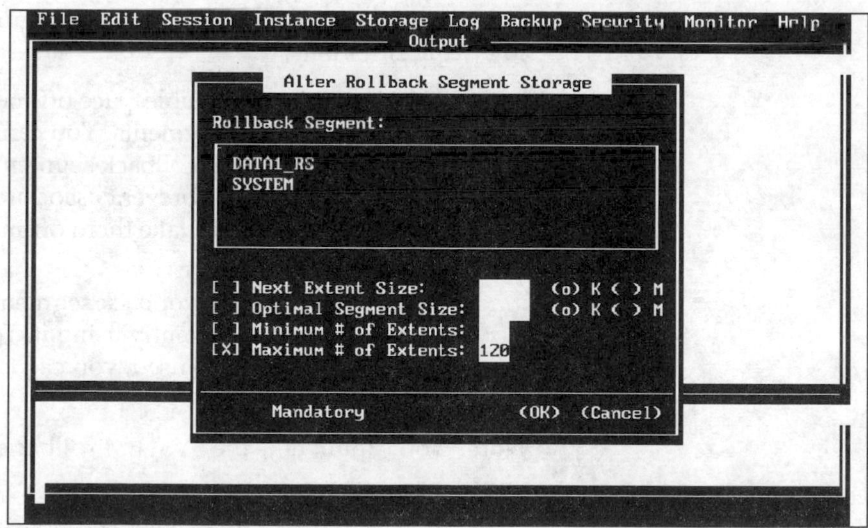

The following statement is the command equivalent of the Alter Rollback Segment Storage dialog box in Figure 9-2:

```
ALTER PUBLIC ROLLBACK SEGMENT data1_rs
  STORAGE (MAXEXTENTS 120);
```

Note: You can alter the settings for the SYSTEM rollback segment, including the OPTIMAL parameter, just as you can alter those of any rollback segment.

For guidance on setting sizes and storage parameters (including OPTIMAL) for rollback segments, see "Guidelines for Managing Rollback segments" on page 9-2.

Note: If you are altering a public rollback segment, you must include the keyword PUBLIC in the ALTER ROLLBACK SEGMENT command.

Privileges Required to Alter Rollback Segments

To alter rollback segments, you must have the ALTER ROLLBACK SEGMENT system privilege.

Taking Rollback Segments Online and Offline

A rollback segment is either *online* (available to transactions) or *offline* (unavailable to transactions). In most cases, rollback segments are online and available for use by transactions.

You might want to take online rollback segments offline in the following situations:

- You want to take a tablespace offline and the tablespace contains rollback segments. You cannot take a tablespace offline if it contains rollback segments that transactions are currently using. To prevent associated rollback segments from being used, you can take them offline prior to taking the tablespace offline.
- You want to drop a rollback segment, but cannot because transactions are currently using it. To prevent the rollback segment from being used, you can take it offline prior to dropping it.

Note: You cannot take the SYSTEM rollback segment offline.

You might later want to bring a rollback segment back online so that transactions can use it. Also, when a rollback segment is created, it is initially offline; you must explicitly bring a newly created rollback segment online before it can be used by an instance's transactions. An offline rollback segment can be brought online by any instance accessing the database that contains the rollback segment.

Bringing Rollback Segments Online

You can bring online only a rollback segment whose current status (as shown in the DBA_ROLLBACK_SEGS data dictionary view) is

"OFFLINE" or "PARTLY AVAILABLE". To bring an offline rollback segment online, use either the Set Rollback Segment Online dialog box of SQL*DBA or the SQL command ALTER ROLLBACK SEGMENT with the ONLINE option.

Figure 9-3 shows the Set Rollback Segment Online dialog box that brings the rollback segment USER_RS_2 online.

FIGURE 9-3
The Set Rollback Segment Online Dialog

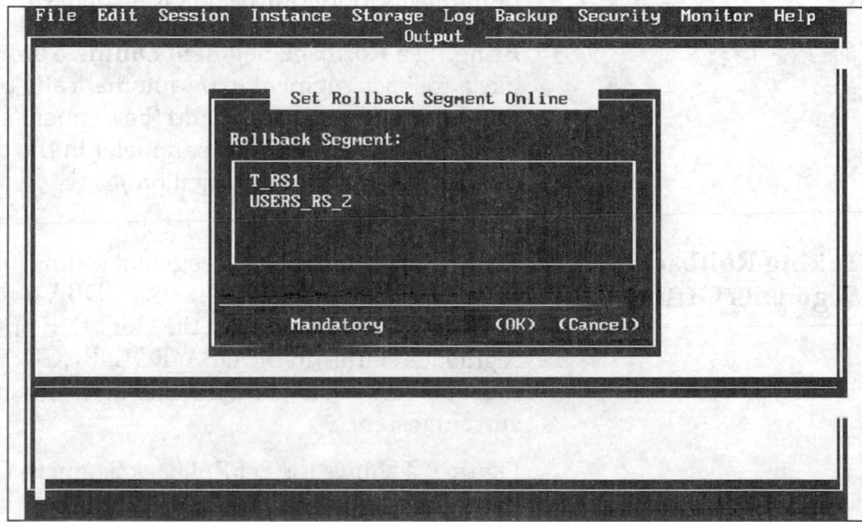

The following statement is the command equivalent of the Set Rollback Segment Online dialog box in Figure 9-3:

```
ALTER ROLLBACK SEGMENT user_rs_2 ONLINE;
```

After you bring a rollback segment online, its status in the data dictionary view DBA_ROLLBACK_SEGS is "ONLINE". See "Displaying Rollback Segment Information" on page 9-16 for a query for checking rollback segment state, and Appendix B for information about DBA_ROLLBACK_SEGS.

Bringing a PARTLY AVAILABLE Rollback Segment Online A rollback segment in the PARTLY AVAILABLE state (ts status in the data dictionary view DBA_ROLLBACK_SEGS is "PARTLY AVAILABLE") contains data for an in-doubt distributed transaction. The rollback segment usually remains in this state until the transaction is resolved (either automatically by RECO or manually by a DBA). However, you might find that all rollback segments are PARTLY AVAILABLE. In this case, you can bring a PARTLY AVAILABLE segment online, as described above.

Some resources used by the rollback segment for the in-doubt transaction remain inaccessible until the transaction is resolved. As a result, the rollback segment may have to grow if other transactions assigned to it need additional space.

As an alternative to bringing a PARTLY AVAILABLE segment online, you might find it easier to create a new rollback segment temporarily, until the in-doubt transaction is resolved.

Bringing a Rollback Segment Online Automatically If you would like a rollback segment to be automatically brought online whenever you start up the database, add the segment's name to the ROLLBACK_SEGMENTS parameter in the database's parameter file. (See Appendix A for information.)

Taking Rollback Segments Offline

To take an online rollback segment offline, use either the Set Rollback Segment Offline dialog box of SQL*DBA or the ALTER ROLLBACK SEGMENT command with the OFFLINE option. The rollback segment's status (in the DBA_ROLLBACK_SEGS data dictionary view) must be "ONLINE", and the rollback segment must be acquired by the current instance.

Figure 9-4 shows the Set Rollback Segment Offline dialog box that takes the rollback segment USER_RS_2 offline.

FIGURE 9-4
The Set Rollback Segment Offline Dialog

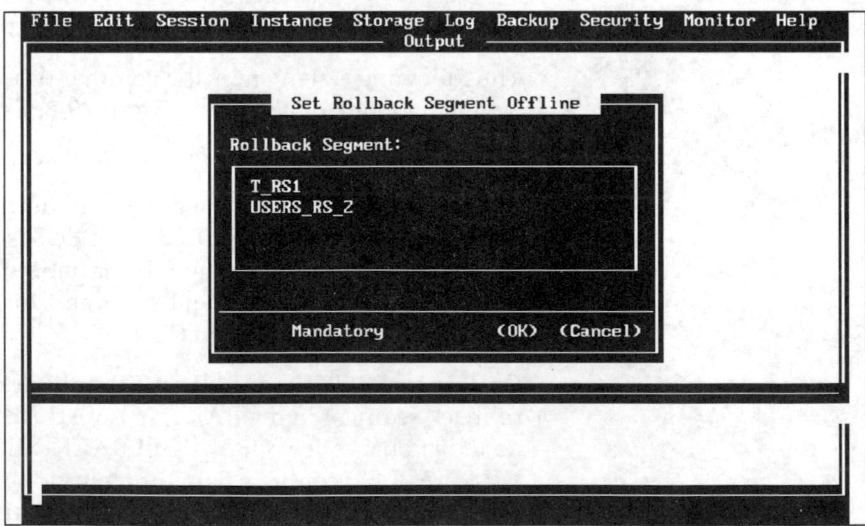

The following statement is the command equivalent of the Set Rollback Segment Offline dialog box in Figure 9-4:

```
ALTER ROLLBACK SEGMENT user_rs_2 OFFLINE;
```

Checking Whether a Rollback Segment Went Offline

If you try to take offline a rollback segment that does not contain active rollback entries, ORACLE immediately takes the segment offline and changes its status to "OFFLINE".

In contrast, if you try to take offline a rollback segment that does contain rollback data for active transactions (whether local, remote, or distributed), ORACLE makes the rollback segment unavailable to future transactions and takes it offline once all the active transactions using the rollback segment complete. Until the transactions complete, the rollback segment cannot be brought online by any instance other than the one that was trying to take it offline. During this period, the rollback segment's status in the view DBA_ROLLBACK_SEGS remains ONLINE; however, the rollback segment's status in the view V$ROLLSTAT is PENDING OFFLINE. (See "Displaying Rollback Segment Information" on page 9-16 for information on viewing rollback segment status; also see Appendix B for information about the views DBA_ROLLBACK_SEGS and V$ROLLSTAT.)

The instance that tried to take a rollback segment offline and caused it to be PENDING OFFLINE can bring it back online at any time; if the rollback segment is brought back online, it will function normally.

Taking Public and Private Rollback Segments Offline

After you take a *public* rollback segment offline, it remains offline (even if the instance is shut down and restarted) until you bring it back online. After you take a *private* rollback segment offline, it remains offline until you explicitly bring it back online *or* you restart the instance (unless the private rollback segment's name is removed from the list in the parameter file).

Privileges Required to Take Rollback Segments Online and Offline

To take a rollback segment online or offline, you must have the ALTER ROLLBACK SEGMENT system privilege.

Explicitly Assigning a Transaction to a Rollback Segment

A transaction can be explicitly assigned to a specific rollback segment using the SET TRANSACTION command with the USE ROLLBACK SEGMENT parameter. Transactions are explicitly assigned to rollback segments so that:

- The anticipated amount of rollback information generated by a transaction can fit in the current extents of the assigned rollback segment.
- Additional extents do not have to be dynamically allocated (and subsequently truncated) for rollback segments, which reduces overall system performance.

To assign a transaction to a rollback segment explicitly, the rollback segment must be online for the current instance, and the SET TRANSACTION USE ROLLBACK SEGMENT statement must be the first statement of the transaction. If a specified rollback segment is not online or a SET TRANSACTION USE ROLLBACK SEGMENT statement is not the first statement in a transaction, an error is returned.

For example, if you are about to begin a transaction that contains a significant amount of work (more than most transactions), you can assign the transaction to a large rollback segment, as follows:

```
SET TRANSACTION USE ROLLBACK SEGMENT large_rs1;
```

After the transaction is committed, the next transaction will be automatically assigned to any available rollback segment by ORACLE unless the new transaction is explicitly assigned to a specific rollback segment by the user.

Privileges Required to Assign a Transaction to a Rollback Segment

No special privileges are required to assign a transaction to a specific rollback segment explicitly; any user can do this.

Dropping Rollback Segments

Rollback segments can be dropped when the extents of a segment become too fragmented on disk or the segment needs to be relocated in a different tablespace.

Before dropping a rollback segment, make sure that status of the rollback segment is "OFFLINE". If the rollback segment that you want to drop is currently "ONLINE", "PARTLY AVAILABLE", "NEEDS RECOVERY", or "INVALID", you cannot drop it. (If the status is "INVALID", the segment has already been dropped.) Before you can drop it, you must take it offline; see "Taking Rollback Segments Offline" on page 9-12.

If a rollback segment is offline, you can drop it using either the Drop Rollback Segment dialog box of SQL*DBA or the SQL command DROP ROLLBACK SEGMENT. Figure 9-5 shows the Drop Rollback Segment dialog box that drops the DATA1_RS rollback segment.

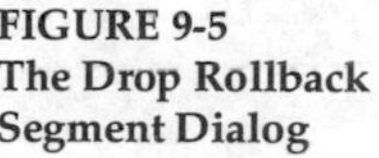

FIGURE 9-5
The Drop Rollback Segment Dialog

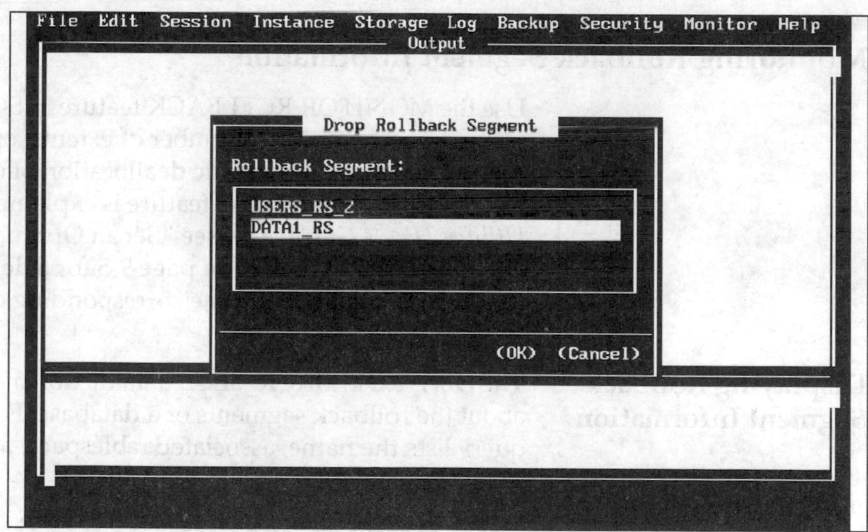

The following statement is the command equivalent of the Drop Rollback Segment dialog box in Figure 9-5:

```
DROP PUBLIC ROLLBACK SEGMENT data1_rs;
```

If you use the DROP ROLLBACK SEGMENT command, indicate the correct type of rollback segment to drop, public or private, by including or omitting the PUBLIC keyword.

Note: If a rollback segment specified in ROLLBACK_SEGMENTS is dropped, make sure to edit the parameter files of the database to remove the name of the dropped rollback segment from the list in the ROLLBACK_SEGMENTS parameter. If this step is not performed before the next instance startup, startup fails because it cannot acquire the dropped rollback segment.

Once a rollback segment is dropped, its status changes to "INVALID." The next time a rollback segment is created, it takes the row vacated by a dropped rollback segment, if one is available, and the dropped rollback segment's row no longer appears in the DBA_ROLLBACK_SEGS view. (See "Displaying Rollback Segment Information" on page 9-16 and Appendix B for more information about the view DBA_ROLLBACK_SEGS.)

Privileges Required to Drop Rollback Segments

To drop a rollback segment, you must have the DROP ROLLBACK SEGMENT system privilege.

Monitoring Rollback Segment Information

Utilities

Use the MONITOR ROLLBACK feature of SQL*DBA to monitor a rollback segment's size, number of extents, optimal number of extents, activity concerning dynamic deallocation of extents, and current usage by active transactions; this feature is explained in the *ORACLE7 Server Utilities User's Guide.* Also see "Set an Optimal Number of Extents for Each Rollback Segment" on page 9-5 for a detailed description of how to use the MONITOR for the corresponding operation.

Displaying Rollback Segment Information

The DBA_ROLLBACK_SEGS data dictionary view stores information about the rollback segments of a database. For example, the following query lists the name, associated tablespace, and status of each rollback segment in a database:

```
SELECT segment_name, tablespace_name, status
   FROM sys.dba_rollback_segs;

SEGMENT_NAME  TABLESPACE_NAME  STATUS
-------------------------------------
SYSTEM        SYSTEM           ONLINE
PUBLIC_RS     SYSTEM           ONLINE
USERS_RS      USERS            ONLINE
```

In addition, the following data dictionary views contain information about the segments of a database, including rollback segments:

- USER_SEGMENTS
- DBA_SEGMENTS

Example 1 Displaying All Rollback Segments

The following query returns the name of each rollback segment, the tablespace that contains it, and its size:

```
SELECT segment_name, tablespace_name, bytes, blocks, extents
    FROM sys.dba_segments
    WHERE segment_type = 'ROLLBACK';

SEGMENT_NAME TABLESPACE_NAME      BYTES     BLOCKS    EXTENTS
------------ --------------- ---------- ---------- ----------
RS1          SYSTEM               20480         10          2
RS2          TS1                  40960         20          3
SYSTEM       SYSTEM              184320         90          3
```

Example 2 Displaying Whether a Rollback Segment Has Gone Offline

When you take a rollback segment offline, it does not actually go offline until all active transactions in it have completed. Between the time when you attempt to take it offline and when it actually is offline, its status in DBA_ROLLBACK_SEGS remains ONLINE, but it is not used for new transactions. To determine whether any rollback segments for an instance are in this state, use the following query:

```
SELECT name, xacts 'ACTIVE TRANSACTIONS'
  FROM v$rollname, v$rollstat
 WHERE status = 'PENDING OFFLINE'
   AND v$rollname.usn = v$rollstat.usn;

NAME       ACTIVE TRANSACTIONS
---------- -------------------
RS2                          3
```

If your instance is part of a Parallel Server configuration, this query displays information for rollback segments of the current instance only, not those of other instances.

Example 3 Displaying Public and Private Rollback Segments

The following query shows which rollback segments are private and which are public. Note that it only displays information about the rollback segments that are currently online for the current instance.

```
SELECT segment_name, tablespace_name, owner
  FROM sys.dba_rollback_segs;

SEGMENT_NAME  TABLESPACE_NAME  OWNER
-------------------------------------
SYSTEM        SYSTEM           SYS
PUBLIC_RS     SYSTEM           PUBLIC
USERS_RS      USERS            SYS
```

Example 4 Displaying Deferred Rollback Segments

The following query shows all deferred rollback segments (rollback segments that were created to hold rollback entries for tablespaces taken offline until the tablespaces are brought back online):

```
SELECT segment_name, segment_type, tablespace_name
  FROM sys.dba_segments
 WHERE segment_type = 'DEFERRED ROLLBACK';

SEGMENT_NAME        SEGMENT_TYPE           TABLESPACE_NAME
------------        ------------           ---------------
USERS_RS            DEFERRED ROLLBACK      USERS
```

PART

IV DATABASE SECURITY

CHAPTER

10

ESTABLISHING SECURITY POLICIES

This chapter provides guidelines for developing security policies for the following areas of database operation:

- determining who manages and monitors the security of each database
- setting the level of system security
- setting the level of object security
- setting the level of security for the different types of users:
    - end-user security
    - administrator security
    - application developer security
- establishing a database auditing policy

Trusted

If you are using Trusted ORACLE, you must consider additional security issues; see the *Trusted ORACLE7 Server Administrator's Guide*.

The Security Administrator

Each database has one or more administrators who are responsible for maintaining all aspects of the security policy: the security administrators. If the database system is small, the database administrator may have the responsibilities of the security administrator. However, if the database system is large, a special person or group of people may have responsibilities limited to those of a security administrator.

Once it has been decided who will manage the security of the system, a security policy must be developed for every database. A database's security policy should include several sub-policies, as explained in the following sections.

System Security Policy

The overall security of a database system should include many considerations. This section discusses issues relevant to any database system.

Management of Database Users

Users (or, more precisely, users) are the access paths to the information in an ORACLE database. Therefore, tight security should be maintained for the management of database users. Depending on the size of a database system and the amount of work required to manage database users, the security administrator may be the only user with the privileges required to create, alter, or drop database users or there may be a number of administrators with the privileges to manage database users. Regardless, only trusted individuals should have the powerful privileges to administer database users.

User Authentication

Database users can be authenticated (verified as the correct person by ORACLE using the operating system or using the database. In most cases, user authentication by the host operating system is preferred for the following reasons:

- Users can connect to ORACLE faster and more conveniently (without specifying a user name or password).
- Centralized control over user authorization in the operating system: ORACLE need not store or manage user passwords and user names if the operating system and database correspond.

- User entries in the database and operating system audit trails correspond.

User authentication by the database is normally used when the host operating system cannot support user authentication. See "Creating Users" on page 11-7 for more information about user authentication.

Operating System Security

If applicable, certain security considerations must also be made for the operating system environment that executes ORACLE and any database applications. For example:

- Database administrators must have the operating system privileges to create and delete files.
- Typical database users should not have the operating system privileges to create or delete files related to the database.
- If the operating system is used to identify database roles for users, the security administrators must have the operating system privileges to modify the security domain of operating system accounts.

IUG

See your installation or user's guide for more information concerning operating system security issues for ORACLE databases.

Data Security Policy

Decisions must be made regarding the security policy of the data in a database. For example, it may be acceptable to have very little data security in a database; it may be tolerable to allow any user to create any schema object and grant access privileges for their objects to any other user of the system. Alternatively, it might be necessary that data security be very controlled; a database or security administrator might be the only person with the privileges to create objects and grant access privileges for objects to roles and users.

Overall data security should be based on the sensitivity of data. If information is not sensitive, then the data security policy can be lax. However, if data is sensitive, a discreet security policy should be developed to maintain tight control over access to objects.

User Security Policy

Decisions must be made regarding the security policy of the users of a database. Specific issues must be considered for each type of database user, including end-users, administrators, and application developers.

General User Security

For all types of database users, consider the following issues:

Password Security

If user authentication is managed by the database, a password security policy should be developed to maintain database access security. For example, database users should be required to change their passwords at regular intervals or if their passwords are revealed to another person. By forcing a user to modify passwords in such situations, unauthorized database access can be reduced if users mistakenly reveal their passwords.

Privilege Management

General decisions must be made for privilege management for all types of users. For example, in a database with a large number of user names, it may be beneficial to use roles to manage the privileges available to users. Alternatively, in a database with a handful of user names, it may be easier to grant privileges explicitly to users and avoid the use of roles.

A database that has a large number of users, applications, or objects should take advantage of the benefits offered by roles. Roles greatly simplify the task of privilege management in complicated environments.

End-User Security

A policy must be made regarding end-user security. For example, if the database is large with many users, the security administrator can decide what groups of users can be categorized, create user roles for these user groups, grant the necessary privileges or application roles to each user role, and assign the user roles to the users. To account for exceptions, the security administrator must also decide what privileges must be explicitly granted to individual users.

Using Roles for End-User Privilege Management

Roles are the easiest way to grant and manage the common privileges needed by different groups of database users.

Example

Consider the following situation:

- Every user in the accounting department of a company needs the privileges to run the ACCTS_RECEIVABLE and ACCTS_PAYABLE database applications.

- Roles are associated with both applications, and contain the object privileges necessary to execute those applications.

To address this simple security situation, the following actions should be performed by the database administrator or security administrator:

1. A role named ACCOUNTANT should be created.
2. The roles for the ACCTS_RECEIVABLE and ACCTS_PAYABLE database applications should be granted to the ACCOUNTANT role.
3. The ACCOUNTANT role should be granted to each user of the accounting department.

This security model is illustrated in Figure 10-1.

FIGURE 10-1
User Roles

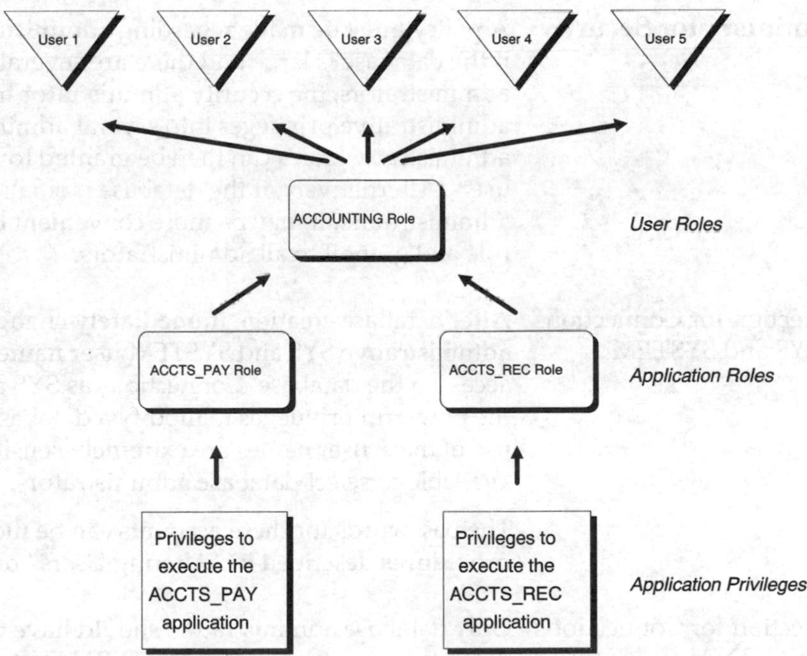

This plan addresses the following potential future situations:

- If accountants subsequently need a role for a new database application, that application's role can be granted to the ACCOUNTANT role, and all users in the accounting department will automatically receive the privileges associated with the new database application. The application's role does not need to be granted to individual users requiring use of the application.

- Similarly, if the accounting department no longer requires the need for a specific application, the application's role can be dropped from the ACCOUNTANT role.
- If the privileges required by the ACCTS_RECEIVABLE or ACCTS_PAYABLE applications change, the new privileges can be granted to (or revoked from) the application's role. The security domain of the ACCOUNTANT role, and all users granted the ACCOUNTANT role automatically reflect the privilege modification.

Roles should be utilized in all possible situations to make end-user privilege management efficient and simple.

Administrator Security

A policy must be made regarding administrator security. For example, if the database is large and there are several types of database administrators, the security administrator may decide to group related administrative privileges into several administrative roles. The administrative roles can then be granted to appropriate administrator users. Alternatively, if the database is small and has only a few administrators, it may be more convenient to create one administrative role and grant it to all administrators.

Protection for Connections as SYS and SYSTEM

After database creation, **immediately** change the passwords for the administrative SYS and SYSTEM user names to prevent unauthorized access to the database. Connections as SYS and SYSTEM allow a user the powerful privileges to modify a database in many ways. Therefore, use of these user names are extremely sensitive, and should only be available to select database administrators.

The passwords for these accounts can be modified using the procedures described in "Altering Users" on page 11-11.

Protection for Connections as INTERNAL

Only database administrators should have the capability to connect to a database using the keyword INTERNAL. Connections as INTERNAL allow a user unrestricted privileges to do anything to a database (such as startup, shutdown, and recover) or the objects within a database (such as create, drop, and delete from). Therefore, use of this keyword is extremely privileged, and should only be available to select database administrators.

If your ORACLE Server supports role identification using the host operating system, the INTERNAL keyword is protected by the OSOPER and OSDBA roles. Each role provides a different level of functionality when connected as INTERNAL. See "Alternatives to INTERNAL: OSOPER and OSDBA" on page 1-5 for more information about the OSOPER and OSDBA roles and their functions.

Note: To be able to configure a database administrator's operating system account with these roles, the security administrator must have the ability to modify the security for operating system accounts.

If your ORACLE Server does not support role identification via the host operating system, the use of INTERNAL is protected in an operating system specific method (usually by passwords). See "Connecting as INTERNAL" on page 1-4 and your installation or user's guide for details.

Using Roles for Administrator Privilege Management

Roles are the easiest way to restrict the powerful system privileges and roles required by administrative personnel of the database.

Example

Assume that the database administrator responsibilities at a large installation are shared among several database administrators, each responsible for specific database management jobs. There might be:

- an administrator responsible for object creation and maintenance
- an administrator responsible for database tuning and performance
- a security administrator, who is responsible for creating new users, granting roles and privileges to database users, etc.
- a database administrator responsible for routine database operation (for example, startup, shutdown, backup)
- an administrator responsible for emergency situations, such as database recovery
- new, inexperienced database administrators who need limited capabilities to experiment with database management

In this situation, the security administrator should structure the security for administrative personnel as follows:

1. Six roles should be defined to contain the distinct privileges required to accomplish each type of job (for example, DBA_OBJECTS, DBA_TUNE, DBA_SECURITY, DBA_MAINTAIN, DBA_RECOV, DBA_NEW).
2. Each role is granted the appropriate privileges.

3. Each type of database administrator can be granted the corresponding role.

This plan will easily solve the following potential future problems:

- If a database administrator's job description changes to include more responsibilities, that database administrator can be granted other administrative roles corresponding to the new responsibilities.
- If a database administrator's job description changes to include fewer responsibilities, that database administrator can have the appropriate administrative roles revoked.
- The data dictionary always stores information about each role and each user, so information is available to disclose the task of each administrator.

Application Developer Security

A special policy must be made for the application developers using a database. For example, the privileges to create necessary objects can be granted to application developers. Alternatively, the privileges to create objects can only be granted to a database administrator, who receives requests for object creation from developers.

Application Developers and Their Privileges

The database application developer is a unique type of database user who requires special groups of privileges to accomplish his job. Unlike end-users, developers need system privileges, such as CREATE TABLE, CREATE PROCEDURE, and so on. However, only specific system privileges should be granted to developers to restrict their overall capabilities in the database.

The Application Developer's Environment: Test and Production Databases

In many cases, application development is restricted to test databases and not allowed on production databases. By imposing this restriction:

- application developers do not compete with end-users for database resources
- application developers cannot detrimentally affect a production database

When an application has been thoroughly developed and tested, the application is allowed to access the production database and made available to the appropriate end-users of the production database.

Free vs. Controlled Application Development

The database administrator has two options when determining the privileges that should be granted to application developers:

Free Development An application developer is allowed to create new schema objects, including tables, indexes, procedures, packages, and so on. This option allows the application developer to develop an application independent of other objects.

Controlled Development An application developer is not allowed to create new schema objects. All required tables, indexes, procedures, and so on are created by a database administrator, as requested by an application developer. This option allows the database administrator to completely control a database's space usage and the access paths to information in the database.

Although some database systems could be purely one of the two options, other systems could be a mix of the options. For example, application developers can be allowed to create new stored procedures and packages, but not allowed to create tables or indexes. A security administrator's decision regarding this issue should be based on:

- the control desired over a database's space usage
- the control desired over the access paths to schema objects
- the database used to develop applications—if a test database is being used for application development, a more liberal development policy would be in order

Roles and Privileges for Application Developers

Roles can be created by the security administrator to manage the privileges required by the typical application developer. For example, a typical role named APPLICATION_DEVELOPER might include the CREATE TABLE, CREATE VIEW, and CREATE PROCEDURE system privileges. Notice two important points when defining roles for application developers:

- CREATE system privileges are usually granted to application developers so that they can create their own objects. However, CREATE ANY system privileges (which allow a user to create an object in any user's domain), such as CREATE ANY TABLE, CREATE ANY PROCEDURE, and so on, are not usually granted to developers. This restricts the creation of new objects only to the developer's user account.
- Object privileges are rarely granted to roles used by application developers. This is often impractical because granting object privileges via roles often restricts their usability in the creation of other objects (primarily views and stored procedures). It is

more practical to allow application developers to create their own objects for development purposes.

Space Restrictions Imposed on Application Developers

While application developers are normally given the privileges to create objects as part of the development process, security administrators must maintain limits on what and how much database space can be used by each application developer. For example, as the security administrator, you should specifically set or restrict the following limits for each individual application developer:

- the tablespaces in which the developer can create tables or indexes
- the quota for each tablespace accessible to the developer

Both limitations can be set by altering a developer's security domain. For more information, see "Altering Users" on page 11-11.

Application Administrator Security

In large database systems with many database applications (for example, precompiler applications and SQL*Forms applications), you might want to have application administrators. An application administrator is responsible for the following types of tasks:

- creating roles for an application and managing the privileges of each application role
- creating and managing the objects used by a database application
- maintaining and updating the application code and ORACLE procedures and packages, as necessary

In many cases, an application administrator is also the application developer that designed the application. However, these jobs might not be the responsibility of the developer and can be assigned to another individual familiar with the database application.

Auditing Policy

A policy should be developed for the auditing procedures of each database. For example, it may be decided to have database auditing disabled unless questionable activities are suspected. When auditing is required, the security administrator must decide what level of detail to audit the database; usually, more general system auditing is followed by more specific types of auditing once the origins of suspicious activity are determined.

CHAPTER

11 MANAGING USERS AND RESOURCES

This chapter explains how to control access to an ORACLE database as a whole. Topics include:

- complying with your ORACLE license agreement
- creating, managing, and dropping database users
- creating, assigning, altering, and dropping profiles (resource limits)
- enabling and disabling resource limits
- displaying information about users and profiles

For guidelines on establishing security policies for users and profiles, see Chapter 10.

Privileges and roles control the access a user has to a database and the schema objects within the database. For information on privileges and roles, see Chapter 12.

Trusted

For databases with Trusted ORACLE, see the *Trusted ORACLE7 Server Administrator's Guide* for additional information about user management in that environment.

Managing Users

Each ORACLE database has a list of valid database users. To access a database, a user must run a database application and connect to the database instance using a valid user name defined in the database. This section explains how to create, manage, and drop users for a database.

Using Session and User Licensing

ORACLE helps you ensure that your site complies with its ORACLE Server license agreement. If your site is licensed by concurrent usage, you can track and limit the number of sessions concurrently connected to a database. If instead your site is licensed by named users, you can limit the number of named users created in a database. In either case, you control the licensing facilities, and must enable the facilities and set the appropriate limits.

To use this facility, you need to know which type of licensing agreement your site has, and what the maximum number of sessions or named users is. Your site might use either type of licensing (concurrent usage licensing or named user licensing), but not both.

Note: In a few cases, your site might not use either of these types of licensing. For example, your site might have an unlimited license. In these cases only, leave the licensing mechanism disabled: omit the parameters LICENSE_MAX_SESSIONS, LICENSE_SESSIONS_-WARNING, and LICENSE_MAX_USERS from the parameter file, or set all three to 0.

The following sections explain how to set the concurrent usage or named user limit, and how to view current settings and the highest number of concurrent sessions.

Using Concurrent Usage Licensing

Concurrent usage licensing limits the number of sessions that can be connected to the database on the specified computer at a time. You can set a limit on the number of concurrent sessions before you start an instance. In fact, you should have set this limit as part of the initial installation procedure; see "Edit New Parameter Files" on page 2-5. You can also change the maximum number of concurrent sessions while the database is running.

Once this limit is reached, only users with RESTRICTED SESSION privilege (usually DBAs) can connect to the database; when such a user connects, ORACLE sends him a message saying that the maximum limit has been reached, and writes a message to the ALERT file. When the maximum is reached, you should connect only to kill unneeded processes. (See "Killing Sessions" on page 4-13.) Do not raise the licensing limits unless you have upgraded your ORACLE license agreement.

In addition to setting a maximum, you can set a warning limit on the number of concurrent sessions. Once this limit is reached, additional users can continue to connect (up to the maximum limit), but ORACLE writes an appropriate message to the ALERT file with each connection, and sends each connecting user who has the RESTRICTED SESSION privilege a warning indicating that the maximum is about to be reached.

If a user is connecting as INTERNAL, the limits still apply; however, ORACLE enforces the limit after the first statement the user executes.

In addition to enforcing the concurrent usage limits, ORACLE tracks the highest number of concurrent sessions for each instance. You can use this "high water mark" to determine if you need to upgrade the ORACLE license for your site; see "Viewing Licensing Limits and Current Values" on page 11-5.

Parallel

For instances running with the Parallel Server, each instance can have its own concurrent usage limit and warning limit. However, the sum of the instances' limits must not exceed the site's concurrent usage license. See the *ORACLE7 Parallel Server Administrator's Guide* for more information about setting and changing these limits in that environment.

Sessions that connect to ORACLE through multiplexing software or hardware (such as a TP monitor) each contribute individually to the concurrent usage limit; however, the ORACLE licensing mechanism cannot distinguish the number of sessions connected this way. If your site uses multiplexing software or hardware, you must take that into consideration and set the maximum concurrent usage limit lower to account for the multiplexed sessions.

The following sections explain how to set and enforce the concurrent usage limit.

Setting the Maximum Number of Sessions To set the maximum number of concurrent sessions for an instance, set the parameter LICENSE_MAX_SESSIONS. For example:

```
LICENSE_MAX_SESSIONS = 80
```

If you set this limit, you are not required to set a warning limit (LICENSE_SESSIONS_WARNING). However, using the warning limit makes the maximum limit easier to manage, since it gives you advance notice that your site is nearing maximum use.

Setting the Session Warning Limit To set the warning limit for an instance, set the parameter LICENSE_SESSIONS_WARNING in the parameter file used to start the instance.

Set the session warning to a value lower than the concurrent usage maximum limit (LICENSE_MAX_SESSIONS).

Changing Concurrent Usage Limits While the Database Runs To change either the maximum concurrent usage limit or the warning limit while the database is running, use the ALTER SYSTEM command with the appropriate option. For example, the following statement changes the maximum limit to 100 concurrent sessions:

```
ALTER SYSTEM SET LICENSE_MAX_SESSIONS = 100;
```

As another example, the following statement changes both the warning limit and the maximum limit:

```
ALTER SYSTEM
  SET LICENSE_MAX_SESSIONS = 64
      LICENSE_SESSIONS_WARNING = 54;
```

If you change either limit to a value lower than the current number of sessions, the current sessions remain; however, the new limit is enforced for all future connections until the instance is shut down. To change the limit permanently, change the value of the appropriate parameter in the parameter file.

To change the concurrent usage limits while the database runs, you must have the ALTER SYSTEM privilege. Also, to connect to an instance once the instance's maximum limit has been reached, you must have the RESTRICTED SESSION privilege.

Do not raise the concurrent usage limits unless you have appropriately upgraded your ORACLE Server license; contact your Oracle representative for information.

Using Named User Limits

Named user licensing limits the number of individuals who are authorized to use ORACLE on the specified computer. To enforce this license, you can set a limit on the number of users created in the database before you start an instance; you can also change the maximum number of users while the instance is running, or disable the limit altogether. Once this limit is reached, you cannot create more users; if you try to do so, ORACLE returns an error saying that the maximum number of users have been created, and writes a message to the ALERT file.

This mechanism assumes that each person accessing the database has a unique user name, and that no people share a user name. Therefore, so that named user licensing can help you ensure compliance with your ORACLE license agreement, do not allow multiple users to connect using the same user name.

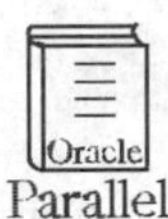

For instances running with the Parallel Server, all instances connected to the same database should have the same named user limit. See the *ORACLE7 Parallel Server Administrator's Guide* for more information on setting this limit in that environment.

The following sections explain how to set and use the named user limit.

Setting User Limits To limit the number of users created in a database, set the LICENSE_MAX_USERS parameter in the database's parameter file. For example:

```
LICENSE_MAX_USERS = 200
```

If the database contains more than LICENSE_MAX_USERS when you start it, ORACLE returns a warning and writes an appropriate message in the ALERT file. You cannot create additional users until the number of users drops below the limit, and you should either delete users or upgrade your ORACLE license.

Changing User Limits To change the maximum named users limit, use the ALTER SYSTEM command with the LICENSE_MAX_USERS option. For example, the following statement changes the maximum number of defined users to 300:

```
ALTER SYSTEM SET LICENSE_MAX_USERS = 300;
```

If you try to change the limit to a value lower than the current number of users, ORACLE returns an error and continues to use the old limit. If you successfully change the limit, the new limit remains in effect until you shut down the instance; to change the limit permanently, change the value of LICENSE_MAX_USERS in the parameter file.

To change the maximum named users limit, you must have the ALTER SYSTEM privilege.

Do not raise the named user limit unless you have appropriately upgraded your ORACLE license; contact your Oracle representative for information.

Viewing Licensing Limits and Current Values

You can see the current limits of all of the license settings, the current number of sessions, and the maximum number of concurrent sessions for the instance by querying the V$LICENSE data dictionary view. You can use this information to determine if you need to upgrade your ORACLE license, to allow more concurrent sessions or named users.

For example:

```
SELECT sessions_max s_max,
       sessions_warning s_warning,
       sessions_current s_current,
       sessions_highwater s_high,
       users_max
  FROM v$license;

S_MAX      S_WARNING  S_CURRENT  S_HIGH     USERS_MAX
-------------------------------------------------------
     100          80         65       88          250
```

In addition, ORACLE writes the session high water mark to the database's ALERT file when the database shuts down, so you can check for it there.

To see the current number of named users defined in the database, use the following query:

```
SELECT COUNT(*) FROM dba_users;

COUNT(*)
----------
       174
```

Authenticating Users

A user connecting to an instance can be authenticated by either the operating system or the database. For simplicity, you might want all users to be authenticated in the same way, but each user can be authenticated a different way; some users can be authenticated by the operating system, while others are authenticated by ORACLE. You specify individually for each user how that user is authenticated when you create the user, and you can later alter any user to change her method of authentication.

Using Operating System Authentication

IUG

If your operating system permits (see your installation or user's guide), you can have it authenticate users. If you do so, set the parameter OS_AUTHENT_PREFIX, and use this prefix in ORACLE user names. This parameter defines a prefix that ORACLE adds to the beginning of every user's operating system account name. ORACLE compares the prefixed user name with the ORACLE user names in the database when a user attempts to connect.

For example, assume that OS_AUTHENT_PREFIX is set as follows:

```
OS_AUTHENT_PREFIX=OPS$
```

If a user with an operating system account named "TSMITH" is to connect to an ORACLE database and be authenticated by the operating system, ORACLE checks that there is a corresponding database user "OPS$TSMITH" and, if so, allows the user to connect. All references to a user authenticated by the operating system must include the prefix, and therefore look like "OPS$TSMITH".

The default value of this parameter is "OPS$" for backward compatibility with previous versions of ORACLE. However, you might prefer to set the prefix value to some other string or a null string (an empty set of double quotes: ""); using a null string eliminates the addition of any prefix to operating system account names, so that ORACLE user names exactly match operating system user names.

Once you set OS_AUTHENT_PREFIX, it should remain the same for the life of a database. If you change the prefix, any database user name that includes the old prefix cannot be used to establish a connection, unless you alter the user name to have it use password authentication.

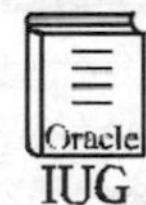

Note: The text of the OS_AUTHENT_PREFIX parameter is case-sensitive on some operating systems. See your installation or user's guide for more information about this initialization parameter.

Operating System Authentication and the Multi-Threaded Server If you want to have the operating system authenticate a user, by default that user cannot connect to the database through the multi-threaded server. This restriction is the default because a remote user could impersonate another operating system user over a network connection.

If you are not concerned with this security risk and want to use operating system user authentication with the multi-threaded server, set the parameter REMOTE_OS_AUTHENT in the database's parameter file to TRUE. The change will take effect the next time you start the instance and mount the database. (The parameter is FALSE by default.)

Using Database Authentication

To have ORACLE authenticate a user, specify a password for the user when you create or alter the user. Any user can change his password at any time. Passwords are stored in an encrypted format. Each password must be made up of single-byte characters, even if your database uses a multi-byte character set.

Creating Users

You create a user with either the Create User dialog box of SQL*DBA or the SQL command CREATE USER. Using either option, you can also specify the new user's default and temporary segment tablespaces, tablespace quotas, and profile. Figure 11-1 shows the Create User dialog box.

FIGURE 11-1
The Create User Dialog

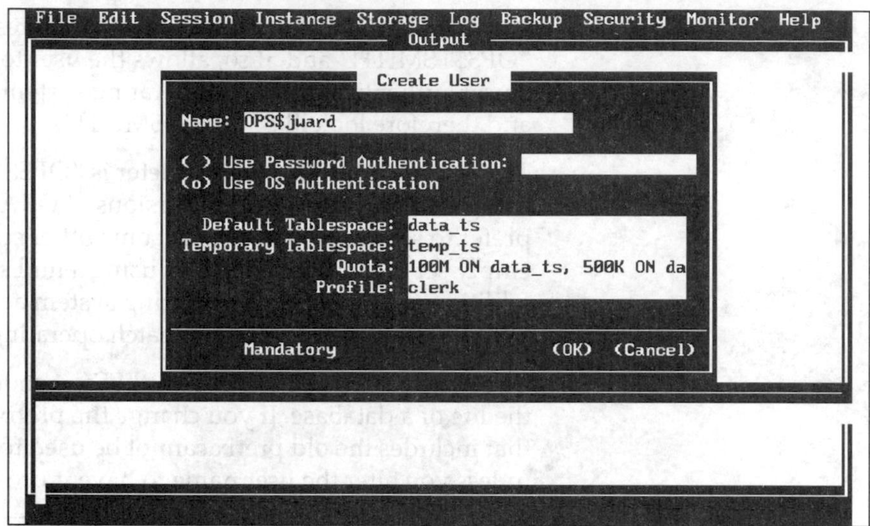

The following statement is the command equivalent of the Create User dialog box in Figure 11-1:

```
CREATE USER OPS$jward
    IDENTIFIED EXTERNALLY
    DEFAULT TABLESPACE data_ts
    TEMPORARY TABLESPACE temp_ts
    QUOTA 100M ON test_ts
    QUOTA 500K ON data_ts
    PROFILE clerk;
```

Note: A newly-created user cannot connect to the database until he is granted the CONNECT system privilege. See "Granting and Revoking Privileges and Roles" on page 12-15.

Specifying a Name

Within each database, a user name must be unique with respect to other user names and roles; a user and role cannot have the same name. Furthermore, each user has an associated schema. Within a schema, each schema object must have unique names. See Chapter 8 for more information about schema objects and their naming rules, and Chapter 12 about roles and their naming rules.

User Names in Multi-Byte Character Sets In a database that uses a multi-byte character set, Oracle Corporation strongly recommends that each user name contain at least one single-byte character. If a user name contains only multi-byte characters, the encrypted user name/password combination is considerably less secure.

Setting a User's Authentication

In the previous example, the new user is to be authenticated using the operating system. The user name includes the default prefix "OPS$." If the OS_AUTHENT_PREFIX parameter is set differently (that is, if it specifies either no prefix or some other prefix), modify the user name accordingly, by omitting the prefix or substituting the correct prefix.

Alternatively, you can create a user so that he is authenticated using the database and a password; the following statement is an example:

```
CREATE USER jward
        IDENTIFIED BY airplane
        . . . ;
```

In this case, the connecting user must supply the correct password to the database to connect successfully.

User Passwords in Multi-Byte Character Sets In a database that uses a multi-byte character set, passwords must include only single-byte characters. Multi-byte characters are not accepted in passwords.

Assigning a Default Tablespace

Each user has a default tablespace; when a user creates a schema object and specifies no tablespace to contain it, ORACLE stores the object in the user's default tablespace.

The default setting for every user's default tablespace is the SYSTEM tablespace. If a user will not create any type of object, this default setting is fine. However, if a user can create any type of object, consider specifically setting the user's default tablespace. You can set user's default tablespace during user creation, and change it later; changing the user's default tablespace affects only objects created after the setting is changed.

Consider the following issues when deciding which tablespace to specify:

- Set a user's default tablespace only if the user has the privileges to create objects (such as tables, views, and clusters).
- Set a user's default tablespace to a tablespace for which the user has a quota. See "Assigning Tablespace Quotas" on page 11-10.
- If possible, set a user's default tablespace to a tablespace other than the SYSTEM tablespace to reduce contention between data dictionary objects and user objects for the same data files.

In the example above, JWARD's default tablespace is DATA_TS.

Assigning a Temporary Tablespace

Each user also has a temporary tablespace; when a user executes a SQL statement that requires a temporary segment, ORACLE stores the segment in the user's temporary tablespace.

If a user's temporary tablespace is not explicitly set, the default is the SYSTEM tablespace. However, setting each user's temporary tablespace reduces file contention among temporary segments and other types of segments. You can set a user's temporary tablespace at user creation, and change it later.

In the example above, JWARD's temporary tablespace is TEMP_TS, a tablespace created explicitly to contain temporary segments only.

Assigning Tablespace Quotas

You can assign each user a tablespace quota for any tablespace. Assigning a quota does two things:

- If the user has a privilege to create some type of object, the user can create objects in the specified tablespace.
- ORACLE limits the amount of space that can be allocated for storage of a user's objects within the specified tablespace to the amount of the quota.

By default, a user has no quota on any tablespace in the database. If the user has the privilege to create some type of schema object, you must assign a quota to allow the user to create objects; at minimum, assign the user a quota for his default tablespace, and assign additional quotas for other tablespace in which the user will create objects.

You can assign a user either individual quotas for a specific amount of disk space in each tablespace, or an unlimited amount of disk space in all tablespaces. Specific quotas prevent a user's objects from consuming too much space in the database.

You can assign a user's tablespace quotas when you create the user, or add or change quotas later. If a new quota is less than the old one, then the following conditions hold true:

- If a user has already exceeded a new tablespace quota, the user's objects in the tablespace cannot be allocated more space until the combined space of these objects falls below the new quota.
- If a user has not exceeded a new tablespace quota, or if the space used by the user's objects in the tablespace falls under a new tablespace quota, the user's objects can be allocated space up to the new quota.

Revoking Tablespace Access You can revoke a user's tablespace access by altering the user's current quota to zero. Once a quota of zero is assigned, the user's objects in the revoked tablespace remain, but the objects cannot be allocated any new space.

The UNLIMITED TABLESPACE System Privilege To permit a user to use an unlimited amount of any tablespace in the database, grant the user the UNLIMITED TABLESPACE system privilege. This overrides all explicit tablespace quotas for the user; if you later revoke the privilege, explicit quotas again take effect. You can grant this privilege only to users, not to roles.

Before granting the UNLIMITED TABLESPACE system privilege, consider the advantages and disadvantages of doing so:

Advantage

- You can grant a user unlimited access to all tablespaces of a database with one statement.

Disadvantages

- The privilege overrides all explicit tablespace quotas for the user.
- You cannot selectively revoke tablespace access from a user with the UNLIMITED TABLESPACE privilege. You can grant access selectively only after revoking the privilege.

Setting Default Roles

You cannot set a user's default roles in the CREATE USER statement. When you first create a user, the user's default role setting is ALL, which causes all roles subsequently granted to the user to be default roles. Use the ALTER USER command to change the user's default roles; see "Altering Users" on page 11-11.

Privileges Required to Create Users

To create a database user, you must have the CREATE USER system privilege. When creating a new user, tablespace quotas can be specified for any tablespace in the database, even if the creator does not have a quota on a specified tablespace. Due to such privileged power, a security administrator is normally the only type of user that has the CREATE USER system privilege.

Altering Users

You can alter a user's security settings with either the Alter User dialog box of SQL*DBA or the SQL command ALTER USER. Changing a user's security settings affects the user's future sessions, not current sessions. Figure 11-2 shows the Alter User dialog box.

FIGURE 11-2
The Alter User Dialog

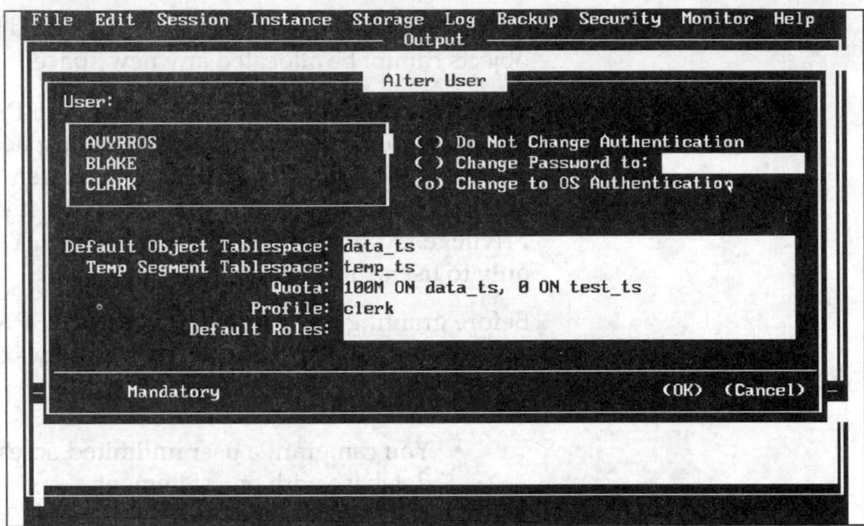

The following statement is the command equivalent of the Alter User dialog box in Figure 11-2:

```
ALTER USER avyrros
    IDENTIFIED EXTERNALLY
    DEFAULT TABLESPACE data_ts
    TEMPORARY TABLESPACE temp_ts
    QUOTA 100M ON data_ts
    QUOTA 0 ON test_ts
    PROFILE clerk;
```

The above examples change AVYRROS's security setting as follows:

- Authentication is changed to use AVYRROS's operating system account.
- AVYRROS's default and temporary tablespaces are explicitly set.
- AVYRROS is given a 100M quota for the DATA_TS tablespace.
- AVYRROS's quota on the TEST_TS is revoked.
- AVYRROS is assigned the CLERK profile.

Changing a User's Password, for Non-DBAs

Most non-DBA users do not use SQL*DBA, but can still change their own passwords with the ALTER USER command, as in the following example:

```
ALTER USER andy
  IDENTIFIED BY swordfish;
```

Any user can change her own password this way, without any special privileges (other than those to connect to the database). Users should be encouraged to change their passwords themselves frequently.

A user must have the ALTER USER privilege to change between ORACLE authorization and operating system authorization; usually only DBAs should have this privilege.

Passwords in Multi-Byte Character Sets In a database that uses a multi-byte character set, passwords must include only single-byte characters. Multi-byte characters are not accepted in passwords.

Changing a User's Default Roles

A default role is one that is automatically enabled for a user when the user creates a session. You can assign a user zero or more default roles. Any role directly granted to a user can potentially be a default role of the user; an indirectly granted role (a role that is granted to a role) cannot be a default role. The number of default roles for a user should not exceed the maximum number of enabled roles that are allowed per user or, when the user tries to connect, errors are returned and the connection is not allowed.

Note: ORACLE automatically enables a user's default roles when the user creates a session. Placing a role in a user's list of default roles bypasses authentication for the role, whether the role is defined to be authorized using a password or the operating system.

If you specify a list of roles, all other roles granted to that user are removed from the user's default role list. For example, suppose user AVYRROS has been granted the roles DEVELOPER and CLERK, and CLERK is his only default role. The following statement removes CLERK from his default role list and adds DEVELOPER:

```
ALTER USER avyrros
  DEFAULT ROLE DEVELOPER;
```

In this case, any roles subsequently granted to AVYRROS will not be default roles, and will be disabled on connection.

If you specify ALL for the user's list of default roles, every role granted directly to the user is automatically added to the user's list of default roles. Subsequent modification of a user's default role list can remove newly granted roles from a user's list of default roles. The following example causes all roles currently granted to AVYRROS to be added to his list of default roles, as well as all roles granted in the future:

```
ALTER USER avyrros
  DEFAULT ROLE ALL;
```

Furthermore, you can specify ALL EXCEPT with a list of role, and those roles will be the only roles granted to the user not on his default role list. For example, the following statement adds all roles currently granted to AVYRROS except the role PAYROLL to the user's default role list; any roles granted to AVYRROS in the future are also added to the default role list:

```
ALTER USER avyrros
  DEFAULT ROLE ALL EXCEPT payroll;
```

To cause a user to have no default roles, specify NONE for the user's list of default roles, as in the following example;

```
ALTER USER avyrros
  DEFAULT ROLE NONE;
```

Changing a user's default role list affects subsequent sessions; it does not affect any session in progress at the time.

Revoking a role from a user automatically removes the role from the user's default role list.

Privileges Required to Alter Users

As noted above, any user can change his own password. However, to change any other option of a user's security domain, you must have the ALTER USER system privilege. Security administrators are normally the only users that have this system privilege, as it allows a modification of **any** user's security domain. This privilege includes the ability to set tablespace quotas for a user on any tablespace in the database, even if the user performing the modification does not have a quota for a specified tablespace.

Dropping Users

When a user is dropped, the user and associated schema is removed from the data dictionary and all schema objects contained in the user's schema, if any, are immediately dropped.

Note: If a user's schema and associated objects must remain but the user must be revoked access to the database, revoke the CREATE SESSION privilege from the user.

A user that is currently connected to a database cannot be dropped. To drop a connected user, you must first kill the user's sessions using either the Kill Session dialog box of SQL*DBA or the SQL command ALTER SYSTEM with the KILL SESSION clause; see "Killing Sessions" on page 4-13.

Drop a user from a database using either the Drop User dialog box of SQL*DBA or the SQL command DROP USER. Figure 11-3 shows the Drop User dialog box.

FIGURE 11-3
The Drop User Dialog

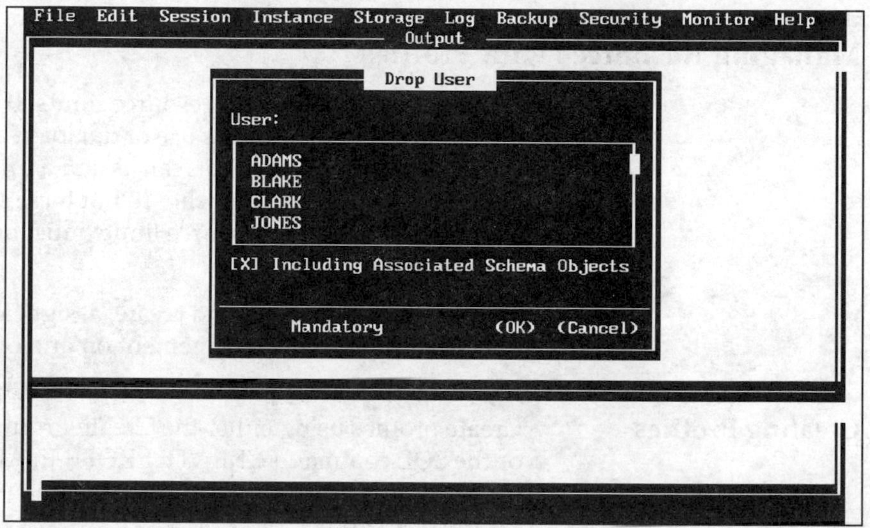

If the user's schema contains any schema objects, the Including Associated Schema Objects check box must be selected to drop the user and all associated objects and foreign keys that depend on the tables of the user successfully; if you do not select this check box and the user's schema contains objects, an error message is returned and the user is not dropped. Before dropping a user whose schema contains objects, thoroughly investigate which objects the user's schema contains and the implications of dropping them before the user is dropped. Pay attention to any unknown cascading effects; for example, if you intend to drop a user that owns a table, check whether any views or procedures depend on the table.

The following statement is the command equivalent of the Drop User dialog box in Figure 11-3:

```
DROP USER jones CASCADE;
```

Privileges Required to Drop Users

To drop a user and all the user's schema objects (if any), you must have the DROP USER system privilege. Because the DROP USER system privilege is so powerful, a security administrator is normally the only type of user that has this privilege.

Managing Resources with Profiles

A profile is a named set of resource limits. If resource limits are turned on, ORACLE limits a user's use of database and instance resources to that given in his profile. You can assign a profile to each user, and a default profile to all users who do not have specific profiles. For profiles to take effect, resource limits must be turned on for the database as a whole.

This section explains how to create, assign, alter, and drop profiles, and how to turn resource management on and off.

Creating Profiles

Create profiles using either the Create Profile dialog box of SQL*DBA or the SQL command CREATE PROFILE. At the same time, you can explicitly set particular resource limits. Figure 11-4 shows the Create Profile dialog box.

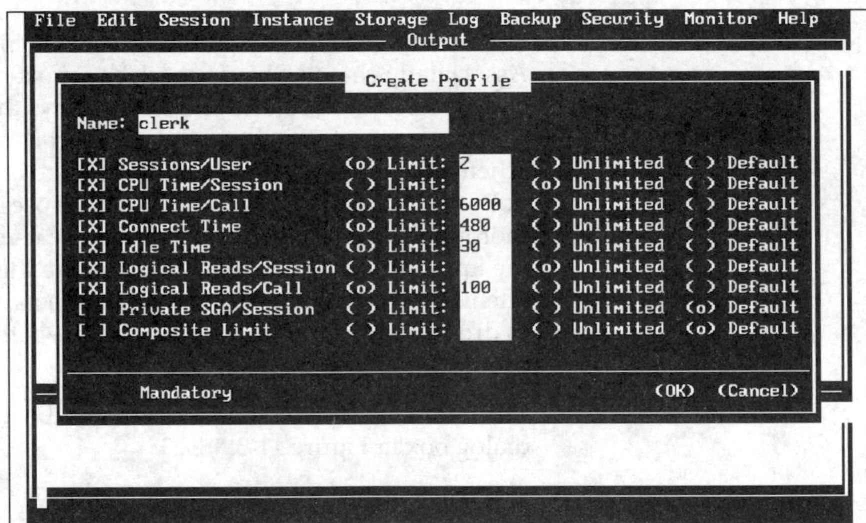

FIGURE 11-4
The Create Profile Dialog

The following statement is the command equivalent of the Create Profile dialog box in Figure 11-4:

```
CREATE PROFILE clerk LIMIT
    SESSIONS_PER_USER 2
    CPU_PER_SESSION unlimited
    CPU_PER_CALL 6000
    LOGICAL_READS_PER_SESSION unlimited
    LOGICAL_READS_PER_CALL 100
    IDLE_TIME 30
    CONNECT_TIME 480;
```

All unspecified resource limits for a new profile take the limit set by the default profile named DEFAULT. You can also specify limits for the DEFAULT profile. (See "Using the Default Profile" on page 11-17.)

Privileges Required to Create Profiles

To create a profile, you must have the CREATE PROFILE system privilege.

Using the Default Profile

Each database automatically has a default profile named DEFAULT. The default profile's limits are used in two cases:

- If a user is not explicitly assigned a profile, then the user conforms to **all** the limits of the default profile.
- All unspecified limits of any profile use the corresponding limit of the default profile.

Initially, all limits of the DEFAULT profile are set to UNLIMITED. However, to prevent unlimited resource consumption by users of the default profile, the security administrator should change the default limits using the Alter Profile dialog box or a typical ALTER PROFILE statement, as in:

```
ALTER PROFILE default LIMIT
    . . . ;
```

Any user with the ALTER PROFILE system privilege can adjust the limits in the DEFAULT profile. The DEFAULT profile cannot be dropped.

Assigning Profiles

Once a profile has been created, you can assign it to database users. Each user can be assigned only one profile at any given time. If a profile is assigned to a user who already has a profile, the new profile assignment overrides the previously assigned profile. Profile assignments do not affect current sessions. Profiles can be assigned only to users and not to roles or other profiles.

Profiles can be assigned to users using the SQL*DBA dialogs Create User and Alter User, or the SQL commands CREATE USER or ALTER USER. See "Creating Users" on page 11-7 and "Altering Users" on page 11-11 for more information about assigning a profile to a user.

Altering Profiles

The resource limit settings of any profile can be altered using either the Alter Profile dialog box of SQL*DBA or the SQL command ALTER PROFILE. Figure 11-5 shows the Alter Profile dialog box.

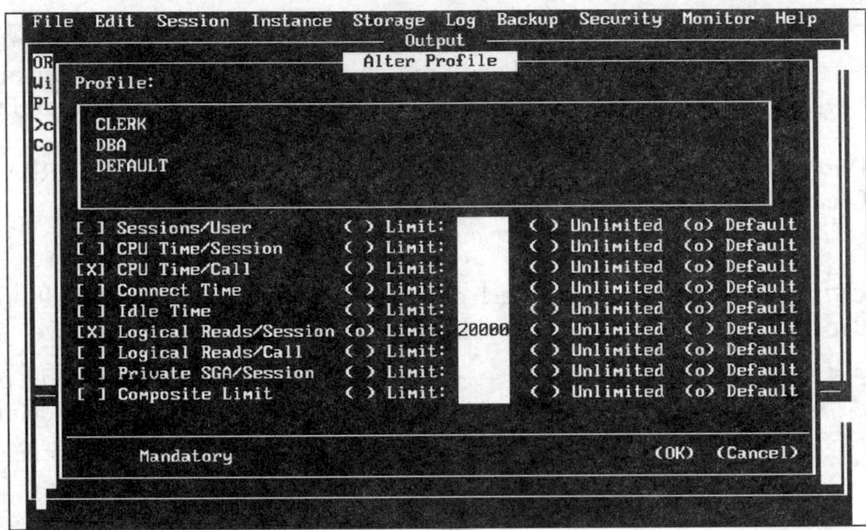

FIGURE 11-5
The Alter Profile Dialog

The following statement is the command equivalent of the Alter Profile dialog box in Figure 11-5:

```
ALTER PROFILE clerk LIMIT
    CPU_PER_CALL default
    LOGICAL_READS_PER_SESSION 20000;
```

Any profile limit adjusted overrides the previous setting for that profile limit. By adjusting a limit with a value of DEFAULT, the resource limit reverts to the default limit set for the database (see "Using the Default Profile" on page 11-17). All profiles not adjusted when altering a profile retain the previous settings. Any changes to a profile do not affect current sessions; new profile settings are used only for sessions created after a profile is modified.

Privileges Required to Alter Profiles

To alter a profile, you must have the ALTER PROFILE system privilege.

Using Composite Limits

In addition to setting specific resource limits explicitly for a profile, a single composite limit can be set that accounts for all resource limits in a profile. A profile's composite limit is set using the Composite Limit checkbox of the Create Profile and Alter Profile dialog boxes of SQL*DBA or the COMPOSITE_LIMIT parameter of the SQL commands CREATE PROFILE or ALTER PROFILE. A composite limit is set in terms of *service units*. A service unit is a weighted sum of all resources used. For example, the following CREATE PROFILE statement is defined using the COMPOSITE_LIMIT parameter:

```
CREATE PROFILE clerk LIMIT
    COMPOSITE_LIMIT 20000
    SESSIONS_PER_USER 2
    CPU_PER_CALL 1000;
```

Notice that both explicit resource limits and a composite limit can exist concurrently for a profile. The limit that is reached first is used to stop the activity in a session. Composite limits allow additional flexibility when limiting the use of system resources.

The correct service unit setting for a composite limit depends on the total amount of resource used by an average profile user. As with each specific resource limit, historical information should be gathered to determine the normal range of composite resource usage for a typical profile user.

Each system has its own characteristics; some system resources may be more valuable than others. Therefore, ORACLE also permits you to give each system resource a *cost*. Costs weight each system resource at the database level. Costs are only applied to the composite limit of a profile; costs do not apply to set individual resource limits explicitly.

Only certain resources can be given a cost, including CPU_PER_-SESSION, LOGICAL_READS_PER_SESSION, CONNECT_TIME, and PRIVATE_SGA. Set costs for a database using either the Alter Resource Cost dialog box of SQL*DBA or the SQL command ALTER RESOURCE COST. Figure 11-6 shows the Alter Resource Cost dialog box.

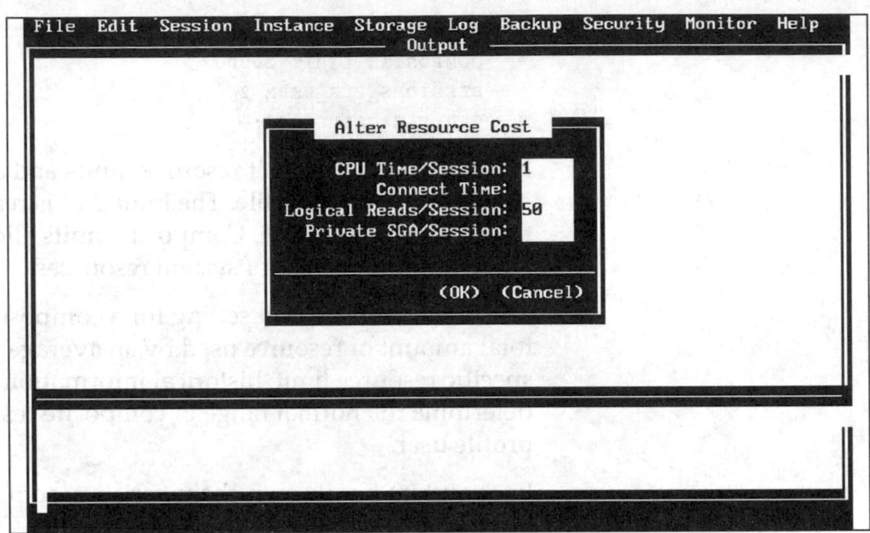

FIGURE 11-6
The Alter Resource Cost Dialog

The following statement is the command equivalent of the Alter Resource Cost dialog box in Figure 11-6:

```
ALTER RESOURCE COST
    CPU_PER_SESSION 1
    LOGICAL_READS_PER_SESSION 50;
```

A large cost means that the resource is very expensive, while a small cost means that the resource is not expensive. By default, each resource is initially given a cost of 0. A cost of 0 means that the resource should not be considered in the composite limit (that is, it does not cost anything to use this resource). No resource can be given a cost of NULL. See your installation or user's guide for additional information and recommendations on setting resource costs.

Privileges Required to Set Resource Costs

To set resource costs, you must have the ALTER RESOURCE system privilege.

Dropping Profiles

A profile can be dropped using either the Drop Profile dialog box of SQL*DBA or the SQL command DROP PROFILE. Figure 11-7 shows the Drop Profile dialog box.

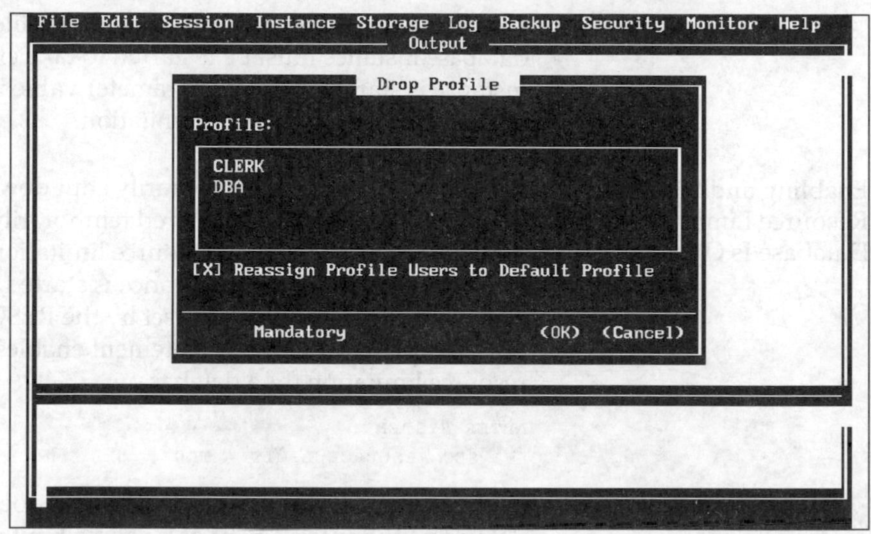

FIGURE 11-7
The Drop Profile Dialog

To drop a profile currently assigned to a user successfully, the Drop Even If Currently Assigned checkbox must be selected.

The following statement is the command equivalent of the Drop Profile dialog in Figure 11-7:

```
DROP PROFILE clerk CASCADE;
```

Any user currently assigned to a profile that is dropped is automatically assigned to the DEFAULT profile. The DEFAULT profile cannot be dropped. Note that when a profile is dropped, the drop does not affect currently active sessions; only sessions created after a profile is dropped abide by any modified profile assignments.

Privileges Required to Drop Profiles

To drop a profile, you must have the DROP PROFILE system privilege.

Enabling and Disabling Resource Limits

A profile can be created, assigned to users, altered, and dropped at any time by any authorized database user, but the resource limits set for a profile are enforced only when you enable resource limitation for the associated database. Resource limitation enforcement can be enabled or disabled by two different methods, as described in the next two sections.

Enabling and Disabling Resource Limits Before Startup

If a database can be temporarily shut down, resource limitation can be enabled or disabled by the RESOURCE_LIMIT initialization parameter in the database's parameter file. Valid values for the parameter are TRUE (enables enforcement) and FALSE; by default, this parameter's value is set to FALSE. Once the parameter file has been edited, the database instance must be restarted to take effect. Every time that an instance is started, the new parameter value is used to enable or disable the enforcement of resource limitation.

Enabling and Disabling Resource Limits While the Database Is Open

If a database cannot be temporarily shut down or the resource limitation feature must be altered temporarily, you can enable or disable the enforcement of resource limitation using the SQL command ALTER SYSTEM. Once an instance is started, an ALTER SYSTEM statement overrides the value set by the RESOURCE_LIMIT parameter. For example, the following statement enables the enforcement of resource limitation for a database:

```
ALTER SYSTEM
    SET RESOURCE_LIMIT = TRUE;
```

However, an ALTER SYSTEM statement does not permanently determine the enforcement of resource limitation; if the database is shut down and restarted, the enforcement of resource limits is determined by the value set for the RESOURCE_LIMIT parameter.

Privileges Required to Enable and Disable Resource Limits To alter the enforcement of resource limitation while the database remains open, you must have the ALTER SYSTEM system privilege.

Listing Information About Database Users and Profiles

The data dictionary stores information about every user and profile, including:

- all users in a database
- each user's default tablespace for tables, clusters, and indexes
- each user's tablespace for temporary segments
- each user's space quotas, if any
- each user's assigned profile and resource limits
- the cost assigned to each applicable system resource
- each current session's memory usage

The following data dictionary views are of interest regarding database users and profiles:

- ALL_USERS
- USER_USERS
- DBA_USERS
- USER_TS_QUOTAS
- DBA_TS_QUOTAS
- USER_RESOURCE_LIMITS
- DBA_PROFILES
- RESOURCE_COST
- V$SESSION
- V$SESSTAT
- V$STATNAME

See Appendix B for detailed information about each view.

Examples

The examples in this section assume a database in which the following statements have been executed:

```
CREATE PROFILE clerk LIMIT
    SESSIONS_PER_USER 1
    IDLE_TIME 30
    CONNECT_TIME 600;

CREATE USER jward
    IDENTIFIED BY wildcat
    DEFAULT TABLESPACE users
    TEMPORARY TABLESPACE temp_ts
    QUOTA 500K ON users
    PROFILE clerk;

CREATE USER tsmith
    IDENTIFIED BY bedrock
    DEFAULT TABLESPACE users
    TEMPORARY TABLESPACE temp_ts
    QUOTA unlimited ON users;
```

Example 1 Listing All Users and Associated Information

The following query lists all users defined in the database:

```
SELECT * FROM sys.dba_users;

USERNA USER_ID PASSWORD         DEFAUL TEMPOR  CREATED   PROFILE
------ ------- ---------------- ------ ------  --------- --------
SYS          % 522D06CDE017CF93 SYSTEM SYSTEM  31-JUL-90 PUBLIC_DEFAULT
SYSTEM       % 9B30B3EB7A7EE46A SYSTEM SYSTEM  31-JUL-90 PUBLIC_DEFAULT
JWARD        % DEE4F647381D62C4 USERS  TEMP_TS 12-SEP-90 CLERK
TSMITH       % 4791F162172E7834 USERS  TEMP_TS 12-SEP-90 PUBLIC_DEFAULT
```

All passwords are encrypted to preserve security.

Example 2
Listing Users' Roles

The following query lists, for each user, the roles granted to that user, and indicates whether each role is granted with the ADMIN OPTION and is a default role:

```
SELECT * FROM sys.dba_role_privs where grantee = 'CCLOSKEY';

GRANTEE                      GRANTED_ROLE                ADM DEF
---------------------------- --------------------------- --- ---
CCLOSKEY                     CLERK                       YES YES
CCLOSKEY                     PAYROLL                     NO  NO
CCLOSKEY                     WEEKLY_ADMIN                NO  NO
```

Example 3
Listing All
Tablespace Quotas

The following query lists all tablespace quotas specifically assigned to each user:

```
SELECT * FROM sys.dba_ts_quotas;

TABLESPACE USERNAME        BYTES  MAX_BYTES     BLOCKS MAX_BLOCKS
---------- ---------- ---------- ---------- ---------- ----------
SYSTEM     SYSTEM              0          0          0          0
SYSTEM     JWARD               0     512000          0        250
SYSTEM     TSMITH              0         -1          0         -1
```

When specific quotas are assigned, the exact number is indicated in the MAX_BYTES column. Unlimited quotas are indicated by "-1".

Example 4 Listing All Profiles and Assigned Limits

The following query lists all profiles in the database and associated settings for each limit in each profile:

```
SELECT * FROM sys.dba_profiles
    ORDER BY profile;

PROFILE           RESOURCE_NAME                      LIMIT
---------------   --------------------------------   -------------
CLERK             COMPOSITE_LIMIT                    UNLIMITED
CLERK             SESSIONS_PER_USER                  1
CLERK             CPU_PER_SESSION                    UNLIMITED
CLERK             CPU_PER_CALL                       UNLIMITED
CLERK             LOGICAL_READS_PER_SESSION          UNLIMITED
CLERK             LOGICAL_READS_PER_CALL             UNLIMITED
CLERK             IDLE_TIME                          30
CLERK             CONNECT_TIME                       600
CLERK             PRIVATE_SGA                        UNLIMITED
DEFAULT           COMPOSITE_LIMIT                    UNLIMITED
DEFAULT           SESSIONS_PER_USER                  UNLIMITED
DEFAULT           CPU_PER_SESSION                    UNLIMITED
DEFAULT           CPU_PER_CALL                       UNLIMITED
DEFAULT           LOGICAL_READS_PER_SESSION          UNLIMITED
DEFAULT           LOGICAL_READS_PER_CALL             UNLIMITED
DEFAULT           IDLE_TIME                          UNLIMITED
DEFAULT           CONNECT_TIME                       UNLIMITED
DEFAULT           PRIVATE_SGA                        UNLIMITED
```

Example 5 Viewing Memory Use Per User Session

The following query lists all current sessions, showing the ORACLE user and current memory use per session:

```
SELECT username, value || 'bytes' "Current session memory"
  FROM v$session sess, v$sesstat stat, v$statname name
WHERE sess.sid = stat.sid
   AND stat.statistic# = name.statistic#
   AND name.name = 'session memory';
```

The amount of space indicated in "Current session memory" is allocated in the shared pool for each session connected through the multi-threaded server. You can limit the amount of memory allocated per user with the PRIVATE_SGA resource limit.

To see the maximum memory ever allocated to each session since the instance started, replace 'session memory' in the query above with 'max session memory'.

CHAPTER

12 Controlling User Privileges and Roles

This chapter explains how to control the capability to execute system operations and access to schema objects using privileges and roles. Topics include:

- system and object privileges
- how to grant and revoke privileges and roles
- how to create, alter, and drop roles
- how to manage role use

For information on controlling access to a database as a whole, see Chapter 11; for suggested general database security policies, see Chapter 10.

Trusted

If you are using Trusted ORACLE in DBMS MAC mode, see the *Trusted ORACLE7 Server Administrator's Guide* for important information about system privileges and role management.

Understanding Privileges

A privilege is a right to execute a particular type of SQL statement, or a right to access another user's object. ORACLE has two kinds of privileges: system privileges and object privileges. ORACLE's privileges are listed in the following sections, along with shortcuts that group privileges commonly granted or revoked together.

System Privileges

There are over 80 distinct system privileges. Each system privilege allows a user to perform a particular database operation or class of database operations. Table 12-1 lists all system privileges and the operations that they permit.

TABLE 12-1
System Privileges

System Privilege	Operations Permitted
ANALYZE	
ANALYZE ANY	Analyze any table, cluster, or index in the database.
AUDIT	
AUDIT ANY	Audit any schema object in the database.
AUDIT SYSTEM	Enable and disable statement and privilege audit options.
CLUSTER	
CREATE CLUSTER	Create a cluster in own schema.
CREATE ANY CLUSTER	Create a cluster in any schema. Behaves similarly to CREATE ANY TABLE.
ALTER ANY CLUSTER	Alter any cluster in the database.
DROP ANY CLUSTER	Drop any cluster in the database.
DATABASE	
ALTER DATABASE	Alter the database; add files to the operating system via ORACLE, regardless of operating system privileges.
DATABASE LINK	
CREATE DATABASE LINK	Create private database links in own schema.

INDEX	
CREATE ANY INDEX	Create an index (in any schema) on any table.
ALTER ANY INDEX	Alter any index in the database.
DROP ANY INDEX	Drop any index in the database.
PRIVILEGE	
GRANT ANY PRIVILEGE	Grant any system privilege (not object privilege).
PROCEDURE	
CREATE PROCEDURE	Create stored procedures, functions, and packages in own schema.
CREATE ANY PROCEDURE	Create stored procedures, functions, and packages in any schema. (Requires that user also have ALTER ANY TABLE, BACKUP ANY TABLE, DROP ANY TABLE, LOCK ANY TABLE, COMMENT ANY TABLE, SELECT ANY TABLE, INSERT ANY TABLE, UPDATE ANY TABLE, DELETE ANY TABLE, or GRANT ANY TABLE.)
ALTER ANY PROCEDURE	Compile any stored procedure, function, or package in any schema.
DROP ANY PROCEDURE	Drop any stored procedure, function, or package in any schema.
EXECUTE ANY PROCEDURE	Execute any procedure or function (stand-alone or packaged), or reference any public package variable in any schema.
PROFILE	
CREATE PROFILE	Create profiles.
ALTER PROFILE	Alter any profile in the database.
DROP PROFILE	Drop any profile in the database.
ALTER RESOURCE COST	Set costs for resources used in all user sessions.
PUBLIC DATABASE LINK	
CREATE PUBLIC DATABASE LINK	Create public database links.
DROP PUBLIC DATABASE LINK	Drop public database links.

PUBLIC SYNONYM	
CREATE PUBLIC SYNONYM	Create public synonyms.
DROP PUBLIC SYNONYM	Drop public synonyms.
ROLE	
CREATE ROLE	Create roles.
ALTER ANY ROLE	Alter any role in the database.
DROP ANY ROLE	Drop any role in the database.
GRANT ANY ROLE	Grant any role in the database.
ROLLBACK SEGMENT	
CREATE ROLLBACK SEGMENT	Create rollback segments.
ALTER ROLLBACK SEGMENT	Alter rollback segments.
DROP ROLLBACK SEGMENT	Drop rollback segments.
SESSION	
CREATE SESSION	Connect to the database.
ALTER SESSION	Issue ALTER SESSION statements.
RESTRICTED SESSION	Connect when the database has been started using STARTUP RESTRICT. (The OSOPER and OSDBA roles contain this privilege.)
SEQUENCE	
CREATE SEQUENCE	Create a sequence in own schema.
CREATE ANY SEQUENCE	Create any sequence in any schema.
ALTER ANY SEQUENCE	Alter any sequence in any schema.
DROP ANY SEQUENCE	Drop any sequence in any schema.
SELECT ANY SEQUENCE	Reference any sequence in any schema.

SNAPSHOT	
CREATE SNAPSHOT	Create snapshots in own schema. (User must also have the CREATE TABLE privilege.)
CREATE ANY SNAPSHOT	Create snapshots in any schema. (User must also have the CREATE ANY TABLE privilege.)
ALTER ANY SNAPSHOT	Alter any snapshot in any schema.
DROP ANY SNAPSHOT	Drop any snapshot in any schema.
SYNONYM	
CREATE SYNONYM	Create a synonym in own schema.
CREATE ANY SYNONYM	Create any synonym in any schema.
DROP ANY SYNONYM	Drop any synonym in any schema
SYSTEM	
ALTER SYSTEM	Issue ALTER SYSTEM statements.
TABLE	
CREATE TABLE	Create tables in own schema. Also allows grantee to create indexes (including those for integrity constraints) on tables in own schema. (The grantee must have a quota for the tablespace or the UNLIMITED TABLESPACE privilege.)
CREATE ANY TABLE	Create a table in any schema. (If grantee has CREATE ANY TABLE privilege and creates a table in another user's schema, the owner's space quotas and default tablespace are used. If a tablespace is explicitly specified, the owner must have space quota on that tablespace. The table owner need not have the CREATE [ANY] TABLE privilege.)
ALTER ANY TABLE	Alter any table in any schema and compile any view in any schema.
BACKUP ANY TABLE	Perform an incremental export using the Export utility.
DROP ANY TABLE	Drop any table in any schema.
LOCK ANY TABLE	Lock any table or view in any schema.
COMMENT ANY TABLE	Comment on any table, view, or column in schema.
SELECT ANY TABLE	Query any table, view, or snapshot in any schema.
INSERT ANY TABLE	Insert rows into any table or view in any schema.

UPDATE ANY TABLE	Update rows in any table or view in any schema.
DELETE ANY TABLE	Delete rows from any table or view in any schema, and truncate any table, cluster, or index.
TABLESPACE	
CREATE TABLESPACE	Create tablespaces; add files to the operating system via ORACLE, regardless of the user's operating system privileges.
ALTER TABLESPACE	Alter tablespaces; add files to the operating system via ORACLE, regardless of the user's operating system privileges.
MANAGE TABLESPACE	Take any tablespace offline, bring any tablespace online, and begin and end backups of any tablespace.
DROP TABLESPACE	Drop tablespaces.
UNLIMITED TABLESPACE	Use an unlimited amount of **any** tablespace. (This privilege overrides any specific quotas assigned. If revoked, the grantee's schema objects remain but further tablespace allocation is denied unless allowed by specific tablespace quotas. **This system privilege can only be granted to users and not to roles. In general, specific tablespace quotas are assigned instead of granting this system privilege.**)
TRANSACTION	
FORCE TRANSACTION	Force the commit or rollback of own in-doubt distributed transactions in the local database.
FORCE ANY TRANSACTION	Force the commit or rollback of any in-doubt distributed transaction in the local database.
TRIGGER	
CREATE TRIGGER	Create a trigger in own schema.
CREATE ANY TRIGGER	Create any trigger (in any schema) associated with any table in any schema.
ALTER ANY TRIGGER	Enable, disable, or compile any trigger in any schema.
DROP ANY TRIGGER	Drop any trigger in any schema.

USER	
CREATE USER	Create users; assign quotas on **any** tablespace, set default and temporary tablespaces, and assign a profile as part of a CREATE USER statement.
BECOME USER	Become another user. (Required by any user performing a full database import.)
ALTER USER	Alter other users: change any user's password or authentication method, assign tablespace quotas, set default and temporary tablespaces, assign profiles and default roles, in an ALTER USER statement. (Not needed to alter own password)
DROP USER	Drop another user.
VIEW	
CREATE VIEW	Create a view in own schema.
CREATE ANY VIEW	Create a view in any schema. (Requires that user also have ALTER ANY TABLE, BACKUP ANY TABLE, DROP ANY TABLE, LOCK ANY TABLE, COMMENT ANY TABLE, SELECT ANY TABLE, INSERT ANY TABLE, UPDATE ANY TABLE, DELETE ANY TABLE, or GRANT ANY TABLE.)
DROP ANY VIEW	Drop any view in any schema.

Because system privileges are very powerful, they should be cautiously granted to roles and trusted users of the database.

Object Privileges

Each type of object has different privileges associated with it. Table 12-2 summarizes the object privileges available for each type of object.

TABLE 12-2
Object Privileges

Object Privilege	Table	View	Sequence	Procedure*
ALTER	✔		✔	
DELETE	✔	✔		
EXECUTE				✔
INDEX	✔**			
INSERT	✔	✔		
REFERENCES	✔**			
SELECT	✔	✔***	✔	
UPDATE	✔	✔		

* Includes stand-alone stored procedures and functions, and public package constructs.

** Privilege cannot be granted to a role.

*** Can also be granted for snapshots.

Granting INSERT Privileges for Columns

You can grant INSERT on individual columns in a table. Before granting a column-specific INSERT privilege, investigate the possible side effects; if a table has one or more columns declared NOT NULL, granting selective insert capability without including the NOT NULL columns prevents the user from inserting any rows into the table. To prevent problems, check that each column with a NOT NULL constraint is either insertable or has a non-NULL default value; if this problem is not accounted for, an error is returned and rows cannot be inserted.

Statements Permitted by Each Privilege

Table 12-3 lists the SQL statements permitted by the object privileges listed previously.

TABLE 12-3
SQL Statements Permitted by Database Object Privileges

Object Privilege	SQL Statements Permitted
ALTER	ALTER object (table or sequence)
DELETE	DELETE FROM object (table or view)
EXECUTE	EXECUTE object (procedure or function) References to public package variables
INDEX	CREATE INDEX ON object (tables only)
INSERT	INSERT INTO object (table or view)
REFERENCES	CREATE or ALTER TABLE statement defining a FOREIGN KEY integrity constraint on object (tables only)
SELECT	SELECT . . . FROM object (table, view, or snapshot) SQL statements using a sequence
UPDATE	UPDATE object (table or view)

Not all types of schema objects are included in Table 12-2. Many of the schema objects not listed here (such as clusters, indexes, triggers, and database links) are controlled exclusively using system privileges. For example, to alter a cluster, a user must own the cluster or have the ALTER ANY CLUSTER system privilege.

Object Privilege Shortcut

The ALL and ALL PRIVILEGES shortcuts grant or revoke all available object privileges for a object. This shortcut is not a privilege itself; rather, it is a way of granting or revoking all object privileges with one word in GRANT and REVOKE statements. Note that if all object privileges are granted using the ALL shortcut, individual privileges can still be revoked.

Likewise, all individually granted privileges can be revoked using the ALL shortcut. However, if you REVOKE ALL, and revoking causes integrity constraints to be deleted (because they depend on a REFERENCES privilege that you are revoking), you must include the CASCADE CONSTRAINTS option in the REVOKE statement.

Managing Roles

A role groups several privileges and roles, so that they can be granted and revoked simultaneously from users. Roles can be enabled and disabled per user. The following sections explain how to create, alter, enable, disable, and drop roles.

Creating Roles

You create a role using either the Create Role dialog box of SQL*DBA or the SQL command CREATE ROLE. Figure 12-1 shows the Create Role dialog box.

FIGURE 12-1
The Create Role Dialog

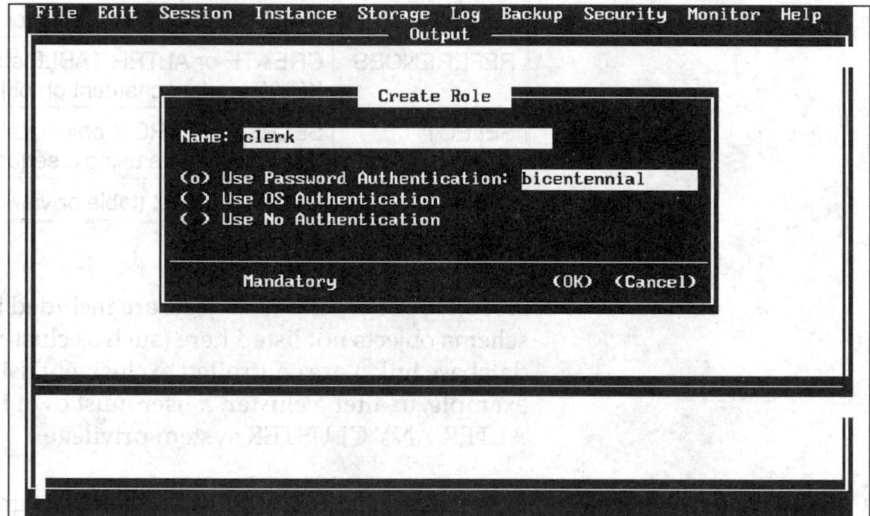

The following statement is the command equivalent of the Create Role dialog box in Figure 12-1:

```
CREATE ROLE clerk IDENTIFIED BY bicentennial;
```

You must give each role you create a unique name among existing usernames and role names of the database. Roles are not contained in the schema of any user.

Immediately after creation, a role has no privileges associated with it. To associate privileges with a new role, you must grant privileges or other roles to the new role. This procedure is discussed in "Granting and Revoking Privileges and Roles" on page 12-15.

Role Names in Multi-Byte Character Sets

In a database that uses a multi-byte character set, Oracle Corporation recommends that each role name contain at least one single-byte character. If a role name contains only multi-byte characters, the encrypted role name/password combination is considerably less secure.

Role Authorization

A database role can optionally require authorization when a user attempts to enable the role. Role authorization can be maintained by the database (using passwords) or, if your operating system permits, by the operating system.

Authorization by the Database The use of a role can be protected by an associated password, as in the examples above. If you are granted a role protected by a password, you can enable or disable the role only by supplying the proper password for the role in a SET ROLE command.

Note: In a database that uses a multi-byte character set, passwords for roles must include only single-byte characters. Multi-byte characters are not accepted in passwords.

Authorization by the Operating System In contrast, the following statement creates a role named ACCTS_REC and requires that the operating system authorize its use:

```
CREATE ROLE role IDENTIFIED EXTERNALLY;
```

Role authentication via the operating system is useful only when the operating system must be able to dynamically link operating system privileges with applications. When a user starts an application, the operating system grants an operating system privilege to the user. The granted operating system privilege corresponds to the role associated with the application. At this point, the application can enable the application role. When the application is terminated, the previously granted operating system privilege is revoked from the user's operating system account.

If a role is to be authorized by the operating system, you must configure information for each user at the operating system level. This operation is operating system dependent.

If roles are granted by the operating system (that is, if OS_ROLES = TRUE; see page 12-22), you do not need to have the operating system authorize them also; this is redundant.

Note: If users connect to the database through the multi-threaded server, by default their roles cannot be authenticated by the operating system. This restriction is the default because a remote user could impersonate another operating system user over a network connection.

If you are not concerned with this security risk and want to use operating system role authentication with the multi-threaded server, set the parameter REMOTE_OS_ROLES in the database's parameter file to TRUE. The change will take effect the next time you start the instance and mount the database. (The parameter is FALSE by default.)

No Authorization A role can also be created without authorization. If a role is created without any protection, the role can be enabled or disabled by any grantee.

Using Pre-Defined Roles

The roles listed in Table 12-4 are automatically defined for ORACLE databases. These roles are provided for backward compatibility to earlier versions of ORACLE. You can grant and revoke privileges and roles to these pre-defined roles, as you can to any role you define.

TABLE 12-4
Pre-Defined Roles

Role Name	Privileges Granted To Role
CONNECT[1]	ALTER SESSION, CREATE CLUSTER, CREATE DATABASE LINK, CREATE SEQUENCE, CREATE SESSION, CREATE SYNONYM, CREATE TABLE, CREATE VIEW
RESOURCE[1, 2]	CREATE CLUSTER, CREATE PROCEDURE, CREATE SEQUENCE, CREATE TABLE, CREATE TRIGGER
DBA[1,3,4]	All system privileges WITH ADMIN OPTION
EXP_FULL_DATABASE[5]	SELECT ANY TABLE, BACKUP ANY TABLE, INSERT, DELETE, and UPDATE on the tables SYS.INCVID, SYS.INCFIL, and SYS.INCEXP
IMP_FULL_DATABASE[5]	BECOME USER, WRITEDOWN[6]

1 created by SQL.BSQ

2 grantees of the RESOURCE role also receive the UNLIMITED TABLESPACE system privilege as an explicitly grant (not as part of the RESOURCE role)

3 grantees of the DBA role also receive the UNLIMITED TABLESPACE system privilege with the ADMIN OPTION as an explicit grant (not as part of the DBA role)

4 also includes the EXP_FULL_DATABASE and IMP_FULL_DATABASE roles if CATEXP.SQL has been run

5 created by CATEXP.SQL

6 a Trusted ORACLE privilege only; see the *Trusted ORACLE7 Server Administrator's Guide*

Privileges Required to Create Roles

To create a role, you must have the CREATE ROLE system privilege. Typically, only security administrators have this system privilege.

Changing Role Authorization

You can set and change the authorization method for a role using either the Alter Role dialog box of SQL*DBA or the SQL command ALTER ROLE. Figure 12-2 shows the Alter Role dialog box.

FIGURE 12-2
The Alter Role Dialog

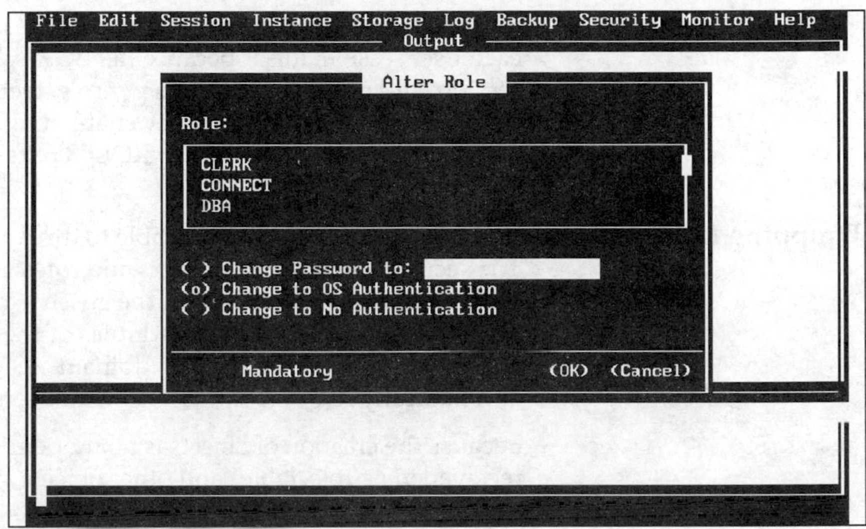

The following statement is the command equivalent of the Alter Role dialog box in Figure 12-2.

```
ALTER ROLE clerk IDENTIFIED EXTERNALLY;
```

For more information about role authorization, see "Role Authorization" on page 12-11.

Privileges Required to Change Role Authorization

To alter the authorization method for a role, you must have the ALTER ANY ROLE system privilege or have been granted the role with the ADMIN OPTION.

Changing a User's Default Roles

A user's list of default roles can be set and altered using either the Alter User dialog box of SQL*DBA or the SQL command ALTER USER. See "Altering Users" on page 11-11 for more information about these options.

If the user's list of default roles is specified as ALL, every role granted to a user is automatically added to the user's list of default roles. Only subsequent modification of a user's default role list can remove newly granted roles from a user's list of default roles.

The MAX_ENABLED_ROLES Parameter

A user can enable as many roles as specified by the initialization parameter MAX_ENABLED_ROLES. All indirectly granted roles enabled as a result of enabling a primary role are included in this count. The database administrator can alter this limitation by modifying the value for this parameter. Higher values permit each user session to have more concurrently enabled roles. However, the larger the value for this parameter, the more memory space is required on behalf of each user session; this is because the PGA size is affected for each user session, and requires four bytes per role. Determine the highest number of roles that will be concurrently enabled by any one user and use this value for the MAX_ENABLED_ROLES parameter.

Dropping Roles

In some cases, it may be applicable to drop a role from the database. The security domains of all users and roles granted a dropped role are immediately changed to reflect the absence of the dropped role's privileges. All indirectly granted roles of the dropped role are also removed from affected security domains. Dropping a role automatically removes the role from all users' default role lists.

Because the creation of objects is not dependent on the privileges received via a role, tables and other objects are not dropped when a role is dropped.

Drop a role using either the Drop Role dialog box of SQL*DBA or the SQL command DROP ROLE. Figure 12-3 shows the Drop Role dialog box.

FIGURE 12-3
The Drop Role Dialog

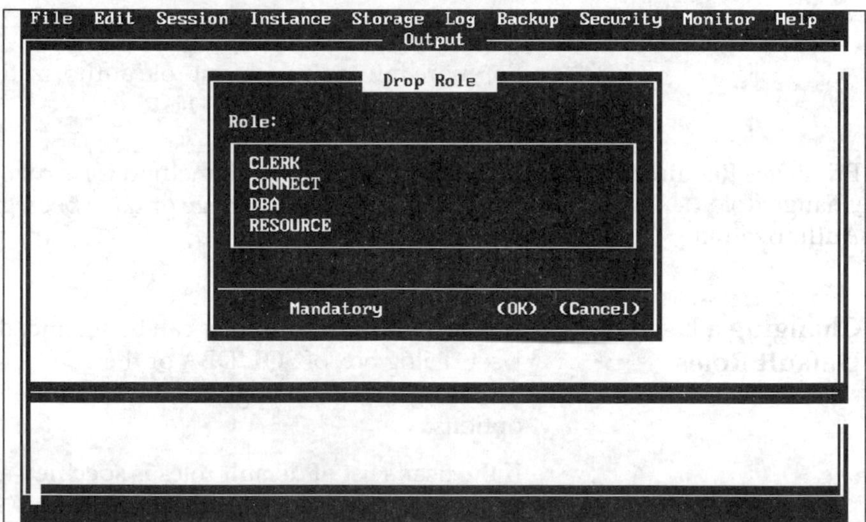

The following statement is the command equivalent of the Drop Role dialog box in Figure 12-3:

```
DROP ROLE clerk;
```

Privileges Required to Drop Roles

To drop a role, you must have the DROP ANY ROLE system privilege or have been granted the role with the ADMIN OPTION.

Granting and Revoking Privileges and Roles

This section explains how to grant and revoke system privileges, roles, and object privileges.

Granting System Privileges and Roles

System privileges and roles can be granted to other roles or users using either the Grant System Privileges/Roles dialog box of SQL*DBA or the SQL command GRANT. Figure 12-4 shows the Grant System Privileges/Roles dialog box.

FIGURE 12-4
The Grant System Privileges/Roles Dialog

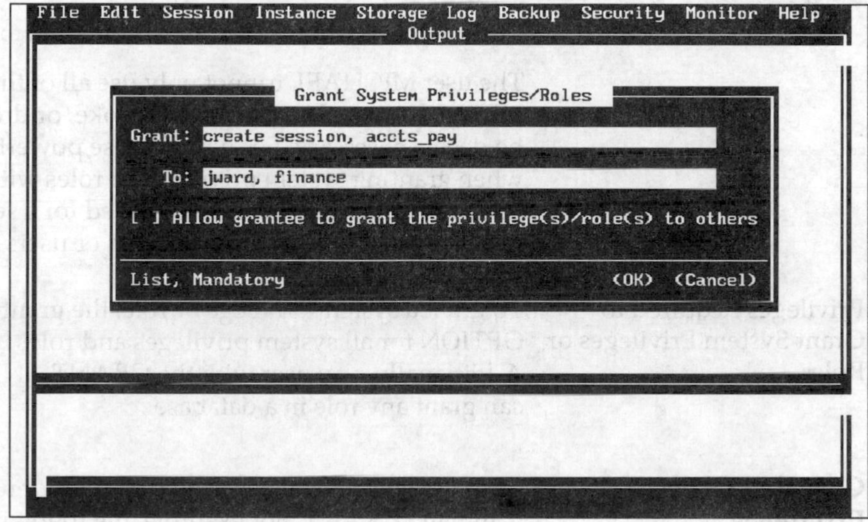

The following statement is the command equivalent of the Grant System Privileges/Roles dialog box in Figure 12-4:

```
GRANT create session, accts_pay
   TO jward, finance;
```

Note: Object privileges **cannot** be granted along with system privileges and roles in the same GRANT statement.

The ADMIN Option

A system privilege or role can be granted with the ADMIN OPTION. (The ADMIN OPTION cannot be included in a GRANT statement that grants a role to another role.) A grantee with this special option has several expanded capabilities:

- The grantee can grant or revoke the system privilege or role to or from **any** user or other role in the database. (A user cannot revoke a role from himself.)

- The grantee can further grant the system privilege or role with the ADMIN OPTION.
- The grantee of a role can alter or drop the role.

A grantee without the ADMIN OPTION cannot perform the above operations.

When a user creates a role, the role is automatically granted to the creator with the ADMIN OPTION.

Assume that the security administrator grants the NEW_DBA role to MICHAEL with the following statement:

```
GRANT new_dba TO michael WITH ADMIN OPTION;
```

The user MICHAEL cannot only use all of the privileges implicit in the NEW_DBA role, but can grant, revoke, or drop the NEW_DBA role as he deems necessary. Because of these powerful capabilities, use caution when granting system privileges or roles with the ADMIN OPTION. Such capabilities are usually reserved for a security administrator and rarely given to other administrators or users of the system.

Privileges Required to Grant System Privileges or Roles

To grant a system privilege or role, the grantor requires the ADMIN OPTION for all system privileges and roles being granted. Additionally, any user with the GRANT ANY ROLE system privilege can grant any role in a database.

Granting Object Privileges

Object privileges can be granted to roles or users using the SQL command GRANT. For example, the following statement grants the SELECT, INSERT, and DELETE object privileges for all columns of the EMP table to the users JWARD and TSMITH:

```
GRANT select, insert, delete ON emp TO jward, tsmith;
```

To grant the INSERT object privilege for only the ENAME and JOB columns of the EMP table to the users JWARD and TSMITH, enter the following statement:

```
GRANT insert(ename, job) ON emp TO jward, tsmith;
```

To grant all object privileges on the SALARY view to the user WALLEN, use the ALL shortcut, as in:

```
GRANT ALL ON salary TO wallen;
```

Note: System privileges and roles cannot be granted along with object privileges in the same GRANT statement.

The GRANT OPTION

An object privilege can be granted to a user with the GRANT OPTION. This special privilege allows the grantee several expanded privileges:

- The grantee can grant the object privilege to any user or any role in the database.
- The grantee can also grant the object privilege to other users, with or without the GRANT OPTION.
- If the grantee receives object privileges for a table with the GRANT OPTION and the grantee has the CREATE VIEW or the CREATE ANY VIEW system privilege, the grantee can create views on the table and grant the corresponding privileges on the view to any user or role in the database.

The user whose schema contains an object is automatically granted all associated object privileges with the GRANT OPTION.

Specifically note that the GRANT OPTION is not valid when granting an object privilege to a role. ORACLE prevents the propagation of object privileges via roles so that grantees of a role cannot propagate object privileges received via roles.

Privileges Required to Grant Object Privileges

To grant an object privilege, the grantor fulfill one of the following conditions:

- Own the object specified.
- Have been granted the object privileges being granted with the GRANT OPTION.

Revoking System Privileges and Roles

System privileges and/or roles can be revoked using either the Revoke System Privileges/Roles dialog box of SQL*DBA or the SQL command REVOKE. Figure 12-5 shows the Revoke System Privileges/Roles dialog box.

FIGURE 12-5
The Revoke System Privileges/Roles Dialog

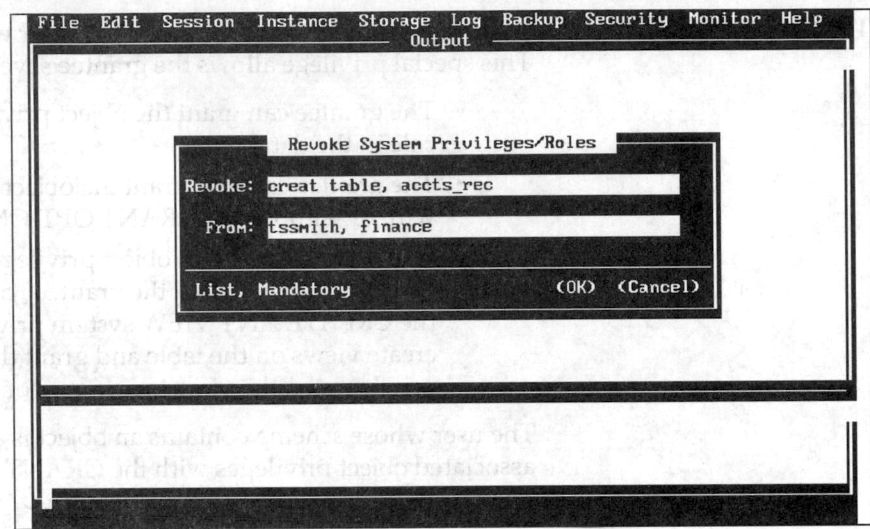

The following statement is the command equivalent of the Revoke System Privileges/Roles dialog box in Figure 12-5:

```
REVOKE create table, accts_rec FROM tsmith, finance;
```

Note: The ADMIN OPTION for a system privilege or role cannot be selectively revoked; the privilege or role must be revoked and then the privilege or role regranted without the ADMIN OPTION.

Privileges Required to Revoke System Privileges and Roles

Any user with the ADMIN OPTION for a system privilege or role can revoke the privilege or role from any other database user or role (the user does not have to be the user that originally granted the privilege or role). Additionally, any user with the GRANT ANY ROLE can revoke any role.

Revoking Object Privileges

Object privileges can be revoked using the SQL command REVOKE. For example, assuming you are the original grantor, to revoke the SELECT and INSERT privileges on the EMP table from the users JWARD and TSMITH, enter the following statement:

```
REVOKE select, insert ON emp
    FROM jward, tsmith;
```

A grantor could also revoke all privileges on the table DEPT (even if only one privilege was granted) that he/she granted to the role HUMAN_RESOURCES by entering the following statement:

```
REVOKE ALL ON dept FROM human_resources;
```

Note: The statement above would only revoke the privileges that the grantor authorized, not the grants made by other users. The GRANT OPTION for an object privilege cannot be selectively revoked; the object privilege must be revoked and then regranted without the GRANT OPTION. Users cannot revoke object privileges from themselves.

Revoking Column Selective Object Privileges

Although users can grant column selective INSERT, UPDATE, and REFERENCES privileges for tables and views, they cannot selectively revoke column specific privileges with a similar REVOKE statement. Instead, the grantor must first revoke the object privilege for all columns of a table or view, and then selectively regrant the column specific privileges that should remain.

For example, assume that role HUMAN_RESOURCES has been granted the UPDATE privilege on the DEPTNO and DNAME columns of the table DEPT. To revoke the UPDATE privilege on just the DEPTNO column, you would enter the following two statements:

```
REVOKE UPDATE ON dept FROM human_resources;
GRANT UPDATE (dname) ON dept TO human_resources;
```

The REVOKE statement revokes UPDATE privilege on all columns of the DEPT table from the role HUMAN_RESOURCES. The GRANT statement regrants UPDATE privilege on the DNAME column to the role HUMAN_RESOURCES.

Revoking the REFERENCES Object Privilege

If the grantee of the REFERENCES object privilege has used the privilege to create a foreign key constraint (that currently exists), the grantor can only revoke the privilege by specifying the CASCADE CONSTRAINTS option in the REVOKE statement:

```
REVOKE REFERENCES ON dept FROM jward CASCADE CONSTRAINTS;
```

Any foreign key constraints currently defined that use the revoked REFERENCES privilege are dropped when the CASCADE CONSTRAINTS options is specified.

Privileges Required to Revoke Object Privileges

To revoke an object privilege, the revoker must be the original grantor of the object privilege being revoked.

Cascading Effects of Revoking Privileges

Depending on the type of privilege, there may or may not be cascading effects if a privilege is revoked. The following sections explain several cascading effects.

System Privileges

There are no cascading effects when revoking a system privilege related to DDL operations, regardless of whether or not the privilege was granted with or without the ADMIN OPTION. For example, assume:

1. The security administrator grants the CREATE TABLE system privilege to JWARD with the ADMIN OPTION.
2. JWARD creates a table.
3. JWARD grants the CREATE TABLE system privilege to TSMITH.
4. TSMITH creates a table.
5. The security administrator revokes the CREATE TABLE system privilege from JWARD.
6. JWARD's table continues to exist. TSMITH continues to have the CREATE TABLE system privilege and his table still exists.

Cascading effects can be observed when revoking a system privilege related to a DML operation. For example, if SELECT ANY TABLE is granted to a user, and that user has created any procedures, all procedures contained in the user's schema must be reauthorized before they can be used again (after the revoke).

Object Privileges

Revoking an object privilege can have several types of cascading effects that should be investigated before a REVOKE statement is issued:

- Object definitions that depend on a DML object privilege can be affected if the DML object privilege is revoked. For example, assume the procedure body of the TEST procedure includes a SQL statement that queries data from the EMP table. If the SELECT privilege on the EMP table is revoked from the owner of the TEST procedure, the procedure can no longer be executed successfully.
- Object definitions that require the ALTER and INDEX DDL object privileges are not affected if the ALTER or INDEX object privilege is revoked. For example, if the INDEX privilege is revoked from a user that created an index on someone else's table, the index continues to exist after the privilege is revoked.
- When a REFERENCES privilege for a table is revoked from a user, any foreign key integrity constraints defined by the user that require the dropped REFERENCES privilege are automatically dropped. For example, assume that the user JWARD is granted the REFERENCES privilege for the DEPTNO column of the DEPT table and creates a foreign key on the DEPTNO column in the EMP table that references the DEPTNO column. If the REFERENCES privilege on the

DEPTNO column of the DEPT table is revoked, the foreign key constraint on the DEPTNO column of the EMP table is dropped in the same operation.

- The object privilege grants propagated through the use of the GRANT OPTION are revoked if a grantor's object privilege is revoked. For example, assume that USER1 is granted the SELECT object privilege with the GRANT OPTION, and grants the SELECT privilege on EMP to USER2. Subsequently, the SELECT privilege is revoked from USER1. This revoke is cascaded to USER2 as well. Any objects that depended on USER1's and USER2's revoked SELECT privilege can also be affected, as described in previous bullet items.

Granting to and Revoking from the User Group PUBLIC

Privileges and roles can also be granted to and revoked from the user group PUBLIC. Because PUBLIC is accessible to every database user, all privileges and roles granted to PUBLIC are accessible to every database user.

Security administrators and database users should only grant a privilege or role to PUBLIC if every database user requires the privilege or role. This recommendation restates the general rule that at any given time, each database user should only have the privileges required to accomplish the current task successfully.

Revokes from PUBLIC can cause significant cascading effects, depending on the privilege that is revoked. If any privilege related to a DML operation is revoked from PUBLIC (for example, SELECT ANY TABLE, UPDATE ON emp), all procedures in the database (including functions and packages) must be *reauthorized* (see "Managing Object Dependencies" on page 8-75) before they can be used again. Therefore, use caution when granting DML-related privileges to PUBLIC.

When Do Grants and Revokes Take Effect?

Depending on what is granted or revoked, a grant or revoke takes effect at different times:

- All grants/revokes of privileges (system and object) to anything (users, roles, and PUBLIC) are immediately observed.
- All grants/revokes of roles to anything (users, other roles, PUBLIC) are only observed when a current user session issues a SET ROLE statement to re-enable the role after the grant/revoke, or when a new user session is created after the grant/revoke.

Granting Database Roles Using the Operating System

Instead of a security administrator explicitly granting and revoking database roles to and from users using GRANT and REVOKE statements, the operating system that operates ORACLE can grant roles to users at connect time; roles can be administered using the operating system and passed to ORACLE when a user creates a session. As part of this mechanism, each user's default roles and the roles granted to a user with the ADMIN OPTION can be identified. Even if the operating system is used to authorize users for roles, all roles must be created in the database and privileges assigned to the role with GRANT statements, as normal.

The advantage of using the operating system to identify a user's database roles is that privilege management for an ORACLE database can be externalized; the security facilities offered by the operating system control a user's privileges. This option may offer advantages of centralizing security for a number of system activities. For example, MVS ORACLE administrators may want RACF groups to identify a database user's roles, UNIX ORACLE administrators may want UNIX groups to identify a database user's roles, or VMS ORACLE administrators may want to use rights identifiers to identify a database user's roles.

The main disadvantage of using the operating system to identify a user's database roles is that privilege management can only be performed at the role level; individual privileges cannot be granted using the operating system, but can still be granted inside the database using GRANT statements.

A secondary disadvantage of using this feature is that by default users cannot connect to the database through the multi-threaded server if the operating system is managing roles. However, you can change this default; see "Using the Multi-Threaded Server with Operating System Role Management" on page 12-24.

Note: The features described in this section are available only on some operating systems. This information is operating system dependent; see your installation or user's guide.

Using Operating System Role Identification

To operate a database so that it uses the operating system to identify each user's database roles when a session is created, set the initialization parameter OS_ROLES to TRUE (and restart the instance, if it is currently running). When a user attempts to create a session with the database, ORACLE initializes the user's security domain using the database roles identified by the operating system.

To identify database roles for a user, each ORACLE user's operating system account must have operating system identifiers (these may be called groups, rights identifiers, or other similar names) that indicate which database roles are to be available for the user. Role specification can also indicate which roles are the default roles of a user and which roles are available with the ADMIN OPTION. No matter which operating system is used, the role specification at the operating system level follows the format:

```
ORA_<ID>_<ROLE>[_[D][A]]
```

where:

ID — ID specifies different things on different operating systems. For example, on VMS, ID is the instance identifier of the database; on MVS, it is the machine type; on UNIX, it is the system ID.

D — This optional character indicates that this role is to be a default role of the database user.

A — This optional character indicates that this role is to be granted to the user with the ADMIN OPTION. This allows the user to grant the role to other roles only. (Roles cannot be granted to users if the operating system is used to manage roles.)

Note: If either the D or A characters are specified, they must be preceded by an underscore.

For example, an operating system account might have the following roles identified in its profile:

```
ORA_PAYROLL_ROLE1
ORA_PAYROLL_ROLE2_A
ORA_PAYROLL_ROLE3_D
ORA_PAYROLL_ROLE4_DA
```

When the corresponding user connects to the PAYROLL instance of ORACLE, ROLE3 and ROLE4 are defaults, while ROLE2 and ROLE4 are available with the ADMIN OPTION.

Granting and Revoking Roles When OS_ROLES=TRUE

If OS_ROLES is set to TRUE, the operating system completely manages the grants and revokes of roles **to users**. Any previous grants of roles to users via GRANT statements do not apply; however, they are still listed in the data dictionary. Only the role grants made at the operating system level to users apply. Users can still grant privileges to roles and users.

Note: If the operating system grants a role to a user with the ADMIN OPTION, the user can grant the role only to other roles.

Enabling and Disabling Roles When OS_ROLES=TRUE

If OS_ROLES is set to TRUE, any role granted by the operating system can be dynamically enabled using the SET ROLE command; if the role was defined to require a password or operating system authorization, that still applies. However, any role not identified in a user's operating system account cannot be specified in a SET ROLE statement, even if a role has been granted using a GRANT statement when OS_ROLES = FALSE. (If you specify such a role, ORACLE ignores it.)

When OS_ROLES = TRUE, a user can enable as many roles as specified by the parameter MAX_ENABLED_ROLES.

Using the Multi-Threaded Server with Operating System Role Management

If you want to have the operating system manage roles, by default users cannot connect to the database through the multi-threaded server. This restriction is the default because a remote user could impersonate another operating system user over a non-secure connection.

If you are not concerned with this security risk and want to use operating system role management with the multi-threaded server, set the parameter REMOTE_OS_ROLES in the database's parameter file to TRUE. The change will take effect the next time you start the instance and mount the database. (The parameter is FALSE by default.)

Listing Privilege and Role Information

To list the grants made for objects, a user can query the following data dictionary views:

- ALL_COL_PRIVS, USER_COL_PRIVS, DBA_COL_PRIVS
- ALL_COL_PRIVS_MADE, USER_COL_PRIVS_MADE
- ALL_COL_PRIVS_RECD, USER_COL_PRIVS_RECD
- ALL_TAB_PRIVS, USER_TAB_PRIVS, DBA_TAB_PRIVS
- ALL_TAB_PRIVS_MADE, USER_TAB_PRIVS_MADE
- ALL_TAB_PRIVS_RECD, USER_TAB_PRIVS_RECD
- DBA_ROLES
- USER_ROLE_PRIVS, DBA_ROLE_PRIVS
- USER_SYS_PRIVS, DBA_SYS_PRIVS
- COLUMN_PRIVILEGES
- ROLE_ROLE_PRIVS, ROLE_SYS_PRIVS, ROLE_TAB_PRIVS
- SESSION_PRIVS, SESSION_ROLES

Note: See Appendix B for a detailed description of these data dictionary views.

Examples

For the following examples, assume the following statements are issued:

```
CREATE ROLE security_admin IDENTIFIED BY honcho;

GRANT create profile, alter profile, drop profile,
   create role, drop any role, grant any role, audit any,
   audit system, create user, become user, alter user, drop user
   TO security_admin WITH ADMIN OPTION;

GRANT SELECT, DELETE ON sys.aud$ TO security_admin;

GRANT security_admin, create session TO swilliams;

GRANT security_admin TO system_administrator;

GRANT create session TO jward;

GRANT SELECT, DELETE ON emp TO jward;

GRANT INSERT (ename, job) ON emp TO swilliams, jward;
```

Example 1
Listing All System Privilege Grants

The following query indicates all system privilege grants made to roles and users:

```
SELECT * FROM sys.dba_sys_privs;

GRANTEE                PRIVILEGE                                        ADM
------------------ ---------------------------------------- ---
SECURITY_ADMIN         ALTER PROFILE                                    YES
SECURITY_ADMIN         ALTER USER                                       YES
SECURITY_ADMIN         AUDIT ANY                                        YES
SECURITY_ADMIN         AUDIT SYSTEM                                     YES
SECURITY_ADMIN         BECOME USER                                      YES
SECURITY_ADMIN         CREATE PROFILE                                   YES
SECURITY_ADMIN         CREATE ROLE                                      YES
SECURITY_ADMIN         CREATE USER                                      YES
SECURITY_ADMIN         DROP ANY ROLE                                    YES
SECURITY_ADMIN         DROP PROFILE                                     YES
SECURITY_ADMIN         DROP USER                                        YES
SECURITY_ADMIN         GRANT ANY ROLE                                   YES
SWILLIAMS              CREATE SESSION                                   NO
JWARD                  CREATE SESSION                                   NO
```

Example 2
Listing All Role Grants

The following query returns all the roles granted to users and other roles:

```
SELECT * FROM sys.dba_role_privs;

GRANTEE                GRANTED_ROLE                                     ADM
------------------ ------------------------------------------ ---
SWILLIAMS              SECURITY_ADMIN                                   NO
```

Example 3
Listing Object Privileges Granted to a User

The following query returns all object privileges (not including column specific privileges) granted to the specified user:

```
SELECT table_name, privilege, grantable FROM sys.dba_tab_privs
    WHERE grantee = 'JWARD';

TABLE_NAME    PRIVILEGE    GRANTABLE
------------ ------------ -----------
EMP           SELECT       NO
EMP           DELETE       NO
```

To list all the column specific privileges that have been granted, the following query can be used:

```
SELECT grantee, table_name, column_name, privilege
    FROM sys.dba_col_privs;

GRANTEE       TABLE_NAME    COLUMN_NAME        PRIVILEGE
------------- ------------- ------------------ -----------------
SWILLIAMS     EMP           ENAME              INSERT
SWILLIAMS     EMP           JOB                INSERT
JWARD         EMP           ENAME              INSERT
JWARD         EMP           JOB                INSERT
```

Example 4 Listing the Current Privilege Domain of Your Session

The following query lists all roles currently enabled for the issuer:

```
SELECT * FROM session_roles;
```

If SWILLIAMS has enabled the SECURITY_ADMIN role and issues this query, ORACLE returns the following information:

```
ROLE
------------------------------
SECURITY_ADMIN
```

The following query lists all system privileges currently available in the issuer's security domain, both from explicit privilege grants and from enabled roles:

```
SELECT * FROM session_privs;
```

If SWILLIAMS has the SECURITY_ADMIN role enabled and issues this query, the following results are returned:

```
PRIVILEGE
----------------------------------------
AUDIT SYSTEM
CREATE SESSION
CREATE USER
BECOME USER
ALTER USER
DROP USER
CREATE ROLE
DROP ANY ROLE
GRANT ANY ROLE
AUDIT ANY
CREATE PROFILE
ALTER PROFILE
DROP PROFILE
```

If the SECURITY_ADMIN role is disabled for SWILLIAMS, the first query would have returned no rows, while the second query would only return a row for the CREATE SESSION privilege grant.

Example 5
Listing Roles of the Database

The DBA_ROLES data dictionary view can be used to list all roles of a database and the authentication used for each role. For example, the following query lists all the roles in the database:

```
SELECT * FROM sys.dba_roles;

ROLE                              PASSWORD
--------------------------------- --------
CONNECT                           NO
RESOURCE                          NO
DBA                               NO
SECURITY_ADMIN                    YES
```

Example 6
Listing Information About the Privilege Domains of Roles

The ROLE_ROLE_PRIVS, ROLE_SYS_PRIVS, and ROLE_TAB_PRIVS data dictionary views contain information on the privilege domains of roles.

For example, the following query lists all the roles granted to the SYSTEM_ADMIN role:

```
SELECT granted_role, admin_option
    FROM role_role_privs
    WHERE role = 'SYSTEM_ADMIN';
GRANTED_ROLE                      ADM
--------------------------------- ---
SECURITY_ADMIN                    NO
```

The following query lists all the system privileges granted to the SECURITY_ADMIN role:

```
SELECT * FROM role_sys_privs WHERE role = 'SECURITY_ADMIN';

ROLE                        PRIVILEGE                                ADM
--------------------------- ---------------------------------------- ---
SECURITY_ADMIN              ALTER PROFILE                            YES
SECURITY_ADMIN              ALTER USER                               YES
SECURITY_ADMIN              AUDIT ANY                                YES
SECURITY_ADMIN              AUDIT SYSTEM                             YES
SECURITY_ADMIN              BECOME USER                              YES
SECURITY_ADMIN              CREATE PROFILE                           YES
SECURITY_ADMIN              CREATE ROLE                              YES
SECURITY_ADMIN              CREATE USER                              YES
SECURITY_ADMIN              DROP ANY ROLE                            YES
SECURITY_ADMIN              DROP PROFILE                             YES
SECURITY_ADMIN              DROP USER                                YES
SECURITY_ADMIN              GRANT ANY ROLE                           YES
```

The following query lists all the object privileges granted to the SECURITY_ADMIN role:

```
SELECT table_name, privilege FROM role_tab_privs
    WHERE role = 'SECURITY_ADMIN';

TABLE_NAME                     PRIVILEGE
------------------------------ -------------------
AUD$                           DELETE
AUD$                           SELECT
```

CHAPTER

13 AUDITING DATABASE USE

This chapter explains how to use the ORACLE auditing facilities. Topics include:

- guidelines for auditing your database
- setting auditing options
- turning auditing on and off
- managing the audit trail
- auditing with database triggers

If you are using Trusted ORACLE, see the *Trusted ORACLE7 Server Administrator's Guide* for additional information about auditing and audit trail management.

Guidelines for Auditing

Here are some guidelines for auditing database activity.

Choose Between Auditing with the Database and Auditing with the Operating System

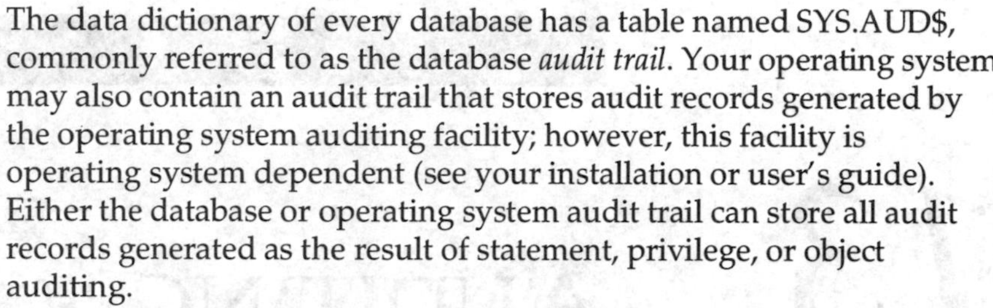

The data dictionary of every database has a table named SYS.AUD$, commonly referred to as the database *audit trail*. Your operating system may also contain an audit trail that stores audit records generated by the operating system auditing facility; however, this facility is operating system dependent (see your installation or user's guide). Either the database or operating system audit trail can store all audit records generated as the result of statement, privilege, or object auditing.

Your operating system may or may not support database auditing to the operating system audit trail. If this option is available, consider the advantages and disadvantages of using either the database or operating system auditing trail to store database audit records.

Using the database audit trail offers the following advantages:

- You can view selected portions of the audit trail with the predefined audit trail views of the data dictionary.
- You can use ORACLE tools (such as SQL*ReportWriter) to generate audit reports.

Alternatively, your operating system audit trail may allow you to consolidate audit records from multiple sources including ORACLE and other applications. Therefore, examining system activity might be more efficient because all audit records are in one place.

Keep Audited Information Manageable

Although auditing is relatively inexpensive, limit the number of audited events as much as possible. This will minimize the performance impact on the execution of statements that are audited, and also minimize the size of the audit trail.

Consider the following two general guidelines when devising an auditing strategy:

1. **Evaluate your purpose for auditing.**
   Once you have a clear understanding of the reasons for auditing, you can devise an appropriate auditing strategy and avoid unnecessary auditing.

   For example, suppose you are auditing to investigate suspicious database activity. This information by itself is not specific enough. What types of suspicious database activity do you suspect or have you noticed? A more focused auditing purpose might be to audit unauthorized deletions from arbitrary tables in the database. This purpose narrows the type of action being audited and the type of object being affected by the suspicious activity.

2. **Audit knowledgeably.**
   Audit the minimum number of statements, users, or objects required to get the targeted information. This prevents unnecessary audit information from cluttering the meaningful information and consuming valuable space in the SYSTEM tablespace. Balance your need to gather sufficient security information with your ability to store and process it.

   For example, if you are auditing to gather information about database activity, determine exactly what types of activities you are tracking, audit only the activities of interest, and audit only for the amount of time necessary to gather the information you desire. Do not audit objects if you are only interested in each session's logical I/O information.

Auditing Suspicious Database Activity

When your auditing purpose is to monitor for suspicious database activity, consider the following guidelines:

- **Audit generally, then specifically..**
  When starting to audit for suspicious database activity, it is common that not much information is available to target specific users or schema objects. Therefore, audit options must be set more generally at first. Once preliminary audit information is recorded and analyzed, the general audit options should be turned off and more specific audit options enabled. This process should continue until enough evidence is gathered to make concrete conclusions about the origin of the suspicious database activity.
- **Protect the audit trail..**
  When auditing for suspicious database activity, protect the audit trail so that audit information cannot be added, changed, or deleted without being audited. See "Protecting the Audit Trail" on page 13-17.

Auditing Normal Database Activity

When your auditing purpose is to gather historical information about particular database activities, consider the following guidelines:

- **Audit only pertinent actions.**
  To avoid cluttering meaningful information with useless audit records and reduce the amount of audit trail administration, only audit the targeted database activities.
- **Archive audit records and purge the audit trail.**
  Once you have collected the required information, archive the audit records of interest and purge the audit trail of this information.

Creating and Deleting the Database Audit Trail Views

The database audit trail (SYS.AUD$) is a single table in each ORACLE database's data dictionary. To help you view meaningful auditing information in this table, several predefined views are provided.

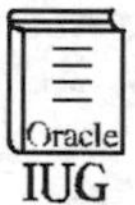

On most operating systems (see your installation or user's guide for more information), the audit trail views are created automatically with the data dictionary. They must be created for you to use auditing; you can later delete them if you decide not to use auditing. The following sections explain how to do this.

Creating the Audit Trail Views

If you decide to use auditing, create the auditing views by connecting as SYS and running the script CATAUDIT.SQL. This script creates the following views:

- STMT_AUDIT_OPTION_MAP
- AUDIT_ACTIONS
- ALL_DEF_AUDIT_OPTS
- DBA_STMT_AUDIT_OPTS
- USER_OBJ_AUDIT_OPTS, DBA_OBJ_AUDIT_OPTS
- USER_AUDIT_TRAIL, DBA_AUDIT_TRAIL
- USER_AUDIT_SESSION, DBA_AUDIT_SESSION
- USER_AUDIT_STATEMENT, DBA_AUDIT_STATEMENT
- USER_AUDIT_OBJECT, DBA_AUDIT_OBJECT
- DBA_AUDIT_EXISTS
- USER_AUDIT_SESSION, DBA_AUDIT_SESSION
- USER_TAB_AUDIT_OPTS

See Appendix B for more information about these views. Also see "Viewing Database Audit Trail Information" on page 13-17 for examples of interpreting audit information.

Deleting the Audit Trail Views

If you disable auditing and no longer need the audit trail views, delete them by connecting to the database as SYS and running the script file CATNOAUD.SQL. The name and location of the CATNOAUD.SQL script are operating system dependent.

Setting Auditing Options

Depending on the auditing options set, audit records can contain different types of information. However, all auditing options generate the following information:

- the user that executed the audited statement
- the action code (a number) that indicates the audited statement executed by the user
- the object or objects referenced in the audited statement
- the date and time that the audited statement was executed

The audit trail does not store information about any data values that might be involved in the audited statement; for example, old and new data values of updated rows are not stored when an UPDATE statement is audited. However, this specialized type of auditing can be performed on DML statements involving tables by using database triggers; see page 13-20 for examples of using triggers for this specialized type of auditing.

ORACLE allows you to set audit options at three levels:

statement	audits based on the type of a SQL statement, such as any SQL statement on a table (which records each CREATE, TRUNCATE, and DROP TABLE statement)
privilege	audits use of a particular system privilege, such as CREATE TABLE
object	audits specific statements on specific objects, such as ALTER TABLE on the EMP table

The following sections explain the audit options you can set.

Statement Audit Options

Valid statement audit options that can be included in AUDIT and NOAUDIT statements are listed in Table 13-1. (Additional statement audit options are listed in Table 13-2.)

TABLE 13-1
Statement Auditing Options

Option	SQL Statements Audited
ALTER SYSTEM	ALTER SYSTEM
CLUSTER	CREATE CLUSTER ALTER CLUSTER TRUNCATE CLUSTER DROP CLUSTER
DATABASE LINK	CREATE DATABASE LINK DROP DATABASE LINK
INDEX	CREATE INDEX ALTER INDEX DROP INDEX
NOT EXISTS	All SQL statements that return an ORACLE error because the specified structure or object does not exist
PROCEDURE	CREATE [OR REPLACE] FUNCTION CREATE [OR REPLACE] PACKAGE CREATE [OR REPLACE] PACKAGE BODY CREATE [OR REPLACE] PROCEDURE DROP FUNCTION DROP PACKAGE DROP PROCEDURE
PUBLIC DATABASE LINK	CREATE PUBLIC DATABASE LINK DROP PUBLIC DATABASE LINK
PUBLIC SYNONYM	CREATE PUBLIC SYNONYM DROP PUBLIC SYNONYM
ROLE	CREATE ROLE ALTER ROLE SET ROLE DROP ROLE
ROLLBACK SEGMENT	CREATE ROLLBACK SEGMENT ALTER ROLLBACK SEGMENT DROP ROLLBACK SEGMENT
SEQUENCE	CREATE SEQUENCE DROP SEQUENCE
SESSION	Connects and Disconnects
SYNONYM	CREATE SYNONYM DROP SYNONYM
SYSTEM AUDIT	AUDIT NO AUDIT

SYSTEM GRANT	GRANT system privilege/role TO user/role REVOKE system privilege/role FROM user/role
TABLE	CREATE TABLE TRUNCATE TABLE DROP TABLE
TABLESPACE	CREATE TABLESPACE ALTER TABLESPACE DROP TABLESPACE
TRIGGER	CREATE TRIGGER ALTER TRIGGER ENABLE or DISABLE ALTER TABLE with ENABLE, DISABLE, and DROP clauses
USER	CREATE USER ALTER USER DROP USER
VIEW	CREATE [OR REPLACE] VIEW DROP VIEW

Shortcuts for Statement Audit Options

Shortcuts are provided to specify several related statement options with one word. Shortcuts are not statement options themselves; rather, they are ways of specifying sets of related statement options with one word in AUDIT and NOAUDIT statements.

CONNECT	equivalent to the SESSION option
RESOURCE	equivalent to the options ALTER SYSTEM, CLUSTER, DATABASE LINK, PROCEDURE, ROLLBACK SEGMENT, SEQUENCE, SYNONYM, TABLE, TABLESPACE, and VIEW
DBA	equivalent to the options SYSTEM AUDIT, PUBLIC DATABASE LINK, PUBLIC SYNONYM, ROLE, SYSTEM GRANT, and USER
ALL	equivalent to all options in Table 13-1, including the NOT EXISTS option

Note: Do not confuse the shortcuts CONNECT, RESOURCE, and DBA with the predefined roles of the same names.

Auditing Connections and Disconnections

The SESSION statement option (and CONNECT shortcut) is unique because it does not generate an audit record when a particular type of statement is issued; this option generates a single audit record for each session created by connections to an instance. An audit record is inserted into the audit trail at connect time and updated at disconnect time. Cumulative information about a session such as connection time, disconnection time, logical and physical I/Os processed, and more is stored in a single audit record that corresponds to the session.

Additional Statement Options

Additional audit options not covered by any of the above shortcuts are listed in Table 13-2.

TABLE 13-2
Additional Statement Auditing Options

Object Option	SQL Statements Audited
ALTER SEQUENCE	ALTER SEQUENCE sequence
ALTER TABLE	ALTER TABLE table
COMMENT TABLE	COMMENT ON table, view, snapshot, column
DELETE TABLE	DELETE FROM table, view
EXECUTE PROCEDURE	Calls to procedures and functions
GRANT PROCEDURE	GRANT privilege ON procedure REVOKE privilege ON procedure
GRANT SEQUENCE	GRANT privilege ON sequence REVOKE privilege ON sequence
GRANT TABLE	GRANT privilege ON table, view, snapshot REVOKE privilege ON table, view, snapshot
INSERT TABLE	INSERT INTO table, view
LOCK TABLE	LOCK TABLE table, view
SELECT SEQUENCE	Reference to a sequence
SELECT TABLE	SELECT . . . FROM table, view, snapshot
UPDATE TABLE	UPDATE table, view

Privilege Audit Options

Privilege audit options exactly match the corresponding system privileges. For example, the option to audit use of the DELETE ANY TABLE privilege is DELETE ANY TABLE. To turn this option on, you would use a statement like the following example:

```
AUDIT DELETE ANY TABLE
  BY ACCESS
  WHENEVER NOT SUCCESSFUL;
```

ORACLE's system privileges are listed beginning on page 12-2.

Object Audit Options

Table 13-3 lists valid object audit options and the schema object types for which each option is available.

TABLE 13-3
Object Audit Options

Object Option	Table	View	Sequence	Procedure*
ALTER	✔		✔	
AUDIT	✔	✔	✔	✔
COMMENT	✔	✔		
DELETE	✔	✔		
EXECUTE				✔
GRANT	✔	✔	✔	✔
INDEX	✔			
INSERT	✔	✔		
LOCK	✔	✔		
RENAME	✔	✔		✔
SELECT	✔	✔**	✔	
UPDATE	✔	✔		

* "Procedure" refers to stand-alone stored procedures and functions, and packages.

** The SELECT option may also be used for snapshots.

Table 13-4 lists the SQL statements audited by each object option.

TABLE 13-4
SQL Statement Audited by Database Object Audit Options

Object Option	SQL Statements Audited
ALTER	ALTER object (table or sequence)
AUDIT	AUDIT (Form II) object
COMMENT	COMMENT object (table or view)
DELETE	DELETE FROM object (table or view)
EXECUTE	EXECUTE object (procedure*)
GRANT	GRANT (Form II) privilege ON object
INDEX	CREATE INDEX ON object (tables only)
INSERT	INSERT INTO object (table or view)
LOCK	LOCK object (table or view)
RENAME	RENAME object (table, view, or procedure*)
SELECT	SELECT . . . FROM object (table, view, snapshot) Any statement using a sequence
UPDATE	UPDATE object (table or view)

* Procedure refers to stand-alone stored procedures and functions, and packages.

Shortcut for Object Audit Options

The ALL shortcut can be used to specify all available object audit options for a schema object. This shortcut is not an option itself; rather, it is a way of specifying all object audit options with one word in AUDIT and NOAUDIT statements.

Enabling Audit Options

The SQL command AUDIT turns on statement and privilege audit options, and object audit options. Audit statements that set statement and privilege audit options can include the BY USER option to specify a list of users to limit the scope of the statement and privilege audit options.The SQL command AUDIT turns on audit options. To use it to set statement and privilege options, you must have the AUDIT SYSTEM privilege. To use it to set object audit options, you must own the object to be audited or have the AUDIT ANY privilege.

You can set any auditing option, and specify the following conditions for auditing:

- WHENEVER SUCCESSFUL/WHENEVER NOT SUCCESSFUL
- BY SESSION/BY ACCESS

Warning: The AUDIT command only turns auditing options on; it does not enable auditing as a whole. To turn auditing on and control

whether ORACLE generates audit records based on the audit options currently set, set the parameter AUDIT_TRAIL in the database's parameter file. (See "Enabling and Disabling Database Auditing" on page 13-14.)

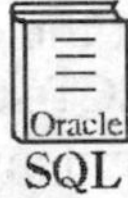

SQL

The following examples illustrate the use of the AUDIT command. For a complete description of the AUDIT command, see the *ORACLE7 Server SQL Language Reference Manual*.

Enabling Statement and Privilege Auditing

To audit all successful and unsuccessful connections to and disconnections from the database, regardless of user, BY SESSION (the default and only value for this option), enter the following statement:

```
AUDIT SESSION;
```

You can set this option selectively for individual users also, as in the next example:

```
AUDIT SESSION
    BY scott, lori;
```

To audit all successful and unsuccessful uses of the DELETE ANY TABLE system privilege, enter the following statement:

```
AUDIT DELETE ANY TABLE;
```

To audit all unsuccessful SELECT, INSERT, and DELETE statements on all tables and unsuccessful uses of the EXECUTE ANY PROCEDURE system privilege, by all database users, BY ACCESS, enter the following statement:

```
AUDIT SELECT TABLE, INSERT TABLE, DELETE TABLE,
 EXECUTE ANY PROCEDURE
    BY ACCESS
    WHENEVER NOT SUCCESSFUL;
```

Privilege Required to Enable Statement and Privilege Auditing Options The AUDIT SYSTEM system privilege is required to set any statement or privilege audit option. Normally, the security administrator is the only user granted this system privilege.

Enabling Object Auditing

To audit all successful and unsuccessful DELETE statements on the EMP table, BY SESSION (the default value), enter the following statement:

```
AUDIT DELETE ON emp;
```

To audit all successful SELECT, INSERT, and DELETE statements on the DEPT table owned by user JWARD, BY ACCESS, enter the following statement:

```
AUDIT SELECT, INSERT, DELETE
    ON jward.dept
    BY ACCESS
    WHENEVER SUCCESSFUL;
```

Setting Default Object Audit Options To set the default object auditing options to audit all unsuccessful SELECT statements, BY SESSION (the default), enter the following statement:

```
AUDIT SELECT
    ON DEFAULT
    WHENEVER NOT SUCCESSFUL;
```

Privilege Required to Enable Object Audit Options A user can set any object audit option for the objects contained in the user's schema. The AUDIT ANY system privilege is required to set an object audit option for an object contained in another user's schema or to set the default object auditing options; normally, the security administrator is the only user granted this system privilege.

Disabling Audit Options

The NOAUDIT command turns off the various audit options of ORACLE. Use it to reset statement and privilege audit options, and object audit options. A NOAUDIT statement that sets statement and privilege audit options can include the BY USER option to specify a list of users to limit the scope of the statement and privilege audit options.

You can use a NOAUDIT statement to disable an audit option selectively using the WHENEVER clause. If the clause is not specified, the auditing option is disabled entirely, for both successful and non-successful cases.

The BY SESSION/BY ACCESS option pair is **not** supported by the NOAUDIT command; audit options, no matter how they were turned on, are turned off by an appropriate NOAUDIT statement.

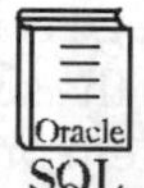

The following examples illustrate the use of the NOAUDIT command. For a complete syntax listing of the NOAUDIT command, see the *ORACLE7 Server SQL Language Reference Manual*.

Warning: The NOAUDIT command only turns auditing options off; it does not disable auditing as a whole. To turn auditing off and stop ORACLE from generating audit records, even though you have audit options currently set, set the parameter AUDIT_TRAIL in the database's parameter file. (See "Enabling and Disabling Database Auditing" on page 13-14.)

Disabling Statement and Privilege Auditing

The following statements turn off the corresponding audit options:

```
NOAUDIT session;
NOAUDIT session BY scott, lori;
NOAUDIT DELETE ANY TABLE;
NOAUDIT SELECT TABLE, INSERT TABLE, DELETE TABLE,
  EXECUTE ANY PROCEDURE;
```

Furthermore, the following statements turn off all statement (system) and privilege audit options:

```
NOAUDIT ALL;
NOAUDIT ALL PRIVILEGES;
```

Privileges Required to Disable Statement and Privilege Auditing Options To disable statement or privilege auditing options, you must have the AUDIT SYSTEM system privilege.

Disabling Object Auditing

The following statements turn off the corresponding auditing options:

```
NOAUDIT DELETE
    ON emp;
NOAUDIT SELECT, INSERT, DELETE
    ON jward.dept;
```

Furthermore, to turn off all object audit options on the EMP table, enter the following statement:

```
NOAUDIT ALL
    ON emp;
```

Disabling Default Object Audit Options To turn off all default object audit options, enter the following statement:

```
NOAUDIT ALL
    ON DEFAULT;
```

Note that all schema objects created before this NOAUDIT statement is issued continue to use the default object audit options in effect at the time of their creation, unless overridden by an explicit NOAUDIT statement after their creation.

Privileges Required to Disable Object Auditing Options To disable object audit options for a specific object, you must be the owner of the schema object. To disable the object audit options of an object in another user's schema or to disable default object audit options, you must have the AUDIT ANY system privilege. A user with privileges to disable object audit options of an object can override the options set by any user.

Enabling and Disabling Database Auditing

Any authorized database user can set statement, privilege, and object auditing options at any time, but ORACLE does not generate and store audit records in the audit trail unless database auditing is enabled. The security administrator is normally responsible for this operation.

Database auditing is enabled and disabled by the AUDIT_TRAIL initialization parameter in the database's parameter file. The parameter can be set to the following values:

DB	enables database auditing and directs all audit records to the database audit trail
OS	enables database auditing and directs all audit records to the operating system audit trail
NONE	disables auditing (This value is the default.)

Once you have edited the parameter file, restart the database instance to enable or disable database auditing as intended.

Note: See Appendix A for more information about editing parameter files.

Controlling the Growth and Size of the Audit Trail

Note: The following sections discuss how to manage the database audit trail. If you are directing audit records to the operating system audit trail, see your installation or user's guide for more information about managing the operating system audit trail.

If the audit trail becomes completely full and no more audit records can be inserted, audited statements cannot be successfully executed until the audit trail is purged; warnings are returned to all users that issue audited statements. Therefore, the security administrator must control the growth and size of the audit trail.

When auditing is enabled and audit records are being generated, the audit trail grows according to two factors:

- the number of audit options turned on
- the frequency of execution of audited statements

To control the growth of the audit trail, you can use the following methods:

- Enable and disable database auditing. If it is enabled, audit records are generated and stored in the audit trail; if it is disabled, audit records are not generated.
- Be very selective about the audit options that are turned on. If more selective auditing is performed, useless or unnecessary audit information is not generated and stored in the audit trail.
- Tightly control the ability to perform object auditing. This can be done two different ways:
  - A security administrator owns all objects and the AUDIT ANY system privilege is never granted to any other user. Alternatively, all schema objects can belong to a schema for which the corresponding user does not have CREATE SESSION privilege.
  - All objects are contained in schemas that do not correspond to real database users (that is, the CREATE SESSION privilege is not granted to the corresponding user) and the security administrator is the only user granted the AUDIT ANY system privilege.

  In both scenarios, object auditing is controlled entirely by the security administrator.

The maximum size of the database audit trail (SYS.AUD$ table) is predetermined during database creation. By default, up to 99 extents, each 10K in size, can be allocated for this table.

Purging Audit Records from the Audit Trail

After auditing is enabled for some time, the security administrator may want to delete records from the database audit trail both to free audit trail space and to facilitate audit trail management.

For example, to delete **all** audit records from the audit trail, enter the following statement:

```
DELETE FROM sys.aud$;
```

Alternatively, to delete all audit records from the audit trail generated as a result of auditing the table EMP, enter the following statement:

```
DELETE FROM sys.aud$
    WHERE obj$name='EMP';
```

If audit trail information must be archived for historical purposes, the security administrator can copy the relevant records to a normal database table (for example, using "INSERT INTO table SELECT ... FROM sys.aud$ ...") or export the audit trail table to an operating

Oracle Utilities

system file. For information about exporting tables, see the *ORACLE7 Server Utilities User's Guide*.

Only the user SYS, a user who has the DELETE ANY TABLE privilege, or a user to whom SYS has granted DELETE privilege on SYS.AUD$ can delete records from the database audit trail.

Note: If the audit trail is completely full and connections are being audited (that is, if the SESSION option is set), typical users cannot connect to the database because the associated audit record for the connection cannot be inserted into the audit trail. In this case, the security administrator must connect as SYS (operations by SYS are not audited) and make space available in the audit trail.

Reducing the Size of the Audit Trail

As with any database table, after records are deleted from the database audit trail, the extents allocated for this table still exist. If the database audit trail has many extents allocated for it, but many of them are not being used, the space allocated to the database audit trail can be reduced using the following steps:

1. If you want to save information currently in the audit trail, copy it to another database table or export it using the EXPORT utility.
2. Connect as INTERNAL.
3. Truncate SYS.AUD$ using the TRUNCATE command.
4. Reload archived audit trail records generated from Step 1.

The new version of SYS.AUD$ is allocated only as many extents that are necessary to contain current audit trail records.

Note: SYS.AUD$ is the only SYS object that should ever be directly modified.

Protecting the Audit Trail

When auditing for suspicious database activity, protect the integrity of the audit trail's records to guarantee the accuracy and completeness of the auditing information.

To protect the database audit trail from unauthorized deletions, grant the DELETE ANY TABLE system privilege to security administrators only.

To audit changes made to the database audit trail itself, audit the audit trail with the following statement:

```
AUDIT INSERT, UPDATE, DELETE
    ON sys.aud$
    BY ACCESS;
```

Audit records generated as a result of object audit options set for the SYS.AUD$ table can only be deleted from the audit trail by someone connected as INTERNAL, which itself has protection against unauthorized use. As a final measure of protecting the audit trail, any operation performed while connected as INTERNAL is audited in the operating system audit trail, if available. See your installation or user's guide for more information about the availability of an operating system audit trail and possible uses.

Viewing Database Audit Trail Information

The following sections give examples that demonstrate how to examine and interpret the information in the audit trail.

Examples Assume that you must audit the database for the following suspicious database activity:

- Passwords, tablespace settings, and quotas for some database users are being altered without authorization.
- A high number of deadlocks are occurring, most likely because of users acquiring exclusive table locks.
- Rows are arbitrarily being deleted from the EMP table in SCOTT's schema.

Also assume that you suspect the users JWARD and SWILLIAMS for several of these detrimental actions.

For the examples below, assume that the following statements are issued by an administrator (in the given order):

```
AUDIT ALTER, INDEX, RENAME ON DEFAULT
             BY SESSION;
CREATE TABLE scott.emp . . . ;
CREATE VIEW scott.employee AS SELECT * FROM scott.emp;
AUDIT SESSION BY jward, swilliams;
AUDIT ALTER USER;
AUDIT LOCK TABLE
  BY ACCESS
  WHENEVER SUCCESSFUL;
AUDIT DELETE ON scott.emp
  BY ACCESS
  WHENEVER SUCCESSFUL;
```

The following statements are subsequently issued by the user JWARD:

```
ALTER USER tsmith QUOTA 0 ON users;
DROP USER djones;
```

The following statements are subsequently issued by the user SWILLIAMS:

```
LOCK TABLE scott.emp IN EXCLUSIVE MODE;
DELETE FROM scott.emp WHERE mgr = 7698;
ALTER TABLE scott.emp ALLOCATE EXTENT (SIZE 100K);
CREATE INDEX scott.ename_index ON scott.emp (ename);
CREATE PROCEDURE scott.fire_employee (empid NUMBER) AS
BEGIN
    DELETE FROM scott.emp WHERE empno = empid;
END;
/
EXECUTE scott.fire_employee(7902);
```

The following sections show the information that can be listed using the audit trail views in the data dictionary.

Example 1 Listing Active Statement Audit Options

The following query returns all the statement audit options that are set:

```
SELECT * FROM sys.dba_stmt_audit_opts;

USER_NAME            AUDIT_OPTION         SUCCESS    FAILURE
-------------------- -------------------- ---------- ----------
JWARD                SESSION              BY SESSION BY SESSION
SWILLIAMS            SESSION              BY SESSION BY SESSION
                     LOCK TABLE           BY ACCESS  NOT SET
```

Notice that the view reveals the statement audit options set, whether or not they are set for success or failure (or both), and whether they are set for BY SESSION or BY ACCESS.

Example 2 Listing Active Privilege Audit Options

The following query returns all the privilege audit options that are set:

```
SELECT * FROM sys.dba_priv_audit_opts;

USER_NAME            AUDIT_OPTION         SUCCESS    FAILURE
-------------------- -------------------- ---------- ----------
                     ALTER USER           BY SESSION BY SESSION
```

Example 3 Listing Active Object Audit Options for Specific Objects

The following query returns all audit options set for any objects contained in SCOTT's schema:

```
SELECT * FROM sys.dba_obj_audit_opts
    WHERE owner = 'SCOTT' AND object_name LIKE 'EMP%';

OWNER  OBJECT_NAME OBJECT_TY ALT AUD COM DEL GRA IND INS LOC REN SEL UPD EXE
------ ----------- --------- --- --- --- --- --- --- --- --- --- --- --- ---
SCOTT  EMP         TABLE     S/S -/- -/- A/- -/- S/S -/- -/- S/S -/- -/- -/-
SCOTT  EMPLOYEE    VIEW      -/- -/- -/- -/- -/- -/- -/- -/- S/S -/- -/- -/-
```

Notice that the view returns information about all the audit options for the specified object. The information in the view is interpreted as follows:

- The character "-" indicates that the audit option is not set.
- The character "S" indicates that the audit option is set, BY SESSION.
- The character "A" indicates that the audit option is set, BY ACCESS.
- Each audit option has two possible settings, WHENEVER SUCCESSFUL and WHENEVER NOT SUCCESSFUL, separated by "/". For example, the DELETE audit option for SCOTT.EMP is set BY ACCESS for successful delete statements and not set at all for unsuccessful delete statements.

Example 4 Listing Default Object Audit Options

The following query returns all default object audit options:

```
SELECT * FROM all_def_audit_opts;

ALT AUD COM DEL GRA IND INS LOC REN SEL UPD
--- --- --- --- --- --- --- --- --- --- ---
S/S -/- -/- -/- -/- S/S -/- -/- S/S -/- -/-
```

Notice that the view returns information similar to the USER_OBJ_AUDIT_OPTS and DBA_OBJ_AUDIT_OPTS views (see previous example).

Example 5
Listing Audit Records

The following query lists audit records generated by statement and object audit options:

```
SELECT username, obj_name, action_name, ses_actions
    FROM sys.dba_audit_object;
```

Example 6
Listing Audit Records for the AUDIT SESSION Option

The following query lists audit information corresponding to the AUDIT SESSION statement audit option:

```
SELECT username, logoff_time, logoff_lread, logoff_pread,
    logoff_lwrite, logoff_dlock
    FROM sys.dba_audit_session;

USERNAME   LOGOFF_TI LOGOFF_LRE LOGOFF_PRE LOGOFF_LWR LOGOFF_DLO
---------- --------- ---------- ---------- ---------- ----------
JWARD      02-AUG-91         53          2         24 0
SWILLIAMS  02-AUG-91       3337        256        630 0
```

Auditing Through Database Triggers

You can use triggers to supplement the built-in auditing features of ORACLE. Although you can write triggers to record information similar to that recorded by the AUDIT command, do so only when you need more detailed audit information. For example, you can use triggers to provide value-based auditing on a per-row basis for tables.

Note: In some fields, the ORACLE AUDIT command is considered a *security* audit facility, while triggers can provide a *financial* audit facility.

When deciding whether or not to create a trigger to audit database activity, consider the advantages that the standard ORACLE database auditing features provide compared to auditing by triggers:

- Standard auditing options cover DML and DDL statements regarding all types of schema objects and structures. In contrast, triggers can audit only DML statements issued against tables.
- All database audit information is recorded centrally and automatically using the auditing features of ORACLE.
- Auditing features enabled using the standard ORACLE features are easier to declare and maintain and less prone to errors than are auditing functions defined through triggers.
- Any changes to existing auditing options can also be audited to guard against malicious database activity.
- Using the database auditing features, you can generate records once every time an audited statement is issued (BY ACCESS) or

once for every session that issues an audited statement (BY SESSION). Triggers cannot audit by session; an audit record is generated each time a trigger-audited table is referenced.

- Database auditing can audit unsuccessful data access. In comparison, any audit information generated by a trigger is rolled back if the triggering statement is rolled back.
- Connections and disconnections, as well as session activity (such as physical I/Os, logical I/Os, and deadlocks), can be recorded by standard database auditing.

When using triggers to provide sophisticated auditing, normally use AFTER triggers. By using AFTER triggers, you record auditing information after the triggering statement is subjected to any applicable integrity constraints, preventing cases where audit processing is carried out unnecessarily for statements that generate exceptions to integrity constraints.

When you should use AFTER row vs. AFTER statement triggers depends on the information being audited. For example, row triggers provide value-based auditing on a per-row basis for tables. Triggers can also allow the user to supply a "reason code" for issuing the audited SQL statement, which can be useful in both row and statement-level auditing situations.

The following trigger audits modifications to the EMP table on a per-row basis. It requires that a "reason code" be stored in a global package variable before the update. The trigger demonstrates:

- how triggers can provide value-based auditing
- how to use public package variables

Comments within the code explain the functionality of the trigger.

```
CREATE TRIGGER audit_employee
AFTER INSERT OR DELETE OR UPDATE ON emp
FOR EACH ROW
BEGIN
/*  AUDITPACKAGE is a package with a public package
    variable REASON.  REASON could be set by the
    application by a command such as EXECUTE
    AUDITPACKAGE.SET_REASON(reason_string). Note that a
    package variable has state for the duration of a
    session and that each session has a separate copy of
    all package variables. */
  IF auditpackage.reason IS NULL THEN
   raise_application_error(-20201,
    'Must specify reason with AUDITPACKAGE.SET_REASON(reason_string)');
  END IF;
```

```
/*  If the above conditional evaluates to TRUE, the
    user-specified error number and message is raised,
    the trigger stops execution, and the effects of the
    triggering statement are rolled back.  Otherwise, a
    new row is inserted into the pre-defined auditing
    table named AUDIT_EMPLOYEE containing the existing
    and new values of the EMP table and the reason code
    defined by the REASON variable of AUDITPACKAGE.  Note
    that the "old" values are NULL if triggering
    statement is an INSERT and the "new" values are NULL
    if the triggering statement is a DELETE. */
  INSERT INTO audit_employee VALUES
    (:old.ssn, :old.name, :old.job_classification, :old.sal,
    :new.ssn, :new.name, :new.job_classification, :new.sal,
    auditpackage.reason, user, sysdate );
END;
```

Optionally, you can also set the reason code back to NULL if you want to force the reason code to be set for every update. The following AFTER statement trigger sets the reason code back to NULL after the triggering statement is executed:

```
CREATE TRIGGER audit_employee_reset
AFTER INSERT OR DELETE OR UPDATE ON emp
BEGIN
  auditpackage.set_reason(NULL);
END;
```

The previous two triggers are both fired by the same type of SQL statement. However, the AFTER row trigger is fired once for each row of the table affected by the triggering statement, while the AFTER statement trigger is fired only once after the triggering statement execution is completed.

PART

V

DISTRIBUTED PROCESSING AND DISTRIBUTED DATABASES

CHAPTER

14 Administering Client-Server Systems

This chapter provides guidelines for managing client-server systems. The following chapters are included:

- placing distributed applications
- developing distributed applications
- connecting between versions of ORACLE

Deciding Where to Locate Client Applications

In a distributed processing environment, you must work with application developers to decide the best location for the client applications. Below are examples of making the proper choice for this location.

- ORACLE is operating on a mainframe computer. The majority of the database users are unfamiliar with mainframe computers; however, they are familiar with personal computers (PCs). To avoid having to educate users on the mainframe's operating system, you might find it easiest to operate the client application code on the local PC and not on the mainframe.
- ORACLE is operating on a mainframe computer. The majority of the database users have PCs locally on their desk top. To boost ORACLE's performance and minimize network traffic, you should operate client applications on the local PCs.
- ORACLE is operating on a minicomputer. All database users have local terminals connected to the centralized minicomputer. The system will see best performance if you execute ORACLE on one processor of the minicomputer, while all client applications are executed by a different processor of the minicomputer. This configuration uses true distributed processing.

Developing Distributed Database Applications

In a distributed processing environment, you must work with the application developer to decide the best location for database applications to be developed and tested. For example, assume the following conditions:

- A company operates ORACLE on a centralized minicomputer.
- Client applications are also executed by the minicomputer. Database users interact with the database via terminals.
- At all times of the day, there is a high throughput of database transactions.

In this configuration, using the minicomputer to develop new database applications might significantly harm the performance of the database system. Instead, developers should develop and test new applications on another system running ORACLE, such as a minicomputer or a PC. Because ORACLE and applications developed for ORACLE are portable, the finished application can then be ported to the minicomputer without changes to the existing environment.

Connecting Between ORACLE Server Versions

In administering a distributed processing network, you must be aware of the version of Oracle software running at networked sites:

- Version 5 client applications can query Version 6 servers and ORACLE7 Servers.
- Version 6 clients can query Version 5 and Version 6 servers, and ORACLE7 Servers; however, Version 6 clients cannot use features unique to Version 6 when communicating with a Version 5 server since the server does not support them.
- ORACLE7 clients can query and update Version 5 and 6 databases, with only one updated database per transaction; however, ORACLE7 clients cannot use features unique to ORACLE7 when communicating with a Version 5 or Version 6 server, since the older versions do not support them.

  Attempting to update a Version 5 or 6 database and either an ORACLE7 database or a different Version 5 or 6 database results in an error message ("ORA-02047: cannot join distributed transaction in progress").

CHAPTER

15 Managing Distributed Databases

This chapter explains how to manage a database that is part of a distributed database system. Topics include:

- guidelines for distributed databases
- managing global database names
- creating, using, and dropping database links
- implementing location transparency
- setting commit point strength
- troubleshooting distributed database problems

The information in this chapter applies only to systems using ORACLE with the distributed option.

Guidelines for Implementing a Distributed Database System

The following sections discuss some important issues that you should consider in implementing a distributed database system.

Assign Distributed Database Administrators

Because nodes in an ORACLE distributed database system are autonomous, one or more database administrators must assume responsibility for each database in a distributed database system. Each database administrator is responsible for issues important only to the associated database, such as space management and local security. However, administrators of different databases in a distributed system also need to coordinate with each other on issues that concern distributed database systems, such as data design issues, backup and recovery issues, and remote security.

Consider Network and Communication Issues

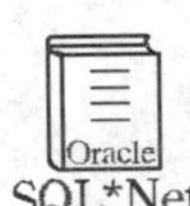

SQL*Net

Database, system, and network administrators can be responsible for guaranteeing that networks connect machines referenced in distributed transactions. This includes installing and executing the proper SQL*Net drivers to facilitate communication among ORACLE database servers. For more information about SQL*Net, see your SQL*Net documentation.

Define Global Database Names and Database Links

Give each database a unique global name and define database links in the local database so that SQL statements issued by users and applications can reference objects of remote databases. See "Managing Global Database Names" and "Managing Database Links" on pages 15-3 and 15-7 for details.

Decide Where to Locate the Data

In a distributed database environment, database administrators must work with application developers to decide the best location for the data. Consider the following items:

- the number of transactions posted from each location
- the amount of data (portion of table) used by each node
- the performance characteristics and reliability of the network
- the speed of various nodes and the capacities of disks
- the criticality of access if a node or link is down
- the need for referential integrity among tables

For more information on trade-offs in locating data, see the *ORACLE7 Application Developer's Guide.*

Enforce Security in a Distributed Database System

In general, security is controlled by the administrator of each database and cannot be administered remotely; for example, you cannot grant system and object privileges to remote users. A remote connection is subject to the security domain of the account a database link uses for the connection. In some cases, you can perform limited local privilege management for remote objects; see "Balancing Location Transparency and Security" on page 15-12.

Resource limits for a user apply only at the node to which a user is directly connected. Remote sessions established on behalf of database links are also subject to resource limits set in the remote database.

Similarly, audit records are generated on behalf of connections established in each database, including connections established via database links. Audit records are generated in the database in which a change occurs.

Plan Distributed Database Backup and Recovery

Consider backup and recovery strategies for the global distributed database before making autonomous decisions for your databases. Several important issues are discussed in the sections "Consider Distributed Database Backups" and "Coordinate Distributed Recovery" on pages 18-4 and 19-3, respectively.

Managing Global Database Names

In a distributed database system, each ORACLE database must have a unique global database name so that objects within the distributed database can be uniquely identified. A database's global database name is comprised of two parts: a name component (used for local administrative operations such as startup, recovery operations, and shutdown) and a network domain component (used to indicate the database's location within a network structure).

Note: Although global database names resemble SQL*Net communities, which similarly have domains, they are not the same thing. See your SQL*Net documentation for information on SQL*Net communities.

Choosing a Global Database Name

Before creating an ORACLE database (or renaming an existing database), choose a global name for the database so that it is uniquely identified among any network of databases; that is, make sure that the combination of database name and domain is unique. Consider the following points when naming a database:

- The name component of a global database name usually corresponds to the information within the database. For example, if a database stores sales information, the database might be named SALES; if a database stores archeological information about prehistoric reptiles, the database might be named DINOSAUR.
- The name component of a global database name should not imply location. This practice is usually avoided to maintain an extra layer of location transparency with respect to global object names; this transparency is lost if users explicitly specify global object names in their SQL statements.
- You should have some administrative control over the network domain that contains the database. For example, you should not create a database in a high-level network domain in which you have no control over name duplication. By having control of the network domain that contains a database, you can ensure that all database names within the domain are unique.
- Anticipate potential database name conflicts within network domains. If you foresee name conflicts within a particular domain, use an additional level in the network domain structure so that no name conflicts occur. However, create only enough levels of domains to make names unique, without creating unnecessarily long and confusing database names.
- Put databases that are related in the same network domain. This improves organization within network domains, and reduces complexity when specifying names for the database links among related databases.

Creating a Global Database Name

Specify both components of a database's global name in the parameter file before database creation; after database creation, changing the database's global name can have a severe impact on existing applications and object definitions.

You establish a database's global name by setting the DB_NAME and DB_DOMAIN parameters. The DB_NAME parameter determines the name component of a database's global object name; the DB_NAME parameter also determines the database's local database name, which you might specify during administrative operations (such as database startup and recovery). The DB_DOMAIN parameter indicates the location (strictly a logical location) of the database within a network structure. The combination of the settings for these two parameters forms a database name that must be unique within a network. For example, to create a database with a global database name TEST.US.ACME.COM, edit the parameters of the parameter file as follows:

```
DB_NAME = TEST
DB_DOMAIN = US.ACME.COM
```

DB_NAME must be an alphanumeric text string of no more than eight characters, without any special characters. During database creation, the name you provide for DB_NAME is recorded in the data files, redo log files, and control file of the database. If during database startup the value of the DB_NAME parameter and the database name in the control file do not match, the database does not start.

DB_DOMAIN must be an alphanumeric text string of no more than 119 characters that specifies the network domain in which the database is created (typically the name of the organization that owns the database). Case is not significant. Levels in the domain name are separated by dots; dots should only separate leafs in the domain structure. The order of domain names is from leaf to root, left to right (in accordance with the standard Internet convention).

Changing a Database's Global Name

In rare situations, you may need to change a database's global name. Changing a database's global name can cause several undesired side effects, including the following effects:

- If existing database links in remote databases point to the renamed database, they are not renamed automatically.
- Existing synonyms in remote databases that point to objects within the renamed database are not updated automatically.
- Existing PL/SQL program units in remote databases that reference data in the renamed database are not updated automatically.

If you absolutely need to change the global name of a database, first coordinate the name change with other database administrators of the system. After this is completed, you should (but are not required to) alter the instance to restricted session mode (using the ENABLE RESTRICTED SESSION option of the SQL command ALTER SYSTEM) and then kill all current sessions. To rename the database, use the RENAME GLOBAL_NAME parameter of the ALTER DATABASE command. For example, assume that during a reorganization of the ACME company, the Sales department is moved to Australia. You could rename the global database name of the Sales department database as follows:

```
ALTER DATABASE RENAME GLOBAL_NAME TO sales.australia.acme.com;
```

After the database name has been changed, you can allow users to connect to the instance; use the DISABLE RESTRICTED SESSION option of the SQL command ALTER SYSTEM.

Enforcing Global Naming

In most cases, you should take advantage of the global object naming features of ORACLE when operating in a distributed database. However, for backward compatibility with earlier releases of ORACLE, you can disable global name resolution. Disabling global name resolution also allows database link names to have no correspondence to global database names.

Enforcement of global name resolution is controlled at two levels:

for the instance — Enforcement of global name resolution can be controlled at the system level by the initialization parameter GLOBAL_NAMES; if set to TRUE, a subsequently started instance enforces global name resolution. The default is FALSE. The current instance setting can be overridden using the SET GLOBAL_NAMES parameter of the ALTER SYSTEM command (specifying TRUE or FALSE).

for a user session — Enforcement of global name resolution can be controlled at the session level using the SET GLOBAL_NAMES parameter of the ALTER SESSION command (specifying TRUE or FALSE).

Examining Global Database Names

Any user can see the global name of a database with the GLOBAL_NAME data dictionary view. For example, the following query lists the global database name of the database to which you are connected (in this case, SALES.US.ACME.COM):

```
SELECT * FROM GLOBAL_NAME;

GLOBAL_NAME
----------------------
SALES.US.ACME.COM
```

Managing Database Links

The database and application administrators of a database that is part of a distributed database are responsible for managing the necessary database links that define paths to related remote databases. The following sections cover the guidelines and procedures to consider when managing database links.

Guidelines for Database Links

In a distributed database, application developers and individual users are often allowed to create private database links. However, you must account for the extra security responsibilities required in a distributed system.

As the administrator, you are responsible for creating all public and network database links. In general, public links are defined so that the following conditions are true:

- All users of the local database can access data in remote databases of the system, providing they have the necessary authorizations in the remote databases.
- Users who create matching private database links do not have to be concerned with specifying complicated database strings.

Application developers and end-users do not need to know anything about SQL*Net connect strings and fully specified global database names, but instead need just a list of remote database names. Using this approach allows you to control how private database links establish connections to remote databases.

Concepts

Tip: Take advantage of the fact that ORACLE can create a full connect string from partial links to make database link management simple and well-defined. Create public links with database strings for all related databases, so that application developers and end-users can create simple private links without having to specify network connection information. See the *ORACLE7 Server Concepts Manual* for details on ORACLE database link search paths.

Creating Database Links

Users and administrators can create database links to facilitate connections to remote databases when a global object name is referenced in a SQL statement or PL/SQL program unit. The name of a database link must be the same as that of the database to which it points. If there is no such database, the link is created, but returns errors when used to resolve object references.

To create a database link and define a path to a remote database, use the CREATE DATABASE LINK command. The optional CONNECT TO clause specifies the remote username/password to use when creating a session in the remote database; if this clause is omitted, the local username and password are used to create the remote ORACLE user session. The optional USING clause indicates the database string (a string containing operating system specific and communications-specific SQL*Net connection information that identifies the communications protocol). See your installation or user's guide and SQL*Net documentation for more information on connect strings.

For example, assume that the local database is named HQ.ACME.COM and a remote database that stores sales information is named SALES.ACME.COM.

```
CREATE PUBLIC DATABASE LINK sales.acme.com
    USING 'dbstring';
```

The example above creates a public database link to the SALES database. Notice the following points:

- A complete database name (both name and network domain) is specified for the database link name.
- The CONNECT TO clause is omitted, so ORACLE uses the local user/password to create a session in the remote database with the database link.
- The USING parameter of the statement specifies a database string *dbstring*.

```
CREATE DATABASE LINK sales
    CONNECT TO scott IDENTIFIED BY tiger
```

The second example creates a private database link for the creator of the link. Notice the following points:

- A partial database name (only the name component) is specified for the database link name. As a result, ORACLE automatically expands the database link name by appending the network domain of the local database to the specified database name to form a global database name.
- A CONNECT TO clause is explicitly specified. The specified remote user/password is used when the database link is used to establish a session in the remote database.
- A USING clause is omitted. Therefore, when the private database link is used, a public or network database link of the same name must be present and must indicate the database

string to use when establishing a connection to the remote database.

In all cases, the complete global name of a database link is accessible in the local data dictionary, in DBA_DB_LINKS, ALL_DB_LINKS, and USER_DB_LINKS. A database link's name must be unique in the scope in which it is created.

Trusted

Note: If you are using Trusted ORACLE in OS MAC mode, see the *Trusted ORACLE7 Server Administrator's Guide* for additional information about creating database links.

Privileges Required to Create a Database Link

The creator of a database link must have either the CREATE DATABASE LINK system privilege (to create private database links) or CREATE PUBLIC DATABASE LINK system privilege (to create public database links).

The remote accounts to which a database link points must exist in the remote database, and must have at least the CREATE SESSION system privilege. If a database link uses individual accounts in the remote database, the local user of the database link must have an account in the remote database. The database administrator of each database must specify privileges for each account. The requirements discussed in this paragraph are not checked when a database link is created; they are checked when a connection is attempted using the database link.

Controlling Connections Established by the RECO Background Process

In its attempt to recover an in-doubt distributed transaction, the RECO background process establishes connections to remote nodes involved in the transaction. To control the costs of connecting to other databases, you might want to control the length of time that such connections are held open on behalf of RECO using the DISTRIBUTED_RECOVERY_-CONNECTION_HOLD_TIME initialization parameter.

Dropping Database Links

A database link is dropped using the DROP DATABASE LINK command. For example, to drop the public database link named SALES, enter the following statement:

```
DROP PUBLIC DATABASE LINK sales.acme.com;
```

Partial global database names are expanded using the network domain component of the local database.

Note: A database link should not be dropped if it is required to resolve an in-doubt distributed transaction. See "Troubleshooting Distributed Transaction problems" on page 15-15 for more information about in-doubt distributed transactions.

Privileges Required to Drop a Database Link

If the database link is private, only the owner can drop the database link. If the database link is public, you must have the DROP PUBLIC DATABASE LINK system privilege.

Examining Available Database Links

The data dictionary of each database stores the definitions of all the database links in that database. The USER/ALL/DBA_DB_LINKS data dictionary views show the database links that have been defined.

For example, assume that the local database's global name is MKTG.ACME.COM. Also assume that the following CREATE DATABASE LINK statements have been issued by the same user:

```
CREATE DATABASE LINK hq.acme.com
   CONNECT TO guest IDENTIFIED BY password

CREATE DATABASE LINK sales USING 'dbstring';
```

The following query lists all of the private database links contained in the schema associated with the current user issuing the query:

```
SELECT db_link, username, host
   FROM user_db_links;
```

For example, if the user that owns the previously created database links (HQ and SALES) issues the query above, results similar to those below are returned:

```
DB_LINK           USERNAME  HOST
----------------  --------  ----------
HQ.ACME.COM       GUEST
SALES.ACME.COM              dbstring
```

Notice that the USERNAME and HOST fields can be null if database link definitions do not indicate complete paths to the remote database.

Limiting the Number of Active Database Links

You can limit the number of connections from a user process to remote databases with the parameter OPEN_LINKS. This parameter controls the number of remote connections that any single user process can use concurrently, within a single SQL statement. To improve application performance, increase the value of this parameter if users need to access more databases at the same time; this allows the user to access all the remote data he needs without waiting for the local instance to close and open connections. For more information, see Appendix A.

Implementing Location Transparency

Location transparency means that the physical location of table data is not specified by (and may not be known by) the end-users and application developers of a database system. Location transparency is beneficial because remote data access is simplified, both local and remote object identities can be hidden from users, and objects can be moved with no effect on users or current applications.

Location transparency is not automatic, but it can be provided to end-users and applications when desired using several different methods:

- A locally defined view can provide location transparency by referencing remote tables in its definition.
- A local synonym can hide the database link used to access a remote table or view.
- The statements of a local procedure can access remote data and remote procedures. Users of the procedure simply call the procedure to access remote data.

Consider these issues when using views, synonyms, and procedures to provide location transparency.

Object Resolution and Location Transparency

When defining views, synonyms, and procedures that reference remote objects, consider the following issues so that your views, synonyms, and procedures always access the intended objects with the intended privileges:

- Unless all remote objects are explicitly qualified with their schema names, the accessed object is dependent on the connection established via the specified database link. For example, if you want a local synonym's remote base table to be SCOTT.EMP, explicitly specify schema SCOTT in the synonym definition:

  ```
  CREATE SYNONYM emp FOR scott.emp@hq.acme.com;
  ```

- Database links defined with a CONNECT TO clause always connect to the remote database as the user specified in the CONNECT TO clause. Views, synonyms, and procedures that use this type of database link are always subject to the privileges and schema resolution of the specified remote user. Alternatively, when database links without a CONNECT TO clause are used in the definition of a view, synonym, or procedure, the remote connection is dependent on the local user. Views and procedures should typically use database links with explicit accounts to ensure that they can function with the proper remote authorizations.

Circular References and Location Transparency

When views, procedures, and synonyms are used to implement location transparency, circular references are not detected by ORACLE, but can be controlled using resource limits (profiles), and specifically the SESSIONS limit. For example, assume that a public synonym in the SALES database, EMP, resolves to the public synonym EMP in the HQ database, and the public synonym EMP in the HQ database references the public synonym EMP in the SALES database. A SQL statement referencing the public synonym EMP in either SALES or HQ would terminate when the maximum number of sessions is exceeded.

Balancing Location Transparency and Security

The choice of using a view, synonym, or procedure for location transparency determines the degree to which the local and remote administrators are responsible for object security. The following example statements and sections outline the issues to consider when choosing among the options for location transparency.

Statement issued at remote database:

```
GRANT SELECT, DELETE ON scott.emp TO user1;
```

Statements issued at local database:

```
CREATE DATABASE LINK hr.acme.com
    CONNECT TO user1 IDENTIFIED BY password
    USING 'db_string';
CREATE VIEW admin.emp_view AS
    SELECT * FROM scott.emp@hr.acme.com;
CREATE PROCEDURE admin.fire_emp (enum NUMBER) AS
BEGIN
    DELETE FROM scott.emp@hr.acme.com
            WHERE empno = enum;
END;
CREATE SYNONYM admin.emp_syn FOR scott.emp@hr.acme.com;
```

Privilege Management With Views

Assume a local view (ADMIN.EMP_VIEW) references a remote table or view. The owner of the local view can grant only the object privileges on his view that have been granted the remote user referenced in the database link; this is similar to privilege management for views that reference local data. Therefore, local privilege management is possible when views are used for location transparency. For example, the user ADMIN can successfully grant the SELECT and DELETE privileges, but not the INSERT and UPDATE privileges for EMP_VIEW.

Views are a good choice for location transparency if unlimited local object privilege management is a requirement. For example, assume the local security administrator needs to selectively grant object privileges for several remote tables. The remote administrator can create a powerful user account that is granted many privileges for many remote tables. Then, the local administrator can create a private database link that connects to the powerful remote account and, in the same schema, create views to "mirror" the remote tables. The local administrator controls local privilege management for the remote tables by granting privileges on the local views. Also note that in this example, a private database link can be used by many users.

Privilege Management With Procedures

Assume a local procedure includes a statement that references a remote table or view (see example on previous page). The owner of the local procedure can grant the EXECUTE privilege to any user, thereby giving that user the ability to execute the procedure and access remote data.

In general, procedures aid in security; users that call a procedure can only perform the controlled operations of the procedure, and privileges for objects referenced within a procedure do not need to be explicitly granted to the calling users. Much like views, procedures are a good choice for location transparency if unlimited local privilege management is a requirement. For example, assume the local security administrator needs to selectively allow users to query and update several remote tables. The remote administrator can create a powerful user account granted many object privileges. Then, the local administrator can create a private database link that connects to the powerful remote account and, in the same schema, create procedures to query and modify the remote tables, as desired. The local administrator can control how local users can access the remote tables by selectively granting the EXECUTE privilege for the local procedures, thus controlling local privilege management for remote objects.

Privilege Management With Synonyms

Assume a local synonym is an alias for a remote object. The owner of the local synonym **cannot** grant any object privileges on the synonym to any other local user. This behavior is different from privilege management for synonyms that are aliases for local tables or views; in the case where a synonym is an alias for a remote object, local privileges for the synonym cannot be granted because this would amount to granting privileges for the remote object, which is not allowed. Therefore, no local privilege management can be performed when synonyms are used for location transparency; security for the base object is controlled entirely at the remote node. For example, the user ADMIN cannot grant any object privileges for the EMP_SYN synonym.

Unlike a database link referenced in a view or procedure definition, a database link referenced in a synonym is resolved by first looking for a private link owned by the schema in effect at the time the reference to the synonym is parsed. Therefore, to ensure the desired object resolution, it is especially important to specify the underlying object's schema in the definition of a synonym.

Limiting the Number of Distributed Transactions Per Node

The parameter DISTRIBUTED_TRANSACTIONS controls the number of possible distributed transactions in which a given instance can concurrently participate, both as a client and a server. If this limit is reached and a subsequent user tries to issue a SQL statement referencing a remote database, the statement is rolled back and the following error message is returned:

```
ORA-2042: too many global transactions
```

For example, assume that DISTRIBUTED_TRANSACTIONS is set to 10 for a given instance. In this case, only ten sessions can concurrently be in the process of a distributed transaction; if an eleventh session attempts to issue a DML statement requiring distributed access, an error message is returned to the session and the statement is rolled back. The database administrator should consider increasing the value of the initialization parameter DISTRIBUTED_TRANSACTIONS when an instance regularly participates in numerous distributed transactions and the above error message is frequently returned as a result of the current limit. Increasing the limit allows more users to concurrently issue distributed transactions.

If the DISTRIBUTED_TRANSACTIONS initialization parameter is set to zero, no distributed SQL statements can be issued in any session. Also, the RECO background process is not started at startup of the local instance and any in-doubt distributed transactions that may be present (from a previous network or system failure) cannot be automatically resolved by ORACLE; therefore, only set this initialization parameter to zero to prevent distributed transactions when a new instance is started and when it is certain that no in-doubt distributed transactions remained after the last instance shut down.

Setting the Commit Point Strength of an Instance

Set the commit point strength for each ORACLE database so that the most critical server can be "non-blocking" in the event of a failure during a two-phase commit. A database's commit point strength should relate to the estimated number of collisions that can result from data locked by in-doubt transactions. For example, databases controlled by ORACLE on mainframe computers most likely have higher commit point strengths than databases controlled by minicomputers. In turn, databases on minicomputers most likely have higher commit point strengths than databases controlled by PC database servers. To determine such settings, it is necessary for all administrators of the distributed database system to communicate and establish proper guidelines for commit point strength settings.

A database instance's commit point strength is set by the initialization parameter COMMIT_POINT_STRENGTH. The range of values is any integer from 0 to 255. For example, to set the commit point strength of a database to 200, include the following line in that database's parameter file:

```
COMMIT_POINT_STRENGTH=200
```

IUG

The default value is operating system specific; see your installation or user's guide for this value on your system.

Troubleshooting Distributed Transaction Problems

After a network or system failure occurs, it can cause the following types of problems for the users of the distributed database system:

- A two-phase commit being processed when a failure occurs may not be completed at all nodes of the session tree.
- If a failure persists (for example, if the network is down for a long period of time), the data exclusively locked by in-doubt transactions is unavailable to statements of other transactions.

The following sections describe these situations.

Failures that Interrupt a Two-Phase Commit

The user program that commits a distributed transaction is informed of a problem by one of the following error messages:

```
ORA-02050: transaction ID rolled back, some remote dbs may be
in-doubt
ORA-02051: transaction ID committed, some remote dbs may be in-doubt
ORA-02054: transaction ID in-doubt
```

An application should save information about a transaction if it receives any of the above errors. This information can be used later if manual distributed transaction recovery is desired.

Note: The failure cases that prompt these error messages are beyond the scope of this book and are unnecessary to understand in order to administer the system.

No action is required by the administrator of any node that has one or more in-doubt distributed transactions due to a network or system failure. The automatic recovery features of ORACLE transparently complete any in-doubt transaction so that the same outcome occurs on all nodes of a session tree (that is, all commit or all roll back) once the network or system failure is resolved. However, in extended outages, the administrator may wish to force the commit or rollback of a transaction to release any locked data. Applications must account for such possibilities.

Failures that Prevent Access of Data

When a user issues a SQL statement, ORACLE attempts to lock the required resources to successfully execute the statement. However, if the requested data is currently being held by statements of other uncommitted transactions and continues to remained locked for an excessive amount of time, a time-out occurs. Consider the following two scenarios.

Example 1: Transaction Time-Out

A DML SQL statement that requires locks on a remote database may be blocked from doing so if another transaction (distributed or non-distributed) currently own locks on the requested data. If these locks continue to block the requesting SQL statement, a time-out occurs, the statement is rolled back, and the following error message is returned to the user:

```
ORA-02049: time-out: distributed transaction waiting for lock
```

Since no data has been modified, no actions are necessary as a result of the time-out. Applications should proceed as if a deadlock has been encountered. The user who executed the statement can try to re-execute the statement later. If the lock persists, the user should contact an administrator to report the problem.

The timeout interval used in the above situation can be controlled using the initialization parameter DISTRIBUTED_LOCK_TIMEOUT. This interval is in seconds. For example, to set the time-out interval for an instance to 30 seconds, the following line should be included in the associated parameter file:

```
DISTRIBUTED_LOCK_TIMEOUT=30
```

With the above time-out interval, the time-out errors discussed in the previous section occur if a transaction cannot proceed after 30 seconds of waiting for unavailable resources.

For more information about initialization parameters and editing parameter files, see Appendix A.

Example 2: Lock From In-Doubt Transaction

A query or DML statement that requires locks on a local database may be blocked from doing so indefinitely due to the locked resources of an in-doubt distributed transaction. In this case, the following error message is immediately returned to the user:

```
ORA-01591: lock held by in-doubt distributed transaction ID
```

In this case, the SQL statement is rolled back immediately. The user who executed the statement can try to re-execute the statement at a later time. If the lock persists, the user should contact an administrator to report the problem, **including** the ID of the in-doubt distributed transaction.

The chances of the above situations occurring are very rare, considering the low probability of failures during the critical portions of a two-phase commit. Even if such a failure occurs and assuming quick recovery from a network or system failure, problems are automatically resolved without manual intervention, and thus are likely to be resolved before they can be detected by users or database administrators.

Manually Overriding In-Doubt Transactions

A database administrator can manually force the COMMIT or ROLLBACK of a local in-doubt distributed transaction. However, a specific in-doubt transaction should be manually overridden **only** when the following situations exist:

- The in-doubt transaction is locking data that is required by other transactions; this happens if users complain that the ORA-01591 error message is interfering with their transactions.
- An in-doubt transaction is preventing the extents of a rollback segment to be used by other transactions. The first portion of an in-doubt distributed transaction's local transaction ID corresponds to the ID of the rollback segment's ID, as listed by

the data dictionary views DBA_2PC_PENDING and DBA_ROLLBACK_SEGS.

- The failure that did not allow the two-phase commit to complete will not be corrected in an acceptable time period. Examples of such cases might include a telecommunication network that has been damaged or a damaged database that needs a substantial amount of time to complete recovery.

Normally, a decision to locally force an in-doubt distributed transaction should be made in consultation with administrators at other locations. Understand that a wrong decision can lead to database inconsistencies that must be manually corrected, which can be difficult to trace.

If the conditions above do not apply, ***always*** allow the automatic recovery features of ORACLE to complete the transaction. However, if any of the above criteria are met, the administrator should consider a local override of the in-doubt transaction. If a decision is made to locally force the transaction to complete, the database administrator should analyze available information with the following goals in mind:

- Try to find a node that has either committed or rolled back the transaction. If you can find a node that has already resolved the transaction, you can follow the action taken at that node.
- See if any information is given in the TRAN_COMMENT column of DBA_2PC_PENDING for the distributed transaction. Comments are included in the COMMENT parameter of the COMMIT command. For example, an in-doubt distributed transaction's comment might indicate the origin of the transaction and what type of transaction it is:

```
COMMIT COMMENT 'Finance/Accts_pay/Trans_type 10B';
```

- See if any information is given in the ADVICE column of DBA_2PC_PENDING for the distributed transaction. An application can prescribe advice about whether to force the commit or force the rollback of separate parts of a distributed transaction using the ADVISE parameter of the SQL command ALTER SESSION. The advice sent during the prepare phase to each node is the advice in effect at the time the most recent DML statement was executed at that database in the current transaction. For example, consider a distributed transaction that is moving an employee record from the EMP table at one node to the EMP table at another node. The transaction could protect the record, even when administrators independently force the in-doubt transaction at each node, by including the following sequence of SQL statements:

```
ALTER SESSION ADVISE COMMIT;
INSERT INTO emp@hq ... ;     /* advice to commit at HQ */

ALTER SESSION ADVISE ROLLBACK;
DELETE FROM emp@sales ... ; /* advice to roll back at SALES */

ALTER SESSION ADVISE NOTHING;
```

If the advice is followed to manually force the in-doubt transaction, the worst that can happen is that each node has a copy of the employee record being moved; the record cannot disappear.

Manual Override Example

The following example shows a failure during the commit of a distributed transaction and how to go about gaining information before manually forcing the commit or rollback of the local portion of an in-doubt distributed transaction. Figure 15-1 illustrates the example.

FIGURE 15-1
An Example of an In-Doubt Distributed Transaction

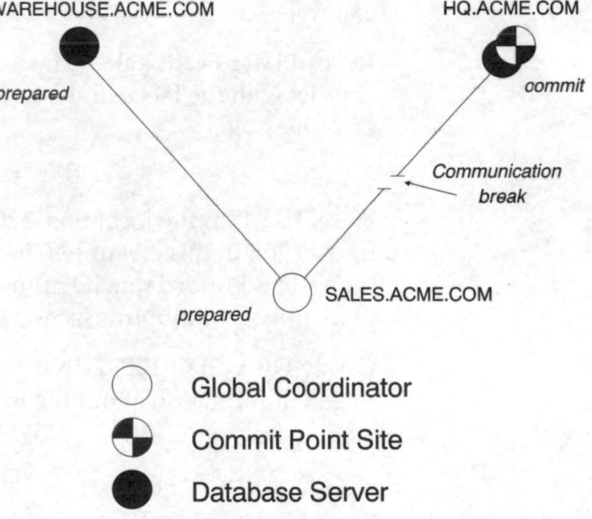

In this failure case, the Prepare phase completed. However, during the Commit phase, the commit point site's commit message (the message telling the global coordinator that the transaction was committed at the commit point site) never made it back to the global coordinator, even though the commit point site committed the transaction. The italicized text indicates the state of all nodes involved in the in-doubt transaction.

You are the WAREHOUSE database administrator. The inventory data locked because of the in-doubt transaction is critical to other transactions, but cannot be accessed because the locks must be held until the in-doubt transaction either commits or rolls back.

Furthermore, you understand that the communication link between sales and headquarters cannot be resolved immediately. Therefore, you decide to manually force the local portion of the in-doubt transaction using the following steps:

1. Record user feedback.
2. Query the local DBA_2PC_PENDING view to obtain the global transaction ID and get other information about the in-doubt transaction.
3. Query the local DBA_2PC_NEIGHBORS view to begin tracing the session tree so that you can find a node that resolved the in-doubt transaction.
4. Check the mixed outcome flag after normal communication is re-established.

The following sections explain each step in detail for this particular example.

Record User Feedback The users of the local database system that conflict with the locks of the in-doubt transaction get the following error message:

```
ORA-01591: lock held by in-doubt distributed transaction 1.21.17
```

Here, 1.21.17 is the local transaction ID of the in-doubt distributed transaction in this example. The local database administrator should request and record this ID number from the users that report problems to identify in-doubt transactions that should be forced.

Query DBA_2PC_PENDING Query the local DBA_2PC_PENDING to gain information about the in-doubt transaction:

```
SELECT * FROM sys.dba_2pc_pending
 WHERE local_tran_id = '1.21.17';
```

For example, when the previous query is issued at WAREHOUSE, the following information is returned. (Here, query results are transposed for clarity.)

```
Column Name           Value
--------------------- ----------------------------------------
LOCAL_TRAN_ID         1.21.17
GLOBAL_TRAN_ID        SALES.ACME.COM.55d1c563.1.93.29
STATE                 prepared
MIXED                 no
ADVICE
TRAN_COMMENT          Sales/New Order/Trans_type 10B
FAIL_TIME             31-MAY-91
FORCE_TIME
RETRY_TIME            31-MAY-91
OS_USER               SWILLIAMS
OS_TERMINAL           TWA139:
HOST                  system1
DB_USER               SWILLIAMS
COMMIT#
```

The global transaction ID is the common transaction ID that is the same on every node for a distributed transaction. It is of the form:

```
global_database_name.hhhhhhhh.local_transaction_id
```

Here, *global_database_name* is the database name of the global coordinator (where the transaction originates), *hhhhhhhh* is an internal database ID at the global coordinator (8 hexadecimal digits), and *local_tran_id* is the corresponding local transaction ID assigned on the global coordinator. Therefore, the last portion of the global transaction ID and the local transaction ID will match at the global coordinator; in the example, you can tell that WAREHOUSE is not the global coordinator because these numbers do not match.

The state of the transaction on this node is "prepared." Therefore, WAREHOUSE is waiting for its coordinator to send either a commit or rollback message.

The transaction's comment or advice may include information about this transaction. If so, use this comment to your advantage. In this example, the origin (the sales order entry application) and transaction type is included in the transaction's comment. This information may reveal something that would help you decide whether to commit or rollback the local portion of the transaction.

If useful comments do not accompany an in-doubt transaction, you must complete some extra administrative work to trace the session tree and find a node that has resolved the transaction. Proceed to Step 3.

Query DBA_2PC_NEIGHBORS The purpose of this step is to climb the session tree such that you find coordinators, eventually reaching the global coordinator. Along the way, you might find a coordinator that has resolved the transaction. If not, you can eventually work your way to the commit point site, which will always have resolved the in-doubt transaction.

The DBA_2PC_NEIGHBORS view provides information about connections associated with an in-doubt transaction. Information for each connection is different, based on whether the connection is inbound or outbound:

- If the connection is inbound, your node is subordinate (a server of) another node. In this case, the DATABASE column lists the name of the client database that connected to your node, and the DBUSER_OWNER column lists the local account used for the database link connection that corresponds to the in-doubt transaction.
- If the connection is outbound, your node is a client of other servers. In this case, the DATABASE column lists the name of the database link used to connect to the remote node, and the DBUSER_OWNER column lists the owner of the database link used within the in-doubt transaction.

Additionally, the INTERFACE column tells whether the local node or a subordinate node is the commit point site.

To trace the session tree, you can query the local DBA_2PC_NEIGHBORS view. In this case, you query this view on the WAREHOUSE database. (Here, query results are transposed for clarity.)

```
SELECT * FROM sys.dba_2pc_neighbors
      WHERE local_tran_id = '1.21.17'
      ORDER BY sess#, in_out;

Column Name              Value
----------------------   --------------------------------------
LOCAL_TRAN_ID            1.21.17
IN_OUT                   in
DATABASE                 SALES.ACME.COM
DBUSER_OWNER             SWILLIAMS
INTERFACE                N
DBID                     000003F4
SESS#                    1
BRANCH                   0100
```

The columns of particular interest in this view are the IN_OUT, DATABASE, DBUSER_OWNER, and INTERFACE columns. In this example, the returned information reveals that this node (WAREHOUSE) is a server of the node SALES, and that the connection to WAREHOUSE was established via a database link that connected to the SWILLIAMS account.

At this point, you can contact the administrator at the located nodes and ask them to repeat Steps 2 and 3, using the global transaction ID.

Note: If you can directly connect to these nodes using another network, you can repeat Steps 2 and 3 yourself.

For example, the following results are returned when Steps 2 and 3 are performed at SALES and HQ, respectively:

At SALES:

```
SELECT * FROM sys.dba_2pc_pending
        WHERE global_tran_id = 'SALES.ACME.COM.55d1c563.1.93.29';

Column Name              Value
------------------------ ----------------------------------------
LOCAL_TRAN_ID            1.93.29
GLOBAL_TRAN_ID           SALES.ACME.COM.55d1c563.1.93.29
STATE                    prepared
MIXED                    no
ADVICE
TRAN_COMMENT             Sales/New Order/Trans_type 10B
FAIL_TIME                31-MAY-91
FORCE_TIME
RETRY_TIME               31-MAY-91
OS_USER                  SWILLIAMS
OS_TERMINAL              TWA139:
HOST                     system1
DB_USER                  SWILLIAMS
COMMIT#

SELECT * FROM dba_2pc_neighbors
        WHERE global_tran_id = 'SALES.ACME.COM.55d1c563.1.93.29'
        ORDER BY sess#, in_out;
```

At SALES, there are three rows for this transaction (one for the connection to WAREHOUSE, one for the connection to HQ, and one for the connection established by the user). Information corresponding to the rows for the SALES and HQ connections is listed below:

```
Column Name             Value
----------------------  --------------------------------------
LOCAL_TRAN_ID           1.93.29
IN_OUT                  OUT
DATABASE                WAREHOUSE.ACME.COM
DBUSER_OWNER            SWILLIAMS
INTERFACE               N
DBID                    55d1c563
SESS#                   1
BRANCH                  1

LOCAL_TRAN_ID           1.93.29
IN_OUT                  OUT
DATABASE                HQ.ACME.COM
DBUSER_OWNER            ALLEN
INTERFACE               C
DBID                    00000390
SESS#                   1
BRANCH                  1
```

The information from the previous query reveals several facts:

- SALES is the global coordinator because the local transaction ID and global transaction ID match. Also, notice that two outbound connections are established from this node, but no inbound links (this node is not a server of another node).
- HQ or one of its servers (none in this example) is the commit point site.

At HQ:

```
SELECT * FROM dba_2pc_pending
      WHERE global_tran_id = 'SALES.ACME.COM.55d1c563.1.93.29';
```

```
Column Name             Value
----------------------  --------------------------------------
LOCAL_TRAN_ID           1.45.13
GLOBAL_TRAN_ID          SALES.ACME.COM.55d1c563.1.93.29
STATE                   COMMIT
MIXED                   NO
ACTION
TRAN_COMMENT            Sales/New Order/Trans_type 10B
FAIL_TIME               31-MAY-91
FORCE_TIME
RETRY_TIME              31-MAY-91
OS_USER                 SWILLIAMS
OS_TERMINAL             TWA139:
HOST                    SYSTEM1
DB_USER                 SWILLIAMS
COMMIT#                 129314
```

At this point, you have found a node that resolved the transaction: it has been committed. Therefore, you can force the in-doubt transaction to commit at your local database (see the following section for information on manually committing or rolling back in-doubt transactions). It is a good idea to contact any other administrators you know that could also benefit from your investigation.

Check for Mixed Outcome After you manually force a transaction to commit or roll back, the corresponding row in the pending transaction table remains. The STATE of the transaction is changed to "forced commit" or "forced abort," depending on how you forced the transaction. Furthermore, once connections between the instances can be resumed, RECO checks the global outcome of the transaction. The MIXED column is changed to "yes" and the row for the transaction is not deleted if you forced the transaction the wrong way. If you ever see a transaction forced the wrong way, you should be aware that some global data inconsistency may exist. Eventually, you can purge unnecessary rows from the pending transaction table.

Manually Committing In-Doubt Transactions

The local database administrator can manually force an in-doubt transaction to commit using either the Recover In-Doubt Transaction dialog box of SQL*DBA or the SQL command COMMIT WORK with the FORCE option and a text string indicating either the local or global transaction ID of the in-doubt transaction to commit. Figure 15-2 shows the Recover In-Doubt Transaction dialog box.

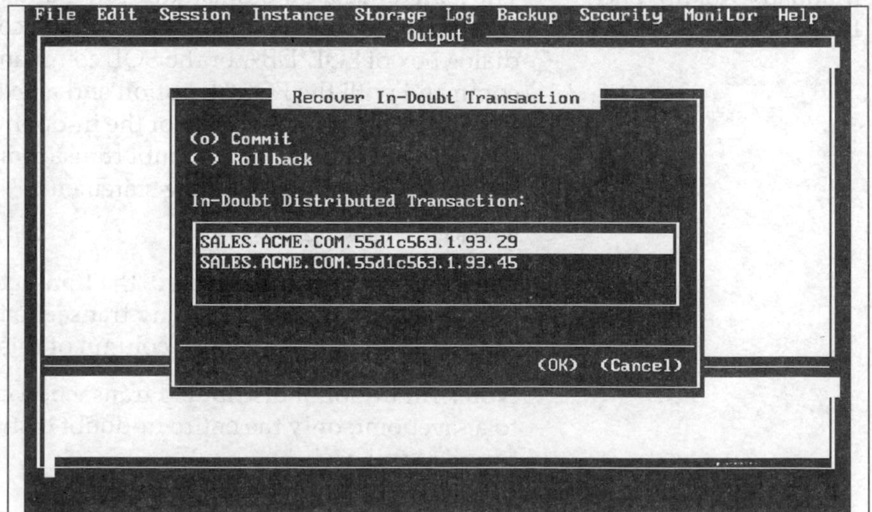

FIGURE 15-2
The Recover In-Doubt Transaction Dialog

The following statement is the command equivalent of the Recover In-Doubt Transaction dialog box in Figure 15-2:

```
COMMIT FORCE 'SALES.ACME.COM.55d1c563.1.93.29';
```

In both examples, the transaction is committed on the local node and the local pending transaction table records a value of "forced commit" for the STATE column of this transaction's row.

Optionally, when forcing a transaction to commit, the SCN for the transaction can be specified; this feature allows you to commit an in-doubt transaction with the SCN assigned when it was committed at other nodes, thus maintaining the synchronized commit time of the distributed transaction even in the event of failure. An SCN should only be specified when you can determine the SCN of the same transaction already committed at another node.

For example, assume you want to manually commit a transaction with the global transaction ID *global_id*. First, query the DBA_2PC_PENDING view of a remote database also involved with the transaction in question and note the SCN used for the commit of the transaction at that node. Specify the SCN (a decimal number) when committing the transaction at the local node. For example, assume the noted SCN is 829381993:

```
COMMIT FORCE 'global_id', 829381993;
```

Manually Rolling Back In-Doubt Transactions

The local database administrator can manually force an in-doubt transaction to roll back using either the Recover In-Doubt Transaction dialog box of SQL*DBA or the SQL command ROLLBACK WORK command with the FORCE option and a text string indicating either the local or global transaction ID of the in-doubt transaction to rollback. For example, to rollback the in-doubt transaction with the local transaction ID of 2.9.4, enter the following statement:

```
ROLLBACK FORCE '2.9.4';
```

Once this statement is executed, the transaction is rolled back on the local node and the local pending transaction table records a value of "forced abort" for the STATE column of this transaction's row.

Note: An in-doubt distributed transaction cannot be forced to roll back to a savepoint; only the entire in-doubt distributed transaction can be forced to roll back.

Privileges Required to Manually Commit or Rollback In-Doubt Transactions

To manually force the commit or rollback of an in-doubt transaction issued by yourself, you must have been granted the FORCE TRANSACTION system privilege. To force the commit or rollback of another user's distributed transaction, you must have the FORCE ANY

TRANSACTION system privilege. Both privileges can be obtained either explicitly or via a role.

Note: Forcing the commit or rollback of an in-doubt distributed transaction does not affect the status of the operator's current transaction.

Changing Connection Hold Time

After a distributed transaction fails, the connection from the local site to the remote site does not necessarily close immediately; instead, it remains open in case communication can be restored quickly, without having to re-establish the connection. You can set the length of time that the connection remains open with the database parameter DISTRIBUTED_RECOVERY_CONNECTION_HOLD_TIME. A high value minimizes the cost of reconnecting after failures, but causes the local database to consume more resources. In contrast, a lower value minimizes the cost of resources kept locked during a failure, but increases the cost of reconnecting after failures. The default value of the parameter is 200 seconds. See Appendix A for more information.

Setting a Limit on Distributed Transactions

The database parameter DISTRIBUTED _TRANSACTIONS sets a maximum on the number of distributed transactions in which a database can participate. You should increase the value of this parameter if your database is part of many distributed transactions; the default value is operating system specific.

In contrast, if your site is experiencing an abnormally high number of network failures, you can temporarily decrease the value of this parameter. Doing so limits the number of in-doubt transactions in which your site takes part, and thereby limits the amount of locked data at your site, and the number of in-doubt transactions you might have to resolve.

For more information on this parameter, see Appendix A.

Testing Distributed Transaction Recovery Features

If you like, you can force the failure of a distributed transaction to observe RECO automatically resolving the local portion of the transaction. Alternatively, you might be interested in forcing a distributed transaction to fail so that you can practice manually resolving in-doubt distributed transactions and observing the results. The following sections describes the features available and the steps necessary to perform such operations.

Forcing a Distributed Transaction to Fail

Comments can be included in the COMMENT parameter of the COMMIT statement. To intentionally induce a failure during the two-phase commit of a distributed transaction, include the following comment in the COMMENT parameter:

```
COMMIT COMMENT 'ORA-2PC-CRASH-TEST-n';
```

where *n* is one of the following integers:

n	*Effect*
1	Crash commit point site after collect
2	Crash non-commit point site after collect
3	Crash before prepare (non-commit point site)
4	Crash after prepare (non-commit point site)
5	Crash commit point site before commit
6	Crash commit point site after commit
7	Crash non-commit point site before commit
8	Crash non-commit point site after commit
9	Crash commit point site before forget
10	Crash non-commit point site before forget

For example, the following statement returns the following messages if the local commit point strength is greater than the remote commit point strength and both nodes are updated:

```
COMMIT COMMENT 'ORA-2PC-CRASH-TEST-7';

ORA-02054: transaction #.##.## in-doubt
ORA-02059: ORA-CRASH-TEST-n in commit comment
```

At this point, the in-doubt distributed transaction appears in the DBA_2PC_PENDING view. If enabled, RECO automatically resolves the transaction rather quickly.

Privileges Required to Induce Two-Phase Commit Failures You can induce two-phase commit failures via the previous comments only if both the local and remote sessions have the FORCE ANY TRANSACTION system privilege. Otherwise, an error is returned if you attempt to issue a COMMIT statement with a crash comment.

Disabling and Enabling RECO

The recoverer background process, RECO, can be enabled and disabled using the ALTER SYSTEM command with the ENABLE/DISABLE DISTRIBUTED RECOVERY options, respectively. For example, you might want to temporarily disable RECO so that you can force the failure of a two-phase commit and manually resolve the in-doubt transaction. The following statement disables RECO:

```
ALTER SYSTEM DISABLE DISTRIBUTED RECOVERY;
```

Alternatively, the following statement enables RECO so that in-doubt transactions are automatically resolved:

```
ALTER SYSTEM ENABLE DISTRIBUTED RECOVERY;
```

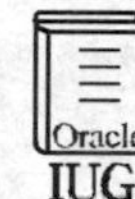

IUG

Note: Single-process instances (for example, a PC running MS-DOS) have no separate background processes, and therefore no RECO process. Therefore, when a single-process instance that participates in a distributed database is first started, distributed recovery must be manually enabled using the statement above. See your installation or user's guide for more information about distributed transaction recovery for single-process instances.

CHAPTER

16 Managing Table Snapshots

This chapter explains how to manage table snapshots (local copies of a remote table). The topics in this chapter include:

- creating, altering, and dropping snapshots
- refreshing snapshots
- troubleshooting snapshot problems
- creating, altering, managing, and dropping snapshot logs
- duplicating tables manually

Except for manual table duplication, the information in this chapter applies only to systems using ORACLE with both the distributed option and the procedural option.

Managing Snapshots

A snapshot is a read-only copy of a table or of data from multiple tables. A snapshot is periodically refreshed to reflect a recent, transaction-consistent state of the tables that it replicates.

The following sections explain how to create, alter, and drop snapshots.

Preparing to Create Snapshots

Before anyone can create any snapshots or snapshot logs in a database, you must run the CATSNAP.SQL script on both the database that contains the master table and the database that will contain snapshots; you must be connected as SYS. The name and location of the CATSNAP.SQL script are operating system specific; see your installation or user's guide. This script is usually run during database creation of sites with the procedural option.

In addition, the procedures described in this chapter for administering snapshots require that you run the script DBMSSNAP.SQL, which creates packages of procedures for refreshing snapshots. You must run this script, while connected as SYS, on both the master table's database and the snapshot's database. The name and location of the DBMSSNAP.SQL script are operating system specific; see your installation or user's guide. This script is also usually run by default during database creation for sites with the procedural option.

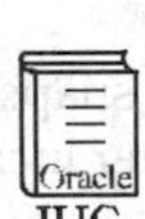

Also, if you want snapshots to be refreshed automatically, you can, depending on your operating system, start a periodic batch job or write a utility to connect periodically to the database containing the snapshots and call the procedure DBMS_SNAPSHOT.REFRESH_-ALL(), which refreshes the snapshots. On many platforms, Oracle provides a utility program like this; you specify when you start the utility the name of a file that indicates which user (and password) the utility should use in connecting, and the interval at which it should connect. The exact name, location, and operation of the refresh utility are operating system dependent; in many cases, the utility is called REFSNAP. See your installation or user's guide for information about this utility on your platform.

Creating Snapshots

You create a local snapshot using the SQL command CREATE SNAPSHOT. As when creating tables, you can specify storage characteristics, extent sizes and allocation, and the tablespace to hold the snapshot, or a cluster to hold the snapshot (in which case all of the previous options do not apply). You can also specify how the snapshot is to be refreshed and the distributed query that defines the snapshot; this is unique to snapshots. For example, the following CREATE

SNAPSHOT statement defines a local snapshot to replicate the remote EMP table located in NY:

```
CREATE SNAPSHOT emp_sf
    PCTFREE 5 PCTUSED 60
    TABLESPACE users
    STORAGE (INITIAL 50K NEXT 50K PCTINCREASE 50)
    REFRESH FAST
            START WITH sysdate
            NEXT sysdate + 7
    AS SELECT * FROM emp@ny;
```

Whenever a snapshot is created, it is immediately filled with the rows returned by the query that defines the snapshot. Thereafter, the snapshot is refreshed as specified by the REFRESH clause; see "Refreshing Snapshots" on page 16-5.

Naming Snapshots

Snapshots are contained in a user's schema. A snapshot's name must be unique with respect to other objects in the schema. Keep snapshot names to 23 or fewer characters. If a snapshot name contains more than 23 characters, ORACLE automatically (and uniquely) truncates the prefixed names of the underlying table and views, so that they comply with the naming rules for schema objects.

Creating a Clustered Snapshot

You can create a snapshot in a cluster, just as you can a table. For example, the following statement creates a snapshot named EMP_DALLAS in the EMP_DEPT cluster:

```
CREATE SNAPSHOT emp_dallas
    ...
    CLUSTER emp_dept
    ... ;
```

The storage parameters of the cluster's data segment are used for the storage of the clustered snapshot, even if storage parameters are specified for the snapshot.

Privileges Required to Create Snapshots

To create a snapshot, the following sets of privileges must be granted:

- To create a snapshot in your own schema, you must have the CREATE SNAPSHOT, CREATE TABLE, CREATE VIEW, and CREATE INDEX (only for simple snapshots) system privileges, as well as SELECT privilege on the master tables.
- To create a snapshot in another user's schema, you must have the CREATE ANY SNAPSHOT, CREATE ANY TABLE, CREATE ANY VIEW, and CREATE ANY INDEX (only for simple snapshots) system privileges, as well as SELECT privilege on the master table. Additionally, the owner of the

snapshot must have the appropriate SELECT privilege on the master tables.

In either case, the owner of the snapshot must also have sufficient quota on the tablespace intended to hold the snapshot.

The large set of privileges required to create a snapshot is due to the underlying objects that must also be created on behalf of the snapshot.

Understanding the Internals of Snapshot Creation

When a snapshot is created, several operations are performed internally by ORACLE:

- ORACLE (at the snapshot node) creates a table to store the rows retrieved by the snapshot's defining query; this is the snapshot's *base table*. The table's name is SNAP$_*snapshotname*. (This base table of a snapshot should not be altered in any way; do not add triggers or integrity constraints to a snapshot's base table or directly modify data in a snapshot's base table.)
- ORACLE creates a read-only view on the SNAP$ table for queries issued against the snapshot. This view uses the name provided by the CREATE SNAPSHOT statement. (No DML operations are allowed on this view because it is read-only.)
- ORACLE creates a second local view on the remote master table. It uses this view when it refreshes the snapshot. This view is named MVIEW$_*snapshotname*.

Additionally, if the snapshot is a simple snapshot, ORACLE creates an index on the SNAP$ table. This index is named PK$_*snapshotname*.

All of these internal objects are created in the schema of the snapshot. Do not alter, change data in, or delete these objects manually.

Setting Storage Parameters for Snapshots

How you should set storage options for a snapshot depends on the type of snapshot (simple or complex):

- In general, a simple snapshot's storage options should mimic the storage options for its master table, since they share the same characteristics. If a number of master tables are clustered in the master database, you should probably cluster the corresponding snapshots in the remote database.

  Note: If a simple snapshot does not duplicate all columns of its master table, modify the snapshot storage items accordingly.

- Because a complex snapshot is always completely refreshed, set its PCTFREE to 0 and PCTUSED to 100 for maximum efficiency.

You can change a snapshot's storage parameters using the ALTER SNAPSHOT command. For example, the following command alters the EMP snapshot's PCTFREE parameter:

```
ALTER SNAPSHOT emp PCTFREE 10;
```

You cannot change a snapshot's defining query; you must first drop the snapshot and then re-create it.

Privileges Required to Alter a Snapshot

To alter a snapshot's storage parameters, the snapshot must be contained in your schema or you must have the ALTER ANY SNAPSHOT and ALTER ANY TABLE system privileges.

Refreshing Snapshots

Each snapshot is individually refreshed in a separate transaction to make the snapshot reflect a more recent state of its master tables. There are two types of refreshes: a fast refresh and a complete refresh. A *fast refresh* uses the snapshot log of a master table to refresh a simple snapshot (only simple snapshots can execute a fast refresh). A *complete refresh* entirely replaces the existing data in a simple or complex snapshot. Also, snapshots can be refreshed automatically or manually.

Consider the following issues when deciding how to refresh a snapshot:

- In most cases with a simple snapshot, use fast refreshes because they are more efficient than complete refreshes.
- If the master tables receive a consistent number of updates in a given time period, automatically refresh dependent snapshots.
- After bulk loads to the master tables, manually refresh all snapshots based on the master table. This propagates the new rows of the master tables to associated snapshots.

Configuring Automatic Refreshes

To configure snapshots to be automatically refreshed, perform the following steps:

1. Create or alter each snapshot to be refreshed automatically, specifying automatic refresh options.
2. Start the refresh utility program on the database server that has the snapshots (not the master table).

To configure a specific snapshot to automatically refresh, specify a refresh option in the REFRESH clause of a CREATE SNAPSHOT or ALTER SNAPSHOT statement. The refresh options available are FAST, COMPLETE, and FORCE. FORCE, the default, performs a fast refresh if possible, or a complete refresh otherwise. The START WITH parameter specifies the time for a snapshot's initial automatic refresh; if omitted, the initial automatic refresh of the snapshot is evaluated using the creation time and the NEXT parameter. The NEXT parameter specifies the automatic refresh interval for the snapshot. NEXT is always evaluated from the last refresh, automatic or manual.

The automatic refresh settings for a snapshot are stored in the data dictionary. Refresh settings in the data dictionary are updated if they are altered via an ALTER SNAPSHOT statement and every time the snapshot is refreshed (automatically or manually). When setting a snapshot's refresh settings, understand the following behavior:

- The dates or date expressions in the START WITH and NEXT parameters must evaluate to a future point in time; if they do not, an error message is returned. A date literal must be enclosed in single quotes, while date expressions do not require quotes (see example below).
- If a snapshot should be refreshed periodically at a set interval, use the NEXT parameter with a date expression similar to "SYSDATE + 7". For example, if you set the automatic refresh interval to "SYSDATE + 7" on Monday and manually refresh the snapshot on Thursday, "SYSDATE + 7" now evaluates to every Thursday, not Monday. Alternatively, if you always want to automatically refresh the snapshot at a specific time, regardless of the last refresh (for example, every Monday), the NEXT parameter should specify a date expression similar to "NEXT_DAY(TRUNC(SYSDATE), 'MONDAY')".

Table 16-1 lists some common date expressions used for snapshot refresh intervals.

TABLE 16-1 Examples of Common Refresh Intervals

Date Expression	Evaluation
SYSDATE + 7	Exactly seven days from the last refresh
NEXT_DAY(TRUNC(SYSDATE), 'MONDAY')+ 15/24	Every Monday at 3PM
NEXT_DAY(ADD_MONTHS(TRUNC(SYSDATE,'Q'),3), 'THURSDAY')	The first Thursday of each quarter

The following examples of the REFRESH clause show valid combinations and date expressions:

```
CREATE SNAPSHOT snap
  . . .
  REFRESH  COMPLETE
           START WITH '01-SEP-92'
           NEXT sysdate + 7
  AS . . . ;

ALTER SNAPSHOT snap REFRESH FAST;
```

```
ALTER SNAPSHOT snap
   REFRESH COMPLETE
                NEXT next_day(trunc(sysdate), 'MONDAY') + 15/24;
```

The first statement creates the SNAP snapshot, specifying complete automatic refreshes, the first of which occurs on September 1st, 1992, with an automatic refresh interval of seven days from the most recent refresh (whether automatic or manual). The second statement specifies that automatic refreshes should be fast. The third statement specifies that automatic refreshes should be complete, and changes the automatic refresh interval to be every Monday at 3PM.

For automatic refreshes to take place, the refresh utility program, supplied with ORACLE, runs on the database server. This utility notifies ORACLE about the automatic refresh of **any** appropriate snapshot. When the refresh utility is started, an interval can be specified that indicates how often the utility "wakes up" to check for snapshots due to be automatically refreshed. The exact name and location of the refresh utility program are operating system dependent.

Troubleshooting Automatic Refresh Problems Several factors can prevent the automatic refresh of snapshots: not executing the refresh utility, an intervening network or instance failure, or an instance shutdown. When any of these factors prevents the automatic refresh of a snapshot, the snapshot remains "due" to be refreshed. Snapshots due to be refreshed are automatically refreshed once the refresh utility is executed and any network failure is resolved.

Manually Refreshing Snapshots

You can refresh a snapshot manually, whether or not it is also automatically refreshed by ORACLE. You refresh an individual snapshot using the REFRESH stored procedure of the package DBMS_SNAPSHOT, with the following syntax:

```
dbms_snapshot.refresh ('[schema.]name' [, 'refresh_option'])
```

The argument *schema.name* is the name of the snapshot to refresh. The optional argument *refresh_option* specifies the type of refresh to perform; 'F' or 'f' indicates a fast refresh, 'C' or 'c' indicates a complete refresh, and '?' indicates the default refresh option of the snapshot.

For example, the following EXECUTE statement within SQL*DBA causes a fast refresh of the EMP snapshot:

```
EXECUTE dbms_snapshot.refresh('emp', 'f');
```

You can refresh all snapshots due to be automatically refreshed (those not yet refreshed by the refresh utility) by calling the REFRESH_ALL stored procedure of the DBMS_SNAPSHOT package. This procedure refreshes each snapshot due to be automatically refreshed, according to its automatic refresh settings:

```
EXECUTE dbms_snapshot.refresh_all;
```

The REFRESH_ALL procedure accepts no arguments. Snapshots not configured for automatic refresh are not affected by the REFRESH_ALL stored procedure. A single execution of the REFRESH_ALL procedure refreshes all snapshots due to be automatically refreshed. As this procedure executes, each snapshot due to be automatically refreshed is individually refreshed in a separate transaction. If a system failure interrupts the procedure, some snapshots may have been refreshed while others are still due to be refreshed. If this happens, execute the REFRESH_ALL procedure again.

Privileges Required to Manually Refresh Snapshots To alter the refresh settings for a snapshot or to manually refresh the snapshot, you must own the snapshot or have the ALTER ANY SNAPSHOT system privilege. If you are manually refreshing a snapshot using the fast method, you must also have access to the snapshot log on the master table: you must either own the snapshot log or have SELECT privilege on it. (The name of a snapshot log is MLOG$_*master_table_name*, where master_table_name is the name of the master table. See "Managing Snapshot Logs" on page 16-10 for more information.)

Any user with the ALTER ANY SNAPSHOT system privilege can execute the REFRESH_ALL procedure to manually refresh any snapshots due to be automatically refreshed.

Refreshing Snapshots and Referential Integrity

If referential integrity is enforced on one master table or between multiple master tables, refresh related snapshots so that the referential integrity of the master tables is propagated to the associated snapshots.

For example, consider the EMP and DEPT master tables, related via referential integrity on the DEPTNO column. Referential integrity of EMP and DEPT is propagated to the corresponding snapshots EMP_SNAP and DEPT_SNAP only if you can refresh EMP_SNAP and DEPT_SNAP without any modifications taking place on the EMP and the DEPT table between the individual refreshes.

To refresh a single snapshot with a master table that has a self-referencing integrity constraint, use the following steps:

1. Lock, in exclusive mode, the master table with the self-referential integrity constraint:

```
LOCK TABLE emp IN EXCLUSIVE MODE;
```

2. Refresh the snapshot using the REFRESH procedure of the DBMS_SNAPSHOT package. For example, when using SQL*DBA, enter the following statement:

```
EXECUTE dbms_snapshot.refresh('emp', '?');
```

To refresh snapshots of master tables related by referential integrity, use the following procedure:

1. Start a session with an interactive tool (such as SQL*Plus or SQL*DBA) and establish a connection with a database in the distributed database system.
2. Issue a LOCK TABLE statement to exclusively lock the tables related via referential integrity:

```
LOCK TABLE emp, dept IN EXCLUSIVE MODE;
```

3. Start a second session with an interactive tool and establish a connection to the database that contains the snapshots to be refreshed. Note that the first session should remain active to preserve the table locks established in Step 2.
4. Refresh the snapshots that correspond to the tables locked in Step 2. For example, the following statements refresh the EMP and DEPT snapshots:

```
EXECUTE dbms_snapshot.refresh('emp', '?');

EXECUTE dbms_snapshot.refresh('dept', '?');
```

Declarative Constraints and Snapshots

Do not create declarative constraints on snapshots or snapshot logs.

Indexing Snapshots

To increase the query performance when using a snapshot, you can create indexes for the snapshot. To index a column (or columns) of a snapshot, you must create the index on the underlying "SNAP$_" table created to hold the rows of the snapshot. Do not use declarative constraints to create an index; instead, use the CREATE INDEX statement.

Operations on a Master Table that Affect Snapshots

All changes made by INSERT, UPDATE, and DELETE statements issued against a table are reflected in associated snapshots when the snapshots are refreshed.

However, changes made by a TRUNCATE command on master tables are not propagated automatically to simple snapshots; they are propagated to complex snapshots. If you truncate a master table, completely refresh any associated simple snapshots.

If you drop a master table, any associated snapshots remain and continue to be accessible. An associated snapshot log (if present) of a dropped master table also remains. However, when you attempt to refresh a snapshot based on a non-existent master table, ORACLE returns an error.

Snapshots and Media Failure

As the result of a media failure, either a database that contains a master table of a snapshot or a database with a snapshot may need to be recovered. If you have a snapshot or master table in a database that you must recover, see "Recover Databases with Snapshots" on page 19-5.

Dropping Snapshots

You can drop a snapshot independently of its master tables or the snapshot log. To drop a local snapshot, use the SQL command DROP SNAPSHOT. For example:

```
DROP SNAPSHOT emp;
```

If you drop the only snapshot of a master table, you should also drop the snapshot log of the master table, if there is one.

Privileges Required to Drop a Snapshot

Only the owner of a snapshot or a user with the DROP ANY SNAPSHOT, DROP ANY TABLE, and DROP ANY VIEW system privileges can drop a snapshot.

Managing Snapshot Logs

A snapshot log is a table, in the same database as the master table for a snapshot, that is associated with the master table. Its rows list changes that have been made to the master table, and information on which snapshots have and have not been updated to reflect those changes. It can be used by simple snapshots to perform a fast refresh; it cannot be used in complex snapshots.

These sections explain how to create, manage, and drop snapshot logs.

Creation Order of a Simple Snapshot and the Snapshot Log

If you are creating a simple snapshot, it is more efficient to create the snapshot log before the snapshot. Figure 16-1 illustrates the two orders of creation.

FIGURE 16-1
Creation Order of a Simple Snapshot and the Snapshot Log

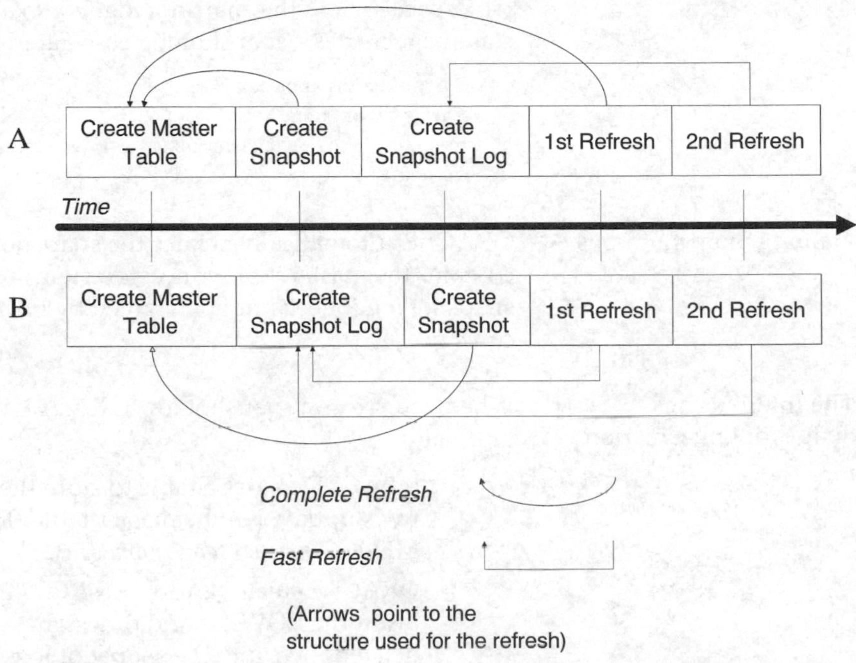

In Method A, the first refresh of the snapshot cannot use the log because the log cannot reflect all updates entered between the creation of the snapshot and the creation of the snapshot log; therefore, two complete refreshes are necessary.

In contrast, Method B only requires one complete refresh (when creating the snapshot); subsequent refreshes can immediately use the snapshot log. If the master table is large or a number of simple snapshots are based on the same master table, creating the snapshot log before the snapshots can be much more efficient.

Creating a Snapshot Log

You can create a snapshot log to decrease the amount of processing and time needed to refresh the simple snapshot. Snapshot logs cannot be used with complex snapshots. A snapshot log is associated with a single master table; likewise, a master table can have only one snapshot log. If multiple simple snapshots are based on the same master table, they all use the same snapshot log.

Create a snapshot log in the same database as the master table using the SQL command CREATE SNAPSHOT LOG. You can set storage options for the snapshot log's data blocks, extent sizes and allocation, and tablespace to hold the snapshot log. For example, the following statement creates a snapshot log associated with the EMP table:

```
CREATE SNAPSHOT LOG ON emp
    TABLESPACE users
    STORAGE (INITIAL 10K NEXT 10K PCTINCREASE 50)
    PCTFREE 5;
```

Naming Snapshot Logs

ORACLE automatically creates the snapshot log in the schema that contains the master table. Since you cannot specify a name for the snapshot log (one is implicitly given by ORACLE), uniqueness is not a concern.

The Internals of Snapshot Log Creation

When you create a snapshot log, ORACLE performs several operations internally:

- ORACLE creates a table to store the ROWID and timestamp of rows updated in the master table. The table is named MLOG$_*master_table_name*.
- ORACLE creates an AFTER ROW trigger on the master table to insert the ROWIDs and timestamps of inserted, updated, and deleted rows into the snapshot log. The trigger is named TLOG$_*master_table_name*.

  Note: Because snapshot log creation implicitly creates an AFTER ROW trigger on the master table, you cannot explicitly create any other AFTER ROW triggers for a master table.

The underlying table for a snapshot log and associated trigger are contained in the same schema as the master table.

Do not alter or change data in these objects.

Privileges Required to Create Snapshot Logs

If you own the master table, you can create an associated snapshot log if you have the CREATE TABLE and CREATE TRIGGER system privileges. If you are creating a snapshot log for a table in another user's schema, you must have the CREATE ANY TABLE and CREATE ANY TRIGGER system privileges. In either case, the owner of the snapshot log must have sufficient quota in the tablespace intended to hold the snapshot log.

The privileges required to create a snapshot log directly relate to the privileges necessary to create the underlying objects associated with a snapshot log.

Setting Storage Parameters for Snapshot Logs

Set a snapshot log's storage options as follows:

- Set PCTFREE to 0, and PCTUSED to 100.
- Set extent storage parameters according to the update activity (number of INSERT, UPDATE, and DELETE statements) on the master table.

Each row in a snapshot log takes approximately 13 bytes (six bytes for a ROWID and seven bytes for a timestamp). Use this number to calculate how much space a snapshot log requires, using the procedure described in "Calculating Space Required by Non-Clustered Tables" on page 8-17.

Altering Snapshot Log Storage Parameters

You can alter a snapshot log's storage parameters using the SQL command ALTER SNAPSHOT LOG. For example:

```
ALTER SNAPSHOT LOG sale_price
   PCTFREE 25
   PCTUSED 40;
```

Privileges Required to Alter Snapshot Logs Only the owner of the master table, or a user with the ALTER ANY TABLE and ALTER ANY TRIGGER system privileges can alter the storage parameters of a snapshot log.

Managing Snapshot Log Space Use

ORACLE automatically tracks which rows in a snapshot log have been used during the refreshes of snapshots, and purges these rows from the log so that the log does not grow endlessly. Because multiple simple snapshots can use the same snapshot log, rows used in the refresh of one snapshot may still be needed to refresh another snapshot; ORACLE does not delete rows from the log until all snapshots have used them. However, this automated feature can cause a snapshot log to grow indefinitely if a single associated snapshot is never refreshed. Figure 16-2 illustrates this case.

FIGURE 16-2
Managing a Snapshot Log

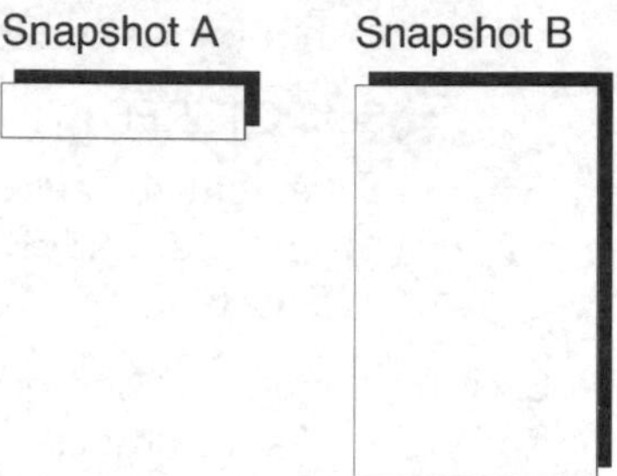

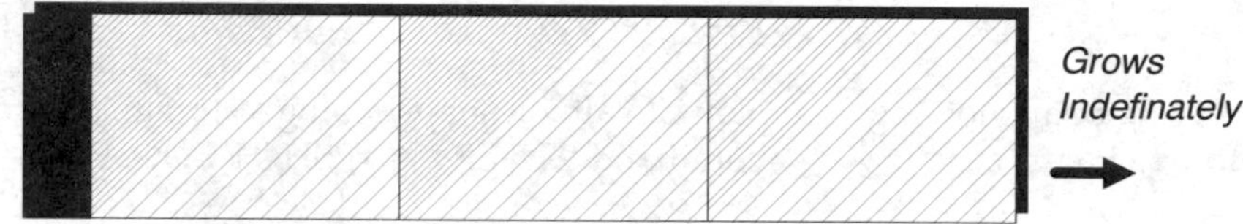

Snapshot B is regularly refreshed. However, ORACLE cannot purge the rows used during the refresh of Snapshot B because Snapshot A needs them for its next refresh. This situation occurs when you have several simple snapshots based on the same master table and either:

- One snapshot is not configured to be automatically refreshed by ORACLE; it has to be manually refreshed.
- One snapshot has a large refresh interval, such as every year.
- A network failure has prevented an automatic refresh of one or more of the snapshots based on the master table.

Keep the snapshot log as small as possible to minimize the space it uses. To reduce the number of rows in a snapshot log, you can either refresh the snapshots associated with the log, or shrink the log by deleting the rows only required by the Nth least recently refreshed snapshots. To do the latter, execute the PURGE_LOG stored procedure of the DBMS_SNAPSHOT package, with the following syntax:

```
dbms_snapshot.purge_log('table', purge_number [, 'DELETE'])
```

The argument *table* is the name of the master table. The argument *purge_number* indicates the number of least recently refreshed snapshots whose rows you want to remove from snapshot log. For example, the following statement deletes rows needed to refresh the two least recently refreshed snapshots:

```
EXECUTE dbms_snapshot.purge_log('master_table', 2);
```

To delete all rows in the snapshot log, indicate a high number of snapshots to disregard, as in this example:

```
EXECUTE dbms_snapshot.purge_log('master_table', 9999);
```

This statement completely purges the snapshot log that corresponds to MASTER_TABLE, if fewer than 9999 snapshots are based on MASTER_TABLE.

Note: A simple snapshot whose rows have been purged from the snapshot log must be completely refreshed the next time it is refreshed.

The optional argument *DELETE* guarantees that rows are deleted from the snapshot log for at least one snapshot, and can override the setting for the argument purge_number. For example, the following statement deletes rows from the least recently refreshed snapshot that actually has dependent rows in the snapshot log:

```
EXECUTE dbms_snapshot.purge_log('master_table', 0, 'DELETE');
```

Reducing Space Allocation for a Snapshot Log

If a snapshot log grows and allocates many extents, purging the log of rows does not reduce the amount of space allocated for the log. To reduce the space allocated for a snapshot log, either truncate or drop and re-create the snapshot log. The first refresh of each simple snapshot subsequent to truncating the log must be a complete refresh. Fast refreshes can then resume.

Privileges Required to Delete Rows From a Snapshot Log The owner of a snapshot log or a user with the DELETE ANY TABLE system privilege can purge rows from the snapshot log by executing the PURGE_LOG procedure.

Dropping Snapshot Logs

You can drop a snapshot log independently of its master table or any existing snapshots. You might decide to drop a snapshot log if one of the following is true:

- All simple snapshots of a master table have been dropped.
- All simple snapshots of a master table are to be completely refreshed, not fast refreshed.

To drop a local snapshot log, use the SQL command DROP SNAPSHOT LOG, as in:

```
DROP SNAPSHOT LOG emp_log;
```

Privileges Required to Drop a Snapshot Log

Only the owner of the master table, or a user with the DROP ANY TABLE system privilege can drop a snapshot log.

Manually Copying Tables Among Nodes of a Distributed Database

As an alternative to creating snapshots, you can manually replicate tables among the nodes of a distributed database. Manual table replication is often useful if the master table experiences high update activity while read-only replicas only need to periodically reflect the changes to the master table.

To create the local replica of the remote master table use a CREATE TABLE statement:

```
CREATE TABLE local_replica
   AS SELECT * FROM remote_master;
```

You can grant local privileges on the replica, create associated indexes and views, and so on.

When you want to update a local replica of the remote master table, drop and re-create the local replica. However, note the following issues:

- When you drop a replica, you also drop any associated indexes, triggers, and integrity constraints. Therefore, you must re-create indexes, triggers, and integrity constraints.
- When you drop a local replica, all object privileges granted to users or roles on the local replica are revoked. After re-creating the replica, regrant object privileges to users and roles.
- When you drop a local replica, all views based on the replica continue to exist, but become invalid. After you create the replica, all dependent views become valid if the new version of the replica has the same structure as the previous replica.

  All privileges granted on a dependent view are preserved throughout the operation of updating a local replica. Therefore, consider creating a view of a local table replica and granting privileges on this view rather than on the replica itself, thereby avoiding regranting privileges on the replica.

PART

VI

DATABASE BACKUP AND RECOVERY

CHAPTER

17 Archiving Redo Information

This chapter explains how to create and maintain the archived redo log. Topics include:

- deciding whether to archive
- specifying the archiving file name format and destination
- turning archiving on and off
- tuning archiving
- checking the archiving status

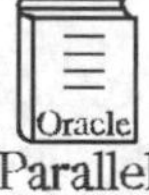

If you are using ORACLE with the Parallel Server, see the *ORACLE7 Parallel Server Administrator's Guide* for additional information about archiving in the environment.

Choosing Between NOARCHIVELOG and ARCHIVELOG Mode

Consider these issues when deciding whether to use archiving:

- In the event of a database failure, including disk failure, you can recover all committed transactions of the database if you are using ARCHIVELOG mode. If you are using NOARCHIVELOG mode, however, you can only **restore** (not recover) the database to the point of the most recent full database backup. You cannot recover subsequent transactions.
- If the database is operating in ARCHIVELOG mode, the entire database can be open and available for normal use while you back up or recover all or part of the database.

In NOARCHIVELOG mode, you cannot perform online tablespace backups. Furthermore, you cannot use online tablespace backups previously taken while the database operated in ARCHIVELOG mode; only full backups taken while the database is closed can be used to restore a database operating in NOARCHIVELOG mode. Therefore, if you decide to operate a database in NOARCHIVELOG mode, take full database backups at regular, frequent intervals.

- If **all** databases in a distributed database operate in ARCHIVELOG mode, you can perform coordinated distributed database recovery. However, if **any** database in a distributed database uses NOARCHIVELOG mode, recovery of a global distributed database (to make all databases consistent) is limited by the last full backup of any database operating in NOARCHIVELOG mode.
- Extra administrative operations are required to manage the files of the archived redo log.
- You must have a dedicated tape drive or additional disk space to store the archived redo log files if the database operates in ARCHIVELOG mode.

If a database operates in ARCHIVELOG mode, you must also decide how filled groups of the online redo log are to be archived; an instance can be configured to have ORACLE automatically archive filled online redo log files, or you can manually archive filled groups.

Turning Archiving On and Off

You set a database's initial archiving mode as part of database creation. In most cases, you can use the default of NOARCHIVELOG mode at database creation because there is no need to archive the redo information generated then. Once the database has been created, decide whether to change from the initial archiving mode.

Note: If a database is automatically created during ORACLE installation, the initial archiving mode of the database is operating system specific. See your installation or user's guide.

Once a database has been created, you can switch the database's archiving mode on demand. However, you should generally not switch the database between archiving modes.

Setting the Initial Database Archiving Mode at Database Creation

When you create the database, you set the initial archiving mode of the redo log in the CREATE DATABASE statement. If you do not specify either ARCHIVELOG or NOARCHIVELOG, NOARCHIVELOG is the default. See Chapter 2 for more information about creating a database.

Changing the Database Archiving Mode After Database Creation

To switch a database's archiving mode between NOARCHIVELOG and ARCHIVELOG mode, use the SQL command ALTER DATABASE with the ARCHIVELOG or NOARCHIVELOG option. For example, the following statement switches the database's archiving mode from NOARCHIVELOG to ARCHIVELOG:

```
ALTER DATABASE ARCHIVELOG;
```

Before switching the database's archiving mode, perform the following operations:

1. Shut down the database instance.

   An open database must be closed and dismounted and any associated instances shut down before the database's archiving mode can be switched. Archiving cannot be disabled if any data files need media recovery.

2. Back up the database.

   Before making any major alteration to a database, always back up the database to protect against any problems that might occur. For more information about database backup, see Chapter 18.

3. Perform any operating system specific steps ***(optional)***.

If you want to archive filled groups, you may have to execute some additional steps at this point, depending on your operating system; see your installation or user's guide for details for your system. These steps may involve exiting SQL*DBA to configure how ORACLE will perform the archiving of the filled groups. Once this operation is complete, start SQL*DBA again and continue to Step 4.

4. Start up a new instance and mount but do not open the database.

   To enable or disable archiving, the database must be mounted but not open. For more information about starting an instance and mounting a database, see Chapter 3.

   Note: If you are using the ORACLE Parallel Server, you must mount the database exclusively, using one instance, to switch the database's archiving mode. See the *ORACLE7 Parallel Server Administrator's Guide* for more information about switching the archiving mode when using the ORACLE Parallel Server.

5. Switch the database's archiving mode.

After using the ALTER DATABASE command to switch a database's archiving mode, open the database for normal operation. If you switched to ARCHIVELOG mode, you should also set the archiving options—decide whether or not to enable ORACLE to archive groups of online redo log files automatically as they fill. See the following sections for more information about the automatic and manual archiving options.

Enabling Automatic Archiving

If your operating system permits, you can enable automatic archiving of the online redo log. Under this option, you need take no action to copy a group after it fills; ORACLE automatically archives groups after they are filled. For this convenience alone, automatic archiving is the method of choice for archiving the filled groups of online redo log files. See your installation or user's guide to determine whether or not this is a valid option for your ORACLE Server.

If automatic archiving is enabled, manual archiving is still possible; see "Performing Manual Archiving" on page 17-6. Always specify an archived redo log destination and filename format when enabling automatic archiving; see "Specifying the Archived Redo Log Filename Format and Destination" on page 17-10.

Automatic archiving can be enabled before or after instance startup.

Enabling Automatic Archiving at Instance Startup

To enable automatic archiving of filled groups each time an instance is started, include the LOG_ARCHIVE_START parameter, set to TRUE, in the database's parameter file:

```
LOG_ARCHIVE_START=TRUE
```

The new value takes effect the next time you start the database.

Enabling Automatic Archiving After Instance Startup

To enable automatic archiving of filled online redo log groups without shutting down the current instance, use the Start Automatic Archiving dialog box of SQL*DBA or the SQL command ALTER SYSTEM with the ARCHIVE LOG START parameter; you can optionally include the archiving destination. Figure 17-1 shows the Start Automatic Archiving dialog box.

FIGURE 17-1 The Start Automatic Archiving Dialog

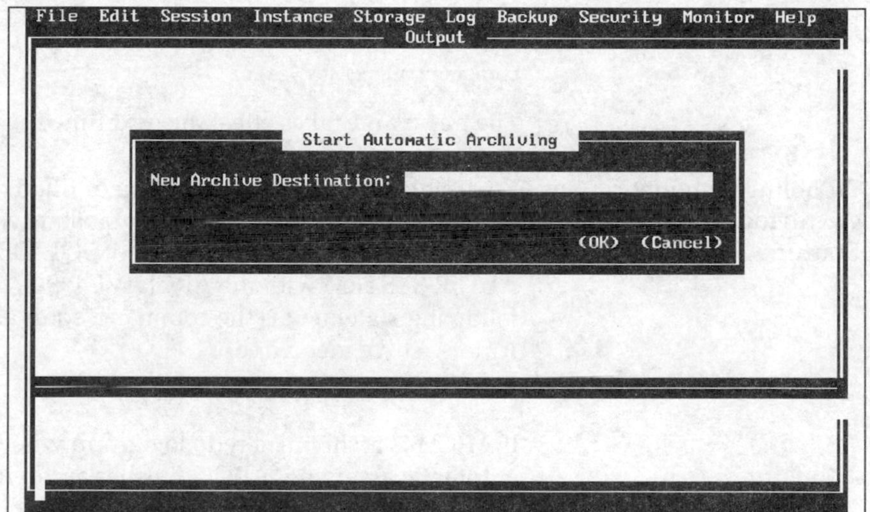

The following statement is the command equivalent of the Start Automatic Archiving dialog box in Figure 17-1:

```
ALTER SYSTEM ARCHIVE LOG START;
```

Using either of the options above, the instance does not have to be shut down to enable automatic archiving; however, if an instance is shut down and restarted after automatic archiving is enabled, the instance is reinitialized using the settings of the parameter file, which may or may not enable automatic archiving.

Privileges Required to Enable Automatic Archiving After Instance Startup To enable automatic archiving after instance startup, you must be connected to ORACLE as INTERNAL. See "Connecting as INTERNAL" on page 1-4.

Disabling Automatic Archiving

You can disable automatic archiving of the online redo log groups at any time. However, once automatic archiving is disabled, you must manually archive groups of online redo log files in a timely fashion. If a database is operated in ARCHIVELOG mode, automatic archiving is disabled, and all groups of online redo log files are filled but not archived, then LGWR cannot reuse any inactive groups of online redo log groups to continue writing redo log entries. Therefore, database operation is temporarily suspended until the necessary archiving is performed.

Automatic archiving can be disabled at or after instance startup.

Disabling Automatic Archiving at Instance Startup

To disable the automatic archiving of filled online redo log groups each time a database instance is started, set the LOG_ARCHIVE_START parameter of a database's parameter file to FALSE:

```
LOG_ARCHIVE_START=FALSE
```

The new value takes effect the next time the database is started.

Disabling Automatic Archiving after Instance Startup

To disable the automatic archiving of filled online redo log groups without shutting down the current instance, use either the Stop Auto Archive option of the Logs menu of SQL*DBA or the SQL command ALTER SYSTEM with the ARCHIVE LOG STOP parameter. The following statement is the command equivalent of selecting the Stop Auto Archive menu option:

```
ALTER SYSTEM ARCHIVE LOG STOP;
```

If ARCH is archiving a redo log group when you attempt to disable automatic archiving, ARCH finishes archiving the current group, but does not begin archiving the next filled online redo log group.

The instance does not have to be shut down to disable automatic archiving; however, if an instance is shut down and restarted after automatic archiving is disabled, the instance is reinitialized using the settings of the parameter file, which may or may not enable automatic archiving.

Privileges Required to Disable Automatic Archiving After Instance Startup To disable automatic archiving after instance startup, you must be connected as INTERNAL and have the ALTER SYSTEM privilege.

Performing Manual Archiving

If a database is operating in ARCHIVELOG mode, inactive groups of filled online redo log files must be archived. You can manually archive groups of the online redo log whether or not automatic archiving is enabled:

- If automatic archiving is not enabled, you must manually archive groups of filled online redo log files in a timely fashion. If all online redo log groups are filled but not archived, LGWR cannot reuse any inactive groups of online redo log members to continue writing redo log entries. Therefore, database operation is temporarily suspended until the necessary archiving is performed.
- If automatic archiving is enabled, but you want to rearchive an inactive group of filled online redo log members to another location, you can use manual archiving. (However, the instance can decide to reuse the redo log group before you have finished manually archiving, and thereby overwrite the files; if this happens, ORACLE will put an error message in the ALERT file.)

Manually archive inactive groups of filled online redo log members using the Begin Manual Archive dialog box of SQL*DBA or the SQL command ALTER SYSTEM with the ARCHIVE LOG clause. Figure 17-2 shows the Begin Manual Archive dialog box.

FIGURE 17-2
The Begin Manual Archive Dialog

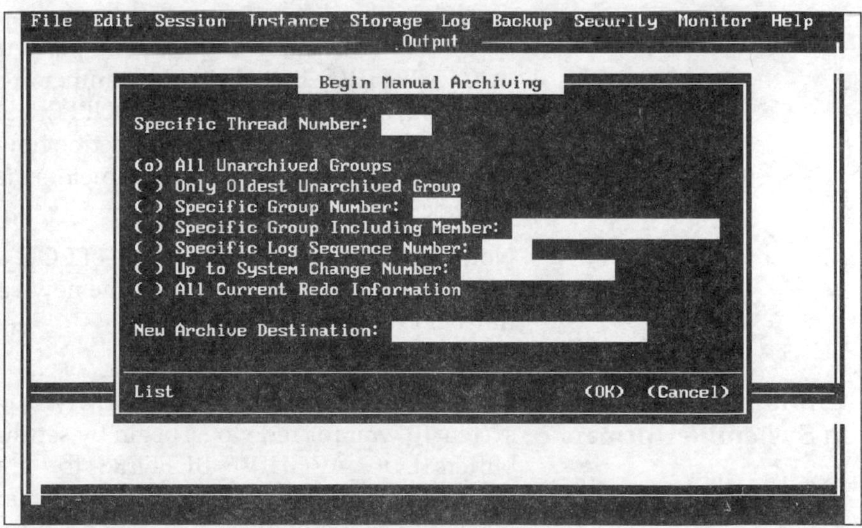

The following statement is the command equivalent of the Begin Manual Archive dialog box in Figure 17-2:

```
ALTER SYSTEM ARCHIVE LOG ALL;
```

With both manual or automatic archiving, you need to specify a thread only when you are using the ORACLE Parallel Server. See the *ORACLE7 Parallel Server Administrator's Guide* for more information.

Privileges Required to Manually Archive an Online Redo Log Group

To manually archive a filled online redo log group, you must be connected as INTERNAL. See "Connecting as INTERNAL" on page 1-4.

Tuning Archiving

For most databases, the archiver process has no effect on overall system performance. In some large database sites, however, archiving can have an impact on system performance. On one hand, if the archiver works very quickly, overall system performance can be reduced while the archiver runs, since CPU cycles are being consumed in archiving. On the other hand, if the archiver runs extremely slowly, it has little detrimental effect on system performance, but it takes longer to archive redo log files, and can be a bottleneck if all redo log groups are unavailable because they are waiting to be archived.

For these large database sites, you can tune archiving, to cause it to run either as slowly as possible without being a bottleneck, or as quickly as possible without reducing system performance substantially. To do so, adjust the values of the initialization parameters LOG_ARCHIVE_BUFFERS (the number of buffers allocated to archiving) and LOG_ARCHIVE_BUFFER_SIZE (the size of each such buffer). The following sections describe how to adjust these parameters for either kind of tuning. The parameters themselves are described in more detail in Appendix A.

Note: When you change the value of LOG_ARCHIVE_BUFFERS or LOG_ARCHIVE_BUFFER_SIZE, the new value takes effect the next time you start the instance.

Minimizing the Impact on System Performance

To cause the archiver to work as slowly as possible without forcing the system to wait for redo logs, begin by setting the number of archive buffers (LOG_ARCHIVE_BUFFERS) to 1 and the size of each buffer (LOG_ARCHIVE_BUFFER_SIZE) to the maximum possible. (This maximum is operating system dependent; see your installation or user's guide.) If the performance of the system drops significantly while the archiver is working, adjust LOG_ARCHIVE_BUFFER_SIZE lower, until system performance is no longer reduced when the archiver runs.

Note: If you want to set archiving to be very slow, but find that ORACLE frequently has to wait for redo log files to be archived before they can be reused, consider creating additional redo log file groups. Adding groups can ensure that a group is always available for ORACLE to use. See Chapter 5 for information.

Increasing Archiving Speed

To increase archiving performance (for example, if you want to stream input to a tape drive), use multiple archive buffers, so that the archiver process can read the archive log at the same time that it writes the output log. You can set LOG_ARCHIVE_BUFFERS to 2, but for a very fast tape drive you might want to set it to 3 or more. Then, set the size of the archive buffers to a moderate number, and increase it until archiving is as fast as you want it to be without impairing system performance.

Displaying Archiving Status Information

Query the V$DATABASE view to see the current archiving mode:

```
SELECT log_mode FROM sys.v$database;

LOG_MODE
------------
NOARCHIVELOG
```

The V$ARCHIVE and V$LOG data dictionary views also contain archiving information of a database. For example, the following query lists all log groups for the database and indicates the ones that remain to be archived:

```
SELECT group#, archived
   FROM sys.v$log;

GROUP#    ARC
---------- ---
         1 YES
         2 NO
```

The List Archive Status option of the Logs menu in SQL*DBA and the command ARCHIVE LOG with the LIST parameter also show archiving information for the connected instance. For example:

```
ARCHIVE LOG LIST;

Database log mode                          ARCHIVELOG
Automatic archival                         ENABLED
Archive destination                        destination
```

```
Oldest online log sequence              30
Next log sequence to archive            32
Current log sequence number             33
```

This display tells you all the necessary information regarding the redo log settings for the current instance:

- The database is currently operating in ARCHIVELOG mode.
- Automatic archiving is enabled.
- The destination of the archived redo log (operating system specific) is *destination* (corresponds to LOG_ARCHIVE_DEST or an overriding destination).
- The oldest filled online redo log group has a sequence number of 30.
- The next filled online redo log group to archive has a sequence number of 32.
- The current online redo log file has a sequence number of 33.

You must archive all redo log groups with a sequence number equal to or greater than the *Next log sequence to archive*, yet less than the *Current log sequence number*. For example, the display above indicates that the online redo log group with sequence number 32 needs to be archived.

Privileges Required to List Archive Status

To list archive status information, you must be connected as INTERNAL. See "Connecting as INTERNAL" on page 1-4.

Specifying the Archived Redo Log Filename Format and Destination

When the database is used in ARCHIVELOG mode, ORACLE must know the archived redo log filename format and destination so that automatic or manual archiving creates uniquely named archived redo log files in the proper location.

Archived redo log files are uniquely named as specified by the LOG_ARCHIVE_FORMAT parameter. Filename format is operating system specific; for most operating systems it consists of a text string, one or more parameters, and a filename extension. When a filled online redo log group is archived, the archiving process concatenates the supplied text string with the return values of the specified parameters to create uniquely identified archived redo log files. Each parameter has an upper bound, which is operating system dependent. Table 17-1 lists the parameters that can be included in a filename format and corresponding examples to show how the parameter affects the filenames created by the archiving process.

TABLE 17-1
Archived Redo Log Filename Format Parameters

Parameter	Description	Example *
%T	Thread number, left-zero-padded.	arch0000000001
%t	Thread number, not padded.	arch1
%S	Log sequence number, left-zero-padded.	arch0000000251
%s	Log sequence number, not padded.	arch251

* Assume LOG_ARCHIVE_FORMAT=arch%parameter, and the upper bound for all parameters is 10 characters.

The different options are provided so that you can customize the archived redo log filenames as you need. For example, you might want to take into account the operating system sorting algorithm used to list filenames.

Parallel

The %T and %t are useful only when the ORACLE Parallel Server is used; see the *ORACLE7 Parallel Server Administrator's Guide* for more information about these filename format parameters and the term "thread."

In a non-Parallel Server configuration, you must decide whether to use %S or %s to identify each archived redo log file uniquely. The following is a typical example of a common archived redo log filename format:

```
LOG_ARCHIVE_FORMAT = arch%S.arc
```

Here, *arch* is the filename, %S is the zero-padded log sequence parameter, and *.arc* is the file extension. Assuming the upper bound for the %S parameter is four, this filename format generates archived redo log filenames of the following format:

```
arch0001.arc
arch0002.arc
arch0003.arc
 .
 .
```

Take into account the maximum operating system filename length when specifying the archive filename format; if ARCH or a user process attempts to archive a file and the supplied filename format is too large, the process fails to archive the file.

Note: If no archived filename format is specified using LOG_-ARCHIVE_FORMAT, a default filename format is used by ORACLE. This default filename format is operating system specific.

The archived redo log destination is also operating system specific. For most operating systems, the archive redo log destination points to a disk drive and a file directory; if permitted by your ORACLE Server, this destination can also point to a tape drive dedicated to ORACLE for archiving filled online redo log files.

The archived redo log destination is determined at instance startup by the LOG_ARCHIVE_DEST initialization parameter, but can be overridden while the instance is up:

- If a database's parameter file is edited to include a destination using the LOG_ARCHIVE_DEST parameter, the current instance must be shut down and restarted to read the new parameter file.
- If the current instance cannot be shut down, but the archived redo log destination must be specified or changed for automatic archiving, use the Start Automatic Archiving dialog box of SQL*DBA or an ALTER SYSTEM ARCHIVE LOG START 'destination' statement to override the automatic archiving destination.
- During manual archiving, a specified destination overrides the default archived redo log destination. However, automatic archiving continues to use the current automatic archive destination. If no destination is specified, ORACLE automatically uses the destination specified by the LOG_ARCHIVE_DEST parameter of the parameter file used to start the instance. If no destination is supplied by the LOG_ARCHIVE_DEST parameter, a default destination is used. The default destination is operating system dependent.

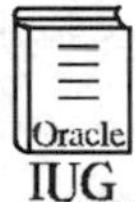

See your installation or user's guide for more information about the LOG_ARCHIVE_FORMAT and LOG_ARCHIVE_DEST initialization parameters, and the default archived redo log filename format and destination.

CHAPTER

18 BACKING UP A DATABASE

This chapter explains how to back up the data in an ORACLE database. Topics include:

- guidelines for backing up
- creating a backup strategy
- taking full and partial database backups
- taking a control file backup
- handling a failure during backup
- using the Export and Import utilities for backups

Guidelines for Database Backups

The following sections provide guidelines to consider in backing up an ORACLE database.

Plan Backup and Recovery Strategies Before Database Creation

Before you create an ORACLE database, you should decide how you plan to protect the database against potential disk failures, etc. If such planning is not considered before database creation, database recovery may not be possible if a disk failure damages the data files, online redo log files, or control files of a database. See "Creating a Backup Strategy" on page 18-4 if you are not familiar with typical backup strategies for a database.

Test Backup and Recovery Strategies

You should test your backup and recovery strategies in a test environment before and after you move to a production system. By testing your backup and recovery strategies, you can test the thoroughness of your strategies and minimize problems before they occur in a real situation. Performing test recoveries on a regular basis ensures that your archiving and backup procedures work. It also helps you stay familiar with recovery procedures, so that you are less likely to make a mistake in a crisis.

Perform Operating System Backups Frequently and Regularly

Frequent and regular full or partial database backups are essential for any recovery scheme. The frequency of backups should be based on the number of changes to database data (such as insertions, updates, and deletions of rows in existing tables, and addition of new tables) that are performed. If a database's data is changed at a high rate, database backup frequency should be proportionally high. Alternatively, if a database is mainly read-only and few updates are issued, the database can be backed up less frequently.

Appropriately Backup the Database Before and After Modifying the Database Structure

If you make any of the following structural changes, perform an appropriate backup of your database immediately before and after completing the alteration:

- Create or drop a tablespace.
- Add or rename (relocate) a data file in an existing tablespace.
- Add, rename (relocate), or drop an online redo log group or member.

The appropriate type of backup depends on the archiving mode of the database, as described below:

- If a database is operated in ARCHIVELOG mode, only a control file backup (using the ALTER DATABASE command with the BACKUP CONTROLFILE option) is required before and after a structural alteration. (You can backup other parts of the database as well, though.)
- If the database is operated in NOARCHIVELOG mode, a full database backup should be taken immediately before and after the modification, including all data files, redo log files, and control files.

Back Up Often-Used Tablespaces Frequently

If a database is operated in ARCHIVELOG mode, it is acceptable to back up the data files of an individual tablespace or even a single data file. This option is useful if a portion of a database is used more extensively than others, such as the SYSTEM tablespace and tablespaces that contain rollback segments. By taking more frequent backups of the extensively used data files of a database, you gather more recent copies of the data files. As a result, if a disk failure damages the extensively used data files, the more recent backup can restore the damaged files and only a small number of changes to data need to be applied to roll the restored file forward to the time of the failure, thereby reducing database recovery time.

Keep Older Backups

How long you should keep an older database backup depends on the choices you want for database recovery. If you might want to recover to a past point-in-time, you need a database backup taken before that point-in-time. For a database operating in NOARCHIVELOG mode, this means a full database backup; for a database operating in ARCHIVELOG mode, this means a backup of each data file, taken individually or together, taken any time before the desired recovery point-in-time, and a backup of the associated control file that reflects the database's structure at the point-in-time of recovery.

For added protection, consider keeping two or more backups previous to the current backup, in case part of the current backup is lost or damaged.

Export Database Data for Added Protection and Flexibility

Because the ORACLE Export utility can selectively export specific objects, you might consider exporting portions or all of a database for supplemental protection and flexibility in a database's backup strategy. However, database exports are not a substitute for operating system backups and cannot provide the same complete recovery advantages that the built-in functionality of ORACLE offers.

Consider Distributed Database Backups

If a database is a node in a distributed database, consider the following guidelines:

- All databases in the distributed database system should be operated in the same archiving mode.
- If the databases in a distributed database system are operating in ARCHIVELOG mode, backups at each node can be performed autonomously (individually, without time coordination).
- If the databases in a distributed database system are operating in NOARCHIVELOG mode, full backups must be performed at the same (global) time, to plan for global distributed database recovery. For example, if a database in New York is backed up at midnight EST, the database in San Francisco should be backed up at 9PM PST. For more information about distributed database recovery when databases are operating in NOARCHIVELOG mode, see "Coordinate Distributed Recovery" on page 19-3.

Creating a Backup Strategy

Before you create an ORACLE database, decide how you plan to protect the database against potential failures. The two primary questions to ask before developing a backup strategy are as follows:

- **Is it acceptable to lose any data if a disk failure damages some of the files that constitute a database?** If it is not acceptable to lose any data in the event of a problem, the database must be operated in ARCHIVELOG mode, ideally with a mirrored online redo log. If it is acceptable to lose a limited amount of data in the event of a disk failure, you can operate the database in NOARCHIVELOG mode and avoid the extra work required to archive filled online redo log files.
- **Does the database need to be available at all times (that is, twenty-four hours per day, seven days per week)?** If so, it is not feasible to operate the database in NOARCHIVELOG mode because the required full database backups (taken while the database is shutdown) cannot be made frequently, if at all. Therefore, high-availability databases always operate in ARCHIVELOG mode to take advantage of online data file backups.

The following sections explain some common backup strategies based on the archiving mode of the database.

Backup Strategies in NOARCHIVELOG Mode

If a database is operated in NOARCHIVELOG mode, filled groups of online redo log files are not being archived. Therefore, the only protection against a disk failure is the most recent full backup of the database. The following list describes when to perform full backups for a database operated in NOARCHIVELOG mode:

- Plan to take full backups regularly, according to the amount of work that you can afford to lose. For example, if you can afford to lose the amount of work accomplished in one week, make a full backup once per week; if you can afford to lose only a day's work, make a full backup every day. For large databases with a high amount of activity, it is usually not acceptable to lose any work. Therefore, the database should be operated in ARCHIVELOG mode, and the appropriate backup strategies should be used.
- Any time that you alter the physical structure of a database operating in NOARCHIVELOG mode, immediately take a full database backup. An immediate full backup protects the new structure of the database not reflected in the previous full backup.

Backup Strategies in ARCHIVELOG Mode

If a database is operating in ARCHIVELOG mode, filled groups of online redo log files are being archived. Therefore, the archived redo log coupled with the online redo log and data file backups can protect the database from a disk failure, providing for complete recovery from a disk failure to the instant that the failure occurred. The following list describes a common backup strategy for a database operating in ARCHIVELOG mode:

- When the database is initially created, perform a full backup of the entire database. This initial full backup is the foundation of your backups because it provides copies of all data files and the control file of the associated database.

Note: When you perform this initial full backup, make sure that the database is in ARCHIVELOG mode first. Otherwise, the backed up database files will contain the NOARCHIVELOG mode setting.

- Subsequent full backups are not required, and if a database must remain open at all times, full backups are not feasible. Instead, you can take partial backups to update the backups of a database.
- Take online or offline data file backups to update backed up information for the database (supplementing the full, initial

backup). In particular, the data files of extensively used tablespaces should be backed up frequently to reduce database recovery time, should recovery ever be required. If a more recent data file backup is used to restore a damaged data file, fewer archived redo logs need to be applied to the restored data file to roll it forward to the time of the failure.

Whether you should take online or offline data file backups depends on the availability requirements of the data—online data file backups are the only choice if the data being backed up must always be available.

- Every time you make a structural change to the database, take a control file backup, using the ALTER DATABASE command with the BACKUP CONTROLFILE option.

Note: If the control file does not contain the name of a data file and you have no backup of that data file, you cannot recover the file if it is lost. Also, do **not** use operating system utilities to backup the control file in ARCHIVELOG mode, unless you are performing a full, offline backup.

- Usually online redo log files never need to be backed up when a database is operated in ARCHIVELOG mode; they are already archived. (However, you should backup online redo log files if you make a full, offline backup of the database.) A mirrored online redo log further safeguards against a single point of failure with respect to the online redo log.

Taking Backups

The following sections cover the procedures necessary to complete full and partial backups.

Listing Database Files Before Backup

Before taking a full or partial database backup, identify the files for backup. Obtain a list of data files for the database by querying the V$DATAFILE view:

```
SELECT name FROM sys.v$datafile;
```

Obtain a list of online redo log files for a database using the query below:

```
SELECT name FROM sys.v$logfile;
```

These queries list the data files and online redo log files of a database, respectively, according to the information in the current control file of the database.

Obtain the names of the current control files of the database by issuing the following statement within SQL*DBA:

```
SHOW PARAMETER control_files;
```

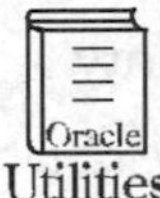

Utilities

Note: For more information about the SHOW command of SQL*DBA, see the *ORACLE7 Server Utilities User's Guide.*

Whenever you take a control file backup, store the full list of data files and online redo log files with the corresponding control file backup; this way, the database's physical structure at the time the control file is backed up is clear and on record.

Performing Full Backups

Take a full backup of all files that constitute a database after the database is shut down to system-wide use in normal priority. **A full backup cannot be taken if the database is open or has been shut down because of an instance failure or abort**; in such cases, a backup is not a full backup because the files are not consistent with respect to the current point-in-time. (The files that constitute the database are the data files, online redo log files, and control file.)

Full backups do not require the database be operated in a specific archiving mode; a full backup can be taken if a database is operating in either ARCHIVELOG or NOARCHIVELOG mode.

The set of backup files that result from a full backup are consistent; all files correspond to the same point in time. If database recovery is necessary, these files can completely restore the database to an exact point in time. After restoring the backup files, additional recovery steps may be possible to restore the database to a more current time if the database is operated in ARCHIVELOG mode and online redo logs are **not** restored.

Note: A backup control file created during a full database backup should only be used with the other files taken in that backup, to restore the full backup. It should not be used for complete or incomplete database recovery. Unless you are taking a full database backup, you should back up your control file using the ALTER DATABASE command with the BACKUP CONTROLFILE option; see "Control File Backups" on page 18-15 for the steps involved.

Preparing to Take a Full Backup

To guarantee that a database's data files are consistent, always shut down the database in **normal** priority before making a full database backup; never perform a full database backup after an instance failure or after the database is shut down with immediate or abort priority (that is, using a SHUTDOWN IMMEDIATE or SHUTDOWN ABORT statement). In both these cases, the data files are likely not to be consistent with respect to a specific point-in-time.

Steps for a Full Backup

To make a full backup, perform the following steps:

1. Shut down the database with normal priority.

   To make a full backup, all files used by the database must be closed by shutting down the database. Do not make a full backup when the instance is aborted or stopped because of a failure; reopen the database and shut it down cleanly before making a full backup.

   See Chapter 3 for more information about database shutdown.

2. Back up all files that constitute the database.

   Use operating system commands or a backup utility to make backups of all data files, online redo log files, and a single control file of the database. If you are mirroring the online redo log, back up all members of each group, since it is not guaranteed that any one member of a group is complete. Also back up the parameter files associated with the database.

   Operating system backups can be performed:

   - within SQL*DBA, using the HOST dialog box or HOST command
   - outside of SQL*DBA, with the operating system commands or a backup utility

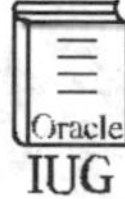

IUG

   See your installation or user's guide for more information about making operating system backups of files.

3. Restart the database.

   Once you have finished backing up all data files, online redo log files, and a single control file of the database, you can restart the database. (See Chapter 3 for more information about database startup.)

Performing Partial Backups

The following sections explain the procedures necessary to complete the different types of partial backups:

- online tablespace and data file backups
- offline tablespace and data file backups

Partial backups should only be taken (and in some cases **can** only be taken) if a database is operating in ARCHIVELOG mode; partial backups cannot be used to restore a database operating in NOARCHIVELOG mode.

Utilities

SQL

Note: For complete information about the dialog boxes of SQL*DBA and SQL commands ALTER TABLESPACE and ALTER DATABASE used in the following sections, see the *ORACLE7 Server Utilities User's Guide* and the *ORACLE7 Server SQL Language Reference Manual*, respectively.

Online Tablespace and Online Data File Backups

All data files of an individual online tablespace or specific data files of an online tablespace can be backed up while the tablespace and data files are currently online and in use for normal database operation. To perform an online backup of an entire tablespace, or a specific data file of an online tablespace, use the following steps:

1. Identify the data files.

   If you are backing up a specific data file, use the fully specified filename of the data file.

   Before beginning a backup on an entire tablespace, identify all of the tablespace's data files using the DBA_DATA_FILES data dictionary view. For example, assume that the USERS tablespace is to be backed up. To identify the USERS tablespace's data file, you can query the DBA_DATA_FILES view:

```
SELECT tablespace_name, file_name
       FROM sys.dba_data_files
       WHERE tablespace_name = 'USERS';

TABLESPACE_NAME        FILE_NAME
---------------        ---------
USERS                  filename1
USERS                  filename2
```

   Here, *filename1* and *filename2* are fully specified filenames corresponding to the data files of the USERS tablespace. See Appendix B for more information about the DBA_DATA_FILES data dictionary view.

2. Mark the beginning of the online tablespace backup.

   To prepare the data files of an online tablespace for backup, use either the Begin Online Tablespace Backup dialog box of SQL*DBA or the SQL command ALTER TABLESPACE with the BEGIN BACKUP option. Figure 18-1 shows the Begin Online Tablespace Backup dialog.

FIGURE 18-1
The Begin Online Tablespace Backup Dialog

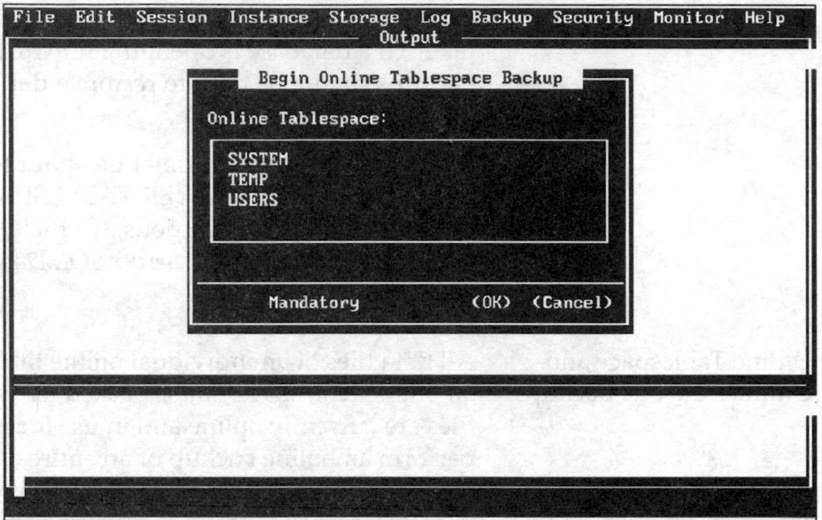

The following statement is the command equivalent of the Begin Online Tablespace Backup dialog in Figure 18-1:

```
ALTER TABLESPACE users BEGIN BACKUP;
```

Note: If you forget to mark the beginning of an online tablespace backup (using either method) before backing up an online tablespace, the backup data files are not useful for subsequent recovery operations. Attempting to recover such a backup might return no errors, but can result in inconsistent data at a later date.

3. Back up the online data files.

   At this point, you can back up the online data files of the online tablespace:

   - from within SQL*DBA, using the HOST command
   - by exiting SQL*DBA and entering the operating system commands or starting the backup utility

   See the *ORACLE7 Server Utilities User's Guide* for information on see your installation or user's guide for more information about making operating system backups of files.

4. Mark the end of the online tablespace backup.

   After the data files of the online tablespace have been backed up, indicate the end of the online backup using either the End Online Tablespace Backup dialog box of SQL*DBA or the SQL command ALTER TABLESPACE with the END BACKUP option. Figure 18-2 shows the End Online Tablespace Backup dialog box.

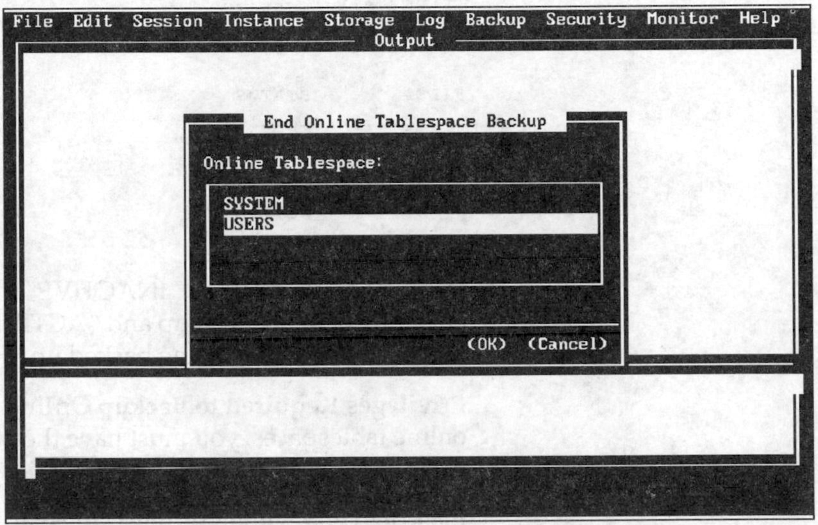

FIGURE 18-2
The End Online Tablespace Backup Dialog Box

The following statement is the command equivalent of the End Online Tablespace Backup dialog box in Figure 18-2:

```
ALTER TABLESPACE users END BACKUP;
```

Note: If you forget to indicate the end of an online tablespace backup and the database is subsequently shut down, ORACLE assumes that media recovery is necessary at the next instance start up. Recovery may require the use of the archived redo log.

Determining Data File Backup Status To see the backup status of a data file (whether it has been backed up), you can often use the data dictionary table V$BACKUP. This table lists all online files and gives their backup status. It is most useful when the database is open; it is also useful immediately after a crash, since it shows the backup status of the files at the time of the crash. You can use this information to determine whether you have left any tablespaces in backup.

Note: V$BACKUP is not useful if the control file currently in use is a restored backup or a new control file created since the media failure occurred; a restored or re-created control file does not contain the information ORACLE needs to fill V$BACKUP accurately. Also, if you have restored a backup of a file, that file's STATUS in V$BACKUP reflects the backup status of the older version of the file, not the most current version's. Thus, this view might contain misleading information on restored files.

For example, the following query displays the current backup status of data files:

```
SELECT file#, status
  FROM v$backup;

FILE#        STATUS
---------------------
   0011      INACTIVE
   0012      INACTIVE
   0013      ACTIVE
  ...
```

In the STATUS column, "INACTIVE" indicates that the file is not currently being backed up and "ACTIVE" indicates that the file is marked as currently being backed up.

Privileges Required to Backup Online Tablespaces To back up online tablespaces, you must have the MANAGE TABLESPACE system privilege.

Backing Up Several Online Tablespaces If you have to back up several online tablespaces, use either of the following procedures:

- Back up the online tablespaces in parallel. For example, prepare all online tablespaces for backup:

  ```
  ALTER TABLESPACE ts1 BEGIN BACKUP;
  ALTER TABLESPACE ts2 BEGIN BACKUP;
  ALTER TABLESPACE ts3 BEGIN BACKUP;
  ```

  Next, back up all files of the online tablespaces and indicate that the online backups have been completed:

  ```
  ALTER TABLESPACE ts1 END BACKUP;
  ALTER TABLESPACE ts2 END BACKUP;
  ALTER TABLESPACE ts3 END BACKUP;
  ```

- Back up the online tablespaces serially. For example, individually prepare, back up, and end the backup of each online tablespace:

```
ALTER TABLESPACE ts1 BEGIN BACKUP;
backup files
ALTER TABLESPACE ts1 END BACKUP;
ALTER TABLESPACE ts2 BEGIN BACKUP;
backup files
ALTER TABLESPACE ts2 END BACKUP;
```

The second option minimizes the time between ALTER TABLESPACE ... BEGIN/END BACKUP commands and is preferred:

- During online backups, more redo information is generated for the tablespace.
- If the instance crashes during online backup and the online log file that was written at BEGIN BACKUP time is reused, then archived redo log files are required for recovery.

Therefore, Oracle Corporation recommends that you back up online tablespaces serially.

Problems that Interrupt Online Tablespace Backups If a system or instance failure interrupts the backup of an online tablespace (after the ALTER TABLESPACE . . . BEGIN BACKUP command is issued, but before the ALTER TABLESPACE . . . END BACKUP command is issued), the database must be recovered using complete media recovery. See "Complete Media Recovery" on page 19-17 for more information.

Offline Tablespace and Offline Data File Backups

All or some of the data files of an individual tablespace can be backed up while the tablespace is offline. All other tablespaces of the database can remain open and available for system-wide use.

Note: You cannot take the SYSTEM tablespace or any tablespace with active rollback segments offline. Therefore, the following procedure cannot be used for such tablespaces.

To perform a backup of the offline data files of an offline tablespace, use the following steps:

1. Identify the data files of the offline tablespace.

   Use the fully specified filename of the data file.

   Before taking the tablespace offline, identify the names of its data files by querying the data dictionary view DBA_DATA_FILES. (See Step 1 of the previous section on page 18-9.)

2. Take the tablespace offline, using normal priority if possible.

If possible, use normal priority (not temporary or immediate) to guarantee that the tablespace can be subsequently brought online without the requirement for tablespace recovery.

To take a tablespace (and all associated data files) offline with normal priority, use the Set Tablespace Offline dialog box of SQL*DBA or the SQL command ALTER TABLESPACE with the OFFLINE parameter. For example, the following statement takes a tablespace named USERS offline normally:

```
ALTER TABLESPACE users OFFLINE NORMAL;
```

After a tablespace is taken offline with normal priority, all data files of the tablespace are closed. See page 7-9 for more information about online and offline tablespaces.

3. Back up the offline data files.

   At this point, you can back up the data files of the offline tablespace:

   - from within SQL*DBA, using the HOST command
   - by exiting SQL*DBA and entering the operating system commands or starting the backup utility

   See your installation or user's guide for more information about making operating system backups of files.

4. Bring the tablespace online. *(Optional)*

   Bring the tablespace back online using either the Set Tablespace Online dialog box of SQL*DBA or the SQL command ALTER TABLESPACE with the ONLINE option. For example, the following statement brings an offline tablespace named USERS online:

```
ALTER TABLESPACE users ONLINE;
```

   Note: If the tablespace was taken offline using temporary or immediate priority, the tablespace may not be able to be brought online unless tablespace recovery is performed. See Chapter 19 for more information about tablespace recovery.

   After a tablespace is brought online, the data files of the tablespace are open and available for use.

Privileges Required to Backup Offline Tablespaces To take tablespaces offline and online, you must have the MANAGE TABLESPACE system privilege.

Control File Backups

Back up the control file of a database after making a structural modification to a database operating in ARCHIVELOG mode.

You can take a backup of a database's control file with the SQL command ALTER DATABASE with the BACKUP CONTROLFILE parameter. For example, the following statement backs up a database's control file:

```
ALTER DATABASE BACKUP CONTROLFILE TO 'filename' REUSE;
```

Here, *filename* is a fully specified filename that indicates the name of the new control file backup.

The REUSE option allows you to have the new control file overwrite a control file that currently exists. You cannot specify this option if you specify any of the following other options in the ALTER DATABASE BACKUP CONTROLFILE command:

- MAXLOGFILES
- MAXDATAFILES
- MAXINSTANCES
- MAXLOGMEMBERS
- MAXLOGHISTORY

Backing Up the Control File to the Trace File

The ALTER DATABASE BACKUP CONTROLFILE command has an option, TRACE, that can help you mange your control file and recover using it. This option causes ORACLE to write SQL commands to the database's trace file, rather than making a physical backup of the control file. These commands start up the database, re-create the control file, and recover and open the database appropriately, based on the current control file; each command is commented. Thus, you can copy the commands from the trace file into a script file, edit them as necessary, and use the script to recover the database if all copies of the control file are lost.

For example, assume the SALES database has three enabled threads, of which thread 2 is public and thread 3 is private; it also has multiplexed redo log files, and one offline and one online tablespace. The command could be used as follows:

```
ALTER DATABASE
  BACKUP CONTROLFILE TO TRACE NORESETLOGS;

3-JUN-1992 17:54:47.27:
# The following commands will create a new control file and use it
# to open the database.
# No data other than log history will be lost. Additional logs may
# be required for media recovery of offline data files. Use this
```

```
# only if the current version of all online logs are available.
STARTUP NOMOUNT
CREATE CONTROLFILE REUSE DATABASE SALES NORESETLOGS ARCHIVELOG
    MAXLOGFILES 32
    MAXLOGMEMBERS 2
    MAXDATAFILES 32
    MAXINSTANCES 16
    MAXLOGHISTORY 1600
LOGFILE
  GROUP 1 'DISK$A:[PROD.SALES.DB]LOG1T1.ORA'  SIZE 100K,
  GROUP 2 (
    'DISK$A:[PROD.SALES.DB]LOG2T1.ORA',
    'DISK$A:[PROD.SALES.DB]G2.ORA'
  ) SIZE 100K,
  GROUP 3 'DISK$A:[PROD.SALES.DB]LOG1T2.ORA'  SIZE 100K,
  GROUP 4 'DISK$A:[PROD.SALES.DB]LOG2T2.ORA'  SIZE 100K,
  GROUP 5 (
    'DISK$A:[PROD.SALES.DB]LOG1T3.ORA',
    'DISK$A:[PROD.SALES.DB]G5.ORA'
  ) SIZE 100K
  GROUP 6 'DISK$A:[PROD.SALES.DB]LOG2T3.ORA'  SIZE 100K
DATAFILE
  'DISK$A:[PROD.SALES.DB]DATABASE1.ORA' SIZE 2M,
  'DISK$A:[PROD.SALES.DB]FILEA.ORA' SIZE 200K
;
# Take files offline to match current control file.
ALTER DATABASE DATAFILE 'DISK$A:[PROD.SALES.DB]FILEA.ORA' OFFLINE;

# Recovery is required if any data files are restored backups,
# or if the last shutdown was not normal or immediate.
RECOVER DATABASE;

# All logs need archiving and a log switch is needed.
ALTER SYSTEM ARCHIVE LOG ALL;

# Database can now be opened normally.
ALTER DATABASE OPEN;

#  Files in normal offline tablespaces are now named.
ALTER DATABASE RENAME FILE 'MISSING0002'
  TO 'DISK$A:[PROD.SALES.DB]FILEB.ORA';
```

Using the command without NORESETLOGS produces the same output. Using the command with RESETLOGS produces a similar script that includes commands that recover the database and open the database, but that resets the redo logs on startup.

Privileges Required to Backup Control Files

To backup a database's control file, you must have the ALTER DATABASE system privilege.

Recovering From a Failure During a Backup

If you crash during an online backup, you must recover the database when you next start it. (You do not need to issue an END BACKUP command once you have restarted the database.)

For this recovery, you do not need to restore previous backups of the data files. You might need archived redo logs.

You can determine whether files were in the process of being backed up by querying the table V$BACKUP. See "Determining Data File Backup Status" on page 18-11.

Perform the recovery in either of two ways:

- Use the SQL*DBA Start Up Instance dialog with the Recover option, or the command STARTUP RECOVER to start and recover the database automatically.
- Start an instance, open and mount the database, and issue the statement RECOVER DATABASE,.

The first method is easier, because it causes ORACLE to perform recovery only if it is needed.

For information on starting the database, see Chapter 3. For information on recovering a database, see Chapter 19.

Using the Export and Import Utilities for Supplemental Database Protection

Export and Import are utilities that move ORACLE data in and out of ORACLE databases. Export writes data from an ORACLE database to an operating system file in a special format. Import reads Export files and restores the corresponding information into an existing database. Although Export and Import are designed for moving ORACLE data, you can also use them to supplement backups of data.

Utilities

Note: Both the Export and Import utilities are discussed in more detail in the *ORACLE7 Server Utilities User's Guide*.

Using Export

Export allows you to backup your database while it is open and available for use. It writes a read-consistent view of the database's objects to an operating system file.

Note: If you use Export for backup, all data must be exported in a logically consistent way so that the backup reflects a single point in time. No one should make changes to the database while the export takes place. Ideally, you should run the database in restricted mode while you export the data, so no regular users can access the data.

There are three Export modes:

User	exports all objects owned by a user
Table	exports all or specific tables owned by a user
Full Database	exports all objects of the database

This section discusses only the full database mode of operation.

There are also three types of exports:

- Incremental
- Cumulative
- Complete

Incremental Export

Only database data that has changed since the last incremental export is exported.

For example, if tables A, B, and C exist, and only table A's information has been modified since the last incremental export, only the changes to table A are exported.

Cumulative Exports

Only database data that has been changed since the last cumulative export is exported. Perform this type of export on a limited basis, such as once a week, to condense the information contained in numerous incremental exports.

For example, if tables A, B, and C exist, and only table A's and table B's information has been modified since the last cumulative export, only the changes to tables A and B are exported.

Complete Exports

All database data is exported. Perform this type of export on a limited basis, such as once a month, to export all data contained in a database.

Using Import

The Import utility allows you to restore the database information held in previously created Export files. It is the complement utility to Export.

To recover a database using Export files and the Import utility, the following operations are required:

1. Re-create the database structure, including the following items:

- all tablespaces
- all users

Note: These recreated structures should not have any objects in them.

2. Import the appropriate Export files to restore the database to the most current state possible. Depending on how your Export schedule is performed, imports of varying degrees will be necessary to restore a database.

For example, assume that the schedule illustrated in Figure 18-3 is used in exporting data from an ORACLE database.

FIGURE 18-3
A Typical Export Schedule

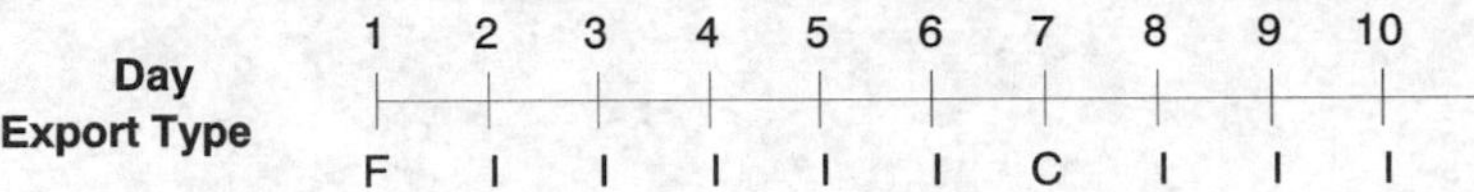

I = Incremental
C = Cumulative
F = Full (Complete)

A complete export was taken on Day 1, a cumulative export was taken every week, and incremental exports were taken daily.

To recover from a disk failure that occurs on Day 10, before the next incremental export is taken on Day 11, perform the following steps:

1. Recreate the database, including all tablespaces and users.
2. Import the complete database export taken on Day 1.
3. Import the cumulative database export taken on Day 7.
4. Import the incremental database exports taken on Days 8, 9, and 10.

CHAPTER

19 Recovering a Database

This chapter explains how to perform database media recovery. Topics include:

- guidelines for media recovery
- recovering from media failure
  - restoring a full backup
  - complete media recovery
  - incomplete media recovery
- examples of media recovery

Guidelines and Prerequisites for Recovering from a Media Failure

The following sections provide some guidelines and prerequisites to consider before recovering a damaged database from a media failure.

Test Backup and Recovery Strategies

You should test your backup and recovery strategies in a test environment before you move to a production system, and continue to test your system regularly. By testing your backup and recovery strategies, you can test the thoroughness of your strategies and minimize problems before they occur in a real situation. Performing test recoveries on a regular basis ensures that your archiving and backup procedures work. It also helps you stay familiar with recovery procedures, so that you are less likely to make a mistake in a crisis.

Decide What Type of Recovery Operation Is Appropriate

Answer the following three questions after media failure damages a database:

1. What recovery operations are available?

   The answer to this first question is determined by whether your database is archiving redo logs:

   - If the database is operated in NOARCHIVELOG mode, usually the only option for recovery from the media failure is to restore the most recent full backup and re-enter all work performed since the backup. (If you have used Export to supplement regular backups, you can instead use Import to restore data.) Some special losses can be repaired more easily.
   - If the database is operated in ARCHIVELOG mode, several recovery operations are available for reconstructing the damaged database.

2. What recovery operations are appropriate for this particular problem?

   If the database is in ARCHIVELOG mode, several recovery operations are available to reconstruct a damaged database to a transaction consistent state prior to the time of the media failure or user error. See "Examples of Media Failures and Appropriate Recovery Procedures" on page 19-27 for a detailed list of the different types of problems that media failures can cause and the appropriate methods of recovery from each type of problem.

3. Is the damaged database part of a distributed database?

   If so, database recovery may need to be coordinated among the nodes of the distributed database. See "Coordinate Distributed Recovery" below for more information.

Correct or Avoid a Disk Problem

The goal of database recovery is to reopen a database for normal operation as soon as possible. If a media failure has occurred because of a hardware problem, the problem should be repaired as soon as possible; however, database recovery is not dependent on the resolution of a long-lasting hardware problem that caused a media failure. Files stored on the damaged device can be restored to other storage devices and the file relocation can be accounted for using the procedures in the following sections:

Type of File	Section Name	Page #
Data File	Renaming and Relocating Data Files for Tablespaces	7-13
Online Redo Log File	Renaming and Relocating Online Redo Log Members	5-7
Control File	Creating Additional Copies of the Control File and Renaming or Relocating Control Files	6-4

Coordinate Distributed Recovery

The ORACLE distributed database architecture is autonomous in nature. Therefore, depending on the type of recovery operation selected for any single damaged database, recovery operations may or may not have to be coordinated globally among all databases in the distributed database system. Table 19-1 summarizes the different types of recovery operations and whether or not coordination among nodes of a distributed database system is required.

TABLE 19-1
Database Recovery in a Distributed Database System

Type of Recovery Operation	Implication for Distributed Database System
Restoring a full backup for a database that was never accessed (updated or queried) from a remote node	Use non-coordinated, autonomous database recovery.
Restoring a full backup for a database that was accessed by a remote node	Shut down all databases and restore them using the same, coordinated full backup.
Complete media recovery of one or more databases in a distributed database	Use non-coordinated, autonomous database recovery.
Incomplete media recovery of a database that was never accessed by a remote node	Use non-coordinated, autonomous database recovery.
Incomplete media recovery of a database that was accessed from a remote node	Use coordinated incomplete media recovery to the same global point-in-time for all databases in the distributed database.

Coordinate Time-Based and Change-Based Distributed Database Recovery

In special circumstances, one node in a distributed database may require recovery to a point-in-time in the past. To preserve global data consistency, it is often necessary that all other nodes in the system also be recovered to the same point-in-time. This is called "coordinated time-based distributed database recovery."

The procedures for autonomous time-based and change-based recovery are given in the following sections of this chapter. However, coordinated time-based distributed database recovery requires some extra steps to correct for the variance in time usually observed among different computers. Therefore, in conjunction with the normal procedures of time-based and change-based recovery, use the following steps to coordinate distributed time-based recovery among many nodes in a distribute database system:

1. Recover the database that is requiring the recovery operation using time-based recovery. For example, if a database needs to be recovered because of a user error (such as an accidental table drop), recover this database first using time-based recovery. Do not recover the other databases yet.

2. After you have recovered the database and opened it using RESETLOGS, look in the ALERT file of the database for the RESETLOGS message.

   If the message says, "RESETLOGS after complete recovery through change nnnnnnnn," you have applied all the changes in the database and actually performed a complete recovery. Do not recover any of the other databases in the distributed system, or you will unnecessarily remove changes in them. **Recovery is finished.**

   If the reset message says, "RESETLOGS after incomplete recovery UNTIL CHANGE nnnnnnnn," you have successfully performed an incomplete recovery. Record the change number from the message and proceed to the next step.

3. Recover all other databases in the distributed database system using change-based recovery, specifying the change number (SCN) from Step 2.

Recover Databases with Snapshots

If a master database is independently recovered to a past point-in-time (that is, coordinated time-based distributed database recovery is not performed), any dependent remote snapshot that refreshed in the interval of lost time will be inconsistent with its master table. In this case, the administrator of the master database should instruct the remote administrators to perform a complete refresh of any inconsistent snapshot.

Performing Media Recovery

The following sections explain the steps necessary to recover from media failures by restoring a full backup, or by using complete or incomplete media recovery operations.

The following sections explain media recovery operations without regard to the media failure itself or the types of files that were damaged by the media failure. Therefore, the following sections should not be used alone to understand the procedures necessary to recover from a media failure; "Examples of Media Failures and Appropriate Recovery Procedures" on page 19-27 provides the appropriate methods of recovery from each type of problem.

Issues Common to All Media Recovery Operations

The following sections discuss topics common to all complete and incomplete media recovery operations (but not restoring a full backup). These topics should be understood before proceeding to the next sections.

Using Messages that Indicate Media Failures

Error messages like those that follow indicate the need for media recovery:

ORA-00204	"error in reading control file '*name*' (block *num*, # blocks *num*)"
ORA-01113	"file *name* needs recovery"
ORA-01168	"file *name*: bad physical block size of *num* bytes expecting *num*"
ORA-01178	"file *name* created before last CREATE CONTROLFILE, cannot recreate"

Message

See the *ORACLE7 Server Messages and Codes Manual* for more information about these and other messages returned by ORACLE.

Determining Whether a File Needs Recovery

To determine which files need recovery, you can often use the table V$RECOVER_FILE. This table lists all files that need recovery, along with information on why they need recovery.

Note: V$RECOVER_FILE is most useful when the database is closed, because when the database is open the table contains information about offline files only. The table is not useful if the control file currently in use is a restored backup or a new control file created since the media failure occurred; a restored or re-created control file does not contain the information ORACLE needs to fill V$RECOVER_FILE accurately.

For example, the following query displays the file ID numbers of data files that require recovery:

```
SELECT file#, online, error
  FROM v$recover_file;

FILE#        ONLINE     ERROR
-----------------------------------------------------
   0014      ONLINE
   0018      ONLINE     FILE NOT FOUND
   0032      OFFLINE    OFFLINE NORMAL
  ...
```

To find the name of a file based on its file number, use the data dictionary view V$DATA_FILE, which contains the file's NAME as well as FILE#.

Deciding Which Recovery Action to Perform

Table 19-2 indicates what to do to recover from the loss of files due to a single media failure. The procedures indicated are detailed in the following sections.

TABLE 19-2
Recovering from the Loss of Files

Types of Damaged Files				Archiving Mode	
Data File	**Online Redo Log File**	**Archived Redo Log File**	**Control File**	**ARCHIVELOG Mode**	**NOARCHIVELOG Mode**
✔				Use complete media recovery (page 19-17).	Restore a full backup (page 19-16).
	✔			Recover the missing files (page 19-29).	Recover the missing files (page 19-29).
		✔		Take a new backup of all data files (page 19-34).	(does not apply)
			✔	Recover the missing files (page 19-34).	Recover the missing files (page 19-34).
✔	✔	✔	✔	Recover the control files, also recovering other files (page 19-34).	(does not apply)
✔	✔	✔		Use incomplete media recovery (page 19-29).	(does not apply)
✔		✔	✔	Recover the control files, also recovering data files (page 19-34).	(does not apply)
✔	✔		✔	Recover the control files, also recovering other files (page 19-34).	Restore a full backup (page 19-16).
✔	✔			Use incomplete media recovery (page 19-29).	Restore a full backup (page 19-16).
✔		✔		Use incomplete media recovery (page 19-34).	(does not apply)
✔			✔	Recover the control files, also recovering data files (page 19-34).	Restore a full backup (page 19-16).
	✔	✔	✔	Recover the control files, resetting the redo log (page 19-34).	(does not apply)
	✔	✔		Use incomplete media recovery (page 19-29).	(does not apply)
	✔		✔	Recover the control files, resetting the redo log (page 19-34).	If the database was shut down normally, re-create the control file (page 19-34). Otherwise, restore a full backup (page 19-16).
		✔	✔	Recover the control files, using incomplete media recovery (page 19-34).	(does not apply)

Restoring Damaged Data Files

If a media failure permanently damages one or more data files of a database, you must restore backups of the damaged data files before you can recover the damaged files.

Relocating Damaged Files If a damaged data file cannot be restored to its original location (for example, a disk must be replaced, so the files are restored to an alternate disk), the new locations of these files must be indicated to the control file of the associated database. Therefore, use the procedure given in "Renaming and Relocating Data Files" on page 7-13, as necessary. (This procedure is referenced throughout the rest of this chapter.)

Recovering a Data File Without a Backup If a data file is damaged and no backup of the file is available, the data file can still be recovered, provided that all log files written since the creation of the original data file are available, and the control file contains the name of the damaged file (that is, the control file is current, or is a backup taken after the damaged data file was added to the database).

Use the CREATE DATAFILE clause of the ALTER DATABASE command to create a new, empty data file, replacing a damaged data file that has no corresponding backup. For example, assume that the data file "disk1:users1" has been damaged and no backup is available. The following statement recreates the original data file (same size) on disk 2:

```
ALTER DATABASE CREATE DATAFILE 'disk2:users1' AS 'disk1:users1';
```

Note: The old data file is implicitly renamed as the new data file when an ALTER DATABASE CREATE DATAFILE statement is issued.

This statement causes ORACLE to create an empty file that matches the lost file. (ORACLE looks at information in the control file and the data dictionary to obtain size information.) You must next perform media recovery on the empty data file. All archived redo logs written since the original data file was created must be mounted and reapplied to the new, empty version of the lost data file during recovery. If the database was created in NOARCHIVELOG mode, the original data files of the SYSTEM tablespace cannot be restored using an ALTER DATABASE CREATE DATAFILE statement because the necessary archived redo logs are not available.

Restoring Necessary Archived Redo Log Files

All archived redo log files required for the pending media recovery eventually need to be on disk so that they are readily available to ORACLE.

To determine which archived redo log files you need, you can often use the tables V$LOG_HISTORY and V$RECOVERY_LOG.

V$LOG_HISTORY lists all of the archived logs, including the names they are most likely to have, given the current archived log file naming scheme (as set by the parameter LOG_ARCHIVE_FORMAT). V$RECOVERY_LOG lists only the archived redo logs that ORACLE believes it needs to perform recovery; it also includes the most likely names of the files, using LOG_ARCHIVE_FORMAT. (See Appendix B for more information on these tables.)

If space is available, restore all of the required archived redo log files to the location currently specified by the initialization parameter LOG_ARCHIVE_DEST. By doing this, you allow ORACLE to locate automatically the correct archived redo log file when required during media recovery. If sufficient space is not available at the location indicated by LOG_ARCHIVE_DEST, you can restore some or all of the required archived redo log files to any disk accessible to ORACLE. In this case, you can specify the location of the archived redo log files before or during media recovery.

After an archived log is applied, you can delete the restored copy of the archived redo log file to free disk space. However, make sure that a copy of each archived log group still exists on offline storage.

Starting Media Recovery

If a damaged database is operating in ARCHIVELOG mode, it is a candidate for either complete media recovery or incomplete media recovery operations. To begin media recovery operations, use one of the following options of SQL*DBA:

- the Recover Closed Database dialog box
- the Recover Offline Tablespaces dialog box
- the Recover Data File dialog box
- the SQL*DBA RECOVER command
- the SQL command ALTER DATABASE
- the Start Up Instance dialog box or the SQL*DBA STARTUP command, with the RECOVER option

This section provides examples for each of the above options. (For information about SQL*DBA, see the *ORACLE7 Server Utilities User's Guide*, and for complete information about the ALTER DATABASE command, see the *ORACLE7 Server SQL Language Reference Manual*.)

Recovering a Closed Database After the database is mounted but closed, start closed database recovery (complete or incomplete) using either SQL*DBA's Recover Closed Database dialog box or the RECOVER command with the DATABASE parameter. Figure 19-1 shows the Recover Closed Database dialog box that begins time-based recovery using a backup version of the control file.

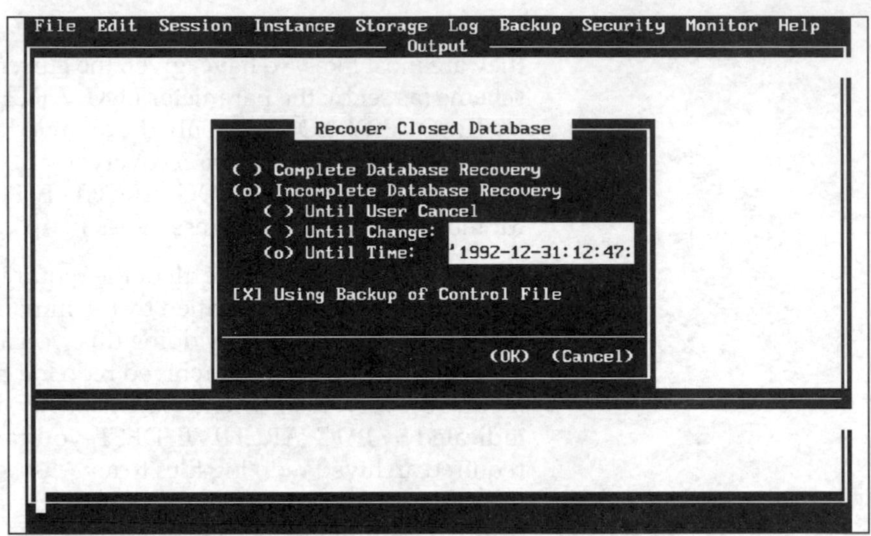

FIGURE 19-1
The Recover Closed Database Dialog

The following statement is the command equivalent of the Recover Closed Database dialog box in Figure 19-1:

```
RECOVER DATABASE
    UNTIL '1992-12-31:12:47:30' USING BACKUP CONTROLFILE;
```

Recovering an Offline Tablespace in an Open Database After the tablespaces of interest are taken offline (see "Taking Tablespaces Offline" on page 7-10), you can start open database-offline tablespace recovery using either of the following options of SQL*DBA: the Recover Offline Tablespaces dialog box or the RECOVER command with the TABLESPACE parameter. Either option begins complete media recovery of one or more offline tablespaces; the remainder of the database may be open and online for normal database operation. Figure 19-2 shows the Recover Offline Tablespaces dialog box.

FIGURE 19-2
The Recover Offline Tablespaces Dialog

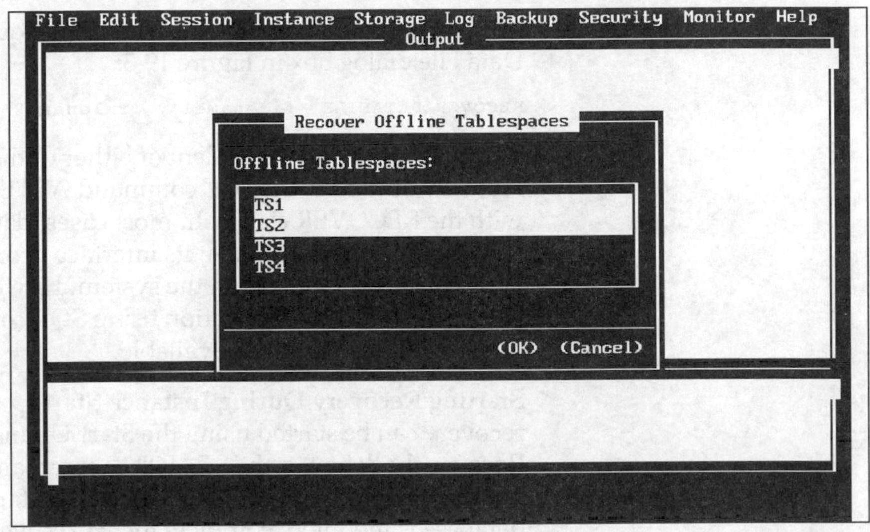

The following statement is the command equivalent of the Recover Offline Tablespaces dialog box in Figure 19-2:

```
RECOVER TABLESPACE ts1, ts2;
```

After the tablespaces that contain the damaged files have been taken offline and you are positive the associated data files are also offline (check in V$DATAFILE to see the file's status), recover selected data files using the Recover Data File dialog box or the RECOVER command with the DATAFILE parameter. Figure 19-3 shows the Recover Data File dialog box.

FIGURE 19-3
The Recover Data File Dialog

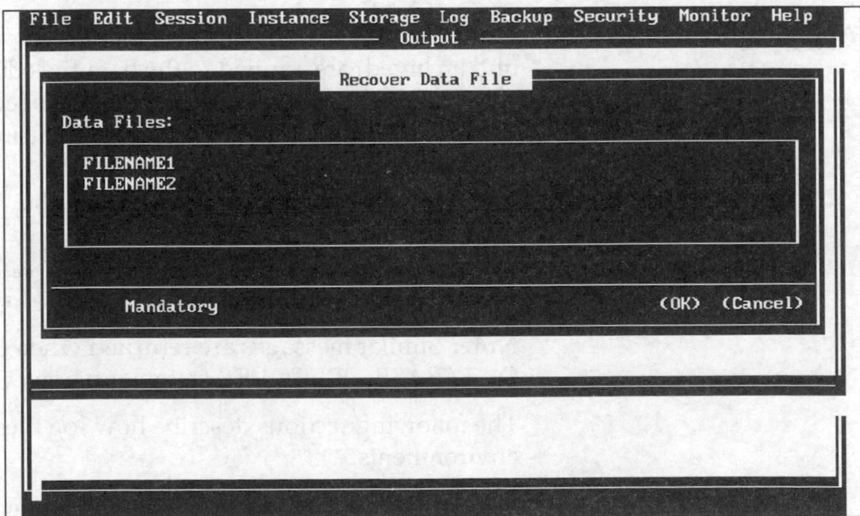

The following statement is the command equivalent of the Recover Data File dialog box in Figure 19-3:

```
RECOVER DATAFILE 'filename1', 'filename2';
```

The SQL command equivalent of either of the SQL*DBA media recovery options is the SQL command ALTER DATABASE command with the RECOVER clause. In most cases, database recovery should be performed using SQL*DBA; its interface prompts you for information and returns messages from the system. However, if you want to design your own recovery application using SQL commands, the ALTER DATABASE command is available.

Starting Recovery During Instance Startup Complete media recovery can be started using the Start Up Instance dialog box with the Recover check box or the STARTUP command with the RECOVER option when using SQL*DBA. Once an instance is started and the database is mounted, complete media recovery proceeds as described in "Complete Media Recovery" on page 19-17. See Chapter 3 and the *ORACLE7 Server Utilities User's Guide* for more information about the Start Up Instance dialog box and STARTUP command.

Utilities

Privileges Required to Start Media Recovery To start any type of media recovery, you must be connected as INTERNAL. All recovery sessions must be compatible; one session cannot start complete media recovery while another performs incomplete media recovery. Also, you cannot start media recovery if you are connected to the database via a multi-threaded server process. See Chapter 4 for more information about multi-threaded server processes.

Applying Redo Log Files

During complete or incomplete media recovery, redo log files (online and archived) are applied to the data files during the roll forward phase of media recovery. As a log file is needed, ORACLE suggests the name of the file. For example, if you are using SQL*DBA, it returns the following lines and prompt:

```
ORA-00279: Change #### generated at DD/MM/YY HH:MM:SS needed for thread #
ORA-00289: Suggestion : logfile
ORA-00280: Change #### for thread # is in sequence #
Specify log: [<RET> for suggested | AUTO | FROM logsource | CANCEL ]
```

Note: Similar messages are returned when using an ALTER DATABASE ... RECOVER statement; however, no prompt is returned.

The following sections describe how log files can be applied in different environments.

Suggested Log Filenames ORACLE suggests log filenames by concatenating the current values of the initialization parameters

LOG_ARCHIVE_DEST and LOG_ARCHIVE_FORMAT and using some information from the control file. Therefore, if all the required archived log files are mounted at LOG_ARCHIVE_DEST and the value for LOG_ARCHIVE_FORMAT is never altered, ORACLE can suggest and apply log files to complete media recovery automatically without intervention from the administrator. If the location specified by LOG_ARCHIVE_DEST is not available (for example, because of media failure), you can change the value for this parameter, mount the log files to the new location, and start a new instance before beginning media recovery.

In some cases, you might want to override the current setting for LOG_ARCHIVE_DEST as a source for log files. For example, assume that a database is open and an offline tablespace must be recovered, but not enough space is available to mount the necessary log files at the location specified by LOG_ARCHIVE_DEST. In this case, the necessary log files can be mounted to an alternate location and the alternate location is indicated to ORACLE for the recovery operation. To specify the location where required log files can be found, use the LOGSOURCE parameter of the SQL*DBA command SET when using SQL*DBA or use the RECOVER ... FROM parameter of the SQL command ALTER DATABASE when using SQL commands.

Note: Overriding the log source does not affect the archive log destination for filled online groups being archived.

Consider overriding the current setting for LOG_ARCHIVE_DEST when not enough space is available to mount all the required log files at any one location. In this case, you can set the log file source to an operating system variable (such as a logical or an environment variable) that acts as a search path to several locations; however, such functionality is operating system dependent; see your installation or user's guide.

IUG

Applying Log Files when Using SQL*DBA If the suggested archived redo log file is correct, apply the suggested archived redo log by pressing the Enter or Return key; you do not have to specify a filename unless the suggested file is incorrect. See your installation or user's guide for an example of this procedure. Once a filename is provided, ORACLE then applies the redo log file to roll forward the restored data files.

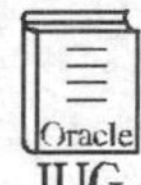
IUG

When using SQL*DBA, you can have ORACLE automatically apply the redo log files that it suggests by using either of two options:

- Before starting media recovery, issue the following SQL*DBA statement to turn automatic recovery on:

  ```
  SET AUTORECOVERY ON;
  ```

  Automatic application of the suggested redo log starts once recovery begins.

- After media recovery is started, enter "auto" when prompted for a redo log file. Automatic application of the suggested redo log starts from this point forward.

Suggested redo log files are automatically applied until a suggested redo log is incorrect or recovery is complete. Online redo log files may need to be manually specified only when cancel-based recovery or a backup of the control file is being used.

Application of Log Files When Using SQL Commands Application of redo log files is similar to the behavior described in the previous section. However, a prompt for log files is not returned once media recovery is started. Instead, you must provide the correct log file using an ALTER DATABASE RECOVER LOGFILE statement. For example, if a message suggests LOG1.ARC, you can apply the suggestion using the following statement:

```
ALTER DATABASE RECOVER LOGFILE 'log1.arc';
```

As a result, restoring a tablespace requires several statements, as indicated in the following example: (DBA input is highlighted in bold; variable information is shown in italics.)

```
> ALTER DATABASE RECOVER TABLESPACE users;
ORA-00279: Change #### generated at DD/MM/YY HH:MM:SS needed for thread #
ORA-00289: Suggestion : logfile1
ORA-00280: Change #### for thread # is in sequence #
> ALTER DATABASE RECOVER LOGFILE 'logfile1';
ORA-00279: Change #### generated at DD/MM/YY HH:MM:SS needed for thread #
ORA-00289: Suggestion : logfile2
ORA-00280: Change #### for thread # is in sequence #
> ALTER DATABASE RECOVER LOGFILE 'logfile2';
(Repeat until all logs are applied.)
Statement processed.
> ALTER TABLESPACE users ONLINE;
Statement processed.
```

Note: This example assumes that the backup files have been restored, and that the user is connected as INTERNAL.

Similarly to the method you would use with SQL*DBA, automatic application of the redo logs can be started with the following statements, before and during recovery, respectively:

```
ALTER DATABASE RECOVER AUTOMATIC ...;

ALTER DATABASE RECOVER AUTOMATIC LOGFILE suggested_log_file;
```

The following is an example of using the first statement:

```
> ALTER DATABASE RECOVER AUTOMATIC TABLESPACE users;
Statement processed.
> ALTER TABLESPACE users ONLINE;
Statement processed.
```

Note: This example assumes that the backup files have been restored, and that the user is connected as INTERNAL.

Similarly, the following is an example of using the "ALTER DATABASE RECOVER AUTOMATIC LOGFILE" statement:

```
> ALTER DATABASE RECOVER TABLESPACE users;
ORA-00279: Change #### generated at DD/MM/YY HH:MM:SS needed for thread #
ORA-00289: Suggestion : logfile1
ORA-00280: Change #### for thread # is in sequence #
> ALTER DATABASE RECOVER AUTOMATIC LOGFILE 'logfile1';
Statement processed.
> ALTER TABLESPACE users ONLINE;
Statement processed.
```

Note: This example assumes that the backup files have been restored, and that the user is connected as INTERNAL.

Successful Application of Redo Logs If you are using SQL*DBA's recovery options (not SQL statements), each time ORACLE finishes applying a redo log file, the following message is returned:

```
Log applied.
```

Make sure that the message "Log applied" is returned after each application of a redo log file. If the suggested file is incorrect or you provide an incorrect filename, an error message is returned instead. If you see an error message instead of "Log applied," a redo log file needed for recovery has not been applied. Recovery cannot continue until the needed redo log file is applied.

If an error message is returned after supplying a redo log filename, the kind of error message that is returned depends upon the kind of error that has been detected:

- If the error message says that the file cannot be found, you may have typed in the wrong filename. Re-enter the correct filename.
- If the redo log file is found, but cannot be opened, then it may be locked. After unlocking the redo log file, re-enter the filename.
- If a redo log file is found and opened, but cannot be read, an I/O error is returned. In this case, the redo log file may have been only partially written or may contain corrupt data. If you can locate an uncorrupted or complete copy of the log, you can simply apply that copy; you do not need to restart recovery. Otherwise, if no other copy of the log exists and if you know the time of the last valid redo entry, you can perform time-based or change-based recovery; in this case, you must restart recovery from the beginning, including restoring backups.

Interrupting Media Recovery

If you start a media recovery operation and then must interrupt it for some reason (for example, because a recovery operation must end for the night and resume the next morning), you can interrupt recovery at any time by using either of these procedures:

- Enter the word CANCEL when prompted for a redo log file.
- If you must abort the procedure of recovering an individual data file or automated recovery is in progress, use your operating system's interrupt signal.

After recovery is canceled, it must be completed before opening a database for normal operation. To resume recovery, restart it; recovery resumes where it left off if it was canceled. If you want to restart recovery beginning with an earlier redo log file or a different backup, restart the entire recovery process by restoring the necessary backups again.

Restoring a Full Backup

If a database is operating in NOARCHIVELOG mode and a media failure damages part or all of the database, usually the only option for recovering the database is to restore the most recent full backup. (If you are using Export to supplement regular backups, you can instead restore the database by importing an exported backup of the database; see "Using the Export and Import Utilities for Supplemental Database Protection" on page 18-17.)

Note: If a database operating in ARCHIVELOG mode is damaged by a media failure, it can be recovered by restoring the data files from the most recent full backup; however, because the database's online redo log is archived, complete or incomplete recovery from the media failure is normally used to reconstruct the database and minimize the amount of work lost.

To recover a damaged database by restoring the most recent full backup, use the following steps:

1. If the database is open, shut it down using either of the following options of SQL*DBA: the Abort Instance option of the Shut Down menu or the SHUTDOWN command with the ABORT option.

2. Repair the hardware problems that caused the database failure. If the hardware problem can be repaired quickly, follow Step 3a; if a hardware failure cannot be repaired quickly and the database must be reopened as soon as possible, follow Steps 3b through 3e.

3. **If the hardware problem has been repaired, follow Step 3a. If the hardware problem has not been corrected and alternative disks are used to store the restored database, follow Steps 3b through 3e:**

a. Restore the most recent full backup, including **all** data files, online redo log files, and control files. Do not restore just the files damaged by the media failure; **all** files must be restored from the most recent full backup to guarantee that the entire database corresponds to a single point in time. Proceed to Step 4.

b. Restore all data files, online redo log files, control files, and the parameter file of the database to operable disks, as desired.

c. Edit the restored parameter file to indicate the new location of the control files, if applicable.

d. Start an instance using the restored and edited parameter file and mount, but do not open, the database.

e. Immediately perform the steps necessary to record the relocation of the restored data files and online redo log files (from Step 3b), as described in "Renaming and Relocating Data Files" and "Renaming and Relocating Online Redo Log Members" on pages 7-13 and 5-7, respectively.

4. Reopen the database.

Complete Media Recovery

The following section explains the steps necessary to complete the different types of complete media recovery operations. The following sections should not be used alone to understand the procedures necessary to recover from a media failure; "Examples of Media Failures and Appropriate Recovery Procedures" on page 19-27 furnishes a detailed list of the different types of problems that media failures can cause and provides the appropriate methods of recovery from each type of problem.

The following sections describe the following types of complete media recovery procedures:

- closed database recovery
- open database, offline tablespace recovery

Performing Closed Database Recovery

Use the following steps to perform closed database recovery, either of all damaged data files in one operation or individual recovery of each damaged data file in separate operations:

1. If the database is open, shut it down using either the Abort Instance option of the Shut Down menu or SQL*DBA, or the SHUTDOWN command with the ABORT option.

2. Correct the hardware problem that caused the media failure. If the hardware problem cannot be repaired quickly, database recovery can proceed by restoring damaged files to an alternative storage device.

3. If files are permanently damaged, restore the most recent backup files (taken as part of either a full backup or partial backup) of **only** the data files damaged by the media failure—do not restore any data files not damaged by the media failure or any online redo log files. If the hardware problem has been repaired and damaged data files can be restored to their original locations, do so, and skip Step 6 of this procedure; if the hardware problem persists, restore the data files to an alternative storage device of the database server and perform Step 6 when you come to it.

   Note: If you do not have a backup of a specific data file, you might be able to create a replacement file, empty of contents, that can be recovered. See "Restoring Damaged Data Files" on page 19-8 for more information about creating data files.

4. Start SQL*DBA and connect to ORACLE as INTERNAL.

5. Start a new instance and mount , but do not open, the database. This operation can be performed using either of the following options of SQL*DBA: the Start Up Instance dialog box with the Mount radio button selected or the STARTUP command with the MOUNT option.

6. If one or more damaged data files were restored to alternative locations in Step 3, the relocation of these files must be indicated to the control file of the associated database. Therefore, use the operation discussed in "Renaming and Relocating Data Files" on page 7-13, as necessary.

7. All data files that are to be recovered must be online during a complete media recovery. You can determine the names of all data files using the list of data files that accompanies the current control file (if available, see "Listing Database Files Before Backup" on page 18-6 for more information about such lists) or query the V$DATAFILE view. Then, use the ALTER DATABASE command and the DATAFILE ONLINE option to make sure that all data files of the database are online. For example, to guarantee that a data file named USERS1 (a fully specified filename) is online, enter the following statement:

```
ALTER DATABASE DATAFILE 'users1' ONLINE;
```

   If a data file is specified that is already online, ORACLE ignores the statement.

8. **Depending on the type of closed database recovery desired, follow either Step 8a or 8b.**

   a. Use either of the following options of SQL*DBA to start closed database recovery of all damaged data files in one step: the Recover Closed Database dialog box or an equivalent RECOVER DATABASE statement. Proceed to Step 9 to continue the closed database recovery operation.

   b. Use either of the following options of SQL*DBA to start closed database recovery of an individual damaged data file: the Recover Offline Data Files dialog box or an equivalent RECOVER DATAFILE statement.

   Note: Multiple, concurrent sessions can be used to recover a few damaged data files simultaneously with each session. If many data files need recovery, this method can potentially expedite the media recovery process. If this option is used, make sure that all damaged data files are recovered. Each session behaves as in Steps 9 and 10.

9. ORACLE now begins the roll forward phase of media recovery by applying the necessary redo log files (archived and online) to reconstruct the restored data files. If automated, the suggested log files are automatically applied; if not automated, ORACLE prompts for the required redo log file. See "Applying Redo Log Files" on page 19-12 for more information.

ORACLE continues to apply archived redo log files until all required archived redo log files have been applied to the restored data files. The online redo log files are then automatically applied to the restored data files to complete media recovery, as indicated by the following message:

```
Media recovery complete.
```

Note: If no archived redo log files are required for complete media recovery, ORACLE does not prompt for any. Instead, all necessary online redo log files are applied, and the "Media recovery complete" message is returned.

If you have completed the above steps, the closed database is now recovered up to the moment that media failure occurred. You can now open the database using the SQL command ALTER DATABASE with the OPEN option.

Performing Open Database-Offline Tablespace Recovery

Use the following steps to perform either open database-offline tablespace recovery or open database-offline tablespace-individual data file recovery. At this point, an open database has experienced a media failure, and the database remains open while the undamaged data files remain online and available for use and the damaged data files are automatically taken offline by ORACLE.

Note: Neither of the following procedures can be used to perform complete media recovery on the data files of the SYSTEM tablespace. If the media failure damages any data files of the SYSTEM tablespace, ORACLE automatically shuts down the database. To proceed with complete media recovery, follow the procedure in the previous section, "Performing Closed Database Recovery."

1. The starting point for this recovery operation can vary, depending on whether you have left the database open after the media failure has occurred.

   a. **If the database has been shut down**, start a new instance, and mount and open the database. This operation can be performed using either of the following options of SQL*DBA: the Start Up Instance dialog box with the Open radio button selected or the STARTUP command with the OPEN option. Once the database is open, take all tablespaces offline that contain damaged data files. Follow Step 1b for this procedure.

b. **If the database is open** with only damaged data files of the database offline, take all tablespaces offline that contain damaged data files. ORACLE should be indicating the damaged data files by the error messages it returns. Tablespaces can be taken offline using either the Set Tablespace Offline dialog box of SQL*DBA or the SQL command ALTER TABLESPACE with the OFFLINE option, as described in "Taking Tablespaces Offline" on page 7-10. If possible, take the damaged tablespaces offline with temporary priority (to minimize the recovery that is required). Also, pay attention to the special instructions in this referenced section concerning tablespaces that contain active rollback segments. After this step is completed, proceed to Step 2.

2. Correct the hardware problem that caused the media failure. If the hardware problem cannot be repaired quickly, database recovery can proceed by restoring damaged files to an alternative storage device.

3. If files are permanently damaged, restore the most recent backup files (taken as part of either a full backup or partial backup) of **only** the data files damaged by the media failure—do not restore any data files not damaged by the media failure, or any online redo log files or control files. If the hardware problem has been repaired and the data files can be restored to their original locations, do so, and skip Step 4 of this procedure; if the hardware problem persists, restore the data files to an alternative storage device of the database server and perform Step 4 next.

   Note: If you do not have a backup of a specific data file, you can create a replacement file, empty of contents, that can be recovered. See "Restoring Damaged Data Files" on page 19-8 for more information about creating data files.

4. If one or more damaged data files were restored to alternative locations in Step 3, the relocation of these files must be indicated to the control file of the associated database. Therefore, use the operation discussed in "Renaming and Relocating Data Files" on page 7-13, as necessary.

5. **Depending on the type of complete media recovery procedure desired, follow Step 5a or 5b after connecting as INTERNAL.**

   a. Use either of the following options of SQL*DBA to start offline tablespace recovery of all damaged data files in one or more offline tablespaces using one step: the Recover Offline Tablespaces dialog box or an equivalent RECOVER TABLESPACE statement. Skip to Step 6 to continue the offline tablespace recovery operation.

b. Use either of the following options of SQL*DBA to start recovery of an individual damaged data file in an offline tablespace: the Recover Offline Data Files dialog box or an equivalent RECOVER DATAFILE statement.

   Note: Multiple, concurrent sessions can be used to recover a few damaged data files simultaneously in each session, if the data files are on separate disks. If many data files need recovery, this method can potentially expedite the media recovery process. If this option is used, make sure that all damaged data files are recovered. Each session behaves as in Steps 6 and 7.

6. ORACLE now begins the roll forward phase of media recovery by applying the necessary redo log files (archived and online) to reconstruct the restored data files. If automated, the suggested log files are automatically applied; if not automated, ORACLE prompts for the required redo log file. See "Applying Redo Log Files" on page 19-12 for more information.

   ORACLE continues to apply archived redo log files until all required archived redo log files have been applied to the restored data files. The online redo log files are then automatically applied to the restored data files to complete media recovery, as indicated by the following message:

   ```
   Media recovery complete.
   ```

   Note: If no archived redo log files are required for complete media recovery, ORACLE does not prompt for any. Instead, all necessary online redo log files are applied, and the "Media recovery complete" message is returned.

7. The damaged tablespaces of the open database are now recovered up to the moment that media failure occurred. The offline tablespaces can be brought online using either the Set Tablespace Online dialog box of SQL*DBA or the SQL command ALTER TABLESPACE with the ONLINE option.

Incomplete Media Recovery

The following section explains the steps necessary to complete the different types of incomplete media recovery operations: time-based, change-based, and cancel-based recovery. The following section should not be used alone to understand the procedures necessary to recover from a media failure; "Examples of Media Failures and Appropriate Recovery Procedures" on page 19-27 furnishes a detailed list of the different types of problems that media failures can cause and provides the appropriate methods of recovery from each type of problem.

Performing Cancel-Based, Time-Based, or Change-Based Recovery

Use the following steps to perform cancel-based, time-based, or change-based recovery:

1. If the database is still open and it has been decided that incomplete media recovery is necessary, shut down the database using either of the following options of SQL*DBA: the Abort Instance option of the Shut Down menu or the SHUTDOWN command with the ABORT option.

2. Make a full backup of the database (all data files, online redo log files, a control file, and the parameter files of the database) as a precautionary measure, in case an error is made during the recovery procedure. (This protects against any problems that might arise in restoring backups in step 5.)

3. If a media failure has occurred, correct the hardware problem that caused the media failure.

4. If the current control files do not match the physical structure (the set of files) of the database at the intended time of recovery (for example, if a data file has been added subsequent to the time to which you intend to recover), then you should restore a backup of the control file that reflects the database's physical file structure (contains only and all the names of data files and online redo log files) at the intended time to which incomplete media recovery is to finish. Review the list of files that corresponds to the current control file and each control file backup to determine the correct control file to use and, if necessary, replace all current control files of the database with the correct control file backup. (You can, alternatively, create a new control file to replace the missing one; see "Creating Additional Control Files and Renaming or Relocating Control Files" on page 6-4.)

   Note: If any control file of the database cannot function or be replaced with a control file backup because a hardware problem that caused a media failure persists, you must edit the parameter file associated with the database to modify the CONTROL_FILES parameter. See the procedure on page 6-4.

5. Restore backup files (taken as part of either a full backup or partial backup) of **all** the data files of the database. All backup files used to replace existing data files must have been taken prior to the intended time of recovery. For example, if you intend to recover to redo log sequence number 38, then restore all data files with backups completed prior to redo log sequence number 38.

   Note: If you do not have a backup of a specific data file, you can create a replacement file, empty of contents, that can be recovered.

See "Restoring Damaged Data Files" on page 19-8 for more information about creating data files.

Note: If a data file was added after the intended time of recovery, it is not necessary to restore a backup for this file, as it will no longer be used for the database after recovery is complete.

If the hardware problem that caused a media failure has been repaired and all data files can be restored to their original locations, do so, and skip Step 8 of this procedure; if a hardware problem persists, restore damaged data files to an alternative storage device and perform Step 8 when you come to it.

6. Start SQL*DBA and connect to ORACLE as INTERNAL.
7. Start a new instance and mount the database. This operation can be performed using either of the following options of SQL*DBA: the Start Up Instance dialog box with the Mount radio button selected or the STARTUP command with the MOUNT option.
8. If one or more damaged data files were restored to alternative locations in Step 5, the relocation of these files must be indicated to the control file of the associated database. Therefore, use the operation discussed in "Renaming and Relocating Data Files" on page 7-13, as necessary.
9. All data files of the database must be online during time-based or change-based recovery (unless an offline tablespace was taken offline normally). You can determine the names of all data files to be recovered using the list of data files that accompanies the control file being used (if available; see "Listing Database Files Before Backup" on page 18-6) or query the V$DATAFILE view. Then, use the ALTER DATABASE command and the DATAFILE ONLINE option to make sure that all data files of the database are online. For example, to guarantee that a data file named USERS1 (a fully specified filename) is online, enter the following statement:

```
ALTER DATABASE DATAFILE 'users1' ONLINE;
```

   If a data file is specified that is already online, ORACLE ignores the statement.

10. **Depending on the type of incomplete media recovery being performed, follow either Step 10a, 10b, or 10c.**

   a. If a backup of the control file is being used with this incomplete recovery (that is, a control file backup or re-created control file was restored in Step 4), indicate this in the dialog box or command used to start recovery (that is, specify USING BACKUP CONTROLFILE).

b. Use either of the following options of SQL*DBA to begin cancel-based recovery: the Recover Closed Database dialog box with the Until User Cancel radio button selected or an equivalent RECOVER DATABASE UNTIL CANCEL statement.

c. Use either of the following options of SQL*DBA to begin time-based recovery: the Recover Closed Database dialog box with the Until Time radio button selected and specified end time, or an equivalent RECOVER DATABASE UNTIL TIME statement. In either case, the time is always specified using the following format, delimited by single quotes, 'YYYY-MM-DD:HH24:MI:SS'.

d. Use either of the following options of SQL*DBA to begin change-based recovery: the Recover Closed Database dialog box with the Until Change radio button selected and specified last change number, or an equivalent RECOVER DATABASE UNTIL CHANGE statement. In either case, the change number (SCN) is specified as a decimal number without quotes.

11. ORACLE now begins the roll forward phase of media recovery by applying the necessary redo log files (archived and online) to reconstruct the restored data files. If automated, the suggested log files are automatically applied; if not automated, ORACLE prompts for the required redo log file. See "Applying Redo Log Files" on page 19-12 for more information.

    ORACLE continues to apply redo log files. Depending on the type of incomplete recovery being performed, follow either of the next two steps:

a. If performing cancel-based recovery, continue applying redo log files until the most recent, undamaged redo log file has been applied to the restored data files.

b. If performing time-based or change-based recovery, continue applying redo log files until the last required redo log file has been applied to the restored data files.

12. Depending on the type of incomplete media recovery being used, follow either Step 12a or 12b:

a. If performing cancel-based recovery, enter "CANCEL" to cancel recovery after ORACLE has applied the redo log file just prior to the damaged file. Cancel-based recovery is now complete.

b. If performing time-based or change-based recovery, ORACLE automatically terminates the recovery operation when it has reached the correct time or change.

In either case, a message is returned to indicate the result of the incomplete recovery. If recovery was indeed incomplete (that is, some redo information was not applied), the following message is reported in the ALERT file:

```
Incomplete recovery done UNTIL CHANGE scn
```

However, if the recovery operation was complete (that is, all available redo was applied), the following messages are reported in the ALERT file:

```
Incomplete recovery applied all redo ever generated.
Recovery completed through change nnnnnnnn
```

13. The first time you open the database subsequent to incomplete media recovery, you must explicitly specify whether or not to reset the log sequence number, by including either the RESETLOGS or NORESETLOGS option. Resetting the redo log discards any redo information that was not applied during recovery, ensuring that it will never be applied; it also reinitializes the control file information about online redo logs and redo threads, clears the contents of the online redo logs, creates the online redo log files if they do not currently exist, and resets the log sequence number to 1. Use the following rules to decide whether to specify RESETLOGS or NORESETLOGS:

    - Reset the log sequence number if you used a backup of the control file in recovery, no matter what type of recovery was performed (complete or incomplete).
    - Reset the log sequence number if the recovery was actually incomplete (see message in Step 12). For example, you must have specified a previous time or SCN, not one in the future.
    - Do not reset logs if recovery was complete (unless you used a backup control file). This applies both when you intentionally performed complete recovery and when you performed incomplete recovery but actually recovered all changes in the redo logs anyway. (See the explanation in step 12 for how to examine the ALERT file to see if incomplete recovery was actually complete.)

    To preserve the log sequence number when opening a database after recovery, use the SQL command ALTER DATABASE with the OPEN NORESETLOGS option. To reset the log sequence number when opening a database after recovery, use the SQL command ALTER DATABASE with the OPEN RESETLOGS option. (If you attempt to reset the log when you should not, or if you neglect to reset the log when you should, ORACLE returns an error and does not open the database. Correct the error and try again.)

If the log sequence number is reset when opening a database, different messages are returned, depending on whether the recovery was complete or incomplete. If the recovery was complete, the following message is reported in the ALERT file:

```
RESETLOGS after complete recovery through change scn
```

If the recovery was incomplete, the following message is reported in the ALERT file:

```
RESETLOGS after incomplete recovery UNTIL CHANGE scn
```

14. If you reset the redo log sequence when opening the database, immediately shut down the database normally and make a full database backup. (See "Performing Full Backups" on page 18-7.) Otherwise, you will not be able to recover changes made after you reset the logs; until you take a full backup, the only way to recover will be to repeat the procedures you just finished, up to resetting the logs. (You do not need to back up the database if you did not reset the log sequence.)

Examples of Media Failures and Appropriate Recovery Procedures

The following sections describe common media failures, the effects of a media failure, and the appropriate steps necessary to recover a database in each situation.

Types of Media Failures

Media failures can be separated into two general categories: permanent and temporary media failures. Permanent media failures are serious hardware problems that cause the permanent loss of data on the disk. Lost data cannot be recovered except by repairing or replacing the failed storage device and restoring backups of the files stored on the damaged storage device. Temporary media failures are hardware problems that do not detrimentally affect the storage of data. The following are two examples of situations that can be categorized as temporary media failures:

- A disk's controller fails. Once the disk's controller is replaced, the data on the disk can be accessed.
- Power to a storage device is cut off. Once the power is returned, the storage device and all associated data is accessible, as normal.

Loss of Data Files

If a media failure has affected data files of a database, the appropriate recovery procedure depends on the archiving mode of the database, the type of media failure, and the exact files affected by the media failure. The following sections explain the appropriate recovery strategy in various situations.

Loss of Data Files, NOARCHIVELOG Mode

If either a permanent or temporary media failure affects **any** data files of a database operating in NOARCHIVELOG mode, ORACLE automatically shuts down the database. Depending on the type of media failure, one of two recovery paths can be used:

- If the media failure is temporary, correct the temporary hardware problem and restart the database. In most cases, instance recovery is possible and all committed transactions can be recovered using the online redo log.
- If the media failure is permanent, follow the steps in "Restoring a Full Backup" on page 19-16 to recover from the media failure.

Loss of Data Files, ARCHIVELOG Mode

If either a permanent or temporary media failure affects the data files of a database operating in ARCHIVELOG mode, the following situations can exist.

- If a temporary or permanent media failure affects any data files of the SYSTEM tablespace or any data files that contain active rollback segments, the database becomes inoperable and should be immediately shut down, if it has not already been shut down by ORACLE.

  If the hardware problem is temporary, correct the problem and restart the database. In most cases, instance recovery is possible and all committed transactions can be recovered using the online redo log.

  If the hardware problem is permanent, follow the procedure given in "Performing Closed Database Recovery" on page 19-18.

- If a temporary or permanent media failure affects only data files not mentioned in the previous item, the affected data files are unavailable, but the database can continue to operate.

If the unaffected portions of the database must remain available, do not shut down the database. First, take all tablespaces that contain problem data files offline using the temporary option. Next, follow the procedure in "Performing Open Database-Offline Tablespace Recovery" on page 19-20. **If the problem that caused the failure is temporary, do not follow Step 3**; recovery can proceed using the intact data files, and often only requires only the online redo log files.

Loss of Online Redo Log Files

If a media failure has affected the online redo log of a database, the appropriate recovery procedure depends on the configuration of the online redo log (mirrored or non-mirrored), the type of media failure (temporary or permanent), and the types of online redo log files affected by the media failure (current, active, not yet archived, or inactive online redo log files). The following sections explain the appropriate recovery strategies in various situations.

Loss of Online Redo Log Members or Mirrored Online Redo Log

If the online redo log of a database is mirrored and at least one member of each online redo log group is not affected by the media failure, ORACLE allows the database to continue functioning as normal (error messages are written to the LGWR trace file and ALERT file of the database). However, the problem should be handled using one of the following actions:

- If the hardware problem is temporary, correct the problem. After it has been fixed, LGWR accesses the previously unavailable online redo log files as if a problem never happened.
- If the hardware problem is permanent, use the following procedure:

    1. Make sure that there are at least two members in each online redo log group, to safeguard against a single point of failure. If any online redo log group contains only one member as a result of a media failure, create additional online redo log files for the group.

    2. Drop the damaged online redo log files.

    3. Repair or replace the damaged storage device, if desired. After you complete this step, you can re-create the damaged set of online redo log files and drop the set of online redo log files made in Step 1 of this procedure.

Note: If all members of an online redo log group in a mirrored online redo log are damaged by a media failure, see the following section.

Loss of All Online Redo Log Members of an Online Redo Log Group

If all members of an online redo log group are damaged by a media failure, different situations can occur, depending on the type of online redo log group affected by the failure and the archiving mode of the database. To determine in which state the damaged online redo log group was, query the view V$LOG:

```
SELECT group#, members, status, archived
  FROM v$log
;

    GROUP#  MEMBERS            STATUS      ARCHIVED
------------------------------------------------
   0001  log1a            INACTIVE    YES
   0001  log1b            INACTIVE    YES
   0002  log2a            ACTIVE      YES
   0002  log2b            ACTIVE      YES
   0003  log3a            CURRENT     NO
   0003  log3b            CURRENT     NO
```

The following sections explain the various situations:

Loss of an Inactive, Archived Online Redo Log Group If all members of an inactive (but archived, if you are in ARCHIVELOG mode) online redo log group are damaged, several situations can arise:

- In either archiving mode, if a temporary media failure affects only an inactive online redo log group, correct the problem; LGWR can reuse the group when required.
- If a media failure permanently prevents access to only an inactive online redo log group, the damaged inactive online redo log group will eventually halt normal database operation.

  If you notice the problem before the database halts, either drop the damaged online redo log group (adding another group if necessary) or, if you are in ARCHIVELOG mode, restore the archive of the online redo log from offline storage, creating enough members for the group and renaming the online redo log to the new location.

  If the database has already halted, use the following steps to resolve this problem:

1. Abort the current instance immediately using either the Abort Instance option of SQL*DBA's Shut Down menu or the SHUTDOWN command with the ABORT option.

2. Start a new instance and mount the database, but do not open the database. This operation can be performed using either of the following options of SQL*DBA: the Start Up Instance dialog box with the Mount radio button selected or the STARTUP command with the MOUNT option.

3. If you are in ARCHIVELOG mode, alter the database's archiving mode by using the ALTER DATABASE command with the NOARCHIVELOG option:

   ```
   ALTER DATABASE NOARCHIVELOG;
   ```

4. Create a new online redo log group to replace the damaged online redo log group using either the Add Online Redo Log Group dialog box of SQL*DBA or the SQL command ALTER DATABASE with the ADD LOGFILE parameter, or restore an archived copy of the damaged redo log group from disk.

5. Drop the damaged online redo log group using either the Drop Online Redo Log Group dialog box of SQL*DBA or the SQL command ALTER DATABASE with the DROP LOGFILE parameter.

6. If you were previously in ARCHIVELOG mode, switch the database's archiving mode back to ARCHIVELOG:

   ```
   ALTER DATABASE ARCHIVELOG;
   ```

7. Immediately back up the database; also back up the database's control file using the ALTER DATABASE command with the BACKUP CONTROLFILE option.

You can now open the database.

Loss of an Unarchived Online Redo Log Group In ARCHIVELOG mode only, if an online redo log group that has not yet been archived is damaged, several situations can arise:

- If the media failure is temporary, correct the problem; LGWR can archive and reuse the group when required.
- If the media failure permanently prevents access to the unarchived redo log, the damaged unarchived online redo log group will eventually halt normal database operation when the

ARCH process cannot archive the log and eventually all logs are waiting to be archived. Use the following steps to repair this problem:

1. Shut down the database normally, using either the Normal option of SQL*DBA's Shut Down dialog or the SHUTDOWN command with the NORMAL option. If you cannot shutdown the database normally, use either the IMMEDIATE option or the ABORT option, then restart the instance using the RECOVER option, mount the database, and shut it down normally.
2. Start cancel-based recovery, canceling immediately, before you apply any redo logs.
3. Rename the damaged online redo log group to a new location. (You do not need to create the files.)
4. Open the database using the RESETLOGS option.
5. Immediately backup the control file of the database using the ALTER DATABASE command with the BACKUP CONTROLFILE parameter.

The damaged log is now repaired.

Loss of an Active Online Redo Log Group If all members of an active online redo log group are damaged, several situations can arise:

- If the media failure is temporary, correct the problem and ORACLE can reuse the group when required.
- If the database is operating in NOARCHIVELOG mode and a permanent media failure permanently prevents access to an active online redo log group, recover the database from a full backup.
- If the database is operating in ARCHIVELOG mode and a permanent media failure permanently prevents access to an active online redo log group, shut down the database normally (if it has not already crashed); how you recover depends on whether the online redo log has been archived or not, as explained below.

  If the active redo log has already been archived, restore the group from the archived copy, renaming it to the restored location, and restart the database. ORACLE can continue to use the group as before

If the active redo log has not yet been archived, use the procedure given in "Performing Cancel-Based, Time-Based, or Change-Based Recovery" on page 19-23, recovering up through the log before the damaged log, and modifying the following steps:

8. Rename the damaged online redo log group to a new location. (You do not need to create the files.)

14. In addition to making a full backup, immediately back up the control file of the database using the ALTER DATABASE command with the BACKUP CONTROLFILE parameter.

The damaged log is now repaired.

Loss of the Current Online Redo Log Group If all members of the current online redo log group are damaged, several situations can arise:

- If the media failure is temporary, correct the problem and ORACLE can reuse the group when required.
- If the database is operating in NOARCHIVELOG mode and a permanent media failure permanently prevents access to an active online redo log group, recover the database from a full backup.
- If the database is operating in ARCHIVELOG mode and a permanent media failure permanently prevents access to an active online redo log group, the database will crash. Use the procedure given in "Performing Cancel-Based, Time-Based, or Change-Based Recovery" on page 19-23, recovering up through the log before the damaged log and modifying the following steps:

8. Rename the damaged online redo log group to a new location. (You do not need to create the files.)

14. In addition to making a full backup, immediately back up the control file of the database using the ALTER DATABASE command with the BACKUP CONTROLFILE parameter.

The damaged log is now repaired.

Loss of Multiple Redo Log Groups If you have lost multiple groups of the online redo log, use the recovery method for the most difficult log to recover. The order of difficulty, from most difficult to least, is as follows: the current online redo log, an active online redo log, an unarchived redo log, an inactive online redo log.

Loss of Archived Redo Log Files

If the database is operating so that filled online redo log groups are being archived and the only copy of an archived redo log file is damaged, it does not affect the present operation of the database. However, the following situations can arise if media recovery is required in the future:

- If **all** data files have been backed up after the filled online redo log group was written (which is now archived), the archived version of the filled online redo log group is not required for any complete media recovery operation.
- Assume the most recent backup file of a data file was taken after the filled online redo log group was written (the group now corresponds to the damaged archived redo log file). At some future point, the corresponding data file is damaged by a permanent media failure. The most recent backup of the damaged data file must be used and incomplete media recovery can only recover the database up to the damaged archived redo log file.
- If time-based recovery is needed, the damaged archived redo log file may be required if old data file backups are used that were taken before the original online redo log group was written. In this case, the incomplete media recovery can only recover the database up to the damaged archived redo log group.

If you know that an archived redo log group has been damaged, immediately backup all data files so that you will have a complete backup that does not require the damaged archived redo log.

Loss of Control Files

If a media failure has affected the control files of a database (whether control files are mirrored or not), the database continues to run until the first time that ORACLE needs to access the control files; at this point, the database and instance are automatically shut down.

If the media failure is temporary and the database has not yet shut down, immediately correcting the media failure can avoid the automatic shut down of the database. However, if the database does shut down before the temporary media failure is corrected, you can simply restart the database after fixing the problem (and restoring access to the control files).

The appropriate recovery procedure for media failures that permanently prevent access to control files of a database depends on whether you have mirrored the control files. The following sections detail the appropriate procedures to follow.

Loss of Mirrored Control Files

Use the following steps to recover a database after one or more control files of a database have been damaged by a permanent media failure and at least one control file has not been damaged by the media failure:

Note: If all control files of a mirrored control file configuration have been damaged, follow the instructions for recovering from the loss of non-mirrored control files.

1. If the instance is still running, immediately abort the current instance using either of the following options of SQL*DBA: the Abort Instance option of the Shut Down menu or the SHUTDOWN command with the ABORT option.
2. Correct the hardware problem that caused the media failure. If the hardware problem cannot be repaired quickly, database recovery can proceed by restoring damaged control files to an alternative storage device; proceed to Step 3.
3. Use an intact copy of the database's control file to copy over the damaged control files. If possible, copy the intact control file to the original locations of all damaged control files; if the hardware problem persists, copy the intact control file to alternate locations. If you restored **all** damaged control files to their original location, proceed to Step 5; if all damaged control files were not restored, or not restored to their original location, proceed to Step 4.
4. If all damaged control files were not restored, or not restored to their original location in Step 3, the parameter file of the database must be edited so that the CONTROL_FILES parameter reflects the current locations of all control files and does not include any control files that are not present.

You can now start a new instance, and mount and open the database.

Loss of Non-Mirrored Control Files

If all control files of a database have been damaged by a permanent media failure, complete media recovery can be performed using a backup of the control file.

Note: If a backup of the control file is not available, you must create a new control file for the database; see "Creating a New Control File" on page 6-4.

If a control file backup is available, use the procedure given in "Performing Closed Database Recovery" on page 19-18 using the following alternative steps when required:

- Between Steps 2 and 3, restore a backup of the control file that reflects the current structure of the database. If the control file is restored to an alternate location, also edit the CONTROL_FILES parameter in the database's parameter file before starting an instance in Step 5 (on page 19-18).
- If no data files are damaged, Steps 3, 6, and 7 can be skipped.
- Choose Step 8a, rather than 8b. Include the USING BACKUP CONTROLFILE option. (This option tells the ORACLE instance that it will detect inconsistencies between the control file and the data and redo file headers; the option is needed any time the control file used in recovery is not current.)
- When you are ready to open the database, first take a full offline backup; this is a precaution in case a problem arises in opening the database with the RESETLOGS option. Then, open the database using the RESETLOGS option. (The redo log sequence number is reset to 1.) Immediately after opening the database, because the log sequence has been reset and all old redo information discarded, make a full backup of the database.

Recovery From User Errors

Serious user errors can detrimentally affect a database and necessitate database recovery. Recovering a database from a user error can be performed so that virtually no data is lost using the following steps:

Note: If the database administrator has properly granted powerful privileges (such as DROP ANY TABLE) to only selected, appropriate users, user errors that require database recovery are minimized.

1. Backup the existing, intact database.
2. Leave the existing database intact, but reconstruct a temporary copy of the database up to the user error using time-based recovery.
3. Export the data lost to the user error from the reconstructed, temporary copy of the database.
4. Import the data lost by the user error into the permanent database.
5. Delete the files associated with the temporary copy of the reconstructed database to conserve disk space.

For example, the steps below recover a table that was accidentally dropped:

1. The database that experienced the user error can remain online and available for normal use. The database can remain open or be shut down. Back up all data files of the existing database in case an error is made during the remaining steps of this procedure.

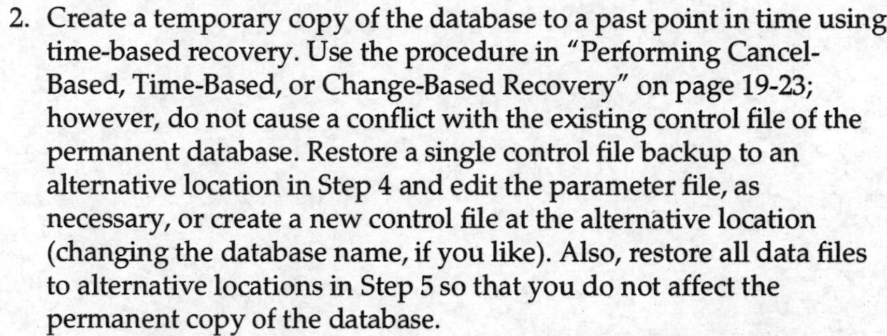

2. Create a temporary copy of the database to a past point in time using time-based recovery. Use the procedure in "Performing Cancel-Based, Time-Based, or Change-Based Recovery" on page 19-23; however, do not cause a conflict with the existing control file of the permanent database. Restore a single control file backup to an alternative location in Step 4 and edit the parameter file, as necessary, or create a new control file at the alternative location (changing the database name, if you like). Also, restore all data files to alternative locations in Step 5 so that you do not affect the permanent copy of the database.

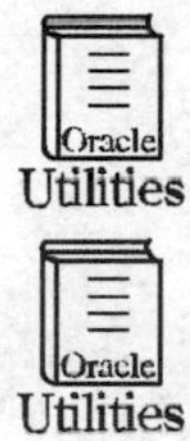

3. Export the lost data using Export from the temporary, restored version of the database. In this case, export the accidentally dropped table. (See the *ORACLE7 Server Utilities User's Guide*.)
4. Import the data exported in Step 3 into the permanent copy of the database using the ORACLE utility Import. (See the *ORACLE7 Server Utilities User's Guide*.)
5. Delete the files of the temporary, reconstructed copy of the database to conserve disk space.

PART

VII Database and Instance Tuning

CHAPTER

20 UNDERSTANDING THE TUNING PROCESS

ORACLE is a sophisticated and highly tunable software product. Its flexibility allows you to make small adjustments that affect performance. By tuning ORACLE, you can tailor its performance to best meet your needs.

In this chapter, you will establish your goals for the tuning process. After establishing these goals, you can more easily choose the tuning measures in this Guide that will most benefit you.

This chapter also presents an overview of the tuning method recommended by Oracle. This method is a complete, step by step process for tuning ORACLE. The overview discusses the scope, importance, and benefits of each step of the method. If you have never tuned ORACLE, you should follow these steps in order. This method provides you with an approach to tuning that is both sound and straightforward. It also introduces you to the performance diagnostic tools provided by ORACLE. If you are already familiar with tuning ORACLE or if you think you know which part of your database needs tuning, this chapter helps you find the specific information you need.

This chapter also lists some of the most important individual tips to consider when tuning ORACLE. These tips highlight the tuning process.

Setting Goals for Tuning

Before you begin tuning ORACLE, you should establish goals for tuning. These goals should stem directly from your reasons for tuning and should be based on the business requirements for which you use ORACLE. For example, you may want to tune ORACLE so that your order entry application can accept a high volume of orders during the peak of the business day.

Your goals for tuning may include one or more of these goals:

- to improve the performance of a specific type of SQL statement
- to improve the performance of a specific database application
- to improve the overall performance of all concurrent users and applications on your database

Keep your goals in mind as you consider each of the tuning measures in this Guide. To decide whether to implement a particular measure, you should consider its performance benefits in light of your goals.

Also keep in mind that your goals may conflict. For example, to achieve best performance for a specific SQL statement, you may have to sacrifice the performance of other SQL statements running concurrently on your database.

Steps of the Tuning Process

The process of tuning ORACLE has three steps. Each step is described in one of the following chapters:

Step One	Chapter 21 "Tuning Memory Allocation" of this Guide
Step Two	Chapter 22 "Tuning I/O" of this Guide
Step Three	Chapter 23 "Tuning Contention" of this Guide

These steps are designed to be as modular and independent as possible. For example, the benefits of tuning I/O in Step Two are separate from the benefits of eliminating contention in Step Three.

However, decisions you make in one step may influence subsequent steps. For example, disk I/O, which is tuned in Step Two, depends on the size of the buffer cache, which is tuned in Step One. The steps that have the greatest effects on other steps as well as the greatest effect on performance appear early in the method. For this reason, you should follow these steps in order.

Before Beginning the Process

Good performance begins with good application design and efficient SQL statements. Before beginning the process of tuning ORACLE itself, you should be certain that your applications have been designed to take full advantage of ORACLE features and that your SQL statements are written to be most efficiently processed by ORACLE. Guidelines for designing applications and writing SQL statements for best performance appear in Chapter 1 "The Application Developer" and Chapter 5 "Tuning SQL Statements" of the *ORACLE7 Server Application Developer's Guide*, respectively. Discuss these chapters with the developers of your applications.

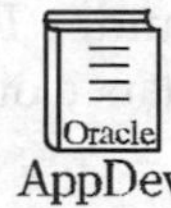

AppDev

Step One: Tuning Memory Allocation

Appropriate allocation of memory resources to ORACLE memory structures can have a large impact on performance. In Step One, you will decide how much memory to allocate to the following structures:

- SQL and PL/SQL areas
- the data dictionary cache
- the buffer cache

Proper allocation of memory resources can yield these benefits:

- improved cache performance
- reduced parsing of SQL statements and PL/SQL blocks
- reduced paging and swapping

Step Two: Tuning I/O

Disk I/O tends to reduce the performance of many software applications. However, ORACLE is designed so that its performance need not be limited by I/O.

Tuning I/O involves these procedures:

- distributing I/O to avoid disk contention
- storing data in data blocks for best access
- creating extents large enough for your data

Step Three: Tuning Contention

Concurrent processing by multiple ORACLE users may create contention for ORACLE resources. Contention may cause processes to wait until resources are available. In Step Three you will reduce contention for:

- rollback segments
- processes of the multi-threaded server architecture
- redo log buffer latches

After Completing the Process

After completing Step Three, reassess performance and decide whether further tuning is necessary. Since some performance gains made in later steps may pave the way for further improvements in earlier steps, additional passes through the tuning process may be useful.

You should also consider the tuning measures discussed in Chapter 24 "Additional Tuning Considerations" of this Guide. These measures tune ORACLE operations that reduce performance only in special cases.

Top Tuning Tips

Some parts of the tuning process are more important than others. The following list highlights the most important parts of tuning. This list is by no means an exhaustive collection of all the material presented in this Guide.

Pay particular attention to the issues addressed in this list. If you have not tuned ORACLE before, this list gives you perspective of the relative importance of the parts of the tuning process. If you are familiar with tuning ORACLE, this list directs you to the parts of this Guide and other ORACLE manuals that discuss these issues.

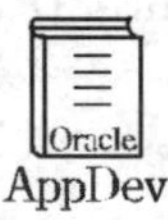

AppDev

1. Index tables appropriately. Proper use of indexes may improve the performance of some SQL statements by orders of magnitude. For information on indexes, see Chapter 5 "Tuning SQL Statements" of the *ORACLE7 Server Application Developer's Guide*.

AppDev

2. Use cost-based optimization whenever possible. With this approach, the optimizer uses statistics for tables, indexes, and clusters to choose the fastest way to execute a SQL statement. This approach reduces the time and effort necessary for you to tune your SQL statements. For information on how to use the cost-based approach, see Chapter 5 "Tuning SQL Statements" of the *ORACLE7 Server Application Developer's Guide*.
3. To direct the optimizer to choose a specific way to execute a SQL statement, use *hints*, or suggestions within a comment within the statement. For information on hints, see Chapter 5 "Tuning SQL Statements" of the*ORACLE7 Server Application Developer's Guide*.

4. Take advantage of other new features of ORACLE7. Enforced integrity constraints are discussed in Chapter 5 "Maintaining Data Integrity" of the *ORACLE7 Server Application Developer's Guide*. Stored Procedures are discussed in Chapter 7 "Using Procedures and Packages" of the *ORACLE7 Server Application Developer's Guide*. Shared SQL and PL/SQL areas are discussed in Chapter 21 "Tuning Memory Allocation" of this Guide.

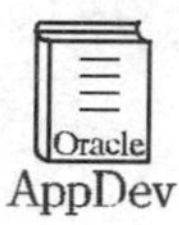

AppDev

5. Reduce the time spent parsing by keeping frequently-used SQL statements and stored procedures parsed after execution and by keeping dictionary data in memory. For information on these measures, see Chapter 21 "Tuning Memory Allocation" of this Guide.

6. If excessive I/O of data blocks occurs, increase the size of the buffer cache in the System Global Area (SGA). For information on resizing ORACLE memory structures, see Chapter 21 "Tuning Memory Allocation" of this Guide.

7. On operating systems with virtual storage, be sure the System Global Area (SGA) fits into real memory to ensure fast access to cached data. For information on allocating memory, see Chapter 21 "Tuning Memory Allocation" of this Guide.

8. Distribute I/O so that none of the disks containing your data files and redo log files are operating near full capacity. For information on distributing I/O, see Chapter 22 "Tuning I/O" of this Guide.

9. Reduce contention for latches if the percentage of latch requests that result in waiting significantly exceeds 1%. For methods of monitoring and reducing latch contention, see Chapter 23 "Tuning Contention" of this Guide.

10. Be sure all ORACLE processes, both foreground and background, have the same operating system process priority. Performance problems may occur if your operating system swaps out a low priority process while that process has exclusive access to a resource. A high priority process in need of that resource may wait indefinitely for the low priority process to be swapped back in. For information on problems caused by contention, see Chapter 23 "Tuning Contention" of this Guide.

CHAPTER

21 Tuning Memory Allocation

This chapter presents Step One of the tuning process: tuning memory allocation. This chapter discusses tuning the performance of the following ORACLE memory structures:

- private SQL and PL/SQL areas
- the shared pool
- the buffer cache

The performance of ORACLE can be improved by proper sizing of these structures. In this chapter, you will allocate memory to these structures to achieve best performance.

The Importance of Memory Allocation

ORACLE stores information in two places:

- in memory
- on disk

Since memory access is much faster than disk access, it is desirable for data requests to be satisfied by access to memory rather than access to disk. For best performance, it is advantageous to store as much data as possible in memory rather than on disk. However, memory resources on your operating system are likely to be limited. Tuning memory allocation involves distributing available memory to ORACLE memory structures.

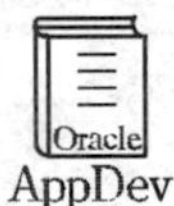

AppDev

Because ORACLE's memory requirements vary depending on your application, you should tune memory allocation after tuning your application and your SQL statements based on the recommendations presented in Chapter 1 "The Application Developer" and Chapter 5 "Tuning SQL Statements" of the *ORACLE7 Server Application Developer's Guide*. Allocating memory before tuning your application and your SQL statements may make it necessary to resize some ORACLE memory structures to meet the needs of your modified statements and application.

Also, you should tune memory allocation before considering the information in Chapter 22 "Tuning I/O" of this Guide. Allocating memory establishes the amount of I/O necessary for ORACLE to operate. This chapter shows you how to allocate memory in order to perform as little I/O as possible. Chapter 22 shows you how to perform that I/O as efficiently as possible.

Steps for Tuning Memory Allocation

This section outlines the process of tuning memory allocation. For best results, you should follow these steps in the order they are presented. Each step is described in more detail in the remainder of this chapter.

Tuning Your Operating System

Ensuring that your operating system runs smoothly and efficiently establishes a solid basis for allocating memory to ORACLE. This step also gives you a good idea of the amount of memory on your operating system that is available for ORACLE.

Tuning Private SQL and PL/SQL Areas

The use of SQL and PL/SQL areas and the frequency of parse calls are primarily determined by your application. Since parsing affects the frequency of access to the data dictionary, you should tune private SQL and PL/SQL areas before tuning the data dictionary cache in the shared pool.

Tuning the Shared Pool

Tuning the shared pool involves allocating memory for these memory structures:

- the library cache containing shared SQL and PL/SQL areas
- the data dictionary cache
- information for sessions connected through shared server processes

A cache miss on the data dictionary cache miss or library cache is more expensive than a miss on the buffer cache. For this reason, you should allocate sufficient memory for the shared pool first.

Tuning the Buffer Cache

After tuning private SQL and PL/SQL areas and the shared pool, you can devote the remaining available memory to the buffer cache.

It may be necessary to repeat the steps of memory allocation after the initial pass through the process. Subsequent passes allow you to make adjustments in earlier steps based on changes in later steps. For example, if you increase the size of the buffer cache, you may need to allocate more memory to ORACLE to avoid paging and swapping.

Tuning Your Operating System

You should begin tuning memory allocation by tuning your operating system with these goals:

- to reduce paging and swapping
- to fit the System Global Area (SGA) into main memory
- to allocate enough memory to individual users

These goals apply in general to most operating systems. However, the details of tuning your operating system vary depending on which operating system you are using.

Reducing Paging and Swapping

Your operating system may store information in any of these places:

- real memory
- virtual memory
- expanded storage
- disk

Your operating system may also move information from one storage location to another. Depending on your operating system, this movement is called paging or swapping. Many operating systems page and swap to accommodate large amounts of information that do not fit into real memory. However, paging and swapping take time. Excessive paging or swapping can reduce the performance of many operating systems.

Monitor your operating system behavior with operating system utilities. Excessive paging or swapping indicates that new information is often being moved into memory. In this case, your system's total memory may not be large enough to hold everything for which you have allocated memory. You should either increase the total memory on your system or decrease the amount of memory you have allocated.

Tuning the System Global Area (SGA)

Since the purpose of the System Global Area (SGA) is to store data in memory for fast access, the SGA should always be contained in main memory. If the SGA is swapped to disk, its data is no longer so quickly accessible. On most operating systems, the disadvantage of excessive paging significantly outweighs the advantage of a large SGA, so you should ensure that the entire SGA always fits into memory and is not paged or swapped.

You can see how much memory is allocated to the SGA and each of its internal structures by issuing this SQL*DBA statement:

```
SQLDBA> SHOW SGA
```

The output of this statement might look like this:

```
Total System Global Area          3554188 bytes
              Fixed Size            22208 bytes
           Variable Size          3376332 bytes
        Database Buffers           122880 bytes
            Redo Buffers            32768 bytes
```

Some operating systems for IBM mainframe computers are equipped with *expanded storage*, or special memory in addition to main memory to which paging can be performed very quickly. These operating systems may be able to page data between main memory and expanded storage faster than ORACLE can read and write data between the SGA and disk. For this reason, allowing a larger SGA to be swapped may lead to better performance than ensuring that a smaller SGA stays in main memory. If your operating system has expanded storage, you can take advantage of it by allocating a larger SGA despite the resulting paging.

User Memory Allocation

On some operating systems, you may have control over the amount of physical memory allocated to each user. Be sure all users are allocated enough memory to accommodate the resources they need to use their application with ORACLE. Depending on your operating system, these resources may include:

- the ORACLE executable image
- the SGA
- ORACLE application tools
- application-specific data

On some operating systems, ORACLE software can be installed so that a single executable image can be shared by many users. By sharing executable images among users, you can reduce the amount of memory required by each user.

Tuning Private SQL and PL/SQL Areas

In this section you learn how to tune private SQL and PL/SQL areas. Tuning private SQL areas involves identifying unnecessary parse calls made by your application and then reducing them. To reduce parse calls, you may have to increase the number of private SQL areas that your application can have allocated at once. Throughout this section, information about private SQL areas and SQL statements also applies to private PL/SQL areas and PL/SQL blocks.

Identifying Unnecessary Parse Calls

To identify unnecessary parse calls, run your application with the SQL trace facility enabled. For each SQL statement in the trace output, examine the *count* statistic for the Parse step. This statistic tells you how many times your application makes a parse call for the statement. This statistic includes parse calls that are satisfied by access to the library cache as well as parse calls that result in actually parsing the statement. Note that this statistic does not include implicit parsing that occurs when an application executes a statement whose shared SQL area is no longer in the library cache. For information on detecting implicit parsing, see the section "Examining Library Cache Activity" on page 21-8.

If the *count* value for the Parse step is near the *count* value for the Execute step for a statement, your application may be deliberately making a parse call each time it executes the statement. Try to reduce these parse calls through your application tool.

Reducing Unnecessary Parse Calls

Depending on the ORACLE application tool you are using, you may be able to control how frequently your application performs parse calls and allocates and deallocates private SQL areas. Whether your application reuses private SQL areas for multiple SQL statements determines how many parse calls your application performs and how many private SQL areas the application requires. In general, an application that reuses private SQL areas for multiple SQL statements does not need as many private SQL areas as an application that does not. However, an application that reuses private SQL areas must perform more parse calls because the application must make a new parse call whenever an existing private SQL is reused for a new SQL statement.

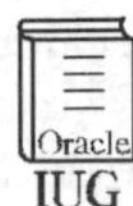

IUG

Be sure that your application can open enough private SQL areas to accommodate all of your SQL statements. If you allocate more private SQL areas, you may need to increase the limit on the number of cursors permitted for a session. You can increase this limit by increasing the value of the initialization parameter OPEN_CURSORS. The maximum value for this parameter depends on your operating system. The minimum value is 5.

The means by which you control parse calls and allocation and deallocation of private SQL areas varies depending on your ORACLE application tool. The following sections introduce the means used for some tools. Note that these means apply only to private SQL areas and not to shared SQL areas.

Reducing Parse Calls with the ORACLE Precompilers With the ORACLE Precompilers, you control private SQL areas and parse calls with these options:

- HOLD_CURSOR
- RELEASE_CURSOR
- MAXOPENCURSORS

These options can be specified in two ways:

- on the precompiler command line
- within the precompiler program

Precomp

With these options, you can employ different strategies for managing private SQL areas during the course of the program. For information on these options, see the *Programmer's Guide to the ORACLE Precompilers* or the *Programmer's Guide to the Pro*Ada Precompiler*.

Reducing Parse Calls with the ORACLE Call Interfaces (OCIs) With the ORACLE Call Interfaces (OCIs), you have complete control over parse calls and private SQL areas with these OCI calls:

OSQL3 OPARSE	An OSQL3 or OPARSE call allocates a private SQL area for a SQL statement.
OCLOSE	An OCLOSE call closes a cursor and deallocates the private SQL area of its associated statement.

OCI

For more information on these calls, see the *Programmer's Guide to the ORACLE Call Interfaces* or the *Pro*Ada ORACLE Call Interface User's Guide*.

Reducing Parse Calls with SQL*Forms With SQL*Forms, you also have some control over whether your application reuses private SQL areas. You can exercise this control in three places:

- at the trigger level
- at the form level
- at runtime

For more information on the reuse of private SQL areas by SQL*Forms, see the *SQL*Forms Designer's Reference* manual.

Tuning the Shared Pool

This section describes tuning these parts of the shared pool:

- library cache
- data dictionary cache
- session information

This section presents these parts of the shared pool in order of importance. Because the algorithm that ORACLE uses to manage data in the shared pool that tends to hold dictionary data in memory longer than library cache data, tuning the library cache to an acceptable cache hit ratio often ensures that the data dictionary cache hit ratio is also acceptable. Allocating space in the shared pool for session information is only necessary if you are using the multi-threaded server architecture.

Tuning the Library Cache

The library cache contains shared SQL and PL/SQL areas. This section tells you how to tune the library cache by:

- examining library cache activity
- reducing library cache misses
- speeding access to shared SQL and PL/SQL areas in the library cache

Throughout this section, information about shared SQL areas and SQL statements also applies to shared PL/SQL areas and PL/SQL blocks.

Examining Library Cache Activity

Library cache misses can occur on either of these steps in the processing of a SQL statement.

Parse If an application makes a parse call for a SQL statement and the parsed representation of the statement does not already exist in a shared SQL area in the library cache, ORACLE parses the statement and allocates a shared SQL area. You may be able to reduce library cache misses on parse calls by ensuring that SQL statements can share a shared SQL area whenever possible.

Execute If an application makes an execute call for a SQL statement and the shared SQL area containing the parsed representation of the statement has been deallocated from the library cache to make room for another statement, ORACLE implicitly reparses the statement, allocates a new shared SQL area for it, and executes it. You may be able to reduce library cache misses on execution calls by allocating more memory to the library cache.

Determine whether misses on the library cache are affecting the performance of ORACLE by querying the dynamic performance table V$LIBRARYCACHE.

The V$LIBRARYCACHE Table Statistics reflecting library cache activity are kept in the dynamic performance table V$LIBRARYCACHE. These statistics reflect all library cache activity since the most recent instance startup. To monitor library cache activity, examine this table. By default, this table is only available to the user SYS and to users granted SELECT ANY TABLE system privilege, such as SYSTEM.

Each row in this table contains statistics for one type of item kept in the library cache. The item described by each row is identified by the value of the NAMESPACE column. Rows of the table with these NAMESPACE values reflect library cache activity for SQL statements and PL/SQL blocks:

- 'SQL AREA'
- 'TABLE/PROCEDURE'
- 'BODY'
- 'TRIGGER'

Rows with other NAMESPACE values reflect library cache activity for object definitions that ORACLE uses for dependency maintenance.

These columns of the V$LIBRARYCACHE table reflect library cache misses on execution calls:

PINS	This column shows the number of times an item in the library cache was executed.
RELOADS	This column shows the number of library cache misses on execution steps.

Querying the V$LIBRARY Cache Table Monitor the statistics in the V$LIBRARYCACHE table over a period of time with this query:

```
SELECT SUM(pins) "Executions",
       SUM(reloads) "Cache Misses while Executing"
    FROM v$librarycache
```

The output of this query might look like this:

```
Executions Cache Misses while Executing
---------- ----------------------------
    320871                          549
```

Interpreting the V$LIBRARYCACHE Table Examining the data returned by the sample query leads to these observations:

- The sum of the PINS column indicates that SQL statements, PL/SQL blocks, and object definitions were accessed for execution a total of 320,871 times.
- The sum of the RELOADS column indicates that 549 of those executions resulted in library cache misses causing ORACLE to implicitly reparse a statement or block or reload an object definition because it had aged out of the library cache.
- The ratio of the total RELOADS to total PINS is about 0.17%. This value means that only 0.17% of executions resulted in reparsing.

Total RELOADS should be near 0. If the ratio of RELOADS to PINS is more than 1%, then you should reduce these library cache misses through the means discussed in the next section.

Reducing Library Cache Misses

You can reduce library cache misses by:

- allocating additional memory for the library cache
- writing identical SQL statements whenever possible

Allocating Additional Memory for the Library Cache You may be able to reduce library cache misses on execution calls by allocating additional memory for the library cache. To ensure that shared SQL areas remain in the cache once their SQL statements are parsed, increase the amount of memory available to the library cache until the V$LIBRARYCACHE.RELOADS value is near 0. To increase the amount of memory available to the library cache, increase the value of the initialization parameter SHARED_POOL_SIZE. The maximum value for this parameter depends on your operating system. This measure will reduce implicit reparsing of SQL statements and PL/SQL blocks on execution.

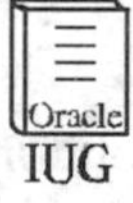

IUG

To take advantage of additional memory available for shared SQL areas, you may also need to increase the number of cursors permitted for a session. You can increase this limit by increasing the value of the initialization parameter OPEN_CURSORS.

Be careful not to induce paging and swapping by allocating too much memory for the library cache. The benefits of a library cache large enough to avoid cache misses can be partially offset by reading shared SQL areas into memory from disk whenever you need to access them.

Writing Identical SQL Statements You may be able to reduce library cache misses on parse calls by ensuring that SQL statements and PL/SQL blocks share a shared SQL area whenever possible. For two different occurrences of a SQL statement or PL/SQL block to share a shared SQL area, they must be identical according to these criteria:

- The text of the SQL statements or PL/SQL blocks must be identical, character for character, including spaces and case.

  For example, these statements cannot use the same shared SQL area:

  ```
  SELECT * FROM emp
  SELECT *    FROM emp
  ```

  These statements cannot use the same shared SQL area:

  ```
  SELECT * FROM emp
  SELECT * FROM Emp
  ```

- References to schema objects in the SQL statements or PL/SQL blocks must resolve to the same object in the same schema.

  For example, if the schemas of the users BOB and ED both contain an EMP table and both users issue the following statement, their statements cannot use the same shared SQL area:

  ```
  SELECT * FROM emp
  ```

  If both statements query the same table and qualify the table with the schema, as in the following statement, then they can use the same shared SQL area:

  ```
  SELECT * FROM bob.emp
  ```

- Bind variables in the SQL statements must match in name and datatype. For example, these statements cannot use the same shared SQL area:

  ```
  SELECT * FROM emp WHERE deptno = :department_no
  SELECT * FROM emp WHERE deptno = :d_no
  ```

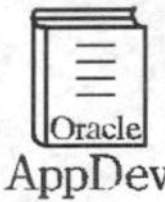

AppDev

- The SQL statements must be optimized using the same optimization approach and, in the case of the cost-based approach, the same optimization goal. For information on optimization approach and goal, see Chapter 5 "Tuning SQL Statements" of the *ORACLE7 Server Application Developer's Guide.*

Shared SQL areas are most useful for reducing library cache misses for multiple users running the same application. Discuss these criteria with the developers of such applications and agree on strategies to ensure that the SQL statements and PL/SQL blocks of an application can use the same shared SQL areas:

- Use bind variables rather than explicitly specified constants in your statements whenever possible.

  For example, the following two statements cannot use the same shared area because they do not match character for character:

  ```
  SELECT ename, empno FROM emp WHERE deptno = 10
  SELECT ename, empno FROM emp WHERE deptno = 20
  ```

  You can accomplish the goals of these statements by using the following statement that contains a bind variable and binding 10 for one occurrence of the statement and 20 for the other:

  ```
  SELECT ename, empno FROM emp WHERE deptno = :department_no
  ```

  The two occurrences of the statement can use the same shared SQL area.

- Be sure that individual users of the application do not change the optimization approach and goal for their individual sessions.

You can also increase the likelihood that SQL statements issued by different applications can share SQL areas by establishing these policies among the developers of these applications:

- Standardize naming conventions for bind variables and spacing conventions for SQL statements and PL/SQL blocks.
- Use stored procedures whenever possible. Multiple users issuing the same stored procedure automatically use the same shared PL/SQL area. Since stored procedures are stored in a parsed form, they eliminate runtime parsing altogether.

Speeding Access to Shared SQL Areas on Execution Calls

If you have no library cache misses, you may still be able to speed execution calls by setting the value of the initialization parameter CURSOR_SPACE_FOR_TIME. This parameter specifies when a shared SQL area can be deallocated from the library cache to make room for a new SQL statement. The default value of this parameter is FALSE, meaning that a shared SQL area can be deallocated from the library cache regardless of whether application cursors associated with its SQL statement are open. The value of TRUE means that a shared SQL area can only be deallocated when all application cursors associated with its statement are closed.

Depending on the value of CURSOR_SPACE_FOR_TIME, ORACLE behaves differently when an application makes an execution call. If the value is FALSE, ORACLE must take time to check that a shared SQL area containing the SQL statement is in the library cache. If the value is TRUE, ORACLE need not make this check because the shared SQL area can never be deallocated while an application cursor associated with it is open. Setting the value of the parameter to TRUE saves ORACLE a small amount of time and may slightly improve the performance of execution calls. This value also prevents the deallocation of private SQL areas until associated application cursors are closed.

Do not set the value of CURSOR_SPACE_FOR_TIME to TRUE if there are library cache misses on execution calls. Such library cache misses indicate that the shared pool is not large enough to hold the shared SQL areas of all concurrently open cursors. If the value is TRUE and there is no space in the shared pool for a new SQL statement, the statement cannot be parsed and ORACLE returns an error saying that there is no more shared memory. If the value is FALSE and there is no space for a new statement, ORACLE deallocates an existing shared SQL area. Although deallocating a shared SQL area results in a library cache miss later, it is preferable to an error halting your application because a SQL statement cannot be parsed.

Do not set the value of CURSOR_SPACE_FOR_TIME to TRUE if the amount of memory available to each user for private SQL areas is scarce. This value also prevents the deallocation of private SQL areas associated with open cursors. If the private SQL areas for all concurrently open cursors fills the user's available memory so that there is no space to allocate a private SQL area for a new SQL statement, the statement cannot be parsed and ORACLE returns an error indicating that there is not enough memory.

Tuning the Data Dictionary Cache

In this section, you will tune the data dictionary cache. These topics are discussed in this section:

- how to monitor the activity of the data dictionary cache
- how to improve the performance of the data dictionary cache

Examining Data Dictionary Cache Activity

Determine whether misses on the data dictionary cache are affecting the performance of ORACLE. You can examine cache activity by querying the V$ROWCACHE table as described in the following sections.

Misses on the data dictionary cache are to be expected in some cases. Upon instance startup, the data dictionary cache contains no data, so any SQL statement issued is likely to result in cache misses. As more data is read into the cache, the likelihood of cache misses should decrease. Eventually the database should reach a "steady state" in which the most frequently used dictionary data is in the cache. At this point, very few cache misses should occur. To tune the cache, examine its activity only after your application has been running.

The V$ROWCACHE Table Statistics reflecting data dictionary activity are kept in the dynamic performance table V$ROWCACHE. By default, this table is only available to the user SYS and to users granted SELECT ANY TABLE system privilege, such as SYSTEM.

Each row in this table contains statistics for a single type of the data dictionary item. These statistics reflect all data dictionary activity since the most recent instance startup. These columns in the V$ROWCACHE table reflect the use and effectiveness of the data dictionary cache:

PARAMETER — This column identifies a particular data dictionary item. For each row, the value in this column is the item prefixed by 'dc_'.

For example, in the row that contains statistics for file descriptions, this column has the value 'dc_files'.

GETS — This column shows the total number of requests for information on the corresponding item.

For example, in the row that contains statistics for file descriptions, this column has the total number of requests for file descriptions data.

GETMISSES — This column shows the number of data requests resulting in cache misses.

Querying the V$ROWCACHE Table Monitor the statistics in the V$ROWCACHE table over a period of time while your application is running with this query:

```
SELECT SUM(gets)       "Data Dictionary Gets",
       SUM(getmisses) "Data Dictionary Cache Get Misses"
   FROM v$rowcache
```

The output of this query might look like this:

```
Data Dictionary Gets  Data Dictionary Cache Get Misses
-------------------- --------------------------------
             1439044                             3120
```

Interpreting the V$ROWCACHE Table Examining the data returned by the sample query leads to these observations:

- The sum of the GETS column indicates that there were a total of 1,439,044 requests for dictionary data.
- The sum of the GETMISSES column indicates that 3120 of the requests for dictionary data resulted in cache misses.
- The ratio of the sums of GETMISSES to GETS is about 0.2%.

Reducing Data Dictionary Cache Misses

Examine cache activity by monitoring the sums of the GETS and GETMISSES columns. For frequently accessed dictionary caches, the ratio of total GETMISSES to total GETS should be less than 10% or 15%. If this ratio continues to increase above this threshold while your application is running, you should consider increasing the amount of memory available to the data dictionary cache. To increase the memory available to the cache, increase the value of the initialization parameter SHARED_POOL_SIZE. The maximum value for this parameter varies depending on your operating system.

Tuning the Shared Pool with the Multi-Threaded Server

In the multi-threaded server architecture, ORACLE stores session information in the shared pool rather than in the memory of user processes. Session information includes private SQL areas and sort areas. If you are using the multi-threaded server architecture, you may need to make your shared pool larger to accommodate session information. You can increase the size of the shared pool by increasing the value of the SHARED_POOL_SIZE initialization parameter. This section discusses measuring the size of session information by querying the dynamic performance table V$SESSTAT.

The V$SESSTAT Table

ORACLE collects statistics on total memory used by a session and stores them in the dynamic performance table V$SESSTAT. By default, this table is only available to the user SYS and to users granted SELECT ANY TABLE system privilege, such as SYSTEM. These statistics are useful for measuring session memory use:

session memory — The value of this statistic is the amount of memory in bytes allocated to the session.

max session memory — The value of this statistic is the maximum amount of memory in bytes ever allocated to the session.

Querying the V$SESSTAT Table

You can use this query to decide how much larger to make the shared pool if you are using the multi-threaded server. Issue these queries while your application is running:

```
SELECT SUM(value) || ' bytes' "Total memory for all sessions"
    FROM v$sesstat
    WHERE name = 'session memory'

SELECT SUM(value) || ' bytes' "Total max mem for all sessions"
    FROM v$sesstat
    WHERE name = 'max session memory'
```

The results of these queries might look like this:

```
Total memory for all sessions
-----------------------------
157125 bytes

Total max mem for all sessions
------------------------------
417381 bytes
```

Interpreting the V$SESSTAT Table

The result of the first query indicates that the memory currently allocated to all sessions is 15,715 bytes. This value is the total memory whose location depends on how the sessions are connected to ORACLE. If the sessions are connected with dedicated servers processes, this memory is part of the memories of the user processes. If the sessions are connected with shared server processes, this memory is part of the shared pool. The result of the second query indicates the sum of the maximum sizes of the memories for all sessions is 417,381 bytes. The second result is greater than the first because some sessions have deallocated memory since allocating their maximum amounts.

You can use the result of either of these queries to determine how much larger to make the shared pool if you use the multi-threaded server. The first value is likely to be a better estimate than the second unless nearly all sessions are likely to reach their maximum allocations at the same time.

Tuning the Buffer Cache

In this section, you will learn how to tune the buffer cache. The following issues are covered in this section:

- how to monitor buffer cache performance
- how to improve buffer cache performance

Examining Buffer Cache Activity

ORACLE collects statistics that reflect data access and stores them in the dynamic performance table V$SYSSTAT. By default, this table is only available to the user SYS and to users granted SELECT ANY TABLE system privilege, such as SYSTEM. These statistics are useful for tuning the buffer cache:

db block gets, consistent gets — The sum of the values of these statistics is the total number of requests for data. This value includes requests satisfied by access to buffers in memory.

physical reads — The value of this statistic is the total number of requests for data resulting in access to data files on disk.

Monitor these statistics over a period of time while your application is running with this query:

```
SELECT name, value
   FROM v$sysstat
   WHERE name IN ('db block gets', 'consistent gets', 'physical reads')
```

The output of this query might look like this:

```
NAME                                                        VALUE
------------------------------------------------------ ----------
db block gets                                               85792
consistent gets                                            278888
physical reads                                              23182
```

Calculate the hit ratio for the buffer cache with this formula:

Hit Ratio = 1 - (*physical reads* / (*db block gets* + *consistent gets*))

Based on the statistics obtained by the example query, the buffer cache hit ratio is 94%.

Reducing Buffer Cache Misses

If your hit ratio is low, say less than 60% or 70%, then you may want to increase the number of buffers in the cache to improve performance. To make the buffer cache larger, increase the value of the initialization parameter DB_BLOCK_BUFFERS. The maximum value for this parameter is 65535.

ORACLE can collect statistics that estimate the performance gain that would result from increasing the size of your buffer cache. With these statistics, you can estimate how many buffers to add to your cache.

The X$KCBRBH Table

The virtual table SYS.X$KCBRBH contains statistics that estimate the performance of a larger cache. Each row in the table reflects the relative performance value of adding a buffer to the cache. This table can only be accessed by the user SYS. The following are the columns of the X$KCBRBH table:

INDX — The value of this column is one less than the number of buffers that would potentially be added to the cache.

COUNT — The value of this column is the number of additional cache hits that would be obtained by adding additional buffer number INDX+1 to the cache.

For example, in the first row of the table, the INDX value is 0 and the COUNT value is the number of cache hits to be gained by adding the first additional buffer to the cache. In the second row, the INDX value is 1 and the COUNT value is the number of cache hits for the second additional buffer.

Enabling the X$KCBRBH Table

The collection of statistics in the X$KCBRBH table is controlled by the initialization parameter DB_BLOCK_LRU_EXTENDED_STATISTICS. The value of this parameter determines the number of rows in the X$KCBRBH table. The default value of this parameter is 0, which means the default behavior is to not collect statistics.

To enable the collection of statistics in the X$KCBRBH table, set the value of DB_BLOCK_LRU_EXTENDED_STATISTICS. For example, if you set the value of the parameter to 100, ORACLE will collect 100 rows of statistics, each row reflecting the addition of one buffer, up to 100 extra buffers.

Collecting these statistics incurs some performance overhead. This overhead is proportional to the number of rows in the table. To avoid this overhead, collect statistics only when you are tuning the buffer cache and disable the collection of statistics when you are finished tuning.

Querying the X$KCBRBH Table

From the information in the X$KCBRBH table, you can predict the potential gains of increasing the cache size. For example, to determine how many more cache hits would occur if you added 20 buffers to the cache, query the X$KCBRBH table with the SQL statement:

```
SELECT SUM(count) ach
    FROM sys.x$kcbrbh
    WHERE indx < 20
```

You can also determine how these additional cache hits would affect the hit ratio. Use the following formula to calculate the hit ratio based on the values of the statistics *db block gets*, *consistent gets*, and *physical reads* and the number of additional cache hits (ACH) returned by the query:

Hit Ratio = 1 - (*physical reads* - ACH / (*db block gets* + *consistent gets*))

Grouping Rows in the X$KCBRBH Table

Another way to examine the X$KCBRBH table is to group the additional buffers in large intervals. You can query the table with a SQL statement similar to this one:

```
SELECT 250*TRUNC(indx/250)+1||' to '||250*(TRUNC(indx/250)+1)
"Interval", SUM(count) "Buffer Cache Hits"
    FROM sys.x$kcbrbh
    GROUP BY TRUNC(indx/250)
```

The result of this query might look like this:

```
Interval        Buffer Cache Hits
--------------- --------------------
1 to 250                       16080
251 to 500                     10950
501 to 750                       710
751 to 1000                    23140
```

where:

INTERVAL	is the interval of additional buffers to be added to the cache.
BUFFER CACHE HITS	is the number of additional cache hits to be gained by adding the buffers in the INTERVAL column.

Examining the query output leads to these observations:

- If 250 buffers were added to the cache, 16,080 cache hits would be gained.
- If 250 more buffers were added for a total of 500 additional buffers, 10,950 cache hits would be gained in addition to the 16,080 cache hits from the first 250 buffers. This means that adding 500 buffers would yield a total of 27,030 additional cache hits.
- If 250 more buffers were added for a total of 750 additional buffers, 710 cache hits would be gained, yielding a total of 27,740 additional cache hits.
- If 250 buffers were added to the cache for a total of 1000 additional buffers, 23,140 cache hits would be gained, yielding a total of 50,880 additional cache hits.

Based on these observations, you should decide how many buffers to add to the cache. In this case, you may make these decisions:

- It is wise to add 250 or 500 buffers, provided memory resources are available. Both of these increments offer significant performance gains.
- It is unwise to add 750 buffers. Nearly the entire performance gain made by such an increase can be made by adding 500 buffers instead. Also, the memory allocated to the additional 250 buffers may be better used by some other ORACLE memory structure.
- It is wise to add 1000 buffers, provided memory resources are available. The performance gain from adding 1000 buffers to the cache is significantly greater than the gains from adding 250, 500, or 750 buffers.

Removing Unnecessary Buffers

If your hit ratio is high, your cache is probably large enough to hold your most frequently accessed data. In this case, you may be able to reduce the cache size and still maintain good performance. To make the buffer cache smaller, reduce the value of the initialization parameter DB_BLOCK_BUFFERS. The minimum value for this parameter is 4. You can apply any leftover memory to other ORACLE memory structures.

ORACLE can collect statistics to predict buffer cache performance based on a smaller cache size. Examining these statistics can help you determine how small you can afford to make your buffer cache without adversely affecting performance.

The X$KCBCBH Table

The virtual table SYS.X$KCBCBH contains the statistics that estimate the performance of a smaller cache. The X$KCBCBH table is similar in structure to the X$KCBRBH table. This table can only be accessed by the user SYS. The following are the columns of the X$KCBCBH table:

INDX	The value of this column is the potential number of buffers in the cache.
COUNT	The value of this column is the number of cache hits attributable to buffer number INDX.

The number of rows in this table is equal to the number of buffers in your buffer cache. Each row in the table reflects the number of cache attributed to a single buffer. For example, in the second row, the INDX value is 1 and the COUNT value is the number of cache hits for the second buffer. In the third row, the INDX value is 2 and the COUNT value is the number of cache hits for the third buffer.

The first row of the table contains special information. The INDX value is 0 and the COUNT value is the total number of blocks moved into the first buffer in the cache.

Enabling the X$KCBCBH Table

The collection of statistics in the X$KCBCBH table is controlled by the initialization parameter DB_BLOCK_LRU_STATISTICS. The value of this parameter determines whether ORACLE collects the statistics. The default value for this parameter is FALSE, which means that the default behavior is to not collect statistics.

To enable the collection of statistics in the X$KCBCBH table, set the value of DB_BLOCK_LRU_STATISTICS to TRUE.

Collecting these statistics incurs some performance overhead. To avoid this overhead, collect statistics only when you are tuning the buffer cache and disable the collection of statistics when you are finished tuning.

Querying the X$KCBCBH Table

From the information in the X$KCBCBH table, you can predict the number of additional cache misses that would occur if the number of buffers in the cache were reduced. If your buffer cache currently contains 100 buffers, you may want to know how many more cache misses would occur if it had only 90. To determine the number of additional cache misses, query the X$KCBCBH table with the SQL statement:

```
SELECT SUM(count) acm
    FROM sys.x$kcbcbh
    WHERE indx >= 90
```

You can also determine the hit ratio based on this cache size. Use the following formula to calculate the hit ratio based on the values of the statistics *db block gets*, *consistent gets*, and *physical reads* and the number of additional cache misses (ACM) returned by the query:

Hit Ratio = 1 - (*physical reads* + ACM / (*db block gets* + *consistent gets*))

Grouping Rows in the X$KCBCBH Table

Another way to examine the X$KCBCBH table is to group the buffers in intervals. For example, if your cache contains 100 buffers, you may want to divide the cache into four 25-buffer intervals. You can query the table with a SQL statement similar to this one:

```
SELECT 25*TRUNC(indx/25)+1||' to '||25*(TRUNC(indx/25)+1) "Interval",
SUM(count) "Buffer Cache Hits"
    FROM sys.x$kcbcbh
    WHERE indx > 0
    GROUP BY TRUNC(indx/25)
```

Note that the WHERE clause prevents the query from collecting statistics from the first row of the table. The result of this query might look like this:

```
Interval          Buffer Cache Hits
--------------- --------------------
1 to 25                         1900
26 to 50                        1100
51 to 75                        1360
76 to 100                        230
```

where:

INTERVAL — is the interval of buffers in the cache.

BUFFER CACHE HITS — is the number of cache hits attributable to the buffers in the INTERVAL column.

Examining the query output leads to these observations:

- The last 25 buffers in the cache (buffers 76 to 100) contribute 230 cache hits. If the cache were reduced in size by 25 buffers, 230 cache hits would be lost.
- The third 25-buffer interval (buffers 51 to 75) contributes 1,360 cache hits. If these buffers were removed from the cache, 1,360 cache hits would be lost in addition to the 230 cache hits lost for buffers 76 to 100. Removing 50 buffers would result in losing a total of 1,590 cache hits.
- The second 25-buffer interval (buffers 26 to 50) contributes 1,100 cache hits. Removing 75 buffers from the cache would result in losing a total of 2,690 cache hits.
- The first 25 buffers in the cache (buffers 1 to 25) contribute 1,900 cache hits.

Based on these observations, you should decide whether to reduce the size of the cache. In this case, you may make these decisions:

- If memory is scarce, it may be wise to remove 25 buffers from the cache. The buffers 76 to 100 contribute relatively few cache hits compared to the total cache hits contributed by the entire cache. Removing 25 buffers will not significantly reduce cache performance, and the leftover memory may be better used by other ORACLE memory structures.
- It is unwise to remove more than 25 buffers from the cache. For example, removing 50 buffers would reduce cache performance significantly. The cache hits contributed by these buffers is a significant portion of the total cache hits.

Reallocating Memory

After resizing your ORACLE memory structures, re-evaluate the performance of the library cache, the data dictionary cache, and the buffer cache. If you have reduced the memory consumption of any one of these structures, you may want to allocate more memory to another structure. For example, if you have reduced the size of your buffer cache, you may now want to take advantage of the additional available memory by using it for the library cache.

Tune your operating system again. Resizing ORACLE memory structures may have changed ORACLE memory requirements. In particular, be sure paging and swapping is not excessive. For example, if the size of the data dictionary cache or the buffer cache has increased, the SGA may be too large to fit into main memory. In this case, the SGA could be paged or swapped.

In the process of reallocating memory, you may determine that the optimum size of ORACLE memory structures requires more memory than your operating system can provide. In this case, you may improve performance even further by adding more memory to your computer.

CHAPTER

22 TUNING I/O

This chapter presents Step Two of the tuning process: tuning I/O. This chapter teaches you how to avoid I/O bottlenecks that could prevent ORACLE from performing at its maximum potential. In this chapter you learn how to:

- reduce disk contention
- allocate space in data blocks
- avoid dynamic space management

The Importance of Tuning I/O

The performance of many software applications is inherently limited by disk I/O. Often, CPU activity must be suspended while I/O activity completes. Such an application is said to be "I/O bound." ORACLE is designed so that performance need not be limited by I/O.

Tuning I/O can help performance if a disk containing database files is operating at its capacity. However, tuning I/O cannot help performance in "CPU bound" cases, or cases in which your computer's CPUs are operating at their capacity.

It is important to tune I/O after following the memory allocation recommendations presented in Chapter 21 "Tuning Memory Allocation" of this Guide. Chapter 21 shows you how to allocate memory in order to reduce I/O to a minimum. After reaching this minimum, follow the instructions in this chapter in order to perform the necessary I/O as efficiently as possible.

Reducing Disk Contention

In this section you will learn how to reduce disk contention. The following issues are discussed in this section:

- what disk contention is
- how to monitor disk activity
- how to reduce disk activity

What Is Disk Contention?

Disk contention occurs when multiple processes try to access the same disk simultaneously. Most disks have limits on both the number of accesses and the amount of data they can transfer per second. When these limits are reached, processes may have to wait to access the disk.

Monitoring Disk Activity

Disk activity is reflected by:

- ORACLE file I/O statistics
- operating system statistics

ORACLE compiles ORACLE file I/O statistics that reflect disk access to database files. Your operating system may also keep statistics for disk access to all files.

Monitoring ORACLE Disk Activity

Examine disk access to database files through the dynamic performance table V$FILESTAT. By default, this table is only available to the user SYS and to users granted SELECT ANY TABLE system privilege, such as SYSTEM. These column values reflect the number of disk accesses for each datafile:

PHYRDS	The value of this column is the number of reads from each database file.
PHYWRTS	This value of this column is the number of writes to each database file.

Monitor these values over some period of time while your application is running with this query:

```
SELECT name, phyrds, phywrts
    FROM v$datafile df, v$filestat fs
    WHERE df.file# = fs.file#
```

This query also retrieves the name of each data file from the dynamic performance table V$DATAFILE. The output of this query might look like this:

```
NAME                                                 PHYRDS    PHYWRTS
-------------------------------------------------- ---------- ----------
DISK$DEV20:[ORACLE.DB_ORA70}ORA_SYSTEM.DBS              7679       2735
DISK$DEV20:[ORACLE.DB_ORA70}ORA_SYSTEM1.DBS               32        546
```

The total I/O for a single disk is the sum of PHYRDS and PHYWRTS for all the database files managed by the ORACLE instance on that disk. Determine this value for each of your disks. Also determine the rate at which I/O occurs for each disk by dividing the total I/O by the interval of time over which the statistics were collected.

Monitoring Operating System Disk Activity

IUG

Disks holding data files and redo log files may also hold files that are not related to ORACLE. Access to such files can only be monitored through operating system facilities rather than through the V$FILESTAT table. Such facilities may be documented in either the ORACLE installation or user's guide for your operating system or your operating system documentation.

Use your operating system facilities to examine the total I/O to your disks. Try to reduce any heavy access to disks that contain database files.

Distributing I/O

Consider the statistics in the V$FILESTAT table and your operating system facilities. Consult your hardware documentation to determine the limits on the capacity of your disks. Any disks operating at or near full capacity are potential sites for disk contention. For example, 40 or more I/Os per second is excessive for most disks on VMS or UNIX operating systems.

To reduce the activity on an overloaded disk, move one or more of its heavily accessed files to a less active disk. Apply this principle to each of your disks until they all have roughly the same amount of I/O. This is referred to as *distributing I/O.*

This section discusses guidelines for distributing I/O:

- Separate data files and redo log files on different disks.
- Separate, or "stripe," table data on different disks.
- Separate tables and indexes on different disks.
- Reduce disk I/O not related to ORACLE.

Separating Data Files and Redo Log Files

ORACLE processes constantly access data files and redo log files. If these files are on common disks, there is potential for disk contention.

Place each data file on a separate disk. Multiple processes can then access different files concurrently without disk contention.

Place each set of redo log files on a separate disk with no other activity. Redo log files are written by the Log Writer process (LGWR) when a transaction is committed. Information in a redo log file is written sequentially. This sequential writing can take place much faster if there is no concurrent activity on the same disk.

Dedicating a separate disk to redo log files usually ensures that LGWR runs smoothly with no further tuning attention. Performance bottlenecks related to LGWR are rare. For information on tuning LGWR, see the section "Reducing Contention for Redo Log Buffer Latches" on page 23-9.

Note that *mirroring* redo log files, or maintaining multiple copies of each redo log file on separate disks, does not slow LGWR considerably. LGWR writes to each disk in parallel and waits until each part of the parallel write is complete. Since the time required for your operating system to perform a single-disk write may vary, increasing the number of copies increases the likelihood that one of the single-disk writes in the parallel write will take longer than average. A parallel write will not take longer than the longest possible single-disk write. There may also be some overhead associated with parallel writes on your operating system.

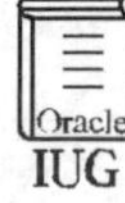

IUG

Dedicating separate disks and mirroring redo log files are important safety precautions. Dedicating separate disks to data files and redo log files ensures that both the data files and the redo log files cannot be lost in a single disk failure. Mirroring redo log files ensures that a single redo log file cannot be lost in a single disk failure.

"Striping" Table Data

"Striping" is the practice of dividing a large table's data into small portions and storing these portions in separate data files on separate disks. This permits multiple processes to access different portions of the table concurrently without disk contention. "Striping" is particularly helpful in optimizing random access to tables with many rows.

To create a "striped" table:

1. Create a tablespace with the CREATE TABLESPACE command. Specify the data files in the DATAFILE clause. Each of the files should be on a different disk.

```
CREATE TABLESPACE stripedtabspace
     DATAFILE 'file_on_disk_1' SIZE 500K,
              'file_on_disk_2' SIZE 500K,
              'file_on_disk_3' SIZE 500K,
              'file_on_disk_4' SIZE 500K,
              'file_on_disk_5' SIZE 500K
```

2. Then create the table with the CREATE TABLE command. Specify the newly created tablespace in the TABLESPACE clause.

   Also specify the size of the table extents in the STORAGE clause. Store each extent in a separate data file. The table extents should be slightly smaller than the data files in the tablespace to allow for overhead. For example:

```
CREATE TABLE stripedtab
     ( col_1  NUMBER(2),
       col_2  VARCHAR2(10)    )
     TABLESPACE stripedtabspace
     STORAGE ( INITIAL 495K  NEXT 495K
               MINEXTENTS 5  PCTINCREASE 0 )
```

These steps result in the creation of table STRIPEDTAB. STRIPEDTAB has 5 initial extents, each of size 495 kilobytes. Each extent takes up one of the data files named in the DATAFILE clause of the CREATE TABLESPACE statement. These files are all on separate disks. These 5 extents are all allocated immediately, since MINEXTENTS is 5. For more information on MINEXTENTS and the other storage parameters, see Chapter 8 "Managing Schema Objects" of this Guide.

Separating Tables and Indexes

Place frequently accessed database structures in separate data files on separate disks. To do this, you must know which of your database structures are used often. For example, separate an often used table from its index. This separation distributes the I/O to the table and index across separate disks.

Follow these steps to separate a table and its index:

1. Create a tablespace with the CREATE TABLESPACE command. Specify the data file in the DATAFILE clause:

```
CREATE TABLESPACE tabspace_1
        DATAFILE 'file_on_disk_1'
```

2. Create the table with the CREATE TABLE command. Specify the tablespace in the TABLESPACE clause:

```
CREATE TABLE tab_1
        ( col_1  NUMBER(2),
          col_2  VARCHAR2(10) )
TABLESPACE tabspace_1
```

3. Create another tablespace. Specify a data file on another disk:

```
CREATE TABLESPACE tabspace_2
        DATAFILE 'file_on_disk_2'
```

4. Create the index. Specify the new tablespace:

```
CREATE INDEX ind_1 ON tab_1 (col_1)
        TABLESPACE tabspace_2
```

These steps result in the creation of table TAB_1 in the file FILE_ON_DISK_1 and the creation of index IND_1 in the file FILE_ON_DISK_2.

Eliminating Other Disk I/O

If possible, eliminate I/O not related to ORACLE on disks that contain database files. This measure is especially helpful in optimizing access to redo log files. Not only does this reduce disk contention, it also allows you to monitor all activity on such disks through the dynamic performance table V$FILESTAT.

Allocating Space in Data Blocks

Table data in the database is stored in data blocks. In this section, you will learn how to allocate space within data blocks for best performance. The following issues are discussed in this section:

- how to control data storage
- how to store data most efficiently based on your application

Migrated and Chained Rows

If an UPDATE statement increases the amount of data in a row so that the row no longer fits in its data block, ORACLE tries to find another block with enough free space to hold the entire row. If such a block is available, ORACLE moves the entire row to the new block. This is called *migrating* a row. If the row is too large to fit into any available block, ORACLE splits the row into multiple pieces and stores each piece in a separate block. This is called *chaining* a row. Rows can also be chained when they are inserted.

Dynamic space management, especially migration and chaining, is detrimental to performance:

- UPDATE statements that cause migration and chaining perform poorly.
- Queries that select migrated or chained rows must perform more I/O.

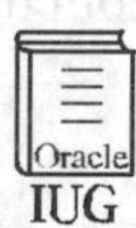

IUG

You can identify migrated and chained rows in a table or cluster by using the ANALYZE command with the LIST CHAINED ROWS option. This command collects information about each migrated or chained row and places this information into a specified output table. The definition of a sample output table named CHAINED_ROWS appears in a SQL script available on your distribution media. The common name of this script is UTLCHAIN.SQL, although its exact name and location may vary depending on your operating system. Your output table must have the same column names, datatypes, and sizes as the CHAINED_ROWS table.

To reduce migrated and chained rows in an existing table, follow these steps:

1. Use the ANALYZE command to collect information about migrated and chained rows. For example:

```
ANALYZE
        TABLE order_hist LIST CHAINED ROWS
```

2. Query the output table:

```
SELECT *
        FROM chained_rows
        WHERE table_name = 'ORDER_HIST'

OWNER_NAME  TABLE_NAME  CLUSTER_NAME  HEAD_ROWID          TIMESTAMP
----------  ----------  ------------  ------------------  ---------
SCOTT       ORDER_HIST                0000186A.0003.0001  04-AUG-92
SCOTT       ORDER_HIST                0000186A.0002.0001  04-AUG-92
SCOTT       ORDER_HIST                0000186A.0001.0001  04-AUG-92
```

3. If the output table shows that you have many migrated or chained rows, follow these steps to eliminate migrated rows:

   a. Create an intermediate table with the same columns as the existing table to hold the migrated and chained rows:

```
CREATE TABLE int_order_hist
     AS SELECT *
                FROM order_hist
                WHERE ROWID IN
                        (SELECT head_rowid
                                FROM chained_rows
                                WHERE table_name = 'ORDER_HIST')
```

   b. Delete the migrated and chained rows from the existing table:

```
DELETE FROM order_hist
     WHERE ROWID IN
             (SELECT head_rowid
                     FROM chained_rows
                     WHERE table_name = 'ORDER_HIST')
```

   c. Insert the rows of the intermediate table into the existing table:

```
INSERT INTO order_hist
     SELECT *
             FROM int_order_hist
```

   d. Drop the intermediate table:

```
DROP TABLE int_order_history
```

4. Delete the information collected in step 1 from the output table:

```
DELETE FROM chained_rows
       WHERE table_name = 'ORDER_HIST'
```

5. Use the ANALYZE command again and query the output table.
6. Any rows that appear in the output table are chained rows. You can eliminate chained rows by increasing your data block size. It may not be possible to avoid chaining in all situations. If your table has a LONG column or long CHAR or VARCHAR2 columns, chaining is often unavoidable.

Avoiding Dynamic Space Management

When an object such as a table or rollback segment is created, space is allocated in the database for the data. This space is called a *segment*. If subsequent database operations cause the data to grow and exceed the space allocated, ORACLE extends the segment. Dynamic extension can reduce performance. This section discusses:

- how to detect dynamic extension
- how to allocate enough space for your data to avoid dynamic extension
- how to avoid dynamic space management in rollback segments

Detecting Dynamic Extension

Dynamic extension causes ORACLE to execute SQL statements in addition to those SQL statements issued by user processes. These SQL statements are called *recursive calls*, because ORACLE issues these statements itself. Recursive calls are also generated by these activities:

- misses on the data dictionary cache
- firing of database triggers
- execution of Data Definition Language statements
- execution of SQL statements within stored procedures, functions, packages, and anonymous PL/SQL blocks
- enforcement of referential integrity constraints

Examine the *recursive calls* statistic through the dynamic performance table V$SYSSTAT. By default, this table is only available to the user SYS and to users granted SELECT ANY TABLE system privilege, such as SYSTEM. Monitor this statistic over some period of time while your application is running with this query:

```
SELECT name, value
    FROM v$sysstat
    WHERE name = 'recursive calls'
```

The output of this query might look like this:

```
NAME                                                               VALUE
----------------------------------------------------------------- ----------
recursive calls                                                       626681
```

If ORACLE continues to make an excess of recursive calls while your application is running, determine whether these recursive calls are due to one of the activities that generate recursive calls other than dynamic extension. If you determine that these recursive calls are caused by dynamic extension, you should try to reduce this extension by allocating larger extents.

Allocating Extents

Follow these steps to avoid dynamic extension:

1. Determine the maximum size of your object. For formulas to predict how much space to allow for a table, see Chapter 8 "Managing Schema Objects" of this Guide.
2. Choose storage parameter values so that ORACLE allocates extents large enough to accommodate all of your data when you create the object.

Larger extents tend to benefit performance for these reasons:

- Since blocks in a single extent are contiguous, one large extent is more contiguous than multiple small extents. ORACLE can read one large extent from disk with fewer multi-block read than would be required to read many small extents.
- Segments with larger extents are less likely to be extended.

However, since large extents require more contiguous blocks, ORACLE may have difficulty finding enough contiguous space to store them. To determine whether to allocate few large extents or many small extents, consider the benefits and drawbacks of each in light of your plans for the growth and use of your tables.

Avoiding Dynamic Space Management in Rollback Segments

The size of rollback segments can also affect performance. Rollback segment size is determined by the rollback segment's storage parameter values. Your rollback segments must be large enough to hold the rollback entries for your transactions. As with other objects, you should avoid dynamic space management in rollback segments.

Use the SET TRANSACTION command to assign transactions to rollback segments of the appropriate size based on the recommendations in the following sections. If you do not explicitly assign a rollback segment to a transaction, ORACLE randomly chooses a rollback segment for it. If you are running multiple concurrent copies of the same application, be careful not to assign the transactions for all copies to the same rollback segment. This leads to contention for that rollback segment.

Also monitor the shrinking, or dynamic deallocation, of rollback segments based on the OPTIMAL storage parameter. For information on choosing values for this parameter and monitoring rollback segment shrinking, and adjusting OPTIMAL accordingly, see Chapter 9 "Managing Rollback Segments" of this Guide.

Example

This statement assigns the current transaction to the rollback segment OLTP_13:

```
SET TRANSACTION USE ROLLBACK SEGMENT oltp_13
```

For Long Queries

Assign large rollback segments to transactions that modify data that is concurrently selected by long queries. Such queries may require access to rollback segments to reconstruct a read-consistent version of the modified data. These rollback segments must be large enough to hold all the rollback entries for the data while the query is running.

For Long Transactions

Assign large rollback segments to long transactions that modify large amounts of data. A large rollback segment can improve the performance of such a transaction. Such transactions generate large rollback entries. If a rollback entry does not fit into a rollback segment, ORACLE extends the segment. Dynamic extension reduces performance and should be avoided whenever possible.

For OLTP Transactions

Some applications perform *online transaction processing*, or OLTP. OLTP applications are characterized by frequent concurrent transactions that each modify small amounts of data. Assign small rollback segments to OLTP transactions provided that their data is not concurrently queried. Small rollback segments are more likely to remain stored in the buffer cache where they can be accessed quickly. A typical OLTP rollback segment might have 2 extents, each on the order of 10 kilobytes in size. To best avoid contention, create many rollback segments and assign each transaction to its own rollback segment.

CHAPTER

23 Tuning Contention

This chapter presents Step Three of the tuning process: tuning contention. Contention occurs when multiple processes try to access the same resource simultaneously. Contention causes processes to wait for access.

ORACLE provides you with methods of handling contention. In this chapter, you will learn how to:

- detect contention that may affect performance
- reduce contention

The ORACLE resources discussed in this chapter include:

- rollback segments
- processes of the multi-threaded server
- redo log buffer latches

Reducing Contention for Rollback Segments

In this section, you will learn how to reduce contention for rollback segments. The following issues are discussed:

- how to identify contention for rollback segments
- how to create rollback segments
- how to assign rollback segments to particular transactions

Identifying Rollback Segment Contention

Contention for rollback segments is reflected by contention for buffers that contain rollback segment blocks. You can determine whether contention for rollback segments is reducing performance by using the dynamic performance table V$WAITSTAT.

The V$WAITSTAT contains statistics that reflect block contention. By default, this table is only available to the user SYS and to other users who have SELECT ANY TABLE system privilege, such as SYSTEM. These statistics reflect contention for different classes of block:

system undo header The value of this statistic is the number of waits for buffers containing header blocks of the SYSTEM rollback segment.

system undo block The value of this statistic is the number of waits for buffers containing blocks other than header blocks of the SYSTEM rollback segment.

undo header The value of this statistic is the number of waits for buffers containing header blocks of rollback segments other than the SYSTEM rollback segment.

undo block The value of this statistic is the number of waits for buffers containing blocks other than header blocks of rollback segments other than the SYSTEM rollback segment.

Monitor these statistics over a period of time while your application is running with this query:

```
SELECT class, count
    FROM v$waitstat
    WHERE class IN ('system undo header', 'system undo block',
                    'undo header', 'undo block')
```

The result of this query might look like this:

```
CLASS                    COUNT
------------------- ----------
system undo header        2089
system undo block          633
undo header               1235
undo block                 942
```

Compare the number of waits for each class of block with the total number of requests for data over the same period of time. You can monitor the total number of requests for data over a period of time with this query:

```
SELECT SUM(value)
    FROM v$sysstat
    WHERE name IN ('db block gets', 'consistent gets')
```

The output of this query might look like this:

```
SUM(VALUE)
----------
    929530
```

If the number of waits for any class is greater than 1% of the total number of requests, you should consider creating more rollback segments to reduce contention.

Creating Rollback Segments

To reduce contention for buffers containing rollback segment blocks, create more rollback segments. Table 23-1 shows some general guidelines for choosing how many rollback segments to allocate based on the number of concurrent transactions on your database. These guidelines are appropriate for most application mixes.

TABLE 23-1
Choosing a Number of Rollback Segments

Number of Concurrent Transactions (*n*)	Recommended Number of Rollback Segments
n < 16	4
16 <= *n* < 32	8
32 <= *n*	*n*/4, but no more than 50

To create rollback segments, use the CREATE ROLLBACK SEGMENT command.

Reducing Contention for Multi-Threaded Server Processes

In this section, you will learn how to reduce contention for these processes used by the ORACLE's multi-threaded server architecture:

- dispatcher processes
- shared server processes

Reducing Contention for Dispatcher Processes

This section discusses these issues:

- how to identify contention for dispatcher processes
- how to add dispatcher processes

Identifying Contention for Dispatcher Processes

Contention for dispatcher processes can be reflected by either of these symptoms:

- high busy rates for existing dispatcher processes
- steady increase in waiting time for responses in the response queues of existing dispatcher processes

Examining Busy Rates for Dispatcher Processes Statistics reflecting the activity of dispatcher processes are kept in the dynamic performance table V$DISPATCHER. By default, this table is only available to the user SYS and to other users who have SELECT ANY TABLE system privilege, such as SYSTEM. These columns reflect busy rates for dispatcher processes:

IDLE	This column shows the idle time for the dispatcher process in hundredths of seconds.
BUSY	This column shows the busy time for the dispatcher process in hundredths of seconds.

Monitor these statistics over a period of time while your application is running with this query:

```
SELECT network                                    "Protocol",
       SUM(busy) / ( SUM(busy) + SUM(idle) ) "Total Busy Rate"
    FROM v$dispatcher
    GROUP BY network
```

This query returns the total busy rate for the dispatcher processes of each protocol or the percentage of time the dispatcher processes of each protocol are busy. The result of this query might look like this:

```
Protocol  Total Busy Rate
--------  ---------------
decnet          .004589828
tcp             .029111042
```

From this result, you can make these observations:

- DECnet dispatcher processes are busy nearly .5% of the time.
- TCP dispatcher processes are busy nearly 3% of the time.

If the dispatcher processes for a specific protocol are busy more than 50% of the time, then you may be able to improve performance for users connected to ORACLE using that protocol by adding dispatcher processes.

Examining Wait Times for Dispatcher Process Response Queues

Statistics reflecting the response queue activity for dispatcher processes are kept in the dynamic performance table V$QUEUE. By default, this table is only available to the user SYS and to other users who have SELECT ANY TABLE system privilege, such as SYSTEM. These columns wait times for responses in the queue:

WAIT: This column shows the total waiting time in hundredths of seconds for all responses that have ever been in the queue.

TOTALQ: This column shows the total number of responses that have ever been in the queue.

Monitor these statistics from time to time while your application is running with this query:

```
SELECT network        "Protocol",
       DECODE( SUM(totalq), 0, 'No Responses',
               SUM(wait)/SUM(totalq) || ' hundredths of seconds')
     "Average Wait Time per Response"
   FROM v$queue q, v$dispatcher d
   WHERE q.type = 'DISPATCHER'
     AND q.paddr = d.paddr
   GROUP BY network
```

This query returns the average time in hundredths of seconds that a response waits in each response queue for a dispatcher process to route it to a user process. This query uses the V$DISPATCHER table to group the rows of the V$QUEUE table by network protocol. The query also uses the DECODE syntax to recognize those protocols for which there have been no responses in the queue. The result of this query might look like this:

```
Protocol  Average Wait Time per Response
--------  ------------------------------
decnet    .1739130 hundredths of seconds
tcp       No Responses
```

From this result, you can tell that a response in the queue for DECNET dispatcher processes waits an average of .17 hundredths of a second and that there have been no responses in the queue for TCP dispatcher processes.

If the average wait time for a specific network protocol continues to increase steadily as your application runs, you may be able to improve performance of those user processes connected to ORACLE using that protocol by adding dispatcher processes.

Adding Dispatcher Processes

You can add more dispatcher processes while ORACLE is running through one of these means:

- the SQL*DBA Configure Multi-Threaded Dispatchers Dialogue Box
- the MTS_DISPATCHERS parameter of the ALTER SYSTEM command

For more information on adding dispatcher processes, see Chapter 4 "Managing ORACLE Processes" of this Guide.

IUG

The total number of dispatcher processes across all protocols is limited by the value of the initialization parameter MTS_MAX_DISPATCHERS. You may need to increase this value before adding dispatcher processes. The default value of this parameter is 5 and the maximum value varies depending on your operating system.

Reducing Contention for Shared Server Processes

This section discusses these issues:

- how to identify contention for shared server processes
- how to increase the maximum number of shared server processes

Identifying Contention for Shared Server Processes

Contention for shared server processes can be reflected by steady increase in waiting time for requests in the request queue. Statistics reflecting the request queue activity for shared server processes are kept in the dynamic performance table V$QUEUE. By default, this table is only available to the user SYS and to other users who have SELECT ANY TABLE system privilege, such as SYSTEM. These columns show wait times for requests in the queue:

WAIT	This column shows the total waiting time in hundredths of seconds for all requests that have ever been in the queue.
TOTALQ	This column shows the total number of requests that have ever been in the queue.

Monitor these statistics from time to time while your application is running with this query:

```
SELECT DECODE( totalq, 0, 'No Requests',
               wait/totalq || ' hundredths of seconds')
        "Average Wait Time Per Requests"
    FROM v$queue
    WHERE type = 'COMMON'
```

This query returns the total wait time for all requests and total number of requests for the request queue. The result of this query might look like this:

```
Average Wait Time per Request
-----------------------------
.090909 hundredths of seconds
```

From the result, you can tell that a request waits an average of .09 hundredths of a second in the queue before it is processed.

You can also determine how many shared server processes are currently running by issuing this query:

```
SELECT COUNT(*) "Shared Server Processes"
    FROM v$shared_servers
    WHERE status != 'QUIT'
```

The result of this query might look like this:

```
Shared Server Processes
-----------------------
                     10
```

Adding Shared Server Processes

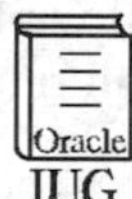

Since ORACLE automatically adds shared server processes if the load on existing shared server processes increases drastically, you are unlikely to improve performance simply by explicitly adding more shared server processes. However, if the number of shared server processes has reached the limit established by the initialization parameter MTS_MAX_SERVERS and the average wait time in the requests queue is still increasing, you may be able to improve performance by increasing the MTS_MAX_SERVERS value. The default value of this parameter is 20 and the maximum value varies depending on your operating system. You can then either allow ORACLE to automatically add shared server processes or explicitly add shared processes through one of these means:

- the MTS_SERVERS initialization parameter
- the SQL*DBA Configure Multi-Threaded Servers Dialog Box
- the MTS_SERVERS parameter of the ALTER SYSTEM command

For more information on adding shared server processes, see Chapter 4 "Managing ORACLE Processes" of this Guide.

Reducing Contention for Redo Log Buffer Latches

Contention for redo log buffer access rarely inhibits database performance. However, ORACLE provides you with methods to monitor and reduce any latch contention that does occur. This section explains:

- how to detect and reduce contention for space in the redo log buffer
- how to detect contention for latches
- how to reduce contention for latches

Space in the Redo Log Buffer

When LGWR writes redo entries from the redo log buffer to a redo log file, user processes can then copy new entries over the entries that have been written to disk. LGWR normally writes fast enough to ensure that space is always available in the buffer for new entries, even when access to the redo log is heavy.

The statistic *redo log space requests* reflects the number of times a user process waits for space in the redo log buffer. This statistic is available through the dynamic performance table V$SYSSTAT. By default, this table is only available to the user SYS and to users granted SELECT ANY TABLE system privilege, such as SYSTEM. Monitor this statistic over a period of time while your application is running with this query:

```
SELECT name, value
   FROM v$sysstat
   WHERE name = 'redo log space requests'
```

The value of *redo log space requests* should be near 0. If this value increments consistently, processes have had to wait for space in the buffer. In this case, increase the size of the redo log buffer. The size of the redo log buffer is determined by the initialization parameter LOG_BUFFER. The value of this parameter is expressed in bytes. Try increasing the size of the redo log buffer by increments of 5% until the value of *redo log space requests* nears 0.

Redo Log Buffer Latches

Access to the redo log buffer is regulated by latches. Two types of latches control access to the redo log buffer:

- the redo allocation latch
- redo copy latches

The Redo Allocation Latch

The *redo allocation latch* controls the allocation of space for redo entries in the redo log buffer. To allocate space in the buffer, an ORACLE user process must obtain the redo allocation latch. Since there is only one redo allocation latch, only one user process can allocate space in the buffer at a time. The single redo allocation latch enforces the sequential nature of the entries in the buffer.

After allocating space for a redo entry, the user process may copy the entry into the buffer while holding the redo allocation latch. Such a copy is referred to as "copying on the redo allocation latch." A process may only copy on the redo allocation latch if the redo entry is smaller than a threshold size. After copying on the redo allocation latch, the user process releases the latch.

The maximum size of a redo entry that can be copied on the redo allocation latch is specified by the initialization parameter LOG_SMALL_ENTRY_MAX_SIZE. The value of this parameter is expressed in bytes. The minimum, maximum, and default values vary depending on your operating system.

Redo Copy Latches

If the redo entry is too large to copy on the redo allocation latch, the user process must obtain a *redo copy latch* before copying the entry into the buffer. While holding a redo copy latch, the user process copies the redo entry into its allocated space in the buffer and then releases the redo copy latch.

If your computer has multiple CPUs, your redo log buffer can have multiple redo copy latches. Multiple redo copy latches allow multiple processes to copy entries to the redo log buffer concurrently. The number of redo copy latches is determined by the initialization parameter LOG_SIMULTANEOUS_COPIES. The default value of LOG_SIMULTANEOUS_COPIES is the value of the initialization parameter CPU_COUNT. ORACLE automatically sets the value of CPU_COUNT to the number of CPUs available to your ORACLE instance. Do not change the value of CPU_COUNT.

On single-CPU computers, there should be no redo copy latches since only one process can by active at once. In this case, all redo entries are copied on the redo allocation latch, regardless of size. ORACLE sets the value of CPU_COUNT to 0.

Examining Redo Log Activity

Heavy access to the redo log buffer can result in contention for redo log buffer latches. Latch contention can reduce performance. ORACLE collects statistics for the activity of all latches and stores them in the dynamic performance table V$LATCH. By default, this table is only available to the user SYS and to other users who have SELECT ANY TABLE system privilege, such as SYSTEM.

Each row in the V$LATCH table contains statistics for a different type of latch. The columns of the table reflect activity for different types of latch requests. The distinction between these types of requests is whether the requesting process continues to request a latch if it is unavailable:

willing-to-wait	If the latch requested with a willing-to-wait request is not available, the requesting process waits a short time and requests the latch again. The process continues waiting and requesting until the latch is available.
immediate	If the latch requested with an immediate request is not available, the requesting process does not wait, but continues processing.

These columns of the V$LATCH table reflect willing-to-wait requests:

GETS	This column shows the number of successful willing-to-wait requests for a latch.
MISSES	This column shows the number of times an initial willing-to-wait request was unsuccessful.
SLEEPS	This column shows the number of times a process waited and requested a latch after an initial willing-to-wait request.

For example, consider the case in which a process makes a willing-to-wait request for a latch that is unavailable. The process waits and requests the latch again and the latch is still unavailable. The process waits and requests the latch a third time and acquires the latch. This activity increments the statistics in these ways:

- The GETS value increases by one, since one request for the latch (the third request) was successful.
- The MISSES value increases by one, since the initial request for the latch resulted in waiting.
- The SLEEPS value increases by two, since the process waited for the latch twice, once after the initial request and again after the second request.

These columns of the V$LATCH table reflect immediate requests:

IMMEDIATE_GETS This column shows the number of successful immediate requests for each latch.

IMMEDIATE_MISSES This column shows the number of unsuccessful immediate requests for each latch.

Monitor the statistics for the redo allocation latch and the redo copy latches over a period of time with this query:

```
SELECT name, gets, misses, immediate_gets, immediate_misses
   FROM v$latch l, v$latchname ln
   WHERE ln.name IN ('redo allocation', 'redo copy')
     AND ln.latch# = l.latch#
```

The output of this query might look like this:

```
NAME                          GETS     MISSES IMMEDIATE_GETS
IMMEDIATE_MISSES
------------------ ---------- ---------- --------------
----------------
redo allocation         252867         83              0
0
redo copy                    0          0          22830
0
```

From the output of the query, calculate the wait ratio for each type of request.

Contention for a latch may be affecting performance if either of these conditions is true:

- if the ratio of MISSES to GETS exceeds 1%
- if the ratio of IMMEDIATE_MISSES to the sum of IMMEDIATE_GETS and IMMEDIATE_MISSES exceeds 1%

IUG

If either of these conditions is true for a latch, try to reduce contention for that latch.

These contention thresholds are appropriate for most operating systems, though some computers with many CPUs may be able to tolerate more contention without performance reduction.

Reducing Latch Contention

Most cases of latch contention occur when two or more ORACLE processes concurrently attempt to obtain the same latch. Latch contention rarely occurs on single-CPU computers where only a single process can be active at once.

Reducing Contention for the Redo Allocation Latch

To reduce contention for the redo allocation latch, you should minimize the time that any single process holds the latch. To reduce this time, reduce copying on the redo allocation latch. Decreasing the value of the initialization parameter LOG_SMALL_ENTRY_MAX_SIZE reduces the number and size of redo entries copied on the redo allocation latch.

Reducing Contention for Redo Copy Latches

On multiple-CPU computers, multiple redo copy latches allow multiple processes to copy entries to the redo log buffer concurrently. The default value of LOG_SIMULTANEOUS_COPIES is the value of the initialization parameter CPU_COUNT. ORACLE automatically sets the value of CPU_COUNT to the number of CPUs available to your ORACLE instance. On single-CPU computers, ORACLE sets the value of CPU_COUNT to 0.

If you observe contention for redo copy latches, add more latches. To increase the number of redo copy latches, increase the value of LOG_SIMULTANEOUS_COPIES. It can help to have up to twice as many redo copy latches as CPUs available to your ORACLE instance.

Another way to reduce contention for redo copy latches is to reduce the time each process holds a latch. You can reduce this time by forcing the ORACLE user process to "pre-build" redo entries before obtaining a redo copy latch.

A redo entry may consist of many pieces. Usually each piece of a redo entry is copied individually from the user process memory into the redo log buffer while a redo copy latch is held. Copying the pieces of a redo entry individually requires many writes to memory. However, when an entry is "pre-built," the user process assembles all the pieces together before requesting the latch. The redo entry can then be copied to the buffer in a single write to memory.

User processes pre-build all entries that are smaller than a threshold size. This threshold size is determined by the initialization parameter LOG_ENTRY_PREBUILD_THRESHOLD. The value of this parameter is expressed in bytes. The default value is 0. This value means that the default behavior is to not pre-build any entries.

To force your user processes to pre-build more of their redo entries, increase the value of LOG_ENTRY_PREBUILD_THRESHOLD.

Assigning All ORACLE Processes Equal Priority

Many processes are involved in the operation of ORACLE. These processes all access the shared memory resources in the SGA.

Be sure that all ORACLE processes, both background processes and user processes, have the same process priority. When you install ORACLE, all background processes are given the default priority for your operating system. You should not change the priorities of background processes. You should also be sure that all user processes have the default operating system priority.

Assigning different priorities to ORACLE processes may exacerbate the effects of contention. Your operating system may not grant processing time to a low priority process if a high priority process also requests processing time. If a high priority process needs access to a memory resource held by a low priority process, the high priority process may wait indefinitely for the low priority process to obtain the CPU, process, and release the resource.

CHAPTER

24 Additional Tuning Considerations

This chapter discusses additional tuning measures you should take after completing the steps presented in the first six chapters of this Guide. These measures tune ORACLE operations that only reduce performance in very special cases. The topics covered by this chapter include:

- sorts
- free lists
- checkpoints

Tuning Sorts

Some applications cause ORACLE to sort data. This section tells you:

- how to allocate memory to optimize your sorts
- how to avoid sorting when creating indexes

Allocating Memory for Sort Areas

The default sort area size is adequate to hold all the data for most sorts. However, if your application often performs large sorts on data that does not fit into the sort area, then you may want to increase the sort area size. Large sorts can be caused by any SQL statement that performs a sort that operates on a large number of rows. SQL statements that perform sorts are listed in Chapter 9 "Memory Structures and Processes" of the *ORACLE7 Server Concepts Manual.*

Concepts

Recognizing Large Sorts

ORACLE collects statistics that reflect sort activity and stores them in the dynamic performance tables V$SYSSTAT. By default, this table is only available to the user SYS and to users granted SELECT ANY TABLE system privilege. These statistics reflect sort behavior:

sorts(memory) — The value of this statistic is the number of sorts small enough to be performed entirely in sort areas without I/O to temporary segments on disk.

sorts(disk) — The value of this statistic is the number of sorts too large to be performed entirely in the sort area requiring I/O to temporary segments on disk.

Monitor these statistics over a period of time while your application is running with this query:

```
SELECT name, value
    FROM v$sysstat
    WHERE name IN ('sorts(memory)', 'sorts(disk)')
```

The output of this query might look like this:

```
NAME                                                        VALUE
----------------------------------------------------------- ----------
sorts(memory)                                                      965
sorts(disk)                                                          8
```

Increasing Sort Area Size

If a significant number of sorts require disk I/O to temporary segments, then your application's performance may benefit from increasing the size of the sort area. In this case, increase the value of the initialization parameter SORT_AREA_SIZE. The maximum value of this parameter varies depending on your operating system.

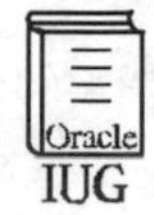

IUG

Performance Benefits of Large Sort Areas

Increasing the size of the sort area increases the size of each run and decreases the total number of runs. This decrease can improve performance in two ways:

- Reducing the total number of runs reduces the number of merges ORACLE must perform to obtain the final sorted result.
- Reducing the total number of runs reduces the disk I/O to the temporary segment necessary to perform the sort.

Performance Tradeoffs for Large Sort Areas

Increasing the size of the sort area causes each ORACLE process that sorts to allocate more memory. This increase reduces the amount of memory available for private SQL and PL/SQL areas. It can also affect operating system memory allocation and may induce paging and swapping. Before increasing the size of the sort area, be sure enough free memory is available on your operating system to accommodate a larger sort area.

If you increase the size of your sort area, you may consider decreasing the retained size of the sort area, or the size to which ORACLE reduces the sort area if its data is not expected to be referenced soon. To decrease the retained size of the sort area, decrease the value of the initialization parameter SORT_AREA_RETAINED_SIZE. A smaller retained sort area reduces memory usage but causes additional I/O to write and read data to and from temporary segments on disk.

Avoiding Sorts

One cause of sorting is the creation of indexes. Creating an index for a table involves sorting all the rows in the table based on the values of the indexed column or columns.

ORACLE also allows you to create indexes without sorting. If the rows in the table are loaded in ascending order, you can create the index faster without sorting.

The NOSORT Option

To create an index without sorting, load the rows into the table in ascending order of the indexed column values. Your operating system may provide you with a sorting utility to sort the rows before you load them.

When you create the index, use the NOSORT option on the CREATE INDEX command. For example, this CREATE INDEX statement creates the index EMP_INDEX on the ENAME column of the EMP table without sorting the rows in the EMP table:

```
CREATE INDEX emp_index
    ON emp(ename)
    NOSORT
```

Choosing When to Use the NOSORT Option

Presorting your data and loading it in order may not always be the fastest way to load a table. If you have a multiple-CPU computer, you may be able to load data faster using multiple processors in parallel, each processor loading a different portion of the data. To take advantage of parallel processing, load the data without sorting it first. Then create the index without the NOSORT option.

On the other hand, if you have a single-CPU computer, you should sort your data before loading, if possible. Then you should create the index with the NOSORT option.

Reducing Free List Contention

Free list contention can reduce the performance of some applications. This section tells you:

- how to identify contention for free lists
- how to increase the number of free lists

Identifying Free List Contention

Contention for free lists is reflected by contention for free data blocks in the buffer cache. You can determine whether contention for free lists is reducing performance by querying the dynamic performance table V$WAITSTAT.

The V$WAITSTAT table contains block contention statistics. By default, this table is only available to the user SYS and to other users who have SELECT ANY TABLE system privilege, such as SYSTEM. The free list statistic reflects contention for free blocks. Monitor this statistic over a period of time while your application is running with this query:

```
SELECT class, count
    FROM v$waitstat
    WHERE class = 'free list'
```

The result of this query might look like this:

```
CLASS              COUNT
------------------ ----------
free list                 459
```

Compare the number of waits for free blocks with the total number of requests for data over the same period of time. You can monitor the total number of requests for data over a period of time with this query:

```
SELECT SUM(value)
    FROM v$sysstat
    WHERE name IN ('db block gets', 'consistent gets')
```

The output of this query might look like this:

```
SUM(VALUE)
----------
    929530
```

If the number of waits for free blocks is greater than 1% of the total number of requests, you should consider adding more free lists to reduce contention.

Adding More Free Lists

To reduce contention for the free lists of a table, re-create the table with a larger value for the FREELISTS storage parameter. Increasing the value of this parameter to the number of ORACLE processes that concurrently insert data into the table may benefit performance for the INSERT statements.

Re-creating the table may simply involve dropping and creating it again. However, you may want to use one of these means instead:

- Re-create the table by selecting data from the old table into a new table, dropping the old table, and renaming the new one.
- Use Import and Export to export the table, drop the table, and import the table. This measure avoids consuming space by creating a temporary table.

Tuning Checkpoints

A checkpoint is an operation that ORACLE performs automatically. Checkpoints can momentarily reduce performance. This section tells you:

- how checkpoints affect performance
- how to choose the frequency of checkpoints
- how to reduce the performance impact of a checkpoint

How Checkpoints Affect Performance

Checkpoints affect:

- recovery time performance
- runtime performance

Recovery Time Performance

Frequent checkpoints can reduce recovery time in the event of an instance failure. If checkpoints are relatively frequent, then relatively few changes to the database are made between checkpoints. In this case, relatively few changes must be rolled forward for recovery.

Runtime Performance

A checkpoint can momentarily reduce runtime performance for these reasons:

- Checkpoints cause DBWR to perform I/O.
- If CKPT is not enabled, checkpoints cause LGWR to update data files and may momentarily prevent LGWR from writing redo entries.

The overhead associated with a checkpoint is usually small and only affects performance while ORACLE performs the checkpoint.

Choosing Checkpoint Frequency

You should choose a checkpoint frequency based on your performance concerns. If you are more concerned with efficient runtime performance than recovery time, choose a lower checkpoint frequency. If you are more concerned with fast recovery time than runtime performance, choose a higher checkpoint frequency.

Because checkpoints on log switches are necessary for redo log maintenance, you cannot eliminate checkpoints entirely. However, you can reduce checkpoint frequency to a minimum by setting these parameters:

- Set the value of the initialization parameter LOG_CHECKPOINT_INTERVAL larger than the size of your largest redo log file.
- Set the value of the initialization parameter LOG_CHECKPOINT_TIMEOUT to 0. This value eliminates time-based checkpoints.

Such settings eliminate all checkpoints except those that occur on log switches.

You can further reduce checkpoints by reducing the frequency of log switches. To reduce log switches, increase the size of your redo log files so that the files do not fill as quickly.

Reducing the Performance Impact of a Checkpoint

You may notice a momentary drop in performance as a checkpoint completes. This drop may be due to an accumulation of redo entries in the redo log buffer. LGWR may be too busy updating data file headers to write these entries to a redo log file. In this case, you can reduce the performance impact of a checkpoint by enabling the Checkpoint process (CKPT).

CKPT updates data file headers when a checkpoint occurs, leaving LGWR free to write redo entries. To enable CKPT, set the value of the initialization parameter CHECKPOINT_PROCESS to TRUE. To disable CKPT, set this value to FALSE. CKPT is disabled by default. Before enabling CKPT, be sure that your operating system can support an additional process. You may also need to increase the value of the initialization parameter PROCESSES.

PART

VIII REFERENCE

APPENDIX

Initialization Parameter Files

This appendix contains detailed descriptions of the database initialization parameters. The initialization parameters are found in the parameter file. A parameter file is required to start an instance.

Though the usual name of the parameter file is INIT.ORA, the actual name of the file may vary depending on the distribution media for your operating system. For example, it may be in mixed or lowercase, or it may have a logical name or a variation on the name INIT.ORA. As the DBA, you can choose a different filename for your parameter file.

The expected location (where the Server expects to find the parameter file upon startup) is documented in the installation or user's guide for your operating system, along with the original name of the file.

A sample parameter file is included on the ORACLE Server distribution media for each operating system. The distributed sample file is appropriate for initial use, but you will want to make changes in the file to tune your database system for best performance. The changes take effect the next time the instance is started after being completely shutdown.

Database administrators can use initialization parameters to:

- optimize performance by adjusting memory structures (for example, the number of database buffers in memory)
- set some database-wide defaults (for example, how much space is initially allocated for a context area when it is created)
- set database limits (for example, the maximum number of database users)
- specify names of files

Many initialization parameters can be "fine-tuned" to improve database performance. Other parameters should never be altered or only be altered under supervision by Oracle Corporation personnel.

Specifying Values in the Parameter File

The parameter file is a text file that contains a list of parameters and a value for each parameter, as in:

```
SAVEPOINTS = 5
PROCESSES = 100
```

The following rules govern the specification of parameters in the parameter file:

- All parameters are optional.
- Only parameters and comments should appear in the parameter file.
- For each parameter, a default value is built into the server. This value may be operating system dependent, depending on the parameter.
- Parameters can be specified in any order.

- Case (upper or lower) is only significant (in filenames) if case is significant on the host operating system. Refer to your installation or user's guide if you require more information.
- To enter several parameters on one line, use spaces between parameter names, as in:

```
PROCESSES = 100 SAVEPOINTS = 5 OPEN_CURSORS = 10
```

- For some parameters (such as INIT_SQL_FILES), multiple values can be entered. Multiple values must be separated by commas and enclosing them in parentheses, as in:

```
INIT_SQL_FILES = (SQL.BSQ, CATALOG.SQL, ENROLL_USERS.SQL)
```

- A backslash (\) can be used to indicate continuation of the parameter specification. If a backslash is used to continue a line, the continued line must not have any preceding spaces. For example:

```
ROLLBACK_SEGMENTS = (SEG1, SEG2, \
SEG3, SEG4, SEG5)
```

- The keyword IFILE can be used to embed another file, which is expected to be in the same format as the original parameter file. Up to three levels of nesting are allowed.
- A pound sign (#) can be used to start a comment; the rest of the line is ignored.
- Double quotes can surround parameter values, such as file names. This syntax option is useful for values that contain special characters.

Tip: It is a good idea to keep parameters in alphabetical order in the control file. That makes it easier to find them and helps to ensure that each parameter is specified only once. (If a parameter is specified more than once and you change its value, then the old value may continue to be used.)

Changing Parameter Values

To change a parameter's value, edit the parameter file. The next time the instance starts it uses the new parameter values in the updated parameter file. *Note that the change does not take effect until the* **next** *time the instance is started.*

Displaying Current Parameter Values

To see the current settings for initialization parameters, use the SQL*DBA command:

```
SQLDBA> SHOW PARAMETERS
```

This displays all parameters in alphabetical order, with their current values. If you enter a text string, as in:

```
SQLDBA> SHOW PARAMETERS BLOCK
```

you will see a display for all parameters having BLOCK in their name. If you display all the parameters, you may wish to use the SPOOL command to write the output to a file.

You can also see the values by including the keyword LIST as the first line in the parameter file. Then when you start an instance using that parameter file, you see a display showing the current settings for the parameters.

Groups of Parameters

Initialization parameters can be grouped in several different ways. For example, there are parameters that:

- set database-wide limits
- set user or process limits
- name files or directories required by a database system
- set limits on database resources
- affect performance (these are called *variable parameters*)

Perhaps the group of parameters of most interest to database administrators is the set of variable parameters, used primarily for improving database performance.

Some parameters may never have to be specified in the parameter file:

- parameters that you never alter except when instructed to do so by Oracle Corporation to resolve a problem
- *derived parameters*, which usually should not be altered because their values are automatically calculated by ORACLE

Variable Parameters

The variable initialization parameters offer the most potential for improving system performance. Some variable parameters set capacity limits but do not affect performance. For example, when the value of OPEN_CURSORS is 10, a user process attempting to open its 11th cursor receives an error. Other variable parameters affect performance but do not impose absolute limits. For example, reducing the value of DB_BLOCK_BUFFERS does not prevent work even though it may slow down performance.

Increasing the values of variable parameters may improve your system's performance, but increasing most parameters also increases the SGA size. A larger SGA can improve database performance up to a point. In virtual memory operating systems, an SGA that is too large can degrade performance if it is swapped in and out of memory. Operating system parameters that control virtual memory working areas should be set with the SGA size in mind. The operating system configuration can also limit the maximum size of the SGA.

Global Constants Parameters (with Prefix "GC")

Initialization parameters with the prefix "GC" (such as GC_DB_LOCKS) apply to systems using the ORACLE Parallel Server. The prefix "GC" stands for Global Constants. The settings of these parameters determine how the ORACLE Parallel Server coordinates multiple instances. The settings you choose have an effect on the use of certain operating system resources. For more information, refer to the *ORACLE7 Parallel Server Administrator's Guide* , your installation or user's guide, system release bulletins, or other operating system specific information.

Operating System Dependent Parameters

For some initialization parameters, the valid values or ranges depend upon the host operating system; this is denoted in the default or range column as O/S dependent. For example, the parameter DB_BLOCK_BUFFERS indicates the *number* of data buffers in main memory, and its maximum value depends on the operating system; the *size* of those buffers, set by DB_BLOCK_SIZE, has a system-dependent default value. Refer to your installation and user's guide for operating-system-specific information on the initialization parameters.

Derived Parameters

Some initialization parameters are noted as *derived*. This means that their values are calculated from the values of other parameters. Normally, you should not alter values for derived parameters but if you do, the value you specify overrides the calculated value.

When Parameters Are Set Incorrectly

Some parameters have a minimum setting below which an ORACLE instance will not start; whereas if the values are too low (or high) for other parameters, ORACLE may perform badly but will still run.

You may see messages indicating that a parameter is too low or too high, or that you have reached the maximum for some resource. Frequently, you can wait a short while and retry the operation when the system is not as busy. If a message occurs repeatedly, you should shut down the instance, adjust the relevant parameter, and restart the instance.

Special Symbols and Keywords

The following special symbols and keywords control the processing of the initialization parameter file.

#

Used to signify a comment.

****

Used to signify that a continuation line follows on the next line. If a backslash is used to continue a line, the continued line must not have any preceding spaces. For example:

```
ROLLBACK_SEGMENTS = (SEG1, SEG2, \
SEG3, SEG4, SEG5)
```

IFILE

Default value: null
Range of values: valid parameter file names
Multiple instances: can have different values

Embeds another parameter file within the current parameter file. For example:

```
IFILE = COMMON.ORA
```

You can have up to three levels of nesting. In this example, the file COMMON.ORA could contain a second IFILE parameter for the file COMMON2.ORA, which could contain a third IFILE parameter for the file GCPARMS.ORA. You can also include multiple parameter files in one parameter file by listing IFILE several times with different values:

```
IFILE = DBPARMS.ORA
IFILE = GCPARMS.ORA
IFILE = LOGPARMS.ORA
```

For more information: Chapter 6 "Managing Control Files"

LIST

If this keyword is included, current parameter values display upon system startup. The LIST keyword must be the first line of the parameter file or an error occurs.

Reading the Parameter Descriptions

The parameter descriptions in this appendix follow the format shown below.

PARAMETER_NAME

Default value:	the value this parameter will assume if not explicitly specified.
Range of values:	the valid range of values that this parameter can assume, shown as a minimum and maximum value. Not applicable to all parameters.
Multiple instances:	how the values for this parameter must be specified for multiple instances in an ORACLE parallel server. Not applicable to all parameters.

The remaining paragraphs provide a textual description of the parameter and the effects of different settings.

For more information: references to chapters or books that contain more detailed information on this subject.

Parameter Descriptions

Descriptions of the individual initialization parameters follow in alphabetical order. Parameter names are shown in uppercase for readability. Refer to the installation or user's guide to see how your operating system expects to read the file and the parameters.

Most initialization parameter values are global (on a database-wide basis), not per user, unless otherwise specified.

AUDIT_TRAIL

Default value: NONE
Range of values: NONE, DB, OS

Enables or disables the writing of rows to the audit trail. Auditing records are not written if the value is NONE or if the parameter is not present. The OS option enables system-wide auditing and causes auditing records to be written to the operating system's audit trail. The DB option enables system-wide auditing and causes audit records to be written to the database audit trail (the SYS.AUD$ table).

The values TRUE and FALSE are also supported, for backward compatibility. TRUE is equivalent to DB. FALSE is equivalent to NONE.

The SQL AUDIT statements can be used to set auditing options regardless of the setting of this parameter.

For more information: Chapter 13 "Auditing Database Use"

AUTO_MOUNTING

This is a Trusted ORACLE parameter.

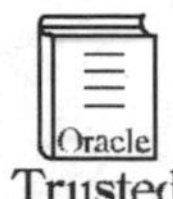

For more information: *Trusted ORACLE7 Server Administrator's Guide*

BACKGROUND_DUMP_DEST

Default value: O/S dependent
Range of values: valid local pathname, directory, or disk

The path name for a directory where debugging trace files for the background processes (LGWR, DBWR, etc.) are written during the course of ORACLE operations.

An ALERT file in the directory specified by BACKGROUND_DUMP_DEST logs significant database events and messages. This file records all instance startups and shutdowns, messages to the operator console, and errors that cause trace files to be written. It also records every CREATE, ALTER, or DROP operation on a database, tablespace, or rollback segment.

The ALERT file is a normal text file. Its filename is operating system specific, generally of the form *nodename_instance-name*_ALERT.LOG. This file grows slowly, but without limit, so the DBA may wish to delete it periodically. The file may be deleted even when the database is running.

For more information: Chapter 4 "Managing ORACLE Processes"

CHECKPOINT_PROCESS

Default value: false
Range of values: true/false
Multiple instances: can have different values

Setting this parameter to TRUE enables the CKPT background process. You should only enable the CKPT process if the performance of the LGWR process decreases significantly during a checkpoint.

Note: Adjust all calculations that depend on the number of background processes to allow for the CKPT process. For example, increase the value of the PROCESSES parameter by one, and increase the values of other parameters whose default values are derived from PROCESSES if you do not use their default values.

For more information: see PROCESSES on page A-39

CLEANUP_ROLLBACK_ENTRIES

Default value: 20 entries

The number of undo records processed at one time when rolling back a transaction. Prevents long transactions from freezing out shorter transactions that also need to be rolled back. Normally this parameter will not need modification.

For more information: Chapter 9 "Managing Rollback Segments"

COMMIT_POINT_STRENGTH

Default value: O/S dependent
Range of values: 0..255

A value used to determine the commit point site in a distributed transaction. The node in the transaction with the highest value for COMMIT_POINT_STRENGTH will be the commit point site. A database's commit point strength should be set relative to the amount of critical shared data in the database. For example, a database on a mainframe computer typically shares more data among users than on a personal computer. Therefore, COMMIT_POINT_STRENGTH should be set to a higher value for the mainframe computer.

The commit point site stores information about the status of transactions. Other computers in a distributed transaction require this information, so it is desirable to have a machines that are always available as commit point sites. Therefore, set COMMIT_POINT_STRENGTH to a higher value on your more available machines.

For more information: *ORACLE7 Server Concepts Manual*, Chapter 22 "Two-Phase Commit" See you installation or users guide for the default value.

COMPATIBLE

Default value: Release Dependent
Range of values: Default Version to Current Version
Multiple instances: Must have the same value

This parameter allows a new release to be used while at the same time guaranteeing backwards compatibility with an earlier version (in case it becomes necessary to retreat to the earlier version). The version that the ORACLE server must remain compatible with is specified by this parameter. In order to maintain compatibility, some features of the current version may be restricted.

The default value is the earliest version with which compatibility can be guaranteed.

For more information: For the default value, see your ORACLE server release notes. For more information, see the *ORACLE7 Server Migration Guide*.

COMPATIBLE_NO_RECOVERY

Default value: Release Dependent
Range of values: Default version to current version
Multiple instances: Must have the same value

This parameter functions like the COMPATIBLE parameter, except that the earlier version may not be usable on the current database if any recovery is needed.

The default value is the earliest version with which compatibility can be guaranteed. In some cases, this version may be earlier than the version specifiable with the COMPATIBLE parameter.

For more information: For the default value, see your ORACLE server release notes. For more information, see the *ORACLE7 Server Migration Guide*.

CONTROL_FILES

Default value: O/S dependent
Range of values: 1..8 filenames

One or more names of control files, separated by commas. Oracle Corporation recommends using multiple files on different devices.

For more information: Chapter 6 "Managing Control Files"

CURSOR_SPACE_FOR_TIME

Default value: false
Range of values: true/false

Setting this parameter to TRUE causes the database to use more space for cursors in order to save time. It affects both the shared SQL area and the client's private SQL area.

Shared SQL areas are kept pinned in the shared pool when this parameter's value is TRUE. As a result, shared SQL areas are not aged out of the pool as long as there is an open cursor that references them. Since each active cursor's SQL area is present in memory, execution is faster. However, since the shared SQL areas never leave memory while they are in use, you should only set this parameter to TRUE when the shared pool is large enough to hold all cursors simultaneously.

Setting this parameter to TRUE also retains the private SQL area allocated for each cursor between executes instead of discarding it after cursor execution. This setting saves cursor allocation and initialization time.

For more information: *ORACLE7 Server Concepts Manual*, Chapter 11 "SQL and PL/SQL"

DB_BLOCK_BUFFERS

Default value: 32 buffers
Range of values: 4..unlimited

The number of database blocks cached in memory in the SGA (one block equals one buffer). This parameter is the most significant determinant of the SGA size and database performance. The advantage of a higher value is that when a user needs a database block that block is more likely to be in memory, thus reducing I/O. The disadvantage of high values is that more memory is consumed. The size of each buffer is equal to the size of the parameter DB_BLOCK_SIZE.

For more information: *ORACLE7 Server Concepts Manual*, Chapter 9 "Memory Structures and Processes"

DB_BLOCK_CHECKPOINT_BATCH

Default value: derived (DB_BLOCK_WRITE_BATCH / 4)
Range of values: 0..DB_BLOCK_WRITE_BATCH

The maximum number of blocks that the database writer process will write in one batch that are devoted to checkpoints. The maximum size of the write-batch is set by DB_BLOCK_WRITE_BATCH. Setting DB_BLOCK_CHECKPOINT_BATCH to a small value, relative to the write-batch size, prevents the I/O system from being flooded with checkpoint writes and allows other modified blocks to be written to disk. Setting it to a higher value allows checkpoints to complete more quickly.

In general, DB_BLOCK_CHECKPOINT_BATCH should be set to a value that allows the checkpoint to complete before the next checkpoint log switch takes place. If a checkpoint log switch takes place every 20 minutes, then this parameter should be set to a value that allows checkpointing to complete within 20 minutes.

Setting DB_BLOCK_CHECKPOINT_BATCH to zero causes the default value to be used. A value larger than DB_BLOCK_WRITE_BATCH can be specified, but its effect is the same as specifying the maximum.

For more information: *ORACLE7 Server Concepts Manual*, Chapter 9 "Memory Structures and Processes"

DB_BLOCK_LRU_EXTENDED_STATISTICS

Default value: 0
Range of values: 0..unlimited

Disables or enables compilation of statistics in the X$KCBRBH table, which measures the effects of increasing the number of buffers in the buffer cache in the SGA. When this facility is enabled, it keeps track of the number of disk accesses that would be saved if additional buffers were allocated. A value greater than zero specifies the additional number of buffers (over DB_BLOCK_BUFFERS) for which statistics are kept. This tuning tool should be turned off during normal operation.

When compiling statistics for the X$KCBRBH table, set this parameter to the maximum size you want to use to evaluate the buffer cache. It should be set to 0 otherwise.

For more information: Chapter 21 "Tuning Memory Allocation"

DB_BLOCK_LRU_STATISTICS

Default value: false
Range of values: true/false

Disables or enables compilation of statistics in the X$KCBCBH table, which measures the effect of fewer buffers in the buffer cache in the SGA. This tuning tool should be turned off during normal operation.

Set this parameter to TRUE when you want to compile statistics for the X$KCBCBH table; otherwise, leave it set to FALSE.

For more information: Chapter 21 "Tuning Memory Allocation"

DB_BLOCK_SIZE

Default value: O/S dependent
Range of values: O/S dependent (1024 - 8192)
Multiple instances: must have the same value

The size in bytes of ORACLE database blocks. Typical values are 2048 and 4096. The value for DB_BLOCK_SIZE in effect at CREATE DATABASE time determines the size of the blocks; at all other times the value must be set to the original value.

This parameter affects the maximum value of the FREELISTS storage parameter for tables and indexes.

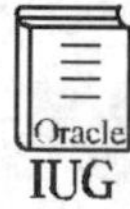

For more information: *ORACLE7 Server Concepts Manual*, Chapter 3 "Database Blocks, Extents, and Segments" (block size). See your installation or user's guide for the default value.

DB_DOMAIN

Default value: WORLD
Range of values: any legal string of name components, separated by periods and up to 128 characters long, including periods
Multiple instances: must have the same value

The extension components of a global database name, consisting of valid identifiers, separated by periods. Specifying DB_DOMAIN as a unique string for every database is highly recommended.

For example, this parameter allows one department to create a database without worrying that it might have the same name as a database created by another department. If one sales department's DB_DOMAIN = "JAPAN.ACME.COM", then their "SALES" database is uniquely distinguished from another department that might also have DB_NAME = "SALES" but with DB_DOMAIN = "US.ACME.COM".

For more information: Chapter 15 "Managing Distributed Databases"

DB_FILES

Default value: O/S dependent
Range of values: minimum: MAXDATAFILES for the database to be mounted
maximum: O/S dependent
Multiple instances: must have the same value

The maximum number of database files that can be opened at runtime for this database. If you increase the value, you must shut down and restart all instances accessing the database before the new value can take effect.

Reduce the value only if you need SGA space and do not anticipate having more database files.

DB_FILES is similar to the MAXDATAFILES argument for the CREATE DATABASE statement, which sets the absolute maximum number of data files at database creation. An instance cannot mount a database unless DB_FILES is equal to or greater than MAXDATAFILES for that database. Greater values are only useful for instances that mount different databases at different times.

For more information: Chapter 7 "Managing the Size and Files of the Database" See your installation or user's guide for the default value.

DB_FILE_MULTIBLOCK_READ_COUNT

Default value: O/S dependent
Range of values: O/S dependent

Used for multi-block I/O, this is the maximum number of blocks read in one I/O operation during a sequential scan. The default is a function of DB_BLOCK_BUFFERS and PROCESSES. Values in the range of 4 to 16 or even 32 are reasonable. The actual maximums vary by operating system.

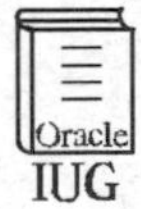

For more information: *ORACLE7 Server Concepts Manual*, Chapter 13 "The Optimizer" See your installation or user's guide for the default value and range of values.

DB_FILE_SIMULTANEOUS_WRITES

Default value: 4
Range of values: 1..24

The number of simultaneous writes ("batches") for each database file when written by DBWR.

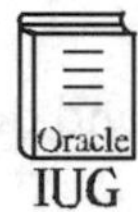

If the operating system only supports one write per device and cannot combine writes to adjacent blocks, then the value should be 1. Though the value has no maximum because DBWR writes blocks in groups, it is not useful to use a value larger than that value. Refer to your installation or user's guide for information specific to your operating system.

For more information: *ORACLE7 Server Concepts Manual*, Chapter 9 "Memory Structures and Processes"

DB_MOUNT_MODE

This is a Trusted ORACLE parameter.

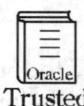

Trusted

For more information: *Trusted ORACLE7 Server Administrator's Guide*

DB_NAME

Default value: null
Range of values: Any valid database name
Multiple instances: must have the same value, or else the same value must be specified in STARTUP OPEN *db_name* or ALTER DATABASE *db_name* MOUNT.

A database identifier of up to eight characters. If specified, it must correspond to the name specified in the CREATE DATABASE statement. Although the use of DB_NAME is optional, it should generally be set before invoking CREATE DATABASE and then referenced in that statement.

If not specified, a database name must appear on either the STARTUP or the ALTER DATABASE MOUNT command line.

The following are valid characters in a database name:

- alphabetic characters
- numbers
- underscore (_)
- sharp (#)
- dollar sign ($)

No other characters are valid. Double quotes are removed before processing the database name. They cannot be used to embed other characters in the name.

Lowercase characters are not treated with any special significance. They are considered the same as their uppercase counterparts.

For more information: DB_DOMAIN, page A-14, Chapter 15 "Managing Distributed Databases", and Chapter 2 "Creating a Database"

DISCRETE_TRANSACTIONS_ENABLED

Default value: false
Range of values: true / false

Implements a simpler, faster rollback mechanism that improves performance for certain kinds of transactions. There are strict limits on the kinds of transactions that can occur in discrete mode, but greater efficiency can be obtained for these transactions.

For more information: *ORACLE7 Server Application Developer's Guide*, Appendix A "Supplied Packages"

DISTRIBUTED_LOCK_TIMEOUT

Default value: 60 seconds
Range of values: 1..unlimited

The amount of time in seconds for distributed transactions to wait for locked resources.

For more information: *ORACLE7 Server Concepts Manual*, Chapter 10 "Data Concurrency" and Chapter 22 "Two-Phase Commit"

DISTRIBUTED_RECOVERY_CONNECTION_HOLD_TIME

Default value: 200 seconds
Range of values: 0..1800 seconds

The length of time to hold a remote connection open after a distributed transaction fails, in hopes that communication will be restored without having to reestablish the connection. Larger values minimize reconnection time, but they also consume local resources for a longer time period. Values larger than 1800 seconds can be specified, but since the reconnection and recovery background process runs every 30 minutes (1800 seconds) whether or not a failure occurs, any value of 1800 or larger means that the connection never closes.

For more information: Chapter 15 "Managing Distributed Databases"

DISTRIBUTED_TRANSACTIONS

Default value: O/S dependent
Range of values: 0..TRANSACTIONS

The maximum number of distributed transactions that this database can concurrently participate in. The value of this parameter cannot exceed the value of the parameter TRANSACTIONS.

If network failures are occurring at an abnormally high rate, causing many in-doubt transactions, you may want to temporarily decrease this parameter's value. This limits the number of concurrent distributed transactions, which then reduces the number of in-doubt transactions. Thus, the amount of blocked data and possible heuristic decision making (because of in-doubt transactions) is reduced.

If DISTRIBUTED_TRANSACTIONS is set to 0, no distributed transactions are allowed for the database and the recoverer (RECO) process does not start when the instance starts up.

For more information: Chapter 15 "Managing Distributed Databases". See your installation or user's guide for the default value.

DML_LOCKS

Default value: derived (4 * TRANSACTIONS)
Range of values: 20..unlimited, 0
Multiple instances: must all have positive values or must all be 0

The maximum number of DML locks — one for each table modified in a transaction. Value should equal the grand total of locks on tables referenced by all users. For example, if 3 users are modifying data in one table, then 3 entries would be required. If 3 users are modifying data in 2 tables, then 6 entries would be required.

The default value assumes an average of 4 tables referenced per transaction. For some systems, this value may not be enough.

If the value is set to 0, enqueues are disabled and performance is slightly increased. However, you cannot use DROP TABLE, CREATE INDEX, or explicit lock statements such as LOCK TABLE IN EXCLUSIVE MODE.

For more information: *ORACLE7 Server Concepts Manual*, Chapter 10 "Data Concurrency"

ENQUEUE_RESOURCES

Default value: derived
Range of values: 10..65535

The number of resources that can be locked by the lock manager. The default value is derived from PROCESSES and should be adequate. For three or fewer processes, the default value is 20. For 4 to 10 processes, the default value is ((PROCESSES – 3) * 5) + 20; and for more than 10 processes it is ((PROCESSES – 10) * 2) + 55.

If many tables are used, the value may be increased. Allow one per resource (regardless of the number of sessions or cursors using that resource), not one per lock. The value should be no greater than DML_LOCKS plus DDL_LOCKS plus overhead of about 20, and generally should be much less.

For more information: *ORACLE7 Server Concepts Manual*, Chapter 10 "Data Concurrency"

EVENT

Default value: null

Modifies the scope of ALTER SESSION SET EVENTS commands so that they pertain to an entire instance, instead of to a single session. Used for system debugging. This parameter should not usually be altered except at the direction of Oracle personnel.

FIXED_DATE

Default value: null

Allows you to set a constant for SYSDATE in the format 'YYYY-MM-DD-HH24:MI:SS'. Also accepts the default ORACLE date format, without a time. Useful primarily for testing.

For more information: *ORACLE7 Server Concepts Manual*, Chapter 6 "Datatypes"

GC_DB_LOCKS

This is a parallel server parameter.

For more information: *ORACLE7 Parallel Server Administrator's Guide*

GC_FILES_TO_LOCKS

This is a parallel server parameter.

For more information: *ORACLE7 Parallel Server Administrator's Guide*

GC_LCK_PROCS

This is a parallel server parameter.

For more information: *ORACLE7 Parallel Server Administrator's Guide*

GC_ROLLBACK_LOCKS

This is a parallel server parameter.

For more information: *ORACLE7 Parallel Server Administrator's Guide*

GC_ROLLBACK_SEGMENTS

This is a parallel server parameter.

For more information: *ORACLE7 Parallel Server Administrator's Guide*

GC_SAVE_ROLLBACK_LOCKS

This is a parallel server parameter.

For more information: *ORACLE7 Parallel Server Administrator's Guide*

GC_SEGMENTS

This is a parallel server parameter.

For more information: *ORACLE7 Parallel Server Administrator's Guide*

GC_TABLESPACES

This is a parallel server parameter.

For more information: *ORACLE7 Parallel Server Administrator's Guide*

GLOBAL_NAMES

Default value: false
Range of values: true / false

This parameter determines whether or not a database link is required to have the same name as the database it connects to. If the value of GLOBAL_NAMES is false, then no check is performed. ORACLE recommends setting this parameter to TRUE to ensure the use of consistent naming conventions for databases and links.

For more information: Chapter 15 "Managing Distributed Databases"

INIT_SQL_FILES

Default value: O/S dependent
Range of values: valid SQL script filenames
Multiple instances: can have different values

Specifies the name of one or more files containing SQL statements to be executed during database creation. Enclose the list in parentheses and separate the filenames with commas, as in:

```
INIT_SQL_FILES = (SQL.BSQ, CATALOG.ORA, SITEDD.SQL)
```

This parameter should always specify SQL.BSQ first. Then other site-specific files can be specified if desired. The default is operating system dependent and should not be altered, except to include additional files. Objects created with additional files that you add belong to the user SYS.

The INIT_SQL_FILES parameter has no effect except when executing the CREATE DATABASE statement. Since CREATE DATABASE can only be executed when a single instance is started up with the NOMOUNT option, this parameter does not apply to instances of an ORACLE Parallel Server running in parallel mode.

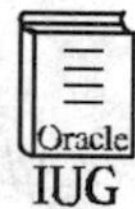

For more information: Chapter 2 "Creating a Database". See your installation or user's guide for the default value.

INSTANCE_NUMBER

This is a parallel server parameter.

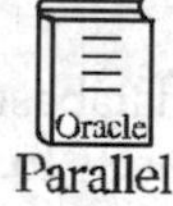

For more information: *ORACLE7 Parallel Server Administrator's Guide*

LABEL_CACHE_SIZE

This is a Trusted ORACLE parameter.

For more information: *Trusted ORACLE7 Server Administrator's Guide*

LICENSE_MAX_SESSIONS

Default value: 0
Range of values: 0..number of session licenses
Multiple instances: can have different values

Sets the maximum number of concurrent user sessions allowed simultaneously. When this limit is reached, only users with the RESTRICTED SESSION privilege can connect to the server. Users who are able to connect receive a warning message indicating that the system has reached maximum capacity.

A zero value indicates that concurrent usage (session) licensing is not enforced. If you set this parameter to a non-zero number, you may also want to set LICENSE_SESSIONS_WARNING.

Concurrent usage licensing and user licensing should not both be enabled. Either LICENSE_MAX_SESSIONS or LICENSE_MAX_USERS should always be zero.

Multiple instances can have different values, but the total for all instances mounting a database should be less than or equal to the total number of sessions licensed for that database.

For more information: Chapter 11 "Controlling Access to the Database"

LICENSE_MAX_USERS

Default value: 0
Range of values: 0..number of user licenses
Multiple instances: should have the same values

Sets the maximum number of users you can create in the database. When you reach this limit, you cannot create any more users. You can, however, increase the limit.

Concurrent usage (session) licensing and user licensing should not both be enabled. Either LICENSE_MAX_SESSIONS or LICENSE_MAX_USERS, or both, should be zero.

If different instances specify different values for this parameter, the value of the first instance to mount the database takes precedence.

For more information: Chapter 11 "Controlling Access to the Database"

LICENSE_SESSIONS_WARNING

Default value: 0
Range of values: 0..LICENSE_MAX_SESSIONS
Multiple instances: can have different values

Sets a warning limit on the number of concurrent user sessions. When this limit is reached, additional users can connect, but ORACLE writes a message in the ALERT file for each new connection. Users with RESTRICTED SESSION privilege who connect after the limit is reached receive a warning message stating that the system is nearing its maximum capacity.

If this parameter is set to zero, no warning is given when approaching the concurrent usage (session) limit. If you set this parameter to a non-zero number, you should also set LICENSE_MAX_SESSIONS.

For more information: Chapter 11 "Controlling Access to the Database"

LOG_ARCHIVE_BUFFER_SIZE

Default value: O/S dependent
Range of values: 1..O/S dependent (in O/S blocks)
Multiple instances: can have different values

The size of each archival buffer, in redo log blocks (operating system blocks). The default should be adequate for most applications.

This parameter, with LOG_ARCHIVE_BUFFERS, can be used to tune archiving so that it runs as fast as necessary, but not so fast that it reduces system performance.

For more information: Chapter 17 "Archiving Redo Information". See your installation or user's guide for the default value and range of values.

LOG_ARCHIVE_BUFFERS

Default value: O/S dependent
Range of values: 1..O/S dependent
Multiple instances: can have different values

The number of buffers to allocate for archiving. The default should be adequate for most applications.

This parameter, with LOG_ARCHIVE_BUFFER_SIZE, can be used to tune archiving so that it runs as fast as necessary, but not so fast that it reduces system performance.

For more information: Chapter 17 "Archiving Redo Information". See your installation or user's guide for the default value and range of values.

LOG_ARCHIVE_DEST

Default value: O/S dependent
Range of values: any valid path or device name
Multiple instances: can have different values

Applicable only if using the redo log in ARCHIVELOG mode. Use a text string to specify the default location and root of the disk file or tape device when archiving redo log files. (Archiving to tape is not supported on all operating systems.)

To override the destination that this parameter specifies, either specify a different destination for manual archiving or use the SQL*DBA command ARCHIVE LOG START *'filespec'* for automatic archiving.

See your user or installation guide for the default value and for example of how to specify the destination path or filename using LOG_ARCHIVE_DEST and LOG_ARCHIVE_FORMAT.

For more information: Chapter 17 "Archiving Redo Information"

LOG_ARCHIVE_FORMAT

Default value: O/S dependent (length for uppercase variables is also O/S dependent)
Range of values: any valid file name
Multiple instances: can have different values, but identical values are recommended.

Applicable only if using the redo log in ARCHIVELOG mode. Use a text string and variables to specify the default filename format when archiving redo log files. The string generated from this format is appended to the string specified in the LOG_ARCHIVE_DEST parameter. The following variables can be used in the format:

%s log sequence number

%t thread number

Using uppercase letters (for example, %S) for the variables causes the value to be a fixed length padded to the left with zeros. The following is an example of specifying the archive redo log filename format:

```
LOG_ARCHIVE_FORMAT = 'LOG%s_%t.ARC'
```

Oracle IUG

For more information: Chapter 17 "Archiving Redo Information". See your installation or user's guide for the default value.

LOG_ARCHIVE_START

Default value: false
Range of values: true/false
Multiple instances: can have different values

Applicable only when you use the redo log in ARCHIVELOG mode, LOG_ARCHIVE_START indicates whether archiving should be automatic or manual when the instance starts up. TRUE indicates that archiving is automatic. FALSE indicates that the DBA will archive filled redo log files manually. (The SQL*DBA command ARCHIVE LOG START or STOP overrides this parameter.)

In ARCHIVELOG mode, if all online redo log files fill without being archived, an error message is issued and instance operations are suspended until the necessary archiving is performed. This delay is more likely if you use manual archiving. You can reduce its likelihood by increasing the number of online redo log files.

To use ARCHIVELOG mode while creating a database, set this parameter to TRUE. Normally, a database is created in NOARCHIVELOG mode and then altered to ARCHIVELOG mode after creation.

For more information: Chapter 17 "Archiving Redo Information"

LOG_BUFFER

Default value: O/S dependent
Range of values: O/S dependent

The number of bytes allocated to the redo log buffer in the SGA. In general, larger values reduce redo log file I/O, particularly if transactions are long or numerous. In a busy system, the value 65536 or higher would not be unreasonable.

The default is set to 4 times the maximum database block size for the host operating system.

For more information: Chapter 23 "Tuning Contention". See your installation or users guide for the default value and range of values.

LOG_CHECKPOINT_INTERVAL

Default value: O/S dependent
Range of values: 2..unlimited (operating system blocks, not database blocks)
Multiple instances: can have different values

The number of newly filled redo log file blocks needed to trigger a checkpoint. Regardless of this value, a checkpoint always occurs when switching from one online redo log file to another. If the value exceeds the actual redo log file size, checkpoints occur only when switching logs.

The number of times DBWR has been notified to do a checkpoint for a given instance is shown in the statistic *dbwr checkpoints* displayed by the SQL*DBA command MONITOR STAT CACHE.

For more information: Chapter 24 "Additional Tuning Considerations" See your installation or users guide for the default value.

LOG_CHECKPOINT_TIMEOUT

Default value: 0 seconds
Range of values: 0..unlimited
Multiple instances: can have different values

The amount of time to pass before another checkpoint occurs. The value is specified in seconds. A value of 0 disables time-based checkpoints. The time begins at the start of the previous checkpoint, then a checkpoint occurs after the amount of time specified by this parameter.

Note: A checkpoint scheduled to occur because of this parameter is delayed until the completion of the previous checkpoint if the previous checkpoint has not yet completed.

For more information: Chapter 24 "Additional Tuning Considerations"

LOG_FILES

Default value: 255
Range of values: 2..255 (should equal MAXLOGFILES)
Multiple instances: must have the same value

The maximum log group number. This value specifies the maximum number of redo log files that can be opened at runtime for the database. It also gives the upper limit on the group numbers that can be specified when issuing log-related commands. Reduce the value only if you need SGA space and have fewer redo log files.

The MAXLOGFILES option for the CREATE DATABASE statement sets the absolute maximum number of redo log files that can ever be created for the database. MAXLOGFILES overrides the LOG_FILES parameter value if LOG_FILES is greater than MAXLOGFILES.

For more information: Chapter 23 "Tuning Contention"

LOG_SIMULTANEOUS_COPIES

Default value: CPU_COUNT
Range of values: 0..unlimited

The maximum number of redo buffer copy latches available to write log entries simultaneously. For good performance, you can have up to twice as many redo copy latches as CPUs. For a single-processor system, set to 0 so that all log entries are copied on the redo allocation latch.

If this parameter is set to 0, redo copy latches are turned off and the parameters LOG_ENTRY_PREBUILD_THRESHOLD and LOG_SMALL_ENTRY_MAX_SIZE are ignored.

For more information: Chapter 23 "Tuning Contention"

LOG_SMALL_ENTRY_MAX_SIZE

Default value: O/S dependent
Range of values: O/S dependent

The size in bytes of the largest copy to the log buffers that can occur under the redo allocation latch, without obtaining the redo buffer copy latch. If the value for LOG_SIMULTANEOUS_COPIES is 0, this parameter is ignored (all writes are "small" and are made without the copy latch).

If the redo entry is copied on the redo allocation latch, the user process releases the latch after the copy. If the redo entry is larger than this parameter, the user process releases the latch after allocating space in the buffer and getting a redo copy latch.

IUG

For more information: Chapter 23 "Tuning Contention". See your installation or user's guide for the default value and range of values.

MAX_DUMP_FILE_SIZE

Default value: 500 blocks
Range of values: 0..unlimited

Maximum size in operating system blocks of any trace files written. Set this limit if you are concerned that trace files may take up too much space.

For more information: Chapter 4 "Managing ORACLE Processes"

MAX_ENABLED_ROLES

Default value: 20
Range of values: 0..48

The maximum number of database roles that a user can enable, including sub-roles.

For more information: Chapter 12 "Controlling User Privileges and Roles"

MAX_ROLLBACK_SEGMENTS

Default value: 30
Range of values: 1..65536

The maximum size of the rollback segment cache in the SGA. The number specified signifies the maximum number of rollback segments that can be kept online (that is, status of INUSE) simultaneously by one instance.

For more information: Chapter 9 "Managing Rollback Segments"

MLS_LABEL_FORMAT

This is a Trusted ORACLE parameter.

Trusted

For more information: *Trusted ORACLE7 Server Administrator's Guide*

MTS_DISPATCHERS

Default value: null

The configuration of the dispatcher processes(es) created when the instance starts up. The value of this parameter is specified as one or more configuration strings. Each configuration string is a quoted string of 2 values separated by a comma that specifies the configuration of a group of one or more dispatchers. The configuration string for each group of dispatcher processes includes the network protocol for that group and the number of dispatcher processes in the group (one or more). Each network protocol that you use on your system requires a separate specification. For example, if you are using TCP/IP and DECNet to connect to the server, you would need to specify two parameters, as follows:

```
MTS_DISPATCHERS = "tcp, 1"
MTS_DISPATCHERS = "decnet, 4"
```

The first configuration string in this example specifies one dispatcher process for the TCP/IP protocol. The second string specifies four dispatcher processes for the DECNet protocol.

For more information: Chapter 15 "Managing Distributed Databases"

MTS_LISTENER_ADDRESS **Default value:** null

The configuration of the Listener process. The Listener process requires an address to listen for connection requests for each network protocol that is used on your system. Addresses are specified as the SQL*Net description of the connection address.

Each address must be specified with its own parameter. (This differs from the SQL*Net syntax.) For example, if you use TCP/IP as well as DECNet, you would provide specifications similar to the following in your initialization file:

```
MTS_LISTENER_ADDRESS =
    "(ADDRESS=(PROTOCOL=tcp)(HOST=myhost)(PORT=7002))"

MTS_LISTENER_ADDRESS =
    "(ADDRESS=(PROTOCOL=decnet)(NODE=name)(OBJECT=mts))"
```

Address specifications for the Listener process are operating system specific and network protocol specific. Refer to your installation or user's guide and SQL*Net documentation for a description of how to specify addresses for the protocols on your system.

For more information: Chapter 14 "Administering Client Server Systems"

MTS_MAX_DISPATCHERS **Default value:** 5
Range of values: O/S dependent

The maximum number of dispatcher processes allowed to be running simultaneously.

For more information: Chapter 14 "Administering Client Server Systems". See your installation or user's guide for the range of values.

MTS_MAX_SERVERS

Default value: 20
Range of values: O/S dependent

The maximum number of shared server processes allowed to be running simultaneously.

For more information: Chapter 14 "Administering Client Server Systems". See your installation or user's guide for the range of values.

MTS_SERVERS

Default value: 0
Range of values: O/S dependent

The number of server processes that you wish to create when an instance is started up.

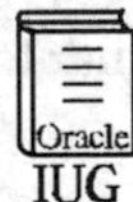

For more information: Chapter 14 "Administering Client Server Systems". See your installation or user's guide for the range of values.

MTS_SERVICE

Default value: null

This parameter specifies the name of the service you wish to be associated with the dispatcher. Using this name in the CONNECT string allows users to connect to an instance via a dispatcher. ORACLE always checks for such a service before establishing a normal database connection.

The name you specify must be unique. It should *not* be enclosed in quotes. It is a good idea for this name to be the same as the instance name. That way, if the dispatcher is unavailable for any reason, the CONNECT string will still connect the user to the database.

If not specified, MTS_SERVICE defaults to the value specified by DB_NAME. If DB_NAME also is not specified, the ORACLE server returns an error at startup indicating that the value for this parameter is missing.

For more information: Chapter 14 "Administering Client Server Systems"

NLS_CURRENCY

Default value: derived
Range of values: any valid character string

Defines the string to use as the local currency symbol for the L number format element. The default value of this parameter is determined by NLS_TERRITORY. For example, the following query uses the L format element to return the default local currency symbol for the territory FRANCE:

```
SELECT TO_CHAR(TOTAL, 'L099') "TOTAL"
    FROM ORDERS WHERE CUSTNO = 586;

  TOTAL
 -------
   F635
```

For more information: Appendix C "National Language Support"

NLS_DATE_FORMAT

Default value: derived
Range of values: any valid date format mask

Defines the default date format to use with the TO_CHAR and TO_DATE functions. The default value of this parameter is determined by NLS_TERRITORY. The value of this parameter can be any valid date format mask. For example:

```
NLS_DATE_FORMAT = 'MM/DD/YYYY'
```

For more information: Appendix C "National Language Support"

NLS_DATE_LANGUAGE

Default value: value for NLS_LANGUAGE
Range of values: any valid NLS_LANGUAGE value

Determines the language to use for day and month names and date abbreviations (AM, PM, AD, BC). The default value of this parameter is the language specified by NLS_LANGUAGE.

For more information: Appendix C "National Language Support"

NLS_ISO_CURRENCY

Default value: derived
Range of values: any valid NLS_TERRITORY value

Defines the string to use as the international currency symbol for the C number format element. The default value of this parameter is determined by NLS_TERRITORY. For example, the following query uses the C format element to return the default international currency symbol for the territory FRANCE:

```
SELECT TO_CHAR(TOTAL, 'C099') "TOTAL"
    FROM ORDERS WHERE CUSTNO = 586;

  TOTAL
 -------
 FRF635
```

The value of this parameter can be any valid territory specified in NLS_TERRITORY.

For more information: Appendix C "National Language Support"

NLS_LANGUAGE

Default value: O/S dependent

Defines the default language of the database. Specifies the language to use for messages, the language of day and month names, symbols to use for AD, BC, AM, and PM, and the default sorting mechanism. This parameter has the format:

```
NLS_LANGUAGE = FRENCH
```

Examples of supported languages are American, French, and Japanese. This parameter determines the default values of the parameters NLS_DATE_LANGUAGE and NLS_SORT. Also see your installation or user's guide and your country release notes for information specific to your operating system.

For more information: Appendix C "National Language Support", your installation or user's guide, and your country release notes for information specific to your operating system.

NLS_NUMERIC_CHARACTERS

Default value: derived

Defines the characters to use as the group separator and decimal. The group separator is the character that separates integer groups (that is, the thousands, millions, billions, etc.). The decimal separates the integer portion of a number from the decimal portion. Any character can be used for the decimal or group separator, but both characters must be different from each other. The characters are specified in the following format:

```
NLS_NUMERIC_CHARACTERS = '<decimal character><group separator>'
```

For example, if you wish to specify a comma as the decimal character and a space as the group separator, you would set this parameter as follows:

```
NLS_NUMERIC_CHARACTERS = ', '
```

The default value of this parameter is determined by NLS_TERRITORY.

Note: When the decimal character is not a period (.) or when the group separator is used, numeric literals must appear in quotes, since the comma is used to separate items in a list in SQL. For example, with the value of NLS_NUMERIC_CHARACTERS above, the following SQL statement requires quotes around the numeric literals:

```
INSERT INTO SIZES ( ITEMID, PRICE, WIDTH )
    VALUES ( 618, '45,50', TO_NUMBER('1 234,11', '9G999D99'));
```

For more information: Appendix C "National Language Support"

NLS_SORT

Default value: derived
Range of values: BINARY or named linguistic sort

If the value is BINARY, then the collating sequence for ORDER BY queries is based on the numeric value of characters (a binary sort that requires less system overhead).

If the value is a named linguistic sort, sorting is based on the order of the defined linguistic sort. Most languages supported by the NLS_LANGUAGE parameter also support a linguistic sort with the same name. Linguistic sorts can be created with NLS*WorkBench if your language doesn't support a linguistic sort with the appropriate sorting rules.

The default value of this parameter is dependent on the NLS_LANGUAGE parameter.

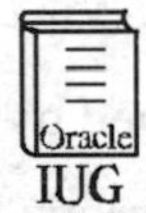

For more information: Appendix C "National Language Support" Also, see your installation or user's guide for linguistic sorts supported by your language and the sorting rules used by the linguistic sorting mechanisms.

NLS_TERRITORY

Default value: O/S dependent

Specifies the name of the territory whose conventions are to be followed for day and week numbering. Also specifies the default date format, the default decimal character and group separator, and the default ISO and local currency symbols. Supported territories include America, France, and Japan.

This parameter determines the default values for the following parameters: NLS_CURRENCY, NLS_ISO_CURRENCY, NLS_DATE_FORMAT, and NLS_NUMERIC_CHARACTERS.

For more information: Appendix C "National Language Support" See your installation or user's guide for the territory-dependent default values for these parameters.

OPEN_CURSORS

Default value: 50
Range of values: 1..O/S limit

The maximum number of open cursors (context areas) a single-user process can have at once. This parameter does not control a system-wide feature, but rather, the maximum address/memory space used by each process. The control of context areas is specific to the application.

For more information: Chapter 21 "Tuning Memory Allocation". See your installation or user's guide for the range of values.

OPEN_LINKS

Default value: 4
Range of values: 0..255

The maximum number of concurrent open connections to remote databases per user process. Value should equal or exceed the number of databases referred to in any single SQL statement that references multiple databases so that all the databases can be open in order to execute the statement. Value should be increased if many different databases are accessed over time. Thus, if queries alternately access databases A, B, and C and OPEN_LINKS is set to 2, time would be spent waiting while one connection was broken and another made.

This parameter refers only to connections used for distributed transactions. Direct connections to a remote database specified as an application connects are not counted.
If set to 0, then no distributed transaction are allowed.

For more information: Chapter 15 "Managing Distributed Databases"

OPEN_MOUNTS

This is a Trusted ORACLE parameter.

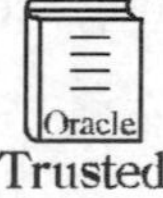

For more information: *Trusted ORACLE7 Server Administrator's Guide*

OPTIMIZER_MODE

Default value: COST
Range of values: RULE/COST

When set to RULE, this parameter causes rule-based optimization to be used, unless hints are specified in the query. When set to COST, the optimizer uses the cost-based approach for a SQL statement if there are statistics in the dictionary for at least one table accessed in the statement. (Otherwise, the rule-based approach is used.)

You can set the goal for cost based optimization within a session by using the ALTER SESSION command. This command lets you specify a goal of maximizing throughput or of minimizing response time.

For more information: *ORACLE7 Server Application Developer's Guide* Chapter 5 "Tuning SQL Statements" and the *ORACLE7 Server Concepts Manual* Chapter 13 "The Optimizer"

OS_AUTHENT_PREFIX

Default value: O/S dependent (typically "OPS$")

This parameter is used to authenticate users attempting to connect to the server with the users' operating system account name and password. The value of this parameter is concatenated to the beginning of every user's operating system account. The prefixed username is compared with the ORACLE usernames in the database when a connection request is attempted. The default value of this parameter is OPS$ for backward compatibility with previous versions. However, you might prefer to set the prefix value to "" (a null string) thereby eliminating the addition of any prefix to operating system account names.

IUG

Note: The text of the OS_AUTHENT_PREFIX parameter is case sensitive with some operating systems. Refer to your installation or user's guide for more information about this initialization parameter.

For more information: Chapter 10 "Establishing Security Policies"

OS_ROLES

Default value: false
Range of values: true/false

Setting this parameter to TRUE causes the database to allow the operating system to identify each username's roles. When a user attempts to create a session, the username's security domain is initialized using the roles identified by the operating system. A user can subsequently enable as many roles identified by the operating system as specified by the parameter MAX_OS_ROLES.

If OS_ROLES is equal to TRUE, the operating system completely manages the role grants for all database usernames. Any revokes of roles granted by the operating system are ignored, and any previously granted roles are ignored.

The default value, FALSE, causes roles to be identified and managed by the database.

For more information: Chapter 10 "Establishing Security Policies"

PROCESSES

Default value: 50
Range of values: 6 to O/S dependent
Multiple instances: can have different values

For a multiple-process operation, this parameter specifies the maximum number of operating system user processes that can simultaneously connect to an ORACLE server. Should include up to 6 for the background processes (or more if MI_BG_PROCS is non-zero or if you use the dispatcher configuration) plus one for logon; so a value of 20 would permit 13 or 14 concurrent users.

The default values of DDL_LOCKS and SESSIONS are derived from PROCESSES. If you alter the value of PROCESSES, you may want to adjust the values of these derived parameters.

For more information: Chapter 4 "Managing ORACLE Processes". See your installation or user's guide for the range of values.

REMOTE_OS_AUTHENT

Default value: false
Range of values: true/false

Setting this parameter to TRUE allows authentication of remote clients with the value of OS_AUTHENT_PREFIX.

For more information: Chapter 15 "Managing Distributed Databases" and OS_AUTHENT_PREFIX on page A-38

REMOTE_OS_ROLES

Default value: false
Range of values: true/false

Setting this parameter to TRUE allows O/S roles for remote clients. The default value, FALSE, causes roles to be identified and managed by the database for remote clients.

For more information: Chapter 15 "Managing Distributed Databases" and OS_ROLES on page A-39

RESOURCE_LIMIT

Default value: false
Range of values: true/false

Changes the enforcement status of resource limits set in database profiles. A value of FALSE disables the enforcement of resource limits. A value of TRUE enables the enforcement of resource limits.

For more information: Chapter 11 "Controlling Access to the Database"

ROLLBACK_SEGMENTS

Default value: null (the instance uses public rollback segments by default if you do not specify this parameter
Range of Values Any rollback segment names listed in DBA_ROLLBACK_SEGS except SYSTEM
Multiple instances: must have different values (different instances cannot specify the same rollback segment)

One or more rollback segments to allocate by name to this instance. If ROLLBACK_SEGMENTS is not overridden, an instance acquires all of the rollback segments named in this parameter, even if the number of rollback segments exceeds the minimum number required by the instance (calculated from the ratio TRANSACTIONS / TRANSACTIONS_PER_ROLLBACK_SEGMENT).

Note: Never name the SYSTEM rollback segment as a value for the ROLLBACK_SEGMENTS parameter.

This parameter has the following syntax:

```
ROLLBACK_SEGMENTS = (rbseg_name [, rbseg_name] ... )
```

Although this parameter usually specifies private rollback segments, it can also specify public rollback segments if they are not already in use.

Different instances in an ORACLE Parallel Server cannot name the same rollback segment for any of the ROLLBACK_SEGMENTS. Query the data dictionary view DBA_ROLLBACK_SEGS to find the name, segment ID number, and status of each rollback segment in the database.

For more information: Chapter 9 "Managing Rollback Segments"

ROW_CACHE_CURSORS

Default value: 10
Range of values: 10..3300

The number of cached recursive cursors used by the row cache manager for selecting rows from the data dictionary. The default value is sufficient for most systems.

For more information: *ORACLE7 Server Concepts Manual,* Chapter 9 "Memory Structures and Processes"

ROW_LOCKING

Default value: ALWAYS
Range of values: ALWAYS/INTENT
Multiple instances: must have the same value

The default of ALWAYS means that only row locks are acquired when a table is updated. INTENT means that only row locks are used on a SELECT FOR UPDATE, but at update time table locks are acquired.

For more information: *ORACLE7 Server Application Developer's Guide*, Chapter 5 "Tuning SQL Statements"

SEQUENCE_CACHE_ENTRIES

Default value: 10
Range of values: 10..32000
Multiple instances: can have different values

The number of sequences that can be cached in the SGA for immediate access. This cache is managed on a least recently used (LRU) basis, so if a request is made for a sequence that is not in the cache and there are no free entries, the oldest one on the LRU list is deleted and replaced with the newly requested one. Highest concurrency is achieved when this value is set to the highest possible number of sequences that will be used on an instance at one time.

Each entry requires approximately 110 bytes in the SGA for an ORACLE Parallel Server.

Sequences created with the NOCACHE option do not reside in this cache. They must be written through to the data dictionary on every use.

For more information: *ORACLE7 Server Application Developer's Guide*, Chapter 2 "Managing Schema Objects"

SEQUENCE_CACHE_HASH_BUCKETS

Default value: 7
Range of values: 1..32000 (if not a prime number, system uses next larger prime)
Multiple instances: can have different values

The number of buckets (at about 8 bytes per bucket) used to speed lookup for newly requested sequences in the cache. The cache is arranged as a hash table; a process making its first request for a sequence looks for it in this table.

This value should be prime; otherwise, the system uses the smallest prime number greater than or equal to the value you specify. Values larger than SEQUENCE_CACHE_ENTRIES are not meaningful.

For more information: *ORACLE7 Server Concepts Manual*, Chapter 9 "Memory Structures and Processes"

SERIALIZABLE

Default value: false
Range of values: true / false
Multiple instances: must have the same value

If TRUE, then queries acquire table-level read locks, preventing any update of objects read until the transaction containing the query is committed. This mode of operation provides repeatable reads and ensures that two queries for the same data within the same transaction see the same values.

Setting SERIALIZABLE to TRUE provides degree three consistency at a considerable cost in concurrency.

For more information: *ORACLE7 Server Concepts Manual*, Chapter 10 "Data Concurrency"

SESSIONS

Default value: derived (1.1 * PROCESSES)

The total number of user and system sessions. The default number is greater than PROCESSES to allow for recursive sessions.

The default value of DDL_LOCKS is derived from SESSIONS. If you alter the value of SESSIONS, you may want to adjust the value of DDL_LOCKS.

For more information: *ORACLE7 Server Concepts Manual*, Chapter 9 "Memory Structures and Processes"

SHARED_POOL_SIZE

Default value: 3.5 Mbytes
Range of values: 300 Kbytes - O/S dependent

The size of the shared pool, in bytes. The shared pool contains shared cursors and stored procedures. Larger values improve performance in multi-user systems. Smaller values use less memory.

For more information: Chapter 21 "Tuning Memory Allocation"

SINGLE_PROCESS

Default value: false
OK to change?: yes (only for an instance in exclusive mode with a single user)
Range of values: true/false
Multiple instances: must be false for all instances

Determines whether a database is brought up in single user (single process) mode or multiuser (multiprocess) mode. TRUE indicates single user and FALSE indicates multiuser. Value must be FALSE for an instance of an ORACLE Parallel Server.

For more information: Chapter 4 "Managing ORACLE Processes"

SMALL_TABLE_THRESHOLD

Default value: 4
Range of values: 0..O/S dependent

This parameter determines the number of buffers in the SGA that are available for scanning a table. Tables that are smaller than this value can be read into the cache in their entirety. When scanning a table that is larger than this value, buffers are reused immediately instead of aging in the cache. Except in very rare cases, the default setting provides optimal performance

For more information: *ORACLE7 Server Concepts Manual*, Chapter 9 "Memory Structures and Processes"

SORT_AREA_RETAINED_SIZE

Default value: derived (= SORT_AREA_SIZE)
Range of values: 0..SORT_AREA_SIZE

This is the maximum amount of session memory, in bytes, that will be used for an in-memory sort. This memory is released when the last row is fetched from the sort space.

If a sort requires more memory, a temporary segment is allocated and the sort becomes an external (disk) sort. The maximum amount of memory to use for the sort is then specified by SORT_AREA_SIZE (described below) instead of by this parameter.

Larger values permit more sorts to be performed in memory. However, multiple sort spaces of this size may be allocated. Usually, only one or two sorts occur at one time, even for complex queries. In some cases, though, additional concurrent sorts are required. Each sort occurs in its own memory area, as specified by SORT_AREA_RETAINED_SIZE.

For more information: Chapter 24 "Additional Tuning Considerations"

SORT_AREA_SIZE

Default value: O/S dependent

The maximum amount of PGA memory to use for an external (disk) sort, specified in bytes. This memory is released when the sorted rows are written to disk.

Increasing SORT_AREA_SIZE size improves the efficiency of large sorts. Multiple allocations never exist: there is only one memory area of SORT_AREA_SIZE for each user process at any given time.

The default is usually fine for most database operations. Only if very large indexes are being created might you want to adjust this parameter. For example, if one process is doing all database access, as in a full database import, then an increased value for this parameter may speed the import, particularly the CREATE INDEX statements.

IUG

For more information: Chapter 24 "Additional Tuning Considerations". See your installation or user's guide for the default value.

SORT_SPACEMAP_SIZE

Default value: O/S dependent

The size in bytes of the sort spacemap in the context area. Only if you have very large indexes should you adjust this parameter. A sort automatically increases its spacemap if necessary, but it does not necessarily do so when it will make best use of disk storage. The sort makes optimal use of disk storage if SORT_SPACEMAP_SIZE is set to

```
[(total-sort-bytes) / (sort-area-size)] + 64
```

where *total-sort-bytes* is:

```
(number-of-records) *
[sum-of-average-column-sizes + (2 * number of col))]
```

where columns include the SELECT list for the ORDER BY, the SELECT list for the GROUP BY, and the key list for CREATE INDEX. Also include 10 bytes for ROWID for CREATE INDEX and GROUP BY or ORDER BY columns not mentioned in the SELECT list for these cases.

For more information: *ORACLE7 Server Concepts Manual*, Chapter 9 "Memory Structures and Processes". See your installation or user's guide for the default value.

SQL_TRACE

Default value: false
Range of values: true/false

Disables or enables the SQL trace facility. Setting this parameter to TRUE provides information on tuning that you can use to improve performance. Because the SQL trace facility causes system overhead, you should run the database with the value TRUE only for the purposes of collecting statistics.

The ALTER SESSION command can override the setting of the SQL_TRACE parameter during a particular session.

For more information: *ORACLE7 Server Application Developer's Guide*, Appendix B "Performance Diagnostic Tools" and the *ORACLE7 Server SQL Language Reference Manual*

TEMPORARY_TABLE_LOCKS

Default value: derived (= SESSIONS)
Range of values: 0..O/S dependent

Determines the number of temporary tables that can be created in the temporary segment space. A temporary table lock is needed any time a sort occurs that is too large too hold in memory, either as the result of a select on a large table with ORDER BY or as a result of sorting a large index. Installations with many users of applications that simultaneously perform several ordered queries on large tables may need to increase this number. Most installations should do well with the default.

For more information: Chapter 24 "Additional Tuning Considerations". See your installation or user's guide for the range of values.

THREAD

Default value: 0
Range of values: 0..maximum number of declared threads
Multiple instances: if specified, must have different values

This parameter is applicable only to instances that intend to run in parallel (shared) mode.

The number of the redo thread that is to be used by the instance. Any available redo thread number can be used, but an instance cannot use the same thread number as another instance. Also, an instance cannot start when its redo thread is disabled. A value of zero causes an available, enabled public thread to be chosen. An instance cannot mount a database if the thread is used by another instance or if the thread is disabled.

Redo threads are specified with the THREAD option of the ALTER DATABASE ADD LOGFILE command. Redo threads are enabled with the ALTER DATABASE ENABLE [PUBLIC] THREAD command. The PUBLIC keyword signifies that the redo thread may be used by any instance.

Thread 1 is the default thread in exclusive mode. An instance running in exclusive mode can specify THREAD to use the redo log files in a thread other than thread 1.

For more information: *ORACLE7 Parallel Server Administrator's Guide* and the *ORACLE7 Server SQL Language Reference Manual*

TIMED_STATISTICS

Default value: false
Range of values: true/false

By default (when set to FALSE), the SQL*DBA statistics related to time (from the buffer manager) always are zero and the Server can avoid the overhead of requesting the time from the operating system. To turn on statistics, set the value to TRUE. Should normally be set to FALSE.

For more information: *ORACLE7 Server Application Developer's Guide*, Appendix B "Performance Diagnostic Tools"

TRANSACTIONS

Default value: derived (1.1 * PROCESSES)
Multiple instances: can have different values

The maximum number of concurrent transactions. Greater values increase the size of the SGA and can increase the number of rollback segments allocated. The default value is greater than PROCESSES to allow for recursive transactions.

For more information: *ORACLE7 Server Concepts Manual*, Chapter 9 "Memory Structures and Processes" and Chapter 12 "Transaction Management"

TRANSACTIONS_PER_ROLLBACK_SEGMENT

Default value: 30
Range of values: 1..O/S dependent
Multiple instances: can have different values

The number of concurrent transactions allowed per rollback segment. The minimum number of rollback segments acquired at startup is TRANSACTIONS divided by the value for this parameter. For example, if TRANSACTIONS is 101 and this parameter is 10, then the minimum number of rollback segments acquired would be the ratio 101/10, rounded up to 11.

More rollback segments can be acquired if they are identified with ROLLBACK_SEGMENT_INITIAL and ROLLBACK_SEGMENT_COUNT or named in ROLLBACK_SEGMENTS.

For more information: Chapter 9 "Managing Rollback Segments". See your installation or user's guide for the range of values.

USER_DUMP_DEST

Default value: O/S dependent
Range of values: valid local pathname, directory, or disk

The path name for a directory where debugging trace files from a user process are written.

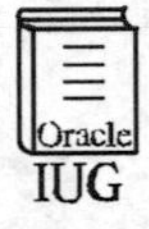

For more information: *ORACLE7 Server Application Developer's Guide,* Appendix B "Performance Diagnostic Tools". See your installation or user's guide for the range of values.

APPENDIX

B

DATA DICTIONARY REFERENCE

This appendix contains descriptions of the data dictionary tables and views. To see the current data dictionary on your system, query the view DICTIONARY.

This appendix contains the following information:

- SQL scripts available for altering the data dictionary or granting access to tables (page B-2)
- Data dictionary views and their columns (page B-5)
- Views of the dynamic performance tables—the V$ views (page B-47)

Trusted

In Trusted ORACLE, each of the dictionary tables and views contains the column which indicates the label of each row in the table or view. There are also additional dictionary tables and views in Trusted ORACLE, as well as additional columns in some tables and views. See the *Trusted ORACLE7 Server Administrator's Guide* for more information.

Data Dictionary SQL Script Files

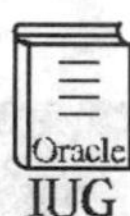

Certain ORACLE SQL script files perform data dictionary functions and can be run during or after database creation. The following is a list of ORACLE SQL scripts that modify the data dictionary. The standard script names are shown. On some operating systems, the names may differ. Consult your installation or user's guide for details.

Standard Scripts

These scripts are run by all installations.

SQL.BSQ	Database bootstrap script.
CATALOG.SQL	Creates the standard data dictionary views.

Data Dictionary Scripts

These scripts are run by SYS to create data dictionary views.

CATAUDIT.SQL	Creates the auditing data dictionary views.
CATBLOCK.SQL	Creates a view called BLOCKING_LOCKS. You can query this view to find out which locks are blocking the system; for example, you could find processes that have died while holding locks, which for some reason have not been cleaned up by PMON.
CATDBSYN.SQL	Creates private synonyms for the DBA data dictionary views.
CATEXP.SQL	Creates roles for import and export and incremental export views.
CATLDR.SQL	Creates SQL*Loader views for direct loads.
CATNOAUD.SQL	Drops the auditing tables.
CATNOPRC.SQL	Drops the procedural object views.
CATPARR.SQL	Creates data dictionary views used for installations with the Parallel Server option.
CATPROC.SQL	Creates data dictionary views for procedural objects and snapshots used in installations with the procedural option.
CATTRUST.SQL	Creates views for Trusted ORACLE.
CATSTAT.SQL	Computes statistics for tables and views created by SQL.BSQ for cost-based optimization.
CATSNAP.SQL	Creates views for storing and maintaining snapshots.

CATRPC.SQL	Creates data dictionary views on distributed database information
STANDARD.SQL	Creates PL/SQL packages for the procedural option
DBMSSTDX.SQL	Includes extensions to the package standard

Procedure Scripts

These scripts are also run by SYS. They create stored procedures and packages.

DBMSALRT.SQL	Creates the user-alert procedures and one supporting view.
DBMSLOCK.SQL	Creates PL/SQL lock management packages that allow applications to create locks, give them names, request them, and release them, as well as to convert a lock from one of several supported lock modes to another. Routines are also provided to wait for a period of time before re-requesting a lock. Deadlock conditions among the locks are detected.
DBMSMAIL.SQL	Creates PL/SQL package to send mail. This routine can be called from a trigger. See also: UTLMAIL.SQL.
DBMSOTPT.SQL	Creates output procedures for use in script debugging and information display.
DBMSPIPE.SQL	Creates procedures for inter-process communication.
DBMSSNAP.SQL	Creates snapshot refresh procedures.
DBMSUTIL.SQL	Creates PL/SQL utility packages, including routines for transaction management, session control, and DDL statement execution. Also supports recompilation of all stored PL/SQL objects.
DBMSDESC.SQL	

User Scripts

These scripts are run by users.

UTLBSTAT.SQL	Creates statistics tables and collects beginning statistics.
UTLCHAIN.SQL	Creates the default table for storing the output of the ANALYZE LIST CHAINED ROWS command.
UTLDIDXS.SQL	Displays index statistics captured by UTLIDXSS.SQL and UTLIDXSO.SQL.
UTLDTREE.SQL	Creates the procedure and view used to show all objects (to which a user has access) that are dependent on a given object, including recursive dependency.
UTLESTAT.SQL	Collects ending statistics and generates a report.
UTLEXCPT.SQL	Creates the exceptions table for recording violations of integrity constraints.
UTLLOCKT.SQL	Shows the lock wait-for graph in tree-structured form to help diagnose systems that are hung on locks.
UTLMAIL.SQL	Upgrades the mail database so that it can be accessed via Remote Procedure Calls (RPC). See also: DBMSMAIL.SQL.
UTLMONTR.SQL	Grants access to the dynamic performance tables to PUBLIC.
UTLOIDXS.SQL	Analyzes a column of a table, generating statistics that can be used to evaluate its suitability for indexing.
UTLSAMPL.SQL	Creates the initial database users and tables for experimentation and illustration.
UTLSIDXS.SQL	Analyzes index statistics for existing index columns. Can analyze multiple tables/columns at one time.
UTLXPLAN.SQL	Creates the table used by EXPLAIN PLAN to store the description of the statement execution plan.

Migration Scripts

For details on these scripts, see the *ORACLE7 Server Migration Guide.*

CATALOG6.SQL	Creates Version 6 views for compatibility.
CATEXP6.SQL	Creates the views needed for a Version 6 export.
DROPCAT6.SQL	Removes the Version 6 views and restores the data dictionary to full ORACLE7 form.

UTLEXP6.SQL	Lists objects not included in a Version 6 export.

Data Dictionary Views

The following is an alphabetical reference of the data dictionary views accessible to all users of an ORACLE server. Most views can be accessed by any user with the CREATE_SESSION privilege.

The data dictionary views that begin with DBA_ are restricted. These views can be accessed only by users with the SELECT_ANY_TABLE privilege. This privilege is assigned to the DBA role when the system is initially installed.

ALL_CATALOG	**All tables, views, synonyms, and sequences accessible to the user**	
	OWNER	Owner of the object
	TABLE_NAME	Name of the object
	TABLE_TYPE	Type of the object
ALL_COL_COMMENTS	**Comments on columns of accessible tables and views**	
	OWNER	Owner of the object
	TABLE_NAME	Name of the object
	COLUMN_NAME	Name of the column
	COMMENTS	Comment on the column
ALL_COL_PRIVS	**Grants on columns for which the user or PUBLIC is the grantee**	
	GRANTOR	Name of the user who performed the grant
	GRANTEE	Name of the user to whom access was granted
	TABLE_SCHEMA	Schema of the object
	TABLE_NAME	Name of the object
	COLUMN_NAME	Name of the column
	PRIVILEGE	Privilege on the column
	GRANTABLE	YES if the privileges was granted with ADMIN OPTION, otherwise NO
ALL_COL_PRIVS_MADE	**Grants on columns for which the user is owner or grantor**	
	GRANTEE	Name of the user to whom access was granted
	OWNER	Username of the owner of the object
	TABLE_NAME	Name of the object
	COLUMN_NAME	Name of the column
	GRANTOR	Name of the user who performed the grant
	PRIVILEGE	Privilege on the column

	GRANTABLE	YES if the privilege was granted with ADMIN OPTION, otherwise NO
ALL_COL_PRIVS_RECD	**Grants on columns for which the user or PUBLIC is the grantee**	
	GRANTEE	Name of the user to whom access was granted
	OWNER	Username of the owner of the object
	TABLE_NAME	Name of the object
	COLUMN_NAME	Name of the column
	GRANTOR	Name of the user who performed the grant
	PRIVILEGE	Privilege on the column
	GRANTABLE	YES if the privilege was granted with ADMIN OPTION, otherwise NO
ALL_CONSTRAINTS	**Constraint definitions on accessible tables**	
	OWNER	Owner of the constraint definition
	CONSTRAINT_NAME	Name associated with the constraint definition
	CONSTRAINT_TYPE	Type of constraint definition: C (check constraint on a table), P (primary key), U (unique key), R (referential integrity), or V (with check option, on a view)
	TABLE_NAME	Name associated with table with constraint definition
	SEARCH_CONDITION	Text of search condition for table check
	R_OWNER	Owner of table used in referential constraint
	R_CONSTRAINT_NAME	Name of unique constraint definition for referenced table
	DELETE_RULE	Delete rule for a referential constraint: CASCADE / NO ACTION
	STATUS	Status of constraint: ENABLED or DISABLED
ALL_CONS_COLUMNS	**Information about accessible columns in constraint definitions**	
	OWNER	Owner of the constraint definition
	CONSTRAINT_NAME	Name associated with the constraint definition
	TABLE_NAME	Name associated with table with constraint definition
	COLUMN_NAME	Name associated with column specified in the constraint definition
	POSITION	Original position of column in definition

ALL_DB_LINKS	**Database links accessible to the user**	
	OWNER	Username of the owner of the database link
	DB_LINK	Name of the database link
	USERNAME	Name of user when logging on
	HOST	SQL*Net string for connect
	CREATED	Creation time of the database link
ALL_DEF_AUDIT_OPTS	**Default object-auditing options that will be applied when objects are created**	
	ALT	Auditing ALTER WHENEVER SUCCESSFUL / UNSUCCESSFUL
	AUD	Auditing AUDIT WHENEVER SUCCESSFUL / UNSUCCESSFUL
	COM	Auditing COMMENT WHENEVER SUCCESSFUL / UNSUCCESSFUL
	DEL	Auditing DELETE WHENEVER SUCCESSFUL / UNSUCCESSFUL
	GRA	Auditing GRANT WHENEVER SUCCESSFUL / UNSUCCESSFUL
	IND	Auditing INDEX WHENEVER SUCCESSFUL / UNSUCCESSFUL
	INS	Auditing INSERT WHENEVER SUCCESSFUL / UNSUCCESSFUL
	LOC	Auditing LOCK WHENEVER SUCCESSFUL / UNSUCCESSFUL
	REN	Auditing RENAME WHENEVER SUCCESSFUL / UNSUCCESSFUL
	SEL	Auditing SELECT WHENEVER SUCCESSFUL / UNSUCCESSFUL
	UPD	Auditing UPDATE WHENEVER SUCCESSFUL / UNSUCCESSFUL
	REF	Auditing REFERENCES WHENEVER SUCCESSFUL / UNSUCCESSFUL
	EXE	Auditing EXECUTE WHENEVER SUCCESSFUL / UNSUCCESSFUL

ALL_DEPENDENCIES	**Dependencies between objects accessible to the user**	
	OWNER	Owner of the object
	NAME	Name of the object
	TYPE	Type of object: PROCEDURE, PACKAGE, FUNCTION, PACKAGE BODY
	REFERENCED_OWNER	Owner of the parent object
	REFERENCED_NAME	Name of the parent object
	REFERENCED_TYPE	Type of the parent object: PROCEDURE, PACKAGE, FUNCTION, PACKAGE BODY
	REFERENCED_LINK_NAME	Name of the link to the parent object (if remote)
ALL_ERRORS	**Current errors on all objects accessible to the user**	
	OWNER	Owner of the object
	NAME	Name of the object
	TYPE	Type of object: VIEW, PROCEDURE, PACKAGE, FUNCTION, PACKAGE BODY
	SEQUENCE	Sequence number, for ordering
	LINE	Line number at which this error occurs
	POSITION	Position in the line at which this error occurs
	TEXT	Text of the error

ALL_INDEXES **Description of indexes on tables accessible to the user**

Column	Description
OWNER	Username of the owner of the index
STATUS	State of the index: DIRECT LOAD or VALID
INDEX_NAME	Name of the index
TABLE_OWNER	Owner of the indexed object
TABLE_NAME	Name of the indexed object
TABLE_TYPE	Type of the indexed object
UNIQUENESS	Uniqueness status of the index: UNIQUE or NONUNIQUE
TABLESPACE_NAME	Name of the tablespace containing the index
INI_TRANS	Initial number of transactions
MAX_TRANS	Maximum number of transactions
INITIAL_EXTENT	Size of the initial extent
NEXT_EXTENT	Size of secondary extents
MIN_EXTENTS	Minimum number of extents allowed in the segment
MAX_EXTENTS	Maximum number of extents allowed in the segment
PCT_INCREASE	Percentage increase in extent size
PCT_FREE	Minimum percentage of free space in a block
BLEVEL	Depth of the index from its root block to its leaf blocks. A depth of 1 indicates that the root block and leaf block are the same.
LEAF_BLOCKS	Number of leaf blocks in the index.
DISTINCT_KEYS	Number of distinct indexed values. For indexes that enforce UNIQUE and PRIMARY KEY constraints, this value is the same as the number of rows in the table (USER_TABLES.NUM_ROWS).
AVG_LEAF_BLOCKS_ PER_KEY	Average number of leaf blocks in which each distinct value in the index appears. This statistic is rounded to the nearest integer. For indexes that enforce UNIQUE and PRIMARY KEY constraints, this value is always 1.
AVG_DATA_BLOCKS_ PER_KEY	Average number of data blocks in the table that are pointed to by a distinct value in the index. This statistic is the average

		number of data blocks that contain rows that contain a given value for the indexed columns. This statistic is rounded to the nearest integer.
	CLUSTERING_FACTOR	Staatistic that represents the amount of order of the rows in the table based on the values of the index. If its value is near the number of blocks, then the table is very well ordered. In such a case, the index entries in a single leaf block tend to point to rows in the same data blocks. If its value is near the number of rows, then the table is very randomly ordered. In such a case, it is unlikely that index entries in the same leaf block point to rows in the same data blocks.
ALL_IND_COLUMNS	**Columns of the indexes on accessible tables**	
	INDEX_OWNER	Index owner
	INDEX_NAME	Index name
	TABLE_OWNER	Table or cluster owner
	TABLE_NAME	Table or cluster name
	COLUMN_NAME	Column name
	COLUMN_POSITION	Position of column within index
	COLUMN_LENGTH	Indexed length of the column

ALL_LABELS

Trusted

A TRUSTED ORACLE view that lists system labels. For details, see the *Trusted ORACLE7 Server Administrator's Guide*.

ALL_MOUNTED_DBS

Trusted

A TRUSTED ORACLE view that lists mounted databases. For details, see the *Trusted ORACLE7 Server Administrator's Guide*.

ALL_OBJECTS	**Objects accessible to the user**	
	OWNER	Username of the owner of the object
	OBJECT_NAME	Name of the object
	OBJECT_ID	Object number of the object
	OBJECT_TYPE	Type of the object
	CREATED	Timestamp for the creation of the object
	LAST_DDL_TIME	Timestamp for the last modification of the object resulting from a DDL command (including grants and revokes)
	TIMESTAMP	Timestamp for the creation of the object (character data)
	STATUS	Status of the object: VALID, INVALID, or N/A
ALL_SEQUENCES	**Description of sequences accessible to the user**	
	SEQUENCE_OWNER	Name of the owner of the sequence
	SEQUENCE_NAME	Sequence name
	MIN_VALUE	Minimum value of the sequence
	MAX_VALUE	Maximum value of the sequence
	INCREMENT_BY	Value by which sequence is incremented
	CYCLE_FLAG	Does sequence wrap around on reaching limit
	ORDER_FLAG	Are sequence numbers generated in order
	CACHE_SIZE	Number of sequence numbers to cache
	LAST_NUMBER	Last sequence number written to disk. If a sequence uses caching, the number written to disk is the last number placed in the sequence cache. This number is likely to be greater than the last sequence number that was used.

ALL_SNAPSHOTS	**All snapshots accessible to the user**	
	OWNER	Owner of the snapshot
	NAME	Name of the view used by users and applications for viewing the snapshot
	TABLE_NAME	Table the snapshot is stored in. This table has an extra column for the master rowid
	MASTER_VIEW	View of the master table, owned by the snapshot owner, used for refreshes
	MASTER_OWNER	Owner of the master table
	MASTER	Name of the master table that this snapshot is a copy of
	MASTER_LINK	Database link name to the master site
	CAN_USE_LOG	YES if this snapshot can use a snapshot log, NO if this snapshot is too complex to use a log
	LAST_REFRESH	Date and time at the master site of the last refresh
	ERROR	Error returned last time an automatic refresh was attempted
	TYPE	Type of refresh for all automatic refreshes: COMPLETE, FAST, FORCE
	NEXT	Date function used to compute next refresh dates
	START_WITH	Date function used to compute next refresh dates
	QUERY	Original query that this snapshot is an instantiation of

ALL_SOURCE	**Text source of all stored objects accessible to the user**	
	OWNER	Owner of the object
	NAME	Name of the object
	TYPE	Type of object: PROCEDURE, PACKAGE, FUNCTION, PACKAGE BODY
	LINE	Line number of this line of source
	TEXT	Text source of the stored object
ALL_SYNONYMS	**All synonyms accessible to the user**	
	OWNER	Owner of the synonym
	SYNONYM_NAME	Name of the synonym
	TABLE_OWNER	Owner of the object referenced by the synonym
	TABLE_NAME	Name of the object referenced by the synonym
	DB_LINK	Name of the database link referenced, if any

ALL_TABLES	Description of tables accessible to the user	
	OWNER	Owner of the table
	TABLE_NAME	Name of the table
	TABLESPACE_NAME	Name of the tablespace containing the table
	CLUSTER_NAME	Name of the cluster, if any, to which the table belongs
	PCT_FREE	Minimum percentage of free space in a block
	PCT_USED	Minimum percentage of used space in a block
	INI_TRANS	Initial number of transactions
	MAX_TRANS	Maximum number of transactions
	INITIAL_EXTENT	Size of the initial extent in bytes
	NEXT_EXTENT	Size of secondary extents in bytes
	MIN_EXTENTS	Minimum number of extents allowed in the segment
	MAX_EXTENTS	Maximum number of extents allowed in the segment
	PCT_INCREASE	Percentage increase in extent size
	BACKED_UP	Has table been backed up since last change
	NUM_ROWS	Number of rows in the table
	BLOCKS	Number of data blocks allocated to the table
	EMPTY_BLOCKS	Number of data blocks allocated to the table that contain no data
	AVG_SPACE	Average amount of free space (in bytes) in a data block allocated to the table
	CHAIN_CNT	Number of rows in the table that are chained from one data block to another, or which have migrated to a new block, requiring a link to preserve the old rowid
	AVG_ROW_LEN	Average length of a row in the table in bytes

ALL_TAB_COLUMNS	**Columns of all tables, views, and clusters accessible to the user**	
	OWNER	Owner of the table, view or cluster
	TABLE_NAME	Table, view, or cluster name
	COLUMN_NAME	Column name
	DATA_TYPE	Datatype of the column
	DATA_LENGTH	Length of the column in bytes
	DATA_PRECISION	Decimal precision for NUMBER datatype; binary precision for FLOAT datatype; NULL for all other datatypes.
	DATA_SCALE	Digits to right of decimal point in a number
	NULLABLE	Does column allow NULLs? Value is N if there is a NOT NULL constraint on the column or if the column is part of a PRIMARY KEY.
	COLUMN_ID	Sequence number of the column as created
	DEFAULT_LENGTH	Length of default value for the column
	DATA_DEFAULT	Default value for the column
	NUM_DISTINCT	Number of distinct values in each column of the table
	LOW_VALUE HIGH_VALUE	For tables with more than three rows, the second-lowest and second-highest values in the column. For tables with three rows or fewer, the lowest and highest values. These statistics are expressed in hexadecimal notation for the internal representation of the first 32 bytes of the values.
ALL_TAB_COMMENTS	**Comments on tables and views accessible to the user**	
	OWNER	Owner of the object
	TABLE_NAME	Name of the object
	TABLE_TYPE	Type of the object
	COMMENTS	Comment on the object

ALL_TAB_PRIVS	**Grants on objects for which the user or PUBLIC is the grantee**	
	GRANTOR	Name of the user who performed the grant
	GRANTEE	Name of the user to whom access is granted
	TABLE_SCHEMA	Schema of the object
	TABLE_NAME	Name of the object
	PRIVILEGE	Privilege on the object
	GRANTABLE	YES if the privilege was granted with ADMIN OPTION, otherwise NO
ALL_TAB_PRIVS_MADE	**User's grants and grants on user's objects**	
	GRANTEE	Name of the user to whom access was granted
	OWNER	Owner of the object
	TABLE_NAME	Name of the object
	GRANTOR	Name of the user who performed the grant
	PRIVILEGE	Privilege on the object
	GRANTABLE	YES if the privilege was granted with ADMIN OPTION, otherwise NO
ALL_TAB_PRIVS_RECD	**Grants on objects for which the user or PUBLIC is the grantee**	
	GRANTEE	Name of the user to whom access was granted
	OWNER	Owner of the object
	TABLE_NAME	Name of the object
	GRANTOR	Name of the user who performed the grant
	PRIVILEGE	Privilege on the object
	GRANTABLE	YES if the privilege was granted with ADMIN OPTION, otherwise NO

ALL_TRIGGERS	**Triggers accessible to the user**	
	OWNER	Owner of the trigger
	TRIGGER_NAME	Name of the trigger
	TRIGGER_TYPE	Type of the trigger: BEFORE ROW, BEFORE STATEMENT, AFTER ROW, AFTER STATEMENT
	TRIGGERING_EVENT	Statement that fires the trigger: INSERT, UPDATE, DELETE
	TABLE_OWNER	Owner of the table the trigger is defined on
	TABLE_NAME	Table the trigger is defined on
	REFERENCING_NAMES	Names used for referencing OLD and NEW column values from within the trigger
	WHEN_CLAUSE	WHEN clause. Must evaluate to TRUE for TRIGGER_BODY to execute
	STATUS	Whether or not the trigger is enabled: ENABLED or DISABLED
	DESCRIPTION	Trigger description. Useful for re-creating a trigger creation statement.
	TRIGGER_BODY	Statement(s) executed by the trigger when it fires
ALL_TRIGGER_COLS	**Shows usage of columns in triggers owned by user, on tables owned by user, or on all triggers if the user has tech CREATE ANY TRIGGER privilege.**	
	TRIGGER_OWNER	Owner of the trigger
	TRIGGER_NAME	Name of the trigger
	TABLE_OWNER	Owner of the table the trigger is defined on
	TABLE_NAME	Table the trigger is defined on
	COLUMN_NAME	Name of the column used in the trigger
	COLUMN_LIST	Column specified in UPDATE clause: Y/N
	COLUMN_USAGE	How the column is used in the trigger. All applicable combinations of NEW, OLD, IN, OUT, and IN OUT.
ALL_USERS	**Information about all users of the database**	
	USERNAME	Name of the user
	USER_ID	ID number of the user
	CREATED	User creation date

ALL_VIEWS	**Text of views accessible to the user**	
	OWNER	Owner of the view
	VIEW_NAME	Name of the view
	TEXT_LENGTH	Length of the view text
	TEXT	View text
AUDIT_ACTIONS	**Description table for audit trail action type codes**	
	ACTION	Numeric audit trail action type code
	NAME	Name of the type of audit trail action
CAT	**Synonym for USER_CATALOG**	
CHAINED_ROWS	**Default table for the ANALYZE LIST CHAINED ROWS command.**	
	OWNER_NAME	Table owner
	TABLE_NAME	Table name
	CLUSTER_NAME	Cluster the table is in, if any
	HEAD_ROWID	RowID the chained row is accessed by
	TIMESTAMP	Date/time that the ANALYZE command was issued
CLU	**Synonym for USER_CLUSTERS**	
CODE_PIECES	**Accessed to create the ALL_OBJECT_SIZE, DBA_OBJECT_SIZE, and USER_OBJECT_SIZE views**	
CODE_SIZE	**Accessed to create the ALL_OBJECT_SIZE, DBA_OBJECT_SIZE, and USER_OBJECT_SIZE views**	
COLS	**Synonym for USER_TAB_COLUMNS**	
COLUMN_PRIVILEGES	**Grants on columns for which the user is the grantor, grantee, or owner, or PUBLIC is the grantee**	
	GRANTEE	Name of the user to whom access was granted
	OWNER	Username of the object's owner
	TABLE_NAME	Name of the object
	COLUMN_NAME	Name of the column
	GRANTOR	Name of the user who performed the grant
	INSERT_PRIV	Permission to insert into the column
	UPDATE_PRIV	Permission to update the column
	REFERENCES_PRIV	Permission to reference the column
	CREATED	Timestamp for the grant

DBA_2PC_NEIGHBORS	Information about incoming and outgoing connections for pending transactions	
	LOCAL_TRAN_ID	Transaction ID on the local database in the format: *n.n.n*
	IN_OUT	IN for incoming transactions, OUT for outgoing transactions
	DATABASE	For incoming transactions, the name of the client database; for outgoing transactions, the name of the database link
	DBUSER_OWNER	For incoming transactions, the name of the local user; for outgoing transactions, the owner of the database link
	INTERFACE	C signifies a request for commit; N signifies prepared state or a request for a read only commit.
	DBID	Remote database ID
	SESS#	Local session number
	BRANCH	Local transaction branch ID

DBA_2PC_PENDING	**Information about failed distributed transactions in PREPARED state**	
	LOCAL_TRAN_ID	Transaction ID on the local database in the format: *n.n.n*
	GLOBAL_TRAN_ID	Global transaction ID in the format: *dbname.yy-mm-dd.hh:mi:ss.cs.n.n.n*
	STATE	State of the transaction: COLLECTING, PREPARED, COMMITTED, HEURISTIC COMMIT, HEURISTIC ABORT
	MIXED	Value of this column is YES if heuristic damage (mixed states) is detected
	ADVICE	Action suggested to take: C (commit), R (rollback), NULL (no advice)
	TRAN_COMMENT	Comment given with the COMMIT WORK COMMENT statement
	FAIL_TIME	Date and time when the row was inserted
	FORCE_TIME	Time of a manual force decision (NULL if the transaction was not forced locally)
	RETRY_TIME	Time that automatic Recoverer process last tried to recover the transaction
	OS_USER	Operating system account for the user
	OS_TERMINAL	Operating system terminal ID for the user
	HOST	Name of the host
	DB_USER	ORACLE username of the user at the commit point site
	COMMIT#	Global commit number for committed transactions

DBA_AUDIT_EXISTS — **Audit trail entries created by the AUDIT EXISTS command**

Column	Description
OS_USERNAME	Operating system logon username of the user whose actions were audited
USERNAME	Name (not ID number) of the user whose actions were audited
USERHOST	Numeric instance ID for the ORACLE instance from which the user is accessing the database
TERMINAL	Identifier for the user's terminal
TIMESTAMP	Timestamp for the creation of the audit trail entry
OWNER	Intended creator of the non-existent object
OBJ_NAME	Name of the object affected by the action
ACTION_NAME	Name of the action type corresponding to the numeric code in ACTION
NEW_OWNER	Owner of the object named in the NEW_NAME column
NEW_NAME	New name of an object after a RENAME or the name of the underlying object
OBJ_PRIVILEGE	Object privileges granted/revoked by a GRANT/REVOKE statement
SYS_PRIVILEGE	System privileges granted/revoked by a GRANT/REVOKE statement
GRANTEE	Name of the grantee specified in a GRANT/REVOKE statement
SESSIONID	Numeric ID for each ORACLE session
ENTRYID	Numeric ID for each audit trail entry in the session
STATEMENTID	Numeric ID for each statement run (a statement may cause many actions)
RETURNCODE	ORACLE message code generated by the action. Some useful values follow: zero — the action succeeded 2004 — security violation

DBA_AUDIT_OBJECT	**All audit trail records for all objects in the system**	
	OS_USERNAME	Operating system logon user name of the user whose actions were audited
	USERNAME	Name (not ID number) of the user whose actions were audited
	USERHOST	Numeric instance ID for the ORACLE instance from which the user is accessing the database
	TERMINAL	Identifier for the user's terminal
	TIMESTAMP	Timestamp for the creation of the audit trail entry or logon time for the CONNECT statement
	OWNER	Creator of object affected by the action
	OBJ_NAME	Name of the object affected by the action
	ACTION_NAME	Name of the action type corresponding to the numeric code in ACTION
	NEW_OWNER	Owner of the object named in the NEW_NAME column
	NEW_NAME	New name of an object after a RENAME or the name of the underlying object
	SES_ACTIONS	Session summary (a string of 11 characters, one for each action type, in the order Alter, Audit, Comment, Delete, Grant, Index, Insert, Lock, Rename, Select, and Update; coded - for none, S for success, F for failure, and B for both)
	COMMENT_TEXT	Text comment on the audit trail entry (inserted by an application program)
	SESSIONID	Numeric ID for each ORACLE session
	ENTRYID	Numeric ID for each audit trail entry in the session
	STATEMENTID	Numeric ID for each statement run (a statement may cause many actions)
	RETURNCODE	ORACLE message code generated by the action (zero if the action succeeded)
	PRIV_USED	System privilege used to execute the action
	OBJECT_LABEL	Optional Trusted ORACLE label associated with the object being audited
	SESSION_LABEL	Trusted ORACLE label associated with the user session

DBA_AUDIT_SESSION	**All audit trail records in the system concerning CONNECT and DISCONNECT**	
	OS_USERNAME	Operating system logon user name of the user whose actions were audited
	USERNAME	Name (not ID number) of the user whose actions were audited
	USERHOST	Numeric instance ID for the ORACLE instance from which the user is accessing the database
	TERMINAL	Identifier for the user's terminal
	TIMESTAMP	Timestamp for the creation of the audit trail entry or logon time for the CONNECT statement
	ACTION_NAME	Name of the action type corresponding to the numeric code in ACTION
	LOGOFF_TIME	Timestamp for user logoff
	LOGOFF_LREAD	Logical reads for the session
	LOGOFF_PREAD	Physical reads for the session
	LOGOFF_LWRITE	Logical writes for the session
	LOGOFF_DLOCK	Deadlocks detected during the session
	SESSIONID	Numeric ID for each ORACLE session
	RETURNCODE	ORACLE message code generated by the action (zero if the action succeeded)
	SESSION_LABEL	Trusted ORACLE label associated with the user session

DBA_AUDIT_STATEMENT

All audit trail records in the system concerning GRANT, REVOKE, AUDIT, NOAUDIT, and ALTER SYSTEM statements

OS_USERNAME	Operating system logon user name of the user whose actions were audited
USERNAME	Name (not ID number) of the user whose actions were audited
USERHOST	Numeric instance ID for the ORACLE instance from which the user is accessing the database
TERMINAL	Identifier for the user's terminal
TIMESTAMP	Timestamp for the creation of the audit trail entry or logon time for the CONNECT statement
OWNER	Creator of object affected by the action
OBJ_NAME	Name of the object affected by the action
ACTION_NAME	Name of the action corresponding to the numeric code in ACTION
NEW_NAME	New name of an object renamed by a RENAME statement
OBJ_PRIVILEGE	Object privileges granted/revoked by a GRANT/REVOKE statement
SYS_PRIVILEGE	System privileges granted/revoked by a GRANT/REVOKE statement
ADMIN_OPTION	Signifies the role or system privilege was granted with ADMIN option
GRANTEE	Username of the grantee specified in a GRANT/REVOKE statement
AUDIT_OPTION	Auditing option set with the AUDIT statement
SES_ACTIONS	Session summary (a string of 11 characters, one for each action type, in the order Alter, Audit, Comment, Delete, Grant, Index, Insert, Lock, Rename, Select, and Update; coded - for none, S for success, F for failure, and B for both)
COMMENT_TEXT	Text comment on the audit trail entry (inserted by an application program)
SESSIONID	Numeric ID for each ORACLE session
ENTRYID	Numeric ID for each audit trail entry in the session
STATEMENTID	Numeric ID for each statement run (a statement may cause many actions)

	RETURNCODE	ORACLE message code generated by the action (zero if the action succeeded)
	PRIV_USED	System privilege used to execute the action
	SESSION_LABEL	Trusted ORACLE label associated with the user session
DBA_AUDIT_TRAIL	**Collection of all audit records in the system**	
	OS_USERNAME	Operating system logon user name of the user whose actions were audited
	USERNAME	Name (not ID number) of the user whose actions were audited
	USERHOST	Numeric instance ID for the ORACLE instance from which the user is accessing the database
	TERMINAL	Identifier for the user's terminal
	TIMESTAMP	Timestamp for the creation of the audit trail entry or logon time for the CONNECT statement
	OWNER	Creator of object affected by the action
	OBJ_NAME	Name of the object affected by the action
	ACTION	Numeric type code corresponding to the action name
	ACTION_NAME	Name of the action type corresponding to the numeric code in ACTION
	NEW_OWNER	Owner of the object named in the NEW_NAME column
	NEW_NAME	New name of an object after a RENAME or the name of the underlying object
	OBJ_PRIVILEGE	Object privileges granted/revoked by a GRANT/REVOKE statement
	SYS_PRIVILEGE	System privileges granted/revoked by a GRANT/REVOKE statement
	ADMIN_OPTION	Signifies the role or system privilege was granted with ADMIN option
	GRANTEE	Username of the grantee specified in a GRANT/REVOKE statement
	AUDIT_OPTION	Auditing option set with the AUDIT statement
	SES_ACTIONS	Session summary (a string of 11 characters, one for each action type, in the order Alter, Audit, Comment, Delete, Grant, Index, Insert, Lock, Rename, Select, and Update; coded - for none, S for success, F for failure, and B for both)

	LOGOFF_TIME	Timestamp for user logoff
	LOGOFF_LREAD	Logical reads for the session
	LOGOFF_PREAD	Physical reads for the session
	LOGOFF_LWRITE	Logical writes for the session
	LOGOFF_DLOCK	Deadlocks detected during the session
	COMMENT_TEXT	Text comment on the audit trail entry (inserted by an application program)
	SESSIONID	Numeric ID for each ORACLE session
	ENTRYID	Numeric ID for each audit trail entry in the session
	STATEMENTID	Numeric ID for each statement run (a statement may cause many actions)
	RETURNCODE	ORACLE message code generated by the action (zero if the action succeeded)
	PRIV_USED	System privilege used to execute the action
	OBJECT_LABEL	Optional Trusted ORACLE label associated with the object being audited
	SESSION_LABEL	Trusted ORACLE label associated with the user session
DBA_BLOCKERS	**All sessions that have someone waiting on a lock they hold that are not themselves waiting on a lock**	
	SESSION_ID	Session holding a lock
DBA_CATALOG	**All database tables, views, synonyms, and sequences**	
	OWNER	Owner of the object
	TABLE_NAME	Name of the object
	TABLE_TYPE	Type of the object

DBA_CLUSTERS	**Description of all clusters in the database**	
	OWNER	Owner of the cluster
	CLUSTER_NAME	Name of the cluster
	TABLESPACE_NAME	Name of the tablespace containing the cluster
	PCT_FREE	Minimum percentage of free space in a block
	PCT_USED	Minimum percentage of used space in a block
	KEY_SIZE	Estimated size of cluster key plus associated rows
	INI_TRANS	Initial number of transactions
	MAX_TRANS	Maximum number of transactions
	INITIAL_EXTENT	Size of the initial extent in bytes
	NEXT_EXTENT	Size of secondary extents in bytes
	MIN_EXTENTS	Minimum number of extents allowed in the segment
	MAX_EXTENTS	Maximum number of extents allowed in the segment
	PCT_INCREASE	Percentage increase in extent size
	AVG_BLOCKS_PER_KEY	Number of blocks in the table divided by number of hash keys
	CLUSTER_TYPE	Type of cluster: B-tree index or hash
	FUNCTION	Hash function used for a hash cluster
	HASHKEYS	Number of hash keys for a hash cluster
DBA_CLU_COLUMNS	**Mapping of table columns to cluster columns**	
	OWNER	Owner of the cluster
	CLUSTER_NAME	Cluster name
	CLU_COLUMN_NAME	Key column in the cluster
	TABLE_NAME	Clustered table name
	TAB_COLUMN_NAME	Key column in the table
DBA_COL_COMMENTS	**Comments on columns of all tables and views**	
	OWNER	Name of the owner of the object
	TABLE_NAME	Name of the object
	COLUMN_NAME	Name of the column
	COMMENTS	Comment on the object

DBA_COL_PRIVS — **All grants on columns in the database**

Column	Description
GRANTEE	Name of the user to whom access was granted
OWNER	Username of the owner of the object
TABLE_NAME	Name of the object
COLUMN_NAME	Name of the column
GRANTOR	Name of the user who performed the grant
PRIVILEGE	Privileges on the column
GRANTABLE	YES if the privilege was granted with ADMIN OPTION, otherwise NO

DBA_CONSTRAINTS — **Constraint definitions on all tables in the database**

Column	Description
OWNER	Owner of the constraint definition
CONSTRAINT_NAME	Name associated with the constraint
CONSTRAINT_TYPE	Type of constraint: C (check constraint on a table), P (primary key), U (unique key), R (referential integrity), V (with check option, on a view)
TABLE_NAME	Name of table associated with the constraint
SEARCH_CONDITION	Text of search condition for table check
R_OWNER	Owner of table used in referential constraint
R_CONSTRAINT_NAME	Name of unique constraint definition for referenced table
DELETE_RULE	The delete rule for a referential constraint: CASCADE / NO ACTION
STATUS	Status of constraint: ENABLED or DISABLED

DBA_CONS_COLUMNS — **Information about all columns in constraint definitions**

Column	Description
OWNER	Owner of the constraint definition
CONSTRAINT_NAME	Name associated with the constraint definition
TABLE_NAME	Name associated with table with constraint definition
COLUMN_NAME	Name associated with column specified in the constraint definition
POSITION	Original position of column in definition

DBA_DATA_FILES	**Information about database files**	
	FILE_NAME	Name of the data file
	FILE_ID	ID of the data file
	TABLESPACE_NAME	Name of the tablespace to which the file belongs
	BYTES	Size of the file in bytes
	BLOCKS	Size of the file in ORACLE blocks
	STATUS	File status: INVALID, AVAILABLE
DBA_DB_LINKS	**All database links in the database**	
	OWNER	Owner of the database link
	DB_LINK	Name of the database link
	USERNAME	Name user should use when logging on
	PASSWORD	Password for logon
	HOST	SQL*Net string for connect
	CREATED	Creation time of the database link
DBA_DDL_LOCKS	**All DDL locks held in the database and all outstanding requests for a DML lock**	
	SESSION_ID	Session Identifier
	OWNER	Owner of the lock
	NAME	Name of the lock
	TYPE	Lock type: Cursor, Table/Procedure, Body, Trigger, Index, Cluster
	MODE_HELD	Lock mode: None, Null, Share, Exclusive
	MODE_REQUESTED	Lock request type: None, Null, Share, Exclusive
DBA_DEPENDENCIES	**Dependencies to and from all objects**	
	OWNER	Owner of the object
	NAME	Name of the object
	TYPE	Type of object: PROCEDURE, PACKAGE, FUNCTION, PACKAGE BODY
	REFERENCED_OWNER	Owner of the parent object
	REFERENCED_NAME	Name of the parent object
	REFERENCED_TYPE	Type of the parent object: PROCEDURE, PACKAGE, FUNCTION, PACKAGE BODY
	REFERENCED_LINK_NAME	Name of the link to the parent object (if remote)

DBA_DML_LOCKS	**All DML locks held in the database and all outstanding requests for a DML lock**	
	SESSION_ID	Session holding or acquiring the lock
	OWNER	Owner of the lock
	NAME	Name of the lock
	MODE_HELD	Lock mode: see the table below
	MODE_REQUESTED	Lock request type: see the table below

Lock Mode	Meaning
ROW-S (SS)	Row share
ROW-X (SX)	Row exclusive
SHARE	Share
S/ROW-X (SSX)	Share row exclusive
EXCLUSIVE	Exclusive
NONE	MODE_HELD: Lock requested, not yet obtained MODE_REQUESTED: Lock identifier obtained, lock not held or requested

DBA_ERRORS	**Current errors on all stored objects in the database**	
	OWNER	Owner of the object
	NAME	Name of the object
	TYPE	Type of object: PROCEDURE, PACKAGE, FUNCTION, PACKAGE BODY
	SEQUENCE	Sequence number, for ordering
	LINE	Line number at which this error occurs
	POSITION	Position in the line at which this error occurs
	TEXT	Text of the error
DBA_EXP_FILES	**Description of export files**	
	EXP_VERSION	Version number of the last export
	EXP_TYPE	Type of export file (full, cumulative, or incremental)
	FILE_NAME	Name of the export file
	USER_NAME	Name of user who executed export
	TIMESTAMP	Timestamp of the last export

DBA_EXP_OBJECTS	**Objects that have been incrementally exported**	
	OWNER	Owner of the exported object
	OBJECT_NAME	Name of the exported object
	OBJECT_TYPE	Type of the exported object
	CUMULATIVE	Date of the last cumulative export
	INCREMENTAL	Date of the last incremental export
	EXPORT_VERSION	Version number of the last export session
DBA_EXP_VERSION	**Version number of the last export session**	
	EXP_VERSION	Version number of the last export session
DBA_EXTENTS	**Extents of all segments in the database**	
	OWNER	Owner of the segment associated with the extent
	SEGMENT_NAME	Name of the segment associated with the extent
	SEGMENT_TYPE	Type of the segment
	TABLESPACE_NAME	Name of the tablespace containing the extent
	EXTENT_ID	Extent number in the segment
	FILE_ID	Name of the file containing the extent
	BLOCK_ID	Starting block number of the extent
	BYTES	Size of the extent in bytes
	BLOCKS	Size of the extent in ORACLE blocks
DBA_FREE_SPACE	**Free extents in all tablespaces**	
	TABLESPACE_NAME	Name of the tablespace containing the extent
	FILE_ID	ID number of the file containing the extent
	BLOCK_ID	Starting block number of the extent
	BYTES	Size of the extent in bytes
	BLOCKS	Size of the extent in ORACLE blocks

DBA_INDEXES	Description for all indexes in the database	
	OWNER	Username of the owner of the index
	STATUS	State of the index: DIRECT LOAD or VALID
	INDEX_NAME	Name of the index
	TABLE_OWNER	Owner of the indexed object
	TABLE_NAME	Name of the indexed object
	TABLE_TYPE	Type of the indexed object
	UNIQUENESS	Uniqueness status of the index: UNIQUE or NONUNIQUE
	TABLESPACE_NAME	Name of the tablespace containing the index
	INI_TRANS	Initial number of transactions
	MAX_TRANS	Maximum number of transactions
	INITIAL_EXTENT	Size of the initial extent
	NEXT_EXTENT	Size of secondary extents
	MIN_EXTENTS	Minimum number of extents allowed in the segment
	MAX_EXTENTS	Maximum number of extents allowed in the segment
	PCT_INCREASE	Percentage increase in extent size
	PCT_FREE	Minimum percentage of free space in a block
	BLEVEL	Depth of the index from its root block to its leaf blocks. A depth of 1 indicates that the root block and leaf block are the same.
	LEAF_BLOCKS	Number of leaf blocks in the index.
	DISTINCT_KEYS	Number of distinct indexed values. For indexes that enforce UNIQUE and PRIMARY KEY constraints, this value is the same as the number of rows in the table (USER_TABLES.NUM_ROWS).
	AVG_LEAF_BLOCKS_PER_KEY	Average number of leaf blocks in which each distinct value in the index appears. This statistic is rounded to the nearest integer. For indexes that enforce UNIQUE and PRIMARY KEY constraints, this value is always 1.
	AVG_DATA_BLOCKS_PER_KEY	The average number of data blocks in the table that are pointed to by a distinct value in the index. This statistic is the average number of data blocks that contain rows that contain a given value for the indexed

		column(s). This statistic is rounded to the nearest integer.
	CLUSTERING_FACTOR	This statistic represents the amount of order of the rows in the table based on the values of the index. If its value is near the number of blocks, then the table is very well ordered. In such a case, the index entries in a single leaf block tend to point to rows in the same data blocks. If its value is near the number of rows, then the table is very randomly ordered. In such a case, it is unlikely that index entries in the same leaf block point to rows in the same data blocks.
DBA_IND_COLUMNS	**Columns of indexes on all tables and clusters**	
	INDEX_OWNER	Index owner
	INDEX_NAME	Index name
	TABLE_OWNER	Table or cluster owner
	TABLE_NAME	Table or cluster name
	COLUMN_NAME	Column name
	COLUMN_POSITION	Position of column within index
	COLUMN_LENGTH	Indexed length of the column
DBA_LOCKS	**All locks or latches held in the database, and all outstanding requests for a lock or latch. This view includes DML locks and DDL locks.**	
	SESSION_ID	Session holding or acquiring the lock
	TYPE	Lock type: See tables beginning on page B-81
	MODE_HELD	Lock mode: see table on page B-29
	MODE_REQUESTED	Lock request type: see table on page B-29
	LOCK_ID1	Type-specific lock identifier, part 1
	LOCK_ID2	Type-specific lock identifier, part 2

DBA_OBJECTS — **All clusters, database links, indexes, packages, package bodies, sequences, synonyms, tables, and views defined in the database**

Column	Description
OWNER	Username of the owner of the object
OBJECT_NAME	Name of the object
OBJECT_ID	Object number of the object
OBJECT_TYPE	Type of the object
CREATED	Timestamp for the creation of the object
LAST_DDL_TIME	Timestamp for the last modification of the object resulting from a DDL command (including grants and revokes)
TIMESTAMP	Timestamp for the creation of the object (character data)
STATUS	Status of the object: VALID, INVALID, or N/A

DBA_OBJECT_SIZE — **All PL/SQL objects in the database**

Column	Description
NAME	Name of the object
TYPE	Type of the object: PROCEDURE, PACKAGE, or PACKAGE BODY
SOURCE_SIZE	Size of source code in bytes
PARSED_SIZE	Size of parsed code in bytes
CODE_SIZE	Size of compiled code in bytes
ERROR_SIZE	Size of error messages in bytes

DBA_OBJ_AUDIT_OPTS	**Auditing options for all tables and views**	
	OWNER	Owner of the object
	OBJECT_NAME	Name of the object
	OBJECT_TYPE	Type of the object: TABLE or VIEW
	ALT	Auditing ALTER WHENEVER SUCCESSFUL / UNSUCCESSFUL
	AUD	Auditing AUDIT WHENEVER SUCCESSFUL / UNSUCCESSFUL
	COM	Auditing COMMENT WHENEVER SUCCESSFUL / UNSUCCESSFUL
	DEL	Auditing DELETE WHENEVER SUCCESSFUL / UNSUCCESSFUL
	GRA	Auditing GRANT WHENEVER SUCCESSFUL / UNSUCCESSFUL
	IND	Auditing INDEX WHENEVER SUCCESSFUL / UNSUCCESSFUL
	INS	Auditing INSERT WHENEVER SUCCESSFUL / UNSUCCESSFUL
	LOC	Auditing LOCK WHENEVER SUCCESSFUL / UNSUCCESSFUL
	REN	Auditing RENAME WHENEVER SUCCESSFUL / UNSUCCESSFUL
	SEL	Auditing SELECT WHENEVER SUCCESSFUL / UNSUCCESSFUL
	UPD	Auditing UPDATE WHENEVER SUCCESSFUL / UNSUCCESSFUL
	REF	Auditing REFERENCES WHENEVER SUCCESSFUL / UNSUCCESSFUL
	EXE	Auditing EXECUTE WHENEVER SUCCESSFUL / UNSUCCESSFUL
DBA_PRIV_AUDIT_OPTS	**Privilege auditing options (one row for each audited privilege)**	
	USER_NAME	Username if auditing by username; NULL for system-wide auditing
	PRIVILEGE	Name of the privilege
	SUCCESS	Mode for WHENEVER SUCCESSFUL system auditing: BY SESSION, BY ACCESS
	FAILURE	Mode for WHENEVER NOT SUCCESSFUL system auditing: BY SESSION, BY ACCESS

DBA_PROFILES	**Resource limits assigned to each profile**	
	PROFILE	Name of the profile
	RESOURCE_NAME	Name of the resource in the profile
	LIMIT	Limit placed on this resource for this profile
DBA_ROLES	**All roles that exist in the database**	
	ROLE	Name of the granted role
	PASSWORD_REQUIRED	Indicates if the role requires a password to be enabled. Values are YES (ORACLE password), NO (no authentication), and EXTERNAL (operating system authentication).
DBA_ROLE_PRIVS	**Description of roles granted to users and to roles**	
	GRANTEE	Name of the user or role receiving the grant
	GRANTED_ROLE	Name of the granted role
	ADMIN_OPTION	"Y" if granted with ADMIN option
	DEFAULT_ROLE	"Y" if it is the grantee's default role
DBA_ROLLBACK_SEGS	**Description of rollback segments**	
	SEGMENT_NAME	Name of the rollback segment
	OWNER	Owner of the rollback segment
	TABLESPACE_NAME	Name of the tablespace containing the rollback segment
	SEGMENT_ID	ID number of the rollback segment
	FILE_ID	ID number of the block containing the segment header
	BLOCK_ID	Starting block number of the extent
	INITIAL_EXTENT	Initial extent size in bytes
	NEXT_EXTENT	Secondary extent size in bytes
	MIN_EXTENTS	Minimum number of extents
	MAX_EXTENTS	Maximum number of extents
	PCT_INCREASE	Percent increase for extent size
	STATUS	Rollback segment status: INVALID, IN USE, AVAILABLE, OFFLINE, NEEDS RECOVERY, PARTLY AVAILABLE
	INSTANCE_NUM	Instance this rollback segment belongs to, or NULL for a single-instance system

DBA_SEGMENTS	**Storage allocated for all database segments**	
	OWNER	Username of the segment owner
	SEGMENT_NAME	Name of the segment, if any
	SEGMENT_TYPE	Type of segment: TABLE, CLUSTER, INDEX, ROLLBACK, DEFERRED ROLLBACK, TEMPORARY, CACHE
	TABLESPACE_NAME	Name of the tablespace containing the segment
	HEADER_FILE	ID of the file containing the segment header
	HEADER_BLOCK	ID of the block containing the segment header
	BYTES	Size of the segment in bytes
	BLOCKS	Size of the segment in ORACLE blocks. This value can be used as a guide when re-creating a segment. The size of the new segment will be approximately the same as the size of the old segment, as long as the value of PCTFREE for the new segment is less than or equal to the average amount of free space in the old blocks.
	EXTENTS	Number of extents allocated to the segment
	INITIAL_EXTENT	Size of the initial extent in ORACLE blocks
	NEXT_EXTENT	Size of the next extent to be allocated in ORACLE blocks
	MIN_EXTENTS	Minimum number of extents allowed in the segment
	MAX_EXTENTS	Maximum number of extents allowed in the segment
	PCT_INCREASE	Percent by which to increase the size of the next extent to be allocated
	FREELISTS	Number of process freelists allocated to this segment
	FREELIST_GROUPS	Number of freelist groups allocated to this segment

DBA_SEQUENCES	**Description of all sequences in the database**	
	SEQUENCE_OWNER	Name of the owner of the sequence
	SEQUENCE_NAME	Sequence name
	MIN_VALUE	Minimum value of the sequence
	MAX_VALUE	Maximum value of the sequence
	INCREMENT_BY	Value by which sequence is incremented
	CYCLE_FLAG	Does sequence wraparound on reaching limit
	ORDER_FLAG	Are sequence numbers generated in order
	CACHE_SIZE	Number of sequence numbers to cache
	LAST_NUMBER	Last sequence number written to disk. If a sequence uses caching, the number written to disk is the last number placed in the sequence cache. This number is likely to be greater than the last sequence number that was used.

DBA_SNAPSHOTS	**All snapshots in the database**	
	OWNER	Owner of the snapshot
	NAME	Name of the view used by users and applications for viewing the snapshot
	TABLE_NAME	Table the snapshot is stored in (it has an extra column for the master rowid)
	MASTER_VIEW	View of the master table, owned by the snapshot owner, used for refreshes
	MASTER_OWNER	Owner of the master table
	MASTER	Master table that this snapshot copies
	MASTER_LINK	Database link name to the master site
	CAN_USE_LOG	YES if this snapshot can use a snapshot log; NO if this snapshot is too complex to use a log
	LAST_REFRESH	Date and time at the master site of the last refresh
	ERROR	Error returned last time an automatic refresh was attempted
	TYPE	Type of refresh for all automatic refreshes: COMPLETE, FAST, FORCE
	NEXT	Date function used to compute next refresh dates
	START_WITH	Date function used to compute next refresh dates
	QUERY	Query used to create the snapshot
DBA_SNAPSHOT_LOGS	**All snapshot logs in the database**	
	LOG_OWNER	Owner of the snapshot log
	MASTER	Name of the master table which the log records changes of
	LOG_TABLE	Log table that holds the rowids and timestamps of rows that changed in the master table
	LOG_TRIGGER	After-row trigger on the master that inserts rows into the log
	CURRENT_SNAPSHOTS	Date the snapshot of the master was last refreshed

DBA_SOURCE	**Text source of all stored objects in the database**	
	OWNER	Owner of the object
	NAME	Name of the object
	TYPE	Type of object: PROCEDURE, PACKAGE, FUNCTION, PACKAGE BODY
	LINE	Line number of this line of source
	TEXT	Text source of the stored object
DBA_STMT_AUDIT_OPTS	**Describes current system auditing options across the system and by user**	
	USER_NAME	Username if auditing by username; NULL for system-wide auditing
	AUDIT_OPTION	Name of the system auditing option
	SUCCESS	Mode for WHENEVER SUCCESSFUL system auditing: BY SESSION, BY ACCESS
	FAILURE	Mode for WHENEVER NOT SUCCESSFUL system auditing: BY SESSION, BY ACCESS
DBA_SYNONYMS	**All synonyms in the database**	
	OWNER	Username of the owner of the synonym
	SYNONYM_NAME	Name of the synonym
	TABLE_OWNER	Owner of the object referenced by the synonym
	TABLE_NAME	Name of the object referenced by the synonym
	DB_LINK	Name of the database link referenced in a remote synonym
DBA_SYS_PRIVS	**Description of system privileges granted to users and to roles**	
	GRANTEE	Name of the user or role receiving the grant
	PRIVILEGE	System privilege granted to the user or role
	ADMIN_OPTION	Signifies that the privilege was granted with the ADMIN option

DBA_TABLES **Description of all tables in the database**

OWNER	Owner of the table
TABLE_NAME	Name of the table
TABLESPACE_NAME	Tablespace containing the table
CLUSTER_NAME	Name of the cluster, if any, to which the table belongs
PCT_FREE	Minimum percentage of free space in a block
PCT_USED	Minimum percentage of used space in a block
INI_TRANS	Initial number of transactions
MAX_TRANS	Maximum number of transactions
INITIAL_EXTENT	Size of the initial extent in bytes
NEXT_EXTENT	Size of secondary extents in bytes
MIN_EXTENTS	Minimum number of extents allowed in the segment
MAX_EXTENTS	Maximum number of extents allowed in the segment
PCT_INCREASE	Percentage increase in extent size
BACKED_UP	Has table been backed up since last modification
NUM_ROWS	Number of rows in the table
BLOCKS	Number of data blocks allocated to the table
EMPTY_BLOCKS	Number of data blocks allocated to the table that contain no data
AVG_SPACE	Average amount of free space (in bytes) in a data block allocated to the table
CHAIN_CNT	Number of rows in the table that are chained from one data block to another or that have migrated to a new block, requiring a link to preserve the old rowid
AVG_ROW_LEN	Average row length in the table in bytes

DBA_TABLESPACES	**Description of all tablespaces in the database**	
	TABLESPACE_NAME	Tablespace name
	INITIAL_EXTENT	Default initial extent size
	NEXT_EXTENT	Default incremental extent size
	MIN_EXTENTS	Default minimum number of extents
	MAX_EXTENTS	Default maximum number of extents
	PCT_INCREASE	Default percent increase for extent size
	STATUS	Tablespace status: ONLINE, OFFLINE, or INVALID (tablespace has been dropped)
DBA_TAB_COLUMNS	**Columns of all tables, views, and clusters**	
	OWNER	Owner of the table, view or cluster
	TABLE_NAME	Table, view, or cluster name
	COLUMN_NAME	Column name
	DATA_TYPE	Datatype of the column
	DATA_LENGTH	Length of the column in bytes
	DATA_PRECISION	Decimal precision for NUMBER datatype; binary precision for FLOAT datatype; NULL for all other datatypes.
	DATA_SCALE	Digits to right of decimal point in a number
	NULLABLE	Does column allow NULLs? Value is N if there is a NOT NULL constraint on the column or if the column is part of a PRIMARY KEY.
	COLUMN_ID	Sequence number of the column as created
	DEFAULT_LENGTH	Length of default value for the column
	DATA_DEFAULT	Default value for the column
	NUM_DISTINCT	Number of distinct values in each column of the table
	LOW_VALUE HIGH_VALUE	For tables with more than three rows, the second-lowest and second-highest values in the column. For tables with three rows or fewer, the lowest and highest values. These statistics are expressed in hexadecimal notation for the internal representation of the first 32 bytes of the values.

DBA_TAB_COMMENTS	**Comments on all tables and views in the database**	
	OWNER	Owner of the object
	TABLE_NAME	Name of the object
	TABLE_TYPE	Type of the object
	COMMENTS	Comment on the object
DBA_TAB_PRIVS	**All grants on objects in the database**	
	GRANTEE	User to whom access was granted
	OWNER	Owner of the object
	TABLE_NAME	Name of the object
	GRANTOR	Name of the user who performed the grant
	PRIVILEGE	Privilege on the object
	GRANTABLE	YES if the privilege was granted with ADMIN OPTION, otherwise NO
DBA_TRIGGERS	**Description of all triggers in the database**	
	OWNER	Owner of the trigger
	TRIGGER_NAME	Name of the trigger
	TRIGGER_TYPE	Type of the trigger: BEFORE ROW, BEFORE STATEMENT, AFTER ROW, AFTER STATEMENT
	TRIGGERING_EVENT	Statement that fires the trigger: INSERT, UPDATE, DELETE
	TABLE_OWNER	Owner of the table the trigger is defined on
	TABLE_NAME	Table the trigger is defined on
	REFERENCING_NAMES	Names used for referencing OLD and NEW column values from within the trigger
	WHEN_CLAUSE	WHEN clause. Must evaluate to TRUE for TRIGGER_BODY to execute
	STATUS	Whether or not the trigger is enabled: ENABLED or DISABLED
	DESCRIPTION	Trigger description. Useful for re-creating a trigger creation statement.
	TRIGGER_BODY	Statement(s) executed by the trigger when it fires

DBA_TRIGGER_COLS	**Shows usage of columns in triggers defined by any user or on any user's table**	
	TRIGGER_OWNER	Owner of the trigger
	TRIGGER_NAME	Name of the trigger
	TABLE_OWNER	Owner of the table the trigger is defined on
	TABLE_NAME	Table the trigger is defined on
	COLUMN_NAME	Name of the column used in the trigger
	COLUMN_LIST	Column specified in UPDATE clause: Y/N
	COLUMN_USAGE	How the column is used in the trigger; all applicable combinations of NEW, OLD, IN, OUT, and IN OUT
DBA_TS_QUOTAS	**Tablespace quotas for all users**	
	TABLESPACE_NAME	Tablespace name
	USERNAME	User with resource rights on the tablespace
	BYTES	Number of bytes charged to the user
	MAX_BYTES	User's quota in bytes or UNLIMITED
	BLOCKS	Number of ORACLE blocks charged to the user
	MAX_BLOCKS	User's quota in ORACLE blocks or UNLIMITED
DBA_USERS	**Information about all users of the database**	
	USERNAME	Name of the user
	USER_ID	ID number of the user
	PASSWORD	Encrypted password
	DEFAULT_TABLESPACE	Default tablespace for data
	TEMPORARY_TABLESPACE	Default tablespace for temporary tables
	CREATED	User creation date
	PROFILE	Name of resource profile assigned to the user
DBA_VIEWS	**Text of all views in the database**	
	OWNER	Owner (creator) of the view
	VIEW_NAME	Name of the view
	TEXT_LENGTH	Length of the view text
	TEXT	View text

DBA_WAITERS	**All sessions waiting for locks and the session that holds the lock**	
	WAITING_SESSION	Session waiting for a lock
	HOLDING_SESSION	Session holding a lock
	TYPE	Lock type: see tables beginning on page B-81
	MODE_HELD	Lock mode: Row-S (SS), Row-X (SX), Share, S/Row-X (SSX), Exclusive
	MODE_REQUESTED	Lock request type: Null, Row-S (SS), Row-X (SX), Share, S/Row-X (SSX), Exclusive
	LOCK_ID1	Type-specific lock identifier, part 1
	LOCK_ID2	Type-specific lock identifier, part 2
DBMS_ALERT_INFO	**Table of registered alerts**	
	NAME	Name of the alert
	SID	Session ID of a session waiting for this alert
	CHANGED	Boolean flag to indicate that an alert has been signaled. Y: Alert signaled. N: No alert.
	MESSAGE	Optional message passed by signaler
DBMS_LOCK_ALLOCATED	**Table of user-allocated locks.**	
	NAME	Name of the lock
	LOCKID	Lock identifier number
	EXPIRATION	Planned lock expiration date (updates whenever the allocation procedure is run)
DEPTREE	**Object dependency tree. Created by DEPTREE.SQL.** For user SYS, this view shows shared cursors (and only shared cursors) that depend on the object. For all other users, it shows objects other than shared cursors. (Other users may access SYS.DEPTREE for information on shared cursors.)	
	NESTED_LEVEL	Nesting level in the dependency tree
	TYPE	Object type
	OWNER	Object owner
	NAME	Object name
	SEQ#	Sequence number in the dependency tree. Used for ordering queries. (See also: the IDEPTREE view)
DICT	**Synonym for DICTIONARY**	

DICTIONARY	**Description of data dictionary tables and views**	
	TABLE_NAME	Name of the object
	COMMENTS	Text comment on the object
DICT_COLUMNS	**Description of columns in data dictionary tables and views**	
	TABLE_NAME	Name of the object that contains the column
	COLUMN_NAME	Name of the column
	COMMENTS	Text comment on the column
ERROR_SIZE	**Accessed to create the ALL_OBJECT_SIZE, DBA_OBJECT_SIZE, and USER_OBJECT_SIZE views**	
EXCEPTIONS	**Information on violations of integrity constraints**	
	ROW_ID	Row that caused the violation
	OWNER	Owner of the table
	TABLE_NAME	Name of the table
	CONSTRAINT	Integrity constraint that was violated
GLOBAL_NAME	**Contains one row that shows the global name of the current database**	
	GLOBAL_NAME	Global name of the database
IDEPTREE	**Indented dependency tree. Created by DEPTREE.SQL. Pre-sorted, pretty-print version of DEPTREE.**	
	NESTED_LEVEL	Nesting level in the dependency tree
	TYPE	Object type
	OWNER	Object owner
	NAME	Object name
IND	**Synonym for USER_INDEXES**	
INDEX_HISTOGRAM	**Contains information from the VALIDATE INDEX command**	
	REPEAT_COUNT	Number of times that one or more index keys is repeated in the table
	KEYS_WITH_REPEAT_COUNT	Number of index keys that are repeated that many times

INDEX_STATS	**Stores information from the VALIDATE INDEX command**	
	HEIGHT	Height of the B-tree
	BLOCKS	Blocks allocated to the segment
	NAME	Name of the index
	LF_ROWS	Number of leaf rows (values in the index)
	LF_BLKS	Number of leaf blocks in the B-tree
	LF_ROWS_LEN	Sum of the lengths of all the leaf rows
	LF_BLK_LEN	Usable space in a leaf block
	BR_ROWS	Number of branch rows in the B-tree
	BR_BLKS	Number of branch blocks in the B-tree
	BR_ROWS_LEN	Sum of the lengths of all the branch blocks in the B-tree
	BR_BLK_LEN	Usable space in a branch block
	DEL_LF_ROWS	Number of deleted leaf rows in the index
	DEL_LF_ROWS_LEN	Total length of all deleted rows in the index
	DISTINCT_KEYS	Number of distinct keys in the index (may include rows that have been deleted)
	MOST_REPEATED_KEY	How many times the most repeated key is repeated (may include rows that have been deleted)
	BTREE_SPACE	Total space currently allocated in the B-tree
	USED_SPACE	Total space that is currently being used in the B-tree
	PCT_USED	Percent of space allocated in the B-tree that is being used
	ROWS_PER_KEY	Average number of rows per distinct key (this figure is calculated without consideration of deleted rows)
	BLKS_GETS_PER_ACCESS	Expected number of consistent mode block reads per row, assuming that a randomly chosen row is accessed using the index. Used to calculate the number of consistent reads that will occur during an index scan.

LOADER_COL_INFO	**SQL*LOADER view used for direct loads**
LOADER_CONSTRAINT_INFO	**SQL*LOADER view used for direct loads**
LOADER_INDCOL_INFO	**SQL*LOADER view used for direct loads**
LOADER_IND_INFO	**SQL*LOADER view used for direct loads**
LOADER_PARAM_INFO	**SQL*LOADER view used for direct loads**
LOADER_TAB_INFO	**SQL*LOADER view used for direct loads**
LOADER_TRIGGER_INFO	**SQL*LOADER view used for direct loads**
OBJ	**Synonym for USER_OBJECTS**
PARSED_PIECES	**Accessed to create the ALL_OBJECT_SIZE, DBA_OBJECT_SIZE, and USER_OBJECT_SIZE views.**
PARSED_SIZE	**Accessed to create the ALL_OBJECT_SIZE, DBA_OBJECT_SIZE, and USER_OBJECT_SIZE views.**

PLAN_TABLE	**Default table for results of the EXPLAIN PLAN statement. One row for each step in the execution plan. Created by UTLXPLAN.SQL.**	
	STATEMENT_ID	Optional statement identifier specified in the EXPLAIN PLAN statement
	TIMESTAMP	Date and time that the EXPLAIN PLAN statement was issued
	REMARKS	Place for comments that can be added to the steps of the execution plan
	OPERATION	Name of the operation performed at this step
	OPTIONS	Options used for the operation performed at this step
	OBJECT_NODE	Name of the database link used to reference the object
	OBJECT_OWNER	Owner of the object
	OBJECT_NAME	Name of the object
	OBJECT_INSTANCE	Numbered position of the object name in the original SQL statement
	OBJECT_TYPE	Descriptive modifier that further describes the type of object
	SEARCH_COLUMNS	Not currently used
	ID	Identification number for this step in the execution plan
	PARENT_ID	ID of the next step that operates on the results of this step
	POSITION	Order of processing for steps with the same parent ID. For cost-based optimization, the value in the first row of the plan is the statement's execution cost. For rule-based optimization, the value is null in the first row.
	OTHER	Additional information on this step.
PUBLIC_DEPENDENCY	**Dependencies to and from objects, by object number**	
	OBJECT_ID	Object number
	REFERENCED_OBJECT_ID	Referenced object (the parent object)
RESOURCE_COST	**Cost for each resource**	
	RESOURCE_NAME	Name of the resource
	UNIT_COST	Cost of the resource

ROLE_ROLE_PRIVS	**Information about roles granted to other roles**	
	ROLE	Name of the role
	GRANTED_ROLE	Role that was granted
	ADMIN_OPTION	Signifies that the role was granted with ADMIN option
ROLE_SYS_PRIVS	**Information about system privileges granted to roles**	
	ROLE	Name of the role
	PRIVILEGE	System privilege granted to the role
	ADMIN_OPTION	Signifies the grant was with the ADMIN option
ROLE_TAB_PRIVS	**Information about table privileges granted to roles**	
	ROLE	Name of the role
	OWNER	Owner of the object
	TABLE_NAME	Name of the object
	COLUMN_NAME	Name of the column, if applicable
	PRIVILEGE	Object privilege granted to the role
	GRANTABLE	YES if the role was granted with ADMIN OPTION, otherwise NO
SEQ	**Synonym for USER_SEQUENCES**	
SESSION_PRIVS	**Privileges that are currently available to the user**	
	PRIVILEGE	Name of the privilege
SESSION_ROLES	**Roles that the user currently has enabled**	
	ROLE	Name of the role
SOURCE_SIZE	**Accessed to create the ALL_OBJECT_SIZE, DBA_OBJECT_SIZE, and USER_OBJECT_SIZE views.**	
STMT_AUDIT_OPTION_MAP	**Description table for auditing option type codes**	
	OPTION#	Numeric auditing option type code
	NAME	Name of the auditing option
SYN	**Synonym for USER_SYNONYMS**	
SYSTEM_PRIVILEGE_MAP	**Description table for system privilege codes**	

TABLE_PRIVILEGES	**Grants on objects for which the user is the grantor, grantee, or owner, or PUBLIC is the grantee**	
	GRANTEE	Name of the user to whom access is granted
	OWNER	Owner of the object
	TABLE_NAME	Name of the object
	GRANTOR	Name of the user who performed the grant
	SELECT_PRIV	Permission to select from the object
	INSERT_PRIV	Permission to insert into the object
	DELETE_PRIV	Permission to delete from the object
	UPDATE_PRIV	Permission to update the object
	REFERENCES_PRIV	Permission to reference the object
	ALTER_PRIV	Permission to alter the object
	INDEX_PRIV	Permission to create or drop an index on the object
	CREATED	Timestamp for the grant
TABLE_PRIVILEGE_MAP	**Description table for access privilege codes**	
TABS	**Synonym for USER_TABLES**	

USER_AUDIT_OBJECT — **Audit trail records for statements concerning objects. Created by CATAUDIT.SQL.**

Column	Description
OS_USERNAME	Operating system logon username of the user whose actions were audited
USERNAME	Name (not ID number) of the user whose actions were audited
USERHOST	Numeric instance ID for the ORACLE instance from which the user is accessing the database
TERMINAL	Identifier for the user's terminal
TIMESTAMP	Timestamp for the creation of the audit trail entry or logon time for the CONNECT statement
OWNER	Creator of object affected by the action
OBJ_NAME	Name of the object affected by the action
ACTION_NAME	Name of the action type corresponding to the numeric code in ACTION
NEW_OWNER	Owner of the object named in the NEW_NAME column
NEW_NAME	New name of an object renamed by a RENAME statement
SES_ACTIONS	Session summary (a string of 11 characters, one for each action type, in the order Alter, Audit, Comment, Delete, Grant, Index, Insert, Lock, Rename, Select, and Update; coded - for none, S for success, F for failure, and B for both)
COMMENT_TEXT	Text comment on the audit trail entry (inserted by an application program)
SESSIONID	Numeric ID for each ORACLE session
ENTRYID	Numeric ID for each audit trail entry in the session
STATEMENTID	Numeric ID for each statement run (a statement may cause many actions)
RETURNCODE	ORACLE message code generated by the action (zero if the action succeeded)
PRIV_USED	System privilege used to execute the action
OBJECT_LABEL	Optional Trusted ORACLE label associated with the object being audited
SESSION_LABEL	Trusted ORACLE label associated with the user session

USER_AUDIT_SESSION	**All audit trail records concerning connections and disconnections for the user. Created by CATAUDIT.SQL.**	
	OS_USERNAME	Operating system logon user name of the user whose actions were audited
	USERNAME	Name (not ID number) of the user whose actions were audited
	USERHOST	Numeric instance ID for the ORACLE instance from which the user is accessing the database
	TERMINAL	Identifier for the user's terminal
	TIMESTAMP	Timestamp for the creation of the audit trail entry or logon time for the CONNECT statement
	ACTION_NAME	Name of the action type corresponding to the numeric code in ACTION
	LOGOFF_TIME	Timestamp for user logoff
	LOGOFF_LREAD	Logical reads for the session
	LOGOFF_PREAD	Physical reads for the session
	LOGOFF_LWRITE	Logical writes for the session
	LOGOFF_DLOCK	Deadlocks detected during the session
	SESSIONID	Numeric ID for each ORACLE session
	RETURNCODE	ORACLE message code generated by the action (zero if the action succeeded)
	SESSION_LABEL	Trusted ORACLE label associated with the user session

USER_AUDIT_STATEMENT

Audit trail entries for the following statements issued by the user: GRANT, REVOKE, AUDIT, NOAUDIT, and ALTER SYSTEM. Created by CATAUDIT.SQL.

OS_USERNAME	Operating system logon username of the user whose actions were audited
USERNAME	Name (not ID number) of the user whose actions were audited
USERHOST	Numeric instance ID for the ORACLE instance from which the user is accessing the database
TERMINAL	Identifier for the user's terminal
TIMESTAMP	Timestamp for the creation of the audit trail entry or logon time for the CONNECT statement
OWNER	Creator of object affected by the action
OBJ_NAME	Name of the object affected by the action
ACTION_NAME	Name of the action type corresponding to the numeric code in ACTION
NEW_NAME	New name of an object after a RENAME
OBJ_PRIVILEGE	Object privileges granted/revoked by a GRANT/REVOKE statement
SYS_PRIVILEGE	System privileges granted/revoked by a GRANT/REVOKE statement
ADMIN_OPTION	Signifies the role or system privilege was granted with ADMIN option
GRANTEE	Username of the grantee specified in a GRANT/REVOKE statement
AUDIT_OPTION	Auditing option set with the AUDIT statement
SES_ACTIONS	Session summary (a string of 11 characters, one for each action type, in the order Alter, Audit, Comment, Delete, Grant, Index, Insert, Lock, Rename, Select, and Update; coded - for none, S for success, F for failure, and B for both)
COMMENT_TEXT	Text comment on the audit trail entry (inserted by an application program)
SESSIONID	Numeric ID for each ORACLE session
ENTRYID	Numeric ID for each audit trail entry in the session
STATEMENTID	Numeric ID for each statement run (a statement may cause many actions)

	RETURNCODE	ORACLE message code generated by the action (zero if the action succeeded)
	PRIV_USED	System privilege used to execute the action
	SESSION_LABEL	Trusted ORACLE label associated with the user session
USER_AUDIT_TRAIL	**Audit trail entries relevant to the user. Created by CATAUDIT.SQL.**	
	OS_USERNAME	Operating system logon username of the user whose actions were audited
	USERNAME	Name (not ID number) of the user whose actions were audited
	USERHOST	Numeric instance ID for the ORACLE instance from which the user is accessing the database
	TERMINAL	Identifier for the user's terminal
	TIMESTAMP	Timestamp for the creation of the audit trail entry or logon time for the CONNECT statement
	OWNER	Creator of object affected by the action
	OBJ_NAME	Name of the object affected by the action
	ACTION	Numeric type code corresponding to the action name
	ACTION_NAME	Name of the action type corresponding to the numeric code in ACTION
	NEW_OWNER	Owner of the object named in the NEW_NAME column
	NEW_NAME	New name of an object renamed by a RENAME statement
	OBJ_PRIVILEGE	Object privileges granted/revoked by a GRANT/REVOKE statement
	SYS_PRIVILEGE	System privileges granted/revoked by a GRANT/REVOKE statement
	ADMIN_OPTION	Signifies the role or system privilege was granted with ADMIN option
	GRANTEE	Username of the grantee specified in a GRANT/REVOKE statement
	AUDIT_OPTION	Auditing option set with the AUDIT statement
	SES_ACTIONS	Session summary (a string of 11 characters, one for each action type, in the order Alter, Audit, Comment, Delete, Grant, Index, Insert, Lock, Rename, Select, and Update; coded - for none, S for success, F for failure, and B for both)

	LOGOFF_TIME	Timestamp for user logoff
	LOGOFF_LREAD	Logical reads for the session
	LOGOFF_PREAD	Physical reads for the session
	LOGOFF_LWRITE	Logical writes for the session
	LOGOFF_DLOCK	Deadlocks detected during the session
	COMMENT_TEXT	Text comment on the audit trail entry (inserted by an application program)
	SESSIONID	Numeric ID for each ORACLE session
	ENTRYID	Numeric ID for each audit trail entry in the session
	STATEMENTID	Numeric ID for each statement run (a statement can cause many actions)
	RETURNCODE	ORACLE message code generated by the action (zero if the action succeeded)
	PRIV_USED	System privilege used to execute the action
	OBJECT_LABEL	Optional Trusted ORACLE label associated with the object being audited
	SESSION_LABEL	Trusted ORACLE label associated with the user session
USER_CATALOG	**Tables, views, synonyms, and sequences owned by the user**	
	TABLE_NAME	Name of the object
	TABLE_TYPE	Type of the object

USER_CLUSTERS	**Description of user's own clusters**	
	CLUSTER_NAME	Name of the cluster
	TABLESPACE_NAME	Name of the tablespace containing the cluster
	PCT_FREE	Minimum percentage of free space in a block
	PCT_USED	Minimum percentage of used space in a block
	KEY_SIZE	Estimated size of cluster key plus associated rows
	INI_TRANS	Initial number of transactions
	MAX_TRANS	Maximum number of transactions
	INITIAL_EXTENT	Size of the initial extent in bytes
	NEXT_EXTENT	Size of secondary extents in bytes
	MIN_EXTENTS	Minimum number of extents allowed in the segment
	MAX_EXTENTS	Maximum number of extents allowed in the segment
	PCT_INCREASE	Percentage increase in extent size
	AVG_BLOCKS_PER_KEY	Number of blocks in the table divided by number of hash keys
	CLUSTER_TYPE	Type of cluster: B-tree index or hash
	FUNCTION	Hash function used for a hash cluster
	HASHKEYS	Number of hash keys for a hash cluster
USER_CLU_COLUMNS	**Mapping of columns in user's tables to cluster columns**	
	CLUSTER_NAME	Cluster name
	CLU_COLUMN_NAME	Key column in the cluster
	TABLE_NAME	Clustered table name
	TAB_COLUMN_NAME	Key column in the table
USER_COL_COMMENTS	**Comments on columns of user's tables and views**	
	TABLE_NAME	Object name
	COLUMN_NAME	Column name
	COMMENTS	Comment on the column

USER_COL_PRIVS	**Grants on columns for which the user is the owner, grantor, or grantee**	
	GRANTEE	Name of the user to whom access was granted
	OWNER	Owner of the object
	TABLE_NAME	Name of the object
	COLUMN_NAME	Name of the column
	GRANTOR	Name of the user who performed the grant
	PRIVILEGE	Privilege on the column
	GRANTABLE	YES if the privilege was granted with ADMIN OPTION; otherwise NO
USER_COL_PRIVS_MADE	**All grants on columns of objects owned by the user**	
	GRANTEE	Name of the user to whom access was granted
	TABLE_NAME	Name of the object
	COLUMN_NAME	Name of the column
	GRANTOR	Name of the user who performed the grant
	PRIVILEGE	Privilege on the column
	GRANTABLE	YES if the privilege was granted with ADMIN OPTION; otherwise NO
USER_COL_PRIVS_RECD	**Grants on columns for which the user is the grantee**	
	OWNER	Username of the owner of the object
	TABLE_NAME	Name of the object
	COLUMN_NAME	Name of the column
	GRANTOR	Name of the user who performed the grant
	PRIVILEGE	Privilege on the column
	GRANTABLE	YES if the privilege was granted with ADMIN OPTION; otherwise NO

USER_CONSTRAINTS	**Constraint definitions on user's tables**	
	OWNER	Owner of the constraint definition
	CONSTRAINT_NAME	Name associated with the constraint definition
	CONSTRAINT_TYPE	Type of constraint definition: C (check constraint on a table), P (primary key), U (unique key), R (referential integrity), V (with check option, on a view)
	TABLE_NAME	Name associated with table with constraint definition
	SEARCH_CONDITION	Text of search condition for table check
	R_OWNER	Owner of table used in referential constraint
	R_CONSTRAINT_NAME	Name of unique constraint definition for referenced table
	DELETE_RULE	The delete rule for a referential constraint: CASCADE, NO ACTION
	STATUS	Status of constraint: ENABLED, DISABLED
USER_CONS_COLUMNS	**Information about columns in constraint definitions owned by the user**	
	OWNER	Owner of the constraint definition
	CONSTRAINT_NAME	Name associated with the constraint definition
	TABLE_NAME	Name associated with table with constraint definition
	COLUMN_NAME	Name associated with column specified in the constraint definition
	POSITION	Original position of column in definition
USER_DB_LINKS	**Database links owned by the user**	
	DB_LINK	Name of the database link
	USERNAME	Name of user to log on as
	PASSWORD	Password for logon
	HOST	SQL*Net string for connect
	CREATED	Creation time of the database link

USER_DEPENDENCIES	**Dependencies to and from a user's objects**	
	NAME	Name of the object
	TYPE	Type of object: PROCEDURE, PACKAGE, FUNCTION, PACKAGE BODY
	REFERENCED_OWNER	Owner of the parent object
	REFERENCED_NAME	Name of the parent object
	REFERENCED_TYPE	Type of the parent object: PROCEDURE, PACKAGE, FUNCTION, PACKAGE BODY
	REFERENCED_LINK_NAME	Name of the link to the parent object (if remote)
USER_ERRORS	**Current errors on all a user's stored objects**	
	NAME	Name of the object
	TYPE	Type of object: PROCEDURE, PACKAGE, FUNCTION, PACKAGE BODY
	SEQUENCE	Sequence number, for ordering
	LINE	Line number at which this error occurs
	POSITION	Position in the line at which this error occurs
	TEXT	Text of the error
USER_EXTENTS	**Extents of the segments belonging to a user's objects**	
	SEGMENT_NAME	Name of the segment associated with the extent
	SEGMENT_TYPE	Type of the segment
	TABLESPACE_NAME	Name of the tablespace containing the extent
	EXTENT_ID	Extent number in the segment
	BYTES	Size of the extent in bytes
	BLOCKS	Size of the extent in ORACLE blocks
USER_FREE_SPACE	**Free extents in tablespaces accessible to the user**	
	TABLESPACE_NAME	Name of the tablespace containing the extent
	FILE_ID	ID number of the file containing the extent
	BLOCK_ID	Starting block number of the extent
	BYTES	Size of the extent in bytes
	BLOCKS	Size of the extent in ORACLE blocks

USER_INDEXES	Description of the user's own indexes	
	STATUS	State of the index: DIRECT LOAD or VALID
	INDEX_NAME	Name of the index
	TABLE_OWNER	Owner of the indexed object
	TABLE_NAME	Name of the indexed object
	TABLE_TYPE	Type of the indexed object
	UNIQUENESS	Uniqueness status of the index: UNIQUE or NONUNIQUE
	TABLESPACE_NAME	Name of the tablespace containing the index
	INI_TRANS	Initial number of transactions
	MAX_TRANS	Maximum number of transactions
	INITIAL_EXTENT	Size of the initial extent in bytes
	NEXT_EXTENT	Size of secondary extents in bytes
	MIN_EXTENTS	Minimum number of extents allowed in the segment
	MAX_EXTENTS	Maximum number of extents allowed in the segment
	PCT_INCREASE	Percentage increase in extent size
	PCT_FREE	Minimum percentage of free space in a block
	BLEVEL	Depth of the index from its root block to its leaf blocks. A depth of 1 indicates that the root block and leaf block are the same.
	LEAF_BLOCKS	Number of leaf blocks in the index.
	DISTINCT_KEYS	Number of distinct indexed values. For indexes that enforce UNIQUE and PRIMARY KEY constraints, this value is the same as the number of rows in the table (USER_TABLES.NUM_ROWS).
	AVG_LEAF_BLOCKS_PER_KEY	Average number of leaf blocks in which each distinct value in the index appears. This statistic is rounded to the nearest integer. For indexes that enforce UNIQUE and PRIMARY KEY constraints, this value is always 1.
	AVG_DATA_BLOCKS_PER_KEY	Average number of data blocks in the table that are pointed to by a distinct value in the index. This statistic is the average number of data blocks that contain rows that contain a given value for the indexed column(s). This statistic is rounded to the nearest integer.

	CLUSTERING_FACTOR	This statistic represents the amount of order of the rows in the table based on the values of the index. If its value is near the number of blocks, then the table is very well ordered. In such a case, the index entries in a single leaf block tend to point to rows in the same data blocks. If its value is near the number of rows, then the table is very randomly ordered. In such a case, it is unlikely that index entries in the same leaf block point to rows in the same data blocks.
USER_IND_COLUMNS	**Columns of the user's indexes or on user's tables**	
	INDEX_NAME	Index name
	TABLE_NAME	Table or cluster name
	COLUMN_NAME	Column name
	COLUMN_POSITION	Position of column within index
	COLUMN_LENGTH	Indexed length of the column
USER_OBJECTS	**Objects owned by the user**	
	OBJECT_NAME	Name of the object
	OBJECT_ID	Object number of the object
	OBJECT_TYPE	Type of the object
	CREATED	Timestamp for the creation of the object
	LAST_DDL_TIME	Timestamp of the last DDL command applied to the object (including grants and revokes)
	TIMESTAMP	Timestamp for the creation of the object (character data)
	STATUS	Status of the object: VALID, INVALID
USER_OBJECT_SIZE	**User's PL/SQL objects**	
	NAME	Name of the object
	TYPE	Type of the object: PROCEDURE, PACKAGE, or PACKAGE BODY
	SOURCE_SIZE	Size of source code in bytes
	PARSED_SIZE	Size of parsed code in bytes
	CODE_SIZE	Size of compiled code in bytes
	ERROR_SIZE	Size of error messages in bytes

USER_OBJ_AUDIT_OPTS	**Auditing options for user's own tables and views. Created by CATAUDIT.SQL.**	
	OBJECT_NAME	Name of the object
	OBJECT_TYPE	Type of the object: TABLE or VIEW
	ALT	Auditing ALTER WHENEVER SUCCESSFUL / UNSUCCESSFUL
	AUD	Auditing AUDIT WHENEVER SUCCESSFUL / UNSUCCESSFUL
	COM	Auditing COMMENT WHENEVER SUCCESSFUL / UNSUCCESSFUL
	DEL	Auditing DELETE WHENEVER SUCCESSFUL / UNSUCCESSFUL
	GRA	Auditing GRANT WHENEVER SUCCESSFUL / UNSUCCESSFUL
	IND	Auditing INDEX WHENEVER SUCCESSFUL / UNSUCCESSFUL
	INS	Auditing INSERT WHENEVER SUCCESSFUL / UNSUCCESSFUL
	LOC	Auditing LOCK WHENEVER SUCCESSFUL / UNSUCCESSFUL
	REN	Auditing RENAME WHENEVER SUCCESSFUL / UNSUCCESSFUL
	SEL	Auditing SELECT WHENEVER SUCCESSFUL / UNSUCCESSFUL
	UPD	Auditing UPDATE WHENEVER SUCCESSFUL / UNSUCCESSFUL
	REF	Auditing REFERENCES WHENEVER SUCCESSFUL / UNSUCCESSFUL
	EXE	Auditing EXECUTE WHENEVER SUCCESSFUL / UNSUCCESSFUL
USER_RESOURCE_LIMITS	**Displays the resource limits for the current user**	
	RESOURCE_NAME	Name of the resource
	LIMIT	Limit placed on this resource

USER_ROLE_PRIVS	**Roles granted to the user**	
	USERNAME	Name of the user, or PUBLIC
	GRANTED_ROLE	Name of the role granted to user
	ADMIN_OPTION	Granted with ADMIN option: Y/N
	DEFAULT_ROLE	Role is designated as the user's default role: Y/N
	OS_GRANTED	Granted by the operating system: Y/N (occurs if configuration parameter OS_ROLES = TRUE)
USER_SEGMENTS	**Storage allocation for database segments belonging to a user's objects**	
	SEGMENT_NAME	Name of the segment, if any
	SEGMENT_TYPE	Type of segment: TABLE, CLUSTER, INDEX, ROLLBACK, DEFERRED ROLLBACK, TEMPORARY, CACHE
	TABLESPACE_NAME	Name of the tablespace containing the segment
	BYTES	Size of the segment in bytes
	BLOCKS	Size of the segment in ORACLE blocks
	EXTENTS	Number of extents allocated to the segment
	INITIAL_EXTENT	Size of the initial extent in ORACLE blocks
	NEXT_EXTENT	Size of the next extent to be allocated in ORACLE blocks
	MIN_EXTENTS	Minimum number of extents allowed in the segment
	MAX_EXTENTS	Maximum number of extents allowed in the segment
	PCT_INCREASE	Percent by which to increase the size of the next extent to be allocated
	FREELISTS	Number of process freelists allocated to this segment
	FREELIST_GROUPS	Number of freelist groups allocated to this segment

USER_SEQUENCES **Description of the user's own sequences**

Column	Description
SEQUENCE_NAME	SEQUENCE name
MIN_VALUE	Minimum value of the sequence
MAX_VALUE	Maximum value of the sequence
INCREMENT_BY	Value by which sequence is incremented
CYCLE_FLAG	Does sequence wraparound on reaching limit
ORDER_FLAG	Are sequence numbers generated in order
CACHE_SIZE	Number of sequence numbers to cache
LAST_NUMBER	Last sequence number written to disk. If a sequence uses caching, the number written to disk is the last number placed in the sequence cache. This number is likely to be greater than the last sequence number that was actually used. This value is *not* continuously updated during database operation. It is intended for use after a warmstart or import.

USER_SNAPSHOTS	**Snapshots the user can view**	
	OWNER	Owner of the snapshot
	NAME	Name of the view used by users and applications for viewing the snapshot
	TABLE_NAME	Table the snapshot is stored in. This table has an extra column for the master rowid
	MASTER_VIEW	View of the master table, owned by the snapshot owner, used for refreshes
	MASTER_OWNER	Owner of the master table
	MASTER	Name of the master table that this snapshot is a copy of
	MASTER_LINK	Database link name to the master site
	CAN_USE_LOG	YES if this snapshot can use a snapshot log, NO if this snapshot is too complex to use a log
	LAST_REFRESH	Date and time at the master site of the last refresh
	ERROR	Error returned last time an automatic refresh was attempted
	TYPE	Type of refresh for all automatic refreshes: COMPLETE, FAST, FORCE
	NEXT	Date function used to compute next refresh dates
	START_WITH	Date function used to compute next refresh dates
	QUERY	Original query that this snapshot is an instantiation of
USER_SNAPSHOT_LOGS	**All snapshot logs owned by the user**	
	LOG_OWNER	Owner of the snapshot log
	MASTER	Name of the master table which the log records changes of
	LOG_TABLE	Log table that holds the rowids and timestamps of rows which changed in the master table
	LOG_TRIGGER	An after-row trigger on the master which inserts rows into the log
	CURRENT_SNAPSHOTS	Date the snapshot of the master was last refreshed

USER_SOURCE	**Text source of all stored objects belonging to the user**	
	NAME	Name of the object
	TYPE	Type of object: PROCEDURE, PACKAGE, FUNCTION, PACKAGE BODY
	LINE	Line number of this line of source
	TEXT	Text source of the stored object
USER_SYNONYMS	**The user's private synonyms**	
	SYNONYM_NAME	Name of the synonym
	TABLE_OWNER	Owner of the object referenced by the synonym
	TABLE_NAME	Name of the object referenced by the synonym
	DB_LINK	Database link referenced in a remote synonym
USER_SYS_PRIVS	**System privileges granted to the user**	
	USERNAME	Name of the user, or PUBLIC
	PRIVILEGE	System privilege granted to the user
	ADMIN_OPTION	Signifies the privilege was granted with ADMIN option

USER_TABLES **Description of the user's own tables**

TABLE_NAME	Name of the table
TABLESPACE_NAME	Name of the tablespace containing the table
CLUSTER_NAME	Name of the cluster, if any, to which the table belongs
PCT_FREE	Minimum percentage of free space in a block
PCT_USED	Minimum percentage of used space in a block
INI_TRANS	Initial number of transactions
MAX_TRANS	Maximum number of transactions
INITIAL_EXTENT	Size of the initial extent in bytes
NEXT_EXTENT	Size of secondary extents in bytes
MIN_EXTENTS	Minimum number of extents allowed in the segment
MAX_EXTENTS	Maximum number of extents allowed in the segment
PCT_INCREASE	Percentage increase in extent size
BACKED_UP	Has table been backed up since last modification
NUM_ROWS	Number of rows in the table
BLOCKS	Number of data blocks allocated to the table
EMPTY_BLOCKS	Number of data blocks allocated to the table that contain no data
AVG_SPACE	Average amount of free space (in bytes) in a data block allocated to the table
CHAIN_CNT	Number of rows in the table that are chained from one data block to another or that have migrated to a new block, requiring a link to preserve the old rowid
AVG_ROW_LEN	Average length of a row in the table in bytes

USER_TABLESPACES	**Description of accessible tablespaces**	
	TABLESPACE_NAME	Tablespace name
	INITIAL_EXTENT	Default initial extent size
	NEXT_EXTENT	Default incremental extent size
	MIN_EXTENTS	Default minimum number of extents
	MAX_EXTENTS	Default maximum number of extents
	PCT_INCREASE	Default percent increase for extent size
	STATUS	Tablespace status: ONLINE, OFFLINE, or INVALID (tablespace has been dropped)
USER_TAB_COLUMNS	**Columns of user's tables, views, and clusters**	
	TABLE_NAME	Table, view, or cluster name
	COLUMN_NAME	Column name
	DATA_TYPE	Datatype of the column
	DATA_LENGTH	Maximum length of the column in bytes
	DATA_PRECISION	Decimal precision for NUMBER datatype; binary precision for FLOAT datatype; NULL for all other datatypes.
	DATA_SCALE	Digits to right of decimal point in a number
	NULLABLE	Does column allow NULLs? Value is n if there is a NOT NULL constraint on the column or if the column is part of a PRIMARY KEY.
	COLUMN_ID	Sequence number of the column as created
	DEFAULT_LENGTH	Length of default value for the column
	DATA_DEFAULT	Default value for the column
	NUM_DISTINCT	Number of distinct values in each column of the table
	LOW_VALUE HIGH_VALUE	For tables with more than three rows, the second-lowest and second-highest values in the column. For tables with three rows or fewer, the lowest and highest values. These statistics are expressed in hexadecimal notation for the internal representation of the first 32 bytes of the values.
USER_TAB_COMMENTS	**Comments on the tables and views owned by the user**	
	TABLE_NAME	Name of the object
	TABLE_TYPE	Type of the object: TABLE or VIEW
	COMMENTS	Comment on the object

USER_TAB_PRIVS	**Grants on objects for which the user is the owner, grantor, or grantee**	
	GRANTEE	Name of the user to whom access was granted
	OWNER	Owner of the object
	TABLE_NAME	Name of the object
	GRANTOR	Name of the user who performed the grant
	PRIVILEGE	Privilege on the object
	GRANTABLE	YES if the privileges was granted with ADMIN OPTION; otherwise NO
USER_TAB_PRIVS_MADE	**All grants on objects owned by the user**	
	GRANTEE	Name of the user to whom access was granted
	TABLE_NAME	Name of the object
	GRANTOR	Name of the user who performed the grant
	PRIVILEGE	Privilege on the object
	GRANTABLE	YES if the privilege was granted with ADMIN OPTION; otherwise NO
USER_TAB_PRIVS_RECD	**Grants on objects for which the user is the grantee**	
	OWNER	Owner of the object
	TABLE_NAME	Name of the object
	GRANTOR	Name of the user who performed the grant
	PRIVILEGE	Privilege on the object
	GRANTABLE	YES if the privilege was granted with ADMIN OPTION; otherwise NO

USER_TRIGGERS	**Description of the user's triggers**	
	TRIGGER_NAME	Name of the trigger
	TRIGGER_TYPE	Type of the trigger: BEFORE STATEMENT, AFTER STATEMENT, BEFORE ROW, AFTER ROW
	TRIGGERING_EVENT	Statement that fires the trigger: INSERT, UPDATE, DELETE
	TABLE_OWNER	Owner of the table the trigger is defined on
	TABLE_NAME	Table the trigger is defined on
	REFERENCING_NAMES	Names used for referencing OLD and NEW column values from within the trigger
	WHEN_CLAUSE	WHEN clause. Must evaluate to TRUE for TRIGGER_BODY to execute
	STATUS	Whether or not the trigger is enabled: ENABLED or DISABLED
	DESCRIPTION	Trigger description. Useful for re-creating a trigger creation statement.
	TRIGGER_BODY	Statement(s) executed by the trigger when it fires
USER_TRIGGER_COLS	**Shows usage of columns in triggers owned by user or on one of user's tables**	
	TRIGGER_OWNER	Owner of the trigger
	TRIGGER_NAME	Name of the trigger
	TABLE_OWNER	Owner of the table the trigger is defined on
	TABLE_NAME	Table the trigger is defined on
	COLUMN_NAME	Name of the column used in the trigger
	COLUMN_LIST	Column specified in UPDATE clause: Y/N
	COLUMN_USAGE	How the column is used in the trigger. All applicable combinations of NEW, OLD, IN, OUT, and IN OUT.
USER_TS_QUOTAS	**Tablespace quotas for the user**	
	TABLESPACE_NAME	Tablespace name
	BYTES	Number of bytes charged to the user
	MAX_BYTES	User's quota in bytes or UNLIMITED
	BLOCKS	Number of ORACLE blocks charged to the user
	MAX_BLOCKS	User's quota in ORACLE blocks or UNLIMITED

USER_USERS	**Information about the current user**	
	USERNAME	Name of the user
	USER_ID	ID number of the user
	DEFAULT_TABLESPACE	Default tablespace for data
	TEMPORARY_TABLESPACE	Default tablespace for temporary tables
	CREATED	User creation date
USER_VIEWS	**Text of views owned by the user**	
	VIEW_NAME	Name of the view
	TEXT_LENGTH	Length of the view text
	TEXT	View text

The Dynamic Performance Tables

The ORACLE Server contains a set of underlying "tables" that are maintained by the Server and accessible to the DBA user SYS. These tables are called *dynamic performance tables* because they are continuously updated while a database is open and in use, and their contents relate primarily to performance.

Although these tables appear to be regular database tables, they are not. Like ROWIDs and ROWNUMs, these tables may be selected from, but never updated or altered.

The file CATALOG.SQL contains definitions of the views and public synonyms for the dynamic performance tables. You must run CATALOG.SQL to create these views and synonyms.

Views created on the dynamic performance tables are identified by the prefix V_$, and public synonyms for these views have the prefix V$. DBAs or users should only access the V$ objects, not the V_$ objects.

In general, these views are not intended for direct access by DBAs or users. Rather, the dynamic performance tables are used by SQL*DBA, which is the primary interface for accessing information about system performance.

Once the instance is started, the V$ views are accessible. The database does not have to be mounted or open. One important consequence of this fact is that the V$LOG view can be used to identify logfiles needed for recovery.

Note: Information about the dynamic performance tables is presented for completeness only; this information does not imply a commitment to support these tables in the future.

Access to the Dynamic Performance Tables

After installation, only username SYS has access to the dynamic performance tables. However, access to these tables is required for any user needing to view the MONITOR displays available in SQL*DBA.

Granting Access to All Tables

The UTLMONTR.SQL script can be run to grant access to PUBLIC on all of the dynamic performance tables. See your installation or user's guide for details on running UTLMONTR.SQL

IUG

Granting Access on Selected Tables

If any user other than SYS wants to use SQL*DBA's MONITOR functions, that user needs access to one or more of the dynamic performance tables. For a list of the views used by each monitor, see the *ORACLE7 Server Utilities User's Guide.*

Descriptions of Individual Tables

This section lists the columns and public synonyms for the dynamic performance tables.

V$ACCESS

Shows objects in the database that are currently locked and the sessions that are accessing them.

SID	VARCHAR2	Session number that is accessing an object
OWNER	VARCHAR2	Owner of the object
OBJECT	VARCHAR2	Name of the object
OB_TYP	NUMBER	Type identifier for the object

V$ARCHIVE

Information on archive logs for each thread in the database system. (Each row provides information for one thread.)

GROUP#	NUMBER	Logfile group number
THREAD#	NUMBER	Logfile thread number
SEQUENCE#	NUMBER	Logfile sequence number
CURRENT	VARCHAR2	Archive log currently in use
FIRST_CHANGE#	NUMBER	First SCN stored in the current log

V$BACKUP

Backup status of all online datafiles.

FILE#	NUMBER	File identifier
STATUS	VARCHAR2	File status: NOT ACTIVE, ACTIVE (backup in progress), OFFLINE NORMAL, or description of an error
CHANGE#	NUMBER	System change number when backup started
TIME	NUMBER	Time the backup started

V$BGPROCESS — **Describes the background processes.**

Column	Type	Description
PADDR	RAW(4)	Address of the process state object
NAME	VARCHAR2	Name of this background process
DESCRIPTION	VARCHAR2	Description of the background process
ERROR	NUMBER	Error encountered

V$CIRCUIT — **Information about virtual circuits** (user connections to the database through dispatchers and servers).

Column	Type	Description
CIRCUIT	RAW(4)	Circuit address
DISPATCHER	RAW(4)	Current dispatcher process address
SERVER	RAW(4)	Current server process address
WAITER	RAW(4)	Address of server process that is waiting for the (currently busy) circuit to become available
SADDR	RAW(4)	Address of session bound to the circuit
STATUS	VARCHAR2	Status of the circuit: BREAK (currently interrupted), EOF (about to be removed), OUTBOUND (an outward link to a remote database), NORMAL (normal circuit into the local database)
QUEUE	VARCHAR2	Queue the circuit is currently on: COMMON (on the common queue, waiting to be picked up by a server process), DISPATCHER (waiting for the dispatcher), SERVER (currently being serviced), OUTBOUND (waiting to establish an outbound connection, NONE (idle circuit)
MESSAGE0	NUMBER	Size in bytes of the messages in the first message buffer
MESSAGE1	NUMBER	Size in bytes of the messages in the second message buffer
MESSAGES	NUMBER	Total number of messages that have gone through this circuit
BYTES	NUMBER	Total number of bytes that have gone through this circuit
BREAKS	NUMBER	Total number of breaks (interruptions) for this circuit

V$DATABASE **Database information from the control file.**

NAME	VARCHAR2	Name of the database
CREATED	VARCHAR2	Creation date
LOG_MODE	VARCHAR2	Archive log mode: NOARCHIVELOG or ARCHIVELOG
CHECKPOINT_CHANGE#	NUMBER	Last SCN checkpointed
ARCHIVE_CHANGE#	NUMBER	Last SCN archived

V$DATAFILE **Datafile information from the control file.**

FILE#	NUMBER	File identification number
STATUS	VARCHAR2	Type of file (system or user) and its status. Values: OFFLINE, SYSOFF, ONLINE, SYSTEM, RECOVER
CHECKPOINT_CHANGE#	NUMBER	SCN at last checkpoint
BYTES	NUMBER	Size in bytes
NAME	VARCHAR2	Name of the file

V$DBFILE **All data files making up the database.** This view is retained for historical compatibility. Use of V$DATAFILE is recommended instead.

FILE#	NUMBER	File identifier
NAME	VARCHAR2	Name of file

V$DB_OBJECT_CACHE **Shows database objects that are cached in the library cache. Objects include tables, indexes, clusters, synonym definitions, PL/SQL procedures and packages, and triggers.**

Column	Datatype	Description
OWNER	VARCHAR2	Owner of the object
NAME	VARCHAR2	Name of the object
DB_LINK	VARCHAR2	Database link name, if any
NAMESPACE	VARCHAR2	Library cache namespace of the object: TABLE/PROCEDURE, BODY, TRIGGER, INDEX, CLUSTER, OBJECT
TYPE	VARCHAR2	Type of the object: INDEX, TABLE, CLUSTER, VIEW, SET, SYNONYM, SEQUENCE, PROCEDURE, FUNCTION, PACKAGE, PACKAGE BODY, TRIGGER, CLASS, OBJECT, USER, DBLINK
SHARABLE_MEM	NUMBER	Amount of sharable memory in the shared pool consumed by the object
LOADS	NUMBER	Number of times the object has been loaded. This count also increases when an object has been invalidated
EXECUTIONS	NUMBER	Total number of times this object has been executed
LOCKS	NUMBER	Number of users currently locking this object
PINS	NUMBER	Number of users currentlypinning this object

V$DISPATCHER	**Information on the dispatcher processes.**		
	NAME	VARCHAR2	Name of the dispatcher process
	NETWORK	VARCHAR2	Network protocol supported by this dispatcher. For example, TCP or DECNET.
	PADDR	RAW(4)	Process address
	STATUS	VARCHAR2	Dispatcher status: WAIT (idle), SEND (sending a message), RECEIVE (receiving a message), CONNECT (establishing a connection), DISCONNECT (handling a disconnect request), BREAK (handling a break), OUTBOUND (establishing an outbound connection)
	ACCEPT	VARCHAR2	Whether this dispatcher is accepting new connections: YES, NO
	MESSAGES	NUMBER	Number of messages processed by this dispatcher
	BYTES	NUMBER	Size in bytes of messages processed by this dispatcher
	BREAKS	NUMBER	Number of breaks occurring in this connection
	OWNED	NUMBER	Number of circuits owned by this dispatcher
	CREATED	NUMBER	Number of circuits created by this dispatcher
	IDLE	NUMBER	Total idle time for this dispatcher, in hundredths of a second
	BUSY	NUMBER	Total busy time for this dispatcher, in hundredths of a second
V$ENABLEDPRIVS	**Which privileges are enabled.**		
	PRIV_NUMBER	NUMBER	Numeric identifier of enabled privileges
V$FILESTAT	**Information about file read/write statistics.**		
	FILE#	NUMBER	Number of the file
	PHYRDS	NUMBER	Number of physical reads done
	PHYWRTS	NUMBER	Number of physical writes done
	PHYBLKRD	NUMBER	Number of physical blocks read
	PHYBLKWRT	NUMBER	Number of physical blocks written
	READTIM	NUMBER	Time spent doing reads if the parameter TIMED_STATISTICS is TRUE; 0 if FALSE
	WRITETIM	NUMBER	Time spent doing writes if the parameter TIMED_STATISTICS is TRUE; 0 if FALSE

V$FIXED_TABLE

Shows all fixed tables, views, and derived tables in the database.

NAME	VATCHAR2	Name of the object
OBJECT_ID	NUMBER	Identifier of the fixed object
TYPE	VARCHAR2	Object type: TABLE, VIEW

V$INSTANCE

State of the current instance.

KEY	VARCHAR2	Name of state variable, from the table below
VALUE	NUMBER	Value of state variable

Instance State Variable	Value
RESTRICTED MODE	0 (False), 1 (True)
SHUTDOWN PENDING	0 (False), 1 (True)
STARTUP TIME – JULIAN	Start time and date in Julian format
STARTUP TIME – SECONDS	Number of seconds since midnight on the startup date

V$LATCH

Information about each type of latch. (The rows of this table and the rows of V$LATCHNAME correspond one-to-one.)

ADDR	RAW(4)	Address of latch object
LATCH#	NUMBER	Latch number
LEVEL#	NUMBER	Latch level
GETS	NUMBER	Number of times obtained wait
MISSES	NUMBER	Number of times obtained with wait but failed first try
SLEEPS	NUMBER	Number of times slept when wanted wait
IMMEDIATE_GETS	NUMBER	Number of times obtained with no wait
IMMEDIATE_MISSES	NUMBER	Number of times failed to get with no wait

V$LATCHHOLDER

Information about the current latch holders.

PID	NUMBER	Identifier of process holding the latch
LADDR	RAW(4)	Latch address

V$LATCHNAME

The decoded latch names for the latches shown in table V$LATCH. (The rows of this table and the rows of V$LATCH correspond one-to-one.)

LATCH#	NUMBER	Latch number
NAME	VARCHAR2	Latch name

V$LIBRARYCACHE	**Statistics on library cache management.**		
	NAMESPACE	VARCHAR2	Library cache namespace: SQL AREA,TABLE/PROCEDURE, BODY, TRIGGER, INDEX, CLUSTER, OBJECT, PIPE
	GETS	NUMBER	Number of times the system requests handles to library objects belonging to this namespace
	GETHITS	NUMBER	Number of times the handles are already allocated in the cache. If the handle is not already allocated, it is a miss. The handle is then allocated and inserted into the cache.
	GETHITRATIO	NUMBER	Number of GETHITS divided by GETS. Values close to 1 indicate that most of the handles the system has tried to get are cached.
	PINS	NUMBER	Number of times the system issues pin requests for objects in the cache in order to access them
	PINHITS	NUMBER	Number of times that objects the system is pinning and accessing are already allocated and initialized in the cache. Otherwise, it is a miss, and the system has to allocate it in the cache and initialize it with data queried from the database or generate the data.
	PINHITRATIO	NUMBER	Number of PINHITS divided by number of PINS. Values close to 1 indicate that most of the objects the system has tried to pin and access have been cached
	RELOADS	NUMBER	Number of times that library objects have to be reinitialized and reloaded with data because they have been aged out or invalidated
	INVALIDATIONS	NUMBER	Number of times that non-persistent library objects (like shared SQL areas) have been invalidated

V$LICENSE — **Information about license limits.**

SESSIONS_MAX	NUMBER	Maximum number of concurrent user sessions allowed for the instance
SESSIONS_WARNING	NUMBER	Warning limit for concurrent user sessions for the instance
SESSIONS_CURRENT	NUMBER	Current number of concurrent user sessions
SESSION_HIGHWATER	NUMBER	Highest number of concurrent user sessions since the instance started
USERS_MAX	NUMBER	Maximum number of named users allowed for the database

V$LOADCSTAT — **SQL*Loader statistics compiled during the execution of a direct load.** These statistics apply to the whole load. Any select against this table results in "no rows returned" since you cannot load data and do a query at the same time.

READ	NUMBER	Number of records read
REJECTED	NUMBER	Number of records rejected
TDISCARD	NUMBER	Total number of discards during the load
NDISCARD	NUMBER	Number of discards from the current file
SAVEDATA	NUMBER	Whether or not save data points are used

V$LOADTSTAT — **SQL*Loader statistics compiled during the execution of a direct load.** These statistics apply to the current table. Any select against this table results in "no rows returned" since you cannot load data and do a query at the same time.

LOADED	NUMBER	Number of records loaded
REJECTED	NUMBER	Number of records rejected
FAILWHEN	NUMBER	Number of records that failed to meet any WHEN clause
ALLNULL	NUMBER	Number of records that were completely null and were therefore not loaded
LEFT2SKIP	NUMBER	Number of records yet to skip during a continued load

V$LOCK

Information about locks and resources. Does not include DDL locks.

ADDR	RAW(4)	Address of lock state object
KADDR	RAW(4)	Address of lock
SID	NUMBER	Identifier of process holding the lock
TYPE	VARCHAR2	Resource type (see following table)
ID1	NUMBER	Resource identifier #1
ID2	NUMBER	Resource identifier #2
LMODE	NUMBER	Lock mode held: 1 (null), 2 (row share), 3 (row exclusive), 4 (share), 5 (share row exclusive), 6 (exclusive)
REQUEST	NUMBER	Lock mode requested (same values as LMODE)

The following locks are obtained by user applications. Any process which is blocking others is likely to be holding one of these locks:

User Lock Type	Description
RW	Row wait enqueue lock
TM	DML enqueue lock
TX	Transaction enqueue lock
UL	User supplied lock

The following system locks are held for extremely short periods of time:

System Lock Type	Description
BL	Buffer hash table instance lock
CF	Cross-instance function invocation instance lock
CI	Control file schema global enqueue lock
CS	Control file schema global enqueue lock
DF	Data file instance lock
DM	Mount/startup db primary/secondary instance lock
DR	Distributed recovery process lock
DX	Distributed transaction entry lock
FI	SGA open-file information lock
FS	File set lock
IR	Instance recovery serialization global enqueue lock
IV	Library cache invalidation instance lock
LA..LP	Library cache lock instance lock (A..P = namespace)
LS	Log start/log switch enqueue lock

System Lock Type	Description
MB	Master buffer hash table instance lock
MM	Mount definition global enqueue lock
MR	Media recovery lock
PA..PZ	Library cache pin instance lock (A..Z = namespace)
QA..QZ	Row cache instance lock (A..Z = cache)
RE	USE_ROW_ENQUEUES enforcement lock
RT	Redo thread global enqueue lock
SC	System commit number instance lock
SH	System commit number high water mark enqueue lock
SN	Sequence number instance lock
SQ	Sequence number enqueue lock
ST	Space transaction enqueue lock
SV	Sequence number value lock
TA	Generic enqueue lock
TD	DDL enqueue lock
TE	Extend-segment enqueue lock
TS	Temporary segment enqueue lock (ID2 = 0)
TS	New block allocation enqueue lock (ID2 = 1)
TT	Temporary table enqueue lock
UN	User name lock
WL	Being-written redo log instance lock
WS	Write-atomic-log-switch global enqueue lock

V$LOG — **Log file information from control file.**

Column	Type	Description
GROUP#	NUMBER	Log group number
THREAD#	NUMBER	Log thread number
SEQUENCE#	NUMBER	Log sequence number
BYTES	NUMBER	Size of the log in bytes
MEMBERS	NUMBER	Number of members in the log group
ARCHIVED	VARCHAR2	Archive status: TRUE, FALSE
FIRST_CHANGE#	NUMBER	Lowest SCN in the log
FIRST_TIME	VARCHAR2	Time of first SCN in the log

V$LOGFILE — **Information about redo log files.**

Column	Type	Description
GROUP#	NUMBER	Redo log group identifier number
STATUS	VARCHAR2	Status of this log member: INVALID (file is inaccessible), STALE (file's contents are incomplete), DELETED (file is no longer used), or blank (file is in use)
MEMBER	VARCHAR2	Redo log member name

V$LOGHIST — **Log history information from the control file. This view is retained for historical compatibility. Use of V$LOG_HISTORY is recommended instead.**

Column	Type	Description
THREAD#	NUMBER	Log thread number
SEQUENCE#	NUMBER	Log sequence number
FIRST_CHANGE#	NUMBER	Lowest SCN in the log
FIRST_TIME	VARCHAR2	Time of first SCN in the log
SWITCH_CHANGE#	NUMBER	SCN at which the log switch occurred; one more than highest SCN in the log

V$LOG_HISTORY — **Archived log names for all logs in the log history.**

Column	Datatype	Description
THREAD#	NUMBER	Thread number of the archived log
SEQUENCE#	NUMBER	Sequence number of the archived log
TIME	NUMBER	Time of first entry (lowest SCN) in the log
LOW_CHANGE#	NUMBER	Lowest SCN in the log
HIGH_CHANGE#	NUMBER	Highest SCN in the log
ARCHIVE_NAME	VARCHAR2	Name of file when archived, using the naming convention specified by the LOG_ARCHIVE_FORMAT initialization parameter

V$NLS_PARAMETERS — **Current values of NLS parameters.**

Column	Datatype	Description
NAME	VARCHAR2	Parameter name: NLS_LANGUAGE, NLS_SORT, NLS_TERRITORY, NLS_CHARACTERSET, NLS_CURRENCY, NLS_ISO_CURRENCY, NLS_NUMERIC_CHARACTERS, NLS_DATE_FORMAT, NLS_DATE_LANGUAGE
VALUE	VARCHAR2	NLS parameter value

V$OPEN_CURSOR — **Cursors that each user session currently has opened and parsed.**

Column	Datatype	Description
SADDR	RAW	Session address
USER_NAME	VARCHAR2	User thjat is logged into the session
ADDRESS	RAW	Used with HASH_VALUE to uniquely identify the SQL statement being executed in the session
HASH_VALUE	NUMBER	Used with ADDRESS to uniquely identify the SQL statement being executed in the session
SQL_TEXT	VARCHAR2	First 60 characters of the SQL statement that is parsed into the open cursor

V$PARAMETER — **Information about current parameter values.**

Column	Datatype	Description
NUM	NUMBER	Parameter number
NAME	VARCHAR2	Parameter name
TYPE	NUMBER	Parameter type
VALUE	VARCHAR2	Parameter value
ISDEFAULT	VARCHAR2	Default value in use: TRUE, FALSE

V$PROCESS

Information about currently active processes.

ADDR	RAW(4)	Address of process state object
PID	NUMBER	ORACLE process identifier
SPID	VARCHAR2	Operating system process identifier
USERNAME	VARCHAR2	Operating system process username. Any Two-Task user coming across the network has "-T" appended to the username.
SERIAL#	NUMBER	Process serial number
TERMINAL	VARCHAR2	Operating system terminal identifier
PROGRAM	VARCHAR2	Program in progress
BACKGROUND	VARCHAR2	1 for a background process; null for a normal process
LATCHWAIT	VARCHAR2	Address of latch waiting for; null if none

V$QUEUE

Information on the multi-thread message queues.

PADDR	RAW(4)	Address of the process that owns the queue
TYPE	VARCHAR2	Type of queue: COMMON (processed by servers), OUTBOUND (used by remote servers), DISPATCHER.
QUEUED	NUMBER	Number of items in the queue
WAIT	NUMBER	Total time that all items in this queue have waited. Divide by TOTALQ for average wait per item.
TOTALQ	NUMBER	Total number of items that have ever been in the queue

V$RECOVERY_LOG

Archived logs needed to complete media recovery. This information is derived from the log history (V$LOG_HISTORY). The amount of information available is limited by the setting of the MAX_LOG_HISTORY initialization parameter.

THREAD#	NUMBER	Thread number of the archived log
SEQUENCE#	NUMBER	Sequence number of the archived log
TIME	NUMBER	Time of first entry (lowest SCN) in the log
ARCHIVE_NAME	VARCHAR2	Name of file when archived, using the naming convention specified by the LOG_ARCHIVE_FORMAT initialization parameter

V$RECOVER_FILE — **Status of files needing media recovery.**

FILE#	NUMBER	File identifier number
ONLINE	VARCHAR2	Online status: ONLINE, OFFLINE
ERROR	VARCHAR2	Why the file needs to be recovered: NULL if reason unknown, or OFFLINE NORMAL if recovery not needed
CHANGE#	NUMBER	SCN where recovery must start
TIME	VARCHAR2	Time of SCN where recovery must start

V$REQDIST — **Histogram of request times, divided into 12 buckets, or ranges of time.** The time ranges grow exponentially as a function of the bucket number.

BUCKET	NUMBER	Bucket number: 0..11; the maximum time for each bucket is (4 * 2^N)/100 seconds
COUNT	NUMBER	Count of requests whose total time to complete (excluding wait time) falls in this range.

V$RESOURCE — **Information about resources.**

ADDR	RAW(4)	Address of resource object
TYPE	VARCHAR2	Resource type
ID1	NUMBER	Resource identifier #1
ID2	NUMBER	Resource identifier #2

V$ROLLNAME — **Names of all online rollback segments.**

USN	NUMBER	Rollback ("undo") segment number
NAME	VARCHAR2	Rollback segment name

V$ROLLSTAT — **Statistics for all online rollback segments.**

Column	Type	Description
USN	NUMBER	Rollback segment number
EXTENTS	NUMBER	Number of rollback extents
RSSIZE	NUMBER	Size in bytes of rollback segment
WRITES	NUMBER	Number of bytes written to rollback segment
XACTS	NUMBER	Number of active transactions
GETS	NUMBER	Number of header gets
WAITS	NUMBER	Number of header waits
OPTSIZE	NUMBER	Optimal size of rollback segment
HWMSIZE	NUMBER	High water mark of rollback segment size
SHRINKS	NUMBER	Number of times rollback segment shrank, eliminating one or more additional extents each time
WRAPS	NUMBER	Number of times rollback segment wraps from one extent to another
EXTENDS	NUMBER	Number of times rollback segment was extended to have a new extent
AVESHRINK	NUMBER	Total size of freed extents divided by number of shrinks
AVEACTIVE	NUMBER	Current average size of active extents, where "active" extents have uncommitted transaction data
STATUS	VARCHAR2	ONLINE if the segment is online,or PENDING OFFLINE if the segment is going offline but some active (distributed) transactions are using the rollback segment. When the transactions complete, the segment goes offline.

V$ROWCACHE

Statistics for data dictionary activity.(Each row contains statistics for one data dictionary cache.)

CACHE#	NUMBER	Row cache ID number
TYPE	VARCHAR2	Parent or subordinate row cache type
SUBORDINATE#	NUMBER	Subordinate set number
PARAMETER	VARCHAR2	Name of the INIT.ORA parameter that determines the number of entries in the data dictionary cache
COUNT	NUMBER	Total number of entries in the cache
USAGE	NUMBER	Number of cache entries that contain valid data
FIXED	NUMBER	Number of fixed entries in the cache
GETS	NUMBER	Total number of requests for information on the data object
GETMISSES	NUMBER	Number of data requests resulting in cache misses
SCANS	NUMBER	Number of scan requests
SCANMISSES	NUMBER	Number of times a scan failed to find the data in the cache
SCANCOMPLETES	NUMBER	For a list of subordinate entries, the number of times the list was scanned completely
MODIFICATIONS	NUMBER	Number of inserts, updates, and deletions
FLUSHES	NUMBER	Number of times flushed to disk

V$SECONDARY

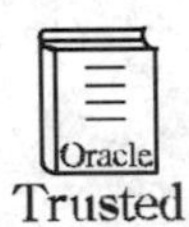

A TRUSTED ORACLE view that lists secondary mounted databases. For details, see the *Trusted ORACLE7 Server Administrator's Guide.*

V$SESSION

Session information for each current session.

Column	Type	Description
SADDR	RAW(4)	Session address
SID	NUMBER	Session identifier
SERIAL#	NUMBER	Session serial number. Used to uniquely identify a session's objects. Guarantees that session-level commands are applied to the correct session objects in the event that the session ends and another session begins with the same session ID.
AUDSID	NUMBER	Auditing session ID
PADDR	RAW(4)	Address of the process that owns this session
USER#	NUMBER	ORACLE user identifier
USERNAME	VARCHAR2	ORACLE username
COMMAND	NUMBER	Command in progress; see the table on the next page
TADDR	VARCHAR2	Address of transaction state object
LOCKWAIT	VARCHAR2	Address of lock waiting for; null if none
STATUS	VARCHAR2	Status of the session: ACTIVE, INACTIVE, KILLED
SERVER	VARCHAR2	Server type: DEDICATED, SHARED, PSEUDO, NONE
SCHEMA#	NUMBER	Schema user identifier
SCHEMANAME	VARCHAR2	Schema user name
OSUSER	VARCHAR2	Operating system client user name
PROCESS	VARCHAR2	Operating system client process ID
MACHINE	VARCHAR2	Operating system machine name
TERMINAL	VARCHAR2	Operating system terminal name
PROGRAM	VARCHAR2	Operating system program name
TYPE	VARCHAR2	Session type
SQL_ADDRESS	RAW	Used with SQL_HASH_VALUE to identify the SQL statement that is currently being executed
SQL_HASH_VALUE	NUMBER	Used with SQL_ADDRESS to identify the SQL statement that is currently being executed

Command Number	Command
1	CREATE TABLE
2	INSERT
3	SELECT
4	CREATE CLUSTER
5	ALTER CLUSTER
6	UPDATE
7	DELETE
8	DROP
9	CREATE INDEX
10	DROP INDEX
11	ALTER INDEX
12	DROP TABLE
13	---
14	---
15	ALTER TABLE
16	---
17	GRANT
18	REVOKE
19	CREATE SYNONYM
20	DROP SYNONYM
21	CREATE VIEW
22	DROP VIEW
23	---
24	---
25	---
26	LOCK TABLE
27	NO OPERATION
28	RENAME
29	COMMENT
30	AUDIT
31	NOAUDIT
32	CREATE EXTERNAL DATABASE
33	DROP EXTERNAL DATABASE
34	CREATE DATABASE
35	ALTER DATABASE
36	CREATE ROLLBACK SEGMENT
37	ALTER ROLLBACK SEGMENT
38	DROP ROLLBACK SEGMENT
39	CREATE TABLESPACE
40	ALTER TABLESPACE
41	DROP TABLESPACE
42	ALTER SESSION

Continued...

Command Number	Command
43	ALTER USER
44	COMMIT
45	ROLLBACK
46	SAVEPOINT

V$SESSION_WAIT — **Lists the reseources or events that active sessions are waiting for.**

SID	NUMBER	Session identifier
SEQ#	NUMBER	Sequence number that uniquely identifies this wait. Incremented for each wait.
EVENT	VARCHAR2	Resource or event the session is waiting for
P1TEXT	VARCHAR2	Description of first additional parameter
P1	VARCHAR2	First additional parameter
P2TEXT	VARCHAR2	Description of second parameter
P2	VARCHAR2	Second additional parameter
P3TEXT	VARCHAR2	Description of third parameter
P3	VARCHAR2	Third additional parameter
WAIT_TIME	NUMBER	A non-zero value is the session's last wait time. A zero value means the session is currently waiting.

V$SESSTAT — **For each current session, the current statistics values.**

SID	NUMBER	Session identifier
STATISTIC#	NUMBER	Statistic number (identifier)
VALUE	NUMBER	Statistic value

V$SESS_IO — **I/O statistics for each user session.**

SID	NUMBER	Session identifier
BLOCK_GETS	NUMBER	Block gets for this session
CONSISTENT_GETS	NUMBER	Consistent gets for this session
PHYSICAL_READS	NUMBER	Physical reads for this session
BLOCK_CHANGES	NUMBER	Block changes for this session
CONSISTENT_CHANGES	NUMBER	Consistent changes for this session

V$SGA — **Summary information on the System Global Area.**

NAME	VARCHAR2	SGA component group
VALUE	NUMBER	Memory size in bytes

V$SGASTAT — **Detailed information on the System Global Area.**

NAME	VARCHAR2	SGA component name
BYTES	NUMBER	Memory size in bytes

V$SHARED_SERVER — **Information on the shared server processes.**

Column	Datatype	Description
NAME	VARCHAR2	Name of the server
PADDR	RAW(4)	Server's process address
STATUS	VARCHAR2	Server status: EXEC (executing SQL), WAIT (ENQ) (waiting for a lock), WAIT (SEND (waiting to send data to user), WAIT (COMMON (idle; waiting for a user request), WAIT (RESET) (waiting for a circuit to reset after a break), QUIT (terminating)
MESSAGES	NUMBER	Number of messages processed
BYTES	NUMBER	Total number of bytes in all messages
BREAKS	NUMBER	Number of breaks
CIRCUIT	RAW(4)	Address of circuit currently being serviced
IDLE	NUMBER	Total idle time in hundredths of a second
BUSY	NUMBER	Total busy time in hundredths of a second
REQUESTS	NUMBER	Total number of requests taken from the common queue in this server's lifetime

V$SQLAREA	**Statistics on the shared cursor cache. Each row has statistics on one shared cursor.**		
	SQL_TEXT	VARCHAR2	Text of the SQL statement requiring the cursor, or the PL/SQL anonymous code
	SHARABLE_MEM	NUMBER	Amount of memory in bytes that is sharable between users
	PERSISTENT_MEM	NUMBER	Amount of per-user memory in bytes that persists for the life of the cursor
	RUNTIME_MEM	NUMBER	Amount of per-user memory, in bytes, that is needed only during execution
	SORTS	NUMBER	Number of sorts performed by the SQL statement.
	VERSION_COUNT	NUMBER	Number of different versions of this cursor. The same SQL text might be used by different users, each on their own version of a table (for example, "SELECT * from EMP" by SCOTT and JONES, when they each have their own version of EMP). In that case, multiple versions of the cursor would exist.
	LOADED_VERSIONS	NUMBER	Versions of the cursor that are currently fully loaded, with no parts aged out
	OPEN_VERSIONS	NUMBER	Number of versions that some user has an open cursor on.
	USERS_OPENING	NUMBER	Number of users that currently have this SQL statement parsed in an open cursor
	EXECUTIONS	NUMBER	Total number of times this SQL statement has been executed
	USERS_EXECUTING	NUMBER	Number of users that are currently executing this cursor
	LOADS	NUMBER	Number of times the cursor has been loaded. after the body of the cursor has been aged out of the cache while the text of the SQL statement remained in it, or after the cursor is invalidated
	FIRST_LOAD_TIME	VARCHAR2	Time at which the cursor was first loaded into the SGA

INVALIDATIONS	NUMBER	Number of times the contents of the cursor have been invalidated. For example: because tables referenced in the cursor are dropped, validated, or indexed
PARSE_CALLS	NUMBER	Number of times users executed a parse call for this cursor
DISK_READS	NUMBER	Number of disk blocks read by this cursor and all cursors caused to be executed by this cursor
BUFFER_GETS	NUMBER	Number of buffers gotten (in any mode) by this cursor and all cursors caused to be executed by this cursor
ADDRESS	RAW	Used together with HASH_VALUE to select the full text of the SQL statement from V$SQLTEXT
HASH_VALUE	NUMBER	Used together with ADDRESS to select the full text of the SQL statement from V$SQLTEXT

V$SQLTEXT

The text of SQL statements belonging to shared SQL cursors in the SGA.

ADDRESS	RAW	Used with HASH_VALUE to uniquely identify a cached cursor
HASH_VALUE	NUMBER	Used with ADDRESS to uniquely identify a cached cursor
PIECE	NUMBER	Number used to order the pieces of SQL text
SQL_TEXT	VARCHAR2	A column containing one piece of the SQL text

V$STATNAME

Decoded statistic names for the statistics shown in the V$SESSTAT table.

STATISTIC#	NUMBER	Statistic number
NAME	VARCHAR2	Statistic name
CLASS	NUMBER	Statistic class : 1 (User), 2 (Redo), 4 (Enqueue), 8 (Cache)

V$SYSLABEL

A TRUSTED ORACLE view that lists system labels. For details, see the *Trusted ORACLE7 Server Administrator's Guide.*

V$SYSSTAT — **The current system-wide value for each statistic in table V$SESSTAT.**

Column	Datatype	Description
STATISTIC#	NUMBER	Statistic number
NAME	VARCHAR2	Statistic name
CLASS	NUMBER	Statistic class: 1 (User), 2 (Redo), 4 (Enqueue), 8 (Cache)
VALUE	NUMBER	Statistic value

V$THREAD — **Thread information from the control file.**

Column	Datatype	Description
THREAD#	NUMBER	Thread number
STATUS	VARCHAR2	Thread status: OPEN, CLOSED
ENABLED	VARCHAR2	Enabled status: DISABLED, (enabled) PRIVATE, or (enabled) PUBLIC
GROUPS	NUMBER	Number of log groups assigned to this thread
INSTANCE	VARCHAR2	Instance name, if available
OPEN_TIME	VARCHAR2	Last time the thread was opened
CURRENT_GROUP#	NUMBER	Current log group
SEQUENCE#	NUMBER	Sequence number of current log
CHECKPOINT_CHANGE#	NUMBER	SCN at last checkpoint
CHECKPOINT_TIME	VARCHAR2	Time of last checkpoint

V$TIMER — **The current time in hundredths of seconds.**

Column	Datatype	Description
HSECS	NUMBER	Time in hundredths of a second

V$TRANSACTION — **Information about transactions.**

Column	Datatype	Description
ADDR	RAW(4)	Address of transaction state object
SCNBASE	NUMBER	First part of the system change number; invalid if inactive
SCNWRAP	NUMBER	Second part of the system change number; invalid if inactive
XIDUSN	NUMBER	Rollback (undo) segment number; invalid if inactive
XIDSLOT	NUMBER	Slot number; invalid if inactive
XIDSQN	NUMBER	Sequence number; invalid if inactive
UBADBA	NUMBER	Database block address for rollback data; invalid if inactive
UBASQN	NUMBER	Sequence number for rollback data; invalid if inactive
UBAREC	NUMBER	Record number for rollback data; invalid if inactive

V$TYPE_SIZE — **Sizes of various database components for use in estimating data block capacity.**

Column	Type	Description
COMPONENT	VARCHAR2	Component name, such as segment or buffer header
TYPE	VARCHAR2	Component type
DESCRIPTION	VARCHAR2	Description of component
SIZE	NUMBER	Size of component

V$VERSION — **Version numbers of core library components in the ORACLE Server. There is one row for each component.**

Column	Type	Description
BANNER	VARCHAR2	Component name and version number

V$WAITSTAT — **Block contention statistics. This table is only updated when timed statistics are enabled.**

Column	Type	Description
CLASS	VARCHAR2	Class of block subject to contention
COUNT	NUMBER	Number of waits by this OPERATION for this CLASS of block
TIME	NUMBER	Sum of all wait times for all the waits by this OPERATION for this CLASS of block

APPENDIX

C NATIONAL LANGUAGE SUPPORT

This appendix describes the database administrator's control of features that enable ORACLE applications to operate with multiple languages using conventions specified by the application user. Topics include:

- specifying language-dependent behavior for a session
- specifying default language-dependent behavior
- overriding the standard defaults
- data and number formats

Specifying Character Sets

Once the database is created, the database character set cannot be changed without re-creating the database. Hence, it is important to consider carefully which character set to use. The database character set should always be a superset of the operating system's native character set. The character sets used by client applications that access the database will usually determine which superset is the best choice.

If all client applications use the same character set, then this is the normal choice for the database character set. When client applications use different character sets, the database character set should be a superset (or equivalent) of all the client character sets. This will ensure that every character is represented when converting from a client character set to the database character set.

Character Set Conversion

Replacement characters may be defined for specific characters as part of a character set definition. Where a specific replacement character is not defined, a default replacement character is used. To avoid the use of replacement characters when converting from client to database character set, the latter should be a superset (or equivalent) of all the client character sets.

Specifying Language-Dependent Behavior for a Session

This section discusses the NLS parameters that specify language-dependent operation of applications.

NLS_LANG Parameter

The NLS_LANG parameter has three components (*language*, *territory*, and *charset*) in the form:

```
NLS_LANG = language_territory.charset
```

Each component controls the operation of a sub-set of NLS features.

language specifies conventions such as the language used for ORACLE messages, day names, and month names. Each supported language has a unique name, for example American, French, or German. The language argument specifies default values for the territory and character set arguments, so either (or both) *territory* or *charset* can be omitted.

territory specifies conventions such as the default date format and decimal character used for numbers. Each supported <*territory*> has a unique name, for example America, France, Canada.

charset specifies the character set used by the client application (normally that of the user's terminal). Each supported character set has a unique acronym, for example US7ASCII, WEISO8859P1, WE8DEC, WE8EBCDIC500, JA16EUC.

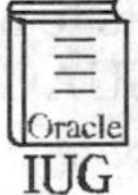

Each language has a default character set associated with it. Default values for the languages available on your system are listed in your installation or user's guide.

The three arguments of NLS_LANG can be specified in any combination, for example:

```
AMERICAN_AMERICA.US7ASCII

FRENCH_FRANCE.ISO8859P1

FRENCH_CANADA.WE8DEC

JAPANESE_JAPAN.JA16EUC
```

Specifying NLS_LANG

NLS_LANG is defined for each session with an environment variable or equivalent platform-specific mechanism. Different sessions connected to the same database can specify different values for their NLS_LANG parameter.

Each operating system handles environment variables differently, so refer to your installation or user's guide to determine how to set NLS_LANG on your system. For example, on VMS you could specify the value of NLS_LANG by entering the following line at the VMS prompt:

```
$ DEFINE NLS_LANG FRENCH_FRANCE.WE8DEC
```

Client/Server Architecture

NLS_LANG sets the NLS environment used by the database for both the Server session and for the client application. Using the one parameter ensures that the language environments of both database and client application are automatically the same.

Default Character Set

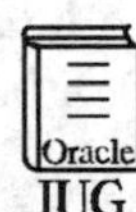

Default values for *language* and *territory* can be specified for an instance by defining the two initialization parameters NLS_LANGUAGE and NLS_TERRITORY when the instance is started. These two parameters are discussed in the next section. See your installation or user's guide for a list of the standard defaults on your system.

Overriding Language and Territory Specifications

The default values for language and territory can be overridden for a session by using the ALTER SESSION statement. For example:

```
ALTER SESSION SET NLS_LANGUAGE = FRENCH NLS_TERRITORY = FRANCE
```

This feature is used implicitly to determine the language environment of the database for each session. An ALTER SESSION statement is automatically executed when a session connects to a database to set the values of the database parameters NLS_LANGUAGE and NLS_TERRITORY to those specified by the *language* and *territory* arguments of NLS_LANG. If NLS_LANG is not defined, an ALTER SESSION statement is not executed.

When NLS_LANG is defined, the implicit ALTER SESSION is executed for all instances the session connects to, for both direct and indirect connections. If the values of NLS parameters are changed explicitly with ALTER SESSION during a session, the changes are propagated to all instances that user session is connected to.

Specifying Default Language-Dependent Behavior

This section describes NLS_LANGUAGE and NLS_TERRITORY, the initialization parameters that specify the default language-dependent behavior for a session.

NLS_LANGUAGE Parameter

NLS_LANGUAGE specifies the default conventions used for the following session characteristics:

- language used for Server messages
- language used for day and month names and their abbreviations (specified in the SQL functions TO_CHAR and TO_DATE)
- symbols used for equivalents of AM, PM, AD, and BC
- default sorting sequence used for character data when ORDER BY is specified (GROUP BY uses a binary sort, unless ORDER BY is specified)

The value specified for NLS_LANGUAGE in the initialization file is the default for all sessions in that instance. Refer to your installation or user's guide to check which language conventions are supported. For example, to specify the default session language as French, the parameter should be set as follows:

```
NLS_LANGUAGE = FRENCH
```

In this case, the Server message

```
ORA-00942: table or view does not exist
```

will appear as:

```
ORA-00942: table ou vue n'existe pas
```

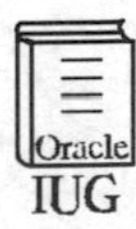

Messages used by the Server are stored in binary-format files that are placed in the ora_rdbms directory, or equivalent. (See your installation or user's guide for the location on your system.) Multiple versions of these files can exist, one for each supported language, using the filename convention:

```
<product_id><language_id>.MSB
```

For example, the file containing the Server messages in French is called ORAF.MSB, 'F' being the language abbreviation used for French.

Messages are stored in these files in one specific character set, depending on the particular machine and operating system. If this is different from the database character set, message text is automatically converted to the database character set. If necessary, it will be further converted to the client character set, if it is different from the database character set. Hence, messages will be displayed correctly at the user's terminal, subject to the limitations of character set conversion.

The default value of NLS_LANGUAGE may be operating system specific. Refer to your installation or user's guide to check the default value. You can alter the NLS_LANGUAGE parameter by changing the value in the initialization file and then restarting the instance.

NLS_TERRITORY Parameter

NLS_TERRITORY specifies the conventions used for the following default date and numeric formatting characteristics::

- date format
- decimal character and group separator
- local currency symbol
- ISO currency symbol
- week start day

The value specified for NLS_TERRITORY in the initialization file is the default for the instance. For example, to specify the default as France, the parameter should be set as follows:

```
NLS_TERRITORY = FRANCE
```

In this case, numbers would be formatted using a comma as the decimal character.

The default value of NLS_TERRITORY may be operating system specific. Refer to your installation or user's guide to check the default value and to see which territory conventions are supported on your system. You can alter the NLS_TERRITORY parameter by changing the value in the initialization file and then restarting the instance.

Overriding the Standard Defaults

The NLS_LANGUAGE and NLS_TERRITORY parameters implicitly specify several aspects of language-dependent operation. Additional NLS parameters provide explicit control over these operations. The parameters listed below can be specified in the initialization file, or they can also be specified for each session with the ALTER SESSION command. (See the *ORACLE7 Server SQL Language Reference Manual* for a complete description of ALTER SESSION.)

The additional NLS parameters are:

Parameter	*Description*
NLS_DATE_FORMAT	default date format
NLS_DATE_LANGUAGE	default language used for dates
NLS_NUMERIC_CHARACTERS	decimal character and group separator
NLS_CURRENCY	local currency symbol
NLS_ISO_CURRENCY	ISO international currency symbol
NLS_SORT	character sort sequence

These parameters are described in the following sections.

NLS_DATE_FORMAT Parameter

This parameter specifies the default date format, overriding that defined implicitly by NLS_TERRITORY. Any format usable in the TO_DATE function can be specified with the NLS_DATE_FORMAT parameter. For example, to set the default date format to display Roman numerals for months, you would include the following line in your initialization file:

```
NLS_DATE_FORMAT = 'DD RM YY'
```

With such a default date format, the following SELECT statement would return the month using Roman numerals (assuming today's date is February 13, 1991):

```
SELECT TO_CHAR(SYSDATE) CURRDATE
    FROM DUAL;

CURRDATE
---------
13 II 91
```

Note: The applications you design may need to allow for a variable-length default date format.

You can alter the default value of NLS_DATE_FORMAT by changing its value in the initialization file and then restarting the instance, and you can alter the value during a session using an ALTER SESSION SET

NLS_DATE_FORMAT command. (See the *ORACLE7 Server SQL Language Reference Manual* for a description of the ALTER SESSION command.)

NLS_DATE_LANGUAGE Parameter

This parameter specifies the language used for the spelling of day and month names by the functions TO_CHAR and TO_DATE, overriding that specified implicitly by NLS_LANGUAGE. NLS_DATE_LANGUAGE has the same syntax as the NLS_LANGUAGE parameter, and all supported languages are valid values. For example, to specify the date language as French, the parameter should be set as follows:

```
NLS_DATE_LANGUAGE = FRENCH
```

In this case, the query

```
SELECT TO_CHAR(SYSDATE, 'Day:Dd Month yyyy')
    FROM DUAL;
```

would return:

```
Mercredi:13 Février 1991
```

Month and day name abbreviations are also in the language specified, for example:

```
Me:13 Fév 1991
```

The default date format also uses the language-specific month name abbreviations. For example, if the default date format is DD-MON-YYYY, the above date would be inserted using:

```
INSERT INTO tablename VALUES ('13-Fév-1991');
```

The abbreviations for AM, PM, AD, and BC are also returned in the language specified by NLS_DATE_LANGUAGE. Note that numbers spelled using the TO_CHAR function always use English spellings, for example:

```
SELECT TO_CHAR(TO_DATE('27-Fév-91'),'Day: ddspth Month')
   FROM DUAL;
```

would return:

```
Mercredi: twenty-seventh Février
```

You can alter the default value of NLS_DATE_LANGUAGE by changing its value in the initialization file and then restarting the instance, and you can alter the value during a session using an ALTER SESSION SET NLS_DATE_LANGUAGE command. (See the *ORACLE7 Server SQL Language Reference Manual* for a description of the ALTER SESSION command.)

NLS_NUMERIC_CHARACTERS Parameter

This parameter specifies the decimal character and grouping separator, overriding those defined implicitly by NLS_TERRITORY. The decimal character separates the integer and decimal parts of a number. The grouping separator is the character returned by the number format mask G. For example, to set the decimal character to a comma and the grouping separator to a period, the parameter should be set as follows:

```
NLS_NUMERIC_CHARACTERS = ',.'
```

Both characters are single-byte and must be different. Either can be a space.

Note: When the decimal character is not a period (.) or when a group separator is used, numbers appearing in SQL statements must be enclosed in quotes, since the comma is usually used to separate list items. For example:

```
INSERT INTO SIZES (ITEMID, WIDTH, QUANTITY)
   VALUES (618, '45,5', TO_NUMBER('1.234','9G999'));
```

You can alter the default value of NLS_NUMERIC_CHARACTERS by changing its value in the initialization file and then restarting the instance, and you can alter its value during a session using an ALTER SESSION SET NLS_DATE_LANGUAGE command. (See the *ORACLE7 Server SQL Language Reference Manual* for a description of the ALTER SESSION command.

NLS_CURRENCY Parameter

This parameter specifies the character string returned by the number format mask L, the local currency symbol, overriding that defined implicitly by NLS_TERRITORY. For example, to set the local currency symbol to 'Dfl ' (including a space), the parameter should be set as follows:

```
NLS_CURRENCY = 'Dfl '
```

In this case, the query

```
SELECT TO_CHAR(TOTAL, 'L099G999D99') "TOTAL"
   FROM ORDERS WHERE CUSTNO = 586
```

would return:

```
      TOTAL
-------------
   Dfl 12.673,49
```

You can alter the default value of NLS_CURRENCY by changing its value in the initialization file and then restarting the instance, and you can alter its value during a session using an ALTER SESSION SET

NLS_CURRENCY command. (See the *ORACLE7 Server SQL Language Reference Manual* for a description of the ALTER SESSION command.)

NLS_ISO_CURRENCY Parameter

This parameter specifies the character string returned by the number format mask C, the ISO currency symbol, overriding that defined implicitly by NLS_TERRITORY.

Local currency symbols can be ambiguous; for example, a dollar sign ($) can refer to US dollars or Australian dollars. ISO Specification 4217 1987-07-15 defines unique 'international' currency symbols for the currencies of specific territories (or countries).

For example, the ISO currency symbol for the US Dollar is USD, for the Australian Dollar AUD. To specify the ISO currency symbol, the corresponding territory name is used.

NLS_ISO_CURRENCY has the same syntax as the NLS_TERRITORY parameter, and all supported territories are valid values. For example, to specify the ISO currency symbol for France, the parameter should be set as follows:

```
NLS_ISO_CURRENCY = FRANCE
```

In this case, the query

```
SELECT TO_CHAR(TOTAL, 'C099G999D99') "TOTAL"
    FROM ORDERS WHERE CUSTNO = 586
```

would return:

```
        TOTAL
-------------
 FRF12.673,49
```

You can alter the default value of NLS_ISO_CURRENCY by changing its value in the initialization file and then restarting the instance, and you can alter its value during a session using an ALTER SESSION SET NLS_ISO_CURRENCY command. (See the *ORACLE7 Server SQL Language Reference Manual* for a description of the ALTER SESSION command.)

NLS_SORT Parameter

This parameter specifies the type of sort used for character data, overriding that defined implicitly by NLS_LANGUAGE. The syntax of NLS_SORT is:

```
NLS_SORT = { BINARY | name }
```

BINARY specifies a binary sort and *name* specifies a particular linguistic sort sequence. For example, to specify the linguistic sort sequence called German, the parameter should be set as follows:

```
NLS_SORT = German
```

IUG

The name given to a linguistic sort sequence has no direct connection to language names. In most cases, however, each supported language will have an appropriate linguistic sort sequence defined that uses the same name. Refer to your installation or user's guide to check which linguistic sort sequences are supported.

You can alter the default value of NLS_SORT by changing its value in the initialization file and then restarting the instance, and you can alter its value during a session using an ALTER SESSION SET NLS_SORT command. (See the *ORACLE7 Server SQL Language Reference Manual* for a description of the ALTER SESSION command.)

Date and Number Formats

Several format masks are provided with the TO_CHAR, TO_DATE, and TO_NUMBER functions in order to format dates and numbers according to the relevant conventions.

Note: The TO_NUMBER function also accepts a format mask.

Date Formats

A format element RM (Roman Month) returns a month as a Roman numeral. Both uppercase and lowercase can be specified, using RM and rm respectively. For example, for the date 7 Sep 1992, 'DD-rm-YY' will return '07-ix-92' and 'DD-RM-YY' will return '07-IX-92'.

Note that the MON and DY format masks explicitly support month and day abbreviations that may not be three characters in length. For example, the abbreviations 'Lu' and 'Ma' can be specified for the French 'Lundi' and 'Mardi', respectively.

Week and Day Number Conventions

The week numbers returned by the WW format mask are calculated according to the algorithm *int((day-jan1)/7)*. This week number algorithm does not follow the ISO standard (2015, 1992-06-15).

To support the ISO standard, a format element IW is provided that returns the ISO week number. In addition, format elements, I IY IYY and IYYY, equivalent in behavior to the format elements Y YY YYY YYYY, return the year relating to the ISO week number.

In the ISO standard, the year relating to an ISO week number can be different from the calendar year. For example 1st Jan 1988 is in ISO week number 53 of 1987. A week always starts on a Monday and ends on a Sunday.

- If January 1 falls on a Friday, Saturday, or Sunday, then the week including January 1 is the last week of the previous year, because most of the days in the week belong to the previous year.
- If January 1 falls on a Monday, Tuesday, Wednesday, or Thursday, then the week is the first week of the new year, because most of the days in the week belong to the new year.

For example, January 1, 1991, is a Tuesday, so Monday, December 31, 1990, to Sunday, January 6, 1991, is week 1. Thus the ISO week number and year for December 31, 1990, is 1, 1991. To get the ISO week number, use the format mask 'IW' for the week number and one of the 'IY' formats for the year. See the *ORACLE7 Server SQL Language Reference Manual* for more information on using date format masks.

Number Formats

Several additional format elements are provided for formatting numbers:

- D (Decimal) returns the decimal character
- G (Group) returns the group separator
- L (Local currency) returns the local currency symbol
- C (international Currency) returns the international currency symbol
- RN (Roman Numeral) returns the number as its Roman numeral equivalent

For Roman numerals, both uppercase and lowercase can be specified, using RN and rn, respectively. The number to be converted must be an integer in the range 1 to 3999.

APPENDIX

D DATABASE LIMITS

This appendix lists the limits of values associated with various database functions and objects.

Limits exist on several levels in the database. There is usually a hard-coded limit in the database that cannot be exceeded. The value may be further restricted for any given operating system. You must refer to your installation or user's guide to determine the maximum value of such limits.

You can also set limits when you create a database. These limits are recorded in the control file and cannot be overridden during the life of the database. Next, you can set limits for the duration of an instance with initialization parameters. These parameters temporarily override the database limits of the control file.

For example, the maximum number of database files allowed by the ORACLE Server can be reduced for a particular database by specifying a lower value for the MAXDATAFILES option of the CREATE DATABASE command. This limit is then recorded in the control file and cannot be exceeded for the life of that database. You can alter the value of the initialization parameter DB_FILES to a value less than MAXDATAFILES for a particular instance. The maximum number of database files is then limited to the number specified by DB_FILES for the life of that instance.

Item	*type*	*Limit*
blocks (ORACLE)	minimum in initial extent	2 blocks minimum (automatically enforced)
blocks (ORACLE)	maximum	2**32-1 (up to 4 terabytes, depending on block size)
characters	CHAR column	255 characters maximum
	index	no absolute limit, but a function of block size
		LONG column 2^{31} - 1 characters (2 gigabytes) maximum
		VARCHAR2 column 2000 characters maximum
columns	index (or cluster index)	16 columns maximum
	table	254 columns maximum
	expression list	254 columns maximum
	view definition	254 columns maximum
(LONG)	table	1 LONG column per table
constraints	CHECK (on columns)	unlimited
context area	size	no absolute limit (1024 is the minimum initial extent size)
control files	number of	one minimum: 2 or more strongly recommended on separate devices
control file	size	typically 50..200Kb, depending on database creation options; maximum is O/S-dependent
database file size	minimum	no absolute limit except for first file whose minimum size is 2 MB
	maximum	O/S dependent, typically 16 million ORACLE blocks

Item	*type*	*Limit*
database files	system	1022 or value of DB_FILES in INIT.ORA, or limited by value of MAXDATAFILES in CREATE DATABASE. Less on some operating systems.
GROUP BY clause	maximum size	number of bytes limited to one ORACLE block, less O/S-dependent block overhead, less 2-bytes per group-by expression, less one of the following: 2 bytes plus size of each aggregate of a non-distinct value Example: COUNT(DISTINCT(x)) *or* two bytes plus size in bytes of the longest aggregate of a *distinct* value Example: COUNT(x)
indexes	table	no limit
instances	parallel server	O/S dependent, subject to ORACLE limit of 255
literals	character string number (+ or -)	255 characters 1.0×10^{-130} to 1.0×10^{125}
locks	transaction distributed	no limit O/S dependent
MAXEXTENTS		O/S dependent
nested queries		255 queries
NUMBER	maximum value	1.0×10^{125}
precision		up to 38 significant digits per numeric value

Item	*type*	*Limit*
redo log files	database	255 or value for LOG_FILES in INIT.ORA, or by MAXLOGFILES in CREATE DATABASE. Ultimately, an operating system limit.
redo log file size	minimum	50 Kbytes
rollback segments	database	no limit
rows	table	no limit
SGA size	maximum	no limit
SQL statement length		64 K maximum length; particular tools may have lower limits
stored packages	size	SQL*FORMS may have limits on the size of stored procedures you can call. Consult your SQL*Forms documentation for details.
tablespaces	database	no limit
tables	cluster database	32 no limit
trigger cascade limit	maximum	32 larger values O/S–dependent

APPENDIX

E

OPERATING SYSTEM SPECIFIC INFORMATION

This Guide occasionally refers to other ORACLE manuals that contain detailed information for using ORACLE on a specific operating system. These ORACLE manuals are often called *installation or user's guides*, although the exact name may vary on different operating systems. Throughout this guide, references to these manuals are marked with the icon shown in the left margin.

This appendix lists all the references in this guide to operating system specific ORACLE manuals, and lists the operating system (OS) dependent initialization parameters. If you are using ORACLE on multiple operating systems, this appendix can help you ensure that your applications are portable across these operating systems.

Operating system specific topics are listed alphabetically, with page numbers of sections that discuss these topics.

Topic	Page

Topic	Page
Initialization parameters	
BACKGROUND_DUMP_DEST	A-9
COMMIT_POINT_STRENGTH	15-15, A-10
CONTROL_FILES	2-6, A-11
DB_BLOCK_SIZE	A-14
DB_FILES	A-15
DB_FILE_MULTIBLOCK_READ_COUNT	A-15
DB_FILE_SIMULTANEOUS_WRITES	A-16
DISTRIBUTED_TRANSACTIONS	A-19
INIT_SQL_FILES	2-13, A-22
INSTANCE_NUMBER	A-22
LOG_ARCHIVE_BUFFER_SIZE	A-24
LOG_ARCHIVE_BUFFERS	A-25
LOG_ARCHIVE_DEST	17-12, A-25
LOG_ARCHIVE_FORMAT	17-12, A-26
LOG_BUFFER	A-27
LOG_CHECKPOINT_INTERVAL	A-27
LOG_SMALL_ENTRY_MAX_SIZE	23-10, A-29
MTS_MAX_DISPATCHERS (maximum value)	23-6, A-31
MTS_MAX_SERVERS (maximum value)	23-8, A-32
MTS_SERVERS	A-32
NLS_LANGUAGE	A-34, A-34, C-5, C-6
NLS_TERRITORY	A-36, C-6
OPEN_CURSORS (value, maximum value)	21-6, A-37
OS_AUTHENT_PREFIX (value, case sensitivity)	7-5, A-38
PROCESSES	A-39
SHARED_POOL_SIZE (value, maximum value)	21-10, 21-15, A-44
SMALL_TABLE_THRESHOLD	A-44
SORT_AREA_SIZE	24-2, A-45
SORT_SPACEMAP_SIZE	A-46
TEMPORARY_TABLE_LOCKS	A-47
TRANSACTIONS_PER_ROLLBACK_SEGMENT	A-48
USER_DUMP_DEST	A-49

INDEX

A

B

C

D

E

F

G

H

I

K

L

M

N

O

P

Q

R

S

T

U

V

W

X

Reader's Comment Form

ORACLE7 Server Administrator's Guide
Part No. 6694-70-1292
December 1992

Oracle Corporation welcomes your comments and suggestions on the quality and usefulness of this publication. Your input is an important part of the information used for revision.

- Did you find any errors?
- Is the information clearly presented?
- Do you need more information? If so, where?
- Are the examples correct? Do you need more examples?
- What features did you like most about this manual?

If you find any errors or have any suggestions for improvement, please indicate the topic, chapter, and page number below:

____

____

____

____

____

____

Please send your comments to:

ORACLE7 Server Documentation Manager
Oracle Corporation
500 Oracle Parkway
Redwood Shores, CA 94065
(415) 506-7000

FAX: (415) 506-7200

If you would like a reply, please give your name, address, and telephone number below:

____

____

____

Thank you for helping us improve our documentation.

TABLE B. Sex and Sex-condition Terminology for Several Livestock and Poultry Species

	Female		Uncastrated Male		Castrated Male	
Species	Young[a]	Mature[b]	Young[a]	Mature[b]	Young[a]	Mature[b]
Cattle	Heifer[c]	Cow	Bull[c]	Bull	Steer	Stag
Chicken	Chick or Pullet	Hen	Chick or Cockerel	Cock/rooster	Capon	—
Goat	Doe	Doe	Buck	Buck	Wether	—
Horse[d]	Filly	Mare	Colt[e]	Stallion	Gelding	—
Sheep	Ewe[f]	Ewe	Ram[f]	Ram/buck	Wether	Stag
Swine	Gilt	Sow	Boar[g]	Boar	Barrow	Stag
Turkey	Young hen or Poult[h]	Hen	Young tom or Poult[h]	Tom	—	—

[a] *Young:* generally prior to puberty or sexual maturity and before the development of secondary sex characteristics.
[b] *Mature:* generally after puberty and before the development of secondary sex characteristics.
[c] Referred to as a *bull calf* (under 1 year of age); *heifer* can be a heifer calf, yearling heifer, or first calf heifer (after the first calf is born and prior to the birth of the second calf).
[d] A close relative of the horse is the *donkey,* also known as an *ass* or a *burro.* The male ass is referred to as a *jack;* the female is known as a *jennet.* A *mule* is produced by crossing a *jackass* with a mare. A *hinny* is produced by crossing a stallion with a jennet. Mules and hinnys are reproductively sterile, although their visual sexual characteristics appear to be normal.
[e] Under 3 years of age.
[f] Referred to as a *ewe lamb* or a *ram lamb* (under 1 year of age).
[g] Referred to as a *boar pig* (under 6 months of age).
[h] Under 10 weeks of age. Chicks or poults are newly hatched or a few days old.

SCIENTIFIC FARM ANIMAL PRODUCTION

FOURTH EDITION

SCIENTIFIC FARM ANIMAL PRODUCTION

AN INTRODUCTION TO ANIMAL SCIENCE

ROBERT E. TAYLOR

Department of Animal Sciences
Colorado State University
Fort Collins, Colorado

MACMILLAN PUBLISHING COMPANY
New York

MAXWELL MACMILLAN CANADA, INC.
Toronto

MAXWELL MACMILLAN INTERNATIONAL
New York Oxford Singapore Sydney

Editor: Paul Corey
Production Supervisor: Helen Wallace
Production Manager: Paul Smolenski
Text Designer: Blake Logan
Cover Designer: Blake Logan

This book was set in Palatino by Progressive Typographers, Inc., and was printed and bound by Arcata Graphics Halliday. The cover was printed by Phoenix Color Corp.

Printed in the United States of America

Macmillan Publishing Company
866 Third Avenue, New York, New York 10022

Macmillan Publishing Company is
part of the Maxwell Communication
Group of companies.

Maxwell Macmillan Canada, Inc.
1200 Eglinton Avenue East
Suite 200
Don Mills, Ontario M3C 3N1

Library of Congress Cataloging-in-Publication Data

Taylor, Robert E. (Robert Ellis) (date)
Scientific farm animal production : an introduction to animal science.—4th ed. / Robert E. Taylor.
p. cm.
Includes index.
ISBN 0-02-419280-5
1. Livestock. I. Title.
SF61.T39 1991
636—dc20 91-11415
CIP

Printing: 2 3 4 5 6 7 8 9 Year: 2 3 4 5 6 7 8 9 0 1

DEDICATION

This book is dedicated to the hundreds of students the author has taught. The positive and rewarding interactions with these students have provided the stimulus to write this book. Hopefully, the reading and studying of *Scientific Farm Animal Production* will be a motivational influence to current and future students as they seek to enhance their education.

PREFACE

Scientific Farm Animal Production is distinguished by an appropriate combination of both breadth and depth of livestock and poultry production and their respective industries. The book gives an overview of the biological principles applicable to the Animal Sciences with chapters on reproduction, genetics, nutrition, lactation, end products, and others. The book also covers the breeding, feeding and management of beef cattle, dairy cattle, horses, sheep, swine, poultry, and goats. Although books have been written on each of these separate chapters, the author has highlighted the significant biological principles, scientific relationships, and management practices in a condensed but informative manner.

TARGET AUDIENCE

This book is designed as a text for the introductory Animal Science course typically taught at universities and junior or community colleges. It is also a valuable reference book for livestock producers, vocational agriculture instructors, and others desiring an overview of livestock production principles and management. The book is basic and sufficiently simple for the urban student with limited livestock experience, yet challenging for the student who has a livestock production background.

The book is designed to accommodate several instructional approaches to teaching the introductory course: (1) the life-cycle biological principles approach, including such areas as end products, reproduction, breeding, nutrition, and animal health; (2) the species approach (teaching the course primarily by the various species); or (3) a combination of the previous two. The latter appears to be the most popular teaching approach by covering principles in lecture and combining principles and species into laboratory exercises.

KEY FEATURES

Chapters 1–9 cover animal products, Chapters 10–21 discuss the biological principles while livestock and poultry management practices are presented in Chapters 22–33.

The glossary of the terms, used throughout the book, has been expanded so students can readily become familiar with animal science terminology. The bold lettered words in the text are included in the glossary.

Many illustrations in the form of photographs and line drawings are used throughout the book to communicate key points and major relationships. If "a picture is worth a thousand words", the numerous photographs and drawings expand the usefulness of the book beyond its 590 pages.

Selected references are provided for each chapter to direct students into greater depth and breadth as they become intrigued with certain topics. Instructors can also use the references to expand their knowledge in current background material. Also included in the selected references section are references to visuals that relate to the specific chapter. Instructors are encouraged to review these visuals and use those which will enrich their course.

CHANGES IN THIS EDITION

This book has been updated with current technical and applied information. A new chapter (Overview of the Livestock and Poultry Industries) has been included which gives both a global and U. S. perspective. A section on biotechnology has been added to the genetics chapter. Several sections of the genetics chapter have been simplified. The chapter on Animal Welfare and Animal Rights has been expanded.

A "costs and returns" section has been added to the management section in most species chapters. Enterprise budgets and analyses have been included and emphasized as a critical ingredient in the management decision process. The management emphasis follows current industry trends where bioeconomics focuses on combining biology with economics.

ACKNOWLEDGMENTS

Appreciation is expressed to those individuals and organizations who have reviewed all or part of the third and fourth editions and offered suggestions for the revision. The following individuals and organizations made a major contribution to the fourth edition: R. L. Belyea (University of Missouri); J. W. Edwards (Texas A&M University); Tom Field (Colorado State University); G. S. Gieger (University of Missouri); Dave Hawkins (Michigan State University); Michael Howard (Morehead State University); G. W. Jesse (University of Missouri); M. D. Kenealy (Iowa State University); D. H. Keisler (University of Missouri); Steve Kopperud (Animal Industry Foundation); Steve LeValley (Colorado State University); D. Lincicome (USDA); W. E. Loch (University of Missouri); H. W. Miller (Mississippi State University); Mark Morando (Washington State University); R. E. Morrow (University of Missouri); R. G. Mortimer (Colorado State University); K. G. Odde (Colorado State University); Paul Sammelwitz (University of Delaware); S. P. Schmidt (Auburn University); Turkey Foundation; Paul Walker (Illinois State University); Jeffrey A. Wood (Illinois State University); F. W. Williams, Jr. (USDA). And last but not least, thanks to Shirley Mitchell, who typed the fourth edition.

ABOUT THE AUTHOR

Dr. Taylor was raised on an Idaho livestock operation where several livestock species were produced. He received a B. S. degree in animal husbandry and a Master's degree in animal production from Utah State University. This background, combined with his Ph.D. work in animal breeding and physiology from Oklahoma State University, has provided much depth to his knowledge of livestock production. He has had practical production experience with beef cattle, dairy cattle, horses, poultry, sheep, and swine.

Dr. Taylor received teaching awards at Iowa State University (where he also managed a swine herd) and at Colorado State University. He also received the Distinguished Teaching Award from the American Society of Animal Science in recognition of his ability to organize and present materials to students. Many of his concepts for effective teaching are used in this book.

CONTENTS

CHAPTER 1

Animal Contributions to Human Needs

Our basic human needs are food, shelter, clothing, fuel, and emotional well-being. Animals and animal products supply many of these basic needs and contribute to a high standard of living associated with a high consumption of animal products.

Since the domestication of dogs, horses, cattle, and sheep, some 6,000 to 10,000 years ago, wide differences have developed among people in various regions of the world in using agricultural technology to improve their standard of living. But in all societies, domestic animals are a source of food, other commercial products, and companionship for people.

Of particular importance among the multitude of benefits that domestic animals provide for humans are food; clothing; slaughter by-products used for various chemical purposes and animal feeds; power; manure for fuel (Fig. 1.1), buildings, and fertilizer; information on human disease through studies of experimental animals; and pleasure for those who keep animals. Table 1.1 shows the major domesticated animal species, their approximate numbers, and how they are used by people throughout the world. Chickens (10.5 billion) are most numerous, followed by cattle (1.3 billion), sheep (1.2 billion), and swine (846 million).

CONTRIBUTIONS TO FOOD NEEDS

When opportunity exists, most humans consume both plant and animal products (Fig. 1.2). Meat is nearly always consumed in quantity when it is available. Its availability in most countries is closely related to the economic status of the people and their agricultural technology. Vegetarianism in countries such as India may be the long-term result of intense population pressures and scarcity of feed for animals because of competition between humans and animals for food. Rising population pressures, particularly in developing regions (Southeast Asia, Africa, and Latin America), force people to consume foods primarily of plant origin. Some major groups in human society practice vegetarianism for ethical reasons. In the Buddhist philosophy and some religions of India, for example, all animal life is considered sacred.

The development of vegetarianism in England and in the United States was closely linked to temperance movements and to conservative attitudes toward sexuality. Vegetarianism was

FIGURE 1.1.
A load of cow-dung cakes en route to a market in India. Courtesy of R. E. McDowell, Cornell University.

thought to cool "animal passions." It has never been practiced to a large extent in the United States. The vegetarian movement in this country developed in the nineteenth century and was based on the view that eating only plant products was healthier than including meat in the diet. However, some medical surveys of vegetarians have shown evidence of anemia and poor health.

The contribution of animal products to the per-capita calorie and protein supply in food is shown in Table 1.2. Animal products comprise approximately 16% of the calories and 34% of the protein in the total world food supply. Large differences exist between developed countries and developing countries in both total daily supply of calories (3,398 vs. 2,434) and protein (103

FIGURE 1.2.
Animal food products, such as meat, milk, and eggs, are the preferred foods in countries with high standards of living. Courtesy of the American Egg Board.

TABLE 1.1. Major Domesticated Animal Species—Their Numbers and Uses in the World

Animal Species	World Numbers (mil)	Leading Countries or Areas with Numbers[a] (mil)	Primary Uses
Ruminants			
Cattle	1,282	India (195), Brazil (137), USSR (120), United States (99), China (77)	Meat, milk, hides
Sheep	1,176	Australia (152), USSR (140), China (102), New Zealand (61), United States (11)	Wool, meat, milk, hides
Goats	526	India (107), China (79), Pakistan (34), Nigeria (26), United States (1.8)	Milk, meat, hair, hides
Buffalo	140	India (74), China (22), Pakistan (14), Thailand (5)	Draft, milk, meat, hides, bones
Camel	19	Somalia (6.7), Sudan (2.9), India (1.4), Ethiopia (1.1)	Packing, riding, draft, meat, milk, hides
Yak	13	USSR,[b] Tibet[b]	Packing, riding, draft, meat, milk, hides
Llama	13	South America[b]	Packing, riding, draft, meat, milk, hides
Nonruminants			
Chickens	10,584	China (1,981), USSR (1,160), United States (1,550), Brazil (600)	Meat, eggs, feathers
Swine	846	China (349), USSR (78), United States (55), Germany (36)	Meat
Turkeys	234	United States (75), USSR (47), Italy (23)	Meat, eggs, feathers
Ducks	527	China (333), Bangladesh (33), Indonesia (29), Vietnam (24), United States (7)	Meat, eggs, feathers
Horses	60	China (11), Mexico (6), USSR (6), Brazil (6), United States (5)	Draft, packing, riding, meat, companion animals
Asses	43	China (11), Ethiopa (5), Mexico (3) United States (0.028)	Draft, packing, riding, meat, companion animals
Mules	15	China (5.4), Mexico (3.2), Brazil (2), United States (0.024)	Draft, packing, riding, meat, companion animals

[a] U.S. numbers are given for comparison; may not always be among the leading countries.
[b] Data not available.
Source: Adapted from several sources, including the 1989 *FAO Production Yearbook.*

vs. 59 g). The comparison of developed and developing countries for the contribution of animal products in calories is 30% versus 9%, respectively, and the comparison for protein is 57% versus 22%.

Table 1.2 also shows calorie and protein data for selected countries in both developed and developing market economies. It is interesting to compare countries that have larger and smaller contributions of calories and protein from animal products to total calories (Iceland and Denmark vs. Nigeria and Bangladesh) and to total protein (Iceland vs. India and China). The United

TABLE 1.2. Animal Product Contribution to Per-capita Calorie and Protein Supply (selected countries (1986–88)

	Per-capita Calorie Supply (calories per day)			Per-capita Protein Supply		
		From Animal Products			From Animal Products	
Country	Total Calories	Calories	Percent	Total Protein (g)	Grams	Percent
Developed Market Economies						
United States	3,644	1,234	34%	109	72	66%
United Kingdom	3,259	1,109	34	89	54	61
Germany	3,855	1,405	36	105	70	67
Canada	3,451	1,125	33	99	61	62
Australia	3,347	1,169	35	100	65	65
Denmark	3,605	1,625	45	100	65	65
Israel	3,133	646	21	98	52	53
Japan	2,822	575	20	90	48	53
Iceland	3,361	1,445	43	136	101	74
USSR	3,382	918	27	106	55	52
Poland	3,434	1,184	34	102	57	56
Developing Market Economies						
Mexico	3,123	514	16	81	30	37
Brazil	2,703	405	15	62	24	39
Egypt	3,196	201	6	79	11	14
Turkey	3,084	279	9	84	18	21
Nigeria	2,083	39	2	46	4	9
China	2,637	258	10	64	12	19
India	2,104	140	7	51	7	14
Kenya	2,016	226	11	56	14	25
Bangladesh	1,925	59	3	41	5	12
All Developed Countries	3,398	1,028	30	103	59	57
All Developing Countries	2,434	220	9	59	13	22
World Total	2,671	419	16	70	24	34

Source: 1989 *FAO Production Yearbook.*

States ranks high compared to other countries in the contribution of animal products to the available calories and protein.

Selected recommended daily intakes (recommended daily allowance) of calories and protein are given in Table 1.3. Although the data in Table 1.3 do not represent an average of the U.S.

TABLE 1.3. Recommended Daily Caloric and Protein Intake for Selected Males and Females in the United States

Sex	Age (years)	Weight (lb)	Height	Average Daily Calories	Protein (g/day)
Female	23–50	120	5 ft 4 in.	2,000	44
Male	23–50	155	5 ft 10 in.	2,700	56

population, a comparison of these data with those in Table 1.2 is interesting. Some countries have a larger supply of calories and protein than needed, whereas other countries have an inadequate calorie and protein supply. This assumes an equal distribution of the available supply, which in reality does not occur.

The large differences among countries in the importance of animal products in their food supply can be partially explained by available resources and development of those resources. Most countries with only a small percentage of their population involved in agriculture have higher standards of living and a higher per-capita consumption of animal products. Comparing Table 1.4 with Table 1.2, note that the countries in Table 1.4 are listed by percentage of their population involved in agriculture. The countries in Table 1.2 are listed in the same order as in Table 1.4.

TABLE 1.4. Population Involved in Agriculture in Selected Countries (countries ranked by percent of population in agriculture)

Country	1989 Population (mil)	1989 Population in Agriculture[a] (mil)	Percent of Population Economically Active in Agriculture (1989)[b]	Number of Tractors (1988) (thou)
Developed Market Economies				
United States	248	7	2%	4,670
United Kingdom	57	1	2	518
Canada	26	1	4	756
Germany	62	2	4	1,460
Israel	4	0.2	4	24
Australia	17	1	5	332
Denmark	5	0.2	5	168
Japan	123	8	7	1,985
Iceland	0.3	0.02	7	13
Ireland	4	0.5	14	164
USSR	289	39	14	2,692
Poland	38	7	22	1,101
Developing Market Economies				
Mexico	87	26	31	165
Egypt	53	22	41	46
Turkey	55	25	49	655
Nigeria	109	71	65	11
India	836	528	67	750
Bangladesh	113	78	69	5
China	1,117	761	68	876
Kenya	24	19	77	9
Nepal	19	17	92	3
All Developed Countries	1,243	106	9	21,005
All Developing Countries	3,962	2,262	60	4,806
World Total	5,205	2,368	47	25,865

[a] *Agricultural population* is defined as all persons depending for their livelihood on agriculture. This comprises all persons actively engaged in agriculture and their nonworking dependents.
[b] Includes all economically active persons engaged principally in agriculture, forestry, hunting, or fishing.
Source: 1989 *FAO Production Yearbook.*

TABLE 1.5. Persons Supplied by One Farm Worker in the United States and the Percent of Income Spent on Food

Year	No. Persons Supplied Per Farm Worker	Percent of Personal Disposable Income Spent on Food
1820	4	—
1850	4	—
1880	6	—
1910	7	—
1940	11	—
1950	16	30.0
1960	26	20.2
1970	48	17.3
1980	76	16.6
1985	78	14.7
1990	80	11.8

Source: USDA.

Developed countries have approximately 9% of their population economically active in agriculture, whereas more than 60% of the population in developing countries are involved in agriculture (Table 1.4). Agriculture mechanization (note tractor numbers in Table 1.4) has been largely responsible for increased food production and allowing many people to work in other industries. This facilitates the provision of many goods and services and thus raises the standard of living in a country.

The tremendous increase in the productivity of U.S. agriculture and the relative cost of food are vividly demonstrated in Table 1.5. From 1820 it took 100 years to double productivity. Then productivity doubled in shorter, successive time periods—30 years (1920–50), 15 years (1950–65), and 10 years (1965–75). A dramatic change occurred after World War II, when productivity increased more than fivefold in 30 years. During that time, the abundant production of feed grains provided a marked stimulus in increasing livestock production, thus providing large amounts of animal products for the human population.

TABLE 1.6. Amount of Food Purchased by an Hour's Pay (average U.S. worker)

Food Item	1950	1970	1980	1989
Frying chicken (lb)	2.3	7.9	9.4	10.7
Milk (half gal)	3.5	9.0	11.6	7.6
Eggs (doz)	2.2	5.3	7.9	9.7
Pork (lb)	2.5	4.2	4.8	5.3
White bread (lb)	9.3	13.3	13.1	14.4
Ground beef (lb)	2.4	5.0	4.2	6.7

NOTE: Average hourly pay: $1.34 (1950), $3.23 (1970), $6.66 (1980), and $9.66 (1989).
Source: USDA.

Releasing people from producing their own food in the United States has given them the opportunity to improve their per-capita incomes. The increased per-capita income associated with an abundance of animal products has resulted in a decrease in relative costs of some animal products with time (Table 1.6).

U.S. consumers allocate a smaller share (12%) of their disposable income for food than people in other countries. In contrast, people of India and China spend 55–65% of their incomes for food.

Table 1.7 shows that cereal grains are the most important source of energy in world diets. The energy derived from cereal grains, however, is twice as important in developing countries (as a group; there are exceptions) as in developed countries. Table 1.7 also shows that meat and milk are the major animal products contributing to the world supply of calories and protein.

Most of the world meat supply comes from cattle, buffalo, swine, sheep, goats, and horses. There are, however, 20 or more additional species, unfamiliar to most Americans, that collectively contribute about 6.5 billion lb of edible protein per year or approximately 10% of the estimated total protein from all meats. These include the alpaca, llama, yak, deer, elk, antelope, kangaroo, rabbit, guinea pig, capybara, fowl other than chicken (duck, turkey, goose, guinea fowl, pigeon), and wild game exclusive of birds. For example, the Soviet Union cans more than 110 million lb of reindeer meat per year, and in West Germany the annual sales of local venison exceed $1 million. Peru derives more than 5% of its meat from the guinea pig.

Meat is important as a food for two scientifically based reasons. The first is that the assortment of amino acids in animal protein more closely matches the needs of the human body than does the assortment of amino acids in plant protein. The second is that vitamin B_{12}, which is required in human nutrition, may be obtained in adequate quantities from consumption of meat or other animal products but not from consumption of plants.

Milk is one of the largest single sources of food from animals. In the United States, 99% of the milk comes from cattle, but on a worldwide basis, milk from other species is important, too; the domestic buffalo, sheep, goat, alpaca, camel, reindeer, and yak supply significant amounts of milk in certain countries. Milk and products made from milk contribute protein, energy, vitamins, and minerals for humans.

TABLE 1.7. Contributions of Various Food Groups to the World Food Supply

Food Group	Calories (%)	Protein (%)
Cereals	49%	43%
Roots, tubers, pulses	10	10
Nuts, oils, vegetable fats	8	4
Sugar and sugar products	9	2
Vegetables and fruits	8	7
All animal products	16	34
Meat	(7)	(15)
Eggs	(1)	(2)
Fish	(1)	(5)
Milk	(5)	(11)
Other	(2)	(1)

Source: Adapted from several FAO World Food Surveys.

Besides the nutritional advantages, a major reason for human use of animals for food is that most countries have land areas unsuitable for growing cultivated crops. Approximately two-thirds of the world's agricultural land is permanent pasture, range, and meadow; of this, about 60% is unsuitable for producing cultivated crops that would be consumed directly by humans. This land, however, can produce feed in the form of grass and other vegetation that is digestible by grazing ruminant animals, the most important of which are cattle and sheep (Fig. 1.3). These animals can harvest and convert the vegetation, which is for the most part undigestible by humans, to high-quality protein food. In the United States, about 385 million acres of range land and forest, representing 44% of the total land area, are used for grazing. Although this

FIGURE 1.3.
Animals produce food for humans by utilizing grass, crop residues, and other forages from land that cannot produce crops to be consumed directly by humans. (A) Sheep grazing a steep hillside. Courtesy of *California Agriculture Magazine*, University of California. (B) Cattle grazing a mountain valley in Switzerland. Courtesy of the American Simmental Association. (C) Cattle produce meat from the mountains and Plains areas of the western United States. Courtesy of the American Simmental Association. (D) Sheep utilizing the crop residue remaining after harvesting the corn grain. Courtesy of Winrock International.

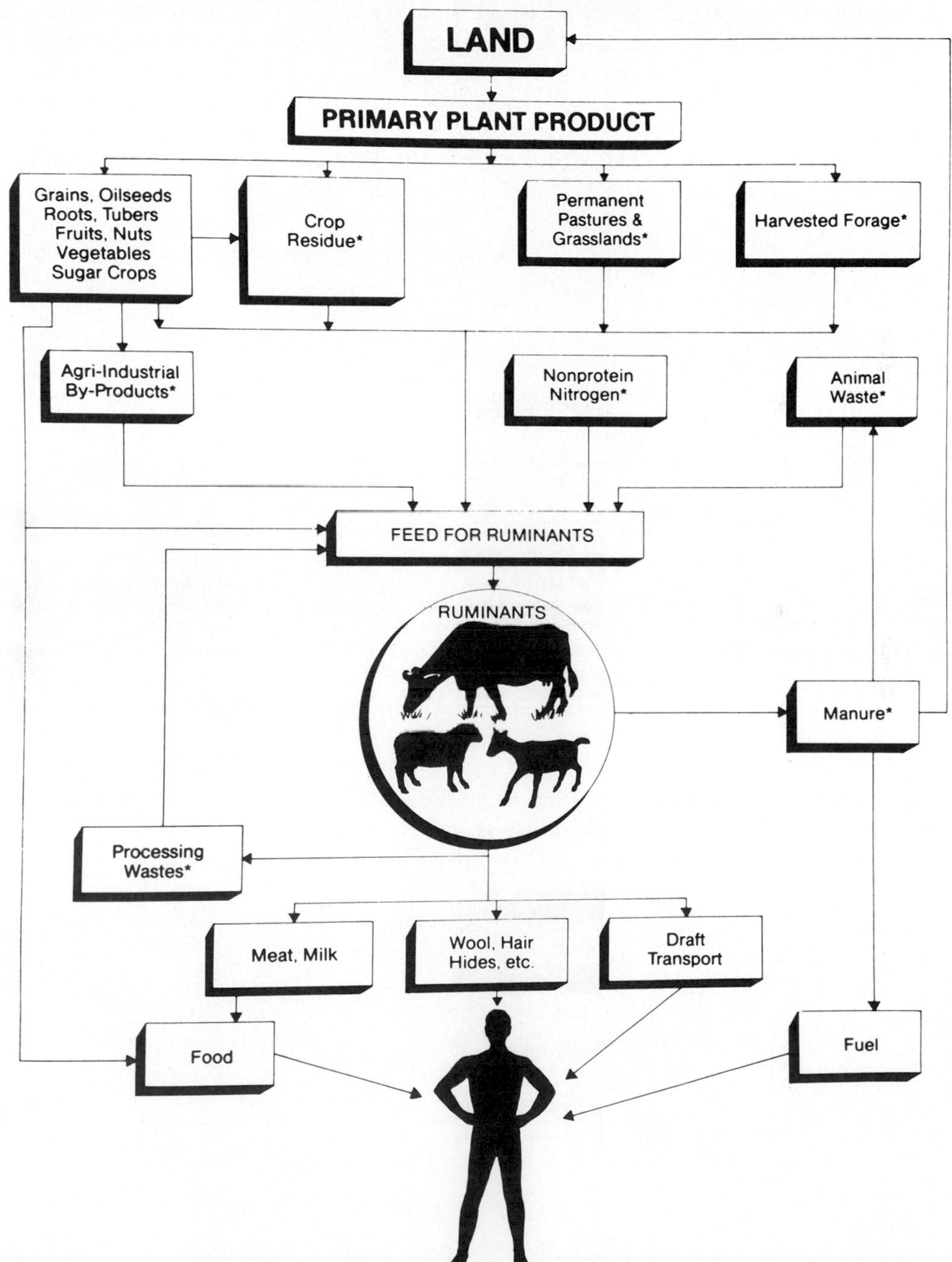

FIGURE 1.4.
A graphic illustration of the land-plant-ruminant-animal-human relationship. Products marked with an asterisk (*) are not normally consumed by humans, but ruminants convert many of these products into useful products for humans. Courtesy of Winrock International.

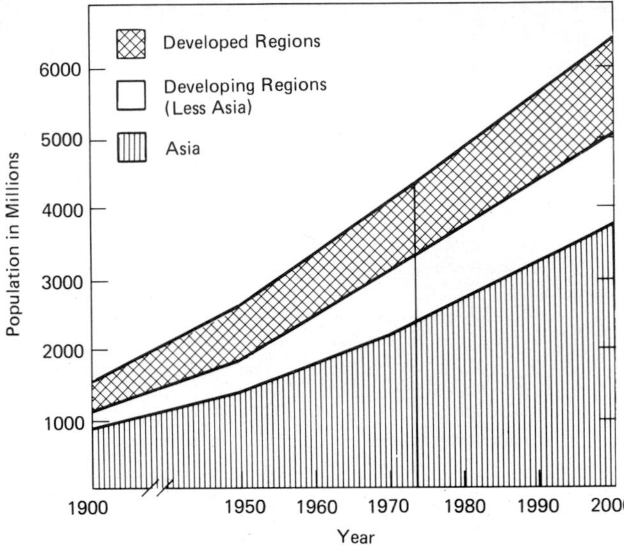

FIGURE 1.5.
Past, present, and projected world population, 1900–2000.

acreage now supports only about 40% of the total cattle population, it could carry twice this amount if developed and managed intensively.

Animal agriculture therefore does not compete with human use for production of most land used as permanent pasture, range, and meadow. On the contrary, the use of animals as intermediaries provides a means by which land that is otherwise unproductive for humans can be made productive (Fig. 1.4).

People today are concerned about energy, protein, population pressures (Fig. 1.5), and land resources as they relate to animal agriculture. Quantities of energy and protein present in foods

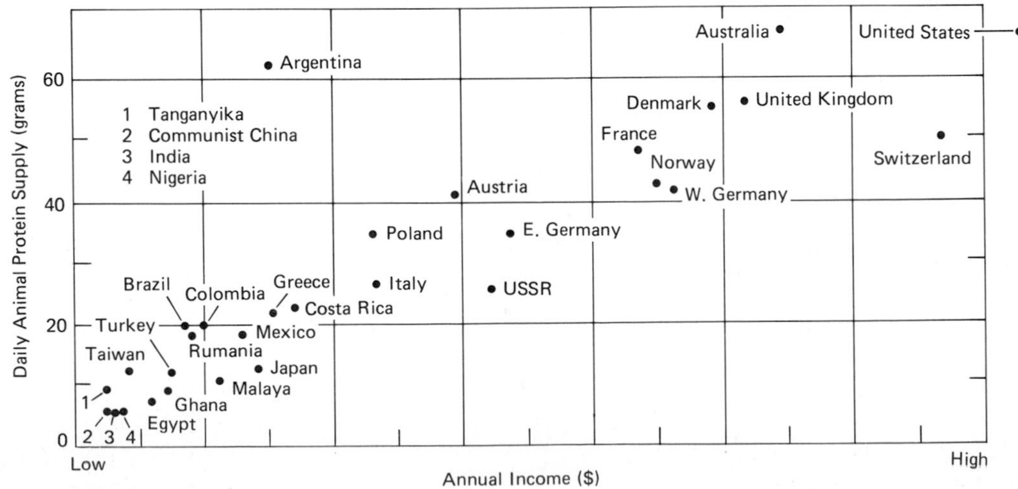

FIGURE 1.6.
Income and supply of animal protein (per person) in selected countries. Courtesy of the USDA.

from animals are smaller than quantities consumed by animals in their feed because animals are inefficient in the ratio of nutrients used to nutrients produced. More acres of cropland are required per person for a diet high in foods from animals than for a diet including only plant products. As a consequence, animal agriculture has been criticized for wasting food and land resources that could otherwise be used to provide persons with a adequate diets. Consideration must be given to economic systems and consumer preferences to understand why agriculture perpetuates what critics perceive as resource-inefficient practices. These practices relate primarily to providing food-producing animals with feed that could be eaten by humans and using land resources to produce crops specifically for animals instead of producing crops that could be consumed by humans.

Hunger does exist, of course. It affects, in varying degrees, nearly 1 billion people in the world. This is almost 25% of the world's population, most of them in developing countries. However, hunger is being reduced, and the potential exists to make even more improvement. The book *Ending Hunger: An Idea Whose Time Has Come* states:

> Since 1900, seventy-five countries have ended hunger within their borders as a basic, society-wide issue. It is both important and heartening to note that there is no single prescribed way to achieve the end of the persistence of hunger in a society. Some countries focused on land reform, while others emphasized food subsidies, collectivized agriculture, or privately owned "family farms." For every country that saw a particular action as crucial to ending hunger, there is a country that ended hunger without it.

Ending Hunger quotes the National Academy of Sciences in its World Food and Nutrition Study, for which 1,500 scientists had been consulted: "If there is the political will in this country and abroad . . . it should be possible to overcome the worst aspects of widespread hunger and malnutrition within one generation."

Agriculture producers produce what consumers want to eat as reflected in the prices consumers can and are willing to pay. Eighty-five percent of the world's population desires food of animal origin in its diets, perhaps because foods of animal origin are considered more palatable than foods from plants. In more countries, as per-capita income rises, consumers tend to increase their consumption of meat and animal products, which are generally more expensive pound for pound than products derived from cereal grains (Fig. 1.6). Table 1.8 shows some comparative food prices for selected world capitals. The total of all food items varies from a low of $33.82 for Mexico City to a high of $107.23 for Stockholm. Even though total prices are highest for Stockholm and Tokyo, these cities devote a smaller percentage of their weekly income for food compared to Buenos Aires and Mexico City.

Sirloin steak is the food item showing the widest price range—$1.07/lb in Buenos Aires versus $20.75/lb in Tokyo. Several factors besides supply and demand are reflected in the differences in these prices.

If many consumers in countries where animal products are consumed at a high rate were to decide to eat only food of plant origin, consumption and price of foods from plants would increase, and consumption and price of foods from animals would decrease. Agriculture would then adjust to produce greater quantities of food from plants and lesser quantities of food from animals. Ruminant animals can produce large amounts of meat without grain feeding. The amount of grain feeding in the future will be determined by cost of grain and the price consumers are willing to pay for meat.

Some people in the United States advocate shifting from the consumption of foods from

TABLE 1.8. Average Retail Food Prices in Selected World Capitals, May 1990 (in $ U.S., converted at exchange rates for date shown)

Item	Buenos Aires	Mexico City	Paris
Steak, sirloin, boneless, (lb)	$ 1.07	$ 2.17	$ 6.57
Roast, pork, boneless (lb)	2.32	3.00	3.29
Broilers, whole (lb)	0.70	0.45	2.95
Eggs, large (doz)	0.90	0.71	2.79
Butter (lb)	1.96	1.27	2.73
Cheese, cheddar (lb)	3.56	2.75	4.38
Milk, whole (qt)	0.61	0.39	1.00
Total, animal products	11.12	10.74	23.71
Total, market basket, May 1990[a]	36.02	33.82	68.66
Average weekly income	35.00	44.00	326.00

[a] Also includes potatoes, apples, oranges, flour, rice, sugar, coffee, and cooking oil.
Source: USDA, FAS, *Agricultural Trade Highlights.*

animals to foods from plants. They see this primarily as a moral issue, believing it is unethical to let people elsewhere in the world starve when our own food needs could be met by eating foods from plants rather than feeding plants to animals. The balance of plant-derived foods could then be sent abroad. These people believe that grain can be shipped with comparative ease because a surplus of grain exists in the United States and because any surplus we have should be

TABLE 1.9. Improvement in Efficiency of Producing Foods of Animal Origin in the United States

Species and Measure of Productivity	1925 Value	1950 Value	1975 Value	1990 Value
Beef cattle				
Liveweight marketed per breeding female (lb)	220	310	482	524
Sheep				
Liveweight marketed per breeding female (lb)	60	90	130	145
Dairy cattle				
Milk marketed per breeding female (lb)	4,189	5,313	10,500	14,000
Swine				
Liveweight marketed per breeding female (lb)	1,600	2,430	2,850	3,500
Broiler chickens				
Age to market weight (weeks)	15.0	12.0	7.5	6.5
Feed per pound of gain (lb)	4.0	3.3	2.1	1.9
Liveweight at marketing (lb)	2.8	3.1	3.8	4.5
Turkeys				
Age to market weight (weeks)	34	24	19	16
Feed per pound of gain (lb)	5.5	4.5	3.1	2.6
Liveweight at marketing (lb)	13.0	18.6	18.4	21.1
Laying hens				
Eggs per hen per year (no.)	112	174	232	250
Feed per dozen eggs (lb)	8.0	5.8	4.2	4.0

Source: Adapted from *Food from Animals,* CAST Report 82. March 1980, p. 13.

TABLE 1.8. continued

Rome	Stockholm	Tokyo	Washington, D.C.
$ 6.78	$ 11.49	$ 20.75	$ 4.43
4.71	11.25	5.48	3.46
2.19	3.82	2.29	1.23
2.02	3.10	1.14	1.11
3.48	3.10	4.14	2.20
4.51	4.73	3.06	3.53
1.08	0.87	1.13	0.60
22.58	34.54	37.99	16.56
69.73	107.23	47.33	52.69
289.00	428.00	446.00	404.00

provided at no cost. Providing free food to other countries has met with limited success in the past. In some situations, it upsets their own agricultural production, and in many cases the food cannot be adequately distributed in the country because transportation and marketing systems are poor. There are strong feelings that the United States has a moral obligation to share its abundance with other people in the world, particularly those in developing countries. It appears that this can best be done by sharing our time and sharing our basic, but not necessarily advanced, technology. People need to have self-motivation to improve, need to be shown how to help themselves step by step, and need to develop fully the agricultural resources in their own countries.

Increases in the efficiency of animal production in the United States have been remarkable during the past half century (Table 1.9). These improvements in efficiency have occurred primarily because people had an incentive to progress under a free-enterprise system. They learned how to improve their standard of living by effectively using available resources. This progress has taken time under the environmental conditions that motivated people to be successful.

Citizens of the United States should not only share their technology with other countries but also share how this technology was developed (Fig. 1.7). These achievements have been built on knowledge developed through experience and research, the extension of knowledge to producers, and the development of an industry to provide transportation, processing, and marketing in addition to production. Dwindling dollars currently being spent to support agricultural research and extension of knowledge in the United States may not provide the technology needed for future food demands.

About 30% of the world human population and 32% of the ruminant animal population live in developed regions of the world, but ruminants of these same regions produce two-thirds of the world's meat and 80% of the world's milk. In developed regions, a higher percentage of animals are used as food producers, and these animals are more productive on a per-animal basis than animals in developing regions. This is the primary reason for the higher level of human nutrition in developed countries of the world.

Possibly many developing regions of the world could achieve levels of plant and animal food productivity similar to those of developed regions (Fig. 1.8). Except perhaps in India,

FIGURE 1.7.
Mechanization has increased plant and animal production in the United States. (A) In the late 1800s and early 1900s, a team of horses, one worker, and a single moldboard plow could plow about 2 acres per day. Courtesy of Charles L. Benn, Iowa State University. (B) An early tractor in 1918 increased agricultural production on a per-worker basis. Courtesy of Michigan State University. (C) In the 1980s, one worker with a powerful modern tractor pulling three plows, each with five moldboards, could plow 110 acres in a 10-hour day, accomplishing the work that once required 55 workers and 110 horses. Courtesy of the USDA and CAST.

abundant world supplies of animal feed resources that do not compete with production of food for people are available to support expansion of animal populations and production. It has been estimated that through changes in resource allocation, an additional 8 billion acres of arable land (twice what is now being used) and 9.2 billion acres of permanent pasture and meadow

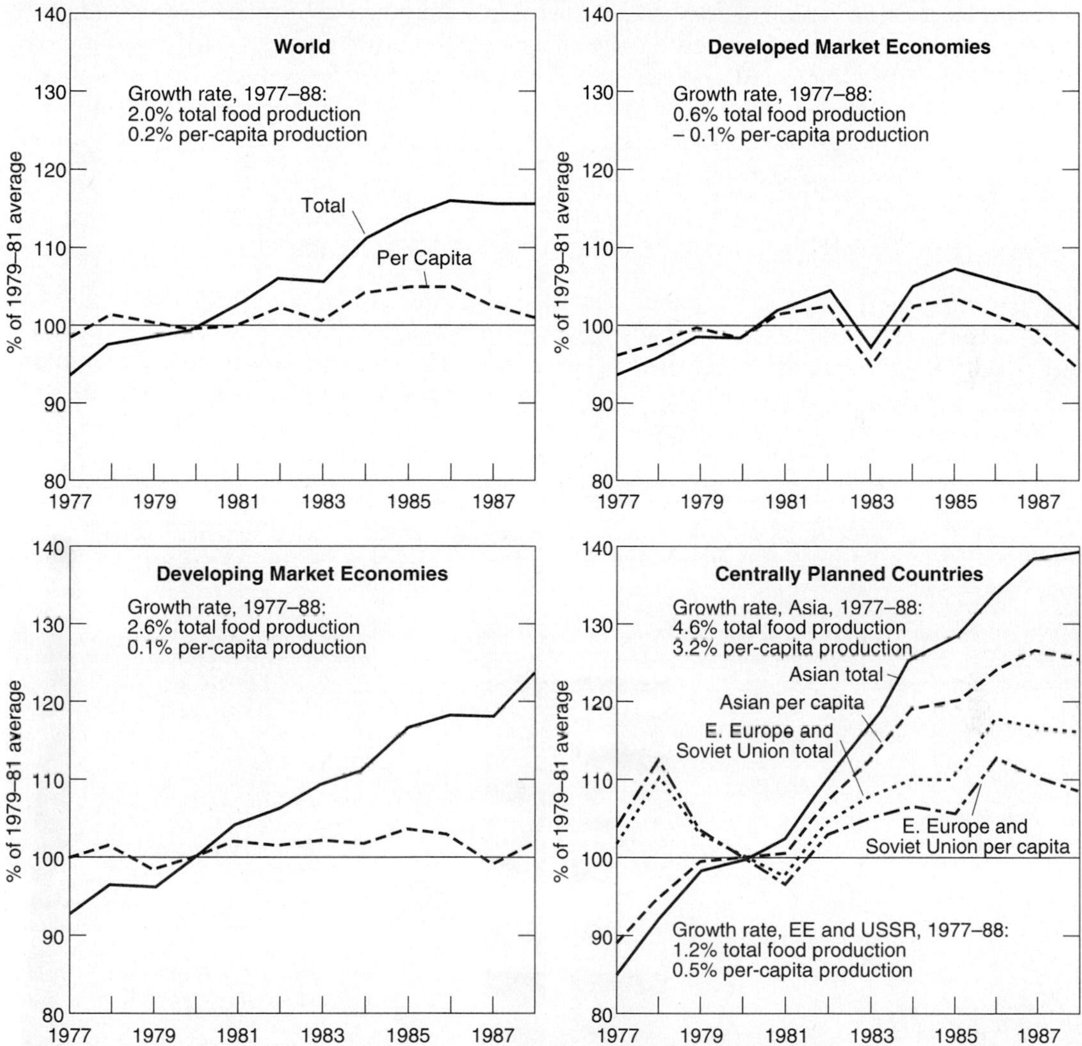

FIGURE 1.8.
Changes in world agricultural production. Developed countries include the United States, Canada, Europe, USSR, Japan, Republic of South Africa, Australia, and New Zealand. Developing countries include South and Central America, Africa (except Republic of South Africa), and Asia (except Japan and Communist Asia). Centrally planned countries include China, Korea, Vietnam, Czechoslovakia, Hungary, Poland, and Romania. Courtesy of the USDA, 1990 *Agricultural Chartbook.*

(23% more than is now being used) could be put into production in the world. These estimates, plus the potential increase in productivity per acre and per animal in developed countries, demonstrate the magnitude of world food production potential. This potential cannot be realized, however, without proper government planning and increased incentive to individual producers.

In the long run, each nation must assume the responsibility of producing its own food supply by efficient production, barter, or purchase and by keeping future food-production technology ahead of population increases and demand. Extensive untapped resources that can greatly enhance more food production exist throughout the world, including an ample supply of animal products. The greatest resource is the human being, who can, through self-motivation, become more productive and self-reliant.

CONTRIBUTIONS TO CLOTHING AND OTHER NONFOOD PRODUCTS

Products other than food from ruminants include wool, hair, hides, and pelts. Although synthetic materials have made some inroads into markets for these products, world wool production has remained relatively stable over the past 15 years. It is important to note that in more than 100 countries, ruminant fibers are used in domestic production and cottage industries for clothing, bedding, housing, and carpets.

A

B

C

FIGURE 1.9.
Animals provide significant contributions to the draft and transportation needs of countries lacking mechanization in their agricultural technology. (A) Cattle used for draft in Honduras. Courtesy of Winrock International. (B) Water buffalos are used to cultivate many of the rice patties in the Far East. Courtesy of Dr. Budi S. Nara. (C) Camels being used to transfer fertilizer to farming areas in Ethiopia. FAO photo, courtesy of C. N. Coombes.

A

B

C

FIGURE 1.10.

(A) The dog serves humans in a variety of ways. A guide dog leads the way for a visually impaired man. Courtesy of Guide Dogs for the Blind, San Rafael, CA. (B) Many people enjoy riding horses. Courtesy of the *Western Horseman*. (C) Horse racing is one of the most highly attended spectator sports in the United States. Courtesy of the Kentucky Derby.

D

E

F

FIGURE 1.10 *(continued).*
(D) Steer wrestling is exciting for the spectator but dangerous for the participants. Fast, well-trained horses and strong participants are needed to wrestle the steers to the ground in less than 5 seconds. Courtesy of Larry Thomas. (E) Calf roping is a favorite rodeo event. Courtesy of Larry Thomas. (F) Bullfighting originated in Spain centuries ago. It is popular in Mexico and several South American countries. Courtesy of José Rafael Cortes, editor of *La Nación* newspaper, San Cristobal, Venezuela.

Annual production of animal wastes from ruminants contains millions of tons of nitrogen, phosphorus, and potassium. The annual value of these wastes for fertilizer is estimated at $1 billion.

Inedible tallows and greases are animal by-products used primarily in soaps and animal feeds and as sources of fatty acids for lubricants and industrial use. Additional tallow and grease by-products are used in the manufacture of pharmaceuticals, candles, cosmetics, leather goods, woolen fabrics, and tin plating. The individual fatty acids can be used to produce synthetic rubber, food emulsifiers, plasticizers, floor waxes, candles, paints, varnishes, printing inks, and pharmaceuticals.

Gelatin is obtained from hides, skins, and bones and can be used in foods, films, and glues. Collagen, obtained primarily from hides, is used to make sausage casings.

CONTRIBUTIONS TO WORK AND POWER NEEDS

The early history of the developed world abounds with examples of the importance of animals as a source of work energy through draft work, packing, and human transport. The horse made significant contributions to winning the wars and exploration of the unknown regions of the world.

In the United States during the 1920s, approximately 25 million horses and mules were used, primarily for draft purposes. The tractor has replaced all but a few of these draft animals. In parts of the developing world, however, animals provide as much as 99% of the power for agriculture even today.

In more than half the countries of the world, animals—mostly buffalo and cattle but also horses, mules, camels, and llamas—are kept primarily for work and draft purposes (Fig. 1.9). About 20% of the world's human population depends largely or entirely on animals for moving goods. Animal draft power makes a significant contribution to the production of major foods (rice and other cereal grains) in several heavily populated areas of the world. India, for example, has more than 200 million cattle and buffalo, the largest number of any country. Although not slaughtered because they are considered sacred, cattle of India contribute significantly to the food supply by providing power for field work and milk for people. It is estimated that India alone would have to spend more than $1 billion annually for gasoline to replace the animal energy it uses in agriculture.

ANIMALS FOR COMPANIONSHIP, RECREATION, AND ENTERTAINMENT

Estimates of the number of companion animals in the world are unavailable. There are an estimated 26 million family-owned dogs and 21 million family-owned cats in the United States. The U.S. pet food industry processes more than 3 million tons of cat and dog food annually valued at more than $1 billion. Many species of animals would qualify as companions where people derive pleasure from them. The contribution of animals as companions, especially to the young and elderly, is meaningful, even though it is difficult to quantify the emotional value. Animals used in rodeos, bullfighting, and other sports provide income for thousands of people and entertainment and recreation for millions (Fig. 1.10).

FIGURE 1.11.
Yucatan miniature pigs are used as experimental animals to help solve human problems such as diabetes, obesity, and atherosclerosis. Courtesy of Colorado State University.

A

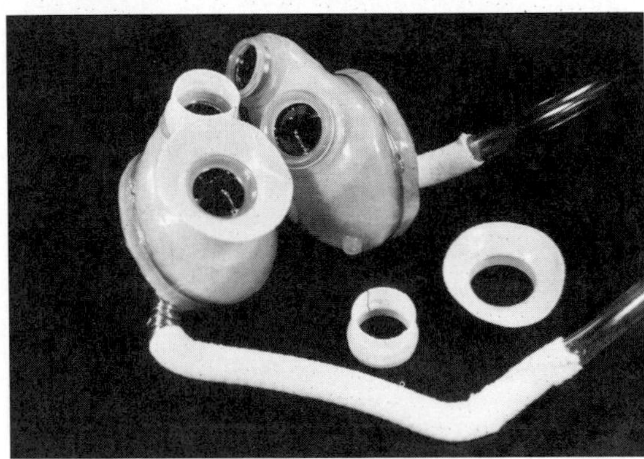

B

C

FIGURE 1.12.
(A) Jarvik 7 artificial heart was used experimentally in sheep and calves before being used in humans. (B) Longest survival time in sheep with Jarvik 7 artificial heart was 289 days. (C) Dairy animal "Charley" had a natural heart for 90 days, a Jarvik 7 artificial heart for 74 days, then a natural heart transplant from a twin sister, until he was slaughtered at 39 months of age. Courtesy of Division of Artificial Organs, University of Utah.

From the livestock that provide high-quality food to the pet that gives pleasure to its owner, domestic animals serve people in diverse and vital ways. This book is intended to discuss the contributions of livestock, a group of domestic animals whose contributions to human welfare have long been, and will continue to be, fundamentally important to meeting human needs.

HUMAN HEALTH RESEARCH

Laboratory animals are commonly used to provide valuable information for improving human life. Larger, domestic farm animals are used less frequently because the initial cost and maintenance costs are high. However, examples of how farm animals have contributed to human health are noteworthy.

Iowa State University has done an extensive study using swine as the model to evaluate how irradiation might increase the frequency of genetic defects. Colorado State University has studied the long-term effects of low levels of irradiation on the incidence of cancer in a beagle dog colony.

Miniature pigs (Yucatan swine whose ancestors came from the wilds of southern Mexico and central South America) have been used as laboratory animals because their pulmonary, cardiac, dental, and even prenatal brain development closely resembles that of humans. The utilization of miniature Yucatan pigs in biomedical research has increased dramatically since 1978. Miniature pigs are considered ideal in studying human aging, disease resistance, and the effect of diet on diabetes and atherosclerosis (Fig. 1.11). In one research study, for example, it was discovered that genetically predisposed pigs became susceptible to diabetes after consuming a low-fiber diet with 40% of the calories coming from saturated fat. There is less cost in maintaining the miniature pigs because their mature weights are approximately 120 lb, compared to 600–800 lb for typical swine. A new breed of Yucatan swine, the micropig, may prove even more useful as an experimental animal; its mature weight range is 50–70 lb.

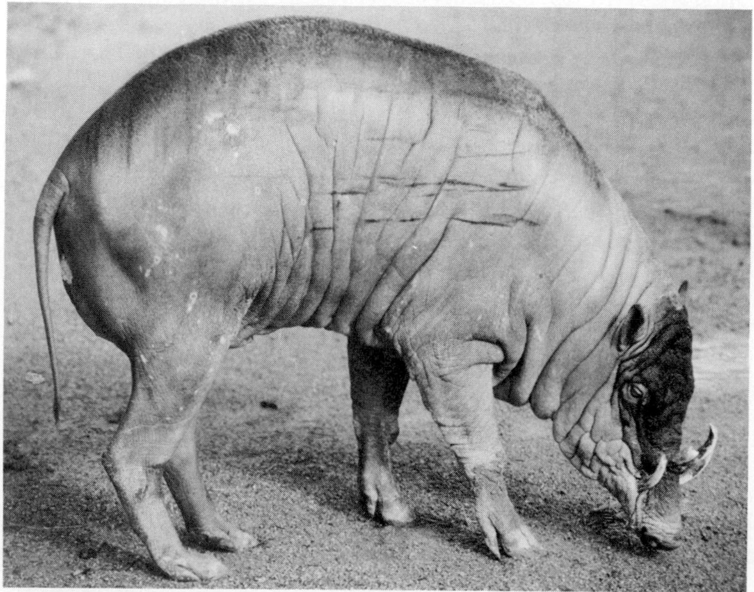

FIGURE 1.13.
The babirusa, a piglike animal unique to a few islands in eastern Indonesia. Courtesy of Phillip Coffey, Jersey Wildlife Preservation Trust.

Cattle and sheep have been used to test artificial organs before these organs have been implanted into humans. Figure 1.12 shows some of the experimental animals used to test the Jarvik 7 artificial heart.

OTHER ANIMALS

This book gives major attention to cattle, sheep, swine, horses, poultry, and goats. Several other useful species are briefly mentioned in this chapter. In addition, there are other animals that provide useful products in specific areas of the world. There are also several domesticated animals about which little is known, and undomesticated animals that have potential for long-term world agricultural development. Some of these domesticated animals, relatives to cattle, are the banteng of Indonesia and the mithan of India, Burma, and Bangladesh. Wild bovines include the kouprey in Thailand and the gaur in India and Southeast Asia.

Among the undomesticated Asian pigs is the babirusa of eastern Indonesia (Fig. 1.13). The stomach of these unusual animals has an extra sac, suggesting they may have the ability to break down cellulose. These "ruminant pigs" browse leaves, a behavior more similar to deer than to pigs.

Several of these rare animals have disease resistance that might be incorporated into breeding programs of our more familiar animals. A realistic question could be posed: Are we overlooking animals that could benefit humankind?

SELECTED REFERENCES

Baldwin, R. L. 1980. *Animals, Feed, Food and People: An Analysis of the Role of Animals in Food Production.* Boulder, CO: Westview Press.

Cravens, W. W. 1981. Plants and animals as protein sources. *J. Anim. Sci.* 53:817.

Devendra, C. 1980. Potential of sheep and goats in less developed countries. *J. Anim. Sci.* 51:461.

Ending Hunger: An Idea Whose Time Has Come. 1985. Sparks, NV: Praeger.

FAO Production Yearbook. Vol. 43, 1989. Rome: FAO.

Fitzhugh, H. A., Hodgson, H. J., Scoville, O. J., Nguyen, T. D., and Byerly, T. C. 1978. *The Role of Ruminants in Support of Man.* Morrilton, AR: Winrock International.

Food from Animals: Quantity, Quality and Safety. 1980. Council for Agricultural Science and Technology (CAST) Report no. 82.

Hodgson, H. J. 1979. Role of the dairy cow in world food production. *J. Dairy Sci.* 62:343.

Kunkel, H. O. 1990. *World Hunger—Grain Versus Meat Production.* College Station, TX: Texas A&M University.

National Research Council. 1983. *Little-Known Asian Animals with a Promising Economic Future.* Washington: National Academy Press.

Reid, J. T., White, O. D., Anrique, R., and Fortin, A. 1980. Nutritional energetics of livestock: Some present boundaries of knowledge and future research needs. *J. Anim. Sci.* 51:1393.

Willham, R. L. 1985. *The Legacy of the Stockman.* Morrilton, AR: Winrock International.

CHAPTER 2

An Overview of the Livestock and Poultry Industries

It is important to see the broad picture of the livestock and poultry industries before delving into the specific biological and economic principles that describe animal function, production, and profitability. These industries are typically described with numbers, pounds, prices, people (producers and consumers), production systems, and products. Products and consumers are covered in the next several chapters.

An understanding of the animal industries begins with basic terminology, especially the various species and sex classifications (see inside front cover). Refer to the glossary, which follows Chapter 37, for a complete listing of defined terms.

U.S. ANIMAL INDUSTRIES: AN OVERVIEW

The livestock and poultry industries in the United States are big businesses — they must be large to meet the high animal product preference of 250 million people and also to supply the export market. The inventory of livestock and poultry in the United States is approximately 1.8 billion head (1,550 million chickens; 99 million cattle, including 10 million dairy cows; 75 million turkeys; 55 million swine; 11 million sheep; 5 million horses; and 2 million goats). The January 1, 1991 commercial inventory value of U.S. livestock and poultry exceeded $100 billion.

Cash Receipts

An evaluation of farm cash receipts from the sale of animals and animal products provides another perspective of U.S. animal industries. Table 2.1 shows the cash receipts for animal commodities ranked against all agricultural commodities. The top 5 states for each commodity are also shown in this table. Note that cash receipts for all livestock products comprise 52% of all agricultural commodities in the United States.

Figure 2.1 shows the farm cash receipts from livestock and poultry products for each state. Note that 15 states each have annual cash receipts exceeding $2 billion.

TABLE 2.1. Leading U.S. States for Farm Cash Receipts, 1989

Commodity	Rank[a]	Value ($mil)	Five Leading States ($mil) 1	2	3	4	5
All Commodities	—	$159,173	Calif. $17,515	Tex. $10,760	Iowa $9,119	Nebr. $8,525	Ill. $6,710
All Livestock	—	83,724	Tex. 6,863	Nebr. 5,643	Iowa 5,209	Calif. 5,093	Wis. 4,337
Cattle and calves	1	36,679	Tex. 5,050	Nebr. 4,634	Kans. 3,753	Colo. 2,233	Iowa 2,027
Dairy products	2	19,401	Wis. 3,183	Calif. 2,431	N.Y. 1,556	Pa. 1,453	Minn. 1,305
Hogs	5	9,426	Iowa 2,421	Ill. 984	Minn. 811	Nebr. 723	Ind. 700
Broilers	6	8,780	Ark. 1,469	Ga. 1,250	Ala. 1,134	N.C. 848	Miss. 594
Eggs	10	3,854	Calif. 402	Ga. 286	Ind. 281	Pa. 257	Ark. 237
Turkeys	14	2,222	N.C. 407	Minn. 290	Calif. 249	Ark. 169	Mo. 144
Sheep/lambs[b]	[a]	471	Calif. 67	Tex. 65	Colo. 45	S.Dak. 35	Wyo. 33
Wool[b]	[a]	124	Tex. 36	Wyo. 13	Calif. 10	Colo. 9	Mont. 8
Horses[b]	[a]	—	Ky. 524	—	—	—	—
Mohair[b]	[a]	32	Tex. 29	—	—	—	—

[a] Ranking is in comparison to all agricultural commodities. Ranking of sheep/lambs, wool, horses, and mohair is below 25th.
[b] Some states list receipts from horses, mohair, and sheep under the category "miscellaneous livestock."
Source: USDA, *Economic Indicators of the Farm Sector.*

World Trade

The economic well-being of U.S. animal industries is influenced by world trade. Table 2.2 shows the export and import markets for several animal commodities. While world trade for all U.S. products shows a deficit, agricultural and animal products show a positive trade balance. The economics of the U.S. export market for animal products is significantly influenced by cattle hides, meat (beef), fat/tallow, and dairy products. The highest import expenditures are for beef, dairy products, pork, and live cattle.

Of course, world trade affects the economics of some states more than others. Table 2.3 shows the export values of animal products for the five leading states in each product area. Live animals and meat ranks fourth in all agricultural commodities. Feed grains ($8.3 billion), wheat ($6.3 billion), and soybeans ($5.8 billion) are the leading agricultural exports.

Commodity Prices

The profitability of U.S. animal industries is partly influenced by the prices paid to producers for animals and animal products. Prices can fluctuate monthly, weekly, even daily. These price changes are influenced primarily by supply and demand.

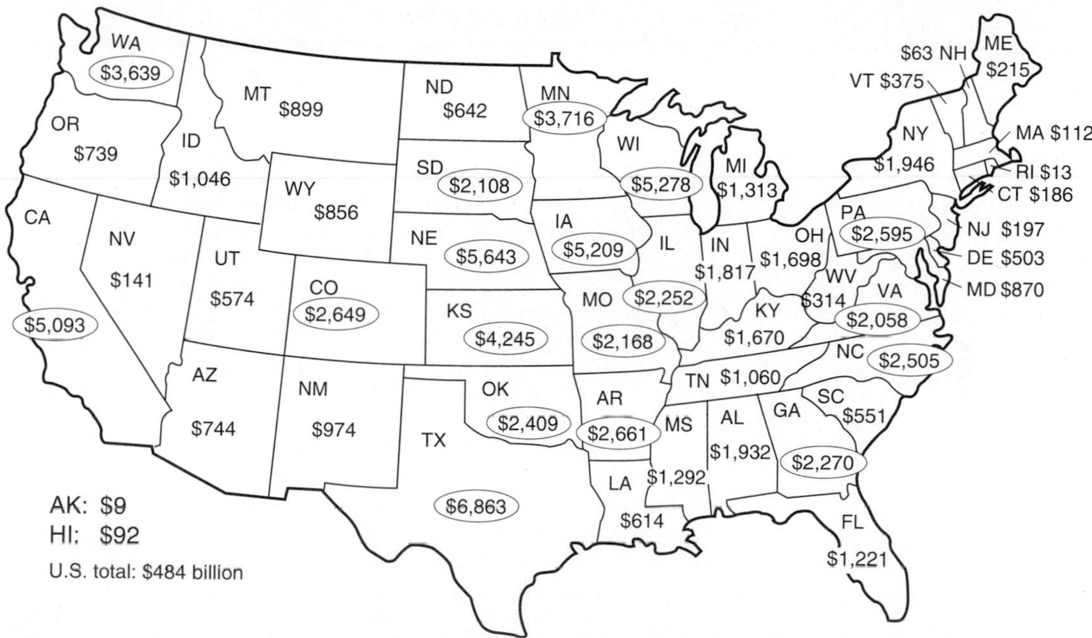

FIGURE 2.1.
Farm cash receipts, by states, for livestock and poultry products, 1989 ($ mil.). States with over $2 billion in receipts are circled. Courtesy of the USDA, *Economic Indicators of the Farm Sector.*

Those individuals interested in animal profitability should know the average prices of animal products. In addition, an understanding of the prices for specific classes and grades of animals, of what causes prices to fluctuate, and of how high prices are obtained is also necessary. Figure 2.2 compares market prices of selected species and products. The intent of this overview of commodity prices is to give a brief exposure to prices producers receive for the animals and products they sell. Details of how some factors influence prices are discussed in later chapters.

THE BEEF INDUSTRY

Global Perspective

Cattle are believed to have been domesticated in Asia and Europe during the New Stone Age. The humped cattle *(Bos indicus)* were developed in tropical countries; the *Bos taurus* cattle were developed in more temperate zones.

Cattle, including the domestic water buffalo, contribute food, fiber, fuel, and draft animal power to the 5.5 billion people of the world. For most developed countries, beef (meat) is a primary product. For developing countries, beef is a secondary product and draft animal power or milk is the primary product. In some countries, cattle are still a mode of currency or a focus of religious beliefs and customs.

For 30 years cattle numbers have continued to increase due to (1) greater demand for beef in developing countries, and (2) increased export demand (the result of more liberal trade policies

TABLE 2.2. U.S. Exports and Imports of Major Animal Products, 1989

Commodity	Exports Quantity	Exports Value ($mil)	Imports Quantity	Imports Value ($mil)
Live Animals (excluding poultry)	NA	$ 409	2,700 (thou head)	$ 824
Cattle and calves	169 (thou head)	108	1,459 (thou head)	598
Hogs	93 (thou head)	17	1,074 (thou head)	101
Sheep and lambs	330 (thou head)	11	142 (thou head)	6
Horses, mules, burros	42 (thou head)	248	11 (thou head)	55
Baby chicks	34,538 (thou head)	76	NA	18
Meats and Meat Products (excluding poultry)	2,013 (mil lb)	2,346	2,444 (mil lb)	2,548
Beef and veal	854 (mil lb)	1,418	1,560 (mil lb)	1,663
Pork	205 (mil lb)	330	761 (mil lb)	754
Lamb and mutton	NA	NA	46 (mil lb)	43
Poultry	1,093 (mil lb)	516	7 (mil lb)	14
Horse meat	130 (mil lb)	134	NA	NA
Other Products				
Tallow, grease, fat, and lard	3,012 (mil lb)	576	31 (mil lb)	13
Variety meats	581 (mil lb)	376	NA	NA
Sausage casings	22 (mil lb)	30	31 (mil lb)	64
Hides and skins	26 (mil lb)[a]	1,466	NA [b]	216
Wool and mohair	15 (mil lb)	41	106 (mil lb)	246
Dairy products	NA	572	NA	857
Eggs and egg products	NA	117	NA	28
Feathers and down	4 (mil lb)	30	29 (mil lb)	76
Bull semen	NA	53		
Total for Animals and Products		6,373		5,067
Total for Agricultural Products		39,991[c]		21,752
Total for All Products		349,576		468,361

[a] Cattle hides only.
[b] All hides and skins (including fur skins).
[c] Grains and soybeans are most important.
Source: USDA, *Foreign Agricultural Trade of the United States.*

in some countries). In recent years, drought in the Southern Hemisphere has slowed the growth in cattle numbers.

Table 2.4 shows the leading countries for cattle numbers, beef production, and beef consumption. India has the largest cattle population; however, its per-capita consumption is low because religious customs forbid cattle, considered sacred, from being slaughtered. The United States produces the most beef, but Argentina and Uruguay are higher in per-capita consumption.

Countries with a high cattle population relative to their human population typically have a high per-capita consumption of beef and high export tonnage. For example, the cattle versus human population in Australia is 24 million versus 16 million, and in Argentina it is 51 million versus 32 million. Both countries rank high in per-capita consumption of beef. Japan, with its 5

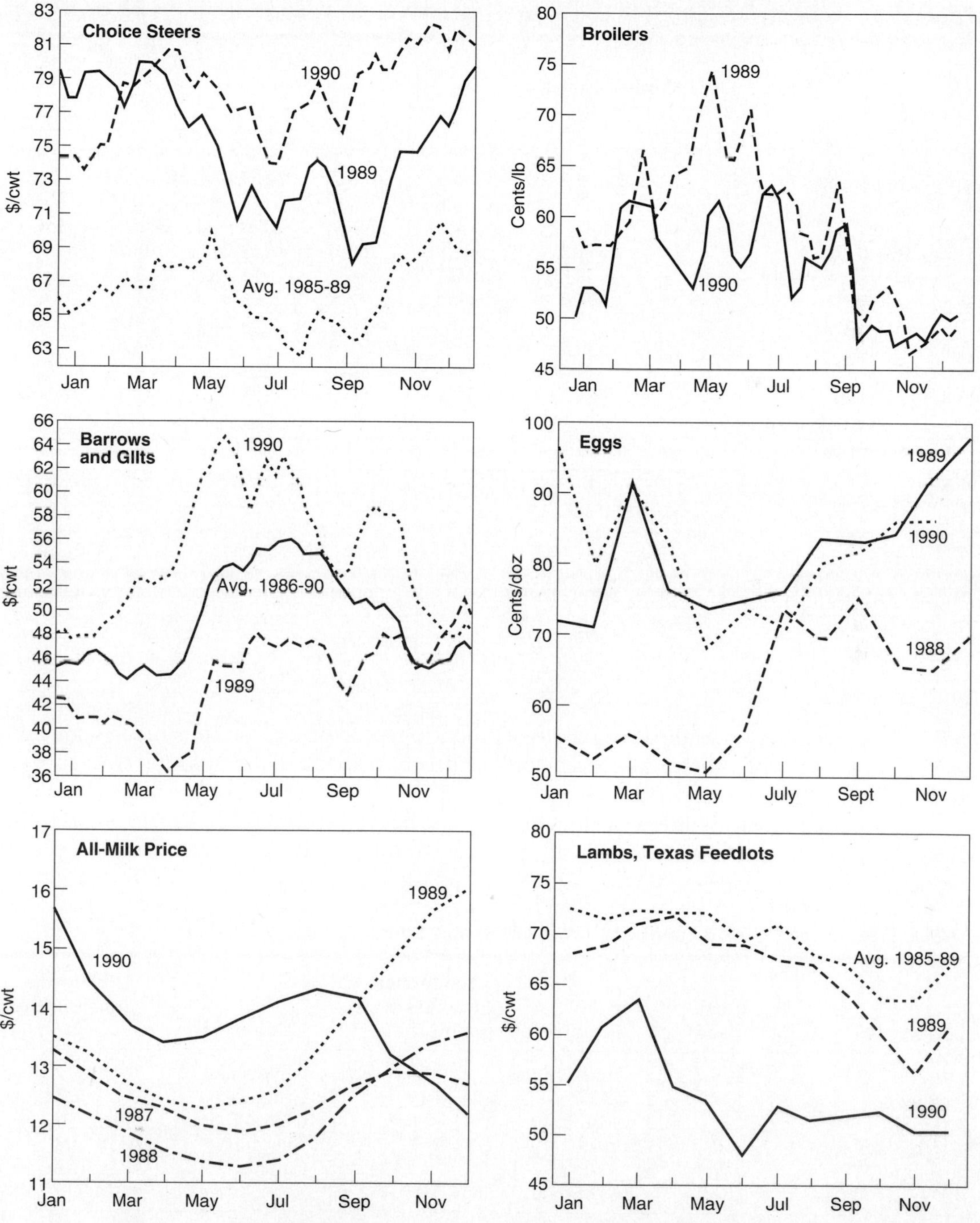

FIGURE 2.2.
Commodity market prices. Courtesy of the USDA.

TABLE 2.3. Leading U.S. States in Animal and Animal Product Export Values, 1989

Commodity	Rank[a]	United States ($mil)	Five Leading States ($mil) 1	2	3	4	5
			Kans.	Nebr.	Tex.	Iowa	Ky.
Live animals and meat	4	$ 2,829.8	$388.4	$385.5	$362.6	$235.7	$216.9
			Kans.	Nebr.	Tex.	Colo.	Iowa
Hides and skins	7	1,657.3	300.0	285.0	268.2	108.7	94.7
			Ark.	Ga.	Ala.	N.C.	Ind.
Poultry	12	728.2	94.7	87.1	66.3	65.3	48.4
			Kans	Nebr.	Tex.	Colo.	Iowa
Animal fats	14	530.1	96.1	91.3	85.9	34.8	30.3
			Wis.	Calif.	Minn.	N.Y.	Pa.
Dairy products	16	474.7	122.7	61.2	54.3	27.1	26.4
Total for All Agricultural Commodities		39,651.0					

[a] Ranking is in comparison to export of all agricultural commodities.
Source: USDA, *Foreign Agricultural Trade of the United States.*

million cattle, 123 million people, and rapidly expanding economy, has an increasing demand for beef (Table 2.5).

United States

The U.S. beef industry is made up of a series of producing, processing, and consuming segments that relate to each other but that operate independently. Table 2.6 identifies the various segments and the products they produce.

Figure 2.3 shows total cattle and amount of carcass beef produced in the United States from 1960–90. Interestingly, 100 million head of cattle currently produce as much carcass beef as

TABLE 2.4. World Cattle Numbers, Production, and Consumption, 1989

Country	No. Cattle (mil head)	Country	Production (carcass wt, bil lb)[a]	Country	Per-capita Consumption (lb)[b]
1. India	195	1. United States	23	1. Argentina	177
2. Brazil	137	2. USSR	19	2. Uruguay	127
3. USSR	120	3. Argentina	6	3. United States	99
4. United States	99	4. Brazil	5	4. Australia	92
5. China	77	5. Mexico	4	5. Canada	86
World total	1,282	World total	109	World average[c]	19

[a] Does not include buffalo meat.
[b] Carcass weight.
[c] Estimated by dividing the annual beef production by the world population.
Sources: USDA, FAS, *World Livestock Situation;* 1989 *FAO Production Yearbook.*

TABLE 2.5. World Beef Trade, 1989

Country	Exports (bil lb)	Country	Imports (bil lb)
1. Australia	1.9	1. United States	2.2
2. Germany	1.4	2. Japan	1.1
3. France	1.1	3. Italy	1.0
4. Ireland	1.0	4. United Kingdom	0.8
5. United States	1.0	5. France	0.8
World total	12.6	World total	10.3

NOTE: Carcass weight.
Source: USDA, FAS, *World Livestock Situation.*

120 million head produced in the 1970s. There are several reasons for this relatively high production of beef from fewer numbers of cattle: (1) the average carcass weight has increased from 579 lb in 1975 to 678 lb in 1989, (2) an increased number of cattle are fed per feedlot (2.4 times the feedlot capacity), (3) the market age of fed cattle has decreased, and (4) more cross-breeding and faster-gaining European breeds (e.g., Simmental and Charolais) are being used in commercial breeding programs.

Cattle Production

Most commercial beef cattle production occurs in three phases: the **cow-calf**, **stocker-yearling**, and **feedlot** operations. The cow-calf operator raises the young calf from birth to 6–10 months of age (400–650 lb). The stocker-yearling operator then grows the calf to 600–850 lb, primarily on roughage. Finally, the feedlot operator uses high-energy rations to finish the cattle to a desirable slaughter weight, approximately 900–1,300 lb. Most fed steers and slaughter heifers are between 15 and 24 months of age when marketed.

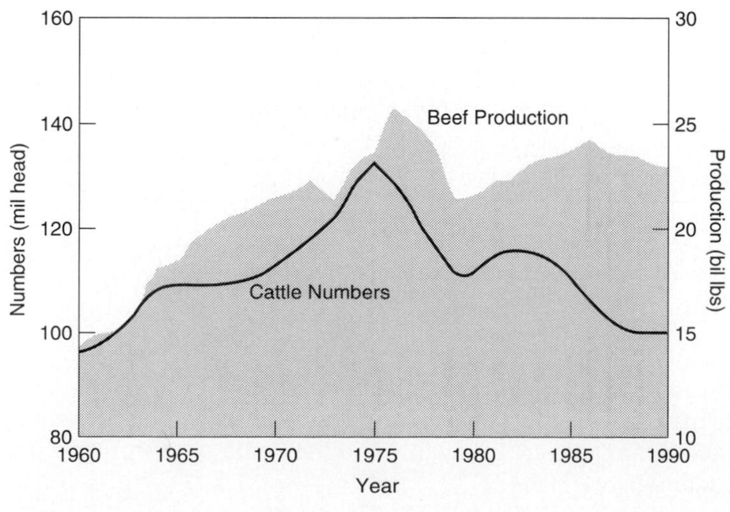

FIGURE 2.3. Total cattle numbers and carcass beef produced in the United States, 1960–90. Courtesy of Cattle-Fax and National Cattlemen's Association.

TABLE 2.6. An Overview of the Beef Industry Segments in the United States

Segment of the Beef Industry	Products Produced or Utilized	Approximate Number	Investment ($bil)
Seedstock Producers	Breeding stock—primarily bulls (14–30 months old) and some heifers and cows. Some steers and heifers for feeding. Slaughter cows and bulls.	150,000 breeders	$ 15.0
↓[a] ↑[b]			
Commercial Cow-Calf Producers	Calves (6–10 months old), weighing 300–600 lb. Slaughter cows and bulls with majority over 5 years of age, weighing 800–1,500 lb (cows) and 1,000–2,500 lb (bulls).	960,000 producers[c]	180.0
↓ ↑			
Yearling or Stocker Operator	Feeder steers and heifers (most of them 12–20 months old, weighing 500–900 lb).		
↓ ↑			
Feeders	Market steers, heifers, cows, and bulls (most steers and heifers 16–30 months old, weighing 900–1,300 lb).	47,000 feedlots (feed 88% of cattle)	7.5
↓ ↑			
Packers	Carcasses (approx. 600–800 lb). Boxed beef (carcasses into subprimal cuts). By-products	1250 packers	3.8
↓ ↑			
Retailers	Retail cuts	250 food chains	50.0
↓ ↑			
Consumers	Cooked products By-products (leather, pharmaceuticals, variety meats, etc.)	248 million consumers	

[a] Animal and/or product flow.
[b] Demands and expectations.
[c] In addition, there are approximately 200,000 dairy farms that produce about 20% of U.S. beef.

However, there are alternatives to the typical three-phase operation. In an **integrated** operation, for instance, the cattle may have a single owner from cow-calf to feedlot, or ownership may change several times before the cattle are ready for slaughter. Alternative production and marketing strategies are diagramed in Fig. 2.4.

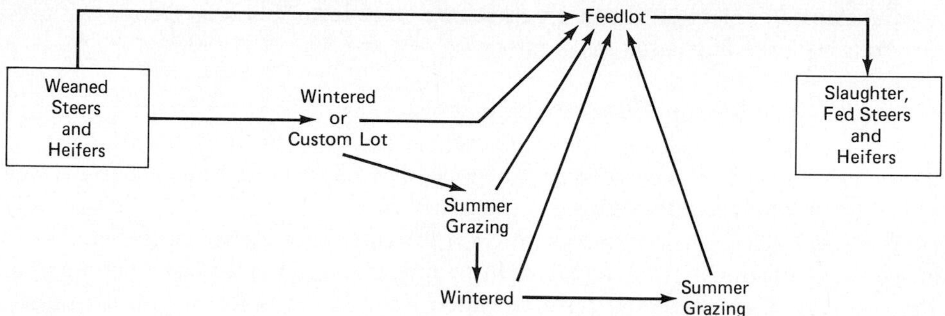

FIGURE 2.4.
Alternative feeding and marketing pathways for weaned calves. Some steers and heifers go to slaughter after the summer grazing period; however, their numbers are relatively small. Courtesy of Colorado State University.

Cow-Calf Production. U.S. cow-calf production involves some 33 million head of beef cows that are distributed throughout the country. Most of the cows are concentrated in areas where forage is abundant. As Fig. 2.5 shows, 14 states each have over 900,000 head of cows (66% of the U.S. total), most of them located in the Plains and Corn Belt areas. Cow numbers fluctuate over the years, depending on drought and on the prices of beef and land.

There are two kinds of cow-calf producers. **Commercial** cow-calf producers raise most of

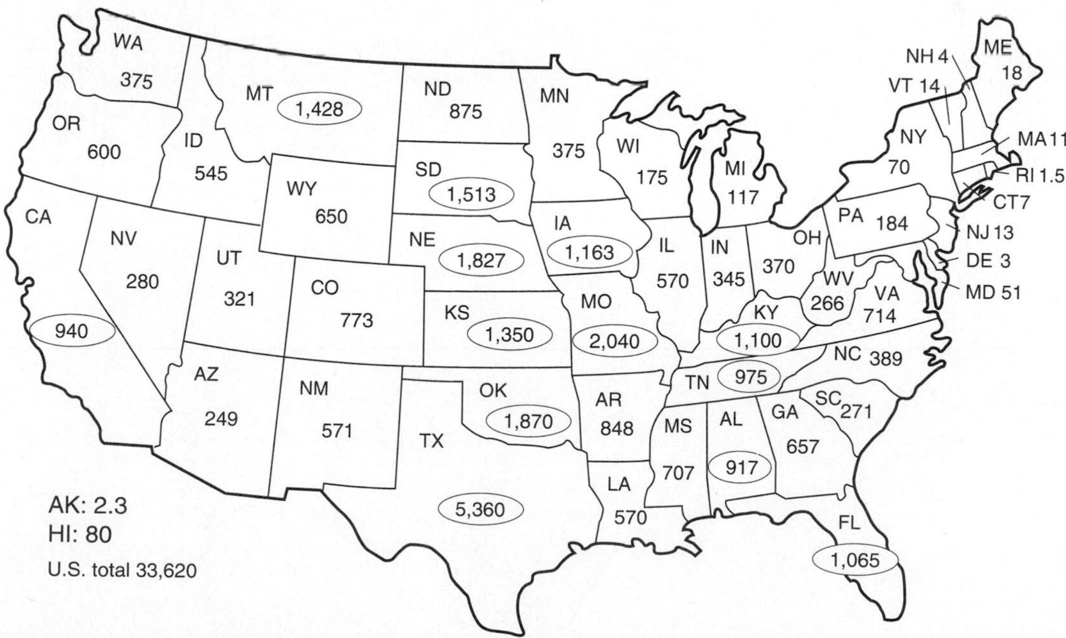

FIGURE 2.5.
U.S. beef cows that have calved, 1 January 1991 (1,000 head). States with more than 900,000 cows are circled. Courtesy of Western Livestock Marketing Information Project.

the potential slaughter steers and heifers. **Purebred breeders**, specialized cow-calf producers, produce primarily breeding cattle and semen.

Stocker-Yearling Production. Stocker-yearling producers feed cattle for growth prior to their going into a feedlot for finishing. Replacement heifers intended for the breeding herd are typically included in the stocker-yearling category. Our focus here, however, is on steers and heifers grown for later feedlot finishing.

Several alternate stocker-yearling production programs are identified in Fig. 2.4. In some programs, a single producer owns the calves from birth through the feedlot finishing phase, and the cattle are raised on the same farm or ranch. In other programs, one operator retains ownership, but the cattle are custom fed during the growth and finishing phases. In still other programs, the cattle are bought and sold once or several times.

The primary basis of the stocker-yearling operation is to market available forage and high-roughage feeds, such as grass, crop residues (e.g., corn stalks, grain stubble, and beet tops), wheat pasture, and silage. Stocker-yearling operations also make use of summer-only grazing areas that are not suitable for the production of supplemental winter feed.

Stocker-yearling operations are desirable for early-maturing cattle. These cattle need slower gains to achieve heavier slaughter weights without being excessively finished. Larger-framed, later maturing cattle usually are more efficient and profitable if they go directly to the feedlot after weaning.

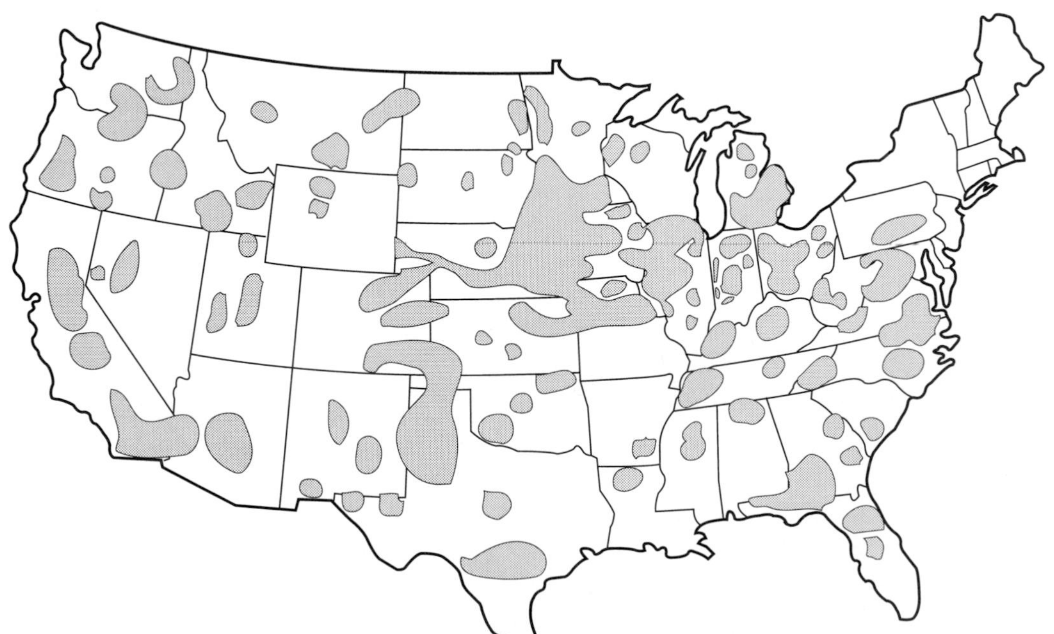

FIGURE 2.6.
Cattle-feeding areas in the United States. The areas (in grey) represent location but not volume of cattle fed. Courtesy of the USDA.

Feedlot Cattle Production. Feedlot cattle are fed in small pens or fenced areas, where harvested feed is brought to them. Some cattle are finished for market on pasture, but they represent only 10%–15% of the slaughter steers and heifers. They are sometimes referred to as *nonfed cattle* because they are fed little, if any, grain or concentrate feeds.

The cattle-feeding areas in the United States (Fig. 2.6) correspond to the primary feed-producing areas where cultivated grains and roughages are grown. These locations are determined primarily by soil type, growing season, and amount of rainfall or irrigation water. Figure 2.7 shows where the approximately 26 million feedlot cattle are fed in the various states. The total number of fed cattle marketed in the 13 leading states is shown in Fig. 2.8. The 22.9 million head represent 88% of the 26.2 million head of fed cattle in all states. By contrasting Figs. 2.7 and 2.8, it is noted that the number of cattle marketed for each state is considerably higher than the number on feed. This is because most commercial feedlots feed more than twice the number of cattle of their one-time feedlot capacity.

Cattle Feeding

The two basic types of cattle-feeding operations are (1) **commercial feeders** and (2) **farmer-feeders**. The two operations are distinguished by type of ownership and size of feedlot (Figs. 2.9 and 2.10).

The farmer-feeder operation is usually owned and operated by an individual or a family and has a feedlot capacity of under 1,000 head. The commercial feedlot is sometimes owned by an individual or partnership, but more often a corporation owns it, especially as feedlot size

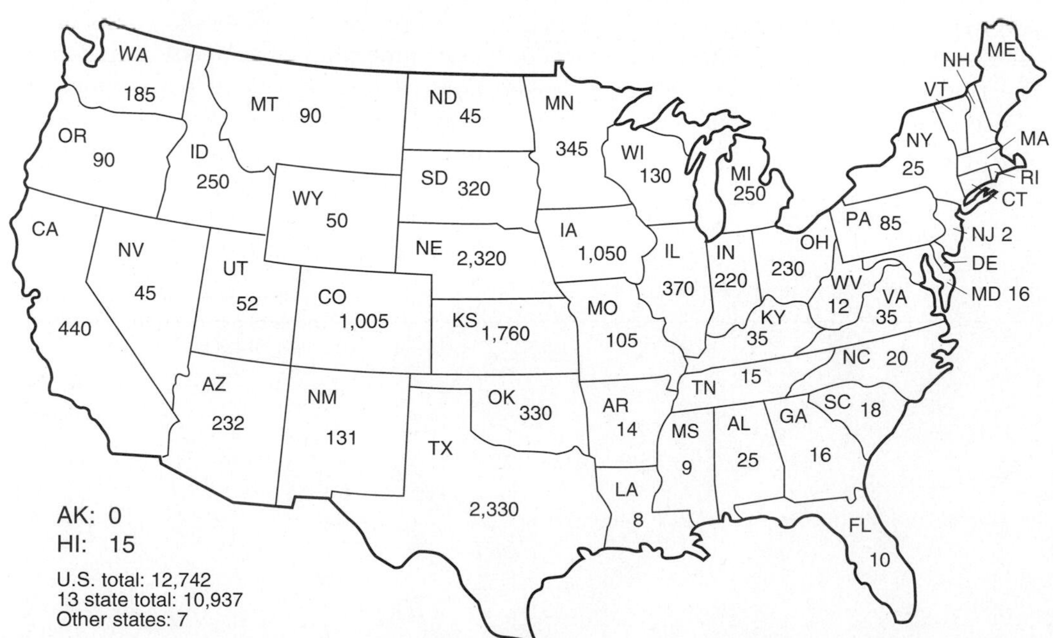

FIGURE 2.7.
U.S. cattle on feed, 1 January 1991 (1,000 head). Courtesy of Western Livestock Marketing Information Project.

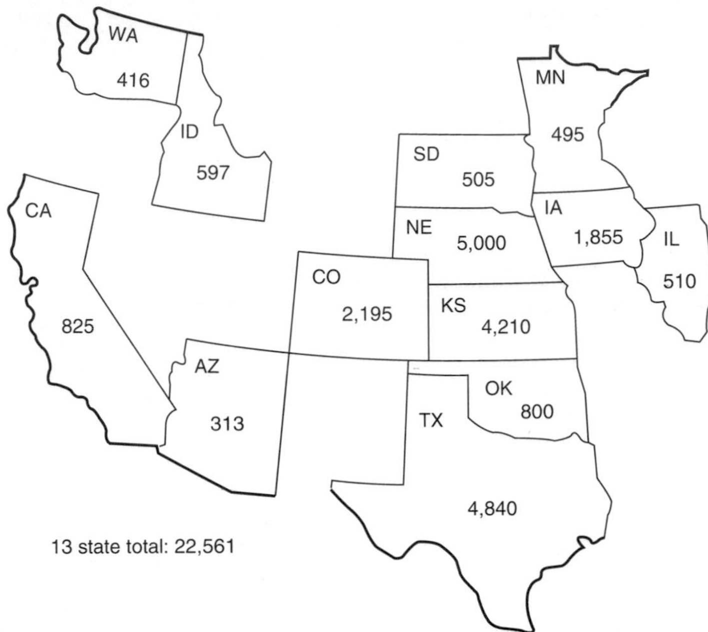

FIGURE 2.8.
Number of fed cattle marketings in 13 U.S. states, 1990 (1,000 head). Courtesy of Western Livestock Marketing Information Project.

increases. It has a feedlot capacity of over 1,000 head. Approximately 70% of fed cattle are fed in feedlots with over 1,000-head capacity, whereas 30% of fed cattle are fed in feedlots with under 1,000-head capacity. A number of U.S. commercial feedlots have capacities of 40,000 head or higher, and a few have capacities of over 100,000 head. Some commercial feedlots custom-feed cattle; that is, the commercial feedlot provides the feed and feeding service to the cattle owner.

Each type of feeding operation has its advantages and disadvantages. What is an advantage to one type of feedlot is usually a disadvantage to the other type. The large commercial feedlot

FIGURE 2.9.
A large commercial feedlot where thousands of cattle can be easily fed in fenceline bunks using feed trucks. Courtesy of *BEEF*.

FIGURE 2.10.
A farmer teedlot. In this operation the feed is fed in troughs located within the pen. Courtesy of *BEEF*.

usually enjoys economic advantages associated with its size as well as professional expertise in nutrition, health, marketing, and financing. The farmer-feeder has the advantages of distributing labor over several enterprises by using high-roughage feeds effectively, creating a market of homegrown feeds through cattle, and more easily closing down the feeding operation during times of unprofitable returns.

Chapters 22 and 23 examine the breeding, feeding, and management of beef cattle in more detail.

THE DAIRY CATTLE INDUSTRY

Global Perspective

Milk and milk products are produced and consumed by most countries of the world. Although buffalo, goat, and other types of milk are important in some areas, our focus here is on cow's milk and its products.

Table 2.7 shows world dairy cattle numbers, fluid milk production, and per-capita consumption of milk. Of the 222 million dairy cows in the world, the Soviet Union leads all other

TABLE 2.7. World Dairy Cattle Numbers, Production, and Consumption, 1990

Country	No. Dairy Cattle (mil head)	Country	Fluid Milk Production (bil lb)	Country	Per-capita Fluid Milk Consumption (lb)
1. USSR	42	1. USSR	239	1. Norway	512
2. India	29	2. United States	136	2. Ireland	378
3. Brazil	19	3. Germany	74	3. Poland	350
4. United States	10	4. France	57	4. Sweden	337
5. France	9	5. India	54	5. Finland	333
World total	222	World total	968	World average	102

Sources: USDA, FAS *World Livestock Situation;* 1990 *FAO Production Yearbook.*

countries with its 42 million. The Soviet Union also has the highest total fluid milk production, even though its annual production per cow is only 5,700 lb. The average annual world production per cow is 4,700 lb, with production in Israel the highest at nearly 19,000 lb. The United States ranks third with 14,000 lb, behind South Korea's approximately 15,000 lb. Countries with high milk-production levels per cow have excellent breeding, feeding, and health-management programs.

World butter production is 14 billion lb. The Soviet Union, the United States, and West Germany are the leading countries in total butter production, while West Germany, New Zealand, and Denmark have the highest per-capita consumption of butter.

The leading countries in cheese production are the United States, France, and the Soviet Union, with all countries producing 24 billion lb of cheese. Greece, France, and Italy have the highest per-capita consumption of cheese.

Milk is produced worldwide but dairy trade is dominated by manufactured dairy products. Dairy products traded internationally account for about 5% of the global milk production on a milk-equivalent basis. Trade restrictions keep trade volume and prices lower than if trade was more liberalized. Most developed countries, including the United States, extensively regulate their dairy industries by subsidizing production and often exportation.

Table 2.8 shows the leading countries and total world trade for cheese and butter. Nonfat dry milk is another milk product produced in large quantities — world production is 7 billion lb. France, West Germany, and the Soviet Union produce the most nonfat dry milk.

United States

The U.S. dairy industry has changed dramatically since the days of the family milk cow. Today it is a highly specialized industry that includes the production, processing, and distribution of milk. A large investment is required in cows, machinery, barns, and milking parlors where cows are milked. Dairy operators who produce their own feed need additional money for land on which to grow the feed. They also require machinery to produce, harvest, and process the crops.

Although the size of a dairy operation can vary from less than 30 milking cows to more than 5,000 milking cows (Fig. 2.11), the average U.S. dairy has approximately 100 milking cows, 30 dry cows, 30 heifers, and 25 calves. Average dairy producers farm 200–300 acres of land, raise much of the forage, and market the milk through cooperatives, of which they are members. The producers sell about 3 tons of milk daily, or about 2.2 million lb annually, valued at about $230,000. Their average total capital investment may exceed $500,000. The average dairy producer has a partnership (with a family member or another person) to make the management of time and resources easier.

One way to stress the importance of dairying in the United States is to examine the number of cows in the states (Fig. 2.12). The five leading states in thousands of dairy cows are, respectively, Wisconsin (1,753), California (1,135), New York (768), Minnesota (710), and Pennsylvania (683). The five leading states in per-cow production are, respectively, New Mexico (18,552 lb), Washington (18,209 lb), California (17,530 lb), Colorado (16,803 lb), and Arizona (16,738 lb). And the five leading states in total pounds of milk produced (given in million pounds) are, respectively, Wisconsin (24), California (19.4), New York (11.1), Minnesota (10.1), and Pennsylvania (10).

As Fig. 2.13 shows, today's 10 million dairy cows are approximately one-half the number of cows 50 years ago, yet during the past decade total milk production has increased 10%–15%

TABLE 2.8. World Dairy Trade, 1990

Exports			
Country	Cheese (mil lb)	Country	Butter (bil lb)
1. Netherlands	0.9	1. Netherlands	0.7
2. France	0.7	2. New Zealand	0.5
3. Germany	0.6	3. Belgium	0.3
4. Denmark	0.5	4. Ireland	0.3
5. New Zealand	0.2	5. France	0.3
World total	4.3	World total	3.1

Imports			
Country	Cheese (mil lb)	Country	Butter (bil lb)
1. Germany	0.7	1. USSR	0.7
2. Italy	0.7	2. Belgium	0.4
3. England	0.4	3. Netherlands	0.3
4. France	0.2	4. Germany	0.3
5. Japan	0.2	5. England	0.3
World total	3.5	World total	2.4

Sources: USDA, ERS; *World Livestock Situation* 1990 *FAO Production Yearbook.*

FIGURE 2.11.
Dairies in the United States continue to increase in herd size. Many dairy cow herds are intensively managed in excellent facilities. Courtesy of Colorado State University.

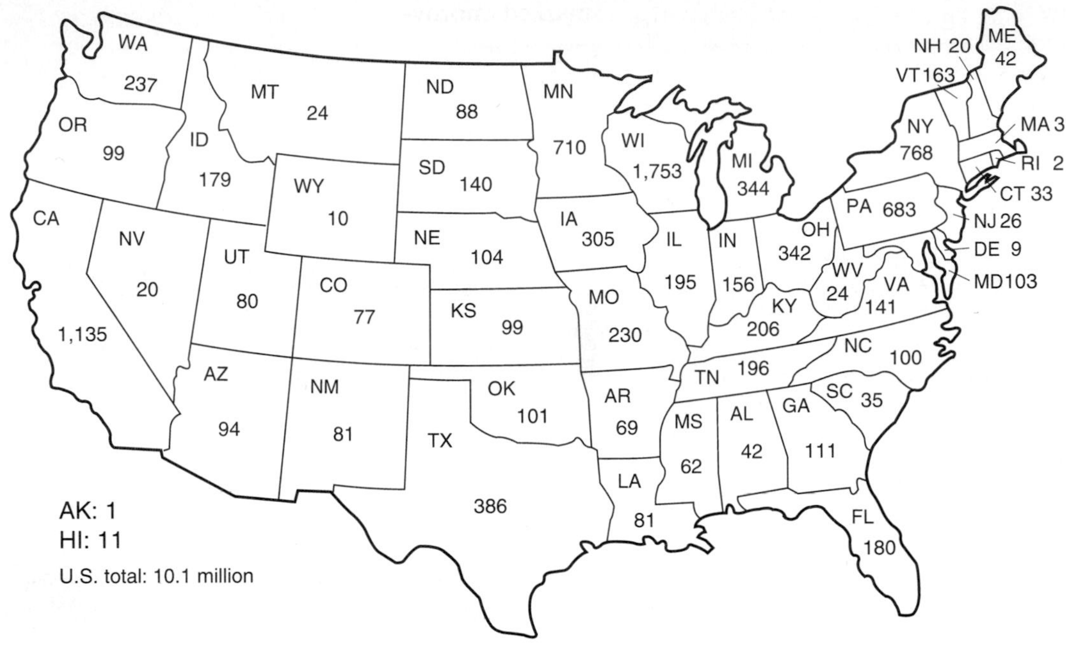

FIGURE 2.12.
U.S. milk cow numbers, 1990 (1,000 head). Courtesy of the USDA.

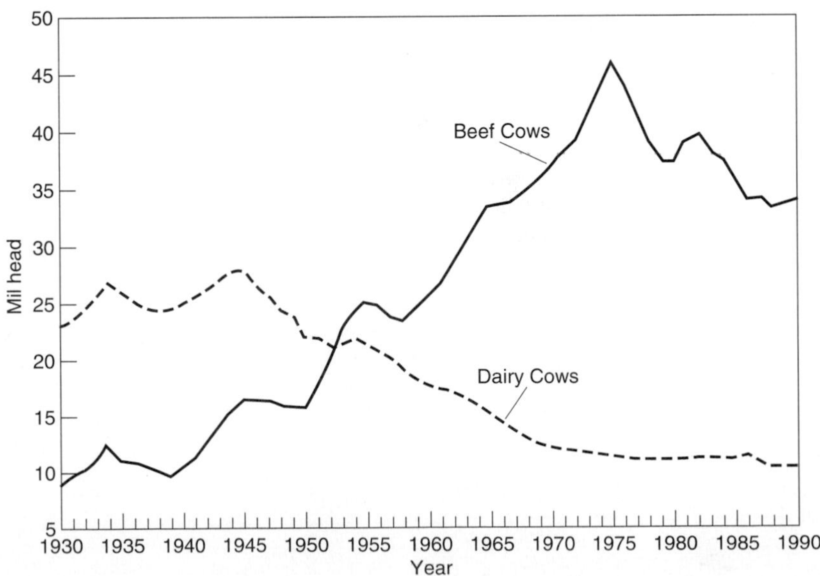

FIGURE 2.13.
U.S. cow inventory, 1 January 1930–90. Courtesy of the Western Livestock Marketing Information Project.

due to increased production per cow. This marked improvement is the result of more effective breeding, feeding, health, and management programs.

Factors affecting dairy cattle productivity and profitability are covered in Chapters 24 and 25.

THE HORSE INDUSTRY

Global Perspective

The horse was domesticated about 5,000 years ago. It was one of the last farm animals to be domesticated. Horses were first used as food, then for war and sports, and also for draft purposes. They were used for transporting people swiftly and for moving heavy loads. In addition, horses became important in farming, mining, and forestry.

The donkey, descended from the wild ass of Africa, was domesticated in Egypt prior to the domestication of the horse. Donkeys and zebras are in the same genus *(Equus),* but are different species from horses (see Fig. 14.9, Chapter 14). Horses mate with donkeys and zebras but the offspring produced are sterile.

Table 2.9 shows the world numbers of horses (60.5 million), donkeys (43.2 million), and mules (14.7 million). The five leading countries are given for each of the three species, with China having the most of all three. Mexico ranks second in horse numbers, while the Soviet Union, Brazil, and United States each have approximately 5–6 million head.

Horses have been companions for people since their domestication. Once important in wars, mail delivery, farming, forest harvesting, and mining, the horse today is used in shows, in racing, in the handling of livestock, and for companionship, recreation, and exercise.

United States

There were no horses on the North American continent when Columbus arrived. However, there is fossil evidence that the early ancestor of the horse was here some 50–60 million years ago. The Eohippus (or dawn horse), a 4-toed animal less than a foot high, is believed to be the oldest relative of the horse. Through evolutionary changes, the Mesohippus (about the size of a collie dog) was believed to have foraged on the prairies of the Great Plains.

The early ancestors of the horse disappeared in pre-Columbian times, supposedly by crossing from Alaska into Siberia. It is from these animals that horses evolved in Asia and Europe.

TABLE 2.9. World Horse, Donkey, and Mule Numbers, 1989

Country	No. Horses (mil head)	Country	No. Donkeys (mil head)	Country	No. Mules (mil head)
1. China	10.7	1. China	11.3	1. China	5.4
2. Mexico	6.2	2. Ethiopia	4.9	2. Mexico	3.2
3. USSR	5.9	3. Mexico	3.2	3. Brazil	2.0
4. Brazil	5.8	4. Pakistan	3.1	4. Columbia	0.6
5. United States	5.2	5. Egypt	1.9	5. Ethiopia	0.6
World total	60.5	World total	43.2	World total	14.7

Source: 1989 *FAO Production Yearbook.*

The draft horses and Shetland ponies developed in Europe, whereas the lighter, more agile horses developed in Asia and the Middle East. The Spaniards and colonists introduced modern horses to the Americas.

In the early 1900s, there were approximately 25 million horses and mules in the United States. Shortly after World War I, however, horse numbers began a rapid decline. The war stimulated the development and use of motor-powered equipment, such as automobiles, trucks, tractors, and bulldozers. Railroads were heavily used for transporting people and for moving freight long distances. By the early 1960s, horses and mules had declined to a mere 3 million in the United States.

In recent years, U.S. horse numbers have increased. With the shorter work week and greater affluence of the working class, there has been more time and money available for recreation. An estimated 1 million American horse owners are involved in the industry. The horse industry made its greatest growth between 1960 and 1976. Pleasure riding is the main contribution made by horses, though many people think of horse racing as more important. Attendance at U.S. racetracks exceeds 70 million and annual wagering exceeds $13 billion.

The U.S. horse industry employs thousands of people and gives pleasure to millions. It also generates more than $15 billion annually, including income for salaries and services; taxes on pari-mutuel betting; income from the breeding, showing, and selling of horses; expenditures for feeds and medicines; and investments in the animals, land, and facilities. Horse shows generate $223 million per year and rodeos $104 million; foreign sales are $200 million annually.

The American Horse Council estimates that there were 5.25 million economically productive horses in the United States in 1987, with Texas (478,000) and California (389,000) the leading states in horse numbers. The American Veterinary Medical Association estimates some 6.6 million equine in the United States in 1988; most of these were considered backyard horses.

Horse breeding, feeding, and management practices are presented in Chapters 30 and 31.

THE POULTRY INDUSTRY

Global Perspective

The term ***poultry*** applies to chickens, turkeys, geese, ducks, pigeons, peafowls, and guineas. Chickens and turkeys dominate the world poultry industry. However, in parts of Asia, ducks

TABLE 2.10. World Poultry Numbers, Production, and Consumption, 1989

Country	No. Poultry (mil head)	Country	Production (bil lb)[a]	Country	Per-Capita Consumption (lb)[a]
1. China	1,977	1. United States	22.3	1. United States	86
2. United States	1,550	2. USSR	7.3	2. Singapore	79
3. USSR	1,160	3. China	6.3	3. Israel	77
4. Brazil	600	4. Brazil	4.7	4. Hong Kong	71
5. Indonesia	444	5. France	3.4	5. Canada	60
World total	10,545	World total[b]	75.2	World average[c]	14

[a] Ready-to-cook equivalent.
[b] Not all countries included.
[c] Estimated by dividing world production by world population.
Source: USDA, FAS, *World Poultry Situation.*

TABLE 2.11. World Poultry Meat Trade, 1989

Country	Exports (mil lb)	Country	Imports (mil lb)
1. France	996	1. Germany	736
2. United States	878	2. Japan	619
3. Netherlands	750	3. USSR	463
4. Brazil	547	4. Hong Kong	437
5. Hungary	384	5. Saudi Arabia	432
World total[b]	5,340	World total[b]	4,350

Note: Dressed weight.
[b] Not all countries included.
Source: USDA, FAS, *World Poultry Situation.*

are commercially more important than broilers (young chickens), and in areas of Europe, there are more geese because they are more economically important than other poultry.

Chickens originated in Southeast Asia and were kept in China as early as 1400 B.C. Charles Darwin concluded in 1868 that domestic chickens originated from the Red Junglefowl, although three other Junglefowl species were known to exist.

Table 2.10 shows the leading countries in world poultry numbers, production, and consumption. China has the highest poultry numbers, while the United States leads in poultry production and consumption.

France and the United States export the largest amounts of poultry, while West Germany, Japan, and the Soviet Union are the leading importers (Table 2.11).

World governments influence world poultry trade by controlling production and pricing and by placing tariffs on incoming goods—all barriers to free international trade. Trade liberalization by countries with industrial market economies would likely increase the trade of and decrease the price of poultry meat. Countries with efficient producers (such as the United States, Brazil, and Thailand), combined with consumers from countries with considerable trade protection (such as Japan, Canada, and 12 countries in the European Economic Community), would benefit most from liberalized trade.

Poultry is the fastest-growing source of meat for people. The industralized countries produce and export more than 50% of the poultry meat in the world.

United States

The annual U.S. income from broilers, turkeys, and eggs exceeds $15 billion (broilers, $8.8 billion; eggs, $3.9 billion, and turkeys, $2.2 billion). Figure 2.14 shows the leading states in broiler, turkey, and egg production. The U.S. poultry industry is concentrated primarily in the southeastern area of the country.

From 1900–40, the primary concerns of the U.S. poultry industry were egg production by chickens and meat production by turkeys and waterfowl. Meat production by chickens was largely a by-product of the egg-producing enterprises. The broiler industry, as it is known today, was not yet established. Egg production was well established near large population centers, but the quality of eggs was often low because of seasonal production, poor storage, and the absence of laws to control grading standards.

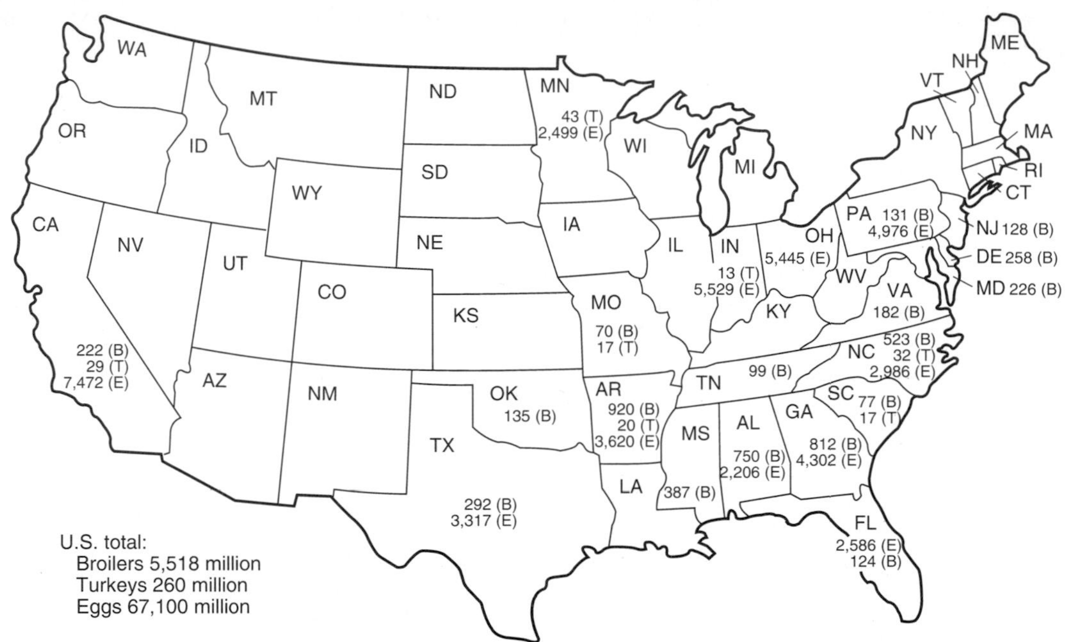

FIGURE 2.14.
States in the U.S. producing at least 50 million broilers (B), 10 million turkeys (T), and 2,000 million eggs (E). Courtesy of the USDA, *The Livestock and Poultry Situation.*

FIGURE 2.15.
Modern broiler houses are ventilated facilities where broilers are raised from chicks to maturity. Each house holds thousands of broilers. Courtesy of Grant Heilman Photography, Inc.

Before 1940, large numbers of small farm flocks existed in the United States, but the management practices applied today were practically unknown. The modern mechanized poultry industry of the United States emerged during the late 1950s as the number of poultry farms and hatcheries decreased and the number of birds per installation dramatically increased. Larger cage-type layer operations appeared, and egg-production units grew, with production geared to provide consumers with eggs of uniform size and high quality. Huge broiler farms (Fig. 2.15) that provided consumers with fresh meat throughout the year were established, and large dressing plants capable of dressing 50,000 or more broilers a day were built. The U.S. poultry industry was thus revolutionized.

One of the most striking achievements of the poultry industry is its increased production of eggs and meat per hour of labor. Poultry operations with 1 million birds at one location are not uncommon. Labor reduction has been accomplished by automatic feeding, watering, egg collecting, egg packing, and manure removal.

Dramatic changes came between 1955 and 1975 with the introduction of integration. It began in the broiler industry and is applied to a lesser degree in egg and turkey operations. Integration brings all phases of an enterprise under the control of one head, frequently the corporate ownership of breeding flocks, hatcheries, feed mills, raising, dressing plants, services, and marketing and distribution of products (Fig. 2.16). After 1975, poultry entered a new period

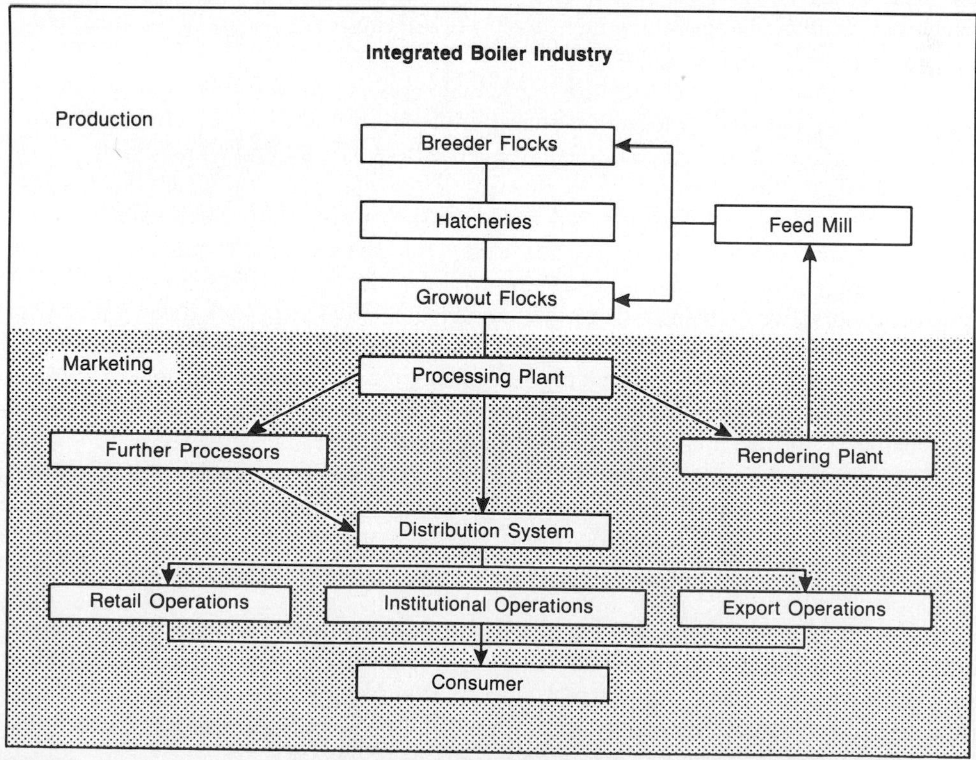

FIGURE 2.16.
Most of the activities in producing and marketing broilers are under the same ownership and management. This integrated system produces broilers very efficiently. Courtesy of CSU Graphics.

of consolidation, in which vertically integrated companies purchased, acquired, or merged with each other, creating a small number of superintegrated companies.

The actual raising of broilers is sometimes accomplished on a contract basis between the person who owns the houses and equipment and who furnishes the necessary labor, and the corporation that furnishes the birds, feed, field service, dressing, and marketing. Payment for raising birds is generally based on a certain price for each bird reared to market age. Bonuses are usually paid to those who do a commendable job of raising birds. An important advantage to the integration system is that all phases are synchronized to ensure the utmost efficiency.

Broiler production is concentrated in the states of Arkansas, Georgia, Alabama, North Carolina, Mississippi, Texas, Maryland, Delaware, California, and Virginia. California is the only state with large production located outside the "broiler belt." These 10 states produce nearly 85% of the total number of broilers in the United States.

Broiler production has increased tremendously over the past three decades, from 3.7 million lb of ready-to-cook broilers in 1960 to 18.6 million lb in 1990. The U.S. broiler industry is concentrating its growout operations into fewer but larger farms. In 1987, there were 27,645 broiler growout operations, compared with 42,185 in 1959. Large farms (those with 100,000 or more birds) constituted over 50% of the total number of growout operations and 93% of total production in 1987. This is a significant change for only 5% large farms in 1959 had 28% of the production.

Although the number of laying hens in the United States has declined over the years, egg production is up because of a dramatic increase in the performance of the individual hen. In 1880, for example, the average laying hen produced 100 eggs per year; in 1950, the average was 175; and in 1986, it increased to 250.

The USDA estimates that 85% of the market eggs produced in the United States are from large commercial producers (those that maintain 1–11 million birds). The 45 largest egg-producing companies in the United States have more than 97 million layers, which is 35.5% of the nation's total.

Important changes have also occurred in U.S. turkey production. Fifty years ago, turkeys were raised in small numbers on many farms; today, they are raised in larger numbers on fewer farms. The average turkey farmer is producing well over 50,000 turkeys per year. The leading turkey-producing states are North Carolina, Minnesota, California, Arkansas, and Missouri.

Most of the turkeys produced today are the heavy or large, broad-breasted white type. At one time, the fryer-roaster-type turkey (5–9 lb) was popular; it bridged the gap between the turkey and the broiler chicken. Today, the broiler industry has taken over the fryer-roaster market because it can produce fryer-roaster chickens at a much lower price.

It takes 16 weeks for turkey hens and 19 weeks for turkey toms to reach market size. Because there is a heavy demand for turkey meat in November and December, turkey eggs are set in large numbers in April, May, and June. However, eggs are set year-round because there is a constant, though lower, demand for fresh turkey meat throughout the year. The normal incubation period for turkey eggs is 28 days.

In the recent past, turkey was considered a seasonal product by most consumers, with consumption occurring primarily at Thanksgiving. Increasingly, turkey is consumed throughout the year, and consumers have available to them a large variety of turkey products. The greater demand for turkey has meant that approximately 1 billion lb more of ready-to-cook turkey is produced today than was produced in the early 1980s.

Product sales in the U.S. poultry industry are approximately $7 billion for broilers, $3 billion for eggs, and $2 billion for turkeys. Broilers and turkeys are experiencing increased growth while egg sales are declining.

Poultry breeding, feeding, and management practices are presented in Chapter 32.

THE SHEEP AND GOAT INDUSTRY

Global Perspective

Sheep and goats are closely related, both originating in Europe and the cooler regions of Asia. Sheep are distinguished from goats by the absence of a beard, less odor (males only) and glands in all four feet. The horns are spiral in different directions; goat horns spiral to the left, while sheep horns spiral to the right (like a corkscrew).

Sheep and goats are important ruminants in temperate and tropical agriculture. They provide fibers, milk, hides, and meat, making them versatile and efficient, especially for developing countries. Sheep and goats are better adapted than cattle to arid tropics, probably because of their superior water and nitrogen economy. Cattle, sheep, and goats often are grazed together because they utilize different plants. Goats graze **browse** (shrubs) and some **forbs** (broadleafed plants), cattle graze tall grasses and some forbs, and sheep graze short grasses and some forbs. Most of the forbs in grazing areas are broadleaf weeds.

More than 60% of all sheep are in temperate zones and fewer than 40% are in tropical zones. Goats, though, are mostly (80%) in the tropical or subtropical zones (0–40°N). Temperature and type of vegetation are the primary factors encouraging sheep production in temperate zones and goat production in tropical zones.

Sheep originated in the dry, alternately hot-and-cold climate of Southwest Asia. To succeed in tropical areas, then, sheep had to adapt the abilities to lose body heat, resist diseases, and survive in an adverse nutritional environment. For sheep to lose heat easily, they require a large body surface-to-mass ratio. Such a sheep is a small, long-legged animal. In addition, a hairy coat allows ventilation and protects the skin from the sun and abrasions. In temperate areas, sheep with large, compact bodies, a heavy fleece covering, and storage of subcutaneous fat have an advantage. Sheep can also constrict or relax blood vessels to the face, legs, and ears for control of heat loss.

TABLE 2.12. World Sheep Numbers, Production, and Consumption, 1989

Country	No. Sheep (mil head)	Country	Production (carcass wt; mil lb)	Country	Per-capita Consumption (lb)[a]
1. Australia	152	1. USSR	1.9	1. New Zealand	68
2. USSR	140	2. New Zealand	1.2	2. Australia	48
3. China	102	3. Australia	1.2	3. Greece	32
4. New Zealand	61	4. China	0.9	4. Ireland	19
5. India	53	5. United Kingdom	0.8	5. Bulgaria	19
World total	1,176	World total	14.2	World average[b]	3

[a] Carcass weight of lamb, mutton, and goat meat.
[b] Estimated by dividing world production by world population.
Sources: USDA, ERS; 1989 *FAO Production Yearbook.*

TABLE 2.13. World Lamb, Mutton, and Goat Meat Trade, 1989

Exports		Imports	
Country	(mil lb)	Country	(mil lb)
1. New Zealand	1,052	1. Japan	306
2. Australia	425	2. France	264
3. United Kingdom	196	3. United Kingdom	260
4. Romania	110	4. Germany	73
5. Ireland	81	5. United States	58
World total	2,097	World total	1,329

Note: Carcass weight.
Source: USDA, FAS, *World Livestock Situation.*

The productivity of sheep is much greater in temperate areas than it is in tropical environments. This difference is the result not only of a more favorable environment (temperature and feed supply) but also a greater selection emphasis on growth rate, milk production, lambing percentage, and fleece weight. Sheep from temperate environments do not adapt well to tropical environments; therefore, it may be more effective to select sheep in the production environment, rather than introduce sheep from different environments.

World sheep numbers of nearly 1.2 billion head in 1989 are the highest on record. Australia, the Soviet Union, China, New Zealand, and India are the leading sheep countries (Table 2.12). New Zealand, Australia, and Greece have the highest per-capita consumption of mutton, lamb, and goat meat.

Countries highly involved in the export and import of lamb and mutton are shown in Table 2.13. New Zealand and Australia are the leading exporters, while Japan and France are the top importers.

The 526 million head of goats in the world are concentrated primarily in India and China, with Pakistan, Nigeria, and Somalia also having large goat populations (Table 2.14). In many countries, goats are important for both milk and meat production. Table 2.14 shows the leading countries in goat meat and milk production.

TABLE 2.14. World Goat Numbers, Meat Production, and Milk Production, 1989

Country	No. Goats (mil head)	Country	Meat Production (carcass wt; mil lb)	Country	Milk Production (bil lb)
1. India	107	1. China	0.9	1. India	3.3
2. China	79	2. India	0.8	2. Somalia	1.5
3. Pakistan	34	3. Pakistan	0.6	3. Pakistan	1.3
4. Nigeria	26	4. Nigeria	0.3	4. Turkey	1.2
5. Somalia	20	5. Turkey	0.2	5. Sudan	1.2
World total	526	World total	5.2	World total	19.0

Source: USDA, FAS, *World Livestock Situation.*

United States

The number of sheep in the United States reached a high of 56 million in 1942, thereafter declining to approximately 11 million in 1990 (Fig. 2.17). U.S. sheep are located on about 111,000 different operations.

Although the price received for lambs increased from $0.15 – $0.70 per pound between 1961 and 1985, this increase has been largely offset by increased production costs, scarcity of good sheep herders, and heavy losses from disease, predators, and adverse weather.

The number of ewes on U.S. farms in 1990 is shown in Fig. 2.18. The five leading states in ewe numbers are, respectively, Texas (1.49 million), California (0.62 million), Wyoming (0.57 million), South Dakota (0.44 million), and Utah (0.41 million). The Midwest and West Coast areas are important in farm-flock sheep production, whereas other western states are primarily range-flock areas. The midwestern states generally raise more lambs per ewe than the western states do, though Washington, Oregon, and Idaho resemble the midwestern states in this regard.

Most of the decline in U.S. sheep numbers during the past 50 years has occurred in the West. However, this region, with its extensive public and private rangelands, still produces 80% of the sheep raised in the country today. Most U.S. sheep growers have small flocks (50 or fewer sheep) and raise sheep as a secondary enterprise. About 40% of the West's sheep producers maintain flocks of more than 50 sheep; these flocks contain about 93% of the sheep in that region. Only about one-third of the operators in the West who have flocks of 50 or more sheep specialize in sheep; the other two-thirds have diversified livestock operations.

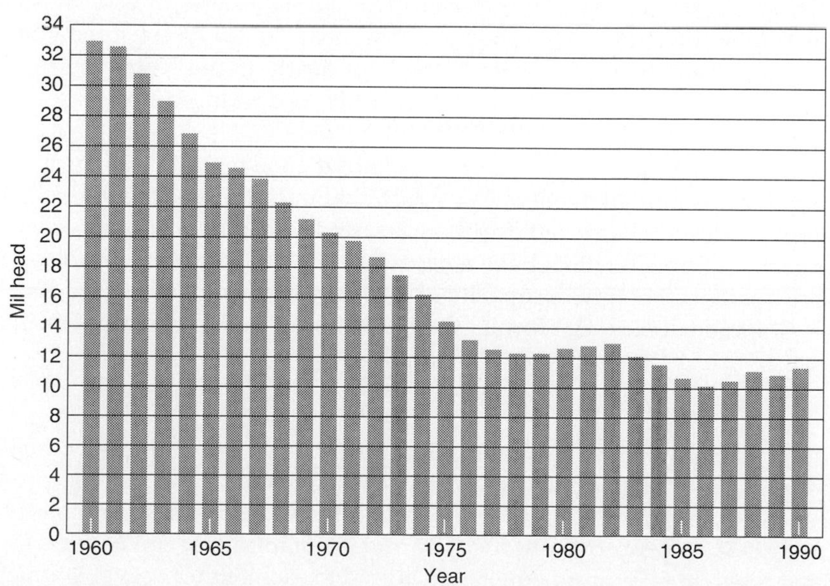

FIGURE 2.17.
U.S. sheep and lamb numbers, 1960–90. Courtesy of Western Livestock Marketing Information Project.

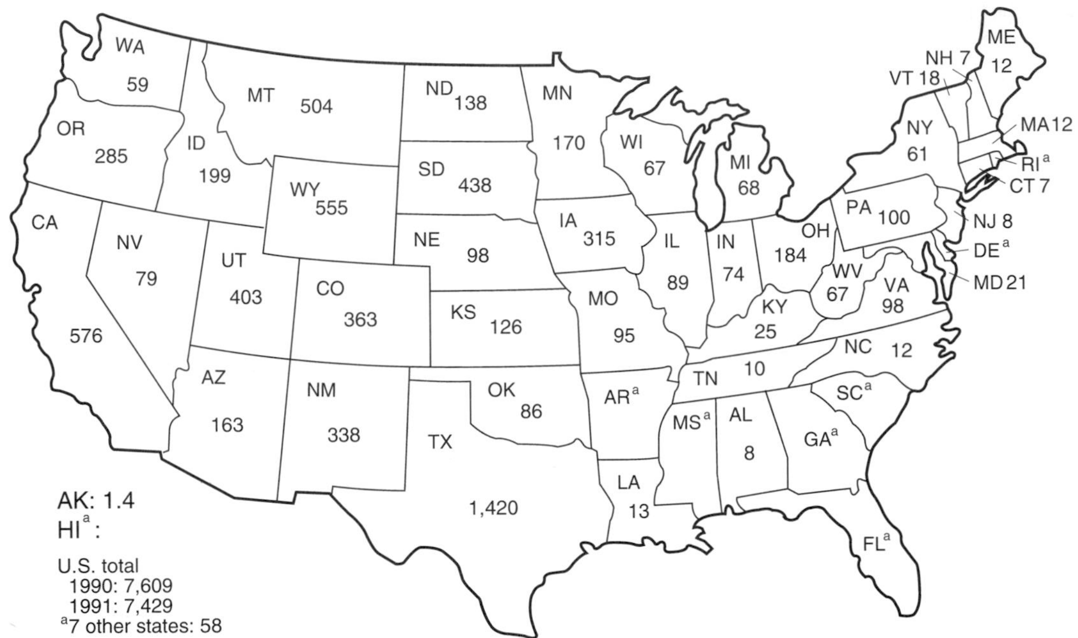

FIGURE 2.18.
U.S. ewe numbers, 1 January 1991 (1,000 head). Courtesy of Western Livestock Marketing Information Project.

About 23% of all sheep born in the western United States and 13% of those born in the North-Central region are lost before they are marketed. In the West, predators, especially coyotes, and weather are the most frequent causes of death. In the North-Central region, the primary causes of death include weather and disease before docking, and disease and attacks by dogs after docking.

The range operator produces some slaughter lambs if good mountain range is available, but most range-produced lambs are feeders (i.e., lambs that must have additional feed before they are slaughtered). Feeder lambs are fed by producers, sold to feedlot operators, or fed on contract by feedlot operators. Some feedlots have a capacity for 10,000 or more lambs on feed at one time, and many feedlots that have a capacity of 1,000 are in operation. The leading lamb-feeding states are Colorado, Texas, California, Oregon, Kansas, and Wyoming (Fig. 2.19).

Purebred Breeder

Some producers raise purebred sheep and sell **rams** for breeding. Purebred breeders have an important responsibility to the sheep industry: they determine the genetic productivity of commercial sheep. The purebred breeder should rigidly select breeding animals and then sell only those rams that will improve productivity and profitability for the commercial producer.

Records are essential to indicate which ram is bred to each of the ewes and which ewe is the mother of each lamb. All ram lambs are usually kept together to identify those that are desirable for sale. The ram lambs are often retained by the purebred breeder until they are 1 year of age, at which time they are offered for sale.

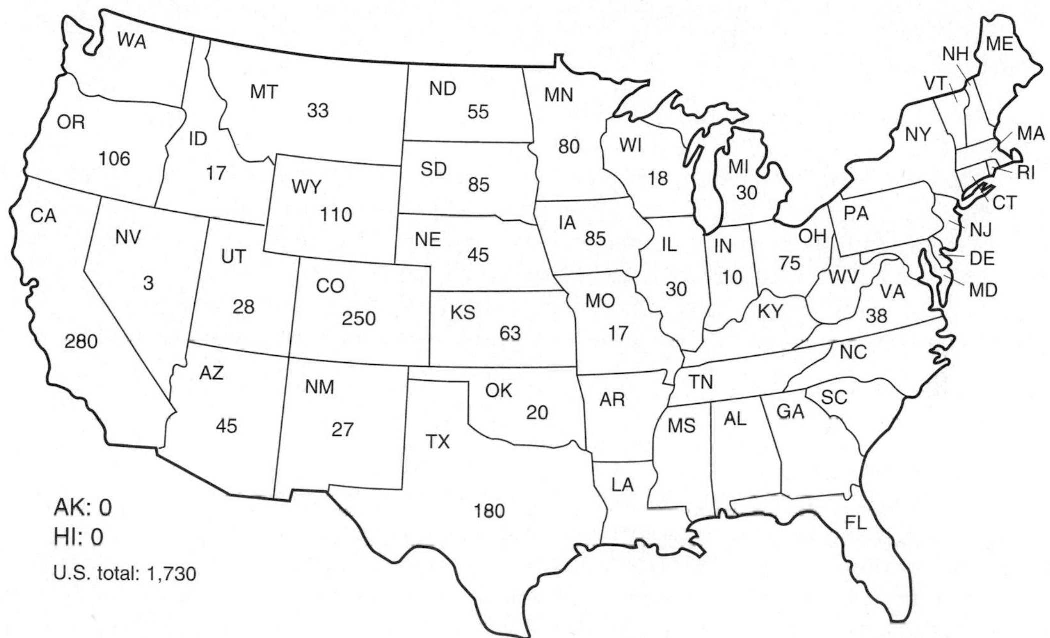

FIGURE 2.19.
U.S. sheep and lambs on feed, 1 January 1991 (1,000 head). Courtesy of Western Livestock Marketing Information Project.

Commercial Market Lamb Producers

Commercial lamb producers whose pastures are productive can produce market wether and ewe lambs on pasture, whereas those whose pastures are less desirable produce feeder lambs. Lambs that are neither sufficiently fat nor large for market at weaning time usually go to feedlot operators, where they are fed to market weight and condition. However, most feedlot lambs are obtained from producers of range sheep. The producer of market lambs, whose feed and pasture conditions are favorable, strives to raise lambs that finish at 90–120 days of age, weighing approximately 110 lb each.

Commercial Feedlot Operator

Lambs are sent to the feedlot if they need additional weight prior to slaughter. The feedlot operator hopes to profit by increasing the value of the lambs per unit of weight and by increasing their weight. Lambs on feed that gain about 0.5–0.8 lb per head per day are considered satisfactory gainers. Feeder buyers prefer feeder lambs weighing 70–80 lb over larger lambs because of the need to put 20–30 lb of additional weight on the lambs to finish them. A feeding period of 40–60 days is usually sufficient for finishing healthy lambs.

Chapters 28 and 29 discuss in detail sheep breeding, feeding, and management practices. Chapter 33 covers goat production.

THE SWINE INDUSTRY

Global Perspective

Swine are widely distributed throughout the world, even though 40% of the world's pigs are located in China (Table 2.15). China far exceeds all other countries in number of pigs and total pork production. However, when pork production (carcass weight) is evaluated on a per-capita basis, then both the United States (64 lb per person) and the Soviet Union (52 lb per person) exceed China (44 lb per person). Other countries where swine numbers and production are important include Germany, France, and Brazil (Table 2.15).

Table 2.16 shows the countries most highly involved in the export and import of pork. Several European countries, the United States, and Canada lead in world pork trade.

United States

Swine production in the United States is concentrated heavily in the nation's midsection known as the Corn Belt. This area produces most of the nation's corn, the principal feed used for swine. The Corn Belt states of Iowa, Missouri, Illinois, Indiana, Ohio, northwest Kentucky, southern Wisconsin, southern Minnesota, eastern South Dakota, and eastern Nebraska produce nearly 75% of the nation's swine, with Iowa alone accounting for almost 25% (Fig. 2.20). Swine numbers decreased about 10 million head in the United States from 1980 to 1990 (Fig. 2.21).

U.S. swine operations have been getting larger over the past 25 years, while the number of farms selling hogs has dropped from 2.1 million to 450,000. Farms selling more than 1,000 hogs annually have increased more than 300% during the same period; these operations now account for 25%–30% of all hogs sold. Most swine producers farm 200–500 acres of land and have other livestock enterprises.

Types of Swine Operations

There are four primary types of swine operations. In **feeder-pig production,** the producer maintains a breeding herd and produces feeder pigs for sale at an average weight of 40 lb. In **feeder-pig finishing,** the feeder pigs are purchased and then fed to slaughter weight. The

TABLE 2.15. World Swine Numbers, Production, and Consumption, 1989

Country	No. Swine (mil head)	Country	Production (carcass wt; bil lb)	Country	Per-capita Consumption (lb)[a]
1. China	349	1. China	49	1. Hungary	195
2. USSR	78	2. United States	16	2. Denmark	144
3. United States	55	3. USSR	15	3. Germany	137
4. Germany	36	4. Germany	10	4. Czechoslovakia	130
5. Brazil	33	5. France	4	5. Austria	116
World total	846	World total	148	World average[b]	27

[a] Carcass weight.
[b] Estimated by dividing world production by world population.
Sources: USDA, FAS, *World Livestock Situation;* 1989 *FAO Production Yearbook.*

TABLE 2.16. World Swine Trade, 1989

Exports		Imports	
Country	(bil lb)	Country	(bil lb)
1. Netherlands	2.3	1. Germany	1.3
2. Denmark	1.9	2. United Kingdom	1.2
3. Belgium, Luxembourg	0.8	3. Japan	1.1
4. Germany	0.8	4. Italy	1.1
5. Canada	0.7	5. France	1.0
World total	9.6	World total	8.6

Note: Carcass weight.
Source: USDA, FAS, *World Livestock Situation.*

farrow-to-finish operation maintains a breeding herd as pigs are produced and fed to market weight on the same farm. Finally, the **purebred** or **seedstock** operation is similar to farrow-to-finish, except the saleable product is primarily breeding boars and gilts.

The various swine operations and the management factors affecting them are discussed in Chapters 26 and 27.

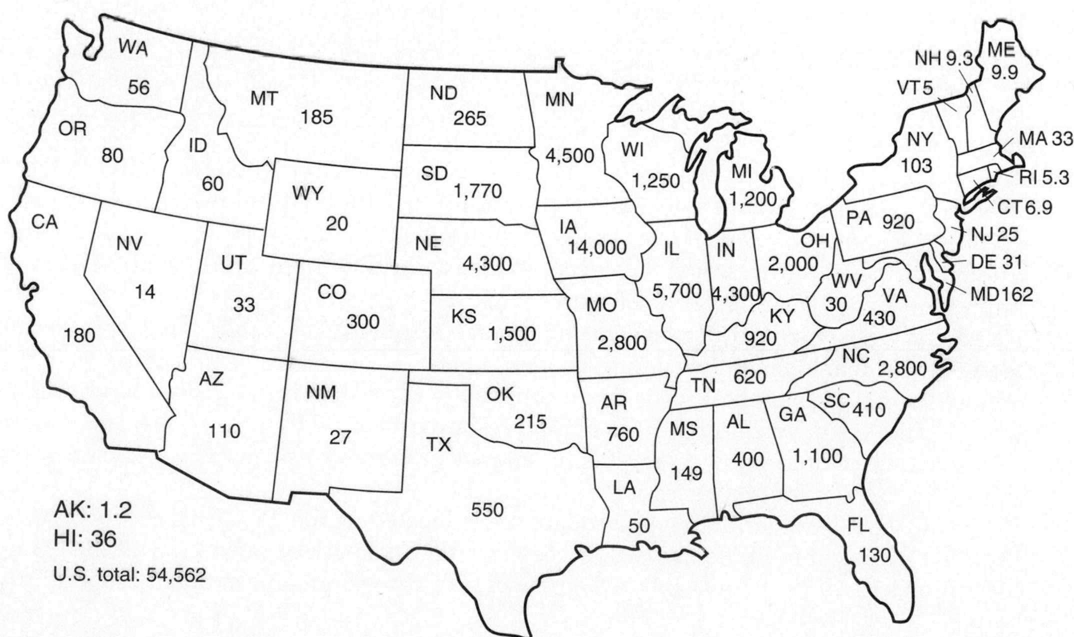

FIGURE 2.20.
Total number of U.S. hogs and pigs, 1 December 1990 (1,000 head). Courtesy of Western Livestock Marketing Information Project.

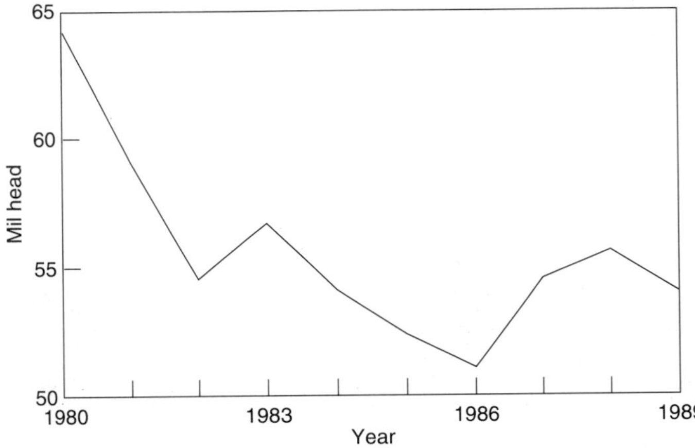

FIGURE 2.21.
U.S. hog inventory, 1980–89. Courtesy of the USDA, *Livestock and Poultry Situation and Outlook Report.*

INDUSTRY ISSUES AND CHALLENGES

The following list identifies some of the significant issues and challenges that the animal industries will encounter during the next decade. Later chapters discuss some of these issues in more detail.

With challenges come opportunities. Jobs are created, recognition is given, and monetary rewards are available to successful problem solvers and decision makers. These individuals will face the problems, meet the challenges, and attempt to resolve them. The challenge is to separate the myths, perceptions, and emotions from the facts, then effectively communicate these differences.

Environmental Issues

—Are livestock and poultry major contributors to environmental problems, such as global warming, water pollution, soil erosion, and misuse of other natural resources?

—Is the methane production of ruminants a significant contributor to global warming, or do ruminants contribute less than 10 percent of the world's methane production? (Methane represents only 18% of greenhouse gases.)

—Who can best ensure the protection of natural resources on public lands, private or government management or both in cooperation?

—Should our environmental focus be on conserving the natural resources of land, water, and wildlife or on preserving those natural resources?
(Preservation would allow little, if any, animal or human use, whereas conservation would encourage multiple uses.)

—If public lands (primarily 550,000 square miles located in the 11 western states) move from single use to multiple use (wilderness and national park expansion), will the elimination of 10% of beef cows and 50% of ewes affect personal and national economics?

Some of the environmental issues can be better perceived and evaluated by viewing videotapes. See the references at the end of this chapter—that is, *Cattlemen Care About the Environment* and *Issues and Answers for the Nineties.*

Animal Rights Issues

—These issues are discussed in detail in Chapter 35.

Health Issues

—Do red meats, eggs, and dairy products fit the health and fitness life-style prevalent among today's consumers? Do these products contain life-threatening amounts of saturated fats and cholesterol? Do large differences exist between consumer perceptions and the nutritional facts of these animal products? If so, how can the animal industries effectively counteract false impressions?

—Are there significant food safety problems with drug residues and antibiotics in meats and life-threatening salmonella in poultry products? (See Chapters 3, 5, and 6 for answers to these questions.)

Convenience Products

—Can the red meat industries provide a greater variety of convenient and taste-satisfying products, similar to the numerous poultry products? (See Chapter 3.)

Marketing Issues

—Can value-based marketing of paying for differences in lean-to-fat ratios become a reality in the red meat industry? Or will the tradition continue of marketing excess fat in boxed products and then trimming the fat at the retail level?

—Can the U.S. poultry and red meat industries make entry into the Soviet Union and other eastern markets?

—Can the U.S. beef industry be competitive with that of Australia (and other countries) for the Japanese and Korean beef demand? Or will the Japanese invest in U.S. beef operations and supply their own market?

—Can world trade, in a global economy, be enhanced by more open markets and fewer trade barriers?

—Are European countries gearing up to become the future superpowers of all member states in the European Community (EC), uniting as one political and economic unit? Does this signal more trade wars like the EC banning of hormone-fed beef from the United States?

—Are there alternatives to hot-iron branding that will increase hide values, satisfy animal rightists' concerns, and give cattle producers positive identification of the animals?

—Can bioengineered products (BST milk and PST pork) enter the market without strong consumer resistance? (See Chapter 12.)

Organizational Issues

—Are the livestock and poultry industries adequately organized, financially capable, and politically influential to counteract and compete with specialized interest groups whose focus may be detrimental to the overall economic well-being of the United States?

SELECTED REFERENCES

Publications

Bell, D. D. 1990. An egg industry perspective: Ready for the 21st century? *Poul. Dig.* 49:22.

Bjerklie, S. 1990. Poultry's decade of issues. *Meat and Poultry* 36:24.

Directions. 1990. *The State of the Beef Industry*. Englewood, CO: National Cattlemen's Association. *FAO Production Yearbook.* Vol. 43, 1989. Rome: FAO.

Helming, B. 1990. Meat's decade of danger. *Meat and Poultry* 36:30.

Horse Industry Directory. 1990–91. Washington, DC: American Horse Council, Inc.

Lasley, F. A., Henson, W. L., and Jones, H. B., Jr. 1984. *The U.S. Turkey Industry.* USDA, ERS Agric. Econ. Rpt. 525.

Lasley, F. A., et al. 1988. *The U.S. Broiler Industry.* USDA, ERS Agric. Econ. Rpt. 591.

Majeskie, J. L. and Eastwood, B. R. 1990. Status of United States Dairy Cattle. National Coop. Dairy Herd Improv. Program Handbook, Fact Sheet K-7.

Meat industry: A sampling of the issues and controversies affecting meat and poultry industries all over the planet. 1989. *Meat and Poultry* 35:12–14, 41, 43.

Roybal, J. 1990. A hassle over hot-iron branding. *BEEF* (Aug.).

Stillman, R., Crawford, T., and Aldrich, L. 1990. *The U.S. Sheep Industry.* Washington, DC: USDA, ERS.

Thompson, K. 1989. The world's meat industry. *Meat and Poultry* 35:12.

USDA. 1988. *Economic Indicators of the Farm Sector: Costs of Production—Livestock and Dairy.* Washington, DC: GPO.

USDA. 1990. *Foreign Agricultural Trade of the United States.* Washington, DC: GPO.

USDA. 1984–88. *Livestock and Meat Statistics.* Statistical Bulletin 784.

USDA. 1990. *Livestock and Poultry Situation and Outlook Report.* LPS39-41.

USDA. 1990. World Livestock Situation.

USDA, FAS. May 1990. *World Dairy Situation.* Cir. Series FD1-90. Washington, DC: GPO.

U.S. Sheep Industry Market Situation Report. 1989–90. American Sheep Industry Association, 6911 S. Yosemite St., Englewood, CO 80112-1414.

Visuals

An Introduction to the Poultry Industry (77 slides and audiotape; 12 min.). Poultry Science Department, Ohio State University, 674 W. Lane Ave., Columbus, OH 43210.

Cattlemen Care About the Environment (1990 Videotape; 9 min.) and *Issues and Answers for the Nineties* (1990 Videotape; 7 min.). Communications Dept., National Cattlemen's Association, Box 3469, Englewood, CO 80111.

CHAPTER 3

Red Meat Products

Red meat products come primarily from cattle, swine, sheep, goats, and, to a lesser extent, horses and other animals. Poultry meat, sometimes called white meat, is discussed in Chapter 6.

Red meats are named according to their source: **beef** is typically from cattle over a year of age; **veal** is from young calves (veal carcasses are distinguished from beef by their grayish-pink color of the lean); **pork** is from swine; **mutton** is from mature sheep; **lamb** is from young sheep; **chevon** is from goats, but more commonly is called **goat meat**.

PRODUCTION

World red meat supply approaches 280 billion pounds, with China, the United States, and Soviet Union leading all other countries (Table 3.1). Buffalo meat comes from the true buffalo; it should not be confused with bison in the United States. The true buffalo has no hump; thus the name *buffalo* belongs only to water buffalo in Asia and the African buffalo.

Red meat production in the United States is shown in Fig. 3.1. Beef and pork comprise most of the annual production of nearly 40 billion lb. The total production has been relatively stable over the past several years.

Figures 3.2, 3.3, and 3.4 show where cattle, hogs, and sheep, respectively, are slaughtered in the United States. Kansas, Texas, Nebraska, Colorado, and Iowa are the leading states in cattle slaughter. Iowa slaughtered more than one-fourth of the nation's hogs in 1990, and Illinois, Minnesota, Nebraska, Michigan, Ohio, Indiana, Missouri, Kentucky, and South Dakota together slaughtered an additional 45%. The leading lamb-slaughtering states are Colorado, California, Texas, Iowa, Kansas, and Minnesota.

The United States has an annual supply of horsemeat of approximately 150 million lb (Table 3.1). While most of the horsemeat goes into pet food, several thousand tons are shipped to Europe for human consumption. Approximately 15 – 20 U.S. packing plants specialize in processing horses, shipping the meat to France, Belgium, the Netherlands, Switzerland, and Italy.

Meat animals are processed in packing plants located near areas of live animal production.

TABLE 3.1. World Red Meat Supply, 1989

Product	Bil lb[a]	Leading Countries (bil lb)
Pork	148	China (49); United States (16); USSR (15); Germany (10)
Beef and veal	109	United States (23.4); USSR (19.4); Argentina (5.7); Brazil (5.4)
Mutton and lamb	14	USSR (1.9); Australia (1.2); New Zealand (1.2); China (0.9)
Goat meat	5	China (0.9); India (0.8); Pakistan (0.6); Nigeria (0.3)
Buffalo meat	3	India (0.8); Pakistan (0.7); China (0.5); Egypt (0.4)
Horsemeat	1	Mexico (0.16); United States (0.15); Italy (0.12); China (0.11)
World total	280	China (53); United States (40); USSR (36); Germany (14)

[a] Carcass weight.
Source: 1989 *FAO Production Yearbook.*

This reduces the transportation costs because carcasses, wholesale cuts, and retail cuts can be transported at less cost than live animals. The top 10 packers are identified in Table 3.2.

PRODUCTS

Animals are transported to packing plants, where they are processed. During the initial processing stage, the animals are made unconscious by using carbon dioxide gas or by stunning

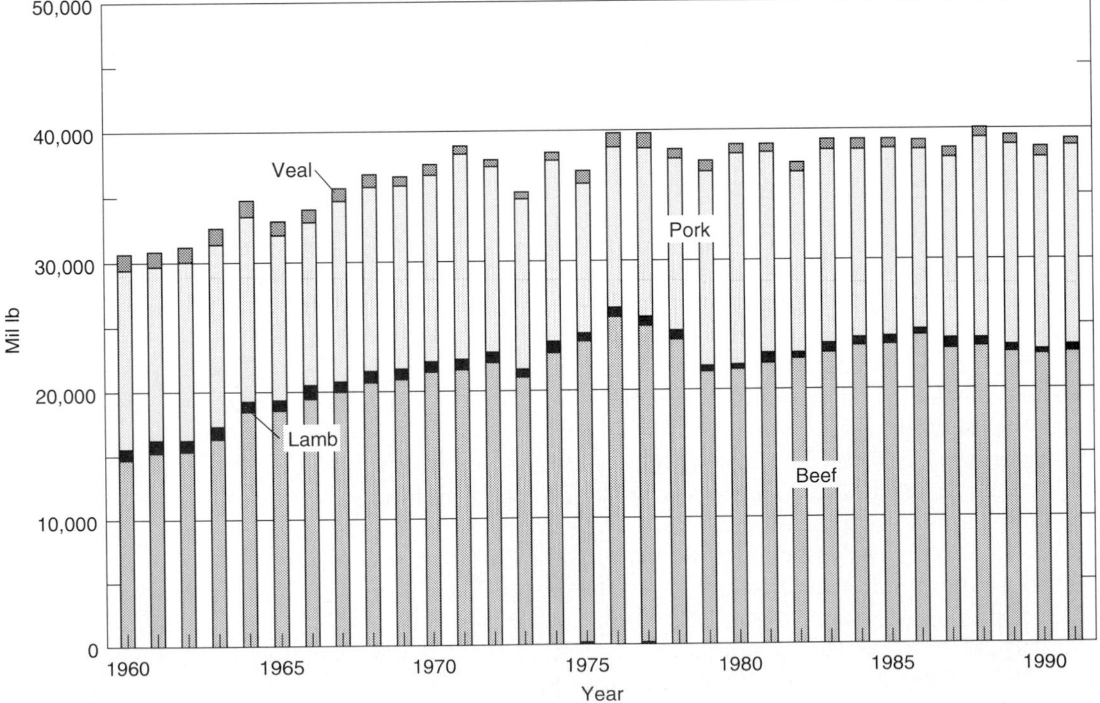

FIGURE 3.1.
Red meat produced in the United States (carcass weight basis), 1960–90. Courtesy of Western Livestock Marketing Information Project.

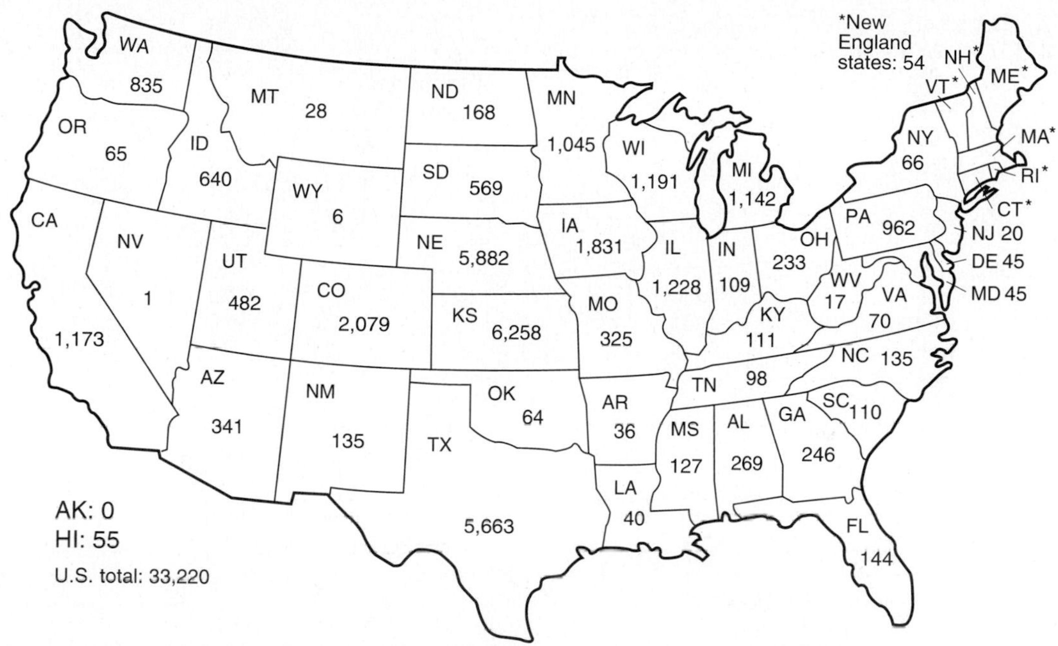

FIGURE 3.2.
U.S. commercial cattle slaughter, 1990 (1,000 head). Courtesy of Western Livestock Marketing Information Project.

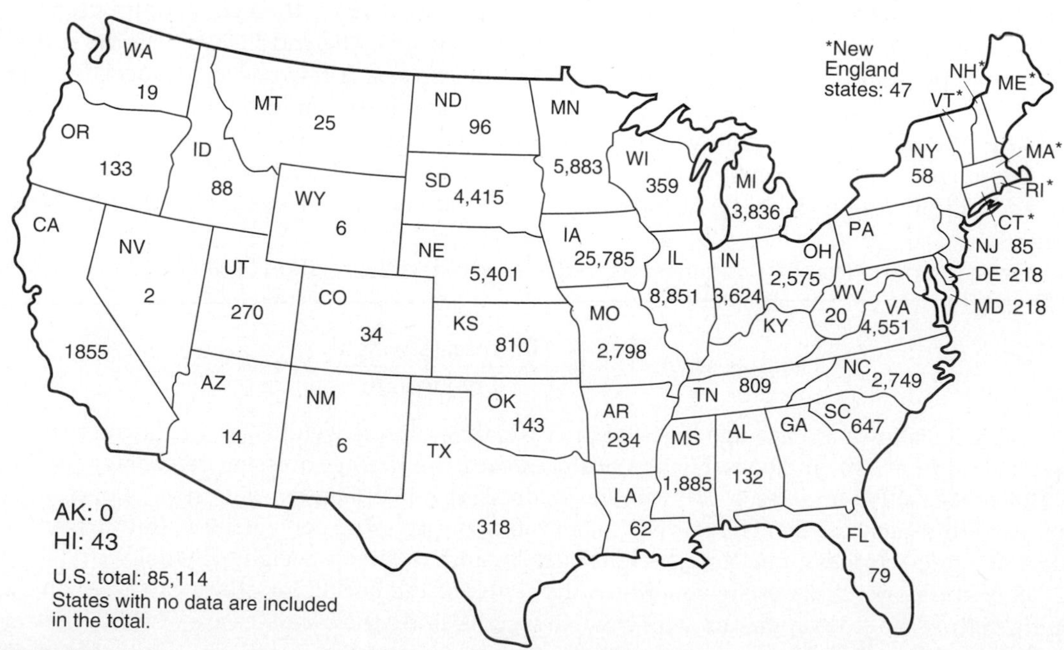

FIGURE 3.3.
U.S. commercial hog slaughter, 1990 (1,000 head). Courtesy of Western Livestock Marketing Information Project.

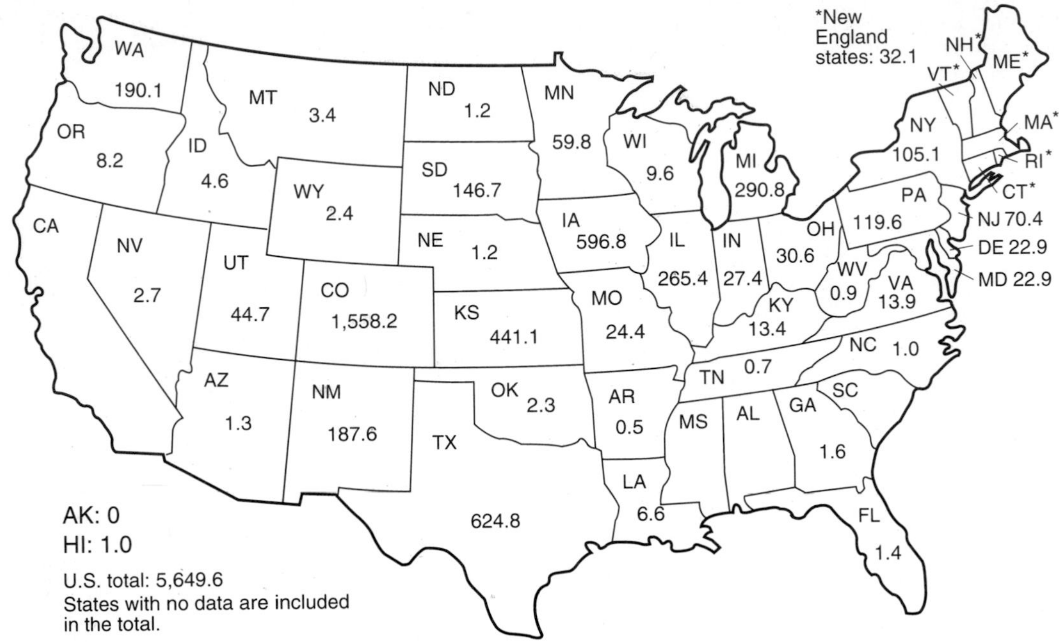

FIGURE 3.4.
U.S. commercial sheep slaughter, 1990 (1,000 head). Courtesy of Western Livestock Marketing Information Project.

(electrical or mechanical). The jugular vein and/or carotid artery is then cut to drain the blood from the animal. After bleeding, the hides are removed from cattle and sheep. Hogs are scalded to remove the hair, but the skin is usually left on the carcass. A few packers (especially small plants) skin hogs, as it is more energy efficient than leaving the skin on.

After the hide or hair is removed, the internal organs are separated from the carcass. Those parts removed from the carcass are sometimes referred to as the **drop, viscera, offal,** or **by-products**. Typically these are the head, hide, hair, shanks (lower parts of legs and feet), and internal organs.

Dressing percentage (sometimes referred to as **yield**) is the relation of hot carcass weight to live weight. It is calculated as follows:

$$\text{Dressing percentage} = \frac{\text{Hot carcass weight}}{\text{Live weight}} \times 100$$

Table 3.3 shows the average live slaughter weights, carcass weights, and dressing percentages for cattle, sheep, and hogs. For practical purposes, the average dressing percentage for hogs is 72%; cattle, 60%; and sheep, 50%; however, dressing percentage can vary several percentage points within each species. The primary factors affecting dressing percentage are fill (contents of digestive tract), fatness, muscling, weight of hide, and, in sheep, weight of wool.

Beef and pork carcasses are split down the center of the backbone (sheep carcasses are not split), giving two sides approximately equal in weight. After the carcasses are washed, they are put in a cooler to chill. The cooler temperature of approximately 35°F removes the heat from the carcass and keeps the meat from spoiling. Carcasses can be stored in coolers for several weeks;

TABLE 3.2. Leading U.S. Meat Packing and Processing Companies

Rank	Company (location)	1989 Sales ($bil)	No. Plants	No. Employees	Products[a]
1	ConAgra (Omaha, NE)	$11.0	63	32,831	*B-P-L-C-T-S*
2	IBP, Inc. (Dakota City, NE)	9.1	18	23,500	*B-P*
3	Excel Corp. (Wichita, KS)	5.0	13	11,500	*B-P*
4	Sara Lee Corp. (Memphis, TN)	2.7	28	13,000	*B-P-T*
5	Tyson Foods, Inc. (Springdale, AR)	2.5	47	43,000	*B-P-C*
6	Geo A. Hormel and Co. (Austin, MN)	2.4	13	8,000	*B-P-C-T-S*
7	Oscar Mayer (Madison, WI)	2.3	21	14,500	*B-P-C-T-S*
8	Internatl. Multifoods (Minneapolis, MN)	2.1	12	2,661	*B-P-C-S*
9	Holly Farms (Memphis, TN)	2.0	26	15,000	*B-P-C*
10	John Morrell and Co. (Cincinnati, OH)	1.9	8	4,950	*B-P-L-C-T*
Total (top 10)		41.0		168,943	
Total (top 50)		61.2		288,924	

[a] *B* = beef; *P* = pork; *L* = lamb; *C* = chicken; *T* = turkey; *S* = seafood.
Source: Meat and Poultry, July 1990.

however, this is uncommon in large packing plants as profitability is dependent on processing live animals one day and shipping carcasses or products out the next day or two. Smaller packers may keep carcasses in the coolers for as long as 2 weeks. This allows the carcasses to age. This **aging** process increases meat tenderness through an enzyme activity that decreases the tensile strength of muscle fibers.

TABLE 3.3. U.S. Livestock Slaughter and Meat Production, 1989

Species/Class	Meat Products	No. Head (mil)	Average Liveweight (lb)	Total Carcass Weight (bil lb)	Average Carcass Weight (lb)	Average Dressing Percentage
Cattle	Beef	34.1	1,130	23.1	680	60%
Calves[a]	Veal	2.2	260	0.3	162	60
Hogs	Pork	89.0	240	15.8	178	72
Sheep and lambs	Mutton and lamb	5.6	120	0.4	62	50

[a] Part of these are classified as calf carcasses, which are intermediate in age and size between veal and beef carcasses.
Sources: USDA; AMI, *Meat Facts,* 1989.

TABLE 3.4. Wholesale Cuts of Beef, Veal, Pork, and Lamb

Beef	Veal	Pork	Lamb
Round	Leg/round	Leg/ham	Leg
Sirloin	Sirloin	Loin	Loin
Short loin	Loin	Blade shoulder	Rib
Rib	Rib	Jowl	Shoulder
Chuck	Shoulder	Arm shoulder	Neck
Foreshank	Foreshank	Spareribs	Foreshank
Brisket	Breast	Side	Breast
Short plate			
Flank			

Source: The National Live Stock and Meat Board.

In the past, most red meat was shipped in carcass form, but today many packing plants process the carcasses into wholesale or primal cuts and even into retail cuts (Table 3.4; Figs. 3.5–3.8). The latter process involves shipping meat in boxes; thus the terms ***boxed beef*** and ***boxed lamb***.

Most red meats are marketed as fresh products. Some are cured, smoked, processed, or canned. Table 3.5 identifies the forms in which major meat products are prepared for sale.

KOSHER MEATS

All **kosher meat** comes from animals that have split hooves, that chew their cud, and that have been slaughtered in a manner prescribed by the Torah (Orthodox Jewish law). Meat from undesirable animals or from animals not properly slaughtered or with imperfections are called **nonkosher** (trefah). Red meats, poultry, and all other foods are classified as kosher or nonkosher. Foods that are kosher bear the endorsement symbol Ⓤ.

Kosher slaughter, inspection, and supervision are performed only by trained individuals approved by rabbinic authority. The trachea and esophagus of the animal must be cut in swift continuous strokes with a perfectly smooth, sharp knife causing instant death and minimum pain to the animal. Various internal organs are inspected for defects and adhesions.

Only the forequarters are identified as kosher, as the hindquarters contain the forbidden sciatic nerve, which is imbedded deep in the muscle tissue and is difficult to remove. Hindquarters are sold as nonkosher meats.

The Torah forbids the eating of blood, including blood of arteries, veins, and muscle tissue. For this reason, certain arteries and veins must be removed from cattle; neck veins of poultry must be severed to allow the free flow of blood. Blood is extracted from meat by broiling and salting. There are specific steps required in proper broiling and salting to endorse the meat as kosher.

There are approximately 2 million Orthodox Jews in the United States who keep kosher. Estimates on quantities of kosher meat consumed are not available.

COMPOSITION

Meat composition can be defined in either physical or chemical terms. Physical composition is observed visually; chemical composition is determined by chemical analysis.

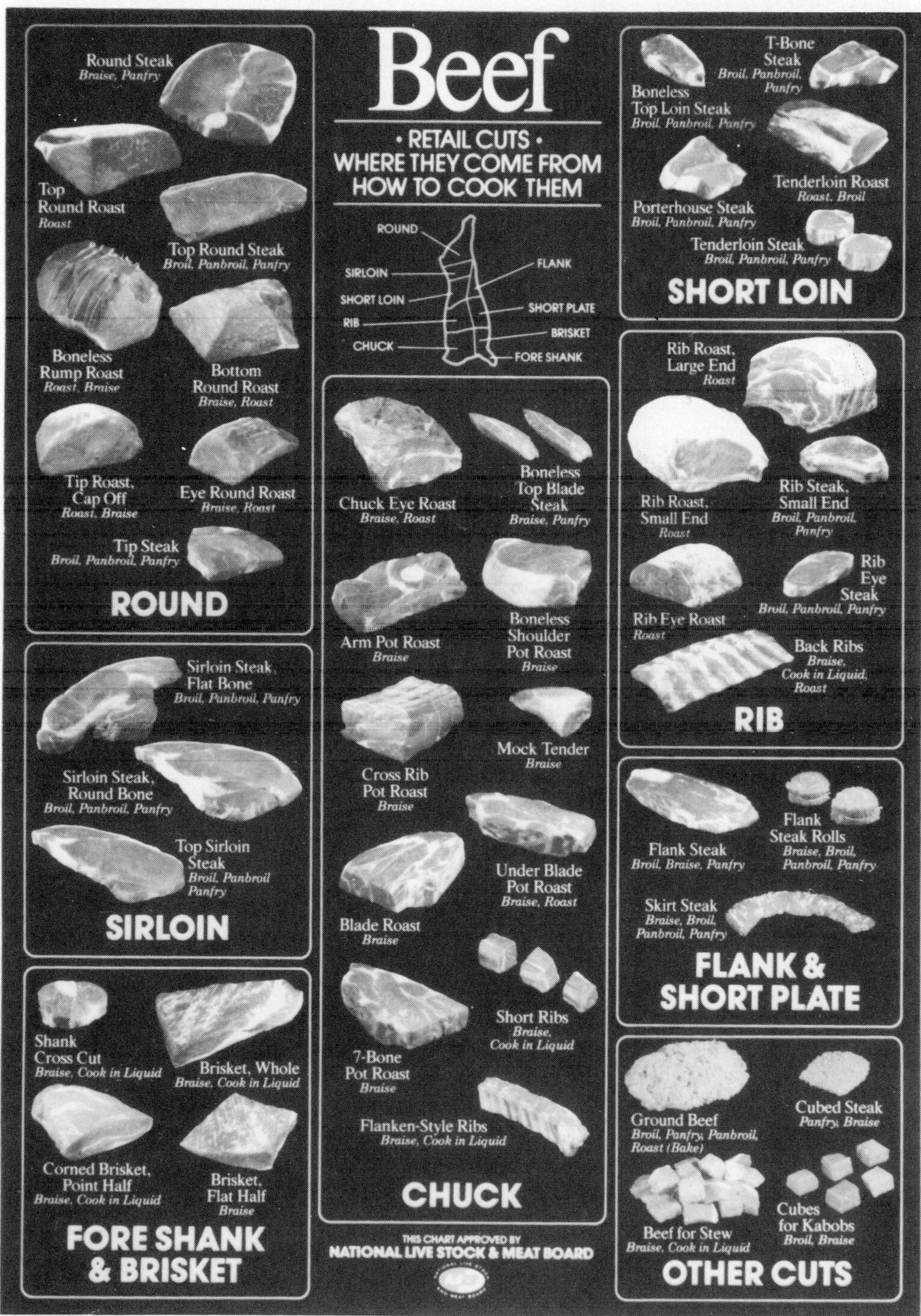

FIGURE 3.5.
Wholesale and retail cuts of beef with recommended types of cooking. Courtesy of the National Live Stock and Meat Board.

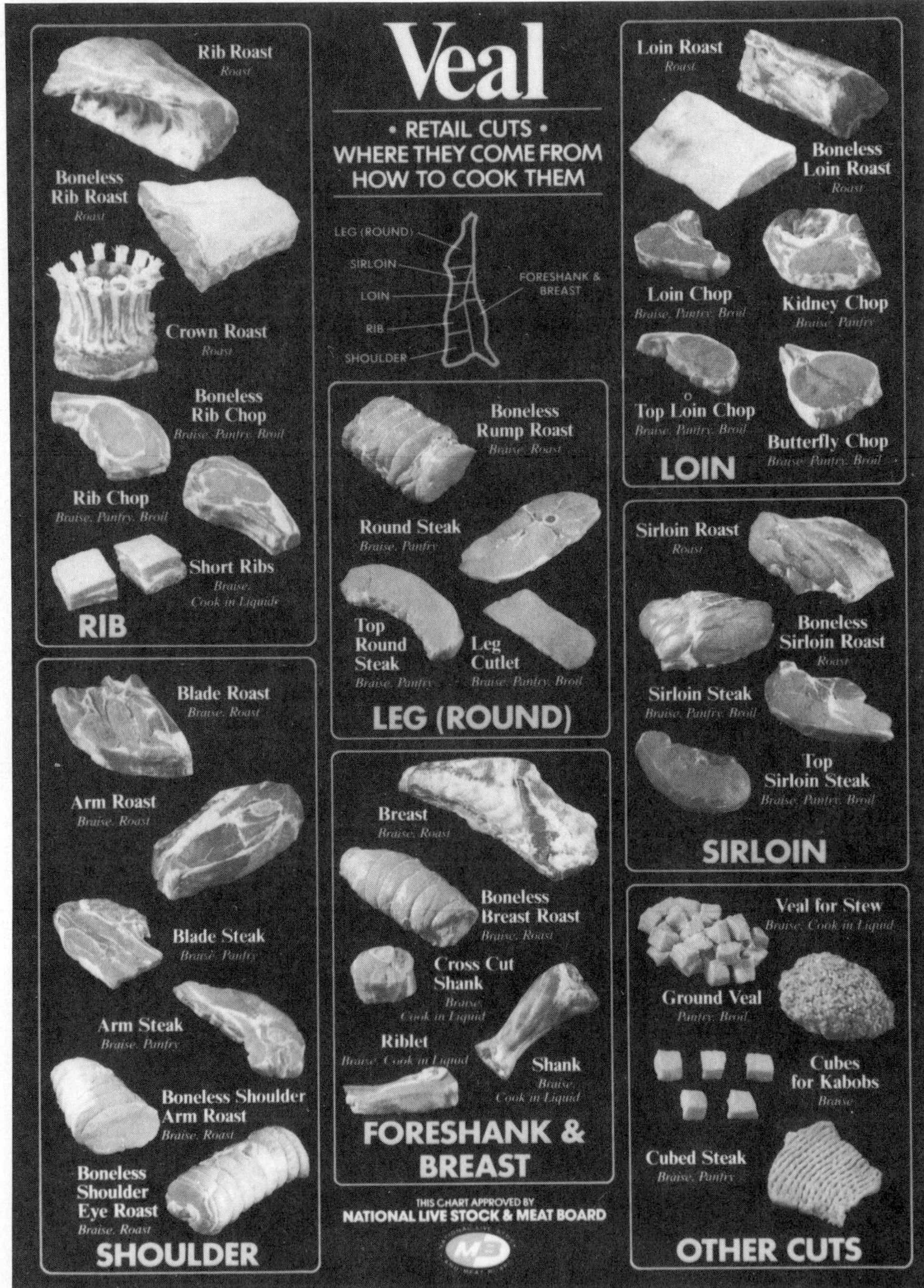

FIGURE 3.6.
Wholesale and retail cuts of veal with recommended types of cooking. Courtesy of the National Live Stock and Meat Board.

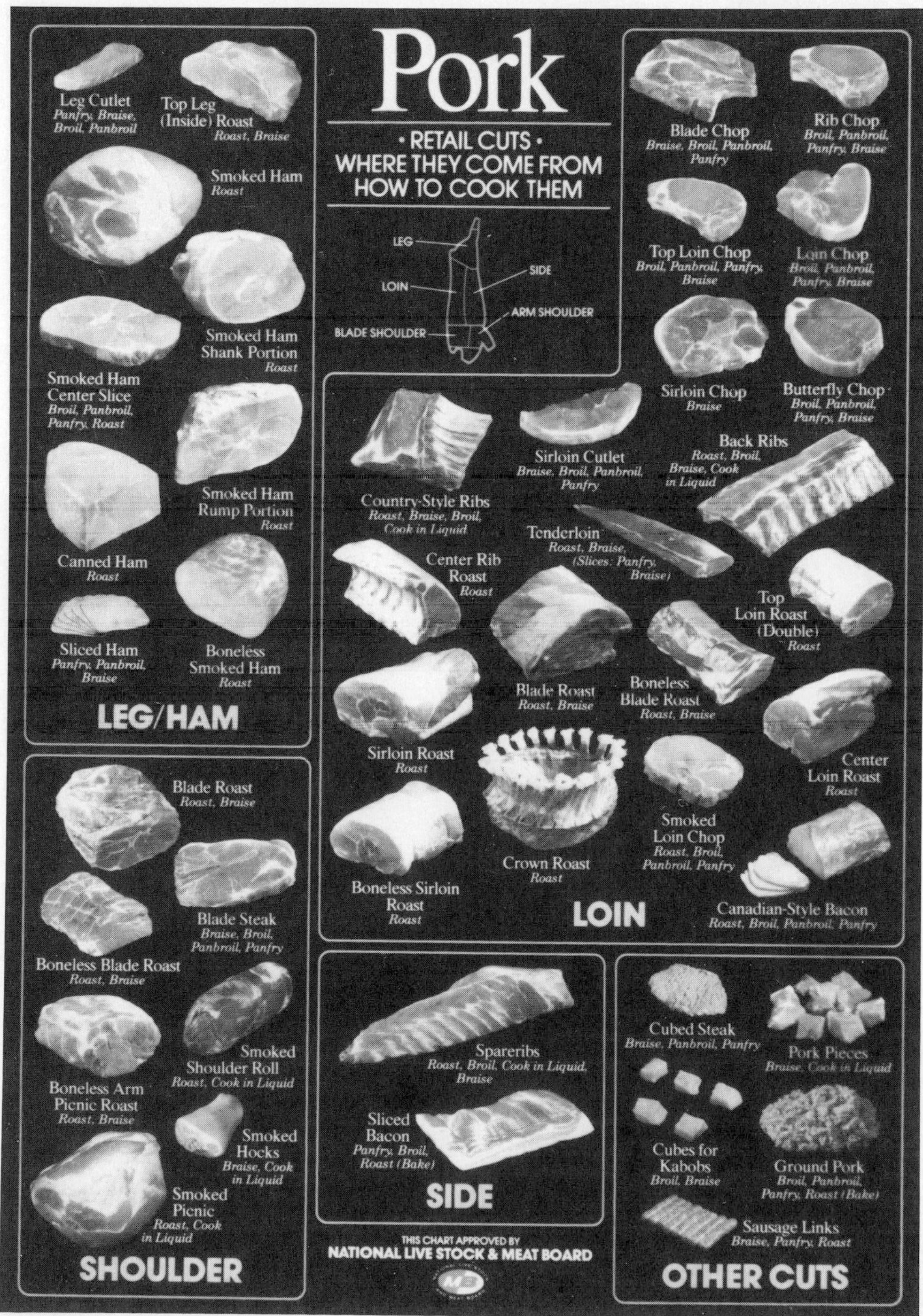

FIGURE 3.7.
Wholesale and retail cuts of pork with recommended types of cooking. Courtesy of the National Live Stock and Meat Board.

FIGURE 3.8.
Wholesale and retail cuts of lamb with recommended types of cooking. Courtesy of the National Live Stock and Meat Board.

TABLE 3.5. Major Red Meat Products (fresh, frozen, and processed) Under Federal Inspection

Meat Product	Mil lb
Cured	
Beef briskets	215
Other beef	160
Pork	3,651
Other meats	22
Smoked, Dried, or Cooked	
Hams	
Bone-in	99
Bone-in, water added	314
Semi-boneless	9
Semi-boneless, water added	63
Boneless	104
Boneless, water added	637
Sectioned and formed	58
Sectioned and formed, water added	348
Hams, dry cured	104
Total hams	1,735
Pork, regular	199
Pork, water added	246
Total other pork	445
Bacon	1,534
Total pork	3,714
Beef, cooked	481
Beef, dried	32
Other meats	350
Fresh/Frozen Products	
Beef cuts	9,944
Beef boning	8,857
Pork cuts	9,679
Pork boning	3,172
Other cuts	486
Other boning	230
Mechanically processed beef	4
Mechanically processed pork	33
Mechanically processed other	4
Steaks, chops, roasts	1,887
Steaks, chops (chopped and formed)	267
Meat patties	483
Hamburger/ground beef	3,659
Other fresh/frozen	962
Convenience Foods	
Pizza	773
Pies	210
Dinners	214
Entrees	425
Other	393

Sources: USDA; AMI, *Meat Facts,* 1988.

Physical Composition

The major physical components of meat are lean (muscle), fat, bone (Fig. 3.9), and connective tissue. The proportions of fat, lean, and bone change from birth to slaughter time. Chapter 18 discusses these compositional changes in more detail. Connective tissue, which to a large extent determines meat tenderness, exists in several different forms and locations. For example, tendons are composed of connective tissue (collagen), which attaches muscle to bone. Other collagenous connective tissues hold muscle bundles together and provide the covering to each muscle fiber. Figure 3.9 shows the physical structure of muscle: **myofibrils** are component parts of muscle fibers, muscle fibers combined together comprise a muscle bundle, and groups of muscle bundles are components of whole muscles or muscle systems.

Chemical Composition

Since muscle or lean meat is the primary carcass component consumed, only its chemical composition is discussed here. Chemical composition is important because it largely determines the nutritive value of meat.

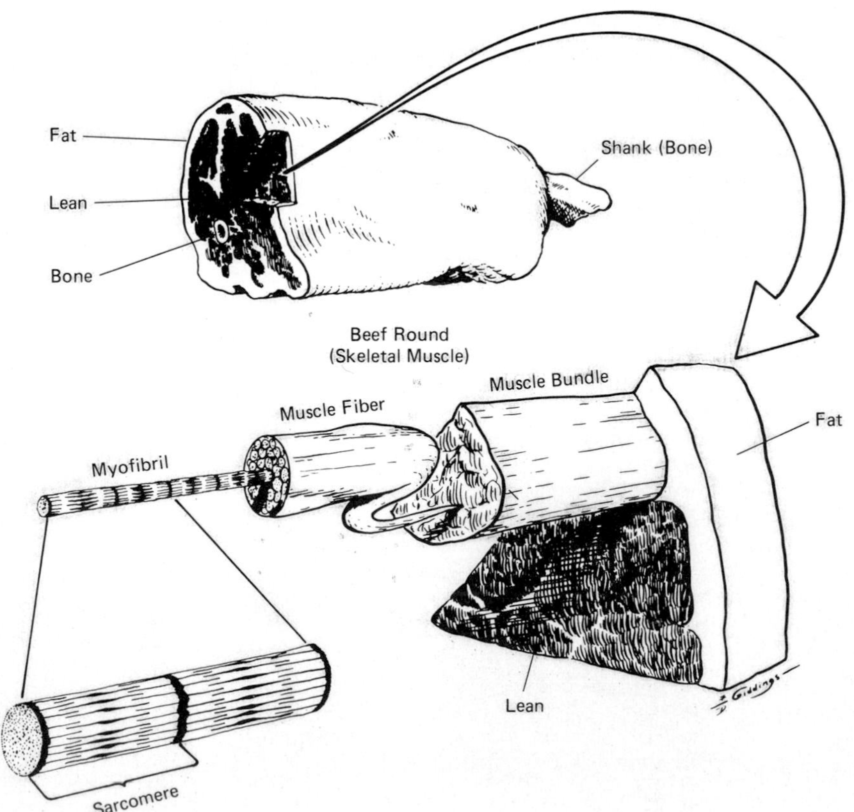

FIGURE 3.9.
The fundamental structure of meat and muscle in the beef carcass. Drawing by Dennis Giddings.

Muscle consists of approximately 65%–75% water, 15%–20% protein, 2%–12% fat, and 1% minerals (ash). As the animal is fattened, water and protein percentages decrease and fat percentage increases.

Fat-soluble vitamins (A, D, E, and K) are contained in the fat component of meat. Most B vitamins (water soluble) are abundant in muscle.

The major protein in muscle is actomyosin, a globulin consisting of the two proteins actin and myosin. Most of the other nitrogenous extracts in meats are relatively unimportant nutritionally. However, these other extracts provide aroma and flavor in meat, which stimulate the flow of gastric juices.

Simple carbohydrates in muscle are less than 1%. Glucose and glycogen are concentrated in the liver. They are not too important nutritionally, but they do have an important effect on meat quality, particularly muscle color and water-holding capacity.

HEALTH CONSIDERATIONS

Nutritive Value

Heightened health awareness in the United States has made today's consumers more astute food buyers than ever before. Consumers look for foods that meet their requirements for a nutritious, balanced diet as well as for convenience, versatility, economy, and ease of preparation. Processed meat products have long been among Americans's favorite foods. Consumers today choose from more than 200 styles or forms of meat, including over 50 cold cuts, dozens of sausages, and a wide variety of hams and bacon. Nutrient-rich red meats—beef, pork, lamb, and veal—are primary ingredients in these products. Meat products in all delicious and unique varieties contain the same nutrients as the fresh meats from which they are made (Table 3.6). More than 40 nutrients are needed by the body for good health. These must be obtained from a variety of foods; no single food contains all nutrients in the desired proportions.

TABLE 3.6. Nutrient Contents of Red Meats (3 oz of cooked, lean portions) and Their Contribution to RDAs (Recommended Daily Allowances)[a]

	Beef		Pork		Lamb	
Nutrient	Amount	% RDA	Amount	% RDA	Amount	% RDA
Calories	192	10%	198	10%	176	9%
Protein	25 g	56	23 g	51	24 g	54
Fat[b]	9.4 g	14	11.1 g	17	8.1 g	12
Cholesterol[b]	73 mg	24	79 mg	26	78 mg	26
Sodium	57 mg	2	59 mg	2	71 mg	2
Iron	2.6 mg	14	1.1 mg	6	1.7 mg	10
Zinc	5.9 mg	39	3.0 mg	20	4.5 mg	30
Thiamin	0.08 mg	6	0.59 mg	39	0.09 mg	6
Niacin	34 mg	17	4.3 mg	22	5.3 mg	27
B_{12}	2.4 mg	79	0.7 mg	24	2.2 mg	37

[a] Based on a 2,000-calorie diet and the RDA for women aged 23–51.
[b] The American Heart Association recommends that fat contribute not more than 30% of total daily calories and that cholesterol be limited to 300 mg/day.
Source: USDA.

Meat is nutrient-dense and is among the most valuable sources of important vitamins and minerals in a balanced diet. **Nutrient density**, a measurement of food value, compares the amount of essential nutrients to the number of calories in food.

Red meats are abundant sources of iron, a mineral necessary to build and maintain blood hemoglobin, which carries oxygen to body cells. Heme iron, one form of iron found in red meat, is used by the body most effectively, and meat enhances the absorption of nonheme iron from meat and other food sources. Red meat is also a rich source of zinc, an essential trace element that contributes to tissue development, growth, and wound healing.

Red meats contain a rich supply of the B vitamins. Pork is a particularly rich source of thiamine. Thiamine is essential to convert carbohydrates into energy. Vitamin B_{12} occurs only in animal products, such as meat, fish, poultry, and milk, and it is essential to protect nerve cells and for the formation of blood cells in bone marrow. Niacin, riboflavin, and vitamin B_6 are also found in significant amounts in red meats.

Finally, red meats are an excellent source of protein, a fundamental component of all living cells. Fresh and processed meats contain high-quality or complete protein with all essential amino acids in good quantity.

Human Disease Risk

Heart disease and cancer are two of the most dreaded human diseases. Over the past several years, millions of dollars have been utilized in research attempting to identify factors causing these diseases. The factors causing heart disease and cancer appear to be many and complex. This has allowed only limited progress in identifying cures for the diseases. Medical scientists do not agree on the major factors causing heart disease and cancer.

Coronary heart disease (CHD) is the leading cause of death in the United States. After several decades of increase, the death rate from CHD in this country reached a peak in the mid-1960s and has been declining ever since. This remarkable phenomenon has not been explained. However, changes in life-style, increased physical activity, and a new level of dietary consciousness have evolved during the same period.

Most CHD results from atherosclerosis, a process by which a complex, lipid-containing lesion develops in the arteries, eventually causing blockage of the blood supply to the heart or the brain. The most important risk factors from CHD are (1) genetics—a family history of CHD, especially premature CHD; (2) cigarette smoking; (3) high blood pressure (hypertension); (4) high blood cholesterol concentration (hypercholesterolemia); and (5) obesity. Each person has a unique set of risk factors determined by environment and genetic susceptibility. Thus, treatment of individuals to alter CHD risk needs to be designed according to each person's risk.

Since meat contains fat and cholesterol, it has been implicated as a cause of hypercholesterolemia and thus a risk for CHD. During the past several years, there has been strong encouragement, primarily through commercial advertising, to lower blood cholesterol by consuming more polyunsaturated fats (vegetables) and decreasing animal fat consumption. Figure 3.10 shows fat and oil consumption by vegetable and animal origin; vegetable oils have replaced some of the animal fat in the diet, although total fat and oil consumption has increased since 1967.

The relationship between dietary and blood cholesterol has not been adequately clarified. Research data indicate that cholesterol intake is one of the least important dietary components that influence blood cholesterol. There is little scientific evidence indicating that dietary changes for most persons will reduce the incidence of CHD except for the obese.

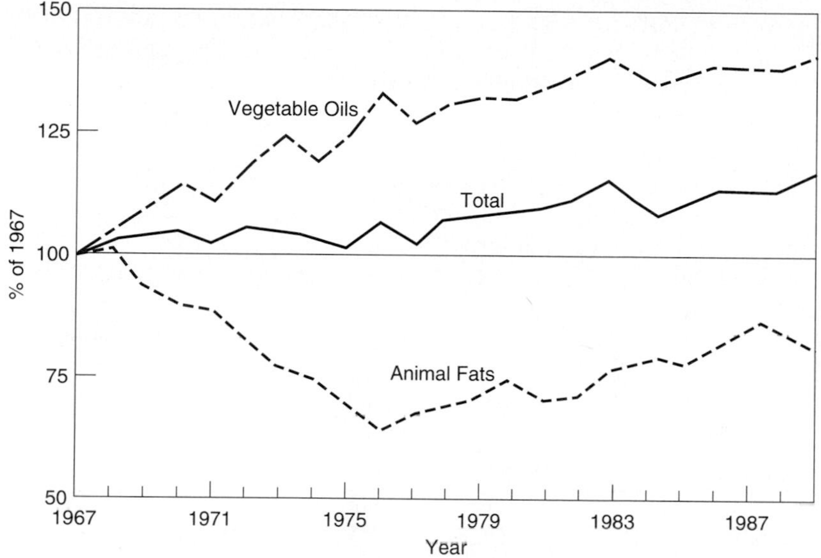

FIGURE 3.10.
Per-capita consumption of fat and oils (animal fats include butter), 1967–89. Courtesy of the USDA.

Many consumers are becoming more health conscious, seeking to reduce their caloric and saturated-fat intake. Numerous food items are marketed as "light" or "lite," which implies that the calorie content is reduced.

Red meat marketing is also being directed to health-oriented consumers. "Light" beef is reduced-fat beef; that is, it contains less fat, both external (subcutaneous) and intramuscular fat. Light beef is at least 25% less fatty than typical USDA choice beef, or at least 90% fat-free on a retail-cut basis (precooked). Light beef is also lower in calories and saturated fat than USDA choice beef. The lower fat content of light beef also leads to very slight reductions in cholesterol content of the beef cut because cholesterol is more highly associated with fat cells than with muscle cells.

The biggest limitation to leaner and lower grading beef is that it has less tolerance for improper cooking methods than USDA choice grade beef. For example, leaner beef may have a higher moisture loss and be less tender when subjected to high cooking temperatures for a longer cooking time than is needed.

Many scientists believe that it is premature to issue broad dietary advice on cancer prevention. There is mounting evidence that total caloric intake may be far more important than the intake of individual nutrients like fat. Energy expenditure (exercise) may also be important. Research supports moderate and balanced diets for decreasing the risk of cancer. This work may take some attention away from fat per se (and fat sources, including meat). However, fat is a concentrated source of calories, so attention will focus on fat to avoid an excessive caloric intake.

In recent years, several retail markets initiated advertisements to show that meat is not high in calories (Fig. 3.11). Additional nutritional information on meat has been made available through the National Live Stock and Meat Board's Meat Nutri-Facts program.

FIGURE 3.11.
Several major supermarkets have advertised the caloric content of lean pork, lamb and beef. Courtesy of the National Live Stock and Meat Board.

CONSUMPTION

Meat is consumed for both nutrient content and eating satisfaction (Figs. 3.12 – 3.14). However, there are food products other than meat that cost less per unit of protein. Visual displays, like the one shown in Fig. 3.15, often appear at retail meat counters. They show that a cooked, trimmed, 3-oz serving of meat (lean portion only) is relatively low in calories, fat, and cholesterol, and that it supplies an abundance of other essential nutrients. However, consumers have a preference for how the protein is packaged, particularly if it is more palatable in texture, flavor, and aroma. Meat has these preferred palatability characteristics.

Consumer acceptance of red meat and poultry is shown in Figure 3.16. Poultry is included here to demonstrate that over the past 20 years the total annual per-capita meat consumption has been increasing, primarily with greater amounts of poultry and less red meat.

Table 3.7 shows the per-capita consumption (disappearance) of red meat on a retail-weight basis. These data do not reflect the amount consumed, as there is fat trim, bone, cooking losses, and plate waste. Consumption data correcting most of these losses is shown in Table 3.8.

During the late 1980s, consumers continued to demand less external fat on retail cuts. Surveys have shown that most retail cuts of beef, pork, and lamb have 0.1 in. or less of external fat covering the lean muscle tissue.

FIGURE 3.12.
A thick, tender, and juicy steak is the most highly preferred beef product. Courtesy of the National Live Stock and Meat Board.

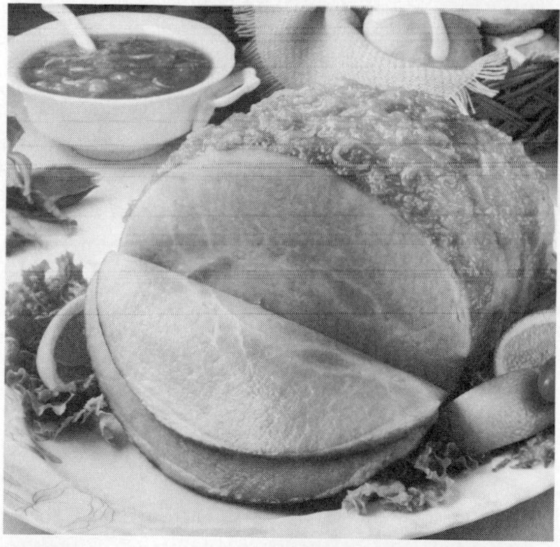

FIGURE 3.13.
A favorite pork dish is smoked, boneless ham. Courtesy of the National Live Stock and Meat Board.

FIGURE 3.14.
Processed beef and pork are popular meat items for sandwich lovers. Courtesy of the National Live Stock and Meat Board.

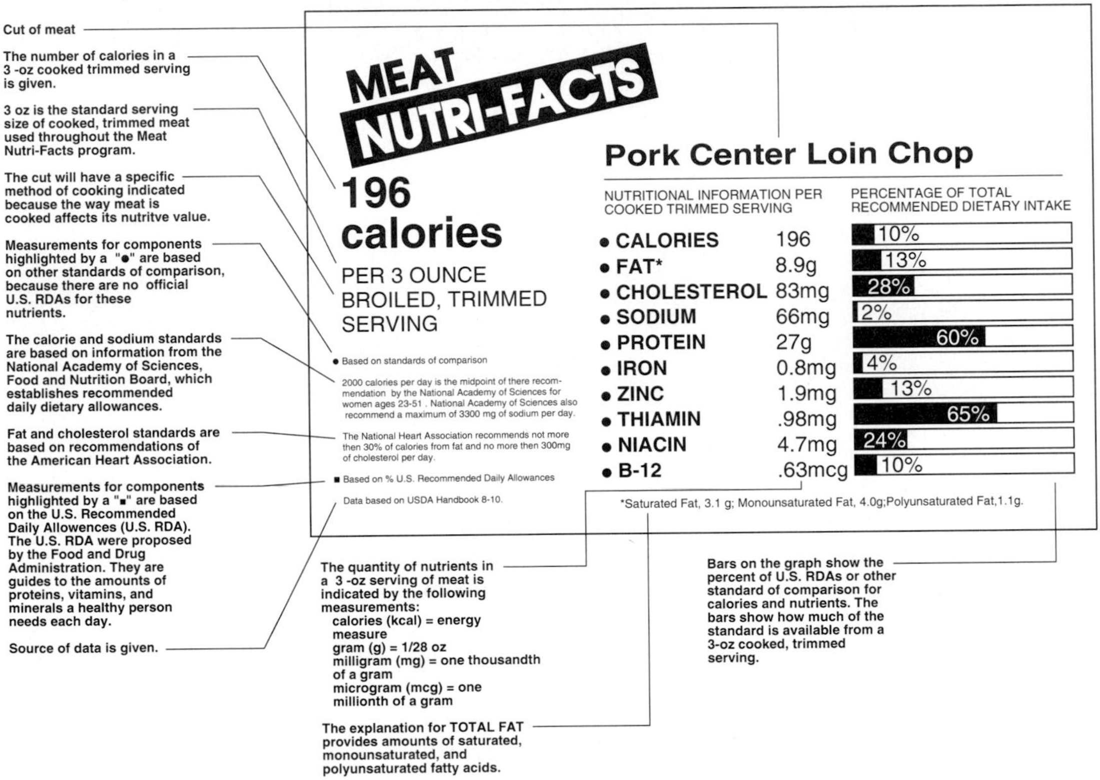

Cut of meat
The number of calories in a 3 -oz cooked trimmed serving is given.
3 oz is the standard serving size of cooked, trimmed meat used throughout the Meat Nutri-Facts program.
The cut will have a specific method of cooking indicated because the way meat is cooked affects its nutritve value.
Measurements for components highlighted by a "●" are based on other standards of comparison, because there are no official U.S. RDAs for these nutrients.
The calorie and sodium standards are based on information from the National Academy of Sciences, Food and Nutrition Board, which establishes recommended daily dietary allowances.
Fat and cholesterol standards are based on recommendations of the American Heart Association.
Measurements for components highlighted by a "■" are based on the U.S. Recommended Daily Allowences (U.S. RDA). The U.S. RDA were proposed by the Food and Drug Administration. They are guides to the amounts of proteins, vitamins, and minerals a healthy person needs each day.
Source of data is given.
MEAT
NUTRI-FACTS
196
calories
PER 3 OUNCE BROILED, TRIMMED SERVING
● Based on standards of comparison
2000 calories per day is the midpoint of there recommendation by the National Academy of Sciences for women ages 23-51. National Academy of Sciences also recommend a maximum of 3300 mg of sodium per day.
The National Heart Association recommends not more then 30% of calories from fat and no more then 300mg of cholesterol per day.
■ Based on % U.S. Recommended Daily Allowances
Data based on USDA Handbook 8-10.
Pork Center Loin Chop
NUTRITIONAL INFORMATION PER COOKED TRIMMED SERVING
PERCENTAGE OF TOTAL RECOMMENDED DIETARY INTAKE
● CALORIES 196 10%
● FAT* 8.9g 13%
● CHOLESTEROL 83mg 28%
● SODIUM 66mg 2%
● PROTEIN 27g 60%
● IRON 0.8mg 4%
● ZINC 1.9mg 13%
● THIAMIN .98mg 65%
● NIACIN 4.7mg 24%
● B-12 .63mcg 10%
*Saturated Fat, 3.1 g; Monounsaturated Fat, 4.0g;Polyunsaturated Fat,1.1g.
The quantity of nutrients in a 3 -oz serving of meat is indicated by the following measurements:
calories (kcal) = energy measure
gram (g) = 1/28 oz
milligram (mg) = one thousandth of a gram
microgram (mcg) = one millionth of a gram
The explanation for TOTAL FAT provides amounts of saturated, monounsaturated, and polyunsaturated fatty acids.
Bars on the graph show the percent of U.S. RDAs or other standard of comparison for calories and nutrients. The bars show how much of the standard is available from a 3-oz cooked, trimmed serving.

FIGURE 3.15.
An explanation of the Meat Nutri-Facts display for a pork center loin chop. Courtesy of the National Live Stock and Meat Board.

Lamb and Mutton
Poultry
Veal
Pork
Beef
240
220
200
180
160
140
120
100
80
60
40
20
0
lb
1960
1964
1968
1972
1976
1980
1984
1988
Year

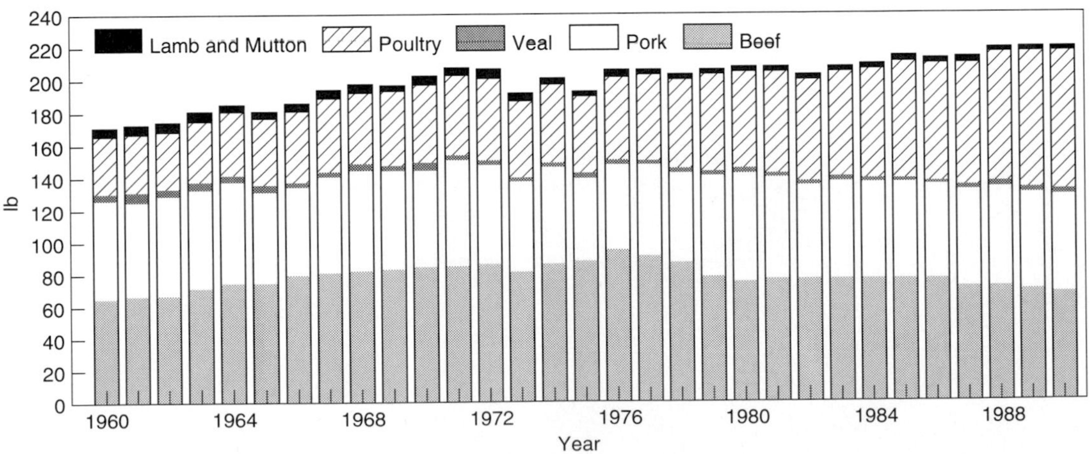

FIGURE 3.16.
Per-capita red meat and poultry consumption (disappearance), retail-weight basis, 1960–90. Courtesy of Western Livestock Marketing Information Project.

TABLE 3.7. Per-capita Consumption (disappearance) of Red Meat (retail weight, lb), 1970–90

Year	Beef	Veal	Pork	Lamb and Mutton	Total Red Meat	Total Meat[a]
1970	84	2.4	62	2.9	152	213
1975	88	3.3	51	1.8	144	206
1980	77	1.5	69	1.4	148	222
1985	79	1.8	62	1.4	144	229
1990	68	1.2	60	1.4	131	236

[a] Includes red meat, poultry, and fish.
Source: USDA.

Data on the consumption and disappearance of meat and other food items can be misleading. What people say they eat and what they purchase does not determine the amount actually consumed. In one study, Dr. Bill Rathje (University of Arizona) evaluated garbage in the Tucson area in an attempt to determine what people eat by what they throw away. Over 10 years of his research data show (1) that people throw away approximately 15% of all the solid food they purchase; and (2) when questioned, consumers in middle- and low-income brackets consistently overestimate their meat consumption, while those in higher-income brackets underestimate their meat consumption.

Per-capita disposable income does affect the total amount of money spent on meat and the amount of product consumed (Table 3.9). However, consumers are spending a smaller percentage of their disposable income on meat and food, indicating that these items are relatively inexpensive compared to other purchases.

Table 3.9 shows that per-capita disposable income has risen more rapidly than the per-capita red meat expenditure, particularly since 1979. This change reflects either a decreased preference for red meat or a preference for other goods and services as income has increased

TABLE 3.8. Red Meat Consumption (cooking, bone, and fat losses removed), 1987

Product	Daily (oz)	Yearly (lb)
Beef	2.09	47.6
Fresh pork	0.35	8.1
Veal	0.04	0.9
Lamb	0.02	0.6
Processed meat (total)	1.50	34.1
Pork (70% of total)	(1.05)	(23.88)
Beef (28% of total)	(0.41)	(9.54)
Lamb (1% of total)	(0.02)	(0.34)
Veal (1% of total)	(0.02)	(0.34)

Source: The National Live Stock and Meat Board.

TABLE 3.9. Per-capita Income and Red Meat Expenditures, 1970–89

Year	Disposable Per-capita Income	Per-capita Red Meat Expenditure	Expenditure for Red Meat as Percentage of: Disposable Per-capita Income	Expenditure for Red Meat as Percentage of: Total Food Expenditure
1970	$ 3,489	$140.38	4.0%	24.5%
1975	5,291	214.31	4.1	24.6
1980	8,421	286.02	3.4	21.2
1985	11,861	294.67	2.5	17.3
1989	15,186	311.16	2.0	15.0

Sources: U.S. Departments of Agriculture and Commerce; AMI, *Meat Facts.*

above a certain level. Lower poultry prices relative to red meat prices has influenced some producers to shift their preference from red meat to poultry (Fig. 3.17).

Table 3.10 shows the consumption patterns for hamburger, processed beef, and beef cuts (steaks and roasts). Comparative prices for hamburger and the average price of retail cuts from choice beef are also shown.

MARKETING

Figure 3.18 shows channels of meat production and processing prior to reaching the retail meat outlets and eventually the consumers. On hog farms, most pigs are raised to slaughter weight. Cattle and sheep are sold by producers to feedlots for added weight gain prior to slaughter.

Packers and processors purchase the animals through several different marketing channels (Table 3.11). Direct purchases can occur at the packing plant, the feedlot, or a buying station

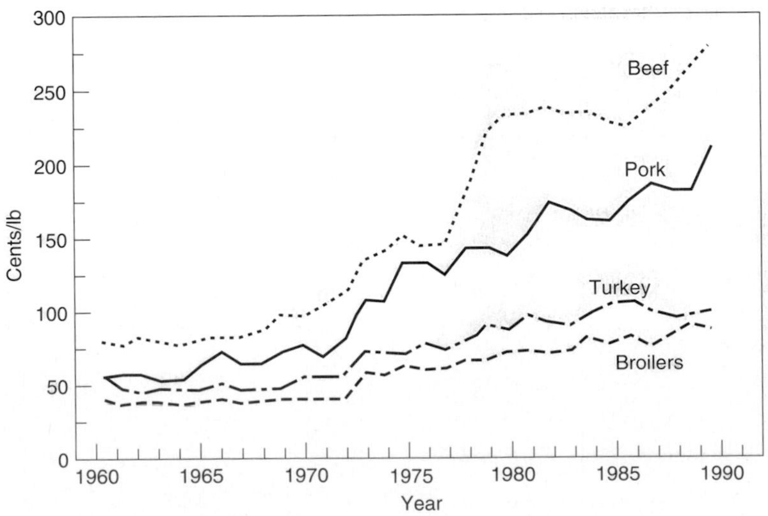

FIGURE 3.17.
Retail meat prices, 1960–90. Courtesy of Western Livestock Marketing Information Project.

TABLE 3.10. Consumption and Prices of Various Beef Products, 1970–89

Year	Per-capita Consumption (lb retail)				Price ($/lb)	
	Hamburger	Processed Beef	Beef Cuts	Total Beef[a]	Hamburger	Choice Beef
1970	21.9	10.8	51.9	84.6	0.66	1.00
1975	30.1	11.7	46.4	88.2	0.88	1.52
1980	24.7	7.4	44.5	76.6	1.36	2.34
1985	27.2	6.0	45.7	78.9	1.24	2.29
1989	28.2	5.0	35.7	68.9	1.44	2.66

[a] Retail-weight basis.
Sources: AMI, *Meat Facts,* 1990; USDA.

near where the animals are produced. Terminal markets are large livestock collection centers where an independent organization serves as a selling agent for the livestock owner. Oklahoma City, Omaha, and Sioux City, Iowa, are examples of some of the larger terminal markets, most of which are located in the midsection of the United States.

Approximately 2,000 auctions, sometimes called sale barns, are located throughout the United States. The auction company has pens, a sale ring, and an auctioneer. Auctioneers sell the livestock to the highest bidder among the buyers attending the auction. Producers pay a marketing fee to the auction company for the sale service.

Most cattle, sheep, and swine are purchased on a live weight basis, with the buyer estimating the value of the carcass and other products. Some animals are purchased on the basis of their carcass weight and the desirability of the carcass produced. For cattle and swine there has been an increased number of purchases on a carcass basis during the past several years (Table 3.12). In this method of marketing, sometimes called **grade and yield**, the seller is paid on a carcass merit basis.

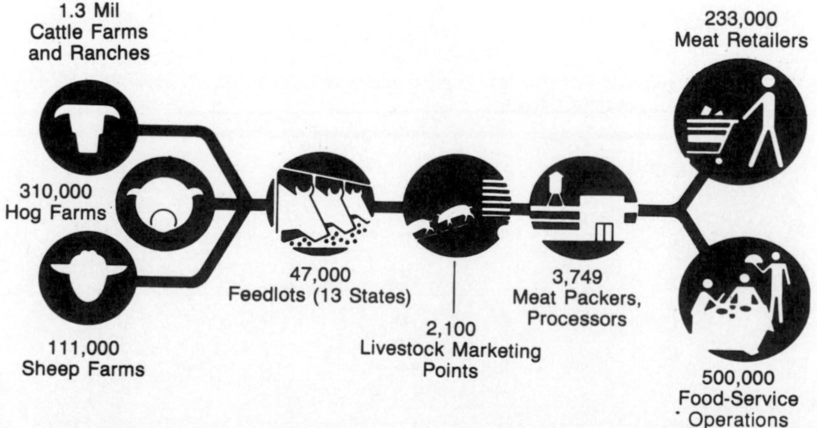

FIGURE 3.18.
Channels of meat production and processing in reaching the retail segment. Courtesy of the National Live Stock and Meat Board.

TABLE 3.11. Market Outlets Used by U.S. Packers in Purchasing Red Meat Animals for Slaughter, 1988

Animals	Total (mil head)	Direct Purchases[a] (%)	Public Markets[b] (%)
Cattle	33.8	81.6	18.4
Calves	2.4	62.5	37.5
Hogs	83.5	89.5	10.5
Sheep and lambs	4.8	83.3	18.7

[a] Direct purchases at packing plants, buying stations, country points, and feedlots.
[b] Public markets consist of terminal markets and auction markets.
Source: USDA, Packers and Stockyards' Statistical Resume.

The Packers and Stockyards Act, passed in 1921 and continually updated, is enforced by the USDA. The act provides for uniform and fair marketing practices. Federal supervision is given at market outlets, including packing plants, for fee and yardage charges, testing of scales, commission charges, and other marketing transactions. Carcass grade and weight sales are covered as well as live animal sales. Marketing protection is provided to both the buyer and the seller.

Consumer attitudes and preferences for meat changed during the 1980s. These attitudes were surveyed, and some are identified in Table 3.13. This information shows that the market is segmented and that different products are needed for each segment. Other market surveys vividly demonstrate that many consumers have a preference for leanness, which in the minds of these consumers means a low level of trimmable fat. Consumers are demanding more convenient (easier to prepare) meat products, as the numbers of two-income families and single

TABLE 3.12. Livestock Purchased by Packers on Carcass Grade and Weight Bases, 1975–88

	Cattle and Calves		Hogs		Sheep and Lambs	
Year	No. Head (mil)	Percent of Total Purchases	No. Head (mil)	Percent of Total Purchases	No. Head (mil)	Percent of Total Purchases
1975	8.6	23%	6.0	9%	0.82	10%
1980	8.4	27	10.2	11	1.54	28
1985	10.2	30	13.0	16	2.19	37
1988	12.1	36	9.0	11	2.01	42

Source: USDA, Packers and Stockyards' Statistical Resume.

TABLE 3.13. Consumer Attitudes Affecting Meat Consumption, 1983–87

Consumer Segments	Percent of Total Population		
	1983	1985	1987
Meat lovers	22%	10%	7%
Creative cooks	20	17	21
Price-driven	25	23	22
Active life-style	16	26	22
Health-oriented	17	24	27

parents have increased dramatically since 1975. There were more (50% vs. 33%) active, health-oriented consumers in 1985 than only 2–3 years previously.

Advertising dollars spent by the livestock industry have been low in recent years. Even though there has been an increase in media advertising, the meat industry's total advertising has been small compared to that of other industries (Table 3.14).

Those consumers who are price-driven (Table 3.13) are continually comparing the prices of different meats. Figure 3.17 shows how retail meat prices for beef, pork, turkey, and chicken have changed over the past several years.

Table 3.15 shows the dollars generated by red-meat products through grocery stores and large supermarket chains. Total red meat represents 18% of total retail sales and 14% of food sales.

TABLE 3.14. Leading Advertisers Compared to Meat Industry

Industry	Spent in 1989 ($ millions)
Procter and Gamble	$1,779
General Motors	1,363
R.J. Reynolds	703
AT&T	567
K Mart	561
McDonalds	774
Dairy	120
Poultry	204
Beef	25
Swine	9
Sheep	less than 2

TABLE 3.15. Consumer Expenditures for Meat Products, Poultry, and Fish in Grocery Stores, 1988 and 1978

Food Item	$Bil		Percent of Food and Beverages		Percent of Total	
	1988	1978	1988	1978	1988	1978
Fresh meat	$ 27.1	$ 18.4	11.7%	14.6%	8.7%	11.3%
Beef	21.3	13.8	9.2	11.0	6.9	8.5
Veal	0.6	0.7	0.2	0.5	0.2	0.4
Lamb	1.1	0.7	0.5	0.5	0.4	0.4
Pork	4.1	3.2	1.8	2.8	1.3	2.0
Processed meats	13.3	11.8	5.8	9.4	4.3	7.3
Cured hams and picnics	2.0	2.0	0.9	1.6	0.7	1.2
Packaged bacon	2.1	2.1	0.9	1.6	0.7	1.3
Frankfurters	1.7	1.2	0.7	1.0	0.5	0.8
Sausage products	4.0	3.0	1.7	2.4	1.3	1.8
Cold cuts and other	3.5	3.5	1.5	2.8	1.1	2.2
Frozen meat	0.2	0.2	0.1	0.1	0.1	0.1
Canned meat	1.3	1.6	0.6	1.3	0.4	1.0
Total meat	41.9	31.9	18.1	25.3	13.5	19.6
Poultry	10.6	5.1	4.6	4.1	3.4	3.2
Fish and seafood	6.2	3.0	2.7	2.4	2.0	1.8
Total meat, poultry, and seafood	58.2	40.1	25.3	31.2	18.9	24.6
Total grocery store sales	310.8	162.6	—	—	—	—
Food and beverages	231.4	126.1	—	—	74.4	77.6
Nonfood and general merchandise	79.5	36.6	—	—	25.6	22.5

Sources: Supermarket Business magazine; AMI, *Meat Facts,* 1990.

SELECTED REFERENCES

Publications

American Meat Institute. 1989. *Meat Facts. A Statistical Summary About America's Largest Food Industry.* Washington: AMI.

Boggs, D. L., and Merkel, R. A. 1990. *Live Animal, Carcass Evaluation and Selection Manual.* Dubuque, IA: Kendall-Hunt.

Diet and Coronary Heart Disease. 1985. CAST Report no. 107.

Facts About Beef; Facts About Pork; Facts About Lamb. Chicago: The National Live Stock and Meat Board.

Forrest, J. C., Aberle, E. D., Hedrick, H. B., and Merkel, R. A. 1975. *Principles of Meat Science.* San Francisco: W. H. Freeman.

Helming, B. 1990. Meat's decade of danger. *Meat and Poultry* 36:30.

Horsemeat. 1980. *Livestock* (Sept. 1980).

Kashruth. Handbook for Home and School. 1972. New York: Union of Orthodox Jewish Congregations of America.

Romans, J. R., Jones, K. W., Costello, W. J., Carlson, C. W., and Ziegler, P. T. 1985. *The Meat We Eat.* 12th ed. Danville, IL: Interstate Printers and Publishers.

Visuals

Cattlemen Care About Beef Safety (1991 Videotape; 9 min.). Communications Dept., National Cattlemen's Association, Box 3469, Englewood, CO 80111.

Lamb Carcass Evaluation Multi-Media Kit. Vocational Education Productions, California Polytechnic State University, San Luis Obispo, CA 93407.

Livestock Slaughter; Carcass Fabrication; Packer to Consumer; Beef Carcass Grading; and *Retail Cut Identification* (videotapes). CEV, P.O. Box 65265, Lubbock, TX 79464-5265.

Marketing Challenges Facing the Beef Industry (10-min. slide presentation produced by the Beef Industry Council, especially for industry audiences). Loan copies available from Beef Industry Council, 444 N. Michigan Ave., Chicago, IL 60611; or State Beef Councils.

Meat Cut Identification (slide set). Vocational Education Productions, California Polytechnic State University, San Luis Obispo, CA 93407.

Meat Identification (slide set), *Meat Evaluation Handbook*, and *The Meat Board Guide to Identifying Meat Cuts (17-203)*. The National Live Stock and Meat Board, 444 N. Michigan Ave., Chicago, IL 60611.

CHAPTER 4

By-products of Meat Animals

By-products are products of considerably less value than the major product. In the United States, meat animals produce meat as the major product; hides, fat, bones, and internal organs are considered by-products. In other countries, primary products may be draft (work), milk, hides, and skins, with meat considered a by-product when old, less useful animals are slaughtered.

There are numerous by-products resulting from animal slaughter and the processing of meat, milk, and eggs. Animals dying during their productive life are also processed into several by-products; however, these by-products are not used in human consumption.

By-products are commonly classified into two categories based on human consumption: edible and inedible (Fig. 4.1; Table 4.1). Some by-products that are not considered edible by

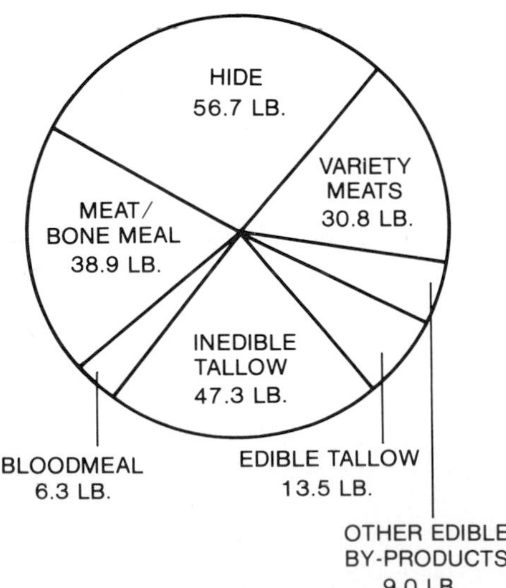

FIGURE 4.1.
Edible and inedible by-products from a 1,050-lb steer. Courtesy of the USDA.

TABLE 4.1. Edible and Inedible By-products from Cattle and Swine

By-product	1,100-lb Steer Expected Yield Per Head (lb)	1,100-lb Steer Market Value Per Cwt (Dec. 1990)	230-lb Hog Expected Yield Per Head (lb)	230-lb Hog Market Value Per Cwt (Dec. 1990)
Edible				
Select liver	13.00	$ 38.00	2.50	$15.00
Heart	3.75	25.80	0.50	24.00
Cheek meat	4.00	95.00	0.88	97.50
Head meat	1.91	86.00	0.25	36.50
Salivary glands	1.25	10.65	—	18.00
Feet	—	—	5.00	21.00
Lips	1.00	72.00	0.25	—
Tail	2.00	112.00	0.25	53.50
Spleen	1.25	8.40	—	—
Tongue	3.23	125.00	0.75	38.00
Weasand meat[a]	0.43	120.00	0.12	—
Tripe (stomach)	8.50	27.40	—	—
Stomach	—	—	1.50	33.00
Sweetbread (thymus)	0.49	44.00	—	—
Ears	—	—	0.62	11.00
Kidneys	2.00	—	0.04	9.00
Snouts	—	—	—	36.50
Tallow/lard	—	15.50	—	13.00
Inedible				
Lung (standard trim)	6.00	6.00	1.00	3.75
Gullet	0.95	5.00	0.62	—
Ox gall (raw bile)	0.30	17.50	—	—
Rendered fat	60.00	14.00	—	12.00
Meat and bone meal (50% protein)	32.00	10.00	—	10.50
Dried blood (80% protein)	6.50	16.00	7.00 (raw)	15.25
Hide	64.00	107.00	2.00	—
Manure	50.00	—	4.00	—

[a] Weasand is the muscular lining that surrounds the esophagus from larynx to first stomach.
Sources: Monfort of Colorado; *National Provisioner.*

humans are edible to other animals. By-products that are processed into animal feeds are good examples.

Figure 4.2 shows the major by-products obtained from a steer in addition to the retail beef products. Average total value of cattle by-products ranges between $0.05 and $0.09 per pound of live weight, with the hide comprising the largest part of the total value.

EDIBLE BY-PRODUCTS

Variety meats are edible products originating from organs and body parts other than the carcass. Liver, heart, tongue, tripe, and sweetbread are among the more typical variety meats. **Tripe** comes from the lining of the stomach; **sweetbread** is the thymus gland.

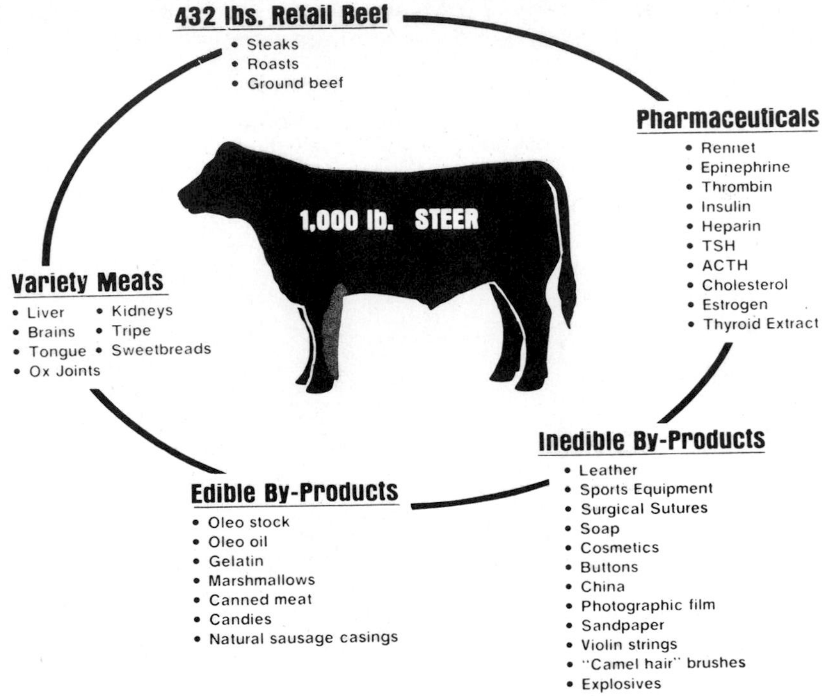

FIGURE 4.2.
In addition to the retail product of beef, there are numerous by-products that come from beef. Courtesy of the National Live Stock and Meat Board.

An average 1,100-lb slaughter steer produces approximately 34 lb of variety meats. Since the U.S. per-capita disappearance is 9 lb, surplus variety meats are exported into countries that have a preference for them.

Other edible products are fats used to produce lard and tallow. These products are eventually used in shortenings, margarine, pastries, candy, and other food items. The United States produces approximately 1.2 billion lb of edible tallow and 5.8 billion lb of inedible tallow. Nearly 50% of the inedible tallow is exported.

INEDIBLE BY-PRODUCTS

Tallow, hides (skins), and inedible organs are the higher-valued inedible by-products. Not all skins are inedible, as some pork skins are processed into consumable food items. Life-saving and life-supporting pharmaceuticals originate from animal by-products, even though many of the same pharmaceuticals are made synthetically. Table 4.2 shows many of these pharmaceuticals and their animal by-product source.

Table 4.3 lists other inedible by-products and their uses. Animals contribute a large number of useful products. The many uses of inedible fats are discussed later in the chapter.

Hides and skins are valuable as by-products or as major products on a worldwide basis. Countries that are most important in hide and skin production are shown in Table 4.4.

TABLE 4.2. Selected Pharmaceuticals from Red Meat Animals—Their Source and Utilization

Pharmaceutical	Source	Utilization
Amfetin	Amniotic fluid	Reduces postoperative pain and nausea and enhances intestinal peristalsis
Cholesterol	Nervous system	Male sex hormone synthesis
Chymotrypsin	Pancreas	Removes dead tissue; for treatment of localized inflammation and swelling
Corticosteriods	Adrenal gland	Treatment for shock, Addison's disease
Corticotrophin (ACTH)	Pituitary gland	Diagnostic assessment of adrenal gland function; treatment of psoriasis, allergies, mononucleosis, and leukemia
Cortisone	Adrenal gland	Treatment for shock, arthritis, and asthma
Desoxycholic acid	Bile	Used in synthesis of cortisone for asthma and arthritis
Epinephrine	Adrenal gland	Relief of hay fever, asthma, and other allergies; heart stimulation
Fibrinolysin	Blood	Dead tissue removal; wound-cleansing agent; healing of skin from ulcers or burns
Glucagon	Pancreas	Counteracts insulin shock; treatment of some psychiatric disorders
Heparin	Intestines	Natural anticoagulant used to thin blood, retards clotting, especially during organ implants
Heparin	Lungs	Anticoagulant; prevention of gangrene
Hyaluranidase	Testes	Enzyme that aids drug penetration into cells
Insulin	Pancreas	Treatment of diabetes for 10 million Americans (primarily synthetic insulin is used)
Liver extracts	Liver	Treatment of anemia
Mucin	Stomach	Treat ulcers
Norepinephrine	Adrenal gland	Shrinks blood vessels, reducing blood flow and slowing heart rate
Ovarian hormone	Ovaries	To treat painful menstruation and prevent abortion
Ox bile extract	Liver	Treatment of indigestion, constipation, and bile tract disorders
Parathyroid hormone	Parathyroid gland	Treatment of human parathyroid deficiency
Plasmin	Blood	Digests fibrin in blood clots, used to treat patients with heart attacks
Rennet	Stomach	Assists infants in digesting milk; cheese making
Thrombin	Blood	Assists in blood coagulation; treatment of wounds; skin grafting
Thyroid extract	Thyroid gland	Treatment of cretinism
Thyrotropin (TSH)	Pituitary gland	Stimulates functions of thyroid gland
Thyroxin	Thyroid	Treatment of thyroid deficiency
Vasopressin	Pituitary gland	Control of renal function

TABLE 4.3. Other Inedible By-products and Their Uses

By-product	Use
Hog heart valves	They replace injured or weakened human heart valves. Since the first operation in 1971, more than 35,000 hog heart valves have been implanted in humans
Pig skins	Used in treating massive human burns. These skins help prepare the patient for permanent skin grafting
Gelatin (from skin)	Coatings for pills and capsules
Brains	Cholesterol for an emulsifier in cosmetics
Blood	Sticking agent for insecticides; a leather finish; plywood adhesive; fabric printing and dyeing
Hides and skins	Many leather goods from coats, handbags and shoes to sporting goods (see Table 4.5)
Bones	Animal feed, glue, buttons, china, and novelties
Gallstones	Shipped to Orient for use as ornaments in necklaces and pendants
Hair	Paint and other brushes; insulation; padding in upholstery, carpet padding, filters
Meat scraps and blood	Animal feed
Inedible fats	Animal feed, fatty acids (see Fig. 4.4)
Wool (pulled from pelts)	Clothing, blankets, lanolin
Poultry feathers	Animal feed, arrows, decorations, bedding, brushes

Cattle and buffalo hides comprise 80% of the farm animal hides and skins produced in the world. The United States has a major contribution in the world hide and skin market, as two-thirds of the 2,081 million lb of cattle hides produced are exported to other countries (Chapter 2). The United States produces very few goat skins but ranks 17th in sheepskins, with an annual production of approximately 37 million lb. Pork skin usually remains on the carcass, although some pigs are skinned.

TABLE 4.4. Leading Countries in Fresh Hide and Skin Production

Cattle and Buffalo Hides		Sheepskins		Goatskins	
Country	(mil lb)	Country	(mil lb)	Country	(mil lb)
1. United States	2,081	1. Australia	603	1. India	196
2. India	1,858	2. USSR	288	2. China	195
3. USSR	1,810	3. New Zealand	286	3. Pakistan	88
4. Brazil	836	4. China	242	4. Nigeria	46
5. Argentina	805	5. Turkey	146	5. Ethiopia	31
World total	15,188	World total	2,847	World total	984

Source: 1989 *FAO Production Yearbook.*

TABLE 4.5. Leather Uses Related to Types of Hides and Skins

Skin Origin	Use
Cow and steer	Shoe and boot uppers, soles, insoles, linings; patent leather; garments; work gloves; waist belts; luggage and cases; upholstery; transmission belting; sporting goods; packings
Calf	Shoe uppers; slippers; handbags and billfolds; hat sweatbands; bookbindings
Sheep and lamb	Grain and suede garments; shoe linings; slippers; dress and work gloves; hat sweatbands; bookbindings; novelties
Goat and kid	Shoe uppers, linings; dress gloves; garments; handbags
Pig	Shoe suede uppers; dress and work gloves; billfolds; fancy leather goods
Horse	Shoe uppers; straps; sporting goods

Source: New England Tanners Club, *Leather Facts.*

The U.S. hide export market yields approximately $1.5 billion on a yearly basis. **Hides, skins,** and **pelts** are made into useful leather products through the tanning process (Table 4.5). The surplus hides are exported primarily to Japan, Korea, Mexico, Taiwan, and Romania.

The general term *hide* refers to a beef hide weighing more than 30 lb. Those weighing less than 30 lb are called *skins*. Skins come from smaller animals, such as pigs, sheep, goats, and small wild animals. Those skins from sheep are usually called sheep pelts with the wool left on. Hides, skins, and pelts are classified according to (1) species, (2) weight, (3) size and placement of brand, and (4) type of packer producing them.

The value of hides may be reduced by branding, by nicking the hide while skinning, or by **warbles** (larvae of heel flies). Warbles emerge from the back region of cattle in the spring, making holes in the hide. Sheep hides may be damaged by outgrowths of grasses in the production of seeds (called beards), which can penetrate the skin, as well as by external parasites called **keds**.

Leather tanning and finishing is a $1.5 billion industry in the United States, employing over 20,000 people in 330 establishments and accounting for $250 million in exports. About 160 plants process raw hides or skins directly into tanned leather. Tanning activities are concentrated in the Northeast, Midwest, Middle Atlantic states, and California. Some tanneries are relatively small concerns specializing in the manufacture of a particular kind of leather, whereas others employ several hundred people and produce a variety of leathers.

TABLE 4.6. U.S. Animal Slaughter and Leather Production

Species	Head Slaughtered (mil)	Leather Production (mil)
Cattle	36	15 hides
Sheep	7	9 skins
Pig	79	4 skins

Source: New England Tanners Club, *Leather Facts,* 1983.

FIGURE 4.3.
Beef hide room where hides are cured, tied, and stored in preparation for shipping. Courtesy of Iowa Beef Processors, Inc.

Every year, U.S. tanneries convert millions of raw hides and skins into leather. The tanners' value added by manufacture constitutes over $500 million annually. Their product—leather—serves in turn as a raw material for the shoe and leather goods industries that provide jobs for over 200,000 people. Table 4.6 shows the most important hides and skins used in leather production. These amounts represent the total of both domestic and imported hides, skins, and pelts.

Table 4.6 shows that less than half of U.S. cattle hides are converted to leather domestically, most being exported for tanning. Some sheepskins are imported, as the domestic supply does not meet the demand. Pigskins are used primarily as food, but interest in leather production is increasing.

Just as meat is perishable, so too are hides and skins. If not cleaned and treated, they begin to decompose and lose leather-making substance within hours after removal from the carcass. Hides are commonly treated (cured) by adding salt as the principal curing agent. The salt solution penetrates the hide in about 12 hours, then the hides are bundled for shipment (Fig. 4.3).

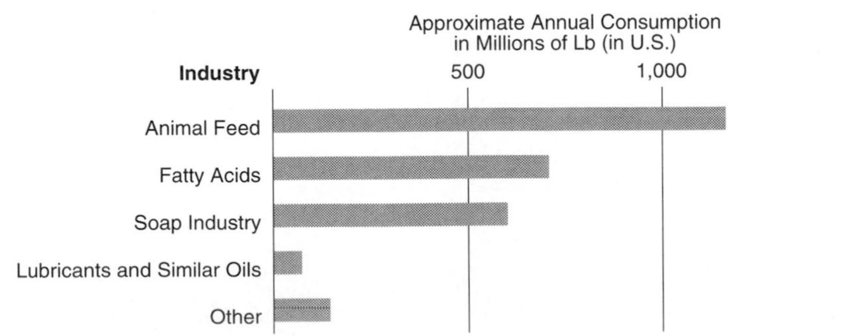

FIGURE 4.4.
The major uses of animal fat. Courtesy of the National Renderers Association.

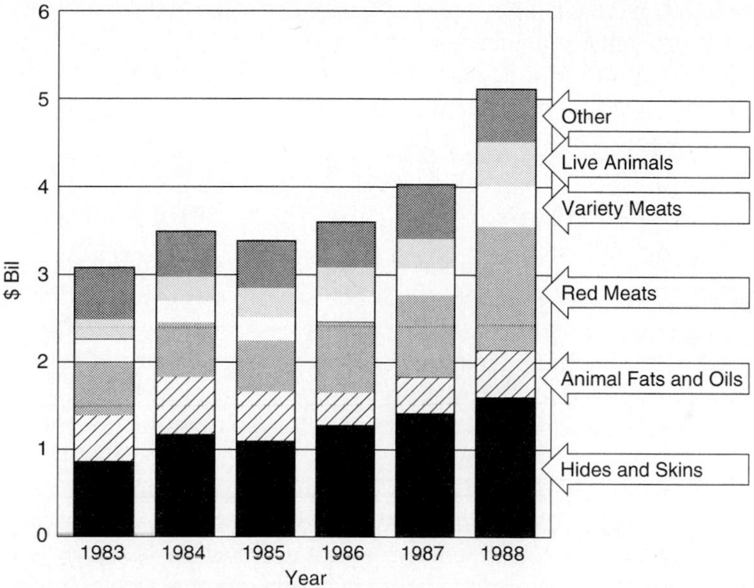

FIGURE 4.5.
U.S. exports of livestock products, 1983–88. Courtesy of the USDA.

THE RENDERING INDUSTRY

A major focal point of by-products is the rendering industry, which recycles offal, fat, bone, meat scraps, and entire animal carcasses. The sources of these raw materials are packing and processing plants, butcher shops, restaurants, supermarkets, farmers, and ranchers. Some large packing and processing plants have their own rendering plants integrated with other operations.

Renderers have a regular pickup service that amounts to approximately 81 million lb of animal material daily. This pickup service is essential to public health, as it reduces a major garbage-disposal problem. Also, since animal by-products have value, consumers can buy meat at a lower price than would otherwise be possible.

Rendering of Red Meat Animal By-Products

Animal fat and animal protein are the primary products of the renderer's art. Originally, animal fats went almost entirely into soap and candles. Today, from the same basic material, renderers produce many grades of tallow and semiliquid fat. The major uses of rendered fat are for animal feeds, fatty-acid production, and soap manufacture (Fig. 4.4).

Fatty acids are used in the manufacture of many products, such as plastic consumer items, cosmetics, lubricants, paints, deodorants, polishes, cleaners, caulking compounds, asphalt tile, printing inks, and others. The fatty-acid industry has had a tremendous growth since 1950.

The rendered animal proteins are processed into several high-protein (more than 50% protein) feed supplements among which are meat and bone meals and blood meals. The supplements are more commonly fed to young monogastric animals—swine, poultry, and pet animals. These animals require a high-quality protein, particularly the amino acid lysine, which is typical of animal protein supplements.

Blood, not processed into blood meal, is used to produce products used in the pet food industry. Such products are blood protein (fresh, frozen whole blood) and blood cell protein (frozen, fresh, dewatered blood).

Rendering of Poultry By-Products

Within a few hours after poultry is slaughtered, the offal is at the rendering plant. There it is cooked in steam-jacketed tanks at temperatures sufficient to destroy all pathogenic organisms. After cooking for several hours, the material is passed through presses that remove most of the fat (poultry fat), while the remaining material becomes poultry by-product meal. While it is still hot, the poultry fat is piped to sterile tanks where appropriate antioxidants or "stabilizers" are added, and thence to tank cars or drums for shipment to feed manufacturers or for other uses as shown in Fig. 4.4.

Poultry by-product meal (PBPM) is high in protein (approximately 58%) and contains 12%–14% fat. PBPM consists of ground dry-rendered clean parts of the carcass of slaughtered poultry, such as heads, feet, undeveloped eggs, and intestines, exclusive of feathers, except in such trace amounts as might occur unavoidably in good factory practice. It should not contain more than 16% ash and not more than 4% acid ash.

EXPORT MARKET

By-products from the livestock and poultry industries are an extremely important part of the export market of livestock products. Hides and skins, fats and oils, and variety meats comprise more than 35% of the $6.4 billion export market in 1989 (Fig. 4.5).

SELECTED REFERENCES

Publications

Hog Is Man's Best Friend; Meat; By-products. Chicago: The National Live Stock and Meat Board.

Renderer Recycling for a Better Tomorrow. 1981. National Renderers Association, 2250 East Devon Ave., Des Plaines, IL 60018.

Romans, J. R., Jones K. W., Costello, W. S., Carlson, C. W., and Ziegler, P. T. 1985. Packing house by-products. Chap. 10 in *The Meat We Eat*. Danville, IL: Interstate Printers and Publishers.

Visuals

Leather Production (VHS Video). VEP, Calif. State Polytechnic Univ., San Luis Obispo, CA 93407.

CHAPTER 5

Milk and Milk Products

The world's population obtains most of its milk and milk products from cows, water buffalo, goats, and sheep (Fig. 5.1). Horses, donkeys, reindeer, yaks, camels, and sows contribute a smaller amount to the total human milk supply. Milk, with its well-balanced assortment of nutrients, is sometimes called "nature's most nearly perfect food." While milk is an excellent food product in many ways, it is not perfect. Nor is any other food. Milk and numerous milk products (e.g., cheese, butter, ice cream, and cottage cheese) are major components of the human diet in many countries.

Changes in dietary preferences and milk marketing are some of the challenges facing the dairy industry. Health considerations and new products are changing the consumption patterns of milk and milk products. Milk surpluses in the United States and the world result in an abundance of consumer products, but the surpluses represent economic challenges to milk producers.

This chapter focuses primarily on milk as human food, but the importance of milk in nourishing suckling farm mammals should not be overlooked. When the term *milk* is used, reference is to milk from dairy cows unless otherwise specified.

MILK PRODUCTION

Table 5.1 shows the most important sources of milk for humans in the world and the United States. Total world milk production has increased during the past 25 years but not at the same rate as world human population (49% vs. 53%). Dairy cows produce over 90% of the world fluid milk supply (Fig. 5.2). During the past 30 years, milk yield from buffalo and sheep has been increasing while goat milk production has been decreasing. Some milk from dairy goats in the United States is marketed through supermarkets and other outlets similar to the marketing of cow's milk (Fig. 5.3). However, most milk from goats is produced and consumed by individuals or families who raise a few goats.

Leading countries for milk production are also shown in Table 5.1. The Soviet Union produces more milk than the United States (239 billion lb vs. 136 billion lb). However, it is

FIGURE 5.1.
(A) Milk plays an important role in human nutrition throughout the world. Courtesy of Heifer Project International. (B) Milking native sheep in the desert of Iran. Courtesy of R. E. McDowell, Cornell University. (C) Goats being milked in Mexico. Courtesy of Winrock International. (D) Milking dairy cows in a modern U.S. dairy. Courtesy of Colorado State University.

interesting to note the difference in cow numbers and productivity per cow. The 42 million cows in the Soviet Union have an average annual production per cow of 5,700 lb, whereas the 10 million cows in the United States have an average yearly production of more than 14,000 lb per cow.

The national dairy herd in the United States has decreased from over 20 million cows in 1956 to approximately 10 million in 1990. Yet total milk production has remained approximately the

TABLE 5.1. Major Sources of World Milk Production

Species	Total Production (bil lb)	Leading Countries (bil lb)
Cows	968	USSR (239); United States (136); Germany (74); France (57)
Buffalo	88	India (56); Pakistan (22); China (4); Egypt (3)
Sheep	19	Turkey (3.3); France (2.4); Iran (1.6); Greece (1.5)
Goats	19	India (3.3); Somalia (1.5); Pakistan (1.3); Turkey (1.2)
All others	52	
World total	1,146	

Source: 1989 *FAO Production Yearbook.*

same. Reduction in cow numbers has been offset by an increased production per cow—from 5,800 lb in 1956 to more than 14,000 lb in 1990. The 14,000 lb per cow comes to 1,624 gal (1 gal = 8.62 lb), which would supply the annual per-capita, fluid-milk consumption for nearly 50 people in the United States. However, since part of the milk is made into other dairy products (Fig. 5.4), the milk from one cow provides milk and manufactured products (cheese, frozen dairy products, and so on) for approximately 20 people.

FIGURE 5.2. Dairy cows have the unique ability to convert feedstuffs into milk. Milk is an important source of nutrients to humans throughout the world. Courtesy of Dairy Council, Inc.

FIGURE 5.3.
Milk products from dairy goats. Courtesy of George F. W. Haenlein, University of Delaware.

Fluid milk sales are important to the U.S. economy. The wholesale and retail values of fluid milk are more than $20 million and $25 million, respectively.

MILK COMPOSITION

Milk is a colloidal suspension of solids in liquid. Fluid whole milk is approximately 88% water, 8.6% **solids-not-fat (SNF),** and 3%–4% milk fat. The SNF is the total solids minus the milk fat. It contains protein, lactose, and minerals.

FIGURE 5.4.
Milk, cheese, and yogurt are among the most highly preferred milk products. Courtesy of the American Dairy Association.

Even though milk is a liquid, its 12% total solids is similar to the solids content of many solid foods. Differences in milk composition for several species of animals are given in Chapter 19.

The first milk a female produces after the young is born is called **colostrum.** True colostrum is milk obtained during the first milking. For the next several milkings, the milk is called transitional milk and is not legally salable until the 11th milking. Colostrum differs greatly in composition from milk. Colostrum is higher in protein, minerals, and milk fat, but it contains less lactose than milk. The most remarkable difference between colostrum and milk produced later is the extremely high immunoglobulin content of colostrum. These protein compounds accumulate in the mammary gland and they are the antibodies that are transferred through milk to the suckling young. People seldom use colostrum from animals because of its unpleasant appearance and odor, although a few may use it for pudding. Additionally, the high globulin content causes a precipitation of proteins when colostrum is pasteurized.

Milk contains a high nutrient density—more than 100 milk components have been identified. **Nutrient density** refers to the concentration of major nutrients in relation to the caloric value of the food. In other words, milk contains important amounts of several nutrients while being relatively low in calories. The major components of milk solids can be grouped into nutrient categories including proteins, fats, carbohydrates, minerals, and vitamins.

Milk Fat

In whole milk, the approximate 3%–4% milk fat is a mixture of lipids existing as microscopic globules suspended in the milk. The fat contributes about 48% of the total calories in whole milk. Fat-soluble vitamins (A, D, E, and K) are normal components in milk fat. Milk fat contains most of the flavor components of milk, so when milk fat is decreased, there may be a concurrent reduction in flavor.

Approximately 500 different fatty acids and fatty-acid derivatives from 2–26 carbon atoms in length have been identified in milk. Milk fat from ruminant animals contains both short-chain and long-chain fatty acids.

Carbohydrates

Lactose, the predominant carbohydrate in milk, is synthesized in the mammary gland. Approximately 4.8% of cow's milk is lactose. It accounts for approximately 54% of the SNF content in milk. Lactose is only about one-sixth as sweet as sucrose, and it is less soluble in water than other sugars. It contributes about 30% of the total calories in milk. Milk is the only natural source of lactose.

Proteins

Milk contains approximately 3.3% protein. Protein accounts for about 38% of total SNF and about 22% of the calories of whole milk. The proteins of milk are of high quality. They contain varying amounts of all amino acids required by humans. A surplus of the amino acid lysine offsets the low lysine content of vegetable proteins and particularly cereals.

Casein, a protein found only in milk, is approximately 82% of the total milk protein. Whey proteins, primarily lactalbumin and lactoglobulin, constitute the remaining 18%. Immunoglobulins, the antibody proteins in colostral milk, were discussed earlier in the chapter.

Vitamins

All vitamins essential in human nutrition are found in milk. Fat-soluable vitamins are in the milk fat portion of milk, and water-soluble vitamins are in the nonfat portion. Milk is usually fortified with vitamin D during processing.

Milk fat from Jersey and Guernsey cows has a rich, yellow color due to carotene (a precursor of vitamin A), which is yellow. Milk fat from Holstein cows has a pale, yellow color, and goat milk fat is white. Carotene can be split into two molecules of vitamin A. Milk fat of Holstein cows is pale yellow because most of the carotene has been split, and the milk fat of goats is white because all of the carotene has been changed to colorless vitamin A.

Water-soluble vitamins (C and B) are relatively constant in milk and are not greatly influenced by vitamin content of the cow's ration. The B vitamins are produced by rumen microorganisms, and vitamin C is formed by healthy epithelial tissue in most animals (excluding humans, other primates, and guinea pigs).

Minerals

Milk is a rich source of calcium for the human diet and a reasonably good source of phosphorus and zinc. Calcium and vitamin D are needed in combination to contribute to bone growth in young humans and to prevent **osteoporosis** in adults, particularly women. Milk is not a good source of iron, and the iodine content of milk varies with the iodine content of the animal's feed.

Table 5.2 and Fig. 5.5 show how the milk supply is used to produce various milk products. More than 80% of the milk produced is marketed as fluid milk, cream, cheese, and butter.

The amount of milk needed to produce each product depends primarily on the milk fat content of the milk. Table 5.3 gives the approximate amount of milk used to produce each product.

MILK PRODUCTS IN THE UNITED STATES

Fluid Milk

Eighty-five percent of the 136 billion lb of milk produced in the United States is grade A quality milk. Grade A milk in excess of fluid milk demand is processed into other milk products. How fluid milk typically moves from farm to consumer is shown in Fig. 5.6.

TABLE 5.2. Milk and Milk Products Resulting from the 1989 Milk Supply

Whole-Milk Product	Total Production (mil lb)	Percent of Total
Fluid milk and cream	55.3	38%
Cheese	43.6	30
Butter	24.5	17
Frozen dairy products	12.5	9
Evaporated and condensed milk	1.8	1
Uses on farms where produced	2.1	2
Other uses	5.3	3

Source: Milk Industry Foundation, 1990 *Milk Facts.*

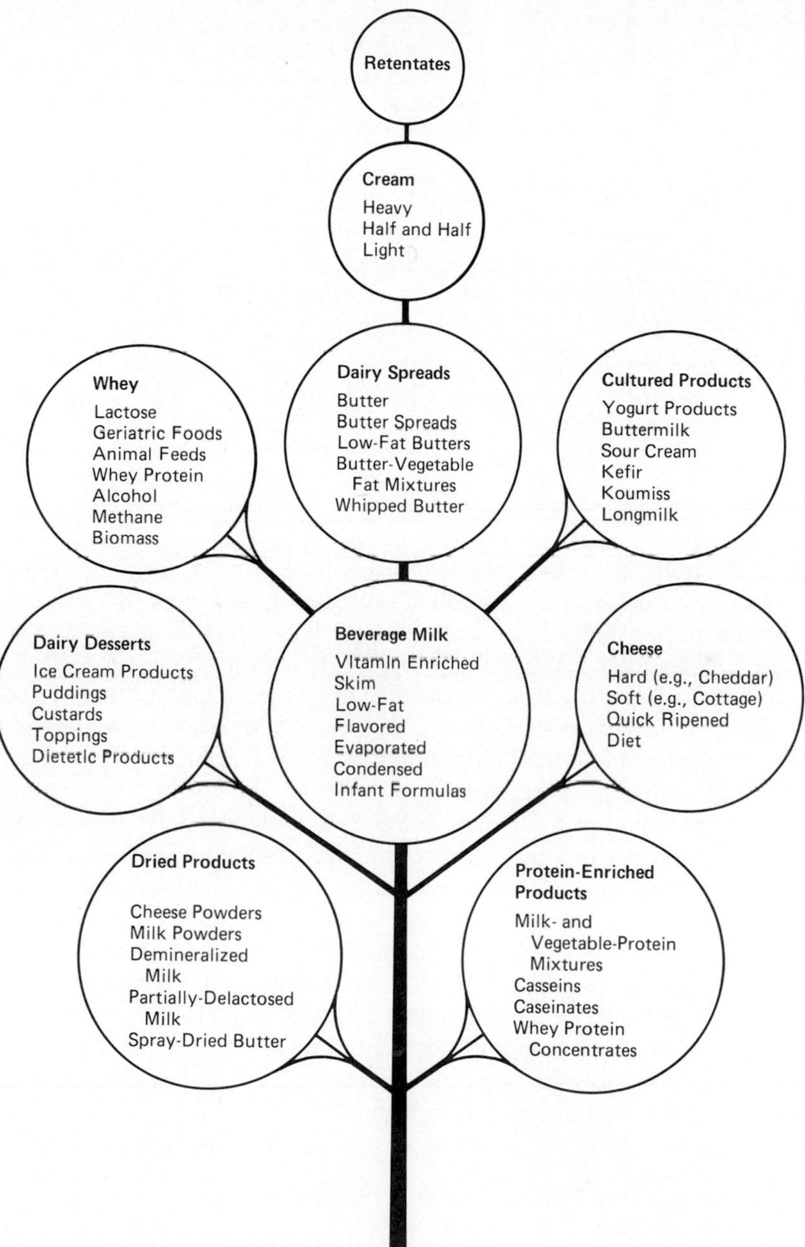

FIGURE 5.5.
The modern dairy tree showing the many products and by-products of milk. Courtesy of *J. Dairy Sci.* 64:1005.

TABLE 5.3. Approximate Amount of Milk Used to Produce Several Selected Dairy Products

Dairy Product (lb)	Whole Milk (lb)
Butter	21.2
Whole-milk cheese	10.0
Evaporated milk	2.1
Condensed milk	7.4
Ice cream (1 gal)	12.0
Cottage cheese	6.2 (skim)
Nonfat dry milk	11.0

Sources: USDA; Milk Industry Foundation, *Milk Facts.*

Depending on the milk fat content and the processing at the plant, the fresh fluid product is labeled whole milk, low-fat milk, or skim milk. In further discussion in this chapter, *milk* refers to whole milk. Whole milk is defined as a lacteal secretion, and when it is packaged for beverage use it must contain not less that 3.25% milk fat and not less than 8.25% milk SNF. Low-fat milk usually has had some or most milk fat removed to have one of the following milk fat levels: 0.5%, 1.0%, 1.5%, or 2.0% with not less than 8.25% milk SNF. Skim milk has had most of the milk fat removed (it contains less than 0.5% milk fat). It must contain at least 8.25% SNF and may be fortified with nonfat solids to 10.25%.

Most fluid milk consumed in the United States is **homogenized** to prevent milk fat from separating from the liquid portion and rising to the top. Homogenization is a physical process resulting in a stable emulsion of milk fat. A "cream line" does not appear in homogenized milk, nor does it form butter if churned.

Fat globules in raw milk average about 6 μm in diameter. Homogenization reduces the fat globule size to less than 2 μm in diameter. To visualize how small the fat globules in homogenized milk are, note that 25,000 μm equal approximately 1 in. Homogenized milk will likely deteriorate by becoming rancid more rapidly than nonhomogenized milk. Rancidity of homogenized milk is forestalled by pasteurizing milk prior to or immediately following homogenization, thus destroying the action of lipolytic enzymes.

Evaporated and Condensed Milk

Evaporated milk is produced by preheating to stabilize proteins and removing about 60% of the water. It is sealed in the container and then heat-treated to sterilize its contents. Milk fat and SNF of evaporated milk must be at least 7.5% and 25%, respectively. Evaporated skim milk must have at least 20% SNF and not more than 0.5% milk fat. Evaporated milk requires no refrigeration until opened. Once the can is opened, refrigeration is necessary to avoid spoilage.

Concentrated, or condensed, milk has milk fat (7.5%) and SNF (25.5%) requirements similar to those for evaporated milk. Concentrated milk also has water removed but, unlike evaporated milk, it is not subjected to further heat treatment to prevent spoilage. Most concentrated milk is

Milk from Farm to Family

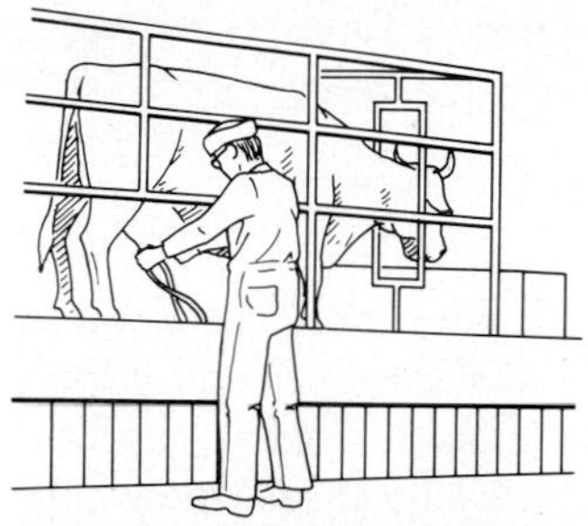

1 Cows are milked twice a day with sanitary milking machines.

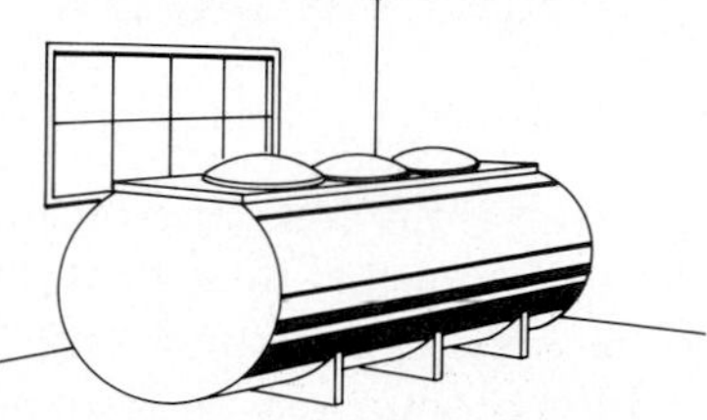

2 The milk is pumped from the milking machine into the refrigerated farm tank.

3 Milk is sampled and checked before it is pumped into the refrigerated truck.

4 Each tank truck rushes cold milk from several farms to dairy plants.

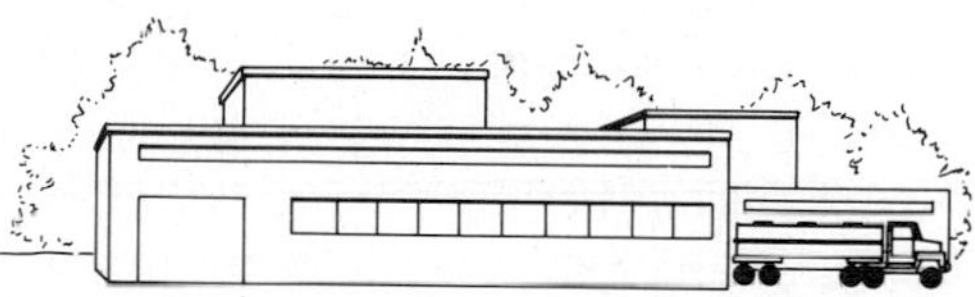

5 Milk is processed and packaged in sterilized equipment.

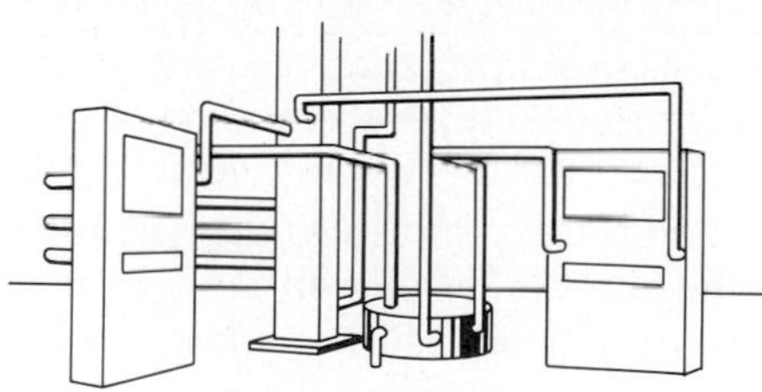

6 The milk is pasteurized in thermostatically controlled equipment, then homogenized (some is not homogenized).

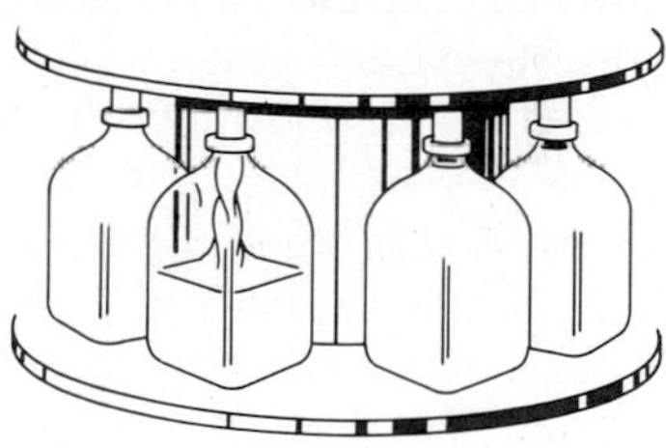

7 Automatic machines package cold pasteurized milk in paper, glass or plastic containers.

8 And put the containers into cases. Conveyors rush the milk, ready for delivery, to a refrigerated room.

9 Refrigerated trucks bring the milk.

10 To stores and homes.

FIGURE 5.6.
The processes involved in making milk available to consumers.

sold bulk for industry use. A common form of concentrated milk on grocery shelves is sweetened (sugar added) condensed milk; it is used for candy and other confections.

Dry Milk

Dry milk is prepared by removing water from milk, low-fat milk, or skim milk. All of these products are to contain no more than 5% moisture by weight. Dry milk can be stored for long periods of time if it is sealed in an atmosphere of nonoxidizing gas, such as nitrogen or carbon dioxide. The spray-dried or foam-dried product can be reconstituted easily in warm or cold water with agitation.

Fermented Dairy Products

Buttermilk, yogurt, sour cream, and other cultured milk products are produced under rigidly controlled conditions of sanitation, inoculation, incubation, acidification, and/or temperature. The word *cultured* appearing in a product name indicates the addition of appropriate bacteria cultures to the fluid dairy product and subsequent fermentation. Selected cultures of bacteria convert lactose into lactic acid, which produces a tart flavor. The specific bacterial cultures used and other controls in the fermentation process determine whether buttermilk, sour cream, yogurt, or cheese is the end product.

Today buttermilk is a cultured product rather than the by-product of churning cream into butter as was the procedure in the past. At the correct stage of acid and flavor development, the buttermilk is stirred gently to break the curd that has formed. It is then cooled to stop the fermentation process.

The word *acidified* in the product name or production process indicates that the food was produced by souring milk or cream with or without the addition of microbial organisms.

Cottage cheese dry curd is soft, unripened cheese; it is produced by culturing or direct acidification. Finished dry curd contains less than 0.5% milk fat and not more than 80% moisture. Cottage cheese is prepared for market by mixing cottage cheese dry curd with a pasteurized creaming mixture called dressing. The finished product contains not less than 4% milk fat and not over 80% moisture. Low-fat cottage cheese is made by the same process; however, the milk fat range is 0.5%–2%.

Sour cream is generally a lactic acid fermentation, although rennet extract is often added in small quantities to produce a thicker-bodied product. Federal standards provide that cultured sour cream contain not less than 18% milk fat. When stored for more than 3–4 weeks, sour cream may develop a bitter flavor as a result of continued bacterial proteolytic enzyme activity.

Yogurt, as a liquid or gel, can be manufactured from fresh whole, low-fat, or skim milk that is heated before fermentation. Federal standards specify that yogurt contain not less than 3.25% milk fat, low-fat yogurt between 0.5–2% milk fat, and nonfat yogurt not more than 0.5% milk fat before any bulky flavors are added.

Today three main types of yogurt are produced: (1) flavored, containing no fruit; (2) flavored, containing fruit (fruit may be at the bottom or blended in); and (3) unflavored.

Cream

Cream is a liquid milk product, high in fat that has been separated from milk. Federal standards require that cream contain not less than 18% milk fat.

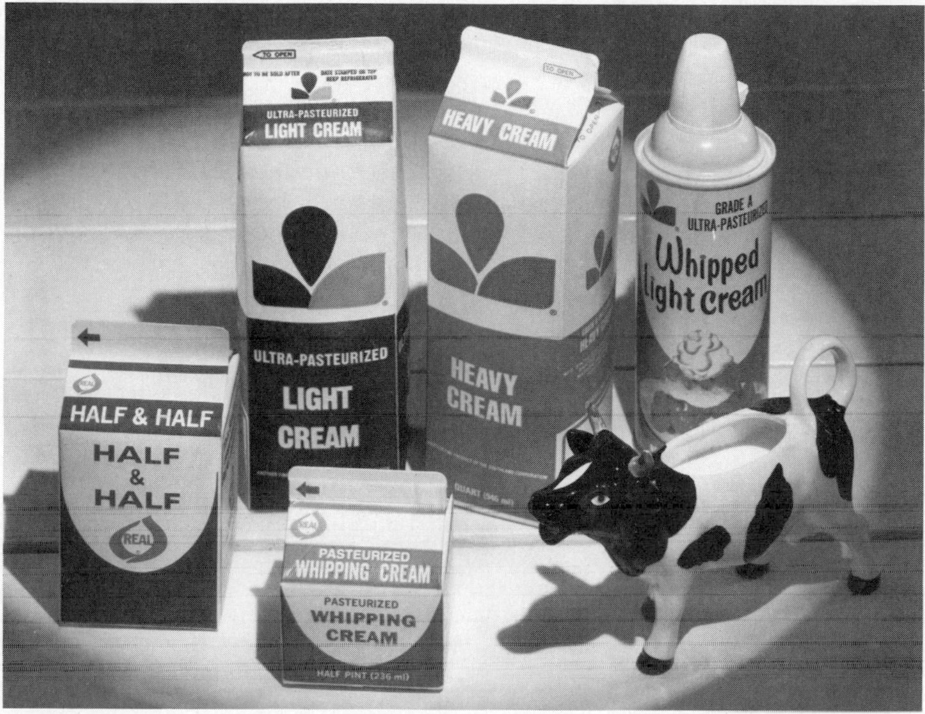

FIGURE 5.7.
There is a range of cream products to meet consumer needs. Courtesy of the American Dairy Association.

Several cream products are marketed (Fig. 5.7). Half-and-half is a mixture of milk and cream containing not less than 10.5% but less than 18% milk fat. Light cream (coffee or table cream) contains not less than 18% but less than 30% milk fat. Light whipping cream or whipping cream contains not less than 30% but less than 36% milk fat. Heavy cream or heavy whipping cream contains not less than 36% milk fat. Dry cream is produced by removal of water only from pasteurized milk and/or cream. It contains not less than 40% but less than 75% milk fat and not more than 5% moisture.

Butter

It is known from food remnants in vessels found in early tombs that the Egyptians cooked with butter and cheese. For many centuries, butter making and cheese making were the only means of preserving milk and cream.

Butter churns are the oldest dairy equipment, dating from prehistoric days when nomads carried milk in a type of pouch made from an animal's stomach. Slung on the back of a horse or camel, the pouch bounced as the animal moved, churning the cream or milk into butter.

Wooden or crockery dasher-type churns used at the turn of the century are today's attic treasures. By jouncing a long-handled, wooden dasher up and down in the deep churn, the cream was sloshed around until butter particles separated from the remaining liquid, called buttermilk.

Butter is the dairy product made exclusively from milk or cream, or both, which contains not less than 80% by weight of milk fat. Federal standards establish U.S. grades for butter based on flavor, color, and salt characteristics.

In modern butter making, fresh sweet milk is weighed, tested for milk fat content, and checked for quality. The cream is then separated by centrifugation to contain 30%–35% milk fat for batch-type churning or 40%–45% milk fat for continuous churning.

Continuous butter-making operations, which can produce 1,800–11,000 lb an hour, are an industry trend. New continuous butter-making processes employ several different scientific principles to form butter.

Cheese

There are more than 400 different kinds of cheese that can be made (Fig. 5.8). The cheeses have more than 2,000 names, since the same cheese may have two or more different names. For example, cheddar cheese is one of the American-type cheeses in the United States, along with Colby, washed or stirred curd, and Monterey.

Most cheeses and cheese products are classified into one of four main groups: (1) soft, (2) semisoft, (3) hard, and (4) very hard. Classification is based on moisture content in the cheese. Thus the body and texture of cheeses range from soft, unripened cheese (such as cottage cheese with 80% moisture) to very hard, grated, shaker cheeses such as Parmesan and Romano. These latter, ripened cheeses have 32%–34% moisture.

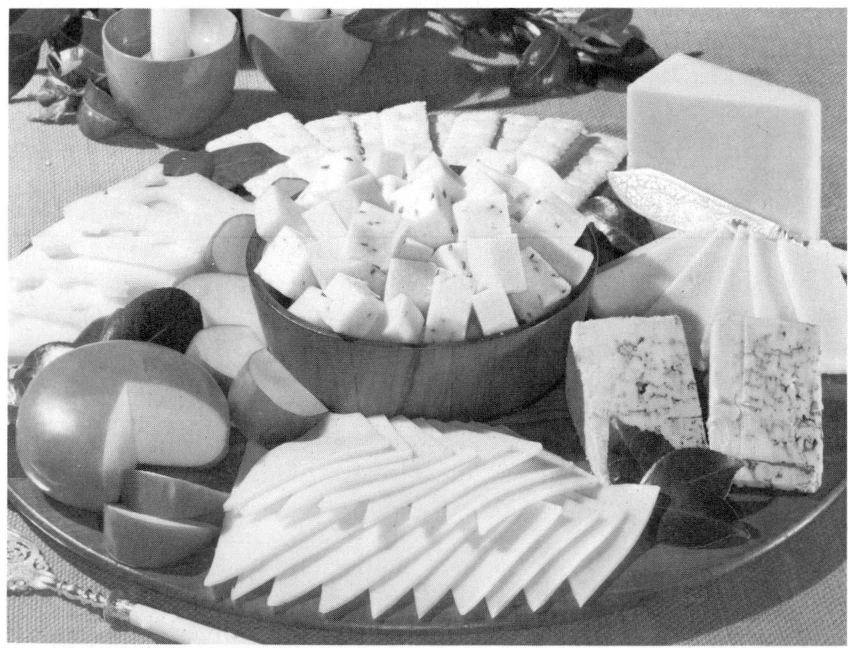

FIGURE 5.8.
There are numerous kinds of cheeses to satisfy varying consumer preferences. Courtesy of the American Dairy Association.

Cheese flavor varies from bland cottage cheese to pungent Roquefort and Limburger. Modern microbiology makes it possible to add specific species and strains of microorganisms required to produce the desired product. For example, a fungus *(Penicillium roqueforti)* is used to produce Roquefort cheese.

The most dramatic increase in cheese production in the United States has occurred with Italian varieties. The phenomenal growth of the pizza industry has caused an increased production and importation of mozzarella cheese.

Cheese making involves a biochemical process called coagulation, or curdling. First the milk is heated, then a liquid starter culture is added. Bacteria from the culture form acids and turn the milk sour. At a later time, rennet is added to thicken the milk. Rennet, obtained from the stomachs of young calves, contains the enzyme rennin. Other enzymes of microbial origin have been used successfully to replace a declining supply of rennin. After stirring this mixture, a custardlike substance called curd is formed. Then the liquid part (whey) is removed. The cheese-making process reduces 100 lb of milk to 8–16 lb of cheese.

In cheese plants, disposal of whey is a problem. It is currently estimated that 35 billion lb of whey containing more than 4 billion lb of solids is produced. Slightly more than half the whey is used to produce human food or animal feeds. The remaining whey poses waste-disposal problems. There continues to be an increasing industrial use of whey for production of food, feed, fertilizer, alcohol, and insulation.

Table 5.4 identifies the leading countries in yearly cheese production and the most important cheese-producing states in the United States.

Ice Cream

Although they come in many variations, ice cream and a group of similarly frozen foods are made in a similar way and have many of the same ingredients. Ice cream, frozen custard, French ice cream, and French custard ice cream are frozen dairy products highest in milk fat and milk solids. Ice cream may contain egg yolk solids. If egg yolks are in excess of 1.4% by weight, the product is called frozen custard, French ice cream, or French custard ice cream.

Ice milk contains less milk fat, protein, and total solids than ice cream. Ice milk usually has more sugar than does ice cream. Soft ice milk and soft ice cream are soft and ready to eat when drawn from the freezer. About three-fourths of the soft-serve products are ice milks. Some

TABLE 5.4. Leading Cheese-producing Countries and States

Country	Total Production (bil lb)	State	Total Production[a] (mil lb)
United States	7	Wisconsin	1,901
USSR	5	Minnesota	635
Germany	4	California	540
France	3	New York	509
Italy	2	Iowa	259
World total	32		

[a] Does not include cottage cheese.
Sources: USDA; 1989 *FAO Production Yearbook.*

of the soft-serve frozen dairy foods contain vegetable fats that have replaced all or most of the milk fat.

Frozen yogurt has become a popular dairy product. Frozen yogurt has less milk fat and higher acidity than ice cream and less sugar than sherbet.

Sherbet is low in both milk fat and milk solids. It has more sugar than ice cream. The tartness of fruit sherbet comes from the added fruit and fruit acid. Nonfruit sherbet is flavored with such ingredients as spices, coffee, or chocolate.

Water ices are nondairy frozen foods. They contain neither milk ingredients nor egg yolk. Ices are made similarly to sherbet.

Mellorine differs from ice cream in that milk fat may be replaced partially by a vegetable fat, another animal fat, or both.

Eggnog

Eggnog contains milk products, egg yolk, egg white, and a nutritive carbohydrate sweetener. In addition, eggnog may contain salt, flavoring, and color additives. Federal standards specify that eggnog shall contain not less than 6% milk fat and 8.25% SNF.

Imitation Dairy Products

The FDA established regulations in 1973 to differentiate between imitation and substitute products. It defined an imitation product as one that looks like, tastes like, and is intended to replace the traditional counterpart but is nutritionally inferior to it. A substitute product resembles the traditional food but also meets the FDA's definition of nutritional equivalency.

Imitation milks usually contain ingredients such as water, corn syrup solids, sugar, vegetable fats, and protein from soybean, sodium caseinate, or other sources. Although imitation fluid milk may not contain dairy products per se, it may contain derivatives of milk such as whey, lactose, casein, salts of casein, and milk proteins, other than casein.

The dairy industry has developed a program for identification of real dairy foods. A "REAL" Seal (observe in Fig. 5.7) on a carton or package identifies milk or other dairy foods made from U.S.-produced milk that meets federal and/or state standards. This seal assures consumers that the food is not an imitation or substitute.

HEALTH CONSIDERATIONS

Nutritive Value of Milk

Milk and other dairy products make a significant contribution to the nation's supply of dietary nutrients. Particularly noteworthy are the relatively large percentages of calcium, phosphorus, protein, and B vitamins (Table 5.5).

Human milk is regarded as the best source of nourishment for infants. Cow's milk for infant feeding is modified to meet the nutrient and physical requirements of infants. Cow's milk is heated, homogenized, or acidified so the nutrients can be utilized efficiently by infants. Sugar is usually added to cow's milk for infant feeding to make milk more nearly like human milk.

Milk is low in iron; therefore, young animals consuming nothing but milk may develop anemia. Baby pigs produced in confinement need a supplemental source of iron, usually given

TABLE 5.5. Contribution of Dairy Foods (excluding butter) to Nutrients Consumed in the United States (1985)

Nutrients	Percent
Energy	10%
Protein	21
Fat	11
Carbohydrate	6
Cholesterol	14
Minerals	
Calcium	76
Phosphorus	36
Magnesium	20
Iron	2
Zinc	20
Vitamins	
Ascorbic acid	3
Thiamin	9
Riboflavin	35
Vitamin B_6	11
Vitamin B_{12}	20
Vitamin A	10

Source: USDA.

as an injection. Babies typically receive supplemental iron, and young children who consume large amounts of milk at the expense of meat should be given supplemental iron.

Milk and milk products are excellent sources of nutrients to meet the dietary requirements of young children, adolescents, and adults. With aging, there is an increased prevalence of osteoporosis, a problem of loss of bone mass. Since osteoporosis involves the loss of bone matrix and minerals, a diet generous in protein, calcium, vitamin D, and fluoride is recommended to overcome the problem. Thus, milk, owing to its content of calcium and other nutrients, is an important food for this segment of the population. Furthermore, for the elderly as well as for the infant and young child, milk is an efficient source of nutrients readily tolerated by a sometimes weakened digestive system.

Wholesomeness

Milk is among the most perishable of all foods owing to its excellent nutritional composition and its fluid form. As it comes from the cow, milk provides an ideal medium for bacterial growth. Properly processed milk can be kept for 10–14 days under refrigeration. With ultra-high-temperature (UHT) processing, milk can be kept for several weeks at room temperature.

Protecting the quality of milk is a responsibility shared by public health officials, the dairy industry, and consumers. The U.S. Food and Drug Administration describes milk as "one of the best controlled, inspected and monitored of all food commodities."

The most important safeguards from a health standpoint are requirements that bacterial counts be low and that milk be pasteurized (Fig. 5.9). Milk sold through commercial outlets is certified to be from herds that are tested and found to be free from brucellosis and tuberculosis. The consumer who buys milk and milk products can be assured of obtaining a safe, desirable, wholesome food. There are definite health risks in consuming milk from a cow or goat where the milk has not been pasteurized. This concern is important where families or individuals have purchased the animal with an unknown health background or purchased milk that has not been processed.

Milk Processing

Milk is taken from the cow by a sanitized milking machine, then transported through sanitized pipes into holding tanks. When withdrawn from the cow, milk is at the cow's body temperature of about 100°F (38°C). It flows into a refrigerated tank, where it is rapidly cooled to 45°F (7°C) or less. Cold temperature maintains the high quality of the milk while it is held for delivery.

Tank truck drivers, who pick up milk, inspect it to see if it is cold and has an acceptable aroma. They take a milk sample for testing later at the processing plant. Then the cold milk is pumped from the refrigerated farm tank through a sanitized hose into the insulated tank on the truck (Fig. 5.10).

After the milk sample passes several tests at the processing plant, it is pumped through sanitized pipes into the processing plant's refrigerated or insulated holding tanks.

Milk is pasteurized at the processing plant. Pasteurization is a process of exposing milk to a temperature that destroys all pathogenic bacteria but neither reduces the nutritional value of milk nor causes it to curdle. Milk is most commonly pasteurized at 161°F (71.5°C) for 15 sec.

FIGURE 5.9.
Milk samples are checked for undesirable bacteria. Courtesy of Dairy Council, Inc.

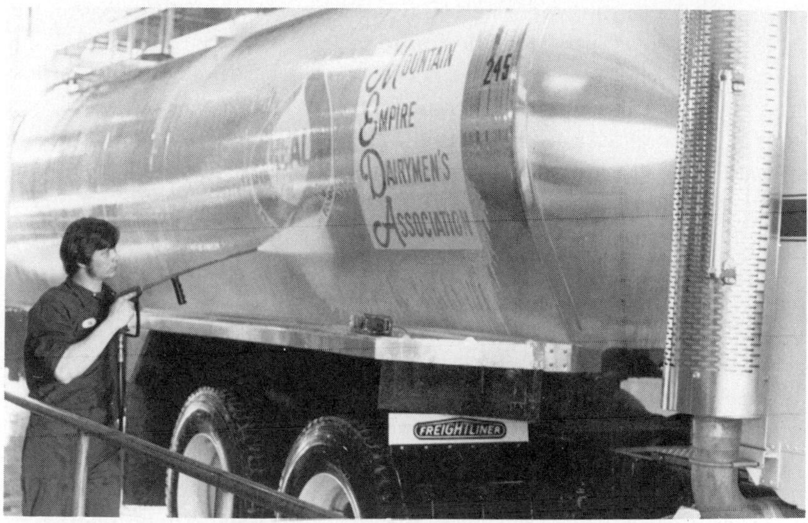

FIGURE 5.10.
Large milk trucks move milk from dairy farms to processing plants. The tanks are washed and sanitized after each delivery. Courtesy of Dairy Council, Inc.

Ultrapasteurized milk and UHT processed milk are heated to 280°F (138°C) for at least 2 sec; this sterilizes milk and increases shelf life.

As it flows out of the pasteurizer, most milk is homogenized by being pumped through a series of valves under pressure. The milk fat is broken up into particles too small to coalesce. As a result, they remain suspended throughout the milk rather than separating to the top as a layer of cream.

The pasteurized, ultrapasteurized, or UHT processed milk is cooled rapidly to below 45°F (7°C). UHT milk is packaged into presterilized containers and aseptically sealed. Since bacteria cannot enter the UHT milk, it can be kept unrefrigerated for at least 3 months. However, once the container is opened, the UHT milk picks up organisms from the air. Then the UHT milk must be handled and stored like any other fluid milk product.

Milk Intolerance

Milk is the main dietary source of carbohydrate lactose. In the 1960s, the potential problem of lactose intolerance was emphasized when reports revealed low levels of the enzyme lactase in digestive tracts of 70% of black and 10% of white persons in the United States. Symptoms include bloating, abdominal cramps, nausea, and diarrhea. Worldwide, lactose intolerance is relatively high among nonwhite populations. However, results of many studies have disclosed the difference between lactose intolerance and milk intolerance. While a large segment of certain populations may be diagnosed as lactose-intolerant, most of these individuals, once adapted, can tolerate the amount of lactose contained in typical servings of dairy foods.

For the few individuals who are truly milk-intolerant, suitable alternatives are available. These include consumption of recommended amounts of milk in smaller but more frequent servings throughout the day, most cheeses, many fermented and culture-containing dairy products (e.g., yogurt), lactose-hydrolyzed milk, and some dairy products containing up to 75% less lactose.

Milk protein allergy may be considered as another form of milk intolerance. An allergic reaction to the protein component of cow's milk may occur in a few infants who experience allergies early in life. The incidence is probably 1% or less in the infant and child population in industrialized countries, although a range of 0.3%–7.5% has been reported. The condition is usually outgrown by 2 years of age, beyond which time true allergic reactions to milk in the general population are rare.

Human Disease Risk

In the 1950s, scientists hypothesized an association between increased dietary intakes of cholesterol and increased risk of atherosclerosis and coronary heart disease (CHD). In 1980, the U.S. government issued dietary guidelines for Americans; one guideline recommended not eating excessive fat, especially saturated fat and cholesterol.

In line with these dietary recommendations, dairy foods have been singled out as being undesirable because of their cholesterol and saturated fatty-acid content. Dairy foods, however, are not particularly high in either cholesterol or saturated fatty acids. Some research demonstrates that whole milk, skim milk, and yogurt exhibit a cholesterol-lowering effect. Further evidence that dairy foods have little or no effect in CHD has been increasing while animal-fat consumption has been decreasing.

The question of whether dietary change is a measure to reduce the incidence of CHD is unresolved. Many scientific investigators and professional organizations believe that the role of dietary cholesterol and saturated fatty acids in the prevention, mitigation, and cure of CHD has been overemphasized.

CONSUMPTION

Population growth by the year 2000 will no doubt cause an increase in consumption of dairy products; however, per-capita consumption is expected to decrease (*J. Dairy Sci.* 64:959).

Table 5.6 shows the per-capita consumption of dairy products in several selected countries. Norway and Germany are highest in fluid milk consumption, and Germany leads in butter consumption. Greece, France, and Germany are the countries with the highest per-capita cheese consumption.

Table 5.7 shows the per-capita sales of milk and milk products in the United States in 1975, 1985, and 1989. There is a noticeable consumer preference toward low-fat products. Figures 5.11 and 5.12 reflect the changes in consumer preferences during the past several years with skim milk, low-fat milk, and cheese showing the most significant changes.

MARKETING

World

Only a small percentage of the world's milk products production enters world trade: butter (4%), cheese (4%), skim milk powder (18%), and casein (80%). The European Economic Community (EEC) and New Zealand account for about 80% of total world exports of dairy products.

TABLE 5.6. Yearly Per-capita Consumption of Selected Dairy Products in Selected Countries

Leading Countries and the United States[a]	Per-capita Consumption (lb)		
	Milk	Butter	Cheese
Finland	343	—	—
Ireland	386	—	—
Netherlands	—	27.1	32.8
Sweden	358	—	32.1
Norway	467	—	—
Germany	413	50.6	53.7
Denmark	—	23.8	—
New Zealand	—	31.1	—
Greece	—	—	50.1
France	—	—	49.2
Italy	—	—	36.4
United States	237	4.3	24.0
Poland	350	—	—

[a] U.S. data shown for comparison to leading countries.
Sources: USDA; Milk Industry Foundation, *Milk Facts.*

TABLE 5.7. Yearly Per-capita Sales of Dairy Products in the United States (lb), 1975–89

Product	1975	1985	1989
Plain whole milk	173.2	116.3	92.0
Lowfat milk	54.9	85.0	95.5
Skim milk	11.9	13.0	20.1
Flavored milk and drinks	10.0	10.7	9.8
Buttermilk	4.8	4.3	3.9
Yogurt	2.1	3.9	4.2
Eggnog	0.4	0.5	0.5
Half-and-half	2.5	3.1	3.0
Light cream	0.4	0.3	0.4
Heavy cream	0.6	0.9	1.2
Sour cream and dips	1.7	2.3	2.5
Butter	4.4	3.8	3.5
American cheese	7.9	9.5	10.8
Other cheese	6.1	10.1	12.7
Cottage cheese	4.6	4.0	3.5
Dry milk	3.2	2.2	2.4
Evaporated milk	8.7	7.6	7.3
Ice cream	18.6	18.1	16.0
Ice milk	7.6	6.9	8.3

Sources: USDA; Milk Industry Foundation, *Milk Facts.*

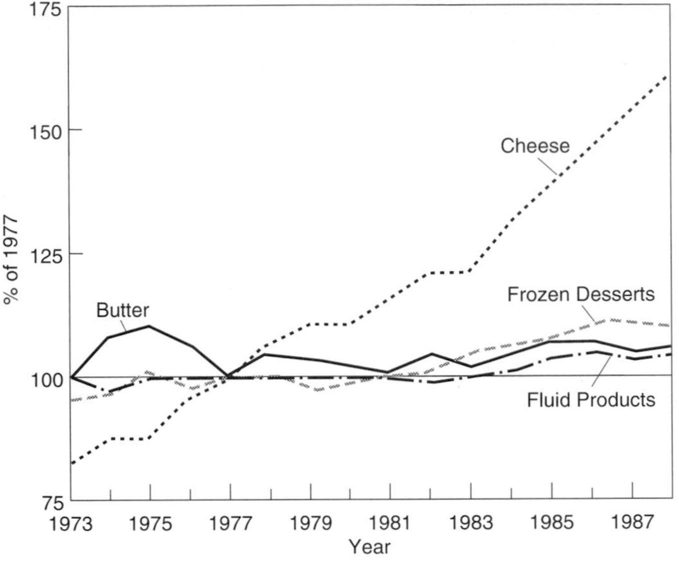

FIGURE 5.11.
U.S. dairy products sales, 1973–87. Fluid products include cheese and specialty items; cheese excludes cottage cheese. Courtesy of the USDA.

The EEC, Canada, and the United States have surpluses of skim milk powder in part because of price stabilization programs and because production costs exceed world market prices. Exports of skim milk powder go principally to countries with a milk deficit and are used in a variety of recombined products. Much of New Zealand and Australian production of casein is exported to the United States.

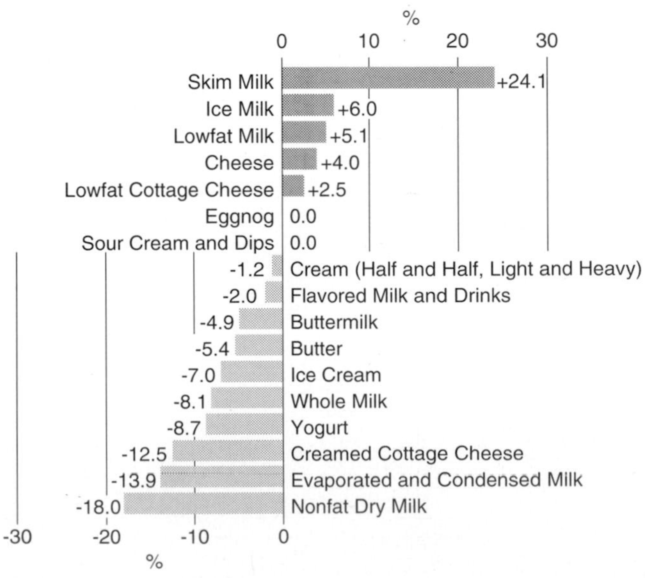

FIGURE 5.12.
Percent change in per-capita sales of selected dairy products, 1988–89. Courtesy of the Milk Industry Foundation.

Nutritionally, the world may need milk, but there is no real market for its present surpluses of dairy products. Surpluses continue to be a major marketing challenge both in the United States and the world.

United States

Most milk produced on U.S. dairy farms goes to plants and dealers for processing. More than 50% of the fluid milk is marketed by supermarkets, primarily in plastic gallon containers.

Prices

Cooperative milk marketing associations, located near large population centers, give producers more bargaining power, as they control approximately 90% of the milk produced. The cooperatives hire professionals to market the milk to prospective purchasers.

There are classes and grades of milk that determine price. Grade A (fluid or market milk) and grade B (manufacturing milk) are determined by the sanitary and microbial quality of the milk. Class I, the highest price class, is grade A milk for fluid use. Classes II and III are for milk used in manufactured products. Class II includes milk for cottage cheese, cream, and frozen desserts; class III is milk used for butter and cheese. Class II is grade A milk, and class III is surplus grade A or grade B milk. Producers receive a "blend" price based on the proportion of milk used in each price class.

Forty-four federal "milk-marketing orders" and 14 states establish the prices that processors must pay diary farmers for about 95% of the fluid milk and fluid milk products consumed in the United States. In some states, milk control commissions not only determine what farmers are to be paid but the price that stores can charge customers. Federal milk orders are to promote orderly marketing conditions for dairy producers and assure consumers an adequate supply of milk.

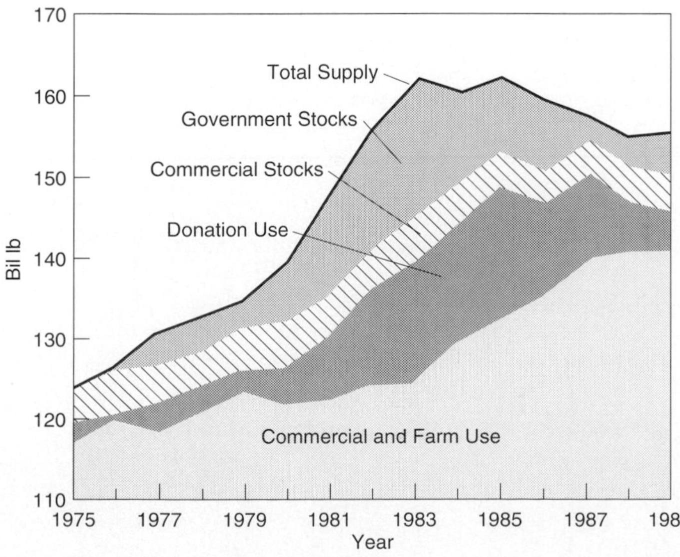

FIGURE 5.13.
U.S. milk supply, use, and stocks, 1975–89. Courtesy of the USDA.

Milk prices in recent years were shown in Fig. 2.2. Lower milk prices in 1990 and 1991 reflect the surplus of dairy products. Total farm receipts from the sale of milk in 1989 were $19.1 billion, while the retail value of the fluid milk industry was $27.8 billion.

Surpluses

Since 1975, there has been a marked increase in milk supply in the United States (Fig. 5.13). Each dairy cow produces 20% more milk than the average cow in 1975. Increased milk production, in addition to government support prices and purchases, has resulted in a surplus of milk and milk products. The excess production and government storage are the major problems facing the dairy industry.

SELECTED REFERENCES

Publications

Dairy Producer Highlights. 1986. National Milk Producers Federation, 1840 Wilson Blvd., Arlington, VA 22201.

Dunkley, W. L., and Pelissier, C. L. 1981. Relationship of United States dairy industry to dairying internationally. *J. Dairy Sci.* 64:695.

Fallert, R. F. 1981. Milk pricing—Past, present, the 1980s. *J. Dairy Sci.* 64:1105.

Hanman, G. E., and Blakeslee, B. 1981. Dairy producer and marketing cooperatives—Past, present and future. *J. Dairy Sci.* 64:1113.

Hedrick, T. I., Harmon, L. G., Chandan, R. C., and Seiberling, D. 1981. Dairy products industry in 2006. *J. Dairy Sci.* 64:959.

Kosikowski, F. V. 1981. Dairy foods of the world—Evolution, expansion and innovation. *J. Dairy Sci.* 64:996.

Larson, B. L. (ed.). 1985. *Lactation.* Ames: Iowa State University Press.

Lowenstein, M., Speck, S. J., Barnhart, H. M., and Frank, J. F. 1980. Research on goat milk products: A review. *J. Dairy Sci.* 63:1629.

Milk Facts. 1990. Milk Industry Foundation, 888 Sixteenth St. NW, Washington, DC 20006.

Newer Knowledge of Cheese and Other Cheese Products. 1983. National Dairy Council, 6300 N. River Road, Rosemont, IL 60018.

Newer Knowledge of Milk and Other Fluid Dairy Products. 1983. National Dairy Council, 6300 N. River Road, Rosemont, IL 60018.

Product Information Sheets (Butter and Cream; Milk; and Ice Cream). 1983. National Dairy Council, 6300 N. River Road, Rosemont, IL 60018.

Sellars, R. L. 1981. Fermented dairy foods. *J. Dairy Sci.* 64:1070.

Speckmann, E. W. L., Brink, M. F., and McBean, L. D. 1981. Dairy foods in nutrition and health. *J. Dairy Sci.* 64:1008.

Tobias, J., and Muck, G. A. 1981. Ice cream and frozen desserts. *J. Dairy Sci.* 64:1077.

Visuals

The Dairy Industry (VHS Video). VEP, Calif. Polytechnic State Univ., San Luis Obispo, CA 93407.

CHAPTER 6

Poultry and Egg Products

Poultry meat and eggs are nutritious and relatively inexpensive animal products used by humans throughout the world. Feathers, down, livers, and other **offal** are additional useful products and by-products obtained from poultry.

Application of genetics, nutrition, and disease control, along with sound business practices, has advanced the commercial poultry industry to where eggs and meat can be produced very efficiently. The industry has developed two specialized and different types of chickens—one for meat production and one for egg production. Broiler lines are superior in efficient, economical meat production but have a lower egg-producing ability than the egg production lines. However, the egg-type birds produce large numbers of eggs very efficiently. They have been bred to mature at light weights and they are therefore slower-growing and inefficient meat producers.

POULTRY MEAT AND EGG PRODUCTION

Broiler chickens provide most of the world's production and consumption of poultry meat. Turkeys and roaster chickens, mature laying hens (fowl), ducks, geese, pigeons, and guinea hens are consumed in smaller quantities, although some of these are important food sources in some areas of the world. The more common kinds of poultry used for meat production in the United States are shown in Table 6.1.

Poultry are slaughtered and processed in large plants owned by integrated poultry companies. Some packing and processing companies that slaughter and process poultry also slaughter and process red meat animals. These companies are identified in Chapter 3 (Table 3.2).

COMPOSITION

Meat

Table 6.1 shows chickens yield approximately 78% of their liveweight as carcass weight whereas the dressing percent for turkeys is 83%. The edible raw meat from carcasses of chickens and turkeys is approximately 67% and 78%, respectively.

TABLE 6.1. Age and Weights of Various Kinds of Poultry Used for Meat Production

Classification	Typical Age (mo)	Average Slaughter Wt (lb)	Average Dressed Wt (lb)	Dressing (%)
Young chickens				
Broiler (fryer)	1.5–2	4–5	3–4	78
Rock Cornish	1.0	2	1.5	75
Roaster	3–5	6–8	5	75
Fowl (mature for stewing)	19	5	3.8	75
Turkeys	4–6	10–25	8–20	83
Ducks	<2	7	4–5	70
Geese	6	11	8–9	75

Sources: USDA and various others.

The gross chemical contents of chickens and turkeys are shown in Table 6.2. Dark meat is higher in calories, lower in protein, and higher in cholesterol than light meat for both chicken and turkey. If the skin remains on poultry, it usually adds cholesterol and total fat.

Eggs

An egg has a spherical shape with one end being rather blunt and larger than the other, smaller, more pointed end. Figure 6.1 shows a longitudinal section of a hen's egg. The mineralized shell surrounds the contents of the egg. Immediately inside the shell are two membranes; one is attached to the shell itself, and the other tightly encloses the content of the egg. The air cell usually forms between the membranes in the blunt end of an egg shortly after it is laid, when the contents of the egg cool and contract.

The egg white, or albumen, exists in four distinct layers. One of these layers surrounds the yolk and keeps the yolk in the center of the egg. The spiral movement of the developing egg in

TABLE 6.2. Composition of Chicken and Turkey per 100 g, Edible Portion

	Water (g)	Food Energy (calories)	Protein (g)	Total Fat (g)	Cholesterol (mg)	Ash (g)
Young chicken						
Light meat (no skin)	74.9	114	23.2	1.6	58	0.98
Dark meat (no skin)	76.0	125	20.1	4.3	80	0.94
Turkey (hen)						
Light meat (no skin)	73.6	116	23.6	1.7	58	1.0
Dark meat (no skin)	74.0	130	20.1	4.9	62	0.95

Source: USDA, *Agricultural Handbook* no. 8–5.

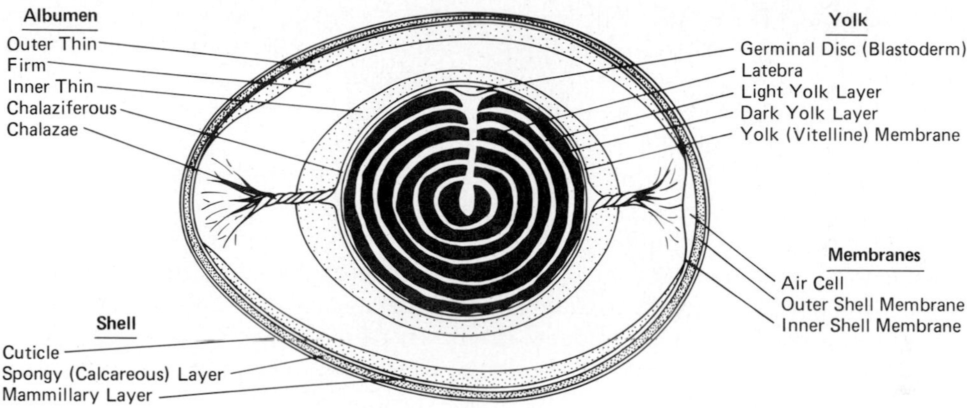

FIGURE 6.1.
Longitudinal section of a hen's egg. Courtesy of the USDA.

the magnum causes the mucin fibers of the albumen to draw together into strands that form the chalaziferous layer and chalazae. The twisting and drawing together of these mucin strands tend to squeeze out the thin albumen to form an inner thin albumen layer.

The yellowish-colored yolk is in the center of the egg, its contents surrounded by a thin, transparent membrane called the vitelline membrane.

Egg weight varies from 1.5 – 2.5 oz, with the average egg weighing approximately 2 oz. The component parts of an egg are shell and membranes (11%), albumen (58%), and yolk (31%). The gross composition of an egg is shown in Table 6.3. The mineral content of the shell is approximately 94% calcium carbonate. The yolk has a relatively high fat and protein percent, although there is more total protein in the albumen.

The weight classes and grades of eggs are discussed in Chapter 8. Egg formation is presented in Chapter 10.

TABLE 6.3. Chemical Composition of the Egg, Including the Shell

	Percent of Total	Water (%)	Protein (%)	Fat (%)	Ash (%)
Whole egg	100	65.5	11.8	11.0	11.7
White	58	88.0	11.0	0.2	0.8
Yolk	31	48.0	17.5	32.5	2.0
	Percent of Total	**Calcium Carbonate (%)**	**Magnesium Carbonate (%)**	**Calcium Phosphate (%)**	**Organic Matter (%)**
Shell and shell membranes	11	94.0	1.0	1.0	4.0

Source: USDA.

POULTRY PRODUCTS

Meat

More than one-half of all broilers leave the processing plant as cut-up chicken (Table 6.4) or selected parts rather than whole birds (compared to less than 30% a decade ago).

Approximately 50% of the broilers, fowl (mature chickens), and turkeys are further processed beyond the ready-to-cook carcass or parts stage. The meat is separated from the bone and formed into products (e.g., turkey roll fingers and nuggets), cut and diced (e.g., for preparation of salads and casseroles), canned, or ground. Some of the cured and smoked ground products are frankfurters, bologna, pastrami, turkey ham, and salami. More than 1 out of 8 lb of all broilers is processed into such products as chicken patties, nuggets, battered and cooked chicken, and hot dogs. Even more of the broilers are expected to be processed in future years.

Eggs

Eggs are unique, prepackaged food products that are ready to cook in their natural state. Eggs find their way into the human diet in numerous ways. They are most popular as a breakfast entree; however, they are commonly used in sandwiches, salads, beverages, desserts, and several main dishes.

Shell eggs can be further processed into pasteurized liquid eggs and dried eggs and other egg products. Pasteurized liquid egg can be blast-frozen and sold to bakeries and other food-processing plants as an ingredient in other fabricated food products or transported to users as a liquid product in refrigerated tank trucks. The dried egg products are sold to food manufacturers to produce products such as cake mixes, candy, and pasta.

The initial step in making egg products is breaking the shell and separating the yolks, whites, and shells. This is done in most egg-breaking plants by equipment completely automated to remove eggs from egg-filler flats, wash and sanitize the shells, break the eggs for individual inspection of the contents by an operator, and separate the yolks from the whites. Processing equipment can also be used to produce various white and yolk products or mixtures of them. Present automatic systems are capable of handling 18,000–50,000 eggs per hour (Fig. 6.2).

Some breeds of chickens lay white-shelled eggs and other breeds produce brown-shelled

TABLE 6.4. The Retail Parts and Cooked Edible Meat of a Broiler-Fryer Chicken

Part	Retail Parts (% of carcass)	Percent Edible[a]
Breast	28	63
Thighs	18	60
Drumsticks	17	53
Wings	14	30
Back and neck	18	27
Giblets	5	100
Total	100	53

[a] Net average yield of meat is 67% without neck and giblets.
Sources: USDA; National Broiler Council.

A

B

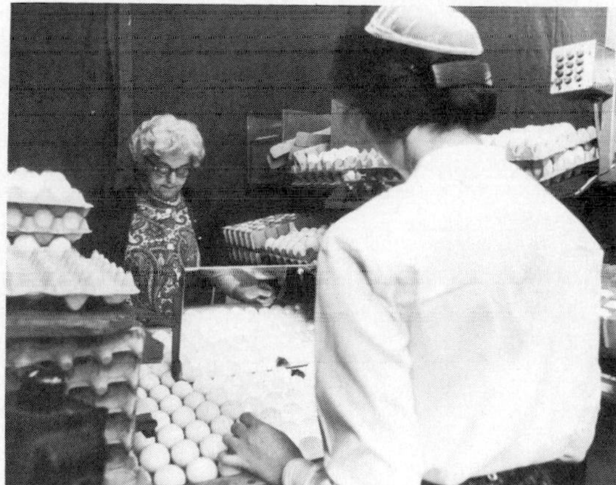

C

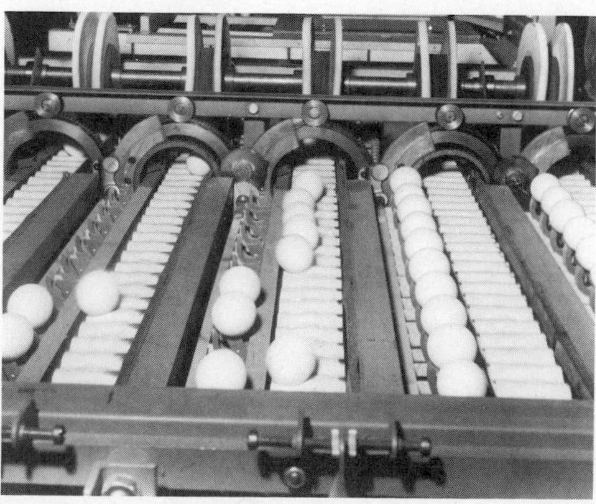

D

FIGURE 6.2.
Automated egg-handling equipment. (A) Overall view. (B) Automatic egg washer. (C) Eggs on the flash-candling area of the in-feed conveyor. (D) In-line scales. Eggs of different sizes are weighed and ejected at different points on the line. Courtesy of the USDA, *Egg Grading Manual*.

eggs. The brown shell color comes from a reddish-brown pigment (ooporhyrin) derived from hemoglobin in the blood. Although there are shell color preferences by consumers in certain parts of the United States, there are no significant nutritional differences related to egg shell color.

Feathers and Down

In some areas of the world, ducks and geese are raised primarily for feathers and down. Down is a small, soft feather found beneath the outer feathers of ducks and geese. Feathers and down provide stuffing for pillows, quilts, and upholstery. They are also used in the manufacture of hats, clothing (outdoor wear), sleeping bags, fishing flies, and brushes.

The duck and goose industry in the United States is too small to meet the manufacturing demand for down. Thus, raw feathers and down are primarily imported (approximately 90% of the product used) from China, France, Switzerland, Poland, and several other European and Asian countries.

Breeder geese are often used for down production, as the older birds produce the best down. Four ducks or three geese will produce 1 lb of feather-and-down mixture, of which 15%–25% is down. Down and feathers are separated by machine, then washed and dried.

TABLE 6.5. Contribution of Poultry and Eggs to Nutrient Supplies Available to U.S. Civilian Consumption, 1985

Nutrients	Meat, Poultry and Fish (%)	Eggs (%)
Food energy	20	2
Protein	43	4
Fat	33	2
Carbohydrate	0.1	0.1
Cholesterol	40	40
Minerals		
Calcium	4	2
Phosphorus	28	4
Iron	29	4
Magnesium	15	1
Vitamins		
Vitamin A	17	2
Thiamin	26	1
Riboflavin	22	4
Niacin	47	0
Vitamin B_6	40	2
Vitamin B_{12}	72	6
Ascorbic acid	2	0

[a] Poultry comprises approximately 30% of the per-capita retail weight consumption of meat, poultry, and fish.
Source: USDA.

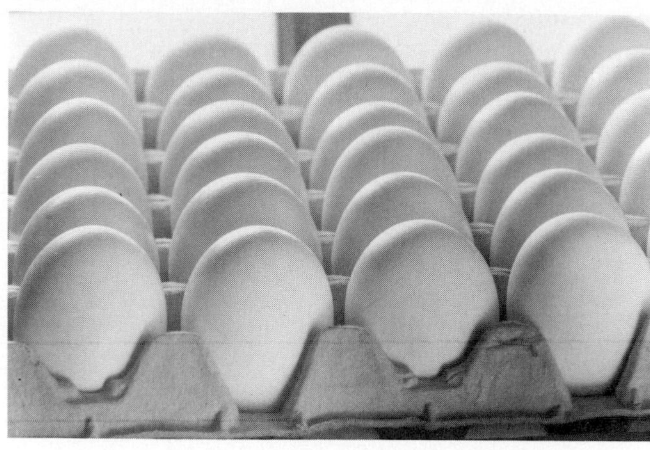

FIGURE 6.3.
"The incredible, edible egg." Courtesy of the American Egg Board.

Other Products and By-Products

Goose livers are considered a gourmet product in European countries. These enlarged fatty livers, weighing as much as 2 lb each, are produced by force-feeding corn to geese three times a day for 4–8 weeks. The liver is used to make a flavored paste called *paté de foie gras* (for hors d'oeuvres or sandwiches).

Poultry by-products include hydrolized feather meal and poultry meat and bone scraps. These by-products are occasionally included in livestock and poultry rations as protein sources (refer to Chapter 4 for more discussion of these by-products).

HEALTH CONSIDERATIONS

Nutritive Value of Poultry Meat

The white meat from fowl is approximately 33% protein, and dark meat is about 28% protein. This protein is easily digested and is of high quality, containing all the essential amino acids. The fat content of poultry meat is lower than that found in many other meats. Poultry meat is also an excellent source of vitamin A, thiamin, riboflavin, and niacin. The nutritive value of poultry and eggs to the U.S. population is shown in Table 6.5.

Nutritive Value of Eggs

Since the egg (Fig. 6.3) contains many essential nutrients, it is recognized as one of the important foods in the major food groups recommended in *Dietary Guidelines for Americans*. These guidelines were developed by the U.S. Department of Agriculture to use in planning diets contributing to good health.

Eggs have a high nutrient density in that they provide excellent protein and a wide range of vitamins and minerals and have a low calorie count. The abundance of readily digestible protein, containing large amounts of essential amino acids, makes eggs a least-cost source of high-quality protein.

TABLE 6.6. Estimated Nutrient Values for a Large Egg (based on 60.9-g shell weight with 55.1-g total liquid whole egg, 38.4-g white, and 16.7-g yolk)

Nutrients and Units (proximate)	Whole	White	Yolk
Solids (g)	13.47	4.6	8.81
Calories (kcal)	84	19	64
Protein (N × 6.25) (g)	6.60	3.88	2.74
Total lipids (g)	6.00	—	5.80
Cholesterol (mg)	213	—	213
Ash (g)	0.55	0.26	0.29

Source: Poultry Sci. 58:131; USDA.

Table 6.6 lists the nutrients and amounts of those nutrients found in eggs. When the values of these nutrients are compared with the dietary allowances recommended by the Food and Nutrition Board of the National Research Council (1980), it is found that two large eggs (a usual serving) supply an impressive percentage of essential nutrients—an average of 10%–30% for adults (Table 6.7). Eggs are an especially rich source of high-quality protein, vitamins (A, D, E,

TABLE 6.7. U.S. Recommended Daily Allowance (RDAs) in Relation to Nutrient Content of Large Eggs

Nutrient	RDA	Percent RDA, Two Eggs
Protein	45.0 g	30%
Vitamins		
A	5,000.0 IU	10
D	400.0 IU	15
E	30.0 IU	6
C	60.0 mg	
Folic acid	0.4 mg	15
Thiamin	1.5 mg	6
Riboflavin	1.7 mg	20
Niacin	20.0 mg	
B_6	2.0 mg	6
B_{12}	6.0 μg	15
Biotin	0.3 mg	8
Pantothenic acid	10.0 mg	15
Minerals		
Calcium	1.0 g	6
Phosphorus	1.0 g	20
Iodine	150.0 μg	35
Iron	18.0 mg	10
Magnesium	400.0 mg	4
Copper	2.0 mg	4
Zinc	15.0 mg	10

Source: Cotterill and Glauert (1981).

folic acid, riboflavin, B_{12}, and pantothenic acid), and minerals (phosphorus, iodine, iron, and zinc). Some consumers believe that the dark yellow yolk is of higher nutrient value than the paler yolks, but there is no evidence to support this belief.

Table 6.7 lists the U.S. recommended daily allowances (RDAs) supplied by two large eggs.

Wholesomeness of Poultry

In the United States, over 90% of the poultry meat is inspected by the USDA for wholesomeness. USDA inspectors give assurance that the meat is free of disease and that it has been processed under sanitary conditions. The inspector gives an antemortem inspection of the poultry before it is slaughtered and a postmortem inspection of the carcasses and viscera.

In 1987, the media focused on salmonella contamination in poultry processing plants. Some consumers were alarmed, but people didn't get sick and poultry markets did not disappear. The USDA had been working with the poultry industry to reduce disease contamination levels. Also, some poultry companies had implemented their own quality control of disease organisms some 15 years previously.

Human Disease Risk

Eggs are relatively high in cholesterol (whole egg, 264 mg; yolk, 258 mg). Eggs have been included in the diet–coronary heart disease controversy, since high blood cholesterol is one of the several risk factors associated with CHD.

Cholesterol, a fatlike substance, is found in blood and nerve tissues and, in fact, in every cell of the body. Its exact function is not fully understood, but cholesterol is known to play a number of important physiological roles.

In addition to being present in all food products of animal origin, cholesterol is synthesized (made) and metabolized (used or excreted) daily in our bodies in amounts far greater than usually consumed in the diet.

High serum cholesterol and CHD are statistically correlated, but CHD does occur in persons having normal or low blood cholesterol. CHD also occurs among vegetarians.

The level of cholesterol in the blood, according to the best scientific knowledge, is not markedly influenced in most people when moderate amounts of cholesterol are present in the foods eaten. It is possible that a high serum cholesterol level is a symptom and not a cause of CHD. There are several known disorders where a high level of cholesterol is a side effect.

TABLE 6.8. World Per-capita Poultry Meat and Egg Consumption, 1989

Country	Poultry Meat (lb)[a]	Country	Hen Eggs (no.)
1. United States	86	1. Netherlands	763
2. Singapore	79	2. Israel	437
3. Israel	77	3. Hungary	402
4. Hong Kong	71	4. Belgium	377
5. Canada	60	5. Germany	361

[a] Ready-to-cook equivalent.
Source: USDA, FAS, *World Poultry Situation.*

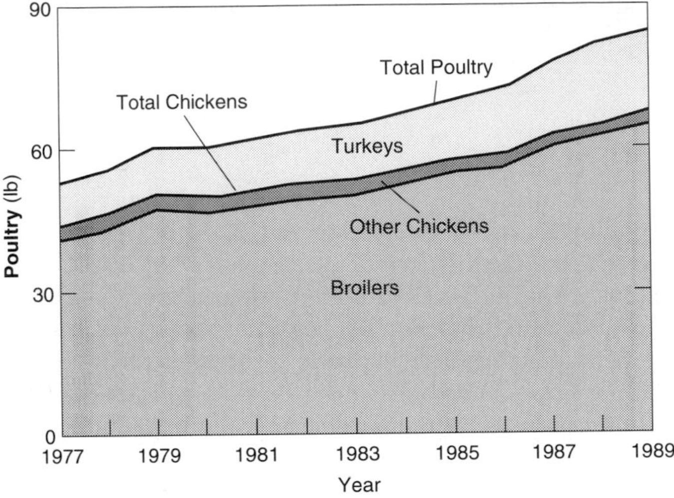

FIGURE 6.4.
Per-capita consumption of poultry (ready-to-cook weight) in the United States, 1977–89. Courtesy of the USDA.

CONSUMPTION

Meat

Table 6.8 shows the poultry and egg consumption for the leading countries of the world. The United States has the highest per-capita consumption of poultry meat, while per-capita egg consumption is highest in the Netherlands. The per-capita consumption of chicken and turkey in the United States is over 80 lb (Fig. 6.4). Poultry consumption is approximately one-half of the total per-capita consumption of red meat and poultry (Fig. 6.5). In recent years, poultry consumption has increased at the expense of red meat consumption. This is due, in part, to the price differential existing between the various meats (Fig. 6.6).

The dollars expended for broilers and turkey is shown in Table 6.9. The percentage of income spent for these two meats has remained relatively stable from 1980–1989, even though the total dollars spent has increased.

A very important reason for marked increase in chicken consumption has been the speed of preparing and serving chicken. The Kentucky Fried Chicken Corporation (KFC) led in preparation and serving chicken in a short time and now chicken is rapidly becoming a major item in fast-food service. The KFC restaurants are found in 56 countries and they sell more than 3 billion pieces of chicken a year. In recent years, other fast-food restaurants have added more chickens items to their menus.

Heavy hens, the type used to produce hatching eggs for broiler production, are sometimes available in retail stores as "stewing hens" or "baking hens." These account for about 10% of the poultry meat consumed by Americans each year.

Consumption of turkey meat per person has increased from 1.7 lb in 1935 and 6.1 lb in 1960 to 8.0 lb in 1970 and 17 lb in 1989. A great deal of the increase in turkey consumption was stimulated by development of processed products such as turkey rolls, roasts, pot pies, and frozen dinners. The selling of prepackaged turkey parts in small packages has also increased consumption.

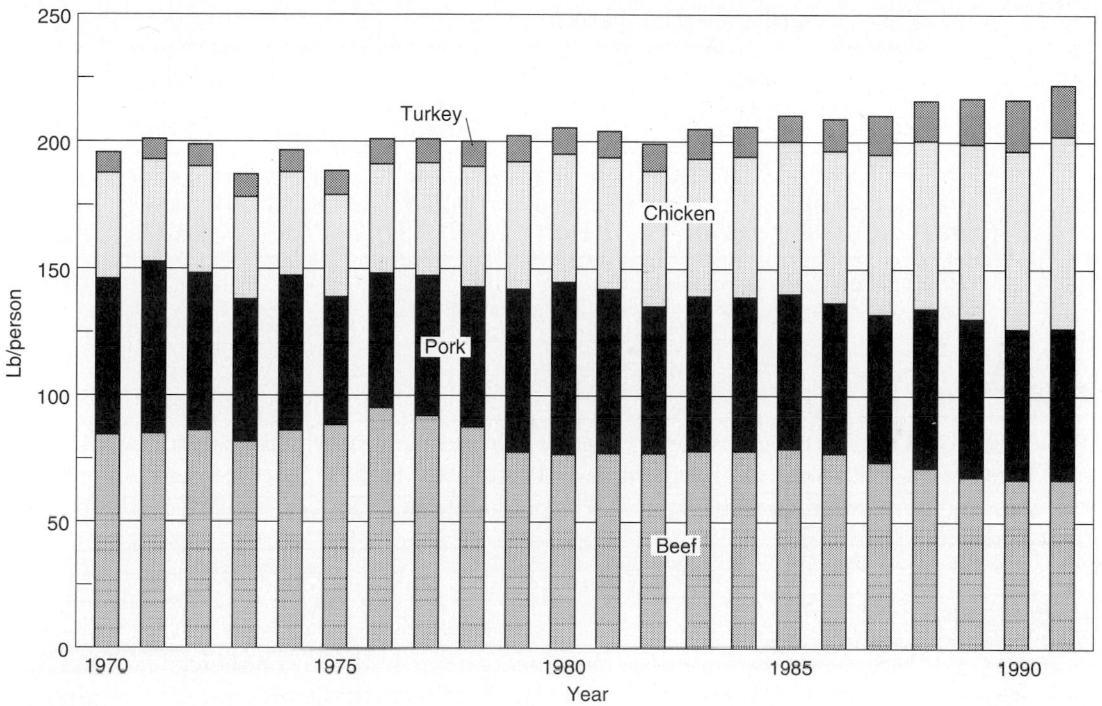

FIGURE 6.5.
Per-capita meat consumption, retail-weight equivalent, 1970–91. Courtesy of the Western Livestock Marketing Information Project.

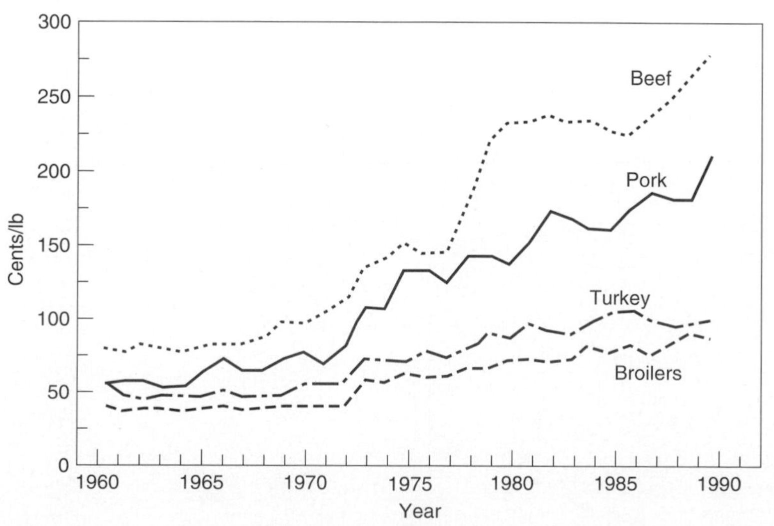

FIGURE 6.6.
Retail prices for chicken and turkey with comparative beef and pork prices, 1960–90. Courtesy of the Western Livestock Marketing Information Project.

TABLE 6.9. Expenditures Per Person for Poultry

	Broilers		Turkey		Total Poultry	
Year	Dollars	Percent[a]	Dollars	Percent[a]	Dollars	Percent[a]
1980	$33.32	0.40%	$ 9.93	0.12%	$43.25	0.51%
1985	42.08	0.35	12.66	0.11	54.75	0.46
1989	61.76	0.41	16.87	0.11	78.63	0.52

[a] Percent of per-capita disposable income.
Source: USDA, *Livestock and Poultry Situation and Outlook.*

Eggs

Per-capita consumption of eggs is approximately 236 eggs per year which is a decrease from 300 eggs in the early 1970s and 263 eggs in the early 1980s. Most of these are consumed as shell eggs (85%) rather than processed eggs (Fig. 6.7). The per-capita consumption is nearly the number of eggs a hen lays per year.

MARKETING

In the United States, large amounts of poultry meat are processed in commercial facilities and then transported under refrigeration to local and world markets. Broilers are the primary poultry meat exported, with more than 900 million pounds exported each year (Fig. 6.8). Approximately 100 million dozen eggs are exported from the United States each year (Fig. 6.9).

Chicken meat is usually marketed fresh in the United States, whereas turkeys are marketed frozen. However, some turkeys are sold fresh year round in some markets. Freshly frozen poultry meat can be marketed on a year-round basis through the use of frozen storage and environmentally controlled production units.

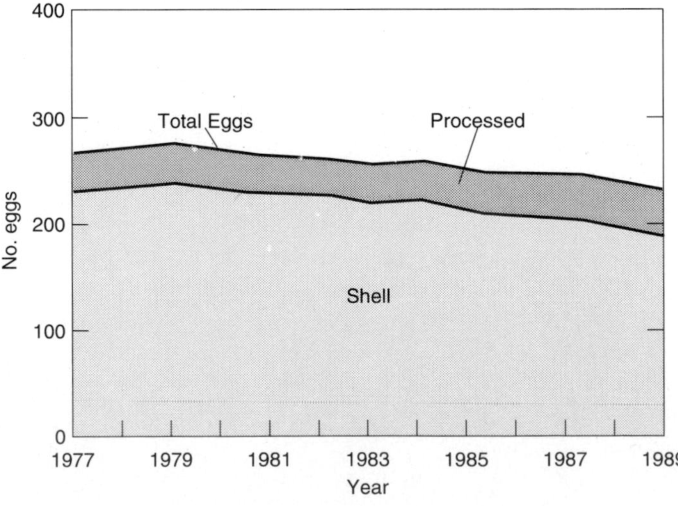

FIGURE 6.7.
Per-capita egg consumption in the United States, 1977–89. Courtesy of the USDA.

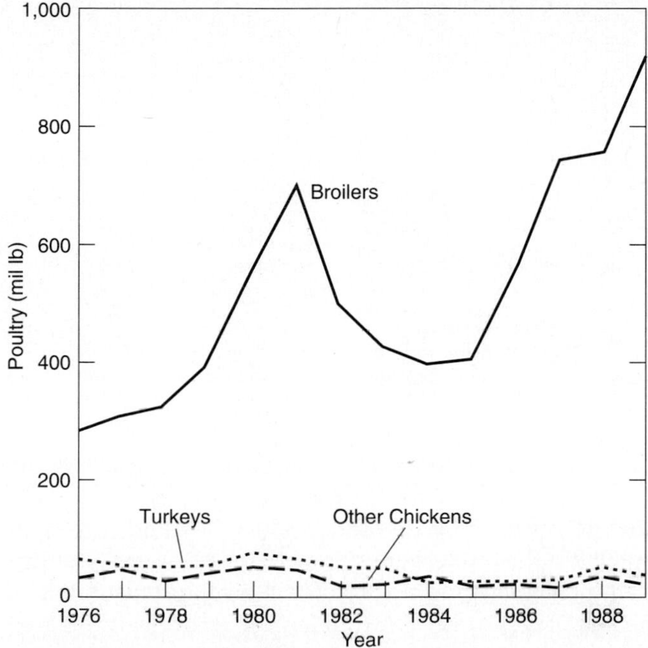

FIGURE 6.8.
U.S. exports of poultry meat (ready-to-cook weight), 1976–88. Courtesy of the USDA.

Most of the broilers are sold to consumers through retail stores (Fig. 6.10). Fresh chicken can reach the retail market counter the day following slaughter. "Sell-by" date on each package is usually 7 days from processing and is the last date recommended for sale of chicken. However, with proper refrigeration (28°F–32°F), shelf life can be extended up to 3 days longer. Some processors guarantee 14 days of shelf life for their broilers.

Almost all commercially available chicken and turkey meat is inspected for wholesomeness

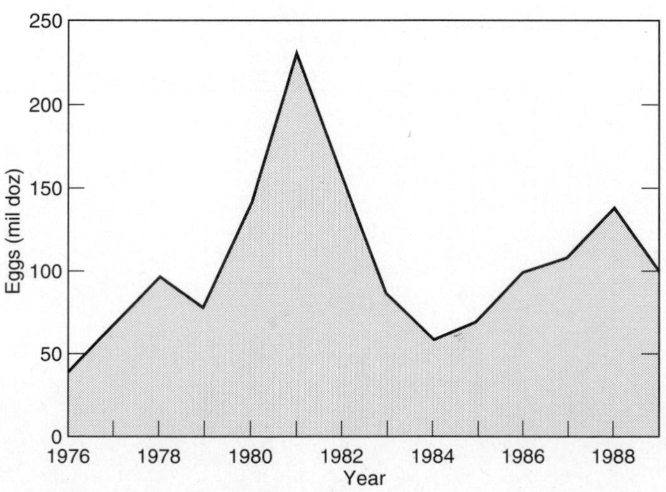

FIGURE 6.9.
U.S. export of eggs, 1976–88. Courtesy of the USDA.

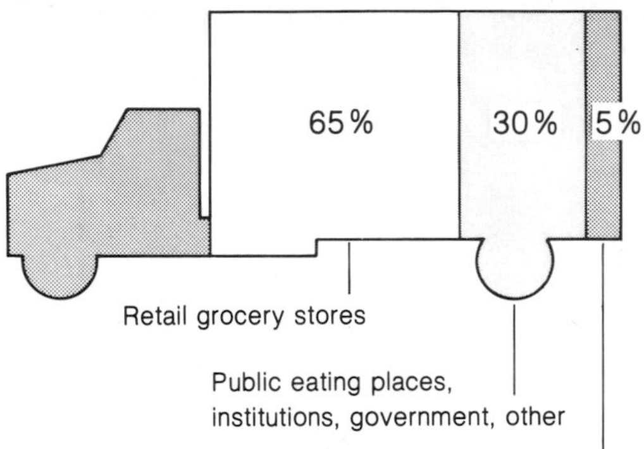

FIGURE 6.10.
Market distribution of several billion pounds of ready-to-cook chicken. Courtesy of the National Broiler Council.

by federal or state government employees. About two-thirds of the chickens are graded by the USDA for quality.

Over 40% of the broilers are marketed to consumers under the producer's brand names. In certain markets, such as New York, over 90% of the broilers are sold with brand names. Poultry brands identify the single firm that raised, processed, and marketed the bird, not just the firm that processed the retail product, as is the case of red meats. The four largest vertically integrated poultry firms represented more than 35% of the broiler market in 1989, compared with only 17% in 1973.

Chicken and turkeys are frequently featured by supermarket stores as loss leaders. Stores knowingly take a loss on the poultry to attract customers to their store where additional items purchased usually more than cover the losses. The practice of using loss leaders is sometimes adopted to stay competitive with other stores that first initiate the practice.

Before and during the 1950s, the marketing of turkey was highly seasonal as 90% of the turkeys were consumed during the last quarter of the year for the Thanksgiving and Christmas holidays. Today less than 40% of turkey sales are made during that period. Current trends

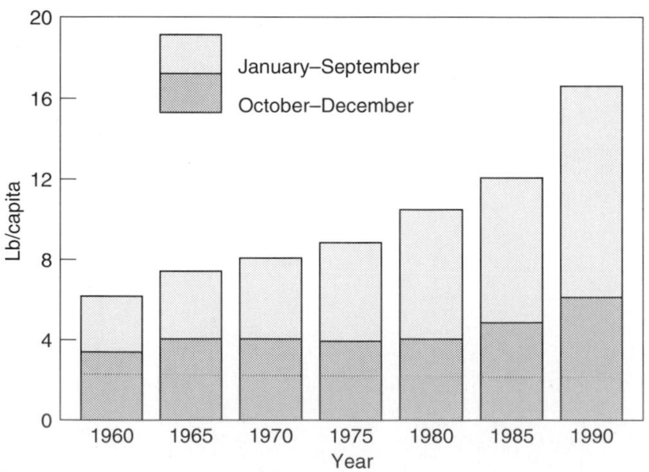

FIGURE 6.11.
U.S. turkey consumption (total and fourth quarter), 1960–90. Courtesy of the USDA.

indicate that turkey is being consumed more on a year-round basis and has become a meat staple (Fig. 6.11).

SELECTED REFERENCES

Publications

A Scientist Speaks About Fowl. 1981. American Egg Board, 1460 Renaissance, Park Ridge, IL 60068.
A Scientist Speaks About Egg Nutrition. 1982. American Egg Board, 1460 Renaissance, Park Ridge, IL 60068.
A Scientist Speaks About Egg Products. 1981. American Egg Board, 1460 Renaissance, Park Ridge, IL 60068.
Cotterill, O. J., and Glauert, J. L. 1981. Shell egg nutritional labeling. *Poultry Tribune* 87:16.
Eggcyclopedia. 1981. American Egg Board, 1460 Renaissance, Park Ridge, IL 60068.
Moreng, R. E., and Avens, J. S. 1985. *Poultry Science and Production.* Reston, VA: Reston Publishing.
Stadelman, W. J., and Cotterill, O. J. 1986. *Egg Science and Technology.* Westport, CT: Avi.
USDA. *Egg Grading Manual.* Apr. 1983. USDA. Agricultural Handbook no. 75. Revised.
USDA. 1989, 1990. Livestock and Poultry Situation and Outlook Report. Washington, D.C.

Visuals

Egg quality film (loan). Information Division, AMS, USDA, Washington, DC 20250.
Egg quality slides. Photography Division, GPA, USDA, Washington, DC 20250.
The Incredible Edible Egg on Video. Northwest Egg Producers Coop. Assoc., P.O. Box 1038, Olympia, WA 98507.
Processing Chicken Broilers (80 slides and tape; 13 min); and *Egg Breaking Operations* (80 slides and tape; 12 min). Poultry Science Dept., Ohio State University, 674 W. Lane Ave., Columbus, OH 43210.
Turkey product slides. National Turkey Federation, 11319 Sunset Hills Rd., Reston, VA 22090.

CHAPTER 7

Wool and Mohair

Skins of common mammals have a covering to which various terms are applied depending on the nature of the growth. For example, cattle, pigs, horses, and dairy goats have hair; sheep have wool; mink and nonangora rabbits have fur; angora rabbits have angora; and angora goats have mohair. Fibers that grow from the skin of animals give protection from abrasions to the skin and help keep animals warm.

Hair from most mammals has little commercial value (it is used mostly in padding and cushions). Fur of mink and nonangora rabbits is either naturally beautiful or can be dyed to give attractive colors; therefore, it has considerable value as fur. Fur is composed of fine short fibers and relatively long, coarse guard hairs, in contrast to the skin covering of cattle, horses, and pigs, which is composed entirely of guard hairs.

Furs made from rabbits, mink, foxes, and bison (American buffalo) may be classed as status clothing because they are usually costly and attractive in appearance. White rabbit furs can be dyed any color (including the pastels), but colored furs cannot. Because colored furs cannot be dyed, color **mutations** have been important in the mink business because they provide a wide array of fur colors. At present, the mink industry in the United States is suffering economically because of competition from furs made in other countries and high costs of producing mink.

Hides from young market lambs are often marketed with wool left on to be processed into heavy winter lambskin coats. Lambs from the **Karakul** breed of fat-tail sheep are used to produce Persian lamb skins. The black, tight curls of fiber are more like fur than wool. Persian lambskins have been produced in the United States, but larger numbers are currently produced in Afghanistan, Iran, and the Soviet Union.

Hides from sheep with longer wool on the pelts also may be marketed intact for processing to produce ornamental rug pieces. The long wool may be dyed. The long wool may also be loosened and removed from the hides after slaughter and sold separately from the hides.

GROWTH OF HAIR, WOOL, AND MOHAIR

Hair or wool fiber grows from a **follicle** located in the outer layers of the skin. Growth occurs at the base of the follicle, where there is a supply of blood, and cells produced are pushed outward.

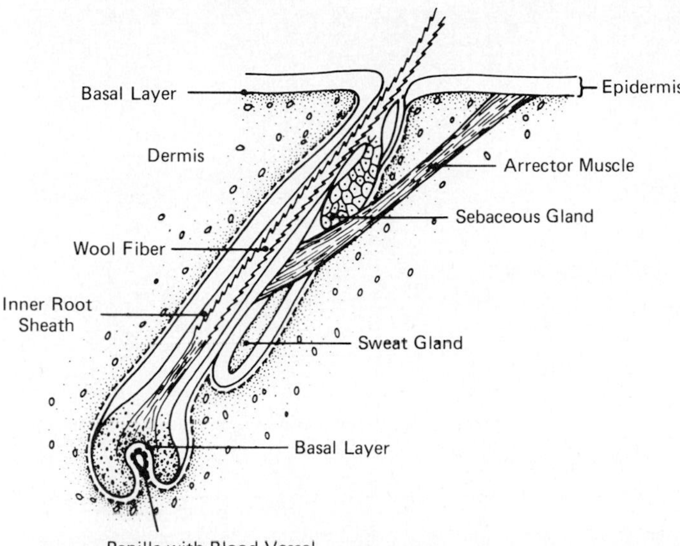

FIGURE 7.1.
Schematic drawing of a wool follicle. Courtesy of R. W. Henderson.

The cells die after they are removed from the blood supply because they can no longer obtain nutrients or eliminate wastes. A schematic drawing of a wool follicle is presented in Fig. 7.1.

The cuticle causes the fibers to cling together. The intermingling of wool fibers is known as **felting**. The felting of wool is advantageous in that wool fibers can be entangled to make **woolens**, but it is also responsible for the shrinkage that occurs when wool becomes wet.

All wool and hair fibers have a similar gross structure, consisting of an outer thin layer (**cuticle**) and a cortex that surrounds an inner core (**medulla**) in medullated fibers (Fig. 7.2). Only medium and coarse wools have a medulla. It is absent in fine wools.

Wool fibers have waves called **crimp** (Fig. 7.3). Crimp is caused by the presence of hard and soft cellular material in the cortex. The soft cortex is more elastic and is on the outer side of the crimp.

Hair does not exhibit any crimp because all the cells in the cortex are hard. Also, the inner

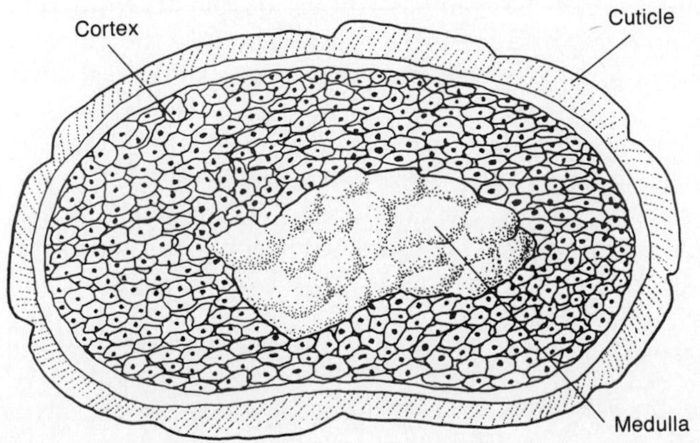

FIGURE 7.2.
Cross section of a medullated wool fiber. Adapted from *The Sheep Production Handbook*.

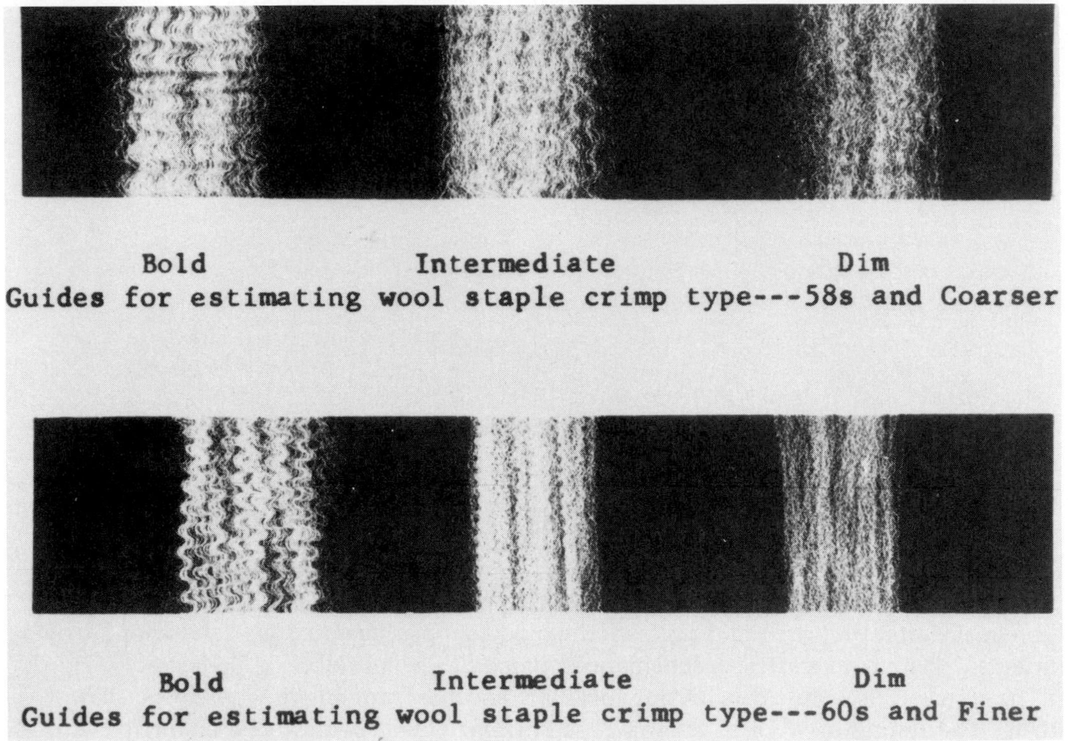

FIGURE 7.3.
Several expressions of crimp in coarser and finer wools. Courtesy of the USDA.

core of hair is not solid, unlike the inner core of most wool fibers. Some fibers in wool of a low quality are large, lack crimp, and do not have a solid inner core. These fibers are called **kemp**, and they reduce the value of the fleece.

Mohair fiber follicles develop in groups consisting of three primary follicles each. Secondary follicles develop later. Mohair fibers have very little crimp (less than 1 crimp for each inch of length). The mohair cortex is composed largely of so-called *ortho* cells, in contrast to the cortex of wool, which is composed of both *ortho* and *para* cells. Mohair has a different scale structure from wool, but it does have scales and will felt. Kemp and **medullated fibers** reduce the value of wool and mohair fleeces because such fibers do not dye well and because they show in apparel made from fleeces containing such fibers.

Skin of young lambs is made up of two layers; the surface skin (outer skin) is the epidermis, and the underlying skin is the dermis (Fig. 7.1). Between these two layers is the basal layer. Development of wool follicles occurs in skin of the fetus. The basal layer thickens and areas that are to become wool follicles push down into the dermis. Two glands develop—the sebaceous gland, which secretes sebum, a greasy secretion; and the sweat gland, which produces and secretes sweat. The downward growth of the basal layer rests on the papilla, which has a supply of blood. The wool fiber grows toward the skin's surface, and as it becomes removed from the blood supply, the cells die.

Two major types of follicles are produced. The first type to develop is known as the primary follicles. They appear on the poll and face of the fetus by 35–50 days' gestation and over all other parts of the body by 60 days. They are arranged in groups of three. All primary follicles are fully developed and are producing fiber at birth.

A second type of follicle, associated with the primary follicles, develops later and is known as the secondary follicles. These follicles have an incomplete set of accessory structures—usually the sweat gland and arrector muscle are absent. The primary and associated secondary follicles are grouped into follicle bundles.

Since all the primary follicles are formed prior to birth of the lamb, the density of primary follicles per square inch of skin declines rapidly during the first 4 months of postnatal life and then declines gradually until the lamb approaches maturity.

Secondary follicles show little activity during the first week of a lamb's life, after which there is a burst of activity of secondary follicles. Activity is maximum between 1 and 3 weeks of age with marked reduction after the third week.

Adverse prenatal environmental conditions can affect the number of secondary follicles initiated in development. Also, early postnatal influence could affect secondary follicle fiber production.

Growth of the wool fiber takes place in the root bulb, which is located in the follicle. Permanent dimensions of the fiber are determined in the area of the bulb, and there are no changes in growth characteristics of the fiber after it is formed. Defective portions of a fiber are caused by a reduction in the size of the fiber that creates a weakened area when sheep are under stressed conditions, such as poor nutrition and high body temperatures. Such fibers are likely to break under pressure.

Two types of undesirable fibers are kemp and medullated fibers. Both are hollow and brittle, and both are produced by primary follicles rather than secondary follicles, as is the case with true wool.

FACTORS AFFECTING THE VALUE OF WOOL

The two most important factors under the control of the producer that affect the amount of wool produced by sheep are nutrition and breeding. The amount of feed available to the sheep (energy intake) and the percentage of protein in the diet influence wool production. Wool production is decreased when sheep are fed diets having less than 8% protein. When the diet contains more than 8% protein, the amount of energy consumed is the determining factor in wool production.

Improving wool production per animal through breeding involves selection for increased clean fleece weight, **staple length, fineness** and uniformity of length, and fineness throughout the fleece. Much progress can be made by performance-testing rams for quantity and quality of wool production, but for overall improvement of the flock, both lamb and wool production must be included (Fig. 7.4).

Sheep and angora goat producers are interested in maximizing net income from their sheep and goat operations. Increasing net income from wool and mohair can be accomplished by selecting to improve wool and mohair production and grade. The values of wool and mohair that are produced can be enhanced by giving attention to the following items:

1. The sheep or goats should be shorn when the wool or mohair is dry.
2. The portions of clips that are loaded with dung (called **tags**) should be sorted from fleeces and sacked separately.

FIGURE 7.4.
The ewe has been bred primarily for wool production with her lamb being a secondary product. Her heavy fleece will soon be shorn from her body. Courtesy of Woolknit Associates, Inc.

3. Wool or mohair should be sacked by wool grades so that when **core samples** are taken from a sack of otherwise good wool, a few fleeces of low-grade wool (or mohair) will not cause the entire sack of wool or mohair to be placed in a low grade.
4. Wool should be shorn without making many double clips.
5. Fleeces should be tied with paper twine after they are properly folded with the clipped side out.
6. A lanolin-based paint should be used for branding animals. This type of paint is scourable.
7. Fleeces from black-faced sheep should be packed separately from other wool. Also, black fleeces should be packed separately. Black fibers do not take on light-colored dyes and consequently stand out in a garment made from black and white fibers dyed a light pastel color.
8. All tags, sweepings, and wool or mohair from dead animals should be packed separately.
9. Hay that has been baled with twine should be carefully fed to sheep; otherwise, pieces of twine will get into the wool or mohair and markedly lower its value.
10. Environmental stresses should be avoided. Being without feed or water for several days or having a high fever can cause a break or weak zone in the wool fibers.
11. Wool containing coarse fibers, or kemp, should be avoided, or kempy fleeces should be packed separately. Cloth and wool containing these coarse fibers are highly objectionable and thus are low in price.

Figure 7.5 identifies several types of undesirable fleeces. These fleeces have a lower value than fleeces containing white fibers and minimal foreign material. Some of the fleeces in Fig. 7.5 not previously discussed include the following:

Burry—contains vegetable matter, such as grass seeds and prickly seeds, which adheres tenaciously to wool
Chaffy—contains vegetable matter such as hay, straw, and other plant material
Cotted—wool fibers are matted or entangled
Dead—wool pulled from sheep that have died but that have not been slaughtered
Murrain—wool obtained from decomposed sheep

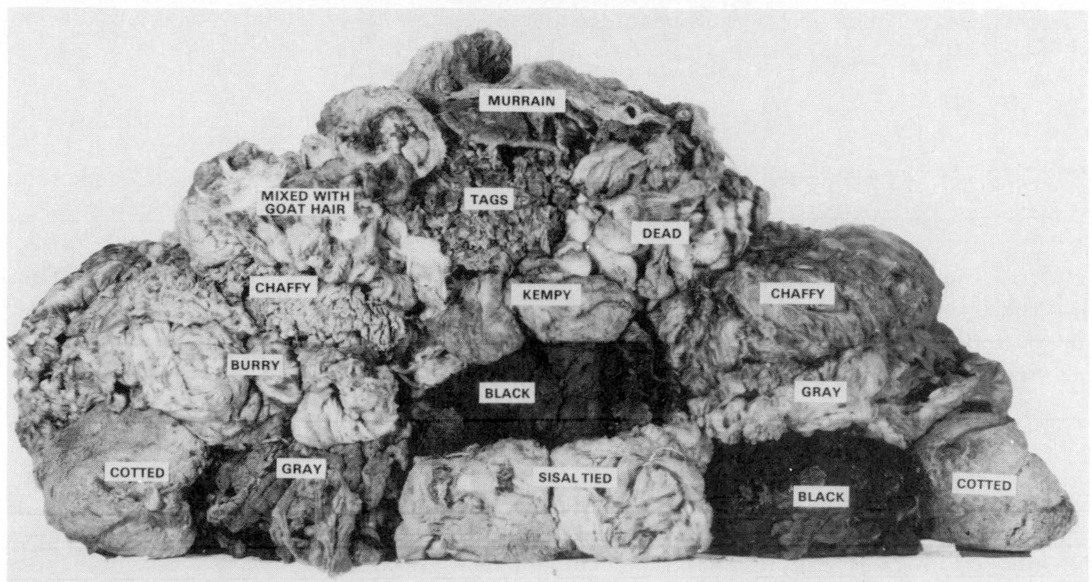

FIGURE 7.5.
Several types of undesirable fleeces are identified. Each of these should be sorted and packed separately from the more desirable fleeces. Courtesy of the USDA.

National Wool Act

In 1954, the U.S. Congress, recognizing that domestic wool is an essential and strategic commodity, established the National Wool Act. An incentive payment program was developed at that time to encourage expansion of sheep production. The National Wool Act seeks to encourage increased wool production by requiring the price of wool to be set each year. A formula determines a price to be paid for the weight of unshorn lambs marketed. The act also provides a means for wool growers to vote a referendum, which, if passed, funds the American Sheep Producers Council so that advertising and promotion can be financed. The money available in the incentive program is limited to a portion of funds derived from duty on imported wool. Thus, the incentive payment program is not financed from tax dollars.

Wool Incentive Payment

The following example shows how the incentive payment is calculated:

$1.81 national incentive level (per lb)
−0.87 actual weighted average U.S. sale price (per lb)
$0.94 difference

The national average is then divided into the difference to obtain the "factor," as follows:

$$0.87\overline{)0.94} = 1.08$$

The factor 1.08 is then used to multiply the individual price received by each grower, as follows:

$$\begin{array}{rl} \$0.87 & \text{price received by producer} \\ \times\underline{1.08} & \\ \$0.94 & \end{array}$$

This makes $0.94 per pound support level received (in addition to the $0.87), which makes this producer's total income per pound of wool $1.81 per lb.

If average price is below the support price, everyone receives payment. If average price is above the support price, no payments are made. If support price has been reached for payment, a producer may receive a percentage or support price incentive even if the wool was sold at prices above the incentive level; that is, if the level is $1.50 and the wool sold for $1.75, the producer would still get incentive payment. Therefore, the term *incentive* to produce better wool is used.

CLASSES AND GRADES OF WOOL

The value of wool is determined by its class and grade. Staple length determines the class, and fineness of fibers determines the grade. The grades of wool are given by any one of three methods, all of which are concerned with a value that indicates the fineness (diameter) of the wool fibers. The three methods of reporting wool grades are these:

1. The **American grade**, or blood (outdated terminology), method is based on the theoretical amount of fine wool breeding (Merino and Rambouillet) represented in the sheep producing the wool (Fig. 7.6). The terms *fine, ½ blood, ⅜ blood, ¼ blood,* and *low-¼ blood* are used to describe typical fiber diameter. Wool classified as fine or ⅝ blood has small fiber diameters, whereas ¼ blood wool is coarse.
2. The **spinning count** system refers to the number of "hanks" of yarn, each 560 yards long, which can be spun from 1 lb of **wool top**. These grades range from 80 (fine) to 36 (coarse). Thus, a grade of 50 by the spinning count method means that 28,000 yards (560 yd × 50 = 28,000 yd) of yarn can be spun from 1 lb of wool top.
3. The **micron diameter** method is based on the average of actual measurements of several wool fibers. This is the most accurate method of determining the grade of wool. A micron is $\frac{1}{25,400}$ of an inch.

Wool samples from each of the major grades are shown in Figs. 7.6 and 7.7. The systems of grading, along with the breeds from which the grades of wool come, are presented in Table 7.1. The Merino and Rambouillet breeds are considered fine wool breeds with the Cotswold, Lincoln, and Romney identified as coarse wool breeds. In Table 7.1, breeds listed between the fine and coarse wool breeds are called medium wool breeds.

Classes of wool are staple, French combing, and clothing; however, fibers of finer grades that do not meet the length requirement may go into a higher class than they would if they were not fine. Much of the staple length wool is combed into **worsted**-type yarns for making garments of a hard finish that hold a press well.

The fineness of wool fibers from a sheep depends on the area of the body from which the fibers came. The body of a sheep can be divided into seven areas. Area 1 is the shoulder, and area 2 is the neck, where wool grows longer and finer than average wool from the same sheep. Area 3 is the back. It has long, average fineness, though it has been exposed to the most weathering. Area 4 is the side. It has long, average fineness and constitutes most of the wool.

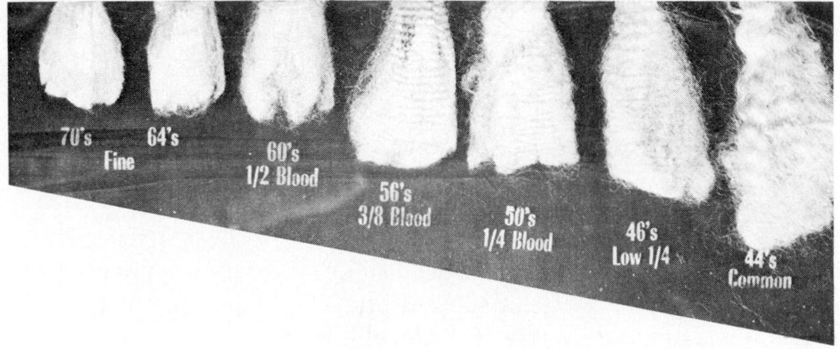

FIGURE 7.6.
Wool samples of the major grades of wool based on spinning count and the blood system. Courtesy of J. H. Landers.

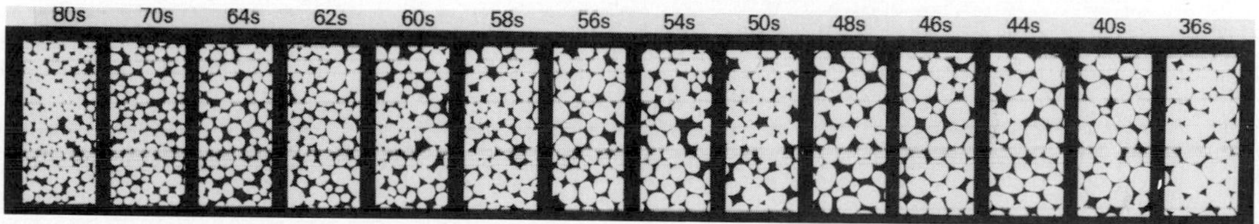

FIGURE 7.7.
Cross section of magnified wool fibers demonstrating the wool grades based on fiber diameter (micron diameter). Courtesy of the USDA.

TABLE 7.1. Market Grades of Wool and Breeds of Sheep That Produce These Grades of Wool

USDA Grades Based on Spinning Count	USDA Grades Based on American (Blood) System	Grades Based on Micron Diameter	Breeds According to Average Grades
80s	Fine	17.70–19.14	Merino
70s	Fine	19.15–20.59	Rambouillet
64s	Fine	20.60–22.04	Targhee, Southdown
62s	½ blood	22.05–23.49	Corriedale, Columbia
50s to 60s	¼ blood to ½ blood	23.50–30.99	Panama, Romeldale
48s to 56s	Low-¼ blood to ½ blood	26.40–32.69	Shropshire, Hampshire, Suffolk, Oxford, Dorset, Cheviot
46s to 48s	Common to low ¼ blood	32.69–38.09	Romney
36s to 40s	Common and braid	36.20–40.20	Cotswold
36s to 46s	Common and braid	32.70–40.20	Lincoln

FIGURE 7.8.
Sheep being shorn for their yearly production of wool. Courtesy of the National Wool Growers (USDA photo).

FIGURE 7.9.
Angora goats with a full growth of mohair. Courtesy of Woolknit Associates, Inc.

TABLE 7.2. World Production of Greasy and Scoured Wools

Country	Greasy Wool (mil lb)	Scoured Wool (mil lb)
Australia	2,072	1,232
USSR	1,043	626
New Zealand	737	442
China	550	275
Argentina	310	180
South Africa	209	102
Uruguay	191	114
United Kingdom	145	112
United States[a]	88	48
World total	7,013	4,270

[a] U.S. production shown for comparison; other countries are higher than the United States in wool production.
Source: 1989 *FAO Production Yearbook.*

Area 5 is the tags. It is long, coarse, dirty, and stained wool. Area 6 is the britch. It is long, coarser-than-average wool that tends to be medullated. Area 7 is the belly. It has short, fine, matted wool that may be very heavy in vegetable matter. Preference is given to a fleece that has uniformity of length and fineness in all areas of the sheep's body.

PRODUCTION OF WOOL AND MOHAIR

Production of wool can be expressed as **greasy wool** or **scoured** (clean) **wool.** Greasy wool is wool or the fleece shorn once each year from sheep (Fig. 7.8). Scoured wool originates in the initial wool-processing stage. Scouring is the washing and rinsing of wool to remove grease, dirt, and other impurities.

Table 7.2 shows the production of greasy and scoured wool for several countries of the world. The world grease wool production is approximately 7 billion lb with the United States producing approximately 88 million lb. Scoured or clean wool production represents 50%–60% of the greasy wool produced.

Growth of wool varies greatly among sheep breeds. Fine-wool sheep grow 4–6 inches of wool per year, $\frac{1}{4}$ to $\frac{1}{2}$ blood breeds of sheep grow 5–10 inches of wool per year, and common to braid wool breeds grow 9–18 inches of wool per year. Mohair growth is approximately 12 inches per year.

Weights of **fleeces** also vary greatly among the breeds of sheep. Even though fine-wool breeds have fleeces of short length, weight of their fleeces varies from 9–12 lb; $\frac{1}{4}$ to $\frac{1}{2}$ blood breeds of sheep produce fleeces weighing 7–15 lb; and coarse wool (common and braid) breeds produce fleeces weighing 9–16 lb.

Annual world mohair production is approximately 59 million lb, of which the United States produces between 29 and 30 million lb or about half the world production. Texas produces about 97% of the mohair that is produced in the United States (Fig. 7.9). Mohair growth is about 1–2 inches per month; therefore, goats are usually shorn twice per year, with length of clip averaging 6–12 inches.

FIGURE 7.10.
Mohair, kid-mohair, and cashmere, strengthened by different proportions of synthetic fibers, are popular yarns for making attractive garments that "breathe" and reduce perspiration. Courtesy of George F. W. Haenlein, University of Delaware.

USES OF WOOL AND MOHAIR

Fibers from sheep, angora rabbits, and goats (Fig. 7.10) are used in making cloth and carpets. The consumption of wool in the United States is small when compared to cotton and numerous manufactured fibers (Fig. 7.11). Figure 7.12 shows the U.S. production and consumption of wool.

Cloth made from wool has both highly desirable and undesirable qualities. Wool has a pleasant warming quality and can absorb considerable quantities of moisture while still providing warmth. It is also highly resistant to fire. However, wool has a tendency to shrink when it becomes wet, and cloth from wool causes some people to itch.

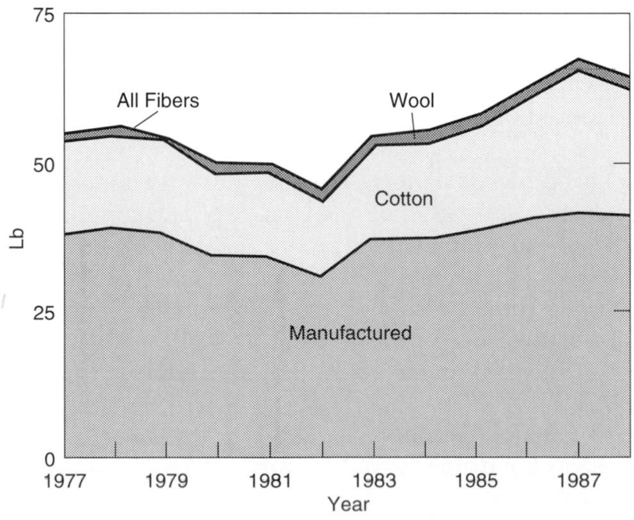

FIGURE 7.11.
U.S. per-capita consumption of fibers, 1977–87. All fibers do not include flax and silk. Manufactured fibers include synthetic fibers such as nylon, dacron, and orlon. Courtesy of the USDA.

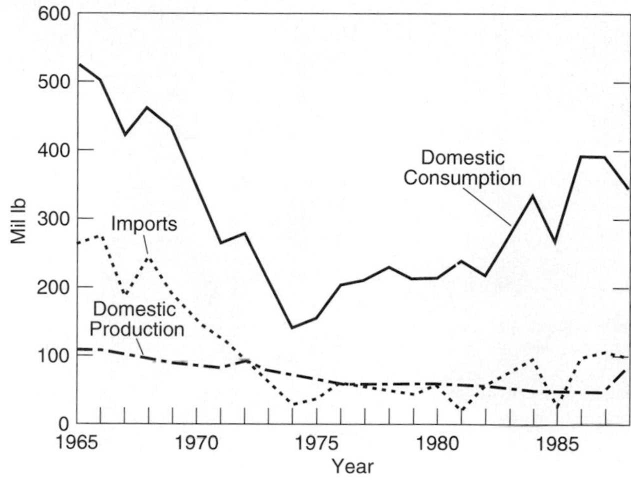

FIGURE 7.12.
U.S. production, imports, and consumption of wool, 1965–88. Imports are on a raw-wool basis. Domestic consumption includes textiles containing wool that are imported. Courtesy of the USDA.

Researchers have contributed greatly to the alteration of wool so that fabrics or garments will not shrink when washed. A process called the WURLAN treatment makes woolen garments machine-washable. In this treatment, the wool fibers are coated with a very thin layer of resin, which adds only 1% to the weight of the wool. The resin does not alter wool in any significant way except to prevent the fibers from absorbing water. There is an increasing trend to blend wool with other fibers. This improves aesthetics and dyability and provides materials with more durability and comfort.

Only fabrics that have passed the quality tests demanded by the International Wool Secretariat and its U.S. branch, the Wool Bureau, Inc., are eligible to carry the Woolmark or Woolblend label (Fig. 7.13).

Woolen garments are as old as the Stone Age, yet as new as today. Wool takes many forms: wovens, knits, piles, and felts, each the result of a different process. It is a long way from a bale of raw wool to a beautiful bolt of fabric and ultimately to beautiful, versatile garments (Fig. 7.14).

FIGURE 7.13.
The sewn-in Woolmark label (pure wool) and Woolblend label (wool blend) give assurance of quality-tested fabrics. Courtesy of the Wool Bureau, Inc.

FIGURE 7.14.
Wool sweaters, wool-knit suits, and wool dresses offer comfort and fashion to the most discerning customers. Courtesy of Woolknit Associates, Inc. (A) Wool sweaters in landscape patterns by Panache and Alps. Knitted in America. (B) The wool suit by Castleberry is the well-dressed delight. Knitted in America. (C) A wool knit dress is designed in a swingy trapeze shape by Geoffrey Beene.

SELECTED REFERENCES

Publications

Botkin, M. P., Field, R. A., and Johnson, C. L. 1988. *Sheep and Wool: Science, Production, and Management.* Englewood Cliffs, NJ: Prentice-Hall.

Rogers, G. E., et al. 1989. *The Biology of Wool and Hair*. New York: Chapman and Hall.

Shelton, M., and Lupton, C. 1986. Where there's wool, there's a way. *Science of Food and Agriculture* (Nov. 6).

Terrill, C. E. 1971. Mohair. In *Encyclopedia of Science and Technology.* 3rd ed. New York: McGraw-Hill.

Visual

From Fleece to Fashion. Pendleton Woolen Mills, P.O. Box 1691, Portland, OR 97207.

CHAPTER 8

Market Classes and Grades of Livestock, Poultry, and Eggs

The production and movement of more than 80 billion lb of highly perishable livestock and poultry products to U.S. consumers is accomplished through a vast and complex marketing system. Marketing is the transformation and pricing of goods and services through which buyers and sellers move livestock and livestock products from the point of production to the point of consumption. Producers need to understand marketing if they are to produce products preferred by consumers, decide intelligently among various marketing alternatives, understand how animals and products are priced, and eventually raise productive animals profitably.

Market classes and grades have been established to segregate animals, carcasses, and products into uniform groups based on preferences of buyers and sellers. The USDA has established extensive classes and grades to make the marketing process simpler and more easily communicated. Use of USDA grades is voluntary. Some packers have their own private grades, though these are often used in combination with USDA grades. An understanding of market classes and grades helps producers recognize quantity and quality of products they are supplying to consumers.

MARKET CLASSES AND GRADES OF RED MEAT ANIMALS

Slaughter Cattle

Slaughter cattle are separated into classes based primarily on age and sex. Age of the animal has a significant effect on tenderness, with younger animals typically producing more tender meat than older animals. Age classifications for meat from cattle are veal, calf, and beef. Veal is from young calves, 1 – 3 months of age, with carcasses weighing less than 150 lb. Calf is from animals ranging in age from 3 – 10 months and carcass weights between 150 – 300 lb. Beef comes from mature cattle (over 12 months of age) having carcass weights higher than 300 lb. Classes and grades established by the USDA for cattle are based on sex, quality grade, and yield grade, all of which are used in the classification of both live cattle and their carcasses (Table 8.1).

TABLE 8.1. Official USDA Grade Standards for Live Slaughter Cattle and Their Carcasses

Class or Kind	Quality Grades (highest to lowest)	Yield Grades (highest to lowest)
Beef		
Steer and heifer	Prime, choice, select, standard, commercial, utility, cutter, canner	1, 2, 3, 4, 5
Cow	Choice, select, standard, commercial, utility, cutter, canner	1, 2, 3, 4, 5
Bullock	Prime, choice, select, standard, utility	1, 2, 3, 4, 5
Bull	(No designated quality grades)	1, 2, 3, 4, 5
Veal	Prime, choice, select, standard, utility	NA
Calf	Prime, choice, select, standard, utility	NA

The sex classes for cattle are **heifer, cow, steer, bull,** and **bullock**. Occasionally, the sex class of **stag** is used by the livestock industry to refer to males that have been castrated after their secondary sex characteristics have developed. Sex classes separate cattle and carcasses into more uniform carcass weights, tenderness groups, and processing methods. **Quality grades** are intended to measure certain consumer palatability characteristics, and **yield grades** measure amount of fat, lean, and bone in the carcass. Slaughter steers representing some of the eight quality grades and five yield grades are shown in Figures. 8.1 and 8.2.

Quality grades are based primarily on two factors: (1) **maturity** (physiological age) of the carcass, and (2) amount of **marbling**. Maturity is determined primarily by observing bone and cartilage structures. For example, soft, porous, red bones with a maximum amount of pearly white cartilage characterize A maturity, whereas very little cartilage and hard, flinty bones characterize C, D, and E maturities. As maturity in carcasses increases from A to E, the meat becomes less tender.

Marbling is intramuscular fat or flecks of fat within the lean, and it is evaluated at the exposed rib-eye muscle between the 12th and 13th ribs. Nine degrees of marbling, ranging from abundant to practically devoid, are designated in the USDA marbling standards. Various combinations of marbling and maturity that identify the carcass quality grades are shown in Figure 8.3. Figure 8.4 shows rib-eye sections representing several different quality grades and several different degrees of marbling. Note that C maturity starts at 42 months of age. Slaughter cows more than 42 months of age will grade commercial, utility, cutter, or canner regardless of amount of marbling.

Yield grades, sometimes referred to as **cutability grades**, measure the quantity of boneless, closely trimmed retail cuts (BCTRC) from the major wholesale cuts of beef (round, loin, rib, and chuck). BCTRC should not be confused with the total percentage of retail cuts (including hamburger) from a beef carcass. A numerical scale of 1–5 is used to rate yield grade, with 1 denoting the highest percentage of BCTRC. Although marketing communications generally quote yield grades in whole numbers, these yield grades are often shown in tenths in research data and information in carcass contests.

Packers can elect to have carcasses quality graded. Table 8.2 shows the yield grades and their respective percentage of BCTRC. As an example, a carcass with a yield grade of 3.0 has a BCTRC of 50%; a 700-lb carcass with this yield grade would produce 350 lb of boneless, closely trimmed retail cuts from the round, loin, rib, and chuck.

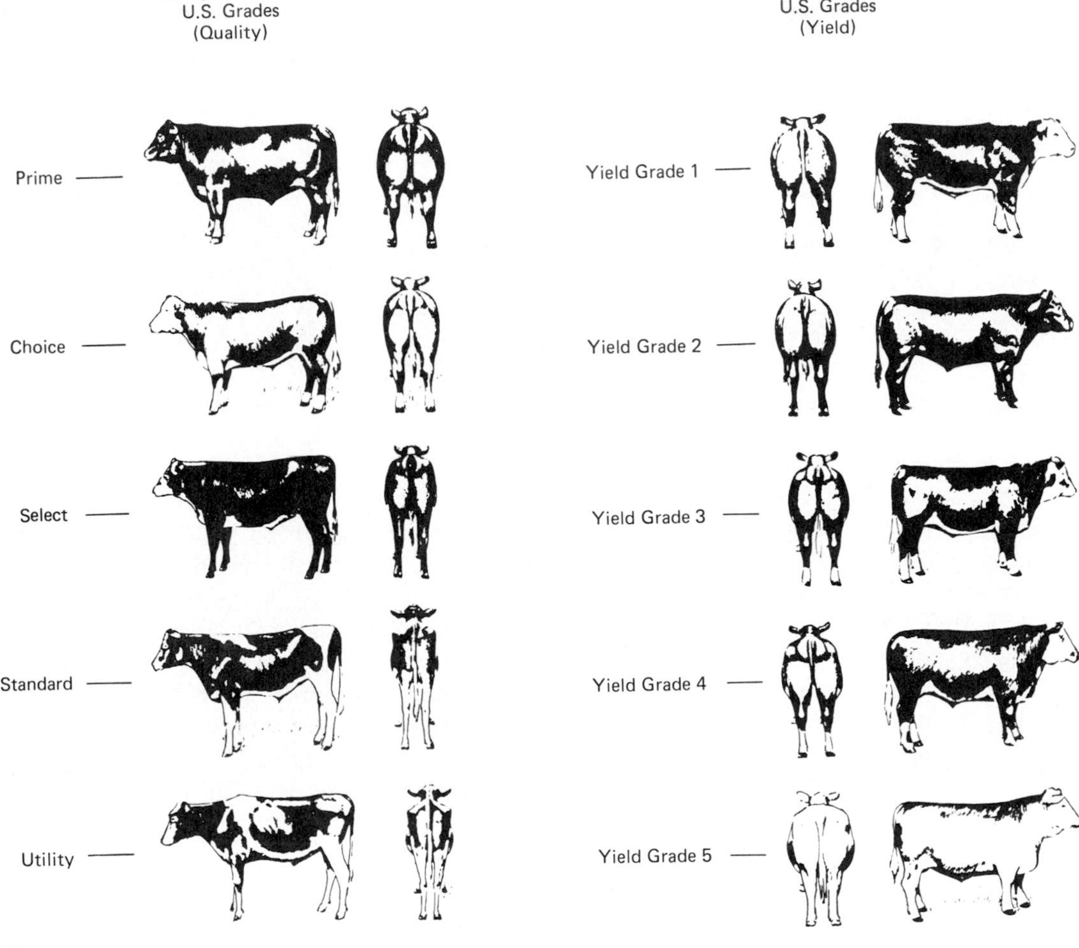

Figure 8.1.
USDA quality grades (commercial, cutter, and canner omitted). Courtesy of the USDA.

FIGURE 8.2.
USDA yield grades for slaughter cattle. Courtesy of the USDA.

Yield grades are determined from the following four carcass characteristics: (1) amount of fat measured in tenths of inches over the rib-eye muscle, also known as the *longissimus dorsi* (Fig. 8.5); (2) kidney, pelvic, and heart fat (usually estimated as percent of carcass weight); (3) area of the rib-eye muscle, measured in square inches (Fig. 8.6); and (4) hot carcass weight. The last measurement reflects amount of intermuscular fat. Generally, as the carcass increases in weight, amount of fat between the muscles increases as well.

Measures of fatness in beef carcasses have the greatest effect in determining yield grade. A tentative yield grade can be determined by estimating or measuring the outside fat of the rib-eye muscle. Figure 8.7 shows the five yield grades with varying amounts of fat over the rib-eye muscle and the area of the rib eye.

Quality grading and yield grading of beef carcasses by packers are voluntary. Approximately 60% of the 23 billion lb of federally inspected carcass beef produced each year is

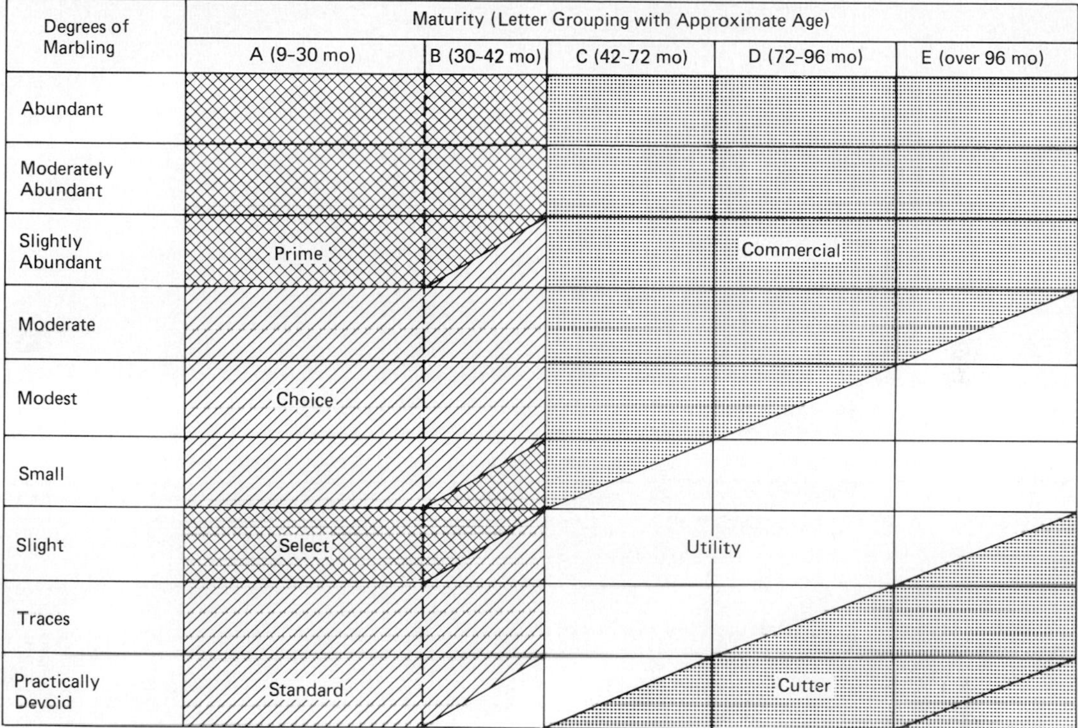

FIGURE 8.3.
Marbling and the maturity of the carcass are the major factors that determine the quality grade of the beef carcass. Courtesy of the USDA.

TABLE 8.2. Beef Carcass Yield Grades and the Yield of BCTRC (boneless, closely trimmed retail cuts) from the Round, Loin, Rib, and Chuck

Yield Grade	BCTRC (%)	Yield Grade	BCTRC (%)	Yield Grade	BCTRC (%)
1.0	54.6	2.8	50.5	4.6	46.4
1.2	54.2	3.0	50.0	4.8	45.9
1.4	53.7	3.2	49.6	5.0	45.4
1.6	53.3	3.4	49.1	5.2	45.0
1.8	52.8	3.6	48.7	5.4	44.5
2.0	52.3	3.8	48.2	5.6	44.1
2.2	51.9	4.0	47.7	5.8	43.6
2.4	51.4	4.2	47.3	—	—
2.6	51.0	4.4	46.8	—	—

Source: USDA.

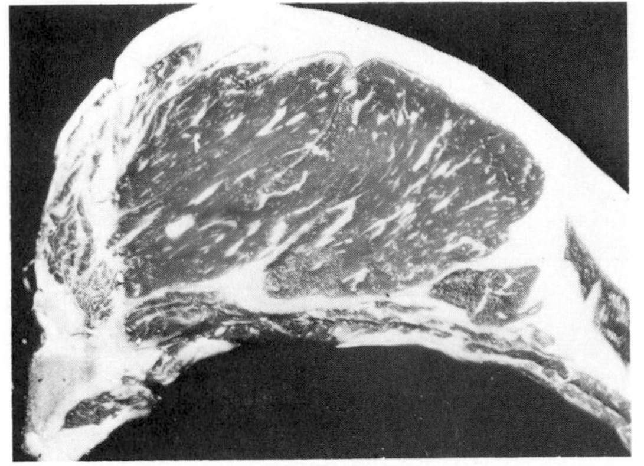

Prime (moderately abundant marbling)

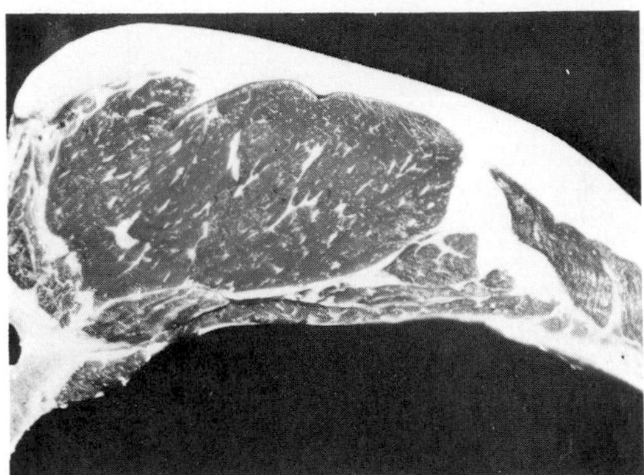

Choice (modest marbling)

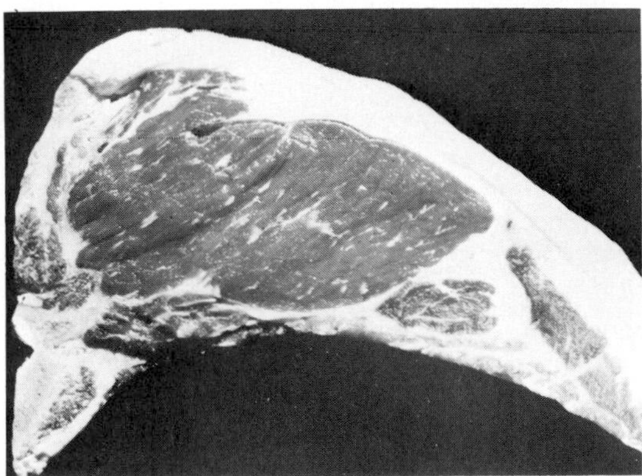

Select (slight marbling)

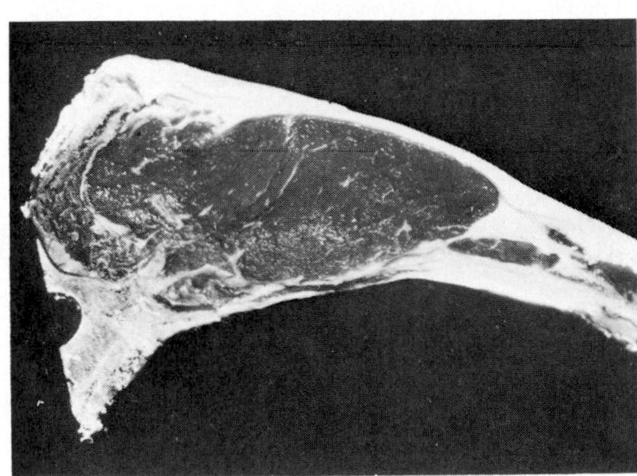

Standard (traces of marbling)

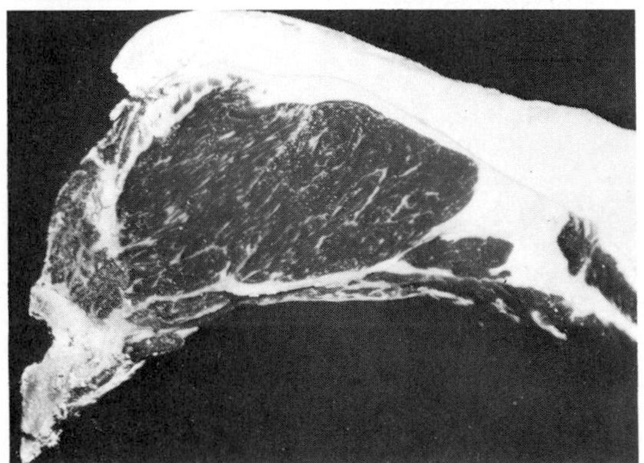

Commercial (moderately abundant marbling; however, E maturity put it into this grade) See Figure 5-3.

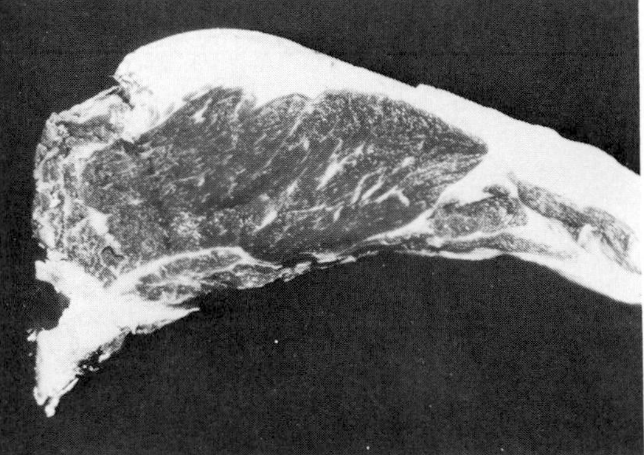

Utility (modest marbling)

FIGURE 8.4.
Exposed rib-eye muscles (between twelfth and thirteenth ribs) showing various degrees of marbling of several beef carcass quality grades. Courtesy of the National Live Stock and Meat Board.

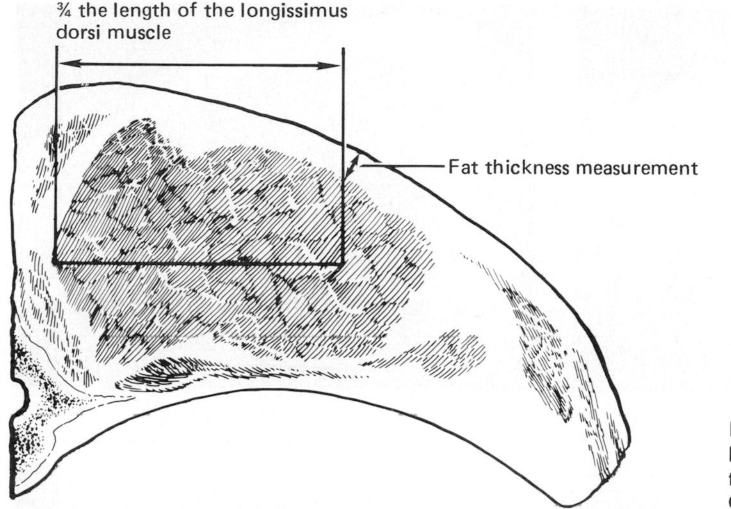

FIGURE 8.5.
Location of the fat measurement over the rib-eye (*longissimus dorsi*) muscle. Courtesy of Dennis Giddings.

quality-graded or yield-graded. Most of the graded beef is slaughter steers and heifers from feedlots. The distribution of quality grades and yield grades is shown in Figure 8.8. Note that the percent of choice is 48% of all beef produced. The percent of choice of the 12.9 million lb that was quality graded in 1989 was 86%.

Feeder Cattle

The revised 1979 USDA feeder grades for cattle are intended to predict feedlot weight gain and the slaughter weight end point of cattle fed to a desirable fat-to-lean composition. The two criteria used to determine feeder grade are frame size and thickness. The three measures of

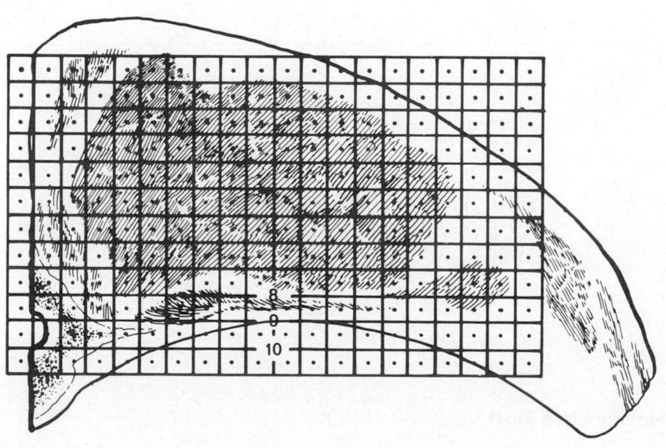

FIGURE 8.6.
Plastic grid is placed over the rib-eye muscle to measure the area. Each square represents 0.1 square inch. Courtesy of Dennis Giddings.

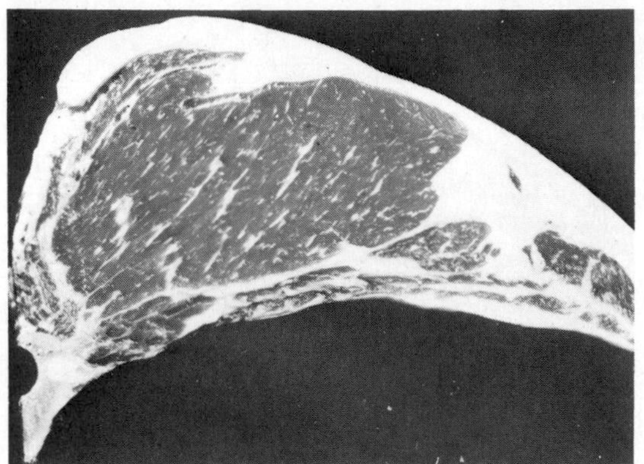

Yield Grade 1
(Fat 0.2 in. ribeye area 13.9 sq in.)

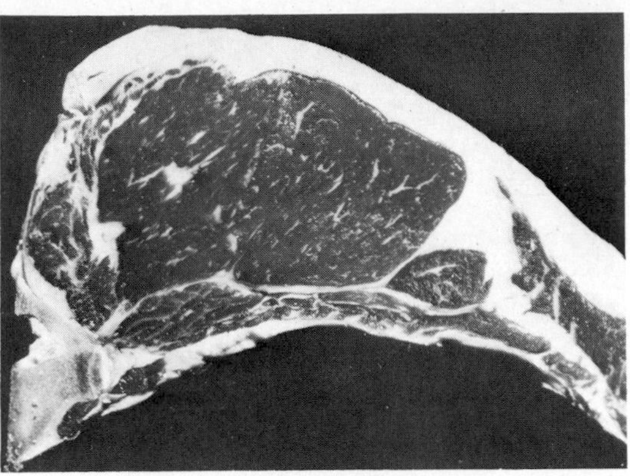

Yield Grade 2
(Fat 0.4 in. ribeye area 12.3 sq in.)

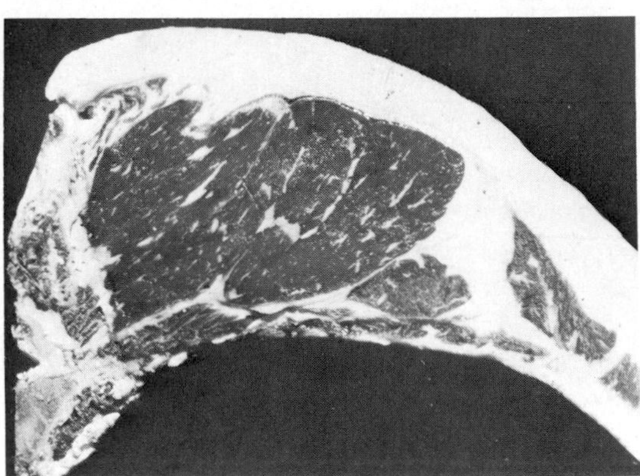

Yield Grade 3
(Fat 0.6 in., ribeye area 11.8 sq in.)

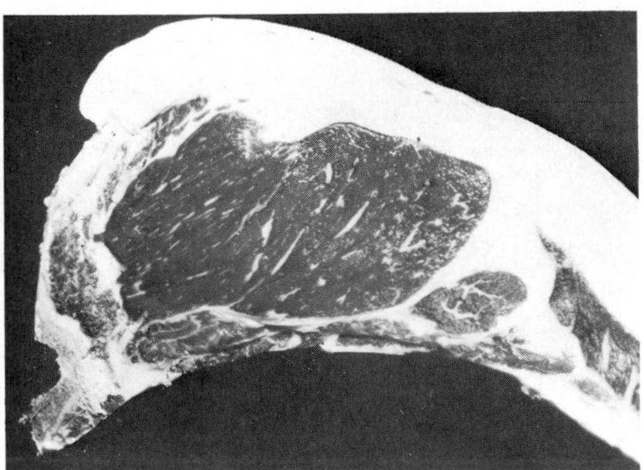

Yield Grade 4
(Fat 0.9 in., ribeye area 10.5 sq in.)

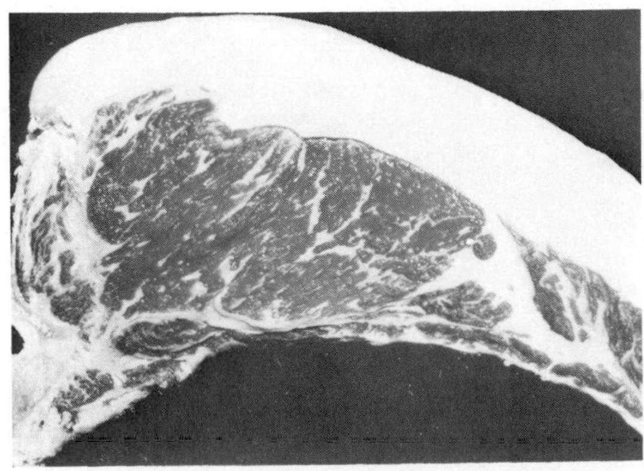

Yield Grade 5
(Fat 1.1 in., ribeye area 10.9 sq in.)

FIGURE 8.7.
The five yield grades of beef shown at twelfth and thirteenth ribs. Courtesy of the National Live Stock and Meat Board.

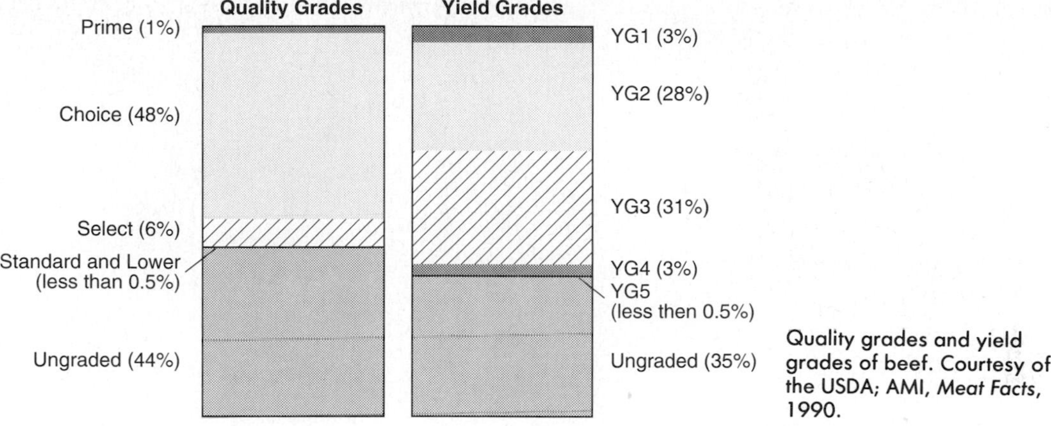

Quality grades and yield grades of beef. Courtesy of the USDA; AMI, *Meat Facts*, 1990.

frame size and thickness are shown in Figures 8.9 and 8.10. Some examples of feeder cattle grade terminology are large no. 1, medium no. 2, and small no. 2. Feeder cattle are given a USDA grade of inferior if the cattle are unhealthy or double-muscled. These cattle would not gain satisfactorily in the feedlot.

Although frame size and ability to gain weight in the feedlot are apparently related in the sense that large-framed cattle usually gain fastest, frame size appears to predict more accurately carcass composition or yield grade at different slaughter weights than gaining ability. The USDA feeder grade specifications identify the different liveweights from the three frame sizes when they reach the choice grade (Table 8.3).

Slaughter Swine

Sex classes of swine are **barrow, gilt, sow, boar,** and **stag**. Boars and sows are older breeding animals, whereas gilts are younger females that have not produced any young. The barrow is the male pig castrated early in life, and the stag is the male pig castrated after it has developed certain boarlike characteristics. Because of relationships between sex and sex condition and the acceptability of prepared meats to the consumer, separate grade standards have been developed

TABLE 8.3. Slaughter Weights of Large-, Medium-, and Small-Frame Slaughter Cattle When They Reach the Choice Grade

	Slaughter Weight	
Frame Size	Steers (lb)	Heifers (lb)
Large	>1,200	>1,000
Medium	1,000–1,200	850–1,000
Small	<1,000	<850

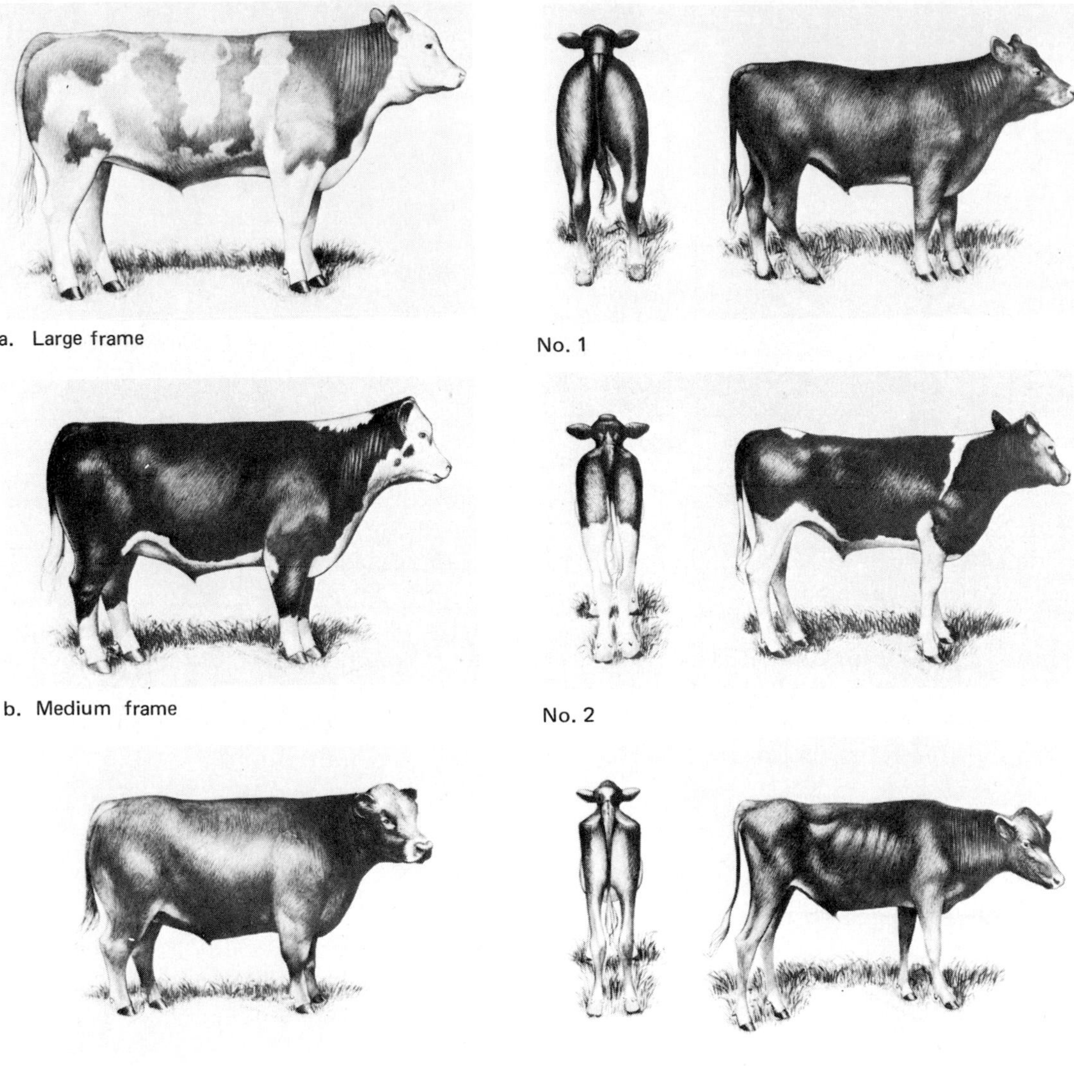

FIGURE 8.9.
The three frame sizes of the USDA feeder grades for cattle. Courtesy of the USDA.

FIGURE 8.10.
The three thickness standards of the USDA feeder grades for cattle. Courtesy of the USDA.

for barrow and gilt carcasses and for sow carcasses. There are no official grades standards for boar and stag carcasses.

The grades for barrow and gilt carcasses are based on two general criteria: (1) quality characteristics of the lean, and (2) expected combined yields of the four lean cuts (ham, loin, blade (Boston) shoulder, and picnic shoulder). There are only two quality grades for lean in a pork carcass: acceptable and unacceptable. Quality of the lean is assessed by observing the exposed surface of a cut muscle, usually between the 10th and 11th ribs. Acceptable lean is

TABLE 8.4. Expected Yields of the Four Lean Cuts, Based on Percent of Chilled Carcass Weight

Grade	Four Lean Cuts (%)
U.S. no 1	53.0 and higher
U.S. no. 2	50.0–52.9
U.S. no. 3	47.0–49.0
U.S. no. 4	<47.0

gray-pink in color, has fine muscle fibers, and has fine marbling. Carcasses that have unacceptable lean quality (too dark or too pale, soft, or watery) or bellies too thin for suitable bacon production are graded U.S. utility, as they are soft and oily carcasses. Carcasses with acceptable lean quality are graded U.S. no. 1, U.S. no. 2, U.S. no. 3, or U.S. no. 4. These grades are based on expected yields of the four lean cuts, as shown in Table 8.4.

Carcasses differ in their yields of the four lean cuts primarily because of differences in amount of fatness and muscling in relation to skeletal size. Back fat thickness and an evaluation of muscling are the two factors used to determine the numerical yield grade (Table 8.5).

Figure 8.11 shows the muscling scores used to determine grades.

Feeder Pig Grades

The USDA grades of feeder pigs are U.S. nos. 1, 2, 3, 4, and utility (Fig. 8.12). These grades correspond to USDA grades for market swine when slaughtered at 220 lb. Utility grade is for unthrifty or unhealthy feeder pigs. Thus, feeder pig grades combine an evaluation for thriftiness and slaughter potential.

TABLE 8.5. Preliminary Grade Based on Back Fat Thickness over the Last Rib (assumes average muscle thickness)

Preliminary Grade[a]	Back Fat Thickness (in.)
U.S. no. 1	<1.00
U.S. no. 2	1.00–1.24
U.S. no. 3	1.25–1.49
U.S. no. 4	1.50 and over[b]

[a] Swine with thick muscling qualify for next higher grade; those with thin muscling are downgraded to next lower grade.
[b] Animals with an estimated last-rib back fat thickness of 1.75 inches or over have to be U.S. no. 4 and cannot be graded U.S. no. 3, even with thick muscling.
Source: USDA.

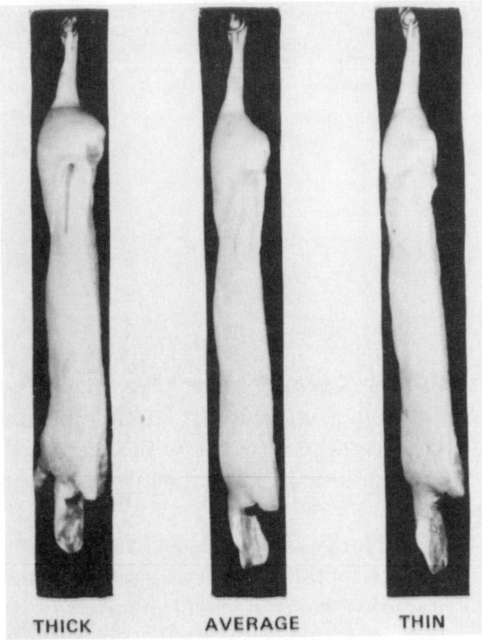

FIGURE 8.11.
Three degrees of muscling in pork carcasses. Thick and average represent the minimum accepted for each of the two degrees. Courtesy of the USDA.

Slaughter Sheep

Slaughter sheep are classified by their sex and maturity. Live sheep and their carcasses are also graded for quality grades and yield grades (Table 8.6).

Lamb carcasses, ranging from approximately 2–14 months of age, always have the characteristic break joint on one of their shanks following the removal of their front legs (Fig. 8.13). Mutton carcasses are distinguished from lamb carcasses by the appearance of the spool joint instead of the break joint (Fig. 8.13). The break joint ossifies as the sheep matures. Yearling mutton carcasses ranging from 12–25 months of age usually have the spool joint present but may occasionally have a break joint. Yearling mutton is also distinguished from lamb and mutton by color of the lean (intermediate between pinkish red of lamb and dark red of mutton) and shape of rib bones. Most U.S. consumers prefer lamb to mutton because it has a milder flavor and is more tender.

Quality grades are determined from a composite evaluation of conformation, maturity, **flank streaking**, and **flank firmness and fullness**. Conformation is an assessment of overall

TABLE 8.6. USDA Maturity Groups, Sex Classes, and Grades of Slaughter Sheep

Maturity Group	Sex Class	Quality Grade (Highest to Lowest)	Yield Grade (Highest to Lowest)
Lamb	Ewe, wether, or ram	Prime, choice, good, utility	1, 2, 3, 4, 5,
Yearling mutton	Ewe, wether, or ram	Prime, choice, good, utility	1, 2, 3, 4, 5,
Mutton	Ewe, wether, or ram	Prime, choice, good, utility	1, 2, 3, 4, 5,

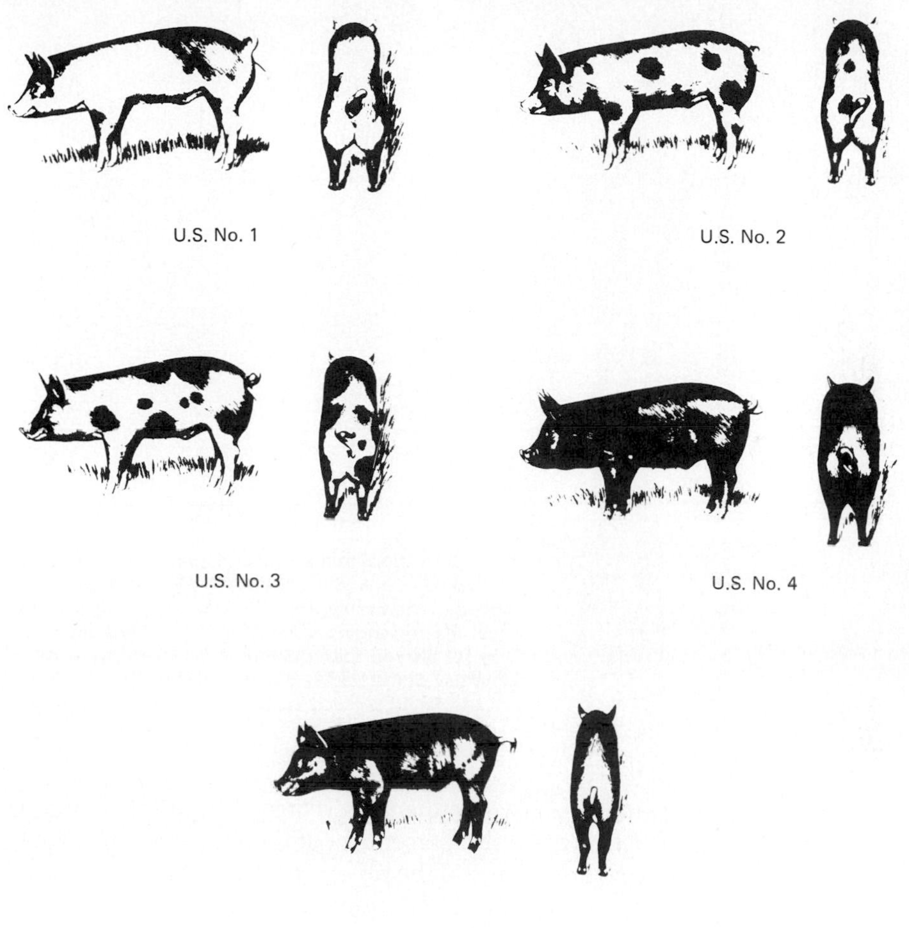

FIGURE 8.12.
The USDA grades for feeder pigs. Courtesy of the USDA.

thickness of muscling in the lamb carcass. Maturity of lamb carcasses is determined by bone color and shape and muscle color. Flank streaking (streaks of fat within the flank muscle) predicts marbling since lamb carcasses are not usually ribbed to expose marbling in the rib-eye muscle. Flank firmness and fullness are determined by taking hold of the flank muscle with the hand. Most lamb carcasses grade either prime or choice, with few carcasses grading in the lower grades.

Lamb carcasses may be quality-graded, yield-graded, or both. Yield grades estimate boneless, closely trimmed retail cuts from the leg, loin, rack, and shoulder. The approximate percentage of retail cuts for selected yield grades are shown in Table 8.7.

Yield grades are determined from a composite evaluation of leg conformation score, percentage of kidney and pelvic fat, and fat thickness. Leg score is subjectively evaluated on a numerical scale from 1–15 by assessing thickness, fullness, and plumpness of muscling in the

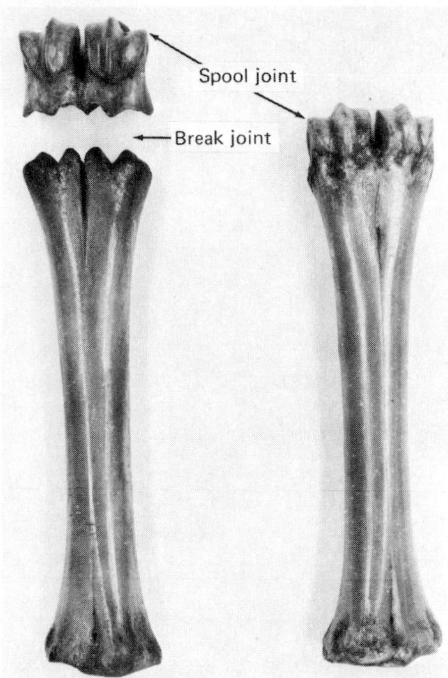

FIGURE 8.13.
Break and spool joints. The cannon bone on the left exhibits the typical break joint in which the foot and pastern are removed at the cartilaginous junction. In the cannon bone on the right, the cartilaginous junction has ossified, making it necessary for the foot and pastern to be removed at the spool joint. Courtesy of the USDA.

hind leg. Figure 8.14 shows examples of two different leg scores. Amount of kidney and pelvic fat is evaluated subjectively and expressed as a percentage of the carcass weight. Fat thickness, in tenths of inches, is measured over the center of the rib-eye muscle between the 12th and 13th ribs. This external fat measurement is the most important yield-grade factor, since it is a good indicator of total fat trimmed in making retail cuts. Figure 8.15 shows cross sections of lamb carcasses representing the five yield grades and amount of fat thickness over the rib eye for each yield grade.

TABLE 8.7. Lamb Carcass Yield Grades and the Percentage of Retail Cuts

Yield Grade	Percent Retail Cuts	Yield Grade	Percent Retail Cuts
1.0	49.0%	3.5	44.6%
1.5	48.2	4.0	43.6
2.0	47.2	4.5	42.8
2.5	46.3	5.0	41.8
3.0	45.4	5.5	41.0

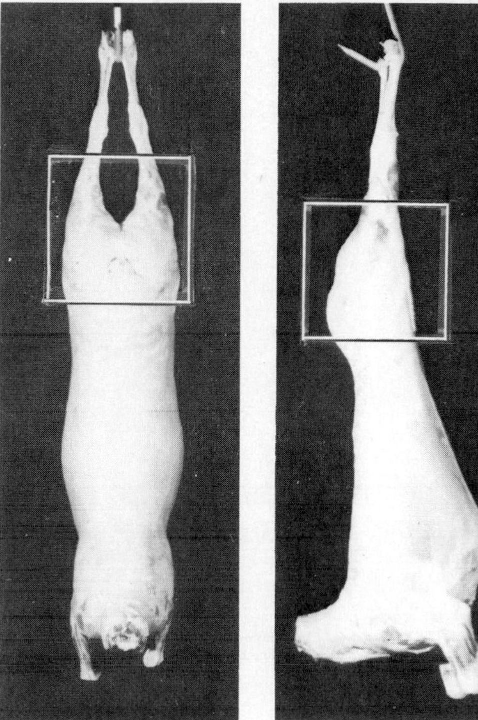
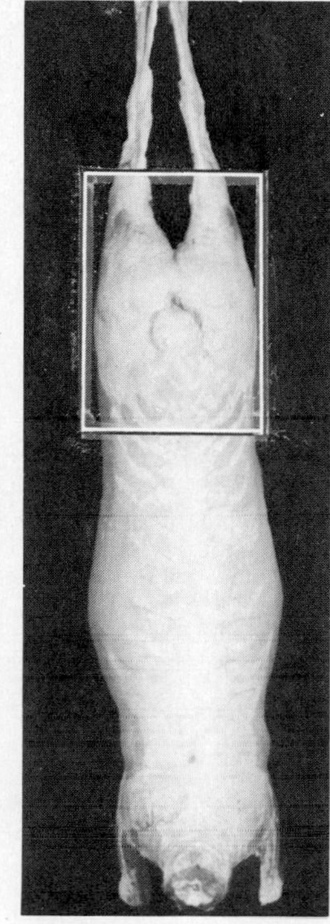
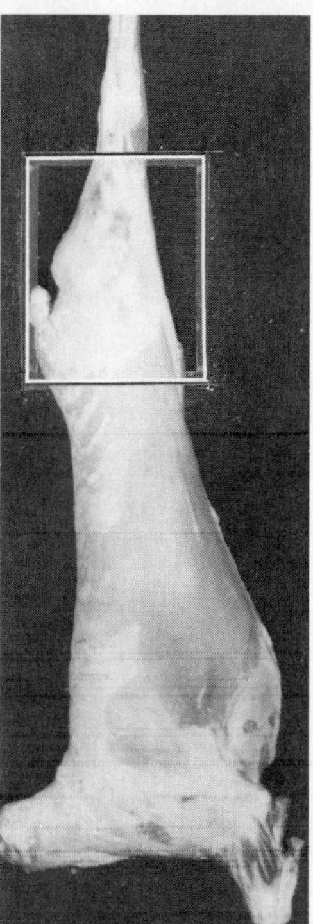

Leg score = Average Prime (score of 14) Leg score = Low Choice (score of 10)

FIGURE 8.14.
Comparison of two different lamb leg scores used as a partial determining factor for yield grade. Boxes define the area evaluated for thickness, fullness, and plumpness of muscling in the hind leg. Courtesy of the National Live Stock and Meat Board.

Feeder Lamb Grades

Choice and prime slaughter lambs are produced in relatively large numbers, fed on grass and their mothers' milk. Lambs weighing less than 100 lb at weaning are considered feeder lambs. They require additional feeding to produce a more desirable carcass.

There are no official USDA grades for feeder lambs. However, some market reports and industry terminology may refer to *prime, choice, good, utility,* and *cull* feeder lambs. These grades are not widely used at the present time, since most lambs, correctly finished for slaughter, are graded choice regardless of their breed or body shape. Most feeder lambs are classified by weight rather than grade. *Lightweight* feeder lambs typically weigh 60–75 lb; *medium weight,* 75–85 lb; and *heavy,* more than 85 lb. Lambs may also be classified as natives (produced in midwestern and eastern farm states) or westerns (produced in the western United States).

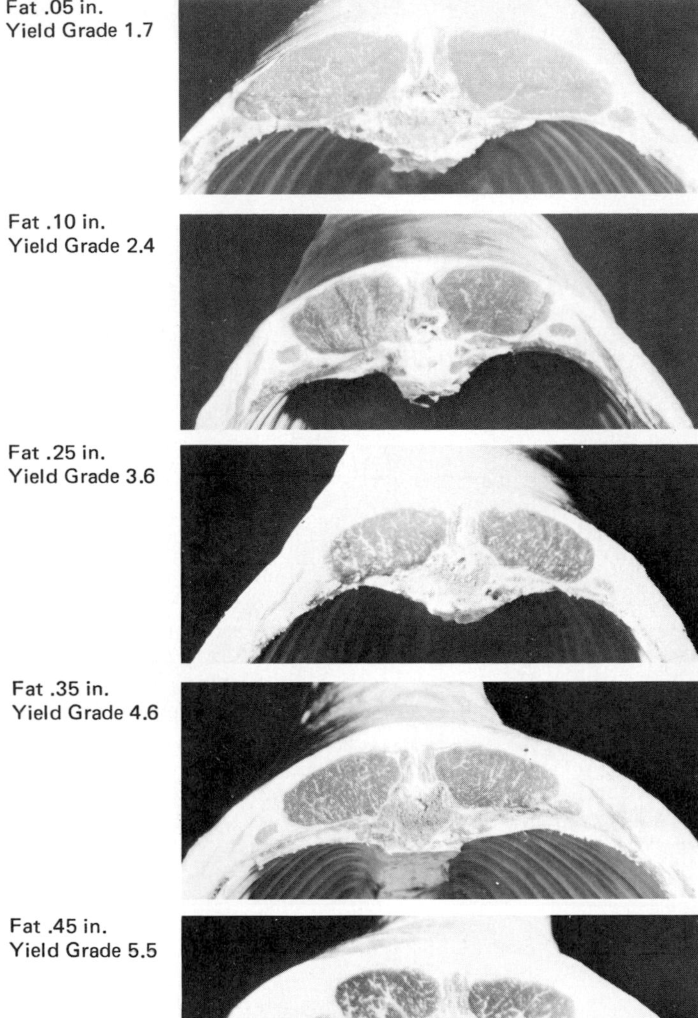

FIGURE 8.15.
The five yield grades of lamb showing the progressive increases in the amount of fat over the loin eye at the twelfth and thirteenth ribs. Courtesy of the National Live Stock and Meat Board.

MARKET CLASSES AND GRADES OF POULTRY PRODUCTS

Poultry Meat

The class of poultry must be displayed on the package label or a tag on the wing of the bird. The age class indicates tenderness, as meat from younger birds is more tender than that from older birds. Table 8.8 shows the age-classification labels for poultry meat.

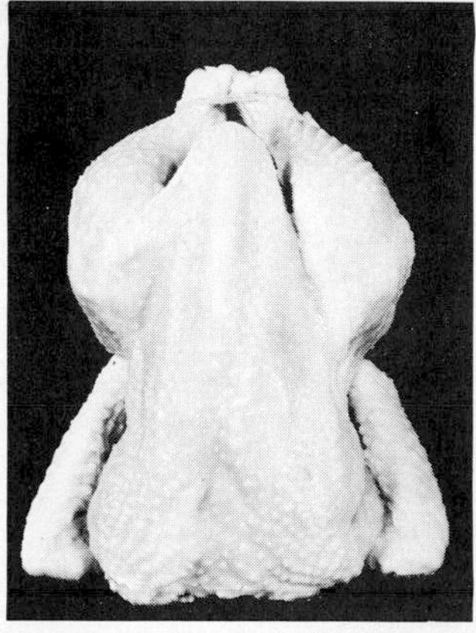

Broiler or fryer, A quality

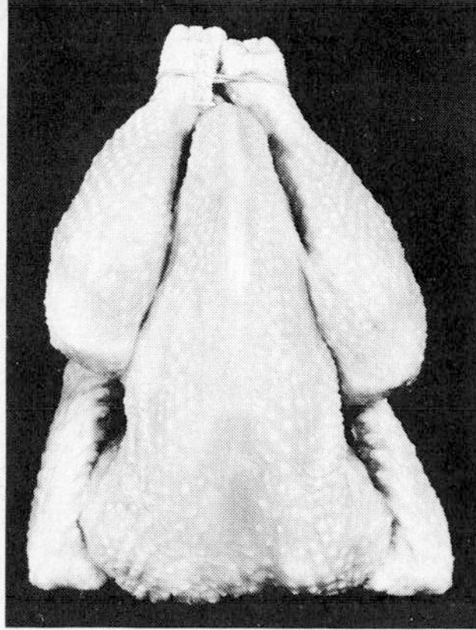

Broiler or fryer, B quality

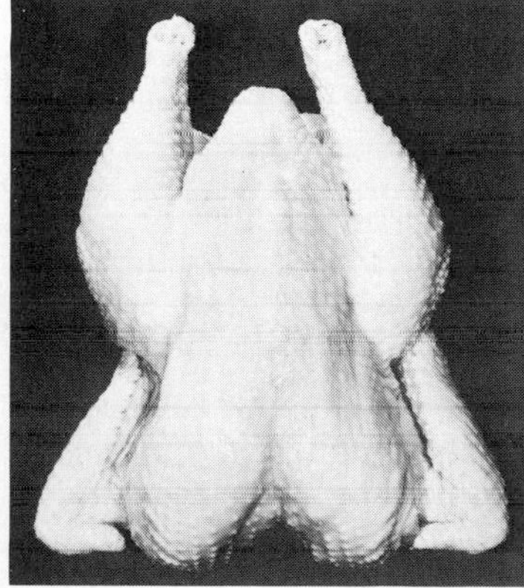

Hen or stewing chicken, A quality

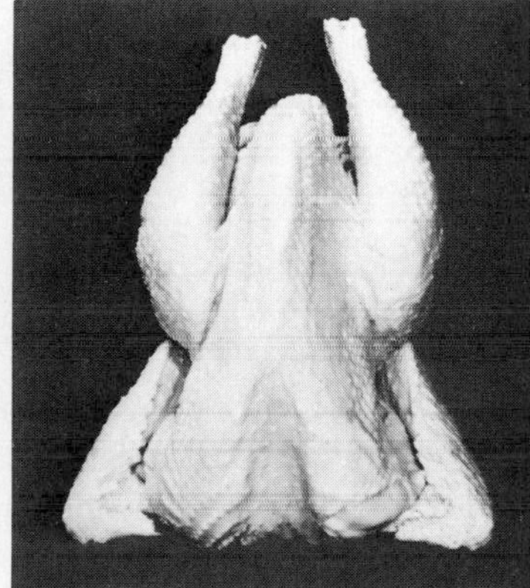

Hen or stewing chicken, B quality

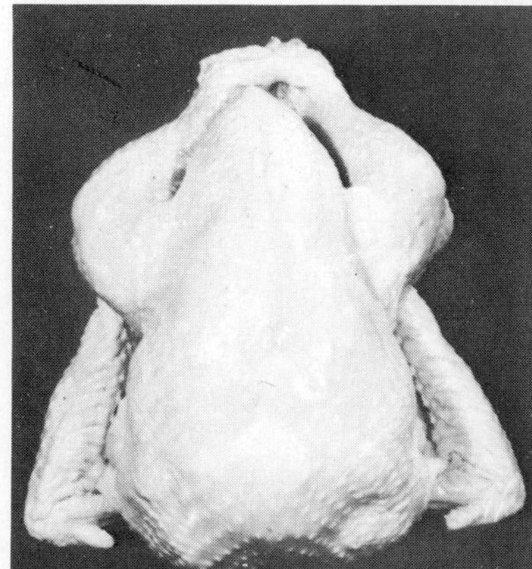

Young turkey, A quality

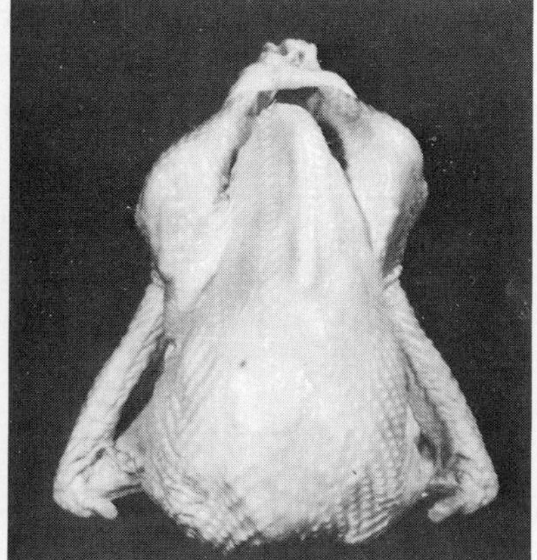

Young turkey, B quality

FIGURE 8.16.
Classes and grades of ready-to-cook poultry. Courtesy of the USDA.

TABLE 8.8. Labels Used to Identify Poultry Age Classes

Type	Young	Mature
Chicken	Young chicken Rock Cornish game hen Broiler Fryer Roaster Capon	Mature chicken Old chicken Hen Stewing chicken Fowl
Turkey	Young turkey Fryer-roaster Young hen Young tom	Mature turkey Yearling turkey Old turkey
Duck	Duckling Young duckling Broiler duckling Fryer duckling Roaster duckling	Mature Old

Meat from the young age classes is usually prepared by broiling, frying, roasting, or barbecuing. The mature, less tender poultry meat is best prepared by baking, stewing, or fabricating or by including it in other prepared dishes.

The grades are U.S. grade A, U.S. grade B, and U.S. grade C for each of the classes, with A being the highest grade (Fig. 8.16). Carcasses of A quality are free of deformities that detract from their appearance or that affect normal distribution of flesh. They have a well-developed covering of flesh and a well-developed layer of fat in the skin. They are free of pinfeathers and diminutive feathers, exposed flesh on the breast and legs, and broken bones. They have no more than one disjointed bone, and they are practically free of discolorations of the skin and flesh and defects resulting from handling, freezing, or storage. Carcasses of B quality may have moderate deformities. They have a moderate covering of flesh, sufficient fat in the skin to prevent a distinct appearance of the flesh through the skin, and no more than an occasional pinfeather or diminutive feather. They may have moderate areas of exposed flesh and discoloration of the

TABLE 8.9. Consumer Weight Classes of Eggs, Minimum Net Weight Per Dozen

Size	Ounces (per doz)
Jumbo	30
Extra large	27
Large	24
Medium	21
Small	18
Peewee	15

Source: USDA.

TABLE 8.10. Summary of U.S. Standards for Quality of Individual Shell Eggs

Quality Factor	Specifications for Each Quality Factor				
	AA Quality	A Quality	B Quality	Dirty	Check
Shell	Clean, unbroken; practically normal	Clean, unbroken, practically normal	Clean to slightly stained[a]; unbroken; abnormal	Unbroken; adhering dirt or foreign material, prominant stains, moderate stained areas in excess of B quality.	Broken or cracked shell but membranes intact, not leaking[c]
Air cell	⅛ in. or less in depth; unlimited movement and free or bubbly	3/16 in. or less in depth; unlimited movement and free or bubbly	Over 3/16 in. in depth; unlimited movement and free or bubbly		
White	Clear, firm	Clear, reasonably firm	Weak and watery; small blood and meat spots present[b]		
Yolk	Outline slightly defined; practically free from defects	Outline fairly well defined; practically free from defects	Outline plainly visible; enlarged and flattened; clearly visible germ development, but no blood; other serious defects		

[a]Moderately stained areas permitted (1/32 of surface if localized, or 1/16 if scattered).
[b]If they are small (aggregating not more than ⅛ in. in diameter).
[c]Leaker has broken or cracked shell and membranes, and contents are leaking or free to leak.
Source: USDA Egg Grading Manual.

FIGURE 8.17.
U.S. Department of Agriculture grade shields showing two egg quality grades. Courtesy of the USDA.

skin and flesh. They may have disjointed parts but no broken bones, and they may have moderate defects resulting from handling, freezing, or storage.

Eggs

The grading of shell eggs involves classifying individual eggs according to established standards. Eggs are graded by sorting them into groups, each group having similar weight and quality characteristics. Table 8.9 shows how eggs are classified according to a size and weight relationship.

The USDA quality standards used to grade individual shell eggs are as follows:

Exterior Quality Factors	*Interior Quality Factors*
Cleanliness of shell	Albumen thickness
Soundness of shell (cracks, checks, and texture)	Condition of yolk
	Size and condition of air cell
Shape	Abnormalities (e.g., blood spots, meat spots)

Exterior quality factors are apparent from external observation; interior quality factors involve an assessment of egg content. The latter is accomplished through a process called **candling** (visually appraising the eggs while light is shown through them).

Although shell color is not a factor in the U.S. standards and grades, eggs are usually sorted by color and sold either as "whites" or "browns." Eggs sell better when sorted by color and packed separately. Contrary to popular opinion, there are no differences between similar quality brown- and white-shelled eggs other than color.

The U.S. standards for quality of individual shell eggs are applicable only to eggs from domestic chickens; these standards are summarized in Table 8.10. Consumer egg grades are U.S. grade AA, U.S. grade A, and U.S. grade B. Figure 8.17 shows selected shields for communicating the quality grade.

SELECTED REFERENCES

Publications

Boggs, D. L., and Merkel, R. A. 1990. *Live Animal Carcass Evaluation and Selection Manual.* 2nd ed. Dubuque, IA: Kendall/Hunt.

Council for Agricultural Science and Technology. Mar. 1980. *Foods from Animals: Quantity, Quality, and Safety.* CAST Report no. 82.

McCoy, J. H. 1988. *Livestock and Marketing.* Westport, CT: AVI.

Meat Evaluation Handbook. 2nd ed., 1977. Chicago: National Live Stock and Meat Board.

USDA. Apr. 1983. *Egg Grading Manual.* USDA Agriculture Handbook no. 75.

USDA. April 1980. *Facts About U.S. Standards for Grades of Feeder Cattle.* Agricultural Marketing Service AMS-586.

USDA. *Official United States Standards for Grades of Feeder Pigs* (Apr. 1, 1969) and *Grades of Slaughter Swine* (Jan. 14, 1985); *Grades of Pork Carcasses* (Jan. 14, 1985); *Grades of Veal and Calf Carcasses* (Oct. 6, 1980); *Grades of Lamb, Yearling Mutton and Mutton Carcasses* (Oct. 17, 1982); *Grades of Carcass Beef and Slaughter Cattle* (Apr. 9, 1989). Agricultural Marketing Service.

Visuals

Grading Eggs for Quality (sound filmstrip). Vocational Education Productions, California Polytechnic State University, San Luis Obispo, CA 93407.

Egg Grades . . . A Matter of Quality (16-mm film, 12 min). National Audio Visual Center, Order Section, 8700 Edgeworth Dr., Capitol Heights, MD 20743-3701.

"Egg Grading" (videotape). CEV, P.O. Box 65265, Lubbock, TX 79464-5265.

Market Animal Grading—Feeder Cattle, Slaughter Cattle, Slaughter Lambs, and Slaughter Hogs (4 videotapes). CEV, P.O. Box 65265, Lubbock, TX 79464-5265.

United States Standards of Poultry and Poultry Parts (three-part slide series: Part 1—whole fryer; part 2—fryer parts; part 3—turkey). 1986. Learning Resources Center, VPI, Blacksburg, VA 24061.

U.S. Standards for Quality of Individual Shell Eggs (photos illustrating interior and exterior grade factors; chart, 15 × 22 in.). 1984. Superintendent of Documents, U.S. Government Printing Office, Washington, DC 20402.

CHAPTER 9

Visual Evaluation of Slaughter Red Meat Animals

Most red meat animals, ready for slaughter, are purchased at market time based on visual appraisal of their apparent carcass merit. Livestock producers attempt to combine high productivity and visual acceptability in these slaughter animals in anticipation of high market prices and positive net returns.

Productivity of breeding and slaughter meat animals is best identified by using meaningful performance records and effective visual appraisal. Opinions regarding the relationship of form and function in red meat animals (cattle, sheep, swine) differ widely among producers. They continually discuss the value of visual appraisal, weights, and body measurements in breeding programs, in determining market grades and in defining the so-called "ideal types." It is important to separate true relationships from opinion in the area of animal form and function.

Type is defined as an ideal or standard of perfection combining all the characteristics that contribute to an animal's usefulness for a specific purpose. *Conformation* implies the same general meaning as type and refers to form and shape of the animal. Both type and conformation describe an animal according to its external form and shape that can be evaluated visually or measured more objectively with a tape or some other device.

Red meat animals have three productive stages: (1) breeding (reproduction), (2) feeder (growth), and (3) slaughter (carcass or product). It has been well demonstrated that performance records are much more effective than visual appraisal in improving reproduction and growth stages. Visual appraisal does have importance in these stages, primarily in identifying reproductive soundness, skeletal soundness, and health status. Visual appraisal has some importance in evaluating productive differences in the carcass composition (fat, lean and bone). Both performance records (such as backfat probes and ultrasonic measurements for fatness) and visual appraisal are important in evaluating slaughter animals. Visual appraisal of slaughter red meat animals can be used effectively to predict primarily carcass composition when relatively large differences exist.

EXTERNAL BODY PARTS

Effective communication in many phases of the livestock industry requires a knowledge of the external body parts of the animal. The locations of the major body parts for swine, cattle, and sheep are shown in Figs. 9.1, 9.2, and 9.3, respectively.

LOCATION OF THE WHOLESALE CUTS IN THE LIVE ANIMAL

The next step for effective visual appraisal, after becoming familiar with the external parts of the animal, is to understand where major meat cuts are located in the live animal. Wholesale and retail cuts of the carcasses of beef, sheep, and swine are identified in Chapter 3. A carcass is evaluated after the animal has been slaughtered, eviscerated, and, in the case of beef and swine, split into two halves. The lamb carcass remains as a whole carcass. Furthermore, when it is evaluated, the carcass is hanging by the hind leg from the rail on the packing plant. This makes it difficult to perceive how the carcass would appear as part of the live animal standing on all four legs. Figure 9.4, which shows the location of the wholesale cuts on the live animal, assists in correlating carcass evaluation to live-animal evaluation.

VISUAL PERSPECTIVE OF CARCASS COMPOSITION OF THE LIVE ANIMAL

The carcass is composed of fat, lean (red meat), and bone. The meat industry's goal is to produce large amounts of highly palatable lean and minimal amounts of fat and bone. These

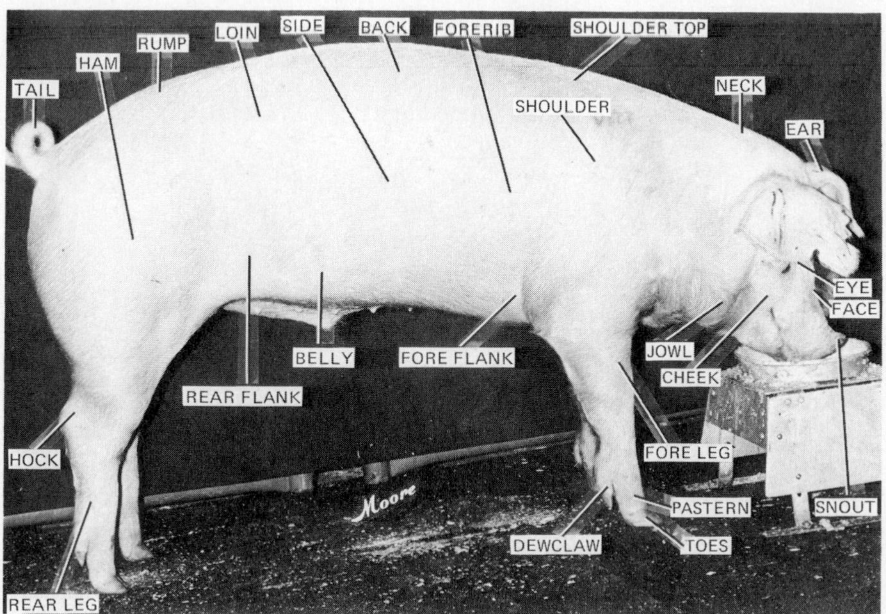

FIGURE 9.1.
The external parts of swine. Courtesy of the Chester White Record Association.

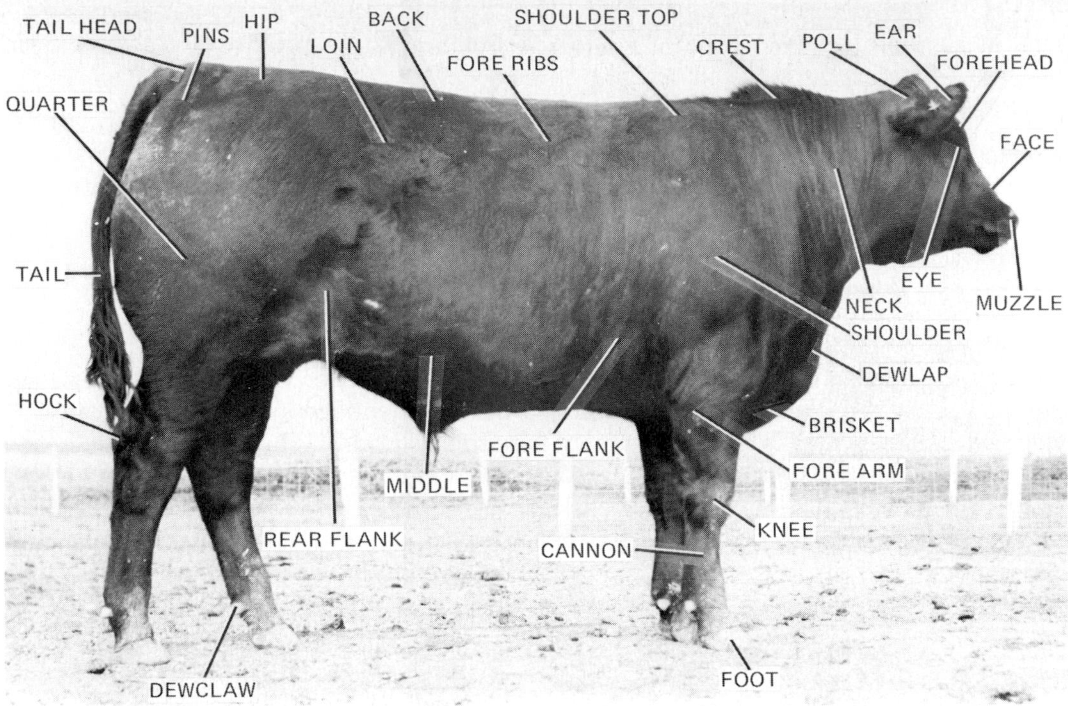

FIGURE 9.2.
The external parts of beef cattle. Courtesy of the American Angus Association.

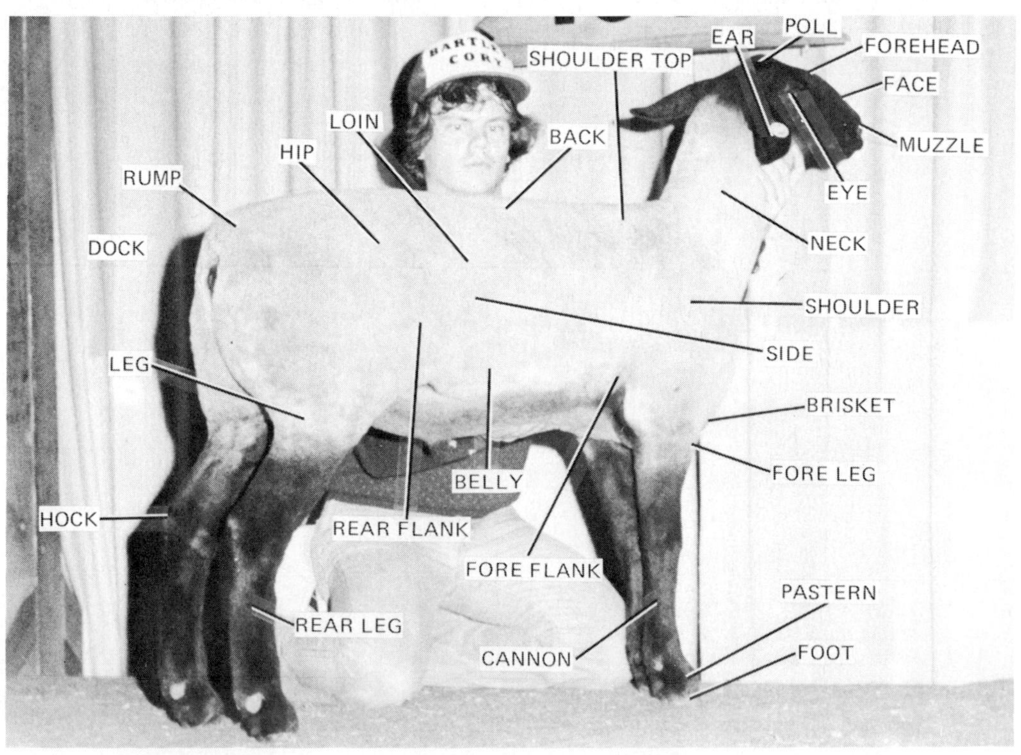

FIGURE 9.3.
The external parts of sheep. Courtesy of *Sheep Breeder and Sheepman* magazine.

1

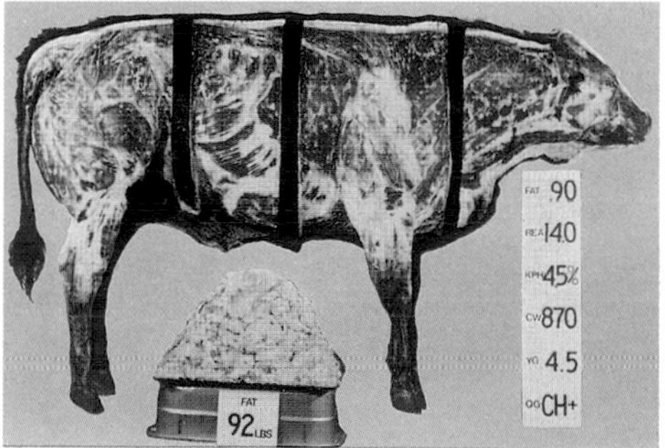

2

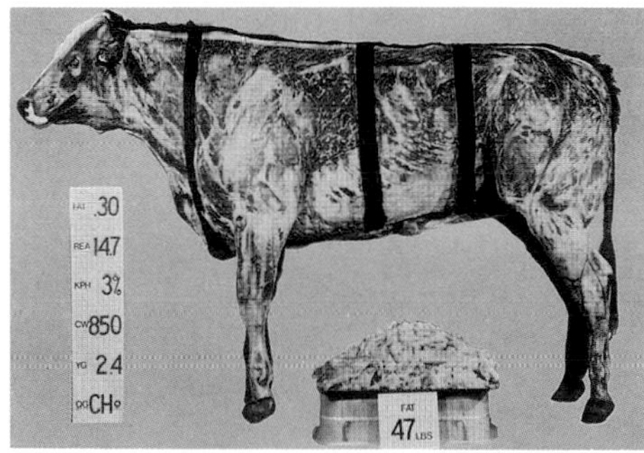

3

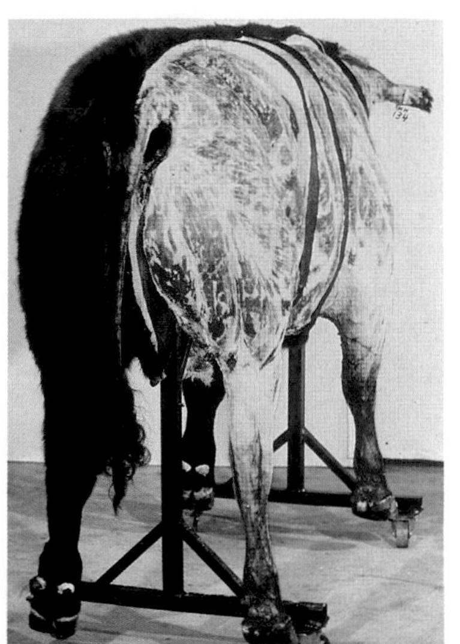

4

5

PLATE A.
Courtesy of Colorado State University.

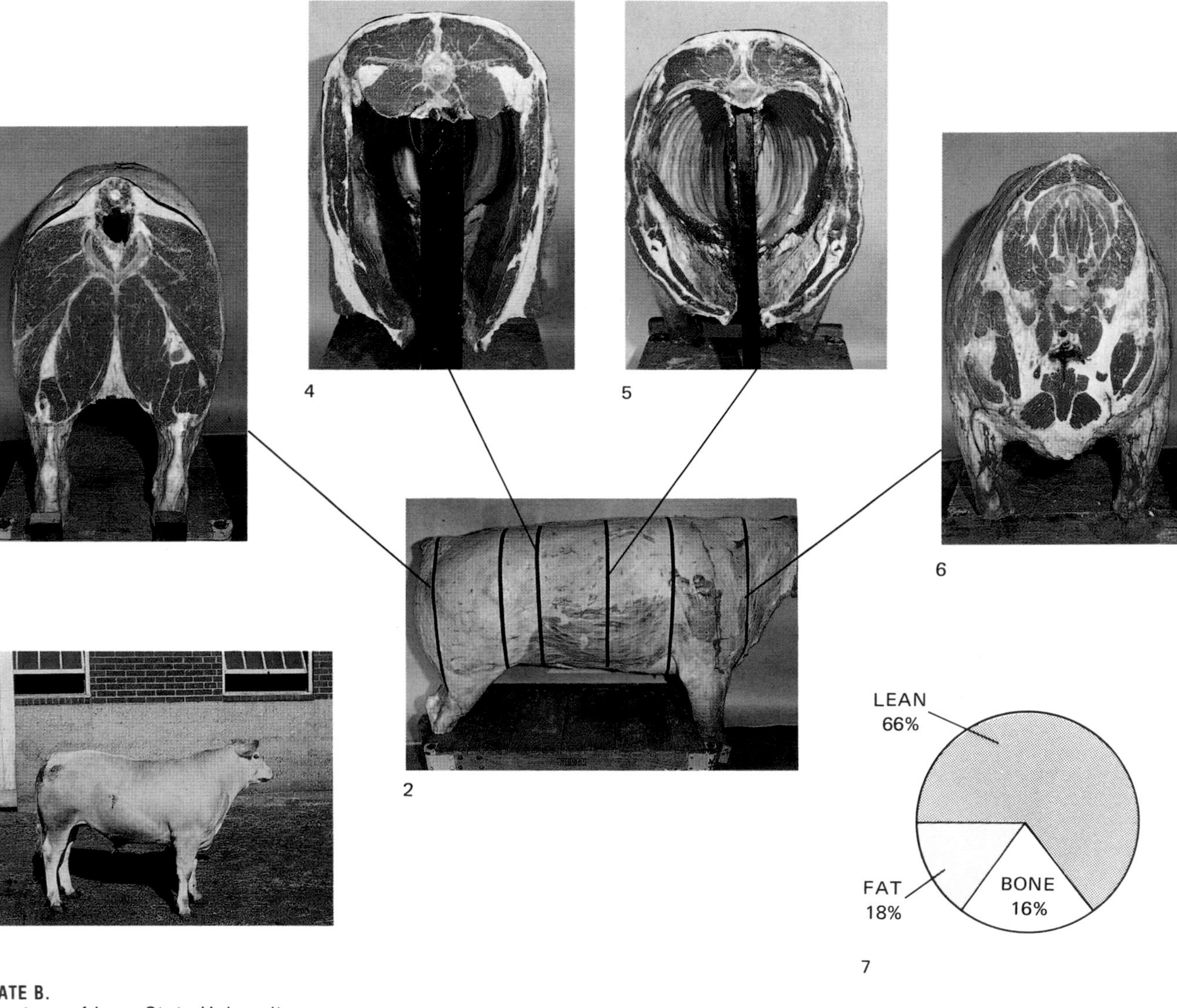

PLATE B.
Courtesy of Iowa State University.

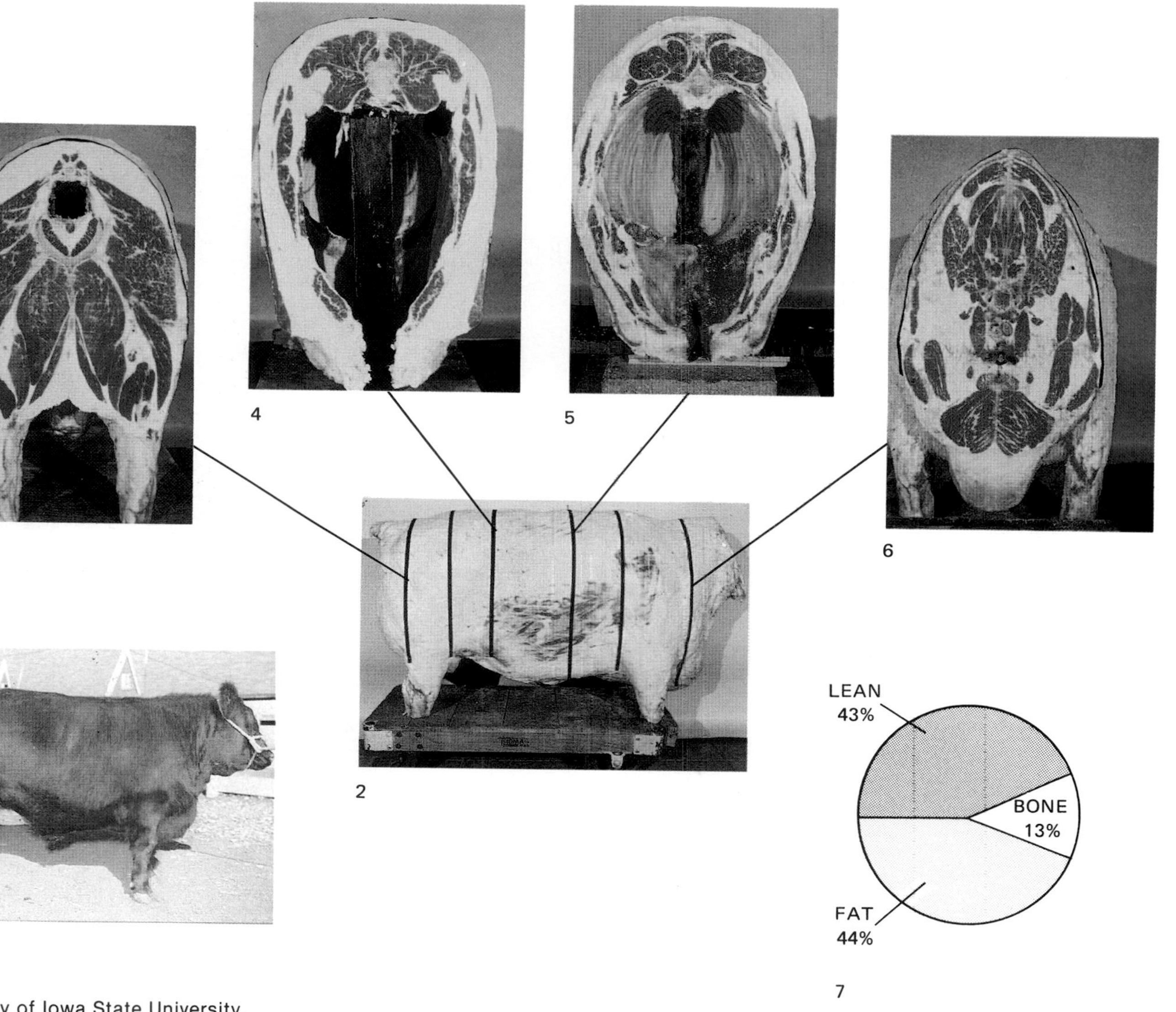

PLATE C.
Courtesy of Iowa State University.

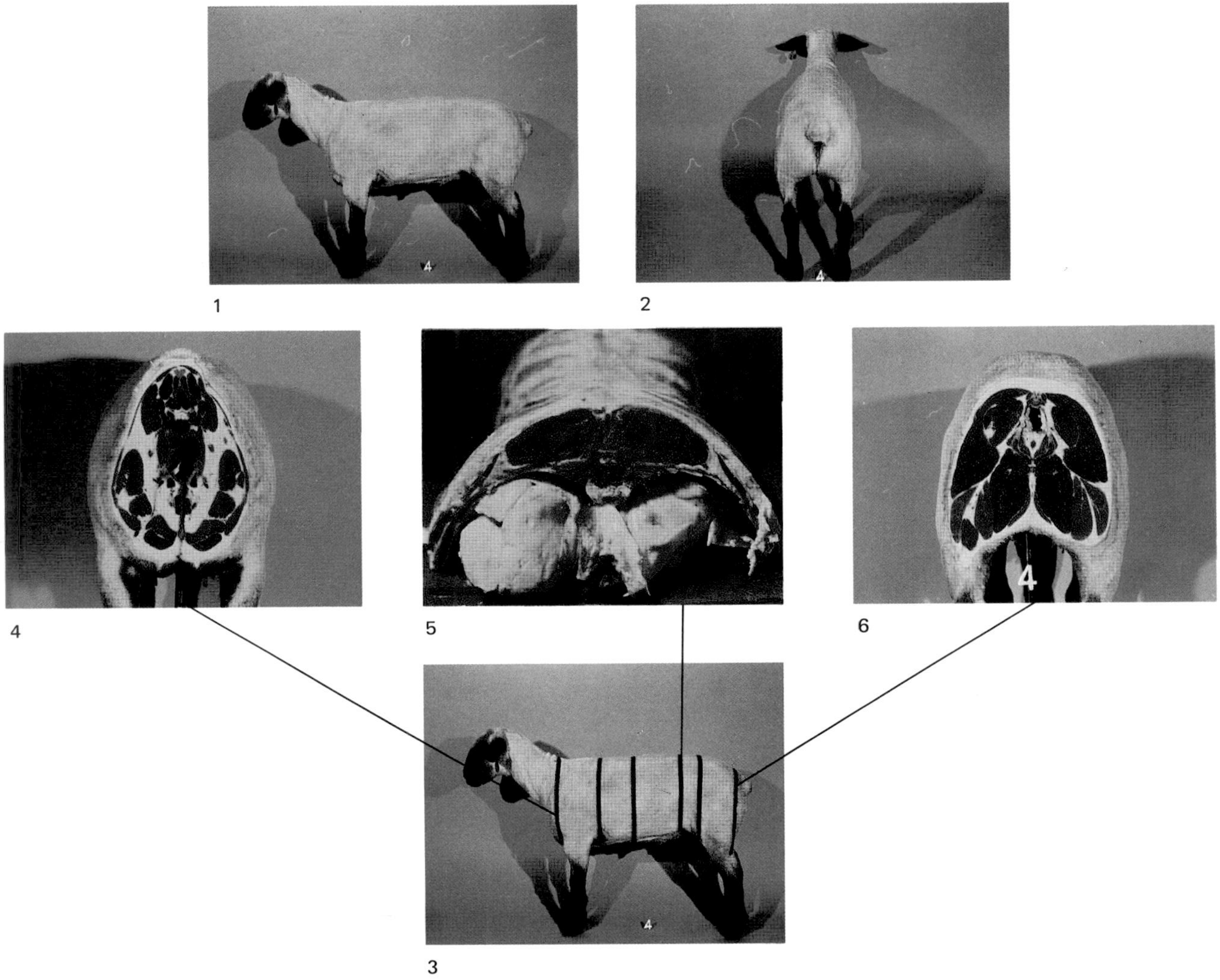

1

2

4

5

6

3

PLATE D.
Courtesy of Iowa State University.

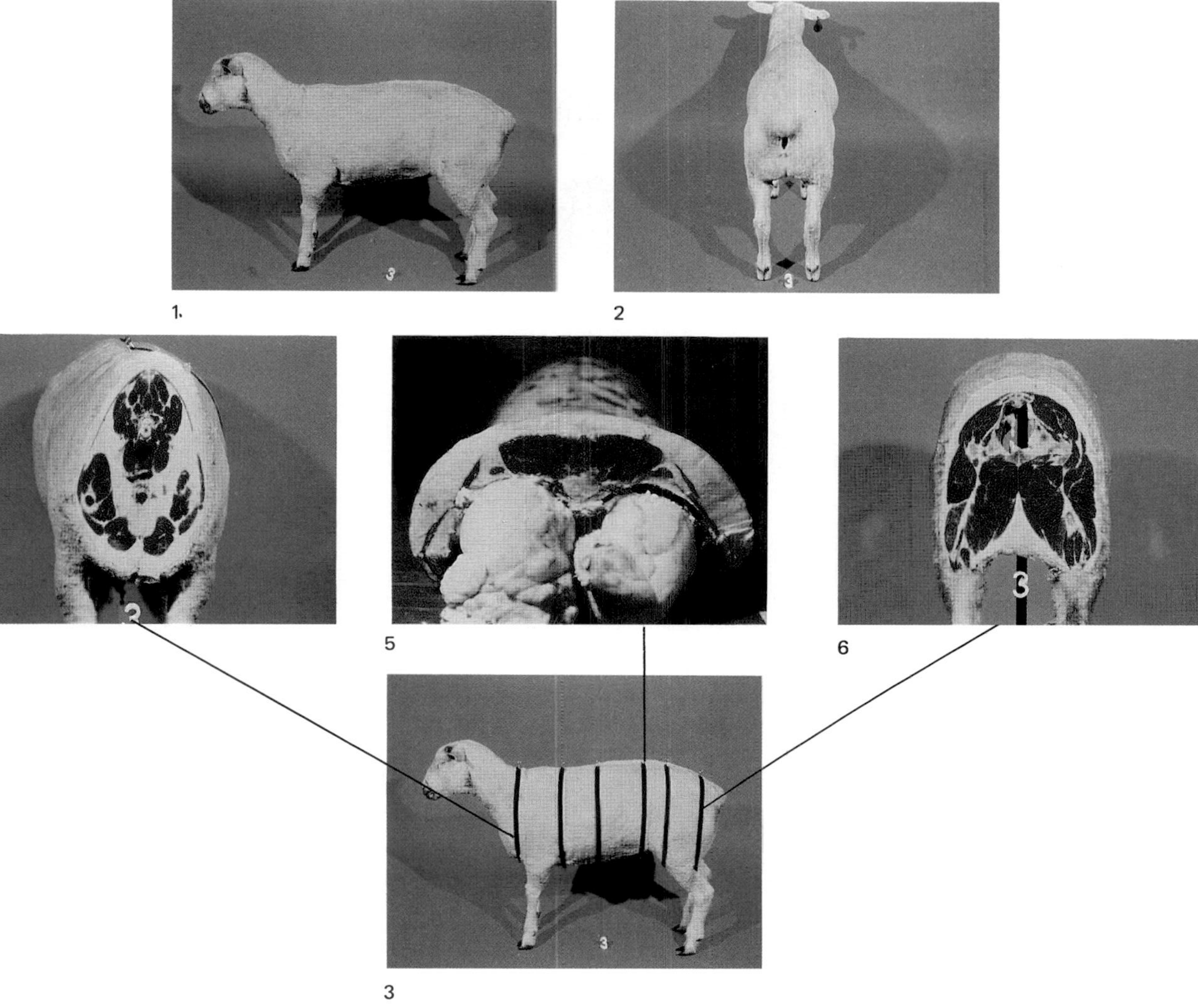

PLATE E.
Courtesy of Iowa State University.

1

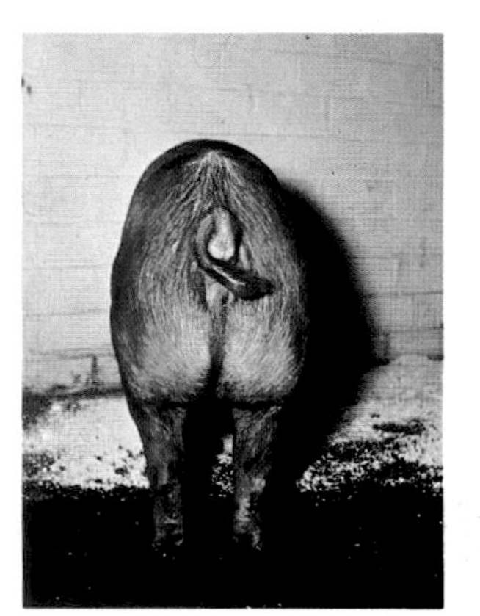

2

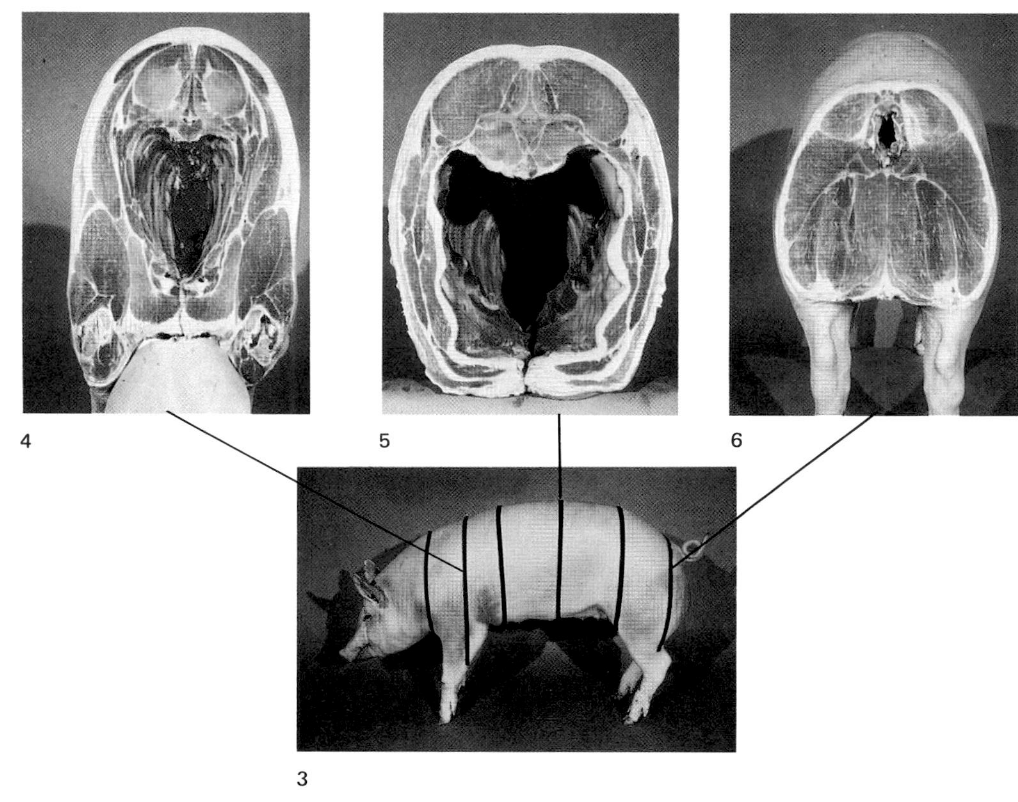

4

5

6

3

PLATE F.
Courtesy of Iowa State University.

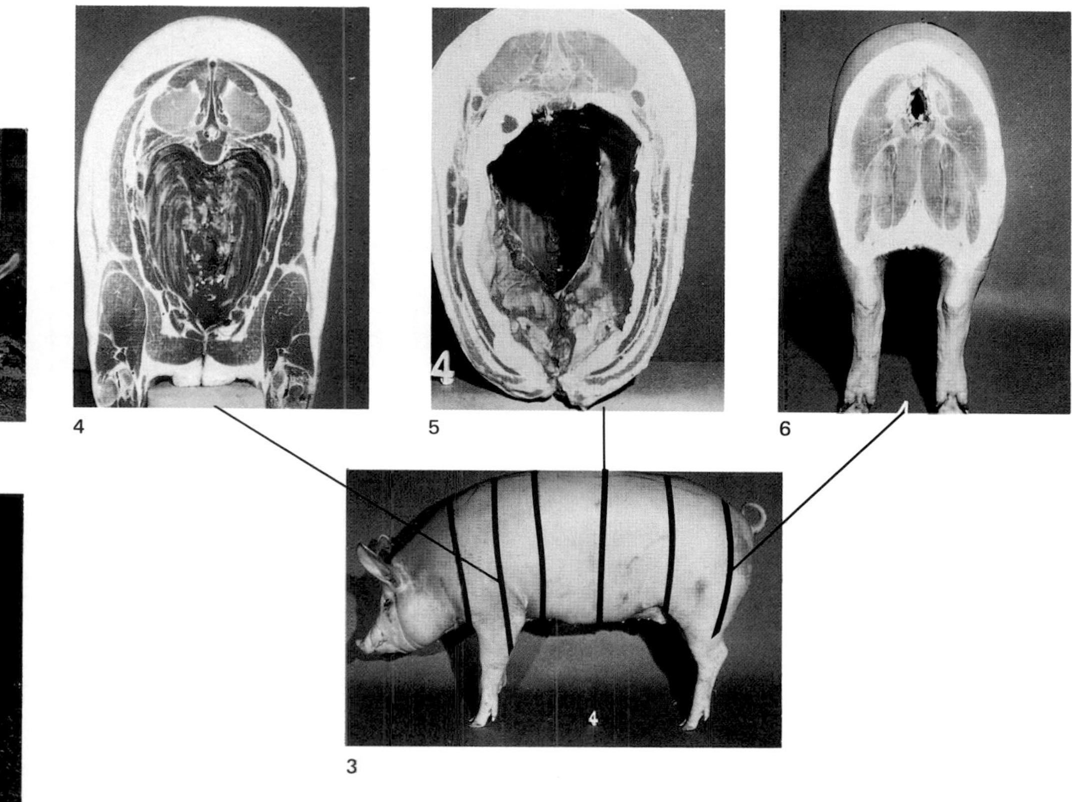

PLATE G.
Courtesy of Iowa State University.

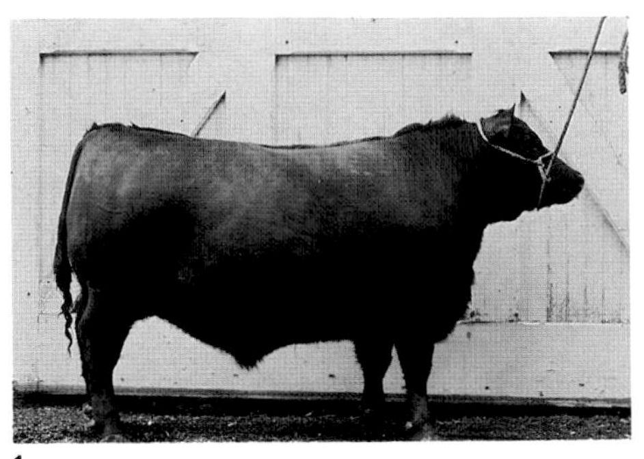

1

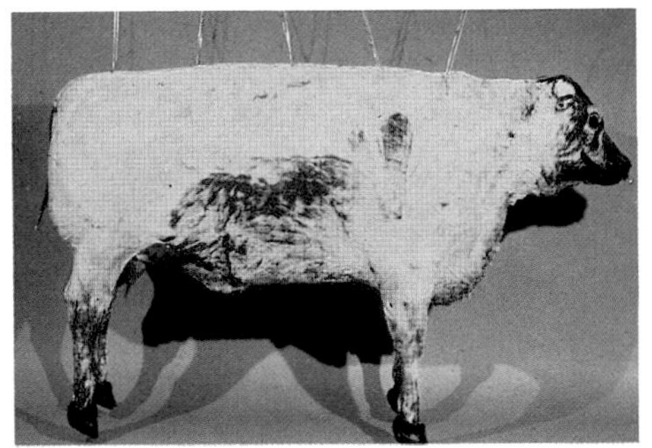

2

3

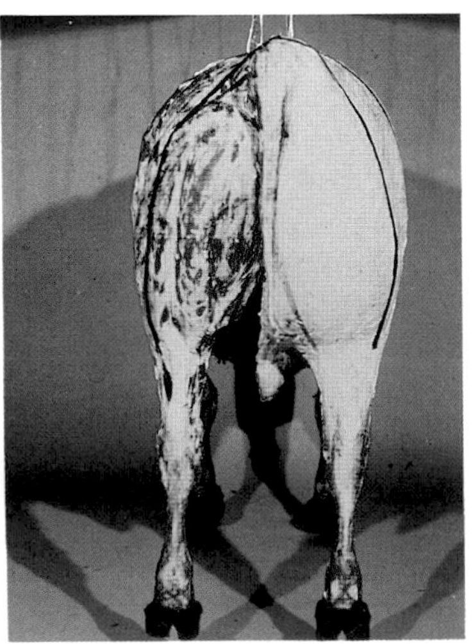

4

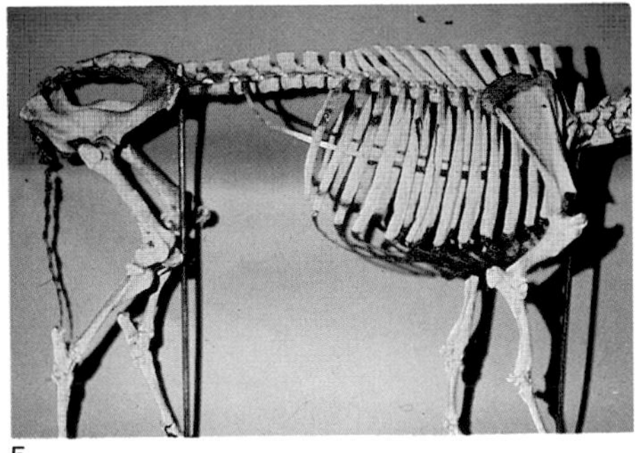

5

PLATE H.
Courtesy of Iowa State University.

Color Plate Section

CARCASS COMPOSITION DISPLAY

The proper ratio of fat to lean in an animal carcass has been a controversial issue among producers, feeders, and packers since the industry began. In the 1940s, fat-type animals, such as the lard-type hog, baby beef, and fat lamb, were the preferred type. Today, however, vegetable oils have largely replaced lard and other animal fats, lean beef has replaced the fatted calf, and the lamb has been made leaner through modern production techniques. Today's consumer demands lean meat, and today's grading system reflects those demands.

By visually appraising carcasses, a person can quickly identify the lean-to-fat compositional differences. Appraisal of similar differences in live animals, however, can be a more difficult and discriminating challenge. The following set of photographs graphically demonstrates a lean/fat ratio both on individual animals and as a comparison between different yield grades. The pictures are courtesy of Iowa State University and Colorado State University, where carcasses were frozen in a standing position. This process allowed technicians to remove different layers of tissue, such as the hide, fat, and muscling, and to cross-section entire carcasses for easy comparison. The photographs are organized by color plates, with the caption for each photo presented here by plate and photo number:

Plate A compares body conformation of different yield grades in both live animals and their carcasses.

1. Thickness of muscling in two medium-framed feeder steers is shown using cut-away sections of the round. The steer on the left has more thickness of lean meat in the round than the steer on the right.

2 & 3. Pounds of fat trimmed from one-half of the body of a yield grade 4 steer (92 lb) and a yield grade 2 steer (47 lb). Black stripes are hide and fat that remain at key locations on the body.

4. Rear view showing how the fat increases in thickness from the middle of the back to the edge of the loin.
5. Two yearling Hereford bulls of approximately the same weight. Breeding cattle can be visually appraised for fat and lean compositional differences. The bull on the left would sire slaughter steers having yield grade 4 or 5 carcasses, while the bull on the right would sire yield grade 1 or 2 steers. This assumes that the bulls would be bred to cows similar in frame-size to themselves, and that the steers would be slaughtered at approximately 1,150 pounds. Compare to plates B and C.

Plates B and **C** compare fat-to-lean composition on a yield grade 2 steer (plate B) and a yield grade 5 steer (plate C).

1. Live animals—side view
2. Black ribbons identify where cross sections were made (3, 4, 5, & 6—cross sections from rump, hip, mid-carcass, and shoulder).
7. The percentages of fat, lean, and bone found in this carcass.

Plates D and **E** compare the fat-to-lean composition of lamb carcasses on yield grade 1 lamb (plate D) and yield grade 5 lamb (plate E).

1. Side view
2. Rear view
3. Black ribbons identify where cross sections were made (4, 5, & 6—cross sections from shoulder, mid-carcass, and rump).

Plates F and **G** compare fat-to-lean composition of a U.S. no. 1 pig (plate F) with a U.S. no. 4 pig (plate G).

1. Live animals—side view
2. Rear view
3. Black ribbons identify where cross sections were made (4, 5, & 6—cross sections from shoulder, mid-carcass, and rump).

Plate H shows the composition and appearance of a steer carcass at various stages of removal of hide, fat, and muscle.

1. Live steer with hair clipped from one side
2. Frozen steer with hide removed and fat exposed
3. Fat removed from one-half of steer's body
4. Rear view with fat removed from the left side. Note cod and twist fat on the right side.
5. Skeleton of the beef animal after all the muscle has been removed.

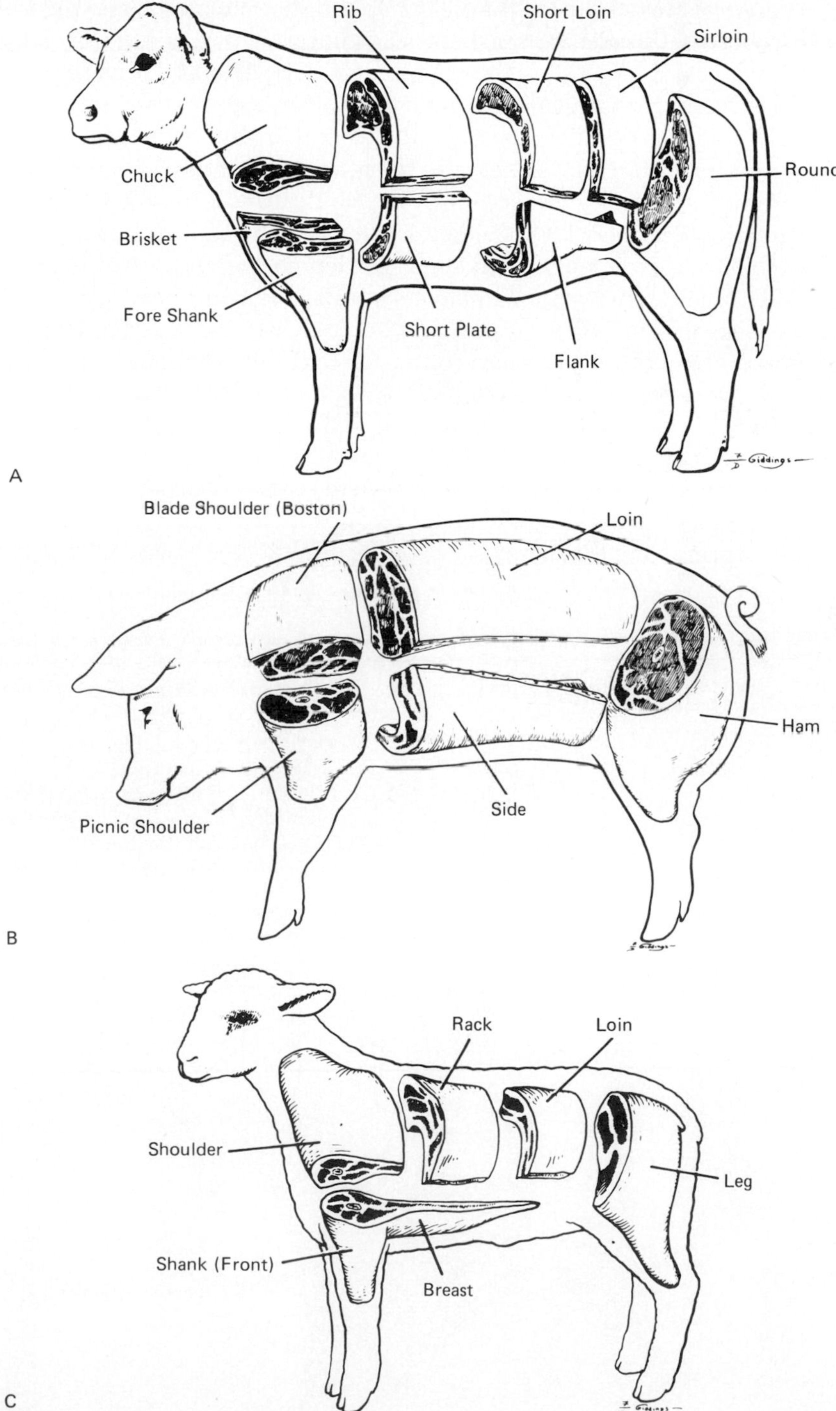

FIGURE 9.4.
Location of the wholesale cuts on the live steer, pig, and lamb. Courtesy of Dennis Giddings.

composition differences are reflected in the yield grades of beef and lamb and the lean percentage of swine discussed in Chapter 8. Effective visual appraisal of carcass composition requires knowing the body areas of the live animal where fat is deposited and muscle growth occurs. Color plates B and C show the fat and lean composition at several cross sections of a yield grade 2 steer and a yield grade 5 steer. The ribbon on the frozen carcasses shows the location of the cross sections. Cross section 3 removes the bulge from the round; cross section 4 is in front of the hip bone down through the flank, cross section 5 is at the 12th and 13th rib, and cross section 6 is at the point of the shoulder down through the brisket. Note the contrasts in fat (18% vs. 44%) and lean (66% vs. 43%) percentages. Both steers graded choice and were slaughtered at approximately 1,100 lb. The conformation characteristics of the two steers, which are primarily influenced by fat deposits and some muscling differences, are contrasted in Figs. 9.5 and 9.6. The conformation of these two steers is also contrasted to the conformation of a slaughter steer that is underfinished and thinly muscled (Fig. 9.7). All body parts referred to in these figures can be identified in Figs. 9.2 and 9.4, with the exception of the twist. The twist is the distance from the top of the tail to where the hind legs separate as observed from a rear view.

Color plates D and E show the cross sections of a yield grade 1 lamb and a yield grade 5 lamb. Cross section 4 is cut through the shoulder area, cross section 5 is at the back, and cross section 6 is through the leg area. Note that many fat deposits and muscle areas are similar to those in Fig. 9.5.

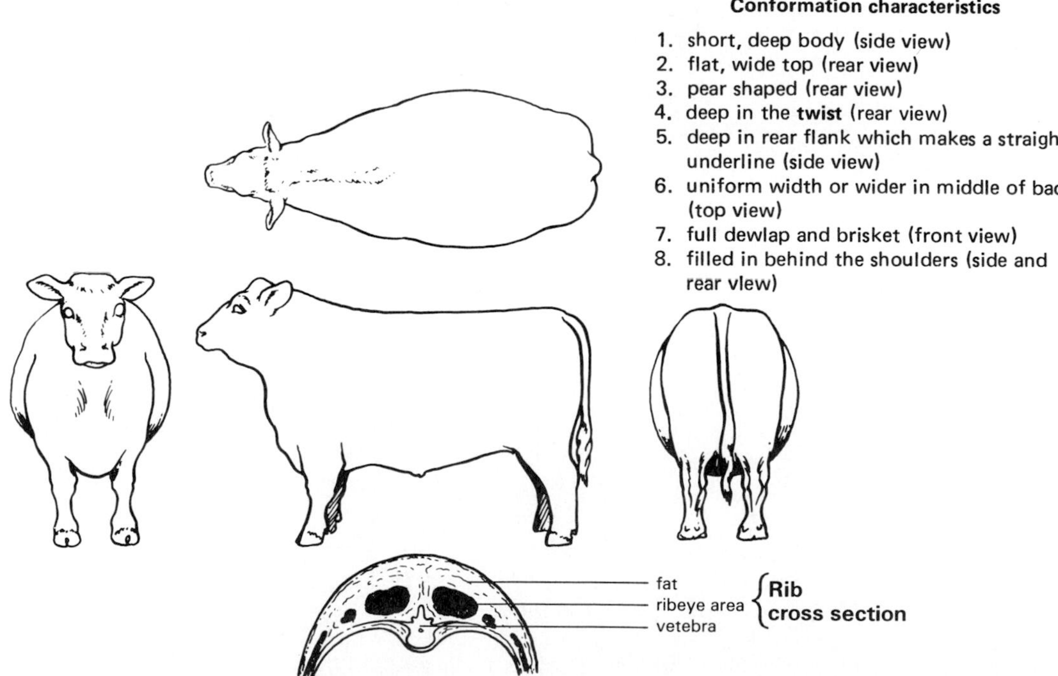

Conformation characteristics
1. short, deep body (side view)
2. flat, wide top (rear view)
3. pear shaped (rear view)
4. deep in the twist (rear view)
5. deep in rear flank which makes a straight underline (side view)
6. uniform width or wider in middle of back (top view)
7. full dewlap and brisket (front view)
8. filled in behind the shoulders (side and rear vlew)
fat
ribeye area
vetebra
Rib cross section

FIGURE 9.5.
Conformation characteristics of slaughter steer typical of yield grade 5. Compare with Plate C. Courtesy of Dennis Giddings.

Conformation characteristics

1. relatively long body with moderate body depth (side view)
2. well turned (curved) top (rear view)
3. wide through center of round (rear view)
4. trim in the **twist** (rear view)
5. higher in rear flank than foreflank (side view)
6. wider in the rump than in the middle of the back (top view)
7. trim in dewlap and brisket (front view)
8. slightly dished behind the shoulders (side and rear view)

fat
ribeye area
vetebra
Rib
cross section

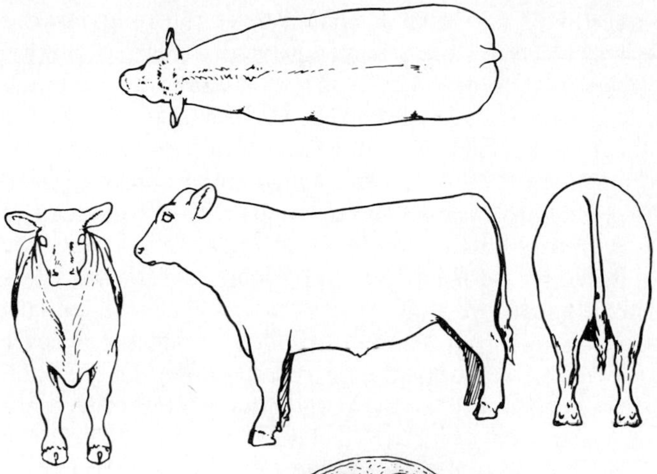

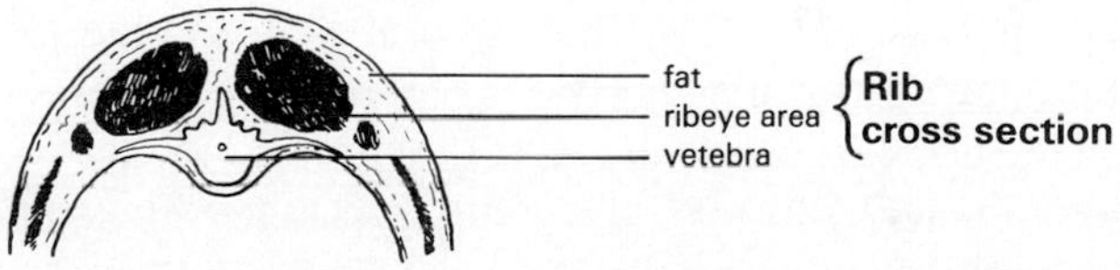

FIGURE 9.6.
Conformation characteristics of slaughter steer typical of yield grade 2. Compare with Plate B. Courtesy of Dennis Giddings.

Underfinished

1. narrow, pleated brisket (front view)
2. relatively shallow body (side view)
3. prominent hip and rib bones (side and rear view)
4. markedly dished behind the shoulders (side and rear view)

Thinly muscled

1. narrow through center of round (rear view)
2. flat and narrow forearm (front and side view)

ribeye area
fat
vetebra
Rib
cross section

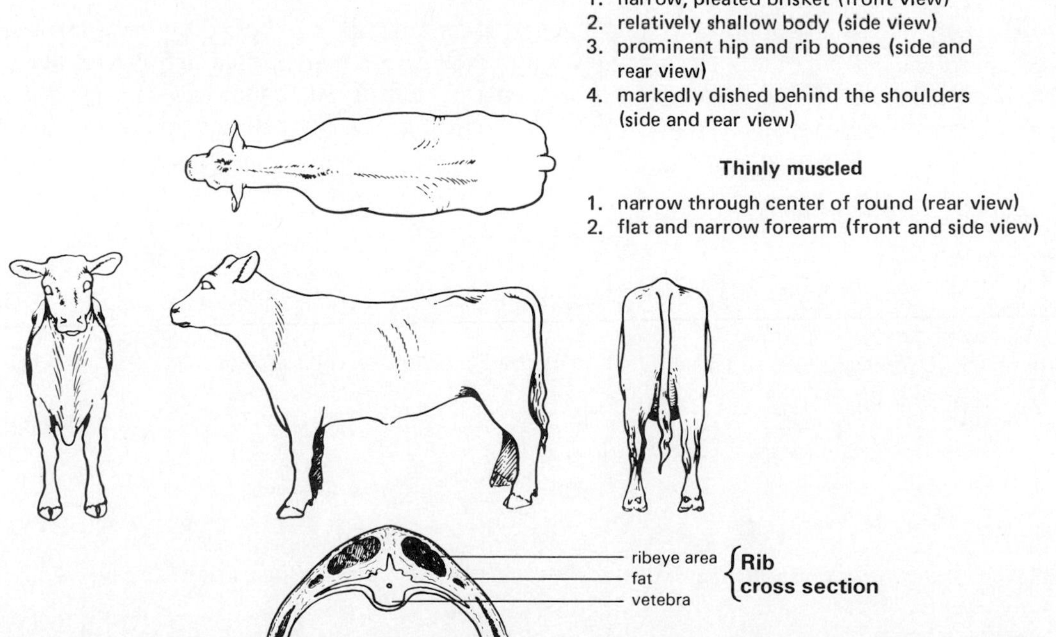

FIGURE 9.7.
Conformation characteristics of slaughter steer that is underfinished (contrast with Fig. 9.5) and thinly muscled (contrast with Fig. 9.6). Courtesy of Dennis Giddings.

Color plates F and G show the cross section of a U.S. no. 1 pig and a U.S. no. 4 pig. Percent lean cuts is used in pork carcass evaluation instead of yield grades. Although the terminology is different, they measure fat-to-lean composition. Percent lean cuts are measured by obtaining the total weight of the trimmed boston shoulder, picnic shoulder, loin, and ham (Fig. 9.4), and then dividing the total by carcass weight. The lean cuts percentage for the U.S. no. 1 would be 53% or more, as contrasted with less than 47% for the U.S. no. 4. The ribbon on the frozen carcass marks the location of the cross sections. Cross section 4 is through the shoulder area, 5 is through the middle of the back, and 6 is through the ham area.

Even though the size and shape of slaughter cattle, sheep, and swine are different, these three species are remarkably similar in muscle structure and fat deposit areas. Therefore, what a person can learn from visual evaluation of one species can be applied to another species. Regardless of species, an animal that shows a square appearance over the top of its back and appears blocky and deep from a side view usually has a large accumulation of fat. Fat accumulates first in flank areas, brisket, dewlap, and throat (jowl); between the hind legs; and over the edge of the loin. Fat also fills in behind the shoulders and gives the animal a smooth appearance. Movement of the shoulder blade can be observed when lean cattle and swine walk. Slaughter red meat animals having an oval turn to the top of their back, while having thickness through the center part of their hind legs (as viewed from the rear), have a high proportion of lean to fat. It is important that slaughter animals have an adequate amount of fat because thin animals typically do not produce a highly palatable consumer product.

The wool covering of sheep can easily camouflage the fat covering. The amount of fat in sheep can be determined by pressing the fingers of the closed hand lightly over the last two ribs and over the spinal processes of the vertebrae. Sheep that have a thick padding of fat in these areas will produce poor yield-grading carcasses.

Accuracy in visually appraising slaughter red meat animals is obtained by making visual estimates of yield grades and percent lean cuts and their component parts, and then comparing the visual estimates with the carcass measurements. Accurate visual appraisal can be used as one tool in producing red meat animals with a more desirable carcass composition of lean to fat.

SELECTED REFERENCES

Publications

Boggs, D. L., and Merkel, R. A. 1990. *Live Animal Carcass Evaluation and Selection Manual.* 2nd ed., Dubuque, IA: Kendall/Hunt.

Crouse, J. E., Dikeman, M. E., and Allen, D. M. 1974. Prediction of beef carcass composition and quality by live-animal traits. *J. Anim. Sci.* 38:264.

Kauffman, R. G., Grummer, R. H., Smith, R. E., Long, R. A., and Shook, G. 1973. Does live-animal and carcass shape influence gross composition? *J. Anim. Sci.* 37:1112.

Visuals

Slaughter Cattle Evaluation, Slaughter Hog Evaluation, and *Slaughter Lamb Evaluation.* (3 Video tapes). CEV, P.O. Box 65265, Lubbock, TX 79464-5265

Swine Evaluation (VHS Video). VEP, Calif. Polytechnic State Univ., San Luis Obispo, CA 93407.

CHAPTER 10

Reproduction

Reproductive efficiency in farm animals, as measured by number of calves or lambs per 100 breeding females or number of pigs per litter, is a trait of great economic importance in farm animal production. It is essential to understand the reproductive process in the creation of new animal life because it is a focal point of overall animal productivity. Producers who manage animals for high reproductive rates must understand the production of viable sex cells, estrous cycles, mating, pregnancy, and birth. (Some aspects of reproductive behavior are presented in Chapter 34.)

FEMALE ORGANS OF REPRODUCTION AND THEIR FUNCTIONS

Figures 10.1 and 10.2 show the reproductive organs of the cow and sow. The female reproductive anatomy of the various farm animal species is similar, although there are a few obvious differences.

The organs of reproduction of the typical female farm mammal include a pair of ovaries, which are suspended by ligaments just back of the kidneys, and a pair of open-ended tubes, the oviducts (also called the Fallopian tubes), which lead directly into the uterus (womb). The uterus itself has two horns, or branches, that in farm mammals merge together at the lower part into one structure so that the lower opening, or exit, from the uterus is a canal. This canal is called the cervix. Its surface is fairly smooth in the mare and the sow, but is folded in the cow and ewe. The cervix opens into the vagina, a relatively large canal or passageway that leads posteriorly to the external parts, which are the vulva and clitoris. The urinary bladder empties into the vagina through the urethral opening.

Ovaries

Ovaries produce ova (female sex cells, also called eggs) and the female sex hormones, estrogen and progesterone. Each ovum (Fig. 10.3) is the largest single cell in the body and it develops inside a recently formed follicle within the ovary (Fig. 10.4). Some tiny follicles develop and ultimately attain maximum size, about 0.8 – 1.5 in. in diameter, after having migrated from deep

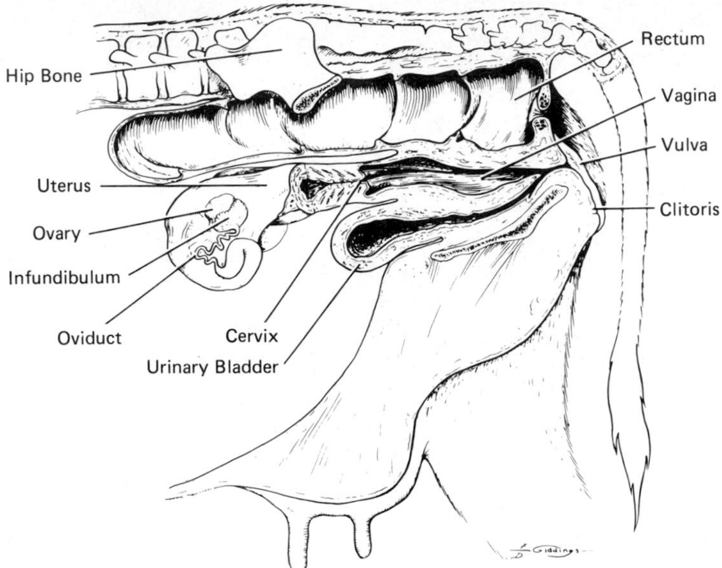

FIGURE 10.1.
Reproductive organs of the cow. Courtesy of Dennis Giddings.

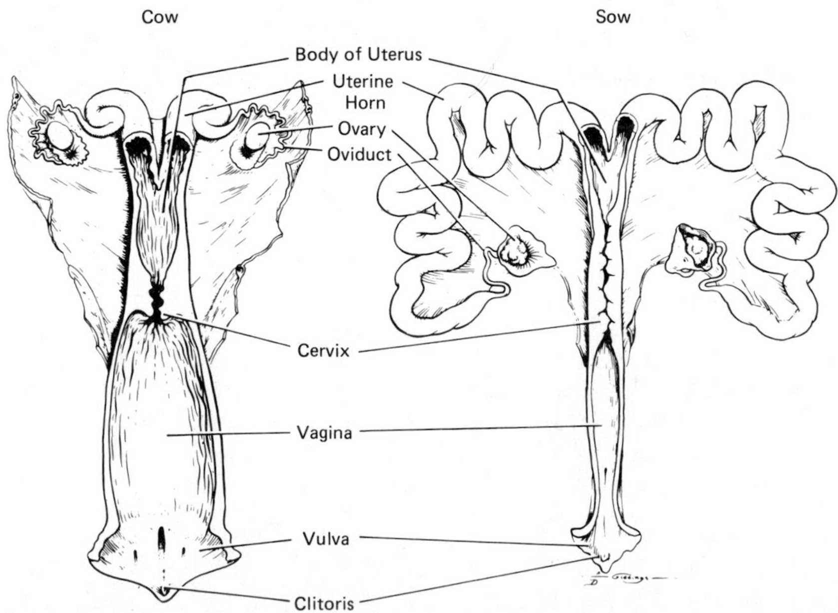

FIGURE 10.2.
A dorsal view of the reproductive organs of the cow and the sow. The most noticeable difference is the longer uterine horns of the sow compared to the cow. Courtesy of Dennis Giddings.

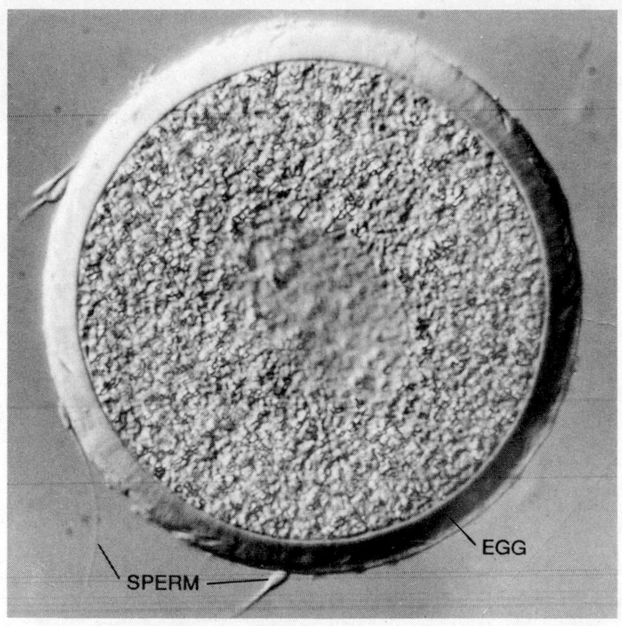

FIGURE 10.3.
Bull sperm and cow egg, each magnified 300 ×. The ovum is about $\frac{1}{200}$ in. in diameter, while the sperm is $\frac{1}{6000}$ in. in diameter. Each is a single cell and contains one-half the chromosome number typical of other body cells. Courtesy of Colorado State University.

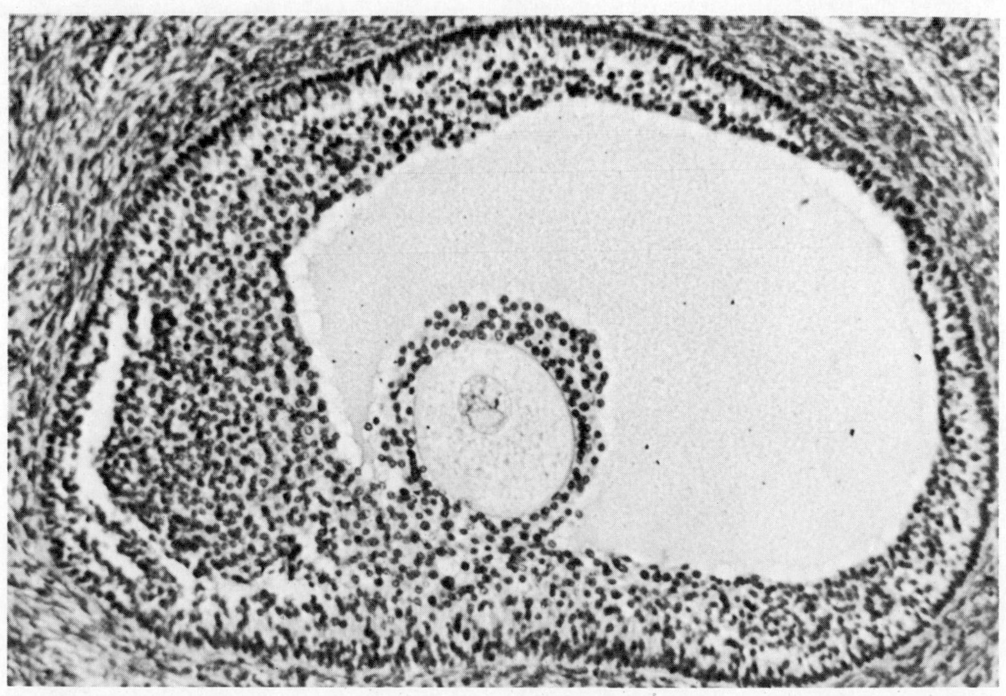

FIGURE 10.4.
The large structure, outlined with a circle of dark cells, is a follicle located on a cow's ovary (magnified 265 ×). The smaller circle, near the center, is the egg. The large light-gray area is the fluid that fills the follicle. When the follicle ruptures, the egg will move into the oviduct by anatomical action of the infundibulum. Courtesy of Colorado State University.

in the ovary to the surface of the ovary. These growing follicles produce estrogens. These mature (Graafian) follicles rupture, thus freeing the ovum (ovulation). Many of the tiny follicles grow to various stages, cease growth, deteriorate, and are absorbed (Fig. 10.5).

After the ovum escapes from the mature follicle, cells of the follicle change into a corpus luteum, or "yellow body." The corpus luteum produces progesterone, which becomes a vitally important hormone for maintaining pregnancy.

The Oviducts

Immediately after ovulation, the ova are caught by the infundibulum of the oviduct. The ova are tiny (approximately $\frac{1}{200}$ in. in diameter), which is approximately the size of a dot made by a sharp

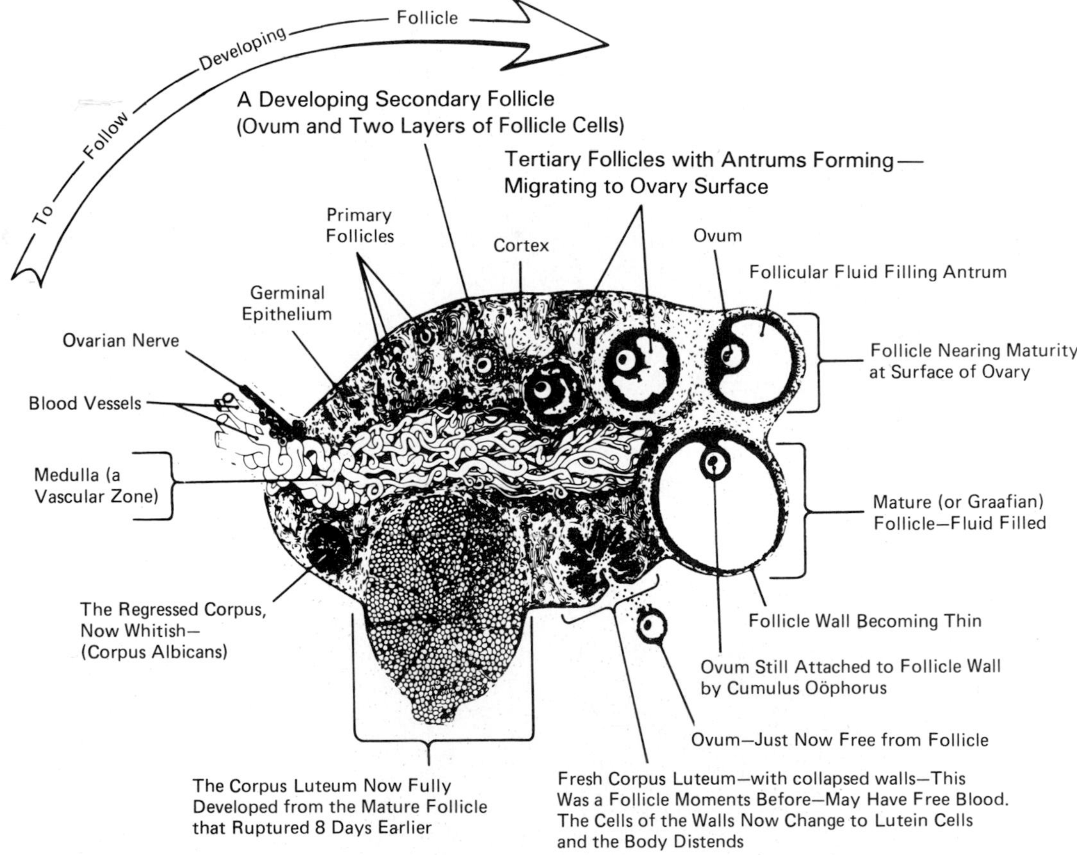

FIGURE 10.5.
A cross section of the bovine ovary showing how a follicle develops to full size and then ruptures, allowing the egg to escape. The follicle then becomes a "yellow body" (*corpus luteum*), which is actually orange-colored in cattle. The corpus luteum degenerates in time and disappears. Of course, many follicles cease development, stop growing, and disappear without ever reaching the mature stage. From J. F. Bone, *Animal Anatomy and Physiology*, 4th ed. (Corvallis: Oregon State University Book Stores, © 1975).

pencil. Sperm are transported through the uterus into the oviduct after the female is inseminated (naturally or artificially). Therefore, the oviducts are the sites where ova and sperm meet and where fertilization takes place. After fertilization, 3–5 days are required in cows and ewes and probably about the same amount of time in other farm animals for the ova to travel down the remaining two-thirds of the oviduct. From the oviduct, the newly developing embryos pass to the uterus and soon attach to it.

The Uterus

The uterus varies in shape from the type that has long, slender left and right horns, as in the sow, to the type that is primarily a fused body with short horns, as in the mare. In the sow, the embryos develop in the uterine horn; in the mare, the embryo develops in the body of the uterus. Each surviving embryo develops into a fetus and remains in the uterus until parturition (birth).

The lower outlet of the uterus is the cervix, an organ composed primarily of connective tissue that constitutes a formidable gateway between the uterus and the vagina. Like the rest of the reproductive tract, the cervix is lined with mucosal cells. These cells make significant changes as the animal goes from one estrous cycle to another and during pregnancy. The cervical passage changes from one that is tightly closed or sealed in pregnancy to a relatively open, very moist canal at the height of estrus.

The Vagina

The vagina serves as the female organ of copulation at mating and as the birth canal at parturition. Its mucosal surface changes during the estrous cycle from very moist, when the animal is ready for mating, to almost dry, even sticky, between periods of heat. The tract from the urinary bladder joins the posterior ventral vagina; from this juncture to the exterior vulva, the vagina serves the dual role of a passageway for the reproductive and urinary systems.

The Clitoris

A highly sensitive organ, the clitoris is located ventrally and at the lower tip of the vagina. The clitoris is the homologue of the penis in the male (i.e., it came from the same embryonic source as the penis). Some research indicates that clitoral stimulation or massage, following AI in cattle, will increase the chance of conception.

Reproduction in Poultry Females

The hen differs from farm mammals in that the young are not suckled, the egg is laid outside the body, and there are no well-defined estrous cycles or pregnancy. Since eggs are an important source of human food, hens are selected and managed to lay eggs consistently throughout the year.

The anatomy of the reproductive tract of the hen is shown in Figures 10.6 and 10.7. At hatching time, the female chick has two ovaries and two oviducts. The right ovary and oviduct do not develop. Therefore, the sexually mature hen has only a well-developed left ovary and oviduct. The ovary appears as a cluster of tiny gray eggs or yolks in front of the left kidney and

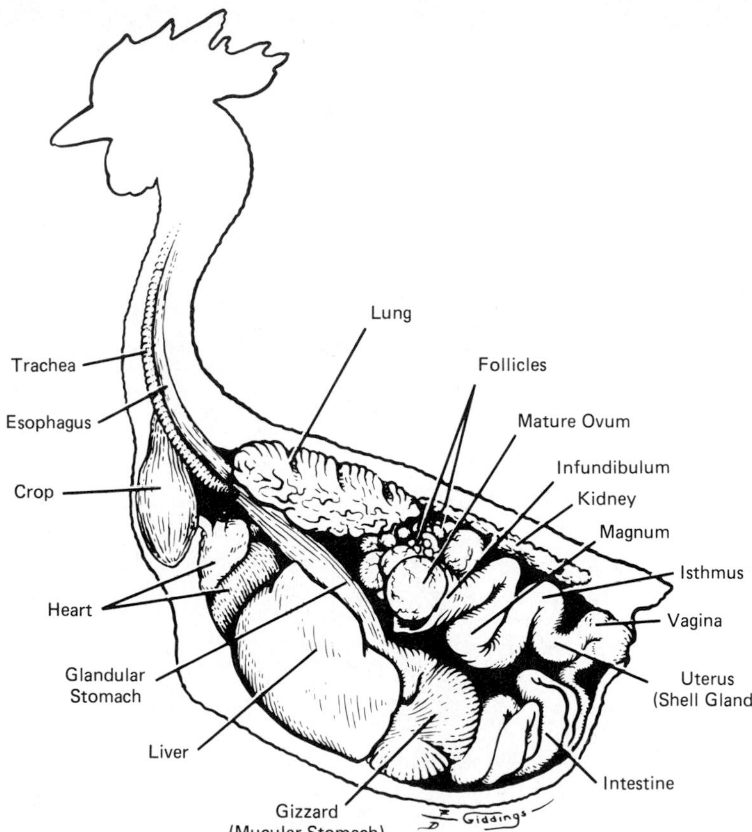

FIGURE 10.6. Reproductive organs of the hen in relation to other body organs. The single ovary and oviduct are on the hen's left side; an underdeveloped ovary and oviduct are sometimes found on the right side, having degenerated in the developing embryo. Courtesy of Dennis Giddings.

attached to the back of the hen. The ovary is fully formed, although very small, when the chick is hatched. It contains approximately 3,600–4,000 miniature ova. As the hen reaches sexual maturity, some of the ova develop into mature yolks (yellow part of the laid egg). The remaining ova are variable in size from the nearly mature to those of microscopic size.

The oviduct is a long, glandular tube leading from the ovary to the cloaca (common opening for reproductive and digestive tracts). The oviduct is divided into five parts: the infundibulum (3–4 in. long), which receives the yolk; the magnum (approximately 15 in. long), which secretes the thick albumen, or white, of the egg; the isthmus (about 4 in. long), which adds the shell membranes; the uterus (approximately 4 in. long), or shell gland, which secretes the thin white, the shell, and the shell pigment; and the vagina (about 2 in. long).

Ovulation is the release of a mature yolk (ovum) from the ovary. When ovulation occurs, the infundibulum engulfs the yolk and starts it on its way through the 25–27-in. oviduct. The yolk moves by peristaltic action through the infundibulum into the magnum area in about 15 minutes.

During the 3-hour passage through the magnum, more than 50% of the albumen is added to the yolk. The developing egg passes through the isthmus in about $1\frac{1}{4}$ hours. Here water and mineral salts and the two shell membranes are added. In the 21-hour stay in the uterus, the

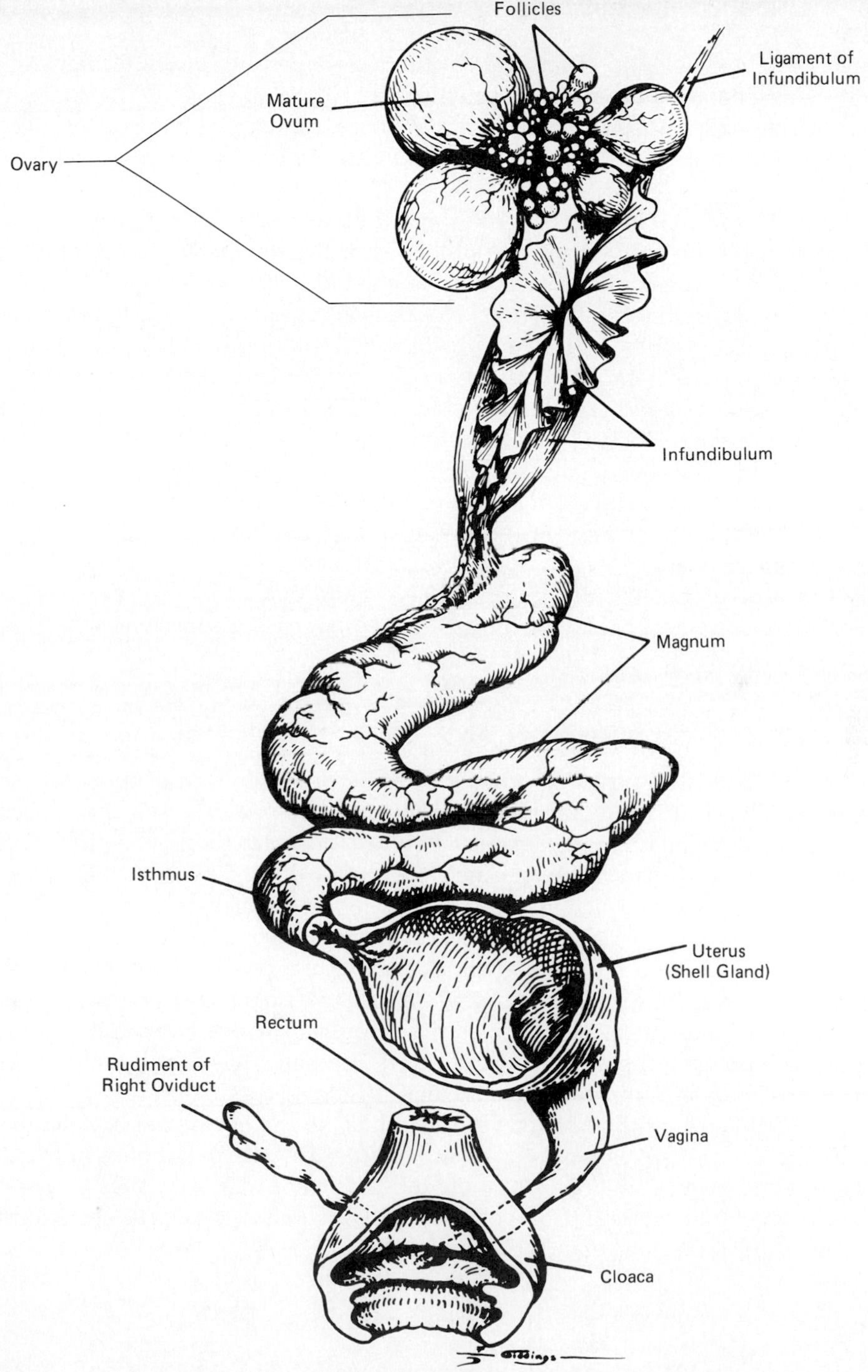

FIGURE 10.7.
Reproductive organs of the hen. Sections of the uterus and cloaca are cut away to better view internal structure. Courtesy of Dennis Giddings.

remainder of the albumen is added, followed by the addition of shell and shell pigment. Moving finally into the vagina, the fully formed egg enters the cloaca and is laid. The entire time from ovulation to laying is usually slightly more than 24 hours. About 30 minutes after a hen has laid an egg, she releases another yolk into the infundibulum, and it will likewise travel the length of the oviduct.

After the fertilized egg is incubated for 21 days, the chick is hatched. The egg is biologically structured to support the growth and life processes of the developing chick embryo during incubation and for 3–4 days after the chick is hatched.

There are several egg abnormalities that occur because of factors affecting ovulation and the developmental process. Double-yolked eggs result when two yolks are released about the same time or when one yolk is lost into the body cavity for a day and is picked up by the funnel when the next day's yolk is released. Yolkless eggs are usually formed about a bit of tissue that is sloughed off the ovary or oviduct. This tissue stimulates the secreting glands of the oviduct and a yolkless egg results. The abnormality of an egg within an egg is due to reversal of direction of an egg by the wall of the oviduct. One day's egg is added to the next day's egg, and shell is formed around both. Soft-shelled eggs generally occur when an egg is laid prematurely and insufficient time in the uterus prevents the deposit of the shell. Thin-shelled eggs may be caused by dietary deficiencies, heredity, or disease. Glassy- and chalky-shelled eggs are caused by malfunctions of the uterus of the laying bird. Glassy eggs are less porous and will not hatch but may retain their quality.

MALE ORGANS OF REPRODUCTION AND THEIR FUNCTIONS

Figures 10.8 and 10.9 show the reproductive organs of the bull and boar. The organs of reproduction of a typical male farm mammal include two testicles, which are held in the scrotum. Male sex cells (called *sperm* or *spermatozoa*) are formed in the tiny seminiferous tubules of the testicles. The sperm from each testicle then pass through very small tubes into the epididymis, which is a highly coiled tube that is held in a covering on the exterior of the testicle. Each epididymal tube leads to a larger tube, the *vas deferens* (also called the *ductus deferens*). The two vasa deferentia converge at the upper end of the urethral canal, where the urinary bladder opens into the urethra. In some species, the wall of the upper end of the vas deferens is thickened and forms a secretory gland called the ampulla. The urethra is the large canal that leads through the penis to the outside of the body. The penis has a triple role: It serves as a passageway for semen and urine and it is the male organ of copulation.

The left and right parts of the seminal vesicles, which lie against the urinary bladder, consist of glandular tissue that secretes a substance into the urethra, which supplies nutrients for the sperm. The prostate gland contains 12 or more tubes, each of which empties into the urethra. Another gland, the bulbourethral (Cowper's) gland, which also empties its secretions into the urethral canal, is posterior to (behind) the prostate.

The Testicles

The testicles produce (1) the sperm cells that fertilize the ova of the female, and (2) a hormone called *testosterone* that conditions the male so that his appearance and behavior are masculine. Details of the structure of the spermatozoa of the bull are shown in Figures 10.10–10.12. The diameter of sperm is approximately $\frac{1}{6000}$ in.

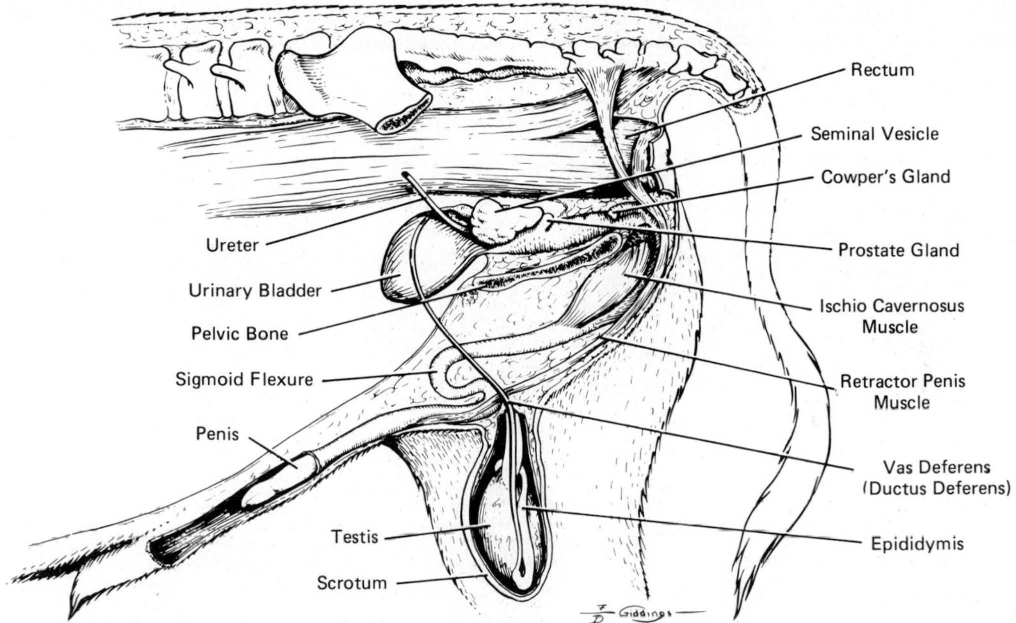

FIGURE 10.8.
Reproductive organs of the bull. Courtesy of Dennis Giddings.

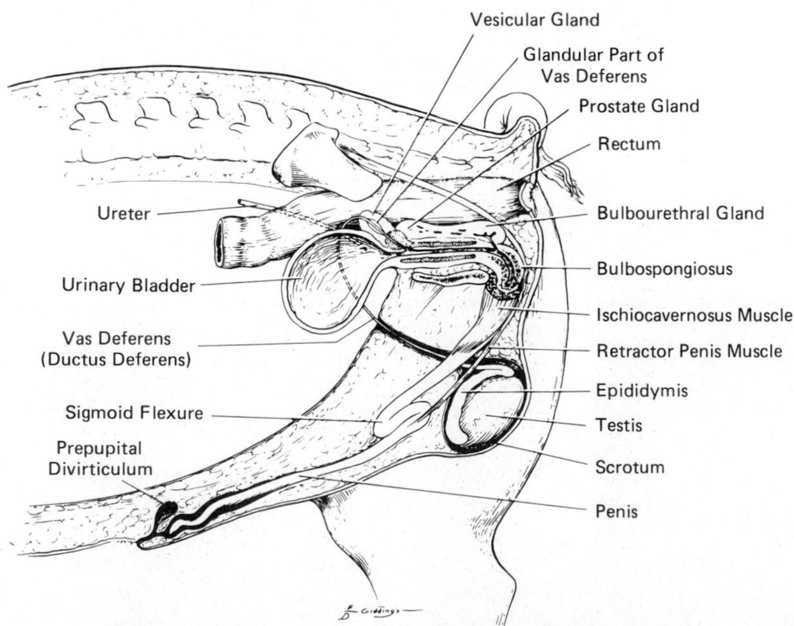

FIGURE 10.9.
Reproductive organs of the boar. Courtesy of Dennis Giddings.

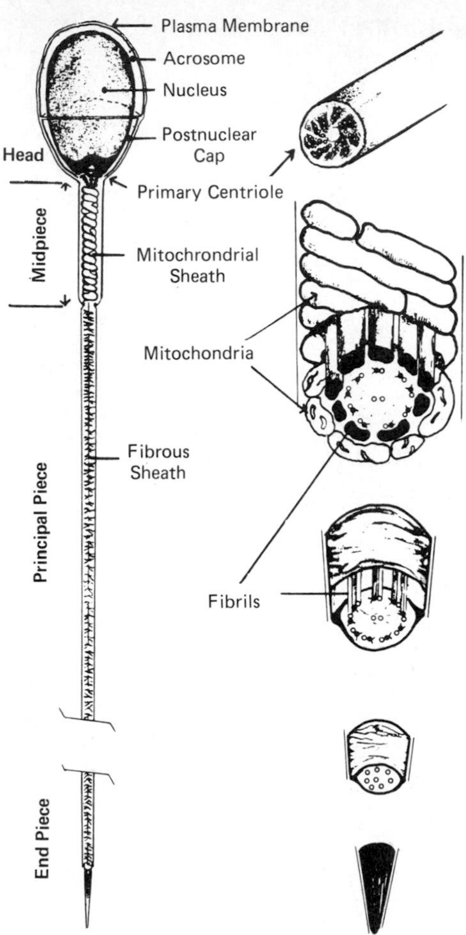

FIGURE 10.10.
A diagrammatic sketch of the structure of bull sperm. Courtesy of Dr. Arthur S. H. Wu, Oregon State University.

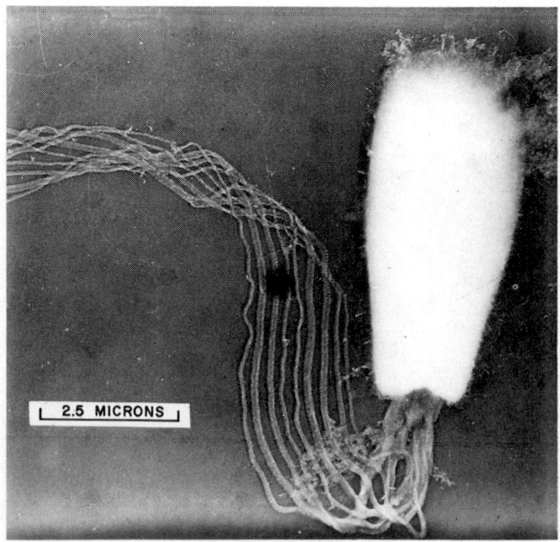

FIGURE 10.11.
A spermatozoa (sperm cell) from a bull (7000 ×) viewed through the electron microscope after treatment with 0.15 N NaOH at 25°C for 16 h. Note how the covering membrane of the neck region of the sperm has been removed, exposing the nine fibrils of the axial filament. Three filaments are larger than the rest. From A. S. H. Wu and F. F. McKenzie, "Microstructure of Spermatozoa After Denudation as Revealed by Electron Microscope," *Journal of Animal Science* 14(4):1151–66, 1955.

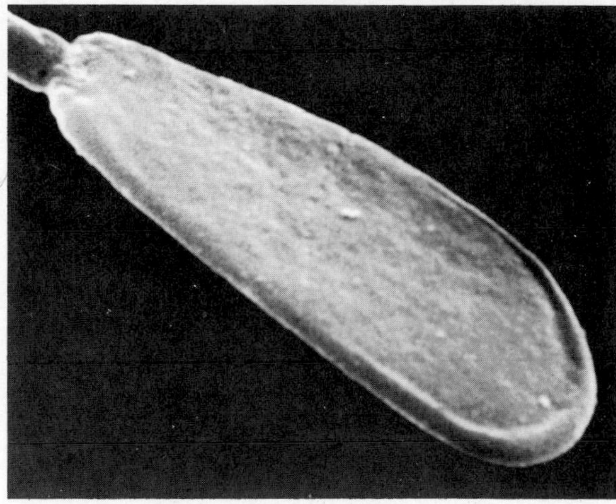

FIGURE 10.12.
Bull sperm (12,000 ×) viewed with the scanning electron microscope showing the depth of the sperm head covered by the raised acrosome. Courtesy of Dr. Arthur S. H. Wu, Oregon State University.

If both testicles are removed (as is done in castration), the individual loses his sperm factory and is sterile. Also, without testosterone his masculine appearance is not apparent, and he approaches the status of a neuter—an individual whose appearance is somewhere between that of a male and that of a female. A steer does not have the crest, or powerful neck, of the bull. The bull has heavier, more muscular shoulders and a deeper voice than a counterpart steer. If a bull calf is castrated, the reproductive organs, such as the vas deferens, seminal vesicles, and prostate and bulbourethral glands, all but cease further development. If castration is done in a mature bull, the remaining genital organs shrink in size and in function.

Within each testicle, sperm cells are generated in the seminiferous tubules, and testosterone is produced in the cells between the tubules, called *Leydig cells* or *interstitial cells* (Fig. 10.13).

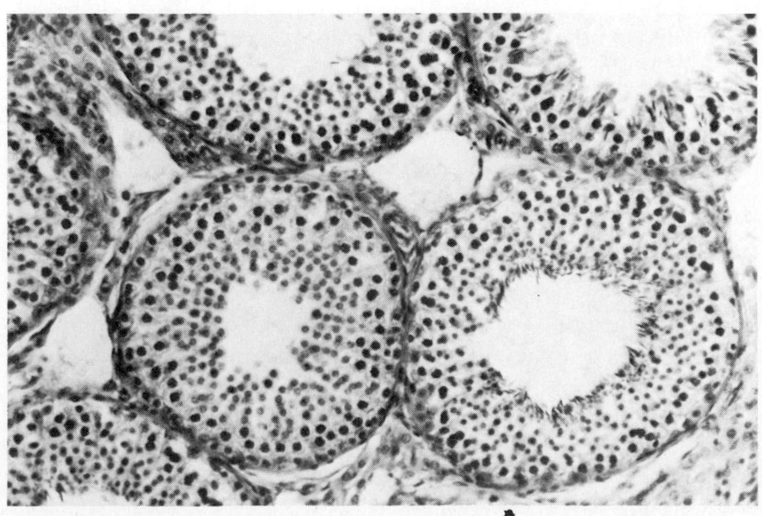

FIGURE 10.13.
A cross section through the seminiferous tubules of the testis of the bull (magnified 240 ×). The tubule in the lower right-hand corner demonstrates the more advanced stages of spermatogenesis as the spermatids are formed near the lumen (opening) of the tubule. Courtesy of Colorado State University.

The Epididymis

The epididymis is the storage site for sperm cells, which enter it from the testicle to mature. In passing through this very long tube (95–115 ft in the bull, longer in the boar and stallion), the sperm acquire the potential to fertilize ova. Sperm taken from the part of the epididymis nearest the testicle and inseminated into females are not likely to be able to fertilize ova, whereas sperm taken near the vas deferens have the potential to fertilize.

In the sexually mature male animal, sperm reside in the epididymis in large numbers. In time, the sperm mature, then degenerate, and are absorbed in the part of the epididymis farthest from the testicle, unless they have been moved on into the vas deferens to be ejaculated.

The Scrotum

The scrotum is a two-lobed sac that contains and protects the two testicles. It also regulates temperature of the testicles, maintaining them at a temperature lower than body temperature (3–7°F lower in the bull and 9–13°F lower in the ram and goat). When the environmental temperature is low, the tunica dartos muscle of the scrotum contracts, pulling the testicles toward the body and its warmth; when the environmental temperature is high, this muscle relaxes, permitting the testicles to drop away from the body and its warmth. This heat-regulating mechanism of the scrotum begins at about the time of puberty. Hormone function precedes puberty by 40–60 days.

When the environmental temperature is elevated such that the testicles cannot cool sufficiently, the formation of sperm is impeded, and a temporary condition of lowered fertility results. Providing shade, keeping the males in the shade during the heat of the day, even providing air conditioning, are ways to manage and prevent this temporary sterility.

The Vas Deferens

The vas deferens is essentially a transportation tube that carries the sperm-containing fluid from each epididymis to the urethra. The vasa deferentia join the urethra near its origin as the urethra leaves the urinary bladder. In the mature bull, the vas deferens is about 0.1 in. in diameter except in its upper end, where it widens into a reservoir, or ampulla, about 4–7 in. long and 0.4 in. wide.

Under the excitement of anticipated mating, the secretion loaded with spermatozoa from each epididymis is propelled into each vas deferens and accumulates in the ampulla of the deferent duct. This brief accumulation of semen in the ampulla is an essential part of sexual arousal. The sperm reside briefly in the ampulla until the moment of ejaculation, when the contents of each ampulla are pressed out into the urethra, and then through the urethra and the penis en route to their deposition in the female tract.

The ampulla is found in the bull, stallion, goat, and ram—species that ejaculate rapidly. It is not present in the boar or dog, animals in which ejaculation normally takes several minutes (8–12 minutes is typical in swine). In such animals, large numbers of sperm travel all the way from the epididymis through the entire length of the vas deferens and the urethra. On close observation of the boar at the time of mating, one can see the muscles over the scrotum quivering rhythmically as some of the contents of each epididymis are propelled into the vasa deferentia and on into the urethra. This slow ejaculation of the boar contrasts to the sudden expulsion of the contents of the ampulla of the vas deferens at the height of the mating reaction, or orgasm, in the bull, stallion, ram, and goat.

The Urethra

The urethra is a large, muscular canal extending from the urinary bladder. The urethra runs posteriorly through the pelvic girdle and curves downward and forward through the full length of the penis. Very near the junction of the bladder and urethra, tubes from the seminal vesicles and tubes from the prostate gland join this large canal. The bulbourethral gland joins the urethra at the posterior floor of the pelvis.

Accessory Sex Glands

The ampullae seminal vesicles, prostate, and bulbourethral glands are known as the accessory sex glands. Their primary functions are to add volume and nutrition to the sperm-rich fluid coming from the epididymis. Semen consists of two components: the sperm and the fluids secreted by the accessory sex glands. The semen characteristics of some farm animals are shown in Table 10.1.

The Penis

The penis is the organ of copulation. It provides a passageway for semen and urine. It is an organ characterized especially by its spongy, erectile tissue that fills with blood under considerable pressure during periods of sexual arousal, making the penis rigid and erect.

The penis of the bull is about 3 ft. in length and 1 in. in diameter, tapering to the free end, or glans penis. In the bull, boar, and ram, the penis is S-shaped when relaxed. This S curve, or sigmoid flexure, becomes straight when the penis is erect. The sigmoid flexure is restored after

TABLE 10.1. Semen Characteristics of Several Male Animals

	Semen Characteristics			
Animal	Volume per Ejaculate (ml)	Composition of Ejaculate	Sperm Concentration per ml $\times 10^9$	Total Sperm per Ejaculate $\times 10^9$
Bull (cattle)	3–10	Single fraction	0.8–1.2	4–18
Ram (sheep)	0.5–2.0	Single fraction	2–3	1–4
Boar (swine)	150–250	Fractionated	0.2–0.3	30–60
Stallion (horse)	40–100	Fractionated	0.15–0.40	8–50
Buck (goat)	0.5–2.5	—	2.0–3.5	1–8
Dog (dog)	1.0–5.0	—	2–7	4–14
Buck (rabbit)	0.5–6.5	—	0.3–1.0	1.5–6.5
Tom (turkey)	0.1–0.7	—	8–30	1–20
Cock (chicken)	0.1–1.5	—	0.4–1.5	0.05–2.0

copulation, when the relaxing penis is drawn back into its sheath by a pair of retractor penis muscles. The stallion penis has no sigmoid flexure; it is enlarged by engorgement of blood in the erectile tissues.

The free end of the penis is termed the *glans penis*. The opening in the ram penis is at the end of a hairlike appendage that extends about 0.8–1.2 in. beyond the larger penis proper. This appendage also becomes erect and, during ejaculation, whirls in a circular fashion, depositing semen in the anterior vagina. It does not regularly penetrate the ewe's cervix, as some investigators claim it does. Only a small portion of the penis of the bull, boar, ram, and goat extends beyond its sheath during erection. The full extension awaits the thrust after entry into the vagina has been made. The stallion and ass usually extend the penis completely before entry into the vagina.

All these accessory male sex organs depend on testosterone for their tone and normal function. This dependence is especially apparent when the testicles are removed (at castration); the usefulness of the accessory sex organs is then diminished or even terminated.

Reproduction in Male Poultry

The reproductive tract of male poultry is shown in Figure 10.14. There are several differences when compared to the reproductive tracts of the farm mammals previously described. The testes of male poultry are contained in the body cavity. Each vas deferens opens into small papillae, which are located in the cloacal wall. The male fowl has no penis but does have a rudimentary organ of copulation. The sperm are transferred from the papillae to the rudimentary copulatory organ, which transfers the sperm to the oviduct of the hen during the mating process. The sperm are stored in primary sperm-host glands located in the oviduct. These sperm

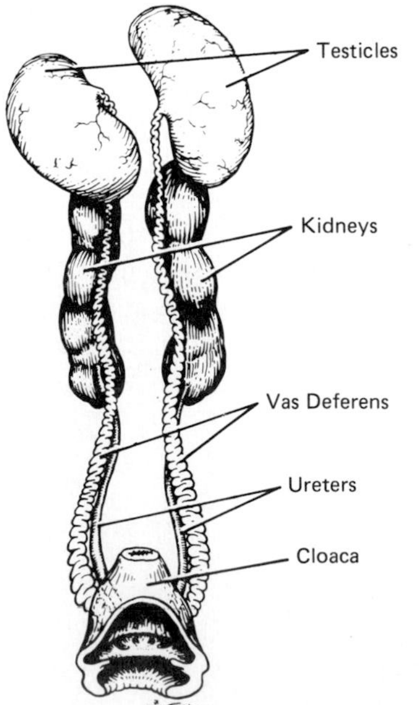

FIGURE 10.14.
Male poultry reproductive tract (ventral view). Courtesy of Dennis Giddings.

are then released on a daily basis and transported to secondary storage glands in the infundibulum. Fertilization occurs in the infundibulum. Sperm stored in the oviduct are capable of fertilizing the eggs for 30 days in turkeys and 10 days in chickens.

WHAT MAKES TESTICLES AND OVARIES FUNCTION

Testicular Function

Testicles produce their hormones under stimuli coming to them from the anterior pituitary (AP) gland situated at the base of the brain. The AP produces and secretes two hormones important to male reproductive performance. Luteinizing hormone (LH) and follicle-stimulating hormone (FSH) are known as gonadotropic hormones because they stimulate the gonads (ovary and testicle). LH produces its effect on the interstitial tissue (Leydig cells) of the testicle, causing the tissue to produce the male hormone, testosterone. FSH stimulates cells in the seminiferous tubules to nourish the developing spermatozoa.

Some species that respond to changes in length of daylight exhibit more seasonal fluctuation than others in reproductive activities. These influences of daylight are on the neurophysiological mechanism in the brain. The hypothalamus is the floor and part of the wall of the third ventricle of the brain and secretes releasing factors through blood vessels that affect the AP and its production of FSH and LH (see Figs. 18.11 and 19.3 in Chapters 18 and 19, respectively).

Ovarian Function

Ovarian hormones in the sexually mature female owe the rhythmicity on their production to hormones that originate in the AP and to the interplay between gonad-stimulating hormones produced there and ovarian hormones whose level and potency vary as the estrous cycle progresses. FSH (the same hormone as FSH in the male) circulates through the bloodstream and affects the responsive follicle cells of the ovary, which respond by secreting the so-called estrogens or estrus-producing hormones, estradiol and estrone. When the amount of estradiol and estrone in the blood reaches a sufficient level, the pituitary is caused to reduce its production of FSH. With this drop in FSH production, the production of estradiol and estrone subsides. When the estrus-producing hormones have been lost from the body and their depressing effect on the AP has been spent, the AP again steps up its production of FSH and the cycle is repeated.

Luteal cells, the successors of the follicle cells, secrete a hormone called progesterone, which plays a role in the female reproductive cycle. Progesterone helps cause the occurrence and recurrence of the desire to mate, which is called **estrus** or **heat**.

Estrus is the period of time when the female will accept the male for breeding purposes. The female of each species exhibits some behavior patterns that demonstrate she is in heat (see Chapter 34). For example, a mare in estrus, when "teased" with the presence of a stallion (Fig. 10.15), will not avoid or kick him. The mare in heat will stand solidly, sometimes squatting and urinating when approached by the stallion.

Synchronized with the estrous cycle is the important and essential phenomenon of ovulation. Ovulation occurs in the cow after estrus. It occurs in the sow, ewe, goat, and mare toward the latter part of, but nevertheless during, estrus. These species all ovulate spontaneously; that is, ovulation takes place whether copulation occurs or not. By contrast, copulation (or some such

FIGURE 10.15.
Estrus is determined in the mare by "teasing" her with the presence of a stallion. Courtesy of Colorado State University.

stimulation) is necessary to trigger ovulation in such animals as the rabbit, cat, ferret, and mink, which are considered "induced ovulators." Ovulation in these animals takes place at a fairly consistent time after mating.

Ovulation is controlled by hormones. The follicle of the ovary grows, matures, fills with fluid, and softens a few hours before rupturing. The follicle ruptures owing to a sudden release of LH rather than bursting as a result of pressure inside.

The FSH of the AP accounts for the increase in size of the ovarian follicle and for the increased amount of estradiol and estrone, which are products of the follicle cells. LH, another hormone from the AP, alters the follicle cells and granulosa cells of the ovary, changing them into luteal cells. These luteal cells are in turn stimulated by LH from the AP to produce progesterone.

In the course of 7–10 days, what was formerly an egg-containing follicle develops into the corpus luteum, a luteal body of about the same size and shape as the mature follicle. The luteal cells of the corpus luteum produce a sufficient quantity of progesterone to depress FSH secretion from the AP until the luteal cells reach maximum development (in nonpregnant animals), cease their development, and (in 3 weeks) lose their potency and disappear.

If pregnancy occurs, the corpus luteum continues to function, persisting in its progesterone production and preventing further estrous cycles. Thus, no more heat occurs until after pregnancy has terminated. The process of follicle development, ovulation, and corpus luteum development and regression is shown in Figure 10.5. Table 10.2 shows the length of estrus, estrous cycles, and time of ovulation for the different farm animals.

The changing length of daylight is a potent factor that influences the estrous cycle, the onset of pregnancy, and the seasonal fluctuations in male fertility. The amount of daylight acts both directly and indirectly on the animal. It acts directly on the central nervous system by influencing the secretion of hormones and indirectly by affecting plant growth, thus altering the level and quality of nutrition available. In cattle, increasing length of day is associated with increased reproductive activity in both males and females. In sheep, the breeding season reaches its height in the autumn, as the hours of daylight shorten. Of course, individuals of both sexes vary in their intensity of sex drive and level of fertility. When selection has resulted in improvements in the

TABLE 10.2. Duration and Frequency of Heat and Time of Ovulation

Animal	Duration of Heat		Length of Cycle (days)		Approximate Time of Ovulation
	Average	Range	Average	Range	
Heifer, cow (cattle)	12 hours	6–27 hours	21	19–23	30 hours after beginning of heat
Ewe (sheep)	30 hours	20–42 hours	17	14–19	26 hours after beginning of heat
Mare (horse)	6 days	1–37 days	21	10–37	1 day before the end of heat
Gilt, sow (swine)	44 hours	$1\frac{1}{2}$–4 days	21	19–23	30–38 hours after beginning of heat
Doe (goat)	39 hours	20–80 hours	17	12–27	On second day of heat
Doe (rabbit)[a]		Constant estrus			8–10 hours after mating
Queen (cat)	5 days	4–7 days	10	8–14	24 hours after mating
Bitch (dog)[a,b]	9 days	4–13 days	—	—	24–48 hours after heat begins
Jill (mink)	2 days	Seasonal breeding (March)			40–50 hours after mating

[a] The dog and rabbit may exhibit a pseudo or false pregnancy after mating has occurred.
[b] The dog has no cycle. There are generally two heats per year—in the fall and spring.

traits associated with reproduction, individuals exhibit higher levels of fertility (i.e., more intense expression of estrus, occurrence of estrus over more months of the year, or occurrence of spermatogenesis at a high level over more months of the year) than unselected individuals.

PREGNANCY

When the sperm and the egg unite (fertilization), conception occurs, which is the beginning of the gestation period. The fertilized egg begins a series of cell divisions (Fig. 10.16). About every 20 hours, embryonic cells duplicate their genes and divide, progressing through the 2-, 4-, 8-, and 16-cell stages, and so on. In farm mammals, the embryo migrates through the oviduct to the uterus in 3–4 days. By then it has developed to the 16- or 32-cell stage. The chorionic and amniotic membranes develop around this new embryo, and the chorion attaches to the uterus. The embryo (and later the fetus) obtains nutrients and discharges wastes through these membranes. This period of attachment (20–30 days in cattle and 14–21 days in swine) is critical. Unless the environment is sufficiently favorable, the embryo dies. Embryonic mortality causes a significant economic loss in farm animals, especially swine, where multiple ovulations and embryos are typical of the species. Good management will help protect the female and embryos early in pregnancy. High temperatures will cause embryonic death. The female should enter the breeding season in a thrifty, weight-gaining condition.

The *embryonic stage* is defined as that period when body parts differentiate and essential organs are formed. This period lasts 45 days in cattle.

When the embryonic stage is completed, the young organism is called a fetus. The fetal period, which lasts until birth, is mainly a time of growth. The duration of pregnancy in cattle is included in Table 10.3. Length of pregnancy varies chiefly with the breed and age of the mother.

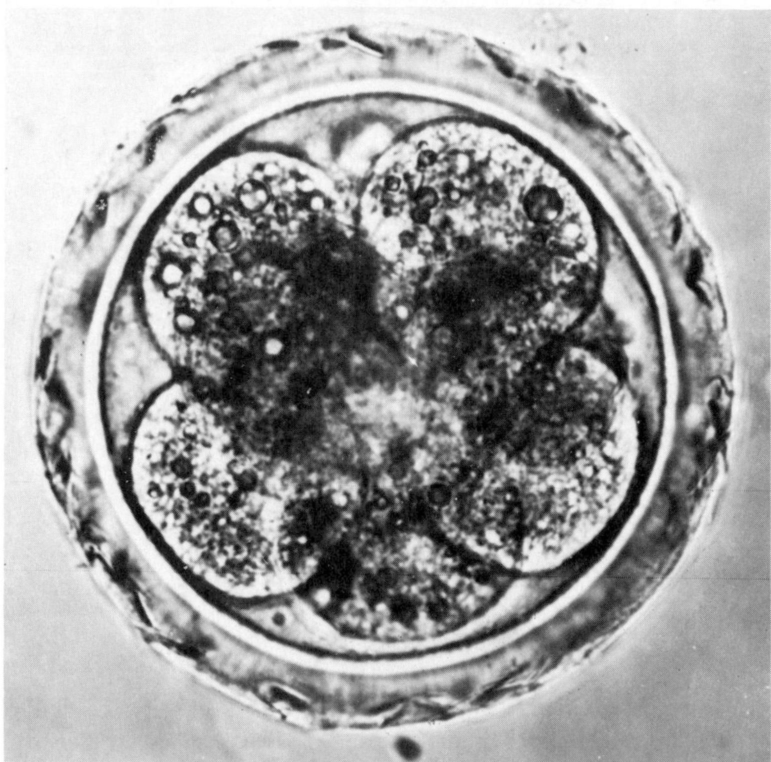

A bovine embryo in the six-cell stage of development (magnified 620 ×). Courtesy of Colorado State University.

PARTURITION

Parturition (birth) marks the termination of pregnancy (Fig. 10.17). Extraembryonic membranes that had been formed around the embryo in early pregnancy are shed at this time and are known as afterbirth. These membranes attach to the uterus during pregnancy and become known as the placenta, which is responsible for the transfer of nutrients and wastes between mother and fetus. The placenta produces hormones, especially estrogens and progesterone, in some farm animal species.

TABLE 10.3. Gestation Length and Number of Offspring Born

Animal	Gestation Length (days)	Usual Number of Offspring Born
Cow (cattle)	285	1
Ewe (sheep)	147	1–3
Mare (horse)	336	1
Sow (swine)	114	6–14
Doe (goat)	150	2–3
Doe (rabbit)	31	4–8
Jill (mink)	50	4
Queen (cat)	52	4
Bitch (dog)	60	7

FIGURE 10.17.
Parturition in the ewe. (A) The water bag (a fluid-filled bag) becomes visible. (B) The head and front legs of the lamb appear. (C) The lamb is forced out by the uterine contractions of the ewe. (D) In a few minutes after birth, the lamb is nursing the ewe. From H. H. Cole and W. N. Garrett (eds.), *Animal Agriculture*, 2nd ed. (New York: W. H. Freeman, © 1980).

The parturition process is initiated by release of the hormone cortisol from the fetal adrenal cortex. Progesterone levels decline whereas estrogen, prostaglandin $F_{2\alpha}$, and oxytocin levels rise, resulting in uterine contractions.

Parturition is a synchronized process. The cervix, until now tightly closed, relaxes. Relaxation of the cervix, along with pressure generated by uterine muscles on the contents of the uterus, permits the passage of the fetus into the vagina and on to the exterior. Another hormone, relaxin, is thought to aid in parturition. Relaxin, which originates in the corpus luteum or placenta, helps to relax cartilage and ligaments in the pelvic region.

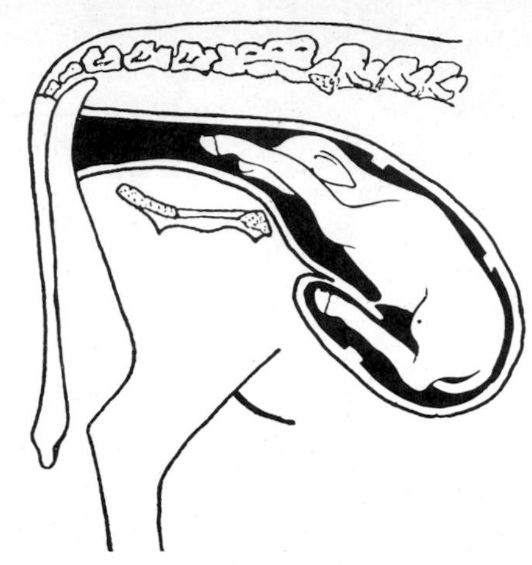

Normal Presentation

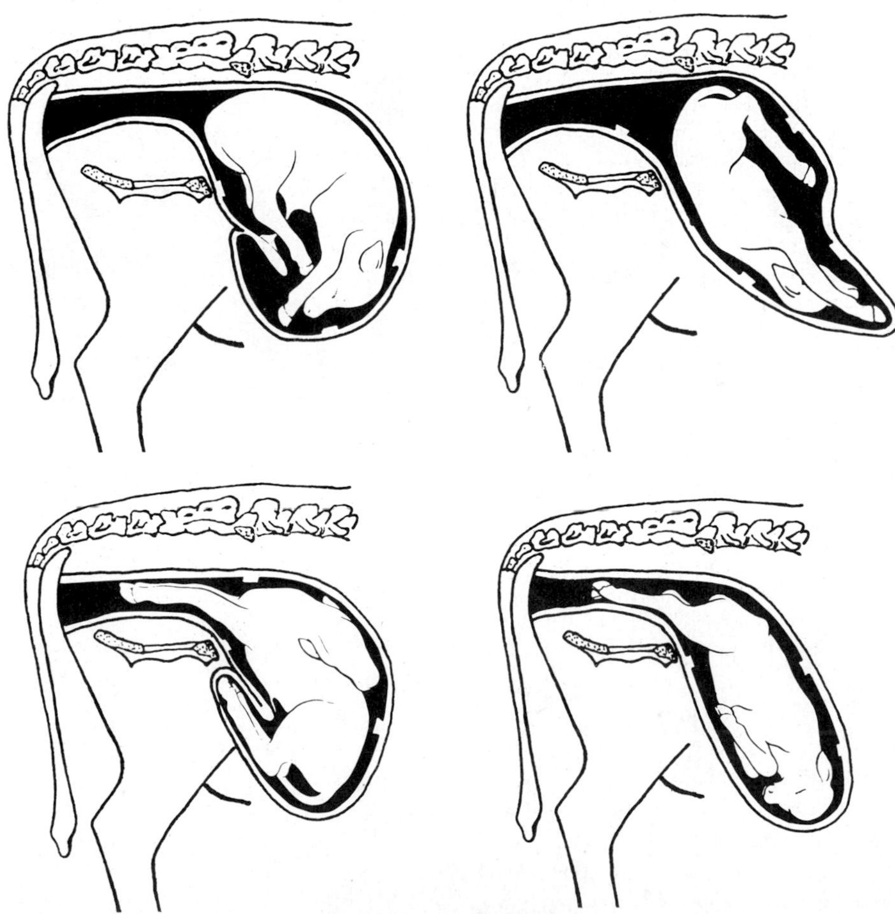

Abnormal Presentation

FIGURE 10.18.
Normal and some abnormal presentations of the calf at parturition. From R. A. Battaglia and V. B. Mayrose, *Handbook of Livestock Management Techniques* (New York: Macmillan, 1981), pp. 131, 134, 135.

At the beginning of parturition, the offspring typically assumes a position that will offer the least resistance as it passes into the pelvic area and through the birth canal. Fetuses of the cow, mare, and ewe assume similar positions in which the front feet are extended with the head between them (Fig. 10.18). Fetal piglets do not orient themselves in any one direction, which does not appear to affect the ease of birth. Calves, lambs, or foals may occasionally present

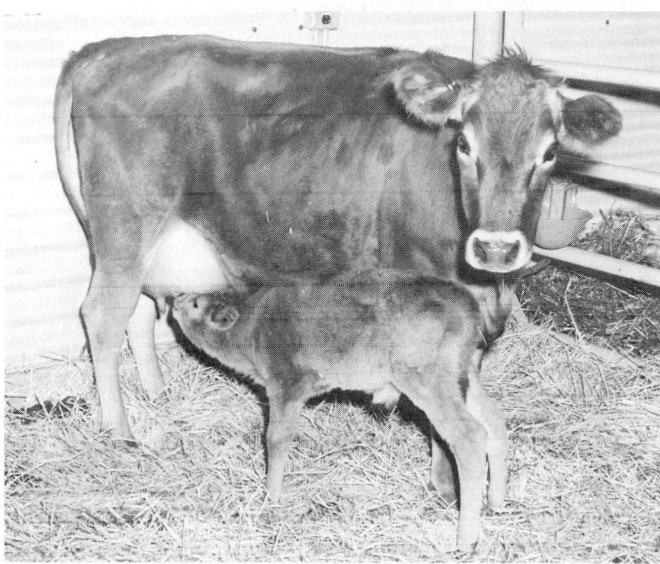

A

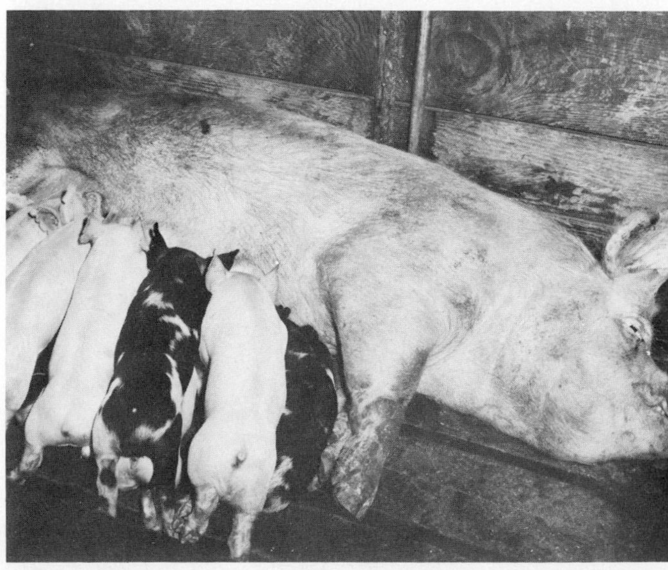

B

FIGURE 10.19.
Live offspring are born to each breeding female in the herd or flock when the intricate mechanisms of reproduction function properly. (A) Dairy cow and calf. Courtesy of Colorado State University. (B) Sow and litter of pigs. Courtesy of D. C. England, Oregon State University. (C) Mare and foal. Courtesy of *The Western Horseman*. (D) Ewe and lambs. Courtesy of Colorado State University. (E) Chicks in the process of hatching. Courtesy of *Poultry Digest*. (F) Beef cow and calf. Courtesy of the American Polled Hereford Association.

C

D

E

F

FIGURE 10.19. *(continued)*

themselves in a number of abnormal positions (Fig. 10.18). In many of these situations, assistance needs to be given at parturition. Otherwise, the offspring may die or be born dead, and in some instances, the mother may die as well. An abnormally small pelvic opening or an abnormally large fetus can cause some mild to severe parturition problems.

Producers can manage their herds and flocks for high reproductive rates. Management decisions are most critical that cause males and females, selected for breeding, to reach puberty at early ages, have high conception rates, and have minimum difficulty at parturition. Keeping animals healthy, providing adequate levels of nutrition, selecting genetically superior animals, and producer attention to parturition are some of the more critical management inputs to minimize reproductive loss. Live offspring born to each breeding female is the key end point to successful farm animal reproduction (Fig. 10.19).

SELECTED REFERENCES

Publications

Battaglia, R. A., and Mayrose, V. B. 1981. *Handbook of Livestock Management Techniques*. New York: Macmillan.

Bearden, H. J., and Fuquay, J. W. 1984. *Applied Animal Reproduction*. Reston, VA: Reston Publishing.

Bone, J. F. 2nd ed., 1988. *Animal Anatomy and Physiology*. Reston, VA: Reston Publishing.

Frandson, R. D. 2nd ed., 1986. *Anatomy and Physiology of Farm Animals*. Philadelphia: Lea and Febiger.

Hafez, E. S. E. (ed.). 2nd ed., 1987. *Reproduction in Farm Animals*. Philadelphia: Lea and Febiger.

Pickett, B. W., Voss, J. L., Squires, E. L., and Amann, R. P. 1981. *Management of the Stallion for Maximum Reproductive Efficiency*. Fort Collins: Colorado State University Press, Animal Reprod. Lab. Gen. Series 1005.

Sorenson, A. M., Jr. 1979. *Animal Reproduction: Principles and Practices*. New York: McGraw-Hill.

Visuals

Beef Cattle Reproduction (3 videotapes). CEV, P.O. Box 65265, Lubbock, TX 79464-5265.

Embryo Development of the Chick (silent filmstrip). Vocational Education Productions, California Polytechnic State University, San Luis Obispo, CA 93407.

Heat Detection in Dairy Cows; Artificial Insemination; and *The Calving Process* (videotapes). Agricultural Products and Services, 2001 Killebrew Dr., Suite 333, Bloomington, MN 55420.

Livestock Parturition (videotape). CEV, P.O. Box 65265, Lubbock, TX 79464-5265.

Swine Reproduction (2 videotapes). CEV, P.O. Box 65265, Lubbock, TX 79464-5265.

The Nature of Foaling (VHS Video). VEP, Calif. Polytechnic State Univ., San Luis Obispo, CA 93407.

CHAPTER 11

Artificial Insemination, Estrous Synchronization, and Embryo Transfer

In the process of artificial insemination (AI), semen is deposited in the female reproductive tract by artificial techniques rather than by natural mating. AI was first successfully accomplished in the dog in 1780 and in horses and cattle in the early 1900s. AI techniques are also available for use in sheep, goats, swine, poultry, laboratory animals, and bees.

The primary advantage of AI is that it permits extensive use of outstanding sires to maximize genetic improvement. For example, a bull may sire 30–50 calves naturally per year over a productive lifetime of 3–8 years. In an AI program, a bull can produce 200–400 units of semen per ejaculate, with four ejaculates typically collected per week. If the semen is frozen and stored for later use, hundreds of thousands of calves can be produced by a single sire (one calf per 1.5 units of semen), and many of these offspring can be produced long after the sire is dead. AI also can be used to control reproductive diseases, and sires can be used that have been injured or are dangerous when used naturally.

SEMEN COLLECTING AND PROCESSING

There are several different methods of collecting semen. The most common method is the artificial vagina (Fig. 11.1), which is constructed to be similar to an actual vagina. The artificial vagina is commonly used to collect semen from bulls, stallions, rams, and buck goats and rabbits. The semen is collected by having the male mount an estrous female or training him to mount another animal or object (Figs. 11.2, 11.3). When the male mounts, his penis is directed into the artificial vagina by the person collecting the semen, and the semen accumulates in the collection tube. Semen from the boar and dog is not typically collected with an artificial vagina. It is collected by applying pressure with a gloved hand, after grasping the extended penis, as the animal mounts another animal or object.

Semen can also be collected by using an electroejaculator, in which a probe is inserted into the rectum and an electrical stimulation causes ejaculation. This is used most commonly in bulls and rams that are not easily trained to use the artificial vagina and from which semen is collected infrequently.

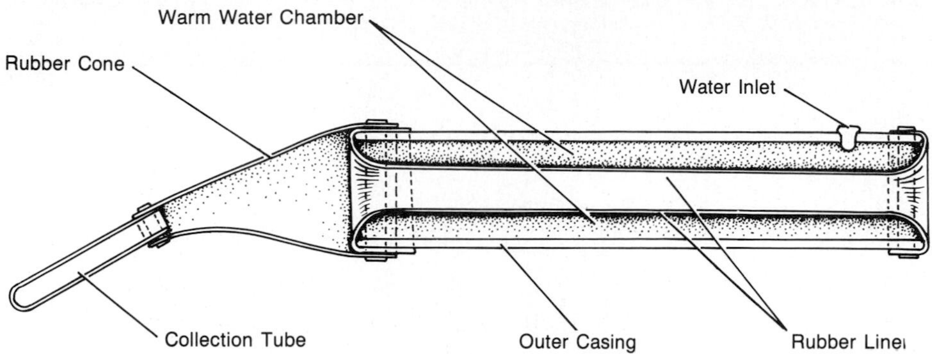

FIGURE 11.1.
Longitudinal section of an artificial vagina. Courtesy of Dennis Giddings.

If semen is collected too frequently, the number of sperm per ejaculate decreases. Semen from a bull is typically collected twice a day for 2 days a week (Fig. 11.4). Semen from rams can be collected several times a day for several weeks, but bucks (goats) must be ejaculated less frequently. Boars and stallions give large numbers of sperm per ejaculate, so semen from them is usually collected every other day at most. Semen is collected from tom turkeys 2–3 times per week. The simplest and most common technique for collecting sperm from toms is the abdominal massage. This technique usually requires two persons: the "collector" helps hold the bird and operates the semen collection apparatus, while the "milker" stimulates a flow of semen by massaging the male's abdomen (Fig. 11.5).

After the semen is collected, it is evaluated for volume, sperm concentration, motility of the sperm, and sperm abnormalities (Fig. 11.6). The semen is usually mixed with an extender that dilutes the ejaculate to a greater volume. This greater volume allows a single ejaculate to be processed into several units of semen, where one unit of semen is used for each female inseminated. The extender is usually composed of nutrients such as milk and egg yolk, a citrate buffer, antibiotics, and glycerol. The amount of extender used is based on the projected number

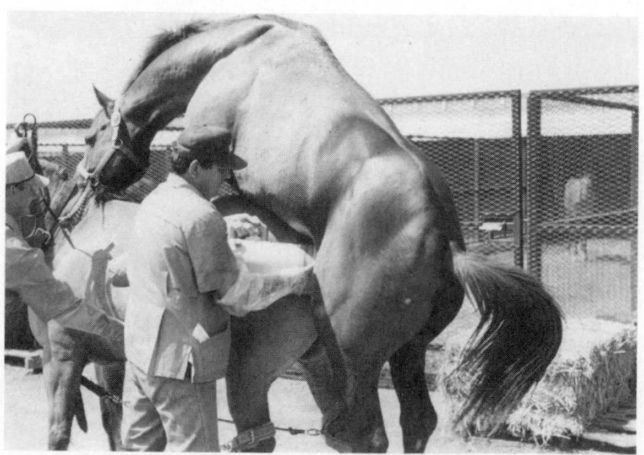

FIGURE 11.2.
Using the artificial vagina to collect semen from the stallion. The handler of the stallion is holding the front leg to prevent the horse from striking the collector. Courtesy of Colorado State University.

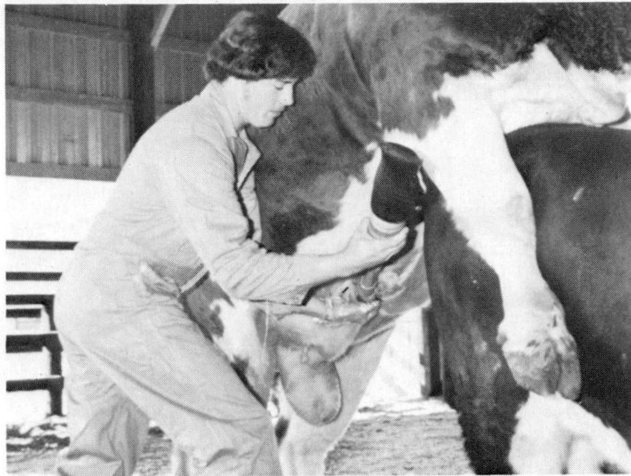

FIGURE 11.3.
Collecting semen from a bull using the artificial vagina. Courtesy of Colorado State University.

of viable sperm available in each unit of extended semen. For example, each unit of semen for insemination in cattle should contain 10 million motile, normal spermatozoa.

Some semen is used fresh; however, it can only be stored this way for a day or two. Most semen is frozen in liquid nitrogen and stored in ampules (glass vials), plastic straws (Fig. 11.7), or pellets. Bull semen can be stored in this manner for an indefinite period of time and retain its fertilization capacity. Most cattle are inseminated with frozen semen that has been thawed. The fertilizing capacity of frozen semen from boars, stallions, and rams is only modestly satisfactory; however, improvement has been noted in recent years. Turkey semen cannot be frozen satisfactorily. For maximum fertilization capacity, it should be used within 30 minutes of collection.

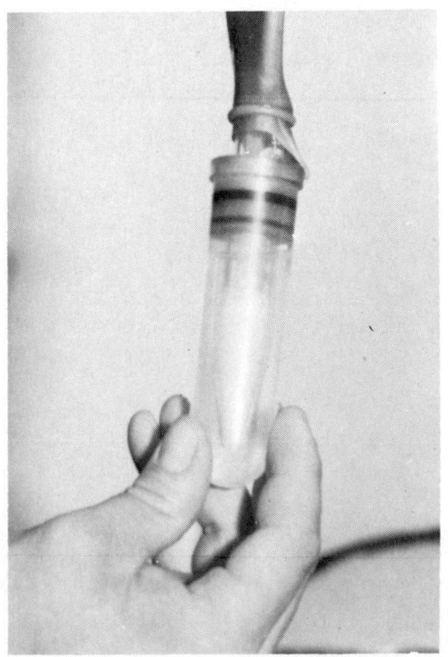

FIGURE 11.4.
Approximately 4 ml of bull semen in the collection tube attached to the artificial vagina. Note that the collection tube is immersed in water to control the temperature. The livability of the sperm is decreased when they are subjected to sudden temperature changes. Courtesy of Colorado State University.

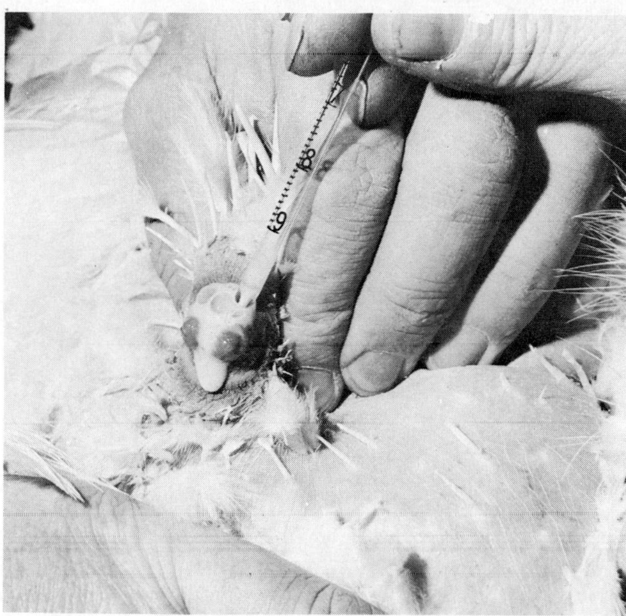

FIGURE 11.5.
Collection of semen from a turkey. Two technicians are usually involved in the collection process. One holds the turkey while the other manually stimulates semen into the cloaca while drawing semen into the collection tube. Courtesy of P. E. Lake, and J. M. Stewart, *Artificial Insemination in Poultry*, 1978, Ministry of Agriculture, Fisheries, and Food. No. 213, London: Her Majesty's Stationery Office, British Crown Copyright.

INSEMINATION OF THE FEMALE

Prior to insemination, the frozen semen is thawed. Thawed semen cannot be refrozen and used again because refreezing will kill the sperm cells.

High conception rates using AI depend on the female's cycling and ovulating; detecting estrus; using semen that has been properly collected, extended, and frozen; thawing and handling the semen satisfactorily at the time of insemination; insemination techniques; and avoiding extremes in stress and excitement to the animal being inseminated.

Detecting Estrus

Estrus must be detected accurately because it signals time of ovulation and determines proper timing of insemination. The best indication of estrus is the condition called *standing heat,* in which the female stands still when mounted by a male or another female.

Cows are typically checked for estrus twice daily, in the morning and evening. They are usually observed for 30 minutes to detect standing heat. Other observable signs are restlessness, attempting to mount other cows, and a clear, mucous discharge from the vagina. Some producers use sterilized bulls or hormone-treated cows as "heat checkers" in the herd. These animals are sometimes equipped with a chin marker that greases or paints marks on the back of the cow when she is mounted.

Estrus in sheep or goats is checked using sterilized males equipped with a brisket-marking harness. Gilts and sows in heat assume a rigid stance with ears erect when hands are placed firmly in their backs. The vulva is usually red and swollen. The presence of a boar and the resulting sounds and odors can help detect heat in swine as the females in estrus will attempt to

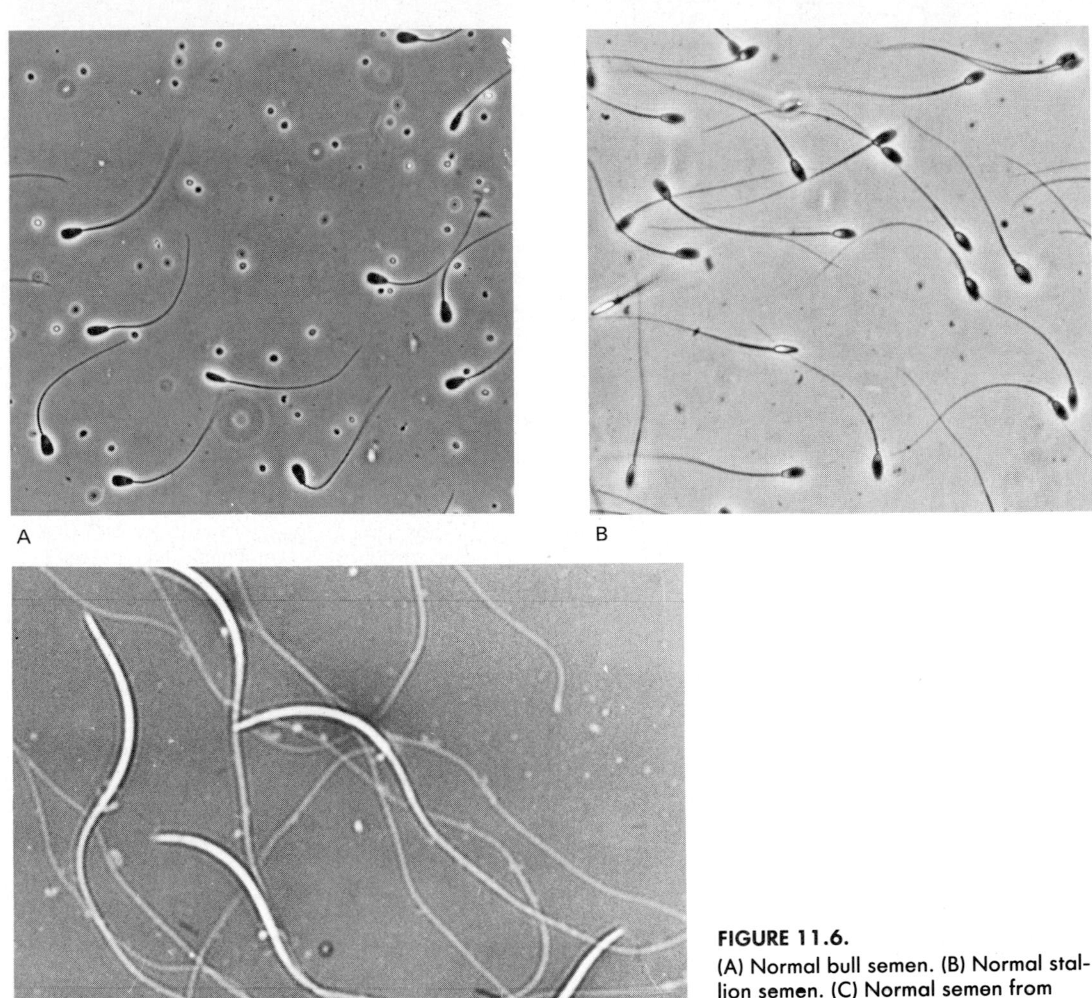

FIGURE 11.6.
(A) Normal bull semen. (B) Normal stallion semen. (C) Normal semen from domestic fowl as viewed under the microscope. Courtesy of Colorado State University (A and B); Dr. P. E. Lake and British Crown Copyright (C).

locate a boar. Signs of estrus in the mare are elevation of the tail, contractions of the vulva (winking), spreading of the legs, and frequent urination.

Proper Timing of Insemination

The duration of estrus and ovulation time are quite variable in farm animals. This variability poses difficulty in determining the best time for insemination. An additional challenge is that sperm are short-lived when put into the female reproductive tract. Also, estrus is sometimes expressed without ovulation occurring; sows, for example, typically show estrus 3–5 days after

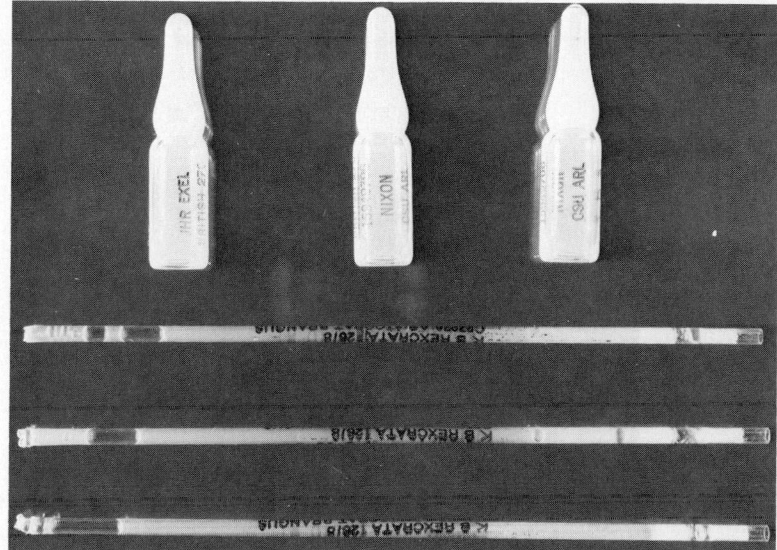

FIGURE 11.7.
Semen is typically stored and frozen in ampules or straws. Three ampules appear at the top of the figure, with three straws of bull semen below. The animal's name, registration number, and location of collection are printed on the ampules and straws. Courtesy of Colorado State University.

farrowing, but ovulation does not occur. Sows should not be bred at this time either artificially or naturally.

Insemination time should be as close to ovulation time as possible; otherwise sperm stay in the female reproductive tract too long and lose their fertilizing capacity. Cows found in estrus in the morning are usually inseminated the evening of the same day, and cows in heat in the

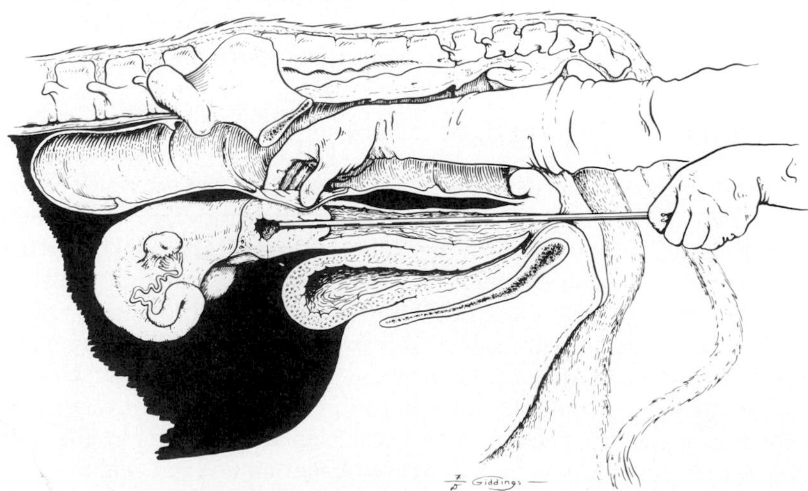

FIGURE 11.8.
Artificial insemination of the cow. Note that the insemination tube has been manipulated through the cervix. The inseminator's forefinger is used to determine when the insemination rod has entered into the uterus. Courtesy of Dennis Giddings.

evening are inseminated the following morning. Insemination, therefore, should occur toward the end or after estrus has been expressed in the cow. Ewes are usually inseminated in the second half of estrus, and goats are inseminated 10–12 hours after the beginning of estrus. Sows ovulate from 30–38 hours after the beginning of estrus, so insemination is recommended at the end of the first day and at the beginning of the second day of estrus. When sows are inseminated both days conception rate is improved compared to insemination on only one day.

Insemination of dairy cows occurs while the cow is standing in a stall or stanchion. Beef cows are penned and inseminated in a chute that restrains the animal. The most common insemination technique in cattle involves the inseminator having one arm in the rectum to manipulate the insemination tube through the cervix (Fig. 11.8). The insemination tube is passed just through the cervix, and the semen is deposited into the body of the uterus. The insemination procedure for sheep and goats is similar to that for cattle; however, a speculum (a tube approximately 1.5 in. in diameter and 6 in. long) allows the inseminator to observe the cervix in sheep and goats. The inseminating tube is passed through the speculum into the cervix, where the semen is deposited into the uterus or cervix.

The sow is usually inseminated without being restrained. The inseminating tube is easily directed into the cervix because the vagina tapers into the cervix. The semen is expelled into the body of the uterus. The mare is hobbled or adequately restrained prior to insemination. The vulva area is washed, and the tail is wrapped or put into a plastic bag. The plastic-covered arm of the inseminator is inserted into the vagina, and the index finger is inserted into the cervix. The insemination tube is passed through the cervix, and the semen is deposited into the uterus.

The turkey hen is inseminated by first applying pressure to the abdominal area to cause eversion of the oviduct (Fig. 11.9). The insemination tube is inserted into the oviduct approximately 2 in., and the semen is released. The first insemination is made when 5%–10% of the flock have started laying eggs. A second insemination a week later assures a high level of fertility. Thereafter, insemination is done at 2-week intervals. Fertility in the turkey usually persists at a high level for 2–3 weeks after insemination. This is possible because sperm are stored in special glands of the hen, where they are nourished and retain their fertilizing capacity. Most of these glands are located near the junction of the uterus and vagina.

EXTENT OF ARTIFICIAL INSEMINATION

The number of farm animals artificially inseminated each year is not well documented. AI is used primarily in the dairy industry where 70% of the cows and 25% of the heifers are bred artificially. Most of the inseminations are in the Holstein breed (Table 11.1). Less than 5% of the beef cows are inseminated, where semen from Angus and Simmental bulls is used most extensively (Table 11.1). The greater use of AI in dairy compared to beef is reflected in Table 11.1, when 13.5 million units of dairy semen is compared to 1.9 million units of beef semen.

It is estimated that approximately 15,000 sows are artificially bred in the United States each year, which is less than 1% of the total sows bred in this country. Satisfactory techniques to freeze boar semen were accomplished in 1971, but frozen semen yields smaller litter sizes than fresh semen. More than 400,000 sows are artificially inseminated each year in certain European countries, which represent 20%–30% of the sows bred in these countries.

AI in horses is still limited because of difficulty in providing extended semen storage. AI in sheep and goats in the United States is limited because herds and flock are dispersed over wide areas and the cost per unit of semen is high. Little AI is done in chickens; however, AI is rather

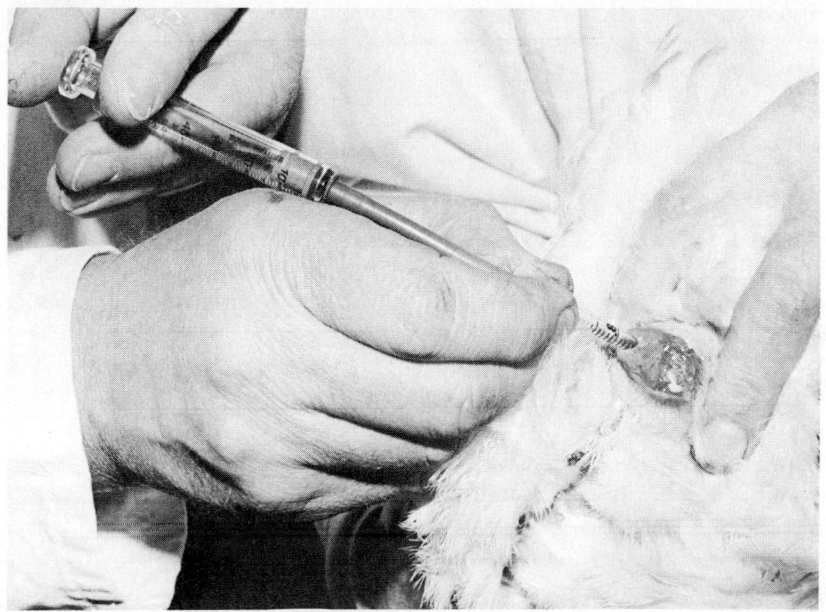

FIGURE 11.9.
Insemination of a hen turkey is accomplished by everting the opening of the oviduct through the opening of the cloaca. The tube is inserted 1 or 2 inches, pressure on the oviduct is relaxed, and the proper amount of semen is deposited as the syringe is slowly withdrawn. Courtesy of P. E. Lake and J. M. Stewart, *Artificial Insemination in Poultry*, 1978, Ministry of Agriculture, Fisheries, and Food, No. 213, London: Her Majesty's Stationery Office, British Crown Copyright.

TABLE 11.1. Semen Production and Sales for Dairy and Beef Bulls, 1989

Breed	Domestic Sales	Custom Frozen	Total	Export Sales No. Units	Export Sales $Mil
	1,000 Units				
Holstein	11,799	630	12,429	3,831	—
Jersey	603	43	646	134	—
Brown Swiss	124	53	177	332	—
Other dairy	244	35	279	9	—
Total dairy	12,770	761	13,531	4,306	$39.2
Angus	374	169	543	55	—
Simmental	126	142	268	50	—
Polled Hereford	96	97	183	31	—
Other beef	226	662	888	106	—
Total beef	822	1,070	1,892	242	1.2

Source: National Association of Animal Breeders.

extensive in turkeys. It is especially important in the broad-breasted turkey, which, because of the size of its breast, has difficulty mating naturally.

ESTROUS SYNCHRONIZATION

Estrous synchronization is controlling or manipulating the estrous cycle so that females express estrus at approximately the same time. Estrous synchronization is a useful part of an AI program because checking heat and breeding animals under extensive management conditions is time-consuming and expensive. Also, estrous synchronization is a successful tool in making embryo transfer programs successful.

Prostaglandin

In 1979, a prostaglandin was cleared for use in cattle. Prostaglandins are naturally occurring fatty acids that have important functions in several of the body systems. The prostaglandin that has a marked effect on the reproductive system is prostaglandin F_2 alpha ($PGF_{2\alpha}$).

It is pointed out in Chapter 10 that the corpus luteum (CL) controls the estrous cycle in the cow by secreting the hormone progesterone. Progesterone prevents the cow from expressing heat and ovulation. The prostaglandin destroys the CL, thus destroying the source of progesterone. About 3 days after the injection of prostaglandin, the cow will be in heat. For prostaglandin to be effective, the cow must have a functional CL. It is ineffective in heifers that have not reached puberty and in noncycling mature cows. Also, prostaglandin is ineffective if the CL is immature or has already started to regress. Prostaglandin is, then, only effective in heifers and cows that are in days 5–18 of their estrous cycle. Because of this relationship, prostaglandin is given on either a 1-injection or a 2-injection system.

One-Injection System

The 1-injection system requires one prostaglandin injection and an 11-day AI breeding season. The first 5 days are a conventional AI program of heat detection and insemination. After 5 days, a calculation can be made to determine what percentage of the females in the herd have been in heat. If a smaller than expected percentage are cycling, the cost of the prostaglandin may not be justified. If the decision is to proceed with the injection, the remaining animals not previously bred are injected on day 6. Then the AI breeding season continues 5 more days, for a total of 11 days.

Field trial results in herds where a high percentage of females are cycling show a 50%–60% pregnancy rate at the end of 11 days of AI breeding for those receiving prostaglandin versus a 30%–40% pregnancy rate for those not receiving it. The amount of prostaglandin required per calf that is produced by AI will be between 1.2 and 2.0 units.

Two-Injection System

In the 2-injection system, all cows are injected with prostaglandin at two different times. Counting the first injection as day 1, the second injection is administered on day 11, 12, or 13. All cows capable of responding to the drug should be in heat during the first 5 days after the second injection of prostaglandin. Heat detection and insemination can occur each of these 5 days, or a fixed-time insemination can be performed 76–80 hours after the second injection.

Field trial results in herds in which a high percentage of the females are cycling show a 35%–55% pregnancy rate at the end of the fifth day or 76- to 80-hour 1-time insemination versus a 10%–12% rate in the cows not receiving prostaglandin. The 2-injection system will require 4–7 units of prostaglandin per AI calf.

Prostaglandin is not a wonder drug. It will only work in well-managed herds where a high percentage of the females are cycling. Biologically, it has been well demonstrated that prostaglandin can synchronize estrus. However, producers must weigh the cost against the economic benefit. Caution should be exercised in administering prostaglandin to pregnant cows, as it may cause abortion. Estrous synchronization in cattle may not be advisable in areas where inadequate protection is given to young calves during severe blizzards. Also, excellent herd health programs must be utilized to prevent high losses from calf scours and other diseases that become more serious where large numbers of newborn calves are grouped together.

MGA and Prostaglandin

MGA (melengestrol acetate) is a feed additive that suppresses estrus in heifers and is widely used in the feedlot industry. MGA and prostaglandin have been used in combination in highly successful estrus synchronization programs. In one such program, MGA is fed at 0.5 mg per head per day for 14 days. Seventeen days after the last MGA feeding, a single injection of prostaglandin is given (Fig. 11.10). Most heifers show estrus approximately 48–72 hours after the prostaglandin injection. In a 30-day breeding program, more than 80% of the heifers usually conceive.

Syncro-Mate-B

Another estrous synchronization product, Syncro-Mate-B, has been available for beef and dairy heifers since 1983. Heifers are injected with 5 mg of estradiol valerate and 3 mg of norgestomet and implanted with 6 mg norgestomet implant subcutaneously on top of the ear. Nine days later, the implant is removed. Most heifers will show estrus approximately 24–48 hours after implant removal. Heifers can be inseminated 12 hours after being detected in estrus or time inseminated 48–54 hours after implant removal. Syncro-Mate-B will cause many noncycling

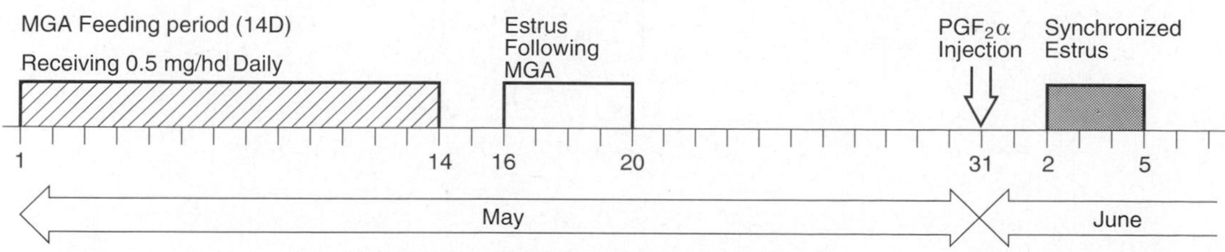

FIGURE 11.10.
The MGA-prostaglandin ($PGF_{2\alpha}$) system for synchronizing estrus. Courtesy of Colorado State University.

heifers to show heat; however, conception rates in these heifers at this estrus are low (~ 20%). In cycling heifers treated with Syncro-Mate-B, conception rates are usually 40% – 60%.

In a sense, there are some natural occurrences of estrous synchronization. The weaning process in swine is an example; the sow will typically show heat 3 – 8 days after the pigs are weaned. Estrus is suppressed through the suckling influence, so when the pigs are removed, the sow will show heat.

EMBRYO TRANSFER

Embryo transfer is sometimes referred to as ova transplant or embryo transplant. In this procedure, an embryo in its early stage of development is removed from its own mother's (the donor's) reproductive tract and transferred to another female's (the recipient's) reproductive tract. The first successful embryo transfer was accomplished in 1890. In the past several decades, successful embryo transfers have been reported in sheep, goats, swine, cattle, and horses.

In recent years, commercial embryo transfer companies have been established in the United States and several other foreign countries. Most commercial work is done with beef and dairy cattle. It is estimated that approximately 65,000 pregnancies from embryo transfers in beef cattle and 35,000 pregnancies in dairy cattle occurred in North America in 1985. This compares to 20 done in 1972. During 1989, more than $8.8 million bovine embryos were exported from the United States, primarily to Western Europe and South America. Approximately 90% of the embryos were from dairy cattle.

Superovulation is the production of a greater than normal number of eggs. Females that are donors of eggs for embryo transfer are injected with hormones to stimulate increased egg production. In cattle, the average donor produces approximately six transferable embryos per superovulation treatment; however, a range of 0 – 25 embryos can be expected (Fig. 11.11). This procedure gives embryo transfer its greatest advantage because it increases the number of

FIGURE 11.11.
Ten Holstein embryo transfer calves resulting from one superovulation and transfer from the Holstein cow in the background. The ten recipient cows are shown on the left-hand side of the fence. Courtesy of Colorado State University.

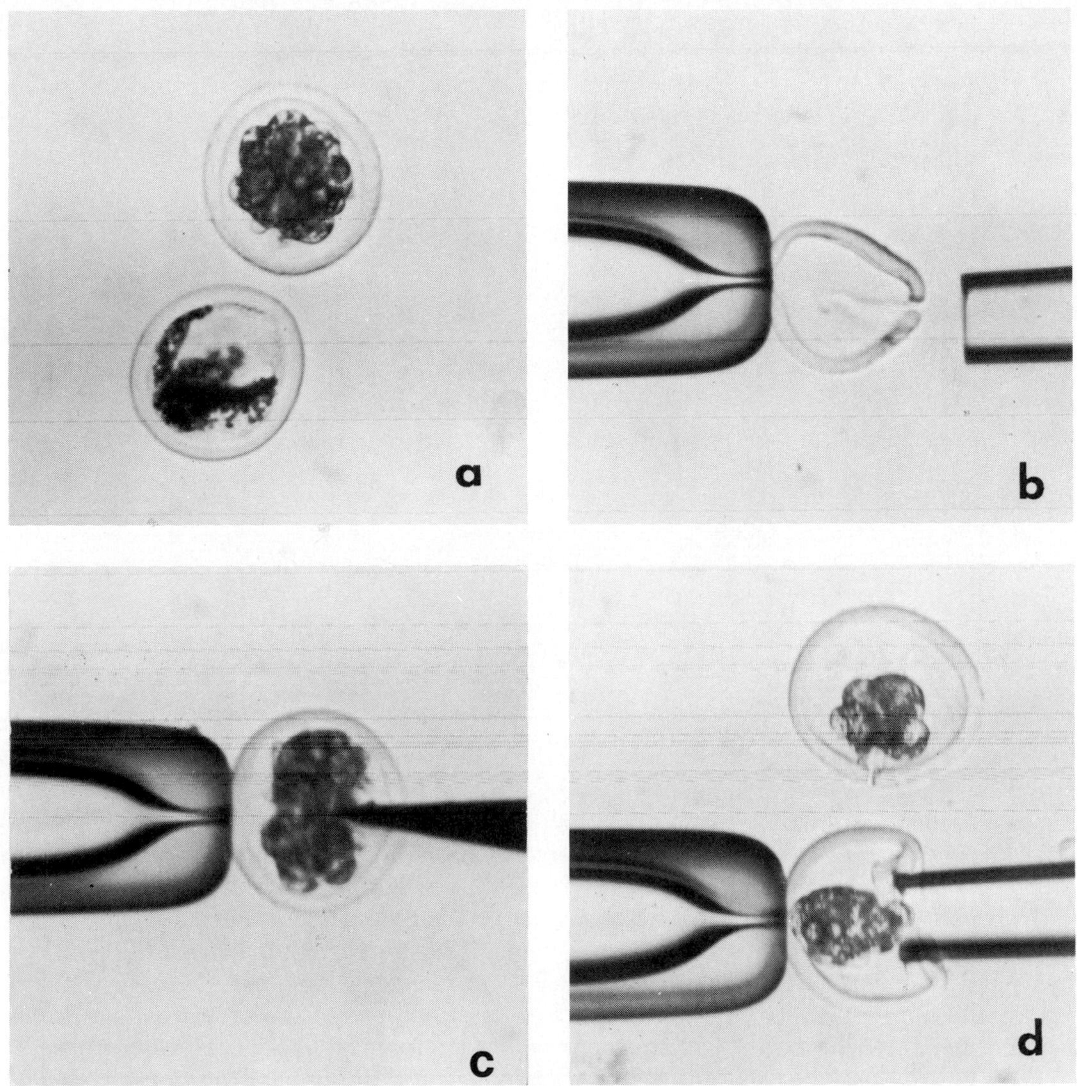

FIGURE 11.12.
The process of embryo splitting. (a) A morula (40–70 cells of the fertilized egg) and an unfertilized egg. (b) The unfertilized egg with the cellular contents sucked out of it. (c) The morula is divided into two groups of cells with the microsurgical blade. (d) One-half of the cells are left in the morula while the other one-half of the cells are placed inside the other unfertilized egg. The result is two genetically identical embryos ready for transfer. Courtesy of Williams et al., *1983 NAAB Conference, Beef AI and Embryo Transfer.*

offspring that a superior female can produce. The key to justification of embryo transfer is identification of genetically superior females. Embryo transfer is usually confined to seed stock herds, where genetically superior females can be more easily identified and where high costs can be justified.

FIGURE 11.13.
"Question" and "Answer" were the world's first split-embryo foals resulting from nonsurgical embryo transfer. Courtesy of Colorado State University.

Until recently, embryo transfer had to be done surgically, but nonsurgical techniques are now used. The procedure after superovulation is to breed the donor 12 and 24 hours after she comes into heat with two doses of semen each time. The fertilized eggs are recovered about a week later by flushing the uterus with a buffered solution. This is essentially the reverse of the AI process and does not require surgery. The embryos are located and evaluated using a microscope and loaded into an AI rod. Nonsurgical transfer of an embryo into a recipient is done with the AI rod. Conception rates are usually higher if the transfer is done surgically. Embryos are usually transferred shortly after being collected, so recipient females need to be in the same stage of the estrous cycle (within 24 hours) for successful transfer to occur. Estrous synchronization of females is necessary, so large numbers of females must be kept for this purpose.

Embryos can now be frozen in liquid nitrogen and remain dormant for months or years. Conception rates are lower when frozen embryos are used than when fresh embryos are used, but research is bringing about improvement. In cattle, approximately 50%–60% of the frozen embryos will be normal after thawing. Thirty percent to forty percent of these normal embryos will result in confirmed pregnancies in 60–90 days. This compares to a pregnancy rate of 55%–65% from fresh embryos transferred the same day of collection.

Recent advances in embryo transfer research have permitted the embryo to be mechanically divided so that identical twins can be produced from a single embryo (Figs. 11.12 and 11.13). Perhaps in the future an embryo of a desired mating and sex could be selected from an inventory of frozen embryos. This embryo would then be thawed and transferred nonsurgically in the cow when she comes into heat. Embryo splitting and embryo transfer are areas of biotechnology that continue to advance rapidly.

SELECTED REFERENCES

Publications

Ernst, R. A., Ogasawara, F. X., Rooney, W. F., Schroeder, J. P., and Ferebee, D. C. 1970. *Artificial Insemination of Turkeys.* University of California Agric. Ext. Publ. AXT-338.

Hafez, E. S. E. 1987. Reproduction in Farm Animals. Philadelphia: Lea and Febiger.

Herman, H. A. 1981. *Improving Cattle by the Millions. NAAB and the Development and Worldwide Application of Artificial Insemination.* Columbia: University of Missouri Press.

Kiessling, A. A., Hughes, W. H., and Blankevoort, M. R. 1986. Superovulation and embryo transfer in the dairy goat. *J. Am. Vet. Med. Assoc.* 188:829.

Lake, P. E., and Steward, J. M. 1978. *Artificial Insemination in Poultry.* Scotland Ministry of Agriculture, Fisheries, and Food no. 213.

Pickett, B. W., and Back, D. G. 1973. *Procedures, Collection, Evaluation and Insemination of Stallion Semen.* Fort Collins: Colorado State University Exp. Sta., Animal Reprod. Lab., Gen. Series 935.

Seidel, G. E., Jr. 1981. Superovulation and embryo transfer in cattle. *Science* 211:351.

Seidel, G. E., Jr., Seidel, S. M., and Bowen R. A. 1978. *Bovine Embryo Transfer Procedures.* Colorado State University Exp. Sta., Animal Reprod. Lab., Gen. Series 975.

Squires, E. L., Cook, V. M., and Voss, J. L. 1984. Collection and transfer of equine embryos. Colorado State University, Animal Reprod. Lab. Bull. no. 01.

Synchronization of Beef Cattle with Prostaglandin. 1979. DeForest, WI: American Breeders Service.

Visuals

Artificial Insemination in Poultry (slide-tape—57 slides; 10 min). Poultry Science Department, Ohio State University, 674 W. Lane Ave., Columbus, OH 43210.

Equine A. I. (sound filmstrips), covering "Introduction to Equine AI," "Teasing and Rectal Palpation," "Semen Collection and Evaluation," "Broodmare Health Care," and "Inseminating and Diagnosing Pregnancy." Vocational Education Productions, California Polytechnic State University, San Luis Obispo, CA 93407.

Modern Cattle Breeding Techniques (sound filmstrips), covering "Artificial Insemination—An Overview" and "Embryo Transfer—The New Horizon." Prentice-Hall Media, 150 White Plains Road, Tarrytown, NY 10591.

Reproduction Kit (sound filmstrips), covering "Embryo Transfer of Beef and Dairy Cattle" and " Artificial Insemination of Beef and Dairy Cattle." Vocational Education Production, California Polytechnic State University, San Luis Obispo, CA 93407.

Swine Reproduction Series (sound filmstrips), covering "Fresh Semen Artificial Insemination" and "Frozen Semen Artificial Insemination." Vocational Education Productions, California Polytechnic State University, San Luis Obispo, CA 93407.

CHAPTER 12

Genetics

Body tissues of animals and plants are composed of cells, whose structure can be observed microscopically. These cells, with certain exceptions, have an outer membrane, an internal cytoplasm, and a nucleus (see Chapter 18, Fig. 18.3). This nucleus contains rodlike bodies called **chromosomes** (Fig. 12.1). Body cells contain these chromosomes in pairs, and each chromosome contains genes, which are the functional units of inheritance. When cells divide to produce more body cells, the chromosomes replicate by a process called **mitosis** (Fig. 12.2). During mitosis, each member of each chromosome pair divides so that the two new cells (daughter cells) are identical to the original cell that divided.

Each species has a characteristic number of chromosomes (Table 12.1), which is maintained through meiosis and fertilization. Poultry have more chromosomes than livestock, whereas swine have the smallest number. For comparative purposes, humans have 23 pairs of chromosomes.

PRODUCTION OF GAMETES

The testicles of the male and the ovaries of the female produce sex cells (gametes) by a process called **gametogenesis.** The gametes produced by the testicles are called sperm; the gametes produced by the ovaries are called eggs, or ova. Specifically, the production of sex cells that become sperm is called **spermatogenesis;** the production of ova, **oogenesis.** The unique type of cell division in which gametes (sperm or ova) are formed is called **meiosis.** Each newly formed gamete contains only one member of each of the chromosome pairs present in the body cells.

Let us examine gametogenesis in a theoretical species in which there are only two pairs of chromosomes in each body cell. Meiosis occurs in the primordial germ cell (cells capable of undergoing meiosis) located near the outer wall of the **seminiferous tubules** of each testicle and near the surface of each ovary. The initial steps in meiosis are similar for the male and female. The chromosomes replicate themselves so that each chromosome is doubled. Then each pair of chromosomes comes together in extremely accurate pairing called synapsis. After chromosome replication and synapsis, the cell is called a primary spermatocyte in the male and a

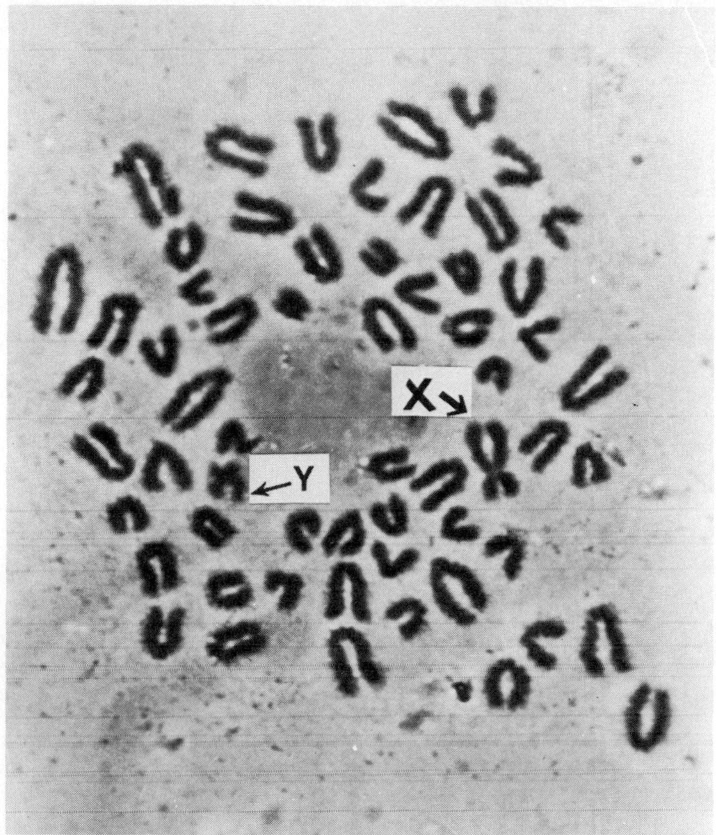

FIGURE 12.1.
The 30 pairs of chromosomes of a bull magnified several hundred times. Note the *X* and *Y* chromosomes. Courtesy of Nat M. Kieffer, Texas A&M University.

TABLE 12.1. Pairs of Chromosomes in Livestock and Poultry

Species	Number of Pairs
Turkeys	41
Chickens	39
Horses	32
Cattle	30
Goats	30
Sheep	27
Humans[a]	23
Swine	19

[a] Shown for comparison.

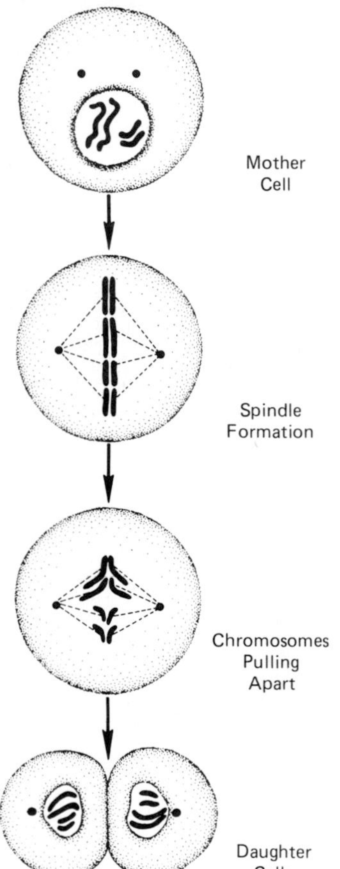

FIGURE 12.2.
Mitosis. Drawing by Dennis Giddings.

primary oocyte in the female. Because subsequent differences exist between spermatogenesis and oogenesis, the two are described here separately.

SPERMATOGENESIS

The process of spermatogenesis in our theoretical species is shown in Figure 12.3. The primary spermatocyte contains two pairs of chromosomes in synapsis. Each chromosome is doubled following replication. Thus, the primary spermatocyte contains two bodies or structures formed by four parts. By two rapid cell divisions, in which no further replication of the chromosomes occurs, four cells, each of which contains two chromosomes, are produced. The spermatid cells each lose much of their cytoplasm and develop a tail. This process, spermatogenesis, results in formation of sperm. Four sperm are produced from each primary spermatocyte. Whereas four chromosomes in two pairs are present in the primordial germ cell, only two chromosomes (one half of each chromosome pair) are present in each sperm. Thus, the number of chromosomes in the sperm has been reduced to half the number in the primordial germ cell.

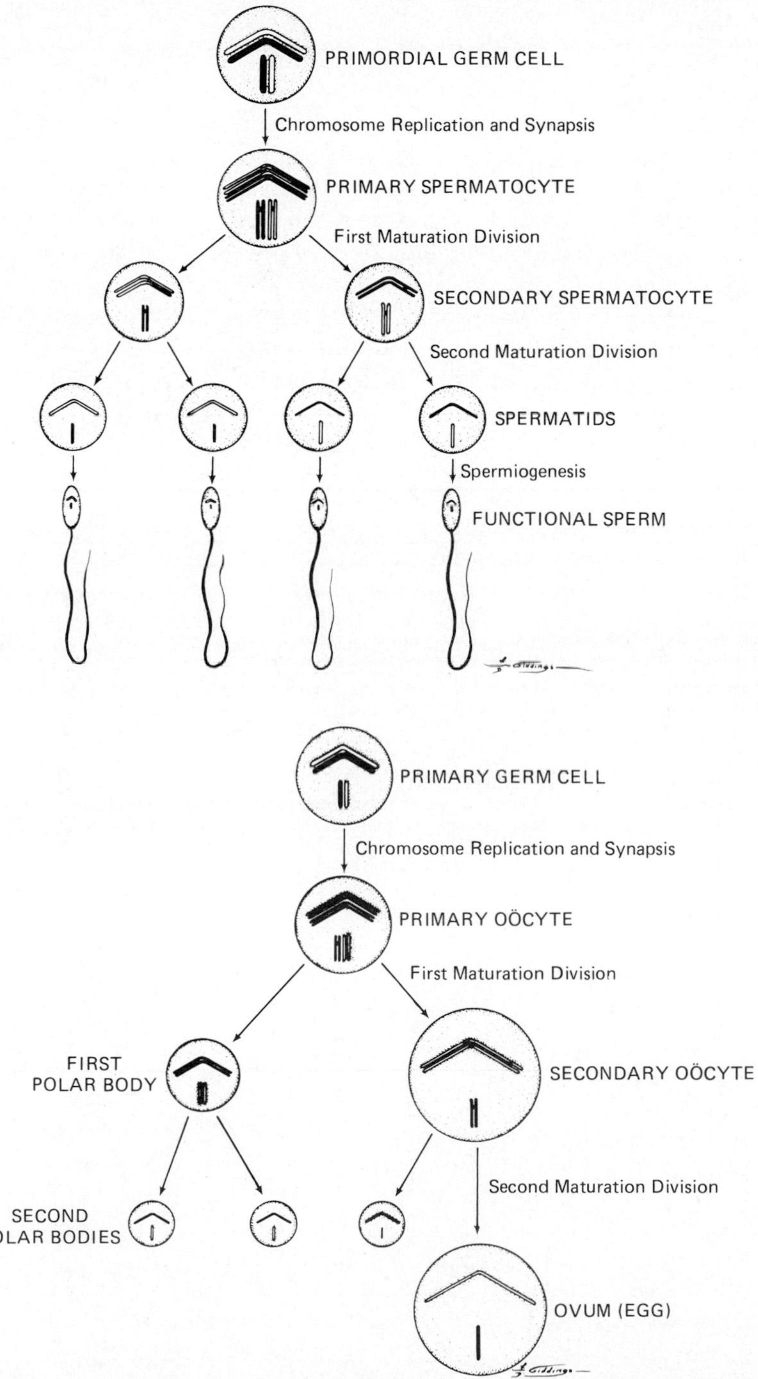

FIGURE 12.3.
Meiosis or reduction cell division in the testicle and ovary (example with two pairs of chromosomes). Drawing by Dennis Giddings.

OOGENESIS

The process of oogenesis in our theoretical species is shown in Figure 12.3. Like the primary spermatocyte of the male, the primary oocyte of the female contains a tetrad. The first maturation division produces one relatively large nutrient-containing cell, the secondary oocyte, and a smaller cell, the first polar body. Each of these two cells contains a dyad. The unequal distribution of nutrients that results from the first maturation division in the female serves to maximize the quantity of nutrients in one of the cells (the secondary oocyte) at the expense of the other (the first polar body). The second maturation division produces the egg (ovum) and the second polar body, each of which contains two chromosomes. The first polar body may also divide, but all polar bodies soon die and are reabsorbed. Note the egg, like the sperm, contains only one chromosome of each pair that was present in the primordial germ cell. The gametes each contain one member of each pair of chromosomes that existed in each primordial germ cell.

FERTILIZATION

When a sperm and an egg of our theoretical species unite to start a new life, each contributes one chromosome to each pair of chromosomes in the fertilized egg, now called a **zygote** (Fig. 12.4). **Fertilization** is defined as the union of the sperm and the egg along with the establishment of the paired condition of the chromosomes. The zygote is termed **diploid** (*diplo-* means "double") because it has chromosomes in pairs; one member of each pair comes from the sire and one member comes from the dam. Gametes have only one member of each pair of chromosomes;

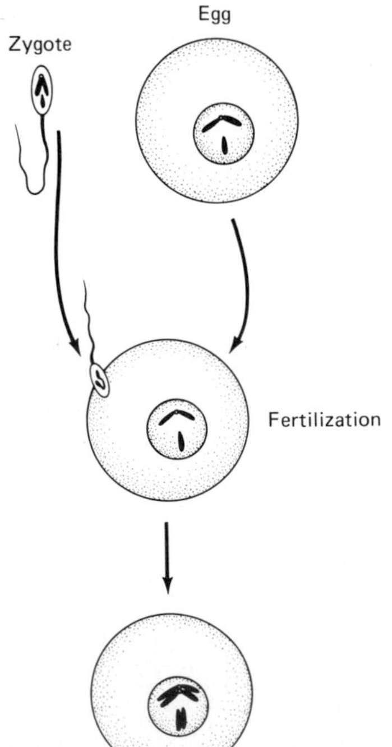

FIGURE 12.4.
Combining of chromosomes through fertilization (two pairs of genes used for simplification of example). Drawing by Dennis Giddings.

therefore, gametes are termed **haploid** (*haplo-* means "half"). Gametogenesis thus reduces the number of chromosomes in a cell to half the diploid number. Fertilization reestablishes the normal diploid number.

DNA AND RNA

The two members of each typical pair of chromosomes in a cell are alike in size and shape and carry **genes** that affect the same hereditary characteristics (Fig. 12.5). Such chromosomes are said to be **homologous.** The genes are points of activity found in each of the chromosomes that govern the way in which traits develop. The genes form the coding system that directs enzyme and protein production. Thus, they control the development of traits.

Chromosomes in advanced organisms like poultry and livestock are composed basically of a protein sheath surrounding **deoxyribonucleic acid (DNA).** Segments of DNA are the genes. DNA is composed of deoxyribose sugar, phosphate, and four nitrogenous bases. The combination of deoxyribose, phosphate, and one of the four bases is called a **nucleotide;** when many nucleotides are chemically bonded to one another, they form a strand that composes one-half of the DNA molecule. (A molecule formed by many repeating sections is called a **polymer.**) Two of these strands wind around each other in a double helix to form the DNA molecule.

The bases of DNA are the parts that hold the key to inheritance. The four bases are adenine (A), thymine (T), guanine (G), and cytosine (C). In the two strands of DNA, A is always complementary to (pairs with) T, and G is always complementary to C (Fig. 12.6). During

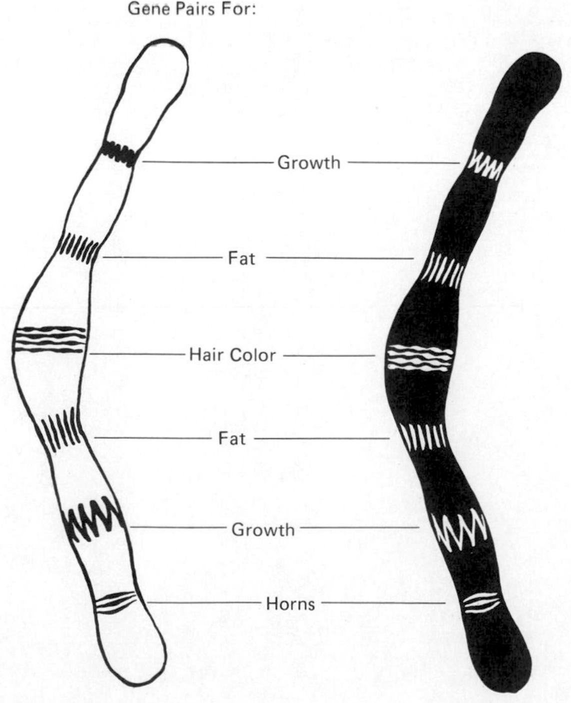

FIGURE 12.5.
A simplified example showing a pair of chromosomes containing several pairs of genes. Drawing by Dennis Giddings.

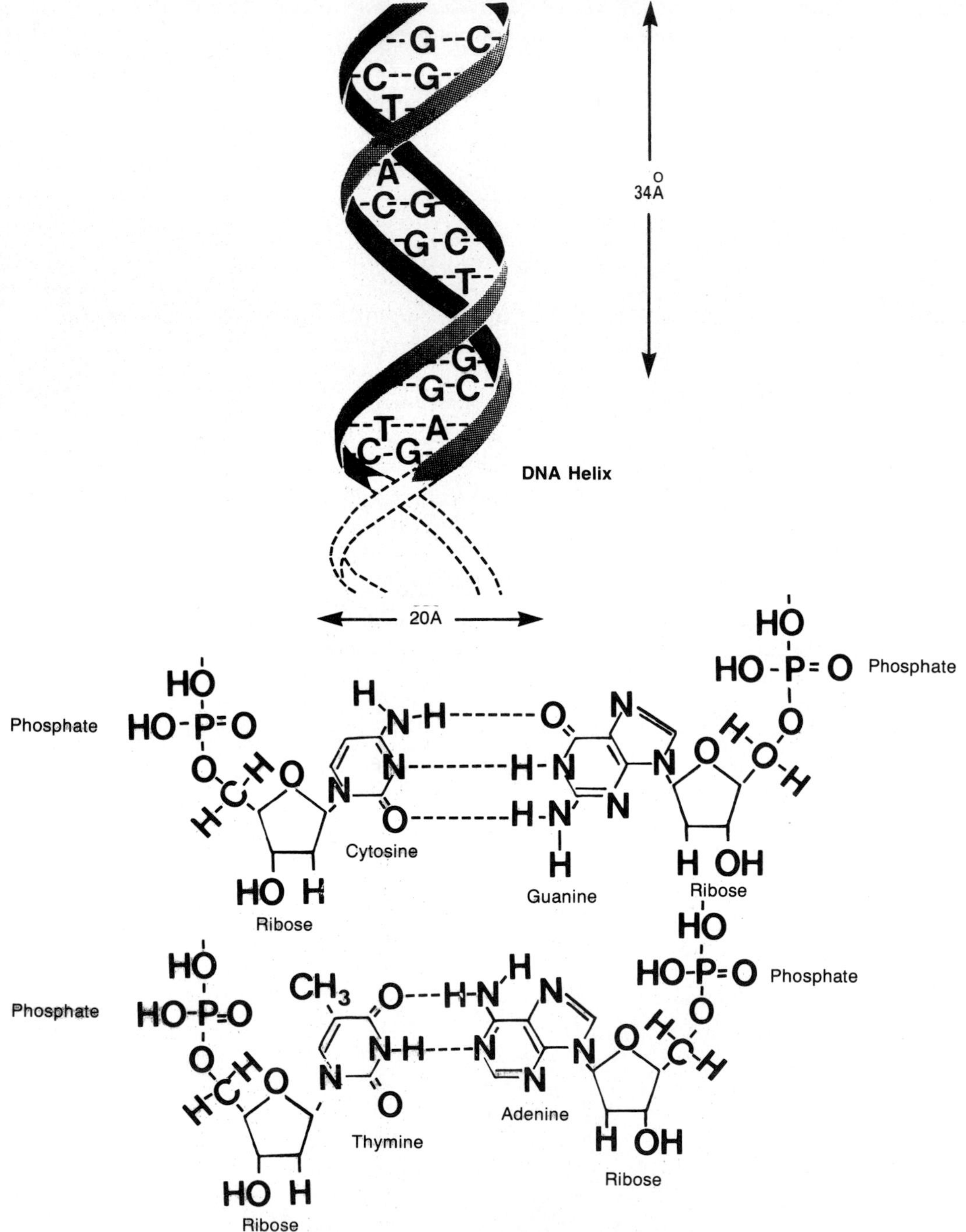

FIGURE 12.6.
DNA helix and structure of nucleotides.

meiosis and mitosis, the chromosomes are replicated by the unwinding and pulling apart of the DNA strands, and a new strand is formed alongside the old. The old strand serves as a template, so that wherever an A occurs on the old strand, a T will be directly opposite it on the new, and wherever a C occurs on the old strand, a G will be placed on the new. Complementary bases pair with each other until two entire double-stranded molecules are formed where originally there was one.

Nearly all genes code for protein, which are also polymers. It is important to realize that DNA and protein are both polymers. For each of the 26 amino acids of which proteins are made, there is at least one "triplet" sequence of three nucleotides. For example, two DNA triplets, TTC and TTT, code for the amino acid lysine; four triplets, CGT, CGA, CGG, and CGC, all code for the amino acid alanine. If we think of a protein molecule as a word, and amino acids as the letters of the word, each triplet sequence of DNA can be said to code for a letter of the word, and the entire encoded message, the series of base triplets, is the gene.

The processes by which the code is "read" and protein is synthesized are called **transcription** and **translation.** To understand these processes, another group of molecules, the **ribonucleic acids (RNAs),** must be introduced. There are three types of RNA; **transfer RNA (tRNA),** which identifies both an amino acid and a base triplet in mRNA; **messenger RNA (mRNA),** which carries the information codes for a particular protein, and **ribosomal RNA (rRNA),** which is essential for ribosome structure and function. All three RNAs are coded by the DNA template.

The first step in protein synthesis is that of transcription. Just as the DNA molecule serves as a template for self-replication using the pairing of specific bases, it can also serve as a template for the mRNA molecule. Messenger RNA is similar to DNA but is single-stranded rather than double-stranded and has the base uracil (U) in place of the base thymine found in DNA. It is shorter, coding for only one or a few proteins. The triplet sequence that codes for one amino acid in mRNA is called a codon. Through transcription, the encoded message held by the DNA molecule becomes transcribed onto the mRNA molecule. The mRNA then leaves the nucleus and travels to an organelle called a ribosome, where protein synthesis will actually take place. The ribosome is composed of rRNA and protein.

The second step in protein synthesis is the union of amino acids to their respective tRNA molecules. The tRNA molecules are coded by the DNA. They have a structure and contain an anticodon that is complementary to an mRNA codon. Each RNA unites with one amino acid. This union is very specific such that, as an example, lysine never links with the tRNA for alanine but only to the tRNA for lysine.

The mRNA attaches to a ribosome for translation of its message into protein. Each triplet codon on the mRNA (which is complementary to one on DNA) associates with a specific tRNA bearing its amino acid, using a base-pairing mechanism similar to that found in DNA replication and mRNA transcription. This matching of each tRNA with its specific mRNA triplets begins at one end of the mRNA and continues down its length until all the codons for the protein-forming amino acids are aligned in the proper order. The amino acids are each chemically bonded to each other by so-called peptide bonding as the mRNA moves through the ribosome, and the fully formed protein disassociates from the tRNA-mRNA complex and is ready to fulfill its role as a part of a cell or as an enzyme to direct metabolic processes. Figure 12.7 summarizes the steps of protein synthesis. It depicts the amino acids arginine (arg), leucine (leu), threonine (thr), and valine (val) being moved into position to join a chain that already includes the amino acids alanine (ala), proline (pro), and leucine (leu).

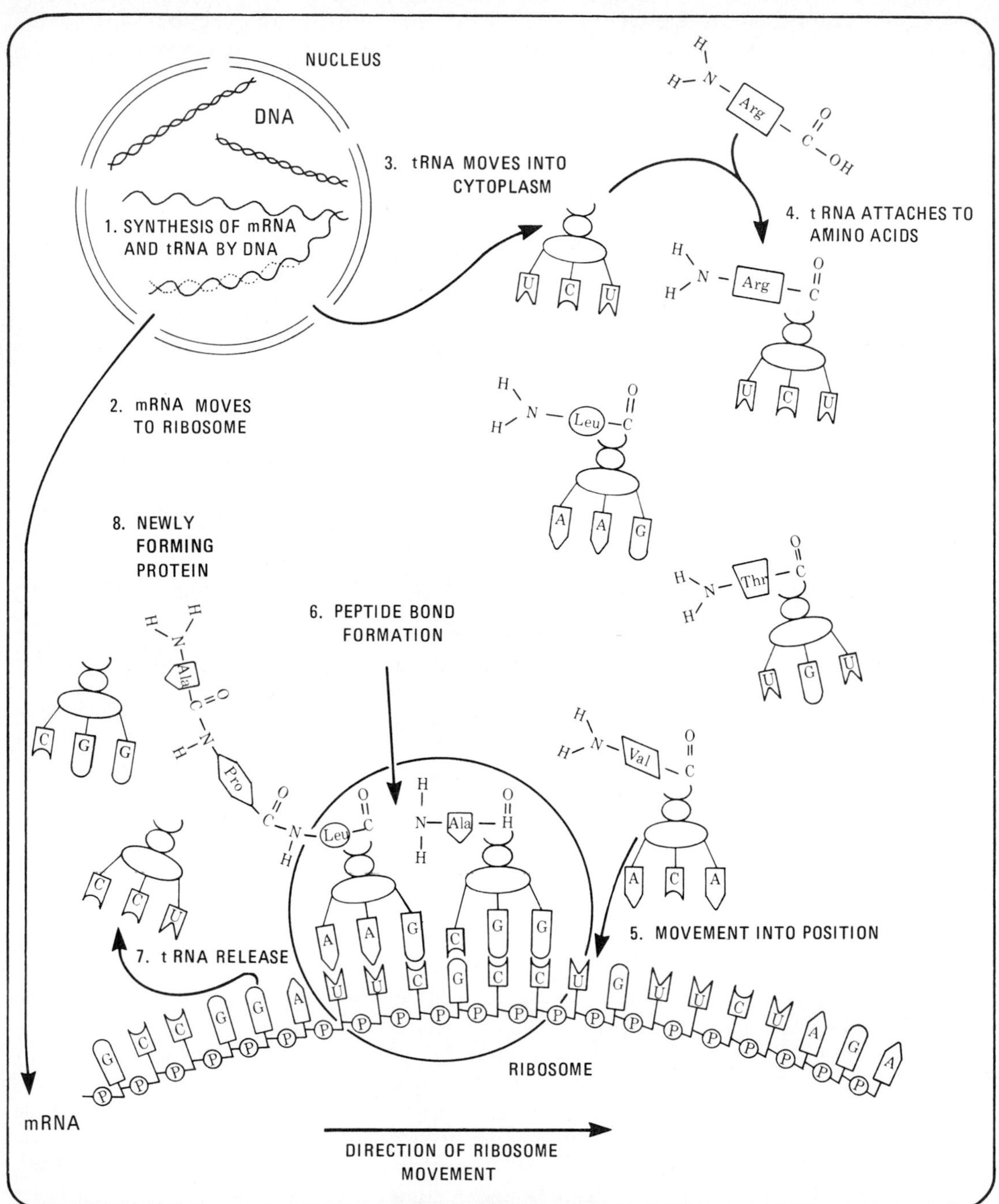

FIGURE 12.7.
Protein synthesis in the cell.

GENES AND CHROMOSOMES

Because chromosomes are in pairs, genes are also in pairs. The location of a gene in a chromosome is called a **locus** (plural, *loci*). For each locus in one of the members of a pair of homologous chromosomes, a corresponding locus occurs in the other member of that chromosome pair. The transmission of genes from parents to offspring depends entirely on the transmission of chromosomes from parents to offspring.

A special pair of chromosomes, the so-called sex chromosomes (*X* and *Y*), exist as a pair in which one of the chromosomes does not correspond entirely to the other in terms of what loci are present. The *Y* chromosome is much shorter in length than the *X* chromosome.

The *X* and *Y* chromosomes determine the sex of mammals. A female has two *X* chromosomes, and the male has an *X* chromosome and a *Y* chromosome. The female, being *XX*, can contribute only an *X* chromosome to the offspring. The male contributes either an *X* or a *Y* (Fig. 12.1), thus determining the sex of the newborn.

In all bird species, including chickens and turkeys, the female determines the sex of the offspring. The sex chromosomes are identical in the sperm (*XX*) but they are different in the egg (*XY*).

The genes located at corresponding loci in **homologous chromosomes** may correspond to each other in the way that they control a trait, or they may contrast. If they correspond, the individual is said to be **homozygous** at the locus (*homo-* means "alike"; *-zygous* refers to the individual); if they differ, the individual is said to be **heterozygous** (*hetero-* means "different"). Those genes that occupy corresponding loci in homologous chromosomes but that affect the same character in different ways (i.e., black or red color) are called **alleles.** Genes that are alike and that affect the character developing in the same way are called **identical genes.** Some authorities speak of alike genes in homologous chromosomes as **identical alleles.**

The geneticist usually illustrates the chromosomes as lines and indicates the genes by alphabetical letters. When the genes at corresponding loci on homologous chromosomes differ, one of the genes often overpowers, or dominates, the expression of the other. This allele is called **dominant.** The allele whose expression is prevented is called **recessive.** The dominant allele is symbolized by a capital letter. The recessive allele is symbolized by a lowercase letter. For example, in cattle, black hair color is dominant to red hair color, so we let B = black and b = red. Three combinations of genes are possible:

$$+B \; +B \qquad +B \; +b \qquad +b \; +b$$

Both *BB* animals and *bb* animals are homozygous for the genes that determine hair color, but one is homozygous-dominant (*BB*) and the other is homozygous-recessive (*bb*). The animal that is *Bb* is heterozygous; it has allelic genes.

SIX FUNDAMENTAL TYPES OF MATING

With three kinds of individuals (homozygous-dominant, heterozygous, and homozygous-recessive) and one pair of genes considered, six types of mating are possible. Using the genes designated as B = black and b = red in cattle, the six mating possibilities are $BB \times BB$, $BB \times Bb$, $BB \times bb$, $Bb \times Bb$, $Bb \times bb$, and $bb \times bb$. Keep in mind that our discussion of these genes is applicable to any other pair of genes in any species.

Homozygous-Dominant × Homozygous-Dominant (*BB* × *BB*). When two homozygous-dominant individuals are mated, each of them can produce only one kind of gamete—the gamete carrying the dominant gene. In our particular example, this gamete carries gene *B*. The union of gametes from two homozygous-dominant parents results in zygote that is homozygous-dominant ($B \times B = BB$). Thus, homozygous-dominant parents produce only homozygous-dominant offspring (Fig. 12.8).

Homozygous-Dominant × Heterozygous (*BB* × *Bb*). The mating of a homozygous-dominant with a heterozygous individual results in an expected ratio of 1 homozygous-dominant : 1 heterozygous. The homozygous-dominant parent produces only one kind of gamete, the one carrying the dominant gene (*B*). The heterozygous parent produces two kinds of gametes, one carrying the dominant gene (*B*) and one carrying the recessive gene (*b*). The latter two kinds of gametes are produced in approximately equal numbers. The chances are equal that a gamete from the parent producing only the one kind of gamete (the one having the dominant gene) will unite with each of the two kinds of gametes produced by the heterozygous parent; therefore, the number of homozygous-dominant offspring ($B \times B = BB$) and heterozygous offspring ($B \times b = Bb$) produced should be approximately equal (Fig. 12.9).

Homozygous-Dominant × Homozygous-Recessive (*BB* × *bb*). The homozygous-dominant individual can produce only gametes carrying the dominant gene (*B*). The recessive individual must be homozygous-recessive to show the recessive trait; therefore, it produces only gametes carrying the recessive gene (*b*). When the two kinds of gametes unite, all offspring produced receive both the dominant and the recessive gene ($B \times b = Bb$) and are thus all heterozygous (Fig. 12.10).

Heterozygous × Heterozygous (*Bb* × *Bb*). Each of the two heterozygous parents produces two kinds of gametes in approximately equal ratios: one kind of gamete carries the dominant gene (*B*); the other kind carries the recessive gene (*b*). The two kinds of gametes produced by one parent each have an equal chance of uniting with each of the two kinds of gametes produced by

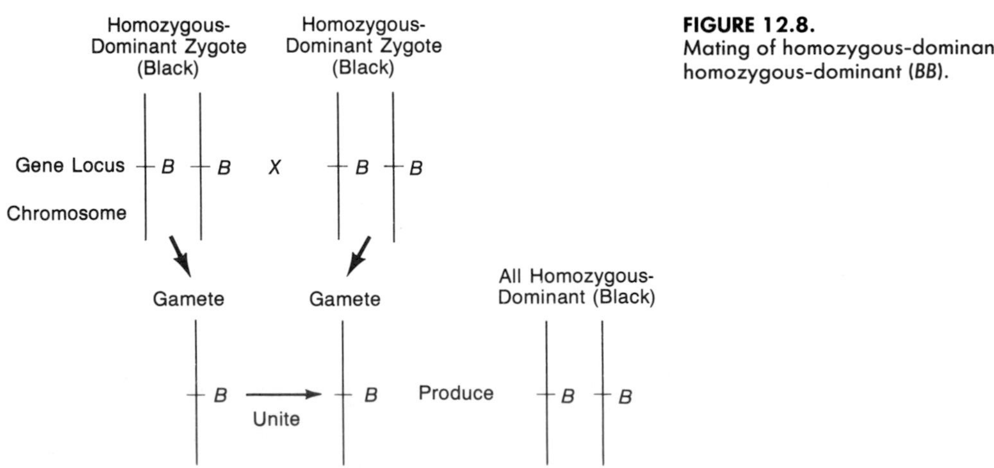

FIGURE 12.8.
Mating of homozygous-dominant (*BB*) × homozygous-dominant (*BB*).

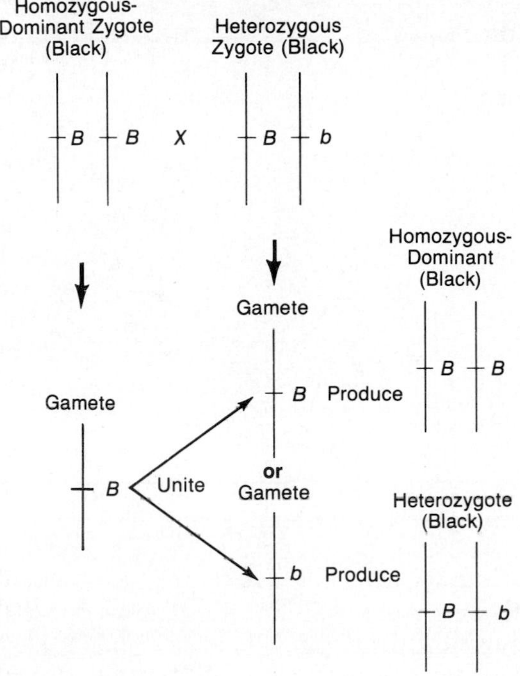

FIGURE 12.9.
Mating of homozygous-dominant (*BB*) × heterozygote (*Bb*).

the other parent. Thus, four equal-chance unions of gametes are possible. If the gamete carrying the *B* gene from one parent unites with the gamete carrying the *B* gene from the other parent, the offspring produced are homozygous-dominant ($B \times B = BB$). If the gamete carrying the *B* gene from one parent unites with the gamete carrying the *b* gene from the other parent, the offspring are heterozygous ($B \times b = Bb$). The latter combination of genes can occur in two ways: the *B* gene can come from the male parent and the *b* gene from the female parent, or the *B* gene can

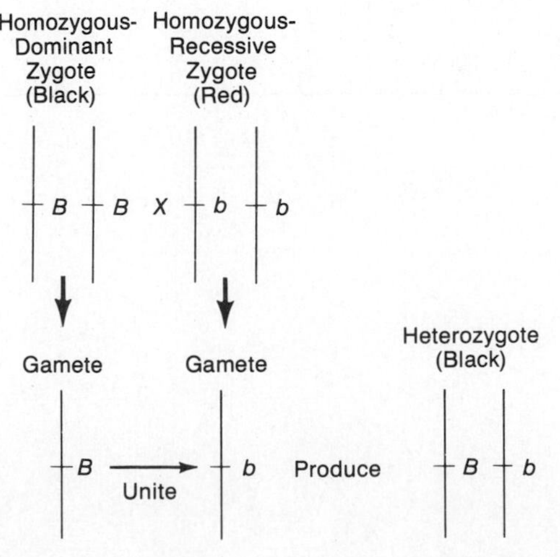

FIGURE 12.10.
Mating of homozygous-dominant (*BB*) × homozygous-recessive (*bb*).

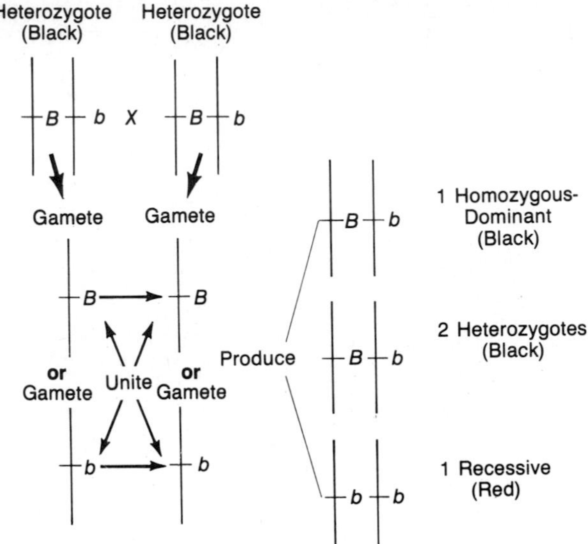

FIGURE 12.11.
Mating of heterozygote (*Bb*) × heterozygote (*Bb*).

come from the female parent and the *b* gene from the male parent. When the gametes carrying the *b* gene from both parents unite, the offspring produced are recessive ($b \times b = bb$). The total expected ratio among the offspring of two heterozygous parents is 1*BB* : 2*Bb* : 1*bb* (Fig. 12.11). This 1 : 2 : 1 ratio is the genetic, or **genotypic** ratio. The appearance of the offspring is in the ratio of 3 dominant : 1 recessive because the *BB* and *Bb* animals are all black (dominant) and cannot be genetically distinguished from one another by looking at them. This 3 : 1 ratio, based on external appearance, is called the **phenotypic** ratio.

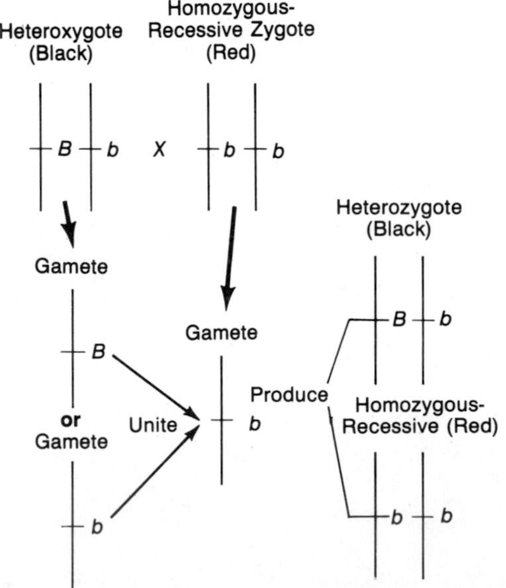

FIGURE 12.12.
Mating of heterozygote (*Bb*) × homozygous-recessive (*bb*).

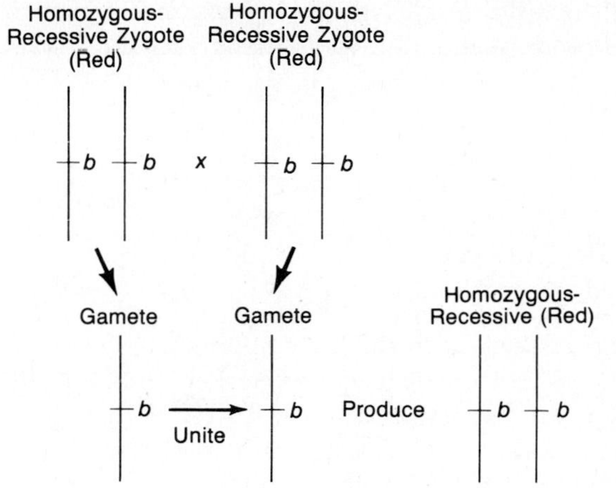

FIGURE 12.13.
Mating of homozygous-recessive (bb) $\times$ homozygous-recessive (bb).

Heterozygous $\times$ Homozygous-Recessive ($Bb \times bb$). The heterozygous individual produces two kinds of gametes, one carrying the dominant gene (B) and the other carrying the recessive gene (b), in approximately equal numbers. The recessive individual produces only the gametes carrying the recessive gene (b). There is an equal chance that the two kinds of gametes produced by the heterozygous parent will unite with the one kind of gamete produced by the recessive parent ($B \times b = Bb$; $b \times b = bb$). The offspring produced when these gametes unite thus occur in the expected ratio of 1 heterozygous : 1 homozygous-recessive (Fig. 12.12).

Homozygous-Recessive $\times$ Homozygous-Recessive ($bb \times bb$). The recessive individuals are homozygous; therefore, they can produce gametes carrying only the recessive gene (b). When these gametes unite ($b \times b = bb$), all offspring produced will be recessive (Fig. 12.13). This example illustrates the principle that recessives, when mated together, breed true.

The knowledge of what results from each of the six fundamental types of matings provides a background for understanding complex crosses. When more than one pair of genes is considered in a mating, one can understand the expected results; that is, one can combine each of the combinations of one pair of genes with each of the other combinations of one pair of genes to obtain the expected ratios.

MULTIPLE GENE PAIRS

Suppose that there are two pairs of genes to be considered, each pair independently affecting a particular trait. Let us consider two pairs of genes, one that determines coat color in cattle and the other whether the animal is polled (hornless) or horned. The genes are designated as follows: B = black (dominant), b = red (recessive), P = polled (dominant), and p = horned (recessive).

If a bull that is heterozygous for both traits ($BbPp$) is mated to cows that are also heterozygous for both traits ($BbPp$), one can determine the expected phenotypic and genotypic ratios. Results of crossing $Bb \times Bb$ (giving a ratio of 3 black : 1 red in the offspring, or 3/4 black and 1/4 red) has previously been shown (Fig. 12.11). Similarly, a cross of $Pp \times Pp$ gives a ratio of 3 polled : 1 horned. Combined, the $BbPp \times BbPp$ produces the following phenotypes:

$$BbPp \times BbPp$$

$$3 \text{ black} \times \begin{cases} 3 \text{ polled} = 9 \text{ black polled} \\ 1 \text{ horned} = 3 \text{ black horned} \end{cases}$$

$$1 \text{ red} \times \begin{cases} 3 \text{ polled} = 3 \text{ red polled} \\ 1 \text{ horned} = 1 \text{ red horned} \end{cases}$$

Of the 3/4 that are black, 3/4 will be polled and 1/4 will be horned. Therefore, 3/4 of 3/4 (or 9/16) will be black and polled; and 1/4 of 3/4 (or 3/16) will be black and horned. Similarly, of the 1/4 that are red, 3/4 will be polled and 1/4 will be horned, and 3/4 of 1/4 (or 3/16) will be red and polled and 1/4 of 1/4 (or 1/16) will be red and horned. This distribution of phenotypes is more often expressed as a 9 : 3 : 3 : 1 ratio instead of a set of fractions. The following demonstrates the different types of genotypes and phenotypes from the $BbPp \times BbPp$ mating:

	Genotypes (9)	*Phenotypes* (3)
1 $BB \times$	1 PP = 1 $BBPP$	black, polled
	2 Pp = 2 $BBPp$	black, polled
	1 pp = 1 $BBpp$	black, horned
2 $Bb \times$	1 PP = 2 $BbPP$	black, polled
	2 Pp = 4 $BbPp$	black, polled
	1 pp = 2 $Bbpp$	black, horned
1 $bb \times$	1 PP = 1 $bbPP$	red, polled
	2 Pp = 2 $bbPp$	red, polled
	1 pp = 1 $bbpp$	red horned

Table 12.2 shows another method of demonstrating the different phenotypes and genotypes that can be produced from a $BbBp$ (bull) $\times$ $BbPp$ (cow) mating. The four different sperm

TABLE 12.2. Genotypes and Phenotypes with Two Heterozygous Gene Pairs

	Eggs			
Sperm	*BP*	*Bp*	*bP*	*bp*
BP	*BBPP*[a] black, polled[b]	*BBPp* black, polled	*BbPP* black, polled	*BbPp* black, polled
Bp	*BBPp* black, polled	*BBpp* black, horned	*BbPp* black, polled	*Bbpp* black, horned
bP	*BbPP* black, polled	*BbPp* black, polled	*bbPP* red, polled	*bbPp* red, polled
bp	*BbPp* black, polled	*Bbpp* black, horned	*bbPp* red, polled	*bbpp* red, horned

[a]Genotype. Number of different genotypes: 1 (*BBPP*), 2 (*BBPp*), 2 (*BbPP*), 4 (*BbPp*), 1 (*BBpp*), 1 (*bbPP*), 2 (*Bbpp*), 2 (*bbPp*), 1 (*bbpp*).

[b]Phenotype. Number of different phenotypes: 9 black, polled; 3 black, horned; 3 red, polled; 1 red, horned.

have opportunity to combine with each of the four different eggs. Nine different genotypes and four different phenotypes are possible.

GENE INTERACTIONS

A gene may interact with other genes in the same chromosome (linear interaction), with its corresponding gene in a homologous chromosome (allelic interaction), or with genes in nonhomologous chromosomes (epistatic interaction). In addition, genes interact with the cytoplasm and with the environment. The environmental factors with which genes interact are internal, such as hormones, and external, such as nutrition, temperature, and amount of light.

Linear interactions are known to exist in lower animals *(Drosophila)*, but have not been demonstrated in farm animals.

Allelic Interactions

When contrasting genes occupy corresponding loci in the same (homologous) pair of chromosomes, each gene exerts its influence on the trait, but the effects of each of the genes depend on the relationship of dominance and recessiveness. **Allelic** interactions may also be called dominance interactions. When unlike genes occupy corresponding loci, complete dominance might exist. In this situation, only the effect of the dominant gene is expressed. A good example, as previously discussed, is provided by cattle, in which the hornless (polled) condition is dominant to the horned condition. The heterozygous animal is polled and is phenotypically indistinguishable from the homozygous polled animal.

There may be lack of dominance, in which heterozygous animals show a phenotype that is different from either homozygous phenotype and is usually intermediate between them. A good example is observed in sheep, in which two alleles for ear length lack dominance to each other. Sheep that are LL have long ears, Ll have short ears, and ll are earless. Thus the heterozygous Ll sheep are different from both homozygotes and are intermediate between them in phenotype.

Lack of dominance can also be considered additive gene action. Additive gene action occurs when each gene has an expressed phenotypic effect. For example, if D gene and d gene influenced rate of gain (where $D = 0.10$ lb/day and $d = 0.05$ lb/day), then $DD =$ increase in gain of 0.20 lb, $Dd =$ increase in gain of 0.15 lb, and $dd =$ increase of gain of 0.10 lb.

There is evidence that many pairs of genes affect production traits (like rate of gain) in an additive manner. For example, consider two pair of genes that influence daily gain, where $D = 0.10$ lb, $d = 0.05$ lb, $N = 0.10$ lb, and $n = 0.05$ lb:

$$DDNN = 0.40 \text{ lb}$$

$$\left.\begin{matrix} DDNn \\ DdNN \end{matrix}\right\} = 0.35 \text{ lb}$$

$$\left.\begin{matrix} DdNn \\ BBnn \\ bbNN \end{matrix}\right\} = 0.30 \text{ lb}$$

$$\left.\begin{matrix} Bbnn \\ bbNn \end{matrix}\right\} = 0.25 \text{ lb}$$

$$bbnn = 0.20 \text{ lb}$$

Sometimes heterozygous individuals are superior to either of the homozygotes. This condition, in which the heterozygotes show overdominance, is an example of a selective advantage for the heterozygous condition. Overdominance means that heterozygotes possess greater vigor or are more desirable in other ways (such as producing more milk or being more fertile) than either of the two homozygotes that produced the heterozygote. Because the heterozygotes of breed crosses are more vigorous than the straightbred parents, they are said to possess **heterosis.** This greater vigor or productivity of crossbreds is also said to be an expression of **hybrid vigor.**

The effects of dominance on the expression of traits that are important in livestock production (production traits like fertility, milk production, growth rate, feed conversion efficiency, carcass merit, and freedom from inherited defects) can be illustrated by bar graphs (Fig. 12.14). Figure 12.14A, which illustrates complete dominance, shows equal performance of the homozygous-dominant and heterozygous individuals, both of which are quite superior to the performance of the recessive individual.

With lack of dominance, one homozygote is superior, the heterozygote is intermediate, and the other homozygote is inferior (Fig. 12.14B). When traits are controlled by genes that show the effects of overdominance, the heterozygote is superior to either of the homozygous types (Fig. 12.14C).

A gene or a pair of genes in one pair of chromosomes may alter or mask the expression of genes in other chromosomes. A gene that interacts with other genes that are not allelic to it is said to be **epistatic** to them. In other cases, a gene or one pair of genes in one pair of chromosomes may influence many other genes in many pairs of chromosomes.

Several coat colors in horses are due to epistatic interactions. For example, the two basic coat colors in horses are black and chestnut. The recessive gene *b* produces the chestnut color; thus, *BB* and *Bb* are black, while *bb* is chestnut. Some horses possess a gene for white color that masks all other genes for color that exist in the genotype. This gene is called the dominant white gene *W*. The recessive gene *w* allows other color genes in the genotype to express themselves. Thus,

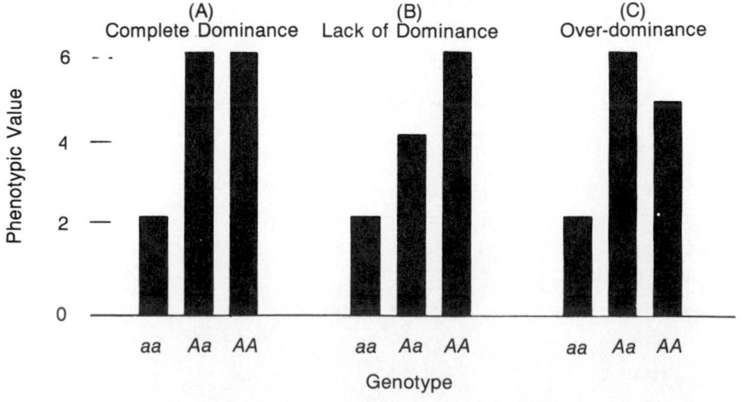

FIGURE 12.14.
Bar graphs illustrating: (A) complete dominance; (B) lack of dominance; (C) overdominance.

the genotypes and phenotypes are:

BBWW or *BBWw*: white	*BBww*: black
BbWW or *BbWw*: white	*Bbww*: black
bbWW or *bbWw*: white	*bbww*: chestnut

Epistasis can result from dominant or recessive genes or a combination of both. For example, in White Rock chickens, C = color, c = albino, W = color, and w = white. Homozygous *cc* prevents W from showing, and *ww* prevents *CC* from showing. In this example, if the mating *CcWw* × *CcWw* was made, there would be only 2 genotypes (colored or white). This contrasts with 4 phenotypes if C and W showed complete dominance, or 9 phenotypes if there was no dominance expressed in the two pairs of genes. Thus, epistasis changes the phenotypic ratio, but the number of different genotypes remains the same.

INTERACTIONS BETWEEN GENES AND ENVIRONMENT

Genes interact with both external and internal environments. The external environment includes temperature, light, altitude, humidity, disease, and feed supply. Some breeds of cattle (Brahman) can withstand high temperatures better than others. Some breeds (Scottish Highland) can withstand the rigors of extreme cold better than others.

Perhaps the most important external environmental factor is feed supply. Some breeds or types of cattle can survive when feed is in short supply for considerable periods of time, and they may consume almost anything that can be eaten. Other breeds of cattle select only highly palatable feeds, and these animals have poor production when good feed is not available.

Allelic, epistatic, and environmental interactions all influence the genetic improvement that can be made through selection. When the external environment has a large effect on production traits, genetic improvement is quite low. For example, if animals in a population are maintained at different nutritional levels, those that are best fed obviously grow faster. In such a case, much of the difference in growth may be due to the nutritional status of the animals rather than to differences in their genetic composition. The producer has two alternatives: (1) standardize the environment so that it causes less variation among the animals, or (2) maximize the expression of the production trait by improving the environment. The first approach is geared to increasing genetic improvement so that selection is more effective. Improvements made by this approach are permanent. The latter approach does not improve the genetic qualities of animals, but it allows animals to express their genetic potentials. The most sensible approach is to expose the breeding animals to an environment similar to one in which commercial animals are expected to perform economically.

BIOTECHNOLOGY

Biotechnology is defined as the use of living organisms to improve, modify, or produce industrially important products or processes. Microorganisms, for instance, have been used for centuries in the production of food and fermented substances, such as some dairy products. **Genetic engineering** of animals by selection and hybridization was first implemented at the turn of the century. Superovulation, sexing of semen, embryo splitting (cloning), and embryo transfer (discussed in Chapter 11) are some of the more recent advances in the field of biotechnology.

During the past several years, research has provided the tools to identify and manipulate DNA genes at the molecular and cellular levels. These genetic-engineering methods, which are used to alter hereditary traits, have created a renewed excitement in biotechnology. The American Association for the Advancement of Science ranks genetic engineering as among the four major scientific advancements of the twentieth century, similar in significance to unlocking the atom, escaping the earth's gravity, and the computer revolution.

Applications

Enzymes are used as "genetic scissors" to cut the DNA at designated places. These genetic components can then be reconstructed into unique combinations not easily achieved with natural selection. In addition to altering existing genes, synthetic genes can be constructed.

Genes can be injected from other animals of the same or different species (Fig. 12.15). The technology mimics nature in that genes can be moved around within and occasionally between species by some types of virus infections. The manipulation of the genetic material does not occur at the whole animal level, but it is performed **in vitro.** The genes are then inserted into either embryos, which are transferred to recipient animals or inserted into cells that are grafted into living animals.

Bovine Somatotropin (BST), a bovine growth hormone, is a natural protein produced in the pituitary gland of cattle. It helps direct the energy in feed to meet the animal's need for growth and milk production. BST can be produced outside the animal's body by the genetic-engineering process shown in Fig. 12.16. Providing supplemental BST to the dairy cow increases feed consumption and milk production. BST directs more of the additional feed to increase milk production than to body maintenance.

Based on extensive research, milk and meat from dairy cows treated with BST are safe for human consumption. Since BST is a protein, any supplemental BST ingested by consumers in the form of milk or meat from BST-supplemented cattle would be digested and degraded in the consumer's stomach just as the process occurs for naturally-produced animal BST and other

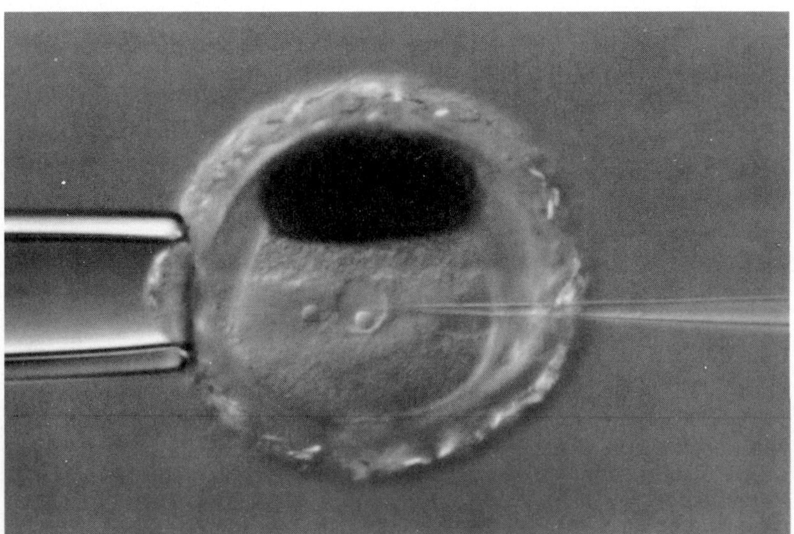

FIGURE 12.15.
A fertilized swine egg photographed at the moment it is microinjected with new genetic material. The vacuum in the large pipette at the bottom anchors the cell while a mixture containing the genes is forced through the smaller pipette into one of the egg's pronucleii. Courtesy of R. E. Hammer and R. L. Brinster, University of Pennsylvania School of Veterinary Medicine.

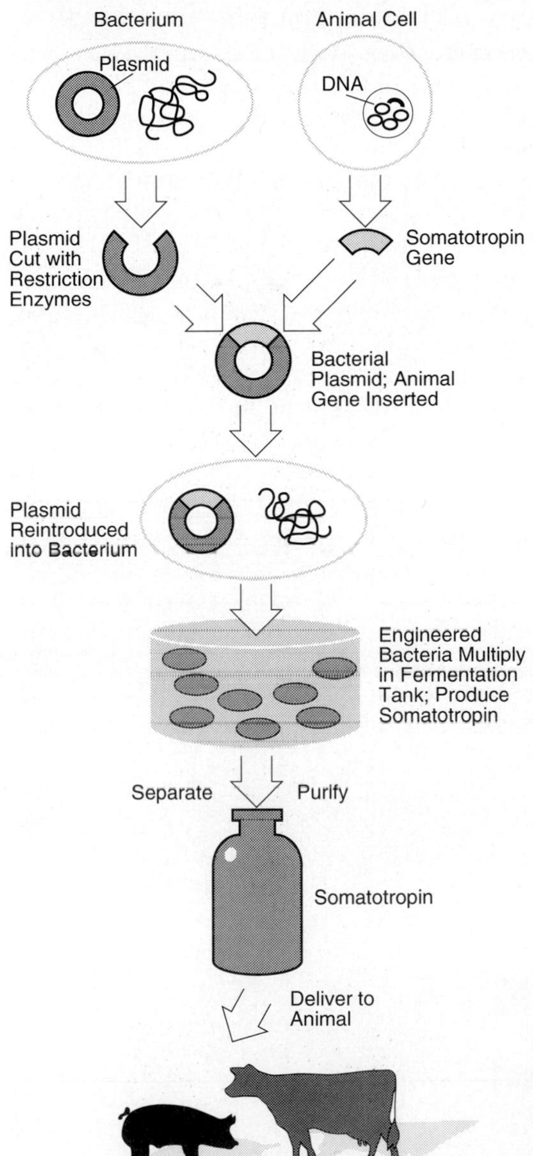

FIGURE 12.16.
Somatotropin production for use in cows and pigs.

proteins. The Food and Drug Administration (FDA) is expected to rule on the commercial use of BST in 1991. However, some consumer groups have expressed concern about potential health risks with foods produced by using any exogenous hormones, including BST. One consumer group has threatened a nationwide boycott of milk produced with BST.

Porcine somatotrophin (PST) has also been produced by a process similar to that used for BST (Fig. 12.16). Research has shown that PST, given as a supplement, increases litter size, reduces the time needed for pigs to reach market weight, improves feed efficiency, and reduces carcass fat production.

Several calves born in Canada, Germany, and the United States (in 1986, 1988, and 1989, respectively) have had genes introduced into them from other species, including genes from humans. A human gene that produces the protein interferon was introduced to improve disease resistance. Other genes have been introduced to stimulate growth and increase milk production. All physiological responses to these introduced genes have not been clearly elucidated.

Figure 12.17 shows a **transgenic** pig. While normal in appearance, the boar contains a new gene composed of the mouse metallothionien promotor/regulator fused to the bovine growth hormone structural gene. This gene, transmitted by the boar in Figure 12.17, causes elevated levels of growth hormone in the blood and results in a 10 to 15% increase in growth rate. The pigs are also more efficient in feed conversion to body weight and have significantly less body fat.

Nuclear fusion is the union of nuclei from two sex cells (sperm and eggs). In terms of biotechnology, this means not only can nuclei from a sperm and egg be united but also the union of nuclei from two eggs or two sperm can occur. The union of nuclei from two females results in all female offspring, while the union of two sperm nuclei produces 1/2 females (XX), 1/4 surviving males (*XY*), and 1/4 lethal males (*YY*). Thus, nuclei from two outstanding males (or females) can be united and then transferred to a recipient female. This has been accomplished in laboratory animals but not in larger, domestic farm animals. Even self-fertilization, once considered possible only in plants, may become a choice in genetically engineered farm animals.

Gene therapy involves inserting genes into a patient's cells to treat or cure certain diseases. In September, 1990, the first federally approved gene therapy for humans was approved. A girl having a hereditary disorder of the immune system had some of her white blood cells removed, genetically altered, then transfused back into her blood stream. The genetically altered cells

FIGURE 12.17.
This normal-appearing boar is a transgenic pig. He received a growth gene (from both mouse and cattle origin) by the process shown in Fig. 12.15. Courtesy of R. L. Brinster and R. E. Hammer, School of Veterinary Medicine, University of Pennsylvania.

were to produce a needed enzyme. Early results of the therapy appear promising. Similar approaches have been used to treat advanced melanoma (skin cancer).

Future Expectations and Concerns

Future advances in biotechnology through genetic manipulation appear to be mind-boggling and ethically challenging. Many of these changes will take years to accomplish because genetic engineering tasks are complicated and expensive. The present state of the art has a high number of failures. Research in the following areas gives insight into future possibilities.

1. Identification of the *genome* (all the genes) of domestic animals may become possible.
2. Animal productivity (i.e., growth, changing the fat-to-lean ratio, milk production) could be significantly increased and the cost of animal production could be reduced.
3. Disease-resistant animals could be genetically engineered.
4. Parasites could be controlled by genetic interference with their immune systems.
5. Domestic and international markets could be expanded through new genetically engineered products.
6. The ability to selectively produce either male or female offspring has had tremendous technological implications since scientists at the USDA Agricultural Research Service developed a method to sex and sort live fertile sperm. Sexed semen used in combination with superovulation, in vitro fertilization, embryo transfer, or just with artificial insemination could significantly affect management practices in the livestock industry.

Genetic engineering of animals raises questions of ethics, food product safety, and environmental safety. The general public has expressed concerns about possible food-safety risks associated with genetically engineered products. While the advantages of implanting genes into cells or putting gene-altered products into the blood of humans and animals to treat inherited genetic abnormalities and diseases are clear, research geared toward altering the genetic material of higher animals and humans is the focus of concern.

Overall, though, future advances in genetic engineering are likely to bring many significant genetic changes and challenges that will benefit both humans and domestic animals.

SELECTED REFERENCES

Publications

American Health Institute. 1988. *Bovine Somatotropin (BST).* Alexandria, VA: AHI.

Genetic Engineering: A Natural Science. St. Louis, MO: Monsanto Company.

Jones, W. E. 1982. *Genetics and Horse Breeding.* Philadelphia: Lea & Febiger.

Lasley, J. F. 1987. *Genetics of Livestock Improvement.* Englewood Cliffs, NJ: Prentice-Hall.

Legates, J. E. 1990. *Breeding and Improvement of Farm Animals. 4th ed.* New York: McGraw-Hill.

Petters, R. M. 1986. Recombinant DNA, gene transfer and the future of animal agriculture. *J. Anim. Sci.* 62:1759.

Pursel, V. G., et al. 1989. Genetic engineering of livestock. *Science* 244:1281.

USDA. 1986. *Biotechnology: An Overview. Biotechnology: Its Application to Animals. 1986 Yearbook of Agriculture (Research for Tomorrow).* Washington, DC: GPO.

Van Vleck, L. D., Oltenacu, E., and Pollack, J. 1986. *Genetics for the Animal Sciences.* New York: W. H. Freeman.

Visuals

Cattle Abnormalities (8861, 16-mm color film; 26 min). Bureau of Audio-Visual Instruction, University of Wisconsin Extension Service, Box 2093, Madison, WI 53701.

Genetics of Coat Color of Horses (SL 501 slide set). Educational Aids, National 4-H Council, 7100 Connecticut Ave., Chevy Chase, MD 20815.

The Nature of Change (videotape 17376 or 16-mm film 17373). Modern Talking Picture Service Film Scheduling Center, 5000 Park St. N., St. Petersburg, FL 33709. A companion booklet, "Genetic Engineering: A Natural Science," can be obtained from Direct Mail Corp., 1533 Washington Ave., St. Louis, MO 63103.

DNA and Genes, VHS Video; *Biotechnology: Science for the Future,* VHS Video. VEP, Calif. Polytechnic State Univ., San Luis Obispo, CA 93407.

CHAPTER 13

Genetic Change Through Selection

CONTINUOUS VARIATION AND MANY PAIRS OF GENES

Most economically important traits in farm animals, such as milk production, egg production, growth rate, and carcass composition, are controlled by hundreds of pairs of genes; therefore, it is necessary to expand one's thinking beyond inheritance involving one and two pairs of genes. The exact number of total genes in a species is not known, although estimates of 50,000 genes in humans and 200,000 genes in cattle have been made. A multibillion dollar project is underway to map the human **genome,** all the genes on the 23 pairs of chromosomes. If this is accomplished by the projected year 2005, it is anticipated that many genes of livestock and poultry will also be identified by that time.

Consider even a simplified example of 20 pairs of heterozygous genes (1 gene pair on each pair of 20 chromosomes) affecting yearling weight in sheep, cattle, or horses. The estimated numbers of genetically different gametes (sperm or eggs) and genetic combinations are shown in Table 13.1. Remember that for one pair of heterozygous genes, there are three different genetic combinations (i.e., *AA*, *Aa*, and *aa*), and for two pairs of heterozygous genes, there are nine different genetic combinations (Table 12.2 in Chapter 12).

TABLE 13.1. Number of Gametes and Genetic Combinations with Varying Numbers of Heterozygous Gene Pairs

No. of Pairs of Heterozygous Genes	No. of Genetically Different Sperm or Eggs	No. of Different Genetic Combinations (genotypes)
1	2	3
2	4	9
n	2^n	3^n
20	$2^n = 2^{20} = \sim 1$ million	$3^n = 3^{20} = \sim 3.5$ billion

TABLE 13.2. Number of Gametes and Genetic Combinations with Eight Pairs of Genes with Varying Amounts of Heterozygosity and Homozygosity

Genes in Sire: Genes in Dam:	*Aa* *aa*		*Bb* *Bb*		*Cc* *CC*		*Dd* *Dd*		*Ee* *Ee*		*FF* *FF*		*GG* *gg*		*Hh* *Hh*		Total
No. different sperm for sire	2	×	2	×	2	×	2	×	2	×	1	×	1	×	2	=	64
No. different eggs for dam	1	×	2	×	1	×	2	×	2	×	1	×	1	×	2	=	16
No. different genetic combinations possible in offspring	2	×	3	×	2	×	3	×	3	×	1	×	1	×	3	=	324

Most farm animals are likely to have some gene pairs heterozygous and some homozygous, depending on the mating system being utilized. Table 13.2 shows the number of gametes and genotypes where eight pairs of genes are either heterozygous or homozygous and each gene pair is located on a different pair of chromosomes.

Many economically important traits in farm animals show continuous variation primarily because they are controlled by many pairs of genes. As these many genes express themselves, and the environment also influences these traits, producers usually observe and measure large differences in the performance of animals for any one trait. For example, if a large number of calves were weighed at weaning (~205 days of age) in a single herd, there would be considerable variation in the calves' weights. Distribution of weaning weights of the calves would be

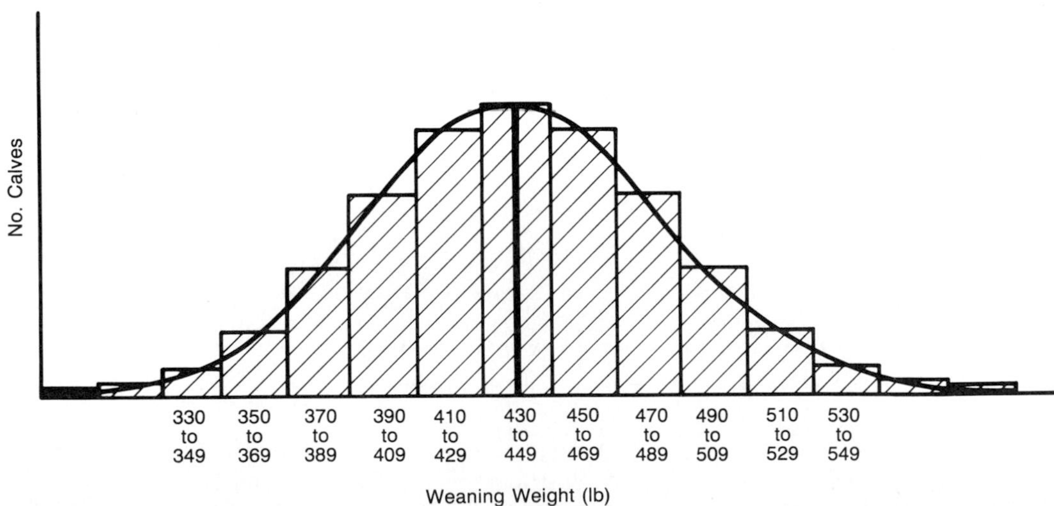

FIGURE 13.1.
Variation or differences in weaning weight in beef cattle. The variation shown by the bell-shaped curve could be representative of a breed or a large herd. The dark vertical line in the center is the average or the mean and, in this example, is 440 lb.

similar to the examples shown in Fig. 13.1 or 13.2. The bell-shaped curve distribution demonstrates that most of the calves are near the average for all calves, with relatively few calves having extremely high or low weaning weights when compared at the same age.

Figure 13.2 shows the use of the statistical measurement of standard deviation (SD) to describe the variation or differences in a herd where the average weaning weight is 440 lb and the calculated standard deviation is 40 lb. Using herd average and standard deviation, the variation in weaning weight is shown in Fig. 13.2 and can be described as follows:

1 SD: 440 lb ± 1 SD (40 lb) = 400–480 lb
(68% of the calves are in this range)
2 SD: 440 lb ± 2 SD (80 lb) = 360–520 lb
(95% of the calves are in this range)
3 SD: 440 lb ± 3 SD (120 lb) = 320–560 lb
(99% of the calves are in this range)

One percent of the calves (4 calves in a herd of 400) would be on either side of the 320–560-lb range. Most likely, two calves would be below 320 lb and two calves would weigh more than 560 lb.

Weaning weight is a phenotype, since the expression of this characteristic is determined by the genotype (genes received from the sire and the dam) and the environment to which the calf is exposed. The genetic part of the expression of weaning weight is obviously not simply inherited. There are many pairs of genes involved, and, at the present time, the individual pairs of genes cannot be identified similarly to traits controlled by one to two pair of genes.

Consider the following formula:

$$phenotype = genotype \pm environment$$

The phenotype will more closely predict the genotype if producers expose their animals to a similar environment; however, the latter must be within economic reason. This resemblance

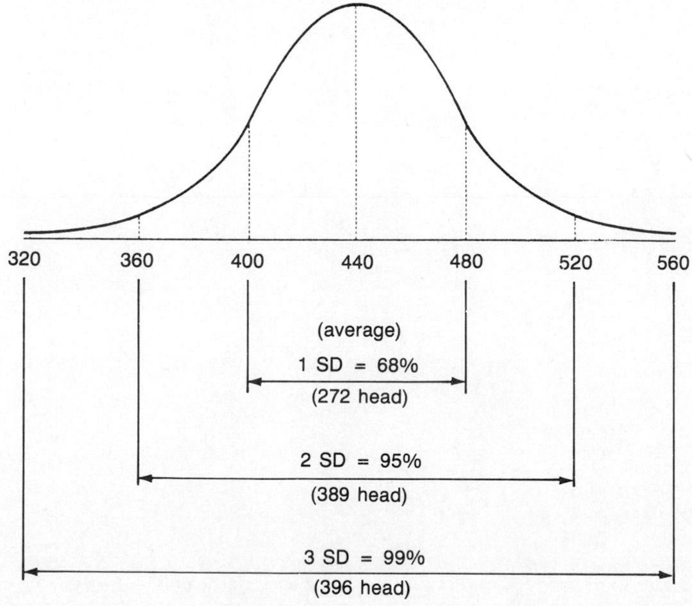

FIGURE 13.2.
A normal, bell-shaped curve for weaning weight showing the number of calves in the area under the curve. (Four hundred calves in the herd.)

between phenotype and genotype, where many pairs of genes are involved, is predicted with the estimate of heritability. Use of **heritability,** along with selecting animals with superior phenotypes, is the primary method of making genetic improvement in traits controlled by many pairs of genes. The application of this method is discussed in more detail later in the chapter.

Traits influenced little by the environment can also show considerable variation. An example is the white belt, a breed-identifying characteristic in Hampshire swine (Fig. 13.3). Note that the white belt can be nonexistent in some Hampshires whereas others can be almost white. To be eligible for pedigree registration, Hampshire pigs must be black with the white belt entirely circling the body, including both front legs and feet. Too much white can also limit registrations. It is difficult to select a herd of purebred Hampshires that will breed true for desired belt pattern. Apparently, some of the genes for this trait exist in heterozygous or epistatic combinations.

In a beef herd where the average weaning weight is 440 lb, or a dairy herd where annual milk production averages 12,500 lb per cow, the managers of these herds may want to increase the herd average. This assumes the increased production is economically feasible—that the economic benefits of improvement will cover the additional costs.

Selection

Selection is differential reproduction—preventing some animals from reproducing while allowing other animals to become parents of numerous offspring. In the latter situation, the selected parents should be genetically superior for the economically important traits. Factors affecting the rate of genetic improvement from selection include selection differential, heritability, and generation interval.

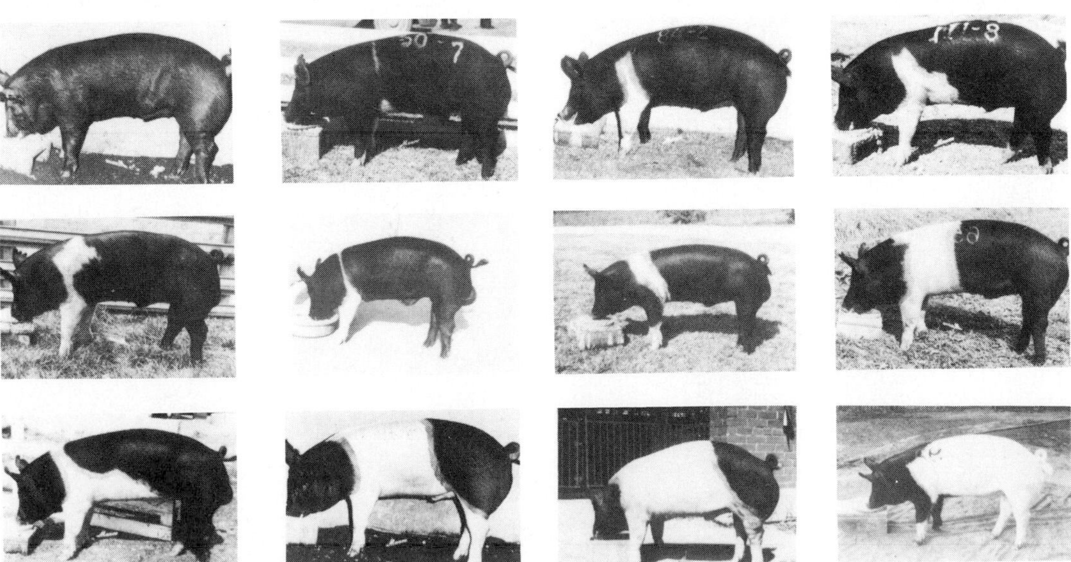

FIGURE 13.3.
Variation in belt pattern in Hampshire swine. Courtesy of *The Hampshire Herdsman.*

Selection Differential

Selection differential, sometimes called **reach,** shows the superiority (or inferiority) of the selected animals compared to the herd average. To improve weaning weights in beef cattle, producers cull as many below-average-producing cows as economically feasible. Then replacement heifers and bulls are selected that are above the herd average for weaning weight. For example, if the average weaning weight of the selected replacement heifers is 480 lb in a herd averaging 440 lb, then the selection differential for the heifers would be 40 lb. Part of this 40-lb difference is due to genetic differences, and the remaining part is due to differences caused by the environment.

Heritability

A **heritability** estimate is a percentage figure that shows what part of the total phenotypic variation (phenotypic differences) is due to genetics. Heritability can also be defined as that portion of the selection differential that is passed on from parent to offspring.

Realized heritability is the portion actually obtained compared to what was attempted in selection. To illustrate realized heritability, let us suppose a farmer has a herd of pigs whose average postweaning gain is 1.80 lb/day. If the farmer selects from this original herd a breeding herd whose members have an average gain of 2.3 lb/day, the farmer is selecting for an increased daily gain of 0.5 lb/day.

If the offspring of the selected animals gain 1.95 lb, then an increase of 0.15 lb (1.95 − 1.80) instead of 0.5 lb (2.3 − 1.8) has been obtained. To find the portion obtained of what was reached for in the selection, one divides 0.15 by 0.5, which gives 0.3. This figure is the realized heritability. If one multiplies 0.3 by 100%, the result is 30%, which is the percentage obtained of what was selected for in this generation.

Table 13.3 shows heritability estimates for several species of livestock. Traits having heritability estimates 40% and higher are considered highly heritable, 20%–39% are classified as having medium heritability, and lowly heritable traits are below 20%.

PREDICTING GENETIC CHANGE

The rate of genetic change that can be made through selection can be estimated using the following equation:

$$\text{Genetic change per year} = \frac{\text{heritability} \times \text{selection differential}}{\text{generation interval}}$$

Consider the following example of selecting for weaning weight in beef cattle and predicting the genetic change. The herd average is 400 lb and bulls and heifers are selected from within the herd.

Bulls	*Weight*
Average of selected bulls	535 lb
Average of all bulls in herd	440 lb
Selection differential	95 lb
Heritability	0.30
Total genetic superiority	28 lb
Only half passed on (28 ÷ 2)	14 lb

Heifers	*Weight*
Average of selected heifers	480 lb
Average of all heifers in herd	440 lb
Selection differential	40 lb
Heritability	0.30
Total genetic superiority	12 lb
Only half passed on (12 ÷ 2)	6 lb

Fertilization combines the genetic superiority of both parents, which in this example is 14 lb + 6 lb = 20 lb. The calves obtain half of their genes from each parent, therefore $\frac{1}{2}$ (28) + $\frac{1}{2}$ (12) equals 20 lb.

The selected heifers represent only approximately 20% of the total cow herd, so the 20 lb is for one generation. Since the heifer replacement rate in the cow herd is 20% it would take 5 years to replace the cow herd with selected heifers. Because of this generation interval, the genetic change per year from selection would be 20 lb ÷ 5 = 4 lb/year.

Generation Interval

This trait is defined as the average age of the parents when the offspring are born. This is calculated by adding the average age of all breeding females to the average age of all breeding males and dividing by 2. The generation interval is approximately 2 years in swine, 3–4 years in dairy cattle, and 5–6 years in beef cattle.

The previous example of 4 lb/year shows genetic change if selection was for only one trait. If selection is practiced for more than one trait, genetic change is $1/\sqrt{n}$ where n is the number of traits in the selection program. If four traits were in the selection program, the genetic change per trait would be $1/\sqrt{4} = 1/2$. This means that only $\frac{1}{2}$ the progress would be made for any one trait compared to giving all the selection to one trait. This reduction in genetic change per trait should not discourage producers from multiple-trait selection, as herd income is dependent on several traits. Maximizing genetic progress in a single trait may not be economically feasible, and it may lower productivity in other economically important traits.

Sometimes traits are genetically correlated. A genetic correlation between two traits means that some of the same genes affect both traits. In swine, the genetic correlation between rate of gain and feed per pound of gain (from similar beginning weights to similar end weights) is negative. This is desirable from a genetic improvement standpoint because animals that gain faster require less feed (primarily less feed for maintenance). This relationship is also desirable because rate of gain is easily measured, whereas feed efficiency is expensive to measure.

Yearling weight or mature weight in cattle is positively correlated with birth weight, which means that as yearling or mature weight increases, birth weight also increases. This weight increase may pose a potential problem, since birth weight to a large extent reflects calving difficulty and calf death loss.

EVIDENCE OF GENETIC CHANGE

The previously shown examples of selection are theoretical. Does selection really work, or is the observed improvement in farm animals a result of improving only the environment? Let's evaluate several examples.

TABLE 13.3. Heritability Estimates for Selected Traits in Several Species of Farm Animals

Species Trait	Percent Heritability	Species Trait	Percent Heritability
Beef Cattle		**Horses** *(Continued)*	
Calving interval	10%	Thoroughbred racing	
Age at puberty	40	Log of earnings	50%
Scrotal circumference	50	Time	15
Birth weight	40	Pacer: best time	15
Body condition score	40	Trotter	
Weaning weight	30	Log earnings	40
Postweaning gain	45	Time	30
Yearling weight	40	**Poultry**	
Yearling hip (frame size)	40	Age at sexual maturity	35
Mature weight	50	Total egg production	25
Carcass quality grade	40	Egg weight	40
Yield grade	30	Body weight	40
Cancer eye susceptibility	30	Shank length	45
Dairy Cattle		Egg hatchability	10
Services per conception	5	Livability	10
Birth weight	50	**Sheep**	
Milk production	25	Number born	15
Fat production	25	Birth weight	30
Protein	25	Weaning weight	30
Solids-not-fat	25	Postweaning gain	40
Type score	30	Mature weight	40
Teat placement	20	Fleece weight	40
Mastitis (susceptibility)	10	Face covering	55
Milking speed	30	Loin eye area	55
Mature weight	35	Carcass fat thickness	50
Excitability	25	Weight of retail cuts	50
Goats		**Swine**	
Milk production	30	Litter size	10
Mohair production	20	Birth weight	5
Horses		Litter weaning weight	15
Withers height	45	Postweaning gain	30
Pulling power	25	Feed efficiency	25
Riding performance		Backfat probe	40
Jumping (earnings)	20	Carcass fat thickness	50
Dressage (earnings)	20	Loin eye area	45
Cutting ability	5	Percent lean cuts	45

There have been marked visual, meat-to-bone ratio changes in the thick-breasted modern turkey selected from the narrow-breasted wild turkey, which is the only animal native to the United States. Estimates for genetic change for meat-to-bone ratio have been 0.5% per year for the modern turkey. Genetic selection and improving the environment, particularly through improved nutrition and health, have produced the modern turkey. Tom turkeys can produce 27 lb of liveweight (22 lb dressed weight) in 5 months; the wild turkey weighs 10 lb in 6 months.

TABLE 13.4. Height and Weight Differences in Mature Draft Horses, Light Horses, Ponies, and Miniature Horses

Horse Type	Approximate Height at Withers		Approximate Mature Weight (lb)
	Hands	Inches	
Draft	17	68	1,600
Light	15	60	1,100
Pony	13	52	700
Miniature	8	32	250

The modern turkey is not likely to survive in the same environment as the wild turkey. The modern turkey needs an environment with intensive management. For example, turkeys are mated artificially because the heavy muscling in the breast prevents them from mating naturally. Selection has been effective in changing rate of growth and meatiness in turkeys, but it has necessitated a change in the environment for these birds to be productive. Therefore, the improvement in turkeys has resulted from improving both the genetics and the environment.

There are tremendous size differences in horses. Draft horses have been selected for large body size and heavy muscling to perform work. The light horse is more moderate in size, and ponies are small. Miniature horses have genetic combinations that result in a very small size. The miniature horse is considered a novelty and a pet. Table 13.4 shows the height and weight variations in different types of horses. Apparently these different horse types have been produced from horses that originally were quite similar in size and weight. The extreme size differences in horses result primarily from genetic differences, as the size differences are apparent when the horses are given similar environmental opportunities.

One of the best documented examples of genetic change in farm animals comes from a back-fat selection experiment in swine. Figure 13.4 shows the results of 13 generations of selection for high and low back-fat thickness. Also, a line of pigs was maintained in which no selection for back-fat thickness was practiced. This nonselected line showed the environmental changes in back-fat thickness from year to year. In this experiment, back-fat thickness was the only trait for which selection was practiced. Selection for and against back-fat thickness was effective, since back-fat thickness is a highly heritable trait (50%).

The back-fat probe has been used to measure differences in back-fat thickness in live pigs (Fig. 13.5). Use of the back-fat probe has improved the effectiveness of selection, as back-fat thickness can be identified in breeding animals without having to slaughter them.

The effectiveness of selection against excessive back-fat thickness in swine is shown in Table 13.5. The reduction in lard production per hog has decreased dramatically, even though the average slaughter weight has increased since 1960.

Selection for milk production in dairy cattle has an additional challenge in a genetic improvement program because the bull does not express the trait. This is an example of a **sex-limited** trait.

A

B

C

FIGURE 13.4.
Examples of 13 generations of selecting for high and low fatness in swine. (A) High-fat slaughter pig. (B) Low-fat slaughter pig. (C) Carcass loin sections (from left to right): high-fat (slaughter weight, 212 lb.; 3.25 in backfat); control pig—no selection (slaughter weight, 216 lb.; 2.10 in backfat); low-fat (214 lb. slaughter weight; 1.30 in backfat). Courtesy of the USDA.

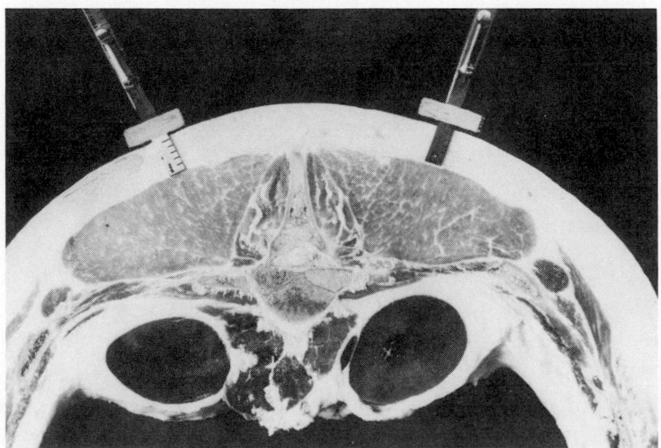

FIGURE 13.5.
A pork carcass cross section demonstrating how the steel ruler back-fat probe measures back-fat thickness in the live pig. Courtesy of Iowa State University.

TABLE 13.5. Trends in U.S. Lard Production

Year	Total Hog Slaughter (mil head)	Total Lard Production (mil lb)	Average Slaughter Weight (lb)	Lard Production per Hog (lb)
1950	79.3	2,631	—	33.2
1960	84.1	2,562	236	30.4
1970	87.0	1,913	240	22.0
1980	97.2	1,217	242	12.5
1985	79.6	852	247	10.7
1989	89.0	938	249	10.5

Source: USDA.

TABLE 13.6. Changes in Milk Production in the United States, 1940–89

Year	No. Cows (mil)	Average Milk Per Cow (lb)	Total Milk (bil lb)
1940	23.7	4,622	109.4
1950	21.9	5,314	116.6
1960	17.5	7,029	123.1
1970	12.0	9,751	117.0
1980	10.8	11,875	128.4
1989	10.1	14,506	143.3

Source: USDA.

Genetic evaluation of a bull is based primarily on how his daughters' milk production compares to that of their **contemporaries.** Milk production is a moderately heritable trait (25%), and the genetic change over the past 50 years is most noteworthy, even though the trait is not expressed in the bull (Table 13.6).

GENETIC IMPROVEMENT THROUGH ARTIFICIAL INSEMINATION

The primary reason for using artificial insemination (AI) is that genetically superior sires can be used more extensively. AI is used more in dairy cattle than any other species of farm animals. Using AI dairy bulls has resulted in higher milk production than using natural service bulls.

Figure 13.6 shows the rate of genetic improvement for yearling weight in beef cattle under different selection schemes. The most significant points are these:

1. Marked difference between herd A (no AI, males and females selected for yearling weight) and herd D (bulls obtained from a herd where no selection is practiced for yearling weight).
2. The small difference between herd B (selects bulls from herd A on yearling weight and selects for yearling weight in his females) and herd C (selects bulls from herd A but practices no selection for yearling weight on females). Effective sire selection accounts for 80%–90% of the genetic change in a herd.

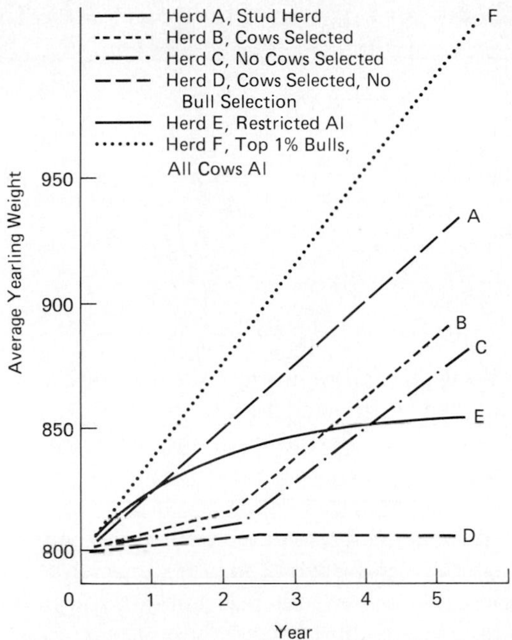

FIGURE 13.6.
Expected genetic change in different types of beef herds. Adapted from Magee, *Mich. State Univ. Qtr. Bul.* 48:4.

3. Greatest change in herd F where the top 1% of the sons of the top 1% of the bulls were used to build generation upon generation of AI selection. The rate of improvement using AI in herd F is 1.5 times that of herd A with natural service. The primary reasons for the greater improvement in herd F is a larger selection differential.

SELECTION METHODS

The three methods of selection are (1) tandem, (2) independent culling level, and (3) selection index, which is based on an index of net merit.

Tandem is selection for one trait at a time. When the desired level is achieved in one trait, then selection is practiced for the second trait. The tandem method is rather ineffective if selection is for more than two traits or if the desirable aspect of one trait is associated with the undesirable aspect of another trait. The tandem method is not generally recommended because it is the least effective of the three methods of selection.

Independent culling level establishes minimum culling levels for each trait in the selection program. Even though it is the second most effective type, it is the most prevalent one used. Independent culling level is most useful when the number of traits being considered is small and when only a small percentage of offspring is needed to replace the parents. For example, with poultry, 100 or more chicks might be produced from each hen and 1,500 or more chicks from each rooster. Here only 1 female out of 50 or 1 male out of 750 is needed to replace the parents. It is simple using this method to select from the upper 10% of the females and the upper 1% of the males.

Table 13.7 shows an example of using independent culling levels in selecting yearling bulls. Birth weight is correlated to calving ease. Weaning weight and postweaning gain measure

TABLE 13.7. Independent Culling Level Selection in Yearling Bulls

Trait	Culling Level	Bull				
		A	B	C	D	E
Birth weight (lb)	85 (max)	(105)	82	85	83	80
Weaning weight (lb)	500 (min)	550	(495)	505	570	600
Postweaning gain (lb/day)	3.0 (min)	3.7	3.6	3.1	3.3	3.5
Scrotal circumference (cm)	30 (min)	34	37	31	(29)	35

growth. Puberty and semen production are measured with scrotal circumference. Any bull that does not meet the minimum or maximum level is culled. Birth weights are evaluated on a maximum level (upper limit) since high birth weights result in increased calving difficulty.

The circled records in Table 13.7 indicate bulls that did not meet the independent culling levels. Bulls A, B, and D would be culled.

In the **selection index** method, each animal is rated numerically in comparison to each other animal for each trait being considered. A simplified example of the selection index method is to rank each of the five bulls in Table 13.7 on a scale of 1 to 5 with 1 representing the best performance and 5 the poorest. Table 13.8 gives the ranks of the bulls based on the 1 to 5 rating scale.

In Table 13.8, the total score (sum of rankings for each of the four traits) is shown for each bull. The bull with the lowest total score would represent the best bull. The bull with the highest total score would be the poorest bull.

A comparison of Tables 13.7 and 13.8 identifies some strengths and weaknesses of independent culling level versus index method of selection. Bull E is evaluated as the best bull under both selection methods.

Bulls B and C identify major weaknesses of independent culling levels. Under the selection index method, bull B was the second-best bull; using independent culling levels, the bull was culled (and likely castrated) when weaned at about 7 months of age. Bull B is superior in four traits but slightly below the culling level for weaning weight.

Bull C barely survives the four culling levels; however, he is ranked second to last in the index method. Therefore, mediocre animals may be selected using independent culling levels but culled using the index method.

TABLE 13.8. Simplified Selection Index Method of Selecting Yearling Bulls Based on Total Score

Trait	Bulls				
	A	B	C	D	E
Birth weight	5	2	4	3	1
Weaning weight	3	5	4	2	1
Postweaning gain	1	2	5	4	3
Scrotal circumference	3	1	4	5	2
Total score	12	10	17	14	7

An advantage of independent culling levels is that selection can occur during different productive stages during the animal's lifetime (e.g., at weaning). This is more cost-effective than the index method, where no culling should occur until records are recorded for all traits. A combination of the two methods may be most useful and cost-effective.

The example in Table 13.8 is oversimplified. Equal emphasis is given to each of the four traits. A selection index could be computed for the traits in Table 13.8 by putting the heritabilities, economic values, genetic correlations, and variabilities of these four traits into a single formula. This process is rather complicated, as it requires the use of complex statistical methods. An example of such an index, used in boar selection, is given in Chapter 26.

BASIS FOR SELECTION

The three primary bases of selection—(1) **pedigree** (names and records of relatives), (2) **individual appearance** or **individual performance,** and (3) **progeny testing**—are shown in Figure 13.7.

Pedigree information is most useful before animals have expressed their own individual performance or their progeny's performance is known. Pedigree is also useful for assessing genetic abnormalities and traits expressed much later in life (longevity), as well as for selecting for traits expressed only in one sex. In evaluating pedigree information, only the information from the animal's closest relatives should be used because of the genetic relationship involved. For example, the genetic relationship of an animal to each parent is 1/2 (50%), to each grandparent 1/4 (25%), and to each great-grandparent 1/8 (12.5%).

Selection on individual appearance and performance should be practiced on traits that are economically important and have high heritabilities. One primary advantage of selection on individual performance is that it permits rapid generation turnover and thus shortens the general interval.

Progeny testing is more accurate than the other two methods, provided the progeny test is accurate and extensive. Progeny tests are particularly useful in selecting for carcass traits (where

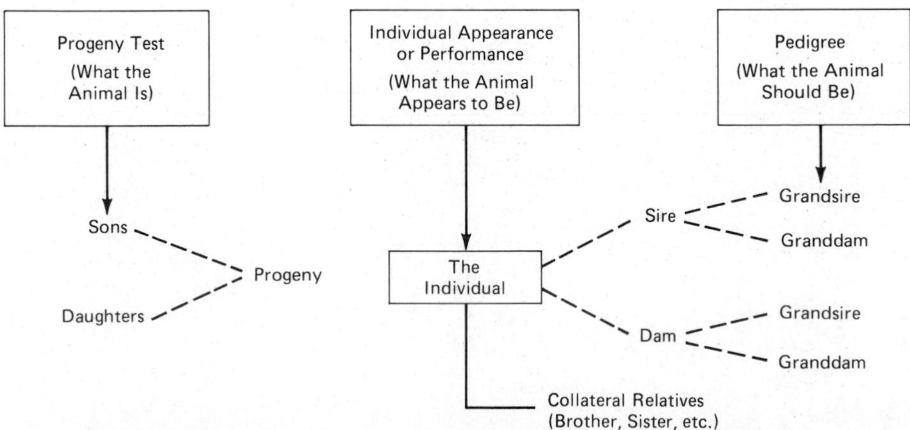

FIGURE 13.7.
The selection methods, how they tie together, and a brief appraisal of each.

good carcass indicators are not available in the live animal), sex-limited traits such as milk production, and traits with low heritabilities.

Disadvantages of progeny testing include (1) that too few animals can be progeny-tested, (2) the longer generation interval required to obtain progeny information, and (3) the decreased accuracy in poorly conducted tests. Progeny testing is usually limited to sires because a sufficient number of offspring cannot be obtained on a dam to give an adequate progeny test.

In a proper progeny test, sires are assigned females at random after the dams have been classified by age, line of breeding, and known performance. A sire, bred to a selected group of females, can give biased information that does not accurately evaluate his breeding ability. An adequate progeny test involves a minimum number of progeny. The greater the number, the greater the validity of the test. Progeny test data are biased and their accuracy is greatly reduced if dams and offspring are not fed and managed uniformly until all data are collected.

All three bases of selection can be used effectively in animal-breeding programs. Outstanding young sires can best be identified by using individual performance and pedigree information on the sire, dam, and half-sibs. These outstanding young sires then need to prove themselves genetically, based on a valid progeny-testing program. Results of progeny tests determine which sires to use extensively in later years.

SELECTED REFERENCES

Publications

Genetics and Goat Breeding. Proceedings of the Third International Conference on Goat Production and Disease. 1982. Scottsdale, AZ: *Dairy Goat Journal.*

Herman, H. A. 1981. *Improving Cattle by the Millions. NAAB and the Development and Worldwide Application of Artificial Insemination.* Columbia: University of Missouri Press.

Hetzer, H. O., and Harvey, W. R. 1967. Selection for high and low fatness in swine. *J. Anim. Sci.* 26:1244.

Hintz, R. L. 1980. Genetics of performance in the horse. *J. Anim. Sci.* 51:582.

Lasley, J. F. 1987. *Genetics of Livestock Improvement.* Englewood Cliffs, NJ: Prentice-Hall.

Legates, J. E. 1990. *Breeding and Improvement of Farm Animals.* 4th ed. New York: McGraw-Hill.

Van Vleck, L. D., Oltenacu, E., and Pollack, J. 1986. *Genetics for the Animal Sciences.* New York: W. H. Freeman.

Visuals

Development of the Modern Chicken (79 slides and audiotape; 15 min); and *Development of the Modern Turkey* (76 slides and audiotape; 14 min). Poultry Science Department, Ohio State University, 674 W. Lane Ave., Columbus, OH 43210.

CHAPTER 14

Mating Systems

Purebred breeders (sometimes called seedstock producers) and commercial breeders (producers) are the two general classifications of animal breeders. **Purebred** livestock typically come from the pure breeds for which their ancestry is recorded on a pedigree by a breed association (Fig. 14.1). Most commercial slaughter livestock are crossbreeds, resulting from crossing two or more breeds or lines of breeding.

A knowledge of breeding or mating systems is important because producers can use mating systems to preserve genetic superiority and utilize hybrid vigor. Genetic improvement can be optimized in most herds and flocks by utilizing a combination of selection and mating systems.

Mating systems are identified primarily by genetic relationship of the animals being mated. The two major systems of mating are **inbreeding** and **outbreeding.** Inbreeding is the mating of animals more closely related than the average of the breed or population. Outbreeding is the mating of animals not as closely related as the average of the population.

Since mating systems are based on the *relationship* of animals being mated, it is important to understand more detail about genetic relationship. Proper pedigree evaluation also involves understanding the genetic relationship between animals. Relationship is best described in knowing which genes two animals have in common and whether the genes in an animal or animals exist primarily in a heterozygous or homozygous condition. Figure 14.2 shows the mating systems and their relationship to a homozygous or heterozygous condition.

Because inbreeding is the mating of related animals, the resulting inbred offspring have an increased homozygosity of gene pairs compared to noninbred animals in the same population (breed or herd). An example of inbreeding is shown in Figure 14.3, where animal A has resulted from mating B (the sire) to C (the dam). Note that B and C have the same parents (D and E). B and C are genetically related because they have a brother–sister relationship. B and C do not have the same identical genetic makeup because each has received a sample half of genes from each

CERTIFICATE OF REGISTRY

No.579621 F

National Suffolk Sheep Association

P. O. Box 324 Columbia, Missouri 65205

EWE Single

~~"Naxos"~~

Strahl 85-1

Sire Strahl Y414 N186304M

Sire Marshall 82-518 N170065M

Dam Strahl S14 Enf N371105F

Ear Tag

Year Born January 21, 1985

Production Registry Index

Dam Strahl VG 30 N395647F

Sire "Vegas" Nelsh MG202 N180403M

Dam Strahl BL160 N219401F

Breeder Maurice Strahl & Sons, Greenfield, Indiana

Owner (2nd) August 29, 1985, Burke & Nelsh Suffolks, Platte City, Missouri

DATE August 19, 1985

Secretary *Betty Biellier*

SAMPLE CERTIFICATE OF REGISTRY - Not Valid for Registry purposes

The above pedigree is on record in the NATIONAL SUFFOLK SHEEP ASSOCIATION.

FIGURE 14.1.
Pedigree of a Suffolk ewe, Strahl 85-1 (registration number 579621 F). Note in this pedigree that the sire, dam, and four grandparents are listed, with a registration number following each of their names. Courtesy of the National Suffolk Sheep Association.

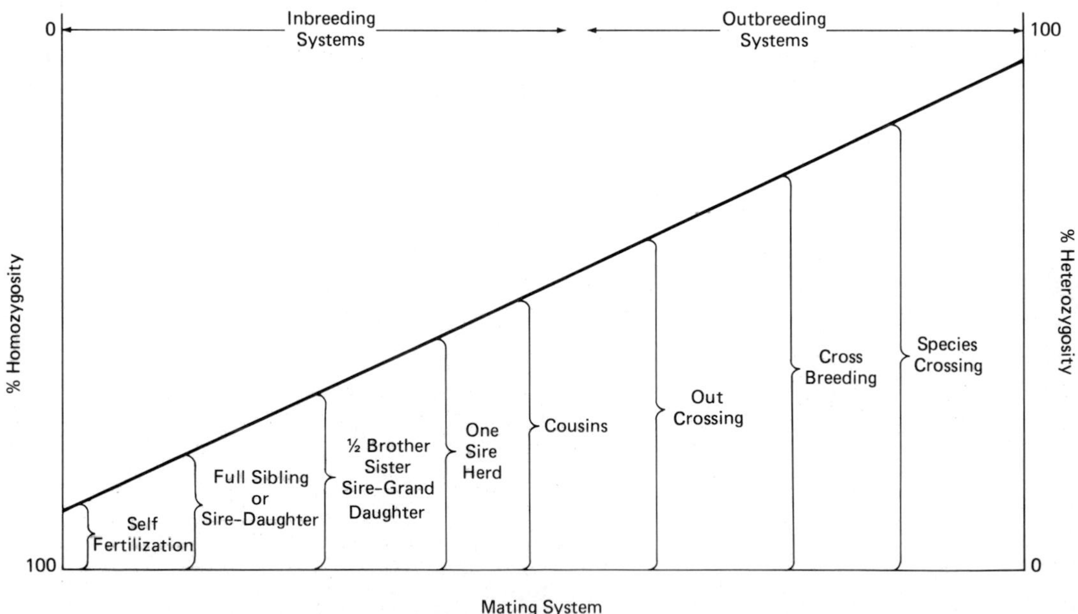

FIGURE 14.2.
Relationship of the mating system to the amount of heterozygosity or homozygosity. Self-fertilization is currently not an available mating system in animals.

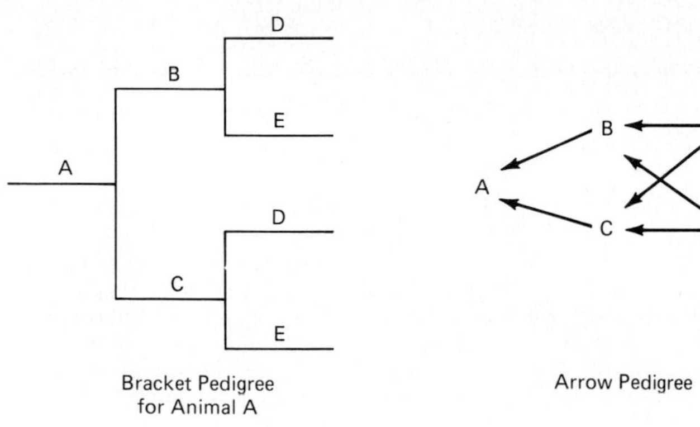

FIGURE 14.3.
Bracket pedigree and arrow pedigree showing animal A resulting from a full brother–sister mating.

parent. The arrow in the arrow pedigree represents a sample half of genes from the parent to the offspring.

Animal A is inbred because it has resulted from the mating of related animals. Although the calculations are not shown in the figure, animal A has 25% more homozygous genes as compared with a noninbred animal in the same population.

Figure 14.4 shows another example of inbreeding, where animal X has resulted from a sire–daughter mating. Sire A was mated to dam D, with D being sired by A. The increased homozygosity of animal X is 25%, which is the same as animal A in Fig. 14.3.

The two different forms of inbreeding are these:

1. *Intensive inbreeding*—mating of closely related animals whose ancestors have been inbred for several generations.
2. *Linebreeding*—a mild form of inbreeding where inbreeding is kept relatively low while maintaining a high genetic relationship to an ancestor or line of ancestors.

Intensive Inbreeding

Intensive inbreeding occurs by mating closely related animals for several generations. Figure 14.5 shows an example of intensive inbreeding. The increase in the homozygosity of animal H's genes is higher than 25% (compare with Fig. 14.4) because both the sire and grandsire of animal H were also inbred.

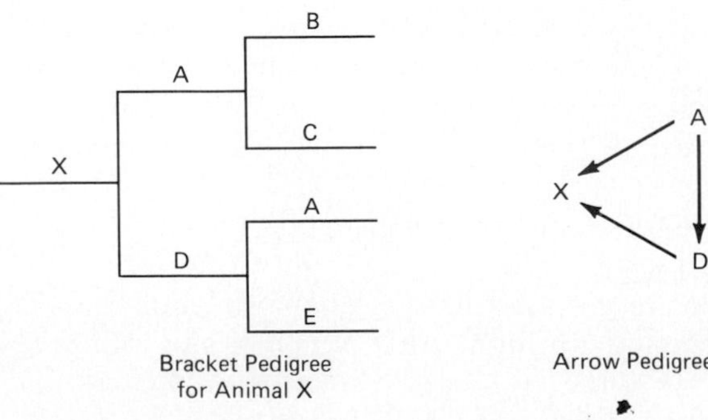

FIGURE 14.4.
Bracket pedigree and arrow pedigree showing animal X resulting from a sire–daughter mating.

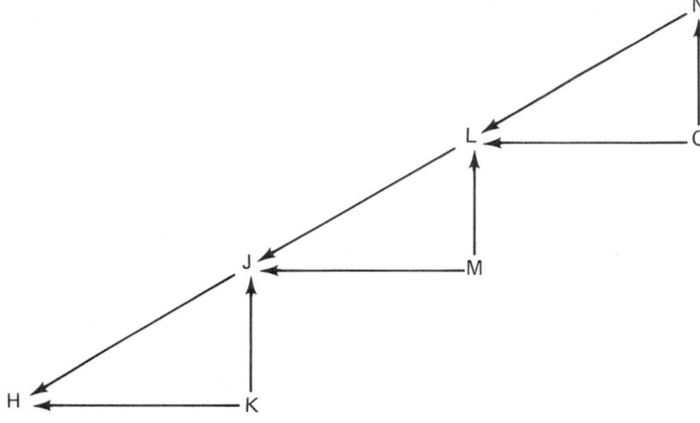

FIGURE 14.5.
An arrow pedigree showing animal H resulting from three generations of sire–daughter matings. Note that J is the sire of H and also the sire of K, the latter being the dam of H. Animal J has resulted from two previous, successive generations of sire–daughter matings.

There are numerous, genetically different inbred lines that can be produced in a given population such as a breed. The number of different, completely homozygous inbred lines is 2^n, where n is the number of heterozygous gene pairs. For example, with 2 pairs of heterozygous gene pairs, there are 2^2 or 4 different inbred lines that are possible. For example, with *BbPp* genes in a herd completely heterozygous (see Chapter 12), the different, completely homozygous lines that can result from inbreeding are *BBPP, BBpp, bbPP,* and *bbpp.* Each of these inbred lines is genetically pure and will breed true.

There have been research projects with swine and beef cattle in which inbred lines have been produced, anticipating that the crossing of these inbred lines would produce results similar to hybrid corn (Fig. 14.6). One continuing research project is at the San Juan Basin Research Center (SJBRC) in Hesperus, Colorado, where cattle have been inbred for more than 30 years. Figure 14.7 shows the arrow pedigree of an inbred bull (Royal 4160) produced in the Royal line of Hereford cattle. Note that College Royal Domino 3 is the sire of 10 animals in Royal 4160's pedigree, while Royal 3016 has sired 6 animals in the same pedigree. The increased homozygosity of this bull is 58%, which represents some of the most highly inbred cattle in the world.

Information obtained from inbreeding studies with farm animals demonstrates the following results and observations:

1. Increased inbreeding is usually detrimental to reproductive performance and preweaning and postweaning growth. Also, inbred animals are more susceptible to environmental stresses. Whereas 60%–70% of the inbred lines show the detrimental effects to increased inbreeding, there are 30%–40% of the lines that show no detrimental effect with some lines demonstrating improved productivity.
2. In a Colorado research beef herd, the inbred lines showed a yearly genetic increase of 2.6 lb in weaning weight over a 26-year period, while the crosses of inbred lines made a 4.6 lb increase over the same time period. Heterosis is demonstrated in the line crosses, and the 4.6 lb increase is typical of what breeders might expect from using intense selection in an outbred herd.
3. Inbreeding quickly identifies some desirable genes and also undesirable genes, particularly the hidden, serious recessive genes.
4. Inbred animals with superior performance are the most likely to have superior breeding values, which result in more uniform progeny with high levels of genetically influenced productivity.

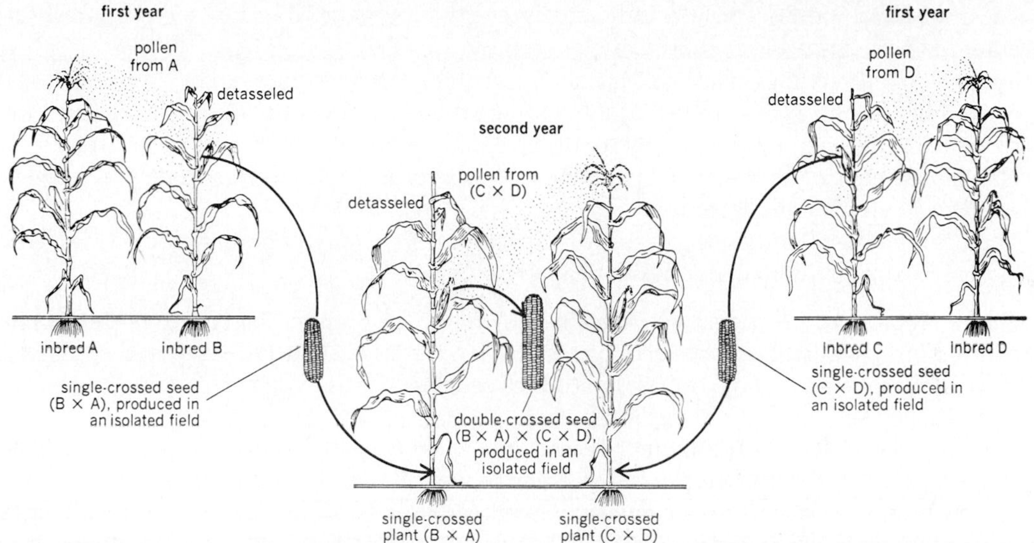

FIGURE 14.6.
Crossing of inbred lines of corn to produce the double-crossing hybrid corn seed utilized widely today. Note the relative size of the corn ears from the inbred lines compared with the resulting hybrid cross. Courtesy of the USDA.

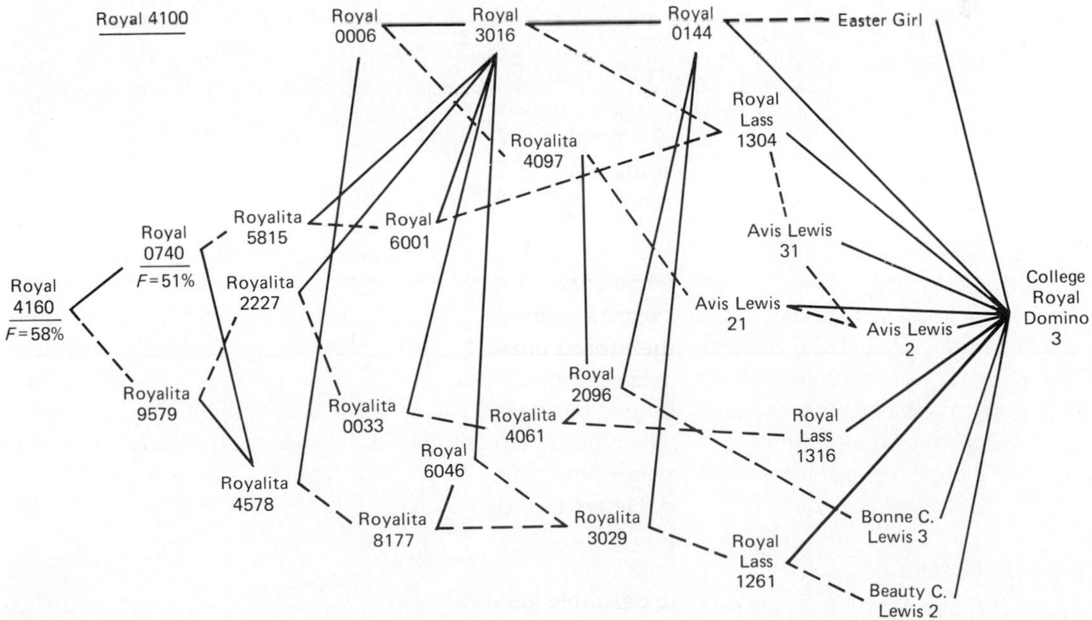

FIGURE 14.7.
Arrow pedigree of Royal 4160, which has an inbreeding coefficient of 58%. Solid lines represent the genetic contribution of the bulls, whereas the cow's contribution is represented by a broken line. Courtesy of the CSU Expt. Sta. (San Juan Basin Research Center) General Series 982.

5. Crossing of inbred lines results in heterosis (see definition p. 252); however, in most cases heterosis compensates for inbreeding depression.
6. Crossing of inbred lines of animals has not yielded the same results as crossing inbred lines of corn. The reasons appear to be: (a) inbreeding animals is slower (cannot self-fertilize as in corn); (b) it is easier and less costly to produce more inbred lines of corn; (c) inbred lines of animals are eliminated because of extremely poor reproductive performance and being less adapted to environmental stress.
7. There is merit in using some inbreeding in developing new lines of poultry and swine. (This is discussed in more detail later in the chapter.)

It is not logical for breeders to develop their own lines of highly inbred beef cattle. Inbreeding depression usually affects the economics of the operation. Both purebred and commercial producers can take advantage of highly productive inbred lines by crossing these inbred bulls on unrelated cows.

Inbreeding such as sire–daughter matings are logical ways to test for undesirable recessive genes. Also, seedstock producers use inbreeding in well-planned linebreeding programs. Consideration should be given to implementing linebreeding when breeders have difficulty introducing sires from other herds that are genetically superior to those they are producing.

Linebreeding

Linebreeding is a mild form of inbreeding used to maintain a high genetic relationship to an outstanding ancestor, usually a sire. This mating system is best used by seedstock producers who have a high level of genetic superiority in their herd. They find it difficult to locate sires that are superior to the ones they are raising in their herds.

Occasionally a breeder may produce a sire with a superior combination of genes, where the sire consistently produces high-producing offspring. Some of these sires may not be outproduced by younger sires. This is observed in some dairy bulls, when they remain competitively superior as long as they produce semen. These sires warrant use in a linebreeding program.

Figure 14.8 gives an example of linebreeding. Impressive, an outstanding quarter horse stallion, is linebred to his ancestor, Three Bars, by three separate pathways. The inbreeding of Impressive is approximately 9%, whereas the genetic relationship of Impressive to Three Bars is approximately 44%. Inbreeding below 20% is considered low, whereas a genetic relationship is high when it approaches 50%.

Impressive has nearly the same genetic relationship as if Three Bars had been his sire (44% vs. 50%). Progeny of Impressive have produced outstanding records, particularly as halter-point and working-point winners in the show ring.

OUTBREEDING

The four types of outbreeding are as follows:

1. *Species cross*—crossing of animals of different species (e.g., horse to donkey or cattle to bison).

2. *Crossbreeding*—mating of animals of different established breeds.
3. *Outcrossing*—mating of unrelated animals within the same breed.
4. *Grading up*—mating of purebred sires to commercial grade females and their female offspring for several generations. Grading up can involve some crossbreeding or it can be a type of outcrossing system.

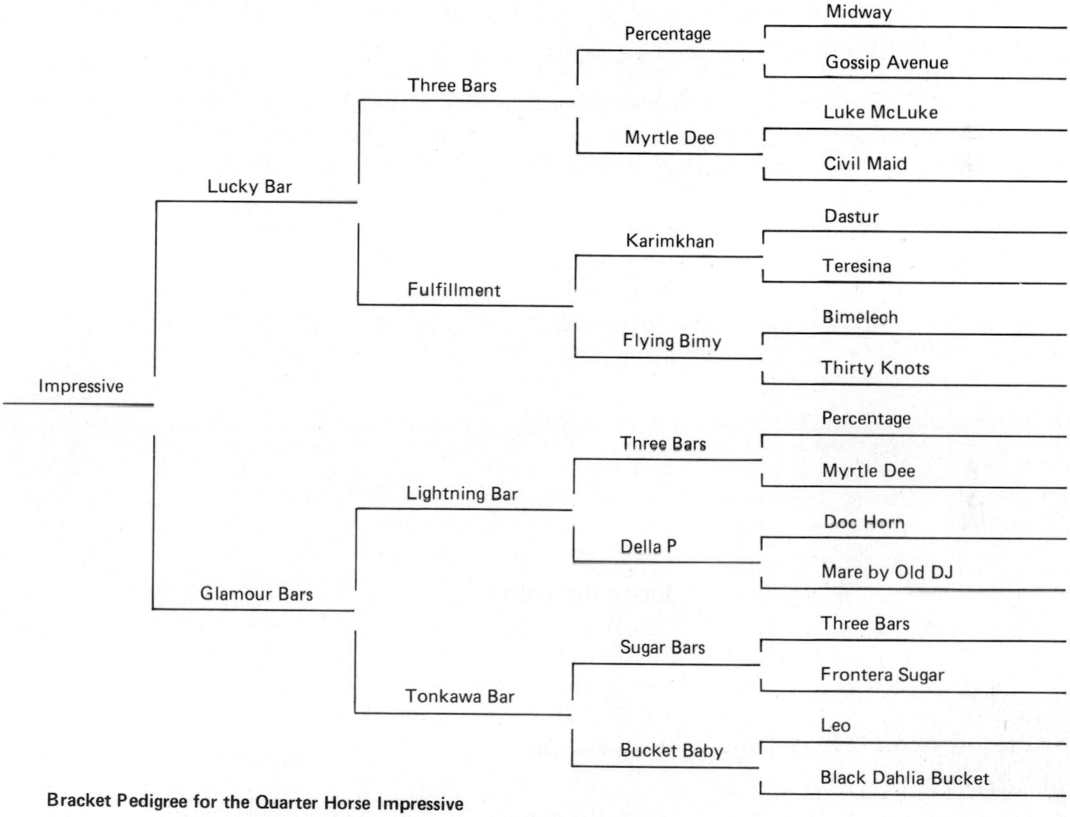

Impressive	Lucky Bar	Three Bars	Percentage	Midway
				Gossip Avenue
			Myrtle Dee	Luke McLuke
				Civil Maid
		Fulfillment	Karimkhan	Dastur
				Teresina
			Flying Bimy	Bimelech
				Thirty Knots
	Glamour Bars	Lightning Bar	Three Bars	Percentage
				Myrtle Dee
			Della P	Doc Horn
				Mare by Old DJ
		Tonkawa Bar	Sugar Bars	Three Bars
				Frontera Sugar
			Bucket Baby	Leo
				Black Dahlia Bucket

Bracket Pedigree for the Quarter Horse Impressive

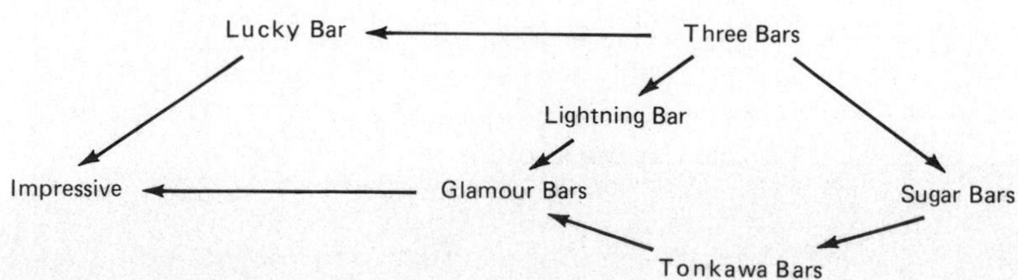

Arrow Pedigree Showing the Genetic Pathways by which Three Bars Contributes to the Inbreeding and Linebreeding of Impressive

FIGURE 14.8.
Horse pedigree showing linebreeding. Courtesy of the American Quarter Horse Association.

Species Cross

A species designation is part of the zoological classification (Fig. 14.9) used in taxonomy (a branch of zoology) to classify animals on similarities in body structure. These differences and similarities in body structure translate to genetic differences and similarities. For example, some animals of different species but the same genus can be crossed to produce viable offspring. Animals of different genus cannot be successfully crossed because chromosome number and other genes are different. Therefore, a **species cross** is the widest possible kind of outbreeding that can be achieved.

One of the most common species cross is the **mule,** resulting from crossing the jack of the ass species and the mare of the horse species *(Equus asinus × Equus caballus).* Mules existed in large numbers as work animals before the advent of the tractor. The **hinny** is the reciprocal cross of the mule (*Equus caballus* stallion × *Equus asinus* jennet). The hinny never became as popular as the mule.

Mare mules are usually sterile, which gives verification to genetic differences between the ass and horse. There have been a few reports of fertile mare mules.

Crossing of the zebu or humped cattle on European-type cattle *(Bos indicus × Bos taurus)* is common in the southeastern part of the United States. These crosses are more adaptable and productive in hot, humid environments than either of the straight species. Some authorities

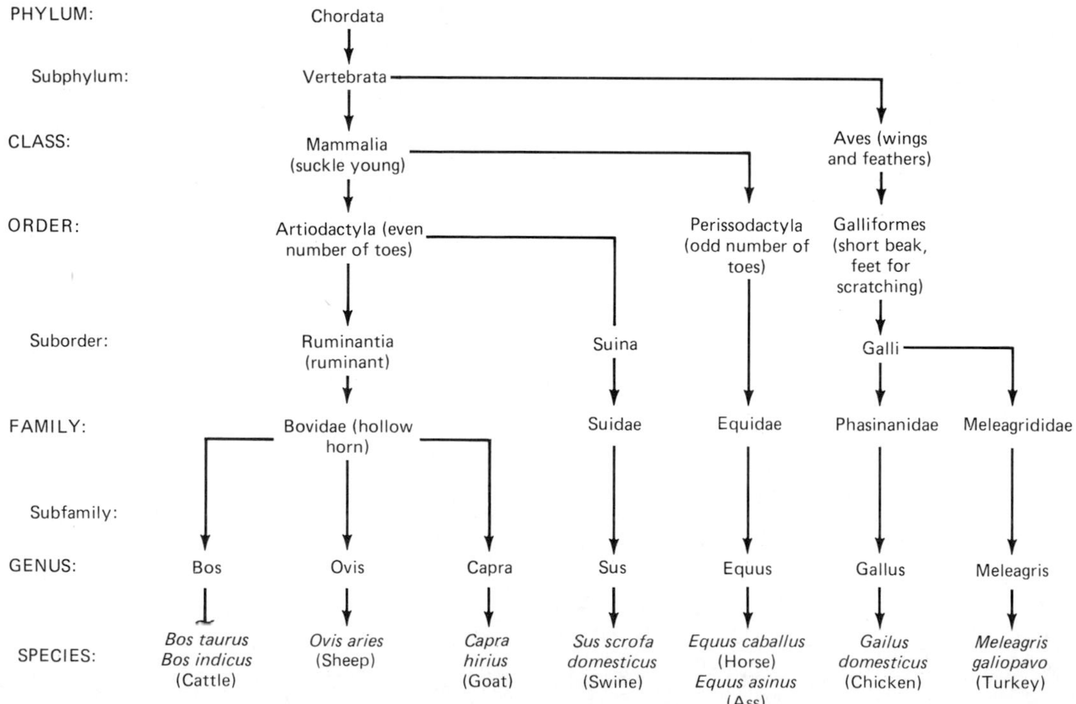

FIGURE 14.9.
Zoological classification that identifies the major species of farm animals. Adapted from R. F. Plimpton, and J. F. Stephens, *Animal and Science for Man: A Study Guide* (Minneapolis: Burgess, 1979).

raise questions about *Bos indicus* and *Bos taurus* being separate species, and their crosses are usually referred to as crossbreds rather than species crosses.

Numerous crosses of American bison and cattle have been made. Some of these crosses have been designated as separate breeds called **Cattalo** or **Beefalo.** These crosses are intended to be more adaptable to harsh environments (cold temperatures and limited forage). Fertility problems have existed in some of these crosses, and these numbers are limited.

Sheep and goats have been crossed even though they have different genus classification. Fertilization occurs but embryos die in early gestation.

There are other species crosses that have occurred. Most species crosses have little commercial value, although insight into the evolutionary process is interesting. Recent advances in genetic engineering might make some genetic combinations between species more feasible. Gene-splicing (inserting a gene or genes from one animal to another) has occurred between species. In the future, opportunity to combine desirable genes, both within a species and between species, could become a reality.

Crossbreeding

There are two primary reasons for using **crossbreeding:** (1) breed complementation and (2) heterosis (hybrid vigor). Breed complementation implies crossing breeds so their strengths and weaknesses complement one another. There is no one breed superior in all desired production characteristics; therefore, planned crossbreeding programs that use breed complementation can significantly increase herd productivity.

Crossbreeding, if properly managed, allows for the effective use of heterosis, which has a

TABLE 14.1. Computation of Heterosis for Percent Calf Crop and Weaning Weights

	Calf Crop (%)	Weaning Weight (lb)	Lb Calf Weaned per Cow Exposed
Breed A	82%	460	377
Breed B	78	540	421
Average of the two breeds (without heterosis)	80	500	399
Average of crossbreds (with heterosis)	84	520	447
Superiority of crossbreds over average of two breeds	4	20	
Percent heterosis	5% (4 ÷ 80)	4% (20 ÷ 500)	

TABLE 14.2. Relationship of Heritability and Heterosis for Most Traits

Traits	Heritability	Heterosis
Reproduction	Low	High
Growth	Medium	Medium
Carcass	High	Low

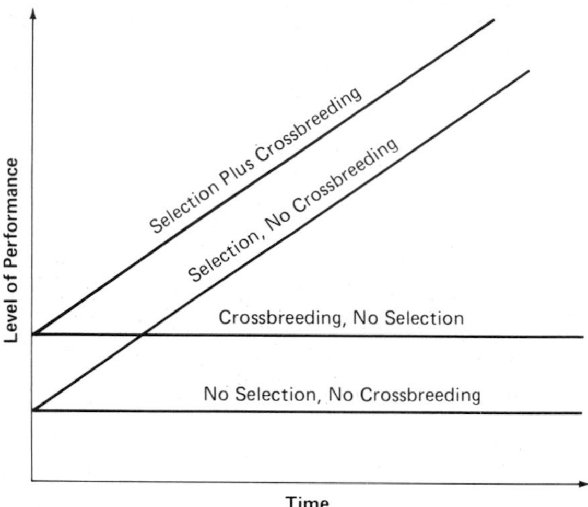

FIGURE 14.10.
Improvement in performance with various combinations of selection and crossbreeding.

marked effect on productivity in swine, poultry, and beef cattle. **Heterosis** is defined as the increase in productivity in the crossbred progeny above the average of breeds or lines that are crossed. An example of calculating heterosis is shown in Table 14.1. The calculated heterosis for calf crop percent in this example is 5%, whereas heterosis for weaning weight is 4%.

Crossbreeding is sometimes questioned when the crossbred performance is less than the parent breed. In Table 14.1, for example, the weaning weight of the crossbreds is 520 lb, while one parent (Breed B) is 540 lb. However, for calf crop percent, the crossbreds are 84%, which is higher than either Breed A or Breed B. The value of crossbreeding, in this example, is best demonstrated by combining calf crop percent and weaning weight (calf crop percent × weaning weight = lb calf weaned per cow exposed). Note in Table 14.1 that lb of calf weaned per cow exposed is 447 lb for the crossbreds, whereas Breed A is 377 lb and Breed B is 421 lb.

The amount of heterosis expressed is related to the heritability of the trait. Table 14.2 shows that heterosis is highest for lowly heritable traits and lowest for highly heritable traits. These relationships are helpful to commercial producers in selecting and crossbreeding to enhance genetic improvement. Figure 14.10 shows the relative importance of selection and crossbreeding in an improvement program. This figure demonstrates that selecting genetically superior

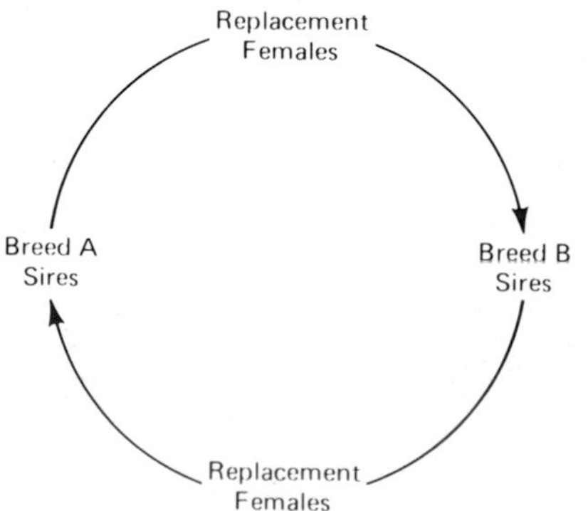

FIGURE 14.11.
Two-breed rotation cross. Females sired by breed A are mated to breed B sires, and females sired by breed B are mated to breed A sires.

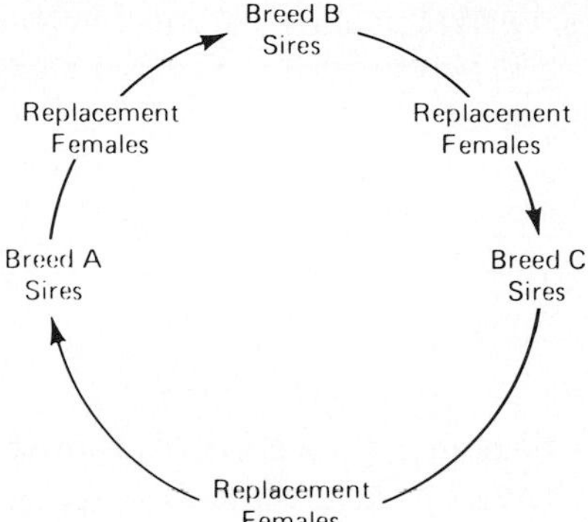

FIGURE 14.12.
Three-breed rotation cross. Females sired by a specific breed are bred to the breed of sire next in rotation.

animals is more important than crossbreeding. However, using the two in combination gives the highest level of performance.

Crossbreeding is most commonly used in swine, beef cattle, and sheep. Little crossbreeding is done in dairy cattle because of the primary emphasis on one trait (milk production) and the superiority of the Holstein breed for that trait. Poultry breeders utilize heterosis primarily through crossing lines that have been developed from crossing breeds and inbreeding separate and distinct lines.

Figures 14.11, 14.12, and 14.13 show the crossbreeding systems most frequently used in swine, beef cattle, and sheep. More specific detail in using these crossbreeding systems for these species is given in Chapters 22, 26, and 28.

Outcrossing

The most widely used breeding system for most species is **outcrossing.** As unrelated animals within the same breed are mated, the gene pairs are primarily heterozygous, although there is a

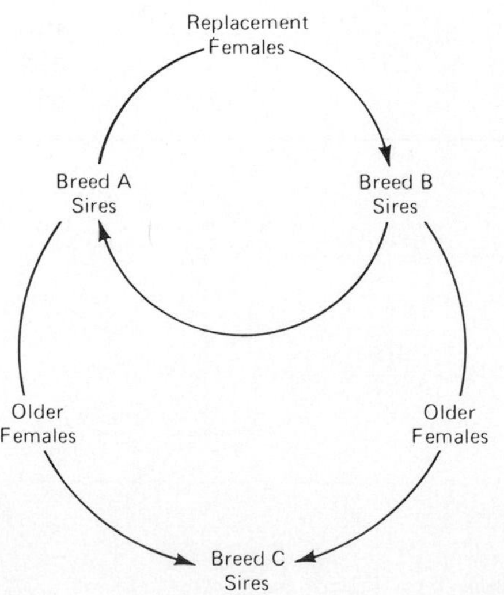

FIGURE 14.13.
Terminal (static) or modified-terminal crossbreeding system. It is terminal or static if all females in herd (A × B) are then crossed to breed C sires. All male and female offspring are sold. It is a modified-terminal system if part of females are bred to A and B sires to produce replacement females. The remainder of the females are terminally crossed to breed C sires.

slight increase in homozygosity over time. Homozygosity for several breeds has been estimated between 10% and 20%. This slight increase in homozygosity occurs because the animals mated are somewhat related in that they are members of the same breed.

Usefulness of outcrossing is primarily dependent on the effectiveness of selection (selection differential × heritability). The gene pairs stay primarily in a heterozygous condition as there is no attempt to maximize homozygosity or heterozygosity.

Grading Up

The continuous use of purebred sires of the same breed in a grade herd or flock is called **grading up.** In this situation, grading up is similar to outcrossing. The accumulated percentage of inheritance of the desired purebred is 50% (1/2), 75% (3/4), 84.5% (7/8), and 94% (15/16) for four generations when grading up is practiced. The fourth generation resembles the purebred sires so closely in genetic composition that it approximates the purebred level.

The grading up system is useful in the breeding of cattle and horses, but it has little value in breeding sheep, swine, or poultry. High-producing purebred sheep, swine, and poultry breeding stock are available at reasonable prices; therefore, the breeder can buy them for less than he can produce them by grading up. The use of production-tested males that are above average in performance in a commercial herd can grade up the herd not only to a general purebred level but also to a high level of production.

A recent use of grading up on a large scale has occurred with the introduction of many beef cattle breeds. Most of the introduction has been with males (bulls or semen), as females have been less available and more expensive because of the numbers needed.

Imported bulls (or their semen) have been used on commercial cows or purebred cows of another breed. Grading up, as used here, is a type of crossbreeding, although the intent is not to maintain heterosis but to increase the frequency of genes from the introduced breed.

After several successive generations of mating the new breed to cows carrying a certain percentage of the new breed, the resulting offspring have been designated purebreds. In most breeds, this designation has been given when the calves had 7/8 or 15/16 of the genetic composition of the new breed. Figure 14.14 shows how these matings are made. It would require a minimum of 7 years to produce the first 15/16 calves of the new breed.

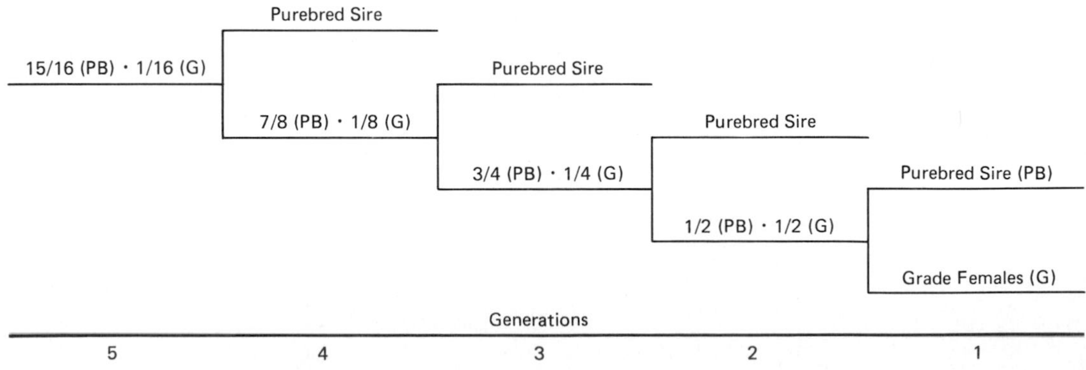

FIGURE 14.14.
Utilizing grading up to produce purebred offspring from a grade herd.

FORMING NEW LINES OR BREEDS

New breeds have been formed and are currently being formed by crossing several breeds. These are sometimes given a general classification of **synthetic breeds** and **composite breeds.** In beef cattle, the Brangus, Barzona, Beefmaster, and Santa Gertrudis breeds are composite (synthetic) breeds formed several years ago, whereas MARC I (crosses of Charolais, Brown Swiss, Limousin, Hereford, and Angus breeds) and RX3 (crosses of Red Angus, Hereford, and Red Holstein breeds) are examples of composites currently being developed. Columbia, Targhee, and Polypay are examples of synthetic breeds of sheep.

Crossing several swine breeds, a practice associated with some inbreeding, has been used to develop the hybrid boars now being merchandised by several companies. Hybrid boars are used extensively in the swine industry.

In poultry, breeding for egg production differs from breeding for broiler production. Different traits are emphasized in the production of these two products. Both inbreeding and heterosis are utilized in the production of specific lines and strains of birds that are highly productive in the production of either eggs or broilers.

Figure 14.15 shows the change from poultry breeds to crossmated lines and strains of birds. The incrossmated represents many of the synthetic egg-type strains or lines. These are primarily

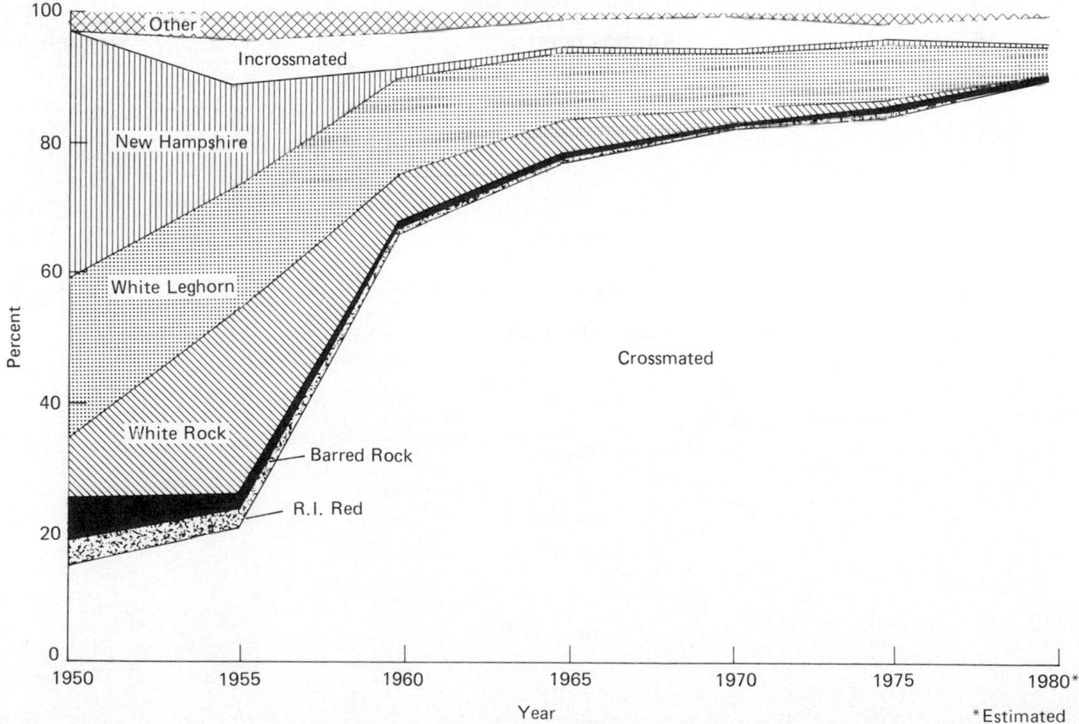

FIGURE 14.15.
In poultry breeding the specific breeds are losing their identity in the production of crossmated and incrossmated lines. Data is from over 30 million birds recorded in the National Poultry improvement Plan. Courtesy of the USDA.

two- and three-way crosses of primarily Mediterranean breeds (e.g., White Leghorns). The crossmated chickens are the commercial broiler chickens that are primarily cornish-type males or White Plymouth females. The area of the chart depicting crossmated shows the tremendous changes of breeding methods utilized by the broiler industry.

SELECTED REFERENCES

Lasley, J. F. 1987. *Genetics of Livestock Improvements.* Englewood Cliffs, NJ: Prentice-Hall.
Legates, J. E. 1990. *Breeding and Improvement of Farm Animals.* 4th ed. New York: McGraw-Hill.

CHAPTER 15

Nutrients and Their Functions

A **nutrient** is any feed constituent that functions in the support of life. There are many different feeds available to animals to provide these nutrients.

Most animal feeds are classified as **concentrates** and **roughages.** Concentrates include cereal grains (e.g., corn, wheat, barley, oats, and milo), oil meals (e.g., soybean meal, linseed meal, and cottonseed meal), molasses, and dried milk products. Concentrates are high in energy, low in fiber, and highly (80%–90%) digestible. Roughages include legume hays, grass hays, and straws, the latter being by-products from the production of grass, seed, and grain. Additional roughages are silage, stovers (dried corn, cane, or milo stalks and leaves with the grain portion removed), soilage (cut green feeds), and grazed forages. Roughages are less digestible than concentrates. Roughages are typically 50%–65% digestible, but the digestibility of some straws is significantly lower.

NUTRIENTS

The six basic classes of nutrients—water, carbohydrates, fats, proteins, vitamins, and minerals—are found in varying amounts in animal feeds. Nutrients are composed of at least 20 of the more than 100 known chemical elements. These 20 elements and their chemical symbols are: calcium (Ca), carbon (C), chlorine (Cl), cobalt (Co), copper (Cu), fluorine (F), hydrogen (H), iodine (I), iron (Fe), magnesium (Mg), manganese (Mn), molybdenum (Mo), nitrogen (N), oxygen (O), phosphorus (P), potassium (K), selenium (Se), sodium (Na), sulphur (S), and zinc (Zn).

Water

Water contains hydrogen and oxygen. The terms **water** and **moisture** are used interchangeably. Typically, water refers to drinking water, whereas moisture is used in reference to the amount of water in a given feed or ration. The remainder of the feed, after accounting for moisture, is referred to as dry matter. Moisture is found in all feeds, ranging from 10% in air-dry feeds to more than 80% in fresh green forage. Livestock and poultry consume several times more water than dry matter each day and will die from lack of water more quickly than from lack of any other nutrient. Water in feed is no more valuable than water from any other source. This knowledge is important to assessing feeds that vary in their moisture content.

Water has important body functions. It enters into most of the metabolic reactions, assists in transporting other nutrients, helps maintain normal body temperature, and gives the body its physical shape (water is the major component within cells).

Carbohydrates

Carbohydrates contain carbon, hydrogen, and oxygen in either simple or complex forms. The more simple carbohydrates, such as starch, supply the major energy source for cattle diets, particularly feedlot diets. The more complex carbohydrates, such as cellulose, are the major components of the cell walls of plants. These complex carbohydrates are not as easily digested as simple carbohydrates and they require host or microbial interaction for effective utilization.

Fats

Fats and oils, also referred to as **lipids,** contain carbon, hydrogen, and oxygen, although there is more carbon and hydrogen in proportion to oxygen than with carbohydrates. Fats are solid and oils are liquid at room temperature due generally to relative saturation. Fats contain 2.25 times more energy per pound than carbohydrates.

Most fats are comprised of three fatty acids attached to a glycerol backbone.

Example:

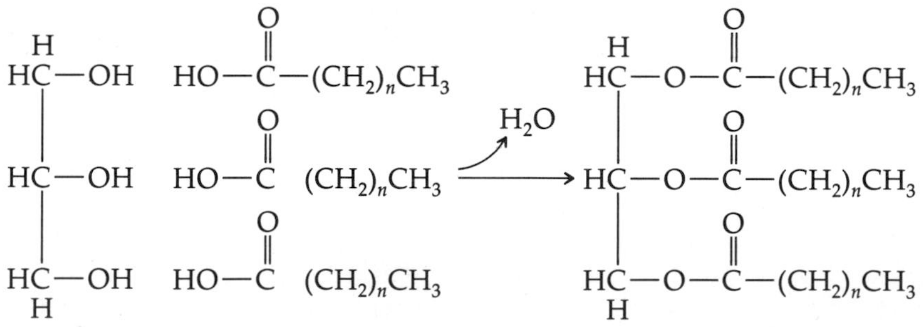

$$
\begin{array}{l}
\text{H} \\
\text{HC—OH} \\
\;| \\
\text{HC—OH} \\
\;| \\
\text{HC—OH} \\
\text{H}
\end{array}
\quad
\begin{array}{l}
HO-\overset{\overset{\displaystyle O}{\|}}{C}-(CH_2)_nCH_3 \\[1em]
HO-\overset{\overset{\displaystyle O}{\|}}{C}\;\;(CH_2)_nCH_3 \\[1em]
HO-\overset{\overset{\displaystyle O}{\|}}{C}\;\;(CH_2)_nCH_3
\end{array}
\xrightarrow{H_2O}
\begin{array}{l}
\text{H} \\
HC-O-\overset{\overset{\displaystyle O}{\|}}{C}-(CH_2)_nCH_3 \\
\;| \\
HC-O-\overset{\overset{\displaystyle O}{\|}}{C}-(CH_2)_nCH_3 \\
\;| \\
HC-O-\overset{\overset{\displaystyle O}{\|}}{C}-(CH_2)_nCH_3 \\
\text{H}
\end{array}
$$

$$\text{Glycerol} + \text{three fatty acids} \longrightarrow \text{a triglyceride} + \text{water}$$

There are saturated and unsaturated fats, depending on their particular chemical composition. Saturated fatty acids have single bonds tying the carbon atoms together (e.g., -C-C-C-C-), whereas unsaturated fatty acids have one or more double bonds (e.g., -C=C-C=C-): The term *polyunsaturated fatty acids* is applied to those having more than one double bond. Although more than 100 fatty acids have been identified, only one has been determined to be dietary essential (linoleic acid). The two apparent functions of the essential fatty acids are (1) as precursors of prostaglandins and (2) as structural components of cells.

Proteins

Proteins always contain carbon, hydrogen, oxygen, and nitrogen and sometimes iron, phosphorus or sulphur, or both. Protein is the only nutrient class that contains nitrogen. Proteins in feeds, on average, contain 16% nitrogen. This is why feeds are analyzed for the percent nitrogen in the feed, with the percent multiplied by 6.25 (100% ÷ 16% = 6.25) to convert it to percent protein. If, for example, a feed is 3% nitrogen, 100 g of the feed contains 3 g nitrogen. Multiplying 6.25 × 3 gives 18.75%, meaning that 100 g of this feed contains 18.75 g protein.

Proteins are composed of various combinations of some 25 amino acids. Amino acids are called the building blocks of the animal's body. The building blocks for growth (including growth of muscle, bone, and connective tissue), milk production, and cellular and tissue repair are amino acids that come from proteins in feed. The interstitial (between cells) fluid, blood, and lymph require amino acids to regulate body water and to transport oxygen and carbon dioxide. All enzymes are proteins, so amino acids are also required for enzyme production. Amino acids have an amino group (NH_2) in each of their chemical structures. There are many different combinations of amino acids that can be structured together. The chemical, or peptide, bonding of amino acids is illustrated using alanine and serine, which results in the formation of a dipeptide:

$$\underset{\text{alanine}}{CH_3-\underset{H}{\overset{NH_2}{C}}-C\begin{matrix}{}^{/\!/O}\\{}_{\backslash OH}\end{matrix}} + \underset{\text{serine}}{HO-CH_2-\underset{H}{\overset{NH_2}{C}}-C\begin{matrix}{}^{/\!/O}\\{}_{\backslash OH}\end{matrix}} \xrightarrow{H_2O} \underset{\text{dipeptide}}{NH_2-\underset{H}{\overset{CH_3}{C}}-\overset{O}{\overset{\|}{C}}-O-\overset{H}{N}-\underset{H}{\overset{HO-CH_2}{C}}-C\begin{matrix}{}^{/\!/O}\\{}_{\backslash OH}\end{matrix}}$$

It can be seen that amino acids have both a basic portion, NH_2, and an acid portion, $C\begin{matrix}{}^{/\!/O}\\{}_{\backslash OH}\end{matrix}$ and it is because of these that they can combine into long chains to make proteins. When digestion occurs, the action is at the peptide linkage to free amino acids from one another.

Some amino acids are provided in abundance in many proteins but others are quite limited. Thus, monogastric animals might have difficulty obtaining scarce amino acids that they cannot synthesize. Of the 15 nonessential amino acids, some (alanine, aspartic acid, glutamic acid, hydroxyproline, proline, and serine) can be synthesized by monogastric animals if carbon, hydrogen, oxygen, and nitrogen are available. Other amino acids, however, either cannot be synthesized at all by monogastric animals (isoleucine, leucine, lysine, methionine, phenylalanine, threonine, tryptophan, and valine) or are produced so slowly that they are called semiessential and must be provided in the feed of growing animals (arginine, histidine—also glycine for the chick).

All amino acids are needed by all animals; the terms *essential* and *nonessential* merely refer to whether or not they must be supplied through the diet. The shortage of any particular amino acid can prevent an animal from using other amino acids for needed functions, and a protein deficiency results. Ruminants do not need a dietary supply of amino acids because the amino acids are synthesized in the ruminant stomach.

Minerals

Chemical elements other than carbon, hydrogen, oxygen, and nitrogen are called minerals. They are inorganic because they contain no carbon; organic nutrients do contain carbon. Some minerals are referred to as macro (required in larger amounts) and others are micro or trace minerals (required in smaller amounts).

The macrominerals include calcium, chlorine, magnesium, phosphorus, potassium, sodium, and sulfur. Calcium and phosphorus are required in certain amounts and in a certain ratio to each other for bone growth and repair and for other body functions. The blood plasma contains sodium chloride; the red blood cells contain potassium chloride. The osmotic relations between the plasma and the red blood cells are maintained by proper concentrations of sodium chloride and potassium chloride. Sodium chloride may be depleted by excessive sweating that results from heavy physical work in hot weather. It is essential that salt and plenty of water be available under such conditions. The acid–base balance of the body is maintained at the proper level by minerals.

The essential microminerals for farm animals include cobalt, copper, fluorine, iodine, iron, manganese, molybdenum, selenium, and zinc. Microminerals may become a part of the molecule of a vitamin (e.g., cobalt is a part of vitamin B_{12}) and they may become a part of a hormone (e.g. thyroxine, a hormone made by the thyroid gland, requires iodine for its synthesis).

Hemoglobin of the red blood cells carries oxygen to tissues and carbon dioxide from tissues. Iron is required for production of hemoglobin because it is a part of the hemoglobin molecule. A small quantity of copper is also necessary for protection of hemoglobin (even though it does not normally become a part of the hemoglobin molecule in farm animals) because it apparently is necessary for normal iron absorption from the digestive tract and for release of iron to the blood plasma.

Certain important metabolic reactions in the body require the presence of minerals. Selenium and vitamin E both appear to work together to help prevent white muscle disease, which is a calcification of the striated muscles, the smooth muscles, and cardiac muscles. Both vitamin E and selenium are more effective if the other is present. Excesses of certain minerals may be quite harmful. For example, excess amounts of fluorine, molybdenum, and selenium are highly toxic.

Vitamins

Vitamins are organic nutrients needed in very small amounts to provide for specific body functions in the animal. There are 16 known vitamins that function in animal nutrition. Vitamins may be classed as either fat-soluble or water-soluble.

The fat-soluble vitamins are vitamins A, D, E, and K. Vitamin A helps maintain proper repair of internal and external body linings. Because the eyes have linings, lack of vitamin A adversely affects the eyes. Vitamin A is also a part of the visual pigments of the eyes. Vitamin D is required for proper use of calcium and phosphorus in bone growth and repair. A major function of vitamin D is to regulate the absorption of calcium and phosphorus from the intestine. Vitamin D is produced by the action of sunlight on steroids of the skin; therefore, animals that are exposed to sufficient sunlight make all the vitamin D they need. Vitamin K is important in blood clotting; hemorrhage might occur if the body is deficient in vitamin K.

The water-soluble vitamins are ascorbic acid (vitamin C), biotin, choline, cyanacobalamin (vitamin B_{12}), folic acid, niacin, pantothenic acid, pyridoxine (vitamin B_6), riboflavin (B_2), and thiamin (vitamin B_1). More diseases caused by inadequate nutrition have been described in the human than in any other animal, and among the best known are those caused by a lack of certain vitamins: beri-beri (lack of thiamin); pellagra (lack of niacin); pernicious anemia (lack of vitamin B_{12}); rickets (lack of vitamin D); and scurvy (lack of vitamin C).

In ruminant animals, all of the water-soluble vitamins are made by microorganisms in the rumen. Water-soluble vitamins also appear to be readily available to horses; perhaps some are made by fermentation in the cecum. Water-soluble vitamins cannot be synthesized by monogastric animals and must therefore be in their feed. Most fat-soluble vitamins are not synthesized by either ruminants or monogastrics and must be supplied in the diets of both groups (an exception is vitamin K, which is synthesized by rumen bacteria in ruminants). Many vitamins are supplied through feeds normally given to animals.

PROXIMATE ANALYSIS OF FEEDS

The nutrient composition of a feed cannot be determined accurately by visual inspection. A system has been devised by which the value of a feed can be approximated. **Proximate analysis** separates feed components into groups according to their feeding value. This analysis is based on a feed sample and analysis, and therefore is no more accurate than how representative the sample is of the entire feed source.

The inorganic and organic components resulting from a proximate analysis are water, crude protein, crude fat (sometimes referred to as ether extract), crude fiber, nitrogen-free extract, and ash (minerals). Figure 15.1 shows these components resulting from a feed that would have a laboratory analysis of 88% dry matter, 13% protein, 4% fat, 10% crude fiber, and 56% nitrogen-free extract (NFE) on a natural or air-dry basis. The analysis might be reported on a

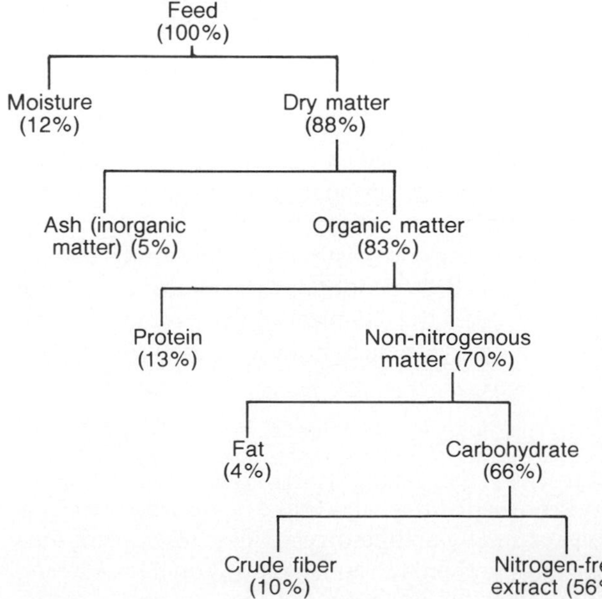

FIGURE 15.1.
Proximate analysis showing the inorganic and organic components of a feed (similar to wheat) on a natural or air-dry basis. Courtesy of CSU Graphics.

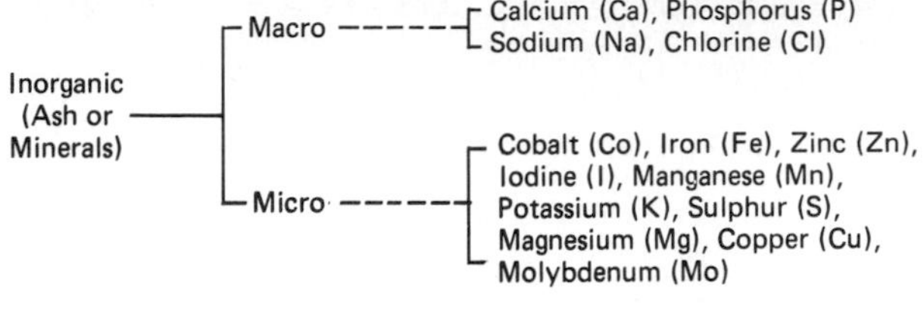

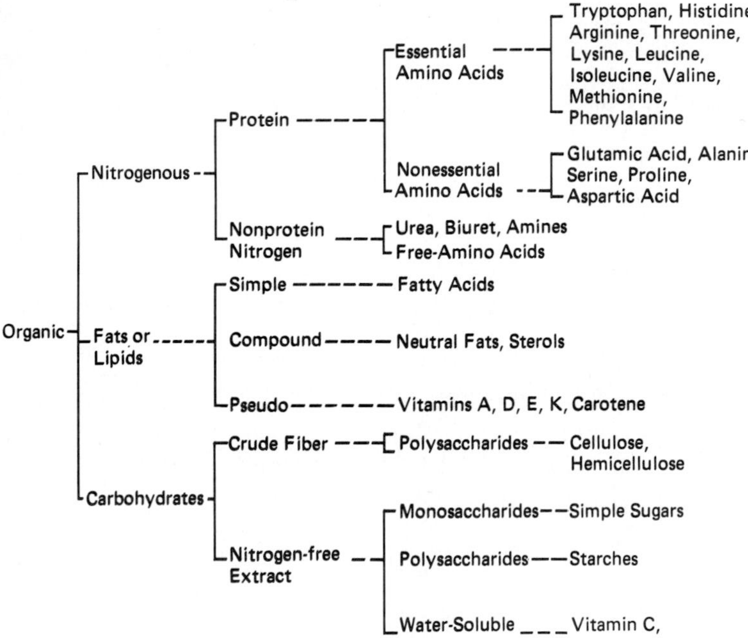

FIGURE 15.2.
Chemical analysis scheme of inorganic and organic nutrients. Courtesy of CSU Graphics.

dry-matter basis (no moisture) as 14.8% protein, 4.5% fat, 11.4% crude fiber, and 63.6% nitrogen-free extract. Therefore, caution needs to be exercised in interpreting the proximate analysis results because different laboratories may report their analytical values on either an air-dry (or as-fed) basis or a dry-matter basis.

The proximate analysis for the six basic nutrients does not distinguish the various components of a nutrient. For example, ash content of a feed does not tell the amount of calcium, phosphorus, or other specific minerals. Figure 15.2 gives the chemical analysis for organic and inorganic nutrients. There are specific chemical analyses for each of these nutrients in a feed if such an analysis is needed.

DIGESTIBILITY OF FEEDS

Digestibility refers to the amount of various nutrients in a feed that are absorbed from the digestive tract. Different feeds and nutrients vary greatly in their digestibility. Many feeds have been subjected to digestion trials, in which feeds of known nutrient composition have been fed to livestock and poultry. Feces have been collected and the nutrients in the feces analyzed. The difference between nutrients fed and nutrients excreted in the feces is the apparent digestibility of the feed.

For example, the digestibility of protein is obtained by determining the digestibility of nitrogen in a feed. Digestibility is expressed as a percentage for nitrogen, for example, as follows:

$$\frac{\text{Nitrogen in feed} - \text{Nitrogen in feces}}{\text{Nitrogen in feed}} \times 100 = \text{Percentage digestibility}$$

As an example, if 100 g feed contains 3.2 g nitrogen and 100 g feces contains 0.8 g nitrogen, the percent digestibility of nitrogen is:

$$\frac{3.2 - 0.8}{3.2} \times 100 = 75\%.$$

Note that the determination of 3.2 g nitrogen in 100 g feed enables one to estimate the percentage of protein in the feed as 20% ($3.20 \times 6.25 = 20$).

ENERGY EVALUATION OF FEEDS

Nutrients that contain carbon provide the energy for animals. Carbohydrates, fats, and proteins can all be used to provide energy; however, carbohydrates supply most of the energy, as they are a more economical energy source than proteins. Complete oxidation (burning or taking on oxygen) of carbon releases the energy. Energy is the force, or power, that is used to drive a variety of body systems.

Energy can be used to power movement of the animal, but most of it is used as chemical energy to drive reactions necessary to convert feed into animal products and to keep the body warm or cool.

Energy needs of animals generally account for the largest portion of feed consumed. Several systems have been devised to evaluate feedstuffs for their energy content. **Total digestible nutrients (TDN)** once was the most commonly used energy system; however, it is being replaced by **metabolizable energy (ME)** and **net energy (NE).** TDN is typically expressed in pounds, kilograms, or percentages after obtaining the proximate analysis and digestibility figures for a feed. The formula for calculating TDN is TDN = (digestible crude protein) + (digestible crude fiber) + (digestible nitrogen-free extract) + (digestible crude fat × 2.25). The factor of 2.25 is used to equate fat to a carbohydrate basis, since fat has 2.25 times as much energy as an equivalent amount of carbohydrate.

An example of calculating TDN in 100 grams of feed is shown in Table 15.1.

TDN is roughly comparable to digestible energy (DE) but it is expressed in different units. TDN and DE both tend to overvalue roughages.

Even though there are some apparent shortcomings in using TDN as an energy measurement of feeds, it works well in balancing rations for cows and growing cattle. There is more precision in the energy measurement of feeds by using the net energy (NE) system. This system usually measures energy values in megacalories per pound or kilogram of feed. The calorie basis, which measures the heat content of feed, is as follows:

Calorie (cal)—amount of energy or heat required to raise the temperature of 1 gram of water 1°C.

TABLE 15.1. An Example of Calculating Total Digestible Nutrients (TDN)

Nutrient	Amount of Nutrient (g)	Digestibility (%)	Amount of Digestible Nutrient
Protein	20	75	15.00
Carbohydrates			
Soluble (NFE)	55	85	46.75
Insoluble (fiber)	10	20	2.00
Fat 5 (×2.25)	11.15	85	9.50
			TDN = 73.25

Kilocalorie (Kcal)—amount of energy or heat required to raise the temperature of 1 kilogram of water 1°C.

Megacalorie (Mcal)—equal to 1,000 kilocalories or 1,000,000 calories.

Figure 15.3 shows various ways that the energy of feeds is utilized by animals and the various energy measurements of feeds. Note that some energy in the feed is lost in the feces (not

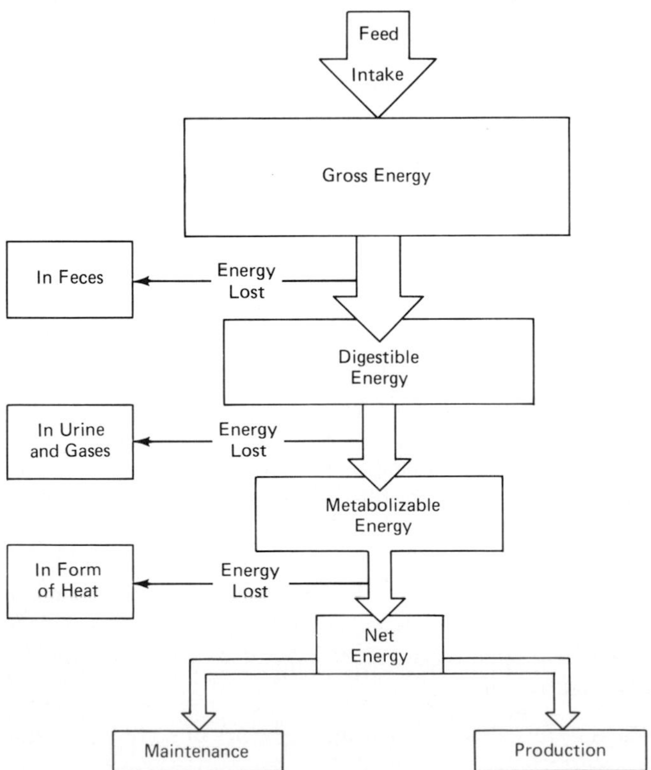

FIGURE 15.3.
Measures of energy and energy utilization.

digested), the urine (digested but not used by the body cells), gases from microbial fermentation of the feed, and heat, resulting from digestion and metabolism of the feed.

Feeds provide energy that the animal uses to supply two basic functions: (1) maintenance energy and (2) production energy. Maintenance energy is used to keep the basal metabolism functioning, to provide for the voluntary activity of the animal, to generate heat to keep the body warm, and to provide energy to cool the body.

Production energy becomes stored energy and energy needed for work. The stored energy exists in fetus development, semen production, growth, fat deposition, and milk, eggs, and wool production.

Gross energy (GE) is the quantity of heat (calories) released from the complete burning of the feed sample in an apparatus called a bomb calorimeter. GE has little practical value in evaluating feeds for animals because the animal does not metabolize feeds in the same manner as a bomb calorimeter. For example, oat straw has the same GE value as corn grain. Digestible energy (DE) is GE of feed minus fecal energy. Metabolizable energy (ME) is GE of feed minus energy in the feces, urine, and gaseous products of digestion. Net energy (NE) is the ME of feed minus the energy used in the consumption, digestion, and metabolism of the feed. This energy lost between ME and NE is called **heat increment.**

Another way to illustrate the several measures of feed energy and how they are utilized is shown in Figure 15.4. In this example, 2,000 kcal of GE (in approximately 1 lb of feed) is fed to a laying hen. The DE shows that 400 kcal was lost in the feces. The ME (1,450 kcal) is used for heat increment, maintenance, and production (eggs and tissue). There are 300 kcal lost in the heat increment, which leaves 1,150 kcal for maintenance and production. For maintenance, 750 kcal are needed, which leaves 400 kcal for egg production and tissue growth. Therefore only 20% (400/2,000) of the GE is used for production.

Net energy for maintenance (NEm) and net energy for gain (NEg) are more commonly used for formulating diets for feedlot cattle than any other energy system. Net energy for lactation (NE_l) is used in dairy cow ration formulation. NEm in animals is the amount of energy needed to maintain a constant body weight. Animals of known weight, fed for zero energy gain, have a constant level of heat production.

The NEg measures the increased energy content of the carcass after feeding a known quantity of feed energy. All feed fed above maintenance is not utilized at a constant level of efficiency. Higher rates of gain require more feed per unit of gain as composition of gain varies with rate of gain.

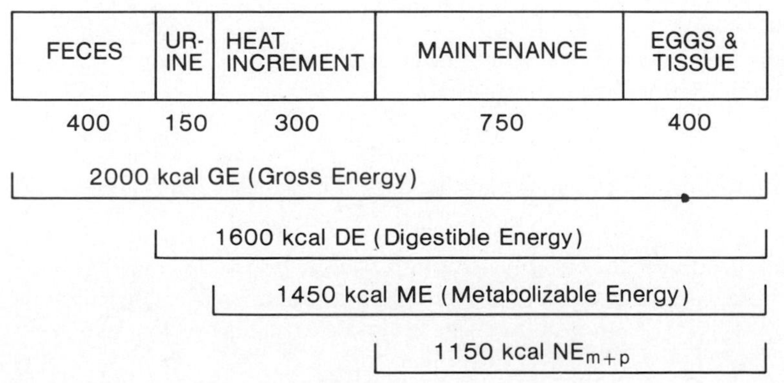

FIGURE 15.4.
Energy utilization by a laying hen. Data represent approximately 1 lb of feed containing 2,000 kcal of gross energy. Courtesy of CSU Graphics.

TABLE 15.2. Comparison of TDN and NE Systems for a Yearling Steer with Varying Rates of Gain

	Rate of Gain (lb/day)		
Energy System	0	2	2.9
TDN (lb)	6.40	12.80	15.00
NEm (Mcal)	6.24	6.24	6.24
NEg (Mcal)		4.29	6.48
Total lb feed			
TDN basis	8.2	16.5	19.3
NE basis	7.2	15.0	19.0
Feed per lb gain (NE)		7.5	6.6
Feed per lb gain (TDN)		8.2	6.6

The TDN and NE systems are compared in Table 15.2. Information in the table is based on feeding a simple diet of ground ear corn (90%) and supplement (10%) to a yearling steer (772 lb) for different rates of gain.

FEEDS AND FEED COMPOSITION

Classification of Feeds

Feeds are naturally occurring ingredients in diets of farm animals used to sustain life. The terms *feeds* and *feedstuffs* are generally used interchangeably; however, *feedstuffs* is a more inclusive term. Feedstuffs can include certain nonnutritive products such as additives to promote growth and reduce stress, for flavor and palatability, to add bulk, or to preserve other feeds in the ration.

The National Research Council (NRC) classification of feedstuffs is as follows:

1. Dry roughages and forages
    Hay (legume and nonlegume)
    Straw
    Fodder
    Stover
    Other feeds with greater than 18% fiber (hulls and shells)
2. Range, pasture plants, and green forages
3. Silages (corn, legume, and grass)
4. Energy feeds (cereal grains, mill by-products, fruits, nuts, and roots)
5. Protein supplements (animal, marine, avian, and plant)
6. Mineral supplements
7. Vitamin supplements
8. Nonnutritive additives (antibiotics, coloring materials, flavors, hormones, preservatives, and medicants)

Roughages and forages are used interchangeably,although roughage usually implies a bulkier, coarser feed. In the dry state, roughages have more than 18% crude fiber. The crude fiber is primarily a component of cell walls that is not highly digestible. Roughages are also relatively

TABLE 15.3. Nutrient Composition of Selected Feeds Commonly Used in Diets of Ruminants

	On a Dry-matter Basis (moisture-free)									
Feed	Dry Matter (%)	TDN (%)	ME (Mcal/ lb)	NEm (Mcal/ lb)	NEg (Mcal/ lb)	NE_l (Mcal/ lb)	Crude Protein (%)	Vitamin A (carotene) (mg/lb)	Calcium (%)	Phos- phorus (%)
Alfalfa hay (early bloom)	90.0%	57.0%	0.94	0.55	0.25	0.59	18.4%	57.8	1.25%	0.23%
Barley	89.0	83.0	1.36	0.97	0.64	0.85	13.0	—	0.09	0.47
Bermuda grass (grazed)	31.0	66.0	—	0.67	0.38	0.61	14.6	150.2	0.49	0.27
Bluegrass (grazed)	30.6	58.0	0.95	0.56	0.27	0.73	17.0	86.4	0.39	0.39
Bone meal (steamed)	95.0	16.0	—	—	—	—	12.7	—	30.51	14.31
Brome (grazed early)	32.5	63.0	1.04	0.62	0.34	0.62	20.3	208.8	0.59	0.37
Buffalo grass	47.7	56.0	0.92	0.54	0.23	0.60	9.2	42.6	0.52	0.16
Corn (no. 2 dent)	89.0	91.0	1.50	1.04	0.67	0.96	10.0	0.91	0.02	0.35
Corn (ground ear)	87.0	90.0	1.48	1.01	0.63	0.85	9.3	—	0.05	0.31
Corn silage	27.9	70.0	1.15	0.71	0.45	0.80	8.4	—	0.28	0.21
Corn stover (no ears, husks)	87.2	59.0	0.97	0.55	0.25	0.52	5.9	—	0.49	0.09
Cottonseed meal	93.5	74.0	1.22	0.75	0.49	0.77	42.4	—	0.20	1.09
Dicalcium phosphate	96.0	—	—	—	—	—	—	—	23.10	18.65
Grama (early vegetation)	41.0	64.0	1.05	0.63	0.36	0.50	13.1	—	0.54	0.19
Limestone (ground)	100.0	—	—	—	—	—	—	—	33.84	0.02
Meadow hay (native)	92.9	51.0	0.84	0.50	0.14	0.56	9.1	—	0.57	0.17
Milk	12.0	130.0	2.14	2.09	0.91	1.52	25.8	—	0.93	0.75
Milo (sorghum)	89.0	80.0	1.31	0.84	0.56	0.81	12.4	—	0.04	0.33
Molasses (cane)	75.0	72.0	1.25	2.27	1.48	0.77	4.3	—	1.19	0.11
Oats (grain)	89.0	76.0	1.25	0.79	0.52	0.80	13.2	—	0.11	0.39
Prairie hay (midbloom)	91.0	51.0	0.84	0.50	0.14	—	8.1	9.1	0.34	0.21
Sorghum, Sudan grass (grazed)	22.7	63.0	1.04	0.62	0.35	0.72	8.7	—	0.43	0.35
Soybean meal (solvent)	89.0	81.0	1.33	0.88	0.59	0.84	51.5	—	0.36	0.75
Wheat (hard, red winter)	89.1	88.0	1.45	0.98	0.64	0.92	14.6	—	0.06	0.57
Wheat (grazed early)	21.5	73.0	1.20	0.75	0.49	0.79	28.6	236.4	0.42	0.40
Wheat (straw)	90.1	48.0	0.79	0.47	0.09	0.37	3.6	1.0	0.17	0.08
Wheatgrass, crested (early)	30.8	67.0	1.10	0.66	0.40	0.57	23.6	197.1	0.46	0.35

Sources: **Adapted from the National Research Council, 1989, and Preston, 1990.**

TABLE 15.4. Nutrient Composition of Selected Feeds Commonly Used in Rations of Monogastric Animals (air-dry basis)

			Minerals					Vitamins							Amino Acids		
Feed	ME	Protein (%)	Calcium (%)	Phosphorus (%)	Iron (mg/lb)	Manganese (mg/lb)	Zinc (mg/lb)	A (IU/lb)	Niacin (mg/lb)	Pantothenic Acid (mg/lb)	Riboflavin (mg/lb)	Choline (mg/lb)	B_{12} (mg/lb)	Lysine (%)	Methionine (%)	Tryptophan (%)
Alfalfa meal (dehydrated)	1032	**17.5**	**1.44**	**0.22**	141	13	8	12,272	17	13	7	497	0.002	**0.73**	**0.2**	**0.28**
Barley	1304	11.6	0.05	0.36	23	4	8	—	29	4	1	450	—	0.40	0.2	0.14
Blood meal	876	85.0	0.30	0.25	1364	3	139	—	10	1	1	340	0.20	8.10	1.5	1.10
Bone meal	—	—	28.00	13.00	—	—	—	—	—	—	—	—	—	—	—	—
Corn	1511	8.8	0.02	0.28	16	2	4	454	15	3	0.5	241	—	0.24	0.2	0.05
Dicalcium phosphate	—	—	26.0	20.0	—	—	—	—	—	—	—	—	—	—	—	—
Feather meal	1032	86.4	0.20	0.80	—	10	—	—	12	4	1	405	0.27	1.10	0.4	0.50
Fish meal (menhaden)	1014	60.5	5.11	2.88	200	15	67	—	25	4	2	1389	0.07	4.83	1.8	0.68
Limestone	—	—	39.0	—	—	—	—	—	—	—	—	—	—	—	—	—
Meat and bone meal	1106	50.4	10.1	4.96	223	6	42	—	21	2	2	907	0.03	2.60	0.7	0.28
Milo (sorghum)	1468	8.9	0.28	0.32	18	6	6	—	19	5	0.5	308	—	0.22	0.1	0.10
Oats	1213	11.4	0.06	0.27	32	20	—	—	7	13	0.5	500	—	0.40	0.2	0.16
Skim milk (dried)	1527	33.5	1.28	1.02	23	1	18	—	5	15	10	568	—	2.40	0.9	0.44
Soybean meal (solvent)	1404	48.5	0.27	0.62	54	12	20	—	10	7	1	1295	—	3.18	0.7	0.67
Wheat, hard (red winter)	1464	14.1	0.05	0.37	23	28	6	—	25	6	2	495	—	0.40	0.2	0.18
Whey (dried)	1450	13.6	0.97	0.76	59	3	—	—	5	20	12	900	—	0.97	0.2	0.19

Source: Adapted from the National Research Council, 1989.

low in TDN, although there are exceptions; for example, corn silage has over 18% crude fiber and approximately 70% TDN.

Feedstuffs that contain 20% or more protein, such as soybean meal and cottonseed meal, are classified as protein supplements. Feedstuffs having less than 18% crude fiber and less than 20% protein are classified as energy feeds or concentrates. Cereal grains are typical energy feeds, which is reflected by their high TDN values.

Nutrient Composition of Feeds

Feeds are analyzed for their nutrient composition, as discussed earlier. The ultimate goal of nutrient analysis of feeds is to predict the productive response of animals when they are fed rations of a given composition.

The nutrient composition of some of the more common feeds is shown in Tables 15.3 (ruminants) and 15.4 (monogastric animals). The information in Table 15.3 represents averages of numerous feed samples. Feeds are not constant in composition, and an actual analysis should be obtained whenever economically feasible. The actual analysis is not always feasible or possible because of lack of available laboratories and insufficient time to obtain the analysis. Therefore, feed-analysis tables become the next best source of reliable information on nutrient composition of feeds. It is not uncommon to expect the following deviations of actual feed analysis from the table values for several feed constituents: crude protein (±15%), energy values (±10%), and minerals (±30%).

Digestible protein is included in some feed composition tables, but because of the large contribution of body protein to the apparent protein in the feces, digestible protein is more misleading than crude protein. For this reason, crude protein is more commonly found in feed-composition tables and used in formulating diets for ruminants.

Digestible protein (DP) can be calculated from crude protein (CP) content by using the following equation (%DP and %CP are on a dry-matter basis):

$$\%DP = 0.9\ (\%CP) - 3$$

Five measures of energy values—TDN, ME, NEm, NEg, and NE_l)—are shown in Table 15.3. TDN is shown because there are more TDN values for feeds and because TDN has been a standard system of expressing the energy value of feeds. Some individuals seek ME (metabolizable energy) values for feed because these values are in calories rather than pounds. NEm and NEg values are used primarily to formulate feedlot diets and diets for growing replacement heifers, as these values offset the major problem associated with the TDN energy system. NE_l is used in formulating diets for dairy cows.

SELECTED REFERENCES

Publications

Church, D. C. 1991. *Livestock Feeds and Feeding.* 3rd ed. Englewood Cliffs, NJ: Prentice-Hall.

Cullison, A. E. 1987. *Feeds and Feeding.* Reston, VA: Reston Publishing Co.

Ensminger, M. E., Oldfield, J. E., and Heinemann, W. W. 1990. *Feeds and Nutrition.* 2nd ed. Clovis, CA: Ensminger Publishing Co.

Jurgens, M. H. 1988. *Animal Feeding and Nutrition.* 4th ed. Dubuque, IA: Kendall-Hunt.

National Research Council. *Nutrient Requirements of Beef Cattle,* 1984; *of Dairy Cattle,* 1978; *of Goats,* 1981; *of Horses,* 1989; *of Poultry,* 1986; *of Sheep,* 1985; and *of Swine,* 1988. Washington, DC: National Academy Press.

Visuals

Introduction to Feeds and Feeding (VHS Video), VEP, Calif. Polytechnic State Univ., San Luis Obispo, CA 93407.

CHAPTER 16

Digestion and Absorption of Feed

Animals obtain substances needed for all body functions from the feeds they eat and the liquids they drink. Before the body can absorb and use them, feeds must undergo a process called digestion. **Digestion** includes mechanical action, such as chewing and contractions of the intestinal tract; chemical action, such as the secretion of hydrochloric acid (HCl) in the stomach and bile in the small intestine; and action of enzymes, such as maltase, lactase, and sucrase (which act on disaccharides), lipase (which acts on lipids), and peptidases (which act on proteins). Enzymes are produced either by the various parts of the digestive tract or by microorganisms. The role of digestion is to reduce feed particles to molecules so they can be absorbed into the blood and eventually support body functions.

CARNIVOROUS, OMNIVOROUS, AND HERBIVOROUS ANIMALS

Animals are classed as carnivores, omnivores, or herbivores according to the types of feed they normally eat. Carnivores, such as dogs and cats, normally consume animal tissues as their source of nutrients; herbivores, such as cattle, horses, sheep, and goats, primarily consume plant tissues. Humans and pigs are examples of omnivores, who eat both plant and animal products.

Carnivores and omnivores are monogastric animals, meaning that the stomach is simple in structure, having only one compartment. Some herbivores, such as horses and rabbits, are also monogastric. Other herbivores, such as cattle, sheep, and goats, are ruminant animals, meaning that the stomach is complex in structure, containing four compartments. Animals classified as carnivores, omnivores, and herbivores can utilize certain feeds they do not normally consume. For example, animal products can be fed to herbivorous ruminants, and certain cereal products can be fed to carnivores.

The digestive tracts of pigs and humans are similar in anatomy and physiology; therefore, much of the information gained from studies on pig nutrition and digestive physiology can be applied to the human. Both the pig and the human are omnivores and both are monogastric animals. Neither can synthesize the B-complex vitamins or amino acids to a significant extent. Both pigs and humans tend to eat large quantities, which can result in obesity. Humans can control obesity by controlling food intake and exercising as a means of using, rather than storing, excess energy. Obesity in swine can be controlled by limiting the amount of feed available to them and through genetic selection of leaner animals. The latter has received the greater emphasis as pigs are typically fed ***ad libitum.***

DIGESTIVE TRACT OF MONOGASTRIC ANIMALS

The anatomy of the digestive tract varies greatly from one species of animal to another. The basic parts of the digestive tract are mouth, stomach, small intestine and large intestine, or colon. The primary function of the parts preceding the intestine is to reduce the size of feed particles. The small intestine functions in splitting food molecules and in nutrient absorption, whereas the large intestine absorbs water and forms indigestible wastes into solid form called feces. In a mammal having a simple stomach (such as the pig), the mouth has teeth and lips for grasping and holding feed that is masticated (chewed), and salivary glands that secrete saliva for moistening feed so it can be swallowed.

Feed passes from the mouth to the stomach through the esophagus. A sphincter (valve) is at the junction of the stomach and esophagus. It can prevent feed from coming up the esophagus when stomach contractions occur. The stomach empties its contents into that portion of the small intestine known as the duodenum. The pyloric sphincter, located at the junction of the stomach and the duodenum, can be closed to prevent feed from moving into or out of the stomach. Feed goes from the duodenum to the jejunum portion and then to the ileum portion of the small intestine. It then passes from the small intestine to the large intestine, or colon. The ileocecal valve, located at the junction of the small intestine and the colon, prevents material in the large intestine from moving back into the small intestine.

The small intestine actually empties into the side of the colon near, but not at, the anterior end of the colon. The blind anterior end of the colon is the cecum, or, in some animals, the vermiform appendix. The large intestine empties into the rectum. The anus has a sphincter, which is under voluntary control so that defecation can be prevented by the animal until it actively engages in the process. The structures of the digestive system of the pig are shown in Figure 16.1.

Animals such as pigs, horses, and poultry are classed as monogastric animals, but they differ markedly in certain ways. For example, the horse (Fig. 16.2) has a large structure called the **cecum,** where feed is fermented. Because the cecum is posterior to the area where most feed is absorbed, horses do not obtain all of the nutrients made by microorganisms in the cecum. Digestive tract sizes and capacities of monogastric animals are contrasted in Table 16.1.

The digestive tracts of most poultry species differ from the pig in several respects. Because they have no teeth, poultry break their feed into a size that can be swallowed by pecking with their beaks or by scratching with their feet. Feed goes from the mouth through the esophagus to the crop, which is an enlargement of the esophagus where feed can be stored. Some fermentation may occur in the crop, but it does not act as a fermentation vat. Feed passes from the crop to the proventriculus, which is a glandular stomach in birds that secretes gastric juices and HCl but does not grind feed. Feed then goes to the gizzard, where it is ground into finer particles by strong muscular contractions. The gizzard apparently has no function other than to reduce the size of feed particles; birds from which it has been removed digest a finely ground ration. Feed moves from the gizzard into the small intestine. Material from the small intestine empties into the large intestine. At the junction of the small and large intestines are two ceca, which

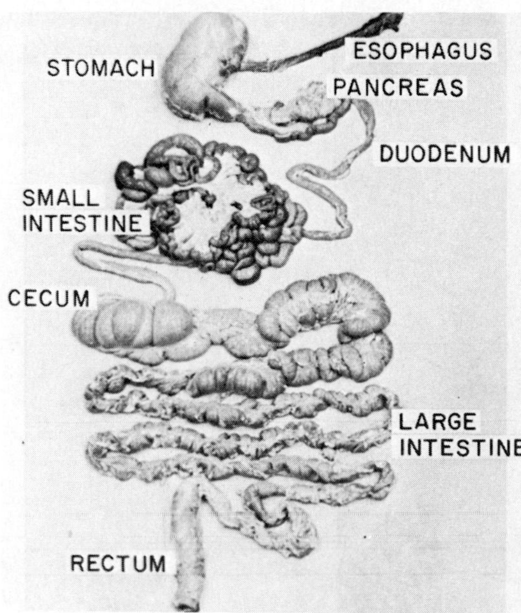

FIGURE 16.1.
Digestive tract of the pig as an example of the digestive tract of a monogastric animal. Reprinted with permission from D. C. Church and W. G. Pond, *Basic Animal Nutrition and Feeding* (Corvallis, OR: D. C. Church, copyright © 1974).

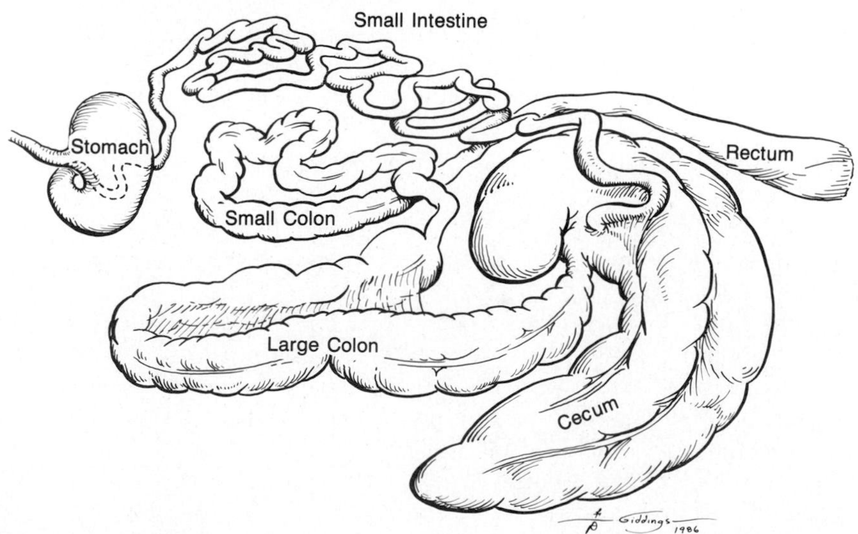

FIGURE 16.2.
Digestive system of the horse. The posterior view shows the colon or large intestine proportionally larger than the rest of the digestive tract. Note particularly the location of the cecum at the anterior end of the colon. Drawing by Dennis Giddings.

TABLE 16.1. Digestive Tract Sizes and Capacities of Selected Monogastric Animals

Part of Digestive Tract	Species: Human	Pig	Horse	Chicken
Esophagus	—	—	4 ft	Total length of digestive tract in mature chickens is approximately 7 ft (beak to crop, 7 in.; beak to proventriculus, 14 in.; duodenum, 8 in.; ileum and jejunum, 48 in.; and cecum, 7 in.)
Stomach	1 qt	2 gal	4 gal	
Small intestine	1 gal	2 gal	12 gal 70 ft	
Large intestine	1 qt	3 gal		
Cecum			8 gal 4 ft	
Large colon			18 gal 10 ft	
Small colon			4 gal 12 ft	

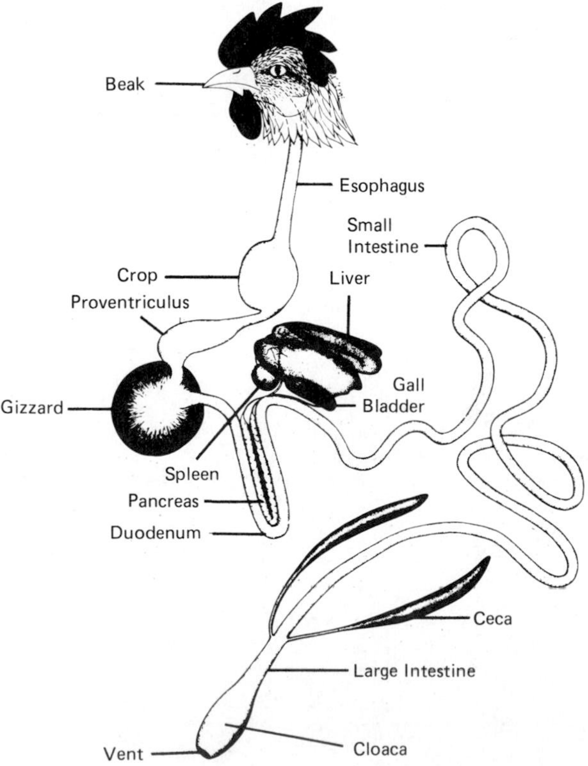

FIGURE 16.3.
Digestive tract of the chicken showing crop, proventriculus, and gizzard, all of which are characteristic of poultry. Courtesy of J. E. Parker, Oregon State University.

contribute little to digestion. Material passes from the large intestine into the cloaca, into which urine also empties. Material from the cloaca is voided through the vent (Fig. 16.3).

STOMACH COMPARTMENTS OF RUMINANT ANIMALS

In contrast to the single stomach of monogastric animals, stomachs of cattle, sheep and goats have four compartments—**rumen, reticulum, omasum,** and **abomasum** (Figs. 16.4 and 16.5). The rumen is a large fermentation vat where bacteria and protozoa thrive and break down

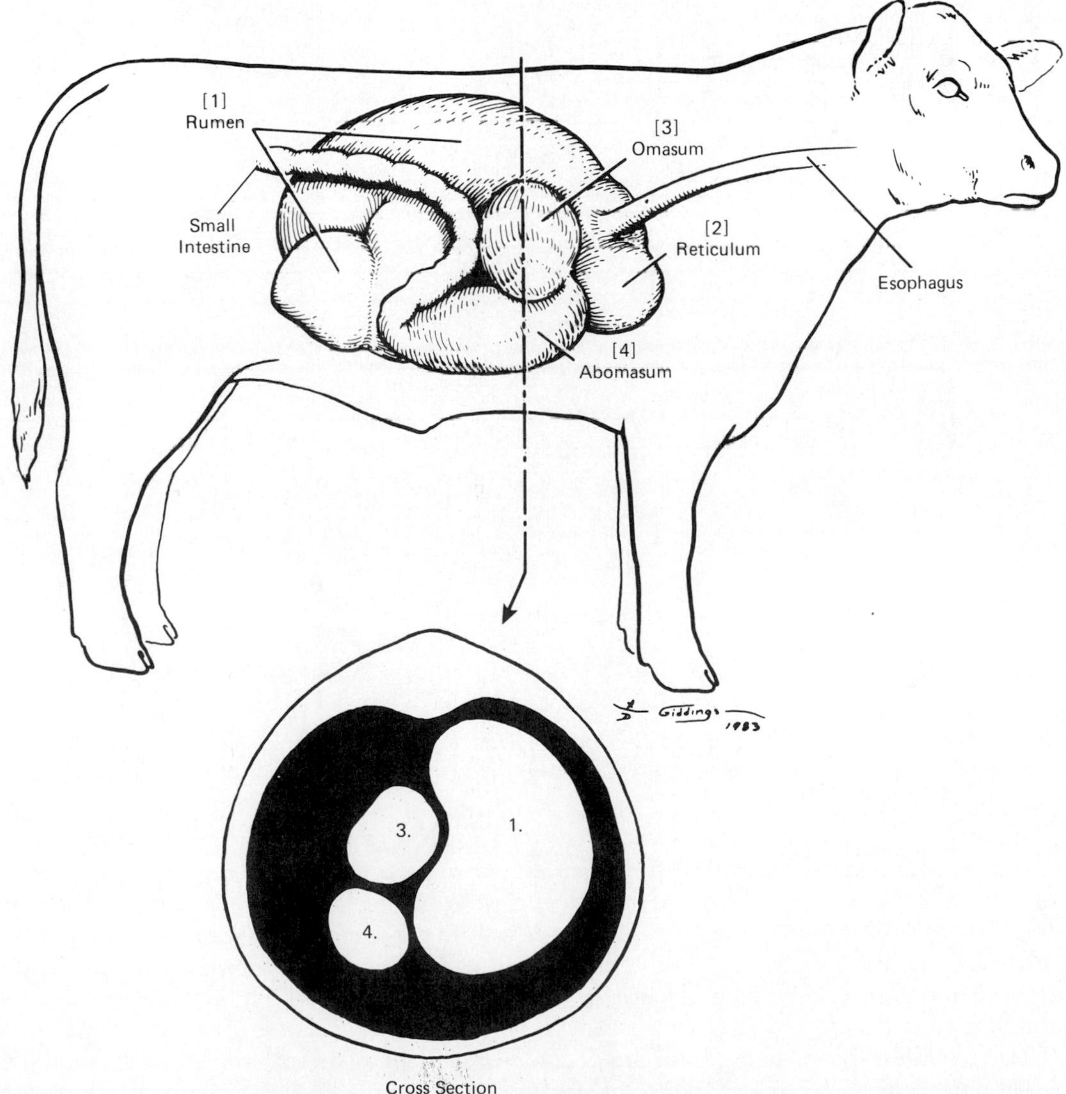

FIGURE 16.4.
Beef cattle digestive tract. Drawing by Dennis Giddings.

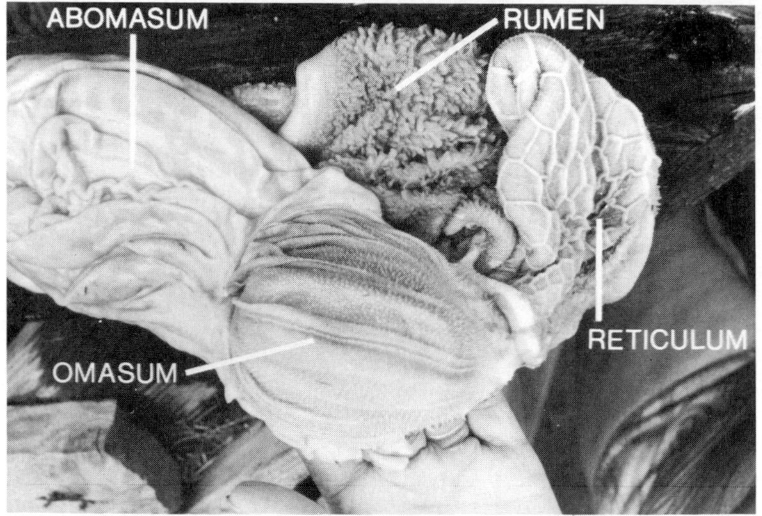

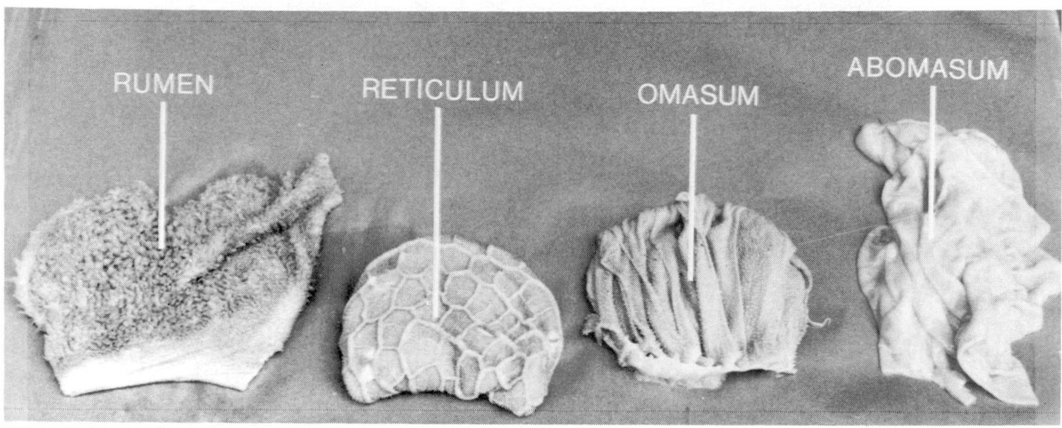

FIGURE 16.5.
Lining of the four compartments of the ruminant stomach (goat). (A) Compartments connected. (B) Compartments separated. Courtesy of George F. W. Haenlein, University of Delaware.

roughages to obtain nutrients for their use. It is lined with numerous papillae, which give it the appearance of being covered with a thick coat of short projections. The papillae increase the surface area of the rumen lining. The microorganisms in the rumen can digest cellulose and can synthesize amino acids from nonprotein nitrogen as well as the B-complex vitamins. Later, these microorganisms are digested in the small intestine to provide these nutrients for the ruminant animal's use.

The reticulum has a lining with small compartments similar to a honeycomb, thus it is occasionally referred to as the honeycomb. Its function is to interact with the rumen in initiating the mixing activity of the rumen and providing an additional area for fermentation. The omasum has many folds, so it is often called the manyplies. The omasum may not have a major

TABLE 16.2. Digestive Tract Sizes and Capacities of Mature Ruminant Animals

Part of Digestive Tract	Species	
	Cow	Ewe
Stomach		
Rumen	40 gal	5 gal
Reticulum	2 gal	2 qt
Omasum	4 gal	1 qt
Abomasum	4 gal	3 qt
Small intestine	15 gal (130 ft)	2 gal (80 ft)
Large intestine	10 gal	6 qt

digestive function, although some believe that the folds produce a grinding action on the feed. The abomasum, or true stomach, corresponds to the stomach of monogastric animals and performs a similar digestive function.

The size and capacity of the ruminant stomach and intestinal tract are given in Table 16.2. The data in Table 16.2 are for mature ruminants, as the relative proportions of the stomach compartments are considerably different in the young lamb and calf. At birth, the abomasum comprises 60% of the total stomach capacity, whereas the rumen is only 25% of the total.

Animals having the four-compartment stomach eat forage rapidly and later, while resting, they regurgitate each bolus of feed known as the **cud.** The regurgitated feed is chewed more thoroughly, swallowed, then another bolus is regurgitated and chewed. This process continues until the feed is thoroughly masticated. The regurgitation and chewing of undigested feed is known as **rumination.** Animals that ruminate are known as ruminants. As feeds are fermented by microorganisms in the rumen, large amounts of gases (chiefly methane and carbon dioxide) are produced. The animal normally can eliminate the gases by controlled belching, also called **eructation.**

DIGESTION IN MONOGASTRIC ANIMALS

Feed that is ingested (taken into the mouth) stimulates the secretion of saliva. Chewing reduces the size of ingested particles and saliva moistens the feed. The enzyme amylase, present in saliva of some species including pigs and humans, acts on starch. Ruminants do not secrete salivary amylase. However, little actual breakdown of starch into simpler compounds occurs in the mouth, primarily because feed is there for a short time.

An **enzyme** is an organic catalyst that speeds a chemical reaction without being altered by the reaction. Enzymes are rather specific; that is, each type of enzyme acts on only one or a few types of substances. Therefore, it is customary to name enzymes by giving the name of the substance on which it acts and adding the suffix *-ase,* which, by convention, indicates that the molecules so named are enzymes (Table 16.3). For example, lipase is an enzyme that acts on lipids (fats); maltase is an enzyme that acts on maltose to convert it into two molecules of glucose; lactase is an enzyme that acts on lactose to convert it into one molecule of glucose and one molecule of galactose; and sucrase is an enzyme that acts on sucrose to convert it into one

TABLE 16.3. Important Enzymes in the Digestion of Feed

Enzyme	Substrate	Substances Resulting from Enzyme Action
Amylase	Starch	Disaccharides, dextrin
Chymotrypsin	Peptides	Amino acids and peptides
Lactase	Lactose	Glucose and galactose
Lipase	Lipids	Fatty acids and glycerides
Maltase	Maltose	Glucose and glucose
Pepsin	Protein	Polypeptides
Peptidases	Peptides	Amino acids
Sucrase	Sucrose	Glucose and fructose
Trypsin	Protein	Polypeptides

molecule of glucose and one molecule of fructose. Some lipase is present in saliva but little hydrolysis of lipids into fatty acids and glycerides occurs in the mouth.

As soon as it is moistened by saliva and chewed, feed is swallowed and passes through the esophagus to the stomach. The stomach secretes HCl, mucus, and the digestive enzymes pepsin and gastrin. The strongly acidic environment in the stomach favors the action of pepsin. Pepsin breaks proteins down into polypeptides. The HCl also assists in coagulation, or curdling, of milk. Little breakdown of proteins into amino acids occurs in the stomach. Mucous secretions help to protect the stomach lining from the action of strong acids.

In the stomach, feed is mixed well and some digestion occurs; the mixture that results is called **chyme.** The chyme passes next into the duodenum, where it is mixed with secretions from the pancreas, bile, and enzymes from the intestine.

Secretion from the pancreas and discharge of bile from the gall bladder are stimulated by secretin, pancreozymin, and cholecystokinin, three hormones that are released from the duodenal cells. The enzymes from the pancreas are lipase, which hydrolyzes fats into fatty acids and glycerides; trypsin, which acts on proteins and polypeptides to reduce them to small peptides; chymotrypsin, which acts on peptides to produce amino acids; and amylase, which breaks starch down to disaccharides, after which the disaccharides are broken down to monosaccharides. The liver produces bile that helps emulsify fats; the bile is strongly alkaline and so helps to neutralize the acidic chyme coming from the stomach. Some minerals that are important in digestion also occur in bile.

By the time they reach the small intestine, amino acids, fatty acids, and monosaccharides (simple sugars or carbohydrates) are all available for absorption. Thus, the small intestine is the most important area for both digestion and absorption of feed. Absorption of feed molecules may be either passive or active. Passive passage results from diffusion, which is the movement of molecules from a region of high concentration of those molecules to a region of low concentration. Active transport of molecules across the intestinal wall may be accomplished through a process in which cells of the intestinal lining (**villi,** shown in Fig. 16.6) engulf the molecules and then actively transport these molecules to either the bloodstream or the lymph. Energy is expended in accomplishing the active transport of molecules across the gut wall.

When molecules of digested feed enter the capillaries of the blood system, they are carried directly to the liver. Molecules may enter the lymphatic system, after which they go to various

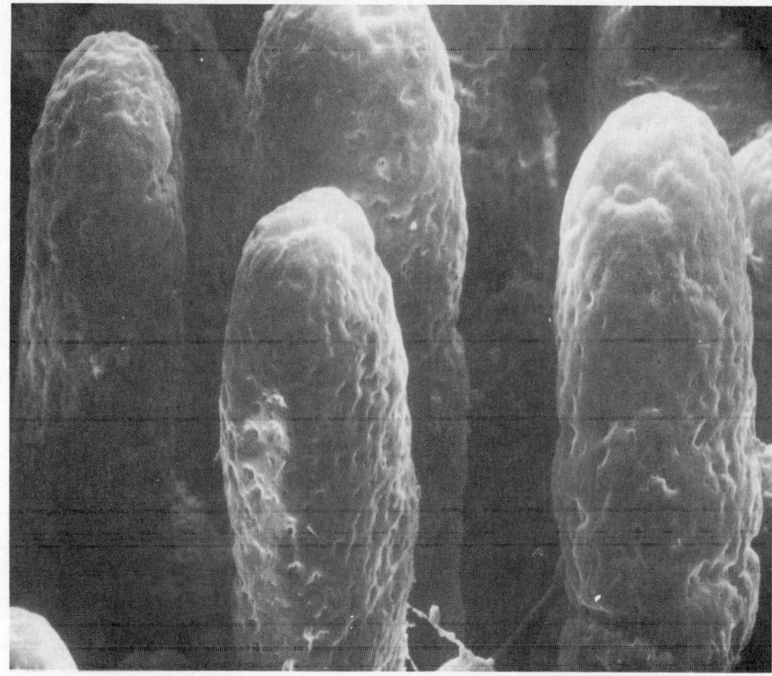

FIGURE 16.6.
Electron micrograph of the lining of the small intestine. These projections (villi) increase the surface area and are covered with cells that digest and absorb nutrients from the feed. Magnification is approximately × 200. Courtesy of Dr. G. L. Waxler, 1972. *Am. J. Vet. Res.* 33:1323.

parts of the body including the liver. The liver is an extremely important organ both for metabolizing useful substances and for detoxifying harmful ones.

In some monogastric animals, such as the horse, postgastric (cecal) fermentation of roughages occurs. In these animals, the feed that can be digested by a monogastric animal is digested and absorbed before the remainder reaches the cecum. These animals are perhaps more efficient than ruminants in their use of feeds such as concentrates. In the ruminant animals, the concentrates given along with roughages are used by the bacteria and protozoa. Because the microorganisms in ruminants use starches and sugars, little glucose is available to ruminants for absorption. The microorganisms do provide volatile fatty acids, which are absorbed by the ruminant and converted to glucose as an energy source. The postgastric fermentation that occurs in horses breaks down roughages, but this takes place posterior to the areas where nutrients are most actively absorbed; consequently, all nutrients in the feed are not obtained by the animal in postgastric fermentation.

DIGESTION IN RUMINANT ANIMALS

In mature ruminant animals (cattle, sheep, and goats), predigestive fermentation of feed occurs in the rumen and reticulum. The bacteria and protozoa in the rumen and reticulum use roughages consumed by the animal as feed for their growth and multiplication; consequently, billions of these microorganisms develop. The rumen environment is ideal for microorganisms because moisture, a warm temperature, and a constant supply of nutrients are present. Excess microorganisms are continuously removed from the rumen and reticulum along with small feed particles that escape microbial fermentation and pass through the omasum into the abomasum.

When feed passes into the abomasum, strong acids destroy the bacteria and protozoa. The ruminant animal then digests the microorganisms in the small intestine and uses them as a source of nutrients. The digested microbial cells provide the animal with most of its amino acid needs and some energy. Thus, ruminant animals and microorganisms mutually benefit each other. All digestive processes in ruminants are the same as those in monogastric animals after the feed reaches the abomasum, which corresponds to the stomach of monogastric animals.

The rumen fermentation process also produces **volatile fatty acids** (acetic, propionic, and butyric acids), which are waste products of microbial fermentation of carbohydrates. The animal then uses these volatile fatty acids (VFA), as its major source of energy. In the process of fermenting feeds, methane gas is also produced by the microorganisms. The animal releases the gas primarily through belching. Occasionally, the gas-releasing mechanism does not function properly and gas accumulates in the rumen, causing **bloat** to occur. Death will occur owing to suffocation if gas pressure builds to a high level and interferes with adequate respiration.

A young, nursing ruminant consumes little or no roughage. Consequently, at this early stage of life, its digestive tract functions similar to a monogastric animal. Milk is directed immediately into the abomasum in young ruminants by the **esophageal groove** (Fig. 16.7). The sides of the esophageal groove extend upwards by a reflex action and form a tube through which milk

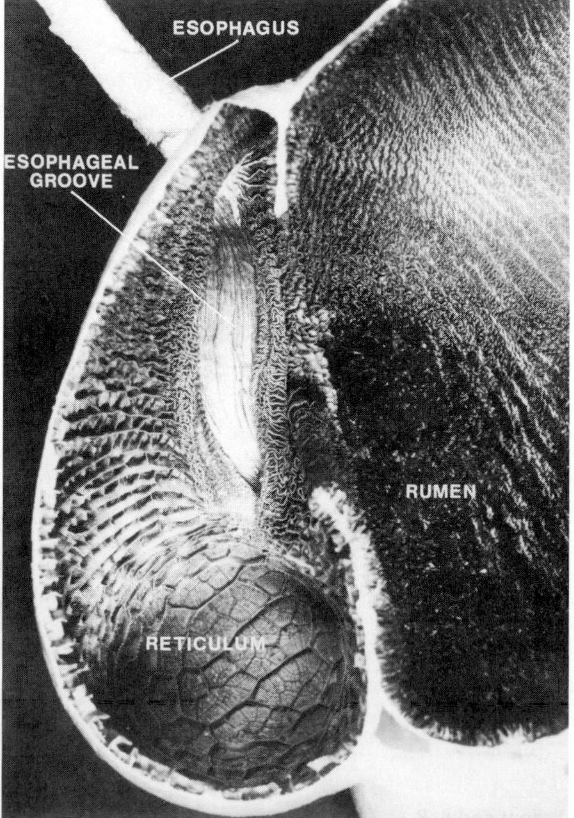

FIGURE 16.7.
The esophageal groove with its location relative to the esophagus, reticulum, and rumen. Courtesy of N. J. Benevenga et al., 1969. Preparation of the ruminant stomach for classroom demonstration. *J. Dairy Sci.* 52:1294.

passes directly from the esophagus to the abomasum. This allows milk to bypass fermentation in the rumen. Rumen fermentation is an inefficient use of energy and protein in a high-quality feed such as milk.

When roughage is consumed it is directed into the rumen, where bacteria and protozoa break it down into simple forms for their use. The rumen starts to develop functionally as soon as roughage enters it, but some time is required before it is completely functional. Complete development of the rumen, reticulum, and abomasum requires about 2 months in sheep and about 3–4 months in cattle. One can influence development of the rumen by the type of feed one gives to the animal. If only milk and concentrated feeds are given, the rumen shows little development. If very young ruminants are forced to live on forage, the rumen develops much more rapidly.

Energy Pathways

Figure 16.8 shows the digestion and utilization of carbohydrates and fats contained in the ingested forages and grains. The primary energy end products of glucose and fatty acids supply

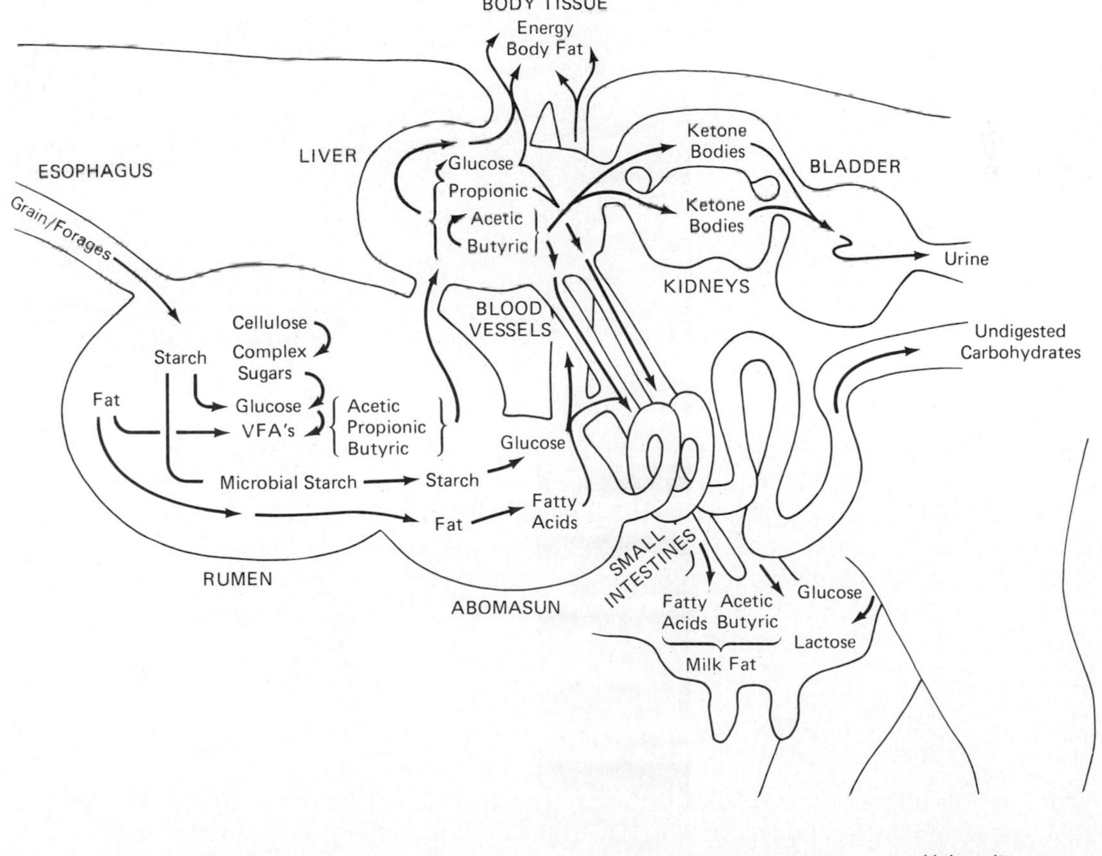

University.

FIGURE 16.8.
Energy pathways in the ruminant. Courtesy of J. Bryant and B. R. Moss, Montana State University.

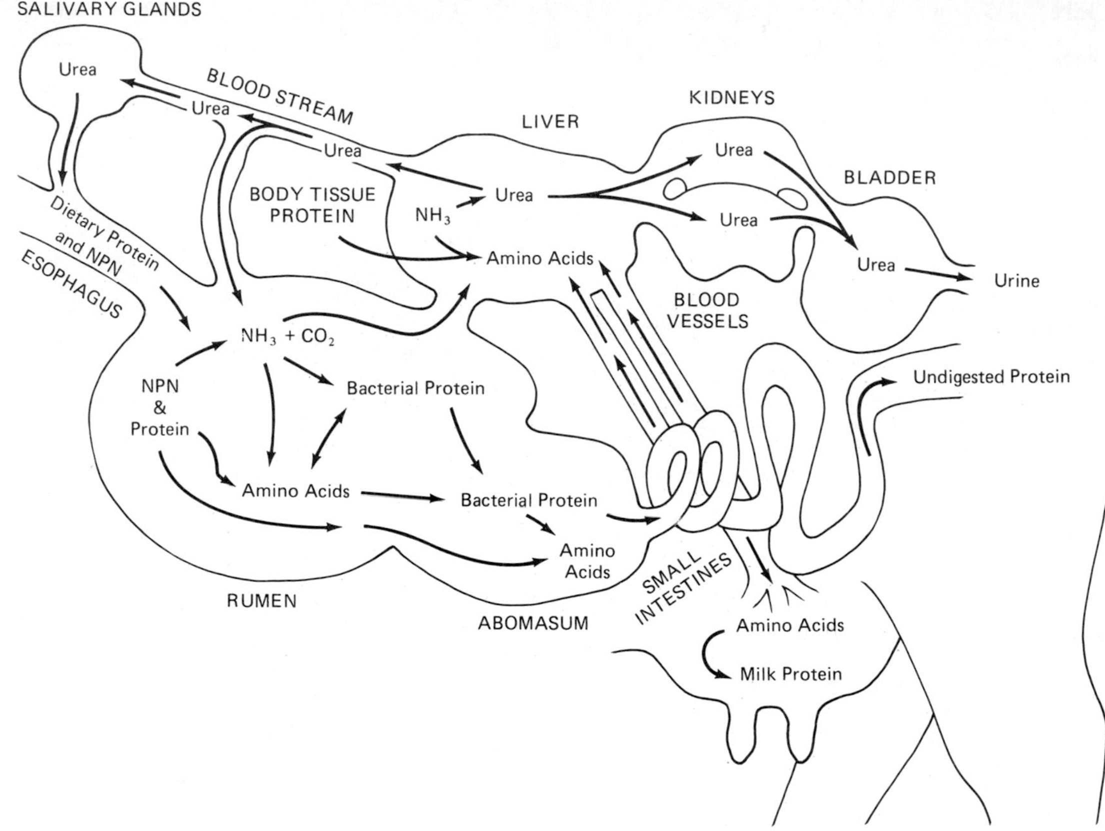

FIGURE 16.9.
Protein pathways in the ruminant. Courtesy of J. Bryant and B. R. Moss, Montana State University.

energy in the body tissues and become milk fat and lactose in the lactating ruminant. Excess energy is stored as body fat in the body tissues.

The primary organs and tissues in energy metabolism are shown in Fig. 16.8. These are the rumen, abomasum, small intestines, liver, blood vessels, mammary gland, and body tissues. Undigested carbohydrates (primarily complex carbohydrates such as lignin) are excreted through the large intestine. Other energy waste products such as ketone bodies are excreted through the kidneys in the urine.

Protein Pathways

The digestion, utilization, and excretion of dietary protein and **nonprotein nitrogen (NPN)** are shown in Fig. 16.9. The end products of protein and NPN are amino acids, ammonia (NH_3), and synthesized amino acids. Excess NH_3 can be formed into urea in the liver, then excreted through the urine, with some urea returning to the rumen as a component of saliva.

SELECTED REFERENCES

Publications

Church, D. C. 1991. *Livestock Feeds and Feeding.* Englewood Cliffs, NJ: Prentice-Hall.

Cullison, A. E. 1987. *Feeds and Feeding.* Reston, VA: Reston Publishing Co.

Ensminger, M. E., Oldfield, J. E., and Heinemann, W. W. 1990. *Feeds and Nutrition.* 2nd ed. Clovis, CA: Ensminger Publishing Co.

Jurgens, M. H. 1988. *Animal Feeding and Nutrition.* 4th ed. Dubuque, IA: Kendall/Hunt.

Visuals

Introduction to Livestock Nutrition (VHS Video). VEP, Calif. Polytechnic State Univ., San Luis Obispo, CA 93407.

CHAPTER 17

Providing Nutrients for Body Functions

Feeding animals is of fundamental importance to any livestock or poultry production program because animals must be healthy to function efficiently and yield maximum profits to the producer. The basic task of the producer, then, is to supply animals with feed that satisfies their body functions for maintenance, growth, fattening, reproduction, lactation, egg laying, wool production, and work. Each of these functions has a unique set of nutrient requirements, and they are additive when more than one function is occurring.

Profits derived from any feeding program must be assessed against production costs. Knowledgeable producers can increase their profits by feeding their animals both adequately and economically.

NUTRIENT REQUIREMENTS FOR BODY MAINTENANCE

Body maintenance requires that nutrients are supplied to keep the body functioning in a state of well-being. There is no gain or loss of weight or production. Maintenance functions that have a high priority for nutrients are (1) body tissue repair, (2) control of body temperature, (3) energy to keep all vital organs (respiratory, digestive, and so on) functioning, and (4) water balance maintenance.

Nutrients first meet maintenance needs before supplying any of the other body functions. Approximately half of all feed fed to livestock and poultry is used to fill the maintenance requirement. Feedlot animals on full feed may only use 30%–40% of their nutrients for maintenance, while some mature breeding animals may need 90% of their feed for maintenance. Highly efficient dairy cows, producing over 100 lb of milk per day, have a daily feed consumption four to five times their maintenance requirement.

Body Size and Maintenance

Maintenance needs are related to body size. A large animal obviously needs more feed than a small one, but maintenance requirements are not linearly related to body weight. Small animals

TABLE 17.1. TDN Needed for Maintenance of Cattle in the Growing–Finishing Period

Weight of Cattle (lb)	TDN Needed Daily for Maintenance (lb)
400	5.7
600	7.7
800	9.7
1,000	11.4
1,100	12.3

require more feed per unit of body weight for maintenance than large ones. The approximate maintenance requirement in relation to weight is expressable as $Wt^{0.75}$, rather than $Wt^{1.00}$. Thus, if a 500-lb animal requires 15 lb of feed per day for maintenance, a 1,000-lb animal of the same type does not require twice as much feed even though the latter animal weighs twice as much as the first. The quantity of $1{,}000^{0.75}$ can be determined and applied to show that the 1,000-lb animal requires approximately 1.7 times as much feed for maintenance as the 500-lb animal. The 1,000-lb animal requires, therefore, approximately 25.5 lb daily (15 lb $\times$ 1.7 = 25.5 lb). Table 17.1 shows how the TDN requirement changes with increasing weight. Where corn is 91% TDN, on an air-dry basis, it would take approximately 12.5 lb (12.5 lb $\times$ 0.91 = 11.4 lb TDN) of corn to fill the maintenance requirement of a 1,000-lb animal.

NUTRIENT REQUIREMENTS FOR GROWTH

Growth occurs when protein synthesis is in excess of its breakdown. Growth occurs when cells increase in number or size, or when a combination of both takes place. Growth at the tissue level is accomplished primarily through the building of muscle, bone, and connective tissue.

There are several important nutrient requirements for growth, including energy, protein, minerals, vitamins, and energy. The dry matter of muscle and connective tissue is composed largely of protein; therefore, young, growing animals that need feed to sustain growth in addition to maintenance have greater protein requirements. A young, growing animal is like a muscle-building factory, and protein in the feed is the raw material for the manufacturing process. If provided with only a maintenance amount of feed for an extended period, a young animal may be permanently stunted.

Monogastric animals not only need a certain quantity of protein but they also must have certain amino acids for proper growth. The protein needs of hogs, for example, are usually supplied by feeding them soybean meal as a supplemental source of amino acids. Young ruminant animals cannot consume enough roughage to make maximum growth. If young ruminant animals are being nursed by dams that produce adequate amounts of milk, the young will do well on good pastures, good quality hay, or both together.

The mineral needs of a young, growing animal include calcium and phosphorus for proper bone growth, salt or a normal sodium level in the body,and any mineral that may be deficient in the area in which the animal lives. Calcium is usually plentiful in legume forages, and phosphorus is usually plentiful in grains, so a combination of hay and grain should provide all the calcium and phosphorus that young ruminant animals need. Animals fed on hay alone may need additional phosphorus, and those fed diets high in concentrates may need additional calcium. Some producers feed a mixture of steamed bone meal or dicalcium phosphate and salt at all times to assure that their animals have the necessary calcium and phosphorus.

Two minerals, iodine and selenium, require special consideration. Some areas may be deficient in one or both of these elements. An insufficient amount of iodine in the ration of pregnant females might cause an iodine deficiency in the fetus, which prevents thyroxine from being produced and thus causes a goiter in the newborn. Young animals with goiters die shortly after they are born. Iodized salt can be easily provided to the pregnant females to avoid the iodine deficiency.

A lack of selenium might cause the young to be born with white muscle disease, it can be prevented by giving the pregnant female an injection of selenium. The injectable selenium is distributed commercially and directions for proper dosages that are supplied by the distributor should be followed closely because an overdose in natural feeds or supplements can kill the animal.

Vitamins are needed by young, growing animals. Young ruminant animals are usually on pasture with their dams and thus are exposed to sunshine. The action of ultraviolet rays from the sun converts steroids in the skin into vitamin D, providing the animal with this vitamin. Vitamin D is needed for the proper use of calcium and phosphorus in bone growth. Because pigs, poultry,and rabbits are often raised inside, where sunshine is limited or lacking, they need a dietary source of vitamin D.

Most vitamins must be supplied to pigs and poultry through feeds. The only vitamin commonly fed to ruminant animals is vitamin A, and then only when they are on dry pasture are they fed hay that is quite mature or hay that has been moistened in processing and has, therefore, been dried in the sun for several days. Vitamin A is easily lost in sunlight and during extended dry storage. The activity of vitamin A in silage is often quite high because this vitamin is usually preserved by the acid fermentation that takes placed when silage is made. Silage, however, is usually quite low in vitamin D because the plants used in making silage do not make this vitamin through the action of sunlight and they are not exposed to sunlight for long periods after they are cut.

Young animals need sufficient energy to sustain their growth, high metabolic rate, and activities. They obtain some energy from their mother's milk, and additional energy is supplied as carbohydrates (starch and sugar) and fats from grazed forage or supplemental feeds. Feed grains are high in carbohydrates and also contain some fats. Young ruminants on good pasture typically obtain sufficient energy from pasture and from milk.

The energy needs of young pigs and poultry are generally supplied by feeding them grains such as corn, barley, or wheat. Young horses can usually obtain their energy needs when they are on pasture with their dams since most mares produce much milk; however, for adequate growth after weaning, they need some grain in addition to good pasture or good quality hay.

NUTRIENT REQUIREMENTS FOR FATTENING

Fattening is the storing of surplus feed energy as fat both within and around body tissues. Fattening is desirable to give meat some of its palatability characteristics and to provide energy reserves for postpartum reproductive performance.

Gain from growth is usually less costly than gain from fattening. It takes 2.25 times the energy to produce a pound of fat compared with a pound of protein tissue.

Fattening is the result of excess energy from carbohydrates, fats, or protein above that required for maintenance and growth. Usually fattening animals are full-fed high-energy rations during the last phase of the growing–finishing feeding program.

NUTRIENT REQUIREMENTS FOR REPRODUCTION

The requirements for **reproduction** fall into two categories—those for (1) gamete production and (2) fetal growth in the uterus. In general, healthy males and females are capable of producing gametes. The energy needs for germ cell production are no greater than those needed to keep animals in a normal, healthy condition. For example, ruminant animals grazing on pastures of mixed grass and legumes are generally neither deficient in phosphorus nor lacking in fertility. A lack of phosphorus may cause irregular estrous cycles and impaired breeding in females.

Animals that are losing weight rapidly because of poor feed conditions and animals that are overly fat may be low in fertility. To attain optimum fertility from female animals, they should be in moderately low to moderate body fat conditions as breeding season approaches, but should, ideally, be increasing in condition (i.e., gaining weight) for 2–4 weeks before and during the breeding season.

The nutrients required by the growing **fetus** are much greater in the last trimester of pregnancy than earlier, as little fetal growth occurs during the first two trimesters for pregnancy. Because the fetus is growing, its requirements are the same as those for growth of a young animal after it is born. Healthy females can withdraw nutrients from their bodies to support the growing fetus temporarily while the amount or quality of their feed is low, but reproductive performance will be lower if nutrition is inadequate for 2–3 months in cattle and a few weeks in swine and sheep.

NUTRIENT REQUIREMENTS FOR LACTATION

Among common farm animals, dairy cows and dairy goats produce the most milk; however, most all females are expected to produce milk for their young. Milk production requires considerable protein, minerals, vitamins, and energy. The need for protein is greater because milk contains more than 3% protein. As an example, a cow that weighs 1,500 lb and produces 30 lb of milk per day needs at least 30 lb of feed per day, which contains 15% protein; this giver her 4.5 lb protein for her body and the milk she produces. If the protein she eats is 60% digestible, there is 2.7 lb of digestible protein, of which 1.5 lb is present in her milk. If a cow of this weight is to produce 100 lb of milk per day, she must now consume 50 lb of feed containing 15% protein to compensate for the 3 lb of protein in the 100 lb of milk that she gives. Generally, during peak milk production, feed consumption cannot compensate for nutrient output and the cow does mobilize some body protein. Actually, more body energy is mobilized than body protein to meet the nutrient deficit.

Calcium and phosphorus are the two most important minerals needed for lactation. Milk is rich in these minerals; their absence or imbalance may result in decreased lactation or even cause death. The dairy cow may develop milk fever shortly after calving if there is an exceptionally heavy drain of calcium from her system. Cows afflicted by milk fever might become comatose and die if not treated. An intravenous injection of calcium gluconate usually helps the cow recover in less than a day. Milk fever rarely occurs in species or animals that produce relatively small quantities of milk.

Dairy cows produce milk that contains considerable quantities of vitamin A and most B-complex vitamins. Because cows are ruminants, it is unnecessary to feed them B-complex vitamins, and they require vitamin D supplementation only if confined indoors.

Exceptions occur with beef cows that give large amounts of milk. If they do not have adequate feed while they are nursing their calves, they may not conceive for the next calf crop. In those parts of the world where sheep and dairy goats are the principal dairy animals, the energy needs of these animals are quite similar to those of dairy cows that produce much milk.

The requirements for milk production in sows are usually provided by increasing the percentage of protein in the ration, by increasing the amount of feed allowed, and by providing a mineral mix (a combination of minerals that usually contains calcium, phosphorus, salt, and some trace minerals).

Energy is perhaps the most vital requirement for the production of much milk. The energy need is based on the amount of milk being produced. A lactating cow needs energy for body maintenance while she also produces milk and provides the energy stored in it. She cannot eat enough hay to obtain the quantity of energy needed so she must receive high-energy feeds such as concentrates; even then her production may be limited by the amount of feed she can eat. A high-producing dairy cow may need three to four times the energy of a nonlactating cow of the same size. Even when fed large amounts of concentrates, a cow that is producing much milk often loses weight and body condition because she cannot consume enough feed to produce at her maximum level; therefore, she draws on her body reserves to supply part of her energy needs.

In the dairy cow, the roughage-to-concentrate ratio should be approximately 40 : 60, as a certain amount of roughage is needed to maintain the desired fat content in milk. Therefore, simply feeding more concentrates is not the only answer to increased milk production.

NUTRIENT REQUIREMENTS FOR EGG LAYING

The nutrient requirements of poultry are dependent on the specific purposes of production—for example, broilers primarily for growth with less emphasis on egg production; Leghorn-type (layers) with primary emphasis on eggs and less on growth. Nutrient requirements for growth are discussed earlier in this chapter.

Leghorn-type chickens are smaller in body size than broilers so their maintenance requirements are less. They are prolific in egg production so they are usually fed *ad libitum* during the growing and laying period. Because layers eat *ad libitum* to satisfy their energy needs, rations need to have adequate concentrations of energy, protein (amino acids), vitamins, and minerals.

NUTRIENT REQUIREMENTS FOR WOOL PRODUCTION

Nutrient requirements for wool production are in addition to nutrients needed for maintenance, growth, and reproduction. Insufficient energy, owing to amount or quality of feed, is usually the most limiting nutritional factor affecting wool production. As wool fibers are primarily protein in composition, the ration should be adequate in protein content.

Shearing removes the natural insulation and may cause an increase in energy requirements owing to heat loss. This is especially true when periods of cold weather occur shortly after shearing.

NUTRIENT REQUIREMENTS FOR WORK

Animals used for work, either for pulling heavy loads or for being ridden, require large amounts of energy in addition to the needs for maintenance. Horses are the primary work animals in the United States, but elsewhere, donkeys, cattle, and water buffaloes are used.

Horses, mules, and donkeys rely partly on perspiration to remove nitrogenous wastes. If a horse is used for hard work for five days of the week and is not allowed to exercise the next two days, a strain is placed on the kidneys and illness may result.

The primary requirement is energy above that needed for maintenance and growth. If energy in the ration is not sufficient to meet the work needs, then body fat stores will provide the additional energy needs.

RATION FORMULATION

This chapter is not intended to cover the details of ration formulation. Attempting to expose the reader to this area without providing the details can be misleading. Books are written and

TABLE 17.2. Daily Nutrient Requirements of Sheep (dry matter basis)

Weight (lb)	Gain (lb)	Dry Matter (lb)	TDN (lb)	ME (Mcal)	Crude Protein (lb)	Ca (g)	P (g)	Vitamin A (IU)	Vitamin E (IU)
Ewes (maintenance)									
110	0.02	2.2	1.2	2.0	0.21	3.0	2.8	2,350	15
176	0.02	2.9	1.6	2.6	0.27	3.3	3.1	3,760	20
Ewes (nonlactating and first 15 weeks of gestation)									
110	0.07	2.6	1.5	2.4	0.25	3.0	2.8	2,350	18
176	0.07	3.3	1.8	3.0	0.31	3.3	3.1	3,760	22
Ewes (last 4 weeks of gestation with 200% lambing rate)									
110	0.5	3.7	2.4	4.0	0.43	4.1	3.9	4,250	26
176	0.5	4.4	2.9	4.7	0.49	4.8	4.5	6,800	30
Ewes (first 8 weeks of lactation, suckling singles)									
110	−0.06	4.6	3.0	4.9	0.67	10.9	7.8	4,250	32
176	−0.06	5.7	3.7	6.1	0.76	12.6	9.0	6,800	39
Ewes (first 8 weeks of lactation, suckling twins)									
110	−0.13	5.3	3.4	5.6	0.86	12.5	8.9	5,000	36
176	−0.13	6.6	4.3	7.0	0.96	14.4	10.2	8,000	45
Lambs (finishing)									
66	0.65	2.9	2.1	3.4	0.42	4.8	3.0	1,410	20
88	0.60	3.5	2.7	4.4	0.41	5.0	3.1	1,880	24
110	0.45	3.5	2.7	4.4	0.35	5.0	3.1	2,350	24

Source: National Research Council, *Nutrient Requirements of Sheep,* 1985.

courses taught on feeds and feeding or animal nutrition that provide an in-depth coverage of this topic. The reader who desires to pursue ration formulation should refer to the references at the end of this chapter.

Chapters 15, 16, and 17 give a brief background on nutrition, which leads into ration formulation. The primary objective of ration formulation is economically matching the animal's nutrient requirements (Tables 17.2–17.8) with the available feeds, taking into consideration the nutrient content of the feeds. Additional considerations are the palatability of the ration, physical form of the feed, and other factors that affect feed consumption.

Additional material on feeding farm animals can be found in the following chapters on individual species: beef cattle (Chapter 23), dairy cattle (Chapter 25), swine (Chapter 27), sheep (Chapter 29), horses (Chapter 31), poultry (Chapter 32), and goats (Chapter 33).

NUTRIENT REQUIREMENTS OF RUMINANTS

The following are some major comparisons that demonstrate changes in nutrient requirements for maintenance growth, lactation, and reproduction:

1. For ewes (maintenance), note the increased requirement in dry matter, energy (TDN or ME), protein, calcium, phosphorus, vitamin A, and vitamin D as body weight changes from 110 lb to 176 lb (Table 17.2). More nutrients are needed to maintain a heavier body weight.

TABLE 17.3. Daily Nutrient Requirements (NRC) for Breeding Heifers and Cows

Weight (lb)	Daily Gain (lb)	Minimum Dry Matter Consumption (lb)	Crude Protein (lb)	TDN (lb)	ME (Mcal)	Ca (g)	P (g)	Vitamin A (1000 IU)
Pregnant Heifers—Last 3–4 Months of Pregnancy								
800	0.9	16.8	1.4	9.2	15.2	21	15	21
950	0.9	19.0	1.5	10.3	16.9	23	17	24
Cows Nursing Calves—Average Milking Ability[a]—First 3–4 Months Postpartum								
900	0	18.8	1.9	10.8	17.7	24	19	33
1,100	0	21.6	2.0	12.1	19.9	27	22	38
1,400	0	25.6	2.3	14.0	23.0	31	26	46
Cows Nursing Calves—Superior Milking Ability[b]—First 3–4 Months Postpartum								
900	0	18.7	2.4	13.1	21.5	35	24	33
1,100	0	22.3	2.6	14.5	23.8	38	27	40
1,400	0	26.7	2.9	16.5	27.1	42	31	47
Dry Pregnant Mature Cows—Middle Third of Pregnancy								
900	0	16.7	1.2	8.2	13.4	14	14	21
1,100	0	19.5	1.4	9.5	15.6	17	17	25
1,400	0	23.3	1.6	11.4	18.7	21	21	30
Dry Pregnant Cows—Last Third of Pregnancy								
900	0.9	18.2	1.5	9.8	16.2	22	17	23
1,100	0.9	21.0	1.6	11.2	18.3	25	20	26
1,400	0.9	24.9	1.9	13.1	21.5	29	24	32

[a]Ten pounds of milk per day (equivalent of approximately 450 lb of calf at weaning if there is adequate forage).
[b]Twenty pounds of milk per day (equivalent of approximately 650 lb of calf at weaning if there is adequate forage).
Source: National Research Council, *Nutrient Requirements of Beef Cattle,* 1984.

TABLE 17.4. Daily Nutrient Requirements for Growing–Finishing Heifers and Steers

Weight[a] (lb)	Daily Gain (lb)	Minimum Dry-Matter Consumption (lb)	Protein (%)	Crude Protein (lb)	NEm (Mcal)	NEg (Mcal)	TDN (lb)	Ca (g)	P (g)
Growing–Finishing Heifer Calves (medium-frame)									
500	1.0	11.8	9.4%	1.10	4.84	3.81	10.1	21	17
500	2.0	11.8	11.4	1.35	4.84	5.37	11.9	27	21
800	1.0	16.7	8.1	1.36	6.24	2.52	11.2	15	15
800	2.0	16.8	9.0	1.51	6.24	6.91	15.2	21	20
1,000	2.0	19.8	8.1	1.61	7.52	6.71	16.3	19	19
Growing–Finishing Steer Calves (medium-frame)									
500	1.0	12.3	9.5%	1.16	4.84	2.53	8.8	18	16
500	2.0	13.1	11.4	1.49	4.84	3.33	9.9	22	19
500	3.0	11.8	14.4	1.69	4.84	4.17	10.4	26	21
800	2.0	18.6	9.2	1.72	6.89	5.33	15.0	21	20
800	3.0[b]	16.8	10.8	1.81	6.89	7.80	17.0	26	23
1,000	2.0	22.0	8.4	1.85	8.14	7.73	18.1	21	21
1,000	3.0[b]	19.8	9.5	1.88	8.14	8.47	19.2	22	22

[a] Average weight for a feeding period.
[b] Most steers of the weight indicated, and not exhibiting compensatory growth, fail to sustain the energy intake necessary to maintain this rate of gain for an extended period.
Source: National Research Council, *Nutrient Requirements of Beef Cattle, 1984.*

TABLE 17.5. Daily Nutrient Requirements of Dairy Cows

Body Weight (lb)	NE_1 (Mcal)	TDN (lb)	Crude Protein (lb)	Ca (lb)	P (lb)	Vitamin A (IU)
Mature Lactating Cows (maintenance)						
800	7.16	6.9	0.70	0.029	0.024	30
1,100	8.46	8.1	0.80	0.044	0.031	38
1,300	9.70	9.3	0.89	0.053	0.037	46
1,550	10.89	10.5	0.99	0.062	0.044	53
Mature Dry Cows (last 2 months of gestation)						
800	9.30	9.1	1.96	0.057	0.035	30
1,100	11.00	10.8	2.32	0.073	0.044	38
1,300	12.61	12.4	2.66	0.086	0.053	46
1,550	14.15	13.9	2.98	0.101	0.062	53
Milk Production (Meal or lb of nutrient per lb of milk for various fat percentages)						
Percentage fat						
3.0	0.291	0.282	0.077	0.0025	0.00170	
3.5	0.313	0.304	0.082	0.0026	0.00175	
4.0	0.336	0.326	0.087	0.0027	0.00180	
4.5	0.354	0.344	0.092	0.0028	0.00185	
5.0	0.377	0.365	0.098	0.0029	0.00190	

Source: National Research Council, *Nutrient Requirements of Dairy Cattle,* 1989.

TABLE 17.6. Daily Nutrient Requirements (or percent of ration) for Swine

	Growing-Fishing (fed *ad libitum*)			Breeding Swine	
Live Weight (lb) Expected Daily Gain (lb) Expected FE (feed/gain)	11-22 0.55 1.84	48-110 1.54 2.71	110-242 1.81 3.79	Bred Gilts and Sows (4 lb daily air-dry feed intake)	Lactating Gilts and Sows (10.5 lb daily air-dry feed intake)
ME (kcal, daily)	1,490	6,200	10,185	5,836	15,320
Crude protein, lb(%)[a]	0.20(20)	0.63(15)	0.89(13)	(12)	(13)
Indispensable amino acids					
Lysine g (%)	5.3(1.15)	14.3(0.75)	18.7(0.60)	(0.43)	(0.60)
Arginine g (%)	2.3(0.50)	4.3(0.05)	3.1(0.10)	(0)	(0.40)
Histidine g (%)	1.4(0.31)	4.2(0.22)	5.6(0.18)	(0.15)	(0.25)
Isoleucine g (%)	3.0(0.15)	8.7(0.46)	11.8(0.38)	(0.30)	(0.39)
Leucine g (%)	3.9(0.85)	11.4(0.60)	15.6(0.50)	(0.30)	(0.48)
Methionine plus cystine g (%)	2.7(0.58)	7.8(0.41)	10.6(0.34)	(0.23)	(0.36)
Phenylalanine plus tyrosine g (%)	4.3(0.94)	12.5(0.66)	17.1(0.55)	(0.45)	(0.70)
Threonine g (%)	3.1(0.68)	9.1(0.48)	12.4(0.40)	(0.30)	(0.43)
Tryptophan g (%)	0.8(0.17)	2.3(0.12)	3.1(0.10)	(0.09)	(0.12)
Valine g (%)	3.1(0.68)	9.1(0.48)	12.4(0.40)	(0.32)	(0.60)
Minerals (selected)					
Calcium g (%)	3.7(0.80)	11.4(0.60)	15.6(0.50)	(0.75)	(0.75)
Phosphorus g (%)	3.0(0.65)	9.5(0.50)	12.4(0.40)	(0.60)	(0.60)
Sodium g (%)	0.5(0.10)	1.9(0.10)	3.1(0.10)	(0.15)	(0.20)
Chlorine g (%)	0.4(0.08)	1.5(0.08)	2.5(0.08)	(0.12)	(0.16)
Magnesium g (%)	0.2(0.04)	0.8(0.04)	1.2(0.04)	(0.04)	(0.04)
Iron mg	46	114	124	144	380
Zinc mg	46	114	155	90	238
Manganese mg	2	4	6	18	48
Vitamins (selected)					
A IU	1,012	2,470	4,043	7,200	9,500
D IU	101	285	466	360	950
E IU	7	21	34	18	47.5
Riboflavin mg	1.61	4.75	6.22	5.4	14.2
Niacin mg	6.90	19	21.77	18	47.5
Panothenic acid mg	4.60	15.20	21.77	21.6	57
B_{12} mg	8.05	19	15.55	27	71.2

[a] Pounds per day or percentage of the ration.
Source: National Research Council, *Nutrient Requirements of Swine,* 1988.

2. In Table 17.2, compare the requirements under ewes (last 6 weeks of gestation) with the requirements of ewes (maintenance) and ewes (nonlactating and first 15 weeks of gestation). During the latter part of gestation, there are greater nutrient demands owing to rapid fetal growth. During the latter part of gestation compared with maintenance only, energy and protein requirements almost double with mineral and vitamin requirements showing significant increases.
3. During lactation, nutrient requirements are even higher than those during gestation. Even with larger amounts of dry matter being supplied, the ewes lose weight. Compare the requirements of ewes nursing single lambs versus twins and note the even higher requirements.
4. The nutrient requirements for lambs being finished for slaughter show the gains approximately the same with increased nutrient requirements due to increased body weight. The increased nutrient requirements are primarily due to an increased maintenance requirement.

TABLE 17.7. Daily Nutrient Requirements for Horses

	Weight (lb)	Daily Gain (lb)	Daily Feed[a] (lb)	Digestible Energy (Mcal)	Crude Protein (g)	Ca (g)	P (g)	Vitamin A (1000 IU)
Ponies (approximate mature weight, 440 lb)								
Maintenance	440	0	8.2	7.4	296	8	6	6
Mares, last 90 days of gestation	440	0.60	8.1	8.2	361	16	12	12
Lactating mares, first 3 months (18 lb of milk per day)	440	0	11.0	13.7	688	27	18	12
Yearling (12 months of age)	308	0.44	6.4	8.7	392	12	7	6
Horses (approximate mature weight, 880 lb)								
Maintenance	880	0	13.9	13.4	536	16	11	12
Mares, last 90 days of gestation	880	1.17	13.7	14.9	654	28	21	24
Lactating mares, first 3 months (26 lb of milk per day)	880	0	17.1	22.9	1,141	45	29	24
Yearling (12 months of age)	583	0.88	10.9	15.6	700	23	13	12
Horses (approximate mature weight, 1,320 lb)								
Maintenance	1,320	0	18.8	19.4	776	24	17	18
Mares, last 90 days of gestation	1,320	1.47	18.5	21.5	947	41	31	36
Lactating mares, first 3 months (40 lb of milk per day)	1,320	0	26.0	33.7	1,711	67	43	36
Yearling (12 months of age)	847	1.32	14.8	22.7	1,023	36	20	17

[a] Air dry basis.

Source: National Research Council, *Nutrient Requirements of Horses,* 1989.

TABLE 17.8. Nutrient Requirements for Leghorn-Type Chickens and Broilers (as percentages or as milligrams or units per kilogram [2.2 lb] of diet)

	Leghorn-Type Chickens					
	Growing		Laying		Broilers	
Energy Base kcal ME/kg Diet[a]	0–6 Weeks 2,900	14–20 Weeks 2,900	2,900	Daily Intake per Hen (mg)[b]	0–3 Weeks 3,200	6–8 Weeks 3,200
Protein (%)	18	12	14.5	16,000	23.0	18.0
Arginine (%)	1.00	0.67	0.68	750	1.44	1.00
Glycine and serine (%)	0.70	0.47	0.50	550	1.50	0.70
Histidine (%)	0.26	0.17	0.16	180	0.35	0.26
Isoleucine (%)	0.60	0.40	0.50	550	0.80	0.60
Leucine (%)	1.00	0.67	0.73	800	1.35	1.00
Lysine (%)	0.85	0.45	0.64	700	1.20	0.85
Methionine plus cystine (%)	0.60	0.40	0.55	600	0.93	0.60
Methionine (%)	0.30	0.20	0.32	350	0.50	0.32
Phenylalanine plus tyrosine (%)	1.00	0.67	0.80	880	1.34	1.00
Phenylalanine (%)	0.54	0.36	0.40	440	0.72	0.54
Threonine (%)	0.68	0.37	0.45	500	0.80	0.68
Tryptophan (%)	0.17	0.11	0.14	150	0.23	0.17
Valine (%)	0.62	0.41	0.55	600	0.82	0.62
Linoleic acid (%)	1.00	1.00	1.00	1,100	1.00	1.00
Calcium (%)	0.80	0.60	3.40	3,750	1.00	0.80
Phosphorus, available (%)	0.40	0.30	0.32	350	0.45	0.35
Potassium (%)	0.40	0.25	0.15	165	0.40	0.30
Sodium (%)	0.15	0.15	0.15	165	0.15	0.15
Chlorine (%)	0.15	0.12	0.15	165	0.15	0.15
Magnesium (mg)	600	400	500	55	600	600
Manganese (mg)	60	30	30	3.30	60.0	60.0
Zinc (mg)	40	35	50	5.50	40.0	40.0
Iron (mg)	80	60	50	5.50	80.0	80.0
Copper (mg)	8	6	6	0.88	8.0	8.0
Iodine (mg)	0.35	0.35	0.30	0.03	0.35	0.35
Selenium (mg)	0.15	0.10	0.10	0.01	0.15	0.15
Vitamin A (IU)	1,500	1,500	4,000	440	1,500	1,500
Vitamin D (ICU)	200	200	500	55	200	200
Vitamin E (IU)	10	5	5	0.55	10	10
Vitamin K (mg)	0.50	0.50	0.50	0.055	0.50	0.50
Riboflavin (mg)	3.60	1.80	2.20	0.242	3.60	3.60
Pantothenic acid (mg)	10.0	10.0	2.20	0.242	10.0	10.0
Niacin (mg)	27.0	11.0	10.0	1.10	27.0	11.0
Vitamin B_{12} (mg)	0.009	0.003	0.004	0.00044	0.009	0.003
Choline (mg)	1,300	500	?	?	1,300	500
Biotine (mg)	0.15	0.10	0.10	0.011	0.15	0.10
Folacin (mg)	0.55	0.25	0.25	0.0275	0.55	0.25
Thiamin (mg)	1.8	1.3	0.80	0.088	1.80	1.80
Pyridoxine (mg)	3.0	3.0	3.0	0.33	3.0	2.5

[a]These are typical dietary energy concentrations.
[b]Assumes an Average daily intake of 110 g of feed/hen.
Source: National Research Council, *Nutrient Requirements of Poultry,* 1986.

SELECTED REFERENCES

Publications

Church, D. C. 1991. *Livestock Feeds and Feeding.* Englewood Cliffs, NJ: Prentice-Hall.

Cullison, A. E. 1987. *Feeds and Feeding.* 2nd ed. Reston, VA: Reston Publishing Co.

Ensminger, M. E., Oldfield, J. E., and Heinemann, W. W. 1990. *Feeds and Nutrition.* 2nd ed. Clovis, CA: Ensminger Publishing Co.

Jurgens, M. H. 1988. *Animal Feeding and Nutrition.* 4th ed. Dubuque, IA: Kendall/Hunt.

National Research Council. *Nutrient Requirements of Beef Cattle,* 1984; *of Dairy Cattle,* 1989; *of Goats,* 1981; *of Horses,* 1989; *of Poultry,* 1986; *of Sheep,* 1985; and *of Swine,* 1989. Washington, DC: National Academy Press.

——— 1982. *United States–Canadian Tables of Feed Composition.* Washington, DC: National Academy Press.

Visuals

Decision Making: Energy Utilization for Feedlot Cattle (videotape). CEV, P.O. Box 65265, Lubbock, TX 79464-5265.

CHAPTER 18

Growth and Development

Profitable and efficient production of livestock and poultry involves understanding their growth and development. Manipulation of genetic and environmental factors can change growth patterns in farm animals.

Many aspects of growth and development are contained in other chapters of this book. The material on reproduction, genetics, nutrition, and products should be integrated with this chapter to understand more fully animal growth and development.

Generally, **growth** is an increase in body weight until mature size is reached. This growth is an increase in cell size and cell numbers with protein deposition resulting. More specifically, growth is an increase in the mass of structural tissues (bone, muscle, and connective tissue) and organs accompanied by a change in form or composition of the animal's body.

Development is defined as the directive coordination of all diverse processes until maturity is reached. It involves growth, cellular differentiation, and changes in body shape and form. In this chapter, growth and development are combined and discussed as one entity.

PRENATAL (LIVESTOCK)

The three phases of prenatal life — sex cells, the embryo, and the fetus — are briefly discussed in Chapter 10. Embryological development is a fascinating process; a spherical mass of cells differentiates into specific cell types and eventually into recognizable organs (Figs. 18.1 and 18.2). The endoderm (Fig. 18.2D) differentiates into the digestive tract, lungs, and bladder; the mesoderm (Fig. 18.2D) into the skeleton, skeletal muscle, and connective tissue; while the ectoderm (Fig. 18.2D) differentiates into the skin, hair, brain, and spinal cord. The growth, development, and differentiation processes, involving primarily protein synthesis, are directed by DNA chains of chromosomes and the organizers in the developing embryo (see Chapter 12). Thus the nucleus is a center of activity for different types of cells, directing the growth and development process (Fig. 18.3).

The fetus undergoes marked changes in shape and form during prenatal growth and development. Early in the prenatal period, the head is much larger than the body. Later, the body and

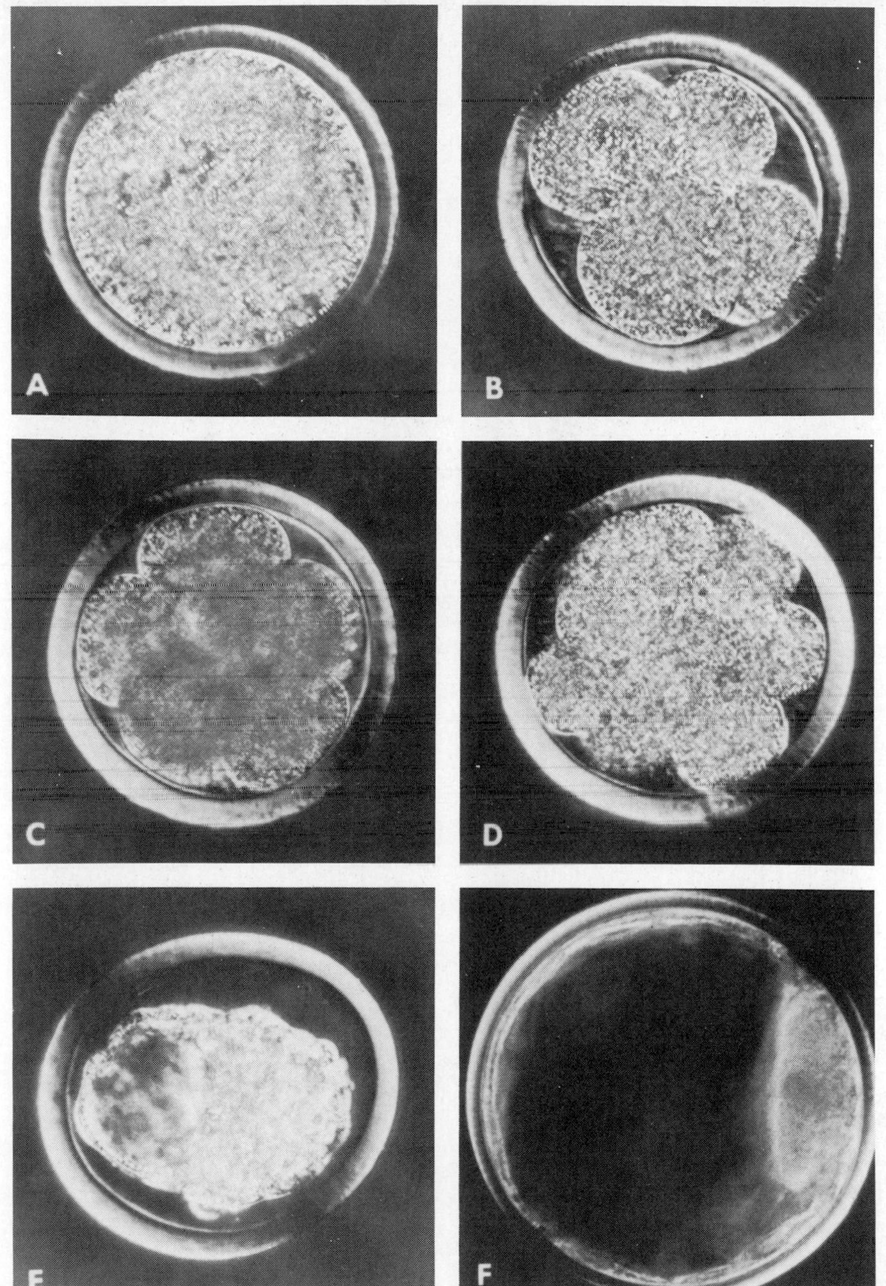

FIGURE 18.1.

Embryonic development during the first 8 days of pregnancy in cattle. (A) Unfertilized egg. (B) Four-cell embryo on day 2 of pregnancy (estrus = day 0). (C) Eight-cell embryo on day 3 of pregnancy. (D) An 8- to 16-cell embryo on day 4 of pregnancy. (E) Very early blastocyst stage (approximately 60 cells). (F) Expanded blastocyst (> 100 cells) recovered from the uterus on day 8 of pregnancy. Magnification approximately × 300. Courtesy of G. E. Seidel, Jr., 1981, Superovulation and embryo transfer in cattle, *Science* 211:351. Copyright © 1981 by the American Association for the Advancement of Science.

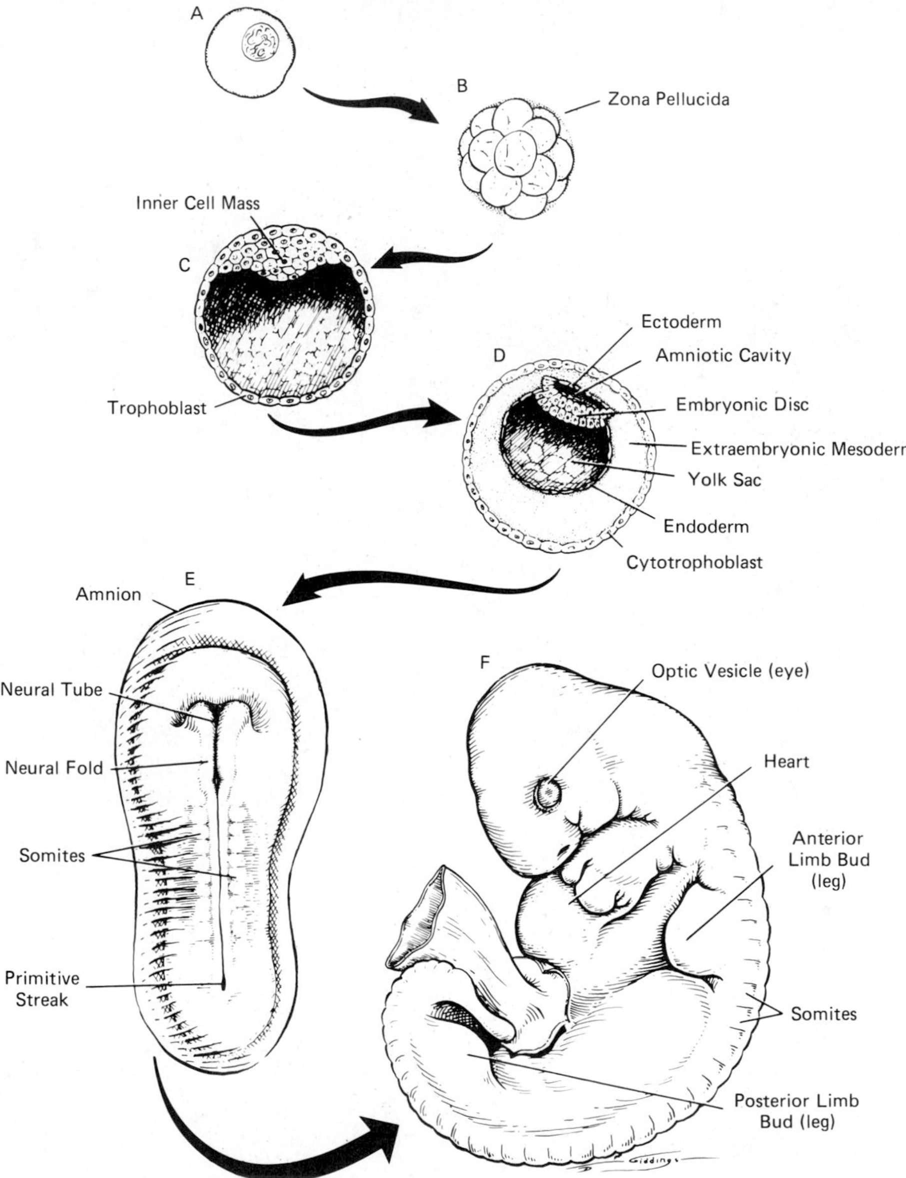

FIGURE 18.2.
The morphogenesis of (A) a single egg cell into (B) a morula, then to (C) a blastocyst. (D) The stage at which the two cavities have formed in the inner cell mass; an upper (amniotic) cavity and a lower cavity yolk sac. The embryonic disc containing the ectoderm and endoderm germ layers is located between cavities. (E) A cattle embryo showing the neural tube and somites. (F) The development of the 14-day cattle embryo. Drawing by Dennis Giddings.

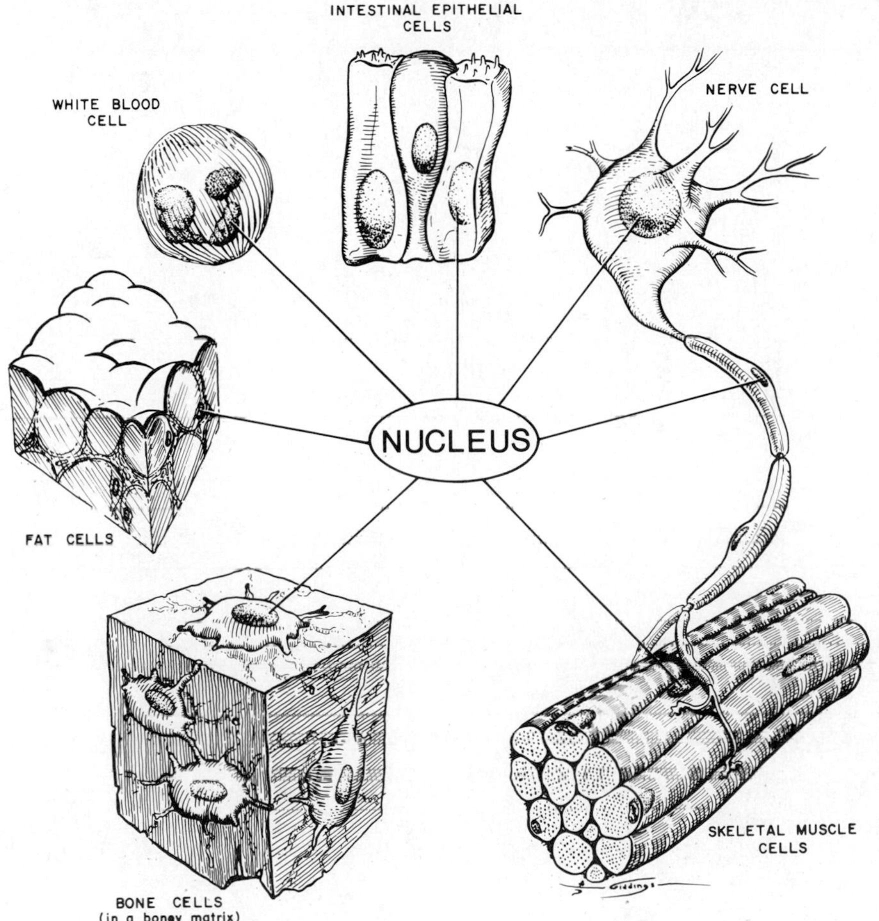

FIGURE 18.3.
Cells of selected tissues showing similarity in cell structure but not cell shape. The nucleus gives direction to differentiation of cells and their function. Drawing by Dennis Giddings.

limbs grow more rapidly than other parts. The order of tissue growth follows a sequential trend determined by physiological importance, starting with the central nervous system and progressing to bones, tendons, muscles, intermuscular fat, and subcutaneous fat.

During the first two-thirds of the prenatal period, most of the increase in muscle weight is due to hypertrophy (increase in size of fibers). During the last 3 months of pregnancy, hyperplasia (increase in number of fibers) represents most of the muscle growth. Individual muscles vary in their rate of growth, with larger muscles (those of the legs and back) having the greatest rate of postnatal growth. Water content of fetal muscle declines with fetal age, and this decline in water content continues through postnatal growth as well.

The relative size of the fetus changes during gestation, with the largest increase in weight occurring during the last trimester of pregnancy (Fig. 18.4).

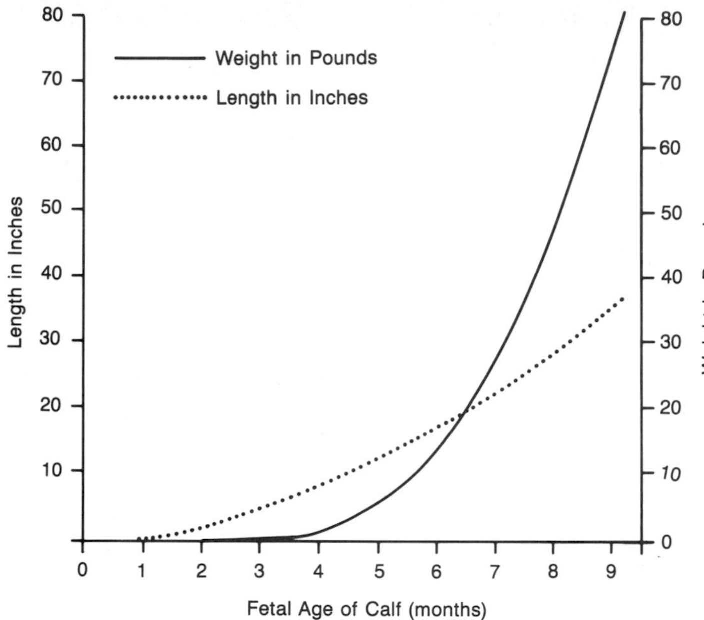

FIGURE 18.4.
Growth of the fetal calf. Drawing by CSU Graphics.

BIRTH (LIVESTOCK)

After birth, the number of muscle fibers does not appear to increase significantly; therefore, postnatal muscle growth is primarily by hypertrophy. In red meat animals, all muscle fibers appear to be red at birth, but shortly thereafter some of them differentiate into white and intermediate muscle types.

At birth, the various body parts have considerably different proportions when compared with mature body size and shape. At birth, the head is relatively large, the legs are long, and the body is small; whereas in the mature animal, the head is relatively small, the legs are relatively short, and the body is relatively large. Birth weight represents approximately 5%–7% of the mature weight, while leg length at birth is approximately 60%; height at withers is approximately 50% of those same measurements at maturity. Hip width and chest width at birth are approximately one-third of the same measurements at maturity. This shows that the distal parts (leg and shoulder height) are developed earlier than proximal parts (hips and chest).

POULTRY

Embryonic Development

The development of a chick differs from mammals because there is no connection with its mother. The chick develops in the egg, entirely outside the hen's body. Embryonic development is much more rapid in chicks than the farm mammals.

Every egg whether fertile or nonfertile has a germ spot called the blastoderm (See Fig. 6.1). This is where the chick embryo develops if the fertile egg is properly incubated.

A controlled environment must be maintained during incubation to produce live chicks from the fertile eggs. The major components of the controlled environment are (1) temperature 99.5°F–100°F); (2) 60%–75% relative humidity; (3) turning the egg every 1–8 hours; and (4) providing adequate oxygen.

Three hours after fertilization, the blastoderm divides to form two cells. Cell division occurs until maturity except during the holding period before incubating the eggs.

There are four membranes that are essential to the growth of the chick embryo (Fig. 18.5). The **allantois** is the membrane that allows the embryo to breathe. It takes oxygen through the porous shell and oxygenates the blood of the embryo. The allantois removes the carbon dioxide, receives excretions from the kidneys, absorbs albumen used as food for the embryo, and absorbs calcium from the shell for use by the embryo. The **amnion** is a membrane filled with a colorless fluid that serves as a protection from the mechanical shock. The **yolk sac** is a layer of tissue growth over the surface of the yolk. This tissue has special cells that digest and absorb the yolk material for the developing embryo. The **chorion** surrounds both the amnion and yolk sac.

Table 18.1 identifies some of the primary changes in the growth and development of the chick embryo. Many of these phenomenal changes occur rapidly, sometimes in only hours.

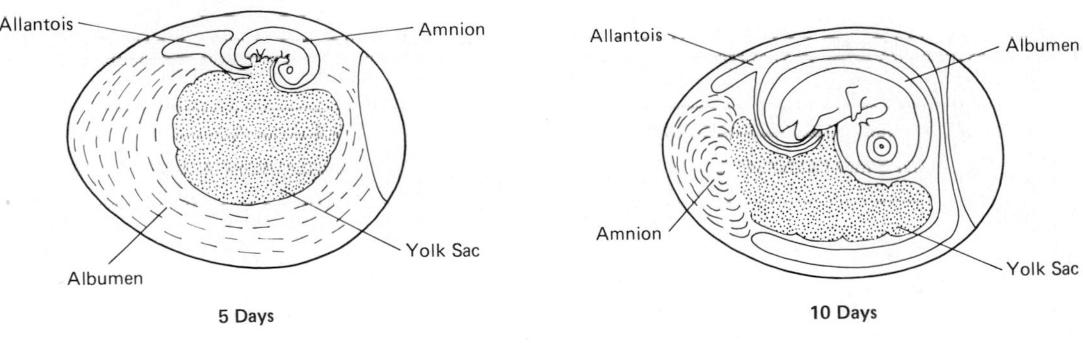

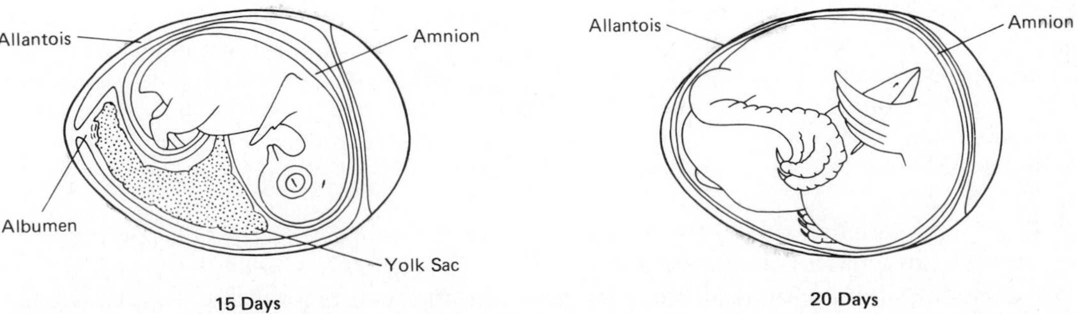

FIGURE 18.5.
Changes in the development of the chick embryo with associated changes in membranes and other contents of the egg.

TABLE 18.1. Major Changes in Weight, Form, and Function of the Chick Embryo (white Leghorn) during Incubation

Day	Weight (g)	Developmental Changes
1	00.0002	Head and backbone are formed; central nervous system begins
2	00.0030	Heart forms and starts beating; eyes begin formation
3	00.0200	Limb buds form
4	00.0500	Allantois starts functioning
5	00.1300	Formation of reproductive organs
6	00.2900	Main division of legs and wings; first movements noted
7	00.5700	
8	01.1500	Feather germs appear
9	01.5300	Beak begins to form; embryo begins to look birdlike
10	02.2600	Beak starts to harden; digits completely separated
11	03.6800	
12	05.0700	Toes fully formed
13	07.3700	Down appears on body; scales and nails appear
14	09.7400	Embryo turns its head toward blunt end of egg
15	12.0000	Small intestines taken into body
16	15.9800	Scales and nails on legs and feet are hard; albumen is near gone; yolk is main food
17	18.5900	Amniotic fluid decreases
18	21.8300	
19	25.6200	Yolk sac enters body through umbilicus
20	30.2100	Embryo becomes a chick; it breaks amnion, then breathes air in air cell
21	36.3000	Chick breaks shell and hatches

Source: Rollins, 1984.

BASIC ANATOMY AND PHYSIOLOGY

In the developmental process, cells become grouped in appearance and function. Specialized groups of cells that function together are called **tissues.** The primary types of tissues are (1) muscle, (2) nerves, and (3) connective and epithelial, with examples shown in Figure 18.3.

Organs are groups of tissues that perform specific functions. For example, the uterus is an organ that functions in the reproductive process. A group of organs that function in concert to accomplish a larger, general function comprise a **system.** The reproductive system (Chapter 10), digestive system (Chapter 16), and mammary system (Chapter 19) are discussed in their respective chapters.

It is not the intent of this chapter to discuss all the different systems even though they are important in growth and development. A few additional systems are briefly surveyed—those considered important in understanding farm animals and their productivity. Figures are provided, showing selected systems for one or two species. The systems are similar and generally comparable among the various species of farm animals, although some large differences between poultry and farm mammals do exist.

Skeletal System

Figure 18.6 shows the skeletal system of the horse and Figure 18.7 portrays the chicken's skeletal system. Even though only bones and some joints are shown in these figures, teeth and cartilage are also considered part of the skeletal system.

The skeleton protects other vital organs and gives a basic form and shape to the animal's body. Bones function as levers, store minerals, and the bone marrow is the site of blood cell formation.

Chicken bones are more pneumatic (bone cavities are filled with air spaces), harder, thinner, more brittle, and have a different ossification process than those for mammals.

Muscle System

There are three types of muscle tissue—skeletal, smooth, and cardiac. Skeletal muscle is the largest component of red meat animal products. Smooth muscle is located in the digestive, reproductive, and urinary organs. The heart is composed of cardiac muscle.

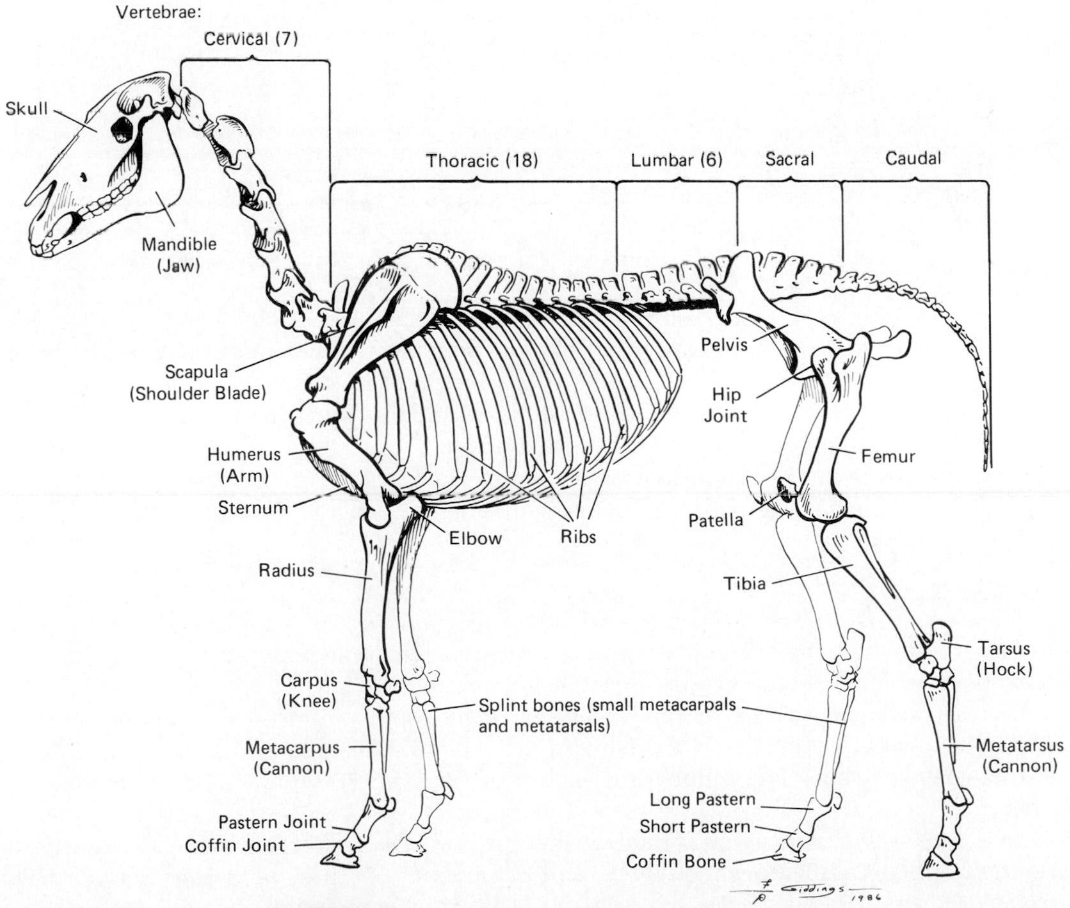

FIGURE 18.6.
Skeletal system of the horse. Drawing by Dennis Giddings.

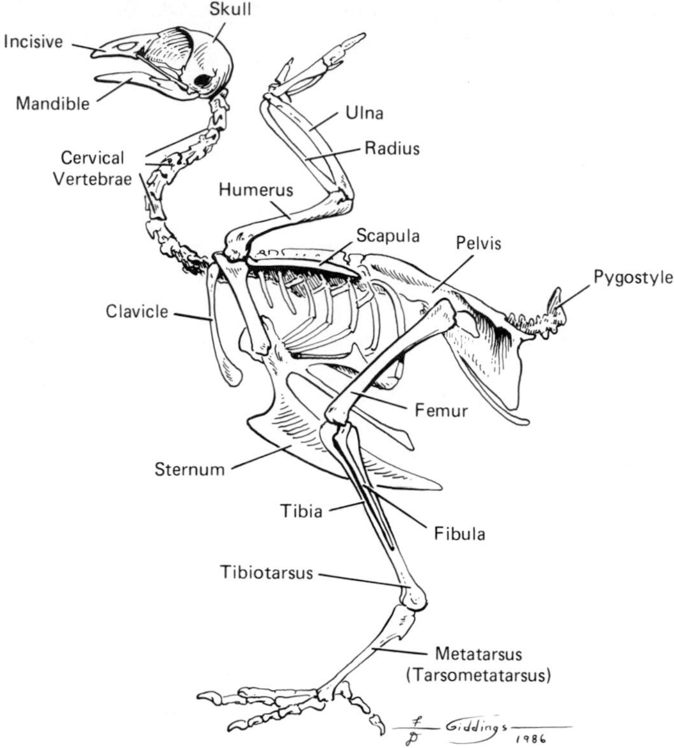

FIGURE 18.7.
Skeletal system of the chicken. Drawing by Dennis Giddings.

Figure 18.8 identifies some of the major muscles similar in name and location in the meat animal species and horses. Of special note is the longissimus dorsi, which is discussed in Chapter 3. The size of this muscle and the marbling it contains are important factors in determining yield grades and quality grades of meat animals.

The primary muscles of the turkey are shown in Figure 18.9. The muscles of poultry are referred to as dark meat (legs and thighs) and white meat (breast and wings).

Circulatory System

Figure 18.10 shows the major components of the dairy cow's circulatory system. The circulatory systems of other farm animal species are similar to that of the dairy cow.

The heart, acting as a pump, and the accompanying vessels comprise the circulatory system. Arteries are vessels transporting blood away from the heart, while the vessels carrying blood to the heart are called veins. The lymph vessels transport lymph (intercellular fluid) from tissues to the heart.

The circulatory system is important in growth and development; the blood transports oxygen, nutrients, cellular waste products, and hormones.

Milk production in all species is dependent on the nutrients in milk arriving through the circulatory system. Dairy cows producing 20,000 – 40,000 lb milk per year (over 100 lb per day)

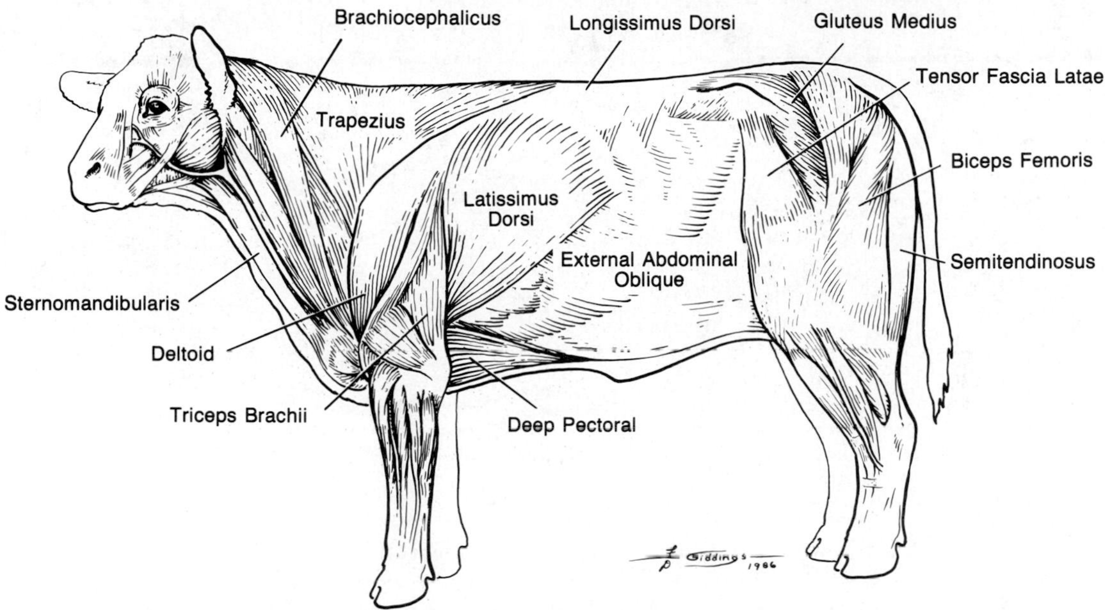

FIGURE 18.8.
Primary muscles of the beef steer. Drawing by Dennis Giddings.

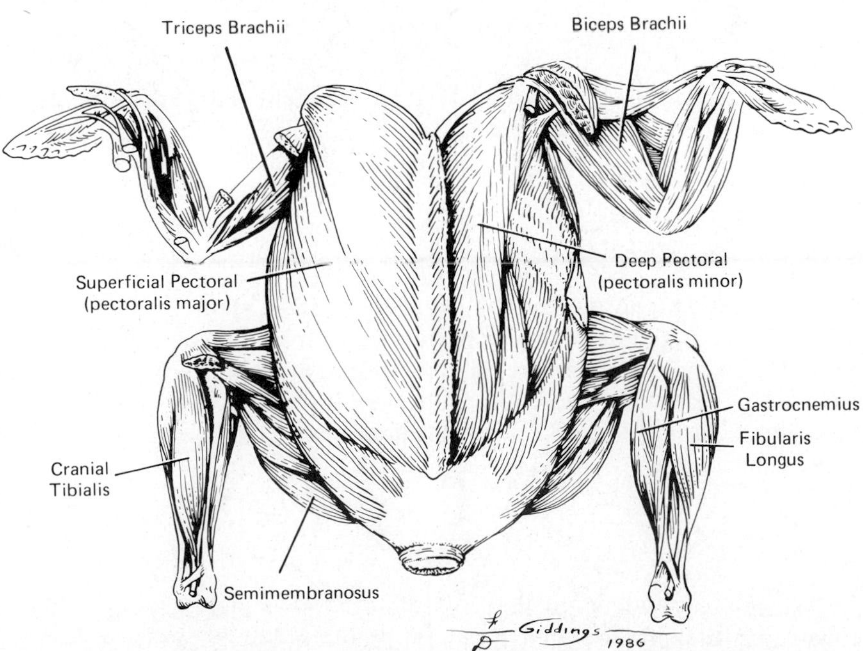

FIGURE 18.9.
Primary muscles of the turkey. Drawing by Dennis Giddings.

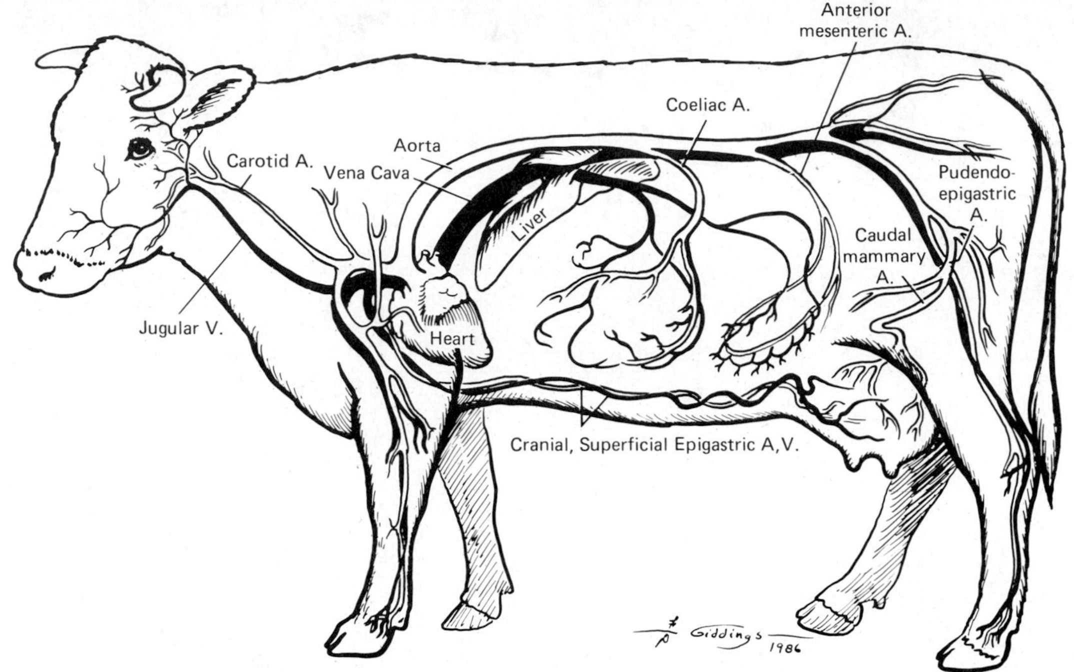

FIGURE 18.10.
Circulatory system of the dairy cow (A = artery, V = vein). Drawing by Dennis Giddings.

must consume large amounts of feed, with these feed nutrients circulating in high concentration through the mammary blood supply. Approximately 400–500 lb of blood circulates through the dairy cow's mammary gland for each pound of milk produced.

Endocrine System

Growth and development is highly dependent on the endocrine system. This system consists of several endocrine (ductless) glands that secrete **hormones** into the circulatory system. Hormones are chemical substances that affect a gland (or organ) or, in some cases, all body tissues.

The major endocrine glands are shown in Figure 18.11; the hormones produced and their major effects are identified in Table 18.2. The hormones affecting mammary gland growth, development, and function are identified in Chapter 19.

GROWTH CURVES

Postweaning growth is a curved-line function regardless of how it is expressed mathematically. If growth is considered an increase in body weight, then most of the early growth follows a straight line or is linear in the age–weight relationship (Fig. 18.12). As the animal increases in

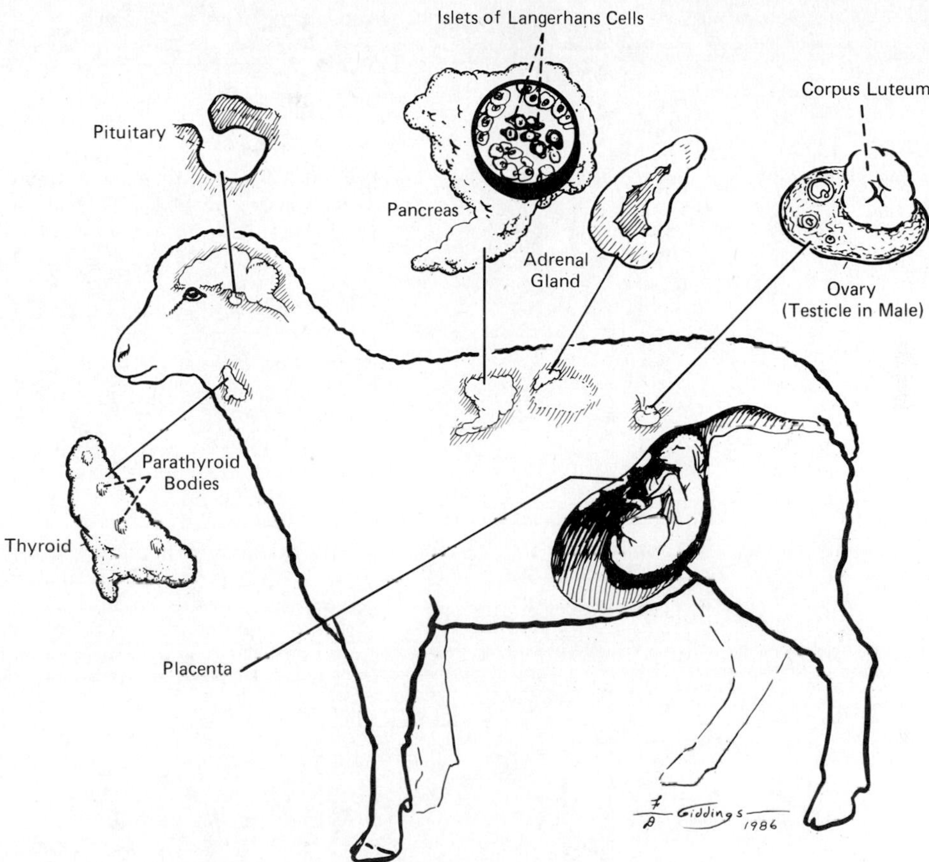

FIGURE 18.11.
Primary endocrine organs of the sheep. Drawing by Dennis Giddings.

age and approaches puberty, rate of growth usually declines, and true growth ceases when the animal reaches maturity.

After an animal reaches maturity, it may have large fluctuations in body weight simply by increasing or decreasing the amount of fat or water that is stored. This increase in weight owing to fattening is not true growth because no net increase in body protein occurs. In fact, animals tend to lose body protein as they grow older. The loss of body protein is one of the phenomena in the aging process.

Figures 18.13 and 18.14 show typical growth curves for most farm animals. The different curves for large and small breeds is primarily a function of differences in skeletal frame size. Maturity is reached at heavier weights in larger breeds, which have larger skeletal frame sizes than smaller-framed animals.

The relatively straight-lined growth shown for turkeys and broilers (Figure 18.14) does curve and level off as shown for the other species. This occurs when the birds become older; for broilers, at approximately 11 weeks of age.

TABLE 18.2. Major Hormones Affecting Growth and Development in Farm Animals

Hormone	Source	Major Effect
Growth (Somatotrophic, STH)	Pituitary (anterior)	Body cell growth—especially muscle and bone cells
Adrenocorticotropic (ACTH)	Pituitary (anterior)	Stimulates adrenal cortex to produce adrenal cortical steroid hormones
Glucocorticoids	Adrenal (cortex)	Conversion of proteins to carbohydrates
Mineralocorticoids	Adrenal (cortex)	Regulates sodium and potassium balance; water balance
Thyroid-stimulating (TSH)	Pituitary (anterior)	Stimulates thyroid gland to produce thyroid hormones
Thyroid	Thyroid	Regulates metabolic rate
Testosterone	Testicles (interstitial cells)	Libido; accessory sex gland development; male secondary sex characteristics; spermatogenesis
Follicle-stimulating (FSH)	Pituitary (anterior)	Development of ovarian follicles; spermatogenesis
Luteinizing (LH)	Pituitary (anterior)	Ovum maturation; ovulation; formation of corpus luteum (CL); stimulates interstitial cells (testicle) to produce testosterone
Prolactin (luteotropic, LTH)	Pituitary (anterior)	Milk secretion (initiation and maintenance); CL maintenance during pregnancy
Estrogen	Ovary (follicle) Placenta	Female reproductive organ growth; female secondary sex characteristics; mammary gland duct growth
Progesterone	Corpus luteum; placenta	Uterine growth; maintenance of pregnancy; alveoli growth in mammary gland growth
Antidiuretic (ADH) (Vasopressin)	Pituitary (posterior)	Controls water loss in kidney
Oxytocin	Pituitary (posterior) (released with nursing reflex)	Causes uterine contractions during parturition; causes milk letdown in mammary gland
Relaxin	Ovary; placenta	Relaxes pelvic ligaments during parturition
Epinephrine	Adrenal (medulla)	Increases blood glucose concentration
Norepinephrine	Adrenal (medulla)	Maintains blood pressure
Insulin	Pancreas	Lowers blood sugar
Parathormone (PTH)	Parathyroid	Calcium and phosphorus metabolism
Glucagon	Pancreas	Raises blood sugar

Source: Compiled from several sources.

CARCASS COMPOSITION

Products from meat animals and poultry are composed primarily of fat, lean, and bone. A superior carcass is characterized by a low proportion of bone, a high proportion of muscle, and an optimum amount of fat. Understanding the growth and development of these animals is important in knowing when animals should be slaughtered to produce the desirable combinations of fat, lean, and bone.

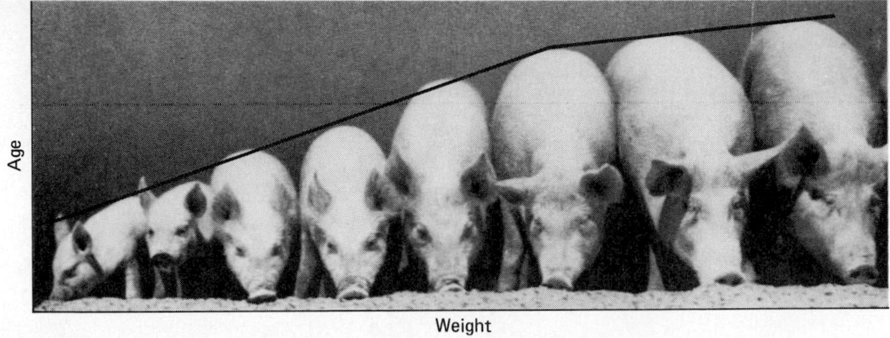

FIGURE 18.12.
Early growth in pigs is linear (straight line), whereas later in life the rate of growth decreases. Courtesy of Elanco Products Co.

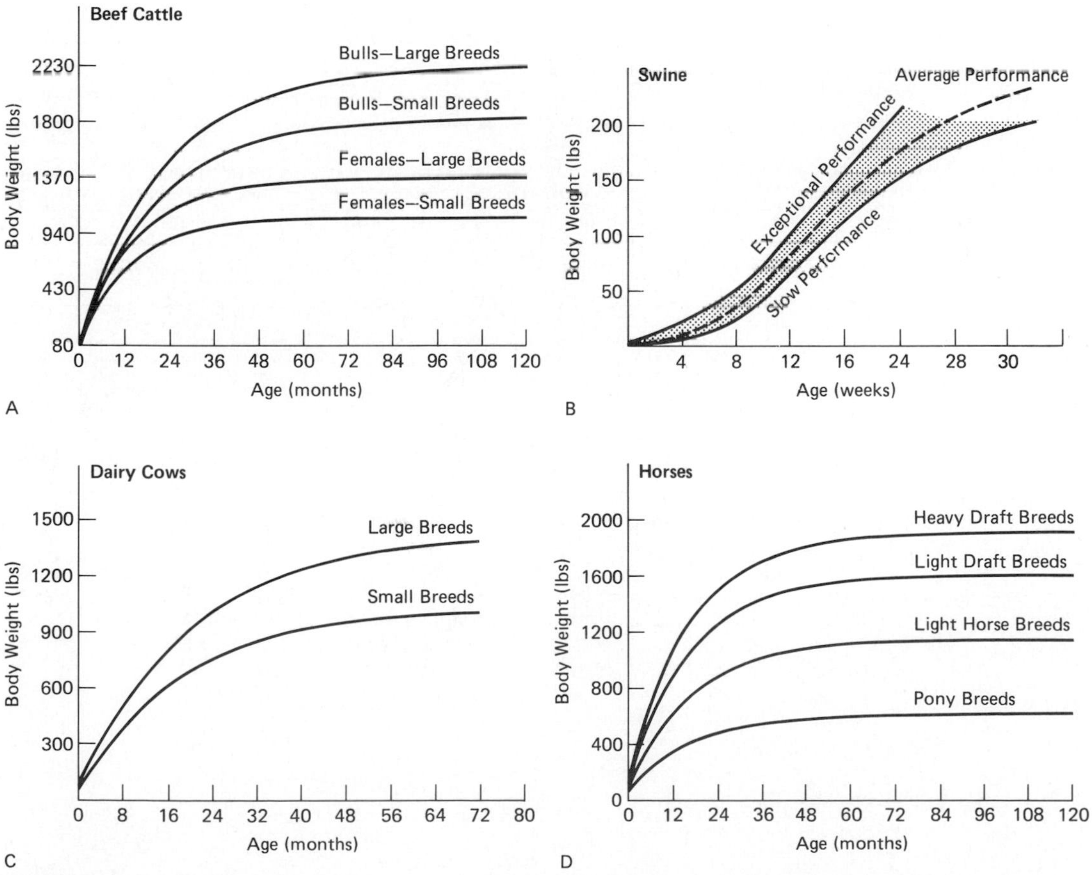

FIGURE 18.13.
Typical growth curves for (A) beef cattle, (B) swine, (C) dairy cows, and (D) horses. Courtesy of R. A. Battaglia and V. B. Mayrose, *Handbook of Livestock Management Techniques* (New York: Macmillan, 1981). Copyright © Macmillan Publishing Co.

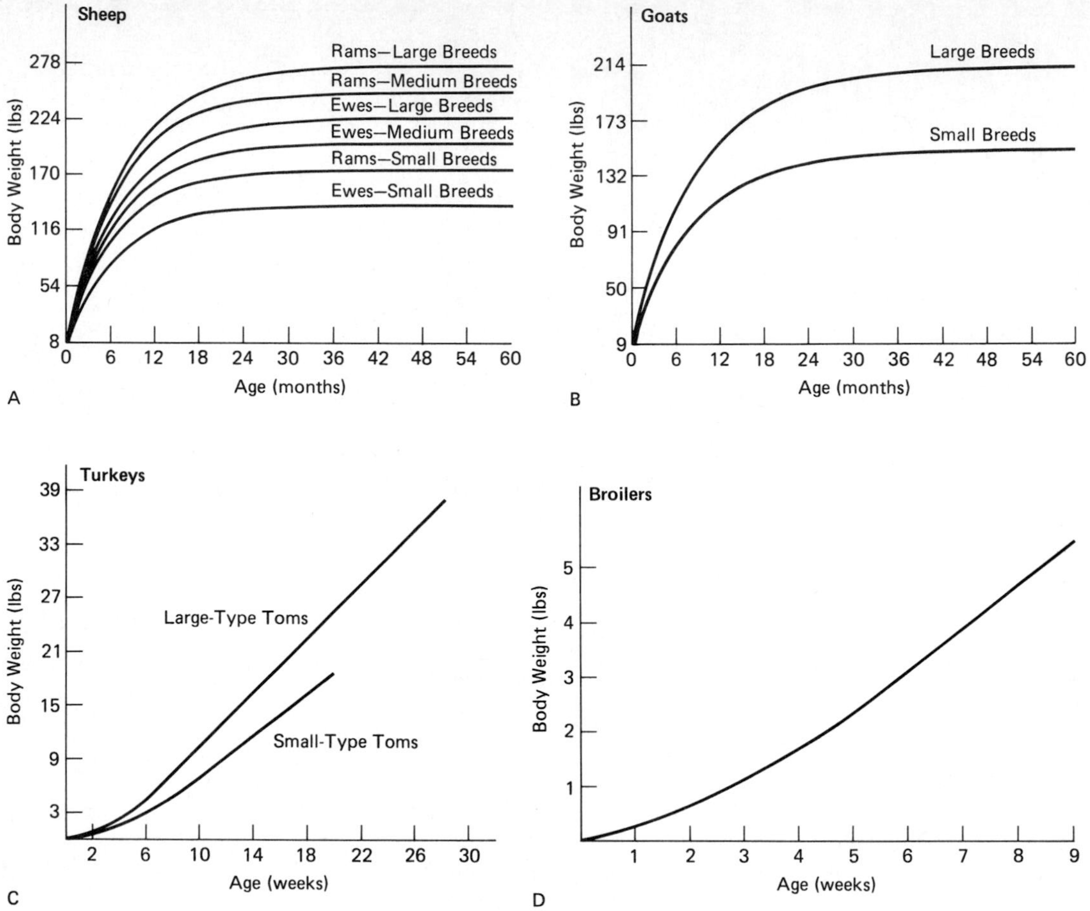

FIGURE 18.14.
Typical growth curves for (A) sheep, (B) goats, (C) turkeys, and (D) broilers. Courtesy of R. A. Battaglia and V. B. Mayrose, *Handbook of Livestock Management Techniques* (New York: Macmillan, 1981). Copyright © Macmillan Publishing Co.

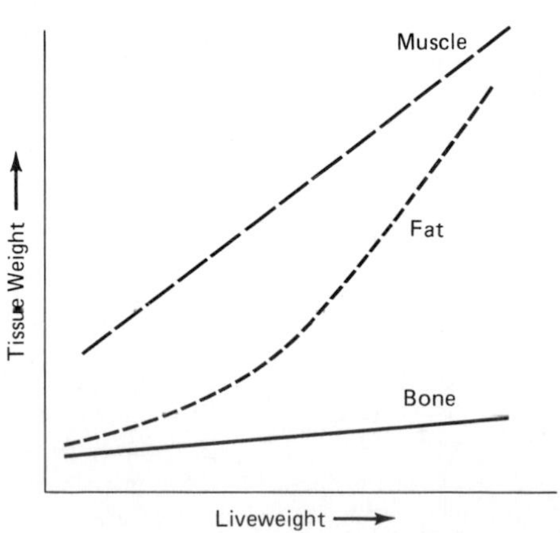

FIGURE 18.15.
Tissue growth relative to increased liveweight. Adapted from Berg and Walters (1983), courtesy of the American Society of Animal Science.

Figure 18.15 shows the expected changes in fat, muscle, and bone as animals increase in liveweight during the linear-growth phase. As the animal moves from the linear-growth phase into maturity, the growth curves shown in Fig. 18.15 are extended similar to those shown in Figure 18.13.

At light weights, fat deposition begins rather slowly, then increases geometrically when muscle growth slows as the animal approaches physiological maturity. Muscle comprises the greatest proportion and its growth is linear during the production of young slaughter animals. Bone has a smaller relative growth rate than either fat or muscle. Because of the relative growth rates, the ratio of muscle to bone increases as the animal increases in weight.

Effects of Frame Size

Different maturity types of animals (sometimes referred to as breed types or biological types) have a marked influence on carcass composition at similar liveweights (Fig. 18.16). The earlier maturing types increase fat deposition at lighter weights than either the average or later maturing types.

Skeletal frame size, measured as hip height, is a more specific way of defining maturity type. Figure 18.17 shows the difference in fat, lean, and bone composition for small-, medium-, and large-framed beef steers at different liveweights. Note that the three different frame sizes have a similar composition at 900 lb (small frame), 1,100 lb (medium frame), and 1,300 lb (large frame).

Effect of Sex

The effect of sex is primarily on the fat component, although there are differences among species. Heifers deposit fat earlier than steers or bulls, with bulls being leaner at the same slaughter weight (Fig. 18.18A). Heifers are typically slaughtered at lighter weights (100–200 lb less) than steers to have a similar fat-to-lean composition.

Swine are different from cattle as barrows are fatter than gilts or boars at similar slaughter weights (Fig. 18.18B). The reason for this species difference is not known.

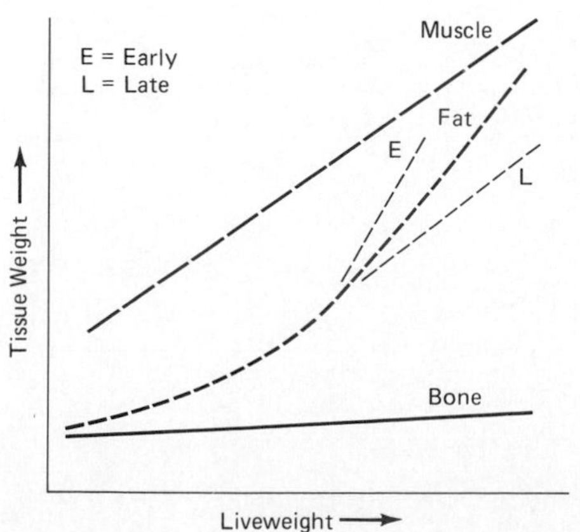

FIGURE 18.16.
Effects of different maturity types on carcass composition. Adapted from Berg and Walters (1983), courtesy of the American Society of Animal Science.

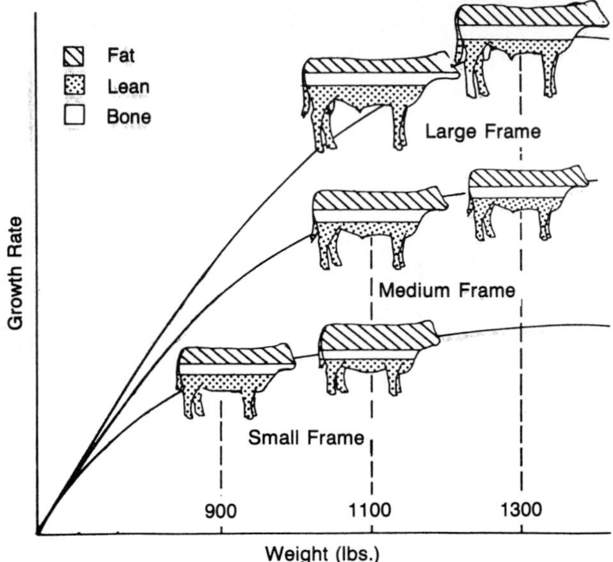

FIGURE 18.17.
The relationship of frame size and weight to carcass composition in beef steers. Drawing by CSU Graphics.

At typical slaughter weights, the sex differences in sheep do not have a marked effect on fat and lean composition. Apparently, sheep are slaughtered in an earlier stage of development (before puberty) than cattle and swine. Compositional differences in sheep are similar to cattle if sheep are fed longer than their usual slaughter weights.

Effect of Muscling

Relatively large differences exist in muscling among the various species of farm animals. The proportion of muscle in the carcass varies indirectly with fat, and a higher proportion of fat is

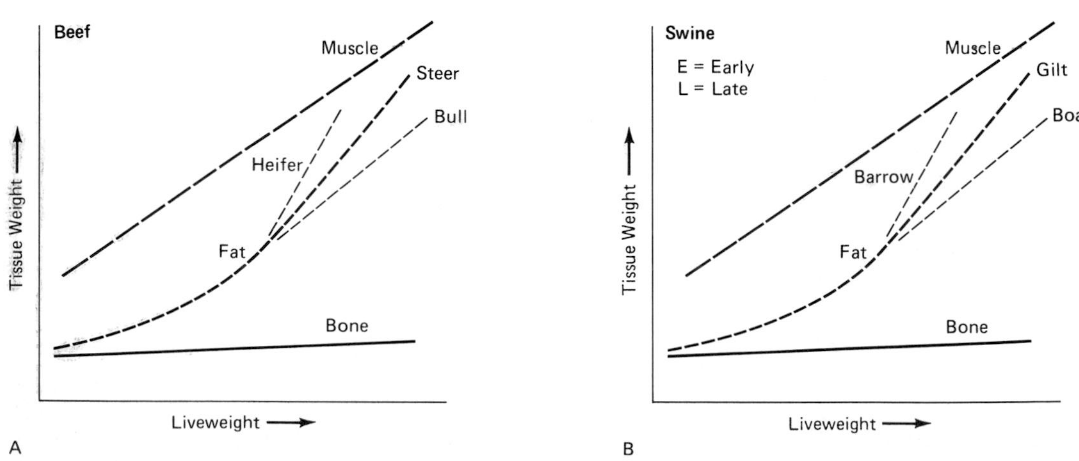

FIGURE 18.18.
Influence of sex on carcass composition in (A) beef cattle and (B) swine. Adapted from Berg and Walters (1983), courtesy of the American Society of Animal Science.

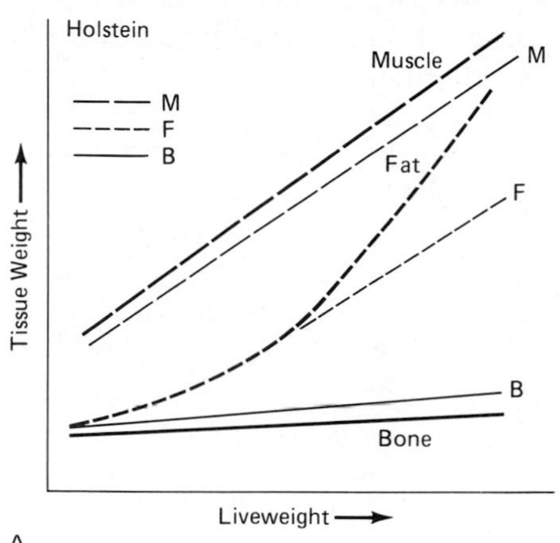

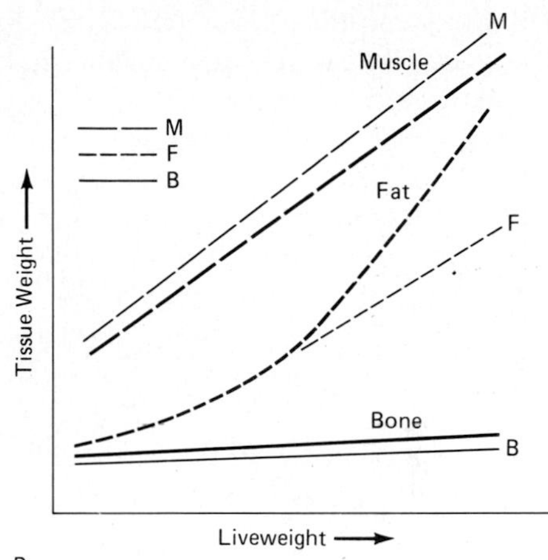

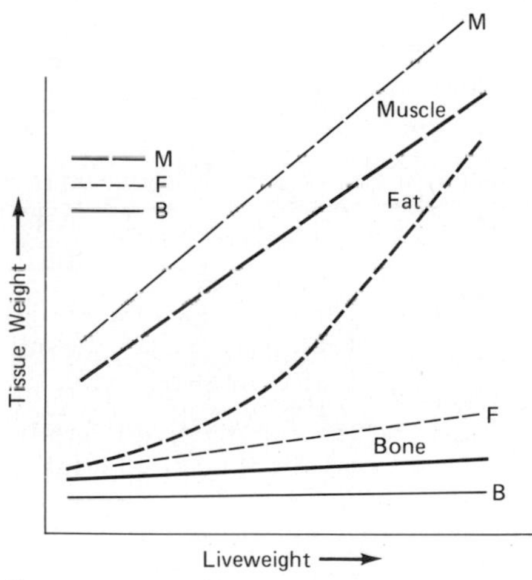

FIGURE 18.19.
Effect of muscling on fat, lean, and bone composition in cattle: (A) light-muscled Holsteins, (B) heavily muscled, (C) double-muscled. Adapted from Berg and Walters (1983), courtesy of the American Society of Animal Science.

associated with a lower proportion of muscle. Muscle has a much faster relative growth rate than bone. Muscle weight relative to liveweight or muscle-to-bone ratio can be used as a valuable measurement of muscle yield.

Most of the current cattle population in the United States does not have large differences in muscling. There are, however, muscling differences in 10% – 15% of the cattle, which are best expressed by a muscle-to-bone ratio (pounds of muscle ÷ pounds of bone). Muscle-to-bone ratios can range from 3 lb of muscle to 1 lb of bone in thinly muscled slaughter steers and heifers to 5 lb of muscle to 1 lb of bone in more thickly muscled cattle. Muscle-to-bone ratios higher than 5 : 1 are found in double-muscled cattle. These differences in muscle-to-bone ratio are economically important, particularly if more boneless cuts are merchandised.

Some of the muscling differences for cattle are shown in Figure 18.19: lighter-muscled Holsteins (Fig. 18.19A), heavy-muscled (Fig. 18.19B), and double-muscled cattle (Fig. 18.19C).

Double-muscled cattle do not have a duplicate set of muscles but they do have an enlargement (hypertrophy) of the existing muscles.

Extreme muscling, as observed in double-muscled or heavy-muscled types of animals, can be associated with problems in total productivity. Some heavy-muscled swine might die when subjected to stress conditions and reproductive efficiency is lower in some heavy-muscled animals. There is some latitude in increasing muscle-to-bone ratio in slaughter animals without encountering negative side effects.

Individual muscle dissection has shown a similarity of proportion of individual muscles to the total body muscle weight. Small differences in muscle distribution have been shown, but the differences do not seem to be economically significant for the industry. Thus it appears that increasing muscle weight in areas of high-priced cuts, at the expense of muscle weight in lower-priced cuts, is not commercially feasible. Even though muscle distribution is not important, muscling as previously defined—as muscle-to-bone ratio—has high economic importance.

AGE AND TEETH RELATIONSHIP

For many years, producers have observed teeth of farm animals to estimate their age or their ability to graze effectively with advancing age. Some animals are **mouthed** to classify them into appropriate age groups for show ring classification. The latter has not always proven exact because of animal variation in teeth condition and the ability of some exhibitors to manipulate the condition of the teeth.

Table 18.3 gives some of the guidelines used in estimating the age of cattle by observing their teeth. The **incisors** (front cutting teeth) are the teeth used. There are no upper incisors, and the molars (back teeth) are not commonly used to determine age.

Figure 18.20 shows the incisor teeth of cattle of different ages. If the grazing area is sandy and the grass is short, wearing of the teeth progresses faster than that previously described.

TABLE 18.3. Description of Cattle's Teeth to Estimate Age

Approximate Age	Description of Teeth
Birth	Usually only one pair of middle incisors
1 mon	All eight, temporary incisors
1.5–2 yr	First pair of permanent (middle incisors)
2.5–3 yr	Second pair of permanent incisors
3.25–4 yr	Third pair of permanent incisors
4–4.5 yr	Fourth (corner) pair of permanent incisors
5–6 yr	Middle pair of incisors begins to level off from wear; corner teeth might also show some wear
7–8 yr	Both middle and second pair of incisors show wear
8–9 yr	Middle, second, and third pair of incisors show wear
10 yr and over	All eight incisors show wear

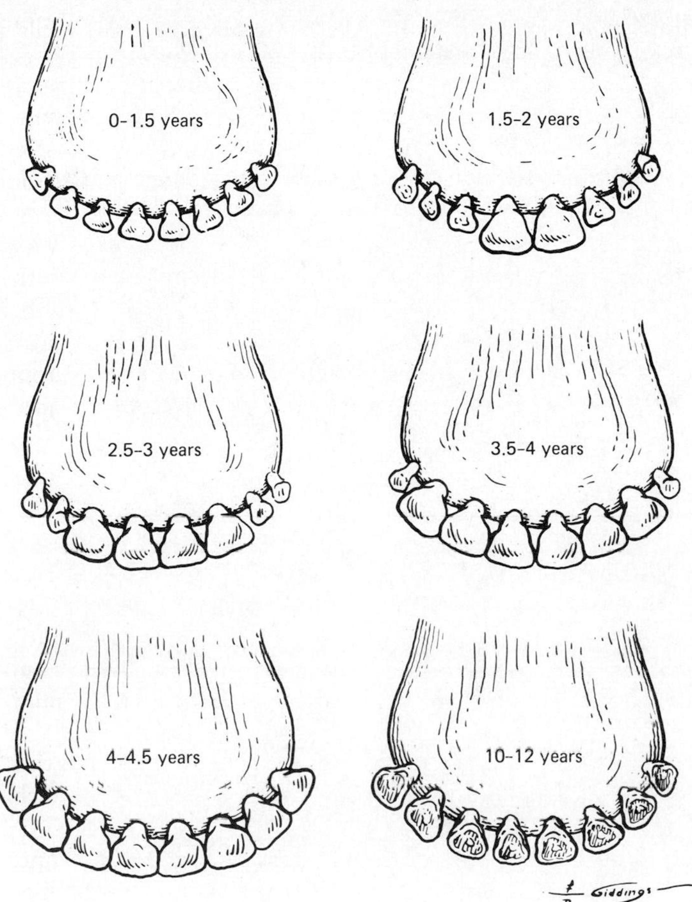

FIGURE 18.20.
Incisor teeth of cattle of different ages. Drawing by Dennis Giddings.

Also, some cows may be **broken-mouthed,** which means some of their permanent incisor teeth have been lost.

The age relationship to teeth condition for sheep and horses is given in Chapters 29 and 30, respectively.

SELECTED REFERENCES

Publications

Berg, R. T., and Butterfield, R. M. 1976. *New Concepts of Cattle Growth.* Sydney, Australia: Sydney University Press.

——— and Walters, L. E. 1983. The meat animal. Changes and challenges. *J. Anim. Sci.* 57:133 (Suppl. 2).

Bone, J. F. 1988. *Animal Anatomy and Physiology.* 4th ed. Reston, VA: Reston Publishing Co.

Currie, W. B. 1988. *Structure and Function of Domestic Animals.* Boston, MA: Butterworths Publishers.

Frandson, R. D. 1986. *Anatomy and Physiology of Farm Animals.* 4th ed. Philadelphia: Lea & Febiger.
Hammond, J., Jr., Robinson, T., and Bowman, J. 1983. *Hammond's Farm Animals.* Baltimore: Edward Arnold University Park Press.
Prior, R. L., and Lasater, D. B. 1979. Development of the bovine fetus. *J. Anim. Sci.* 48:1546.
Rollins, F. D. 1984. Development of the embryo. *Arizona Coop. Ext. Serv. Publication* 8427.
Swatland, H. J. 1984. *Structure and Development of Meat Animals.* Englewood Cliffs, NJ: Prentice-Hall.
Trenkle, A. H., and Marple, D. N. 1983. Growth and development of meat animals. *J. Anim. Sci.* 57:273 (Suppl. 2).

Visual

Anatomy of the Fowl (sound filmstrip). Vocational Education Productions, California Polytechnic State University, San Luis Obispo, CA 93407.

CHAPTER 19

Lactation

Lactation, the production of milk by the mammary gland, is a distinguishing characteristic of mammals whose young at first feed solely on milk from their mothers. Even after they start to eat other feeds, the young continue to nurse until they are weaned (separated from their mothers so they cannot nurse).

The mammary gland serves two functions: (1) it provides nutrition to animal offspring and (2) it is a source of passive immunity to the offspring. The importance of milk as a nutritional source to perpetuate each mammalian species has been known since the beginning of history. Only during the past few decades have the basic mechanisms of immunity through milk been determined.

Humans consume milk and recognize it as a palatable source of nutrients. Milk consumed in the United States comes primarily from dairy cows and, to a much lesser extent, from goats and sheep. In other countries, the human milk supply also comes from water buffalo, yak, reindeer, camel, donkey, and sow.

MAMMARY GLAND STRUCTURE

The mammary gland is an **exocrine gland** that produces the external secretion of milk transported through a series of ducts. The cow has four separate mammary glands that terminate into four teats; sheep and goats have two glands and two teats; and the mare has four mammary glands that terminate into two teats. The mammary glands of these species are located in the groin area (Fig. 19.1).

Sows have 6–20 mammary glands located in two rows along the abdomen, with each gland having a teat. Typically there are 10–14 of the sow's mammary glands that are functional (Fig. 19.1). There is evidence that teat number in swine is not related to litter size or litter-weaning weight.

Figure 19.2 shows the basic structure of the cow's udder. The udder is supported horizontally and laterally by suspensory ligaments (Fig. 19.2A). The internal structure of the udder is similar for all farm animal species, except for the number of glands and teats.

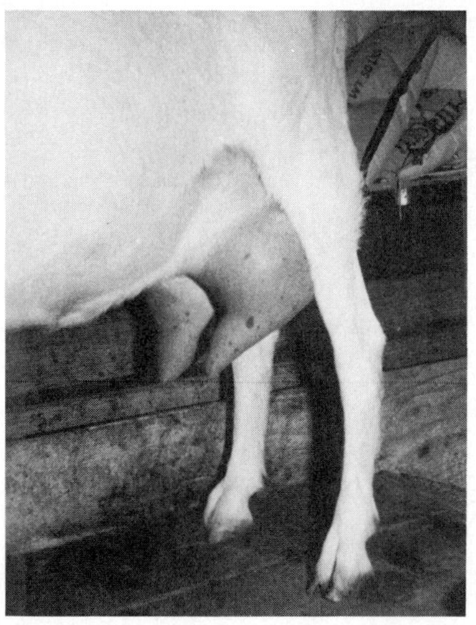

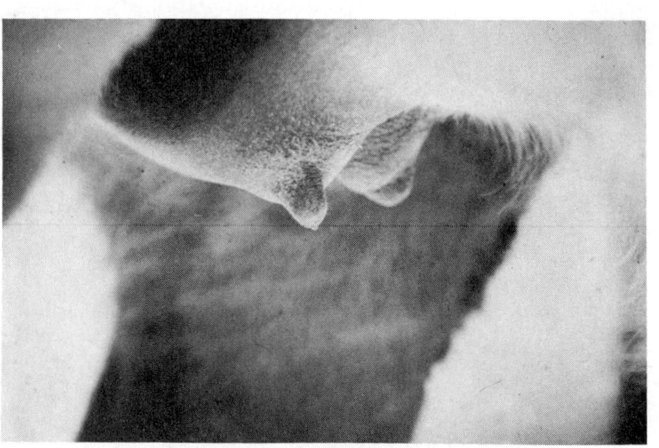

A B C D

FIGURE 19.1.
Mammary glands of (A) cow, (B) sow, (C) goat, and (D) mare. Courtesy of (A) *Hoards Dairyman*, (B) University of Nebraska, (C) George F. W. Haenlein, and (D) Colorado State University.

Secretory tissue of the mammary gland (Fig. 19.2C) is composed of millions of grapelike structures called **alveoli.** Each **alveolus** has its separate blood supply from which milk constituents are obtained by epithelial cells lining the alveolus. Milk collects in the alveolus lumen and, during milk letdown, travels through ducts to a larger collection area called the gland cistern.

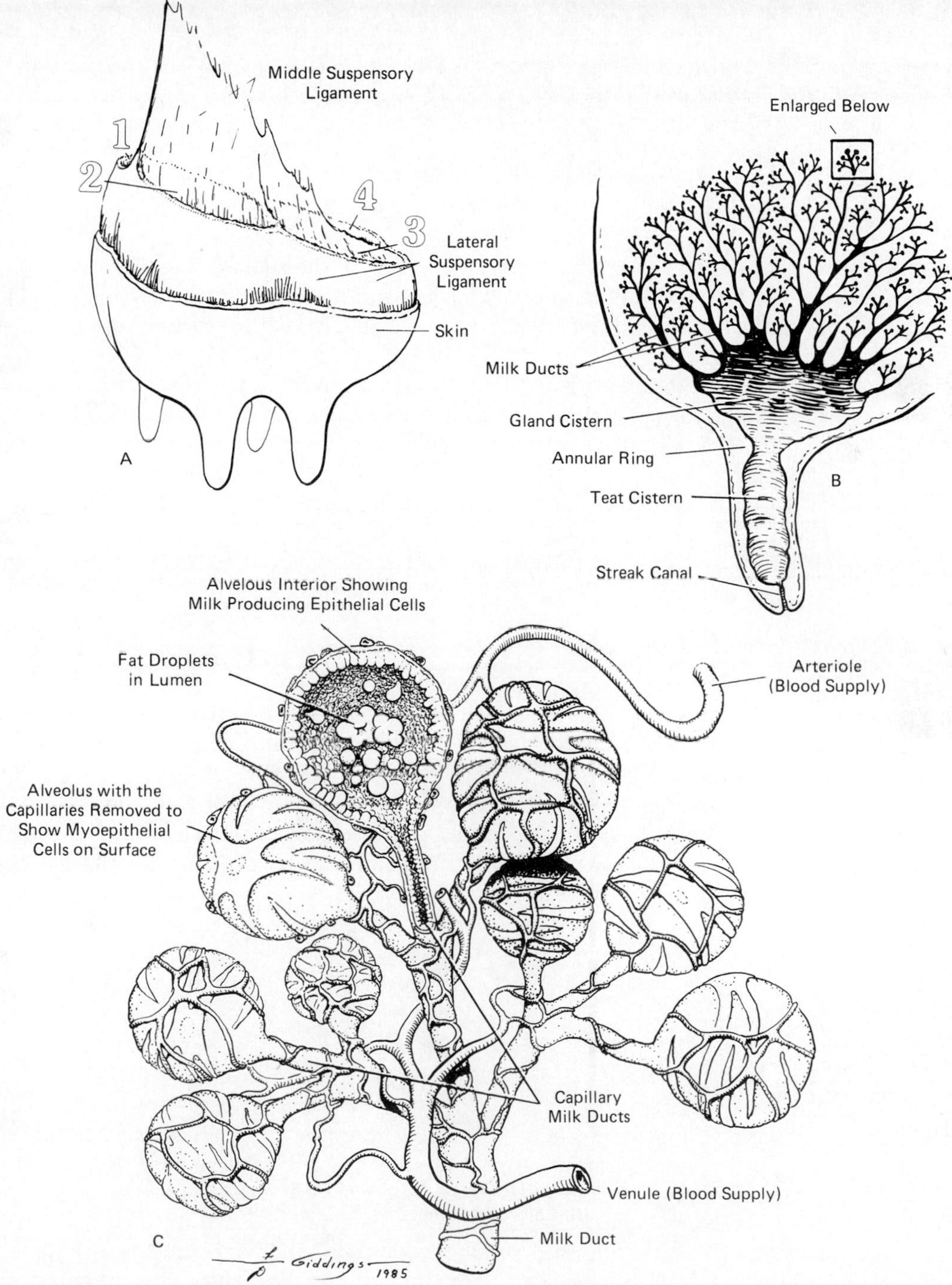

FIGURE 19.2.
(A) Basic structure of the cow's udder, showing suspensory ligaments and the location of the four separate quarters. (B) A section through one of the quarters, showing secretory tissue, ducts, and milk-collecting cisterns. (C) An enlarged lobe with several alveoli and their accompanying blood supply. Drawing by Dennis Giddings.

During milk letdown and the milking process, milk is forced into the teat cistern and through the streak canal to the outside of the teat.

MAMMARY GLAND DEVELOPMENT AND FUNCTION

Development

Mammary gland growth and development occur rapidly as the female reaches puberty. The ovarian hormones (estrogen and progesterone) have a large effect on development. Estrogen is primarily responsible for duct and cistern growth, whereas progesterone stimulates growth of the alveoli.

Estrogen and progesterone are produced by the ovary under the stimulation of FSH and LH from the anterior pituitary (Fig. 19.3). The pituitary also has a direct influence on mammary growth through the production of growth hormone. Growth hormone stimulates general cell growth of the mammary gland.

Figure 19.3 also identifies the additional indirect effect (other than FSH and LH) on mammary growth and development. Thyroid hormones are produced under the influence of TSH, and the adrenal gland produces the corticosteroids when stimulated by ACTH from the pituitary. All of these hormones work in concert to produce mammary growth and function.

Milk Secretion

Growth hormone, adrenal corticoids, and prolactin are primarily responsible for the initiation of lactation. These hormones become effective as parturition nears and when estrogen and progesterone hormone levels decrease.

Through milking or nursing, the milk in the gland cistern is soon removed. There remains a large amount of milk in the alveoli that is forced into the ducts by the contractions of the myoepithelial cells (Fig. 19.2). These cells contract under the influence of the hormone oxytocin, which is secreted by the posterior pituitary (Fig. 19.3).

Oxytocin, released by the suckling reflex, can also be released by other stimuli. The milk letdown can be associated with feeding the cows or washing the udder. The latter is a typical management practice before milking cows. Oxytocin release can be inhibited by pain, loud noises, and other stressful stimuli.

Maintenance of Lactation

Lactation is maintained primarily through hormonal influence. Prolactin, thyroid hormones, adrenal hormones, and growth hormone are all important in the maintenance of lactation.

Daily milk production typically increases during the first few weeks of lactation, peaks at approximately 4–6 weeks, then decreases over the next several weeks of the lactation period. Persistency of lactation measures how milk production is maintained over time. For example, in dairy cattle persistency is determined by calculating milk production of the current month as a percentage of the last month's production.

Figure 19.4 shows lactation curves for the various species of farm animals. The curve for dairy cows (Fig. 19.4A) represents approximately 14,000 lb produced in 305 days.

Decreased milk production during the lactation period is due primarily to a decreased

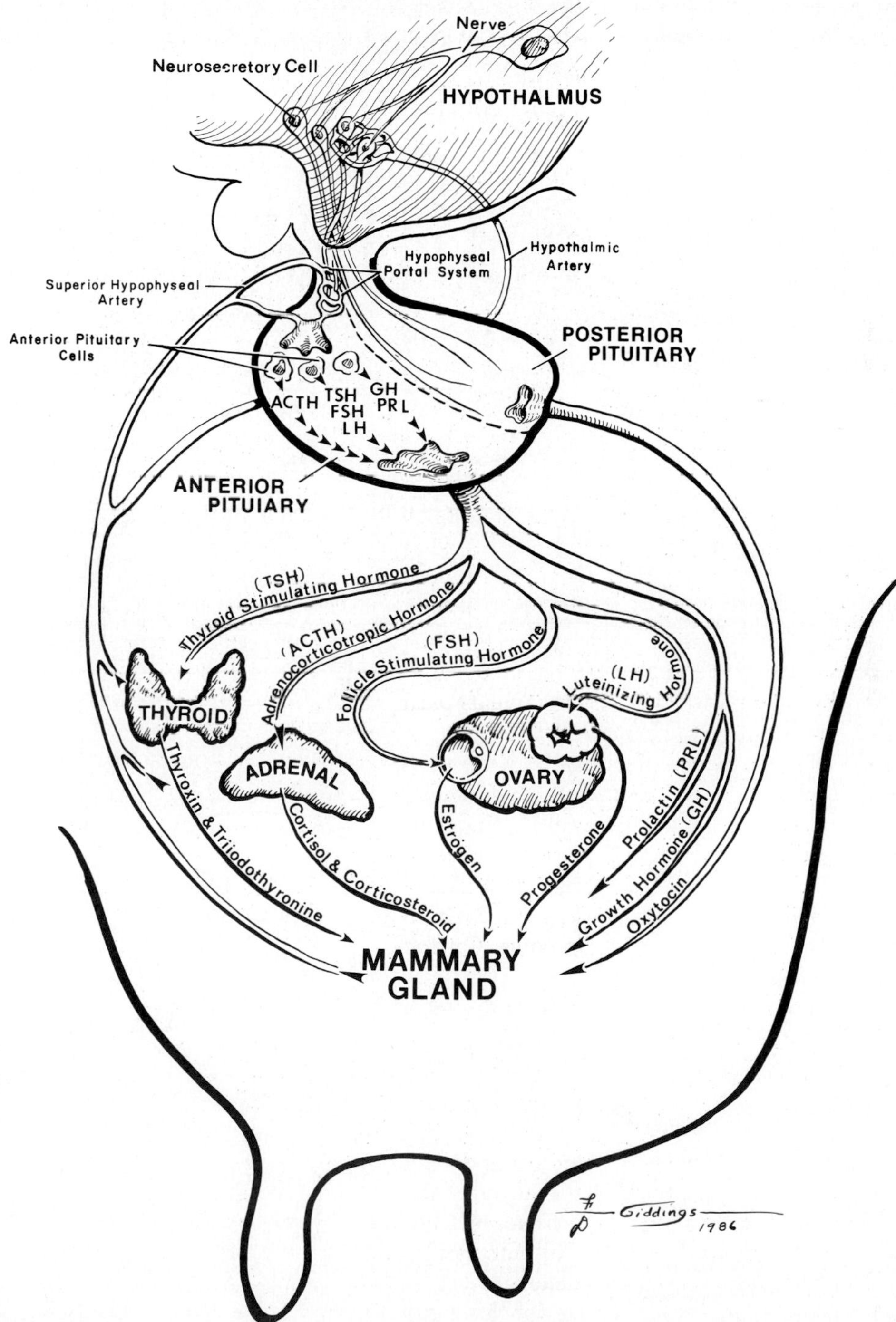

FIGURE 19.3.
Major hormones (and their sources) influencing the anatomy and physiology of the mammary gland. Refer to Figure 18.11 for the locations of the endocrine glands throughout the body. Drawing by Dennis Giddings.

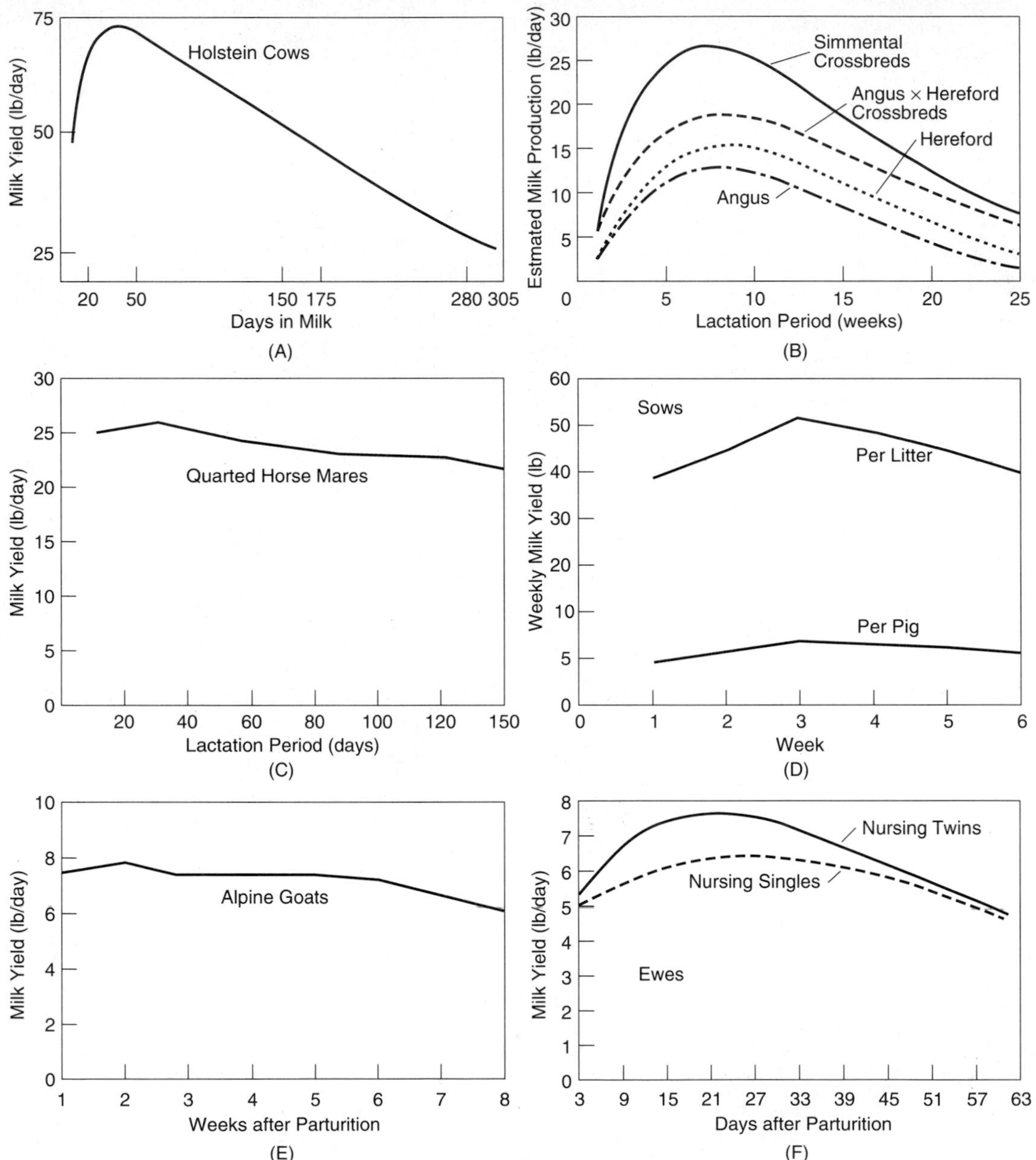

FIGURE 19.4.
Lactation curves for several species of farm animals. (A) Dalry cows. Courtesy of Colorado State University (CO, ID, and UT DHIA records). (B) Beef cows. Courtesy of Jenkins and Ferrell, 1984 Beef Cow Efficiency Forum. (C) Quarter horse mares. Courtesy of *J. Anim. Sci.* 54:496. (D) Sows. Courtesy of *Missouri Agric. Research Bull.* 712. (E) Alpine goats. Courtesy of *J. Dairy Sci.* 63:1677. (F) Ewes. Courtesy of *Michigan State Agric. Expt. Sta. Research Report* 491.

number of active alveoli and less secretory tissue (epithelial cells) in the alveoli. These and other changes are associated with hormonal changes.

When milking or suckling is stopped, the alveoli are distended and the capillaries are filled with blood. After a few days the secretory tissue becomes involuted (reduced in size and activity) and the lobes of the mammary gland consist primarily of ducts and connective tissue. The female then becomes **dry** as milk secretion is not occurring. After the dry period (approximately 2 months in the dairy cow) and when parturition approaches, hormones and other influences prepare the mammary gland to resume its secretion and production of milk.

FACTORS AFFECTING MILK PRODUCTION

Inheritance determines the potential for milk production, but feed and management determine whether or not this potential is attained. The best feed and care will not make a high-producing female out of one that is genetically a low producer. Likewise, a female with high genetic potential will not produce at a high level unless she receives proper feed and care. Production is also influenced by the health of the animal. For example, **mastitis** (an inflammation of the udder) in dairy cows can reduce production by 30% or more. Proper management of dairy cows, particularly adherence to routine milking and feeding schedules, contribute to a high level of production.

In lactating farm animals, the level of milk production is important because milk from these females provides much of the required nutrients for optimal growth in the young. If beef cows, for example, are inherently heavy milkers, their milk-producing levels will be established by the ability of the young to consume milk. Normally, if the cow is not milked, she will adjust her production to the consumption level of the calf. However, if the cow is milked early in lactation, her milk flow may be far greater in amount than the calf can consume. This situation makes it necessary either to continue milking the cow until the calf becomes large enough to consume the milk or to put another calf onto the cow.

Anything that causes a female to reduce her production of milk is likely to cause some regression of the mammary gland, thereby preventing resumption of full production. If the young animal lacks vigor, it does not consume all the milk that its mother can supply, and her level of production is lowered accordingly. This is one reason inbred animals grow more slowly and crossbred animals more rapidly during the nursing period. Crossbreds are usually larger and more vigorous at birth and can stimulate a high level of milk production by their dams, whereas inbred animals are smaller and less vigorous and cause their dams to produce milk at a comparatively low rate.

Females with male offspring produce more milk than females with female offspring. Male offspring are usually heavier at birth and have a faster growth rate than females. This puts a greater demand on the milk-producing ability of the dam.

Females with multiple births usually produce more total milk than females with single births. Age of the female also affects milk yield, younger and older females producing less milk compared to females who have had several lactations. For example, sows are usually at peak milk yields during third or fourth lactation, beef cows produce the most milk at 5–9 years of age, and dairy cows have the highest milk yields between 5–8 years of age.

Large amounts of nutrients are needed to supply the requirements of lactating females producing high levels of milk because much energy is required for milk secretion and because milk contains large quantities of nutrients. Adequate nutrition is much greater for lactation than for gestation; for example, a cow producing 100 lb of milk daily could yield 4.0 lb of butterfat, 3.3 lb of protein, and almost 5.0 lb of lactose in that milk. If nutrition is inadequate in quality or quantity, a cow that has the inherent capacity to produce 100 lb of milk daily will draw nutrients from her own body as the body attempts to sustain a high level of milk production. Withdrawal of nutrients reduces the body stores. This withdrawal usually occurs to a limited extent in high producers even when they are well fed. Cows reduce their milk production in response to inadequate amounts or quality of feed, but they usually do so only after the loss of nutrients is sufficiently severe to cause a loss in body weight. In gestation, a cow becomes relatively efficient in digesting her feed, so feed restrictions in gestation are less harmful than they might be at other times.

MILK COMPOSITION

Species Differences

Milk composition is markedly different for the mammalian species (Table 19.1). Milk from reindeer and aquatic mammals is exceptionally high in total solids, whereas the mare's milk is low in this regard. Large differences in milk fat percentages exist in mammals; donkeys are low (1.4%) and fur seals are high (53.3%).

Except in protein, milk from cows and goats is similar in composition to milk from humans. Milk from cows or goats is much higher in protein than milk from humans. This is not a problem in bottle-feeding babies as the additional protein is not harmful.

In dairy cows, the amount or percentage of fat is easily changed through changing the diet fed. Carbohydrates (lactose) remain relatively constant even with dietary fluctuations. Varying the protein content of the ration has little change on the protein content of the milk.

COLOSTRUM

The fetus develops in a sterile environment. Its immune system has not yet been challenged by the microorganisms existing in the external environment. Before or shortly after birth, the fetal immune system must be made functional or death is imminent.

TABLE 19.1. Average Milk Composition of Several Species

Species	Total Solids (%)	Fat (%)	Protein (%)	Lactose (%)	Minerals (%)
Human	13.3	4.5	1.6	7.0	0.2
Cow *(Bos taurus)*	12.7	3.9	3.3	4.8	0.7
Cow *(Bos indicus)*	13.5	4.7	3.4	4.7	0.7
Goat	12.4	3.7	3.3	4.7	0.8
Water buffalo	19.0	7.4	6.0	4.8	0.8
Ewe	18.4	6.5	6.3	4.8	0.9
Sow	19.0	6.8	6.3	5.0	0.9
Mare	10.5	1.2	2.3	5.9	0.4
Reindeer	33.7	18.7	11.1	2.7	1.2

Immunoglobulins (Ig) are involved in the passive immunity transfer maternally to the offspring. In some animals, the Ig are transferred *in utero* through the bloodstream, whereas in other animals immunoglobulins are transferred through colostrum. Certain animals utilize both methods of Ig transfer; however, the colostrum method is most common for larger, domestic animals.

These Ig antibodies give the newborn protection from harmful microorganisms that invade the body and cause illness. The intestinal wall of the newborn is quite porous, permitting absorption of colostrum antibodies to enter the bloodstream. Within a few hours (no more than 24), the gut wall becomes less porous, allowing little absorption of the antibodies to occur. Thus, passive immunity of the newborn is dependent on an adequate supply of antibodies in the colostrum and on consuming the colostrum within a few hours after parturition.

SELECTED REFERENCES

Publications

Allen, A. D., Lasley, J. F., and Tribble, L. F. Milk production and related factors in sows. *Missouri Agric. Research Bull.* 712.

Gibbs, P. G., Potter, G. D., Blake, R. W., and McMullan, W. C. 1982. Milk production of quarter horse mares during 150 days of lactation. *J. Anim. Sci.* 54:496.

Henry, M. S., and Benson, M. E. 1990. Milk production and efficiency of lactating ewe lambs. *Michigan State Agric. Expt. Sta. Report* 491.

Keown, J. F., Everett R. W., Empet, N. B., and Wadell, L. H. 1986. Lactation curves. *J. Dairy Sci.* 69:769.

Larson, B. L. (ed.). 1985. *Lactation.* Ames, IA: Iowa State University Press.

Offedal, O. T. Hintz, H. F., and Schryver, H. F. 1983. Lactation in the horse: Milk composition and intake by foals. *J. Nutr.* 113:2196.

Visuals

External Features of the Udder; Internal Features of the Udder; Removal of Milk and Proper Milking Practices; Abnormalities in Mammary Glands; and *Milk Composition and Factors Affecting Milk Yield* (videotapes). Agricultural Products and Services, 2001 Killebrew Dr., Suite 333, Bloomington, MN 55420.

CHAPTER 20

Adaptation to the Environment

Livestock throughout the world are expected to produce under an extremely wide range of environments. Variations in temperature, humidity, wind, light, altitude, feed, water, and exposure to parasites and disease organisms are some of the environmental conditions to which livestock are exposed (Fig. 20.1).

Under **intensive management,** such as integrated poultry enterprises, confinement swine operations, and large dairies, many environmental conditions are highly controlled. Feed and water are plentiful, rations are carefully balanced, excellent health programs are carefully monitored, and, in many cases, temperature, humidity, and other weather influences are controlled.

Extensive management involves less producer control over the environmental conditions in which animals are expected to produce. Many ruminant animals are extensively managed while also exposed to numerous climatic conditions as they graze the forage, often sparse. Livestock that produce and survive under these conditions must have physiological mechanisms for adaptability.

Economics dictate to a large extent whether animals will be managed intensively or extensively. Under intensive management, many environmental conditions are changed to fit the animals. Under extensive management, animals are changed (selected for adaptability) to fit the environment.

It is important to understand the major environmental effects on animal productivity. Management decisions can then be made to determine whether changing the environment or changing the adaptability of animals is the most economically feasible alternative. In some situations, environmental changes and changes in animal adaptability can produce optimal results.

MAJOR ENVIRONMENTAL EFFECTS

Adjusting to Environmental Changes

As the seasons change, two major kinds of changes occur in the environment: changes in temperature and changes in length of daylight. As summer approaches, temperature and length

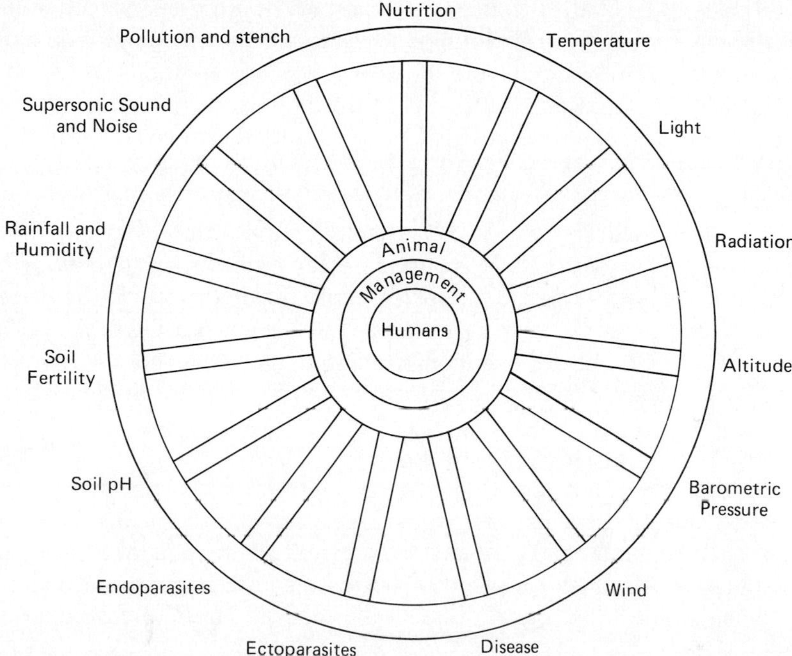

FIGURE 20.1.
The livestock ecology wheel. Human's management decisions with farm animals play a role in determining how the animals will interact with their environment. Courtesy of J. Bonsma, *Livestock Production* (Cody, WY: Agi Books, 1983). Copyright © Agi Books.

of daylight increase, thus increasing the amount of heat available to the animal. As autumn approaches, length of daylight and temperature decrease. Hormone changes help the animal respond physiologically to these seasonal changes.

The thyroid gland, the lobes of which are located on both sides of the trachea, regulates the metabolic activity of the animal. When the environmental temperature is cool, the air inhaled tends to cool the thyroid gland. The thyroid responds by increasing its production of the hormone thyroxine; the thyroxine, in turn, stimulates metabolic activity and heat is generated. The growing and shedding of insulating coats of fiber are slow changes that are also influenced by hormones. Sudden warm periods before shedding occur in spring, and sudden cool periods before a warm coat has been produced in autumn can have severe effects on an animal. These sudden temperature changes are the greatest predisposers for the onset of respiratory diseases such as pneumonia, influenza, and shipping fever.

Temperature Zones of Comfort and Stress

The **comfort zone,** or **thermoneutral zone (TNZ),** identifies a range of temperatures where heat production and heat loss from the body are about the same. When the temperature is below the TNZ, animals increase their feed intake and reduce blood flow to the surface and the extremities. Mammals generate heat by shivering. Fowl fluff their feathers to create a large space of dead air about themselves to prevent rapid heat transfer from their bodies. Some animals hunch to expose less body surface. Cattle congregate in an area that provides protection from blizzards, and they huddle closely so that each animal receives heat from the others. During a severe blizzard, some animals can be killed from crowding, trampling, and suffocation.

To avoid excessive heat loss, animals maintain the temperature of their extremities at a level below that of the rest of the body through a unique mechanism called countercurrent blood flow action. Blood in arteries coming from the core of the body is relatively warm and blood in veins in the extremities is relatively cool. The blood in veins in the extremities cools the warmer arterial blood so that the extremities are kept at a cool temperature. With the extremities thus kept at a relatively cool temperature, loss of heat to the environment is reduced.

Between 65°F and 80°F, dilation of blood vessels near the skin and in the extremities occurs so that the surface of the animal becomes warmer, water consumption increases, respiration increases, and, in animals that can sweat, perspiration increases. Above 80°F, animals that have the capacity of sweating keep their body surfaces wet with sweat so that evaporation can help cool them.

When the environmental temperature exceeds 90°F, farm animals may die, have lower daily gains and poor feed conversion, and have lower reproductive performance through higher embryonic deaths. During these high temperatures, animals become less active to reduce the amount of heat they generate, and lie down in the shade to reduce their exposure to the sun. Animals typically increase their consumption of water and excretion of urine. If the water consumed is cooler than the temperature of the animal, it can help considerably to cool the body.

CHANGING THE ENVIRONMENT

Adjusting Rations for Weather Changes

Nutrient requirements and predicted gains of farm animals are published from research studies in which animals are protected from environmental extremes. The most common environmental factor that alters both performance and nutrient requirements is temperature. Thus livestock producers should be aware of critical temperatures that affect performance of their animals and consider making changes in their feeding and management programs if economics so dictate.

The TNZ is the range in effective temperature where rate and efficiency of performance is optimum. Critical temperature is the lower limit of the TNZ, and is typified by the ambient temperature below which the performance of animals begins to decline as temperatures become colder. Figure 20.2 shows that the maintenance energy requirement increases more rapidly during cold weather than does rate of feed intake. This results in a reduction of gain and more feed required per pound of gain, which typically causes cost per pound of gain to be higher.

Effective ambient temperatures below the lower critical temperature (below the TNZ) constitute cold stress, and those above the TNZ constitute heat stress. The term ***effective ambient temperature*** is an index of the heating or cooling power of the environment in terms of dry-bulb temperature. It includes any environmental factor—such as radiation, wind, humidity, or precipitation—that can alter environmental heat demand.

The critical temperatures and optimal temperature ranges are shown for some animals in Figure 20.3. Effective ambient temperatures have not been calculated for all farm animals, although the effects of some combined environmental factors are known. For example, the windchill index for cattle is shown in Table 20.1. An example in Table 20.1 shows that with a temperature of 20°F and a wind speed of 30 mph, the effective ambient temperature is −16°F.

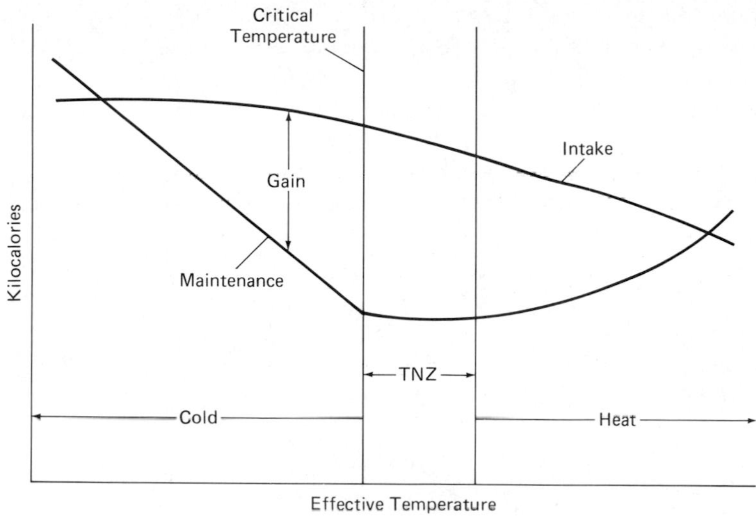

FIGURE 20.2. Effect of temperature on rate of feed intake, maintenance energy requirement, and gain. Adapted from Ames, 1980.

The lower critical temperature (LCT) for cattle depends on how much insulation is provided by the hair coat, whether the animal is wet or dry, and how much feed the cow consumes. Table 20.2 shows some lower critical temperatures for beef cattle. For example, a cow being fed a maintenance ration may have a low critical temperature of 32°F when dry but a low critical temperature of 60°F when wet.

Coldness of a specific environment is the value that must be considered when adjusting rations for cows. Coldness is simply the difference between effective temperature (windchill) and lower critical temperature. Using this definition for coldness, instead of using temperature on an ordinary thermometer, helps explain why wet, windy days in March might be colder for a cow than extremely cold but dry, calm days in January.

The major effect of cold on nutrient requirements of cows is increased need for energy, which usually means increasing the total amount of daily feed.

Feeding tables recommend that a 1,200-lb cow receive 16.5 lb of good mixed hay to supply energy needs during the last one-third of pregnancy. How much feed should the cow receive if

TABLE 20.1. Windchill Factors for Cattle with Winter Coat

Wind Speed (mph)	Temperature (°F)												
	−10	−5	0	5	10	15	20	25	30	35	40	45	50
Calm	−10	−5	0	5	10	15	20	25	30	35	40	45	50
5	−16	−11	−6	−1	3	8	13	18	23	28	33	38	43
10	−21	−16	−11	−6	−1	3	8	13	18	23	28	33	38
15	−25	−20	−15	−10	−5	0	4	9	14	19	24	29	34
20	−30	−25	−20	−15	−10	−5	0	4	9	14	19	24	29
25	−37	−32	−27	−22	−17	−12	−7	−2	2	7	12	17	22
30	−40	−41	−36	−31	−26	−21	−16	−11	−6	−1	3	8	13
35	−60	−55	−50	−45	−40	−35	−30	−25	−20	−15	−10	−5	0
40	−78	−73	−68	−63	−58	−53	−48	−43	−38	−33	−28	−23	−18

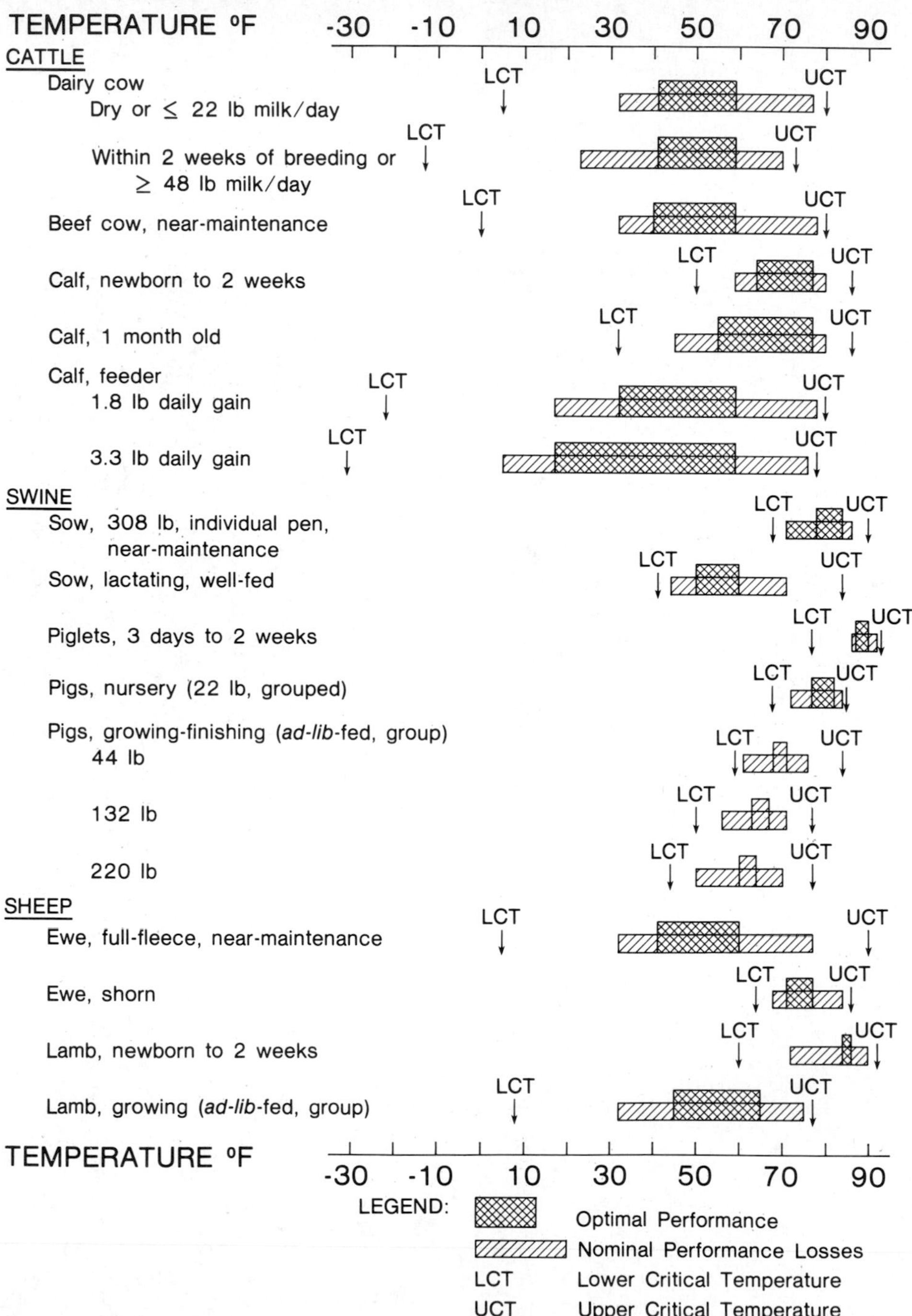

FIGURE 20.3.
Critical ambient temperatures and temperature zones for optimal performance in cattle *(Bos taurus)*, swine, and sheep. Adapted from Yousef, 1985.

TABLE 20.2. Estimated Lower Critical Temperatures for Beef Cattle

Coat Description	Critical Temperature (°F)
Summer coat or wet	59
Fall coat	45
Winter coat	32
Heavy winter coat	18

she is dry and has a winter hair coat but the temperature is 20°F with a 15-mph wind? The coldness is calculated by subtracting the windchill or effective temperature (4°F) from the cow's lower critical temperature (32°F). Thus the magnitude of coldness is 28°F. A rule of thumb (more detailed tables are available) is to increase the amount of feed 1% for each degree of coldness. A 28% increase of the 16.5 lb (the original requirement) would mean that 21.1 lb of feed must be fed to compensate for the coldness.

This example is typical of many feeding situations; however, if the cow was wet, the same increase in feed would be required at 31°F windchill (28°F of coldness).

Inability of Animals to Cope with Heat

Animals are sometimes unable to control their body temperatures in conditions of extreme heat or cold. When the body temperature exceeds normal because the animal cannot dissipate its heat, a condition known as fever results. Fever is often caused by systemic infectious diseases and is often most severe when environmental temperatures are extremely high or low. Keeping the ill animal comfortable while medication is given will assist recovery.

When the temperature becomes excessively high, some animals (notably pigs) might lose normal control of their senses and do things that aggravate the situation. If nothing is done to prevent them from doing so, pigs that get too hot will often run up and down a fence line, squealing, until they collapse and die. Pigs seen doing this should be cooled with water and encouraged to lie down on damp soil.

Most dairy cows will have a reduction in milk production when the environmental temperature exceeds 80°F. This occurs primarily because appetite is depressed and feed consumption declines. Milk yields will improve when thermal stress is alleviated by providing shade, fans, or refrigerated air.

CHANGING THE ANIMALS

One of the most impressive examples of adaptability under extensive management are the small Black Bedouin goats that graze the Negev desert of Israel and the eastern Sinai. Owing to the arid and desert conditions, they are watered only once in 2–4 days, which greatly increases their foraging range.

Ninety Bedouin goats (2,970 lb total body mass) can be herded successfully 2 days away from water points, where only one fat-tail Awassi sheep (110 lb) or 1.5 Black Mediterranean goats (165 lb) would be able to live because of more frequent watering needs.

During water deprivation for 4 days, the Bedouin goats lose 25%–30% of their body weight from reduction of total body water and blood plasma volume. Nevertheless, these goats have relatively high milk yields, as 35-lb goats produce over 4.5 lb of milk per day. The Bedouin goats also have relatively low daily caloric demands for maintenance per unit of metabolic weight. Milk production efficiencies have exceeded 33% of energy consumed. The Bedouin goats have developed this adaptability over several centuries of natural selection as they have survived and produced in these arid, desert environments.

Inability of Animals to Cope with Other Stresses

Some animals are unable to adjust to environmental stresses. This inability may be genetically controlled.

When cattle are grazed at high altitudes, 1%–5% develop high mountain (brisket) disease. This disease usually occurs at altitudes of 7,000 feet or more. It is characterized as right heart failure (deterioration of the right side of the heart). It was considered that this disease was caused by chronic **hypoxia** (lack of oxygen), which leads to pulmonary **hypertension** (high blood pressure). As the animal becomes more affected, marked subcutaneous edema (filling of tissue with fluid) develops in the brisket area. Some recent studies at the U.S. Poisonous Plant Center at Logan, Utah, however, have shown that certain poisonous plants that grow only at high altitudes can cause brisket disease when fed to cattle maintained at low altitudes.

Some young cattle and sheep whose dams are fed plants in selenium-deficient areas develop **white muscle disease.** The disease is characterized by calcification of the heart and voluntary muscles, giving the muscles a white appearance. White muscle disease can be prevented by administering selenium to the mother during pregnancy and to the young at birth. In the absence of treatment, some animals are affected and some are not; therefore, resistance and susceptibility appear to be inherited.

SELECTED REFERENCES

Ames, D. R. 1981. Feeding beef cows in winter. *Angus J.*, Jan.

———. 1980. Livestock nutrition in cold weather. *Anim. Nutr. and Health,* Oct.

Bonsma, J. 1983. *Livestock Production.* Cody, WY: Ag Books.

Hahn, G. L. 1985. Weather and climate impacts on beef cattle. *Beef Research Progress Report* no. 2, MARC, USDA, ARS-42.

McDowell, L. R. (ed.). 1985. *Nutrition of Grazing Ruminants in Warm Climates.* New York: Academic Press.

National Research Council. 1981. *Effect of Environment on Nutrient Requirements of Domestic Animals.* Washington, DC: National Academy Press.

Yousef, M. K. 1985. *Stress Physiology in Livestock. Vol. II: Ungulates.* Boca Raton, FL: CRC Press.

CHAPTER 21

Animal Health

Productive animals are typically healthy animals. Death loss **(mortality rate)** is the most dramatic sign of health problems; however, lower production levels and higher costs of production, which are due to sickness **(morbidity),** are economically more serious.

Disease is defined as any deviation from normal health in which there are marked physiological, anatomical, or chemical changes in the animal's body. Noninfectious diseases and infectious diseases are the two major disease types. Noninfectious diseases result from injury, genetic abnormalities, ingestion of toxic materials, and poor nutrition. Microorganisms are not involved in noninfectious diseases. Examples of noninfectious diseases are plant poisoning, bloat, and mineral deficiencies.

Infectious diseases are caused by microorganisms such as bacteria, viruses, and protozoa. A **contagious disease** is an infectious disease that spreads rapidly from one animal to another. Brucellosis, ringworm, and transmissible gastroenteritis (TGE) are examples of infectious diseases.

PREVENTION

The old adage, "An ounce of prevention is worth a pound of cure," is an important part of herd health. Preventative herd health programs can eliminate or reduce most of the health-related livestock losses. Most major animal disease problems are associated with health management.

The components of a herd health-management program include (1) veterinarian-assisted planning, (2) sanitation, (3) proper nutrition, (4) record analysis, (5) physical facilities, (6) source of livestock, (7) proper use of biologics and pharmaceuticals, (8) minimizing stress, and (9) personnel training. All of these components require cooperative efforts between the producer and veterinarian.

Planning with the Veterinarian

Veterinarians are professionally educated and trained in animal health. Veterinarians located near animal producers are familiar with the disease and health problems common in the producer's area. Producers having the most successful herd health programs use veterinarians in planning such programs. Important parts of the plan include regularly scheduled visits by the veterinarian throughout the year to assess preventative programs, as well as to provide animal treatment. The veterinarian can also train farm and ranch personnel in simple herd health-management practices and serve as a reference for new products.

In most livestock and poultry operations, it is more economically feasible to have veterinarians assist in planning and implementing preventative health programs than to use their services only in crisis situations.

Producers should keep cost-effective health records as recommended by the veterinarian. These records are needed to assess problem areas and to develop a more effective herd health plan. The records can include such information as when and what was done in the preventative and treatment programs, descriptions of the conditions during health problems, and deaths. Possible causes of death also should be recorded, with **necropsy** records obtained when economically feasible.

Sanitation

The severity of some diseases is dependent on the number and virulence of microorganisms entering the animal's body. Many microorganisms live and multiply outside the animal, so the number of microorganisms can be reduced by implementing sanitation practices. These practices, in turn, reduce the incidence of disease outbreaks.

Manure and other organic waste materials are ideal environments for the proliferation of microorganisms. A good sanitation program includes cleaning of organic materials from buildings, pens, and lots. This allows the effective destruction of microorganisms from high temperatures and drying. Buildings, pens, and pastures should be well drained, preventing prolonged wet areas or mud holes. These sanitation practices help both in disease prevention and controlling parasites.

Antiseptics and **disinfectants** are carefully selected and effectively utilized in a good sanitation program. Antiseptics are substances, usually applied to animal tissue, that kill or prevent the growth of microorganisms. Disinfectants are products that destroy pathogenic microorganisms. They are usually agents used on inanimate objects. In the absence of disinfectants, sanitizing with clean water is helpful.

Other important sanitation measures include the prompt and proper disposal of dead animals, either to rendering plants or by burial.

Proper Nutrition

Well-nourished animals receive an adequate daily supply of essential nutrients. Undernourished animals usually have a weak immune system, thus making them more vulnerable to invading microorganisms.

Nutrition principles are presented in Chapters 15, 16, and 17. Feeding programs for the various species of farm animals are covered in Chapters 23, 25, 27, 29, 31, 32, and 33.

Record Analysis

Herd health must be approached from an economic standpoint. Does a health problem exist, or is it just a perception? Proper records permit health problems to be identified, determine what is causing them, and thereby allow alternative methods of prevention and treatment to be assessed.

Physical Facilities

Physical facilities contribute to animal health problems by causing physical injury or stress, or by allowing dissemination of pathogens through a group of animals. They can contribute to the spread of disease by not preventing its transmission (e.g., venereal disease transmission owing to poor or inadequate fences). Even proper facilities that are misused, such as at a feedlot, can provide an easier transmission of disease owing to crowding, stress, and poor sanitation.

Source of Livestock

Producers can reduce the spread of infectious diseases into their herds and flocks by (1) purchasing animals (entering their herds) from other producers who have effective herd health-management programs; (2) controlling exposure of their animals to other people and vehicles; (3) providing clothing, boots, and disinfectant to people who must be exposed to the animals and facilities; (4) isolating animals to be introduced into their herds so that disease symptoms can be observed for several weeks; (5) controlling insects, birds, rodents, and other animals that can carry disease organisms; and (6) keeping their animals out of drainage areas that run through their farm from other farms.

Use of Biologics and Pharmaceuticals

Drugs are classified as biologicals or pharmaceuticals. **Biologics** are used primarily to prevent diseases, whereas **pharmaceuticals** are used mainly to treat diseases. Both are needed in a successful herd health-management program.

Most biologicals are used to stimulate immunity against specific diseases. Vaccines are biological agents that stimulate active immunity in the animal.

Other biologicals stimulate the body's immune system to produce antibodies that fight diseases. This is similar to immunity through natural infection. An antibody is a protein molecule that circulates in the bloodstream and neutralizes disease-causing microorganisms. An animal is immunized when sufficient antibodies are produced to prevent the disease from developing. Specific antibodies must be produced for specific diseases, thus vaccination for several different diseases may be necessary. Also periodic revaccination might be needed to maintain antibodies in the blood at an adequate level.

Immunity from vaccination occurs only if the immune system properly responds. In some situations vaccination is not effective. In most animal species, for example, the immune systems of newborn young are not yet developed enough to respond. This is why their immunity is dependent on the maternal antibodies ingested from their mother's milk. Also, undernourished animals, stressed animals, or those animals already exposed to the disease rarely give a positive response to vaccination.

The amount of vaccine, frequency, route of administration, and duration of immunity vary with the specific vaccine. The manufacturer's directions should be followed carefully.

Vaccines (biologicals) and drugs (pharmaceuticals) can be administered as follows:

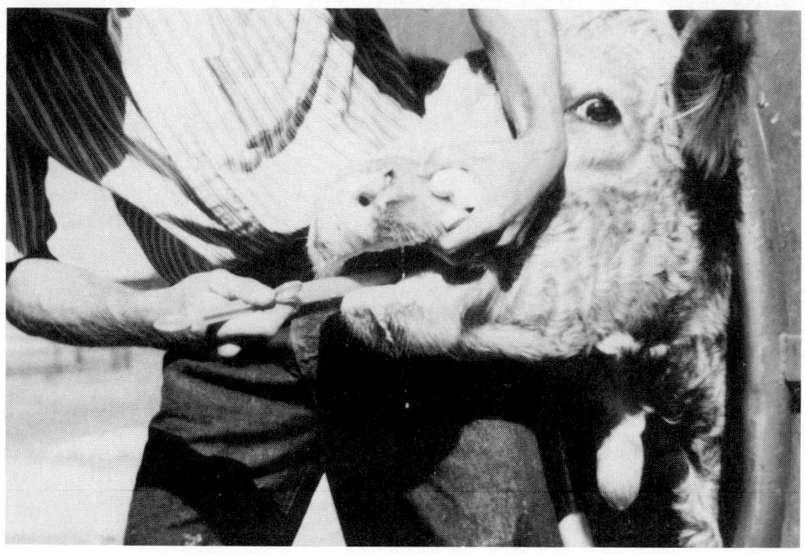

FIGURE 21.1.
Using a balling gun to give a bolus or capsule to a cow. After the instrument is placed on the back of the tongue, the plunger is pushed to deposit the pill onto the back of the tongue. The animal then swallows the pill. Courtesy of Norden Laboratories.

1. Topically—applied to the skin.
2. Orally—through the mouth by feeding, drenching, or using balling guns. The latter is used to give pills such as capsules or boluses (Fig. 21.1).
3. Injected directly into the animal's body by using a needle and syringe.

Types of injections include (1) subcutaneous (under the skin but not into the muscle), (2) intramuscular (directly into the muscle), (3) intravenous (into a vein), (4) intramammary (through a cannula in the teat canal and injecting the drug into the milk cistern), (5) intraperitoneal (into the peritoneal cavity), and (6) intrauterine (using an infusion pipette or a tube through the cervix). Some injection sites are shown in Figures 21.2–21.4.

Pharmaceuticals are used to kill or reduce the growth of microorganisms in the treatment of diseases and infections. Pharmaceuticals comes in a variety of forms: liquid, powder, boluses, drenches, and feed additives. They should be administered only after a specific diagnosis has been made. Examples of pharmaceuticals are antibiotics, steroids, sulfa compounds, hormones, and nitrofurans.

Other pharmaceuticals are used to control external and internal parasites. Losses owing to external and internal parasites are usually reduced weight gains, poor feed conversion, lower milk and egg production, reduced hide value, and excessive carcass trim, rather than high death losses.

Common external parasites are flies, lice, mites, and ticks, which live off the flesh and blood of animals. These parasites can also transmit infectious diseases from one animal to another. Insecticides are used to control external parasites. They can be applied as systemics, spraying, fogging, dipping, back rubbers, ear tags, or dust bags.

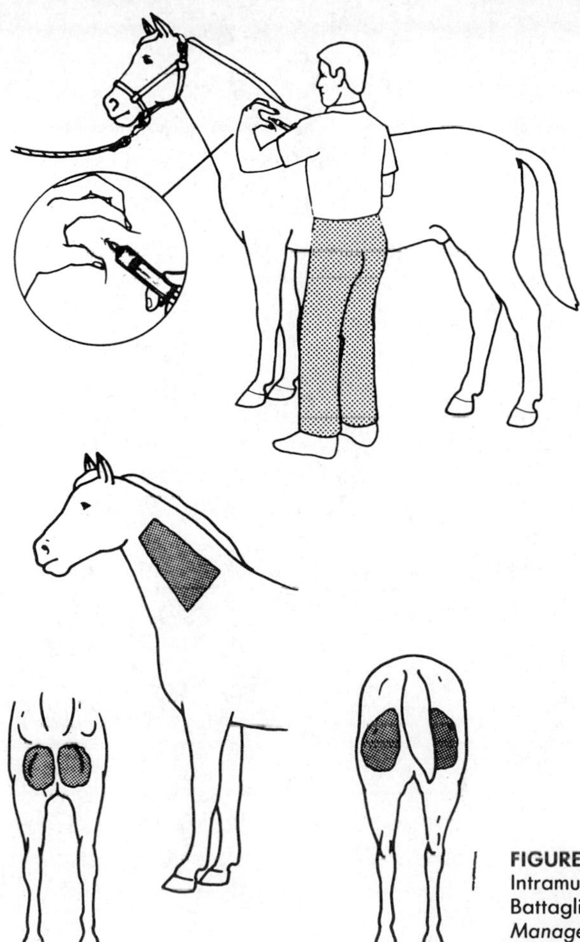

FIGURE 21.2.
Subcutaneous injection in the horse. Courtesy of R. A. Battaglia, and V. B. Mayrose, *Handbook of Livestock Management Techniques* (New York: Macmillan, 1981). Copyright © Macmillan Publishing Co.

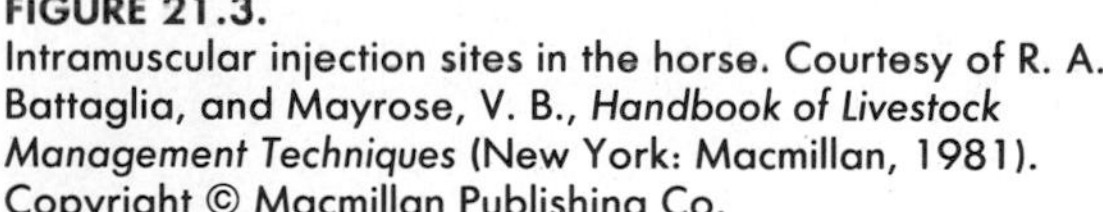

FIGURE 21.3.
Intramuscular injection sites in the horse. Courtesy of R. A. Battaglia, and Mayrose, V. B., *Handbook of Livestock Management Techniques* (New York: Macmillan, 1981). Copyright © Macmillan Publishing Co.

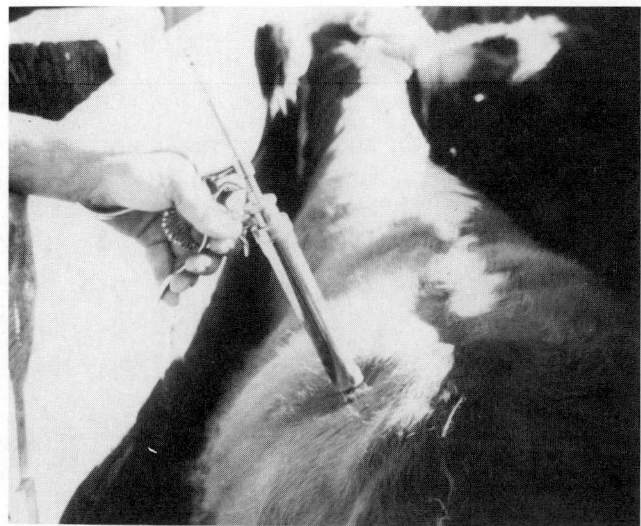

FIGURE 21.4.
Intramuscular injection into the muscles of the hip. Courtesy of Norden Laboratories.

Roundworms and tapeworms are the most common internal parasites, with flukes causing problems in certain environments. Internal parasites are controlled by interrupting their life cycle by (1) the presence of unfavorable climatic conditions (wet, warm weather favors the proliferation of many internal parasites); (2) destroying intermediate hosts; (3) managing animals so they will not ingest the parasites or their eggs; and (4) giving therapeutic chemical treatment. **Anthelmintics** are drugs that are given to kill the internal parasites.

Stress

Stress is any environmental factor that can cause a significant change in the animal's physiological processes. Physical sources of stress are temperature, wind velocity, nutritional deficiency or oversupply, mud, snow, dust, fatigue, weaning, ammonia buildup, transportation, castration, dehorning, and abusive handling. Social or behavior-related stress can result from aggression or overcrowding.

Prolonged stress can impair the body's immune system, causing a reduced resistance to disease. Stressful conditions in animals should be minimized within economic constraints.

Personnel Training

Maintaining good animal health requires continuous training of personnel. This is one of the most difficult areas to accomplish, particularly in a livestock operation that employs many people. While the owner understands what needs to be done, this may differ from what the employees actually accomplish. Cooperative training programs and informative sessions with the veterinarian can assist in the implementation of effective herd health-management programs.

DETECTING UNHEALTHY ANIMALS

Visual Observation

Detecting sick animals and separating them from the healthy animals is an important key to a successful treatment program. Animals treated in the early stages of sickness usually respond more favorably to treatment than do animals whose illness has progressed to advanced stages.

Early signs of sickness are not easily detected; however, the following are some of the observable signs, several of which can be observed in Figure 21.5:

1. loss of appetite
2. animal appears listless and depressed
3. ears may be droopy or not held in an alert position
4. animal has a hump in the back and holds its head in a lower position
5. animal stays separated from the rest of the herd or flock
6. coughing, wheezing, or labored breathing

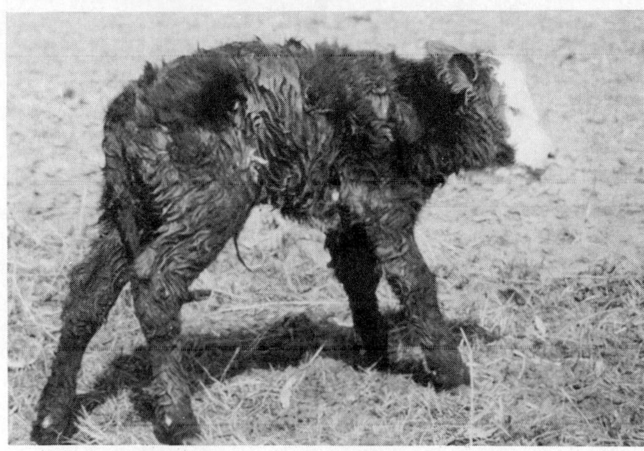

FIGURE 21.5.
This calf is sick with diarrhea (calf scours). Note the visual signs of illness. Courtesy of Norden Laboratories.

Vital Signs

Body temperature, respiration rate, and heart rate are the vital signs of the animal. Health problems are usually evident when one or more of the vital signs deviate from the normal range. The average and normal range for the vital functions are given in Table 21.1.

Body temperature is taken rectally. An elevated body temperature occurs in overheated animals or with most infectious diseases. A subnormal temperature indicates chilling or a critical condition of the animal.

TABLE 21.1. Vital Functions of Selected Livestock and Poultry Species

Animal	Rectal Temperature (°F)	Respiration Rate (per min)	Heart Rate (per min)
Cattle	101.5[a] (100.4–102.8)[b]	30[a]	50[a]
Swine	102.5 (101.6–103.6)	16	60
Sheep	102.3 (100.9–103.8)	19	75
Goat	102.3 (101.3–103.5)	15	90
Horse	100.0 (99.1–100.8)	12	45
Chicken	107.1 (105.0–109.4)	12–36[b]	275
Turkey	105	28–49[b]	165

[a] Average.
[b] Normal range.
Source: R. A. Battaglia, and V. B. Mayrose, *Handbook of Livestock Management Techniques* (New York: Macmillan, 1981). Copyright © Macmillan Publishing Co.

By evaluating the animals' vital signs and visually observing their appearance, health problems can be identified in their early stages. This allows for early treatment, which usually prevents serious losses.

MAJOR DISEASES OF FARM ANIMALS

Table 21.2 identifies some of the major diseases and health problems of beef cattle, dairy cattle, swine, horses, poultry, and sheep.

TABLE 21.2. Selected Major Diseases and Health Problems of Beef Cattle, Dairy Cattle, Swine, Horses, Poultry, and Sheep

Species/Disease/Cause	Signs	Prevention	Treatment
Beef Cattle			
Bovine viral diarrhea (BVD) Virus. Laboratory diagnosis imperative for accuracy	(Feeder cattle) Ulcerations throughout digestive tract Diarrhea (often containing mucus or blood)	Vaccination prior to exposure Avoid contact with infected animals	Symptomatic treatment; antibiotics; sulfonamids; "Hyper" serums; force feed
	(Breeding cattle) Abortions	Vaccination prior to breeding	None Symptomatic treatment
Brucellosis bacteria	Abortions	Calfhood vaccination (in some states) between the ages of 2–12 months Test and slaughter reactors	None
Campylobacteriosis (vibriosis) bacteria	Repeat services Abortions (1%–2%)	Vaccination of females and bulls prior to breeding Use of artificial insemination Untried bulls on virgin heifers Avoid sexual contact with infected animals	None
Leptospirosis Leptospira spp Several bacteria	(Breeding cattle) Fever, off feed, abortions, icterus, discolored urine	Vaccination at least annually (in high risk areas, more frequently) Control rodents Avoid contact with wildlife and other infected animals	Streptomycin Penicillin Oxytetracycline (i.m.), 1 mg/lb/body weight/7 days Chlortetracycline, 1 mg/lb/body weight/7 days
	(Feeder cattle)	Vaccination on arrival	Dihydrostreptomycin

TABLE 21.2 (Continued)

Species/Disease/Cause	Signs	Prevention	Treatment
Infectious bovine rhinotracheitis (IBR) Virus. Laboratory diagnosis imperative for accuracy	Respiratory involvement Fever, vaginitis, abortion, eye and nose discharges Abortions or stillborn calves Pneumonia in calves	Vaccination prior to exposure	Chlortetracycline, 350 g/day Sulfamethazine, 350 mg to keep down secondary infections "Hyper" serums
Scours, calf colibacillosis "septicemia" *E. coli* (bacteria) plus stress factors	Diarrhea, weakness, and dehydration Rough hair and coat	Dry, clean calving areas Adequate colostrum	Fluid therapy Antibiotics to prevent secondary infections
Scours (viral) Virus (reovirus and corona virus)	Acute diarrhea, high mortality Affects calves shortly after birth (See Figs. 21.5 and 21.6).	Vaccination with specific viral vaccines	Fluid therapy not effective in severe cases
"Shipping fever" Para-influenza Virus plus bacteria plus stress May be accompanied by other viral diseases	Respiratory involvement Differential diagnosis	Chlortetracycline, 350 mg/head/day Sulfamethazone, 350 mg/head/day Oxytetracycline, 0.5–2 mg/head/day for 3 days	Sulfonamides; antibiotics; antiserums; serums; "hyper" serums; Tylan 200
Trichomoniasis protozoa	Repeat services Abortion	Use of artificial insemination Untried bulls on virgin heifers Avoid sexual contact with infected animals	

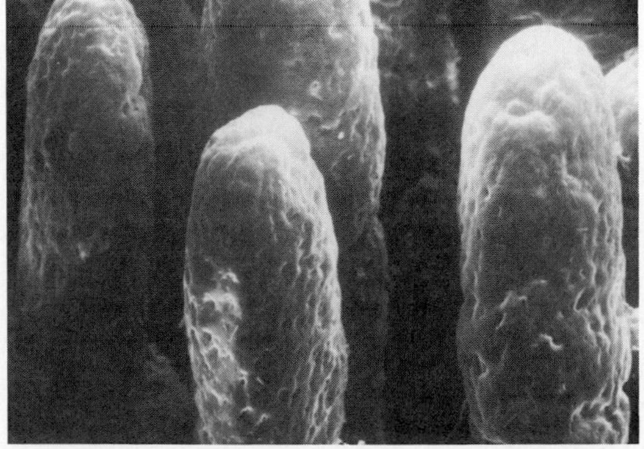

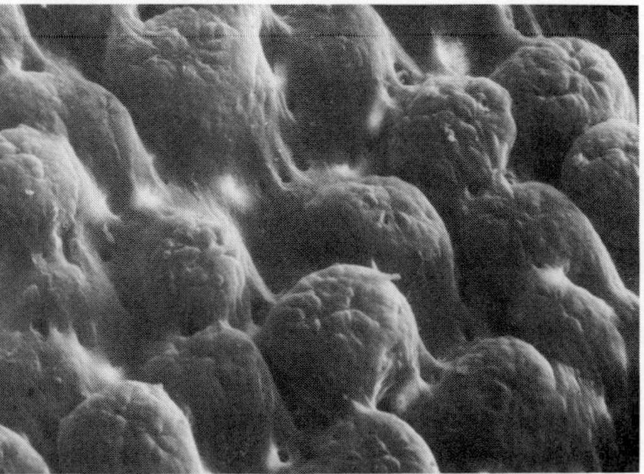

FIGURE 21.6.
(A) Normal villi that line the intestinal wall. (B) De-nuded villi after virus infection in pigs and calves. Severe diarrhea results as the animal has lost the ability to digest and absorb nutrients. If the animal survives, the villi will regain their natural form in 1–2 weeks. Courtesy of Dr. G. L. Waxler, 1972. *Am. J. Vet. Res.* 33:1323.

TABLE 21.2 *(Continued)*

Species/Disease/Cause	Signs	Prevention	Treatment
Dairy Cattle			
Mastitis Primarily infectious bacteria *(Streptococci, Staphylococci,* or *E. coli)*	Inflammation of the udder Decreased milk production	Use CMT (California mastitis test) or SCC (somatic cell counts)—checks for white blood cells in milk Avoid injury to udder Use proper milking techniques	Determine specific organism causing the problem, then select most effective antibiotic. For example, cloxacillin, penicillin, erythromycin, and neomycin are effective against several streptococcus and staphylococcus organisms
Milk fever (Parturient Daresis) Metabolic disorder (low blood calcium level associated with a deficiency of vitamin D and phosphorus)	Occurs at onset of lactation Muscular weakness; drowsiness; cow lies down in curled position	Proper nutrition and management of cows during dry period	Intravenous injection of calcium borogluconate
Respiratory diseases (See *Infectious Bovine Rhinotracheitis, "Shipping Fever" parainfluenza,* under **Beef Cattle**)			
Uterine infections Usually result from bacterial contamination at the time of calving	Infections classified according to tissues involved Animal may be systemically or only locally affected **Endometritis:** inflammation of lining of uterus **Metritis:** infection of all tissues of uterus **Pyometra:** pus in the uterus.	Sanitation; cleanliness when giving calving assistance	Early detection; antibiotics, hormone therapy, prostaglandins
Venereal diseases (See *BVD, IBR, leptospirosis, vibriosis and trichomoniasis,* under **Beef Cattle**)			
Swine			
Atrophic rhinitis Bordetella bronchiseptica (bacteria); Pasteurella (secondary invader)	Sneezing (most common); sniffling; snorting; coughing; nose shape (twisted to one side) Nasal infection (inflammation of	Monitor performance; monitor contact with animals from outside the herd; correct environmental deficiencies (sanitation, temperature,	Vaccinate against Bordetella and Pasteurella organisms; medicate sow feed with sulfamethazine or oxytetracycline; improve environment

TABLE 21.2 *(Continued)*

Species/Disease/Cause	Signs	Prevention	Treatment
Swine *(continued)*	membranes in nose) Diagnosis confirmed by observing turbinate bone atrophy (in nose) during postmortem examination (Fig. 21.7)	humidity, ventilation, dust, drafts, excessive ammonia and overcrowding)	
Colibacillosis E. coli (bacteria)	Diarrhea (pale, watery feces); weakness; depression Most serious in pigs under 7 days of age	Good sanitation; good management practices (nutrition, pigs suckle soon after birth, prevent chilling); vaccinate sows to increase protective value of colostrum	Effective treatment is limited; identify strain of *E. coli,* then use specific antibacterial drug
Mycoplasmal infections (Pneumonia and arthritis) Mycoplasma bacteria	Pneumonia: death loss low; dry cough; reduced growth rate; lesions in lungs Arthritis: inflammation in lining of chest and abdominal cavity; lameness; swollen joints; sudden death	Pneumonia: reduce animal contact; good nutrition, warm and dust-free environment and parasite (ascarid and lung worm) control minimizes effects of the disease	Pneumonia: adequate treatment not available; sulfas and antibiotics prevent secondary penumonia infections Arthritis: no satisfactory treatment; can depopulate and restock with disease-free animals
Pseudorabies Virus of herpesvirus group	Baby pigs (less than 3 weeks old): sudden death Pigs (3 weeks to 5 months): fever,	Prevent direct contact with infected swine; humans should wear clean clothes and disin-	Drugs and feed additives are not effective; quarantine; blood test and slaughter those in-

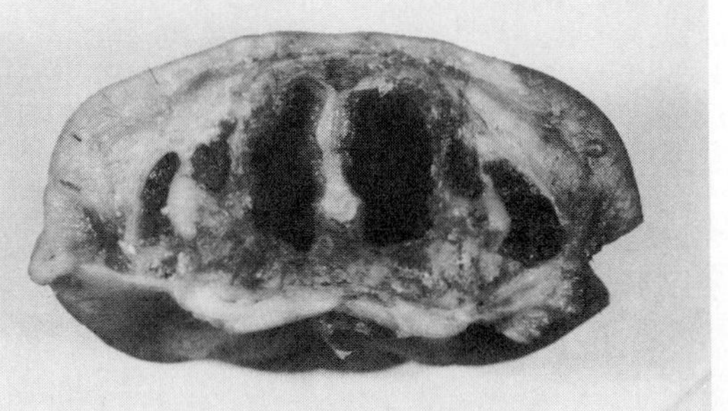

FIGURE 21.7.
Cross sections through the hog's snout showing the effects of atrophic rhinitis. (A) Normal snout with turbinate bones. (B) Diseased snout showing severe atrophy or absence of turbinate bones. Courtesy of Elanco Products Company.

TABLE 21.2 *(Continued)*

Species/Disease/Cause	Signs	Prevention	Treatment
Swine *(continued)*	loss of appetite, labored breathing, trembling and incoordination of hindlegs Mature pigs: less severe fever, loss of appetite; abortion and reproductive failure	fect boots when entering and leaving the premises Recovered swine are immune but should be considered carriers	fected; repopulate
Transmissable gastroenteritis (TGE) Virus of coronavirus group	Vomiting; diarrhea; weakness; dehydration; high death rate in pigs under 3 weeks of age (see Fig. 21.6)	Sanitation is most cost effective Prevent transfer of virus from infected animals through exposure to other pigs, birds, equipment, and people	No drugs are effective Fresh water and a draft-free environment will reduce losses Antibiotics may prevent some secondary infections
Horses			
Colic Noninfectious; a general term indicating abdominal pain	Looking at flank; kicking at abdomen; pawing; getting up and down; rolling; sweating	Parasite control, avoiding moldy or spoiled feeds; avoid overeating or drinking too much water when hot; have sharp points of teeth filed (floated) annually to assure proper chewing of feed	Quiet walking of horse; avoid undue stress; bran mash and aspirin; milk of magnesia; mild, soapy, warm water enema for impaction
Lameness Most common are stone bruises, puncture wounds, sprains, and navicular disease	Departure from normal stance or gait; limping; head bobbing; dropping of the hip; alternate resting on front feet; pointing (extends one front foot in front of the other); stiffness Navicular disease: soft tissue bursitis in the foot	Bruise: avoid running horse on graveled roads or rocky terrain Puncture wounds: avoid areas where nails and other sharp objects may be present Sprains: avoid stress and strains on feet and legs Navicular disease: exact cause not known; avoid continual concussion on hard surfaces; provide proper shoeing, and trimming	Varies with cause of lameness Bruises: soaking foot in bucket of ice water or standing horse in mud; aspirin Puncture wound: tetanus protection; antibiotic; aspirin; soaking foot in hot epsom salts Navicular disease: no known cure; drug therapy and corrective shoes for temporary relief; surgery

TABLE 21.2 *(Continued)*

Species/Disease/Cause	Signs	Prevention	Treatment
Horses *(continued)*			
Respiratory Three viral diseases: viral rhinopneumonitis; viral arteritis; influenza One bacterial disease: strangles	Nasal discharge; coughing; lung congestion; fever Rhinopneumonitis may cause abortion	Isolate infected animals; avoid undue stress; draft-free shelter; parasite control; avoid chilling Rhinopneumonitis, influenza, and strangles vaccines are available	Follow prevention guidelines Strangles: drain abscess
Parasites 150 different internal parasites with strongyles (blood worms), ascarids (roundworms), bots, pinworms, and stomach worms most common External parasites (most common are lice, ticks, and flies)	Unthrifty appearance ("pot-bellied," rough hair coat); weakness; poor growth Lice, ticks, and flies can be visually observed on the horse	Good sanitation practices (clean feeding and watering facilities; regular removal of manure); periodic rest periods for pastures; avoid overcrowding of horses; avoid spreading fresh manure on pastures.	Internal parasites: worm horses twice a year (usually spring and fall); bot eggs can be shaved from the hairs of the legs External parasites: application of insecticides
Poultry			
Avian influenza Virus	Drop in egg production; sneezing; coughing; in the severe systemic form, deep drowsiness and high mortality are common	Vaccine (but has short immunity); select eggs and poults from clean flocks	No effective drug available
Coccidiosis Coccida	Depends on type of coccidiosis—there are nine or more types. Some signs, prevention, and treatment of three more common types are identified		
	Weight loss; unthriftiness; pallor; blood in droppings; lesions in intestinal wall	Use coccidiostat (kills coccida organism)	Sulfa drugs in drinking water
Lymphoid leukosis Virus	Combs and wattles may be shriveled, pale and scaly; enlarged, infected liver Lesions common in liver and kidneys	Sanitation; development of resistant strains through breeding methods	None
Marek's disease Herpesvirus	Can cause high mortality in pullet flocks; paralysis; death might occur without any clinical signs	Vaccination	None

TABLE 21.2 (Continued)

Species/Disease/Cause	Signs	Prevention	Treatment
Poultry *(continued)*			
Mycoplasma infections Mycoplasma organisms	There are several diseases caused by mycoplasma organisms. Most important are chronic respiratory disease (CRD) and infectious synovitis.		
	CRD—difficult breathing; nasal discharge; rattling in windpipe; death loss may be high in turkey poults; swelling of face in turkeys Synovitis—swollen joints, (Fig. 21.8) tendon sheaths and footpads; ruffled feathers	For both CRD and synovitis: use chicks or poults from disease-free parent stock; sanitation (cleaning and disinfecting the premises)	Antibiotic in feed or drinking water
Newcastle Disease	Gasping, coughing, hoarse chirping; paralysis; mortality may be high (Fig. 21.9)	Vaccination	None

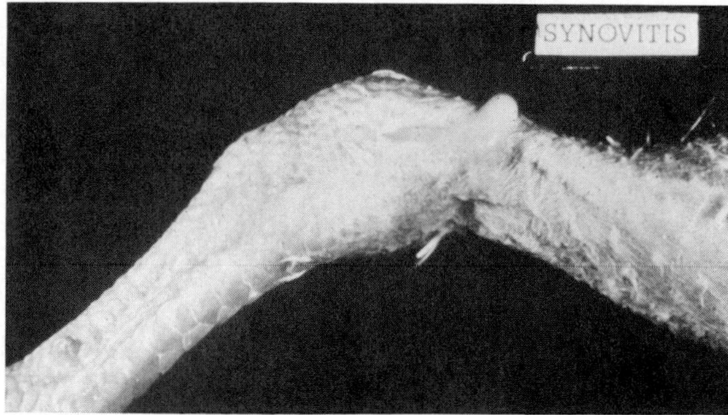

FIGURE 21.8.
Infectious synovitis. A swollen hock and lameness are characteristic. When opened, the hock usually contains a creamy exudate. Courtesy of Salisbury Laboratories.

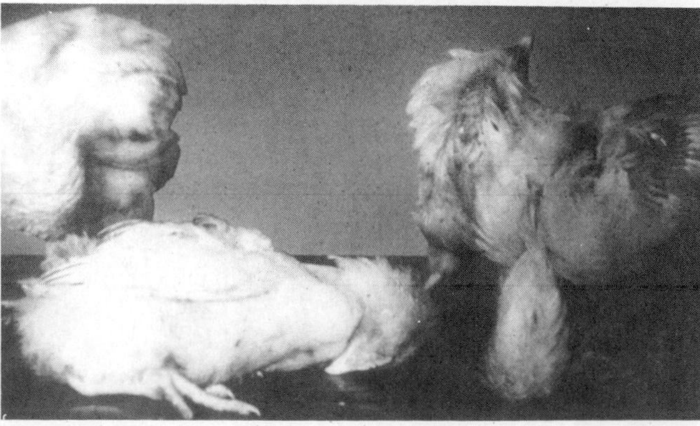

FIGURE 21.9.
Newcastle disease. Birds may have complete or partial paralysis of legs and wings. The photo shows common signs when nerves are affected. Courtesy of Salisbury Laboratories.

TABLE 21.2 *(Continued)*

Species/Disease/Cause	Signs	Prevention	Treatment
Sheep			
C. pseudotuberculosis Bacteria	Enlarged lymph nodes	Sanitation; reduce opportunity for wound infection at docking, castration and, shearing	Antibiotics
Enterotoxemia (overeating disease) Bacteria	Often sudden death occurs without warning; sick lambs might show nervous symptoms; e.g., head drawn back, convulsions	Vaccination (most effective in young lambs under 6 weeks of age nursing heavy-milking ewes, and in weaned lambs on lush pasture or in feedlots)	None; antitoxins can be used but they are expensive and immunity is temporary (2–3 weeks)
Epididymitis Bacteria	Most common in western United States; swelling of epididymis; poor semen quality; low conception rates	Rigid culling and vaccination	Rigid culling
Footrot Bacteria	Lameness; interdigital skin is usually red and swollen	Remove from wet pastures or stubble pastures; vaccines in some cases	Disinfectants such as 5% formalin or 10% copper sulfate; antibiotics
Pneumonia Many types; caused by viruses, stress, bacteria, and parasites	Sudden death; nasal discharge; depression; high temperature	Reduce stress factors	Antibiotics; sulfonamindes
Pregnancy toxemia Undernutrition in late pregnancy; stress associated with poor body condition	Listlessness; loss of appetite; unusual postures; progressive loss of reflexes; hypoglycemia; coma; death	Prevent obesity in early pregnancy; good nutrition during last 6 weeks of pregnancy; reduce environmental stresses	In early stages the administration of some glucogenic materials may reduce mortality; in advanced stages no treatment improves survival

SELECTED REFERENCES

Publications

Battaglia, R. A., and Mayrose, V. B. 1981. *Handbook of Livestock Management Techniques.* New York: Macmillan. (Esp. Chap. 10, Animal health management.)

Gaafar, S. M., Howard, W. E., and Marsh, R. E. (eds.). 1985. *Parasites, Pests and Predators.* New York: Elsevier Science.

Haynes, N. B. 1985. *Keeping Livestock Healthy.* Pownal, VT: Storey.

Keeler, R. F., VanKampen, K. R., and James, L. F. (eds.). 1978. *Effects of Poisonous Plants on Livestock.* New York: Academic Press.
Kirkbride, C. A. 1986. *Control of Livestock Diseases.* Springfield, IL: Charles C Thomas.
Naviaux, J. L. 1985. *Horses in Health and Disease.* Philadelphia: Lea & Febiger.
Radostits, O. M., and Blood, D. C. 1985. *Herd Health.* Philadelphia: W. B. Saunders.
Sainsbury, D. 1983. *Animal Health.* Boulder, CO: Westview Press.

Visual

Distinguishing Normal and Abnormal Cattle (videotape). Agricultural Products and Services, 2001 Killebrew Dr., Suite 333, Bloomington, MN 55420.

CHAPTER 22

Beef Cattle Breeds and Breeding

A **breed** of cattle is defined as a race or variety, the members of which are related by descent and similar in certain distinguishable characteristics. More than 250 breeds of cattle are recognized throughout the world, and several hundred other varieties and types have not been identified with a breed name.

Some of the oldest recognized breeds in the United States were officially recognized as breeds during the middle to late 1800s. Most of these breeds originated from crossing and combining existing strains of cattle. When a breeder or group of breeders decided to establish a breed, distinguishing that breed from other breeds was of paramount importance; thus, major emphasis was placed on readily distinguishable visual characteristics, such as color, color pattern, polled or horned condition, and rather extreme differences in form and shape.

New cattle breeds, such as Brangus, Santa Gertrudis, and Beefmaster, have come into existence in the United States during the past 50–75 years. These breeds have been developed by attempting to combine the desirable characteristics of several existing breeds. Currently there are new breeds of cattle being developed. They are sometimes called **composite breeds** or **synthetic breeds.** In most cases, however, the same visual characteristics as previously mentioned are used to give the new breeds visual identity.

After some of these first breeds were developed, it was not long until the word ***purebred*** was attached to them. Herd books and registry associations were established to assure the "purity" of each breed and to promote and improve each breed. *Purebred* refers to purity of ancestry, established by the pedigree, which shows that only animals recorded in that particular breed have been mated to produce the animal in question. Purebreds, therefore, are cattle within the various breeds that have pedigrees recorded in their respective breed registry associations.

When viewing a herd of purebred Angus or Herefords uniformity is noted, particularly uniformity of color or color pattern. Because of this uniformity of one or two characteristics, the word *purebred* has come to imply genetic uniformity (homozygosity) of all characteristics. Cattle within the same breed are not highly homozygous because high levels of homozygosity occur only after many generations of close inbreeding. This close inbreeding has not occurred in cattle breeds. If breeds were uniform genetically, they could not be improved or changed even if changes were desired.

WHAT IS A BREED?

The genetic basis of cattle breeds and their comparison is not well understood by most livestock producers. Often the statement is made, "There is more variation within a breed than there is between breeds." The validity of this claim needs to be examined carefully. Considerable variation does exist within a breed for most of the economically important traits. This variation is depicted in Figure 22.1, which shows the number of calves, of a particular breed, that fall within certain weight-range categories at 205 days of age. A bell-shaped curve is formed by connecting the high points of each bar. The breed average is represented by the solid line that separates the bell curve into equal halves. Most of the calves are near the breed average; however, at the outer edge of the bell curve are high- and low-weaning weight calves. Note that they are fewer in number at these extremes.

Figure 22.2 allows us to compare, hypothetically, three breeds of cattle in terms of weaning weight. The breed averages are different; however, the variation within each breed is comparable among all three. The statement, "There is more variation within a breed than between breed averages," is more correct than the statement, "There is more variation within a breed than there is between breeds."

Figures 22.1 and 22.2 are hypothetical examples; however, they are based on realistic samples of data obtained from the various breeds of cattle. Figure 22.3 shows how breeds can differ greatly when only one trait is considered. Note how distinctly different the Charolais-sired calves are from the Jersey or Angus and Hereford calves. The statement, "There is more variation within the Charolais breed than between the Simmental and Jersey breeds" is not valid in this case. Rather, "There is more variation within the Charolais breed than between breed averages" is a more correct statement.

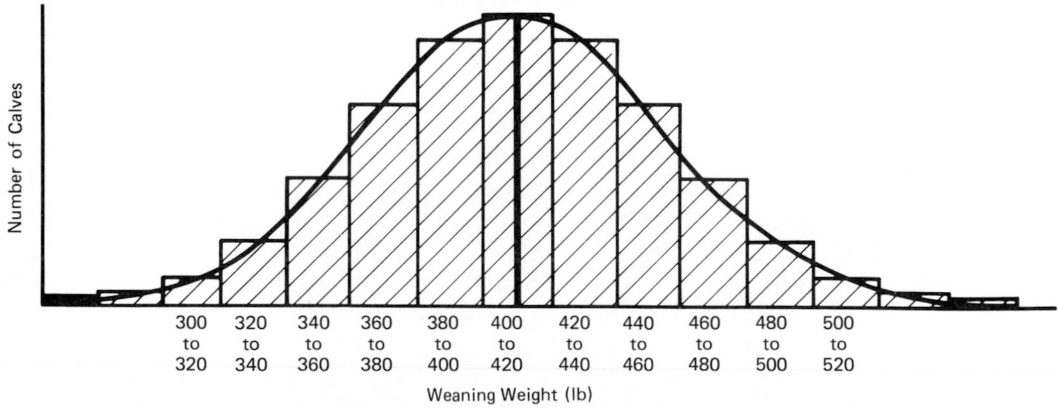

FIGURE 22.1.
Variation or differences in weaning weight in beef cattle. The variation shown by the bell-shaped curve could be representative of a breed or a large herd. The vertical line in the center is the average or the mean, which is 410 lb. Note that the number of calves is greater around the average and is less at the extremely light and extremely heavy weights. Courtesy of Colorado State University.

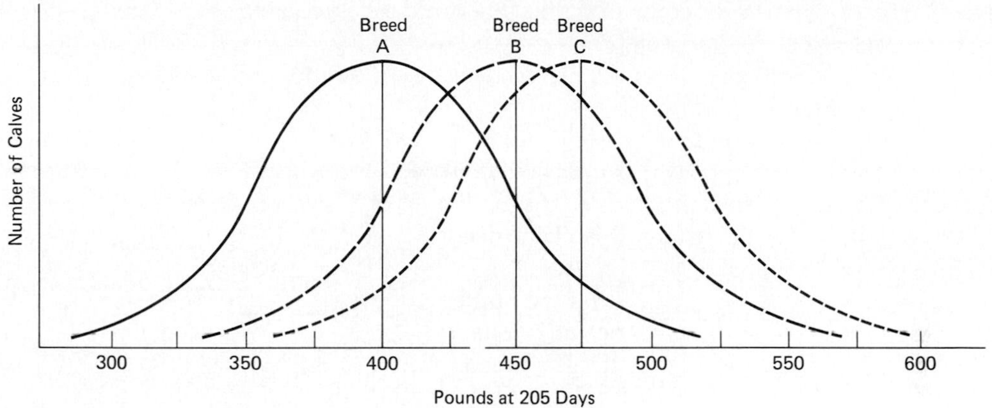

FIGURE 22.2.
Comparison of breed averages and the variation within each breed for weaning weight in beef cattle. The vertical lines are the breed averages. Note that some individual animals in breeds B and C can be lower in weaning weight than the average of breed A. Courtesy of Colorado State University.

The information in Figure 22.3 supports Charolais as being the most superior breed based on breed averages. However, this is only for one trait, and other breeds show superiority to the Charolais breed when other economically important traits are considered.

MAJOR U.S. BEEF BREEDS

Shorthorn, Hereford, and Angus were the major beef breeds in the United States during the early 1900s (Fig. 22.4). During the 1960s and 1970s, the number of cattle breeds remained relatively stable at between 15 and 20. Today, more than 60 breeds of cattle are available to U.S. beef producers. Why the large importation of the different breeds from several different countries? Following are several possible reasons:

1. Feeding more cattle larger amounts of grain, a practice started in the 1940s, resulted in many overfat cattle—cattle that had been previously selected to fatten on forage diets. Therefore,

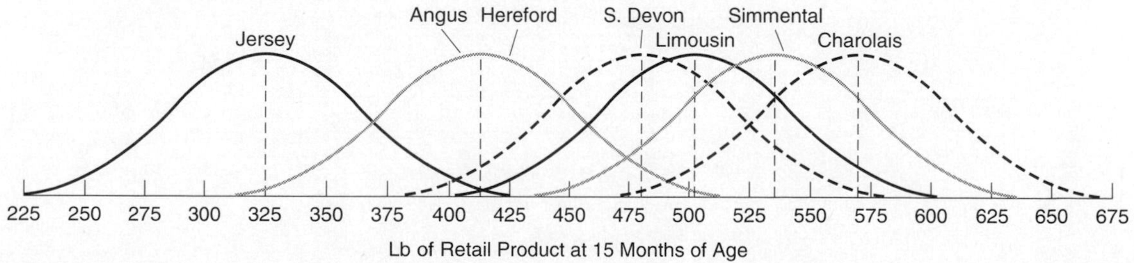

FIGURE 22.3.
Breed differences in retail product when breeds are slaughtered at the same age. Courtesy of U.S. Meat Animal Research Center.

a need was established for grain-fed cattle that could produce a higher percentage of lean to fat at the desired slaughter weight.

2. Economic pressure to produce more weight in a shorter period of time demonstrated a need for cattle with more milk and more growth.
3. An opportunity was available for some promoters to capitalize on merchandising a certain breed as being the ultimate in all production traits. This opportunity was easily accomplished because there was little comparative information on breeds.

Color Plates I through L (following p. 354) identify the most numerous breeds of beef cattle in the United States. Table 22.1 gives some distinguishing characteristics and brief background information for more of these breeds.

The relative importance of the various breeds' contributions to the total beef industry is best estimated by the registration numbers of the breeds (Table 22.2). Although registration numbers are for purebred animals, they reflect the commercial cow-calf producers' demand for the different breeds. Registration numbers show that Angus, Hereford, and Simmental are the most important breeds of the beef cattle industry in the United States.

The numbers of cattle belonging to various breeds in this country have changed over the past years, as shown in Figure 22.4. No doubt some breeds will become more numerous in future years and others will decrease significantly in numbers. These changes will be influenced by economic conditions and how well the breeds meet the needs of the commercial beef industry.

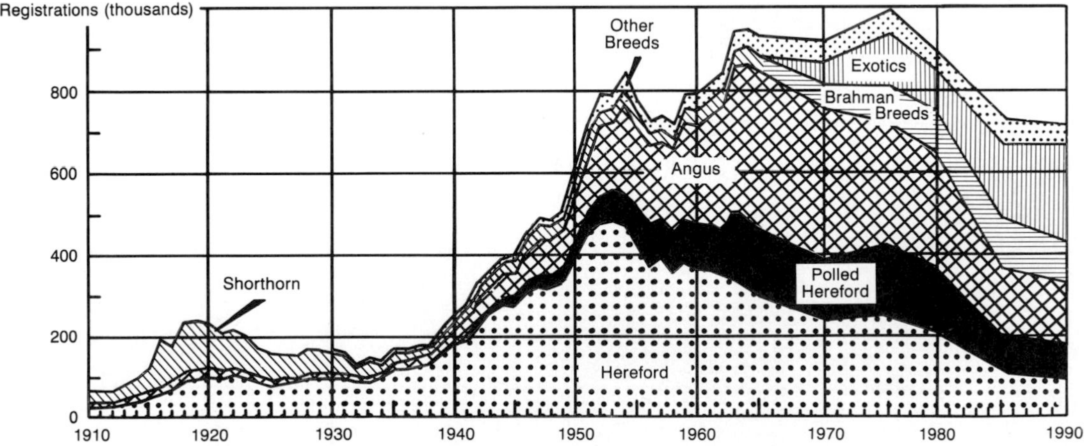

Prior to 1963: Some Polled Herefords were registered only in the Ameircan Hereford Association; others were registered in the American Polled Hereford Association.

Prior to 1965: Brahman breeds were included in other breeds. Very few exotics registered.

After 1985: Shorthorn ends, included in other breeds.
Brahman breeds (Brahman, Brangus, Beefmaster, Santa Gertrudis).
Exotics (Charolais, Limousin, Gelbvieh, Salers, Simmental).

FIGURE 22.4.
Registration numbers of beef cattle in the United States, 1910–1990. Courtesy of the USDA.

TABLE 22.1. Background and Distinguishing Characteristics of Major Beef Breeds in the United States

Breed	Distinguishing Characteristics	Brief Background
Angus	Black color; polled	Originated in Aberdeenshire and Angushire of Scotland Imported into the United States in 1873 to cross with Longhorn
Beefmaster	Has various colors; horned	Developed in the United States from Brahman, Hereford, and Shorthorn breeds Selected for its ability to reproduce, produce milk, and grow under range conditions
Brahman	Various colors, with gray predominant. They are one of the Zebu breeds, which have the hump over the top of the shoulder. Most Zebu breeds also have large, drooping ears and excess skin in the throat and dewlap	Major importations to the United States from India and Brazil Largest introductions in early 1900s These cattle are heat tolerant and well adapted to the harsh conditions of the Gulf Coast region
Brangus	Black and polled predominate, although there are Red Brangus	Breed developed around 1912 in the United States from three-eighths Brahman and five-eighths Angus
Charolais	White color with heavy muscling; horned or polled	One of the oldest breeds in France Brought into the United States soon after World War I, but its most rapid expansion occurred in the 1960s
Chianina	White color with black eyes and nose; extremely tall cattle	An old breed originating in Italy Acknowledged to be the largest breed, with mature bulls weighing more than 3,000 lb First used for breeding in the United States in 1971
Gelbvieh	Golden colored; horned or polled	Originated in Austria and Germany Dual-purpose breed used for draft, milk, and meat
Hereford	Red body with white face; horned	Introduced in the United States in 1817 by Henry Clay. Followed the Longhorn in becoming the traditionally known range cattle
Limousin	Golden color with marked expression of muscling; polled or horned	Introduced into the United States in 1969, primarily from France
Longhorn	Multicolored with characteristically long horns	Came to West Indies with Columbus. Brought to the United States through Mexico by the Spanish explorers Longhorns were the noted trail-drive cattle from Texas into the Plains States
Polled Hereford	Red body with white face; polled	Bred in 1901 in Iowa by Warren Gammon, who accumulated several naturally polled cattle from horned Hereford breeders

TABLE 22.1. *(Continued)*

Breed	Distinguishing Characteristics	Brief Background
Red Angus	Red color; polled	Founded as a performance breed in 1954 by sorting the genetic recessives from Black Angus herds
Salers	Uniform mahogany red with medium to long hair; horned	Raised in the mountainous area of France, where they were selected for milk, meat, and draft
Santa Gertrudis	Red color; horned	First U.S. breed of cattle developed on the King Ranch in Texas Combination of five-eighths Shorthorn and three-eighths Brahman
Shorthorn	Red, white, or roan in color; horned and polled	Introduced into the United States in 1783 under the name *Durham* Most prominent in the United States around 1920
Simmental	Yellow to red and white color pattern; polled and horned	A prominent breed in parts of Switzerland and France First bull arrived in Canada in 1967 Originally selected as a dual-purpose milk and meat breed
Tarentaise	Solid wheat-colored hair ranging from light cherry to dark blond; horned	Mountain cattle derived from an ancient Alpine strain in France Originally a dairy breed in which maternal traits have been emphasized

TABLE 22.2. **Annual Registration Numbers for Major U.S. Beef Breeds**

	Annual Registrations (in thousands)					Year Association Formed
Breed[a]	1989	1985	1980	1975	1970	
Angus	156.7	175.5	257.6	306.5	346.2	1883
Hereford	92.4	95.8	201.5	251.8	237.8	1881
Simmental	77.5	73.0	66.1	75.5	2.8	1969
Polled Hereford	72.5	84.2	151.7	167.4	160.4	1901
Limousin	59.4	44.5	13.8	9.5	2.0	1968
Charolais	42.6	23.2	23.0	45.2	45.3	1957
Beefmaster	35.5	32.1	30.0	12.0	2.8	1961
Brangus	26.6	30.3	24.5	13.4	6.5	1949
Salers	21.5	11.4	—	0.2	—	1974
Gelbvieh	21.5	16.1	—	—	—	1971
Shorthorn	18.0	16.7	19.4	29.2	35.6	1872
Brahman	16.8	29.9	36.4	27.5	18.2	1924
Santa Gertrudis	16.0	28.2	31.2	19.0	—	1951
Red Angus	14.0	12.0	12.5	10.1	—	1954
Longhorn (Texas)	12.4	14.9	6.5	2.4	0.4	1964

[a] Only breeds with more than 10,000 registrations are listed.
Source: Various beef breed associations.

Angus

Beefmaster

Brahman

Brangus

Charolais

Chianina

PLATE I.

PLATES I-L.
Some of the breeds of cattle used for beef production in the United States. Courtesy of the American Angus Association, BBU, American Brahman Breeders Association, International Brangus Breeders Association, Charolais Journal, American Breeders Service, North American Gelbvieh Association, North American Limousin Foundation, American Polled Hereford Association, Dickinson Ranch, Santa Gertrudis Breeders International, Leachman Cattle Co., American Scotch Highland Breeders Association, American Shorthorn Association, and American Simmental Association.

Devon

Galloway

Gelbvieh

Hereford

Limousin

Longhorn

PLATE J.

Maine Anjou

Murray Grey

Pinzgauer

Polled Hereford

Red Angus

Red Poll

PLATE K.

Salers

Santa Gertrudis

Scotch Highland

Shorthorn

Simmental

Tarentaise

PLATE L.

IMPROVING BEEF CATTLE THROUGH BREEDING METHODS

Genetic improvement in beef cattle can occur by selection and by using a particular mating system. Significant improvement by selection results when the selected animals are superior to the herd average and when the heritabilities of the traits are relatively high (40% and higher). It is important that the traits included in a breeding program be of economic importance and that they are measured objectively.

TRAITS AND THEIR MEASUREMENT

Most economically important traits of beef cattle are classified as follows: (1) reproductive performance, (2) weaning weight, (3) postweaning growth, (4) feed efficiency, (5) carcass merit, (6) longevity (functional traits), (7) conformation, and (8) freedom from genetic defects.

Reproductive Performance

Reproductive performance has the highest economic importance of all the traits. Most cow–calf producers have a goal for percent calf crop weaned (number of calves weaned compared to the number of cows in the breeding herd) of 85% or higher. Beef producers also desire each cow to calve every 365 days or less and to have a calving season for the entire herd of less than 90 days. All of these are good objective measures of reproductive performance.

The heritability of fertility in beef cattle is quite low (less than 20%), so little genetic progress can be made through selection for that specific trait. Heritabilities for birth weight and scrotal circumference are higher; therefore, selection for these traits will improve the percent calf crop weaned. The most effective way to improve certain reproductive traits (such as rebreeding after calving) is to improve the environment, through adequate nutrition and good herd health practices, for example. Selecting bulls based on a reproductive soundness examination, which includes semen testing, will also improve reproductive performance in the herd.

Reproductive performance can be improved through breeding methods by crossbreeding to obtain heterosis for percent calf crop weaned, using bulls with relatively light birth weights (heritability of birth weight is 40%), which decreases calving difficulty, as well as by selecting bulls that have a relatively large scrotal circumference. Scrotal circumference has a high heritability (40%); bulls with a larger scrotal size (over 30 cm for yearling bulls) produce a larger volume of semen and have half-sister heifers that reach puberty at earlier ages than heifers related to bulls with a smaller scrotal size.

Weaning Weight

Weaning weight, as measured objectively by weighing on scales, reflects the milking and mothering ability of the cow and the preweaning growth rate of the calf. Weaning weight is commonly expressed as the adjusted 205-day weight, where the weaning weight is adjusted for the age of the calf and age of the dam. This adjustment puts all weaning-weight records on a comparable basis since older calves will weigh more than younger calves and mature cows (5–9 years of age) will milk heavier than younger cows (2–4 years of age) and older cows (10 years and older).

Weaning weights of calves are usually compared by dividing the calf's adjusted weight by the average weight of the other calves in the herd. This is expressed as a ratio. For example, a calf with a weaning weight of 440 lb, where the herd average is 400 lb, has a ratio of 110. This calf's weaning weight ratio is 10% above the herd average. Ratios can be used primarily for selecting cattle within the same herd in which they have had similar environmental opportunity. Comparing ratios between herds is misleading from a genetic standpoint because most differences between herds are caused by differences in the environment. Weaning weight will respond to selection because it has a heritability of 30%.

Postweaning Growth

Postweaning growth measures the growth from weaning to a weight that approaches slaughter weight. Postweaning growth might take place on a pasture or in a feedlot. Usually animals with relatively high postweaning gains make efficient gains at a relatively low cost to the producer.

Postweaning gain in cattle is usually measured in pounds gained per day after a calf has been on a feed test for 100–160 days. Weaning weight and postweaning gain are usually combined into a single trait; namely, adjusted 365-day weight (or yearling weight). It is computed as follows:

$$\text{Adjusted 365-day weight} = (160 \times \text{average daily gain}) + \text{adjusted 205-day weight}$$

Average daily gain for 140 days and adjusted 365-day weight both have high heritabilities (40%); therefore, genetic improvement can be quite rapid when selection is practiced on postweaning growth or yearling weight.

Feed Efficiency

Feed efficiency is measured by the pounds of feed required per pound of liveweight gain. Specific records for feed efficiency can be obtained only be feeding each animal individually and keeping records on the amount of feed consumed. With the possible exception of some bull-testing programs, determining feed efficiency on an individual animal basis is seldom economically feasible.

Interpretation of feed-efficiency records can be somewhat difficult, depending on the endpoint to which the animals are fed. Feeding endpoint can be a certain number of days on feed (e.g., 140 days) to a specified slaughter weight (e.g., 1,200 lb), or to a carcass compositional endpoint (e.g., low Choice quality grade). Most differences in feed efficiency, shown by individual animals, are related to the pounds of body weight maintained through feeding periods and the daily rate of gain or feed intake of each animal. Cattle fed from a similar initial feedlot weight (e.g., 600 lb) to a similar slaughter weight (e.g., 1,100 lb) will demonstrate a high relationship between rate of gain and efficiency of gain. In this situation, cattle that gain faster will require fewer pounds of feed per pound of grain. Thus, a breeder can select for rate of gain and thereby make genetic improvement in feed efficiency. However, when cattle are fed to the same compositional endpoint (approximately the same carcass fat), there are small differences in the amount of feed required per pound of gain. This is true for different sizes and shapes of cattle, and even for various breeds that vary greatly in skeletal size and weight.

The heritability of feed efficiency, at similar beginning and final weights, is high (45%), so selection for more efficient cattle can be effective. It seems logical to use the genetic correlation between gain and efficiency where possible.

Carcass Merit

Carcass merit is presently measured by quality grades and yield grades, which are discussed in detail in Chapter 8. Many cattle-breeding programs have goals to produce cattle that will grade Choice and have yield grade 2 carcasses. Objective measurements using backfat thickness probes on the live animal and hip height measurement can assist in predicting the yield grade at certain slaughter weights. Visual appraisal, which is more subjective, can be used to predict amount of fat or predisposition to fat and skeletal size. These visual estimates can be relatively accurate in identifying actual yield grades if cattle differ by as much as one yield grade.

Because quality grade cannot be evaluated accurately in the live animal, it is necessary to evaluate the carcass. Steer and heifer progeny of different bulls are slaughtered to identify the genetic superiority or inferiority of bulls for both quality grade and yield grade. The heritabilities of most beef carcass traits are high (over 40%), so selection can result in marked genetic improvement for these traits.

Longevity

Longevity measures the length of productive life. It is an important trait, particularly for cows, when replacement heifer costs are high or when a producer reaches an optimum level of herd performance and desires to stabilize it. Bulls are usually kept in a herd for 3–5 years, or inbreeding might occur. Some highly productive cows remain in the herd at age 15 years or older, whereas other highly productive cows have been culled before reaching 8 or 9 years of age. These cows may have been culled because of such problems as skeletal unsoundness, poor udders, eye problems (i.e., cancer eye), and lost or worn teeth. Little selection opportunity for longevity exists because few cows remain highly productive past the age of 10 years. Most cows that leave the herd early have poor reproduction performance.

Some producers need to improve their average herd performance as rapidly as possible rather than improve longevity. In this situation, a relatively rapid turnover of cows is needed. Some selection for longevity occurs because producers have the opportunity to keep more replacement heifers born to cows that are highly productive in the herd for a longer period of time than heifers born to cows that stay in the herd for a short time. Some beef producers attempt to identify bulls that have highly productive, relatively old dams. Certain conformation traits, such as skeletal soundness and udder soundness, may be evaluated to extend the longevity of production.

Conformation

Conformation is the form, shape and visual appearance of an animal. How much emphasis to put on conformation in a beef cattle selection program has been, and continues to be, controversial. Some producers believe that putting a productive animal into an attractive package contributes to additional economic returns. It is more logical, however, to place more selection emphasis on traits that will produce additional numbers and pounds of lean growth for a given number of cows. Placing some emphasis on conformation traits such as skeletal, udder, eye, and teeth soundness is justified. Conformation differences such as fat accumulation or predisposition to fat can be used effectively to make meaningful genetic improvement in carcass composition.

Most conformation traits are medium to high (30%–60%) in heritability, so selection for these traits will result in genetic improvement.

Genetic Defects

Genetic defects, other than those previously identified under longevity and conformation, need to be considered in breeding productive beef cattle. Cattle have numerous known hereditary defects; most of them, however, occur infrequently and are of minor concern. Some defects increase in their frequency, and selection needs to be directed against them. Most of these defects are determined by a single pair of genes that are usually recessive. When one of these hereditary defects occurs, it is a logical practice to cull both the cow and the bull.

Some common occurring genetic defects in cattle today are double muscling, syndactyly (mule foot), arthrogryposis (palate-pastern syndrome), osteopetrosis (marble bone disease), hydrocephalus, and dwarfism. **Double muscling** is evidence by an enlargement of the muscles with large grooves between the muscle systems of the hind leg. Double-muscled cattle usually grow slowly and their fat deposition in and on the carcass is much less than that of the normal beef animal. **Syndactyly** is a condition in which one or more of the hooves are solid in structure rather than cloven. Mortality rate is high in calves with syndactyly. **Arthrogryposis** is a defect in which the pastern tendons are contracted, and the upper part of the mouth has not properly fused together. **Osteopetrosis** is characterized by the marrow cavity of the long bones being filled with bone tissue. All calves having osteopetrosis have short lower jaws, protruding tongue, and impacted molar teeth. A bulging forehead where fluid has accumulated in the brain area is typical of the defect of **hydrocephalus.** Calves with arthrogryposis, hydrocephalus, or osteopetrosis usually die shortly after birth. The most common type of **dwarfism** is snorter dwarfism, in which the skeleton is quite small and the forehead has a slight bulge. Some snorter dwarfs exhibit a heavy, labored breathing sound. This defect was most common in the 1950s, and it has decreased significantly since that time.

BULL SELECTION

Bull selection must receive the greatest emphasis if optimum genetic improvement of a herd is to be achieved. Bull selection accounts for 80%–90% of the herd improvement over a period of several years. This does not diminish the importance of good beef females because genetically superior bulls have superior dams. However, most of the genetic superiority or inferiority of the cows will depend on the bulls previously used in the herd. Also the accuracy of records is much higher in bulls than in cows and heifers because bulls produce more offspring and are used in more herds (especially with AI).

All commercial and purebred producers should identify breeders who have honest, comparative records on their cattle. Most performance-minded seedstock producers record the birthweights, weaning weights, and yearling weights of their bulls. Some breeders also obtain feedlot and carcass data on their own bulls, or they use bulls from sires for whom these test data are known.

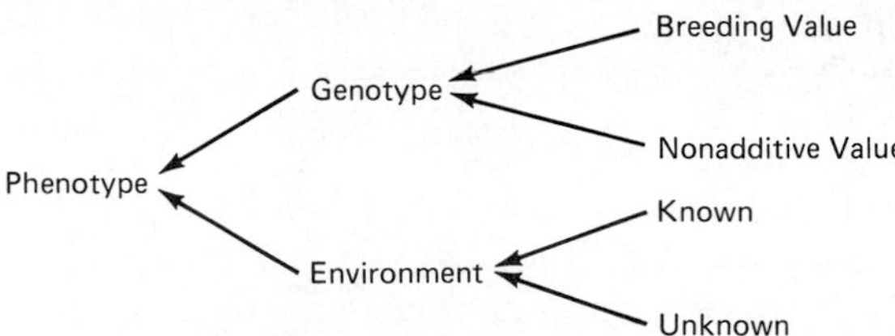

FIGURE 22.5.
Breeding value and its relationship to genotype and phenotype. Courtesy of Gibb, Wallace, and Wagner, 1985.

Purebred breeders should provide accurate performance data on their bulls, and commercial producers should request the information. Excellent performance records can be obtained and made available on the farm or ranch. The trait ratios are useful and comparative if the bulls have been fed and managed in similar environments.

Breeding Values

Phenotype is the appearance or performance of an animal determined by the genotype (genetic makeup) and the environment in which it was raised. Genotype is determined by two factors: (1) breeding value (what genes are present), and (2) nonadditive (how genes are combined). Environmental factors influence the phenotype through known and unknown effects. Age of dam, resulting in different levels of milk production, is a known environmental effect adjusted for in an adjusted 205-day weight (phenotype). Unknown effects are things like injury or health problems for which it is difficult to adjust the phenotypic record. Figure 22.5 shows how breeding value relates to the phenotype of an animal.

An example depicting breeding values is shown in Figure 22.6. In the "brick wall concept," each brick represents a gene. Some genes have positive, additive effects, whereas other genes have negative effects. The different sized bricks represent the magnitude of the gene's effect. In this example (Fig. 22.6), the 10 pairs of genes (20 bricks) are used to show a superior breeding value and a negative breeding value. The superior breeding value (higher brick wall) is where the sum of the additive gene effects (bricks) is above herd average.

Breed associations have developed computer programs that utilize performance records on the individual calf and its relatives. This information is used to calculate breeding values. Breeding values are most frequently reported on birth weight, maternal weaning weight, weaning weight, and yearling weight by using **expected progeny difference (EPD).**

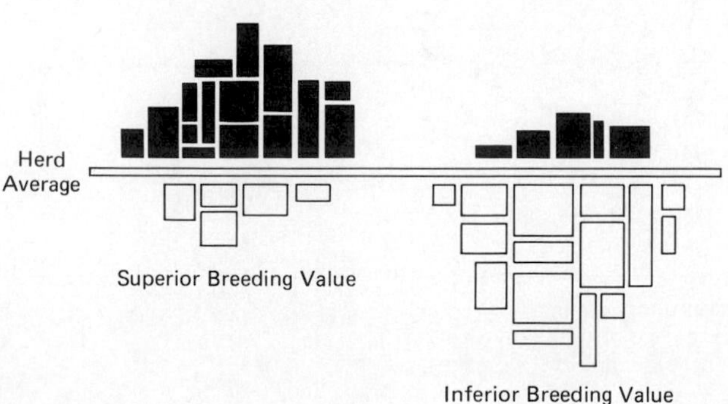

FIGURE 22.6.
Breeding value as depicted by the "brick wall concept." Courtesy of Gibb, Wallace, and Wagner, 1985.

Sire Summaries

The development of sire summaries has led to more effective sire selection. Most breed associations publish a sire summary that is updated annually or biannually.

Expected progeny difference (EPD) and **accuracy (ACC)** are the important terms used in understanding sire summaries. An EPD combines into one figure a measurement of genetic potential based on the individual's performance and the performance of related animals such as the sire, dam, and other relatives. EPD is expressed as a plus or minus value, reflecting the genetic-transmitting ability of a sire. The most common EPDs reported for bulls, heifers, and cows are birthweight EPD, milk EPD, weaning growth EPD, maternal EPD (includes milk and preweaning growth), and yearling weight EPD. Some additional traits are included as well (Table 22.3).

Accuracy (ACC) is a measure of expected change in the EPD as additional progeny data become available. EPDs with ACC of 0.90 and higher would be expected to change very little, whereas EPDs with ACC below 0.70 might change dramatically with additional progeny data.

Table 22.4 shows sire summary data for several Angus bulls.

If bull B and bull C were used in the same herd (each on an equal group of cows) the expected performance on their calves would be:

Bull B's calves to be 16 lb heavier at birth
Bull B's calves to weight 59 lb more at weaning
Bull B's calves to weigh 78 lb more as yearlings
Bull B's daughters to wean 7 lb less calf

Bull A and bull D have an optimum combination calving case (birth weight) and growth traits (weaning weight and yearling weight). Bull E is a promising young sire with an excellent

TABLE 22.3 Sire Summary Data (EPDS or ratios)

Trait	Breed					
	Angus (Red and Black)	Charolais	Gelbvieh	Hereford	Polled Hereford	Simmental
Calving ease						
First calf[b]	0	0[a]	+[a]	0	+	+
Maternal[c]	0	0	+	0	+	+
Birth weight	+	+	+	+	+	+
Weaning weight	+	+	+	+	+	+
Yearling weight	+	+	+	+	+	+
Milk	+	+	+	+	+	+
Maternal	+	+	+	+	+	+
Milk + weaning						
Gestation length	0	0	+	0	0	0
Yearling height	0	0	0	+	0	0
Scrotal circumference	0	0	0	+	+	0

[a]0 = absent from sire summary; + = appears in sire summary.
[b] Expressed as a ratio, not as an EPD. Measures calving ease of bull's own calves.
[c] Expressed as a ratio, not as an EPD. Measures calving ease of a bull's daughters.
Source: Breed Sire Summaries.

TABLE 22.4. Selected Data from an Angus Sire Evaluation Report

	Birth Weight		Weaning Weight Direct		Weaning Weight Maternal				Yearling Weight	
					Milk[a]					
Sire	EPD	ACC	EPD	ACC	EPD	ACC	DTS[b]	Combination Index[c]	EPD	ACC
A	−1	0.95	+20	0.95	+1	0.93	331	+11	+39	0.94
B	+9	0.95	+47	0.95	−17	0.89	88	6	+74	0.90
C	−7	0.83	−12	0.85	−10	0.79	29	−16	−4	0.85
D	+1	0.95	+22	0.95	+3	0.92	230	+14	+54	0.94
E	1	0.73	+15	0.70	+12	0.42	0	+20	+45	0.66

[a] Milk EPD is measured by comparing calf weaning weights from daughters of bulls.
[b] DTS is daughters.
[c] Calculated by taking $\frac{1}{2}$ of weaning weight (direct) + Milk EPD.

combination of EPDs. However, the ACC is relatively low and could significantly change with more progeny and as daughters start producing.

Bull selection becomes more complex in that desired genetic improvement is for a combination of several traits. "Stacking pedigrees" for only one trait may result in some problems in other traits. A good example is selecting for yearling weight alone, which results in increased birth weight because the two traits are genetically correlated. Birth weight is associated with calving difficulty, so increased birth weight might be a problem. Large increases in birth EPD can occur and calving difficulty can be serious.

The most difficult challenge in bull selection is selecting bulls that will improve maternal traits. Frequently too much emphasis is placed on yearling growth, frame size, and large mature size. These traits can be antagonistic to maternal traits such as birthweight, early puberty, and maintaining a cow size consistent with an economical feed supply. Figure 22.7 shows an example of stacking a pedigree for maternal traits for yearling bull selection where the bull is used naturally on heifers. If an older bull can be used AI, then emphasis would be on higher accuracies than available on young bulls.

Table 22.5 identifies bull-selection criteria that would apply to a large number of commercial producers. First the breeding program goals and the maternal traits are identified. Second, the bull-selection criteria are identified, giving emphasis to the maternal traits. These traits would receive emphasis if a commercial producer was using only one breed or a rotational crossbreeding program or in producing the cows used in a terminal crossbreeding program. Finally, Table

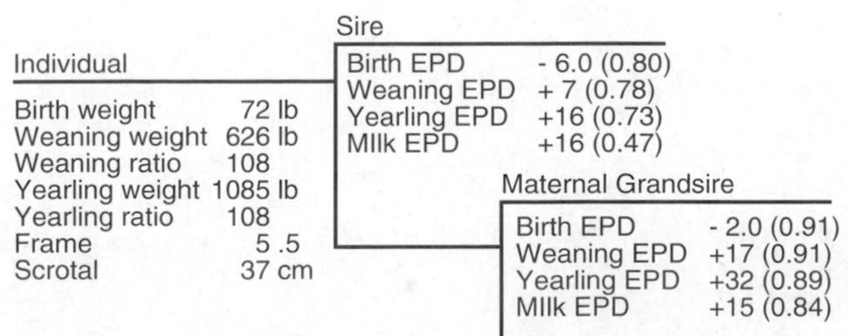

FIGURE 22.7.
Yearling bull selection emphasizing maternal traits. Bull is used naturally on replacement heifers. Courtesy of Taylor Hybrids.

TABLE 22.5. Bull-Section Criteria for Commercial Beef Producers

Goals and Maternal Traits	Bull-Selection Criteria for Maternal Traits	Selection Criteria for Terminal Cross Bulls
Breeding Program Goals 1. Select for an **optimum** combination of **maternal traits** to **maximize profitability** (Avoiding genetic antagonisms and environmental conflicts that come with maximum production or single-trait selection) 2. Provide genetic input so **cows** can be **matched with their environment**—cows that wean more lifetime pounds of calf without overtaxing the forage, labor, or financial resources 3. Stack pedigrees for maternal traits **Maternal Traits** **Mature weight:** Medium-sized cows (1,000–1,250-lb under average feed supply) **Milk production:** Moderate (wean 500–550-lb calves under average feed) **Body condition** ("fleshing ability"): "5" condition score at calving without high-cost feeding **Early puberty/high conception:** Calve by 24 months of age **Calving ease:** Moderate birthweights (65–75-lb hfrs; 75–90-lb cows). Calf shape (head, shoulders, hips), which relates to unassisted births **Early growth and composition:** Rapid gains—relatively heavy weaning and yearling weights within medium (4–6) frame size. Yield grade 2 (steers slaughtered at 1,150 lb) **Functional traits (longevity):** Udders (shape, teats, pigment); eye pigment; disposition; structural soundness	**Yearling frame size:** 4.0–6.0 (smaller frame size will adapt better to harsher environments—e.g., less feed, more severe weather, less care) **Mature weight:** Under 2,000 lb in average condition (preference for future). Now we likely will have to consider bulls under 2,500 lb **Milk EPD:** 0 to +15 lb (prefer +10) **Maternal EPD:** +20 to +40 (prefer +25) **Body condition:** Backfat of 0.20–0.35 in. at yearling weights of 1,100–1,250 lb Monitor reproduction of daughters **Scrotal circumference:** 34–40 cm at 365 days of age. Passed breeding soundness examination **Birth weight EPD:** Preferably under +1.0 lb. Evaluate calving ease of daughters **Weaning weight EPD:** Approximately +20 lb **Yearly weight EPD:** Approximately +40 lb **Accuracies:** All EPDs of 0.90 and higher (older, progeny-tested sires) **Functional traits:** Visual evaluation of bull and his daughters **Visual:** Functional traits Sufficiently attractive to sire calves that would not be economically discriminated against in the marketplace Preference for "adequate middle" as medium-frame-size cattle need middle for feed capacity **Young bulls** without EPDs or with accuracies below 0.90—evaluate trait ratios and pedigree EPDs to predict mature bulls with above average EPDs and accuracies. Select sons of bulls that meet EPDs listed above	**Yearling frame size:** 6.0–8.0 (should be evaluated with frame size of cows so slaughter progeny will average 5.0 and 6.0) **Mature weight:** No upper limit as long as birth weight and frame size are kept in desired range **Milk EPD:** Not considered **Maternal EPD:** Not considered **Body condition:** Evaluate with body condition of cows so that progeny will be between 0.25 and 0.45 in. at 1,100–1,300 lb slaughter weights **Scrotal circumference:** 32–38 cm at 365 days of age. Passed breeding soundness exam **Birth weight EPD:** Preferably no higher than +5.0; want calves birthweights in 85–95-lb range with few, if any, over 100 lb **Weaning weight EPD:** +40 lb or higher **Yearling weight EPD:** +60 lb or higher **Accuracies:** All EPDs of 0.90 and higher (older, progeny-tested sires) **Visual:** Functional traits: Disposition and structural soundness Sufficiently attractive to sire calves that would not be economically discriminated against in the marketplace. **Young bulls without EPDs** or with accuracies below 0.90—evaluate trait ratios and pedigree EPDs to predict mature bulls with above average EPDs and accuracies. Select sons of bulls that meet EPDs listed above

22.5 identifies the traits emphasized in selecting terminal cross bulls. In selecting terminal cross sires, little emphasis is placed on maternal traits as no replacement heifers from this cross are kept in the herd.

SELECTING REPLACEMENT HEIFERS

Heifers, as replacement breeding females, can be selected for several traits at different stages of their reproductive life. The objective is to identify heifers that will conceive early in the breeding season, calve easily, give a flow of milk consistent with the feed supply, wean a heavy calf, and make a desirable genetic contribution to the calf's postweaning growth and carcass merit.

Beef producers have found it challenging to determine which of the young heifers will make the most productive cows. Table 22.6 shows the selection process that producers use to select the most productive replacement heifers. This selection process assumes that more heifers will

TABLE 22.6. Replacement Heifer Selection Guidelines at the Different Productive Stages

Stage of Heifer's Productive Life	Emphasis on Productive Trait	
	Primary	Secondary
Weaning (7–10 months of age)	Cull only the heifers whose actual weight is too light to prevent them from showing estrus by 15 months of age. Also consider the economics of the weight gains needed to have puberty expressed	Weaning weight ratio Weaning EPD Milk EPD Maternal EPD Predisposition to fatness Adequate skeletal frame Skeletal soundness
Yearling (12–15 months of age)	Cull heifers that have not reached the desired target breeding weight (e.g., minimum of 650–750 lb for small- to medium-sized breeds or cross, minimum of 750–850 lb for large-sized breeds and crosses)	Milk, weaning, and maternal EPDs Yearling weight ratio Yearling EPD Predisposition to fatness Adequate skeletal frame Skeletal soundness
After breeding (19–21 months of age)	Cull heifers that are not pregnant and those that will calve in the latter one-third of the calving season	Milk, weaning, and maternal EPDs Yearling weight ratio Yearling EPD Predisposition to fatness Adequate skeletal frame Skeletal soundness
After weaning First calf (31–34 months of age)	Cull to the number of first-calf heifers actually needed in the cow herd based on the weaning weight performance of the first calf. Preferably all the calves from these heifers have been sired by the same bull. Heifers should also be pregnant.	

be selected at each stage of production than the actual numbers of cows to be replaced in the herd. The number of replacement heifers that producers keep is based primarily on how many they can afford to raise. More heifers than the number needed should be kept through pregnancy-check time. Heifers are selected on the basis that they become pregnant early in life primarily for economic reasons rather than expected genetic improvement from selection.

COW SELECTION

Cows should be culled from the herd based on the productivity of their calves and additional evidence that they can be productive the following year, such as soundness of udders, eyes, skeleton, and teeth. Cow productivity is measured by pregnancy test, weaning and yearling weights (ratios) of their calves, and the EPD of the cow. Table 22.7 shows the weaning and yearling values of the high- and low-producing cows in a herd. Cow 1 is a high-producing cow, whereas cow 2 is the low-producing cow. Cow 2 should be culled and replaced with a heifer of higher breeding potential.

CROSSBREEDING PROGRAMS FOR COMMERCIAL PRODUCERS

Most commercial beef producers use crossbreeding programs to take advantage of heterosis in addition to the genetic improvement from selection. A crossbreeding system should be determined according to which breeds are available and then adapted to the commercial producers' feed supply, market demands, and other environmental conditions. A good example of adaptability is the Brahman breed, which is more heat and insect resistant than most other breeds. Because of this higher resistance, the level of productivity (in the southern and Gulf regions of the United States) is much higher for the Brahman and Brahman crosses.

Most commercial producers travel 150 or fewer miles to purchase bulls used in natural mating. Therefore, a producer should assess the breeders with excellent breeding programs in a 150-mile radius, as well as available breeds. This assessment, in most cases, should be determined before planning which breeds to use and in which combination to use them.

Breeds should be chosen for a crossbreeding system based on how well the breeds complement each other. Table 22.8 gives some comparative rankings of the major beef breeds for productive characteristics. Although the information in Table 22.8 is useful, it should not be considered the final answer for decisions on breeds to use. First, a producer needs to recognize that this information reflects breed averages; therefore, there are individual animals and herds of the same breed that are much higher or lower than the ranking given (Figs. 22.1–22.3). Producers need to use some of the previously described methods to identify superior animals

TABLE 22.7. Performance Data on High- and Low-producing Cows in the Same Herd

Cow Number	Number of Calves	Weaning Weight (lb)	Weaning Weight Ratio	Yearling Weight Ratio
1	9	583	112	108
2	9[a]	464	89	94

[a] One calf died before weaning (not computed in averages).

TABLE 22.8. Breed Crosses Grouped in Biological Types on Basis of Four Major Criteria

Breed Group[a]	Growth Rate and Mature Size	Lean-to-Fat Ratio	Age at Puberty	Milk Production
Jersey	X	X	X	XXXXX
Longhorn	X	XX	XXX	XX
Hereford-Angus	XX	XX	XXX	XX
Red Poll	XX	XX	XX	XXX
Devon	XX	XX	XXX	XX
Shorthorn	XX	XX	XXX	XX
South Devon	XXX	XXX	XX	XXX
Tarentaise	XXX	XXX	XX	XXX
Pinzgauer	XXX	XXX	XX	XXX
Salers	XXX	XXX	XXX	XXX
Brangus	XXX	XX	XXXX	XX
Santa Gertrudis	XXX	XX	XXXX	XX
Beefmaster	XXX	XX	XXX	XX
Sahiwal	XX	XXX	XXXXX	XXX
Brahman	XXXXX	XXX	XXXXX	XXX
Brown Swiss	XXXX	XXXX	XX	XXXX
Gelbvieh	XXXX	XXXX	XX	XXXX
Holstein	XXXX	XXXX	XX	XXXXXX
Simmental	XXXXX	XXXX	XXX	XXXX
Maine Anjou	XXXXX	XXXX	XXX	XXX
Limousin	XXX	XXXXX	XXXX	X
Charolais	XXXXX	XXXXX	XXXX	X
Chianina	XXXXX	XXXXX	XXXX	X

Note: Increasing numbers of X's indicate relatively higher levels of performance, except for age at puberty, where smaller numbers of X's reflect earlier age at puberty.
[a] Breed group based on these breeds of sires mated to Hereford and Angus cows.
Source: Adapted from *MARC Res. Prog. Rpt.* no. 3 (1988) and no. 12 (1990).

within each breed. Second, it should be recognized that these average breed rankings can change with time, depending on the improvement programs used by the leading breeders within the same breed. Obviously, those traits that have high heritabilities would be expected to change most rapidly, assuming the same selection pressure for each trait. A careful analysis of the information in Table 22.8 shows that no one breed is superior for all important productive characteristics. This gives an advantage to commercial producers using a crossbreeding program if they select breeds whose superior traits complement each other. An excellent example of breed complementation is shown by the Angus and Charolais breeds, which complement each other for both quality grade and yield grade.

Most of the heterosis achieved in cattle as a result of crossbreeding is expressed by weaning time. The cumulative effect of heterosis on pounds of calf weaned per cow exposed is shown in Fig. 22.8, in which maximum heterosis is obtained when crossbred calves are obtained from crossbred cows. The traits that express an approximate heterosis of a 20% increase in pounds of

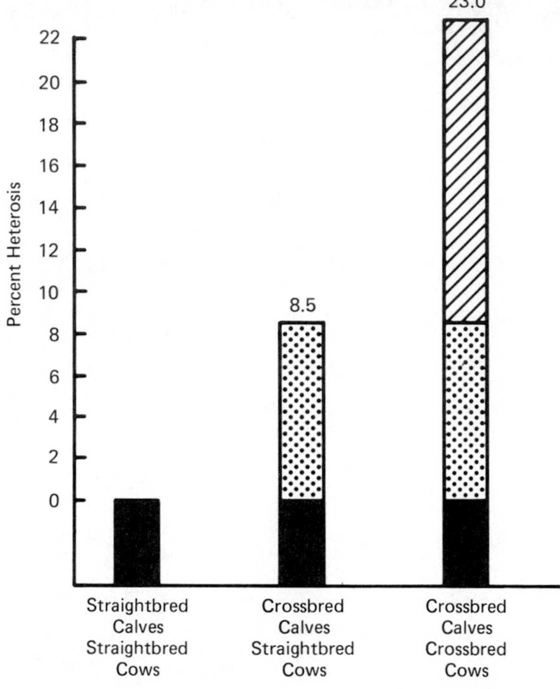

FIGURE 22.8.
Heterosis, resulting from crossbreeding, for pounds of calf weaned per cow exposed to breeding. Courtesy of the USDA.

calf weaned per cow exposed to breeding are early puberty of crossbred heifers, high conception rates in the crossbred female, high survival rate of calves, increased milk production of crossbred cows, and a higher preweaning growth rate of crossbred calves.

Consistent high levels of heterosis can be maintained generation after generation if crossbreeding systems such as those shown in Figures 22.9–22.11 are used. The crossbreeding system shown in Figure 22.11 combines a two-breed rotation with a terminal cross. In this system, the two-breed rotation is used primarily to produce replacement females for the entire cow herd. In most cow herds, approximately 50% of the cows are bred to sires to produce replacement females with the remaining 50% being bred to terminal cross sires. All terminal cross calves are sold. This crossbreeding system maintains heterosis as high as the three-breed rotation system.

In the rotational crossing, breeds with maternal trait superiority (high conception, calving ease, and milking ability) would be selected. The terminal cross sire could come from a larger breed where growth rate and carcass cutability are emphasized. A primary advantage of the rotational-terminal cross system is that smaller- or medium-sized breeds can be used in rotational crossing and a larger breed could be used in terminal crossing. Terminal crossbreeding systems will maximize heterosis at approximately 25%–30%. Some of the systems that will fit a one-breeding pasture program include (1) using a composite (synthetic) breed, (2) rotating two or three breeds of bulls (each breed every 3–5 years, and (3) putting multiple-sire breeds of bulls with crossbred cows. Each of these crossbreeding systems will maintain heterosis at approximately 15%. These systems may be more cost-effective and profitable than some of the more complex crossbreeding system discussed earlier.

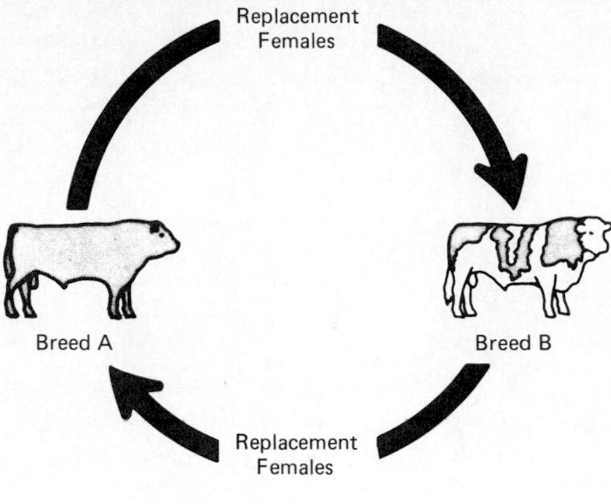

FIGURE 22.9.
Two-breed rotation cross. Females sired by breed A are mated to breed B bulls, and heifers sired by breed B are mated to breed A bulls. This will increase the pounds of calf weaned per cow bred by approximately 15%. Courtesy of Colorado State University.

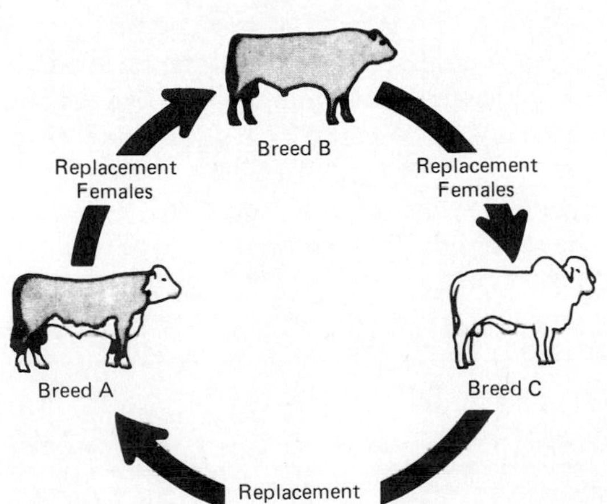

FIGURE 22.10.
Three-breed rotation cross. Females sired by a specific breed are bred to the breed of the next bull in rotation. This will increase the pounds of calf weaned per cow by approximately 20%. Courtesy of Colorado State University.

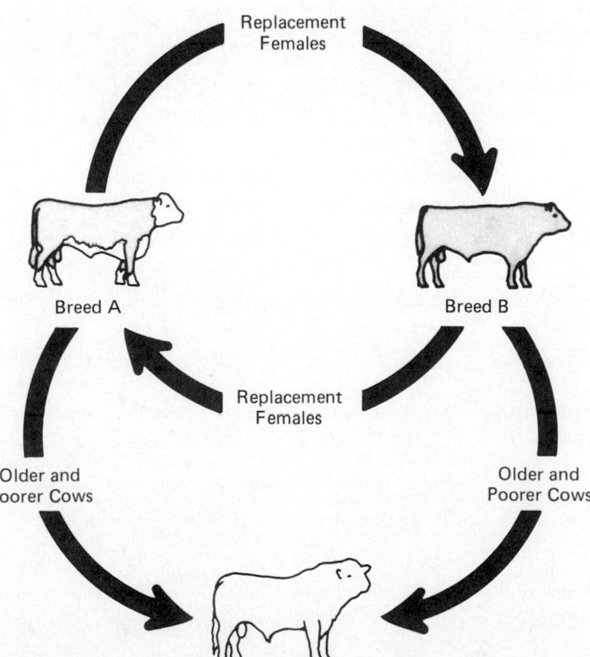

FIGURE 22.11.
Two-breed rotation and terminal sire crossbreeding system. Sires are used in the two-breed rotation primarily to produce replacement heifers. Terminal cross sires are mated to the less productive females. This system will increase the pounds of calf weaned per cow bred by more than 20%. Courtesy of Colorado State University.

TABLE 22.9. Heritability and Heterosis for the Major Beef Cattle Traits

Traits	Heritability	Heterosis
Reproduction	Low	High
Growth	Medium	Medium
Carcass	High	Low

Table 22.9 shows the advantage a commercial producer has over a purebred breeder in being able to use more of the breeding methods for genetic improvement. Commercial producers can use crossbreeding, whereas purebred breeders cannot use crossbreeding if they maintain breed purity.

Traits with a low heritability respond little to genetic selection, but they show a marked improvement in a sound crossbreeding program. The commercial producer needs to select sires carefully to improve the traits with a high heritability.

SELECTED REFERENCES

Publications

Briggs, H. M., and Briggs, D. M. 1980. *Modern Breeds of Livestock.* New York: Macmillan.

Bull and Heifer Replacement Workshops (proceedings). 1990. Fort Collins, CO: Colorado State University.

Gibb, J., Wallace, R., and Wagner, W. 1985. Understanding performance pedigrees. *Beef Improvement Federation,* BIF:FS2.

Gregory, K. E., and Cundiff, L. V. 1980. Crossbreeding in beef cattle: Evaluation of systems. *J. Anim. Sci.* 51:1224.

Kress, D. D. 1989. Practical breeding programs for managing heterosis. *The Range Beef Cow Symposium XI.*

Lamm, D., Hixon, D., and Mankin, J. D. 1986. Culling the commercial cow herd. *Beef Improvement Federation,* BIF-FS7.

Lasley, J. F. 1987. *Genetics of Livestock Improvement.* Englewood Cliffs, NJ: Prentice-Hall.

Long, C. R. 1980. Crossbreeding for beef production: Experimental results. *J. Anim. Sci.* 51:1197.

Mankin, J. D. 1985. Utilizing performance records in commercial beef herds. *Beef Improvement Federation,* BIF-FS4.

McGraw, R., Wallace, R., and Gosey, J. A. 1986. Modern commercial beef sire selection. *Beef Improvement Federation,* BIF-FS9.

Taylor, R. E. 1984. *Beef Production and the Beef Industry: A Commercial Producer's Perspective.* Minneapolis: Burgess.

Thomas, V. M. 1986. *Beef Cattle Production.* Philadelphia: Lea & Febiger.

Wagner, W., Gibb, J., Farmer, J., and Strohbehn, D. 1985. Understanding and using sire summaries. *Beef Improvement Federation,* BIF-FS3.

Visuals

Basic Genetics in Beef Cattle Selection; and *Selecting the Beef Heifer* (slide sets with audiotapes). Beef Improvement Federation, K. W. Ellis, Cooperative Extension Service, University of California, Davis, CA 95616.

Beef Breed Identification (slides). VEP, Calif. Polytechnic State Univ., San Luis Obispo, CA 93407.

Breeding Cattle Selection, Yearling Bull Test (sound filmstrips). Vocational Education Productions, California Polytechnic State University, San Luis Obispo, CA 93407.

Cows That Fit Montana (1985, videotape; 12 min). Department of Animal Science, Montana State University, Bozeman, MT 59715.

Introduction to Beef Breed Selection, Breed Identification: British Breeds; Breed Identification: Continental Breeds; Breed Identification: Brahman and Brahman Crossbreeds; Selecting Beef Sires; and *Designing a Beef Breeding System* (sound filmstrips). Prentice-Hall Media, 150 White Plains Rd., Tarrytown, NY 10591.

Like Begets Like (1989, videotape; 8.5 min). American Angus Association, 3201 Frederick Blvd., St. Joseph, MD 64501.

Using EPDs in Sire Selection (1988, videotape, 11 min). American Simmental Association, One Simmental Way, Bozeman, MT 59715.

CHAPTER 23

Feeding and Managing Beef Cattle

An overview of the beef industry and beef production is presented in Chapter 2. This chapter will identify the primary factors affecting beef cattle productivity and profitability.

COW-CALF MANAGEMENT

Cow-calf producers are interested in managing their operations as economical units. The profitability of a commercial cow-calf operation can be assessed easily by analyzing the following criteria: (1) calf crop percentage weaned (i.e., number of calves produced per 100 cows in the breeding herd), (2) average weight of calves at weaning (7–9 months of age), and (3) annual cow cost (based on the dollar amount required to keep a cow each year).

TABLE 23.1. Break-even Price (per 100 lb) for Commercial Cow-Calf Operations with Varying Calf Crop Percentages, Annual Cow Costs, and Weaning Weights

Calf Crop Percent Weaned	Annual Cow Cost	Breakeven Prices for Calves of Different Weaning Weights		
		400 lb	500 lb	600 lb
95	$ 350.	$ 92.10	$ 73.68	$ 61.40
	300.	78.95	63.16	52.63
	250.	65.79	52.63	43.85
85	350.	102.94	82.35	68.63
	300.	88.24	70.59	58.82
	250.	73.53	58.25	49.02
75	350.	116.67	93.33	77.78
	300.	100.00	80.00	66.67
	250.	83.33	66.67	55.56

An example of the economic assessment of a commercial cow-calf producer who has an 85% calf crop weaned, 500-lb weaning weights, and a $300 annual cost would be as follows:

Calf crop % (0.85) × weaning weight (500 lb) =
425 lb of calf weaned per cow in the breeding herd.
Annual cow cost ($300) ÷ lb of calf weaned (425 lb) = $70.59 per hundredweight.

A break-even price of $70.59 per hundredweight means that the producer would have to receive more than 70¢ per pound, or $70.59 per 100 lb of calf sold, to cover the yearly cost of each cow in the breeding herd. Table 23.1 shows the break-even price for several levels of calf crop percentage, weaning weight, and annual cow cost. This information reflects different management levels in which the break-even price ranges from more than $1.00 per pound to less than $0.50 per pound. Profitability of the commercial cow-calf operation is determined by comparing the market price of the calves at the time they are sold with the break-even price.

Cow-calf operations are managed best by operators who know the factors that affect calf crop percentage (Fig. 23.1), weaning weight, and annual cow cost. The primary management objective should be to improve pounds of calf weaned per cow and reduce or control the annual cow costs.

Costs and Returns

Figure 23.2 shows the dollars returned over cash costs for an average U.S. cow-calf operation. Note the wide deviation in net returns over the 10-year period. During 1986–89, higher prices for calves resulted in higher levels of profitability.

FIGURE 23.1.
Percent calf crop, as measured by a live calf born and raised per cow, is the most economically important trait for the cow-calf producer. The bull, cow, calf, and producer each make a meaningful contribution to the level of productivity for this trait. Courtesy of Norden Laboratories, Inc.

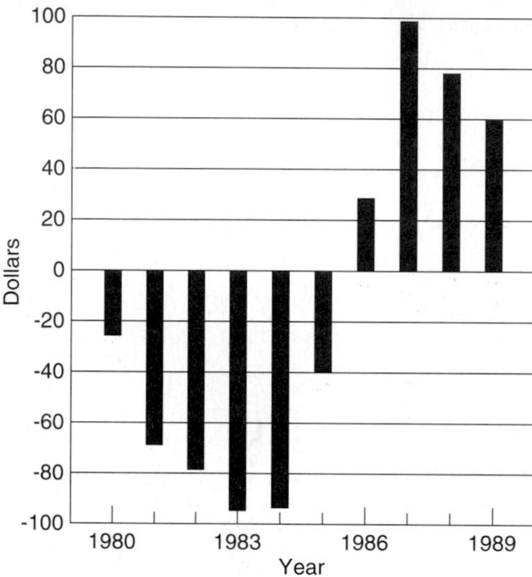

FIGURE 23.2.
Estimated average cow-calf returns (dollars per head above cash costs), 1980–89. Courtesy of the Western Livestock Marketing Information Project.

Costs and returns are computed from an **enterprise budget** (sometimes called an **enterprise analysis**). The enterprise budget is one of the best financial forms used to make management decisions.

The component parts of receipts and expenses for an average cow-calf enterprise are shown in Table 23.2. On a per-cow basis, the total receipts are $350.90 and the total expenses are $295.15. This means there is a return of $55.75; that is, a net return above cash costs. There are additional costs such as unpaid producer's labor, capital replacement, return to land, and so on. When all costs are included, the net return is −$168.88.

MANAGEMENT FOR OPTIMUM CALF CROP PERCENTAGES

The primary management factors affecting calf crop percentages are as follows:

1. Heifers need to be fed adequate levels of a balanced ration to reach puberty at 15 months of age if they are to calve at the desired age of 2 years. Medium-frame-sized heifers of English breeds and crosses (e.g., Angus and Hereford) should weigh 650–750 lb at 15 months of age. Cattle of larger frame-sized exotic breeds or crosses should weigh 100–150 lb more to assure a high percentage of heifers cycling at breeding.
2. Heifers should be bred to calve early in the calving season. Heifers calving early are more likely to be pregnant as 2- and 3-year-olds, whereas heifers calving late will likely not conceive during the next breeding season. Some producers save more heifers as potential replacements at weaning and as yearlings so selection for early pregnancy can be made at pregnancy test time.
3. Heifers typically have a longer postpartum interval than cows. This interval becomes shorter if first-calf heifers (heifers with their first calves) are separated from mature cows 60 days prior to calving and after calving. This separation allows the heifers to obtain their share of the feed essential for a rapid return to estrus.

TABLE 23.2. U.S. Cow-Calf Production Costs and Returns (all sizes of operation)

Item	Dollars per Cow (1988)
Gross value of production	
Steer calves (112.7 lb)	$ 114.78
Heifer calves (79.7 lb)	61.95
Feeder steers (106.7 lb)	85.47
Feeder heifers (76.5 lb)	56.75
Cull cows (80.9 lb)	31.95
Total	350.90
Cash expenses	
Feed	
Grain (2.05 cwt)	9.05
Protein supplements (1.47 cwt)	17.17
Salt and minerals (0.33 cwt)	1.98
Hay (1.25 ton)	44.59
Silage (0.29 ton)	7.00
Pasture	34.90
Public grazing	.75
Crop residue	.08
Other	
Veterinary and medicine	6.91
Livestock hauling	1.89
Marketing	4.54
Custom feed mixing	.29
Fuel, lube, and electricity	12.71
Machinery and building repairs	22.20
Hired labor (3.20 hr)	15.06
Miscellaneous	.23
Total, variable cash expenses	179.35
General farm overhead	49.13
Taxes and insurance	28.07
Interest	38.60
Total, fixed cash expenses	115.80
Total, cash expenses	295.15
Value of production less cash expenses	55.75

Source: USDA, ERS, *Economic Indicators of the Farm Sector. Costs of Production—Livestock and Poultry,* 1988.

4. Feeding programs are designed to have cows and heifers in a moderate body condition (visually estimated by the fat over the back and ribs) at calving time. Table 23.3 shows a body condition scoring system (BCS) currently being used. Thin cows at calving usually have a longer postpartum interval (Fig. 23.3). Cows that are too fat reflect a higher feed cost than is necessary for high and efficient production.

TABLE 23.3. System of Body Condition Scoring (BCS) for Beef Cattle

Group	BCS	Description
Thin condition	1	*Emaciated*—Cow is extremely emaciated with no palpable fat detectable over spinous processes, tranverse processes, hip bones, or ribs. Tail-head and ribs project quite prominently.
	2	*Poor*—Cow still appears somewhat emaciated but tail-head and ribs are less prominent. Individual spinous processes are still rather sharp to the touch but some tissue cover over dorsal portion of ribs.
	3	*Thin*—Ribs are still individually identifiable but not quite as sharp to the touch. There is obvious palpable fat along spine and over tail-head with some tissue cover over dorsal portion of ribs.
Borderline condition	4	*Borderline*—Individual ribs are no longer visually obvious. The spinous processes can be identified individually on palpation but feel rounded rather than sharp. Some fat cover over ribs, transverse processes, and hip bones.
Optimum moderate condition	5	*Moderate*—Cow has generally good overall appearance. On palpation, fat cover over ribs feel spongy and areas on either side of tail-head now have palpable fat cover.
	6	*High moderate*—Firm pressure now needs to be applied to feel spinous processes. A high degree of fat is palpable over ribs and around tail-head.
	7	*Good*—Cow appears fleshy and obviously carries considerable fat. Very spongy fat cover over ribs and around tail-head. In fact "rounds" or "pones" beginning to be obvious. Some fat around vulva and in crotch.
Fat condition	8	*Fat*—Cow very fleshy and overconditioned. Spinous processes almost impossible to palpate. Cow has large fat deposits over ribs, around tail-head, and below vulva. "Rounds" or "pones" are obvious
	9	*Extremely fat*—Cow obviously extremely wasty and patchy and looks blocky. Tail-head and hips buried in fatty tissue and "rounds" or "pones" of fat are protruding. Bone structure no longer visible and barely palpable. Animal's mobility might even be impaired by large fatty deposits.

Source: Richards, et al. 1986. *J. Anim. Sci.* 62:300.

5. Cows, particularly first-calf heifers, should be observed every few hours at calving time. Some females will have difficulty calving **(dystocia)** and will need assistance in delivery of the calf. Calving difficulties should be kept to a minimum to prevent potential death of calves and cows. Calving difficulty is also undesirable because cows given assistance will usually have longer postpartum intervals.
6. Calving difficulty should be minimized but usually cannot be eliminated. A balance should be maintained between the number of calves born alive and the weight of the calves at weaning. Heavier calves at birth usually have heavier weaning weights. When calves are too heavy at birth, however, the death loss of the calves increases. Birth weight is the primary cause of calving difficulty; therefore, management decisions should be made to

keep birth weights moderate. Bulls of the larger breeds or larger frame sizes should not be bred to heifers, and large, extremely growthy bulls, even in the breeds known for calving ease, should not be bred to heifers. Birth weight within a herd is influenced by genetics. Genetic differences are more important than certain environmental differences such as amount of feed during gestation. Bulls, to be used artificially, should have extensive progeny test records for birth weight and calving ease in addition to an individual birthweight record.

7. The bulls' role in affecting pregnancy rate has a marked influence on calf crop percentage. Before breeding, bulls should be evaluated for breeding soundness by addressing physical conformation and skeletal soundness, palpating the genital organs, measuring scrotal circumference, and testing the semen for motility and morphology. **Libido** (sex drive) and mating capacity are additional important factors in how the bull affects pregnancy rate. These traits are not easily measured in individual bulls before breeding or even after breeding in multiple-sire herds. The typical cow-to-bull ratio is quoted by most cattle producers as 30 to 1. However, some bulls can settle more than 50 cows in a 60-day breeding season. In some large pastures with rough terrain, the cow-to-bull ratio might have to be less to assure a high calf crop percentage.
8. Crossbreeding affects calf crop percentage in several ways. Crossbred heifers usually cycle earlier and have higher conception rates than their straightbred counterparts. Crossbred calves are more vigorous and have a higher survival rate. An effective crossbreeding program can increase the calf crop by 8%–12%.
9. The primary nutritional factor influencing calf crop percentage is adequate intake of energy which can be expressed in pounds of total digestible nutrients (TDN). The quantity of TDN intake is important in helping initiate puberty, maintaining proper body condition at calving, and keeping the postpartum interval relatively short. Other nutrients of major importance are protein, calcium and phosphorous. Additional vitamins and minerals are important only in areas where the soil or feed is deficient.
10. Calf losses during gestation are usually low (2%–3%) unless certain diseases are present in the herd. Serious reproductive diseases such as brucellosis, leptospirosis, vibriosis, and infectious bovine rhinotracheitis (IBR) can cause abortions, which may markedly reduce the calf crop percentage. These diseases can be managed by blood testing animals entering the herd or vaccinating for the diseases. Herd health programs vary for different operations depending on the incidence of the diseases in the area. Details of these programs should be worked out with the local veterinarian.
11. Calf losses after 1–2 days following birth are usually small (2%–3%) in most cow-calf operations. Severe weather problems, such as spring blizzards, can cause high calf losses where protection from the weather is limited. In certain areas and in certain years, health problems can also cause high death losses. Infectious calf scours and secondary pneumonia can occasionally reduce the potential calf crop 10%–30%.

MANAGEMENT FOR OPTIMUM WEANING WEIGHTS

The primary management factors affecting calf weaning weights are as follows:

1. Calves born early in the calving season are heavier at weaning primarily because they are older. Calves are typically born over a several week period but are weaned together on one

FIGURE 23.3.
The cow on the left is a body condition score (BCS) 4, whereas the cow on the right is a BCS 6. Cows with BCSs below 5 have a longer interval (days) between calving and pregnancy compared to cows having BCSs of 5 and higher. Courtesy of Oklahoma State University.

specified day. Every time the cow cycles during the breeding season and fails to become pregnant, the weaning weight of her calf is reduced by 30 – 40 lb. Most commercial producers have a breeding season of 90 days or less so the calves are heavier at weaning and can be managed in uniform groups (Fig. 23.4).

2. The amount of forage available to the cow and the calf has a marked influence on weaning

FIGURE 23.4.
This calf is approximately 7 months old and soon will be weaned or separated from its dam. Commercial cow-calf producers manage their cows so that the calves will be heavy at weaning time. Courtesy of the *Charolais Banner*.

weights. The cow needs feed to produce milk for the calf. The calf, after about 3 months of age, will consume forage directly in addition to the milk it receives.

3. Growth stimulants, commonly given to nursing calves, will increase the weaning weight by 5%–15% (Fig. 23.5). Ralgro (Zeranol), Synovex C, and Compudose, common growth stimulants, are implanted as pellets under the skin of the ear. The pellets dissolve over a period of several weeks and supply the growth-stimulating substance that is absorbed into the bloodstream. This implant, however, should not be used on bulls and heifers to be used for breeding purposes. The implant sometimes interferes with the proper development and functioning of the reproductive organs.
4. Providing supplemental feed to the calves where it is inaccessible to the cows will increase the weaning weight of the calves. This practice of **creep feeding** should be used with caution because it is not always economical. It can be used on calves that have the ability to grow and not fatten. It helps calves make the transition of the weaning process and is a feasible practice under drought or marginal feed-supply conditions. Creep feeding of breeding heifer calves can impair the development of their milk secretory tissue and subsequently reduce milk production. This impairment is apparently caused by fat accumulating in the udder and crowding the secretory tissue.
5. Any diseases that affect the milk supply of the cow or growth of the calf will cause a reduction in the weaning weight of the calf (See Chapter 21).
6. Genetic selection for milk production and calf growth rate will increase calf weaning weight. Selection based on EPDs (weaning weight and milk) is the most effective way to change

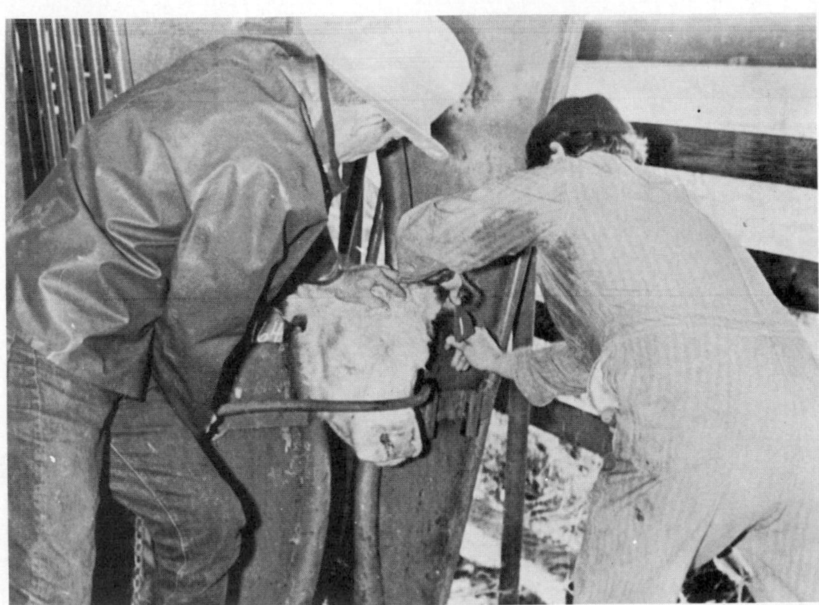

FIGURE 23.5.
The squeeze chute is an essential piece of equipment for restraining cattle. The head can be restrained for inserting ear tags, treating eyes, implanting growth stimulants, or administering medication orally. Note the numbered ear tag, which is the most common form of individual animal identification. Courtesy of Dr. A. T. Ralston, Oregon State University.

weaning weights in a herd genetically. Effective bull selection will account for 80%–90% of the genetic improvement in weaning weight, although weaning-weight information can also be used in culling cows and in selecting replacement heifers. It has been well demonstrated that effective selection can result in a 4–6-lb per-year increase in weaning weight on a per-calf basis.

7. Crossbreeding for the average cow-calf producer can result in a 10%–30% (average 20%) increase in pounds of calf weaned per cow exposed in the breeding herd. Most of the increase occurs from improved reproductive performance; however, one-fourth to one-third of the 20% increase is due to the effect of heterosis on growth rate of the calf and increased milk production of the crossbred cow.

MANAGEMENT FOR LOW ANNUAL COW COSTS

In times of inflationary economic conditions, it may be difficult for a producer to lower annual cow costs. Some producers manage to lower costs, while other producers keep costs at a level similar to past years. Adequate expense records must be maintained so that cost areas can be carefully analyzed (Fig. 23.6).

The greatest consideration should be given to feed costs as they constitute the largest part of annual cow costs, usually 50%–70%. The period from the weaning of a calf to the last one-third of gestation in the next pregnancy is the time when cows can be maintained on comparatively small amounts of relatively cheap, low-quality feeds. Cow-calf operations having available crop aftermath feeds (e.g., corn stalks, grain stubble, and straw) usually have the greatest opportunity to keep feed costs lower than other operations (Fig. 23.7). Nutrient costs of available feeds should be evaluated continually.

Labor costs usually compose 15%–20% of the annual cow costs. Labor costs are usually lower on a per-cow basis as herd size increases and in areas where moderate weather conditions

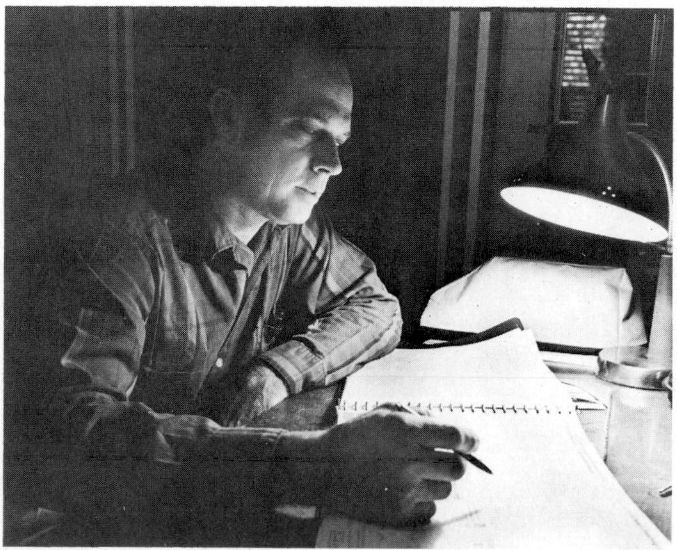

FIGURE 23.6.
Cattle producers must keep accurate income and expense records to assess annual cow costs and the profitability of their operations. Courtesy of Duane Dailey, University of Missouri.

FIGURE 23.7.
Corn-stalk fields are available to cattle after the grain has been harvested. There are millions of acres of stalk fields and other crop-aftermath feeds that can be grazed by cattle and other livestock. Courtesy of *BEEF*.

prevail. It typically takes 15 – 20 hours of labor per cow unit per year. Operations that use labor inefficiently require twice as much labor per cow.

Interest charges on operating capital account for another 10% – 15% of the annual cow cost. Producers can reduce interest charges by carefully analyzing the costs of different credit sources.

Cows and heifers should be palpated at approximately 45 days after the end of the breeding season to determine if pregnancy has occurred. The producer should consider all marketing alternatives to maximize profits when selling open cows. Failing to check cows for pregnancy contributes to higher annual cow costs, lower calf crop percentages, and higher break-even costs of the calves produced.

STOCKER-YEARLING PRODUCTION

Several alternate stocker-yearling production programs are identified in Fig. 2.4. Good producers understand the factors that affect the productivity and profitability of these various programs.

The primary factors affecting the costs and returns of stocker-yearling operations are marketing (both purchasing and selling the cattle), the gaining ability of the cattle, the amount and quality of available forage and roughage, and the health of the cattle. (Table 23.4 shows that management decisions affecting purchase price and sale price have the greatest impact on profitability.

Stocker-yearling producers need to be aware of current market prices for the cattle they purchase or sell. They also need to understand the loss of weight of the cattle from the time of purchase to the time the cattle are delivered to their farm or ranch. This loss in weight, called

TABLE 23.4. Effect of a 10-percent Change on the Break-even Price ($78/cwt) of a Stocker/Yearling Budget

Factor	Change (%)	Decrease in Breakeven Price ($/cwt)	Increase in Profit ($/head)
Sale price	+10%	$ 0.00	$ 56.01
Purchase price	−10	6.95	48.63
Average gain	+10	2.44	18.01
Pasture cost	−10	0.59	4.10
Interest cost	−10	0.33	2.29
Death loss	−10	0.20	1.42
All factors	10	10.02	130.59

Source: Cattle-Fax, Englewood, CO.

shrink can sometimes reflect the difference in the profit or loss of the stocker-yearling operation. It is common for calves and yearlings to shrink 3%–12% from purchased weight to delivered weight. For example, yearlings purchased at 700 lb that shrink 8% will have a delivered weight of 644 lb. It typically takes 2–3 weeks to recover the weight loss.

The gaining ability of most stocker-yearling cattle is estimated visually. Cattle that are lightweight for their age, thin but healthy, with a relatively large skeletal frame size usually have a high gain potential. Cattle that are light for their age are typically most profitable for the stocker-yearling operator, whereas heavier cattle are most profitable for the cow-calf producer.

Stocker-yearling cattle that are purchased and sold several times encounter stress situations of fatigue, hunger, thirst, and exposure to many disease organisms. The most common diseases include shipping fever complex and other respiratory diseases. These stress conditions make it necessary for stocker-yearling producers to have effective health programs for newly purchased cattle. Producers who have poor herd health programs typically experience higher costs of gain and higher death losses.

The primary objective of the stocker-yearling operation is to obtain the most pounds of cattle gain within economic reason, while having assurance that high-quality forage yields can be obtained consistently each year. Forage management to obtain efficient production and consumption of nutritious feed is another essential ingredient of a successful stocker-yearling operation. Time of grazing and intensity of grazing (number of animals per acre) are important considerations if maximum forage production and utilization are to be maintained.

FEEDLOT CATTLE MANAGEMENT

The primary factors needed to analyze and properly manage a feedlot operation are the investment in facilities, cost of feeder cattle, feed cost per pound of gain, nonfeed costs per pound of gain, and marketing. A more detailed analysis of these factors is shown in Table 23.5.

Facilities Investment

The investment in facilities varies with type and location of feedlots. Larger commercial feedlots are quite similar regardless of where they are located in the United States. The general layout is

TABLE 23.5. The Major Component Parts of a Feedlot Business Analysis

Major Component, with Primary Factors Influencing Them				
Investment in Facilities	Cost of Feeder Cattle	Feed Cost per Pound of Gain	Nonfeed Cost per Pound of Gain	Total Dollars Received
Land	Grade	Ration	Death loss	Market choice
Pens	Weight	Rate of gain	Labor	Transportation
Equipment	Shrink	Feed efficiency	Taxes	Shrink
Feed mill	Transportation	Length of time	Insurance	Dressing percentage
Office	Gain potential		Utilities	Quality grade
			Veterinary expenses	Yield grade
			Repairs	Manure value

an open lot of dirt pens with pen capacities varying from 100–500 head. The pens are sometimes mounded in the center to provide a dry resting area for cattle. The fences are pole, cable, or pipe. A feedmill, to process grains and other feeds, is usually a part of the feedlot. Special trucks distribute feed to fence-line feedbunks where cattle stand and eat inside the pens. Bunker trench silos hold corn silage and other roughages. Grains might be stored in these silos; however, they are more often stored in steel bins above the ground. The investment cost per head for this type of feedlot is approximately $150.

Feedlots for farmer-feeder operations vary from unpaved, wood-fenced pens to paved lots with windbreaks, sheds, or total confinement buildings. The latter might have manure collection pits located under the cattle, which stand on slotted floors. The feed might be stored in airtight structures. In most farmer-feeder operations, however, feeds are stored in upright silos and grain bins, particularly where rainfall is high. Feeds are typically processed on the farm and distributed with tractor-powered equipment to feedbunks located either inside or outside the pens. Investment costs for these feedlots vary from $200 to $500 per head.

Cost of Feeder Cattle

Before buying feeder cattle, the feedlot operator first estimates anticipated feed costs and the price the fed slaughter cattle will bring. These figures are then used to project the cost of feeder cattle or what the operator can afford to pay for them. Feeder cattle are priced according to weight, sex, **fill** (content of the digestive tract), skeletal size, thickness, and body condition. Most commercial feeders prefer to buy cattle with **compensatory gain.** These cattle are thin and relatively old for their weight. They have usually been grown out on a relatively low level of feed. When placed on feedlot rations, they gain rapidly and compensate for their previous lack of feed.

The feeder cattle buyer typically projects a high gain potential in cattle that have a large skeletal frame and little finish or body condition. However, not all cattle of this type will gain fast.

Heifers are usually priced a few cents a pound under steers of similar weight. The primary reason is that heifers gain more slowly, the cost per pound of gain is higher, and some feeder heifers are pregnant.

Feeder cattle of the same weight, sex, frame size, and body condition can vary several cents a pound in cost. This value difference is usually due to differences in fill. The differences in fill can amount to 10–40 lb in live weight of feeder cattle. Feed and water consumed before weighing, distance and time of shipping, temperature, and the manner in which cattle are loaded and transported are some major factors affecting the amount of shrink. Shrink results primarily from loss of fill, but weight losses can occur in other parts of the body as well.

Feed Costs

Feed costs per pound of gain form the major costs of putting additional weight on feeder cattle. Typically, feed costs are 60%–75% of the total costs of gain.

Feed costs per pound of gain are influenced by several factors, and the knowledge of these factors is important for proper management decision making. The choice of feed ingredients and how they are processed and fed are key decisions that affect feed costs.

Cattle that gain more rapidly and efficiently on the same feeding program have lower feed costs. Some of these differences are genetic and can sometimes be identified with the specific producer of the cattle. Most feeder cattle receive feed additives (e.g., Rumensin®) and ear implants (e.g., Ralgro® or Synovex®) that improve gain and efficiency and eventually the cost of gain (Figs. 23.8 and 23.9).

Feed cost per pound of gain gets progressively higher as days on feed increase. Therefore, cattle feeders should avoid feeding cattle beyond their optimum combination of slaughter weight, quality grade, and yield grade.

Nonfeed Costs

Nonfeed costs per pound of gain is sometimes referred to as **yardage** cost. Yardage cost includes costs of gain other than feed. These costs can be expressed as either cost per pound of gain or cost per head per day. Obviously, cattle that gain faster move in and out of feedlots sooner and accumulate fewer total dollar yardage costs.

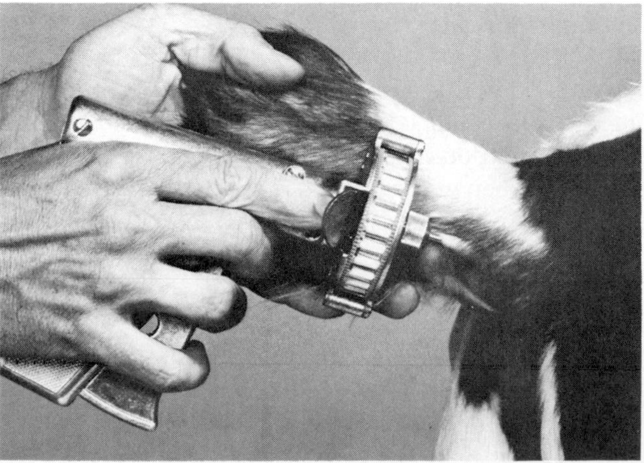

FIGURE 23.8. Implanting a steer with the growth stimulant Ralgro®. Courtesy of International Minerals and Chemical Corporation.

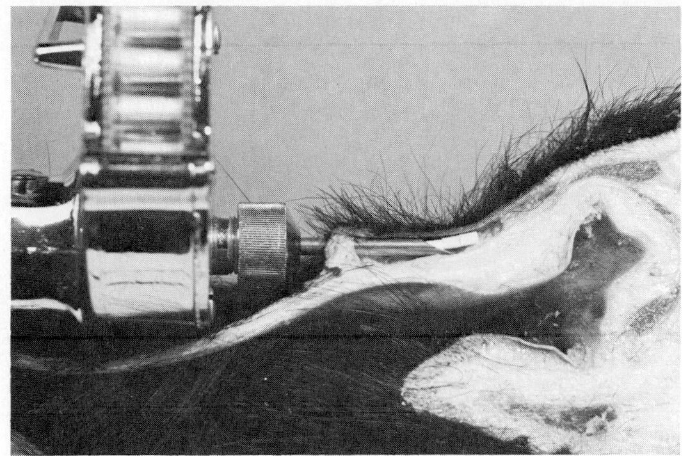

FIGURE 23.9.
Cut-away section of the ear showing the location of three Ralgro® pellets. Note that they are located approximately 1 in. from the base of the ear, just under the skin. Courtesy of International Minerals and Chemical Corporation.

Death loss and veterinary expenses caused by feeder cattle health problems can increase the nonfeed costs significantly. Most cattle feeders prefer to feed yearlings rather than calves because the death loss and health problems in yearlings are significantly lower than in calves.

Gross Receipts

The total dollar amount received for slaughter cattle emphasizes the need for the cattle feeder to be aware of marketing alternatives and the kinds of carcasses the cattle will produce. Most finished cattle from feedlots are sold directly to the packer, through a terminal market when professionals make the marketing transaction, or through an auction where the cattle are sold to the highest bidder. Nearly 80% of the fed cattle are sold direct to a packer. This marketing alternative requires the cattle feeder to be aware of current market prices for the weight and grade of cattle being sold.

Many slaughter cattle at large commercial feedlots are sold on a standard shrink (pencil shrink) of 4%, with the cattle being weighed at the feedlot without being fed the morning of weigh day. Feeders who ship their cattle some distance before a sale weight is taken should manage their cattle to minimize the shrink.

Most slaughter steers and heifers are sold on a live-weight basis with the buyer estimating the carcass weight, quality grade, and yield grade. Slaughter cattle of yield grades 4 and 5 usually have large price discounts. The price spread between the Select and Choice quality grades can vary considerably over time. Some marketing alternatives will not show a price differential between Select and Choice if the cattle have been well fed for a minimum number of days (120 days for yearling feeder cattle).

Cattle feeders who manage their cattle consistently for profitable returns know how to purchase high-performing cattle at reasonable prices. These cattle feeders formulate rations that will optimize cattle performance with feed costs. Also, their cattle have minimum health problems with a low death loss. The feeder feeds cattle the minimum number of days required to assure carcass acceptability and palatability, and develops a marketing plan that will yield the maximum financial returns.

TABLE 23.6. Fed Cattle Production Costs (all operations), 1975–87

Item	1975	1980	1985	1986	1987
	Dollars/cwt				
Cash receipts					
Fed beef	$ 41.79	$ 66.11	$ 59.79	$ 58.52	$ 65.61
Cash expenses					
Feeder cattle	18.41	48.54	39.75	37.66	39.85
Feed					
Silage	1.13	0.32	0.34	0.26	0.19
Dry grain	15.41	12.63	11.68	9.92	7.59
Protein supplements	1.76	1.98	1.96	2.06	2.17
Legume hay	0.68	0.92	1.13	0.92	1.64
Other roughages	0.22	0.38	0.68	1.00	0.96
Total feed costs	19.20	16.23	15.79	13.71	12.05
Other					
Veterinary and medicine	0.37	0.47	0.51	0.52	0.47
Fuel, lube, and electricity	0.33	0.47	0.38	0.36	0.46
Machinery and building repairs	0.40	0.26	0.30	0.29	0.29
Hired labor	0.37	0.60	0.81	0.85	0.85
Miscellaneous	0.45	1.03	1.25	1.39	1.49
Manure credit	−0.07	−0.10	−0.07	−0.07	−0.07
Total variable expenses	39.71	67.50	58.72	55.16	55.39
Taxes and insurance	0.15	0.07	0.07	0.08	0.07
Hired management	0.08	0.15	0.14	0.15	0.13
Interest	2.42	3.76	3.92	4.21	4.72
Total fixed expenses	3.10	3.98	4.13	4.44	4.92
Total cash expenses	42.81	71.48	62.85	59.60	60.31
Receipts less cash expenses	−1.02	−5.37	−3.06	−1.08	5.30

Source: USDA, ERS, *Economic Indicators of the Farm Sector—Livestock and Dairy,* 1975–87.

Some cattle are sold on a grade and yield basis (carcass weight and carcass grade), where total value is determined after the cattle have been slaughtered. This method of marketing is most useful to producers who know the carcass characteristics of their cattle.

COSTS AND RETURNS

The costs and returns for average fed cattle production in the United States are shown in Table 23.6. The enterprise budget is calculated on dollar-per-hundredweight (cwt) basis. Note that the value of fed beef for 1987 was $65.61/cwt and total cash expenses were $60.31/cwt. The net return of receipts over expenses was $5.30/cwt, or $63.60 for a 1,200-lb market steer.

Chapter 36 examines in greater detail how to make effective management decisions.

SELECTED REFERENCES

Publications

Albin, R. C., and Thompson, G. B. 1990. *Cattle Feeding: A Guide to Management.* Amarillo, TX: Trafton Printing, Inc.

Lasley, J. F. 1981. *Beef Cattle Production.* Englewood Cliffs, NJ: Prentice-Hall.

National Research Council. 1984. *Nutrient Requirements of Beef Cattle.* Washington, DC: National Academy Press.

Price, D. P. 1981. *Beef Production.* Dalhart, TX: Southwest Scientific.

Richards, M. W., Spitzer, J. C., and Warner, M. B. 1986. Effect of varying levels of nutrition and body condition at calving on subsequent reproductive performance. J. Anim. Sci. 62:300.

Ritchie, H. D. 1985. *Calving Difficulty in Beef Cattle.* Beef Improvement Federation, BIF-FS6.

Taylor, R. E. 1984. *Beef Production and the Beef Industry: A Commercial Producer's Perspective.* New York: Macmillan.

Thomas, V. M. 1986. *Beef Cattle Production.* Philadelphia: Lea & Febiger.

Visuals

Beef Management Practices (sound filmstrips) covering: *Basic Beef Cattle Nutrition; Preventative Health Care; Handling Equipment and Facilities; Beef Cattle Castration; Dehorning Beef Cattle; Beef Cattle Identification;* and *Calving Management.* Vocational Education Productions, California Polytechnic State University, San Luis Obispo, CA 93407.

Beef Production Systems (sound filmstrips) covering: *Purebred Operations; Cow/Calf Production; and Feedlot Production.* Vocational Education Productions, California Polytechnic State University, San Luis Obispo, CA 93407.

Beef Selection Kit (sound filmstrips) covering: *Breeding Cattle Selection; Market and Feeder Cattle Selection;* and *Fitting and Showing Beef Cattle.* Vocational Education Productions, California Polytechnic State University, San Luis Obispo, CA 93407.

Conception to Feeder (videotape); *Energy Utilization in Feedlot Cattle* (videotape); *Cattle Handling and Transport* and *Beef Cattle Reproduction* (videotapes); *The Feedyard* (videotape); and *Cattle Production* (videotape). CEV, P.O. Box 65265, Lubbock, TX 79464-5265.

CHAPTER 24

Dairy Cattle Breeds and Breeding

Production of milk per cow has been increased markedly in the past 50 years by improvements in breeding, feeding, sanitation, and management. The application of genetic selection, coupled with the extensive use of artificial insemination, has contributed to a successful dairy herd improvement program.

CHARACTERISTICS OF BREEDS

Six major breeds of dairy cattle—Holstein, Ayrshire, Brown Swiss, Guernsey, Jersey, and Red and White—are used for milk production in the United States. These breeds are shown in Color Plates M and N (following p. 386) where production characteristics and other information about the breeds is also given.

It is important to recognize the variation for milk yield and percent fat that exists between breeds and within a breed. Figure 24.1 shows the variation in fat percentage for the Holstein and Jersey breeds. While the two breeds are distinctly different based on breed averages, it is possible to identify Holstein cows that have higher fat percentages than Jersey cows.

Holstein cows produce extremely large amounts of milk—up to 150 lb/day at peak lactation. Thus, in Holsteins and other high milk-producing cows, great stress is placed on udder ligaments, which can break down and no longer support the udder. If an udder breaks down, it is more susceptible to injury and disease, often necessitating culling the cow.

Ayrshires and Brown Swiss produce milk over a greater number of years than Holsteins, but their production levels are lower. Efficiency of milk production per 100 lb body weight is about the same for the major breeds of dairy cows.

Guernsey and Jersey cows produce milk having high percentages of milk fat and solids-not-fat, but the total amount of milk produced is relatively low. The efficiency of energy production of different breeds varies less among the breeds than do either total quantity of milk produced or percentage of fat in the milk.

Ayrshire

Origin: Scotland
Average Weight:
Bulls 1,850 lb
Cows 1,200 lb
Color: Mahogany and white spotted, may have pigmented legs
Average milk yield (1988): 14,125 lb
Percentage of fat: 3.86%

Brown Swiss

Origin: Switzerland
Average Weight:
Bulls 2,000 lb
Cows 1,400 lb
Color: Solid blackish; hairs dark with light tips
Average milk yield (1988): 15,883 lb
Percentage of fat; 3.97%

Guernsey

Origin: Guernsey Island
Average Weight:
Bulls 1,600 lb
Cows 1,100 lb
Color: Light red and white; yellow skin.
Average milk yield (1988): 12,880 lb
Percentage of fat: 4.54%

PLATE M.
Major breeds of dairy cows with origin, identifying characteristics, and production listed. Photographs courtesy of Agri-Graphics.

Holstein

Origin: Holland
Average Weight:
Bulls 2,200 lb
Cows 1,500 lb
Color: Black and white
Average milk yield (1988): 19,444 lb.
Percentage of fat: 3.61%

Jersey

Origin: Jersey Island
Average Weight:
Bulls 1,500 lb
Cows 1,000 lb
Color: Blackish hairs have white tips to give gray color or red tips to give fawn color; also can be solid black or white spotted.
Average milk yield (1988); 12,888 lb
Percentage of fat: 4.73%

Red and White

Origin: Holland
Average Weight:
Bulls 2,100 lb
Cows 1,400 lb
Color: Red and white
Average milk yield (1988): 17,980 lb
Percentage of fat: 3.63%

PLATE N.
Major breeds of dairy cows with origin, identifying characteristics, and production listed. Photographs courtesy of Agri-Graphics.

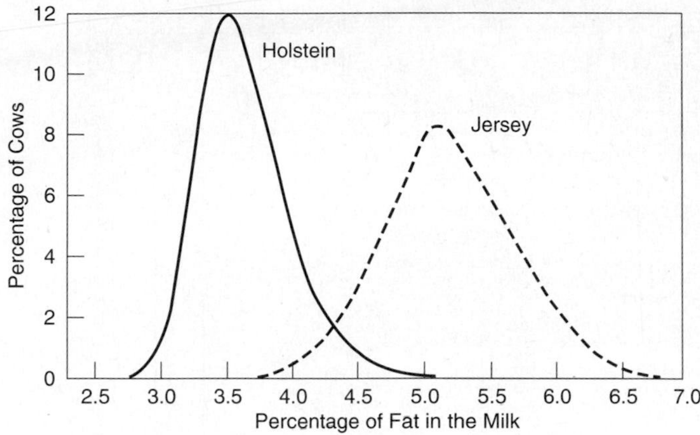

Breed differences in percentage of fat in the milk of Holstein and Jersey cows. Courtesy of G. E. Shook and W. H. Freeman and Company, © 1974.

Registration Numbers

Breed popularity can be estimated from registration numbers, as shown in Table 24.1. Most dairy cows are grade cows, which means they do not have pedigrees (with individual registration numbers) recorded in a breed association. However, producers with registered cattle are a source of breeding for the total dairy industry. Breeds with the largest registration numbers reflect the demand from the commercial dairy industry.

DAIRY TYPE

Some descriptive terms describing ideal dairy type are *stature, angularity, level rump, long and lean neck, milk veins,* and *strong feet and legs.* In the past, dairy producers have placed great emphasis on dairy type, but research studies indicate that some components of dairy type may have little or no value in improving milk production and might even be deleterious if overstressed in selection. However, a properly attached udder and strong feet and legs are good indicators that a cow will remain a high producer for a long time.

TABLE 24.1. Annual Registration Numbers for Major U.S. Breeds of Dairy Cattle

	Annual Registrations (in thousands)					
Breed	1989	1985	1980	1975	1970	Year Association Formed
Holstein	380.0	394.5	353.9	279.2	281.6	1871
Jersey	53.3	65.4	61.0	39.7	37.1	1868
Guernsey	16.1	25.1	20.9	27.4	43.8	1877
Brown Swiss	12.5	11.9	12.9	14.0	16.4	1800
Ayrshire	9.5	11.1	10.9	12.0	15.0	1875
Red and White	7.2	5.3	4.8	1.7	—	1964
Milking Shorthorn	3.1	3.4	4.9	4.6	5.4	1912

Source: Various dairy cattle breed associations; 1990, *Natl. Coop. Dairy Herd Improv. Prog. Handbook.* K-7.

DAIRY COW UNIFIED SCORE CARD

Breed characteristics should be considered in the application of this score card — **Perfect Score**

Order of observation

1. GENERAL APPEARANCE — **35**

(Attractive individuality with feminity, vigor, stretch, scale and harmonious blending of all parts with impressive style and carriage.)

BREED CHARACTERISTICS — (see reverse side) — 5

STATURE — height including moderate length in the leg bones with a long bone pattern throughout the body structure. — 5

FRONT END — adequate constitution with strength and dairy refinement. **SHOULDER BLADES** and elbow set firmly and smoothly against the chest wall and withers to form a smooth union with the neck and body. **CHEST** deep and full with ample width between front legs. — 5

BACK — straight and strong; **LOIN** — broad, strong and nearly level **AND RUMP** — long, wide and nearly level with pin bones slightly lower than hip bones. **THURLS** high and wide apart; **TAIL HEAD** set nearly level with topline and with tail head and tail free from coarseness. — 5

LEGS AND FEET — bone flat and strong. **FRONT LEGS** straight, wide apart and squarely placed; **HIND LEGS**, nearly perpendicular from hock to pastern from a side view and straight from the rear view; **HOCKS** cleanly molded free from coarseness and puffiness; **PASTERNS** short and strong with some flexibility and **FEET** short, well rounded with deep heel and level sole. — 15

2. DAIRY CHARACTER — **20**

(Angularity and general openness without weakness, freedom from coarseness, and evidence of milking ability with udder quality giving due regard to stage of lactation)

NECK — long, lean and blending smoothly into shoulders; clean cut throat, dewlap, and brisket; **WITHERS** — sharp with chine prominent; **RIBS** — wide apart, rib bones wide, flat and long; **THIGHS** — incurving to flat and wide apart from the rear view, providing ample room for the udder and its rear attachment, and **SKIN** — thin, loose and pliable.

3. BODY CAPACITY — **10**

(Relatively large in proportion to size, age and period of gestation of animal, providing ample capacity, strength and vigor)

CHEST — large, deep and wide floor with well sprung fore ribs blending into the shoulders; crops full. **BODY** — strongly supported, long, deep and wide; depth and spring of rib tending to increase toward the rear; **FLANKS** — deep and refined.

4. UDDER — **35**

(Strongly attached, well-balanced with adequate capacity possessing quality indicating heavy milk production for long period of usefulness)

FORE UDDER — strongly and smoothly attached, moderate length and uniform width from front to rear. — 6

REAR UDDER — strongly attached, high, wide with uniform width from top to bottom and slightly rounded to udder floor. — 8

UDDER SUPPORT — udder carried snugly above the hocks showing a strong suspensory ligament with clearly defined halving. — 11

TEATS — uniform size of medium length and diameter, cylindrical, squarely placed under each quarter, plumb, and well spaced from side and rear views. — 5

BALANCE, SYMMETRY AND QUALITY — symmetrical with moderate length, width and depth, no quartering on sides and level floor as viewed from the side; soft, pliable and well collapsed after milking; quarters evenly balanced. — 5

Because of the natural undeveloped udder in heifer calves and yearlings, less emphasis is placed on udder and more on general appearance, dairy character and body capacity. A slight to serious discrimination applies to overdeveloped, fatty udders in heifer calves and yearlings.

TOTAL — **100**

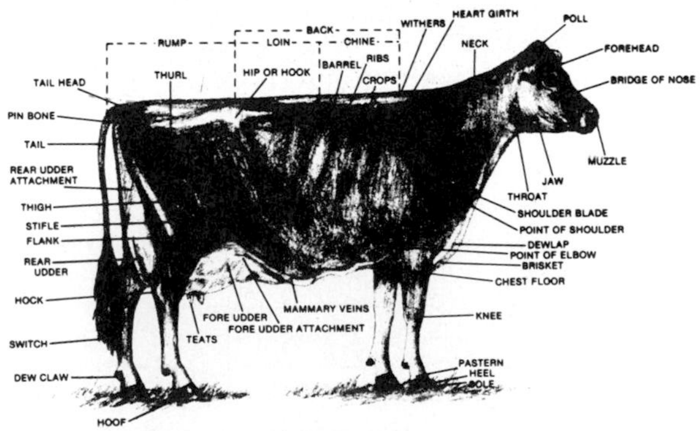

PARTS OF A DAIRY COW

FIGURE 24.2.
Parts of the dairy cow and a description of the preferred dairy type. Courtesy of the Purebred Dairy Cattle Association.

Figure 24.2 shows the parts of a dairy cow and also gives a description of the component parts (general appearance, dairy character, body capacity, and udder) of preferred dairy type. The points on the score card show greatest emphasis for general appearance (especially feet and legs) and udder, where each receives 35 points out of a possible 100 points.

Some dairy breed associations have a classification program to evaluate the type traits. For example, the Holstein Association Linear Classification Program has 29 primary and secondary linear descriptive traits that measure functional conformation or type. A classifier, approved by the association, scores each cow or bull for the several traits and gives a final score if these scores are to be official records recognized by the association.

In the Holstein Association program a final score is calculated from rating the four major categories of classification traits: general appearance, dairy character, body capacity, and mammary system. The emphasis for each category for cows and bulls is shown in Table 24.2.

The final score represents the degree of physical perfection of any given animal. It is expressed in the following numbers and words:

Excellent (EX): 90–100	Good (G): 75–79
Very good (VG): 85–89	Fair (F): 65–74
Good plus (G+): 80–84	Poor (P): 50–64

The final score is used in computing PTAT (predicted transmitting ability for type). The PTAT identifies genetic differences in sires that can be considered in selection programs to improve dairy cattle type.

Type has value from a sales standpoint. Although some components of type score are negatively related to milk production, type is important as a measure of the likelihood that a cow will sustain a high level of production over several years.

IMPROVING MILK PRODUCTION

Great strides have been made over the past 50 years in improving milk production through improved management and breeding (Table 24.3). For example, the amount of milk produced in the United States in the 1980s was about the same as that produced in the 1960s, yet the number of dairy cows in 1989 was less than half the number in 1960. Thus, average production per cow

TABLE 24.2. Classification Traits Used for Final Scores in Holstein Cattle

Trait	Emphasis (%) Cows	Bulls
General appearance	30	45
Dairy character	20	30
Body capacity	20	25
Mammary system	30	—

Source: Holstein Association, Linear Classification Program.

TABLE 24.3. Changes in Milk Production in the U.S., 1940–1989

Year	No. Cows (mil)	Ave. Milk per Cow (lb)	Total Milk (bil lb)
1940	23.7	4,622	109.4
1950	21.9	5,314	116.6
1960	17.5	7,029	123.1
1970	12.0	9,751	117.0
1980	10.8	11,875	128.4
1989	10.1	14,506	143.3

Source: USDA.

in 1989 was more than double that in 1960. From 1975 to 1989, milk production per cow has increased 30% (Fig. 24.3). During this same time period, cow numbers have decreased, thus total milk production has dramatically increased. In the past 10 years alone, annual milk production by the major breeds of dairy cattle in the United States has increased by approximately 250 lb per cow per year.

SELECTION OF DAIRY COWS

The average productive life of a dairy cow is short (approximately 3–4 years). Many cows are culled primarily because of reproductive failure, low milk yield, udder breakdown, feet and leg weaknesses, and mastitis.

Heifers whose ancestral records indicate they will be high producers should be used to replace cows that are **culled** for low production. Such heifers should also be used to replace

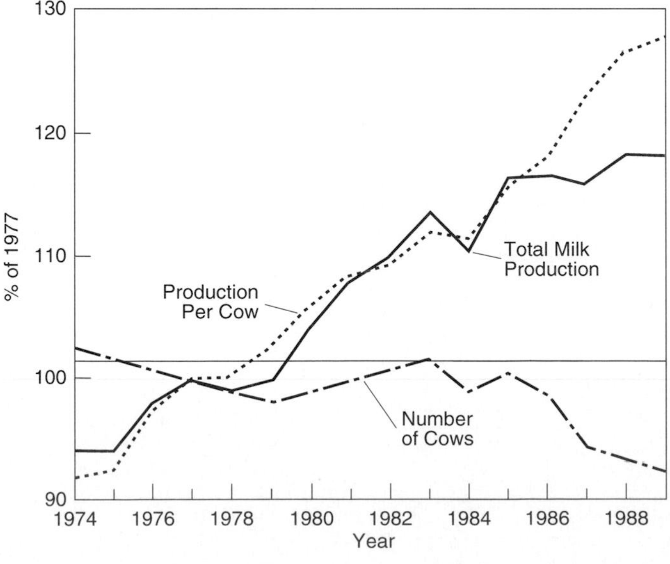

FIGURE 24.3. Total milk production, number of cows, and milk production per cow, 1974–88. Courtesy of the USDA.

cows that leave the herd because of infertility, mastitis, or death, although the improvement gained therby is generally modest.

A basis for evaluating a dairy cow is the quantity of milk (lb) and quality (total solids) that she produces. For a dairy operator to know which cows are good producers and which cows should be culled, a record of milk production is essential.

The **National Cooperative Dairy Herd Improvement Program (NCDHIP)** is a national industry-wide dairy production testing and record-keeping program. It is often referred to as the **Dairy Herd Improvement (DHI) program.** In this program, USDA and Extension Service personnel work with dairy producers to help them improve milk production and dairy management practices. Records obtained are analyzed so dairy operators know how each cow compares with all cows in the herd and how the herd compares with other herds in the area. Producers can use several testing plans; some are official and others are unofficial, but any of them may be useful to a dairy operator interested in improving production in a herd. Six important types of testing plans follow.

Dairy Herd Improvement Association (DHIA) is the most common official testing plan in the NCDHIP. All cows must be properly identified and all Dairy Herd Improvement (DHI) rules enforced. The results of official records might be published and are then used by the USDA to evaluate sires.

Dairy Herd Improvement Registry (DHIR) is another official testing program in NCDHIP. The same rules and procedures apply as in official DHIA records. The main difference is that records are sent to the offices of the breed associations and additional "surprise tests" may be conducted. DHIA and DHIR regulations are the same, and both are official testing programs. The DHIR program is for registered cattle. The following rules apply to both programs.

1. All cows in the herd must be entered into the official testing program.
2. All animals in the herd must be permanently identified.
3. Copies of pedigress of all registered cows must be made available for DHIR.
4. Testing is done each month with not less than 15 days nor more than 45 days allowed between test periods.
5. Testing is conducted over a 24-hour period.
6. An independent supervisor must be present for supervising the weighing of the milk and the sampling of the milk for milk fat and other determinations.
7. Milk or milk fat records that are above values established by the breed association require retesting of the cow to assure that an error was not made. An owner may request retesting if he or she feels the test does not properly reflect the production of the cows.
8. Surprise tests may be made if the supervisor suspects that they are needed to verify previous tests.
9. Any practice that is intended to or does create an inaccurate record of production is considered a fraudulent act and is not allowed.

Figure 24.4 shows an individual cow's record used in the DHIR program. Especially note the milk and milk fat recorded under the heading, "305 ME Season Production." Records are standardized to a lactation length of 305 days, two milkings per day (2x), and to a mature age of cow (ME = mature equivalent). Adjustments are made to records so they can be more accurately compared on a standardized basis.

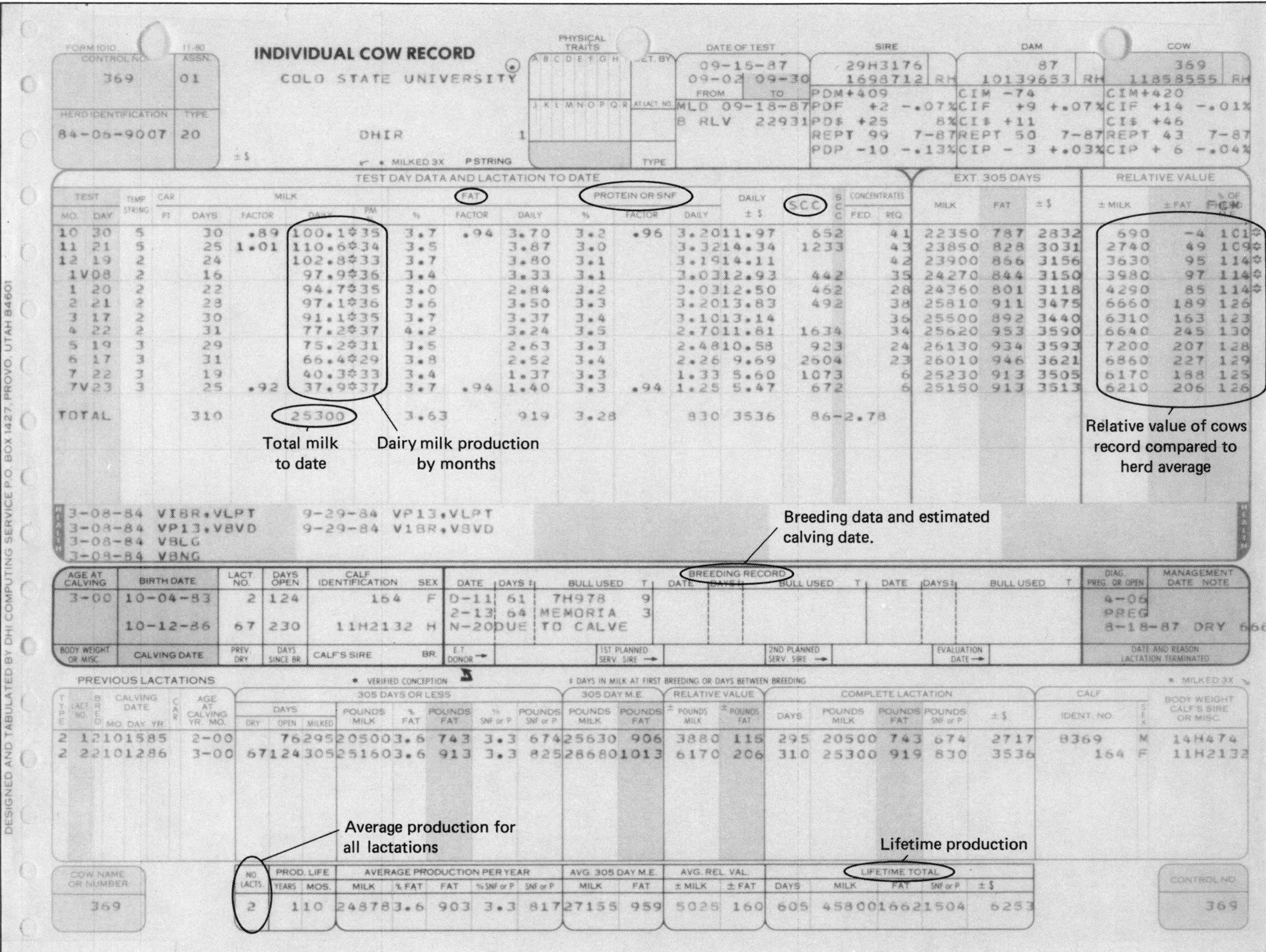

FORM 1010 11-80

INDIVIDUAL COW RECORD

COLO STATE UNIVERSITY

CONTROL NO.	ASSN.
369	01

HERD IDENTIFICATION	TYPE
84-06-9007	20

DHIR 1

± $ ← • MILKED 3X P STRING

PHYSICAL TRAITS A B C D E F G H J K L M N O P Q R — SET. BY — AT LACT. NO. — TYPE

DATE OF TEST	SIRE	DAM	COW
09-15-87	29H3176	87	369
FROM 09-02, TO 09-30	1698712 RH	10139653 RH	11858555 RH
MLD 09-18-87	PDM +409	CIM -74	CIM +420
B RLV 22931	PDF +2 -.07%	CIF +9 +.07%	CIF +14 -.01%
	PD$ +25 8%	CI$ +11	CI$ +46
	REPT 99 7-87	REPT 50 7-87	REPT 43 7-87
	PDP -10 -.13%	CIP - 3 +.03%	CIP + 6 -.04%

TEST DAY DATA AND LACTATION TO DATE — EXT. 305 DAYS — RELATIVE VALUE

TEST MO.	TEST DAY	TEMP STRING	CAR PT	DAYS	MILK FACTOR	MILK DAILY	PM	FAT %	FAT FACTOR	FAT DAILY	PROTEIN OR SNF %	PROTEIN OR SNF FACTOR	PROTEIN OR SNF DAILY	DAILY ± $	SCC	CONCENTRATES FED.	CONCENTRATES REQ.	EXT. 305 MILK	EXT. 305 FAT	EXT. 305 ± $	± MILK	± FAT	% OF FCM
10	30	5		30	.89	100.1	35	3.7	.94	3.70	3.2	.96	3.20	11.97	652		41	22350	787	2832	690	-4	101
11	21	5		25	1.01	110.6	34	3.5		3.87	3.0		3.32	14.34	1233		43	23850	828	3031	2740	49	109
12	19	2		24		102.8	33	3.7		3.80	3.1		3.19	14.11			42	23900	866	3156	3630	95	114
1V	08	2		16		97.9	36	3.4		3.33	3.1		3.03	12.93	442		35	24270	844	3150	3980	97	114
1	20	2		22		94.7	35	3.0		2.84	3.2		3.03	12.50	462		28	24360	801	3118	4290	85	114
2	21	2		28		97.1	36	3.6		3.50	3.3		3.20	13.83	492		38	25810	911	3475	6660	189	126
3	17	2		30		91.1	35	3.7		3.37	3.4		3.10	13.14			36	25500	892	3440	6310	163	123
4	22	2		31		77.2	37	4.2		3.24	3.5		2.70	11.81	1634		34	25620	953	3590	6640	245	130
5	19	3		29		75.2	31	3.5		2.63	3.3		2.48	10.58	923		24	26130	934	3593	7200	207	128
6	17	3		31		66.4	29	3.8		2.52	3.4		2.26	9.69	2604		23	26010	946	3621	6860	227	129
7	22	3		19		40.3	33	3.4		1.37	3.3		1.33	5.60	1073		6	25230	913	3505	6170	188	125
7V	23	3		25	.92	37.9	37	3.7	.94	1.40	3.3	.94	1.25	5.47	672		6	25150	913	3513	6210	206	126
TOTAL				310		25300		3.63		919	3.28		830	3536	86-2.78								

3-08-84 VIBR.VLPT 9-29-84 VP13.VLPT
3-08-84 VP13.V8VD 9-29-84 V18R.V8VD
3-08-84 VBLG
3-08-84 VBNG

AGE AT CALVING	BIRTH DATE	LACT. NO.	DAYS OPEN	CALF IDENTIFICATION	SEX
3-00	10-04-83	2	124	164	F
	10-12-86	67	230	11H2132	H
BODY WEIGHT OR MISC	CALVING DATE	PREV. DRY	DAYS SINCE BR	CALF'S SIRE	BR.

BREEDING RECORD

DATE	DAYS ‡	BULL USED	T
D-11	61	7H978	9
2-13	64	MEMORIA	3
N-20	DUE	TO CALVE	

E.T. DONOR → 1ST PLANNED SERV. SIRE → 2ND PLANNED SERV. SIRE → EVALUATION DATE →

DIAG. PREG. OR OPEN	MANAGEMENT DATE NOTE
4-06	
PREG	
8-18-87 DRY	

DATE AND REASON LACTATION TERMINATED

PREVIOUS LACTATIONS • VERIFIED CONCEPTION ‡ DAYS IN MILK AT FIRST BREEDING OR DAYS BETWEEN BREEDING * MILKED 3X

TYPE	LACT. NO.	BRED	CALVING DATE MO. DAY YR.	CAR	AGE AT CALVING YR. MO.	DAYS DRY	DAYS OPEN	DAYS MILKED	305 POUNDS MILK	305 % FAT	305 POUNDS FAT	305 % SNF or P	305 POUNDS SNF or P	305 M.E. POUNDS MILK	305 M.E. POUNDS FAT	REL. VALUE ± POUNDS MILK	REL. VALUE ± POUNDS FAT	COMPLETE DAYS	COMPLETE POUNDS MILK	COMPLETE POUNDS FAT	COMPLETE POUNDS SNF or P	± $	CALF IDENT. NO.	SEX	BODY WEIGHT CALF'S SIRE OR MISC
2	1	2	101585		2-00		76	295	20500	3.6	743	3.3	674	25630	906	3880	116	295	20500	743	674	2717	8369	M	14H474
2	2	2	101286		3-00	67	124	305	25160	3.6	913	3.3	825	28680	1013	6170	206	310	25300	919	830	3536	164	F	11H2132

COW NAME OR NUMBER	NO. LACTS.	PROD. LIFE YEARS	PROD. LIFE MOS.	AVG. PER YEAR MILK	% FAT	FAT	% SNF or P	SNF or P	AVG. 305 DAY M.E. MILK	AVG. 305 DAY M.E. FAT	AVG. REL. VAL. ± MILK	AVG. REL. VAL. ± FAT	LIFETIME TOTAL DAYS	MILK	FAT	SNF or P	± $	CONTROL NO.
369	2	1	10	24878	3.6	903	3.3	817	27155	959	5025	160	605	45800	1662	1504	6253	369

DESIGNED AND TABULATED BY DHI COMPUTING SERVICE P.O. BOX 1427, PROVO, UTAH 84601

FIGURE 24.4.
An individual cow record used in the DHIR program (some selected information is circled with a brief explanation given). Courtesy of Colorado State University.

Owner-sampler records form a program where the herd owner, rather than the DHIA supervisor, records the milk weights and takes the samples. The information recorded is the same as in official tests, but the records are for private use and are not published.

Tester-sampler records are similar to official records in that the DHIA supervisor samples and weighs the milk. The records are unofficial, however, and the enforcement of cow identification and other DHIA rules is less rigid than in official tests. These records are not for publication.

"A.M.-P.M." records can be official if a milking-time monitor is installed in the milking facilities. In this plan the herd is tested each month throughout the year, but the supervisor takes only the morning (a.m.) milking for 1 month and the afternoon (p.m.) milking for the 2nd month. Each daily milk weight is doubled to determine the daily milk weight for calculation by the test interval method. The daily milk weights printed on the herd report are the average daily milk weights for the last two consecutive tests (one a.m. and one p.m.).

Milk Only records are unofficial records in which only milk weights are used; no tests are made. Each cow's record and the herd summary are based only on amount of milk produced. Unofficial records may also be combined in that owner-sampler records can be a.m.-p.m. or Milk Only. It is also possible to combine Milk Only and a.m.-p.m.

A registry association for purebred animals exists for each dairy cattle breed in the United States. In addition, some breed associations honor cows with outstanding production performance and bulls with daughters that are outstanding in production. The Holstein selective registry, for example, has the Gold Medal Dam and Gold Medal Sire awards. A Gold Medal-winning cow must produce an average of 24,881 lb of milk and 500 lb of milk fat per year during her productive life; she must also have a minimum type score of 83 points based on 100 points. The Gold Medal cow should also have three daughters that meet the requirements. A Gold Medal-winning sire must have 10 or more daughters that meet high standards in milk and fat production and also in type score. Other breed associations have selective registries as a means of encouraging improvement in production.

BREEDING DAIRY CATTLE

The time of breeding is an important phase in dairy cattle management. Because they are milked each day, dairy cows are more closely observed than beef cows, allowing visual detection. When in estrus, dairy cows may show restlessness, enlarged vulvas, and a temporary decline in milk production. Also, when cows are in standing heat they will permit other cows to mount them.

Technicians are available to artificially inseminate cattle, but well-trained dairy producers or employees are excellent inseminators. The use of semen from genetically proven sires is highly desirable, even though this semen may cost more than semen from an average bull. Considering the additional milk production that can be expected from heifers sired by a good bull, the extra investment can return high dividends. Semen costing \$25-\$150 per unit from genetically superior bulls may be a better investment than semen from less desirable bulls at \$10-\$20 per unit. Bulls should not run with the milking cows, because bulls are often dangerous. Bulls that provide semen for artificial insemination should be handled with caution as well.

The heritability of traits is indicative of the progress that can be made by selection. The susceptibilities to cystic ovaries, ketosis, mastitis, and milk fever are all lowly heritable (5%-10%). The percentages of fat, protein, and solids-not-fat are all high (50%). Yearly milk (ME), protein, solids-not-fat, and fat yields are medium in heritability (25%–30%). With the exception of teat locations and spacings, which are moderately heritable (25%–30%), all udder characteristics are lowly heritable (10%–20%).

Strength of head and upstandingness are highly heritable (45% and 50% respectively). Body weight, type score, levelness of rump, height of tail setting, depth of body, tightness of shoulders, and dairy characters are all moderately heritable (25%–35%). Strength of pasterns, arch of back, heel depth, and straightness of hocks are lowly heritable (10%–20%).

The genetic correlation betwen two traits is indicative of the amount of genetic change in trait A that might be expected from a certain amount of selection pressure applied to trait B. The most important genetic correlations are those that might be associated with milk yields during the first lactation. Fat, solids-not-fat, protein yield, lifetime milk yields, and length of productive life have high genetic correlations with first lactation milk yield (0.70–0.90). Overall type score, levelness of rump, udder texture, and strength of fore and rear udder are all negatively correlated with first lactation milk yield (−0.20 to −0.40). Dairy character and udder depth are positively correlated (0.35–0.40) with first lactation yield. Inbreeding tends to increase mortality rate and to reduce all production traits except fat percentage of milk and mature body weight.

There are several inherited abnormalities known in dairy cattle. This does not mean that dairy cattle have a higher number of inherited abnormalities than other farm animals, but that more is known about dairy cattle than about most other farm animals because dairy cattle are observed more closely. No breed of dairy cattle is free from all inherited abnormalities. Some of these abnormalities include achondroplasia (short bones), weavers, limber limbs, rectal-vaginal constriction, dumps, flexed pasterns (feet turned back), fused teats (teats on same side of udder are fused), hairless (almost no hair on calf), and syndactylism (only one toe on a foot). Many of these inherited abnormalities are lethal and most are recessive in their mode of inheritance.

Usually the occurrence of inherited abnormalities is infrequent. However, occasionally an outstanding sire might carry an abnormality or a specific dairy herd may have several genetically abnormal calves. As most inherited abnormalities result from recessive genes, both the sire and dam of genetically abnormal calves carry the undesirable gene. Breeding stock should not be kept from either parent.

One reason such rapid progress has been made in improving milk production is that genetically superior sires were identified and used widely in artificial insemination programs. Genetically superior bulls today might become the sires of 100,000 calves or more each in their productive lives by use of artificial insemination. Generally, the better sires will sire more calves than ordinary sires because dairy producers know the value of semen from outstanding bulls. Thus, selection is enhanced markedly for greater milk production by use of artificial insemination (Fig. 24.5).

Milk production, milk composition, efficiency of production, and characteristics that indicate that a cow will likely remain productive for several years are all highly important in selecting dairy cows. These traits are usually emphasized according to their relative heritability and economic importance. Milk and milk fat production are 20%–30% heritable, and udder attachment is 30% heritable. Fertility is extremely important but low in heritability, so marked improvement in this trait is more likely to be accomplished environmentally through good nutrition and management rather than through selection.

Most dairy cattle in the United States are straightbred because crossing breeds has failed to make a significant improvement in milk production. No combination of breeds, for example, equals the straightbred Holstein in total milk production. Because milk production is controlled

FIGURE 24.5.
Cows being artificially inseminated with semen from a genetically superior bull. A well-managed AI program can make a significant contribution to improving milk production in dairy herds. Courtesy of Colorado State University.

by many genes and the effect of each of the genes is unknown, it is impossible to manipulate genes that control milk production by the same method that one can use in the case of simple inheritance. Also, milk production is a sex-linked trait expressed only in the female. Furthermore, milk production is highly influenced by the environment. To improve milk production by genetic selection, the environment must be standardized among all animals present to ensure, insofar as possible, that differences between animals are due to inheritance rather than environment.

In addition to a high level of milk production, characteristics of longevity, regularity of breeding, ease of milking, and quiet disposition are important in dairy cows. Milk production, milk composition, efficiency of production, and characteristics that indicate that a cow will likely remain productive for several years are all highly important in selecting dairy cows.

Bulls are evaluated for their ability to transmit the characteristic of high-level milk production both by considering the production level of their ancestors (pedigree) and by considering the production level of their daughters (progeny testing). An index is used as a predictive evaluation of the bull's ability to transmit the characteristic of high-level milk production.

The **Sire Index,** computed by the USDA, is based on comparing daughters of a given sire with their contemporary herd mates. Each sire is assigned a **predicted difference** based on the superiority or inferiority of his daughters to their herd mates. Many sires have daughters in 50–100 different herds, so the PTA (predicted transmitting ability) for milk, fat, and type is generally highly reliable and provides a sound basis for the selection of semen. The USDA publishes PTAs among sires semi-annually.

SIRE SELECTION

The dairy industry (breed associations, National Association of Animal Breeders, and the USDA) use the **Best Linear Unbiased Prediction (BLUP)** method for estimating Predicted Transmitting Ability (PTA) among sires. This method was developed primarily at Cornell

FIGURE 24.6.
S-W-D Valiant is an outstanding Holstein bull. He ranks in the top percentage of all Holstein bulls in transmitting milk production traits and type to his offspring. Courtesy of American Breeders Service.

University by Dr. C. R. Henderson. The BLUP procedure accounts for genetic competition among bulls within a herd, genetic progress of the breed over generations, pedigree information available on young bulls, and differing numbers of herdmate's sires, and partially accounts for the differential culling of daughters among sires. In the BLUP method, direct comparisons are made among bulls that have daughters in the same herd. Indirect comparisons are made by using bulls that have daughters in two or more herds. An example presented by the Holstein Association (1980) depicts the use of three different sires in two herds:

Herd 1	**Herd 2**
Daughters of sire A	Daughters of sire B
Daughters of sire C	Daughters of sire C

Direct comparisons can be made between sires B and C in herd 2. Indirect comparisons between sires A and B can be made by using the common sire C as a basis for comparison. PTAs are calculated for milk, protein, fat, type, and dollars returned.

The **Total Performance Index (TPI)** combines differences for milk production traits and difference for type traits into a single value. Figure 24.6 identifies a Holstein bull that is genetically superior in combination of type and milk traits. Figure 24.7 shows the Holstein cow that ranked first out of 700,000 cows for the best combination of milk production traits and type traits.

FIGURE 24.7.
Beecher Arlinda Ellen is an outstanding Holstein cow. She has a 305-day milk record of 55,543 lb with a type score of Excellent-91. Courtesy of Agri-Graphics.

SELECTED REFERENCES

Publications

Bath, D. L., Dickinson, F. N., Tucker, H. A., and Appleman, R. D. 1985. *Dairy Cattle: Principles, Practices, Problems, Profits.* Philadelphia: Lea & Febiger.

Holstein Friesian Association of America. 1980. *New Developments in Holstein Type Evaluations. BLUP. Best Linear Unbiased Prediction, TPI-Summaries.* Brattleboro, VT.

Lasley, J. F. 1987. *Genetics of Livestock Improvement.* Englewood Cliffs, NJ: Prentice-Hall.

Schmidt, G. H., et al. 1988. *Principles of Dairy Science.* Englewood Cliffs, NJ: Prentice-Hall.

Trimberger, G. W., Etgen, W. E., and Galton, D. M. 1987. *Dairy Cattle Judging Techniques.* Englewood Cliffs, NJ: Prentice-Hall.

Visuals

Animal Acquisition/Reproduction: *Introduction to Animal Acquisition—Breed Identification/Advantages and Disadvantages; Heat Detection in Dairy Cows; Artificial Insemination;* and *The Calving Process* (videotapes). Agricultural Products and Services, 2001 Killebrew Dr., Suite 333, Bloomington, MN 55420.

Dairy Breed Selection; Selecting Dairy Females; and *Dairy Breeding Systems* (sound filmstrips). Prentice-Hall Media, 150 White Plains Rd., Tarrytown, NY 10591.

Fitting and Showing Dairy Heifers (sound filmstrip); *The Dairy Judging Kit* (slides, manual and cassette). Vocational Education Production, California Polytechnic State University, San Luis Obispo, CA 93407.

CHAPTER 25

Feeding and Managing Dairy Cattle

The U.S. dairy industry has changed greatly from the days of the family milk cow. Today, it is a highly specialized industry that produces, processes, and distributes milk. A large investment in cows, machinery, barn, and milking parlor is necessary. Dairy operators who produce their own feed need additional money for land on which to grow the feed. They also need machinery to produce, harvest, and process the crops.

Although the size of dairy operations varies from 30 milking cows or less to more than 5,000 milking cows, the average dairy has approximately 100 milking cows, 30 dry cows, and 100 replacement heifers. The average dairy producer farms 200–300 acres of land, raises much of the forage, and markets the milk through cooperatives, of which he or she is a member. These producers sell about 3 tons of milk daily, or about 2.2 million lb annually, worth about $230,000. Their average total capital investment may exceed a half million dollars. The average producer has a partnership with a family member or another person to make management of time and resources easier.

The dairy operator must provide feed and other management inputs to keep animals healthy and at a high level of efficient milk production. Feed and other inputs must be provided at a relatively low cost compared with the price of milk if the dairy operation is profitable.

NUTRITION OF LACTATING COWS

The average milk production per cow in the United States for a lactation period of 305 days is approximately 14,000 lb. Some herd averages exceed 25,000 lb, and some top-producing cows yield more than 40,000 lb of milk per year. Thus, some lactating cows may produce more than 150 lb of milk, more than 5 lb of milk fat, and more than 4.5 lb of protein per day. A great need for energy and total amount of feed is created by lactation. For example, a cow weighing 1,400 lb that produces 40 lb milk daily needs 1.25 times as much energy for lactation as it needs for maintenance. If she is producing 80 lb of milk daily, she needs 2.5 times the energy for milk production than is needed for maintenance.

Providing adequate nutrition to lactating dairy cows is challenging and complex. Some reasons for this complexity are shown in Figure 25.1. The dairy cow's nutritional needs vary widely during the production cycle. Dairy producers must formulate rations to match each period of the production cycle so as to optimize milk yield and reproduction, prevent metabolic disorders, and increase longevity.

It is difficult during the first 2–4 months after calving to provide adequate nutrition because milk yield is high and intake is limited. As the nutrient intake is less than the nutrient demand for milk, the cow uses her body fat and protein reserves to make up the difference. Thus the cow is in a negative energy balance and usually loses body weight during the months of heavy milk production (Fig. 25.1). This same period of time can also be challenging to reproduction as conception rates are usually lower when cows are losing weight.

Body condition scores (1 = thin, 3 = average, 5 = fat) can be used to monitor nutrition, reproduction, and health programs for dairy herds. Condition scores of low 3s and high 2s are acceptable during the first few weeks after calving, but body condition scores in the low 4s are necessary as the cows move into the dry period. Scores lower or higher than these signal potential management problems. Cows can be grouped by condition score and stage of lactation to provide adequate nutrition at effective costs.

At 2–3 months into the lactation period, daily milk production peaks and then starts to decline; feed intake is adequate or higher than milk production demands. This contributes to bodyweight gain (Fig. 25.1). The energy content of the ration should be monitored after approximately 5 months of lactation to prevent the cow from becoming too fat.

Different types and amounts of feeds can be used to provide the needed energy, protein, vitamins, and minerals to lactating cows. The availability, palatability, and relative costs of different feeds are the primary factors influencing ration composition. Basic nutrition principles, presented in Chapters 15, 16, and 17, provide the foundation for developing dairy cattle feeding programs.

Most dairy cattle rations are based on roughages (hays and silages). Roughages are usually the cheapest source of nutrients; often they are produced by dairy farms, but increasing herd

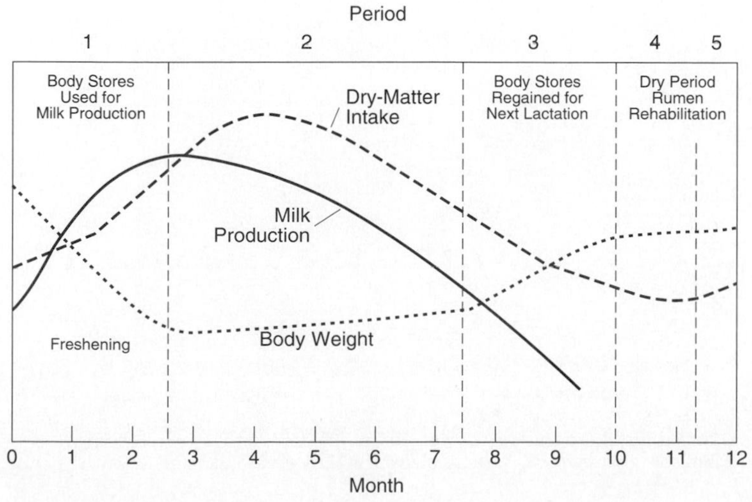

FIGURE 25.1. Nutrient and milk yield relationships during lactation and gestation. Courtesy of Hoffmann-LaRoche, Inc. *Nutritional needs of dairy cows.* (Growthlines). Fall 1989.

size, greater managerial demands, higher land-tax costs, and cheaper feeds are changing this traditional role. In some cases, roughages are fed free-choice and separate from the concentrates, which are fed in restricted amounts. In other cases, silages and concentrates are mixed together before being fed to the cows; this is known as a **total mixed ration,** which is becoming the preferred way of feeding dairy cows. Chopped hay and silage can be delivered to mangers on each side of an open alleyway (Fig. 25.2).

Lactating dairy cows cannot obtain an adequate supply of nutrients from an all-roughage ration. Concentrates are supplied in amounts consistent with the level of milk production, body weight of the cow, amount of nutrients in the roughage, and the nutrient content of the concentrates. Concentrates are usually provided to cows while they are being milked. However, high-producing cows requiring large amounts of concentrates do not have sufficient time in the milking parlor to consume all the necessary grain; therefore, additional concentrates are usually fed at another location.

The computer is increasingly involved with dairy feeding programs today. Many dairy farms have feeding stations that use computers to determine how much concentrate a cow will be fed based on need for milk production and to control the rate (lb/hour) the concentrate is made available to the cow. These devices have two advantages: (1) they prevent cows from overconsuming concentrates, and (2) they prevent cows from eating concentrates too rapidly so as to prevent metabolic upsets.

There are economic advantages in feeding concentrates in relation to quantity of milk produced by each cow. However, this method tends to feed a cow that is declining in production too generously and to feed a cow that is increasing in production inadequately. It is a poor economic practice to allow cows in their last 2 months of lactation to have all the concentrates

FIGURE 25.2.
Arrangement used for feeding chopped hay and silage to dairy cows. The feed is delivered to the feeding area from a truck that proceeds along the open alleyway. Courtesy of Dr. Lloyd Swanson, Animal Science Department, Oregon State University.

TABLE 25.1. Examples of Rations Needed to Meet the Nutrient Requirements of a 1,350-lb Dairy Cow with 3.8% Fat Test

Period[a]	Daily Milk Production (lb)	Daily Dry-matter Intake (lb)	Ration (lb/day; as fed)
1	90	49	Alfalfa hay (28 lb)[b]; corn-oats grain mix (21 lb); soybean oil meal (5 lb); dical (0.5 lb); salt, vitamin, trace mineral mix (0.3 lb)
3	50	38	Alfalfa hay (27 lb)[b]; corn-oats grain mix (16 lb); soybean oil meal (4.5 lb); dical (0.3 lb); salt, vitamin, trace mineral mix (0.25 lb)
4	dry	24	Alfalfa hay (12 lb)[b]; corn silage (43 lb); monosodium phosphate (0.1 lb); salt, vitamin, trace mineral mix (0.1 lb)

[a] Refer to Fig. 25.1
[b] Contains 20% crude protein.
Source: Hoffmann-LaRoche, Inc. *Nutritional needs of dairy cows.* Growthlines. Fall 1989.

that they can consume. Heavy feeding at this stage of lactation does not result in increased milk production.

Young (2-year-old) cows that are genetically capable of high production should be fed large amounts of concentrates to provide the nutrition they need to grow as well as produce milk. Without adequate nutrition, their subsequent breeding and lactation may be hindered.

Forages vary immensely in nutrient concentrations. Legumes (alfalfa) have high calcium, protein, and potassium relative to animal nutrient requirements, whereas other forages such as grasses and corn silage are considerably lower. Concentrates (grains) usually are low in calcium and high in phosphorus. The amount of protein supplement (soybean meal) and mineral supplement that must be added to a concentrate formulation obviously depends on the type and amount of forage being fed. Trace mineralized salt and vitamins A, D, and E are usually added to concentrates.

Table 25.1 shows examples of rations formulated to meet the nutrient requirements of dairy cows in various periods of production.

NUTRITION OF DRY COWS

How dry cows are fed and managed may influence their milk production level and health in the next lactation.

A common practice of drying off lactating cows is abruptly to stop milking the cow; with high producers, however, this may be traumatic and dry-off may need to be more gradual (intermittent milking). The buildup of pressure in the mammary gland causes the secretory tissues to stop producing milk. At the last milking, the cow should be infused with a treatment for preventing mastitis.

Dairy producers plan for a 50–60-day dry period. Short dry periods usually reduce future milk yield because the cow has not adequately improved body condition and the mammary tissue has not properly regenerated. Long dry periods can lower milk yield by the cow becoming overly fat, and profitability may be less because feed costs are increased.

Dry cows should be separated from the lactating cows so they can be fed and managed consistent with their needs. Dry cows need less concentrates than lactating cows. If dry cows overeat, they will likely become fat. This excessive body fat may lower future milk yield and cause health problems, such as fatty liver, ketosis, mastitis, retained placenta, metritis, milk fever, or even death.

NUTRITION OF REPLACEMENT HEIFERS

Young heifers (5 months of age and older) can meet most of their nutritional needs from good-quality legume or grass-legume pasture in addition to 2–3 lb of grain. If the pasture quality is poor, they will need good-quality legume hay and 3–5 lb of grain. In winter, good-quality legume hay or silage and 2–3 lb of grain are needed. If the forage is grass (hay or silage), the heifers will need 3–5 lb of grain to keep them growing well.

Heifers should be large enough to breed at about 15 months of age and calve as 2-year-olds. Weight recommendations for heifers from different breeds are shown in Table 25.2. Weight is important because it affects when the heifer reaches puberty and can be bred. Also, heavier heifers at first calving produce more milk. For example, the optimum weight at calving for Holstein heifers is 1,200–1,250 lb. Lighter heifers produce less milk and heavier heifers are too costly for the increased production.

NUTRITION OF BULLS

It is recommended that dairy bulls not be kept on the farm and that all breeding be done AI. By not keeping bulls on the farm, producers (1) decrease the risk of a dangerous bull and (2) increase genetic progress by using Superior AI bulls.

CALVING OPERATIONS

Dairy cows that are close to calving should be separated from other cows, and each cow should be placed in a maternity stall that has been thoroughly cleaned and bedded with clean bedding. The cow in a maternity stall can be fed and watered there. A cow that delivers her calf without

TABLE 25.2. Recommended Weights at Breeding for Replacement Heifers

Breed	Weight (lb)
Ayrshire	720–750
Brown Swiss	800–875
Guernsey	720–750
Holstein	800–875
Jersey	630–650

Source: Hoffmann-LaRoche, Inc. *Nutritional needs of dairy cows.* Growthlines. Fall 1989.

difficulty should not be disturbed; however, assistance may be necessary if the cow has not calved by 4–6 hours from the start of labor. Extreme difficulties in delivering a calf may require the services of a veterinarian, who should be called as early as possible.

As soon as a calf arrives, it should be wiped dry. Any membranes covering its mouth or nostrils should be removed, and its **navel** should be dipped in a tincture of iodine solution to deter infection. Producers should be sure newborn calves have an adequate amount of colostrum because colostrum contains antibodies to help the calf resist any invading microorganisms that might cause illness. The cow should be milked to stimulate her milk production.

Many commercial dairy operators dispose of bull calves shortly after the calves are born. Some bull calves are fed for veal, while others are castrated and fed for beef. Heifer calves are grown, bred, and milked for at least one lactation to evaluate their milk-producing ability.

Dairy calves rarely nurse their dams. Usually they are removed from their dam and fed milk or milk replacer for several days. Calves that are separated from one another usually have fewer health problems and thus a higher survival rate (Fig. 25.3).

Milk that is not salable or milk substitutes are fed to the young calves. Grain and leafy hay are provided to young calves to encourage them to start eating dry feeds and to stimulate rumen development. As soon as calves are able to consume dry feeds (45–60 days of age), milk or milk replacer is removed from the diet because of its high cost.

MILKING AND HOUSING FACILITIES FOR DAIRY COWS

Dairy farming is labor intensive, so labor-saving machines are common parts of the facilities. Dairy cows usually are managed in groups of 20–50 head; they may be housed in free-stall (cows have access to stalls but are not tied) or loose housing systems. These facilities reduce cleaning, feeding, and handling time as well as labor. In tie-stall barns, cows are tied in a stanchion and remain there much of the year; feeding and milking are done individually in the

FIGURE 25.3.
An example of calf separation and isolation. These individual fiberglass calf huts are used for dairy calves from birth to weaning. The huts are 3.5 ft × 7.5 ft with an attached wire pen in front. Courtesy of Colorado State University.

FIGURE 25.4.
A water flush-free stall barn with individual lock-in stanchions. These facilities provide for inside feeding of totally mixed rations. Courtesy of Colorado State University.

stanchion. In this case, a pipeline milking system is used. Cows are milked in place and milk is carried by a stainless-steel or glass pipe to the bulk tank, where it is cooled and stored. In loose housing systems, such as the loaf shed or free stall (Fig. 25.4), cows are brought to a specialized milking facility, called a **parlor,** for milking.

All housing systems require daily or twice daily removal of manure and waste feed; this may be done mechanically (tractor-blade) or by flushing with water. Manure, urine, and other wastes usually are applied directly to land and/or stored in a lagoon, pit, or storage tank for breakdown before being sprayed or pumped (irrigated) onto land.

MILKING OPERATIONS

The modern milking parlor is a concrete platform raised about 30 inches above the floor (pit) of the parlor (Fig. 25.5). It is designed to speed the milking operation, reduce labor, and make milking easier for the operator. Cows enter the parlor in groups or individually, depending on the facility. The udder and teats are washed clean, dried, and massaged for about 20–30 seconds. Milking begins about 1 minute later and continues for about 6–8 minutes. After milking is completed, the milking unit is removed manually or by computer, and the teats are dipped in a weak iodine solution.

Modern milking machines (Figs. 25.6 and 25.7) are designed to milk cows gently, quickly, and comfortably. Some have a takeoff device to remove the milking cup once the rate of flow drops below a designated level. Removal of the milking unit as soon as milking is complete is important because prolonged exposure to the machine can cause teat and udder damage and lead to disease problems (mastitis).

FIGURE 25.5.
A trigon milking parlor equipped with computer units and automatic milker takeoffs. Two sides of the milking parlor will accommodate six cows each, while the third side handles four cows. Courtesy of Colorado State University.

The milking machine operates on a two-vacuum system: one vacuum is located inside the rubber liner and the other vacuum outside the rubber liner of the teat cup (Fig. 25.8). There is a constant vacuum on the teat to remove the milk and keep the unit on the teat. The intermittent vacuum in the pulsation chamber causes the rubber liner to collapse around the teat. This assists blood and lymph to flow out of the distal teat into the upper part of the teat and udder.

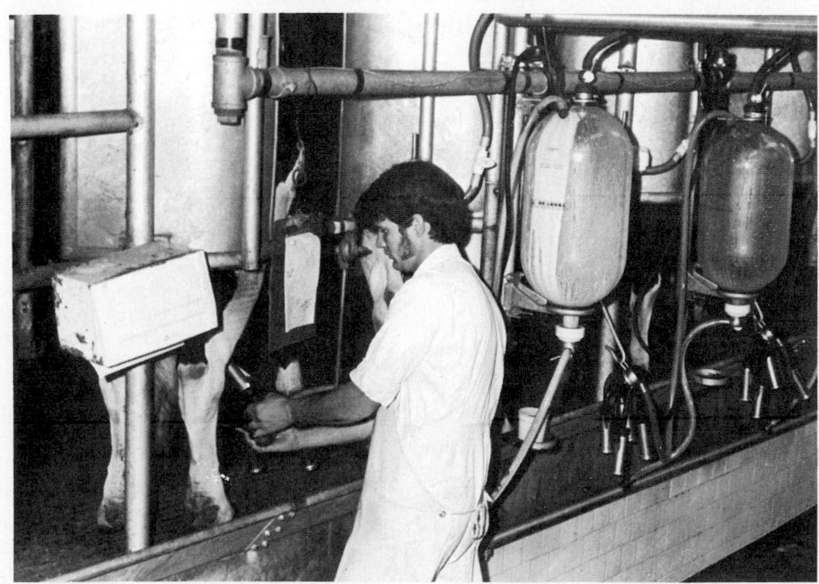

FIGURE 25.6.
The suction cups are applied to the teats of the cow so that she can be milked by machine after she has come to her place in the milking parlor. Courtesy of Dr. Lloyd Swanson, Animal Science Department, Oregon State University.

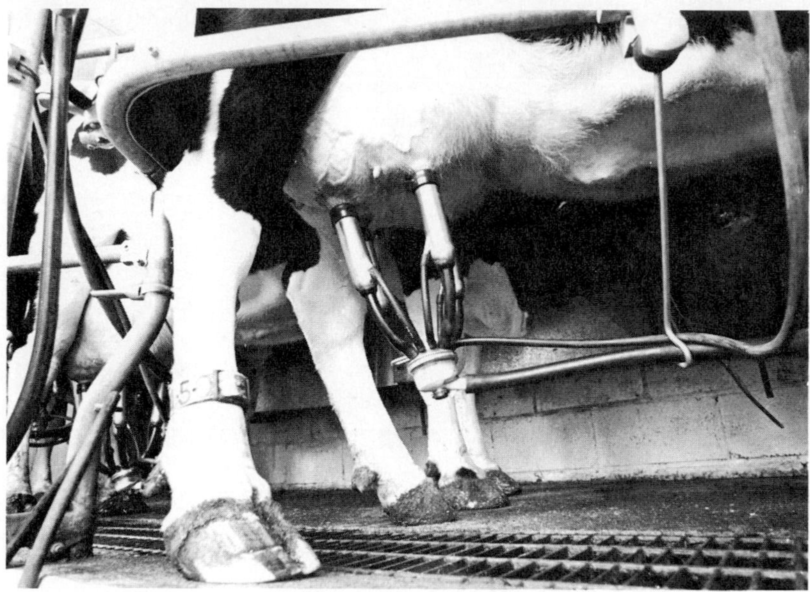

FIGURE 25.7.
Modern milker on cow. The personnel in charge of milking observe closely to be certain that the suction cups are removed as soon as the cow has been milked (unless the machine can automatically reduce its suction at that time). Injury to the udder can result if suction continues for some time after milking has been completed. Courtesy of De Laval Agricultural Division, Alfa-Laval, Inc., Poughkeepsie, NY.

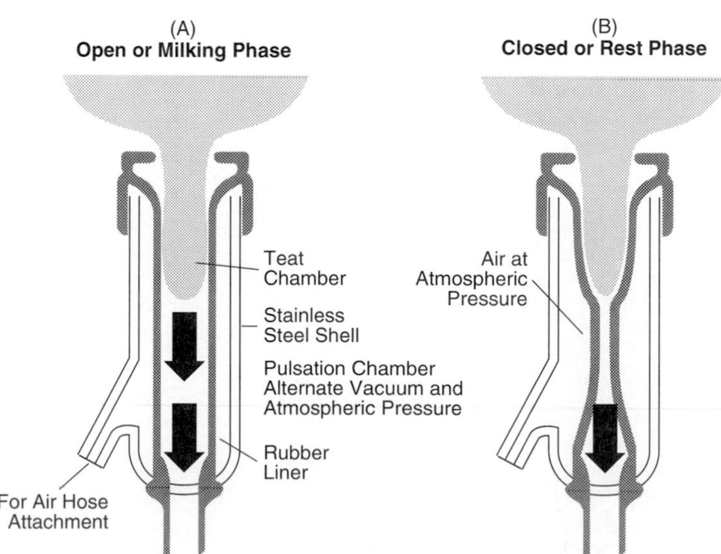

FIGURE 25.8.
Cross section of the teat cup of a milking machine. (A) During the open or milking phase, the vacuum level is the same on both sides of the liner, permitting it to be in an open position. (B) During the closed or rest phase, atmospheric air is admitted into the pulsation chamber by the pulsator. The pressure differential between the inside of the liner and the outside causes the liner to collapse. Courtesy of De Laval Agricultural Division, Alfa-Laval, Inc., Poughkeepsie, NY.

The milking parlor and its equipment must be kept sanitary. The pipes are cleaned and sanitized between milkings.

Regular milking times are established with equal intervals between milkings. Most cows are milked twice per day; however, high-producing cows produce more milk if they are milked three times a day. The latter is labor intensive and economically feasible only in herds with high levels of productivity.

CONTROLLING DISEASES

Dairy and beef cattle are afflicted by the same diseases but some diseases are more serious in dairy cattle than in beef cattle. Certain disease organisms can be transmitted through milk and can be a major problem for people who consume unpasteurized milk.

Several diseases, such as tuberculosis and brucellosis, can affect the health of dairy cattle and of humans consuming their milk. Requirements for the production of grade A milk include that the herd (1) must be checked regularly with the ring test for tuberculosis, and (2) must be bled and tested for brucellosis. Further, milking and housing facilities must be clean and meet certain specifications. Grade A milk must have a low bacteria count and somatic cell count (low mastitis). Grade A milk sells at a higher price than lower grades of milk; therefore, most dairy producers strive to produce grade A milk.

Bang's disease (brucellosis) is caused by the *Brucella abortus* organism. It can markedly reduce fertility in cows and bulls and it can be contracted by humans as a disease known as *undulant fever.* Heifers should be calfhood vaccinated to provide immunity from disease. Since most dairy cows are bred by artificial insemination, there is little danger of a clean herd becoming contaminated from breeding. Persons drinking unpasteurized milk are taking a serious risk unless they know that the milk comes from a clean herd.

Perhaps the most troublesome disease in dairy cattle is **mastitis**—inflammation and infection of the mammary gland. The disease destroys tissue, impedes milk production, and lowers

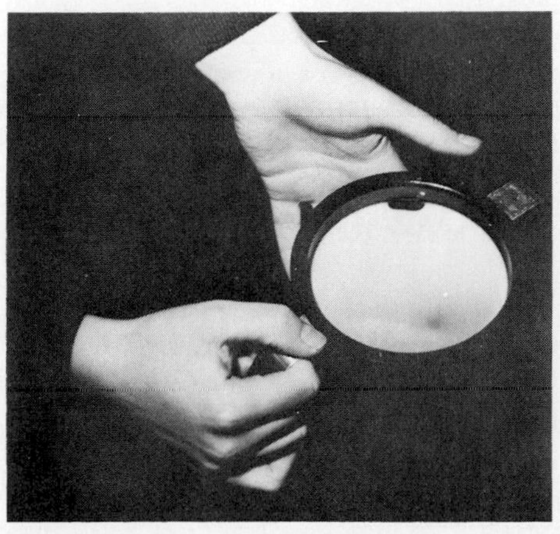

A

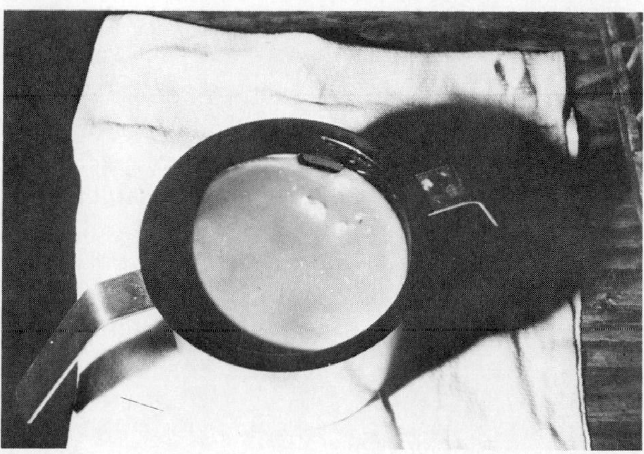

B

FIGURE 25.9.
(A) Normal milk. (B) Ropey milk in strip cups. Courtesy of Dr. Lloyd Swanson, Animal Science Department, Oregon State University.

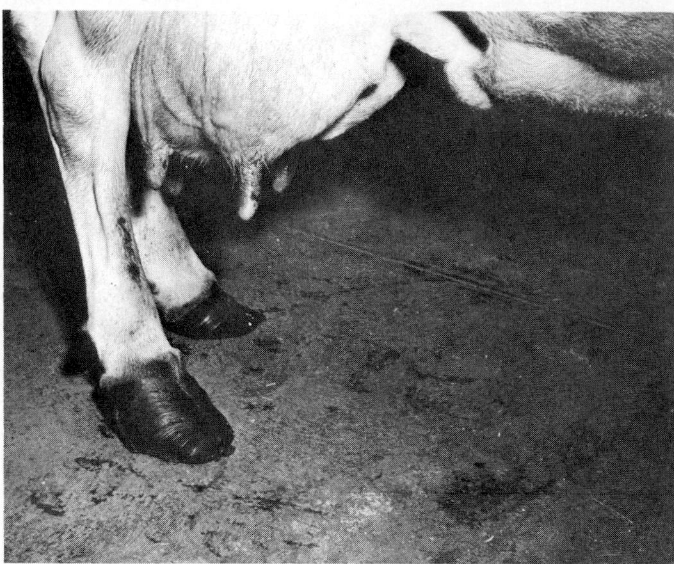

FIGURE 25.10.
A pendulous udder afflicted with mastitis. An udder is pendulous when the udder floor is below the hock and the fore and rear attachments are broken down. Courtesy of Dr. H. P. Adams, Oregon State University.

milk quality. Mastitis costs the U.S. dairy industry more than $1.5 billion each year or approximately $200 per cow annually.

In its early stage of development, subclinical mastitis is undetectable by the human eye. This type of mastitis can be detected only with laboratory equipment (Somatic Cell Counter at the DHI testing laboratory) or with a cow-side test called the California Mastitis Test (CMT). In the latter test, a reagent is added with a paddle to small wells, then milk is squirted from each quarter into a specific well. If a reaction occurs, then the relative degree of subclinical mastitis infection can be determined (Fig. 25.9). As mastitis progresses, small white clots appear in the milk. At this stage it is called **clinical mastitis** and it is easily observed. One can also collect milk using a strip cup, which has a fine screen on a dark background such that white flakes, strings, or blood (from infected areas) can be seen. As mastitis progresses, the milk shows more clots, watery milk, and acute infection. At this stage of mastitis, the signs of mastitis in the cow are obvious: the udder is swollen, red, and hot and gives pain to the cow when touched. In the final stages of mastitis, the gel formation becomes dark and is present in a watery fluid. At this stage, the udder has been so badly damaged that it no longer functions properly.

Susceptibility to mastitis may be genetically related to a certain degree, but environmental factors such as bruises, improper milking, and unsanitary conditions are more prevalent causes of mastitis. High-producing animals may be more prone to stress and mastitis than low-producing animals. Also, cows with **pendulous** udders or odd-shaped teats are more likely to develop mastitis (Fig. 25.10). Housing facilities and milking procedures are other important factors.

The best approach to controlling mastitis is using good management techniques to prevent its outbreak. These include using routine mastitis tests (DHI or CMT), treating infected animals, preventing infection from spreading, dipping tests after milking, using dry-cow therapy, and practicing good husbandry for cleanliness. Chronically infected cows may have to be sold.

TABLE 25.3. Enterprise Analysis of 37 Dairy Farms

Item	Enterprise Average
1. Number of farms	37
2. Number of cows	82
3. Percent of breeding herd sold	39%
4. Number of young stock	100
5. Lb milk sold/cow	15,247
6. Lb milk sold/farm	1,246,748
7. Total capital managed, business unit	$463,088
8. Acres operated	424
9. Person years of labor (operator, family, hired—3,000 hr/person)	2.6
10. Value of total farm production	$149,408
11. Total operating costs, except feed fed	$105,221
12. Net farm-operating profit—business	$ 44,187
13. Net farm-operating profit—operator	$ 40,702
14. Return to management, business unit	$ 486
15. Cash available—operator	$ 43,457
16. Total lb milk equivalent produced	1,472,547
17. Lb milk equivalent from beef and miscellaneous income	225,799
18. Capital used in enterprise	$222,725
19. Return to management, dairy enterprise	$ 7,214
20. Gross milk price received/cwt	$13.46
Total Allocated Costs to Produce 100 Lb Milk Equivalent	
Operating or Variable Costs	
21. Feed	
Grain ration	$ 4.54
Hay and haylage	1.57
Silage and green chop	0.67
Pasture	0.19
Total feed	$ 6.97
22. Veterinary and medicine	0.26
23. Other livestock supplies and hauling	1.06
24. Labor: operator, family, and hired	1.96
25. Machinery and equipment repairs and hire	0.60
26. Utilities	0.26
27. Insurance and property and sales taxes	0.12
28. Real estate repairs	0.18
29. Miscellaneous overhead	0.04
30. Operating interest	0.52
31. Total variable costs	$11.97
Overhead or Fixed Costs	
32. Real estate tax, depreciation, and interest on buildings	$ 0.40
33. Interest on cow herd	0.42
34. Interest and depreciation on machinery and equipment	0.28
35. **Total fixed costs**	$ 1.10
36. **Total allocated costs** (line 31 + line 35)	$13.07
37. **Return to management and risk**	$ 0.39

Source: University of Missouri Farm Management Newsletter, September 1990.

When mastitis is diagnosed, treatment must begin immediately if the udder is to be saved. Most treatments involve infusing an antibiotic into the udder through the teat canal. Depending on the antibiotic used, milk from treated cows should not be sold for human use for 3–5 days after the final treatment is given.

Other diseases and health practices are discussed in Chapter 21.

COSTS AND RETURNS

Table 25.3 shows enterprise averages for 37 dairy farms. Milk production and costs of production are also shown in the table. Note that costs and returns are calculated on a per-hundred-pounds-of-milk basis. In this example, the milk price received was $13.07/cwt. Net return was $0.39/cwt; small operations (those with less than 50 cows) had a net return of −$0.89, while large operations (those with over 70 cows) had a net return of $0.64/cwt. The item with the highest cost was feed, ranging from $6.82/cwt for large operations to $7.89/cwt for small operations.

Refer to Chapter 36 for a more detailed discussion of costs and returns.

SELECTED REFERENCES

Publications

Babson Brothers Dairy Research Service. 1980. *The Way Cows Will Be Milked on Your Dairy Tomorrow.* 8th ed. Oak Brook, IL: Babson Brothers Dairy Research Service.

Bath, D. L., Dickinson, F. N., Tucker, H. A., and Appleman, R. D. 1985. *Dairy Cattle: Principles, Practices, Problems, Profits.* Philadelphia: Lea & Febiger.

The changing dairy farm. 1986. *New York's Food and Life Sciences Quarterly* 16.

Etgen, W. M. 1987. *Dairy Cattle Feeding and Management.* New York: Wiley.

Hoffmann-LaRoche, Inc. 1989–90. *Nutritional Needs of Dairy Cows.* Nutley, NJ: Hoffmann-LaRoche.

National Research Council. 1988. *Nutrient Requirements of Dairy Cattle.* Washington, DC: National Academy Press.

Schmidt, G. H., et al. 1988. *Principles of Dairy Science.* Englewood Cliffs, NJ: Prentice-Hall.

Visuals

Nutrition—*Common Feeds for Dairy Cattle; Nutrition Related Problems;* and *Storage and Handling of Feed.* Herd Health/Husbandry—*Distinguishing Normal and Abnormal Cattle; Normal Movements and Body Positions of Dairy Cattle; Animal Handling;* and *Young Stock Management.* Waste Management/Buildings and Equipment—*Waste Storage;* and *Buildings* (videotapes). Agricultural Products and Services, 2001 Killebrew Dr., Suite 333, Bloomington, MN 55420.

CHAPTER 26

Swine Breeds and Breeding

Breeds of swine are genetic resources available to swine producers. Most market pigs in the United States today are crossbreds, but these crossbreds have their base and continued perpetuation from seedstock herds that maintain pure breeds of swine. A knowledge of the breeds, their productive characteristics, and their crossing abilities is an important part of profitable swine production.

CHARACTERISTICS OF SWINE BREEDS

In the early formation of swine breeds, breeders distinguished one breed from another primarily through visual characteristics. These visual, distinguishing characteristics for swine were, and continue to be, hair color and erect or drooping ears. Figure 26.1 shows the major breeds of swine and their primary distinguishing characteristics.

Relative importance of swine breeds is shown by registration numbers recorded by the different breed associations (Table 26.1). Although the registration numbers are for registered purebreds, the numbers do reflect the demand for breeding stock by commercial producers who produce market swine primarily by crossbreeding two or more breeds. Note how the popularity of breeds has changed with time. This change has resulted, in part, from using more objective measurements of productivity and the breeds' ability to respond to the demand and selection for higher productivity and profitability.

Competitors of purebred breeders are large corporate seedstock suppliers who offer boars and gilts of specialized bloodlines. These lines of breeding, usually called **hybrids,** originated from crossing two or more breeds, then applying some specialized selection programs. Farmers Hybrid Company was the first swine-breeding corporation; it formed in the 1940s. Since 1960 it has been joined by DeKalb, Kleen Leen, Land O' Lakes, and Pig Improvement Company (PIC). An example of a hybrid boar is shown in Figure 26.1.

Landrace (white, large drooped ears)

Chester White (white, drooped ears)

Yorkshire (white, erect ears)

Hampshire (black with white belt; erect ears)

Poland China (black with white on legs, snout, and tail; drooped ears)

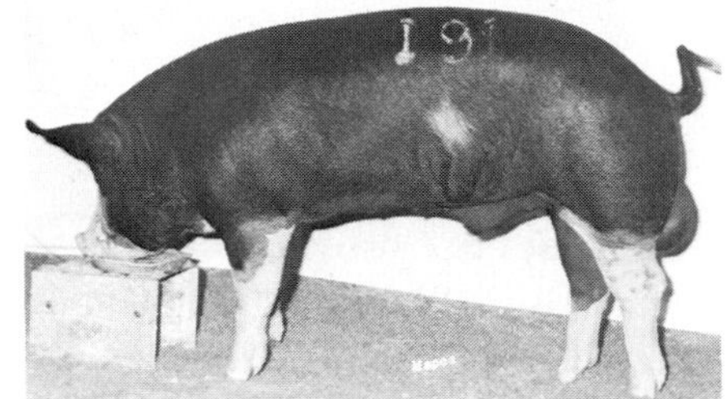

Berkshire (black with white on legs, snout, and tail; erect ears)

Duroc (red, drooped ears)

Spotted (black and white spots, drooped ears)

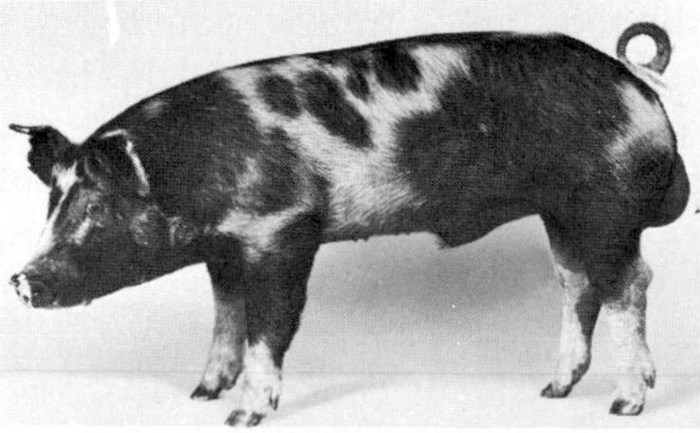

Boar Power (Hybrid boar)
(hybrids are not considered to be purebred breeds but are used similarly to purebred breeds. Foundation breeding of hybrids comes from several breeds and hybrids are bred as pure lines; no consistent color or ear set.)

FIGURE 26.1.

The major breeds of swine in the United States. Courtesy of Poland China Record Association, Knoxville, Illinois (Poland China); National Spotted Swine Record, Bainbridge, Indiana (Spotted); American Landrace, Lebanon, Indiana (Landrace); USDA (Hampshire and Chester White); American Yorkshire Club, West Lafayette, Indiana (Yorkshire); American Berkshire Association, Springfield, Illinois (Berkshire); United Duroc Swine Registry, Peoria, Illinois (Duroc); and Farmers Hybrid Company, Des Moines, Iowa (Boar Power).

TABLE 26.1. Annual Registration Numbers for Major U.S. Breeds of Swine

Breed	Annual Registrations (in thousands)					Year Association Formed
	1989[a]	1985	1980	1975	1970	
Yorkshire	211.6	216.0	220.8	121.0	42.2	1935
Duroc	193.3	206.2	224.4	178.6	62.8	1883
Hampshire	147.9	109.9	120.7	131.1	74.1	1893
Spotted	62.6	87.5	124.0	—	14.0	1914
Chester White	54.6	41.1	44.1	25.5	16.5	1930
Landrace	33.8	38.6	82.3	—	6.1	1950
Berkshire	19.1	20.0	21.0	—	7.2	1875
Poland China	16.0	22.0	20.4	18.8	11.2	1876

[a] Breeds having 10,000 or more registrations are listed.
Source: Various swine breed associations.

TRAITS AND THEIR MEASUREMENTS

Sow Productivity

Sow productivity, which is of extremely high economic importance, is measured by litter size, number weaned per litter, 21-day litter weight, and number of litters per sow per year. A combination of pig number (born alive) and litter weight at 21 days best reflects sow productivity (Fig. 26.2). Litter weight at 21 days is used to measure milk production because the young pigs have consumed little supplemental feed before that time. Sow productivity traits are lowly heritable, which means they can be best improved through changing the environment (e.g., feed, health, and so on), rather than through selective breeding. Eliminating sows low in productivity while keeping highly productive sows is still a logical practice for economic reasons but not when making major genetic change. It is important for commercial producers with effective crossbreeding programs to use breeds that rank high in sow and maternal productivity traits.

Growth

Growth rate is economically important to most swine enterprises and has a heritability of sufficient magnitude (35%) to be included in a selection program. Seedstock producers need a scale to measure weight in relation to age (Fig. 26.3). Growth rate can be expressed in several ways and typically it is adjusted to some constant basis, such as days required for swine to reach 230 lb.

Feed Efficiency

Feed efficiency measures the pounds of feed required per pound of gain. This trait is economically important because feed costs account for 60%–70% of the total production costs for commercial producers. Obtaining feed-efficiency records requires keeping individual or group feed records. However, feed efficiency can be improved without keeping feed records, such as by testing and selecting individual pigs for gain and backfat. This improvement occurs because

FIGURE 26.2.
This crossbred sow farrowed 17 pigs and raised 15 of them. The number of pigs raised per sow and the weight of the litter at 21 days of age effectively measure sow productivity. Courtesy of D. C. England, Oregon State University.

FIGURE 26.3.
Using scales to measure the growth rate of individual boars is an essential part of a sound breeding system. Courtesy of Iowa State University.

fast-gaining pigs and lean pigs tend to be more efficient in their feed utilization. Feed-efficiency records are obtained in some central boar-testing stations; however, costs and other factors need to be considered before similar records are taken on the farm.

Carcass traits are used to estimate the pounds or percentage of acceptable quality lean pork (10% fat) in the carcass. The traits used to predict carcass composition are, in order of importance, (1) fat depth over the loin at the tenth rib, (2) loin muscle area, and (3) carcass muscling score (see Chapter 8). Fortunately, measures of fatness can be predicted reliably by backfat measurements taken on live pigs by either a metal ruler or ultrasonics (Fig. 26.4). The metal probe is considerably less expensive and as accurate as ultrasonic machines. Experienced persons can visually predict significant differences in lean-to-fat composition in live pigs with a fairly high degree of accuracy.

Structural soundness—the capacity of breeding and slaughter animals to withstand the rigors of confinement rearing and breeding—is vital to the swine industry today. Breeders commonly consider unsoundness as one of the results of confinement; actually, though, confinement rearing only makes unsoundness more noticeable. Some seedstock producers raise their breeding stock in confinement (similar to the manner in which most commercial producers raise their offspring) and then cull the unsound ones.

Recent studies report unsoundness to be medium in heritability; therefore, improvement can be made through selection. Soundness can be improved through visual selection if breeders decide to cull restricted, too straight-legged, unsound boars lacking the proper flex at the hock, set of the shoulder, even size of toes, or proper curvature and cushion to the forearm and pastern.

Inherited defects and abnormalities generally occur with a low degree of frequency across the swine population. It is important to know they exist and that certain herds may experience a relatively high incidence. Certain structural unsoundness characteristics might be categorized as inherited defects. **Cryptorchidism** (retention of one or both testicles in the abdomen),

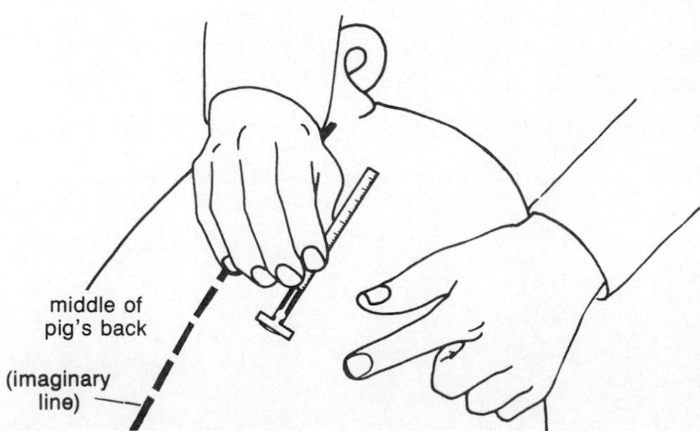

FIGURE 26.4.
A metal ruler is being used to probe this pig. The amount of backfat, measured in inches, will allow the swine breeder to predict the carcass desirability of a boar's offspring. The ruler goes through the hide and fat until it stops at the loin muscle (see Chapter 9, Plates F and G, no. 5 for fat and muscle reference points). Adapted from R. A. Battaglia, and V. B. Mayrose, *Handbook of Livestock Management Techniques* (New York: Macmillan, 1981), p. 264.

umbilical and scrotal **hernias** (rupture), and **inverted nipples** (nipples or teats do not protrude but are inverted into the mammary gland), and **PSE** carcasses (pale, soft, and exudative) are considered the most common occurring genetic defects and abnormalities. The PSE condition and the porcine stress syndrome (PSS) have occurred in recent years from selecting for extreme muscling. Most of the important genetic abnormalities are inherited as a simple recessive genes.

SELECTING REPLACEMENT FEMALES

Sow productivity is the foundation of commercial pork production. The sow herd also contributes half of the genetic composition to the growing–finishing pigs. These two factors show the importance of replacement gilt selection so that highly productive gilts can be retained in the swine herd. Fast growing, sound, moderately lean gilts with body capacity from large litters should be selected for sow herd replacements (Fig. 26.5). Among sows that have farrowed and will rebreed, those that have physical problems, bad dispositions, extremely small litters (two pigs below the herd average), and poor mothering records should be culled.

A balance between sow culling and gilt selection needs to be established. Replacement gilts should be available in sufficient numbers to replace culled sows. Gilts, replacing sows, represent a major opportunity for genetic change in the sow herd. As sows generally produce larger litters of heavier pigs than gilts, replacing large numbers of sows with gilts may reduce production levels. This production differential and the low relationship among the performance of successive litters argue for low rates of culling based on sow performance to maintain high levels of production.

The higher productive rate of sows over gilts must be balanced against the genetic change made possible by bringing gilts into production. A total gilt replacement level of 20%–25% is suggested for each farrowing. Pork producers may find economic advantages in timing the culling of sows to take advantage of high prices for sows.

The gilt selection and sow culling scheme suggested assumes that there are no major genetic antagonisms between maternal traits (litter size and milking ability) and rate of gain and

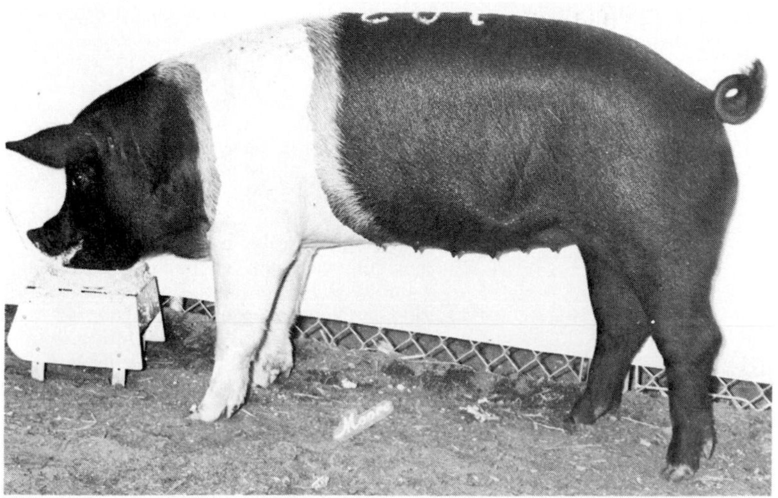

FIGURE 26.5.
This gilt has outstanding performance records for genetic superiority in the economically important traits. Courtesy of the Hampshire Swine Registry.

low-backfat thickness. Some evidence indicates that the so-called "meaty gilt" does not make a good sow. There is, however, no documented evidence that selecting fast-growing, low-backfat gilts that are not too extreme in muscling will adversely affect sow performance. Guidelines for gilt selection by age and weight are given in Table 26.2.

BOAR SELECTION

Boar selection is extremely important in making genetic change in a swine herd. Over several generations, selected boars will contribute 80%–90% of the genetic composition of the herd. This contribution does not diminish the importance of female selection. Boars should have dams that are highly productive sows. Productivity of replacement gilts is highly dependent on the level of sow productivity passed on by the boars.

The review of performance records is a must in selecting boars effectively (Fig. 26.6). The heritability and economic importance of some of their available records is shown in Table 26.3.

TABLE 26.2 Gilt Selection Calendar

When	What
Birth	Identify gilts born in large litters. Hernias, cryptorchids, and other abnormalities should disqualify all gilts in a litter from which replacement gilts are to be selected. Record birth dates, litter size, identification. Equalize litter size by moving boar pigs from large litters to sows with small litters. Pigs should nurse before moving. Keep notes on sow behavior at time of farrowing and check on dispositioin, length of farrowing, any drugs (such as oxytocin) administered, condition of udder, and extended fever.
3–5 weeks	Take 21-day weight of litter. Wean litters. Feed balanced, well-fortified diets for excellent growth and development. Screen gilts identified at birth by examining underlines and reject those with fewer than 12 well-spaced teats. If possible, at this time select and identify about two to three times the number of gilts needed for replacement.
180–200 lb	Weigh and backfat-probe potential replacement gilts. Evaluate for soundness. Select for replacements the fastest-growing, leanest gilts that are sound and from large litters. Save 25–30% more than needed for breeding. Remove selected gilts from market hogs. Place on restricted feed. Allow gilts to have exposure to a boar along the fence that separates them. Observe gilts for sexual maturity. If records are kept, give advantage to those gilts that have had several heat cycles prior to final selection.
Breeding time	Make final cull when the breeding season begins and keep sufficient extra gilts to offset the percentage nonconception in the herd. Make sure all sows and gilts are ear-marked, ear-tagged, or otherwise identified.

Source: Pork Industry Handbook, PIH-27, Guidelines for Choosing Replacement Females, 1985

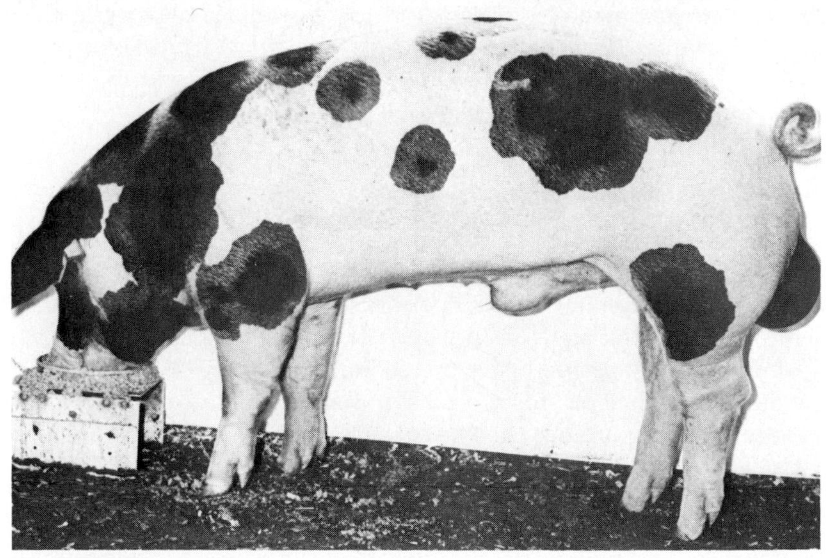

FIGURE 26.6.
This boar has outstanding records for growth, feed efficiency, and backfat thickness. He is from a sow that produced several large litters of heavy pigs at weaning time. Courtesy of the National Spotted Swine Record, Inc.

TABLE 26.3 Economic Value of Production Records of Boars

	Daily Gain (lb/day)	Feed Efficiency (lb F/G)[a]	Adjusted Backfat (in.)
Heritability	0.30	0.40	0.50
Economic value/unit change	$4.00/lb/day	$12.00/lb F/G	$3.50/in.
Records			
Boar A	2.26	2.53	0.89
Group average	2.06	2.71	1.00
Boar B	1.86	2.89	1.11
Superiority of A over B	+0.40	−0.36	−0.22

Value of Boar A over Boar B

Trait	(Superiority)	×	(Heritability)	×	(Genetic Influence)	×	(Economic Value)	=	Added Value/ 230-lb Hog
Daily gain	0.40		0.30		0.50		$ 4.00		$0.24
Feed efficiency	0.36		0.40		0.50		12.00		0.86
Backfat	0.22		0.50		0.50		3.50		0.19
									$1.29

[a]Pound of feed per pound of gain.
Source: Pork Industry Handbook (PIH-9), Boar selection guidelines for commercial producers, 1988.

TABLE 26.4 Suggested Selection Standards for Replacement Boars

Trait	Standard
Litter size	10 or more pigs farrowed; 8 or more pigs weaned.
Underline	12 or more fully developed, well-spaced teats.
Feet and legs	Wide stance both front and rear; free in movement; good cushion to both front and rear feet; equal-sized toes.
Age at 230 lb	155 days or less.
Feed/gain, boar basis (60–230 lb)	275 lb of feed/100 lb (cwt) of gain.
Daily gain (60–230 lb)	2.00 lb/day or more.
Backfat probe (adjusted to 230 lb)	1.0 in. or less.

Source: Pork Industry Handbook, PIH-9, Boar selection for commercial production, 1988.

Based on the comparison of boar A with boar B in Table 26.3, if boar A sired 700 pigs, he would return to the producer an extra $903 ($1.29 × 700). The superiority of replacement gilts retained in the herd would increase boar A's value even more. This comparison shows the value of genetically superior boars and the justification for paying more for them.

Boars should be selected from the top 50% of the test group regardless of whether the selected boars come from a central test station or from the farm. Boars meeting the standards shown in Table 26.4 should be considered as potential herd sires.

EFFECTIVE USE OF PERFORMANCE RECORDS

Records are valuable when used in breeding programs, whereas records obtained only for promotion are eventually self-defeating. The primary reason for obtaining records is to improve accuracy of selection. Records of different pigs should be obtained under a similar environment for the records to be comparable and useful. Breeders who give a small group of pigs preferential treatment are only deceiving themselves. If this procedure is used, breeders can no longer compare accurately even the individuals in their own herds, and the records thus obtained yield false conclusions.

The ultimate objective in an improvement program is to predict an animal's breeding value. Breeding value is a measure of the animal's ability to transmit desired genetic traits to the resulting offspring. Proper records on the individual and on his or her relatives can help a great deal in predicting breeding values.

Heritability estimates are medium (20% – 39%) for growth traits and high (40% and higher) for carcass traits. Genetic principles indicate that the most rapid rate of improvement for these traits is through objectively measuring the traits and selecting pigs based on their superior individual performance. Thus, the performance value of an animal for most traits can be predicted at the young age of 5–6 months and will generally result in more rapid genetic progress than a selection scheme based on sib or progeny tests or on pedigree information. Regardless of the types of facilities available, individual performance tests can be conducted on the farm if all animals are treated similarly. On-the-farm testing is essential to a program of rapid genetic improvement because it permits testing of a larger sample of the potential breeding population than is possible in central testing stations.

The principle of using on-the-farm records to identify genetically superior animals is simple. After the environment is standardized, the traits that estimate each animal's potential breeding value are measured. If the animal is superior because of environment, this animal will breed poorer than its record suggests. By contrast, an animal that has received a poorer than average environment will probably breed better than its record indicates. Therefore, it is important to determine if an animal is superior because of environment or because of genetics. In comparing animals in different herds, this determination is difficult to make.

To compare animals within a group more objectively, indexes have been developed for use in testing stations and farm programs. The index is a single numerical value that is determined from a formula that combines the values for several traits. One such index, currently in use, combines the performance of daily gain, feed efficiency, and backfat into one numerical value for individual boars. In the formula that follows, $\overline{\text{ADG}}$ (average daily gain), $\overline{\text{F/G}}$ (feed per pound of gain), and $\overline{\text{BF}}$ (backfat) represent the averages for all the pigs in the group that are tested together. The index is as follows:

$$\begin{aligned} \text{I (index)} = {} & 100 + 60 \text{ (averaging daily gain of individual} - \overline{\text{ADG}}) \\ & - 75 \text{ (feed efficiency of individual or group of litter mates} - \overline{\text{FG}}) \\ & - 70 \text{ (backfat probe or sonoray of individual} - \overline{\text{BF}}) \end{aligned}$$

An example of this index would be the index of boar A in Table 26.3. Computing this index shows that boar A is 33 points superior for a combination of daily gain, feed efficiency, and backfat when compared with the average of other boars in the test group. The index of the average boar is 100. About 20% of the boars are expected to exceed 120 index points, and 20% are expected to fall below the recommended minimum culling level of 80.

CROSSBREEDING FOR COMMERCIAL SWINE PRODUCERS

The primary function of purebred or seedstock breeders is to provide breeding stock for commercial producers. Breeding programs for seedstock producers are designed to improve genetically the economically important traits. Within a specific breed, rate of improvement will be dependent on heritability of the traits, how much selection is practiced, and how quickly generation turnover occurs. The most rapid genetic changes that have occurred over the past few decades are growth rate and leanness.

Commercial producers and seedstock producers select for the same economically important traits. Commercial producers have an added advantage over seedstock producers, in making genetic change, because crossing two or more swine breeds will increase productivity. This genetic phenomenon of heterosis or hybrid vigor is shown in Table 26.5. There is a 40% increase in total litter market weight of crossbreds, which is a cumulative effect of larger litters, high pig survival, and increased growth rate of individual pigs. This marked increase in productivity tells why 90% of the market hogs in commercial production are crossbreds. Crossbreeding allows genetic improvement in some traits with low heritabilities, such as sow productivity. There is little hybrid vigor for traits with high heritabilities, such as carcass traits.

An effective crossbreeding program takes advantage of using hybrid vigor and selecting genetically superior breeding animals from breeds that best complement one another. A pro-

TABLE 26.5. Heterosis Advantage for Production Traits

Item	First Cross Purebred Sow	Multiple Cross Crossbred Sow	Crossbred Boar
Percentage of Advantage over Purebred			
Reproduction			
Conception rate	0.0%	8.0%	10.0%
Pigs born alive	0.5	8.0	0.0
Litter size at 21 days	9.0	23.0	0.0
Litter size, weaned	10.0	24.0	0.0
Production			
21-day litter weight	10.0	27.0	0.0
Days to 220 lb	7.5	7.0	0.0
Feed/gain	2.0	1.0	0.0
Carcass composition			
Length	0.3	0.5	0.0
Backfat thickness	−2.0	−2.0	0.0
Loin muscle area	1.0	2.0	0.0
Marbling score	0.3	1.0	0.0

Source: Pork Industry Handbook, (PIH-39), 1988.

ducer needs to know the relative strengths and weaknesses of the available breeds shown in Table 26.6. These breed comparisons can change over time as a result of genetic changes made in the individual breeds. Thus, breed comparisons must be made on a regular basis. In addition, the variation within a breed must be considered; individual pig selection could vary from the performance evaluations shown in Table 26.6.

The crossbred female is an integral and important part of an effective crossbreeding program. Even though crossbreeding provides an opportunity to reap the benefits of many genetic sources, an unplanned crossing program will not yield success or profit for the pork producer. A well-planned crossbreeding system capitalizes on heterosis, takes advantage of breed strengths, and fits the producer's management program.

The two basic types of crossbreeding systems are the **rotational cross** system and the **terminal cross** system. The rotational cross system combines two or more breeds, where a different breed of boar is mated to the replacement crossbred females produced by the previous generation (Fig. 26.7). In a simple terminal cross system, a two-breed single or rotational cross female is mated to a boar of a third breed. A more complex terminal crossing system, shown in Figure 26.8, uses four breeds. In this example, crossbred boars are mated to crossbred females.

Figure 26.9 shows a **rotaterminal** crossbreeding system, which combines the three-breed rotational system and the terminal system of crossbreeding. Thus, all the pigs produced by terminal cross boars are sold because the gilts would lack the superiority needed in maternal traits (reproduction and milk). The female stock can be purchased through a system primarily emphasizing reproductive performance. This latter system maximizes heterosis; however, purchasing replacement females increases the risk of introducing disease into the herd.

TABLE 26.6 Comparative Performance Evaluations for Swine Breeds

Trait	Berkshire	Chester White	Duroc	Hampshire	Landrace	Poland China	Spotted	Yorkshire
Conception rate (%)	+	+	A	A	−−	A	A	−
Litter size (no. pigs raised to weaning)	−	++	A	−	++	−−	−	++
21-day litter weight (lb)	−	−	A	A	++	−	−−	+
Rate of gain (lb/day)	−	−	++	A	A	−	−	A
Feed efficiency (lb feed/lb gain)	A	A	+	+	A	−	A	A
Backfat (in.)	A	A	A	+	A	A	A	A
Loin eye area (sq in.)	A	A	A	+	A	+	A	A

Evaluation system:
++ = substantially superior to average
+ = superior to average
A = average or near average
− = below average
−− = substantially below average

Sources: Adapted from the *Pork Industry Handbook* (PIH-39), 1988; and *National Hog Farmer* (June and Oct. 1990).

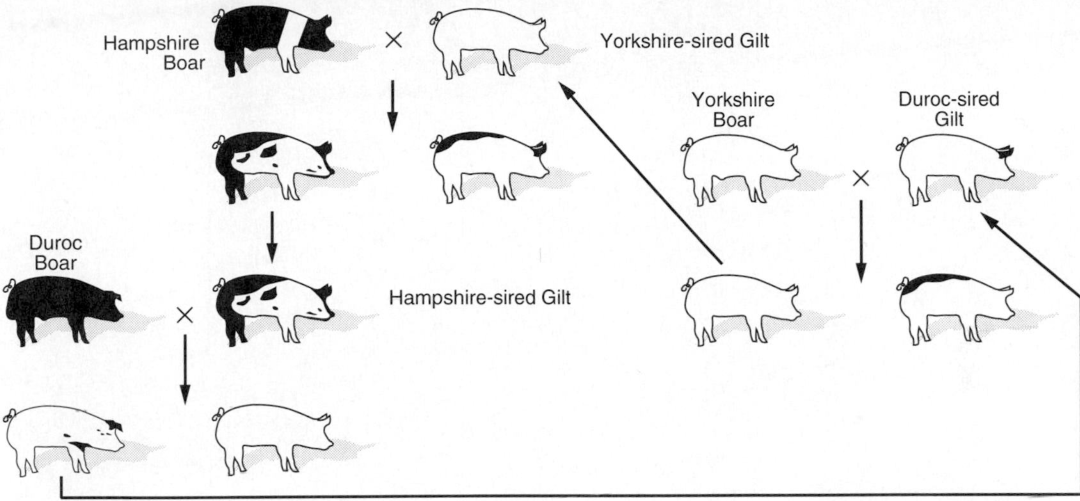

FIGURE 26.7.
Three-breed rotational crossbreeding system. Adapted from the *Pork Industry Handbook* (PIH-39), 1988.

A two- or three-breed rotational crossbreeding system may better fit a producer's management program even though heterosis is less than with a terminal cross system. A two-breed rotation results in 67% of the heterosis of a terminal cross, whereas a three-breed rotation gives 86% of the heterosis of a terminal crossing system.

The three-breed rotational cross is the most popular crossbreeding system. It combines the strong traits of a third breed not available in the other two breeds. Sires from three breeds are systematically rotated each generation and replacement crossbred females are selected each generation. These females are mated to the sire breed to which they are least related. Because reproductive performance is to be stressed in the initial two-breed cross, growth, feed efficiency,

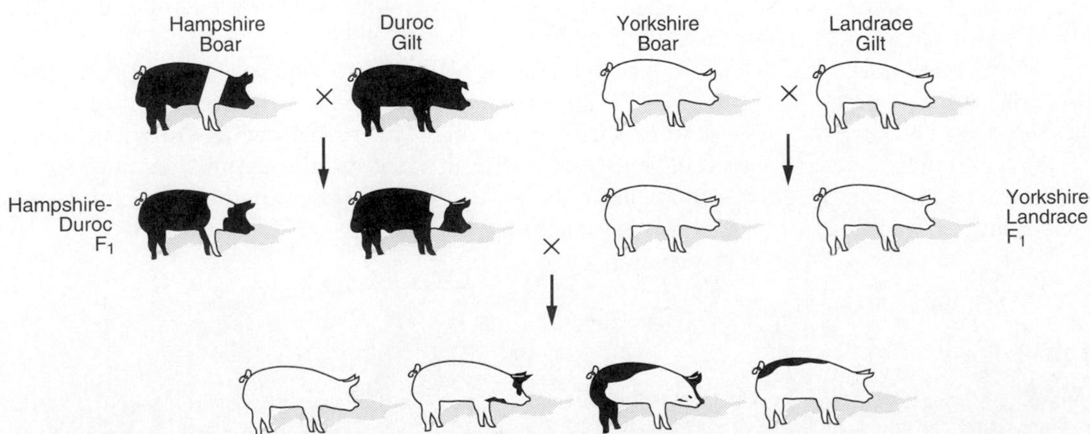

FIGURE 26.8.
Four-breed terminal crossbreeding system. Adapted from the *Pork Industry Handbook* (PIH-39), 1988.

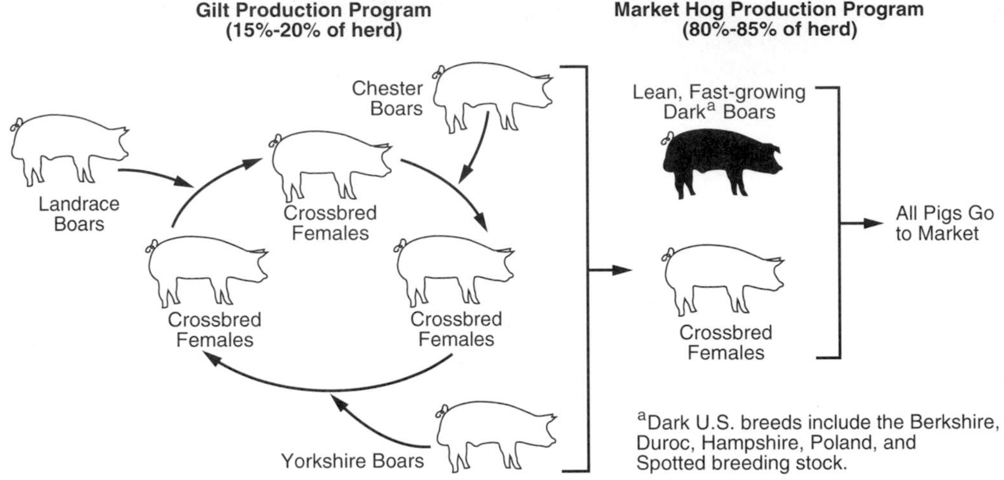

FIGURE 26.9.
A rotaterminal crossbreeding system that combines both rotational crossing and terminal crossing. Adapted from the *Pork Industry Handbook* (PIH-106), Genetic principles and their applications, 1988.

and superior carcass composition may be lower than desired. These traits can be emphasized in the individual boars selected from the third breed, although the reproduction and maternal traits should also receive attention.

Although limited research information is available on the use of crossbred boars, crossbred boars are apparently more aggressive breeders, have fewer problems in leg soundness, and improve conception rate (Table 26.5) in comparison to straightbred boars. A crossbred boar could combine those traits that may not be available in one straightbred breed.

Hybrid boars sold by some commercial companies should not be confused with crossbred boars sold by private breeders. Hybrid boars are developed from specific line crosses. These lines have been selected and developed for specific traits. When specific crosses are made, the hybrid boar is used on specific cross females to obtain the recommended breed combination and to realize a high level of heterosis in their offspring.

Commercial pork producers have many selection tools, crossing systems, and genetic breeding stock sources for their use. Producers should capitalize on heterosis and breed strengths, and require complete performance records on all selected breeding stock. Although there is no one best system, breed, or source of breeding stock, producers must evaluate their total pork production program and integrate the most profitable combination of factors associated with a crossbreeding program.

SELECTED REFERENCES

Publications

Battaglia, R. A., and Mayrose, V. B. 1981. *Handbook of Livestock Management Techniques.* New York: Macmillan.

Briggs, H. M., and Briggs, D. M. 1980. *Modern Breeds of Livestock.* New York: Macmillan.

Crossbreeding systems for commercial pork production. 1988. In *Pork Industry Handbook.* Stillwater, OK: Oklahoma State University.
Ensminger, M. E. and Parker, R. O. 1984. *Swine Science.* Danville, IL: Interstate.
Lasley, J. F. 1987. *Genetics of Livestock Improvement.* Englewood Cliffs, NJ: Prentice-Hall.
Legates, J. E. 1990. *Breeding and Improvement of Farm Animals.* 4th ed. New York: McGraw-Hill.
National Hog Farmer, 1999 Shepard Road, St. Paul, MN 55116.
Pond, W. G., and Maner, J. H. 1984. *Swine Production and Nutrition.* Westport, CT: AVI Publishing Co.
USDA. 1981. *Guidelines for Uniform Swine Improvement Programs.* USDA Program Aid 1157.

Visuals

Breeding Herd Selection and Management (sound filmstrip). Vocational Education Productions, California Polytechnic State University, San Luis Obispo, CA 93407.
Swine Breed I.D. (slide set). Vocational Education Productions, California Polytechnic State University, San Luis Obispo, CA 93407.
Swine Breed Identification; Female Selection in Swine; Boar Selection; and *Swine Breeding Systems* (sound filmstrips). Prentice-Hall Media, 150 White Plains Rd., Tarrytown, NY 10591.
The Swine Industry in the U.S.; Breeds of Swine; Types of Breeding Programs; Selection of Breeding Stock; Low Cost Swine Breeding Units; How to Handle Newly Purchased Breeding Stock; and *Breeding Management* (videotapes). Agricultural Products and Services, 2001 Killbrew Dr., Suite 333, Bloomington, MN 55420.

CHAPTER 27

Feeding and Managing Swine

Swine production in the United States is concentrated heavily in the nation's midsection known as the Corn Belt. This area produces most of the nation's corn, which is the principal feed used for swine.

TYPES OF SWINE OPERATIONS

There are four primary types of swine operations: (1) **feeder pig production,** in which the producer maintains a breeding herd and produces feeder pigs for sale at an average weight of approximately 40 lb; (2) **feeder pig finishing,** in which feeder pigs are purchased and then fed to slaughter weight; (3) **farrow-to-finish,** in which a breeding herd is maintained where pigs are produced and fed to slaughter weight on the same farm; and (4) **purebred** or **seedstock** operations, which are similar to farrow-to-finish except that their saleable product is primarily breeding boars and gilts.

FARROW-TO-FINISH OPERATIONS

Since farrow-to-finish is the major type of swine operation, primary emphasis is given to it in this chapter. The information presented here is also pertinent to the other operations, as most of them represent a certain phase of a farrow-to-finish operation.

The selecting and breeding practices used to produce highly productive swine are presented in Chapter 26. The primary objective in the farrow-to-finish production phase is to feed and manage sows, gilts, and boars economically to assure a large litter of healthy, vigorous pigs from each breeding female.

Boar Management

Boars should be purchased at least 60 days before the breeding season so they can adapt to their new environment. A boar should be purchased from a herd that has an excellent herd health program and then isolated from the new owner's swine for at least 30 days. During this time, the boar can be treated for internal and external parasites if the past owner has not recently done so. The boar should be revaccinated for erysipelas and leptospirosis. Boars not purchased from a validated brucellosis-free herd should have passed a negative brucellosis test within 30 days of the purchase date. An additional 30-day period of fence-lined exposure to the sow herd is recommended to develop immunities before the boar's use.

Younger boars (8–12 months of age) should be fed 5–6 lb/day of a balanced ration containing 14% protein, whereas older boars should receive 4–5 lb/day. The amount of feed should be adjusted to keep the boar in a body condition that is neither fat nor thin.

Young, untried boars should be test-mated to a gilt or two before the breeding season, as records show that approximately 1 of 12 young boars are infertile or sterile. The breeding aggressiveness, mounting procedure, and ability to get the gilts pregnant should be evaluated.

Successful breeding of a group of females requires an assessment of the number of boars required and the breeding ability of each boar. Generally, a young boar can pen-breed 8–10 gilts during a 4-week period. A mature boar can breed 10–12 females. Handmating (producers individually mate the boar to each female) takes more labor but extends the breeding capacity of the boar. Young boars can be handmated once daily, and mature boars can be used twice daily or approximately 10–12 times a week. Handmating can be used to mate heavier, mature boars with the use of a breeding crate. The breeding crate takes most of the boar's weight off the female. Breeding by handmating should correspond with time of ovulation (approximately 40 hours from the beginning of estrus) or litter size will be reduced.

Boars should be considered dangerous at all times and handled with care. It is unsafe for a boar to have tusks as he may inflict injury on the handler or on other pigs. All tusks should be removed prior to the breeding season and every six months thereafter.

Management of Breeding Females

Proper management of females in the breeding herd is necessary to achieve optimum reproductive efficiency. Gilts may start cycling as early as 5 months of age. It is recommended that breeding be avoided during their first heat cycle as the number of ova ovulated is usually less than in subsequent heat cycles. Mixing pens of confinement-reared gilts and regrouping them with direct boar contact initiates early puberty.

Hot weather is detrimental to a high reproductive rate in the breeding females. High temperatures (above 85°F) will delay or prevent the occurrence of estrus, reduce ovulation rate, and increase early embryonic deaths. The animals will suffer heat stress when they are sick and have an elevated body temperature as well as when the environmental temperature is high.

Besides reducing litter size, diseases such as leptospirosis, pseudorabies, and those associated with stillbirths, mummified fetuses, and embryonic deaths may also increase the problem of getting the females pregnant. Attention to a good herd health program will assure a higher reproductive performance over the years.

It is important that sows and gilts obtain adequate nutrients during gestation to assure optimum reproduction. Feeding in excess is not only wasteful and costly but is also likely to increase embryonic mortality. A limited feeding system using balanced, fortified diets is recommended (Fig. 27.1). It assures that each sow gets her daily requirements of nutrients without consuming excess energy. As a rule of thumb, 4 lb of a balanced ration provides adequate protein and energy; however, during cold weather an additional pound of feed may prove

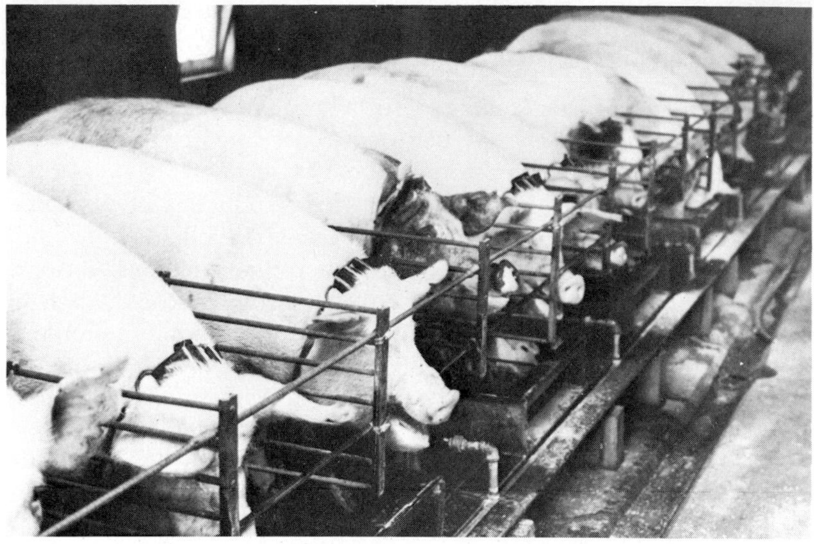

FIGURE 27.1.
Sows in individual feeding units to control the feed intake for each sow. Courtesy of the University of Illinois.

beneficial, especially for bred gilts. With limited feeding, it is important that each sow gets her portion of feed and no more. The individual feeding stall for each sow is best because it prevents the "boss sows" from taking feed from slower-eating or timid sows. During gestation, gilts should be fed so they will gain about 70–80 lb, and sows should gain approximately 30–40 lb.

Table 27.1 shows several sow rations that utilize different grains. Note how the rations are balanced for protein, specific amino acids, minerals, and vitamins.

Management of the Sow During Farrowing and Lactation

Farrowing is the process of the sow or gilt giving birth to her pigs. On the average, there are approximately 8.5 pigs farrowed per litter, with approximately 7.2 pigs weaned per litter. Well-managed swine herds typically have three to four more pigs per litter than these average figures. Extremely large litters are usually undesirable because the pigs are small and weak at birth and death losses can be high.

Proper care of the sow during farrowing and lactation is necessary to assure large litters of pigs at birth and at weaning. Sows should be dewormed about 2 weeks before being moved to the farrowing facility. The sow should be treated for external parasites, at least twice, a few days prior to farrowing time. The farrowing facility should be cleaned completely of organic matter, disinfected, and left unused for 5–7 days before sows are placed in the unit.

Before the sow is put in the farrowing pen or stall, her belly and teats should be washed with a mild soap and warm water. This helps eliminate bacteria that can cause diarrhea in nursing pigs.

Sows should be in the farrowing facility at the right time. Breeding records and projected farrowing dates should be used to determine the proper time. If farrowing is to occur in a crate or pen, the sow should be placed there no later than the 110th day of gestation. This gives some

TABLE 27.1. Suggested Sow Rations (with corn, grain sorghum, barley, or wheat as the grain source)

Ingredient	Ration Number and lb/Ration					
	1	2	3	4	5	6
Corn, yellow	1,635	1485	—	—	—	—
Grain sorghum	—	—	1,620	—	—	—
Barley	—	—	—	1,715	—	—
Wheat	—	—	—	—	1,730	1,575
Soybean meal, 44%	295	250	310	220	200	165
Dehydrated alfalfa meal, 17%	—	200	—	—	—	200
Calcium carbonate	20	13	20	23	25	15
Dicalcium phosphate	38	40	38	30	33	33
Salt	7	7	7	7	7	7
Vitamin-trace mineral mix	5	5	5	5	5	5
Total	2,000	2,000	2,000	2,000	2,000	2,000
Protein, %	13.70	13.70	14.10	14.90	15.00	14.90
Lysine, %	0.62	0.62	0.62	0.62	0.62	0.62
Tryptophan, %	0.15	0.18	0.16	0.21	0.19	0.21
Threonine, %	0.53	0.50	0.52	0.52	0.51	0.52
Methionine + cystine, %	0.49	0.50	0.44	0.45	0.43	0.44
Calcium, %	0.85	0.86	0.86	0.85	0.89	0.84
Phosphorus, %	0.65	0.65	0.66	0.66	0.66	0.66
Metabolizable energy, kcal/lb	1,444	1,403	1,383	1,255	1,446	1,408

Source: Pork Industry Handbook (PIH-23), Swine rations, 1983.

assurance the sow will be in the facility at farrowing time, as the normal gestation is 111–115 days in length. Farrowing time can be estimated by observing an enlarged abdominal area, swollen vulva, and filled teats. The presence of milk in the teats indicates that farrowing is likely to occur within 24 hours.

Before farrowing, while the sows are in the farrowing facilities, they can be fed a ration similar to the one fed during gestation. A laxative ration can be helpful at this time to prevent constipation. The ration can be made bland or bulky by the addition of 10 lb/ton of epsom salts, part of the protein as linseed meal, or the addition of oats, wheat bran, alfalfa meal, or beet pulp.

Sows need not be fed for 12–24 hours after farrowing, but water should be continuously available. Two or three pounds of a laxative feed may be fed at the first post-farrow feeding; the amount fed should be gradually increased until the optimum feed level is reached by 10 days after farrowing. Sows that are thin at farrowing may benefit from generous feeding early after farrowing. Sows nursing fewer than eight pigs may be fed a basic maintenance amount (6 lb/day) with an added amount, such as 0.5 lb for each pig being nursed. It is unnecessary to reduce feed intake before weaning. Regardless of level of feed intake, milk secretion in the udder will cease when pressure reaches a certain threshold level.

Baby Pig Management from Birth to Weaning

Most sows and gilts are farrowed in farrowing stalls or pens to protect baby pigs from the female lying on them (Fig. 27.2). Producers who give attention at farrowing will decrease the number of

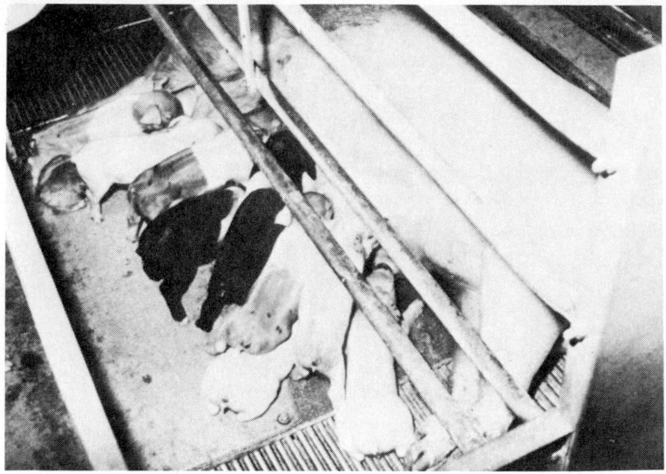

FIGURE 27.2.
Sow and litter of baby pigs in a farrowing crate. The farrowing crate is a pen (approximately 5 ft × 7 ft) that confines the sow to a relatively small area. The panel, a few inches off the floor, separates an area for the baby pigs where the sow cannot lay on them. There is ample space for the pigs to nurse the sow. Courtesy of the University of Illinois.

pigs that die during birth or within the first few hours after birth. Pigs can be freed from membranes, weak pigs can be revived, and other care can be given that will reduce baby pig death loss (Fig. 27.3). Manual assistance of the birth process should not be given unless obviously needed. Duration of labor ranges from 30 minutes to more than 5 hours, with pigs being born either head or feet first. The average interval between births of individual pigs is approximately 15 minutes, but this can vary from almost simultaneously to several hours in

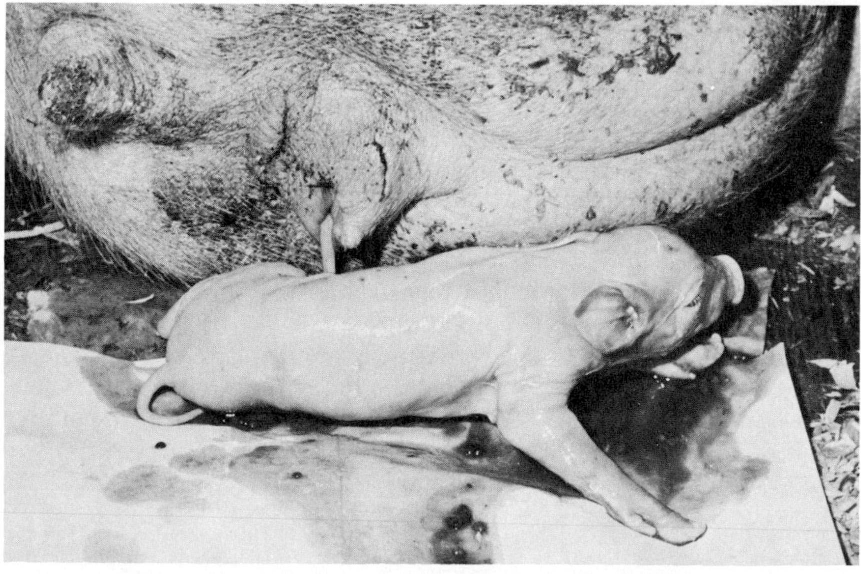

FIGURE 27.3.
A baby pig just farrowed with its umbilical cord still extending into the vulva. Proper attention by the swine producer at farrowing time can assure a higher number of pigs weaned per litter. Courtesy of R. W. Henderson, Oregon State University.

individual cases. An injection of oxytocin can be given to speed the rate of delivery after one or two pigs have been born.

Manual assistance, using a well-lubricated gloved hand, can be used to assist difficult deliveries. The hand and arm should be inserted into the reproductive tract as far as is needed to locate the pig; the pig should be grasped and gently but firmly pulled to assist delivery. Difficult births often enhance the occurrence of the symptoms of **MMA**—**mastitis** (inflammation of the udder), **metritis** (inflammation of the uterus), and **agalactia** (inadequate milk supply). Antibacterial solutions such as nitrofurazone are infused into the reproductive tract after farrowing, and sometimes intramuscular injections of antibiotics are used to decrease or prevent some of these infections.

It is important that the newborn pig receive colostrum to give immediate and temporary protection against common bacterial infections. Pigs from extremely large litters can be transferred to sows having smaller litters to equalize the size of all litters. Care should be given to ensure that baby pigs receive adequate colostrum before the transfer takes place.

Air temperature in the farrowing facility should be 70–75°F with the creep area for baby pigs equipped with zone heat (heat lamps, gas brooders, or floor heat) having a temperature of 85–95°F. Otherwise the pigs will chill and die or become susceptible to serious health problems. Moisture should be controlled or removed from the farrowing facility without creating draft on the pigs.

Management of environmental temperature from birth to 2 weeks of age is critical. At 2 weeks of age, the baby pig has developed the ability to regulate its own body temperature.

Soon after birth, the navel cord should be cut to 3–4 in. from the body and then treated with iodine. This disinfects an area that could easily allow bacteria to enter the body and cause joints to swell and abscesses to occur.

The producer should also clip the 8 sharp needle teeth of the baby pig. This prevents the sow's udder from being injured and facial lacerations from occurring when the baby pigs fight one another. Approximately one-half of each tooth can be removed by using side-cutting pliers or toenail clippers.

Good records are important to the producer interested in obtaining optimum production efficiency. The basis of good production records is pig identification. Ear notching pigs at 1–3 days of age with a system shown in Figure 27.4 provides positive identification for the rest of the pig's life.

Baby pig management from 3 days to 3 weeks of age includes anemia and scour control, castration, and tail docking. Sow's milk is deficient in iron so iron dextran shots are given intramuscularly at 3–4 days of age and again at 2 weeks of age (Fig. 27.5).

Baby pig scours are ongoing problems for the swine producer. Colostrum and a warm, dry, draft-free, and sanitary environment are the best preventative measures against scours. Orally administered drugs determined to be effective against specific bacterial strains have been found to be the best control measures for scours. Serious diarrhea problems resulting from diseases such as **transmissible gastroenteritis (TGE)** and swine **dysentery** should be treated under the direction of a local veterinarian.

Castration is usually done before the pigs are 2 weeks old. Pigs castrated at this age are easier to handle, heal faster, and are not subjected to as much stress as those castrated later. The use of a clean, sharp instrument, low incisions to promote good drainage, and antiseptic procedures make castration a simple operation.

Tail docking has become a common management practice to prevent tail biting during the

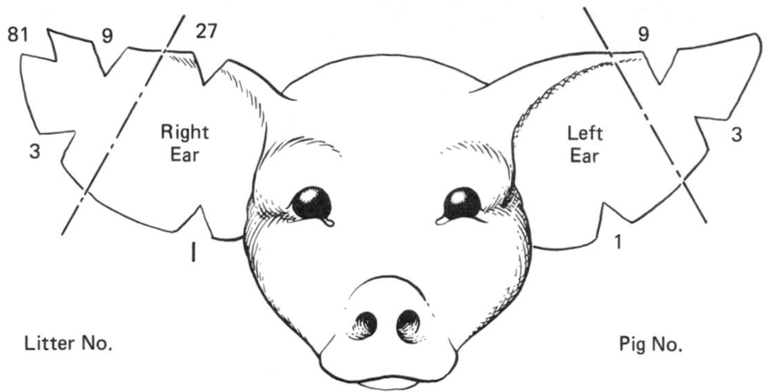

Examples:

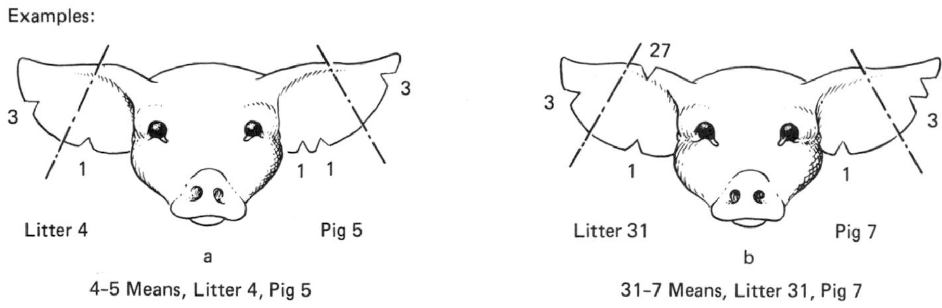

FIGURE 27.4.
An ear-notching identification system for swine. Individual pig identification is necessary for meaningful production and management records. Drawing by Dennis Giddings.

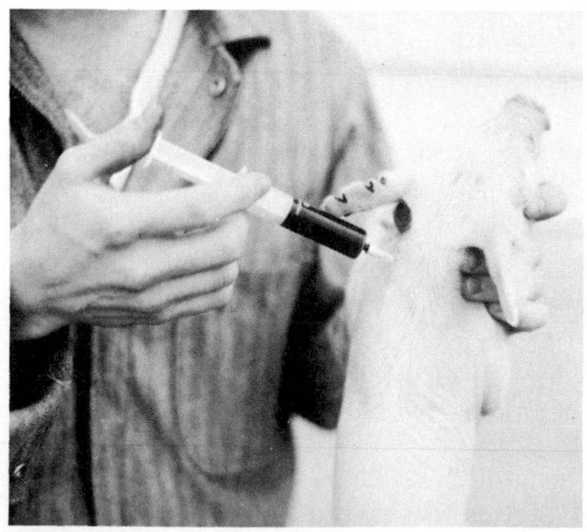

FIGURE 27.5.
Iron shots being given to baby pigs. These injections can be given in either the ham or neck muscles. Courtesy of E. R. Miller, Michigan State University.

confinement raising of pigs. Tails are removed $\frac{1}{4}-\frac{1}{2}$ in. from the body, and the stump should be disinfected along with the instrument after each pig is docked.

Pigs should be offered feed at 1–2 weeks of age in the creep area. These starter feeds can be placed on the floor or in a shallow pan. By 3–4 weeks after farrowing, the sow's milk production has likely peaked; however, the baby pigs should be eating the supplemental feed and growing rapidly (Fig. 27.6).

Rations for baby pigs (weighing 10–25 lb or 25–40 lb) are shown in Table 27.2. Note the components of the rations, especially that milk products (dried whey or dried skim milk) are included in the rations of 10–25-lb pigs.

Pigs can be weaned from their dams at a time that is consistent with the available facilities and the management of the producer. Pigs weaned at young ages should receive a higher level of management. General weaning guidelines include weaning only pigs over 12 lb, weaning pigs over a 2- to 3-day period, weaning the heavier pigs in the litter first, grouping pigs according to size in pens of 30 pigs or less, providing one feeder hole for 4–5 pigs and one waterer for each 20–25 pigs, limiting feed for 48 hours, and using medicated water if scours develop.

Feeding and Management from Weaning to Market

A dependable and economical source of feed is the backbone of a profitable swine operation. Since approximately 55%–77% of the total cost of pork production is feed, the swine producer should be keenly aware of all aspects of swine nutrition.

The pig is an efficient converter of feed to meat. With today's nutritional knowledge, modern meat-type hogs can be produced with a feed efficiency of less than 3.0 lb of feed per pound of gain from 40 lb to market. To obtain maximum feed use, it is necessary to feed well-balanced rations designed for specific purposes.

Swine rations for growing–finishing market pigs as well as rations for breeding stock are formulated around cereal grains, the largest component of swine rations. The most common

FIGURE 27.6.
Baby pigs in a modern nursery unit. The pigs were weaned from the sow and placed into these pens when they weighed 15–20 lb. The pigs will be moved into pens for growing and finishing when they weigh approximately 40 lb. Courtesy of the University of Illinois.

TABLE 27.2. Suggested Baby Pig Rations

	Ration Number and lb/Ration				
	Pigs 10–25 lb		Pigs 25–40 lb		
Ingredient	1	2	1	2	3
Corn, yellow	1,088	975	1,395	1,045	615
Grain sorghum	—	—	—	—	615
Ground oats	—	—	—	200	—
Soybean meal, 44%	500	570	543	500	513
Dried whey	—	400	—	200	200
Dried skim milk	200	—	—	—	—
Sugar	100	—	—	—	—
Fat	50	—	—	—	—
Calcium carbonate	15	13	15	13	15
Dicalcium phosphate	35	30	35	30	30
Salt	7	7	7	7	7
Vitamin-trace mineral mix	5	5	5	5	5
Total	2,000	2,000	2,000	2,000	2,000
Protein, %	19.11	19.20	18.10	18.00	18.00
Lysine, %	1.10	1.10	0.95	0.95	0.95
Tryptophan, %	0.23	0.23	0.21	0.21	0.21
Threonine, %	0.81	0.90	0.72	0.77	0.76
Methionine + cystine, %	0.64	0.62	0.60	0.58	0.57
Calcium, %	0.85	0.84	0.75	0.75	0.77
Phosphorus, %	0.71	0.71	0.65	0.66	0.66
Metabolizable energy, kcal/lb	1,457	1,440	1,446	1,419	1,421

Source: Pork Industry Handbook (PIH-23), Swine rations, 1983.

TABLE 27.3. Percentage of Protein Required for Varying Weights of Pigs from Weaning to Slaughter

Period and Weight	Percentage of Protein in Ration
Starter	
10–40 lb	18–20
Grower	
40–100 lb	16
Finisher I	
100–160 lb	14
Finisher II	
160–240 lb	13

cereal grains—those that provide the basic energy source—are corn, milo, barley, wheat, and their by-products. Because of its abundance and readily available energy, corn is used as the base cereal for comparing the nutritive value of other cereal grains. Milo (grain sorghum) is similar in nutritional content to corn and can completely replace corn in swine rations however milo needs more processing (grinding, rolling, steaming, etc.). Its energy value is about 95% the value of corn. Barley contains more protein and fiber than corn, but its relative feeding value is 85%–95% of corn and it is less palatable than corn. Wheat is equal to corn in feeding value and is highly palatable. However, for best feeding results, wheat should be mixed half and half with some other grain. Which grain or combination of grains to use can best be determined by availability and relative cost.

Grinding the grains improves all grains for feeding, especially those high in fiber such as barley and oats. Pelleting the ration may increase gains and efficiency of gains from 5%–10%. However, advantages of pelleting are usually offset by the higher cost of pelleting the ration.

Cereal grains usually contain lesser quantities of proteins, minerals, and vitamins than swine require; therefore, rations must be supplemented with other feeds to increase these nutrients to recommended levels. Soybean meal has been proven to be the best single source of protein for pigs when palatability, uniformity, and economics are considered. Other feeds rich in protein (meat and bone meal or tankage) can compose as much as 25% of the supplemental protein, if economics so dictate. Cottonseed meal is not recommended as a protein source unless the gossypol has been removed. **Gossypol,** in relatively high levels, is toxic to pigs. Table 27.3

TABLE 27.4. Suggested Growing Rations, 40–125 lb (with corn, barley, grain sorghum, or wheat as the grain source)

	Ration Number and lb/Ration				
Ingredient	1	2	3	4	5
Corn, yellow	1,558	—	—	800	—
Barley	—	1,643	—	—	—
Grain sorghum	—	—	1,548	—	1,558
Wheat, hard winter	—	—	—	800	—
Soybean meal, 44%	390	310	400	350	345
Calcium carbonate	15	20	17	18	12
Dicalcium phosphate	27	17	25	22	15
Salt	7	7	7	7	7
Vitamin-trace mineral mix	3	3	3	3	3
Total	2,000	2,000	2,000	2,000	2,000
Protein, %	15.40	16.40	15.80	16.10	16.10
Lysine, %	0.75	0.74	0.75	0.75	0.74
Tryptophan, %	0.17	0.22	0.18	0.19	0.17
Threonine, %	0.60	0.59	0.59	0.60	0.60
Methionine + cystine, %	0.53	0.49	0.48	0.51	0.49
Calcium, %	0.64	0.66	0.66	0.65	0.70
Phosphorus, %	0.56	0.55	0.56	0.55	0.58
Metabolizable energy, kcal/lb	1,456	1,275	1,398	1,457	1,397

Source: Pork Industry Handbook (PIH-23), Swine rations, 1983.

shows recommended protein levels in corn-soybean oil meal diets for different weights of pigs being grown and finished for slaughter.

If economics dictate, a producer can supplement specific amino acids in place of some of the protein supplement. Typically, lysine may be supplemented separately because lysine is the most limiting amino acid in swine rations.

Calcium and phosphorus are the minerals most likely to be deficient in swine rations, so care should be exercised to assure adequate levels in the ration. The standard ingredients for supplying calcium and phosphorus in the swine diet are limestone and either dicalcium phosphate or defluorinated rock phosphate. If an imbalance of calcium and zinc exists, a skin disease called **parakeratosis** is likely to occur.

Swine producers may formulate their swine rations several ways: (1) by using grain and a complete swine supplement; (2) by using grain and soybean meal plus a complete base mix carrying all necessary vitamins, minerals, and antibiotics; or (3) by using grain, soybean meal, vitamin premix, trace mineral premix, calcium and phosphorus source, and antibiotic and salt mixed together. Which ration is used depends on the producer's expertise, the cost, and the availability of ingredients. The trace mineral premix typically includes vitamin A, vitamin D, vitamin E, vitamin B_{12} and other B vitamins (niacin, pantothenic acid, and choline).

Table 27.4 shows example rations for growing pigs (40–125 lb). Rations for finishing pigs (125 lb to market) are noted in Table 27.5. These rations are formulated using the common grains (corn, grain sorgham, barley, or wheat).

TABLE 27.5. Suggested Finishing Rations, 125 lb to Market (with corn, barley, grain sorghum, or wheat as the grain source)

	Ration Number and lb/Ration				
Ingredient	1	2	3	4	5
Corn, yellow	1,666	—	—	—	—
Barley	—	1,749	—	—	—
Grain sorghum	—	—	1,652	—	—
Wheat, hard winter	—	—	—	1,752	—
Wheat, soft winter	—	—	—	—	1,705
Soybean meal, 44%	290	212	304	208	256
Meat and bone meal, 50%	—	—	—	—	—
Calcium carbonate	17	20	17	21	20
Dicalcium phosphate	7	9	17	9	9
Salt	7	7	7	7	7
Vitamin-trace mineral mix	3	3	3	3	3
Total	2,000	2,000	2,000	2,000	2,000
Protein, %	13.70	14.90	14.10	15.30	14.30
Lysine, %	0.62	0.62	0.62	0.62	0.62
Tryptophan, %	0.15	0.20	0.16	0.19	0.17
Threonine, %	0.54	0.52	0.52	0.51	0.51
Methionine + cystine, %	0.50	0.45	0.45	0.45	0.50
Calcium, %	0.55	0.56	0.56	0.55	0.55
Phosphorus, %	0.45	0.46	0.47	0.45	0.46
Metabolizable energy, kcal/lb	1,464	1,271	1,401	1,467	1,468

Source: Pork Industry Handbook (PIH-23), Swine rations, 1983.

Feed additives are used by most swine producers because the additives have the demonstrated ability to increase growth rate, improve feed efficiency, and reduce death and sickness from infectious organisms. Feed additives available to swine producers fall into three classifications: (1) **antibiotics** (compound coming from bacteria and molds that kill other microorganisms, (2) **chemotherapeutics** (compounds that are similar to antibiotics but are produced chemically rather than microbiologically, and (3) **anthelmintics** (dewormers). Antibiotics and chemotherapeutics should not be substituted for poor management (e.g. unsanitary conditions and poor health care.

Feed additive selection and the level to be used will vary with the existing farm environment, management conditions, and stage of the production cycle. Disease and parasite levels will vary from farm to farm. Also, the first few weeks of a pig's life are far more critical in terms of health protection. Immunity acquired from colostrum diminishes by 3 weeks of age, and the pig does not begin producing sufficient amounts of antibodies until 5–6 weeks of age. Also during this time, the pig is subjected to stress conditions of castration, vaccinations, and weaning. Therefore, at this age the additive level of the feed is much higher than when the pig is more than 75 lb and growing rapidly toward slaughter weight. Producers should be cautious because some additives have withdrawal times, which means the additive should no longer be included in the ration. This is necessary to prevent additives from occurring as residues in meat.

MANAGEMENT OF PURCHASED FEEDER PIGS

Feeder pigs marketed from one producer to another producer are subjected to more stress than pigs produced in a farrow-to-finish operation. These stresses are fatigue, hunger, thirst, temperature changes, diet changes, different surroundings, and social problems. Almost every group has a shipping fever reaction. Care of newly arrived pigs must be directed to relieving stresses and treating shipping fever correctly and promptly.

Management priorities for newly purchased feeder pigs should include (1) a dry, draft-free, well-bedded barn or shed with no more than 50 pigs per pen; (2) a specially formulated starter ration, having 12%–14% protein, more fiber, and a higher level of vitamins and antibiotics than a typical starter ration; (3) an adequate intake of medicated water containing electrolytes or water-soluble antibiotics and electrolytes; and (4) prompt and correct treatment of any sick pigs.

MARKET MANAGEMENT DECISIONS

Slaughter weights of market hogs and which market is selected can have a marked effect on income and profitability of the swine enterprise. For many years the recommended weight to sell barrows and gilts was, in most instances, 200–220 lb. The primary reasons for selling these animals at a maximum weight of 220 lb were increased cost of gain and increased fat accumulations at heavier weights. Market discounts were common on pigs weighing over 220 lb because of the increased amount of fat. Today, swine producers can maximize income by marketing pigs weighing up to 250 lb. These heavier pigs are leaner, and they are not subject to the same market discounts of fatter pigs marketed several years ago (Fig. 27.7). Decisions to market pigs at heavier weights should be based on feed costs and the gaining ability of the pigs.

Prices for slaughter pigs can vary among markets. Marketing costs, such as selling charges, transportation, and shrink (loss of live weight) can also vary. If more than one market is

FIGURE 27.7.
A group of pigs in a growing and finishing production unit. The building is totally enclosed and the floor is totally slatted. The manure from the pigs drops through the slats into a 36-in.-deep pit. The waste is removed from the pit through a water method. Courtesy of the University of Illinois.

TABLE 27.6. Farrow-to-Finish Hog Production Costs and Returns (1,600-head annual sales, North-Central region), 1989–90

	Dollars/cwt		
Item	Dec. 1989	July 1990	Dec. 1990
Cash receipts			
Market hogs (94.25 lb)	$46.41	$58.76	$48.57
Cull sows (5.75 lb)	2.22	2.73	2.56
Total	48.63	61.49	51.13
Cash expenses			
Feed			
Corn (345.6 lb)	14.49	14.20	14.92
Soybean meal (70.6 lb)	10.80	8.76	7.92
Mixing concentrates (14.3 lb)	2.99	2.95	2.86
Total feed	28.28	25.91	25.70
Veterinary and medicine	0.78	0.77	0.74
Fuel, lube, and electricity	1.54	1.47	1.46
Machinery and building repairs	2.52	2.45	2.42
Hired labor	1.48	1.36	1.32
Miscellaneous	0.69	0.64	0.63
Total variable expenses	35.29	32.60	32.37
General farm overhead	1.90	2.25	1.83
Taxes and insurance	0.70	0.68	0.65
Interest	3.97	4.89	4.07
Total fixed expenses	6.57	7.82	6.55
Total cash expenses	41.86	40.42	38.82
Receipts less cash expenses	6.77	21.07	12.31
Capital replacement	6.06	5.92	5.87
Receipts less cash expenses and replacement	0.71	15.15	6.44

Source: USDA, ERS, *Livestock and Poultry Situation and Outlook Report*, 1991.

TABLE 27.7. **Costs and Returns for Feeding Feeder Pigs Under Average Corn Belt Conditions, 1989–90**

Purchased during 1989–90 Marketed during 1989–90	Jan. May	July Nov.	Dec. Apr.
Expenses ($/head)			
40–50-lb feeder pig	44.58	46.35	49.63
Corn (11 bu)	24.42	28.88	23.98
Protein supplement (130 lb)	19.83	19.50	19.50
Total feed	44.25	48.38	43.48
Labor and management (1.3 hr)	13.48	12.61	13.26
Vet medicine	2.95	2.99	3.05
Interest on purchase (4 mo)	1.79	1.84	1.96
Power, equipment, fuel, shelter depreciation	7.18	7.29	7.44
Death loss (4% of purchase)	1.78	1.85	1.99
Transportation (100 miles)	0.48	0.48	0.48
Marketing expenses	1.14	1.14	1.14
Miscellaneous and indirect costs	0.74	0.75	0.76
Total	118.37	123.68	123.19
Selling price required to cover ($/cwt):			
Feed and feeder costs (220 lb)	40.38	43.06	42.32
All costs (220 lb)	53.80	56.22	56.00
Feed cost per 100-lb gain (180 lb)	24.58	26.88	24.16
Barrows and gilts (7 markets)	62.18	49.70	—
Net margin	8.38	−6.52	—
Prices			
40-lb feeder pig (S. Missouri) $/head	44.58	46.35	49.63
Corn $/bu	2.22	2.63	2.18
Protein supplement, 38–42% ($/cwt)	15.25	15.00	15.00
Labor and management ($/hr)	10.37	9.70	10.20
Interest rate, annual	12.02	11.88	11.87
Transportation rate ($/cwt, 100 miles)	0.22	0.22	0.22
Marketing expenses ($/cwt)	1.14	1.14	1.14
Index of prices paid by farmers (1910–14 = 100)	1246	1265	1291

Source: USDA, ERS, *Livestock and Poultry Situation and Outlook Report,* 1991.

available, producers should occasionally patronize different markets as a check against their usual marketing program. No single market is consistently the best market.

COSTS AND RETURNS

Enterprise budgets and analyses for farrow-to-finish hog production are shown in Table 27.6; similar information is given for finishing feeder pigs in Table 27.7. Note the costs and returns for farrow-to-finish operations and the net margin (i.e., the difference between selling price/cwt and all costs/cwt) for feeding feeder pigs.

Costs and returns over several years are noted for farrow-to-finish operations (Fig. 27.8). Excellent managers have larger positive returns and lower losses than shown in this figure. These top managers have low-cost production (especially low feed costs), while buying and selling pigs below and above average market prices.

Additional information on costs and returns is given in Chapter 36.

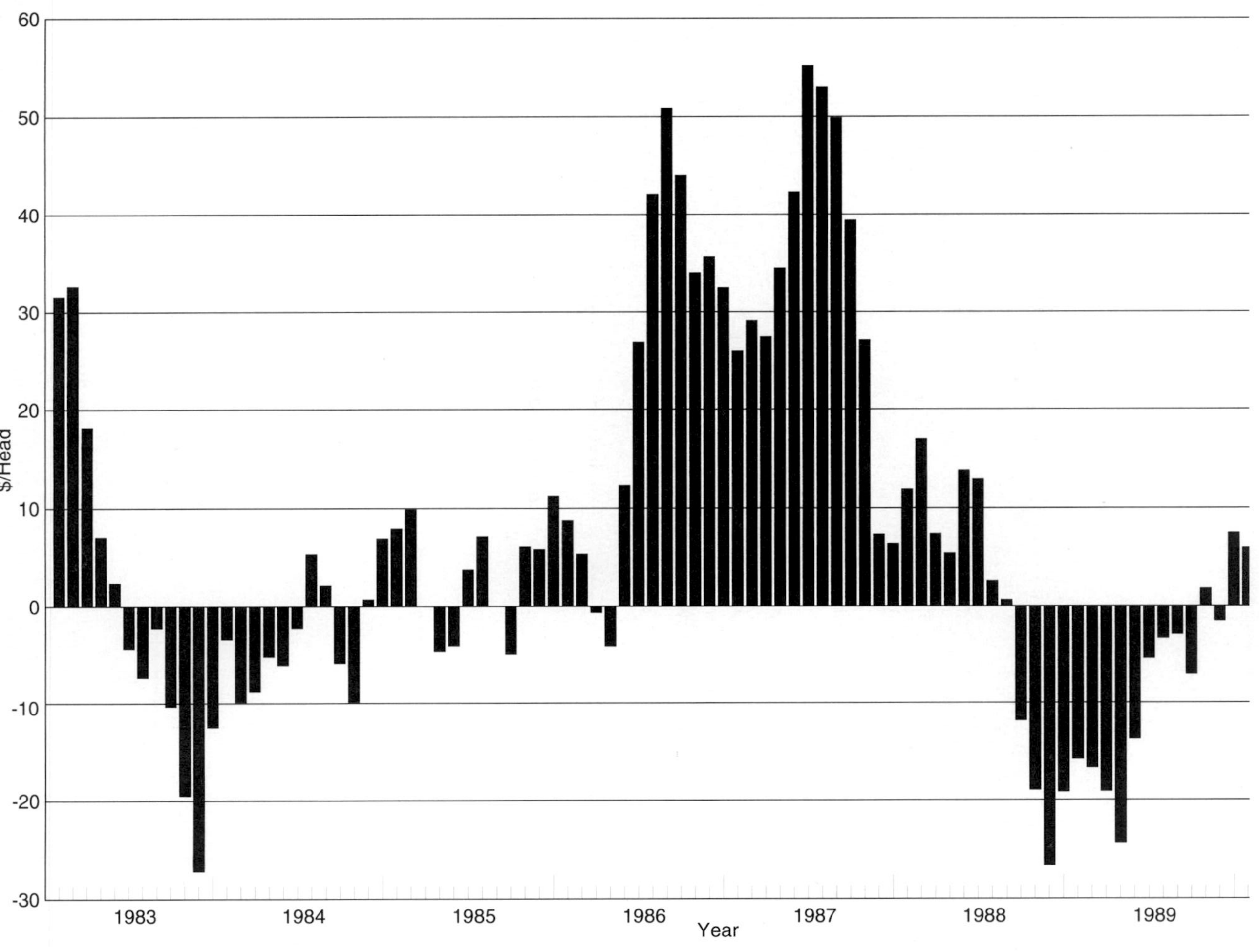

FIGURE 27.8.
Returns to farrow-to-finish operations, 1983–90. Courtesy of the USDA.

SELECTED REFERENCES

Publications

Dubman, R. 1989. *Financial Performance of Specialized Hog Farms*. Washington, DC: USDA, ERS.

Krider, J. L., Conrad, J. H., and Carroll, W. E. 1982. *Swine Production*. 5th ed. Hightstown, NJ: McGraw-Hill.

National Hog Farmer (monthly periodical). P.O. Box 202162, Minneapolis, MN 55420-7162.

National Research Council. 1988. *Nutrient Requirements of Swine*. Washington, DC: National Academy Press.

Pond, W. G., and Maner, J. H. 1984. *Swine Production and Nutrition*. Westport, CT: AVI Publishing Co.

Pork Industry Handbook (various years). Stillwater, OK: Cooperative Extension Service, Oklahoma State University.

van Arsdall, R. N. 1978. *Structural Characteristics of the United States Hog Production Industry*. Washington, DC: USDA Agricultural Economic Report no. 415.

Visuals

Feeding Equipment Choices; Swine Manure Handling Systems; Environmental Control in Swine Buildings; Swine Buildings and Equipment: Material Alternatives; Swine Building Systems: Labor and Cost Comparisons; Gestation Management and Health; Sow Management During Farrowing; Baby Pig Management; Farrowing House Equipment; Farrowing Systems; Swine Nursery Facilities; Purchasing Feeding Pigs/Transporting Feeder Pigs; Facilities for a Feeder-to-Finish Swine Enterprise/Nutrition, Health; and *Management of a Feeder-to-Finish Swine Enterprise, Personal Capabilities of Feeder Pig Producers* (videotapes). Agricultural Products and Services, 2001 Killebrew Dr., Suite 333, Bloomington, MN 55420.

Swine Management Practices (2 videotapes); *Swine Reproduction* (2 videotapes); and *Swine Handling and Transport* (videotape). CEV, P.O. Box 65265, Lubbock, TX 79464-5265.

The Swine Management Series: *Introduction to Swine Management; Brood Sow and Litter; Swine Health Care; Swine Nutrition; Fitting and Showing Swine; Feeder Pig Selection;* and *Swine Nutrition* (sound filmstrips). Vocational Education Productions, California Polytechnic State University, San Luis Obispo, CA 93407.

Swine: Life-cycle Feeding (VHS videotape). VEP, Calif. Polytechnic State Univ., San Luis Obispo, CA 93407.

CHAPTER 28

Sheep Breeds and Breeding

Sheep apparently evolved in the dry mountainous areas of southwest and central Asia. Present-day domesticated sheep were derived from wild animals that existed in Asia some 8,000 – 10,000 years ago. It is believed that domestication occurred during the early civilizations of southwest Asia. The Romans introduced a white, wooled sheep into western Europe, and these sheep contributed heavily to the British breeds. Some 100 – 200 years ago, Europeans took the Merino and British breeds of sheep to South America, Australia, South Africa, and New Zealand. Additional information on the world and U.S. sheep industry is in Chapter 2.

MAJOR U.S. SHEEP BREEDS

Sheep have been bred for three major purposes: production of fine wool for making high-quality clothing; production of long wool for making heavy clothing, upholstering, and rugs; and production of mutton and lamb. In recent years, dual-purpose sheep breeds (which produce both wool and meat) have been developed by crossing fine-wool breeds with long-wool breeds and then selecting for both improved meat and wool production. Some breeds serve specific purposes; an example is the Karakul breed, which supplies pelts for clothing items such as caps and Persian coats.

Sheep breeds can be divided into three major categories:

1. **Ewe breeds** are usually white-faced and have fine or medium wool, or long wool or crosses of these types. They are noted for reproductive efficiency, wool production, size, milking ability, and longevity. The Delaine Merino, Rambouillet, Debouillet, Corriedale, Targhee, **Finnsheep,** and Border Leicester are breeds in the ewe breed category.
2. **Ram breeds** are meat-type breeds raised primarily to produce rams for crossing with ewes of the ewe breed category. They are noted for growth rate and carcass characteristics. The Suffolk, Hampshire, Shropshire, Oxford, Southdown, Montadale, and Cheviot are classed as ram breeds.
3. **Dual-purpose breeds** are used either as ewe breeds or as ram breeds. The Dorset and Columbia are good examples of breeds that are often used as ewe breeds to be crossed with a

good ram breed. The Dorset, Lincoln, and Romney are often used as ram breeds to cross on other breeds of ewes to improve milking ability and fertility of the ewe flock.

Characteristics

Breeds of sheep and their characteristics are listed in Table 28.1. Most breeds are distinguished by wool characteristics, color of face, size, and horned or polled condition. Inheritance of the horned or polled condition is sex-influenced and generally controlled by a single pair of genes. In the heterozygote, the genes are usually expressed as recessive in the ewe and dominant in the ram (Table 28.2).

The sheep breeds commonly used in the United States are shown in Figures 28.1 and 28.2. The Merino and Rambouillet (fine wool) breeds and the dual-purpose breeds that possess fine-wool characteristics have a herding instinct, so one sheepherder with dogs can handle a band of 1,000 ewes and their lambs on the summer range. Winter bands of 2,500–3,000 ewes are common. Ram breeds, by contrast, tend to scatter over the grazing area. They are highly adaptable to grazing fenced pastures where feed is abundant. Rams of the ram breeds (meat type) are often used for breeding ewes of fine-wool breeding on the range for the production of market lambs. Crossbreeding in sheep has been used for more than a half century.

The Columbia and Targhee breeds were developed by the U.S. Sheep Experiment Station in Dubois, Idaho. Both breeds have proven useful on western ranges because they have the herding instinct and, when bred to a meat breed of ram, they raise better market lambs than do fine-wool ewes. The U.S. Sheep Experiment Station has made great strides in improving the Rambouillet, Columbia, and Targhee breeds.

The most important trait in meat breeds of sheep is weight at 90 days of age, with some emphasis also given to conformation and finish of the lambs. Weight at 90 days of age can be calculated for lambs that are weaned at younger or older ages than 90 days as follows:

$$\text{90-day weight} = \frac{\text{weaning weight} - \text{birth weight}}{\text{age at weaning}} \times 90 + \text{birth weight}$$

If a lamb weighs 10 lb at birth and 100 lb at 100 days, the 90-day weight is:

$$\frac{100\text{ lb} - 10\text{ lb}}{100\text{ days}} \times 90\text{ days} + 10\text{ lb} = 91\text{ lb}.$$

If birth weight was not recorded, an assumed birth weight of 8 lb can be used.

Approximately 85%–90% of the total income from sheep of the meat breeds is derived from the sale of lambs, with only 10%–15% coming from the sale of wool. By contrast, the sale of wool accounts for 30%–35% of the income derived from fine-wool and long-wool breeds. Even with wool breeds, the income from lambs produced constitutes the greater portion of total income.

The U.S. Sheep Experiment Station in Dubois, Idaho, has developed a new synthetic breed of sheep, called the **Polypay,** which has superiority in lamb production and in carcass quality. Four breeds (Dorset, Targhee, Rambouillet, and Finnsheep) provided the basic genetic material for the Polypay. Targhees were crossed with Dorsets and Rambouillets were crossed with Finnsheep, after which the two crossbred groups were crossed. The offspring produced by crossing the two crossbred groups were intermated and a rigid selection program was practiced.

TABLE 28.1 Characteristics of Breeds of Sheep Within Each Type

Breed	Size[a]	Carcass Conformation	Wool Fineness	Wool Length[b]	Fleece Weight[c]	Color	Horns or Polled	Other
Fine-wool breeds								
Merino	Small to medium	Poor	Very fine	Medium	Heavy	White	Rams horned, ewes polled	Good herding instinct; skin folds
Rambouillet	Large	Medium	Fine	Medium	Heavy	White	Rams horned, ewes polled	Good herding instinct
Long, coarse-wool breeds								
Romney	Medium large	Medium	Coarse	Long	Heavy	White	Polled	Lambs do not fatten at small size
Lincoln	Large	Good	Coarse	Long	Heavy	White	Polled	Lambs do not fatten at small size
Ram (meat) breeds								
Suffolk	Large	Excellent	Medium	Short	Light	White with black, bare face and legs	Polled	Bare bellies; black fibers
Hampshire	Large	Excellent	Medium	Medium	Medium	White with black face	Polled	Wool blindness, good milkers, black fibers
Shropshire	Medium to large	Good	Medium	Medium	Medium	White, dark face and legs	Polled	Wool blindness, excellent milkers
Southdown	Very small	Excellent	Medium	Short	Very light	White with brown face and legs	Polled	Used in hot-house lamb production

TABLE 28.1 Characteristics of Breeds of Sheep Within Each Type (continued)

Breed	Size[a]	Carcass Conformation	Wool Fineness	Wool Length[b]	Fleece Weight[c]	Color	Horns or Polled	Other
Dorset	Medium	Good	Medium	Medium	Medium	White	Polled or horned	Highly fertile; good milkers
Cheviot	Small	Excellent	Medium	Medium	Medium	White	Polled	Very rugged
Oxford	Large	Excellent	Medium	Medium	Medium to heavy	White with brown face and legs	Polled	
Finnsheep	Small to medium	Poor	Medium	Medium	Medium	White	Polled	Very fertile
Dual-purpose breeds								
Corriedale	Medium	Good	Medium	Medium long	Heavy	White	Polled	Herding instinct
Columbia	Large	Good	Medium	Medium long	Heavy	White	Polled	Rugged; herding instinct
Targhee	Medium to large	Medium to good	Medium to fine	Medium	Heavy	White	Polled	Herding instinct
Miscellaneous breeds								
Navajo	Medium	Poor	Coarse	Long	Medium	Variable	Polled or horned	Wool for making Navajo rugs
Karakul	Large	Poor	Coarse	Long	Medium	Black or brown	Rams horned, ewes polled	Used for pelts

[a] Small—ewes weigh 120–160 lb and rams weigh 160–200 lb; medium—ewes weigh 140–180 lb and rams 180–250 lb; large—ewes weigh 150–200 lb and rams 225–350 lb.
[b] Short—2.0–3.5 in.; medium—2.5–4.5 in.; long—4–6 in. or longer.
[c] Light—5–8 lb; medium—6–10 lb; heavy—10–18 lb.

TABLE 28.2 Horn Inheritance in Sheep

Genotype	Phenotype of Ewes	Phenotype of Rams
HH	Horned	Horned
Hh	Polled	Horned
hh	Polled	Polled

This population was closed to outside breeding. The Rambouillet and Targhee breeds contributed hardiness, herding instinct, size, a long breeding season, and wool of high quality. The Dorset contributed good carcass, high milking quality, and a long breeding season. The Finnsheep contributed early puberty, early postpartum fertility, and high lambing rate.

The Polypay breed has shown outstanding performance in conventional once-a-year lambing under range conditions and superior performance in twice-a-year lambing when compared with other breeds or breed crosses.

There are several U.S. breeds of sheep that are not listed in Table 28.1. Some of these breeds possess certain genes that may be useful for improving the most popular U.S. breeds either through systematic crossbreeding or in the establishment of new breeds.

Popularity of Breeds

Based on annual registration numbers, the Suffolk, Dorset, Rambouillet, and Hampshire are the most numerous breeds of sheep (Table 28.3). Suffolk and Hampshire are used extensively in crossbreeding programs to produce market lambs both in farm flocks and on the range. The most popular ewe breeds on the range are the Rambouillet, Columbia, and Corriedale. In a farm flock lamb-production system, the Dorset, Shropshire, Finnsheep, and Polypay are important ewe breeds.

BREEDING SHEEP

Reproduction

Sheep differ from many farm animals in having a breeding season that occurs mainly in the fall of the year. The length of the breeding season varies with breeds. Ewes of breeds with a long breeding season show heat cycles from mid- to late summer until mid-winter. The breeds in this category are the Rambouillet, Merino, and Dorset. Breeds with an intermediate breeding season (Suffolk, Hampshire, Columbia, and Corriedale) start cycling in late August or early September and continue to cycle until early winter. Ewes of breeds having long or intermediate breeding seasons are more likely to fit into a program of three lamb crops in 2 years.

Ewes of breeds with short breeding seasons (Southdown, Cheviot, and Shropshire) do not start cycling until early fall and discontinue cycling at the end of the fall period.

Puberty is reached at 5 – 12 months of age and is influenced by breed, nutrition, and date of birth. The average length of **estrous cycles** is slightly over 16 days, and the length of estrus (when the ewe is receptive to the ram) is about 30 hours. The length of gestation (time from

Dorset

Montadale

Polled Dorset

Cheviot

Hampshire

Suffolk

FIGURE 28.1.
Some breeds of sheep commonly used either as straightbreds or for crossbreeding to produce market lambs. Photographs courtesy of Continental Dorset Club, Hudson, Iowa (Dorset and Polled Dorset); Montadale Sheep Breeders' Association, Indianapolis, Indiana (Montadale); American Cheviot Sheep Society, Lebanon, Virginia (Cheviot); American Hampshire Sheep Association, Columbia, Missouri (Hampshire); and National Suffolk Sheep Association, Logan, Utah (Suffolk).

Rambouillet | Cotswold

Lincoln | Romney

Targhee | Finnsheep

FIGURE 28.2.
Some breeds of sheep commonly used either as straightbreds or for crossbreeding to produce market lambs. Photographs courtesy of American Rambouillet Sheep Breeders Association, San Angelo, Texas (Rambouillet); American Cotswold Record Association, Rochester, New Hampshire (Cotswold); National Lincoln Sheep Breeders' Association, West Milton, Ohio (Lincoln); American Romney Breeders Association, Corvallis, Oregon (Romney); USDA, ARS, Western Region, U.S. Sheep Experiment Station, Dubois, Idaho (Targhee); and Animal Science Department, University of Minnesota (Finnsheep).

TABLE 28.3 Major U.S. Sheep breeds Based on Annual Registration Numbers (in thousands), 1970–89

Breed	1989	1985	1980	1975	1970	Year U.S. Association Formed
			thousand			
Suffolk[a]	50.4	49.1	60.3	31.8	24.5	1935
Dorset	18.7	12.8	15.2	8.7	8.6	1898
Hampshire	17.4	16.9	60.4	17.2	22.6	1889
Rambouillet	16.2	12.2	11.9	10.0	6.6	1889
Polypay	11.4	3.2	0	0	0	1979
Columbia	9.5	8.0	10.0	6.0	6.4	1942
Southdown	5.8	4.8	4.4	3.6	5.7	1882
Corriedale	5.0	4.4	6.5	6.1	9.0	1816
Shropshire	3.4	3.4	4.4	3.8	5.2	1884
Montadale	3.4	3.1	3.1	1.9	3.0	1945
Cheviot	2.8	2.5	2.5	2.3	2.8	1891

Note: Only breeds with more than 2,500 annual registrations are listed.
[a] Registrations in the National Suffolk Sheep Association. In 1989, there were 19,000 registrations in the American Suffolk Sheep Society. An undetermined number of Suffolks are double registered in both associations.
Source: Various breed associations.

breeding until the lamb is born) averages 147 days but varies; medium-wooled and meat breeds have shorter gestation periods whereas fine-wooled breeds have longer gestation periods.

Several factors affect **fertility** in sheep. Lambing rates vary both within and between breeds, with some ewes consistently producing only one lamb per year and others producing three or four lambs each year. To improve lambing rate, producers keep replacements from ewes that consistently produce two to four lambs each year.

Fertility of rams used in a breeding program should be checked by examining the semen. Semen can be collected by use of an artificial vagina and examined with a microscope. Ram fertility is evaluated by (1) checking for abnormal sperm (tailless, bent tails, no heads, and so on), (2) observing the percentage of live sperm (determined by a staining technique using fresh semen), and (3) checking the sperm motility and concentration in freshly collected semen. Two semen collections 3–4 days apart should be examined. When rams have not ejaculated for some time, there may be dead sperm in the **ejaculate.**

Other Factors Affecting Reproduction

Selection and Crossbreeding. Crossbred ewe lambs, when adequately fed, are usually bred to lamb at 1 year of age. Generally, crossbred lambs are more likely to conceive as lambs than are purebred lambs.

Age. Mature (3–7-year-old) ewes are more fertile and raise a higher percentage of lambs born than do younger or older ewes.

Light. Light, temperature, and relative humidity affect reproduction in sheep. Sheep respond to decreased day lengths both by showing greater proportion of ewes in estrus and by higher **conception** rates.

Temperature. Temperature has a marked effect on both ewes and rams. High temperatures cause heat sterility in rams because the testicles must be at a temperature below normal body temperature for viable sperm production. Embryo survival in the ewe is also influenced by temperature. When ambient temperature exceeds 90°F, embryo survival decreases during the first 8 days after breeding.

Health. Environmental factors that affect the health and well-being of sheep—disease, **parasites,** lack of feed, or imbalance of the ration—reduce the number of lambs produced. Producers can increase their income and profit from a sheep operation by controlling diseases and parasites and by providing the sheep with an adequate supply of good feed. Sheep in moderate body condition are usually more productive than fat sheep. Ewes that are in moderate condition and are gaining weight before and during the breeding season will have more and stronger lambs than ewes that are either overfat or **emaciated** at breeding.

Estrus Synchronization and AI. In some intensively managed sheep operations, hormones can be used to synchronize estrus. Hormones can also be used to bring ewes into estrus at times other than during their normal breeding season.

Estrus can be synchronized if progesterone is given for a 12–14-day period in the feed, as an implant, via a pessary (intravaginal device), or by daily injections followed by injections of pregnant mare serum (PMS) the day progesterone is discontinued. Conception rates at this estrus are low; therefore, a second injection of pregnant mare serum 15–17 days later will bring the ewes into estrus and fertile matings will occur. There must be sufficient ram power to breed naturally a large number of ewes if they are synchronized or if artificial insemination can be used.

This system of synchronizing estrus can also be used to obtain pregnancies out of the normal breeding season and to obtain a normal lamb crop from breeding ewe lambs. Also, producers can use estrus synchronization for accelerated lambing if it is desired to raise two lamb crops per year.

If the ewes are to be artificially inseminated, high-quality fresh semen should be diluted with egg yolk-citrate diluter shortly before insemination. Ram semen has been frozen but conception rates have been low.

Estrogen in Feeds. Sometimes a flock of sheep may show very low fertility because of high estrogen content of the legume pasture or hay that the sheep are eating. Producers are advised to have the legume hay or legumes in the pasture checked for estrogen if they are experiencing fertility problems in their sheep.

The Breeding Season

Sheep may be hand mated or pasture mated. If they are **hand mated,** some **teaser rams** are needed to locate ewes that are in heat. Either a **vasectomized** ram (each vas deferens has been

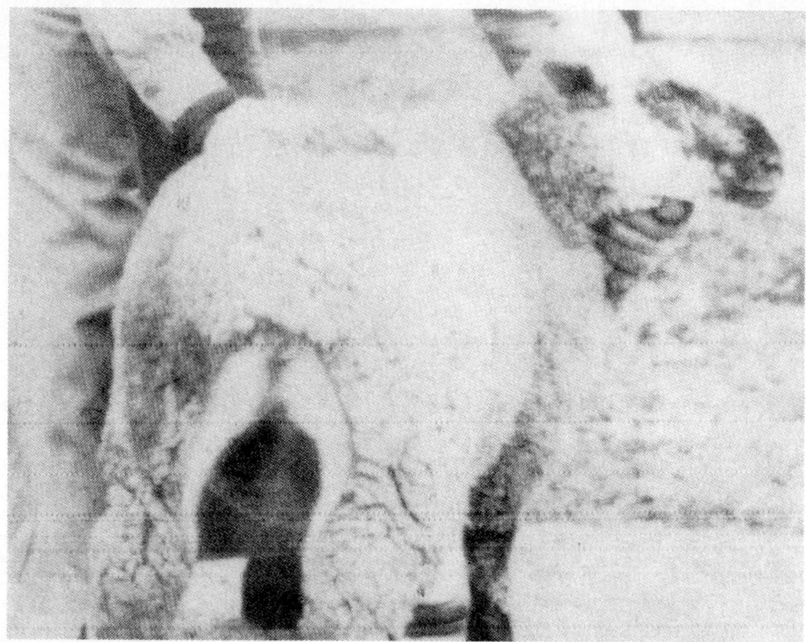

FIGURE 28.3.
Ewe that has been tagged prior to breeding. Wool has been shorn from the dock and vulva region. Courtesy of the *Sheep Production Handbook.*

severed so sperm are prevented from moving from the testicles) can be used, or an apron can be put on the ram such that a strong cloth prevents copulation.

Tagging ewes (Fig. 28.3) before breeding will result in a larger percentage of lambs as well as a lamb flock of more uniform age.

Ewes should be checked twice daily for **heat.** Ewes normally stay in heat for 30 hours and ovulate near the end of heat. It is desirable to breed ewes the morning after ewes are found in heat in the afternoon. Ewes that are found in heat in the morning should be bred in the late afternoon.

If ewes are to be hand mated, the ram should breed them once. Recently bred ewes should be separated from other ewes for 1 or 2 days so that the teaser ram does not spend his energies mounting the same ewe repeatedly.

If ewes are to be **pasture mated,** they are sorted into groups according to the rams to which they are to be mated. It is best to have an empty pasture between breeding pastures so as not to entice rams to be with ewes in another breeding group.

Sheep can be identified by using numbered branding irons to apply scourable paint. The brisket of the breeding ram can be painted with scourable paint so that he marks the ewe when he mounts her. A light-colored paint should be used initially, then a dark color can be used about 14 days later to detect ewes that return in heat. An orange paint can be used initially, followed, successively, with green, red, and black. The paint color should be changed each

16–17 days. Because the ewes are numbered, they can be observed daily and the breeding date of each can be recorded. Also, a ram that is not settling his ewes can be detected and replaced. Occasionally, a ram may be low in fertility even though his semen was given a satisfactory evaluation before the breeding season.

A breeding season of 40 days results in a lamb crop of uniform age and identifies ewes for culling that have an inherent tendency for late lambing.

The Purebred Breeder

The goal of purebred breeders is to make genetic change in the economically important traits. These breeders use selection as their method for genetic improvement, as crossbreeding is limited primarily to commercial producers. Purebred breeders with large operations may find it desirable to close their flocks and select ewe and ram replacements from within the closed flocks.

Normally, purebred breeders have selection programs to produce superior rams for commercial producers. At the same time, commercial producers prefer rams that contribute outstanding performance in a commercial crossbreeding program.

In general, great progress in sheep improvement can be made by selection within a breed for traits that are highly heritable and economically important. Crossbreeding can give significant genetic improvement in traits of low heritability such as fertility. Traits that are only moderately heritable can be improved by selecting genetically superior breeding animals and also by using crossbreeding.

Highly heritable traits (40% or higher) include mature body size, yearling type score, face cover, **skin folds,** clean fleece yield, yearling staple length, gestation length, loin eye area, fat weight, and retail cut weight. Lowly heritable traits (below 20%) include weaning type score, weaning condition score, multiple births, number of lambs weaned, fat thickness over loin, carcass weight per day of age, carcass grades, and dressing percentage. Moderately heritable traits (20%–39%) include birth weight, 90-day weight, rate of gain, neck folds, grease fleece weight, fleece grade, lambing date, milk production, carcass length, and bone weight.

Principles applicable to breeding and improving sheep are presented in Chapters 12 (genetics), 13 (selection), and 14 (systems of mating).

Commercial Sheep Production

Lambs born in December or January and sold as small, finished lambs for Easter or early spring markets can be produced by breeding ewes of a highly fertile breed that produces large quantities of milk (such as Dorset) to a ram of a small breed that has excellent meat conformation (such as the Southdown). The lambs produced by such a mating receive ample milk to make rapid growth. Smaller size and excellent conformation contributed by the Southdown result in lambs having desirable conformation finishing at a relatively small size. They should be sufficiently finished for slaughter at 70–80 lb and make excellent small carcasses.

Lambs produced for slaughter directly from pasture at weaning time are usually produced in areas where good pastures are available. A producer may raise lambs of only one breed as straightbred animals; but more likely the producer with good pastures and an interest in marketing finished lambs at 90–100 days has some type of crossbreeding program. By crossbreeding, the producer can use ewes of a breed or breeds that are strong in traits like high fertility, wool that is fairly long and fine, high milking ability, and a long life, such as the Dorset, Rambouillet, Columbia, and Finnsheep. The producer can use rams of breeds that are rapidly growing, have desirable carcass conformation, and that finish well at 90–115 lb live weight, such as the Suffolk or Hampshire.

Most lambs produced in farm flock operations are marketed at weaning (when they are approximately 100 days of age and weigh 90–120 lb). They are sufficiently finished by then to grade USDA Choice or Prime if they have good carcass conformation and have been adequately fed. A good method for producing such lambs is to use a three-breed rotational crossbreeding system. Producers can use breeds such as the Dorset, Suffolk, and Columbia in areas where relatively good grazing conditions exist.

Some range sheep operations have summer grazing areas that are sufficiently productive to supply the nutrients needed for lambs to grow and fatten on the range. Other range areas produce only enough forage for sheep to raise lambs that must be finished after weaning by placing them in feedlots and feeding grain and some hay for a period of 50–80 days. The use of good meat-type rams for breeding to ewes under this less desirable condition, as well as for breeding to ewes under highly desirable range conditions, is recommended. Under the more favorable summer range conditions, finished lambs at weaning can be produced. Under less desirable summer range conditions, **feeder lambs** can be produced when desirable meat-type rams are used. A range-sheep operator could use Rambouillet, Columbia, Panama, or Targhee ewes and breed them to Suffolk or Hampshire rams. All lambs would be marketed either as slaughter or feeder lambs. Replacement ewes could be purchased or raised by breeding the best range ewes to good rams of the same breed as that of the ewes.

Most market lambs are crossbreds (produced either from crossing breeds or from mating crossbred ewes with purebred rams), but the key to the success of **crossbreeding** is the improvement in production traits made by the purebred breeders in their selection programs. Crossbreeding can be used to combine meat conformation of the sire breeds with lambing ability and wool characteristics of the ewe breeds, and also to obtain the advantage of the fast growth rate of lambs that results from heterosis. The additive as well as the heterotic effects are evident in crossbred lambs. Maximum **heterosis** is obtained in three- or four-breed crosses, either rotational or terminal.

Crossing meat-type sheep with **Finnsheep** offers a means for rapidly increasing efficiency of lamb meat production. The Finnsheep breed was introduced into the United States in 1968, and its numbers are increasing rapidly in this country. Finnsheep (Fig. 28.4) are extremely prolific (two to six lambs per lambing), and research studies show that crossbred ewes of 25%–50% Finnsheep breeding produce more lambs than straightbred or crossbred ewes of the meat breeds.

Some research shows that two lamb crops can be raised per year or, if feed and other conditions do not support such intensive production, three lamb crops every 2 years can be produced. To achieve intense production of this type, producers need ewes that will breed throughout the year. At present, the Polypay seem to fit into such a program fairly well. Also, the Rambouillet and Dorset have a tendency to breed out of season.

To raise three lamb crops in 2 years, ewes should be bred in late summer, probably for a 30-day period (August), for lambs to arrive in January (lamb crop 1). The ewes and lambs need to be well fed so the lambs are sufficiently finished to go to market at 90 days of age (in April). The ewes are then bred in April (30-day breeding period) to lamb in August (lamb crop 2), and the ewes and lambs need good feed so the lambs are well finished and sufficiently large to be

FIGURE 28.4.
One of the first Finnsheep ewes imported into the United States with her first lambs, illustrating the high productivity of Finnsheep. Courtesy of Dwight and Mae Holaway.

marketed at 90 days of age (November). The ewes are bred in November to lamb in April (3rd lamb crop) and the lambs are marketed at 90 days of age in July.

Three-Breed Terminal Crossbreeding

In some production schemes, crossbred ewes are bred to rams of a third breed as a terminal cross (all offspring are marketed). Some producers cross Columbias with Dorsets to develop large ewes that have long, fairly fine fleece, are hardy, and produce much milk. These crossbred ewes are bred to good Suffolk or Hampshire rams. A high percentage of lambs from these crosses are finished at weaning and weigh 90–100 lb at about 90–100 days of age. The entire lamb crop from this terminal mating is marketed. All the two-breed crossbred ewes that are productive are kept until they reach an age at which their production of lambs declines. Replacement ewes are produced by crossing Columbias and Dorsets. A producer carrying out such a program keeps a small flock of either straightbred Dorsets or Columbias to produce the two-breed crossbred ewes. Purebred Suffolk or Hampshire rams are purchased as needed and used for breeding as long as they are sound and inbreeding is not a problem.

INHERITED ABNORMALITIES

It is important to guard against certain genetic abnormalities when managing sheep. Although exceptions occur, sheep showing obvious genetic defects are usually culled. Some inherited abnormalities include the following.

Cryptorchidism is inherited as a simple recessive; therefore, a ram with only one testis descended into the scrotum should never be used for breeding. In addition, producers should cull rams that sire lambs having cryptorchidism, as well as the ewes that produced the lambs.

Dwarfism is inherited as a recessive and is lethal; therefore, ewes and rams producing dwarf offspring should be culled.

The mode of inheritance of **entropion** (turned-in eyelids) has not been determined, but it is known to be under genetic control. A record should be made of any lamb having entropion so that the lamb can be marketed.

Sheep have lower front teeth but lack upper front teeth. They graze by closing the lower teeth against the dental pad of the upper jaw. If the lower jaw is either too short **(overshot** or **Parrot mouth)** or too long **(undershot),** the teeth cannot close against the dental pad and grazing is difficult. The mode of inheritance of these jaw abnormalities is unknown, but the conditions are under genetic control. Sheep having abnormal jaws should be culled.

Rectal prolapse is common in black-faced sheep. It is a serious defect, and both inheritance and the environment are influential in its occurrence. Lambs on heavy feeding or lush pastures are more likely to show rectal prolapse. If surgery is used to correct the condition, the animal should not be used as a breeding animal.

Skin folds, open-faced, closed-faced, and **wool blindness** are inherited and selection against these traits have been effective.

Spider Syndrome is a severe skeletal deformity occurring in Suffolk sheep. The most striking feature is an outward bending of the forelimbs from the knees. Angular deformities of the hindlimbs are generally present. The genetic abnormality is due to a recessive gene and can be effectively selected against.

Many wool defects are known, including black fibers, black tipped fibers, hairiness, fuzziness, and "high belly wool" in which wool that is typical of wool on the belly is present on the sides of the sheep. Selection against all of these fleece defects should be practiced as a means of reducing the frequency of their occurrence.

SELECTED REFERENCES

Publications

Botkin, M. P., Field, R. A., and Johnson, C. L. 1988. *Sheep and Wool: Science, Production, and Management.* Englewood Cliffs, NJ: Prentice-Hall.

Dickerson, G. E. 1978. *Crossbreeding Evaluation of Finnsheep and Some U.S. Breeds for Market Lamb Production.* North Central Regional Publication #246. ARS, USDA, and University of Nebraska.

Ensminger, M. E., and Parker, R. O. 1986. *Sheep and Goat Science.* Danville, IL: Interstate Printers and Publishers.

Land, R. B., and Robinson, D. W. 1985. *Genetics of Reproduction in Sheep.* Boston: Butterworths.

Lasley, J. F. 1987. *Genetics of Livestock Improvement.* Englewood Cliffs, NJ: Prentice-Hall.

Neimann-Sorenson, A. and Tube, D. E. (eds. in chief). 1982. World Animal Science, *Series C:* Production System Approach. 1982. I. E. Coop (ed.). *Sheep and Goat Production.* New York: Elsevier.

Ross, C. V. 1989. *Sheep Production and Management.* Englewood Cliffs, NJ: Prentice-Hall.

The Sheepman's Production Handbook. 1988. Denver, CO: Sheep Industry Development Program.

Visuals

Farm Flock (videotape; 10 min.). National Sheep Improvement Program, Dept. of Animal Science, Iowa State University, Ames, IA 50010.

Farm Flock Production Systems; and *Personal Requirements/Personal Rewards* (videotapes). Agricultural Products and Services, 2001 Killebrew Dr., Suite 333, Bloomington, MN 55420.

An Introduction to Sheep Breed Identification (sound filmstrip). Prentice-Hall Media, 150 White Plains Rd., Tarrytown, NY 10591.

Range Flock (videotape; 10 min.). National Sheep Improvement Program, Dept. of Animal Science, Iowa State University, Ames, IA 50010.

Sheep Breed Identification (slide kit; 15 breeds of sheep). Vocational Education Productions, California Polytechnic State University, San Luis Obispo, CA 93407.

CHAPTER 29

Feeding and Managing Sheep

Sheep feeding and management are essential for the success of an operation. These areas must be integrated with a knowledge of how breeding and environmental factors affect sheep productivity and profitability. Several areas of feeding and management that affect efficient production are discussed in this chapter.

PRODUCTION REQUIREMENTS FOR FARM FLOCKS

Pastures

Good pastures are essential to the typical farm flock operator. Grass-legume mixtures, such as rye grass and clover or orchard grass and alfalfa, are ideal for sheep. Sheep can also graze on temporary pastures of such plants as Sudan grass or rape, which are often used to provide forage in the dry part of summer when permanent pastures may show no new growth. Crops of grain and grass seed may also provide pasture for sheep during autumn and early spring. Sheep do not trample wet soil as severely as do cattle; pasturing sheep on grass-seed and small-grain crops in winter and early spring when the soil is wet does not cause serious damage to the plants or soil.

Fencing

A woven-wire or electric fence is necessary to contain sheep in a pasture. Forage can be best utilized by rotating (moving) sheep from one pasture to another. This also assists in the control of internal parasites. Some sheep operators use temporary fencing (such as electric fencing) to divide pastures and for predator control. It is necessary to use two electrified wires, one located low enough to prevent sheep from going underneath the fence, and the other located high enough to prevent them from jumping over it.

Corrals and Chutes

It is occasionally necessary to put sheep in a small enclosure so to sort them into different groups or to treat any ailing animals. Proper equipment is helpful in this task because sheep are often difficult to drive, particularly when ewes are being separated from their lambs. A **cutting chute** can be constructed to direct sheep into various small lots (Fig. 29.1). A well-designed cutting chute is sufficiently narrow to keep sheep from turning around and can be blocked so that sheep can be packed together closely for such purposes as treating diseases and reading ear tags. The chute can be constructed of lumber that is nailed to wooden posts set into the ground and properly spaced so that the correct width (14 – 16 in.) is provided when the boards are nailed on the inside. Pens used to enclose small groups of sheep can be constructed of a woven-wire fencing. A loading chute is used to place sheep onto a truck for hauling. A portable loading chute (Fig. 29.2) is ideal because it can be moved to different locations where loading and unloading sheep is necessary.

Shelters

Sheep do not normally suffer from cold because they have a heavy wool covering; therefore, open sheds are excellent for housing and feeding wintering ewe lambs, pregnant ewes, and rams. Although the ewes can be lambed in these sheds, the newborn need an enclosed and heated room when the weather is cold.

Lambing Equipment

Small pens, about 4 × 4 ft, can be constructed for holding ewes and their lambs until they are strong enough to be put with other ewes and lambs. Four-foot panels can be constructed from 1 × 4-in. lumber, and the two panels can be hinged together. The lambing pens (called **lambing jugs**) can be made along a wall by wiring these hinged panels. Heat lamps are extremely valuable for keeping newborn lambs warm. A heat lamp above each lambing jug can be located at a height that provides a temperature of 90°F at the lamb's level (Fig. 29.3).

It is advisable to identify each lamb and to record which lambs belong to which ewes. Often, a ewe and her lambs are branded with a scourable paint to identify them. Numbered ear tags

FIGURE 29.1. Sheep being directed into a special pen by use of a cutting chute.

FIGURE 29.2. Sheep being unloaded directly onto pasture by use of a portable loading chute.

can be applied to the lamb at birth. If newborn lambs are to be weighed, a dairy scale and a large bucket are needed. The lamb is placed in the bucket, which hangs from the scale, for weighing. It is advisable to immerse naval cords of newborn lambs in a tincture of iodine.

Feeding Equipment

All sheep are given hay in the winter feeding period. Feeding mangers (Fig. 29.4) should be provided because hay is wasted if it is fed on the ground. Some sheep may require limited

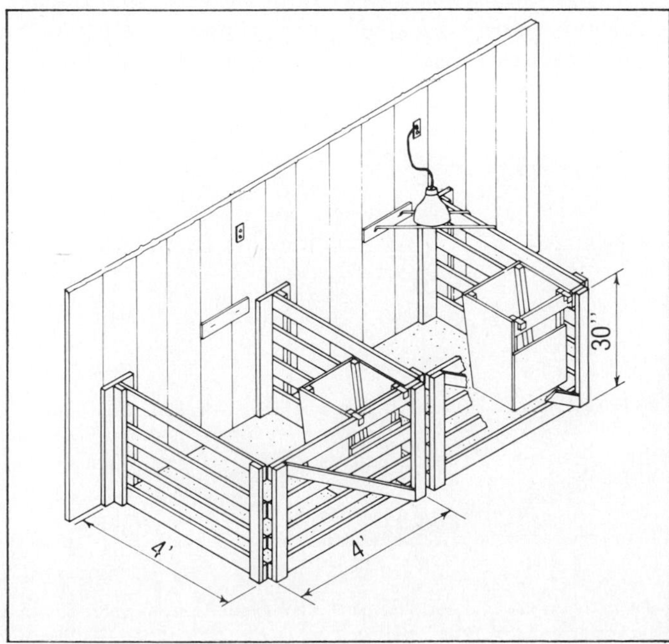

FIGURE 29.3. A lambing jug with heat lamp for ewes with newborn lambs. Courtesy of John H. Pedersen, Midwest Plan Service, Agricultural Engineering, Iowa State University.

FIGURE 29.4.
Sheep eating from a hay bunk.

amounts of concentrates. Concentrates can be fed in the same bunk as hay if the hay bunk is properly constructed, or separate feed troughs (Fig. 29.5) may be preferable.

Additional concentrates can be provided for lambs by placing the concentrate in a **creep** (Fig. 29.6), which is constructed with openings large enough to allow the lambs to enter but small enough to keep out the ewes. In addition to concentrates, it is advisable to provide good-quality legume hay, a mineral mix containing calcium, phosphorus, and salt. Examples of creep diets that are balanced for needed nutrients are shown in Table 29.1. Wheat or barley could replace

FIGURE 29.5.
A feed trough for providing concentrates for sheep. Note the iron rod that prevents the sheep from getting into the trough. Courtesy of the Sheep Production Handbook, 1988.

FIGURE 29.6.
Creep with feeder and heat lamp for lambs. A heat lamp is provided if the weather is cold. From R. A. Battaglia and V. B. Mayrose, *Handbook of Livestock Management Techniques* (New York: Macmillan, 1981), p. 381.

up to a half of the corn or sorghum (milo) in these diets. Lambs normally eat 1.5 lb of the creep diet daily from 10–120 days of age (0.10 lb at 3 weeks and 3.0 lb at 120 days).

Water is essential for sheep at all times. It can be provided by tubs or automatic waterers. Tubs should be cleaned once each week. Large buckets are usually used for watering ewes in lambing jugs.

A separate pen equipped with a milk feeder may be needed for orphan lambs. Milk or a milk replacer can be provided free-choice if it is kept cold. Heat lamps kept some distance from the milk feeder can be provided.

Feed Storage

Areas should be provided for storage of hay and concentrates so that feeds can be purchased in quantity or so homegrown feeds can be stored in a dry place. An open shed is satisfactory for hay storage. Some operators prefer a feed bin for concentrates; it is designed so that the feed can be put in at the top and removed from the bottom.

TABLE 29.1. Example Creep Diets for Lambs

	Ration (percent)			
Ingredient	1	2	3	4
Corn grain (yellow)	51.5%	61.0%	—	—
Sorghum grain	—	—	53.0%	65.0%
Soybean meal (44%)	22.0	12.5	—	—
Cottonseed meal (41%)	—	—	25.0	13.0
Alfalfa hay (mid-bloom)	20.0	20.0	15.0	15.0
Molasses (cane)	5.0	5.0	5.0	5.0
Trace mineral salt (sheep)	0.5	0.5	0.5	0.5
Calcium carbonate	1.0	1.0	1.5	1.5
Vitamin A	500 IU/lb			
Vitamin E	10 IU/lb			

Source: Sheep Production Handbook, 1988.

TYPES OF FARM FLOCK PRODUCERS

Some producers raise purebred sheep and sell **rams** for breeding. Commercial producers whose pastures are productive can produce slaughter lambs on pasture, whereas those whose pastures are less desirable produce feeder lambs. Lambs that are neither sufficiently fat nor large for slaughter at weaning time usually go to feedlot operators where they are fed to slaughter weight and condition. However, most feedlot lambs are obtained from producers of range sheep.

Purebred Breeder

Purebred sheep are usually given more feed than commercial sheep because the purebred breeder is interested in growing sheep that express their growth potential. Records are essential to indicate which ram is bred to each of the ewes and which ewe is the mother of each lamb. All ram lambs are usually kept together to compare and identify those most desirable for sale. The ram lambs are usually retained by the purebred breeder until they are a year of age, at which time they are offered for sale. Buyers usually seek to obtain rams from purebred breeders in early summer.

Purebred breeders have major responsibilities to the sheep industry. Because purebred breeders determine the genetic productivity of commercial sheep, they should rigidly select animals that are kept for breeding and should offer only those rams for sale that will contribute improved productivity for the commercial producer.

Commercial Slaughter Lamb Producers

The producer of slaughter lambs, whose feed and pasture conditions are favorable, strives to raise lambs that finish at 90–120 days of age weighing approximately 120 lb each. Any lamb that is small or lacks finish requires additional feeding. Usually, the price decline that occurs from June through September offsets the improvement that is made in value of lambs by feeding, so that feeding the cull farm flock lambs is generally unprofitable. Creep feeding of concentrates early in the life of lambs helps, but, because lambs may be disoriented when their creep is moved, they may not come to the creep after being put onto a new pasture. Therefore, creep feeding on pasture on which pasture rotation is practiced may not be beneficial. Keeping sheep healthy while providing adequate water on lush pasture will result in early market lambs.

Commercial producers can give some assurance to raising heavy, well-finished market lambs at weaning by using good ram selection and crossbreeding programs. Rams that are heavy at 90 days of age are more likely to sire lambs that are heavy at this age than are rams that are light in weight at 90 days of age. The breeds used in a three-breed rotation should include one that is noted for milk-producing ability, one that is noted for rapid growth, and one that is noted for ruggedness and adaptability. The Dorset could be considered for milk production, either the Hampshire or Suffolk for rapid growth, and the Cheviot for its ruggedness. All of these breeds make desirable carcasses.

Commercial producers castrate all ram lambs. Young ewes that are selected to replace old ewes should be large and growthy and should be daughters of ewes that produce relatively many lambs. Ewes that have started to decline in production and poorly productive ewes should be culled.

Commercial Feeder Lamb Producers

Some commercial sheep are produced under pasture conditions that are insufficient for growing the quantity or quality of feed needed for heavy slaughter lambs at weaning. Lambs produced under such conditions may be either fed out in the summer or carried through the summer on pasture with their dams and finished in the fall. Sudan grass or rape can be seeded so that good pasture is available in the summer, and lambs can be finished on pasture by giving them some concentrates. If good summer pasture cannot be made available, it is advisable to wait until autumn, at which time the lambs are put on full feed in a feedlot.

Commercial Feedlot Operator

Lambs that come to the feedlot for finishing are treated for internal **parasites** and for certain diseases, particularly **overeating disease.** They are provided water and hay initially, after which concentrate feeding is allowed and increased until they receive all the concentrates they will consume. Death losses may be high in unthrifty lambs.

The feedlot operator hopes to profit by efficiently increasing their weight. Lambs on feed should gain about 0.5–0.8 lb per head per day. Feeder buyers prefer feeder lambs weighing 70–80 lb over larger lambs because of the need to put 20–30 lb of additional weight on the lambs to finish them. A feeding period of 40–60 days should be sufficient for finishing thrifty lambs. Table 29.2 shows some example diets for growing–finishing lambs.

Feeding lambs is riskier than producing them because of death losses, price fluctuations of feed and sheep, and the necessity of making large investments.

FEEDING EWES

Figure 29.7 shows the expected weight changes in a 160-lb ewe raising twin lambs. A ewe of similar weight, raising a single lamb, would have about two-thirds of the weight changes shown

TABLE 29.2. Example Diets for Growing–Finishing Lambs

	Ration (lb)			
Ingredient	1	2	3	4
Corn grain (yellow)	620	1,465	—	—
Sorghum grain (milo)	—	—	390	1,475
Alfalfa hay (mature)	1,100	300	300	300
Cottonseed hulls	—	—	800	—
Soybean meal (44%)	140	100	—	—
Cottonseed meal (41%)	—	—	350	80
Molasses (cane)	120	100	120	100
Calcium carbonate	—	15	20	25
Trace mineral salt (sheep)	10	10	10	10
Ammonium chloride	10	10	10	10

Source: Sheep Production Handbook, 1988.

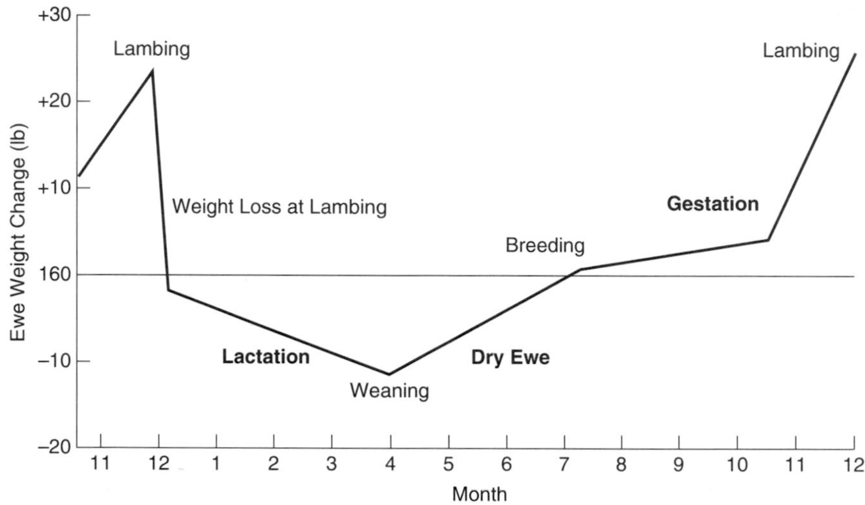

FIGURE 29.7.
Weight changes normally expected during the year for a 160-lb ewe giving birth to and raising twin lambs. Courtesy of the *Sheep Production Handbook*.

in Fig. 29.7. Economical feeding programs are implemented to correspond with these expected weight changes.

Mature, pregnant ewes usually need nothing more than lower quality roughages (e.g. hay, wheat straw or corn stover) during the first half of pregnancy, after which some concentrates and good-quality legume hay should be fed. Any grains such as corn, barley, oats, milo, and wheat are satisfactory feeds. Sheep usually chew these grains sufficiently so that grinding or rolling is not essential. Rolled or cracked grains may be digested slightly more efficiently and may be more palatable, but finely ground grains are undesirable for sheep unless the grains are pelleted.

Sheep need energy, protein, salt, iodine, phosphorus, and vitamins A, D, and E. In some areas selenium is deficient and must be supplied either in the feed or by injection. Mature, ruminating sheep have little need for quality protein or B vitamins, but immature sheep have variable requirements. Rumen microorganisms can synthesize protein from nonprotein nitrogenous substances in the ration.

Sheep will perform poorly or die quickly when the water supply is inadequate, so the importance of supplying water cannot be overstated. Water that is not clean will not be well accepted by sheep. Water intake is influenced by amount of food eaten, protein intake, environmental temperature, mineral intake, water temperature, pregnancy, water content of feed eaten (including rain and dew on pastures), and the odor and taste of the water.

Energy is perhaps the most common limiting nutrient for ewes. Underfeeding is the primary cause for a deficiency of energy because most feed materials are high in energy. Dry range grasses and mature forages such as grain straws may be high in gross energy but so low in digestibility that sheep cannot obtain all their energy needs from them.

The amount of protein in the ration for sheep is of greater importance than the quality of protein because sheep can make the essential amino acids by action of microorganisms in the rumen. The oil meals (soybean, linseed, peanut, and cottonseed) are all high in protein. Soybean meal is the most palatable and its use in a ration encourages a high feed intake. Nonprotein sources of nitrogen such as urea and **biuret** can be used to supply a portion but not all of the nitrogen needs of sheep. Not more than one-third of the nitrogen need should be supplied by urea or biuret, and these materials are not recommended for young lambs with developing rumens or for range sheep on low-energy diets. If protein intake is limited by mixing with salt, adequate water must be provided. The mineral needs for sheep are calcium, phosphorus, sulfur, potassium, sodium, chlorine, magnesium, iron, zinc, copper, manganese, cobalt, iodine, molybdenum, and selenium. All of these minerals are found in varying amounts in different tissues of the body. For example, 99% of the calcium, 80%–95% of the phosphorus, and 70% of the magnesium occurs in the skeleton and more than 80% of the iodine is found in the thyroid gland.

The requirement for minerals is influenced by breed; age, sex, and growth rate of young animals; reproduction and lactation of the ewe; level and chemical form injected or fed; climate; and balance and adequacy of the ration.

Salt is important in sheep nutrition and it can become badly needed when sheep are grazing on lush pastures. Also, sheep may consume too much salt when they are forced to drink brackish water.

In some areas, iodine and selenium are deficient. The use of iodized salt in an area where iodine is deficient may supply the iodine needs. Selenium can be added to the concentrate mixture that is being fed or it can be given by injection.

The most critical periods of nutritional needs for the ewe are at breeding and just before, during, and shortly after lambing. A lesser but still important period for the ewe is during lactation. After the lamb is weaned, the ewe normally can perform satisfactorily on pasture or range without any additional feed. If accelerated lamb production is practiced, the ewes should be well fed after the lamb is weaned so the ewe can be bred again.

Example diets for ewes are shown in Table 29.3. Note how the amount of feed changes from maintenance to gestation to lactation. In both the gestation and lactation periods, the maintenance requirement must be met first.

Ewes are normally run on pasture or range where they obtain all their nutritional needs from grasses, browse, and forbs, except during the winter or dry periods when these plants are not growing. During these periods when there is no plant growth, the sheep must be given supplemental feed.

Occasionally lambs are raised on milk replacer or on cow's milk if the ewe dies during lambing or her udder becomes nonfunctional. During these two periods, frozen colostrum should be available for the lambs. If milk or milk replacer is used, it can be bottle-fed twice daily or it can be self-fed if it is kept cold. It is important to feed cold milk when it is self-fed to prevent the lamb from overconsumption. There should be heat lamps not far from where the lambs consume the cold milk so they can go to the heated area to become warm and to sleep.

Rams should be fed to keep them healthy but not fat. A small amount of grain along with good-quality hay satisfies their nutritional needs in winter. Young bred ewes should be fed some grain along with all the legume hay they will consume because they are growing and also need some nutritional reserve for the subsequent lactation. Ewe lambs should be grown out but not fattened in the winter. Limited grain feeding along with legume hay satisfies their nutritional needs.

At lambing time, the grain allowance of ewes needs to be increased to assist them in

TABLE 29.3. Example Diets (as fed) for 155-lb Ewes at Different Stages of Production

Stage of Production	Ration No.	Alfalfa Hay (mid-bloom; lb)	Corn Silage (mature; lb)	Corn Grain (lb)	Soybean Meal (44% CP; lb)	Salt/Trace Mineral Mix (lb)[a]
Maintenance	1	3.0	—	—	—	0.05
	2	—	6.0	—	0.20	0.05
Gestation	1	3.5	—	—	—	0.05
(first 15 weeks)	2	—	6.0	—	0.25	0.05
Gestation (last 4 weeks)						
130%–150% lambing	1	3.5	—	0.75	—	0.05
	2	—	6.0	0.75	0.40	0.05
180%–225% lambing	1	3.5	—	1.25	—	0.05
	2	—	7.0	1.00	0.50	0.05
Lactation (first 6–8 weeks)						
Suckling single	1	4.0	—	2.00	—	0.05
	2	—	9.0	1.00	0.85	0.05

[a] Contains 50% trace mineral salt (for sheep) and 50% dicalcium phosphate.
Source: Sheep Production Handbook, 1988.

producing a heavy flow of milk. Also, the lambs need to be fed a high-energy ration in the creep. Lambs obtain sufficient protein in the milk given by their mothers, but they need more energy. Rolled grains provided free-choice in the creep are palatable and provide the energy needed.

Lambs on full feed are allowed some hay of good quality and all the concentrates they will consume. Some feedlot operators pellet the hay and concentrates, whereas others feed loose hay and grains. After the grasses and legumes start to grow in the spring, all sheep generally obtain their nutritional needs from the pasture.

CARE AND MANAGEMENT OF FARM FLOCKS

The handling of sheep is extremely important. A sheep should never be caught by its wool because the skin is pulled away from the flesh, causing a bruise. When a group of sheep is crowded into a small enclosure, the sheep will face away from the person who enters the enclosure. When the sheep's rear flank is grasped with one hand, the sheep starts walking backward; this allows one to reach out with the other hand and grasp the skin under the sheep's chin. When a sheep is being held, grasping the skin under the chin with one hand and grasping the top of the head with the other hand enables the holder to pull the sheep forward so its brisket is against the holder's knee. If a sheep is to be moved forward, the skin under the chin can be grasped with one hand and the **dock** (the place where the tail was removed) can be grasped with the other hand. Putting pressure on the dock makes the sheep move forward, while holding its chin with the other hand prevents it from escaping.

Lambing Operations

Before the time the ewes are due to lamb, wool should be clipped from the dock, udder, and vulva regions. This process is called **crutching** or tagging. If weather conditions permit, the ewes may be completely shorn. Also, all **dung tags** (small pieces of dung that stick to the wool) should be clipped from the rear and flank of pregnant ewes. Young lambs will try to locate the teat of the ewe and may try to nurse a dung tag if it is present.

Ewes should be checked periodically to locate those that have lambed. The ewe and newborn lamb should be placed in a lambing jug. The ewe that is about ready to lamb can be watched carefully but with no interference if delivery is proceeding normally. In a normal presentation, the head and front feet of the lamb emerge first. If the rear legs emerge first **(breech presentation),** assistance may be needed if delivery is slow because the lamb can suffocate if deprived of oxygen for too long. If the front feet are presented but not the head, the lamb should be pushed back enough to bring the head forward for presentation.

As soon as the lamb is born, membranes or mucus that may interfere with its breathing should be removed. When the weather is cold, it may be necessary to dry the lamb by rubbing it with a dry cloth. If a lamb becomes chilled, it can be immersed in warm water from the neck down to restore body temperature, after which it should be wiped dry. The lamb should be encouraged to nurse as soon as possible. A lamb that has nursed and is dry should survive without difficulty if a heat lamp is provided. The lamb can be identified by an ear tag, a tattoo, or both.

Some ewes may not want to claim their lambs. It may be necessary to tie a ewe with a rope halter so she cannot butt or trample her lamb.

Castrating and Docking

Because birth is a period of stress for lambs, it is best to wait 3–4 days before castrating and **docking** lambs. To use the elastrator method of castration and docking, a tight rubber band is placed around the scrotum above the testicles (for castration) and around the tail about an inch from the buttocks (for docking). Some death losses can occur when tetanus-causing bacteria invade the tissue where the elastrator was applied. Another castration and docking practice is to remove surgically the testicles and tail. The emasculator is also useful for docking; the skin of the tail is pulled toward the lamb, the emasculator is applied about an inch from the lamb's buttocks, and the tail is cut loose next to the emasculator. A fly repellent should be applied around any wound to lessen the possibility of **fly strike** (fly eggs are deposited during warm weather).

Occasionally, ewes develop a vaginal or uterine **prolapse** (the reproductive tract protrudes to the outside through the vulva). This condition is extremely serious and leads to death if corrective measures are not taken by trained personnel. The tissue should be pushed back in place, even if it is necessary to hoist the ewe up by her hind legs as a means of reducing pressure that the ewe is applying to push the tract out. After the tract is in place, the ewe can be harnessed so that external pressure is applied on both sides of the vulva. In some cases, it may be necessary to suture the tract to make certain that it stays in place. Once a ewe has prolapsed her reproductive tract, the tract shows a weakness that is likely to recur; therefore, a record should be kept so that the ewe can be culled after she weans her lamb.

Shearing

Sheep are usually shorn in the spring, before the hot weather months. Shearing is typically done by professional personnel, though shearing classes are available to teach the operator. The usual method of shearing involves clipping the fleece from the animal with power-driven shears, leaving sufficient wool covering to protect the sheep's skin. In the shearing operation, the sheep is set on its dock and cradled between the shearer's legs, which are used to maneuver the sheep into the positions needed to ease the shearing.

The wool that is properly removed during shearing remains in one large piece. It is spread with the clipped side out, rolled with the edges inside, and tied with paper twine. It is best to remove dung tags and coarse material that is clipped from the legs and put these items in a separate container. The tied fleece is put into a huge sack. When buyers examine the wool, they can obtain core samples from the sack. The core sample is taken by inserting a hollow tube that is sharp at the end into the sack of wool. The sample obtained is examined to evaluate the wool in the sack rather than having to remove the fleeces to examine them. If undesirable material is obtained in the core sample, the price offered will be much lower than if only good wool is found.

If the wool is kept for some time before it is sold, it should be stored in a dry place and on a wooden or concrete floor to avoid damage from moisture.

FACILITIES FOR PRODUCTION OF RANGE SHEEP

Sheep differ from cattle in that they graze weedy plants and brush as well as grasses and legumes. Because of their different grazing patterns, cattle and sheep can be effectively grazed together in some range areas. Total pounds of liveweight produced can be higher compared to grazing the separate species on the same range.

Range sheep are produced in large flocks primarily in arid and semiarid regions. Sheep of fine-wool breeding tend to stay together as they graze, which makes herding possible in large range areas. Range sheep are moved about either in trucks or by trailing so they can consume available forage at various elevations. Requirements for the production of range sheep are usually different from those for farm flock operations. One type of range sheep operation is described here, but it must be noted that variations exist.

Range sheep are usually bred to lamb later than sheep in farm flocks; therefore, they can be lambed on the range. Few provisions are needed for lambing when sheep are lambed on the range, but under some conditions a tent or a lambing shed may be used to give range sheep protection from severe weather at lambing time. Temporary corrals can be constructed using snow fences and steel posts when it is necessary to contain the sheep at the lambing camp or at lambing sheds.

Sheep on range are usually wintered at relatively low elevations in areas where little precipitation occurs. Wintering sheep are provided **feed bunks** if hay is to be fed, and windbreaks to give protection from cold winds. Some producers of range sheep provide pelleted feed to supplement the winter forage. Pellets are usually placed on the ground but are sometimes dispersed in grain troughs.

A sheep camp or sheep wagon is the mobile housing used by the sheep herder. The camp is moved by truck or horses because the sheep need to be moved over large grazing areas. A sheep herder usually has a horse and dogs to assist in herding the sheep. The sheep are brought together to a night bedding area each evening.

MANAGING RANGE SHEEP

Range sheep are grazed in three general areas: (1) the **winter headquarters,** which is a relatively low and dry area and which sometimes provides forage for winter grazing; (2) the **spring–fall**

range, which is a somewhat higher elevation area and which receives more precipitation; and (3) the **summer grazing** area, which is at high mountainous elevations and which receives considerable precipitation, resulting in lush feeds.

The Winter Headquarters

The forage on the winter range, where there is usually less than 10 inches of precipitation annually, is composed of sagebrush and grasses. The grasses are cured on the ground from the growth of the previous summer; consequently, winter forage is of lower quality than green forage because the plants in the winter forage are mature and because they have lost nutrients. The soil in these areas is often alkaline and the water is sometimes alkaline.

Because forage in the wintering area is of poor quality, supplemental feeding that provides needed protein, carotene, and minerals (such as copper, cobalt, iodine, and selenium) is usually necessary. A pelleted mixture made by mixing sun-cured alfalfa leaf meal, grain, solvent-extracted soybean or cottonseed meal, beet pulp, molasses, bone meal or dicalcium phosphate, and trace-mineralized salt is fed at the rate of 0.25–2.0 lb per head per day, depending on the condition of the sheep. The feed may be mixed with salt to regulate intake so that feed can be before the sheep at all times. If the intake of feed is to be regulated through the use of salt, trace-mineralized salt should be avoided. Adequate water must also be provided at all times, because heavy salt intake is quite harmful if sheep do not have water for long periods of time.

The ewes are brought to the winter headquarters about the first of November. Rams are turned in with the ewes for breeding in November if lambing is to take place in sheds or if a spring range that is not likely to experience severe weather conditions is available for lambing. Otherwise, the rams are put with the ewes in December for breeding.

January, February, and March are critical months because the sheep are then in the process of exhausting their body stores and because severe snowstorms can occur. If sheep become snowbound, they should each be given 2 lb of alfalfa hay plus 1 lb of pellets per day containing at least 12% protein. Adequate feeding of ewes while they are being bred and afterward results in at least a 30% increase in lambs produced and about a 10% increase in wool produced. In addition, death losses are markedly reduced. Sheep that are stressed by inadequate nutrition, either as a result of insufficient feed or a ration that is improperly balanced, are highly susceptible to pneumonia. Heavy death losses can result.

The Spring–Fall Range

Pregnant ewes are shorn at the winter headquarters (usually in April). They are then moved to the spring–fall range, where they are lambed. If they are lambed on the range, a protected area is necessary. An area having scrub oak or big sagebrush on the south slopes of foothills and ample feed and water is ideal for range lambing. Portable tents can be used if the weather is severe.

Ewes that have lambed are kept in the same area for about 3 days until the lambs become strong enough to travel. The ewes that have lambs are usually fed a pelleted ration that is high in protein and fortified with trace-mineralized salt and either bone meal or dicalcium phosphate. Feeding at this time can help prevent sheep from eating poisonous plants.

Ewes with lambs are kept separate from those yet to lamb until all ewes have borne their lambs. In addition, ewes that are almost ready to lamb are separated from those that will not lamb for some time yet. Thus, after lambing gets underway, three separate groups of ewes are usually present until lambing is completed.

If the ewes are bred to lamb earlier than is usual for range lambing and a crested wheat-grass pasture is available, ewes may be lambed in open sheds. If good pasture is unavailable, the ewes may be confined in yards around the lambing sheds, starting a month before lambing. In this event, the ewes must be fed alfalfa or other legume hay and 0.50–0.75 lb of grain per head per day. The ewes should have access to a mixture of trace-mineralized salt and bone meal or dicalcium phosphate.

Although shed lambing is more expensive than range lambing, higher prices for lambs marketed earlier have made shed lambing advantageous. Fewer lambs are lost in shed lambing, and lambing can take place earlier in the year. The heavy market lambs that result produce enough income to offset the costs of shed lambing.

Summer Grazing

The Summer Range. Sheep are moved to summer range shortly after lambing is completed if weather conditions have been such that snow has melted and lush plant growth is occurring. The sheep are put into bands of about 1,000–1,200 ewes and their lambs. In some large operations, the general practice is to put ewes with single lambs in one band and ewes with twins in another. The ewes with twin lambs are given the best range area so the lambs will have added growth from the better forage supply. Sheep are herded on the summer range to assist them in finding the best available forage.

In October, prior to the winter storms, the lambs are weaned. Lambs that carry sufficient finish are sent to slaughter and other lambs are sold to lamb feeders. It is the general practice among producers of Rambouillet, Columbia, and Targhee sheep to breed some of the most productive and best-wooled ewes to rams of the same breed to raise replacement ewe lambs. Most of these ewe lambs are kept and grown out, and only the less desirable ones are culled. The remainder of the ewes are bred to meat-type rams, such as the Suffolk or Hampshire, and all their lambs are marketed for slaughter, as feeders or as stockers (animals used in the flock for breeding).

The Fall Range. As soon as the lambs are weaned, the ewes are moved to the spring–fall range. Later they go to the winter headquarters for wintering.

The number of ewes that can be bred per ram during the breeding period of about 2 months is 15 for ram lambs, 30 for yearling rams, and 35 for mature, but not aged, rams. These numbers are general and depend greatly on the type of conditions existing on the range.

CONTROLLING DISEASES AND PARASITES

Sheep raised by most producers are confronted with a few serious diseases, several serious internal parasites, and some external parasites. Some common diseases of sheep include the following types.

Enterotoxemia (overeating disease) is often serious when sheep are in a high nutritional state (e.g., lambs in the feedlot), though it can also affect sheep that are on lush pastures. The disease can be prevented by administering Type D toxoid. Usually, three treatments are given:

two about 4 weeks apart and a booster treatment 6 months later. Losses from this disease among young lambs can be prevented by vaccinating pregnant ewes.

E. coli* complex—*Clostridium E is another disease common in sheep. At least three organisms are involved: (1) *E. coli,* (2) *Clostridium perfringens,* and (3) a virus called *rotavirus.* This disease affects lambs from birth to a few days of age. The disease can be prevented by vaccinating all pregnant ewes twice in later pregnancy with type C and D *Clostridium perfringens* toxoid. The lambing pen should be thoroughly cleaned. Broad spectrum **antibiotics** given to afflicted lambs help. The ewe flock should be vaccinated with *Clostridium perfringens* type C and D toxoid. Enterotoxemia may be caused by *Clostridium perfringens* type D or C. The *Clostridium perfringens* type CD toxoid given to the ewe will give the lamb protection from both types of enterotoxemias.

Lamb dysentery. *C. perfringens* type B occurs very early in life and often during wet weather. It can be prevented by vaccinating ewes with Type BCD vaccine.

Footrot is one of the most serious and common diseases affecting the sheep industry. The disease can be treated with systemic medication. It can be cured by severe trimming so that all affected parts are exposed, treating the diseased area with a solution of one part formalin solution to nine parts of water, and then turning the sheep onto a clean pasture so that reinfection does not occur. A tilting squeeze is useful for restraining sheep that need treatment (Fig. 29.8). Formaldehyde must be used with caution because the fumes are damaging to the respiratory system of both the sheep and the person applying the formaldehyde.

Once all sheep in the flock are free of footrot, it can best be prevented by making sure that it is not reintroduced into the flock. Rams introduced for breeding should be isolated for 30–60 days for observation. If footrot develops, rams should continue in isolation until free of the disease. A vaccine is available for footrot.

Pneumonia usually occurs when animals have been stressed by other diseases, parasites, improper nutrition, or exposure to severe weather conditions. When pneumonia is recognized

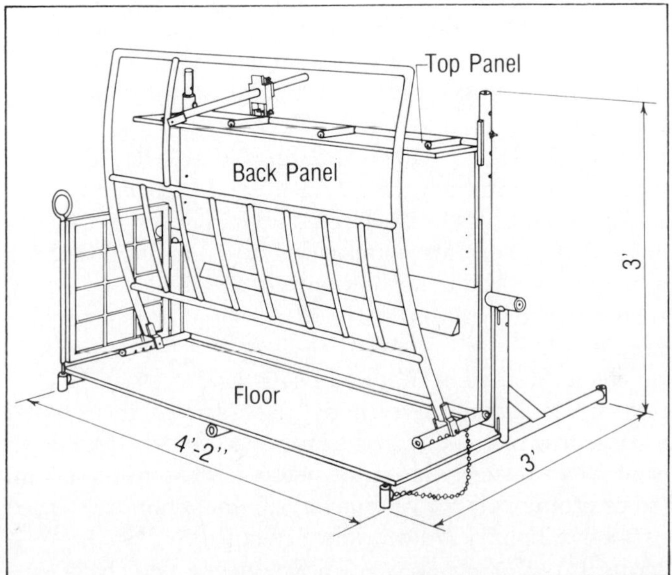

FIGURE 29.8.
A tilting-squeeze chute for restraining sheep. Courtesy of John H. Pedersen, Midwest Plan Service, Agricultural Engineering, Iowa State University.

early, antibiotics are usually effective against it. The afflicted animal should be given special care and kept warm and dry.

Ram epididymitis is an infection of the epididymis that reduces fertility. No effective treatment is available.

Sore mouth usually affects lambs rather than adult sheep. It is caused by a virus and can be contracted by humans. It can be controlled by vaccination, and sheep should be vaccinated as a routine practice.

Sheep are subject to a nutritional disease known as **white muscle disease.** To prevent it, pregnant ewes should be given an injection of selenium during the last one-third of pregnancy and the lambs should be given an injection of selenium at birth.

Selenium can be added to the feed of pregnant ewes to prevent white muscle disease of their lambs. If trace mineralized salt is provided, it should contain sufficient selenium to supply the needs of sheep.

Shipping fever is a highly infectious and contagious disease complex that usually affects lambs after stress of transportation. The most common type of shipping fever is *Pasteurellosis.* Bacterial agents associated with this disease are *Pasteurella hemolytica, Pasteurella multocida, Cornybacterium pyogenes,* and, to a lesser extent, *micrococci, streptococci,* and *pseudomonas.* Antibiotics and **sulfonamides** are usually effective as treatment. Care in transporting lambs helps prevent this disease.

Caseous lymphadenitis is a disease that occurs in greater frequency as sheep increase in age from lambs to old animals. It is due to a bacterium, *Corynebacterium pyogenes var pseudotuberculosis,* which grows in lymph glands and causes a large development of caseous (a thick, cheese-like accumulation) material to form. It is a serious disease and one that is difficult to control. The abscesses can be opened and flushed with a solution of equal parts of 0.2% nitrofurazone solution and 3% hydrogen peroxide. One should not open an abscess and let the thick pus go onto the floor or soil where well sheep will be traveling because this may cause the disease to spread. All infected animals should be culled and they should be isolated from noninfected sheep immediately on appearance of being infected.

Salmonellosis causes dysentery in lambs and abortion by ewes. The organism is found in feces of animals and may contaminate water in stagnant pools. It usually occurs after lambs or other sheep have been stressed. There is no cure for this disease. If lambs show symptoms of the disease, they should be isolated from pregnant ewes and from well lambs.

Polyarthritis (stiff lamb disease usually associated with overeating) affects lambs. It responds to treatment with the oxytetracycline, chlortetracycline, tylosin, and penicillin.

Milk fever is due to hypocalcemia. Afflicted animals can be treated with injection of calcium salts. A 20% solution of calcium borogluconate given **intravenously** at the rate of 100 ml per sheep should have an afflicted animal up and in good condition within 2 hours.

Abortion may occur in late pregnancy due to vibriosis, enzootic abortion, or leptspirosis. Most of these are controlled by vaccination.

Sheath rot may occur in rams. There is no treatment that gives satisfactory results.

Urinary calculi (kidney stones) occurs when the salts in the body that are normally excreted in the urine are precipitated and form stones that may lodge in the kidney's ureters, bladder, or urethra. Providing a constant supply of clean water helps immensely in preventing calculi formation. The ideal ratio of calcium to phorphorus is 1.6 calcium to 1.0 phosphorus. Ammonium chloride can be included in the ration to help prevent urinary calculi.

TABLE 29.4. Summary of Compounds for Control of Internal Parasites of Sheep

Internal Parasites	Drench	Remarks
Coccidia Coccidiosis	Sulfonamides Sulfamethazine Sulfaguanidine	Relatively effective; will form crystals in kidney of lamb, which can cause death
Liver fluke	Albendazole	A new drug released by the FDA for experimental use in Texas, Oregon, Washington, Idaho, and Louisiana
	Carbon tetrachloride	Toxic—use at recommended doses; effective only against adult flukes
Lung worm	Levamisol (Tramisol)	Effective only against adult lungworm
Stomach and round worms	Tramisol	Safe, effective; will kill arrested worms
	Phenothiazine	Control is much improved with the use of fine particle size
	Thiabendazole	Safe, effective
Tapeworm Broad	Lead arsenate Dipenthane 70 (teniatol, teniazine)	May be mixed with phenothiazine or thiabendazole for control of roundworms and tapeworms with one drench
Fringe	No approved control	

Pregnancy disease (ketosis) is a metabolic disease that affects ewes in late pregnancy, particularly if they are carrying twins or triplets. The problem is that ewes carrying twins or triplets must break down body fat to provide their energy needs in later pregnancy. It is possible that use of fat breakdown may not provide the glucose needs, resulting in hypoglycemia. Pregnancy disease may be prevented by feeding some high-energy grain such as corn, barley, or milo, but it is aggravated by one or more large lambs reducing rumen space.

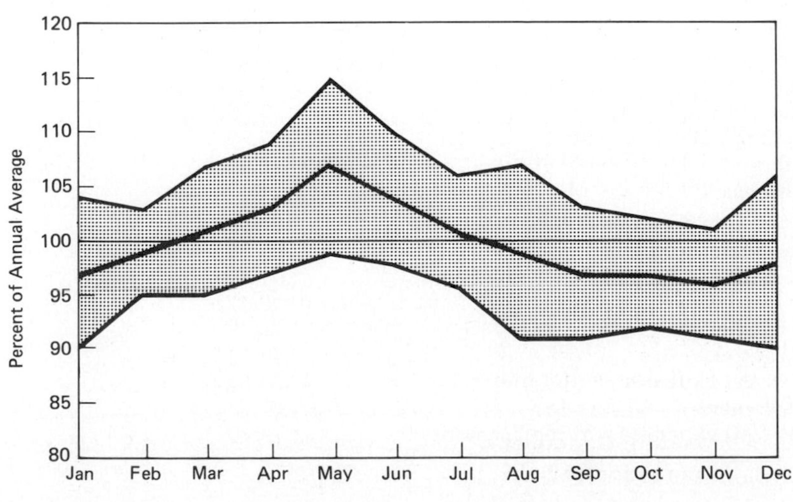

FIGURE 29.9. Seasonal lamb price index (1970–84). The dark line is the average monthly price compared with the average for all years (100). The shaded area shows the range in prices by years. Courtesy of the Western Livestock Marketing Information Project.

Grass tetany (or **grass staggers**) is due to a deficiency of magnesium at a particular time, most frequently in spring when lactating ewes are put onto lush pasture where there is insufficient magnesium available to the sheep. An injection of 50–100 ml of 20% calcium borogluconate or an injection of magnesium sulfate should give rapid recovery.

Johnes disease and **progressive ovine pneumonia** are two debilitating diseases that affect sheep. The lamb may be infected through colostrum of the ewe that has Johnes disease but no ill

TABLE 29.5. U.S. Sheep Production Costs and Returns per Ewe

Item	1987
Cash receipts	**Dollars/head**
Slaughter lambs	$22.96
Feeder lambs	24.02
Cull ewes	6.18
Wool	7.62
Wool payments	10.48
Unshorn lamb payments	1.79
Total cash receipts	73.05
Cash expenses	
Feed	
Grain	1.19
Protein supplements	4.00
Salt and minerals	0.40
Hay	2.82
Pasture	3.41
Public grazing (AUM)[a]	0.67
Crop residues	0.05
Total feed costs	12.54
Other	
Veterinary and medicine	1.11
Livestock hauling	1.26
Marketing	0.30
Ram death loss	0.27
Shearing and tagging	1.34
Fuel, lube, and electricity	1.25
Machine and building repair	2.35
Hired labor	6.98
Miscellaneous	1.19
Total variable expenses	28.59
General farm overhead	5.50
Taxes and insurance	1.80
Interest	8.77
Total fixed expenses	16.07
Total cash expenses	44.66
Receipts less cash expenses	28.39
Capital replacement	7.79
Receipts less cash expenses and replacement	20.60

[a] Animal Unit Month.

Source: Stillman, Crawford, and Aldrich, *The U.S. Sheep Industry,* July 1990.

effects of the disease are exhibited until later when the animal becomes unthrifty and its condition deteriorates. Afflicted animals that are in thin condition do not sell well, but they must be culled because they can help spread the disease to other sheep and they are unlikely to produce lambs when they are emaciated.

Sheep have internal and external parasites, though internal parasites are the more serious of the two. The most important internal parasites are coccidiosis, stomach worms, nodular worms, liver flukes, lungworms, roundworms, and tapeworms.

The treatments effective in controlling internal parasites of sheep are summarized in Table 29.4 (see p. 473).

Common external parasites of sheep include blowfly maggots, **keds** (sheep ticks), lice, mites, screw-worms, and sheep bots. External parasites can be controlled by making two applications of an effective insecticide that is not harmful to sheep. The two applications should be spaced so that eggs hatched after the first application will not result in egg-laying adults prior to the second application.

DETERMINING THE AGE OF SHEEP BY THEIR TEETH

The age of a sheep can be determined by its teeth. Lambs have four pairs of narrow lower incisors called milk teeth or baby teeth. At approximately a year of age the middle pair of milk teeth is replaced by a pair of larger, permanent teeth. At 2 years, a second is replaced. This process continues until, at 4 years of age, the sheep has all permanent incisors. The teeth start to spread apart and some are lost at about 6–7 years of age. When all the permanent incisors are lost, the sheep has difficulty grazing and should be marketed.

COSTS AND RETURNS

The objective of farm flock operators is the efficient production of slaughter lambs ready for market in April and May, when prices are usually highest (Fig. 29.9 on p. 473).

The items used to evaluate costs and returns for ewes are shown in Table 29.5. Note that the total cash receipts per ewe ($73.05) and the total cash expenses per ewe ($44.66) represent a net of $28.39. The costs and returns for several years are shown in Fig. 29.10.

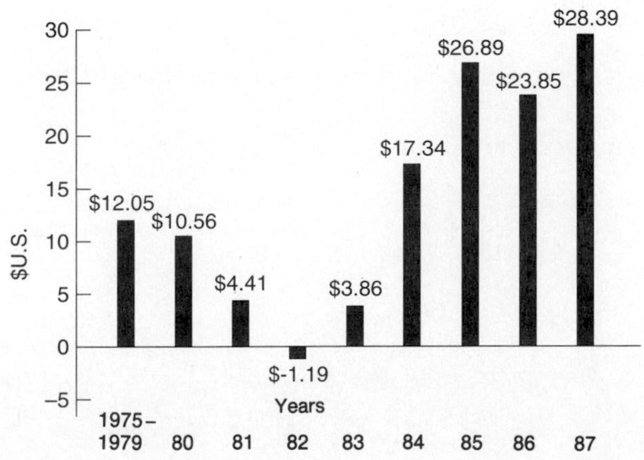

FIGURE 29.10.
U.S. sheep production costs and return, per ewe (receipts less cash expenses). Courtesy of Stillman, Crawford, and Aldrich, *The U.S. Sheep Industry*, July 1990.

TABLE 29.6. Colorado Lamb-Feeding Budget

Item	1985	1986	1987	1988
		Dollars/head		
Costs				
Feeder lamb (83 lbs)	$55.67	$59.96	$71.45	$70.47
Feed				
Corn (3 bu)	7.96	6.74	4.89	6.59
Hay pellets (64 lbs)	2.64	2.65	2.76	3.42
Protein supplement	0.17	2.03	2.18	3.00
Feed additives	2.00	1.98	1.94	1.96
Total feed	12.76	13.40	11.77	14.97
Labor	0.60	0.62	0.65	0.65
Death loss	1.28	1.38	1.64	1.62
Veterinary and medicine	0.37	0.37	0.38	0.38
Miscellaneous and indirect costs	0.78	0.77	0.77	0.81
Machine hire	1.61	1.60	1.62	1.65
Interest on operating capital	1.45	1.45	1.45	1.45
Total costs	73.37	78.17	88.10	90.38
		Dollars/cwt		
Selling price per cwt required to cover costs				
Feed and feeder costs (121 lbs)	56.56	60.63	68.78	70.61
All costs (121 lbs)	60.64	64.60	72.81	74.69
Feed costs per 100-lb gain	33.58	35.27	30.98	39.40
Choice slaughter lambs, South St. Paul	67.22	68.04	75.19	66.24
Net margin	6.58	3.44	2.38	−8.46
Prices				
Choice slaughter lambs, South St. Paul	67.22	68.04	75.19	66.24
Feeder lamb, choice, South St. Paul	67.08	72.24	86.08	84.90
Corn ($/bu)	2.65	2.25	1.63	2.20
Alfalfa pellets ($/ton)	82.37	82.88	86.36	106.98
Soybean meal, 44% ($/ton)	129.25	158.93	170.35	234.85
Annual interest rate (%)	13.43%	11.15%	9.98%	10.58%

Source: Stillman, Crawford, and Aldrich, *The U.S. Sheep Industry,* July 1990.

Table 29.6 shows an enterprise budget for lamb feeding. Note the range in net margin, from +$6.58/cwt to −$8.46/cwt.

For a more detailed discussion of managing costs and returns, see Chapter 36.

SELECTED REFERENCES

Publications

American Feed Industry Association. 1985. *Proceedings of the 1985 Meetings of the American Feed Industry Association Nutrition Council.* Arlington, VA: American Feed Industry Association.

Battaglia, R. A., and Mayrose, V. B. 1981. *Handbook of Livestock Management Techniques.* New York: Macmillan.

Botkin, M. P., Field, R. A., and Johnson, C. L. 1988. *Sheep and Wool: Science, Production, and Management.* Englewood Cliffs, NJ: Prentice-Hall.

Chevelle, N. F. 1977. *Foot Rot of Sheep.* Washington, DC: Agric. Res. Serv. Farmers' Bull. 2206.

Ensminger, M. E., and Parker, R. O. 1986. *Sheep and Goat Science.* Danville, IL: Interstate Printers and Publishers.

Gee, C. K. 1979. *A New Look at Sheep for Colorado Ranchers and Farmers.* Ft. Collins: Colorado State Univ. Exp. Stat. Gen. Series 981.

———, and Madsen, A. G. 1974. *Structure and Operation of the Colorado Lamb Feeding Industry.* Ft. Collins: Colorado State Univ. Expt. Stat. Tech. Bull. 121.

———, and Magleby, R. S. 1978. *Characteristics of Sheep Production in the Western Region.* Washington, DC: USDA Econ. Res. Serv. Agric. Econ. Rpt. 345.

———, Magleby, R. S., Nielson, D. B., and Stevens, D. M. 1977. *Factors in the Decline of the Western Sheep Industry.* Washington, DC: USDA Res. Serv. Agric. Econ. Rpt. 377.

———, and Van Arsdall, R. 1978. *Structural Characteristics and Costs of Producing Sheep in the North-Central States.* Washington, DC: USDA Econ. Stat. and Coop. Serv. SCS-19.

Michalk, D. L. 1979. Sheep production in the United States. *Wool Technology and Sheep Breeding* (Mar.–Apr.).

National Research Council. 1985. *Nutrient Requirements of Sheep.* Washington, DC: National Academy Press.

Sheep Housing and Equipment Handbook. 1982. Ames, IA: Midwest Plan Service.

SID. 1988. *The Sheep Production Handbook.* Denver, CO: Sheep Industry Development Program.

Stillman, R., Crawford, T., and Aldrich, L. July 1990. *The U.S. Sheep Industry.* USDA/ERS, Staff Report no. AGES 9048.

Tomes, G. L., Robertson, D. E., and Lightfoot, R. J. (eds.). 1979. *Sheep Breeding.* Boston: Butterworth & Co.

Ulman, M., and Gee, C. K. 1975. *Prices and Demand for Lamb in the United States.* Fort Collins: Colorado State Univ. Expt. Sta. Tech. Bull. 132.

Visuals

Production Systems for Sheep; Sheep Reproduction and Management Programs; and *Nutrition and Health in Sheep* (sound filmstrips). Prentice-Hall Media, 150 White Plains Rd., Tarrytown, NY 10591.

Sheep Management Practices (2 videotapes). CEV, P.O. Box 65265, Lubbock, TX 79464-5265.

The Sheep Management Series (sound filmstrips): *Ewe and Lamb Management; Fitting and Showing Sheep; Docking Sheep; Controlling Internal Parasites of Sheep; Sheep Castration;* and *Basic Sheep Handling Skills.* Vocational Education Productions, California Polytechnic State University, San Luis Obispo, CA 93407.

Sheep Obstetrics; Assuring Baby Lamb Survival; Castration, Docking and Identification; Raising Orphan Lambs; Marketing Practices; Feeding the Farm Flock; Applying Health Care Practices; Feed and Water Delivery Systems; Sheep Handling; and *Using Equipment and Sheep Psychology* (videotapes). Agricultural Products and Services, 2001 Killebrew Dr., Suite 333, Bloomington, MN 55420.

CHAPTER 30

Horse Breeds and Breeding

BREEDS OF HORSES

Horses have been used for so many different purposes that many breeds have been developed to fill specific needs. The major breeds of horses and their primary uses are listed in Table 30.1. No attempt has been made in Table 30.1 to indicate all the ways each of the breeds is used. For example, the Thoroughbred (Fig. 30.1) is classified primarily as a racehorse for long races, but it is used for several other functions as well.

The "light" breeds of horses provide pleasure for their owners through activities such as racing, riding, and exhibition in shows. Color Plates O and P (following p. 482) and figure 30.2 show examples of these breeds. Quarter Horses are excellent as cutting horses (horses that separate individual cattle out of a herd) and for running short races. Ponies such as the Shetland and Welsh, are selected for their friendliness and safety with children. The American Saddle Horse and the Tennessee Walking Horse have been selected for their comfortable gaits and responsive attitudes. The Palomino, Appaloosa, and Paint horses are color breeds developed for showing and working livestock.

Beauty in color and markings is important in horses used for show and breeding purposes, and color breeds have been developed accordingly. The Appaloosa, for example, has color markings of three patterns: leopard, blanket, and roan. It appears that these color patterns are under different genetic controls. In Appaloosas, Paints, and Palominos, coloration can be affected or eliminated by certain other genes, such as the gene for roaning and the gene for graying. The gene for gray can eliminate both colors and markings, as shown by gray horses that turn white with age.

Another important group of horses is the draft horse (Fig. 30.3 and Color Plate P)—large and powerful animals that are used for heavy work. The Percheron, Shire, Clydesdale, Belgian, and Suffolk are examples of draft horses (Table 30.1).

Popularity of Breeds

Registration numbers are a measure of breed popularity. Table 30.2 shows the registration numbers for draft, light, and pony breeds.

TABLE 30.1. Characteristics and Uses of Selected Breeds of Horses

Breed	Color	Height (in hands)[a]	Weight (lb)	Uses
Riding and Harness Horses				
American Quarter Horse	All colors	14.2–15.2	1,000–1,250	Short racing, showing, stock work
American Saddle Horse	Chestnut, bay, brown, black	15.0–16.0	1,000–1,150	Showing, pleasure riding, 3 and 5 gaited
Arabian	Bay, chestnut, brown, gray, black	14.2–15.2	850–1,000	Pleasure riding, showing
Morgan	Bay, chestnut, brown, black	14.2–15.1	950–1,150	Pleasure riding, driving, showing
Standardbred	Bay, chestnut, roan, brown, black, gray	14.2–16.2	850–1,200	Harness racing
Tennessee Walking Horse	All colors	15.0–16.0	1,000–1,200	Pleasure riding, showing
Thoroughbred	Bay, brown, gray, chestnut, black, roan	15.2–17.0	1,000–1,300	Long racing
Ponies				
Hackney	Bay, chestnut, black, brown	11.2–14.2	450–850	Light harness, showing
Pony of America	Appaloosa			Riding by children, showing
Shetland	Bay, chestnut, brown, black, spotted, mouse	9.2–10.0	300–400	Riding by children, showing
Welsh	Bay, chestnut, black, roan, gray	11.0–13.0	350–850	Riding by children, showing
Draft[b]				
Belgian	Chestnut, roan usually	15.2–17.0	1,900–2,400	Heavy pulling
Clydesdale	Bay, brown, black	15.2–17.0	1,700–2,000	Heavy pulling
Percheron	Black, gray usually	15.2–17.0	1,600–2,200	Heavy pulling
Shire	Bay, brown, usually black	16.2–17.0	1,800–2,200	Heavy pulling
Suffolk	Chestnut	15.2–16.2	1,500–1,900	Heavy pulling
Color Registries				
Appaloosa	Leopard, blanket, roan	14–16	900–1,250	Pleasure riding, showing, stock work
Buckskin	Buckskin, dun, grulla	14–16	900–1,250	Pleasure riding, showing, stock work
Paint	Tobiano, overo	14–16	900–1,250	Pleasure riding, showing, stock work
Palomino	Palomino	14–16	900–1,250	Pleasure riding, showing, stock work
Pinto	Pinto	14–16	900–1,250	Pleasure riding, showing, stock work
White and cremes	White and creme	14–16	900–1,250	Pleasure riding, showing, stock work

[a] Height is measured in inches but reported in "hands." One "hand" equals 4 in.
[b] Draft horses are heavy horses used for pulling; other horses are called light horses and are used primarily as pleasure horses.

FIGURE 30.1.
The Thoroughbred, Foolish Pleasure, in action. Thoroughbreds are great race horses. Note the extreme muscular development.
Courtesy of New York Racing Association, Louis Weintraub, Photo Communication Company, and the Jockey Club, New York, New York.

BREEDING PROGRAM

Reproduction

Mares of the light breeds reach sexual maturity at 12–18 months of age, whereas draft mares are 18–24 months of age when sexual maturity is reached. Mares come into heat every 21 days during the breeding season if they do not become pregnant. Heat lasts for 5–7 days. Ovulation occurs toward the end of heat. Because of the relatively long duration of heat and because ovulation occurs toward the end of heat, horse owners often delay breeding the mare for 2 days after she has first been observed in heat.

Although about 10% of all ovulations in mares are multiple ovulations, twinning occurs in only about 0.5% of the pregnancies that carry to term. The uterus of the mare apparently cannot support twin fetuses; consequently, most twin conceptions result in the loss of both embryos. The length of gestation is about 340 days (approximately 11 months) with usually only one foal being born. Mares usually come into heat 5–12 days following foaling, and fertile matings occur at this heat if the mare has recovered from the previous delivery.

Selection

Most breeders know that weaknesses exist either in their entire herd or in some individuals of the herd. Breeders generally attempt to find a stallion that is particularly strong in the trait or traits that need strengthening in the herd. Obviously, it is also necessary to be sure that no other weaknesses are brought into the herd, so it is better to use a stallion with no undesirable traits, even if he is only average in the trait that needs correcting in the herd. To emphasize one trait only for correcting a weakness while bringing another weakness into the herd will mean, after 25–30 years of breeding, little or no improvement.

An effective breeding program is a completely objective one. There is no place in a breeding program for sympathy toward an animal or for personal pets. Every attempt should be made to see that the environment is the same for all animals in a breeding program. A particularly appealing foal that is given special care and training may develop into a desirable animal.

Quarter Horse

Pinto

Appaloosa

American White Horse

Palomino

United States Trotting Horse

FIGURE 30.2.

Some breeds of pleasure horses. Courtesy of American Quarter Horse Association, Amarillo, Texas (portrait by Orren Mixer); United States Trotting Association, Columbus, Ohio; Appaloosa Horse Club, Moscow, Idaho; Pinto Horse Association, San Diego, California; Palomino Horse Breeders of America, Mineral Wells, Texas (portrait by Orren Mixer); American White Horse Registry, Crabtree, Oregon.

FIGURE 30.3.
A Clydesdale stallion. Courtesy of the USDA.

However, many foals less appealing in early life might also develop into desirable animals if given special care and training. A desirable animal that has had special care and training may transmit favorable hereditary traits no better than a less desirable animal that has not had this treatment. Selecting a horse for breeding that has had special care and training may in fact be selecting only for special care and training. Certainly, these environmentally produced differences in horses are not inherited and will not be transmitted. In fact, it is often wise to select animals that were developed under the type of environment in which they are expected to perform. If stock horses are being developed for herding cattle in rough, rugged country, selection under such conditions is more desirable than where conditions are less rigorous. Horses that possess inherited weaknesses tend to become unsound in a rugged environment, and as a result are not used for breeding. Such animals might never show those inherited weaknesses in a less rugged environment.

An ideal environment for most horse-breeding programs has quality forage distributed over an area that requires horses to exercise as they graze. Where the land is limited, highly productive, and valuable, the animals may have to be kept in a small area and forced to exercise a great deal. Forced exercise tends to keep the animals from becoming too fat and gives strength to the feet and legs. Horses need regular, not sporadic, exercise. Regular exercise, even if quite strenuous, is healthy for genetically sound animals and may reveal the weaknesses of those that are not. Strenuous exercise can, however, be harmful to animals that have not previously exercised for a considerable period of time.

Appaloosa

Arabian

Morgan

Paint

Miniature

PLATE O.
Breeds of light horses and a pony breed (Miniature). Courtesy of Appaloosa Horse Club, (Appaloosa); International Arabian Horse Association (Arabian); American Morgan Horse Association (Morgan); American Paint Horse Association (Paint); and Thomas Nebbia, © National Geographic Association (Miniature).

Quarter Horse

Standardbred

Thoroughbred

Tennessee Walking Horse

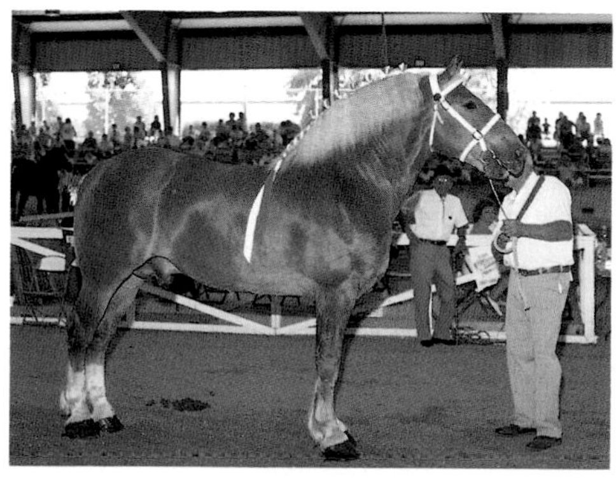

Belgian

PLATE P.
Breeds of light horses and a draft breed (Belgian). Courtesy of the American Quarter Horse Association (Quarter Horse); the U.S. Trotting Association (Standardbred); Gainesway Farm (Thoroughbred); Tennessee Walking Horse Breeders and Exhibitors Association (Tennessee Walking Horse); and the Belgian Draft Horse Corporation (Belgian).

TABLE 30.2. Major U.S. Draft, Light Horse, and Pony Breeds Based on Annual Registration Numbers (in thousands), 1975–89

Breed	1989	1985	1980	1975	Year Association Formed
Light Horse					
Quarter Horse	123.3	157.4	137.1	97.2	1956
Thoroughbred	49.0	50.4	39.4	29.2	1894
Arabian	21.7	30.0	19.7	15.0	1908
Standardbred	17.0	18.4	15.2	12.8	1871
Paint	14.4	12.7	9.7	5.3	1956
Appaloosa	10.8	16.2	25.4	20.2	1938
Tennessee Walking	8.8	7.6	6.8	6.6	1935
Morgan	2.2	4.5	4.5	3.4	1909
Pinto	2.5	3.9	NA	NA	—
Palomino	2.1	1.2	1.6	1.5	1936
Racking Horse	5.5	—	—	—	
Anglo and Half Arab	5.0	10.1	14.3	11.4	—
Saddlebred	3.7	4.4	3.9	4.1	1891
Paso Fino	1.4	1.3	0.6	0.4	—
National Show Horse	0.9	0.9	0.6	0.4	—
Draft					
Belgian	3.5	4.2	0.7	1.3	1887
Percheron	1.4	1.5	0.3	0.1	1905
Clydesdale	0.4	0.2	0.2	0.1	1879
Pony					
Shetland	—	0.6	1.0	—	1888
Miniature	4.1	0.6	—	—	1909
Welsh	0.8	0.5	0.9	—	1906
Hackney	0.6	0.8	0.6	1.0	1891

Sources: Adapted from the American Horse Council, *Horse Industry Directory,* 1990–91; and various breed associations.

An environment should be provided that will identify horses having genetic superiority for the purposes they are to fulfill. For example, horses that are being bred for endurance in traveling should be made to travel long distances on a regular basis to determine if they can remain sound. Horses bred for jumping should be trained to jump as soon as they are physically mature so that those lacking the ability to jump or those that become unsound from jumping can be removed from the breeding program. Draft horses should be trained to pull heavy loads early in life (3 or 4 years of age) to determine their ability to remain sound and their willingness to pull. Performance is needed before animals are used in a breeding program.

Any horse that is unsound should not be used for breeding regardless of the purposes for which the horse is being bred. Such abnormalities as toeing in or toeing out, sickle hocks, cow hocks, and contracted heels will likely lead to unsoundness and difficulties or lack of safety in traveling. Interference and forging actions are extremely objectionable because they can cause the horse to stumble or fall. Defects of the eyes, of the mouth, and of respiration should be selected against in all horses.

CONFORMATION OF THE HORSE

Body Parts

To understand the conformation of the horse, one should be familiar with the body parts (Fig. 30.4). (A more detailed skeletal structure of the horse is shown in Chapter 18.)

Feet and Legs

Major emphasis is placed on feet and legs in describing conformation in the horse—for identifying both correctness and conditions of unsoundness. The old saying, "no feet, no horse" is still considered valid by most horse producers. As feet and leg structure is important, a review of skeletal structure of the front leg and hind leg is given in Figures 30.5 and 30.6.

Figure 30.7 shows the front legs from a front view. From this view, a vertical line from the point of the shoulder should fall in the centers of the knee, pastern, cannon, and foot. Each leg is divided into two equal halves. Deviations from this ideal position are shown with the common terminology associated with them.

The front legs from a side view are shown in Figure 30.8. A vertical line from the shoulder should fall through the center of the elbow and the center of the foot. The angle of the pastern in the ideal position is 45°.

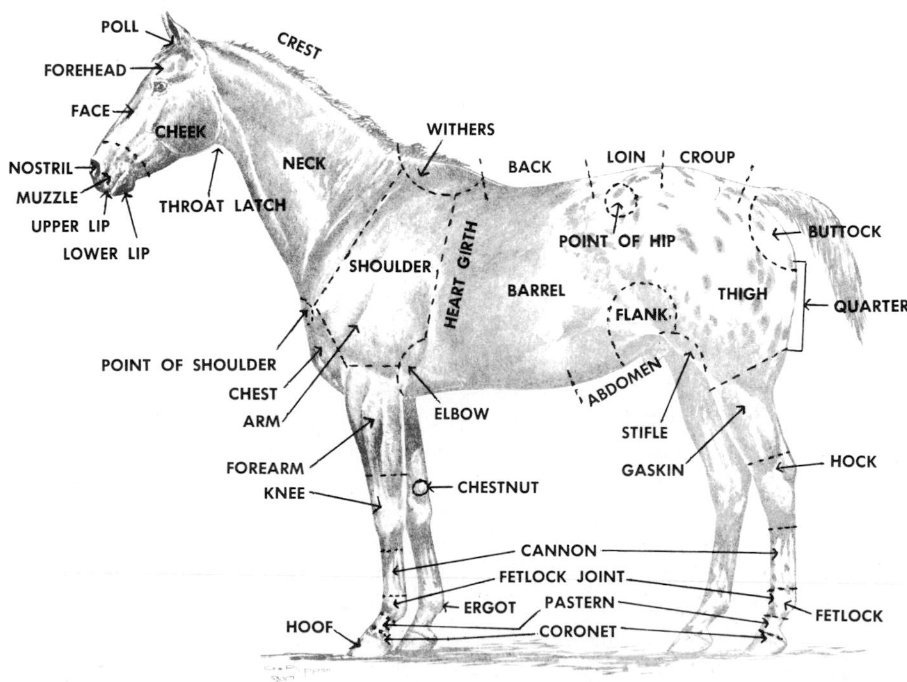

FIGURE 30.4.
The external parts of a horse. Courtesy of the Appaloosa Horse Club, Moscow, Idaho.

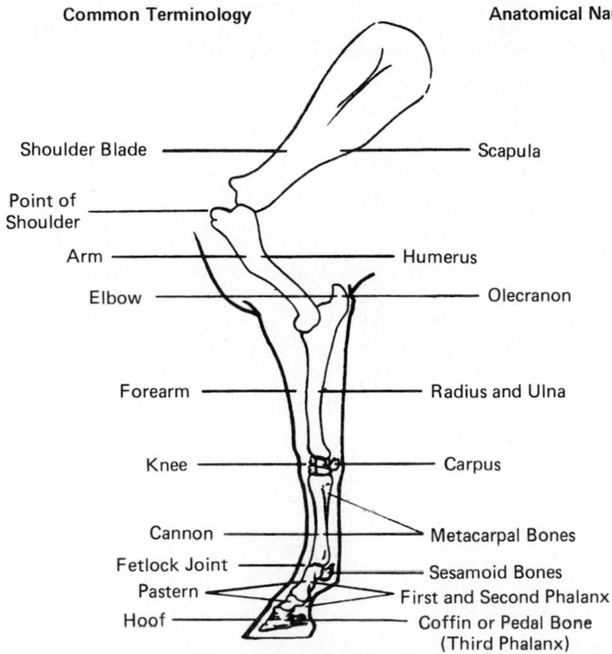

FIGURE 30.5.
Skeletal front leg with common terminology and anatomical names. Courtesy of Rich (1981), Colorado State University Extension Service Publication MOOOOOG.

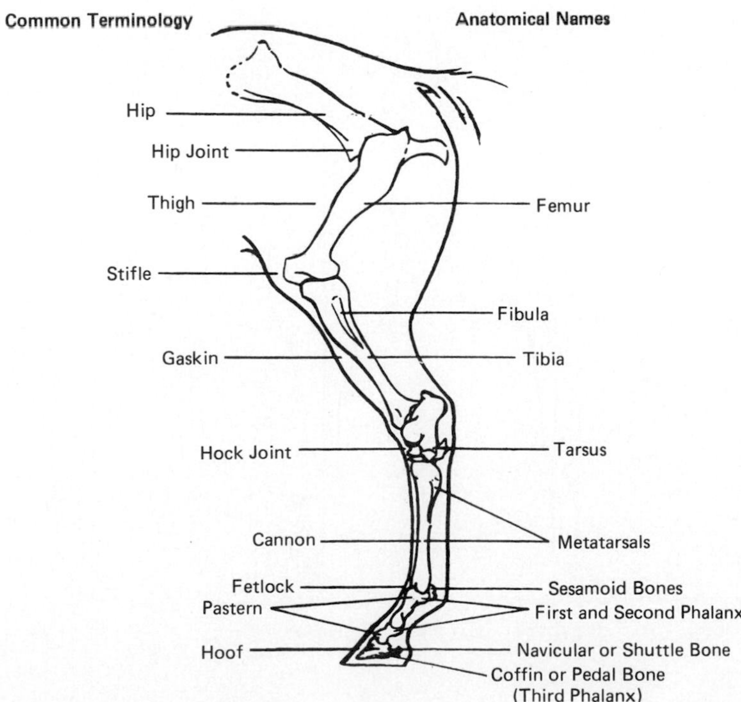

FIGURE 30.6.
Skeletal hind leg with common terminology and anatomical names. Courtesy of Rich (1981), Colorado State University Extension Service Publication MOOOOOG.

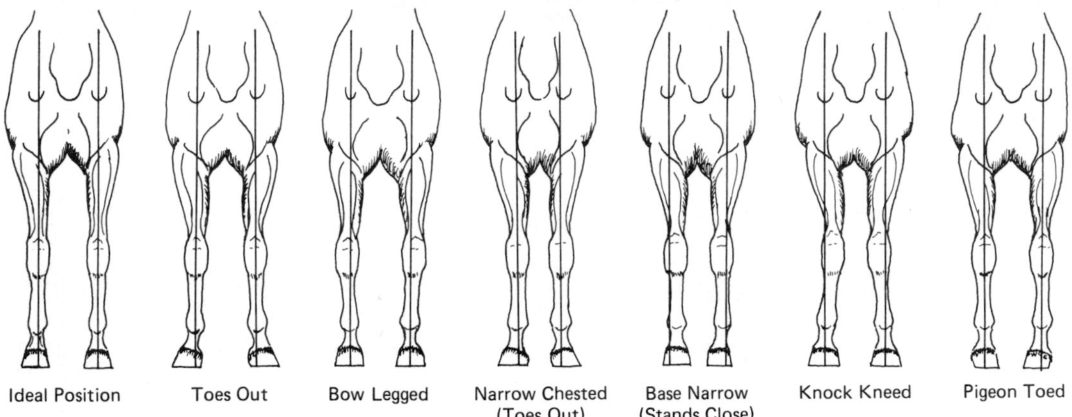

FIGURE 30.7.
Correct and faulty conformation of front feet and legs from a front view. Courtesy of Bill Culbertson.

Figure 30.9 shows the correct hind leg position from a rear view; the less desirable positions of the feet and legs are also shown. In the ideal position, a vertical line from the point of the buttocks should fall through the centers of the hock, cannon, pastern, and foot.

The ideal position of the hind legs from a side view is shown in Figure 30.10. Deviations from the ideal position are shown and described. The ideal position is shown where a vertical line from the point of the buttocks touches the rear edge of the cannon from the hock to the fetlock and meets the ground behind the heel.

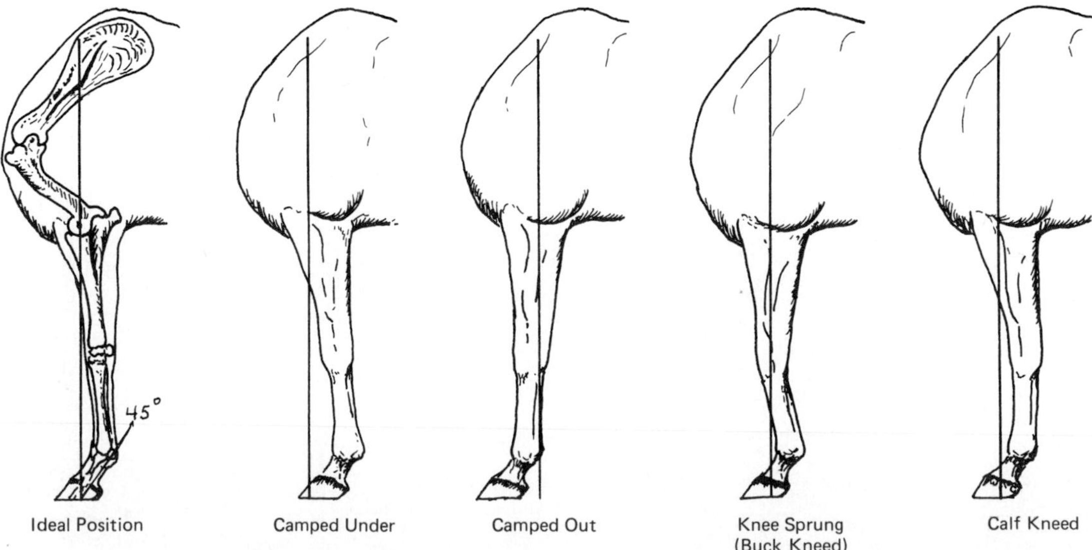

FIGURE 30.8.
Correct and faulty conformation of front feet and legs from a side view. Courtesy of Bill Culbertson.

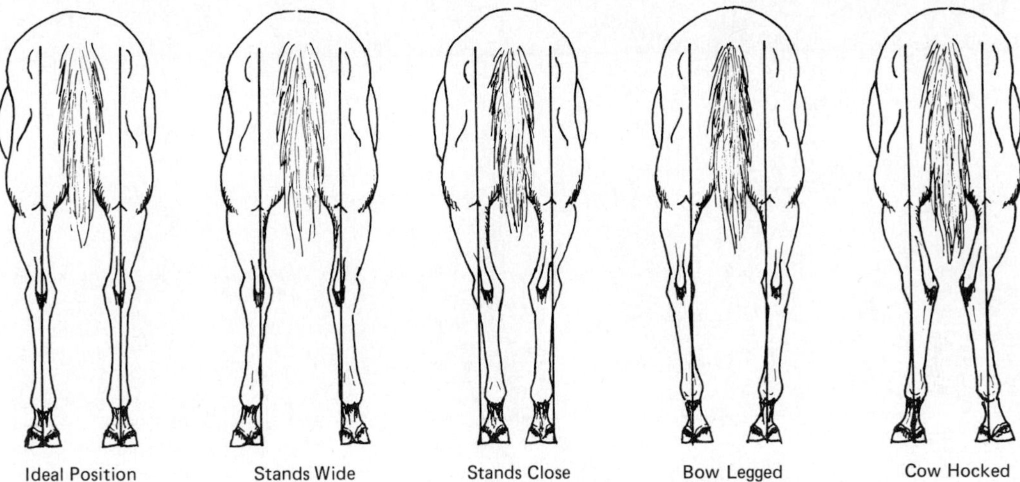

FIGURE 30.9.
Correct and faulty conformation of hind feet and legs as shown in a rear view. Courtesy of Bill Culbertson.

The Hoof

Care of the horse's feet is essential to keep the horse sound and serviceable. Regular cleaning, trimming, and shoeing (depending on frequency of use) are needed. The hoof will, in mature horses, grow $\frac{1}{4}$–$\frac{1}{2}$ inch per month, so trimming is needed every 6–8 weeks.

The external parts of the hoof are shown in Figure 30.11.

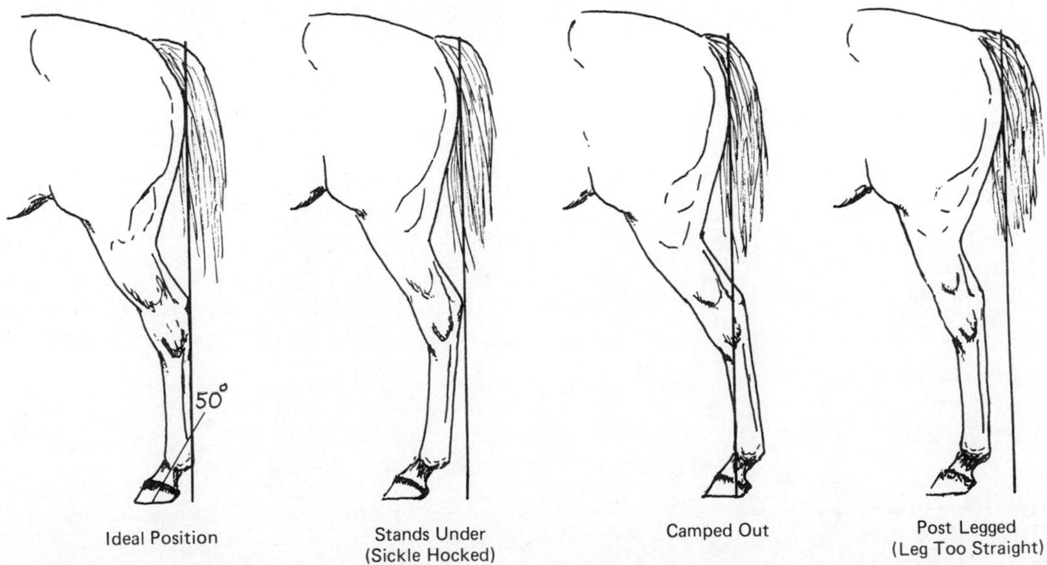

FIGURE 30.10.
Correct and faulty conformation of hind feet and legs from a side view. Courtesy of Bill Culbertson.

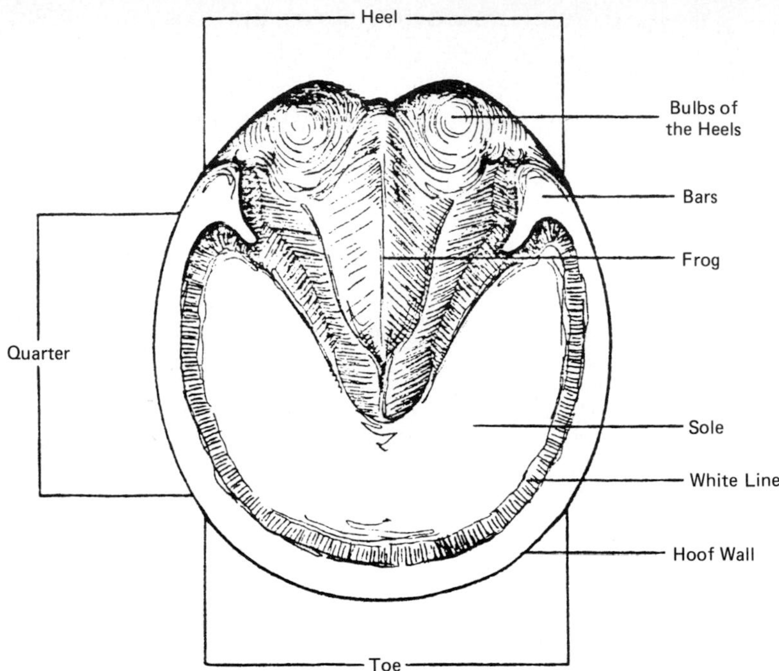

FIGURE 30.11.
The conformation of the hoof (viewed from the bottom side) with several parts identified. Courtesy of Rich (1981), Colorado State University Extension Service Publication MOOOOOG.

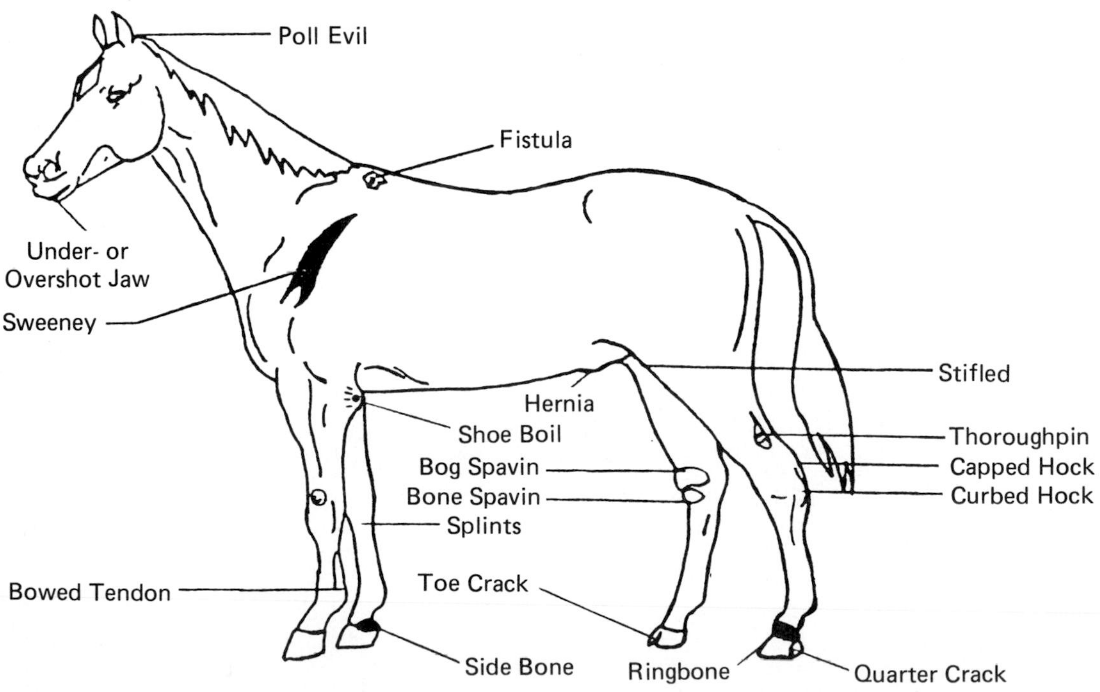

FIGURE 30.12.
Locations of several potential unsoundnesses and blemishes. Courtesy of Rich (1981), Colorado State University Extension Service Publication MOOOOOG.

UNSOUNDNESS AND BLEMISHES OF HORSES

Two terms, *unsoundness* and *blemish,* are used in denoting abnormal conditions in horses. An **unsoundness** is any defect that interferes with the usefulness of the horse. It may be caused by an injury or improper feeding, be inherited, or develop as a result of inherited abnormalities in conformation. A **blemish** is a defect that detracts from the appearance of the horse but does not interfere with its usefulness. A wire cut or saddle sore, for instance, may cause a blemish without interfering with the usefulness of the horse.

Horses may have anatomical abnormalities that interfere with their usefulness. Many of these abnormalities are either inherited directly or develop because of an inherited condition. Abnormalities of the eyes, respiratory system, circulatory system, and conformation of the feet and legs are all important.

Some of the major unsoundnesses and blemishes include the following (several of which are identified by location on the body in Figure 30.12).

Bog spavin is a soft swelling on the inner, anterior aspect of the hock. Although unsightly, the condition usually does not cause lameness. **Bone spavin** is a bony enlargement on the inner aspect of the hock. Both bog and bone spavin arise when stresses are applied to horses that have improperly constructed hocks. Lameness usually accompanies this condition, but most animals return to service after rest and, in some cases, surgery.

Capped hock is a thickening of the skin at the point of the hock. **Curb** is a hard swelling at the upper-rear portion of the cannon bone. The plantar ligament becomes inflamed and swollen, usually owing to poor conformation or a direct blow.

Cataract is inherited as a dominant trait. It can be eliminated if the afflicted horse does not produce several foals before the cataract develops.

Contracted heels can be inherited or acquired through improper shoeing and foot care. Contracted heels may result when the frog or cushion of the foot is damaged and shrinks, allowing the heels to come together. The bottom surface of the foot becomes smaller in circumference than at the coronet band.

The term ***cow hocked*** (Fig. 30.9) indicates that the points of the hocks turn inward. Such hocks are greatly stressed when the horse is pulling, running, or jumping.

Heaves is a respiratory disease in which the horse experiences difficulty in exhaling air. The horse can exhale a certain volume of air normally, after which an effort is exerted to complete exhalation. A horse with a mild case of heaves can continue with light work, but horses with moderate to severe heaves have a limited ability to work.

Laminitis, also called **founder,** is an inflammation of the laminae of the foot causing severe pain and lameness. The front feet are affected more frequently than the hind feet. Overeating of grain, consumption of large amounts of water by overheated horses, and overworking horses on hard surfaces are frequent causes of laminitis.

Moon blindness is periodic ophthalmia in which the horse is blind for a short time, regains its sight, and then again becomes blind for a time. Periods of blindness may initially be spaced as much as 6 months apart. The periods of blindness become progressively closer together until the horse is continuously blind. This condition received the name *moon blindness* because the trait is first noticed when the periods of blindness occur about a month apart. It was originally thought that the periods of blindness were associated with changes in the moon.

Navicular disease is an inflammation of the navicular bone in the front foot. The exact cause is unknown, but hard work, small feet, and trimming heels too low may contribute to the development of the disease. Corrective shoeing or surgery (cutting the navicular nerve) are recommended treatments, although the latter may not restore horses to their original usefulness.

Quittor is a deep sore that drains at the coronet. The infection is caused by puncture wounds, corns, and the like, and results in severe lameness.

Ring bone is a condition in which the cartilage around the pastern bone ossifies. Ring bone shows as a hard bony enlargement encircling the areas of the pastern joint and coronet.

Ruptured blood vessels is a defect of circulation in which the blood vessels in the lungs are fragile and may rupture when the horse is put under the stress of exercising. Some racehorses have died due to hemorrhage from these fragile blood vessels.

Shoe boil, or **capped elbow,** is a soft swelling on the elbow. Common causes are injury to the elbow while the horse is lying down or injury from a long heel on a front shoe.

Sickle hocked (Fig. 30.10) is the term used to describe the hock when it has too much set or bend. As a result, the hind feet are set too far forward. The strain of pulling, jumping, or running is much more severe on a horse with sickle hocks than on a horse whose hocks are of normal conformation.

Sidebones is an abnormality that occurs when the lateral cartilages in the foot ossify. During the ossification process, lameness can occur, but many horses regain soundness with proper rest and shoeing.

A **stifled** horse is one in which the patella (the knee cap in humans) has been displaced. Older horses seldom become sound once they are stifled, while younger horses usually recover.

Stringhalt is an involuntary flexion of the hock during movement. It is considered a nerve disorder. Surgery can improve the condition.

Sweeny refers to atrophied muscles at any location, although many people use it to refer only to shoulder muscles. In the shoulder sweeny, the nerve crossing the shoulder blade has been injured.

A **thoroughpin** is a soft enlargement between the large tendon (tendon of Achilles) of the hock and the fleshy portion of the hind leg. Stress on the flexor tendon allows synovial fluid to collect in the depression of the hock. Lameness rarely occurs.

Toeing-in, or **pigeon-toed** (Fig. 30.7), refers to the turning in of the toes of the front feet. **Toeing-out** (Fig. 30.7) refers to the turning out of the toes of the front feet. These conditions influence the way in which the horse will move its feet when traveling. Toeing-out or moving the front feet inward is considered the more serious defect because it can lead to further interference and faults.

Windgalls, sometimes referred to as **wind puffs** or puffs, occurs when the fluid sacs around the pastern or fetlock joints are enlarged. The disease is common, but not serious, in hardworking horses.

GAITS OF HORSES

The major gaits of horses, along with their modifications, are as follows:

1. **Walk** is a four-beat gait in which each of the four feet strikes the ground separately from the others.
2. **Trot** is a rapid diagonal two-beat gait in which the right front and left rear feet hit the ground

in unison, and the left front and right rear feet hit the ground in unison. The horse travels straight without weaving sideways when trotting.

3. **Pace** is a lateral two-beat gait in which the right front and rear feet hit the ground in unison and the left front and rear feet hit the ground in unison. There is a swaying from right to left when the horse paces.
4. **Gallop** is the fastest gait with four beats.
5. **Canter** is a fast three-beat gait. Depending on the lead, the two diagonal legs hit the ground at the same time with the other hind leg and foreleg hitting at different times.
6. **Rack** is a snappy four-beat gait in which the joints of the legs are highly flexed. The forelegs are lifted upward to produce a flashy effect. This is an artificial gait, whereas the walk, trot, pace, gallop, and canter are natural gaits. The rack is popular in the show ring for speed and animation.
7. **Running walk** is the fast ground-covering walk of the Tennessee Walking Horse. It is an artificial gait that is faster than the normal walk. The horse moves with a gliding motion as the hind leg oversteps the forefoot print by 12–18 inches.

EASE OF RIDING AND WAY OF GOING

When a horse's foot strikes the ground, a large shock is created that would be objectionable to the rider if no shock absorption occurred. There are several shock-absorbing mechanisms existing in horses' feet and legs. The horse has lateral cartilages on all four feet that expand outward when the foot strikes the ground. This absorbs some of the shock. The pastern on each leg absorbs some of the shock when the foot strikes the ground by bending somewhat. A pastern that is too straight will not absorb much of the shock and one that is too long and weak will let the leg go to the ground. These kinds of pasterns will soon result in unsound horses. Thus, it is very important that a pastern has the proper slope so it can absorb the optimal amount of shock without the leg going to the ground or causing too much concussion on the joints and ultimately the rider.

The front legs each have two joints that allow movement and absorb shock: the joint between the ulna and the humerus, and the joint between the humerus and the scapula. Having movement at these joints results in some absorbing of shock. Also, the hind legs each have two joints that bend and, thus, absorb some shock. These joints are between the metatarsus and tibia and between the tibia and femur.

If the horse's feet and legs have proper conformation, a pleasant ride can be enjoyed. If there are abnormalities due to inheritance, injury, improper nutrition, or disease, the horse will give the rider a less comfortable ride.

Abnormalities in Way of Going

A horse that toes out with its front feet tends to dish or swing its feet inward (wings in) when its legs are in action. Swinging the feet inward can cause the striding foot to strike the supporting leg so that **interference** to forward movement results. A horse that toes in (pigeon toed) tends to swing its front feet outward, giving a **paddling** action.

Some horses overreach with the hind leg and catch the heel of the front foot with the toe of the hind foot. This action, called **forging,** can cause the horse to stumble or fall.

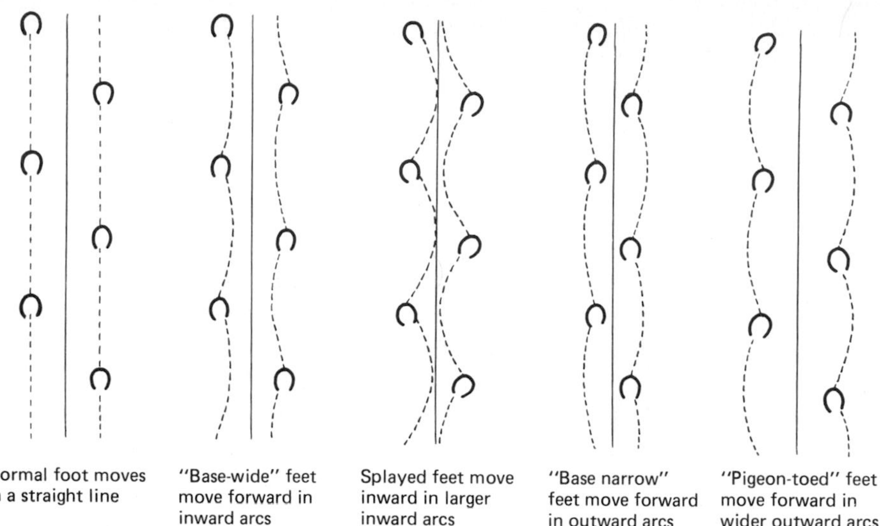
Normal foot moves in a straight line
"Base-wide" feet move forward in inward arcs
Splayed feet move inward in larger inward arcs
"Base narrow" feet move forward in outward arcs
"Pigeon-toed" feet move forward in wider outward arcs

FIGURE 30.13.
Path of the feet (way of going) as seen from above, which relates to feet and leg structure. Courtesy of Rich (1981), Colorado State University Extension Service Publication MOOOOOG.

Figure 30.13 shows the way of going well as the horse moves straight and true, each foot moving in a straight line. The other illustrations show the path of flight of each foot when the structure of the foot and leg deviates from the desired norm. How the length and slope of the hoof affects way of going is shown in Figure 30.14.

Since few horses move perfectly true, it is important to know which movements may be

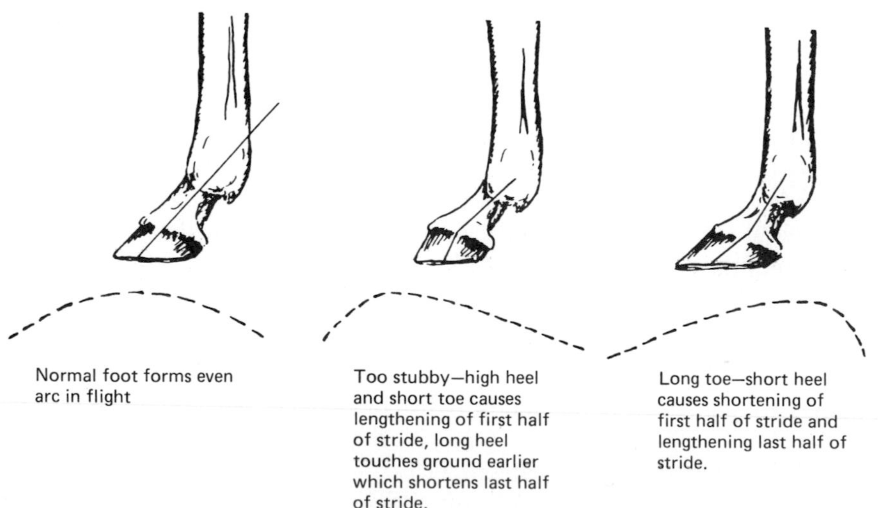
Normal foot forms even arc in flight
Too stubby—high heel and short toe causes lengthening of first half of stride, long heel touches ground earlier which shortens last half of stride.
Long toe—short heel causes shortening of first half of stride and lengthening last half of stride.

FIGURE 30.14.
Illustration of how length and slope of the hoof affects way of going. Courtesy of Rich (1981), Colorado State University Extension Service Publication MOOOOOG.

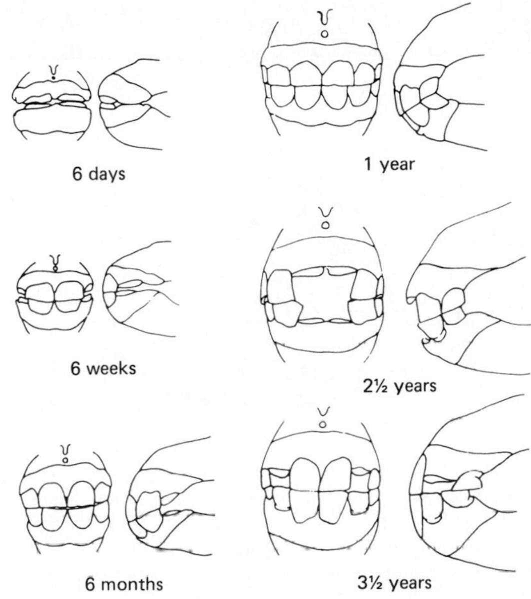

FIGURE 30.15.
Front and side views of the teeth of the horse from 6 days to 3.5 years of age. The young horse has a full set of baby or milk teeth by 6 months of age. It starts shedding the baby teeth and developing permanent teeth at 2.5 years of age. From J. F. Bone, *Animal Anatomy and Physiology*, 5th ed. (Corvallis, OR: State University Book Stores, © 1988).

unsafe. A horse that wings in (interferes) is potentially more unsafe than a horse that wings out (paddles), as the former horse may trip itself.

DETERMINING THE AGE OF A HORSE BY ITS TEETH

The age of a horse can be estimated by its teeth (Figs. 30.15, 30.16, and 30.17). A foal at 6–10 months of age has 24 baby or milk teeth (12 incisors and 12 molars). The incisors include three pairs of upper and three pairs of lower incisors.

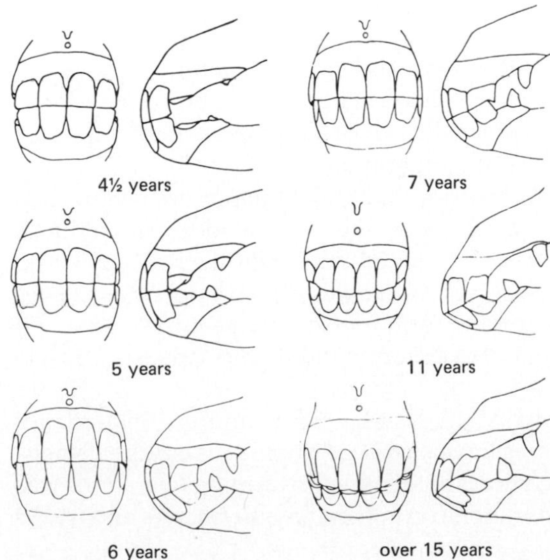

FIGURE 30.16.
Front and side views of the teeth of the horse from 4.5 to 15 years of age. The horse's mouth changes in shape as it becomes older, such that the front teeth protrude somewhat forward. From J. F. Bone, *Animal Anatomy and Physiology*, 5th ed. (Corvallis, OR: Oregon State University Book Stores, © 1988).

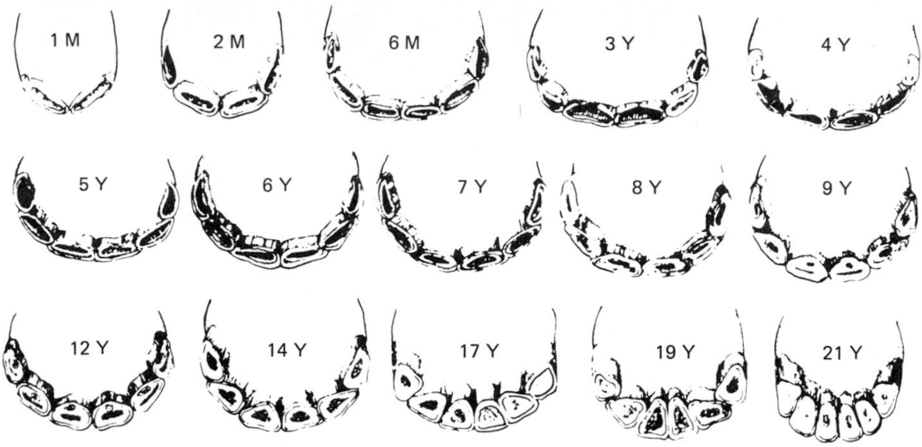

FIGURE 30.17.
Table surfaces of the lower incisors of the horse from 1 month (M) to 21 years (Y) of age. From J. F. Bone, *Animal Anatomy and Physiology*, 5th ed. (Corvallis, OR: Oregon State University Book Stores, © 1988).

Chewing causes the incisors to become worn. The wearing starts with the middle pair and continues laterally. At 1 year of age, the center incisors show wear; at 1.5 years, the intermediates show wear; and at 2 years, the outer, or lateral, incisors show wear. At 2.5 years, shedding of the baby teeth starts. The center incisors are shed first. Thus, at 2.5 years, the center incisors become permanent teeth; at 4 years, the intermediates are shed; at 5 years, the outer, or lateral, incisors are shed and replaced by permanent teeth.

A horse at 5 years of age is said to have a **full mouth,** because all the teeth are permanent. At 6 years, the center incisors show wear; at 7 years, the intermediates show wear; and at 8 years, the outer, or lateral, incisors show wear. Wearing is shown by a change from a deep groove to a rounded dental cup on the grinding surface of a tooth.

DONKEYS, MULES, AND HINNIES

Mules and hinnies have been used as draft animals in mining and farming operations as well as pack animals. When mules were needed for heavy loads, it was important to breed mammoth jacks to mares of one of the draft breeds. Crossing of smaller jacks with mares of medium size produced mules that were useful in mining and farming operations.

Donkeys, mules, and hinnies have some characteristics that make them more useful than horses for certain purposes. Their sure-footedness, for instance, makes them ideal pack animals for moving loads over rough areas. In addition, they are rugged, can endure strenuous work, and have the characteristic of taking care of themselves (e.g., mules do not gorge themselves when given free access to grain, so they do not normally founder from overeating). However, donkeys, mules, and hinnies do not respond to the wishes or commands of humans as well as do horses.

Recently, there has been a movement to use small donkeys as pets for children. Small mules from crosses between male donkeys and pony mares have also been popular as children's pets.

The primary reason trucks and tractors replaced horses and mules in farming operations was that work could be done more rapidly; one person could do much more with tractors and trucks than with horses and mules. The high cost of petroleum products (gasoline and diesel fuels) and the possible scarcity of these items may result in more use of horses and mules in farming, logging, and mining operations and a partial return to horsepower. It is unlikely that horses and mules will ever replace trucks and tractors, but certain operations on farms and in the timber industry may be done to advantage by horses and mules.

SELECTED REFERENCES

Publications

American Horse Council. 1990. *Horse Industry Directory.* Washington, DC: American Horse Council.

Blakely, J. 1981. *Horses and Horse Sense: The Practical Science of Horse Husbandry.* Reston, VA: Reston Publishing Co.

Blakely, R. L. 1985. Miniature horses. *National Geographic* 167:384.

Bone, J. F. 1988. *Animal Anatomy and Physiology.* 5th ed. Corvallis, OR: Oregon State University Book Stores.

Bradley, M. 1981. *Horses: A Practical and Scientific Approach.* Highstown, NJ: McGraw-Hill.

Ensminger, M.E. 1990. *Horses and Horsemanship.,* Danville, IL: Interstate Publishers, Inc.

Evans, J. W. 1989. 4th ed. *Horses: A Guide to Selection, Care and Enjoyment.* San Francisco: W. H. Freeman.

———, Borton, A., Hintz, H. F., and Van Vleck, L. D. 1990. *The Horse.* 2nd ed. San Francisco: W. H. Freeman.

Jones, W. E. 1982. *Genetics and Horse Breeding.* Philadelphia: Lea & Febiger.

Lasley, J. F. 1987. *Genetics of Livestock Improvement.* Englewood Cliffs, NJ: Prentice-Hall.

Rich, G. A. 1981. *Horse Judging Guide.* Colorado State University Extension Service Publication MOOOOOG.

Visuals

Beginner's Guide to Buying a Horse (sound filmstrip). Vocational Education Productions, California Polytechnic State University, San Luis Obispo, CA 93407.

Care of Your Horse's Feet (SL529—slide set). Educational Aids, National 4-H Council, 7100 Connecticut Ave., Chevy Chase, MD 20815.

Horse Breeds and Color Types (slides). Vocational Education Productions, California Polytechnic State University, San Luis Obispo, CA 93407.

Horse Judging (21 videotapes). CEV, P.O. Box 65265, Lubbock, TX 79464-5265.

Survival of the Fittest (two-part 16-mm film; 26 min. each). Covers Quarter Horse conformation—the relation of form to function. American Quarter Horse Association, Amarillo, TX 79168.

The Nature of Foaling (VHS video). VEP, Calif. Polytechnic State Univ., San Luis Obispo, CA 93407.

CHAPTER 31

Feeding and Managing Horses

Horses relate well to people and provide many forms of pleasure. Although many people enjoy horses, most own only a few; however, whether a person keeps only one horse for personal recreation or operates a large breeding farm, basic horse knowledge is vital. Information on managing horses, such as feeding, facilities, disease prevention, and parasite control, is important. Additional material on management is discussed in Chapter 36.

FEEDS AND FEEDING

Horses graze on grass and legume pastures and eat roughages such as hay and grains of all kinds. Concentrate mixtures containing grains, protein supplements, and vitamin and mineral additives are prepared and sold by commercial feed companies, especially to owners with only one or two horses. Wet molasses can be added to these concentrate mixtures to make sweet feed. The forage and concentrate mixtures may be mixed and pelleted to make a complete, higher-priced convenience feed for horse owners.

Although horses spend less time chewing than ruminants, the normal, healthy horse with a full set of teeth can grind grains such as oats, barley, and corn so that cracking or rolling these feeds is unnecessary. Wheat and milo, however, should be cracked to improve digestibility. The horse's stomach is relatively small, composing only 10% of the total digestive capacity. Only a small amount of digestion takes place in the stomach, and food moves rapidly to the small intestine. From 60%–70% of the protein and soluble carbohydrates are digested in the small intestine, and about 80% of the fiber is digested in the cecum and colon. The large intestine has about 60% of the total digestive capacity, with the colon being the largest component. Bacteria that live in the cecum aid digestion there. Minerals, proteins as amino acids, lipids, and readily available carbohydrates such as glucose are absorbed in the small intestine.

Owners of pleasure horses are interested in having them make a desirable appearance, so many liberally feed their horses. Perhaps more horses are overfed than are underfed. Also, many people want to be kind to their animals, keeping them housed in a box stall when weather conditions are undesirable. This may not be best for the physiological state of the horse.

Certainly, if any deficiency exists in the feed provided, such a deficiency is much more likely to affect horses that are not running on good pasture, where they can forage for themselves.

Young, growing foals should be fed well to allow for proper growth, but overfeeding and obesity are discouraged. Quality of protein and amounts of protein, minerals, and energy are important for young growing horses. Soybean meal or dried milk products in the concentrate mixture provide the amino acids and minerals that might otherwise be deficient or marginal in the weanling ration.

Good-quality pasture or hay supplemented with grain can provide the nutrition needed by young horses. An appropriate salt-mineral source should be provided at all times and clean water is essential (Fig. 31.1).

During the first 8 months of gestation, pregnant mares perform well on good pastures or on good-quality hay supplemented with a small amount of grain and an appropriate source of salt-mineral. As the fetus grows during the last trimester of pregnancy, the mare requires more concentrate and less fibrous, bulky hay. Oats, corn, or barley make an excellent feed grain for pregnant mares. Pregnant mares should be in good body condition but avoid obesity as in any horse. Animals used for riding or working, whether they are pregnant or not, need more energy than those not working. Horses being exercised heavily should be fed ample amounts of concentrates to replace the energy used in the work.

Generally, lactating mares require more grain feeding than do geldings and pregnant or nonpregnant mares. Lactation is the most stressful nutritional period for a mare. If lactating mares are exercised, they must be fed additional grain and hay to meet the nutrient demand of the physical activity.

FIGURE 31.1.
Horses need a readily available supply of fresh, clean water. Courtesy of Robert Henderson, Oregon Agricultural Experimental Station.

TABLE 31.1. Sample Rations for Horses of Different Ages and in Various Stages of Production

Creep feed for nursing foals. The grain should be fed at the rate of 0.5–0.75 lb of grain/100 lb body weight.

	Percentage in Grain Mix
Corn, rolled or flaked	34.0%
Oats, rolled or flaked	34.0
Soybean oil meal	22.0
Molasses	6.0
Dicalcium phosphate	2.0
Limestone	1.5
Trace mineral salt	0.5

Grain mix for weanlings. The grain should be fed at the rate of 0.75 – 1.5 lb of grain/100 lb body weight. Select the grain according to the type of roughage fed. Allow free-choice consumption of either roughage type.

	Percentage in Grain Mix	
	Alfalfa Hay	Grass Hay
Corn, rolled or flaked	40.0%	34.0%
Oats, rolled or flaked	40.0	34.0
Soybean oil meal	12.0	23.0
Molasses	5.0	5.0
Dicalcium phosphate	2.5	3.0
Limestone	0	0.5
Trace mineral salt	0.5	0.5

Grain mix for yearlings and mares. The grain should be fed at the rate of 0.5 – 1.0 of grain/100 lb of body weight. Select the grain according to the type of roughage fed. Allow free-choice consumption of either roughage.

Mares during late gestation and lactation can be fed the same grain mixes as yearlings. The grains should be fed at the rate of 0 – 0.5 lb/100 lb of body weight. Roughage consumption can vary from 1.5 – 2.5 lb/100 lb of body weight.

	Percentage in Grain mix	
	Alfalfa Hay	Grass Hay
Corn, rolled or flaked	46.5%	38.0%
Oats, rolled or flaked	46.5	38.0
Soybean oil meal	0	15.5
Molasses	5.0	5.0
Dicalcium phosphate	1.5	2.0
Limestone	0	1.0
Trace mineral salt	0.5	0.5

Grain mix for horses at maintenance and at work, dry mares during the first 8 months of gestation, or stallions. The grain should be fed as needed (to maintain body condition). Roughage consumption can vary from 1.5 – 2.5 lb/100 of body weight.

	Percentage in Grain Mix	
	Alfalfa Hay	Grass Hay
Corn	46.5%	46.5%
Oats	46.5	46.5
Molasses	5.0	5.0
Dicalcium phosphate	0	1.5
Monosodium phosphate	1.5	0
Trace mineral salt	0.5	0.5

Source: Ginger Rich, *Horse Judging Guide,* Colorado State University Extension Service Publication, M00000G, 1981.

Stallions need to be fed as working horses during the breeding season and given a maintenance ration during the nonbreeding season. Feeding good-quality hay with limited amounts of grain is usually sufficient for the stallion.

Feed companies provide properly balanced rations for horse farms of all sizes. An owner who has only one or two horses may find it highly advantageous to use a prepared feed, since it is difficult and laborious to prepare balanced rations for only a few animals. Using commercially prepared feeds or custom-blended rations can prevent nutritional errors, save time, and, for larger farms, be more cost effective.

Table 31.1 shows some examples of horse rations and describes when and how these rations should be fed.

MANAGING HORSES

Proper management of horses is essential at several critical times: the breeding season, foaling, weaning of foals, castration, and during strenuous work.

Breeding Season

Mares should be **teased** daily with a stallion to determine the stage of their estrous cycle (Fig. 31.2). When the mare is in standing heat (estrus), she is ready to be bred. When the stallion approaches the front of the mare, the mare reacts violently against the stallion if not in heat, but squats and urinates with a winking of the vulva if in heat.

To insure safety for the mare, stallion, and handlers, breeding hobbles (Fig. 31.3) should be fitted to the mare. Cleanliness is paramount for both natural breedings and artificial insemination (AI) programs.

Mares bred naturally should have the vulva washed and dried and the tail wrapped before being served by the stallion (Fig. 31.4). If the mare can be bred twice during heat without overusing the stallion, breeding 2 and 4 days after the mare is first noticed in heat is desirable. A

FIGURE 31.2.
Chute teasing. As the stallion is led along a chute holding several mares, the behavior of each mare determines whether she is in estrus. Courtesy of Colorado State University.

FIGURE 31.3.
Breeding hobbles. From R. A. Battaglia and V. B. Mayrose, *Handbook of Livestock Management Techniques* (New York: Macmillan, 1981).

mature stallion can serve twice daily over a short time and once per day over a period of 1 or 2 months. A young stallion should be used lightly at about three or fewer services per week. In an AI program, the stallion can be collected every other day to cover as many mares as possible, depending on the stallion's sperm numbers and motility. AI programs allow better management of the stallion.

Foaling Time

Mares normally give birth to foals in early spring, at which time the weather can be unpleasant. A clean box stall that is bedded with fresh straw should be made available. If the weather is pleasant, mares can foal on clean pastures. When a mare starts to foal, she should be observed carefully but not disturbed unless assistance is necessary. If the head and front feet of the foal are being presented, it should be delivered without difficulty (Fig. 31.5). If necessary, however, a qualified person can assist by pulling the foal as the mare labors. Do not pull when the mare is not laboring and do not use a tackle to pull the foal. If the front feet are presented but not the head (Fig. 31.6), it may be necessary to push the foal back enough to get the head started along

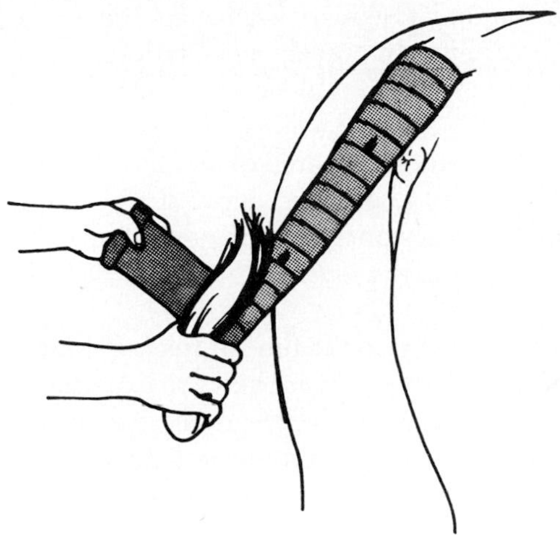

FIGURE 31.4.
Tail of horse being wrapped prior to breeding. From R. A. Battaglia and V. B. Mayrose, *Handbook of Livestock Management Techniques* (New York: Macmillan, 1981).

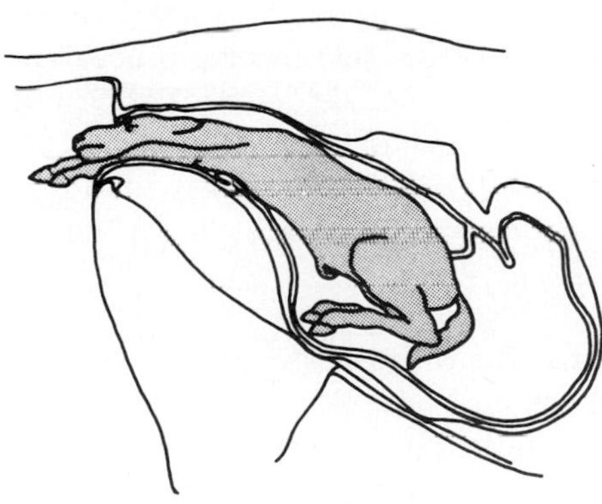

FIGURE 31.5.
Correct presentation position of foal for delivery. From R. A. Battaglia and V. B. Mayrose, *Handbook of Livestock Management Techniques* (New York: Macmillan, 1981).

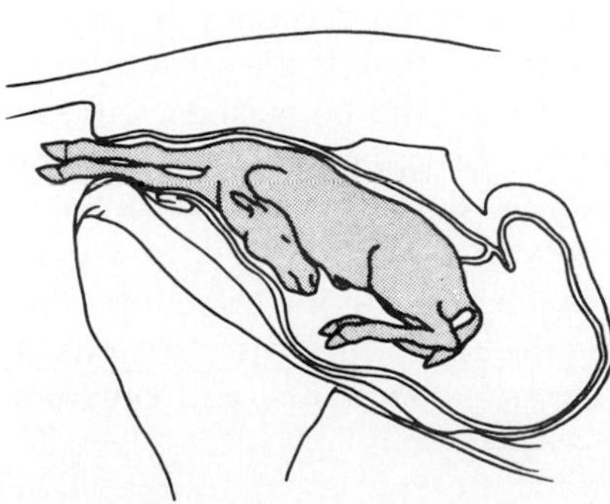

FIGURE 31.6.
Malpresentation of foal for delivery; head and neck back. From R. A. Battaglia and V. B. Mayrose, *Handbook of Livestock Management Techniques* (New York: Macmillan, 1981).

with the front feet. Breech presentations can endanger the foal if delivery is delayed; therefore, assistance should be given to help the mare make a rapid delivery if breech presentation occurs. If it appears that difficulties are likely to occur, a veterinarian should be called as soon as possible.

As soon as the foal is delivered, its mouth and nostrils should be cleared of membranes and mucus so it can breathe. If the weather is cold, the foal should be wiped dry and assisted in nursing. As soon as the foal nurses, its metabolic rate increases and helps it stay warm. The **umbilical cord** should be dipped in a tincture of iodine solution to prevent harmful microorganisms from invading the body.

In general, it is highly desirable to exercise pregnant mares up to the time of foaling. Mares that are exercised properly while pregnant have better muscle tone and are likely to experience less difficulty when foaling than those that get little or no exercise while pregnant. During the horsepower era, many mares used for plowing and similar work foaled in the field without difficulty. The foal was usually left with the mare for a few days, after which the foal was left in a box stall while the mare was worked.

Weaning the Foal

When weaning time arrives, it is best to remove the mare and allow the foal to remain in the surroundings to which it is accustomed. Since the foal will make every attempt to escape to find its mother, it should be left in a box stall or a secure and safe fenced lot. Fencing other than barbed wire should be used. Prior to weaning, the foal should become accustomed to eating and drinking on its own. High-quality hay or pasture and a balanced concentrate feed should be provided for the foal.

Castration

Colts that are not kept for breeding can be castrated any time after the testicles have descended; however, the stress of castration should not be imposed at weaning time. Some people prefer to delay castration until the colt has reached a year of age, whereas others prefer an earlier time. Genetic potential and nutrition, not time of castration, determine mature height and weight.

The colt can be put onto a turntable or manually restrained with ropes for castration. Pain killers and muscle relaxants can be used. The scrotum is opened on each side, by a qualified person, and the membrane around each testicle is split to expose the testicle. The testicle is pulled from the body cavity far enough to expose the cord for clamping. The cord is crushed by the clamp and then severed. The crushing of the cord prevents excessive bleeding. It may be desirable to give the colt an injection of an antibiotic to prevent infection. If the scrotum was cleaned with a mild disinfectant before castration, the wound need not be washed with an antiseptic. Harsh disinfectants should not be applied to the wound. After the colt is castrated, he should be in a small clean pasture for close observation. If fly infestation is a problem, a fly repellant should be applied about the scrotal area.

Horses can be permanently identified by tattooing them on the inside of the upper lip. This does not disfigure the animals and can be easily read by raising the upper lip. Other methods of identification include freeze branding, hot-iron branding, electronic implants, and chestnut implants.

Care of Hardworking Animals

Hardworking horses that are sweating and have elevated temperature, pulse, and respiration rates should be washed ("cooled down") before receiving water and feed. The animals should be given only small amounts of water and walked until they have stopped sweating and their pulse and respiration are within 10% of resting levels. At that time, water, hay, and grain can be given.

Hardworking horses do require extra energy, usually in the form of grain. However, care must be taken to avoid overfeeding grain to horses. Excess grain and sometimes lush green pasture can cause a horse to founder. Founder can cause death or severe lameness.

HOUSING AND EQUIPMENT

Barns should be located on a higher elevation than the surrounding area to assure good drainage. They should be accessible to utilities and vehicles, and preferably have a southeast exposure.

Although many styles of barns exist, one constructed with an aisleway between two rows of stalls provides easy access and efficient use of space. Feed can be placed in the stalls on either side as the feed cart goes down the aisle. If the stalls can be opened from the outside and cleaned with mechanical equipment, labor also is saved. The hay manger in stalls should be constructed at chest height to the horse. Hay racks placed above the horse's head force the horse to inhale hay dust when reaching for the hay and health problems can result.

To alleviate mixing hay with grain, a separate grain feeder should be placed several feet from the hay rack. The waterer or water bucket should be located along the outside wall for drainage purposes. The water source should also be placed some distance from the hay and grain so feed will not drop in the water. Electric waterers save labor but are prone to malfunction. Although water buckets require more labor, they allow water intake to be easily monitored.

Box stalls are used for foaling and for the mare and the foal when the weather is severe. The stall should be constructed to allow complete cleaning and proper drainage. Minimum dimensions for a foaling stall are 14 ft × 14 ft, whereas a regular box stall should be at least 10 ft. × 10 ft.

Feed should be stored in an area connected with or adjacent to the barn. Truck access to the feed storage area is vital. The floor should be solid (i.e., concrete) and the rodent-proof bins should be easily cleaned. Overhead (loft) storage of hay requires a great deal of labor and expensive construction. Large amounts of hay stored in the barn where the horses are housed increases dust and danger of fire.

Lot **fences** should be constructed with wooden or steel posts and cable, or with wooden posts and 2-inch lumber. Barbed wire should not be used because it can cut a horse severely.

A dry, dust-free **tack room** is needed to house riding equipment, including saddles, blankets, bridles, and halters. In addition, it may be advisable to have a **washroom** where horses can be washed.

A **chute** is essential to care for horses that have been injured and need attention. If the horse is in a chute, it is unlikely that the animal can kick the person working around the horse. The chute can be used for AI, teasing, palpation, or treating health problems. The chute is also useful for injections or when blood samples are being taken. Often, horses strike with a front foot when a needle is inserted for vaccinations or blood samples; a properly constructed chute will protect people as well as the horse.

CONTROLLING DISEASES AND PARASITES

Sanitation is of vital importance in controlling diseases and parasites of horses. Horses should have clean stalls and be groomed regularly. A horse that is to be introduced into the herd should be isolated for a month to prevent exposing other horses to diseases and parasites.

Horses may have illnesses caused by bacteria or viruses, internal or external parasites, poisonous plants such as Tanzy Ragwort or Brachen fern, inhalation or ingestion of chemicals that have been used about the barn, or imbalanced rations.

The person who owns and cares for one horse or a dozen horses should engage the services of a trusted veterinarian. Veterinarians can help prevent diseases as well as treat animals that are diseased. Most veterinarians prefer to assist in preventing health problems rather than treating the animals after they are ill.

Horse manure is an excellent medium for microorganisms that cause **tetanus.** Horses should be given shots to prevent tetanus, which can develop if an injury allows tetanus-causing microorganisms to invade through the skin. Usually two shots are given to establish **immunity,** after which a booster shot is given each year. Because the same microorganisms that cause tetanus in horses also affect humans, those who work with horses should also have tetanus shots.

Strangles, also known as distemper, is a bacterial disease that affects the upper respiratory tract and associated lymph glands. High fever, nasal discharge, and swollen lymph glands are signs of strangles. The disease is spread by contamination of feed and water. Afflicted horses must be isolated and provided clean water and feed. A strangles bacterin is available, but postvaccinal reactions limit its use to stables and ranches in which the disease is endemic.

Brood mares are subject to many infectious agents that invade the uterus and cause **abortion;** examples include *Salmonella* and *Streptococcus* bacteria and the viruses of **rhinopneumonitis** and **arteritis.** Should abortion occur, professional assistance should be obtained to determine the specific cause and to develop a preventative plan for the future.

Sleeping sickness, or **equine encephalomyelitis,** is caused by viral infections that affect the brain of the horse. Different types, such as the eastern, western, and Venezuelan, are known. Encephalomyelitis is transmitted by vectors such as mosquitoes. It can also be spread by horses rubbing noses together or sharing water and feed containers. The disease is also transmissible to humans. Vaccination against the disease consists of two intradermal injections spaced a week to 10 days apart. These injections should be given in April. The vaccination ensures immunity for only 6 months; therefore, the injections should be repeated each six months when the disease is prevalent.

Influenza is a common respiratory disease of horses. The virus that causes influenza is airborne, so frequent exposure may occur where horses congregate. The acute disease causes high fever and a severe cough when the horse is exercised. Rest and good nursing care for 3 weeks usually gives the horse an opportunity to recover. Severe aftereffects are rare when complete rest is provided. Horse owners who plan for shows should vaccinate for influenza each spring. Two injections are required the first year, with one annual booster thereafter.

Horses can become infested with internal and external parasites. Control of internal parasites consists of rotating horses from one pasture to another, spreading manure from stables on land that horses do not graze, and treating infested animals.

Pinworms develop in the colon and rectum from eggs that are swallowed as the horse consumes contaminated feed or water. These parasites irritate the anus, which causes the horse to rub the base of its tail against objects even to the point of wearing off hair and causing skin abrasions. Pinworms are controlled by oral administration of proper vermifuges.

Bots are the larvae stage of the bot fly. The female bot fly lays eggs on the hairs of the throat, front legs, and belly of the horse. The irritation of the bot fly causes the horse to lick itself. The eggs are then attached to the tongue and lips of the horse, where they hatch into larvae that burrow into the tissues. The larvae later migrate down the throat and attach to the lining of the stomach, where they remain for about 6 months and cause serious damage. The chemicals used to control bots can be injurious if they are not properly administered or given in improper dosages, so professional assistance should be obtained for treatment.

Adult **strongyles** (bloodworms) firmly attach to the walls of the large intestine. The adult female lays eggs that pass out with the feces. After the eggs hatch, the larvae climb blades of grass where they are swallowed by grazing horses. The larvae migrate to various organs and arteries where severe damage results. Blood clots, which form where arteries are damaged, can break loose and plug an artery. Treatment of bloodworms consists of phenothiazine mixed with the feed or a phenothiazine–piperazone mixture administered orally.

Adult **ascaris worms** are located in the small intestine. The adult female produces large numbers of eggs that pass out with the feces. The eggs become infective if they are swallowed when the horse eats them while grazing. The eggs hatch in the stomach and small intestine, and the larvae migrate into the bloodstream and are carried to the liver and lungs. The small larvae are coughed up from the lungs and swallowed. When they reach the small intestine, they mature and produce eggs. The same chemicals used for the control of bots are effective in the control of ascarids.

SELECTED REFERENCES

Publications

Battaglia, R. A., and Mayrose, V. B. 1981. *Handbook of Livestock Management Techniques.* New York: Macmillan.

Bradley, M. 1981. *Horses: A Practical and Scientific Approach.* Highstown, NJ: McGraw-Hill.

Cunha, T. J. 1991. *Horse Feeding and Nutrition.* 2nd ed. San Diego: Academic Press.

Ensminger, M. E. 1990. *Horses and Horsemanship.* Danville, IL: Interstate Publishers, Inc.

Ensminger, M. E., Oldfield, J. E., and Heinemann, W. W. 1990. *Feeds and Nutrition.* Clovis, CA: Ensminger Publishing Co.

Evans, J. W. 1989. *Horses: A Guide to Selection, Care, and Enjoyment.* San Francisco: W. H. Freeman.

———, Borton, A., Hintz, H. F., and Van Vleck, L. D. 1990. *The Horse.* 2nd ed. San Francisco: W. H. Freeman.

Hickman, J. 1987. *Horse Management.* San Diego: Academic Press.

Lewis, L. D. 1982. *Feeding and Care of the Horse.* Philadelphia: Lea & Febiger.

National Research Council. 1989. *Nutrient Requirements of Horses.* Washington, DC: National Academy Press.

Shideler, R. K., and Voss, J. L. 1984. *Management of the Pregnant Mare and Newborn Foal.* Colorado State University Expt. Sta. Spec. Series 35.

Voss, J. L., and Pickett, B. W. *Reproductive Management of the Broodmare.* Colorado State University.

Visuals

Basic Horse Care (videotape). CEV, P.O. Box 65265, Lubbock, TX 79464-5265.

Breaking and Training the Western Horse (sound filmstrip). Vocational Education Productions, California Polytechnic State University, San Luis Obispo, CA 93407.

Feeding Horses (VHS video) and *Basic Horsemanship, Vol. II* (VHS video). VEP, Calif. Polytechnic State Univ., San Luis Obispo, CA 93407.

CHAPTER 32

Poultry Breeding, Feeding, and Management

The term *poultry* applies to chickens, turkeys, geese, ducks, pigeons, peafowls, and guineas. The head and neck characteristics that distinguish several of the poultry types are shown in Figure 32.1. Turkeys have some unusual identifying characteristics including a beard—a black lock of hair on the upper chest of the male turkey. They also have **carnuncles**—a red-pinkish fleshlike covering on the throat and neck, with the **snood** hanging over the beak.

BREEDS AND BREEDING

Characteristics of Breeds

Chickens. Chickens are classified according to class, breed, and variety. A **class** is a group of birds that has been developed in the same broad geographical area. The four major classes of chickens are American, Asiatic, English, and Mediterranean. A **breed** is a subdivision of a class composed of birds of similar size and shape. Some important breeds, strains, lines, and synthetics are shown in Figure 32.2. The parts of a chicken are shown in Figure 32.3. A **variety** is a subdivision of a breed composed of birds of the same feather color and type of comb.

Factors such as egg numbers, eggshell quality, egg size, efficiency of production, fertility, and hatchability are most important to commercial egg producers. Broiler producers consider such characteristics as white plumage color and picking quality, egg production, fertility, hatchability, growth rate, carcass quality, feed efficiency, livability, and egg production. Also, breeds, strains, and lines that cross well with each other are important to broiler breeders.

The breeds of chickens listed in Table 32.1 were developed many years ago. These specific breeds are not easily identified in the commercial poultry industry because the breeds have been crossed to produce different varieties and strains (see Fig. 32.2). Some breeds are exhibited at shows or propagated for specialty marketing and are more a novelty than part of today's poultry industry.

Turkeys. There are eight varieties of turkeys, but most turkeys grown for meat are white. The eight varieties are (1) Bronze, (2) Narragansett, (3) White Holland, (4) Black, (5) Slate, (6)

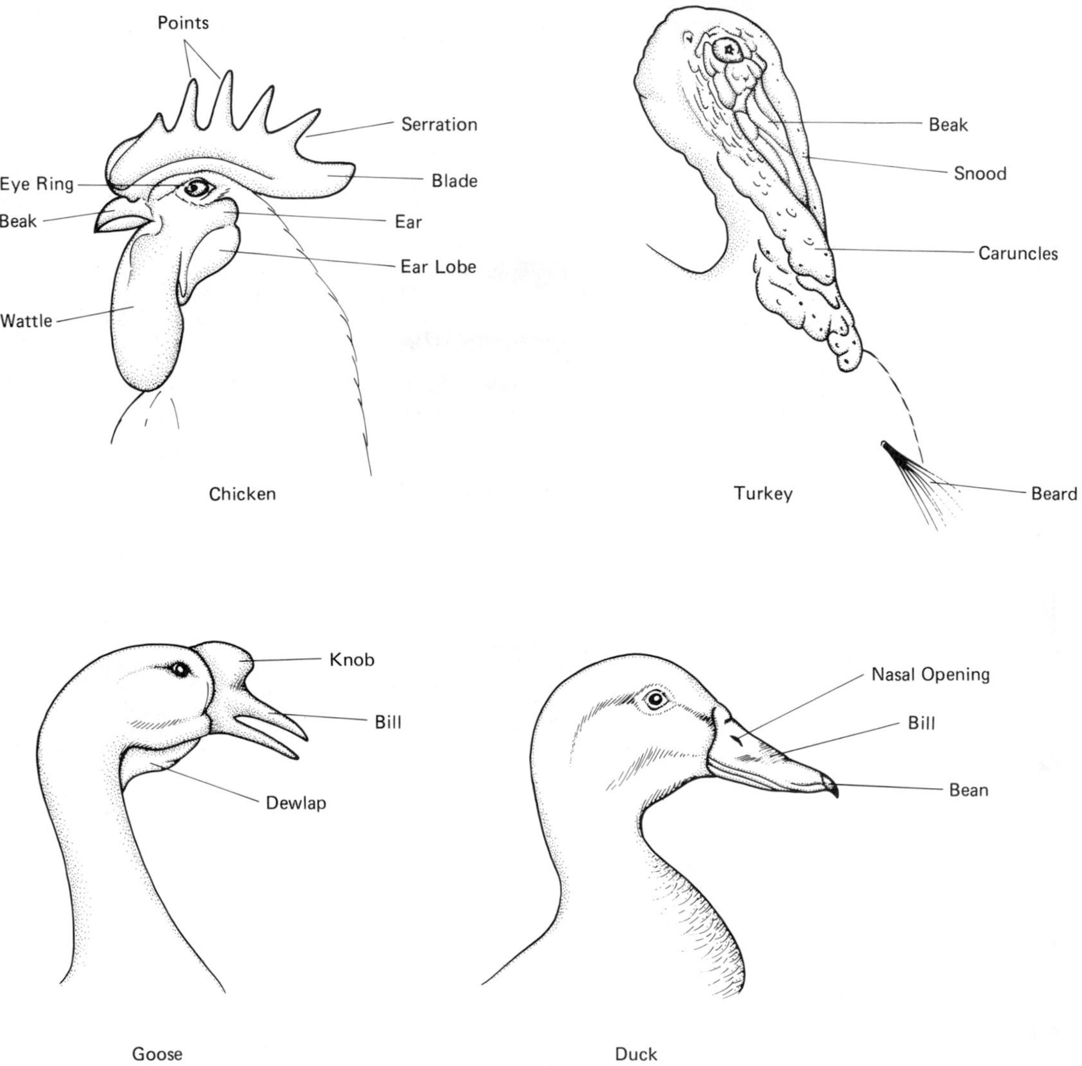

FIGURE 32.1.
Distinguishing characteristics of several different types of poultry.

Bourbon Red, (7) Small Beltsville White, and (8) Royal Palm. Two types of turkey are commercially important in the United States today: the small White and the large Broad White. Since the 1950s, the emphasis has been to produce more large, white turkeys of the type shown in Figure 32.4. A corresponding decrease in the number of small whites has occurred.

Ducks. Many breeds of domestic ducks are known, but only a few are of economic importance. The most popular breed in the United States is the White Pekin. It is most valuable for its meat and produces excellent carcasses at 7–8 weeks of age. Another breed, the Khaki Campbell, is used commercially in some countries for egg production.

FIGURE 32.2.
Breeds, synthetics, lines, or strains of chickens. Courtesy of Dekalb Poultry Research, H&N International, Hubbard Farms, and Watt Publishing Company.

Geese. Several breeds of geese are popular. The Embden, Toulouse, White Chinese, and Pilgrim are all satisfactory for meat production. The characteristics preferred by most commercial geese producers include a medium-sized carcass, good livability (low mortality), rapid growth, and a heavy coat of white or nearly white feathers. The Embden and White Chinese

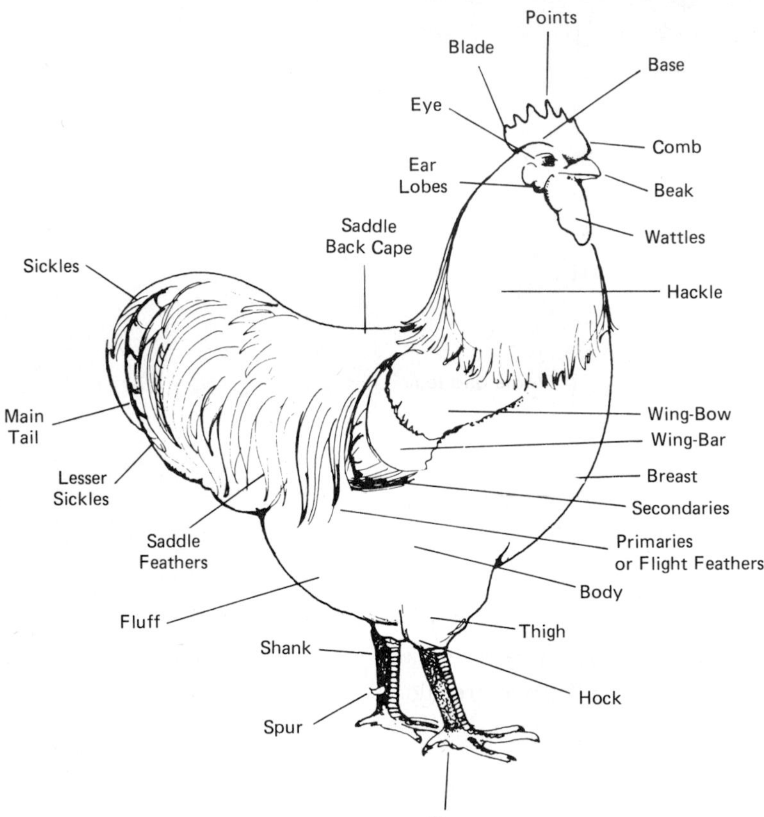

FIGURE 32.3.
The external parts of a chicken.

TABLE 32.1. Certain Breeds of Chickens and Their Main Characteristics

Breed	Purpose	Type of Comb	Color of Egg
American Breeds			
White Plymouth Rock	Eggs and meat	Single	Brown
Wyandotte[a]	Eggs	Rose	Brown
Rhode Island Red	Eggs	Single and rose	Brown
New Hampshire	Eggs and meat	Single	Brown
Asiatic Breeds			
Brahma[a]	Meat	Pea	Brown
Cochin[a]	Meat	Single	Brown
English Breeds			
Australorp	Eggs	Single	Brown
Cornish	Meat	Pea	Brown
Orpington[a]	Meat	Single	Brown
Mediterranean Breed			
Leghorn	Eggs	Single and rose	White

[a]These breeds are of minor importance to the U.S. poultry industry.

FIGURE 32.4.
Male and female turkeys that are nearing maturity. Courtesy of Hubbard Farms.

breeds meet these requirements. One variety of the Toulouse is gray, another variety is buff. The Pilgrim gander is white, the female is grayish. The White Chinese breed is pure white.

Breeding Poultry

Turkeys. There is a specific breeding cycle in the production of baby poults for distribution to growers who raise them to market weight. The pedigree flocks (generation 1) or parent stock are pure lines. The pure lines are crossed one with another to produce generation 2. Generation 2 lines are crossed one with another to produce generation 3. Eggs from these line crosses are selected into female or male lines and sent to hatcheries. Males from the male lines are selected for such meat traits as thicker thighs, meatier drumsticks, plumper breasts, rate of growth, and feed efficiency. The females of the female line are selected for greater fertility, hatchability, egg size, and meat conformation. The male line males are crossed with female line females; the eggs produced are hatched and the poults are sold for the production of market turkeys.

Laying hens are approximately 30 weeks of age when they reach sexual maturity (Fig. 32.5). They are put under controlled lighting to stimulate the start of laying. The average hen usually lays for about 25 weeks and produces 88–93 eggs. The hen is considered "spent" at the end of the 25-week laying cycle. Most hens are marketed at that time for meat. Hens can be molted and stimulated to lay another 25-week cycle. They require 90 days for molting and produce only 75–80 eggs during this later laying cycle; therefore, producers should compare the costs of growing new layers with that of recycling the old ones before deciding if it is economical to recycle old layers. The spent hens usually go into soup products.

Turkey eggs are not produced for human consumption because it costs much more to produce food from turkey eggs than from chicken eggs. It would cost about 50 cents each to produce turkey eggs for this purpose.

All turkey hens are artificially inseminated to obtain fertile eggs. As turkeys have been selected for such broad breasts and large mature size, it is difficult for toms to mate successfully with hens. Semen is collected from the toms and used for inseminating the hens. Usually 1 tom to 10 hens is sufficient for providing the semen needed.

The present-day turkey is much different from the turkeys of many years ago. Today's turkey grows more rapidly, converts feed into meat more efficiently, has more edible meat per

FIGURE 32.5.
A flock of young, pullet turkey hens in the breeding program. Courtesy of Hubbard Farms.

unit of weight, and requires less time to reach market. Most turkeys grown today are white-feathered, so there are no dark pin feathers to discolor the carcass. A turkey requires only 2.8 lb of feed for every pound of gain (Fig. 32.6).

Chickens. Sophisticated selection and breeding methods have been developed in the United States for increased productivity of chickens for both eggs and meat. The discussion here is

FIGURE 32.6.
World's largest turkey feed conversion facility used to accurately measure individual feed efficiency of more than 3,000 female-line pedigree candidate toms per year. The company also tests individual feed conversion on approximately 7,400 other toms for potential use in their breeding program. Courtesy of Nicholas Turkey Breeding Farms.

directed primarily at improvement of chickens; however, methods described for chickens can also be applied to improve meat production in turkeys, geese, and ducks.

Early poultry breeding and selection are concentrated on qualitative traits, which are, from a genetic standpoint, more predictable than quantitative traits. Qualitative traits, such as color, comb type, abnormalities, and sex-linked characteristics, are important; however, quantitative traits, such as egg production, egg characteristics, growth, fertility, and hatchability, are economically more important today.

Quantitative traits are more difficult to select for than are qualitative traits because the mode of inheritance is more complex and the role of the environment is greater. Quantitative traits differ greatly as to the amount of progress that can be attained through selection. For example, increase in body weight is much easier to attain than increase in egg production. Furthermore, a relationship usually exists between body size and egg size. Generally, if body size increases, a corresponding increase in egg size will occur. Most quantitative traits of chickens fall in the low to medium range of heritability, whereas qualitative traits fall in the high range.

Progress in selecting for egg production has been aided by the trapnest, a nest equipped with a door that allows a hen to enter but prevents her from leaving. The trapnest enables accurate determination of egg production of individual hens for any given period and helps to identify and eliminate undesirable egg traits and broodiness (the hen wanting to set on eggs to hatch them). Furthermore, it allows the breeder to begin pedigree work within a flock.

The two most important types of selection applied primarily to chickens and to a lesser extent to other poultry today are mass selection and family selection. In **mass selection,** the older method, the best-performing males are mated to the best-performing females (Fig. 32.7). The program is effective in improving traits of high heritability. **Family selection** is a system whereby all offspring from a particular mating are designated as a family, and selection and culling within a population of birds are based on the performance level of the entire family. This type of selection is most adaptable to selection for traits of low heritability. This is not to say that progress for traits of high heritability cannot be made by using family selection—quite the opposite is true. However, mass selection is effective for traits of high heritability and certainly easier.

Progress through selection is rather slow for the reproductive traits because they are lowly heritable. Most breeding programs are geared toward the improvement of more than one trait at

FIGURE 32.7.
A broiler breeding pen containing 1 male and 12 females. This is a typical breeding unit. Courtesy of Hubbard Farms.

a time. For example, to improve egg-laying lines, it might be necessary to attempt simultaneously to improve egg numbers, shell thickness, interior quality of the egg, and feed efficiency.

Outcrossing. Defined as mating unrelated breeds or strains, ***outcrossing*** is probably more adaptable to the modern broiler industry than to the egg-production industry, though it can be used to improve egg production. Numerous experiments have established fairly accurately which breeds or strains cross well with each other. Knowledge today is sophisticated to the extent that breeders know which strain or line to use as the male line and which to use as the female line.

Crossing Inbred Lines. Development of **inbred lines** for crossing is used largely for increasing egg production. ***Inbreeding*** is defined as the mating of related individuals or as the mating of individuals more closely related than the average of the flock from which they originated. The mating of brother with sister is the most common system of inbreeding for poultry; however, mating parents with offspring gives the same results. Both of these types of inbreeding increase the degree of inbreeding at the same rate per generation.

Hybrid chickens are produced by developing inbred lines and then crossing them to produce chickens that exhibit hybrid vigor. The technique employed in production of hybrid chickens is essentially the same as that used in development of hybrid plants. The breeder works with many egg-laying strains or breeds while producing hybrids. The strains or breeds are inbred (mostly brother or sister) for a number of generations, preferably five or more. In the inbreeding phase, many undesirable factors are culled out—selection is most rigid at this stage.

In all phases of hybrid production, the strains are completely tested for egg production and for important egg-quality traits. After inbreeding the birds for the necessary number of generations, the second step—crossing the remaining inbred lines in all possible combinations—is initiated. These crossbreds are tested for egg production and for egg-quality traits. Crossbreds that show improvement in these traits are bred in the third phase, in which the best test crosses are crossed into three-way and four-way crosses in all possible combinations. Most breeders prefer the four-way cross. The offspring that result from three-way and four-way crosses are known as **hybrid chickens.**

Strain Crossing. Strain crossing is more easily done than inbreeding and crossing inbred lines because it entails only the crossing of two strains that possess similar egg-production traits. It is definitely a type of crossbreeding if the two strains are not related to each other.

The computer is used in chicken breeding largely to help select breeding stock. An overall merit index is computed using data on heritability of each trait considered, the relative economic importance of each trait, and genetic correlations among the traits. Birds having the highest index are used for breeding.

In production of broiler or layer hybrid chicks, the computer is used to determine which lines or strains are most likely to give superior chickens. In broiler hybrids, hatchability, growth rate, economy of feed use, and carcass desirability are important. In layer hybrids, hatchability, egg production, egg size, egg and shell quality, and livability are important.

Practically all line-cross layers are now free from **broodiness** because attempts have been made to eliminate genes for broodiness, and records are available on which lines produce broody chicks when crossed. Lines that produce broody chicks in a line cross are no longer used for producing commercial layers.

FEEDING AND MANAGEMENT

The success of modern poultry operations depends on many factors. Hatchery operators must care for breeding stock properly so that eggs of good quality are available to the hatchery, and they must incubate eggs under environmental conditions that ensure the hatching of healthy and vigorous birds (Fig. 32.8). Feeding, health, and financial programs are essential to sound poultry management.

Incubation Management

Each type of poultry has an incubation period of definite length (Table 32.2), and incubation-management practices are geared to the needs of the eggs throughout that time. The discussion here of incubation management applies specifically to chickens. Although the principles of incubation management generally apply to other types of poultry as well, specific information should be obtained from other sources.

All modern commercial hatcheries have some form of forced-air incubation system. Today's commercial incubator has a forced-air (fan) system that creates a highly uniform environment inside the incubator. Forced-air incubators are available in many sizes. All sizes are equipped

FIGURE 32.8.
Removal of a batch of broiler chicks from the incubator. Courtesy of John Colwell from Grant Heilman.

TABLE 32.2. Incubation Times for Various Birds

Type	Incubation Period (days)
Chicken	21
Turkey	28
Duck	28
Muscovy duck	35–37
Goose	28–34
Pheasant	23–28
Bobwhite quail	23
Coturnix quail	17
Guineas	28

with sophisticated systems that control temperature and humidity, turn eggs, and bring about an adequate exchange of air between the inside and outside of the incubator. The egg-holding capacity of forced-air incubators ranges from several hundred to 100,000 or more eggs (Fig. 32.9).

Temperature, humidity, position of eggs, turning of eggs, oxygen content, carbon dioxide content, and sanitation must be regulated.

FIGURE 32.9.
Large commercial room-type incubator. Courtesy of Chick Master Incubator Co., Medina, Ohio.

Temperature. Proper temperature is probably the most critical requirement for successful incubation of chicken eggs. The usual beginning incubation temperature in the forced-air incubator is 99.5–100.0°F. The temperature should usually be lowered slightly (by 0.25–0.5 °F) at the end of the fourth day and remain constant until the eggs are to be transferred to the hatching compartments (approximately 3 days before hatching). Three days before hatching, the temperature is again lowered, usually by about 1.0–1.5°F. Just before hatching, the chicks change from embryonic respiration to normal respiration and give off considerable heat, which results in a high incubator temperature.

With reference to temperature, there are two especially critical periods during incubation—(1) the first through the fourth day and (2) the last portion of incubation. Higher-than-optimum temperatures usually speed the embryonic process and result in embryonic mortality or deformed chicks at hatching. Lower-than-optimum incubation temperatures usually slow the embryonic process and also cause embryonic mortality or deformed chicks.

Humidity. A relative humidity of 60%–65% is needed for optimum **hatchability.** All modern commercial forced-air incubators are equipped with sensitive humidity controls. The relative humidity should usually be raised slightly in the last few days of incubation. It has been shown that when the relative humidity is close to 70% in the last few days of incubation, successful hatching is greater. Providing optimum relative humidity is essential in reducing evaporation from eggs during incubation.

Position of Eggs. Eggs hatch best when incubated with the large end (the area of the space called the *air cell*) up; however, good hatchability can also be achieved when eggs are set in a horizontal position. Eggs should never be set with the small end up because a high percentage of the developing embryos will die before reaching the hatching stage. The head of the developing embryo should develop near the air cell. In the last few days of incubation, the eggs are transferred to a different type of tray—one in which the eggs are placed in a horizontal position.

Shortly before hatching, the beak of the chick penetrates the air cell. The chick is now able to receive an adequate supply of air for its normal respiratory processes. The horny point (egg tooth) of the beak eventually weakens the eggshell until a small hole is opened. The egg is now said to be "pipped." The chick is typically out of the shell within a few hours. The hatching process varies considerably among different species.

Turning of Eggs. Modern commercial incubators are equipped with time-controlled devices that permit eggs to be turned periodically. Eggs that are not turned enough during incubation have little or no chance of hatching because the embryo often becomes stuck to the shell membrane.

Commercial incubators are equipped with setting trays or compartments that allow eggs to be set in a vertical position. They also have mechanisms that rotate these trays so that the chicken eggs rotate 90° each time they are turned. The number of times the eggs are turned daily is most important. If the eggs are rotated once or twice daily, the percent of hatchability will be much lower than if the eggs are rotated five or more times daily.

Oxygen Content. The air surrounding incubating eggs should be 21% oxygen by volume. At high altitudes, however, the available oxygen in the air may be too low to sustain the physiological needs of developing chick embryos, many of which, therefore, die. Good hatchability can often be attained at high altitudes if supplemental oxygen is provided. This is necessary for commercial turkey hatching, but hatchability can be improved by selecting breeding birds that hatch well in environments in which the supply of oxygen is limited.

Carbon Dioxide Content. It is vital that the incubator be properly ventilated to prevent excessive accumulation of carbon dioxide (CO_2). The CO_2 content of the air in the incubator should never be allowed to exceed 0.5% by volume. Hatchability is lowered drastically if the CO_2 content of air in the incubator reaches 2.0%. Levels of more than 2.0% almost certainly reduce hatchability to near zero.

Sanitation. The incubator must be kept as free of disease-causing microorganisms as possible. The setting and hatching compartments must be thoroughly washed or steam-cleaned and fumigated between settings. In many cases, they should be fumigated more than once for each setting. An excellent schedule is to fumigate eggs immediately after they have been set and again as soon as they have been transferred to the hatching compartment. A good procedure for fumigation is:

1. Prepare 1.5 ml of 40% formalin for each cubic foot of incubator space.
2. Prepare 1.0 g of potassium permanganate for each cubic foot of incubator space.
3. Set the temperature of the setting compartment or hatching compartment at the proper reading (99.5–100.0°F and 98.5–99.0°F, respectively).
4. Turn on the fan.
5. Close the vents.
6. Set the relative humidity at the proper reading (65%).
7. Place potassium permanganate in an open container on the compartment.
8. Pour formalin into the potassium permanganate container and close the incubator door for approximately 20 minutes.
9. Open the door for 5–10 minutes or turn on the exhaust system to allow formaldehyde gas to escape.
10. After the gas has escaped, remove the potassium permanganate container, close the door, and continue normal operating procedures.

Candling of Eggs. In maintaining a healthy and germ-free environment, eggs must be candled—examined by shining a light through each egg to see if a chick embryo is developing—at least once during incubation so that infertile and dead-germ eggs (eggs containing dead embryos) can be identified. Many operators candle chicken eggs on the 4th or 5th day and turkey and waterfowl eggs on the 7th to 10th day. Some operators candle eggs a second time when transferring eggs to the hatching compartment.

Managing Young Poultry

The main objective in managing young poultry is to provide a clean and comfortable environment with sufficient feed and water (Fig. 32.10).

House Preparation. The brooder house should be thoroughly cleaned, **disinfected,** and dried several days before it receives young birds. All necessary brooding equipment should have been tested ahead of time and be in the proper place. One must make sure that the brooders are

FIGURE 32.10.
A commercial poultry house containing young broilers. Environmental conditions are well controlled for these many hundred birds. Courtesy of Hubbard Farms.

working properly and to *check the thermostats and micro-switches!* Such advance preparation is probably as essential to success as any management practice applied to young birds. It is imperative that the disinfectant have no effect on the meat or eggs produced by birds. Food and Drug Administration regulations that govern the use of disinfectants should be strictly observed.

Litter. Litter should be placed in the house when equipment is checked. Some commonly used substances are planer shavings, sawdust, wood chips, peat moss, ground corn cobs, peanut hulls, rice hulls, and sugar cane fiber. The entire floor should be covered by at least 2 inches of litter, which must be perfectly dry when the birds enter.

The primary purpose of litter is to absorb moisture. Litter that gets extremely damp should be replaced. Some operators add small amounts of litter as the birds grow.

Floor Space. The availability of too much or too little floor space can adversely affect growth and efficiency of production. If floor space is insufficient, young birds have difficulty finding adequate feed and water. This can lead to feather picking and actual cannibalism. Too much space can cause birds to become bored, which can lead to problems similar to those caused by overcrowding.

The amount of space required varies with the type and age of the birds. Regardless of type, each bird should have at least 7 – 10 square inches of space around and under the hover (a metal canopy that covers most brooder stoves). Chicks of the egg-producing type and birds of similar size fare well for 5 – 6 weeks on 70 square inches of floor space. Between the time these birds are 6 and 10 weeks old, the space per bird must be increased to nearly 145 square inches.

Broilers, turkeys, and waterfowl should have an area of 110 – 145 square inches for at least their first 8 weeks. In certain situations, such birds could be allowed as much as 145 – 220 square inches before they are 8 weeks old.

Feeder Space. Chick-trough-feeders should be placed within the hover guard area or partially under the hover (0.8 inches/chick or 80 inches/100 chicks to 6 weeks of age). Producers should be sure the 10-watts attraction lights under the hover are working. One linear inch of feeder space per bird is sufficient for most species from the age of 1 day to 3 weeks; 2 inches for 3–6 weeks; and 3 inches beyond 6 weeks. Quail require less space, whereas turkeys, geese, and ducks require slightly more. Most feeders are designed so that birds can eat on either side of them.

The operator can determine how much feeder space is needed through observation. If relatively few birds are eating at one time, the feeding area is probably too large. If too many are eating at once, the area is probably too small. Young birds are usually fed automatically after the brooder stove enclosure is removed.

Water Requirements. Three fountain-type waterers should be placed within the hover guard area (one fountain-type waterer/100 chicks). Generally, two 1-gallon-size water fountains are adequate for 100 birds that are 1 day old. More waterers can be added as necessary. Most commercial producers switch from water fountains to an automatic watering system when birds are put on automatic feeding. If trough-type waterers are used, allow at least 1 inch of water space per bird until 10–12 weeks of age. More space might be needed thereafter. Trough-type waterers designed so that birds can drink from both sides are available. A space of at least 0.5 inch per bird is needed if pan-type waterers are used.

Lighting Requirements. The amount of light provided by the operator varies according to the type of bird being raised. No artificial lights are needed for chicks hatched during April through July. The time clock is set for 12 hours (5 a.m.–5 p.m.) so that lights are available when personnel are working in the area. A step-down lighting program is used for chicks hatched August through March. Many broiler producers use a 24-hour light regime, whereas others use systems such as 20 hours of light alternating with 4 hours of darkness. Growing pullets do not require as much light per day as broilers because the producer desires that future layers not reach sexual maturity too quickly. Generally, about 8–10 hours of light are sufficient for future layers until they are about 12–14 weeks old.

A system of lighting that takes into account the age of the bird, the time of year in which the bird was hatched (seasonal effect), and the type of housing (windowed or windowless) should be used. Pullets should be on a constant day-length regime or a decreasing-light regime at 10 weeks of age to prevent early sexual maturity. In most cases, some type of dim light is provided to prevent young chicks from piling up in periods of darkness. After birds are about 1 week old, some producers substitute light bulbs of relatively low intensity (15–25 watts) for a bulb of higher intensity (40 watts is standard for the first week).

Other Management Factors. Young birds should have access to the proper feed as soon as they are placed in the brooder house. It is important that birds such as turkey poults start eating feed early. Some young poults die for lack of feed; although feed is readily available, they have not learned to eat it.

Young birds are commonly debeaked sometime between their first day of life and several weeks of age. **Debeaking** (also called *beak trimming*) is done with a machine by searing off approximately one-half of the upper mandible and removing a small portion of the lower one.

Care should be taken to avoid searing the bird's tongue while debeaking. Debeaking is done to prevent birds from picking feathers from other birds; it also prevents cannibalism.

Birds should be vaccinated and given health care according to a prescribed schedule; a veterinarian should be consulted.

Managing 10- to 20-Week-Old Poultry

Management of poultry from approximately 10 weeks to 20 weeks of age is quite different from managing younger birds. Improper practices in this most critical period could adversely affect subsequent production.

Confinement rearing is used by commercial producers of replacement birds, the birds that will be kept for egg production. In the three basic systems of confinement rearing, birds are raised on solid floors, slatted floors, or wire floors or cages.

Birds raised on floors in confinement should have from 1–2 square feet of floor space per individual. The amount of space required depends on the environmental conditions and on the condition of the house. Caged birds should be allowed 0.5 square feet to not more than 0.75 square feet.

Replacement chickens raised in confinement are generally fed a completely balanced growing, or developing, ration that is 15%–18% protein. Most birds are kept on a full-feeding program, but in certain conditions some producers restrict the amount of feed provided. Restricted feeding can take different forms: total feed intake, protein intake, or energy intake may be limited. The main purposes of a restricted feeding program are to slow growth rate (thus delaying the onset of sexual maturity and reducing the number of small eggs produced) and to lower feeding cost. Feed intake must not be restricted whenever a restricted lighting system (which is also used to delay sexual maturity) is in effect.

Automatic feeding and watering devices are used in most confinement operations. Watering- and feeding-space requirements are practically the same as those for birds that are 6–10 weeks old. As long as birds are not crowding the feeders and waterers, there is no particular need to increase the feeding and watering space.

The lighting regime used in confinement rearing is very important. Birds raised in window-type housing receive the normal light of long-day periods unless the house is equipped with some type of light-check. In short-day periods, supplemental lighting can be used to meet the requirements of growing chickens. Replacement chickens should receive approximately 14 hours of light daily up to 12 weeks of age. To delay sexual maturity, the amount should then be reduced to about 8–9 hours daily until the birds have reached 20–22 weeks of age. The light is then either abruptly increased to 16 hours per day, or it is increased by 2–3 hours with weekly increments of 15–20 minutes added until 16 hours of light per day are reached.

Regardless of which system replacement pullets are reared under, they should be placed in the laying house when approximately 20 weeks of age so they can adjust to the house and its equipment before beginning to lay.

Management of Laying Hens

The requirements of laying hens for floor space vary from 1.5–2 square feet per bird for egg-production strains and from 2.5–3.5 square feet for dual-purpose and broiler strains. Turkey breeding hens require 4–6 square feet, but less area is needed if hens are housed in cages. If turkey hens have access to an outside yard, 4 square feet of floor space is best. Game birds such as quail and pheasants require less floor space than egg-production hens. In general, 3 square feet or more of floor space is adequate for ducks, whereas geese need approximately 5 square feet.

Breeder hens are housed on litter or on slatted floors, whereas birds used for commercial egg production are kept in cages (Fig. 32.11).

Floor-type houses for breeder hens usually have 60% of the floor space covered with slats. Slatted floors are usually several feet above the base of the building and manure is often allowed to accumulate for a long time before being removed. Many slatted-floor houses are equipped with mechanical floor scrapers that remove the manure periodically. Frequent removal of manure lessens the chance that ammonia will accumulate.

Gathering of eggs in floor-type houses can be done automatically if some type of roll-away nesting equipment is used. In houses equipped with individual nests, the eggs are gathered manually. Some operators prefer colony nests (an open nest that accommodates several birds at a time).

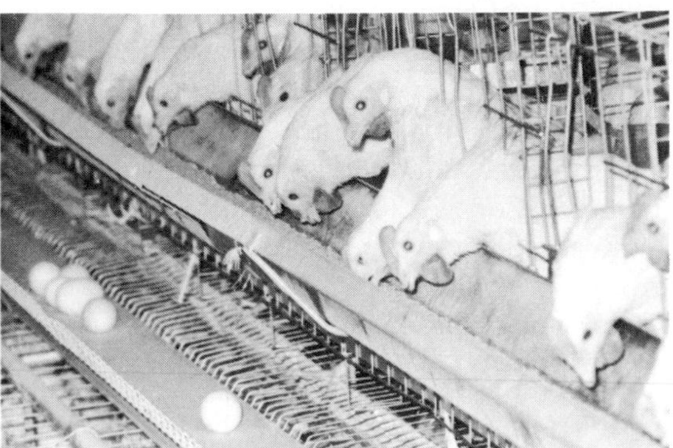

FIGURE 32.11.
Composite pictures of an automated commercial cage house for laying hens. Feeding, watering, egg gathering (vertical elevator at end of row), and manure removal are done automatically.

FIGURE 32.12.
Rearing pullets in cages. Courtesy of J. F. Stephens.

Some type of litter or nesting material must be placed on the bottom of individual and colony nests if eggs are to be gathered manually. Birds should not be allowed to roost in the nests in darkness because dirty nests result.

Cage operations are used by most commercial egg-producing farms. Young chickens may be brooded in colony cages (Fig. 32.12), whereas laying hens may be housed in 4 to 6 tiers of decked laying cages. The individual cages range in size from 8–12 inches in width, 16–20 inches in depth (front to back), and 12–15 inches in height. The number of birds housed per unit varies with the operator. Density of the cage population is an important factor in production.

All cages are equipped with feed troughs that usually extend the entire length of the cage. Some troughs are filled with feed manually, others automatically. It is sometimes advantageous to dub (remove the combs and wattles) caged layers so they can obtain feed from automatic feeders by reaching the head through the openings.

Several types of watering devices (troughs, "nipple" type, or individual "cup-type" waterers) are available for use in individual and colony cages. The watering system should be equipped with a metering device that makes it possible to medicate the birds quickly when necessary by mixing the exact dosage of medicant required with the water.

The arrangement of cages within a house varies greatly. Some producers have a step-up arrangement, such as a double row of cages at a high position with a single row at a low position on either side. Droppings from birds caged in the double row fall free of the birds in the single row. An aisle approximately 3 feet wide is usually between each group of cages. Rather than aisles, some systems have a moveable ramp that can travel above the birds, from one end of the house to the other. In other systems, several double cages are stacked on top of each other.

In cage operations, manure is typically collected into pits below the cages and removed by mechanical pit scrapers or belts. Manure may also drop into pits that are slightly sloped from end to end and partially filled with water. The manure can be flushed out with the water into lagoons.

Housing Poultry

Factors such as temperature, moisture, ventilation, and insulation are given careful consideration in planning and managing poultry houses.

Temperature. Most poultry houses are built to prevent sudden changes in house temperature. A bird having an average body temperature of 106.5°F usually loses heat to its environment except in extremely hot weather. Chickens perform well in temperatures between 35°F and 85°F, but 55°–75°F is optimal.

House temperature can be influenced by such factors as the prevailing ambient temperature, solar radiation, wind velocity, and heat production of the birds. A 4.5-lb laying hen can produce nearly 44 **British thermal units (BTU)** of heat per hour (1 BTU is the quantity of heat required to raise the temperature of 1 lb of water 1°F at or near 39°F). The amount of BTU produced varies with activity, egg-production rate, and the amount of feed consumed. Heat production by birds must be considered in designing poultry houses (about 40 of the 44 BTU produced per hour by a laying hen are available for heating). Although heat produced by birds can be of great benefit in severe cold, the house must be designed so that excess heat produced by birds in hot weather can be dissipated.

Moisture. Excess house moisture, especially in cold weather, can create an environment that is extremely uncomfortable, lead to a drop in production by laying birds, and, if allowed to continue for long, cause illness.

Much of the moisture in a poultry house comes from water spilled from waterers, water in inflowing air, and water vapor from the birds themselves and their droppings. Every effort should be made, of course, to minimize spillage from watering equipment. The amount of moisture in a poultry house can be reduced by increasing the air temperature or by increasing the rate at which air is removed. Because air holds more moisture at high temperatures than at low temperatures (Table 32.3), raising the air temperature causes moisture from the litter to enter the air and thus be dissipated. Air temperature in the house can be increased by retaining the heat produced by the birds themselves and by supplemental heat.

If incoming air is considerably colder than the air in the house, it must be warmed or it will fail to aid in moisture removal. In cold weather, most exhaust ventilation fans are run slower than normal, so most moisture removal is accomplished by increasing the air temperature in the house.

TABLE 32.3. The Water-holding Capacity of Air at Various Temperatures

Temperature (°F)	Pounds of Water per 1,000 lb of Dry Air
50	7.62
40	5.20
30	3.45
20	2.14
10	1.31
0	0.75
−10	0.45

Source: V. M. Meyer and P. Walther, *Ventilate Your Poultry House: For Clean Eggs, Healthy Hens, More Profit* (Ames: Iowa State University Cooperative Extension Service Pamphlet 292, 1963).

Ventilation. A properly designed ventilation system provides adequate fresh air, aids in removing excess moisture, and is essential in maintaining a proper temperature within the house. Type and amount of insulation and heat produced by the birds themselves must be considered in planning for ventilation.

Ventilation is accomplished by positive pressure, through which air is forced into the house to create air turbulence, or by negative pressure, through which air is removed from the house by exhaust fans (Fig. 32.13). The positive pressure system is accomplished by having fans in the attic so that air is forced through holes. The negative pressure system is accomplished by locating exhaust fans near the ceiling. Some houses are ventilated so that the air is fairly warm and dry by having open walls. Also, when outside air is cold and dry, air can enter at low portions of the house and leave through vents near the ceiling as it warms. The heat created by the chickens warms the colder air, which then takes moisture from the house.

Two integral and necessary parts of the most common ventilation systems are the exhaust fan and the air-intake arrangement. The number of exhaust fans varies with size of the house, number of birds, and capacity of the fans (Fig. 32.13). Most fans are rated on the basis of their cubic feet per minute (cfm) capacity; that is, how many cubic feet of air they move per minute. Fans in laying houses should operate at 4–4.5 cfm per bird when the temperature is moderate. In summer, cfm per bird could be as high as 10.

Fans also have a static pressure (water pressure for low house temperatures and a high speed for warm house temperatures). Others operate at only one speed; the amount of air removed is controlled by shutters that open, so that more air can be removed when the temperature of the house exceeds the thermostatically fixed temperature. These shutters then close at lower temperatures.

FIGURE 32.13.
A battery of fans used to ventilate a large poultry house. Courtesy of Big Dutchman, a division of U.S. Industries, Atlanta, Georgia.

An air-intake area must be provided for the ventilation system. It is usually a slotted area in the ceiling or near the top of the walls. There should be at least 100 square inches of inlet space for each 400 cfm of fan capacity.

Insulation. Because energy needs are becoming ever more critical, the insulation of today's poultry houses must be superior to that of the past. Sudden temperature changes inside the house must be avoided, especially for young birds. Houses in cold and windy areas require better insulation than those in milder climates, but good insulation is also essential in areas with high outside temperatures. The insulation ability of any material is measured by its *R* value. This value is based on the material's ability to limit heat loss, as expressed in BTUs. The better the insulating material, the higher its *R* value. For example, if the outside temperature is 11°F cooler than the inside, a material having an *R* value of 11 loses approximately 1 BTU/hour to the outside for each square foot of area when the outside temperature is 20°F cooler than the inside.

By knowing how much heat the birds generate, local variations in ambient temperature, expected wind velocities, and relative humidities experienced, the appropriate *R* value can be established. In many areas of the United States, especially in the cold regions, wall insulation in poultry houses should have an *R* value of 15; ceiling insulation, at least 20 (heat loss through the floor is negligible). In warmer areas, wall insulation should have an *R* value of 5–10; ceiling insulation, 10–15.

When computing the *R* value for a particular area of the house (e.g., walls), resistance of the outer surface, insulation, air space between the studding, inner wall material, resistance of the inner surface, and, if windows are present, presence of glass, must all be considered. Each of these factors has an *R* value, and the total of these values establishes the *R* value for that area of the house. A building materials dealer can furnish the *R*-value ratings of these factors.

Because too much moisture may accumulate in the house, especially in cold weather, some type of vapor barrier should be present in the walls and ceiling. This barrier can be a part of the insulation itself (foil backing) or separate. It should be placed between the insulation and the inside wall. The foil-back portion of the insulation should be placed next to the inside wall.

Feeds and Feeding

Rations fed to poultry today are complex mixtures that should include all ingredients, in a balanced proportion, that have been found to be necessary for body maintenance, maximum production of eggs and meat, and optimum reproduction (**fertility** and hatchability). Poultry nutritionists are constantly searching for and testing new combinations of feedstuffs that, when incorporated into diets, permit better efficiency of production. Feeding can be expensive because an adequate intake of energy, protein, minerals, and vitamins is essential.

The computer is used in formulating least-cost rations that meet the nutritional requirements of poultry. Data input that must be provided includes constraints that depend on age of birds and their productivity, cost of available ingredients, ingredients desired in the ration, composition of the nutritional materials, and requirements of the chickens to be fed.

The constraints set minimum and maximum percentages. For example, an upper limit on the amount of fiber that could be in the ration must be established because birds cannot use fiber effectively. Likewise, a low or minimal level of soybean meal is important to provide the needed amino acids.

Large computers are expensive so only large poultry operations can afford them. However, lower-cost microcomputers are now being used to compute least-cost rations. Most poultry producers can afford a microcomputer.

Energy requirements are supplied mainly by cereal grains, grain by-products, and fats. Some important grains are yellow corn, wheat, sorghum grains (milo), barley, and oats. Most rations contain high amounts of grain (60% or higher, depending on the type of ration). A ration containing a combination of grains is generally better than a ration having only one type. Animal fats and vegetable oils are excellent sources of energy. They are usually incorporated into broiler rations or any high-energy rations.

Protein is so highly essential that most commercial poultry feeds are sold on the basis of their protein content. The types of amino acids present determine the nutritional value of protein (see Chapter 15). Excellent protein can be derived from both plants and animals. Most rations contain both plant and animal protein so that each source can supply amino acids that the other source lacks. The most common sources of plant protein are soybean meal, cottonseed meal, peanut meal, alfalfa meal, and corn gluten meal. Cereal grains contain insufficient protein to meet the needs of birds. The best sources of animal protein are fish meal, milk by-products, meat by-products, tankage, blood meal, and feather meal. The protein requirements of birds vary according to the species, age, and purpose for which they are being raised. The protein requirements of certain birds are shown in Table 32.4. Where variable values are listed, the highest level is to be fed to the youngest individuals.

Whatever ration is adequate for turkeys is generally suitable for game birds. Some game bird producers feed a turkey ration at all times. Others feed a complete game bird ration. The actual nutrient requirements of game birds are not as well known as are the requirement of chickens and turkeys.

A considerable number of minerals are essential, especially calcium, phosphorus, magnesium, manganese, iron, copper, zinc, and iodine. Calcium and phosphorus, along with vitamin D, are essential for proper bone formation. A deficiency of either of these elements can lead to a bone condition known as **rickets.** Calcium is also essential for proper eggshell formation.

TABLE 32.4. Protein Requirements of Poultry

Type	Age (weeks)	Percentage of Protein Required in Diet
Chickens		
Broilers	0–6	20.0–23.0%
Replacement pullets	0–14	15.0–18.0
Replacement pullets	14–20	12.0
Laying and breeding hens		14.5
Turkeys		
Starting	0–8	26.0–28.0
Growing	8–24	14.0–22.0
Breeders		14.0
Pheasant and quail		
Starting and growing		16.0–30.0
Ducks		
Starting and growing		16.0–22.0

Source: National Research Council, *Nutrient Requirements of Poultry,* 8th ed. (Washingtion, DC: National Academy of Sciences, 1984).

TABLE 32.5. Poultry Meat and Egg Production Costs, 1989

	Production Cost (cents per doz/lb)	
Item	Feed	Total
Market eggs	$0.31	$0.49
Broilers	0.18	0.26
Turkeys	0.27	0.40

Source: Livestock and Poultry Situation, 1990. Courtesy of the USDA.

The amount of calcium required varies somewhat with age, rate of egg production, and temperature. Chickens and turkeys up to 8 weeks of age require 0.8% – 1.2% of calcium in their diets. Calcium can be reduced from 0.6% – 0.8% in 8- to 16-week-old birds. Laying hens require at least 3.4% calcium. The amounts of phosphorus required for chickens of different ages are as follows: 0 – 6 weeks, 0.4%; 6 – 14 weeks, 0.35%; and mature, 0.32%. Turkeys require from 0.3% – 0.6% phosphorus; game birds, approximately 0.5%. Requirements for other minerals vary greatly depending on the stage of growth and production.

The vitamins that are most important to poultry are A, D, K, and E (fat soluble), and thiamin, riboflavin, pantothenic acid, niacin, vitamin B_6, choline, biotin, folacin, and vitamin B_{12} (water soluble).

COSTS AND RETURNS

Table 32.5 shows the 1989 costs of production for eggs, broilers, and turkeys. Note that feed costs comprise 60% – 70% of the total costs. Management practices that monitor and lower feed costs usually have a positive effect on net returns.

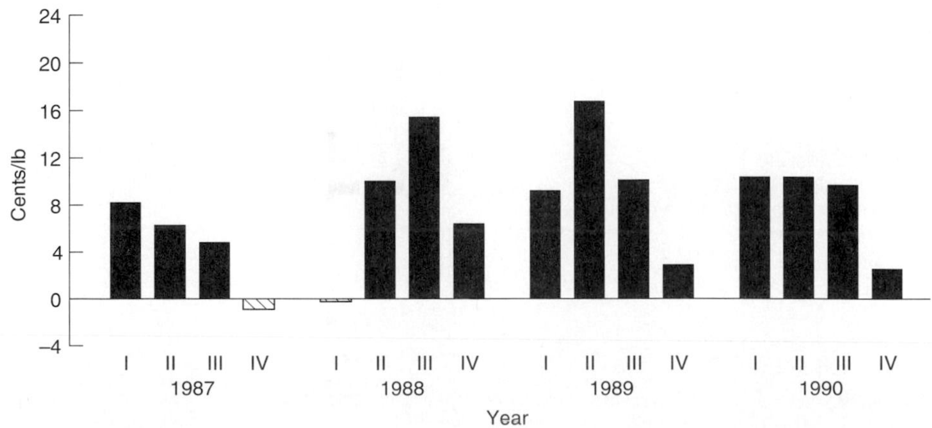

FIGURE 32.14.
Net returns (wholesale) for the broiler industry, 1987 – 90. Courtesy of the USDA.

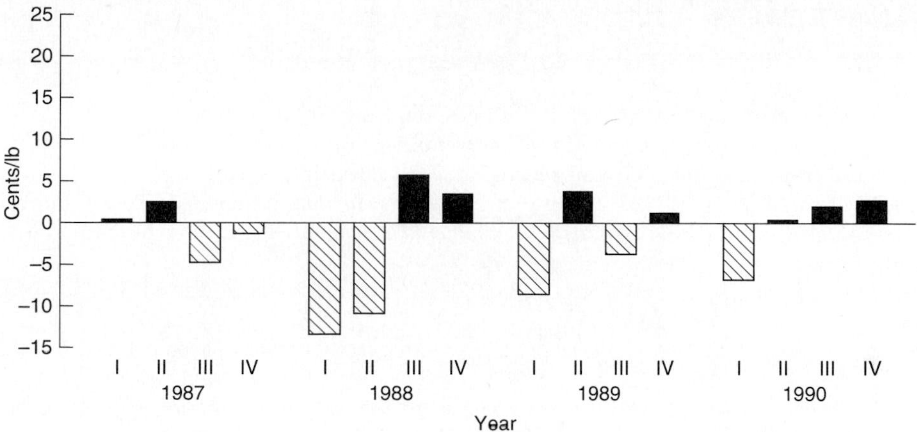

FIGURE 32.15.
Net returns (wholesale) for the turkey industry, 1987–90. Courtesy of the USDA.

The 1987–90 costs and returns for broilers, turkeys, and eggs are shown in Figures 32.14, 32.15, and 32.16, respectively. During these years broilers were the most profitable. Net returns were variable both between and within years.

Additional material on costs and returns is discussed in Chapter 36.

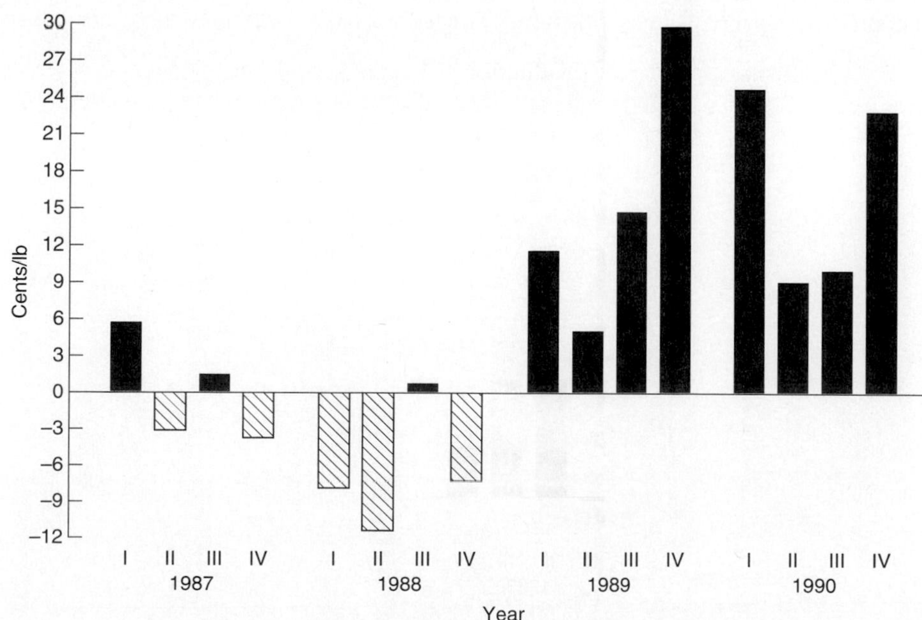

FIGURE 32.16.
Net returns (wholesale) for the egg industry, 1987–90. Courtesy of the USDA.

SELECTED REFERENCES

Publications

Broiler Industry (monthly publication). Mount Morris, IL: Watt Publishing Co.

Day, E. J. 1980. Microcomputers: Ready for least-cost ration formulation. *Feedstuffs* 52:1, 50, 52.

Egg Industry (monthly periodical). Mount Morris, IL: Watt Publishing Co.

Moreng, R. E., and Avens, J. S. 1985. *Poultry Science and Production.* Reston, VA: Reston Publishing Co.

National Research Council. 1984. *Nutrient Requirements of Poultry.* 8th ed. Washington, DC: National Academy Press.

Nesheim, M. C., Austic, R. E., and Card, L. E. 1979. *Poultry Production.* 12th ed. Philadelphia: Lea & Febiger.

North, M. O. and Bell, D. D. 1990. *Commercial Chicken Production Manual.* Westport, CT: Avi Publishing Co.

Plunkett, J. 1980. Four-house, 80,000-hen complex managed by a single employee. *Poult. Dig.* 39:64.

Turkey World (monthly publication). Mount Morris, IL: Watt Publishing Co.

USDA. 1986. *Eggs, Chickens, and Turkeys.* Washington, DC: GPO.

Visuals

The Business of Laying Eggs (videotape; 15 min.). American Farm Bureau Federation, 225 Touhy Ave., Park Ridge, IL 60068.

Commercial Chicken Production (videotape; 57 min.). Dept. of Animal Science, University of Delaware, Newark, DE 19711.

Hatchery Operations (80 slides and audiotape; 18 min.). Poultry Science Department, Ohio State University, 674 W. Lane Ave., Columbus, OH 43210.

How to Do a Poultry Autopsy (silent filmstrip); and *Small Flock Brooding Techniques* (sound filmstrip). Vocational Education Productions, California Polytechnic State University, San Luis Obispo, CA 93407.

CHAPTER 33

Goat Breeding, Feeding, and Management

Geological records reveal that goats existed five million years ago and bones of goats closely associated with people have been found dating back 12,000 years. It appears that people at that time existed in small groups, moving to where food and water could be found for themselves and the goats. The goats were particularly important to people because they provided food (milk and meat), skins for making certain items of clothing, and mohair for many uses.

Goats thrive on **browse** (brushy plants) and **forbs** (broad leaf plants), but they also eat grass extensively, depending on forage species and stage of maturity. Choice of plants and plant parts is important to goats because they are more likely to select the more nutritious parts, and because of their browsing over a wide territory, they are less likely to suffer from internal parasites.

Goats have a large impact on the economy and food supply for people of the tropical world. In many countries, people consume more goat's milk than cow's milk, and goats are an important source of meat. In the United States, the consumption of both goat milk and goat meat is increasing, and the production of mohair is an important industry in Texas.

There are four major kinds of domesticated goats: (1) the **dairy goat** is used largely for the production of milk and to a lesser extent for meat; (2) the **Angora goat** is used mainly for the production of mohair and to a lesser extent for brush clearance and the production of meat; (3) the **meat goat** is used for brush clearance, for the production of meat, and, in some parts of the world, for skins and fine leather; and (4) the **pygmy goat** is used as a laboratory ruminant animal and pet in the United States but is an important disease-resistant meat and milk producer in Africa and other countries.

In some parts of the world, goat meat production is extremely important and, in fact, meat goats outnumber dairy goats worldwide. Goat numbers in the United States are modest compared to cattle and sheep because of the highly specialized and effective dairy industry built around the dairy cow, as well as the specialized beef cattle and sheep industries. Yet in some parts of the world, including Mediterranean countries, France, and Norway, large quantities of dairy products are produced from goats.

Milk produced by dairy goats differs from cow's milk in that all carotene has been converted into vitamin A in goat milk. The type of curd formed from goat milk is different from the curd from cow milk because of differences in the major caseins; milk fat in goat milk is in smaller globules than in cow milk, does not rise or coalesce as readily, and contains much more short-chain fatty acids. Goat milk is more readily digested and assimilated by people and animals because of these differences. The dairy goat is a desirable animal for providing milk for the family because it is small and less expensive to feed than the cow. Goats can consume large quantities of browse, which is not very palatable to cattle.

IMPORTANCE OF GOATS

The number of goats in the different countries of the world is presented in Table 33.1. Most goats are found in developing countries, where they contribute greatly to the needs of the people there. There are many families that have a few goats for the production of milk, meat, and hides for family use.

One major by-product of goats is skins. In areas with extensive goat numbers for milk and meat production, hides become important. The leading countries in the production of goat meat and goatskins are given in Table 33.2.

TABLE 33.1. Number of Goats in the World, in Different Areas of the World, and in Developed and Developing Nations (1989).

Area or Country	Number of Goats (mil)
Africa	169
Nigeria	26
Somalia	20
Asia	296
India	107
China	78
Europe	15
Greece	6
Spain	3
North and Central America	15
Mexico	10
United States	2
South America	22
Brazil	11
Argentina	3
Developed countries	22
Developing countries	412
World	526

Source: FAO Production Yearbook, 1989.

TABLE 33.2. Leading Countries in Goat Meat and Fresh Goatskin Production

Country	Goatmeat (mil lb)	Country	Goatskins (mil lb)
China	882	China	196
India	847	India	189
Pakistan	618	Pakistan	88
Nigeria	295	Nigeria	46
Turkey	165	Ethiopia	31
World total	5,203	World total	984

Source: FAO Production yearbook, 1989.

PHYSIOLOGICAL CHARACTERISTICS

Goats have many characteristics that are similar to sheep. Some of the production traits of goats are summarized in Table 33.3.

CHARACTERISTICS OF BREEDS OF DAIRY GOATS

The external parts of a goat are shown in Fig. 33.1. The dairy goat and dairy cow are about equal in efficiency of converting feed into milk, even though the dairy goat produces much more milk in relation to its size and weight then does the dairy cow. Feed needed for maintenance is higher per unit of body weight for goats than for dairy cows.

Gall (1981) compared the efficiency of Holstein dairy cows with Alpine Beetel dairy goats.

TABLE 33.3. Production Characteristics of Goats

Trait	Time/lb
Gestation length	144–155 days (average 150 days)
Length of estrous cycle	15–18 days (average 16 days)
Length of estrus	1–3 days (average 2 days)
Age at puberty	120 days to over a year[a]
Normal breeding season	Late summer, early fall, or late winter[b] (breeds near the equator are less seasonal)
Size of kids at birth	1.5–11.0 lb[c] (average 5.5 lb)
Adult size	
Does	40–190 lb (average 130 lb)
Bucks	50–300 lb[d] (average 160 lb)

[a] Age of puberty depends on the breed and nutrition. Pygmy goats tend to reach puberty at an early age, some kids at 9 months of age.
[b] Normal breeding season depends on the breed. Pygmy does are capable of breeding over a long breeding season but are more fertile when bred in the fall or early winter. Angora goats usually have a highly restrictive breeding season during the fall.
[c] Pygmy and Angora goats are smaller at birth than are dairy goat kids.
[d] Pygmy goats are the smallest in size, Angora goats are intermediate, and dairy goats are the largest. Bucks of all breeds are larger than corresponding does.

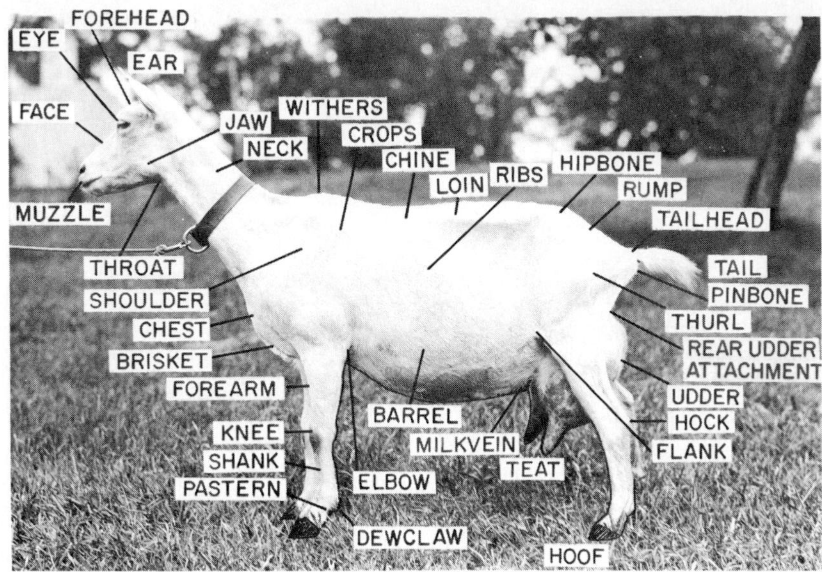

FIGURE 33.1.
The external parts of the dairy goat. Courtesy of R. F. Crawford and Ted Edwards, *Emerald Dairy Goat Association Newsletter*. Photograph by Ole Hoskinson.

The cows weighed 1,325 lb and produced 13,260 lb of milk, whereas the dairy goats weighed 108 lb and produced 1,083 lb of milk per lactation. The dry-matter intakes per lactation and per liter of milk for the Holstein cows were 13,300 lb and 2.3 lb per quart of milk and for the goats 1,173 lb and 2.4 lb per quart of milk.

The six major dairy goat breeds registered in the United States—Toggenburg, Saanen, Alpine, Oberhasli, Nubian, and LaMancha—are all capable of high milk productivity. These breeds are shown in Figs. 33.2–33.7.

The Toggenburg breed is medium in size, is vigorous, and has high milk production (Fig. 33.2). The highest record of milk production for one lactation by a U.S. Toggenburg female is

FIGURE 33.2.
A Toggenburg doe. Note the fore attachment of the udder and the well-placed teats. Courtesy of the *Dairy Goat Journal*.

FIGURE 33.3.
A Saanen doe. Courtesy of Nancy Lee Owen.

5,750 lb. The Saanen is a large, all-white breed capable of producing the most milk (Fig. 33.3). A world-record milk production for one lactation by a Saanen female is 7,713 lb. The Alpine breed is a large, somewhat rangy goat (Fig. 33.4). Alpines also produce much milk; the record for one lactation of a female is 5,729 lb.

The Nubian is a tall, proud-looking goat breed that differs from the other five breeds in being a better meat producer and having long, wide, pendulous ears and a Roman nose (Fig. 33.5). The U.S. record milk production of a Nubian female is 4,420 lb, which is lower than for the three Swiss breeds previously described. However, Nubian milk is distinctive for its higher milk fat content (7.4% vs. 3.5% for Swiss breeds).

The LaMancha goat breed of California origin (Fig. 33.6) is smaller and differs from all other breeds in having almost no external ears ("gopher" ears) or extremely short ears ("elf" or "cookie" ears). Milk production is comparatively lower. Records for one lactation of up to 4,510 lb have been recorded. Fewer females of this breed and the Oberhasli breed have been officially tested for milk production. Therefore, these breeds' true capacities have not yet been demonstrated.

The Oberhasli (Fig. 33.7) is a medium-sized dairy goat breed, also of Swiss origin, with usually solid red or black colors. Production records of up to 3,300 lb milk have been reported.

FIGURE 33.4.
A French Alpine doe. Courtesy of Eva Rappaport.

FIGURE 33.5.
A Nubian doe. Note the ear size and shape. Courtesy of Cindy Schneider.

FIGURE 33.6.
A LaMancha doe. Note the earless condition. This individual is homozygous for earlessness. Courtesy of Cindy Schneider.

FIGURE 33.7.
An Oberhasli doe. Courtesy of Mary Slabach.

Gall (1981) reported the following annual average milk production records from the major dairy goat breeds in the United States (only goats having more than five lactations during 276 to 305 days were used): Toggenburg, 1,940 lb; Saanen, 2,035 lb; Alpine, 2,024 lb; Nubian, 1,662 lb; and LaMancha, 1,719 lb.

CARE AND MANAGEMENT

Simple housing for goats is adequate in areas where the weather is mild because goats do best when they are outside on pasture or in an area where they can exercise freely. If the weather is wet at times, an open shed with a good roof is necessary. Lactating goats can be fed in an open shed in stormy weather and taken to the milking parlor for milking. If the weather is severely cold, an enclosed barn with ample space is needed. At least 20 square feet per goat is needed if goats are to be housed in a barn, but 16 square feet per goat may suffice in open sheds.

The use of several small pastures permits goats to be moved about, thus increasing grazing efficiency and reducing the risk of parasite infestation. Fences must be properly constructed with woven wire and 6-inch stays. Fencing for goats is different from fencing for cows; a woven-wire fence is best for containing goats because they can climb a rail fence. In addition, a special type of bracing at corners of the fence is necessary because goats can walk up a brace pole and jump over the fence. With electric fences, two electric wires should be used — one located low enough to keep goats from going underneath and one high enough to keep them from jumping over. However, an electric fence may not contain bucks of any breed; some may go through the fence despite the shock.

Several pieces of equipment are needed for normal care: a tattoo set, hoof trimmers, a hoof knife, a grooming brush, an emasculator, and a balling gun for administering boluses (large pills for dosing animals).

All breeds of dairy goats are available in polled strains. The polled condition has advantages because a polled goat is less likely to catch its head in a woven-wire fence than is a horned goat. Horned animals should be disbudded during the first week following birth by use of an electric dehorning iron. Goat breeders were plagued by the genetic linkage between hermaphroditism and polledness. However, polled goats with good fertility can be found.

Goat's feet should be kept properly trimmed to prevent deformities and footrot. A good pruning shear is ideal for leveling and shaping the hoof, but final trimming can be done with a hoof knife. Footrot should be treated with formaldehyde, copper sulfate, or iodine. Affected goats are best isolated from the others and placed on clean, dry ground after treatment for footrot.

All kids should be identified by a tattoo in the ear, except for LaMancha and Pygmies, where identification is in the tail-web. Ear tags are also useful and are easy to read. The tattoo serves as permanent identification in case an ear tag is lost. All registered goats must be tattooed because the goat registry associations do not accept ear-tag identification.

Male kids not acceptable for breeding should be castrated. This can be done by constricting the blood circulation to the testicles by use of a rubber band elastrator, or by surgically removing the testicles. Some breeders nonsurgically crush the cords to the testicles with an emasculator. After the blood supply to the testicles is discontinued, they usually atrophy but exceptions occur. After using the emasculator, the blood circulation to the testicles may continue and, although the male is sterile, he continues to produce testosterone and has normal sex drive. A problem with the elastrator is that tetanus can occur when the tissue dies below the elastrator band. Surgical removal of the testicles creates a wound that attracts flies in the warm season. A fly repellant should be applied around the wound. It is recommended that a veterinarian castrate older goats. Whatever method is used, caution must be taken to prevent infection, gangrene, and other complications.

It is important that the udder of dairy goats has strong fore and rear attachments and that the two teats be well spaced. Goats are milked by hand (Fig. 33.8) or by milking machines. The milking stanchion should be elevated to place the goat at a convenient level for the person doing the milking (Fig. 33.9). Clean, sanitary conditions of the milking stanchion, the milking machine, the goat, and her udder and teats are very important prior to milking. After milking, the teats should be dipped in a weak iodine solution.

Considerations of special importance in managing dairy goats are care at time of breeding, kidding, and feeding.

Time of Breeding

The female goat comes into heat at intervals of 15–18 days until she becomes pregnant. Young does can be bred first when they weigh 85–95 lb at about 6–10 months of age, which means that does in good general condition may be bred to have kids at 1 year of age. Goats are seasonal breeders; the normal breeding season occurs in September, October, and November. If no effort is made to breed does at other times, most of the young will be born in February, March, or April. Normal goat lactations are 7–10 months in duration. A period of at least 2 months when no goats are lactating might occur, but with staggered breeding, the kidding and milking seasons can be extended. Housing goats in the dark for several hours each day in the spring and summer months (to stimulate the onset of shorter days) causes some to come into estrus earlier than usual. Conversely, artificial additional light in the goat barn may delay estrus in the autumn.

One service is all that is needed to obtain pregnancy, but it is generally wise to delay breeding for a day after the goat first shows signs of heat. The doe stays in heat from 1–3 days, but the optimum period of standing heat may last only a few hours at the end of estrus. A female in heat is often noisy and restless, and her milk production may decrease sharply. She may disturb other goats in the herd, so it is advisable to keep her in a separate stall until she goes out of heat.

Male goats during the breeding season usually have a rank odor, especially when confined to a pen. Housing the males downwind apart from the does will reduce some of the nuisance of male odors. Cleanliness of the male's long beard and shaggy hair helps reduce "bucky" odors.

Careful records should be kept showing breeding dates and the bucks used. From breeding

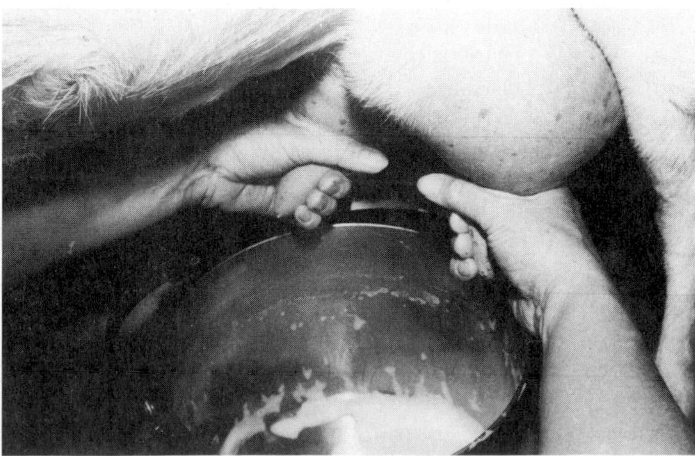

FIGURE 33.8.
Hand-milking the goat. Courtesy of G. F. W. Haenlein, University of Delaware.

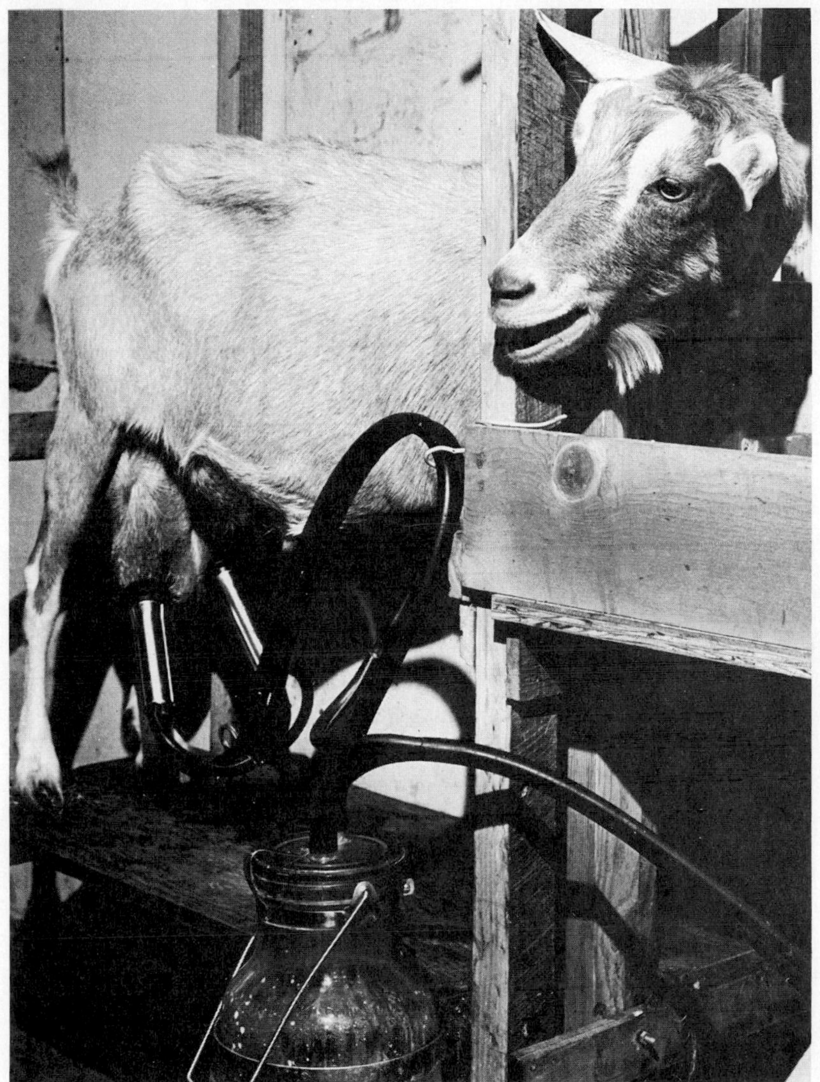

FIGURE 33.9.
A goat being milked by machine in a stanchion at a convenient level for milking. Courtesy of Eva Rappaport.

records, it is possible to calculate when does should deliver kids, as the gestation period is about 150 days. Detailed breeding records are essential for knowing ancestors, which in turn helps in the selection of superior males to produce especially desirable offspring.

Delivery of twins is common and delivery of triplets occurs on occasion, particularly among mature does. More males are conceived and born than are females. The ratio is approximately 115 : 100. Mature does average 2 kids, whereas younger does average 1.5 kids. Kids at birth weighs 5 – 8 lb, but singles may be heavier than twins or triplets, and males are usually heavier than females.

Time of Kidding

A doe, almost ready to deliver young, should be placed in a clean pen that is well bedded with clean straw or shavings. The doe should have plenty of clean water, some laxative feed (such as wheat bran), and fresh soft legume hay. She should be carefully observed but not disturbed unless assistance is necessary, as indicated by excessive straining for 3 hours or more. If the kid presents the front feet and head, delivery should be easy without assistance. If only the front feet, but not the head, are presented, the kid should be pushed back enough to bring the head forward in line with the front feet. Breech presentations are not uncommon, but these deliveries should be rapid to prevent the kid from suffocating. If assistance is needed, a qualified attendant with small well-lubricated hands should pull when contractions occur. Gentleness is essential; harsh or ill-timed pulling can cause severe internal damage.

As soon as the kid arrives, its mouth and nostrils should be wiped clean of membranes and mucus. In cold weather, it is necessary to take the newborn to a heated room for drying. A chilled kid must be helped to regain its body temperature with a heat lamp or even by immersing its body up to the chin in water that is as hot as can be tolerated when the attendant's elbow is immersed in it for 2 minutes. Kids should be encouraged to nurse as soon as they are dry. Nursing helps the newborn kid to keep warm.

Difficulty in kidding may be caused by diseases and internal parasites. It is advisable to use disposable rubber or plastic gloves when assisting with delivery and to wash and disinfect everything diligently. Some diseases (including brucellosis) are transmissible to people; however, brucellosis has not been recently reported in U.S. goats.

Feeding

Because goats are ruminants, they can digest roughage effectively. However, the types and proportions of feed should be related to the functions of the goats. For example, dry (nonmilking) does and bucks that are not actively breeding perform satisfactorily on ample browse, good pasture, and good-quality grass and legume hay. If grass is short and hay is of poor quality, and goats are milking well, feeding of supplemental concentrates is necessary. Overfeeding of supplemental concentrates can cause diarrhea or obesity, which interferes with reproduction and subsequent lactation.

Heavily lactating does and young does that must grow while lactating should be given good-quality hay *ad libitum* and concentrates liberally. Good-quality pasture should supplement hay well, but even then lactating goats require some roughage in the form of hay or other source of long fiber to prevent scouring.

Pregnant does should be fed to gain weight to assure adequate nutrition of the kids. A doe should be in good flesh, but not fat, when she kids because she draws from her body reserves for milk production.

Grains such as corn, oats, barley, and milo may be fed whole because goats crack grains by chewing. If protein supplements are mixed with the grain or if the feed mix is being pelleted, the grain may be rolled, cracked, or coarsely ground. Some people prefer to mix the hay and grain and prepare the ration in a total pellet form. There is added expense in pelleting, but much less feed is wasted.

In some areas, deficiencies in minerals such as phosphorus, selenium, and iodine may exist. The use of iodized or trace-mineralized salt along with dicalcium phosphate or steamed bonemeal usually provides enough minerals if legume hay or good pastures are available. Calcium is usually present in sufficient quantity in legume hay and phosphorus is adequately provided in grain feeds. To be safe, it is best to provide a mixture of trace-mineralized salt and bonemeal free-choice.

Young, growing goats and lactating goats need more protein than do bucks or dry does. A ration containing 12% – 15% protein is desirable for bucks and dry does, but 15% – 20% protein may be better for young goats and for does that are producing much milk.

Generally, kids must be allowed to nurse their dams to obtain the first milk — colostrum. After 3 days, kids may be removed from their mothers and given milk replacer by means of a lamb feeder or hand-held bottle until they are large enough to eat hay and concentrates. It is advisable to encourage young kids to eat solid feed at an early age (2 – 3 weeks) by having leafy legume hay and palatable fresh concentrates such as rolled grain available at all times. Solid feeds are less expensive than milk replacers, and when the kids can do well on solid feeds, milk replacers should not be fed. Small kids need concentrates until their rumens are sufficiently developed to digest enough roughage to meet all their nutritional needs. At 5 – 6 months of age, young goats can do well on good pasture or good-quality legume hay alone.

CONTROLLING DISEASES AND PARASITES

Major diseases affecting goats are Johnes disease, caseous lymphadenitis, caprine pleuropneumonia, ecthyma, enterotoxemia, goat pox, herpesvirus, Pasteurella hemolytica, tetanus, and viral leukocencephalomelitis. As goats are highly resistant to **bluetongue,** there is no reason for alarm even if sheep having bluetongue are grazing in the same pasture.

Johnes disease also affects sheep and it is a serious health problem in goats. Affected goats become unthrifty, emaciated, and unproductive.

A troublesome disease, **caseous lymphadenitis,** is characterized by nodules in the lymph area (throat). When one of the infected nodes is opened, a thick, caseous material is exposed. The disease is difficult to cure or control. One should check animals in a herd from which breeding stock is considered for purchase and then not buy animals from a herd that has infected animals. Also, an isolation program is desirable for purchased animals to see if they develop the disease. Infected animals should be isolated, then infected nodes are opened and flushed with H_2O_2.

Caprine pleuropneumonia results in high mortality. The services of a veterinarian should be obtained to help control this disease.

Contagious ecthyma, also called **soremouth,** is contagious to sheep and humans. Animals that recover from it are immune for several years. A live vaccine can be used on kids on premises that are infected.

Enterotoxemia is caused by *Clostridium perfringes* types *C* and *D*. Animals of all ages are susceptible. *C. perfringes* antitoxin given intraveneously or subcutaneously will give dramatic response. Toxoid vaccination given to month-old kids followed by a second dose in 2 weeks and booster doses each year will control the disease.

Goat pox causes lesions on mucous membranes and skin. It is prevalent in North Africa, the Middle East, Australia, and Scandinavia but not in the United States.

Herpesvirus is serious in neonatal kids.

Young kids are highly susceptible to **Pasteurella hemolytica.** They can be treated with penicillin with successful results.

Tetanus is caused by *Clostridum tetani,* which infects wounds and often causes death. The causative organism is prevalent in soil contaminated with horse feces. Two doses of toxoid to goats over 1 month of age and then an annual booster injection will control the disease.

Mastitis is an inflammation of the udder predisposed by bruising, lack of proper sanitation, and improper milking. The milk becomes curdled and stringy. It is advisable to engage the services of a veterinarian for treating severe mastitic cases. An udder may be treated with a suitable antibiotic by sliding a special dull plastic needle up the teat canal into the udder cistern and depositing the antibiotic, or by systemic antibiotic treatment intramuscularly or intravenously. Hot packs may help reduce the edema and in severe cases frequent milking is necessary. Dry goat treatments can effectively prevent mastitis.

Brucellosis is transmissible to humans. All goats should be tested for brucellosis, and reactor animals or suspects must be slaughtered.

Footrot occurs when goats are kept on wet land. It is contagious, but the bacterial organism causing it does not live long in the soil. Any animal to be introduced into a herd should be isolated for several days to see if footrot is present. Severe hoof trimming of infected feet, followed by treating with formaldehyde (as described in Chapter 29), cures this disease. Generally, dairy goats dislike wet land and footrot is not a common problem in U.S. dairy goats.

Ketosis, or pregnancy disease, rarely occurs in goats. Affected goats are in pain and cannot walk. Exercising goats that are pregnant, reducing the amount of feed in the latter part of the pregnancy to avoid fat conditions, and being certain that they have clean, fresh water at all times helps prevent ketosis.

Milk fever can, but rarely, occur in goats that are lactating heavily. Some heavy-milking goats may deplete their calcium stores. They cannot stand and may die of progressive paralysis. An intravenous injection of calcium gluconate results in rapid recovery. The goat may be up and normal in less than an hour after a calcium gluconate injection.

Goats are subject to many severe external and internal parasites. The external parasites include **lice** and **mites.** The animals may be sprayed, dipped, or dusted with an appropriate insecticide similar to those used on dairy cows. Dairy feed stores are usually good sources of materials and advice for treatment.

Internal parasites of goats include **stomach worms** and **coccidia.** The same treatment for stomach worms that is effective in sheep or horses can be used. **Coccidiosis,** caused by a protozoan organism in the intestinal tract, is found mostly in young goats. **Drenching** the animal with sulfa drugs or certain antibiotics helps control coccidiosis. Routine treatment with thibenzole or phenothiazine, or an alternation of these each six months, helps control internal parasites. Professional help in administering these drugs is advisable.

THE ANGORA GOAT

Angora goats (Fig. 33.10) are raised chiefly to produce mohair, which is made into fine clothing. These goats are produced largely in the Southwest (Texas has the most Angora goats of any state), the Ozarks of Missouri and Arkansas, and the Pacific Northwest. They do best on browse, so they are most commonly kept on rough, brushy areas. They are not as well adapted for intensive grazing pastures because they prefer broadleaf plants over some grasses, and because they are more likely to become parasitized when grazing near the soil level in overgrazed pastures.

FIGURE 33.10.
An Angora goat showing a full fleece of mohair. Angora goats are useful for meat production, brush clearing, and mohair production. Courtesy of Mr. and Mrs. Don F. Kessi.

Good Angora goats are shorn twice a year. Some have a tendency to shed their mohair in the spring, but selection against this trait has been successful. Some Angora goats are not shorn for 2–3 years, which allows the mohair to grow to lengths of 1–2 feet. This special mohair brings a high price and is used for making wigs and doll hair. Shearing is usually done in spring. The clip from does weighs 4–6 lb, whereas bucks and wethers may shear 5–8 lb. Highly improved goats often shear 10–15 lb of mohair per year. Three classes of mohair are produced: the **tight lock** with ringlets the full length of the fibers, the **flat lock,** which is wavy; and the **fluffy,** or **open, fleece.** The tight-lock fleeces are fine in texture but low in yield. The flat lock lacks the fineness of the tight lock but is satisfactory for making cloth and its yield is high. The fluffy fleece is of low quality, often quite coarse, and is easily caught in brush and thereby lost.

Fleeces should be sorted at shearing time. Coarse fleeces and those with burs should be kept separate from good fleeces. The clip from each fleece should be tied separately so that it can be properly graded.

Fertility can be low in Angora goats. Losses of kids on the open range or in scattered timber areas of the West Coast states are often high, especially because of predators such as coyotes, bobcats, and wild dogs. Generally, the kid crop that is raised to weaning is about 80% of the number conceived, as estimated on the basis of the number of does bred. Losses of 20% or more may occur when proper care is lacking at the time kids are born.

Angora goats have straighter horns than dairy goats. When they are in good condition on the range, mature bucks and wethers may weigh 150–200 lb. Mature does weigh 90–110 lb, but well-fed show animals usually weigh more. Kids are usually weaned at 5 months of age, which allows the doe to gain in weight at breeding time. Breeding over a period of days is usually done in late September and October. Since the gestation is 147–152 days, this time of breeding results in the kids arriving in the spring after the weather has moderated. Kidding may take place in open sheds when the weather is severe, or outside when the weather is favorable. Young does are usually first bred to kid at the age of 2 years but, if they are properly developed, they may be bred to kid when they are yearlings.

Angora goats need shelter in rainy periods or wet snows; an open shed is sufficient. The long mohair coats of Angoras keep them warm during cold weather, but they may nevertheless crowd together and smother in severe snowstorms if no shelter is provided.

Angora goats are subject to the same parasites and diseases as dairy goats, and the same treatments are effective for both. In most other respects, though, the care given Angora goats resembles the care given sheep rather than that given dairy goats.

Angora, Spanish meat goats, or cull dairy goats are used in some areas to kill brush. One method is to stock the area heavily with goats and give them little feed as long as their health is not impaired. Keeping the goats hungry for green feed causes all brush to be destroyed in 2 years because the goats nip off the buds of new growth, thus starving the plant. It usually requires 2 years to starve hardy plants, but some of the less hardy ones will succumb the first year. Another method is to mix goats with cattle for 6–10 years. The goats tend to eat leaves of brushy plants while the cattle consume the grasses.

THE MEAT GOAT

Meat goats are found mainly in the southwestern and western U.S. states, though they are raised primarily in Africa and the Middle East, where their main uses are for meat and skins. In Africa there has been a preference for a small, well-muscled, agile goat—the Pygmy. These goats can obtain most of their feed from brushy plants and low trees. As many of the areas away from cities and towns are lacking in refrigeration, small goats that are slaughtered can be consumed by the family before the meat spoils.

Goats of any kind are usually run with sheep outside of the United States; this practice may be advantageous in the United States as well. Goats normally eat more browse and forbs than sheep.

Rams should never be run with doe goats, and buck goats should never be run with ewes. These animals will mate when the females come in heat (estrus); if they conceive, the pregnancy will usually terminate at about 3 or 4 months. There are reports of rare cases of live sheep × goat crosses delivered alive at term.

THE PYGMY GOAT

Pygmy goats were developed in Africa. Those brought to the United States came from the Cameroon area to the Caribbean and were then imported to the United States. Early Pygmy goats were brought to the United States as exotic zoo animals. Zoos sold Pygmy animals not

FIGURE 33.11.
An Agouti Pygmy goat can be a useful 4-H project animal. Courtesy of Deana Mobley.

only to other zoos but also to research scientists. A colony of Pygmy goats was established in Oregon and several other research herds were established, including herds at the University of California. Because Pygmies are small in size, the cost of keeping them is minimal. Pygmy goats are also raised for meat and milk.

Breeders of Pygmy goats enjoy showing their goats just like dairy goat and Angora goat breeders. There are over 50 Pygmy goat shows held annually, in which a total of several hundred goats are shown.

Pygmy goats vary in color from black to white with a dorsal stripe down the back and dark on the legs. On all Pygmy goats except the black ones, the muzzle, forehead, eyes, and ears are accented in tones lighter than the dark portion of the body.

The Pygmy goat is also becoming popular as an animal for 4-H projects (Fig. 33.11). The goats are small and do not require a lot of space or feed. All goats are very friendly animals, which makes them ideal for young people to handle; they are also easily trained.

Refer to Chapter 36 for a more detailed discussion of management principles and their applications.

SELECTED REFERENCES

Publications

Dairy Goat J. (monthly). Schroeder Publications, 6041 Monona Dr., Monona, WI 53716–3989.

Ensminger, M. E., and Parker, R. O. 1986. *Sheep and Goat Science.* Danville, IL: Interstate Printers.

FAO Production Yearbook, 1989. Rome, Italy: Food and Agriculture Organizations of the United Nations.

Gall, C. 1981. *Dairy Goats.* London: Academic Press.

Haenlein, G. F. W. 1981. Dairy goat industry in the United States. *J. Dairy Sci.* 64:1288–1304.

———, and Ace, D. L. (eds.). 1984. *Extension Goat Handbook.* Washington, D.C.: USDA Extension Service.

Hale, L., and Kritzman, E. 1982. *Pygmy Goats: The Best of Memo.* Vashon Island, WA: Island Industries, Inc.; National Pygmy Goat Association.

International symposium: Dairy goats. 1980. *J. Dairy Sci.* 63:1591–1781.

Maclean, J. T. 1987. *Goat Husbandry in the U.S., 1979–1986.* Beltsville, MD: USDA.

National Research Council. 1981. *Nutrient Requirements of Goats.* Washington, D.C.: National Academy Press.

Neimann–Sorenson, A. and Tube, D. E. (eds-in-chief). World Animal Science, Series C: Production System Approach. 1982. I. E. Coop (ed.). *Sheep and Goat Production.* New York: Elsevier.

Proceedings of the Third International Conference on Goat Production and Diseases. 1982. Scottsdale, AZ: Dairy Goat Publishing Co.

Visuals

Dairy Goat Kit: *Dairy Goat Management;* and *Fitting and Showing Dairy Goats* (sound filmstrips). Vocational Education Productions, California Polytechnic State University, San Luis Obispo, CA 93407.

Introduction to Dairy Goat Production, Facilities, Breeding/Prekidding Management, Kidding Management; Care of Kids: Birth to Weaning; Maintaining Herd Health/Milking Management; Marketing/Obtaining Financing; and *Dual-Purposes Goat* (videotapes). Agricultural Products and Services, 2001 Killebrew Dr., Suite 333, Bloomington, MN 55420.

Livestock Judging (slide set no. 7; major breeds of goats illustrated). Vocational Education Productions, California Polytechnic State University, San Luis Obispo, CA 93407.

CHAPTER 34

Animal Behavior

Ethology is the scientific study of an animal's behavior in response to its environment. Only within the past 30 years has animal behavior been accepted as a bona fide discipline within colleges of agriculture and veterinary medicine. A knowledge of animal behavior is essential to understanding the whole animal and its ability to adapt to various management systems imposed by livestock and poultry producers. For example, the value of horses can be increased when horse trainers apply their knowledge of horse behavior.

Animal behavior is a complex process involving the interaction of inherited abilities and environmental experiences to which the animal is subjected. Behavioral changes enable animals to adjust to some external or internal change of conditions, improve their chances of survival, and serve humankind. Also, producers who understand patterns of behavior can manage and train animals more effectively and efficiently.

Instinct (reflexes and responses) is what the animal has at birth. All mammals, at birth, have the instinct to nurse even though they must first learn the location of the teat. Shortly after hatching, chicks begin pecking to obtain feed.

Habituation is learning to respond without thinking. Response to a certain stimulus is established as a result of habituation. **Conditioning** is learning to respond in a particular way to a stimulus as a result of **reinforcement** when the proper response is made. Reinforcement is a reward for making the proper response. Trial and error is the performance of different responses to a stimulus until the correct response is performed, at which time the animal receives a reward. For example, newborn mammals soon become hungry and want to nurse. They search for some place to nurse on any part of the mother's body until they find the teat. This is trial and error until the teat is located; then, when the young nurses, it receives milk as its reward. Soon they learn where the teat is located and find it without having to go through trial and error. Thus, the young become conditioned in nursing behavior through reinforcement.

Reasoning is the ability to respond correctly to a stimulus the first time that a new situation is presented. **Intelligence** is the ability to learn to adjust successfully to certain situations. Both short-term and long-term memory are part of intelligence.

MAJOR TYPES OF ANIMAL BEHAVIOR

Farm animals exhibit several major types of behavior: (1) sexual, (2) maternal, (3) communicative, (4) social, (5) feeding, (6) eliminative, (7) shelter-seeking, (8) investigative, (9) allelomimetic, and (10) maladaptive. Some of these types of behavior are interrelated, though they are discussed separately in this chapter. It is not the intent here to describe, in detail, the different behavior patterns for all farm animals. The major focus is to identify the behavioral activities that most significantly affect animal well-being, productivity, and profitability. By understanding animal behavior, producers can plan and implement more effective management systems for their animals.

SEXUAL BEHAVIOR

Observations on sexual behavior of female farm animals are useful in implementing breeding programs. Cows that are in heat, for example, allow themselves to be mounted by others. Producers observe this condition of "standing heat" or estrus to identify those cows to be **hand-mated** or bred artificially. Ewes in heat are not mounted by other ewes, but vasectomized rams can identify them.

Males and females of certain species produce **pheromones,** chemical substances that attract the opposite sex. Cows, ewes, and mares may have pheromones present in vaginal secretions and in their urine when they are in heat. Bulls, rams, and stallions will smell the vagina and the urine using a nasal organ that can detect pheromones. A common behavioral response in this process is called **flehmen,** during which the male animal lifts its head and curls its upper lip.

It appears that in a sexually active group of cows, the bull is attracted to a cow in heat most often by visual means (observing cow-to-cow mounting) rather than by olfactory clues. The bull follows a cow that is coming into heat, smells and licks her external genitalia, and puts his chin on her rump. When the cow is in standing heat, she stands still when the bull chins her rump. When she reaches full heat, she allows the bull to mount.

When females are sexually receptive, they usually seek out a male if mating has not previously occurred. Females are receptive for varying lengths of time; cows are usually in heat for approximately 12 hours, whereas mares show heat for 5 – 7 days with ovulation occurring during the last 24 hours of estrus.

Vigorous bulls breed females several times a day. If more than one cow is in heat at the same time, bulls tend to mate with one cow once or a few times and then go to others. Other bulls may become attached to one female and ignore the others that are also in heat.

The ram chases a ewe that is coming into heat. The ram champs and licks, puts his head on the side of the ewe, and strikes with his foot. When the ewe reaches standing heat, she stands when approached by the ram.

The buck goat snorts when he detects a doe in heat. The doe shows unrest and may be fought by other does. Mating in goats is similar to that in sheep.

The boar does not seem to detect a sow that is in heat by smelling or seeing. If introduced into a group of sows, a boar chases any sow in the group. The sow that is in heat seeks out the boar for mating, and when the boar is located she stands still and flicks her ears. Boars produce pheromones in the saliva and preputial pouch, which attracts sows and gilts in estrus to the boars. Ejaculation requires several minutes for boars in contrast to an instantaneous ejaculation by rams and bulls.

The sequence of events in estrus detection in horses appears to be similar to swine (previously described). The stallion approaches a mare from the front and a mare not in heat runs and kicks at the stallion. When the mare is in standing heat she stands, squats somewhat, and urinates as he approaches. Her vulva exhibits **winking** (opens and closes) when she is in heat.

In chickens and turkeys, a courtship sequence between the male and female usually takes place. If either individual does not respond to the other's previous signal, the courtship does not proceed further. After the courtship has developed properly, some females run from the rooster, which chases them until they stop and squat for mating. The male chicken or turkey stands on a squatting female and ejaculates semen as his rear descends toward the female's cloaca. Semen is ejaculated at the cloaca and the female draws it into her reproductive tract while the male is mounting her.

Male chickens and turkeys show a preference for certain females and may even refuse to mate with other females. Likewise, female chickens and turkeys may refuse to mate with certain males. This is a serious problem when pen matings of one male and 10–15 females are practiced. The eggs of some females may be infertile. This preferential mating is a greater problem in chickens, as AI is the common breeding practice in turkeys.

Little relationship appears to exist between sex drive and fertility in male farm animals. In fact, some males that show extreme sex drive have reduced fertility because of frequent ejaculations that result in semen with reduced sperm numbers.

Research studies show that many individual bulls have sufficient sex drive and mating ability to fertilize more females than are commonly allotted to them. An excessive number of males, however, are used in multiple-sire herds to offset the few that are poor breeders and to cover for the social dominance that exists among several bulls running with the same herd of cows. The bull may guard a female that he has determined is approaching estrus. His success in guarding the female or actually mating with her is dependent on his rank of dominance in a multiple-sire herd. If low fertility exists in the dominant bull or bulls, then calf crop percentages will be seriously affected even in multiple-sire herds.

Tests have been developed to measure libido and mating ability differences in young bulls. While behavioral differences are evident between different bulls, these tests, based on pregnancy rates, have not proven accurate for use by the beef industry.

Bulls being raised with other bulls commonly mount one another, have a penal erection, and occasionally ejaculate. Individual bulls can be observed arching their back, thrusting their penis toward their front legs, and ejaculating.

Bulls can be easily trained to mount objects that provide the stimulus for them to experience ejaculation. AI studs commonly use restrained steers for collection of semen. Bulls soon respond to the artificial vagina, when mounting steers, which provides them with a sensual reward.

Mating behavior has an apparent genetic base, as there is evidence of more frequent mountings in hybrid or crossbred animals.

Some profound behavior patterns are associated with sex of the animal and changes resulting from castration. This verifies the importance of hormonal-directed expression of behavior.

Intact males have more aggressive behavior, whereas castrates are more docile after losing their source of male hormone.

MATERNAL BEHAVIOR

There is evidence that more cows calve during periods of darkness than during daylight hours. The calving pattern, however, can be changed by when cows are fed. Cows that are fed during late evening have a higher percentage of their calves during daylight hours.

When the young of cattle, sheep, goats, and horses are born, the mothers clean the young by licking them. This stimulates blood circulation and encourages the young to stand and to nurse. Sows do not clean their newborn but encourage them to nurse by lying down and moving their feet as the young approach the udder region. They thus help the young to the teats.

Most animal mothers tend to fight intruders, especially if the young squeal or bawl. Often cows, sows, and mares become aggressive in protecting their young shortly after parturition. Serious injury can occur to producers who do not use caution with these animals.

Strong attachments exist between mother and newborn young, particularly between ewe and lamb and cow and calf. Beef cows diminish their output of milk about 100–120 days after birth of young, and ewes do the same after 60–75 days. This reduction in milk forces the young to search for forage, the consumption of which stimulates rumen development. It is at this time that care-giving by the mother declines.

If young pigs have a high-energy feed available at all times, they nurse less frequently. Without a strong stimulus of nursing, sows reduce their output of milk. Some sows may wean their pigs early and show little concern for them a few days after they are weaned. Pigs are usually weaned by producers at 21–35 days of age.

COMMUNICATION BEHAVIOR

Communication exists when some type of information is exchanged between individual animals. This may occur with the transfer of information through any of the senses.

A distress call, involving a different type of sound, occurs from either the female or her young when they become separated (Fig. 34.1). Young animals cry for help when disturbed or distressed. Lambs bleat, calves bawl, pigs squeal, and chicks chirp. Even adult animals call for help when under stress. The female and her offspring may recognize each other's vocal sound; however, it appears that the most effective way the dam recognizes her offspring is by smell. The young usually nurses with its rear end toward the female's head. This allows a dam to smell her offspring and decide to accept or reject it. A rejected young animal is usually bunted with the head of the dam and kicked with the rear legs when it attempts to nurse. The young animals are less discriminate in their nursing behavior than are their dams.

Females more easily adopt other young through transfer of the odor of one young animal to another. Cows have fostered several calves if their own calves are removed at birth, and the foster calves are smeared with amniotic fluid previously collected from the second "water bag."

Many farm animals learn to respond to the vocal calls or whistles of the producer who wants the animals to come to feed. The animals soon learn that the stimulus of the sound is related to being fed.

FIGURE 34.1.
A calf separated from its dam has a distinct bawl, which communicates distress or dissatisfaction. Courtesy of the American Hereford Association.

The bull vocally communicates his aggressive behavior to other bulls and intruders into his area through a deep bellow. This bellow and aggressive behavior is under the control of the male hormone (testosterone), as the castrated male seldom exhibits similar behavior.

The bull also issues calls to cows and heifers, especially when he is separated from, but still within sight of, them.

Cattle are especially perceptive in their sight, as they have 310–360-degree vision. This affects their behavior in many ways, for example, when they are approached from different angles and when they are handled through various types of facilities.

SOCIAL BEHAVIOR

Social behavior includes behavior activities of fight and flight and those of aggressive and passive behavior when an animal is in contact (physically) with another animal or with livestock and poultry producers.

Interaction with Other Animals

Unless castrated when young, the males of all farm animals fight when they meet other unfamiliar males of the same species. This behavior has great practical implications for management of farm animals. Male farm animals are often run singly with a group of females in breeding season, but it is often necessary to keep males together in a group at times other than the breeding season. The typical producer simply cannot afford to provide a separate lot for each male.

Bulls and other males may exert prolonged physical activity when fighting and thus generate much heat. Therefore, bulls and other potential fighting males should be put together either early in the morning or late in the evening when the environmental temperature is lower than at midday. Often fighting can be reduced when male animals are mixed and put into a new environment.

If a mature bull is put with young bulls, fighting usually occurs until the younger ones concede to the mature one. After the fighting is over, bulls may start mounting one another (one form of homosexuality).

Cows, sows, and mares usually develop a peck order but fight less intensely than males. Sows that are strangers to each other sometimes fight. Ewes seldom, if ever, fight, so ewes that are strangers can be grouped together without harm.

Some cows withdraw from the group to find a secluded spot just before calving. Almost all animals withdraw from the group if they are sick.

Early and continuous association of calves is associated with greater social tolerance, delayed onset of aggressive behavior, and relatively slow formation of social hierarchies.

Status and social rank typically exist in a herd of cows, with certain individuals dominating the other submissive ones. The presence or absence of horns are important in determining social rank, especially when strange cows are mixed together. Also, horned cows usually outrank polled or dehorned cows where close contact is encountered, such as at feedbunks or on the feed ground.

Large differences in age, size, strength, genetic background, and previous experience have powerful effects in determining social rank. Once the rank is established in a herd, it tends to be consistent from one year to the next. There is evidence that genetic differences exist for social rank.

Animals fed together consume more feed than when they are fed individually. This competitive environment evidently is a stimulus for greater feed consumption. Dairy calves, separated from their dams at birth, appear to gain equally well whether fed milk in a group or kept separate. There is, however, evidence that they learn to eat grain earlier when group fed compared with being individually fed. Cattle individually fed in metabolism stalls consume only 50%–60% the amount of feed they will eat if the animals are group fed.

When fed in a group of older cows, 2-year-old heifers have difficulty getting their share of supplemental feed (Table 34.1). Two-year-old heifers and 3-year-old cows can be fed together without any significant age effect in competition for supplemental feed. These behavior differences no doubt explain some of the nutrition, weight gains, and postpartum internal relationships that are age related when cows of all ages compete for the same supplemental feed.

Dominant cows raised in a confinement operation usually consume more feed and wean heavier calves. More submissive cows wean lighter calves (25%), and fewer of them are pregnant compared with more aggressive cows. Figure 34.2 shows a 1-hour feeding pattern for two cows of different social rankings.

TABLE 34.1. Weight Changes of 2-Year-Old Heifers Fed Separately As a Group or Together with Older Cows

Treatment	Weight Change
Pastured and fed with older cows	25-lb loss
Pastured and fed separately	46-lb gain

Source: Wagnon; 1965.

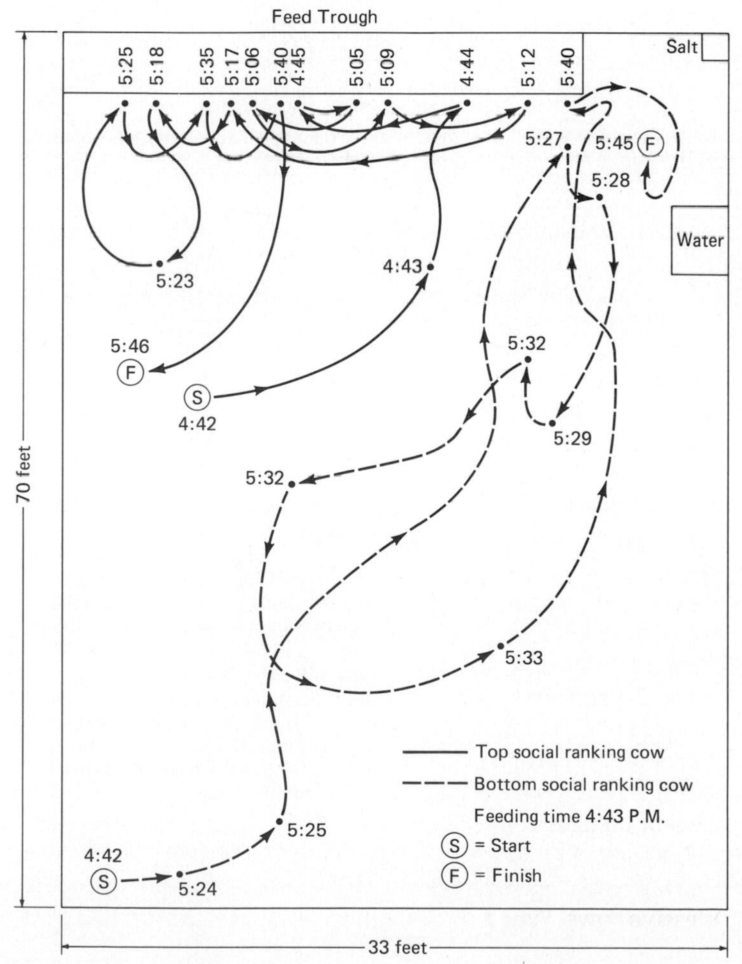

FIGURE 34.2.
One-hour feeding pattern for two cows of different social rankings. Adapted from Schake and Riggs, 1972.

Interactions with Humans

Producers rank the disposition or temperament of animals from docile to wild or "high-strung." This evaluation is usually made when the animals are being handled through various types of corrals, pens, chutes, and other working facilities. The typical behavior exhibited by animals with poor dispositions is one of fear or of aggressive fighting or kicking.

There is evidence that farm animals develop good or poor dispositions from the way they have been treated or handled, though there is evidence that disposition has an inherited basis as well. A few heritability estimates for disposition are in the medium-to-high category, indicating the trait would respond to selection. Some producers cull or eliminate animals with poor dispositions from their herds and flocks because of the potential for personal injury and economic loss (broken fences and facilities) as well as to reduce the excitability of other animals.

Behavior During Handling and Restraint

Most animals are handled and restrained several times during their lifetime. Ease of handling depends largely on the animals' temperament, size, and previous experience and the design of the handling facilities. Understanding animal behavior can assist in preventing injury, undue stress, and physical exertion for both animals and producers. An example is knowing how to approach animals so they will respond to how the producer prefers the animals to move (Fig. 34.3). Most animals have a flight zone. When a person is outside this zone, the animal usually exhibits an inquisitive behavior. When a person moves inside the flight zone, the animal usually moves away.

Blood odor appears to be offensive to some animals; therefore, the reduction or elimination of such odors may encourage animals to move through handling facilities with greater ease. Animals are easily disturbed by loud or unusual noises such as motors, pumps, and compressed air.

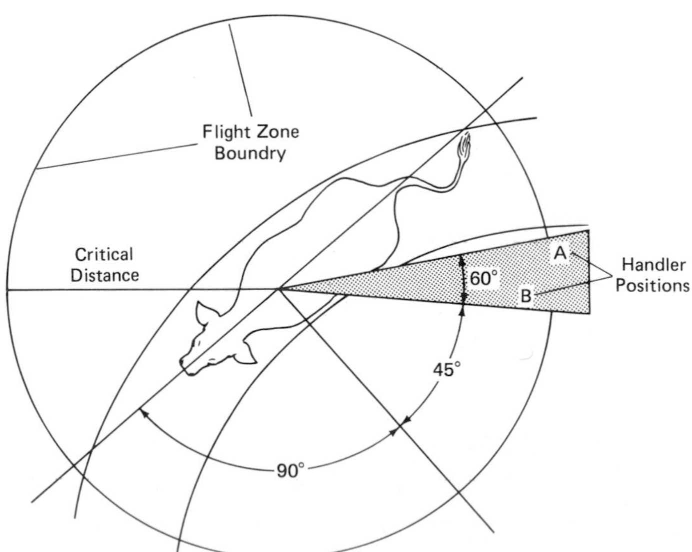

FIGURE 34.3.
Handler positions for moving cattle. Positions A and B are the best places for the handler to stand. The flight zone is penetrated to cause the animal to move forward. Retreating outside the flight zone causes the animal to stop moving. Handlers should avoid standing directly behind the animal because they will be in the animal's blind spot. If the handler gets in front of the line extending from the animal's shoulder, the animal will back up. The solid curved lines indicate the location of the curved, single-file chute. Courtesy of Temple Grandin.

With their 310–360-degree vision, cattle are sensitive to shadows and unusual movements observed at the end of the chute or outside the chutes (Fig. 34.4). For these reasons, cattle will move with more ease through curved chutes with solid sides (Fig. 34.5).

Round pens, having an absence of square corners, handle cattle that are more excitable with less injury occurring to them.

Some breeders claim that AI facilities should permit beef cows to be handled quietly and carefully, and that using facilities where cows have previously felt pain should be avoided. They also state that pregnancy rates will thereby increase. This may sound logical, but research has not substantiated these claims.

FEEDING BEHAVIOR

Ingestive behavior is exhibited by farm animals when they eat and drink. Rather than initially chewing their feed thoroughly, ruminants swallow it as soon as it is well lubricated with saliva. After the animals have consumed a certain amount, they ruminate (regurgitate the feed for chewing). Cattle graze for 4–9 hours/day and sheep and goats graze for 9–11 hours/day.

FIGURE 34.4.
Shadows that fall across a chute can disrupt the handling of animals. The lead animal often balks and refuses to cross the shadows. Courtesy of Temple Grandin.

FIGURE 34.5.
Animals move more easily through curved chutes with solid sides. Courtesy of Temple Grandin.

Grazing is usually done in periods, followed by rest and **rumination.** Sheep rest and ruminate more frequently when grazing than do cattle—cattle ruminate 4–9 hours/day; sheep, 7–10 hours/day. A cow may regurgitate and chew between 300 and 400 **boluses** of feed per day; sheep between 400 and 600 boluses per day.

Under range conditions, cattle usually do not go more than 3 miles away from water, whereas sheep may travel as much as 8 miles a day. When cattle and sheep are on a large range, they tend to overgraze near the water area and to avoid grazing in areas far removed from water. Development of water areas, fencing, placing of salt away from water, and herding the animals are management practices intended to assure a more uniform utilization of the range forage.

Grazing Behavior

Cattle, horses, and sheep have palatability preferences for certain plants and many have difficulty changing from one type or types of plants to other types. Most animals prefer to graze lower areas, especially if they are near water. These grazing behaviors tend to cause overgrazing in certain areas of the pasture and to reduce weight gains.

Age of cow and weather affect the typical behavior of cows grazing native range during the winter (Table 34.2). At the Range Research Station in Miles City, Montana, cows grazed less as temperatures dropped below 20°F, and at a −30°F, 3-year-olds grazed approximately 2 hours less than 6-year-olds. Also, with colder temperatures, cows wait longer before starting to graze in the morning. At 30°F, cows started grazing between 6:30 and 7:00 A.M., but at −30°F, they waited until about 10 A.M. to begin grazing.

TABLE 34.2. Activities of Cows Grazing on Winter Range

Activity	Hours
Grazing	9.45
Ruminating	
Standing	0.63
Lying	8.30
Idle	
Standing	1.11
Lying	3.93
Traveling	0.58
Total	24.00

Eliminative Behavior

Cattle, sheep, horses, goats, and chickens void their feces and urine indiscriminately. Hogs, by contrast, defecate in definite areas of the pasture or pen. Ease of cleaning swine pens can be planned by knowing defecation patterns of the pigs.

Cattle, sheep, goats, and swine usually defecate while standing or walking. All these animals urinate while standing, but not usually when walking. Cattle defecate 12–18 times a day; horses, 5–12 times. Cattle and horses urinate 7–11 times per day. Animals on lush pasture drink less water than when they consume dry feeds; therefore, the amount of urine voided may not differ greatly under these two types of feed conditions.

All farm animals urinate and defecate more frequently and void more excreta than normal when stressed or excited. They often lose a minimum of 3% of their liveweight when transported to and from marketing points. Much of the **shrink** in transit occurs in the first hour, so considerable weight loss occurs even when animals are transported only short distances. Weight loss can be reduced by handling animals carefully and quietly, and by avoiding any excessive stress or excitement of the animals.

SHELTER-SEEKING BEHAVIOR

Animal species vary greatly in the degree to which they seek shelter. Cattle and sheep seek a shady area for rest and rumination if the weather is hot, and pigs try to find a wet area. When the weather is cold, pigs crowd against one another when they are lying down to keep each other warm. In snow and cold winds, animals often crowd together. In extreme situations, they pile up to the extent that some of them smother. Unless the weather is cold and windy, cattle and horses often seek the shelter of trees when it is raining. This may be hazardous where strong electrical storms occur because animals under a tree are more likely to be killed by lightning than those in the open.

INVESTIGATIVE BEHAVIOR

Pigs, horses, and dairy goats are highly curious, investigating any strange object. They usually approach carefully and slowly, sniffing and looking as they approach. Cattle also do a certain amount of investigating (Fig. 34.6). Sheep are less curious and more timid than some other farm animals. They may notice a strange object, become excited, and run away from it.

ALLELOMIMETIC BEHAVIOR

Animals of a species tend to do the same thing at the same time. Cattle and sheep tend to graze at the same time and rest and ruminate at the same time. Range cattle gather at the watering place at about the same time each day because one follows another. This behavior is of practical importance because the producer can then observe the herd or flock with little difficulty, notice anything that is wrong with a particular animal, and have that animal brought in for treatment. If one is artificially inseminating beef cattle, the best time to locate range cows in heat is when they gather at the watering place. This type of behavior is useful in driving groups of animals from one place to another.

MALADAPTIVE OR ABNORMAL BEHAVIOR

Animals that cannot adapt to their environment may exhibit inappropriate or unusual behavior.

Some animals under extensive management systems, such as poultry and swine, are often kept in continuous housing to reduce costs of land and facilities. Frequently, both chickens and swine resort to cannibalism, which may lead to death, if preventive measures are not taken. Some swine producers remove the tails of baby pigs to prevent tail chewing. Tail chewing can cause bleeding, and whenever bleeding occurs, the pigs are likely to become cannibalistic.

Some male uncastrated animals raised with other males masturbate and demonstrate homosexuality. In the latter situation, males mount other males, attempting to breed them. Some

FIGURE 34.6.
Cattle expressing investigative behavior as a producer is approaching them. Courtesy of R. W. Henderson.

of the more submissive males may have to be physically separated from the more aggressive males to prevent injury or death.

The **buller-steer syndrome** is exhibited in steers that have been castrated before puberty. This demonstrates a masculine behavior other than testosterone origin. Certain steers (bullers) are more sexually attractive for other steers to mount. As one steer mounts a buller, other steers are attracted to do the same. Thus, the activity associated with the buller-steer syndrome can cause physical injury, a reduction in feedlot gains, and additional labor and equipment expense as bullers are usually sorted into separate feedlot pens. Some feedlots experience 1%–3% of their steers as bullers.

Growth implants and reduced pen space have been cited as reasons for an increased incidence of buller-steers. Some behaviorists cite evidence of similar homosexual behavior of males in free-ranging natural environments.

SELECTED REFERENCES

Publications

Arave, C. W., and Albright, J. L. 1981. Cattle behavior. *J. Dairy Sci.* 64:1318.

Craig, J. V. 1981. *Domestic Animal Behavior.* Englewood Cliffs, NJ: Prentice-Hall.

Crieger, S. E. 1989. *Farm Animal Ethology: A Guide to Sources.* North Yort, Ontario, Canada: Captus University Publications.

Curtis, S. E., and Houpt, K. A. 1983. Animal ethology: Its emergence in animal science. *J. Anim. Sci.* 57(Suppl.2):234.

Fraser, A. F. (ed.). 1985. *Ethology of Farm Animals. A Comprehensive Study of the Behavioral Features of Common Farm Animals.* New York: Elsevier.

Grandin, T. "Handling facility" fitness. *Managing in Changing Times.* IMC Conference Proceedings, Sept. 16, 1986. Saskatoon, Saskatchewan, Canada.

Hart, B. L. 1985. *The Behavior of Domestic Animals.* New York: W. H. Freeman.

Houpt, K. A. 1985. Behavioral problems in horses. *American Association of Equine Practitioners* 31:113.

——— and Wolski, T. R. 1982. *Domestic Animal Behavior for Veterinarians and Animal Scientists.* Ames, IA: Iowa State University Press.

Kilgour, R., and Dalton, C. 1984. *Livestock Behavior: A Practical Guide.* Boulder, CO: Westview Press.

Monahan, P. and Wood-Gush, D. 1990. *Managing the Behavior of Animals.* New York: Chapman and Hall.

Signoret, J. P. (ed.). 1982. *Welfare and Husbandry of Calves.* Boston: Martinus Nijhoff Publishers.

Visuals

Safety in Handling Livestock (sound filmstrip). Vocational Education Productions. California Polytechnic State University, San Luis Obispo, CA 93407.

CHAPTER 35

Animal Rights and Animal Welfare

All students, especially those in agriculture and veterinary medicine, should understand the issues surrounding animal rights and animal welfare today. Through an understanding of the concerns and challenges of the animal rights movement and livestock producers, people can work together to solve their differences.

While the terms ***animal rights*** and ***animal welfare*** may seem to mean the same thing—and for many people they do—most of those who support the animal welfare movement distinguish themselves from animal rightists because they do not accept many animal rights issues. At the risk of some overlap, then, animal rights and animal welfare are discussed here separately. Also, the discussion focuses primarily on the types of farm animals identified in earlier chapters.

ANIMAL RIGHTS

Should animals have the same basic rights granted human beings? Animal rights activists argue that humans exert excess control over animals and thereby deprive animals of social interaction. Livestock and poultry producers counter that their treatment of animals is humane, otherwise the animals would not be productive. The controversy over animal rights has at times been heated. While several animal rights groups have resorted to extreme measures (e.g., burning livestock facilities, attempted bombings, breaking into animal research facilities) to emphasize their belief in animal liberation, thousands of other animal rightists have marched to the nation's capitol in support of their cause (Fig. 35.1). Activists achieve public awareness through mass demonstrations and the media.

Peter Singer, professor of philosophy and director of the Centre for Human Bioethics at Monash University in Australia, is considered the founder of the animal rights movement. He first promoted many of his animal rights theories while a visiting professor at New York University in 1973–74.

Singer's argument focuses on the common experience of pain among all animals—both human and nonhuman—and, more specifically, on the right of all nonhuman animals to live free of unnecessary pain, especially those used in laboratory experiments or on farms. He uses

FIGURE 35.1.
Animal rights groups protest in Washington, D.C., and in other areas where they can gather support. Courtesy of William E. Carnahan and BEEF.

the term *speciesism,* which means discrimination against a species, especially against animals. According to Singer, any animal, even a rat that eats livestock feed, should have the same basic rights granted human beings. Singer also argues that people should follow a vegetarian diet.

The vegetarian influence appears to be a significant factor in the animal rights movement. According to Dr. Michael W. Fox (1986), vice president of the Humane Society of the United States, an animal rights organization,

> It may seem offensive to vegetarians that I endorse the concept of treating farm animals humanely because it would seem that I support the livestock and poultry industries. Actually, I don't. . . . [V]egetarianism is . . . an enlightened decision, if not a survival imperative in the long term, and producing and consuming less farm-animal produce, especially meat, are essential steps toward the overall restoration of our culture, agriculture, and environment. (pp. 172,176)

The participants in the controversy include vegetarians, livestock producers, philosophers, lawyers, and others who have taken a stand on either side of the debate. The primary concerns of the animal rights movement focus on what it calls "factory farming"—intensive animal production practices such as the use of battery-caged systems for laying hens and of single stalls for growing veal calves, continuous tethering (tying) of sows in confinement, and animal research projects that subject the animals to confinement and painful experiences in the laboratory (Fig. 35.2).

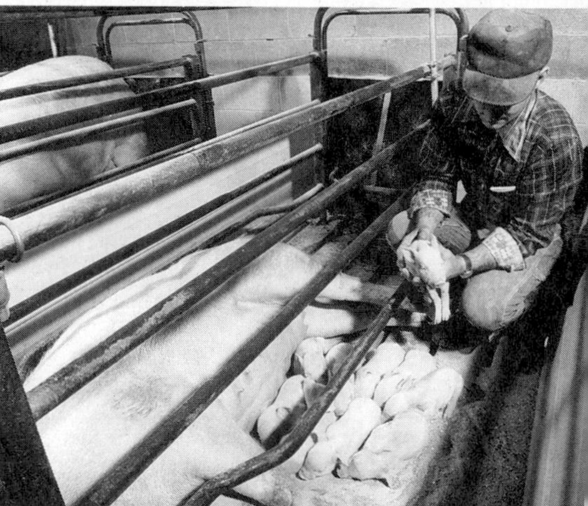

FIGURE 35.2.
Animal rights groups target the confinement practices of the livestock and poultry industries. Producers are concerned with comfort and well-being of their animals. Courtesy of John Colwell and Larry LeFever from Grant Heilman.

In one sense, the domestication of animals deprived them of some of the opportunities they had prior to domestication. However, it has also provided them with an improved year-round feed supply, a decreased incidence of disease, and a longer, more productive life. Further, intensive-management production systems typically control environmental factors like temperature, humidity, and the supply of feed and water to the animals' advantage. Many of these systems also help to prevent the animal suffering and death that are more likely to occur in less intensively managed environments. Animals are observed closely and treated for health problems sooner.

However, some intensive-management systems may cause stress for the animals, resulting in behavioral problems and reduced longevity. Generally, these intensive operations are driven by economic factors—by a consuming public and a government that demands high-quality foods at the lowest possible cost. Livestock producers are faced with a dilemma: If they return to less efficient production methods, they cannot pass on the higher production costs to the consumer. And if supply becomes low because of decreased production, prices may increase and profitability may decrease. Economics, in large part, determines the lifestyles of both humans and farm animals in the U.S. and elsewhere.

During 1900–1990, the intensive farming of animals (and crops) allowed the agricultural producer to feed many more people—an increase of 80 people per producer. This increased efficiency, in turn, allowed other people to move from rural to urban areas in order to produce other goods and services for the benefit of all.

Opponents of the animal rights movement question whether people today have become conditioned into thinking that animals are more human than they really are. They suggest that animated motion pictures and children's books, which depict animals as able to think, feel, and communicate as humans, have been a contributing factor. They claim, for example, that Sweden's enactment in 1988 of a stringent animal rights law, which freed animals from intensive animal production practices, was tied to a childrens' book author, Astrid Lindgren. Opponents of animal rights issues credit Lindgren with making the treatment of farm animals a lively political issue.

Similarly, in November 1988, a ballot question would have put Massachusetts agriculture into the control of animal rights groups. Milk-fed veal production would have been eliminated and restrictive production practices would have been established. Initial polling suggested that 75% of the voters favored the question. Ultimately, though, farmers and livestock producers made their views known and the question was defeated, 79% to 21%.

ANIMAL WELFARE

Livestock producers have been concerned with the welfare of their animals for centuries. Animals were domesticated to give nomadic people a consistent supply of food and companionship. Draft animals were domesticated for transportation and power. People soon learned that the productive response of animals was greater when the animals were given proper care.

Today, the nutrition, health, and management needs of animals are well known and scientifically based. Evidence suggests that many animals in the United States receive a more nutritious diet than some humans consume. The development of the veterinary medical profession has provided on-farm services, health clinics, and hospital care that are in many ways equal to human health-care services.

It is important to note the difference between what an animal may want and what it needs. For example, untended animals may overeat to the point of sickness or death, or they may eat poisonous plants if given the freedom to choose.

Scientific Basis

Some of the issues surrounding animal rights are based on emotion, perception, and personal belief. For example, some people believe that an animal should not suffer or be killed under any circumstances, even if that means limiting human capability. Scientific information is unlikely to resolve differences in personal beliefs, but research can identify measures of well-being for food-producing animals. (It is not the intent of this chapter to make an exhaustive coverage of research data relating to farm animal welfare. Readers should refer to the Selected References at the end of the chapter for more extensive reading on this topic.) Future research will attempt to measure the effect of various management practices on animal behavior, stress, and general well-being.

Some of the items to consider about animal welfare or animal well-being include the following:

1. The principal criteria used by producers and animal scientists as indexes of food-related animal welfare are growth rate, feed efficiency, reproductive efficiency, mortality, and morbidity. These are only indicators of animal well-being, as there is disagreement among producers and scientists on how to define *well-being*. In intensive animal production, the effect of stress on longevity is not critically evaluated because the animals are too rapidly turned over in the production systems.
2. Gonyou (1986) reviewed research data on animal comfort and well-being in terms of physical damage, physiological responses, and behavior. He concluded that:
   a. There is no known universal measure for animal comfort and well-being and one is not likely to be determined.
   b. Because a universal measure of animal comfort and well-being is unknown, it is impossible to make an accurate assessment of different management systems.
   c. A less known but often more productive approach is to identify a problem in a specific system and reduce or eliminate that problem. For example, Tauson (1980) evaluated physical damage in feather density, foot damage, claw length, and throat blisters in hens housed in battery cages. Feather density was improved by using solid partitions between cages; plastic-coated mesh floors reduced foot damage; and horizontal rather than vertical wires in the feeder areas reduced throat blisters. Commercial cages combining these features result in fewer incidences of physical damage to the animals and improved animal comfort and well-being.
   d. Progress is continually being made in each of the preceding areas (a-c). More importantly, the comfort and well-being of animals have been improved in some areas and other attempts are in progress.
3. Recent research attempts to measure stress in animals, including popular measures of stress, alterations in behavior, and changes in hormone secretion, have been unsatisfactory. Some researchers propose that the best indicator of animal stress is the development of some prepathological state; for example, loss of normal reproduction, suppression of the immune systems, or aggressive behavior (Moberg, 1987).

ORGANIZATIONS

Animal Rights Groups

Of the approximately 7,000 animal protectionist groups in the United States, 400 consider themselves animal rights groups. The animal rights groups number both their membership and budgets in the millions and have grown phenomenally during recent years. Many of their members are sophisticated, influential, and well-organized people. In addition, many celebrities support the causes of the animal rights movement. This movement has attracted activists from other areas who know how to protest effectively.

The various animal welfare and animal rights organizations approach the issues differently. Some take the stand that it is acceptable to use animals if they are treated humanely. Others argue for complete animal liberation; they hold that animals should not be exploited in any way for any reason.

As noted earlier in the chapter, intensive animal production is one of the primary concerns of animal rights organizations. Some groups—People for the Ethical Treatment of Animals (PETA), the spokesgroup for the Animal Liberation Front; the Farm Animal Reform Movement (FARM); and Earth First—urge the reduction and eventual elimination of animals for food. These newer groups opt for direct confrontation and the most radical of these, the Animal Liberation Front, has resorted to illegalities, violence, and terrorist activities in pursuit of its goals. Even some of the more traditional organizations are becoming more radical. For example, The Humane Society of the United States denounces bacon and eggs as "the breakfast of cruelty". According to Regan (1985), some of the more extreme animal rights groups argue that "The rights view will not be satisfied with anything less than the total dissolution of the animal industry as we know it today."

Agricultural Groups

The Animal Industry Foundation (AIF) was established to represent the interests of the livestock and poultry industries. AIF focuses its energies and budget on (1) providing the means for livestock producers to educate the public and (2) fostering solid scientific data in the animal rights debate.

The Farm Animal Welfare Coalition (FAWC), an informal organization of agricultural groups, represents animal producers and animal industry organizations on animal welfare issues. FAWC has cooperative projects with AIF such as Media Alert, which makes available transcripts of animal rights activities, consumer articles, and related material. Individual producers are encouraged to avoid direct confrontations with animal rights activists as it gives activists additional media coverage.

State organizations like the Nebraska Food Animal Care Coalition encourage livestock and poultry producers to focus a proactive group effort on food-related animal welfare.

SUMMARY

Table 35.1 summarizes the views of those involved in the animal rights debate on how animals should be perceived and used by humans. The current controversy surrounding animal welfare and animal rights is likely to continue until both sides come to some compromise that includes interests of both humans and animals.

Moderation or balance may be a source of compromise in considering the well-being of animals. Of course, people should not treat animals abusively, nor should their treatment of animals be motivated by profit-oriented interests. People have the responsibility of being caretakers of the earth and its resources, ensuring the welfare of future generations. At the same time, it must be recognized that efficient production of food has made life better for people. High levels of food production could be maintained without overusing the earth's resources if the problems associated with poor land utilization or being abusive to animals were resolved.

The animal rights groups have great strength in membership, organizational structure, and financing. Their combined budgets are in the tens of millions of dollars, whereas the Animal

TABLE 35.1. The Animal Rights Debate: A Summary of the Views

Category/Group	Viewpoint
Animal exploitation	These groups argue that animals exist for human use or even abuse; animals are human property. These groups advocate or conduct activities that are illegal in most states (e.g., dog fighting, cock fighting, live pigeon shooting). Most of their activities involve pain or death of the animals primarily for the entertainment of spectators.
Animal use	These groups believe that animals exist primarily for human use (e.g., livestock production, hunting, fishing, trapping, rodeos, zoos). These organizations have guidelines for the responsible care of the animals. They believe that harvesting of animals for food should be as painless as possible.
Animal control	These organizations enforce the laws, ordinances, and regulations affecting animals. Animals may be supplied for research; surplus animals are destroyed. Many advocate spaying or neutering animals.
Animal welfare	These are national groups, humane societies, and welfare agencies that support the humane treatment of animals. They work within existing laws to accomplish goals. They publicize and document animal abuses to get laws changed. They do not provide animals for research. They require spaying and neutering, and are willing to euthanize surplus pets rather than let them suffer.
Animal rights	These national and local groups believe animals have intrinsic rights that should be guaranteed like human rights. These rights include not being killed, eaten, used for sport or research, or abused in any way. Some hold that pets have the right to breed. Most require spaying or neutering.
Animal liberation	These groups believe that animals should not be forced to work or produce for human benefit. They call for animal liberation.

Source: Adapted from K. B. Morgan, *An Overview of Animal-Related Organizations with Some Guidelines for Recognizing Patterns* (Kansas City, MO: Community Animal Control, 1989.)

Industry Foundation has a budget of a few hundred thousand dollars. Animal scientists and the animal industries have not been as effective in delivering information to Congress, state legislators, and the general public. The animal industries should work harder to make their views known so that people can make more informed decisions about the animal rights debate.

Animal welfare groups, livestock producers, and others concerned about animal welfare should work together to fund and support bonafide research and investigation into those matters of greatest concern. A combination of scientifically based facts and humane treatment of animals may provide the basis for determining the well-being of both humans and animals. It is necessary for the livestock industry and the animal rights groups to cooperate with each other.

SELECTED REFERENCES

Publications

Animal Industry Foundation. 1988. *Animal Agriculture: Myths and Facts.* Arlington, VA: Animal Industry Foundation.

Fox, M. W. 1986. *Agricide.* New York: Schocken Books.

———. 1984. *Farm Animals. Husbandry, Behavior, and Veterinary Practice (Viewpoints of a Critic).* Baltimore: University Park Press.

Gonyou, H. W. 1986. Assessment of comfort and well-being in farm animals. *J. Anim. Sci.* 62:1769.

Hart, B. J. 1985. The behavior of domestic animals. Chap. 10 in *Contributions of Behavioral Science to Issues in Animal Welfare.* New York: W. H. Freeman.

Moberg, G. P. 1987. A model for assessing the impact of behaviorial stress on domestic animals. *J. Anim. Sci.* 65:1228.

Moreng, R. E., and Avens, J. E. 1985. Poultry science and production. Chap. 11 in *Agricultural Animal Welfare.* Reston, VA: Reston Publishing Co.

Regan, T. 1985. *The Case for Animal Rights.* Berkeley: University of California Press.

Rollin, B. E. 1990. Animal welfare, animal rights, and agriculture. *J. Anim. Sci.* 68:3456.

Scientific Aspects of the Welfare of Food Animals. 1981. CAST Report No. 91. Ames, IA: Council for Agri. Sci. and Tech.

Singer, P. 1975. *Animal Liberation.* New York: New York Review of Books.

Smidt, D. 1983. *Indicators Relevant to Farm Animal Welfare.* Boston: Martinus Nijhoft Publishers.

National Cattlemen's Foundation. 1990. *Special Interest Group Profiles.* Washington, D.C.: Hill and Knowlton.

Tannenbaum, J. 1986. Animal rights: Some guideposts for the veterinarian. *JAVMA* 188:1258.

Tauson, R. 1980. Cages: How could they be improved? The Laying Hen and Its Environment. *Curr. Top. Vet. Med. Anim. Sci.* 8:269–99.

Visuals

The Animal Film (videotape; 136 min., pro-animal rights). 1981. The Cinema Guild, 1697 Broadway, New York, NY 10019.

Animal Agriculture: Myths and Facts (videotape, 18 min.). Animal Industry Foundation, P.O. Box 9522, Arlington, VA 22209–0522.

Cattlemen Care About Animal Welfare (1991 videotape; 18 min.). Communication Dept., National Cattlemen's Association, Box 3469, Englewood, CO 80155.

CHAPTER 36

Making Effective Management Decisions

Effective management of livestock operations implies that available resources are used to maximize net profit while the same resources are conserved or improved. Available resources include fixed resources (land, labor, capital, and management) and renewable biological resources (animals and plants). Effective management requires a manager who knows how to make timely decisions based on a careful assessment of management alternatives. Modern technology is providing useful tools to make more rapid and accurate management decisions.

Previous chapters have shown how biological principles determine the efficiency of animal production. It is important to identify other resources that, when combined with the efficiency of animal production, determine the profitability of an operation.

MANAGING FOR LOWER COSTS AND HIGHER RETURNS

Most livestock producers manage their operations with plans to make a profit. Simply stated, the profitability formula is:

$$\begin{matrix}\text{profit}\\ \text{or}\\ <\text{loss}>\end{matrix} = (\text{production} \times \text{price}) - \text{cost}.$$

The formula can be expanded to make management decisions more focused:

$$\begin{matrix}\text{Profit}\\ \text{or}\\ \langle\text{Loss}\rangle\end{matrix} = \left(\text{production} \begin{matrix}\nearrow \text{offspring} \searrow\\ \rightarrow \text{cull females} \rightarrow\\ \searrow \text{cull males} \nearrow\end{matrix} \begin{matrix}\text{pounds per}\\ \text{producing}\\ \text{female}\end{matrix} \times \text{price} \right) - \text{cost}$$

Note: Costs include feed, labor, veterinary, repairs, fuel, interest, other.

Obviously, profit occurs when output value exceeds input cost, and loss occurs when input costs exceed output value. Management decisions should focus on an optimum combination of output value and input costs to maximize profits while maintaining or improving resources.

The primary components of a long-term profitability formula include the following:

Costs—these are identified in earlier chapters (as enterprise budgets) for several species (see Chapter 23 for beef cattle costs, Chapter 25 for dairy cattle, Chapter 27 for swine, and Chapter 29 for sheep).

Production (output)—output is usually pounds and/or numbers sold. The outputs for the various species are shown in the enterprise budgets of the feeding and management chapters.

Price—the amount received per pound, per head, or per dozen (for eggs). Price is influenced primarily by supply and demand.

Maintaining or improving the resources—refers to the land with the forage and crops produced from it. Maximizing short-term profits can easily deplete the land resource by overgrazing, erosion, and the like.

Each component of the profitability formula should initially be evaluated in terms of how it affects output value.

Price has a tremendous effect on output value, though individual producers have little influence over price. Producers accept the price the market offers at the time they sell their products (output). Therefore, the primary management focus for most livestock and poultry producers is to reduce costs while also increasing production and maintaining or improving resources.

The enterprise budget analyses in the species management chapters (Chapters 23, 25, 27, and 29) contain the component parts of input costs. Managers can analyze these costs and make management decisions to reduce them. Throughout all of the chapters in the book, the biological principles affecting production are identified. Producers apply these principles in making cost-effective increases in production.

THE MANAGER

The manager is the individual responsible for planning and decision-making. The management process in simple form is to plan, act, and evaluate. This process is described in more detail in Figure 36.1.

It is imperative that livestock and poultry producers manage their operations as businesses. Current economic pressures associated with keen competition are forcing more producers to manage their operations as business enterprises.

The manager may be an owner-operator with minimum additional labor, or the manager of a more complex organization structure involving several other individuals or businesses (Fig. 36.2). An effective manager, whether involved in a one-person operation or a complex organizational structure, needs to (1) be profit-oriented; (2) identify objectives of the business and establish both short-term and long-range goals to achieve those objectives; (3) keep abreast of the current knowledge related to the operation; (4) know how to use time effectively; (5) attend to the physical, emotional, and financial needs of those employed in the operation; (6) incorporate incentive programs to motivate employees to perform at their full capacity each day; (7) have honest business dealings; (8) effectively communicate responsibilities to all employees and make employees feel they are part of the operation; (9) know what needs to be done and at what time; (10) be a self-starter; (11) set priorities and allocate resources accordingly; (12) remove or alleviate high risks; and (13) set a good example for others to follow.

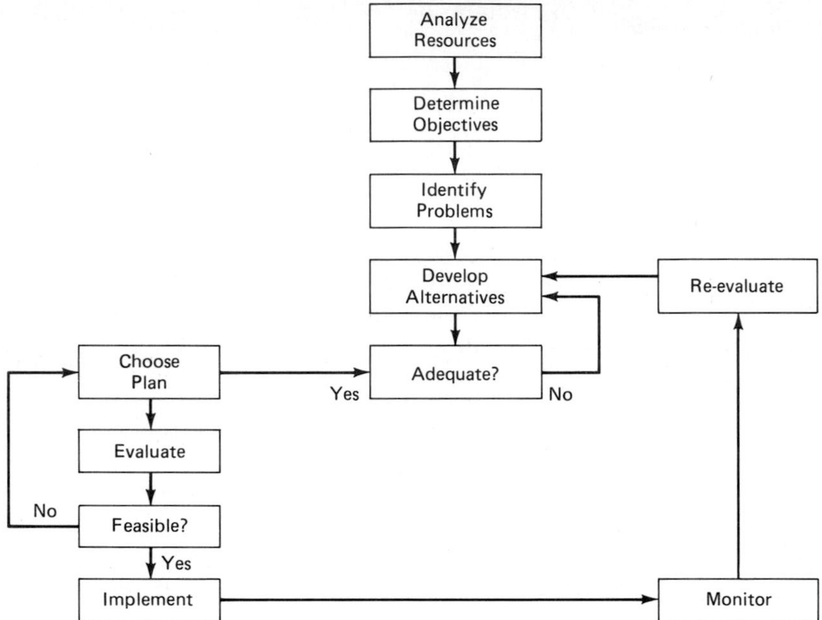

FIGURE 36.1.
Major component parts of the planning process.

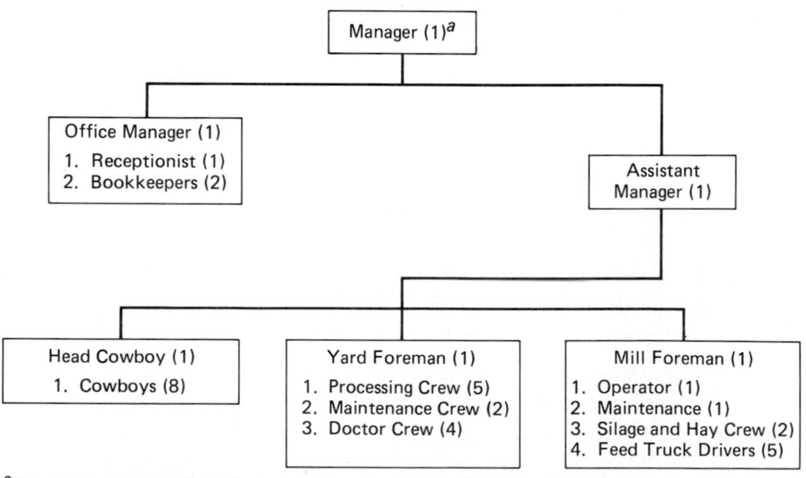

FIGURE 36.2.
Organizational structure of a large commercial feeding operation.

FINANCIAL MANAGEMENT

Costs, returns, and profitability of a livestock operation can only be assessed critically with a meaningful set of records. Table 36.1 identifies the financial records needed by most livestock and poultry operations. Each record is described and its purpose is given. Many producers only keep records sufficient to satisfy the IRS (Fig. 36.3). While this is important, additional records are necessary to make critical management decisions.

TABLE 36.1. Financial Records for Livestock and Poultry Operations

Financial Record	Description and Purpose
Cash transactions	Recording of all cash receipts and expenditures is the simplest yet most time-consuming of all financial records. This provides most of the information needed for filing income-tax returns and in making loan applications.
Balance sheet	Provides a financial picture of the operation at one point in time—usually on the last day of the year. It reflects the net worth of the operation. Net worth = assets (what is owned) − liabilities (what is owed).
Income statement	A moving financial picture that describes most of the changes in net worth from one balance sheet to the next. Net income is calculated by subtracting the expenditures (cash, decrease in inventory and depreciation) from income (cash receipts and increases in inventory).
Cash-flow statement	Shows cash generated and cash needed on a periodic basis (usually monthly) throughout the year. It assesses times when money must be borrowed and times when money is available for additional purchases or investment, or to retire existing debts. A cash-flow budget can be used to plan for the next calendar year. An active cash-flow statement tracks what is actually happening and evaluates the accuracy of the cash-flow budget.
Enterprise budget[a]	Identifies costs and returns associated with a specific product or enterprise. It can aid in making financial decisions by identifying specific problem areas where management changes can be made. Enterprise budgets are also useful where operations have more than one enterprise or where additonal enterprises are being considered. Components include production and marketing assumptions, operating receipts, direct costs, net receipts, and break-even analysis. Estimates of market weight and price can be used in assessing risk in production decisions.
Partial budget	Involves only those income and expense items that would change when implementing a proposed management decision.
Income-tax forms	Form 1040 Schedule F is the primary income-tax form for sole proprietors and individual partners in a partnership. Producers who have completed Schedule F have basically completed an income statement. There are numerous other forms and 1040 schedules (e.g., Asset Sales, Asset Purchases, Self-Empoyment Tax, Farm Rental Income and Expenses, Tax Withholding, Depreciation) that are also completed, depending on individual operations and circumstances.

[a] Enterprise budget analyses are shown for beef cattle, dairy cattle, swine, and sheep in Chapters 23, 25, 27, and 29, respectively.

SCHEDULE F (Form 1040)

Department of the Treasury Internal Revenue Service

Farm Income and Expenses

▶ Attach to Form 1040, Form 1041, or Form 1065.
▶ See Instructions for Schedule F (Form 1040).

OMB No. 1545-0074

1981
16

Name of proprietor(s): JAMES A. BROWN

Social security number: 579 28 6685

Farm name and address ▶ JAMES A. BROWN, RR #1, BOX 25 HOMETOWN YOUR STATE 02115

Employer identification number: 71 9 3 6 7 9 7 4

Part I Farm Income—Cash Method

Do not include sales of livestock held for draft, breeding, sport, or dairy purposes; report these sales on Form 4797.

Sales of Livestock and Other Items You Bought for Resale

a. Description	b. Amount	c. Cost or other basis
1 Livestock ▶ HEIFERS BOUGHT FOR RESALE	6,900	4,000
2 Other items ▶		
3 Totals	6,900	4,000
4 Profit or (loss), subtract line 3, column c, from line 3, column b ▶		2,900

Sales of Livestock and Produce You Raised and Other Farm Income

Kind		Amount
5 Cattle and calves		3,316
6 Sheep		
7 Swine		
8 Poultry		
9 Dairy products		91,454
10 Eggs		
11 Wool		
12 Cotton		
13 Tobacco		
14 Vegetables		
15 Soybeans		
16 Corn		
17 Other grains		
18 Hay and straw		2,266
19 Fruits and nuts		
20 Machine work		1,258
21 a Patronage dividends	272	
b Less: Nonincome items	22	
c Net patronage dividends		250
22 Per-unit retains		
23 Nonpatronage distributions from exempt cooperatives		
24 Agricultural program payments: a Cash		80
b Materials and services		324
25 Commodity credit loans under election (or forfeited)		550
26 Federal gasoline tax credit		100
27 State gasoline tax refund		
28 Crop insurance proceeds		624
29 Other (specify) ▶ FAIR PRIZES		700
30 Add amounts in column for lines 5 through 29		100,922
31 **Gross profits*** (add lines 4 and 30) ▶		103,822

Part II Farm Deductions—Cash and Accrual Method **F**

Do not include personal or living expenses (such as taxes, insurance, repairs, etc., on your home), which do not produce farm income. Reduce the amount of your farm deductions by any reimbursement before entering the deduction below.

Items		Amount
32 a Labor hired		4,438
b Jobs credit		
c WIN credit		
d Total credits		
e Balance (subtract line 32d from line 32a)		4,438
33 Repairs, maintenance		3,236
34 Interest		4,124
35 Rent of farm, pasture		1,200
36 Feed purchased		24,182
37 Seeds, plants purchased		2,286
38 Fertilizers, lime, chemicals		4,498
39 Machine hire		1,200
40 Supplies purchased		3,204
41 Breeding fees		1,078
42 Veterinary fees, medicine		2,020
43 Gasoline, fuel, oil		3,070
44 Storage, warehousing		
45 Taxes		3,050
46 Insurance		2,106
47 Utilities		2,050
48 Freight, trucking		2,056
49 Conservation expenses		1,580
50 Land clearing expenses		
51 Pension and profit-sharing plans		
52 Employee benefit programs other than line 51		
53 Other (specify) ▶		
ADVERTISING		468
FINANCIAL RECORDS		166
FARM ORG. DUES		350
DEATH LOSS - HEIFER BOUGHT FOR RESALE		450
54 Add lines 32e through 53		66,812
55 Depreciation (from Form 4562)		8,483
56 **Total deductions** (add lines 54 and 55) ▶		75,295

57 Net farm profit or (loss) (subtract line 56 from line 31). If a profit, enter on Form 1040, line 18, and on Schedule SE, Part I, line 1a. If a loss, go on to line 58. (Fiduciaries and partnerships, see the Instructions.) 57 | 28,527

58 If you have a loss, do you have amounts for which you are not "at risk" in this farm (see instructions)? ☐ Yes ☐ No
If you checked "No," enter the loss on Form 1040, line 18, and on Schedule SE, Part I, line 1a.

*Use amount on line 31 for optional method of computing net earnings from self-employment. (See Schedule SE, Part I, line 3.)

For Paperwork Reduction Act Notice, see Form 1040 Instructions.

FIGURE 36.3.
Internal Revenue Service form (Schedule F) showing income and expense items for which documented records must be kept.

Profits can be determined by evaluating all cash costs of the operation, all inventory increases or decreases, and the value of opportunity costs. Opportunity costs represent the returns that would be forfeited if debt-free resources (such as owned land, livestock, and equipment) were used in their next best level of employment; for example, the value of pastureland if it were leased, returns if all capital represented by equipment and livestock were invested in a certificate of deposit (or similar investment), and returns if all family labor and management were utilized in other employment. By calculating this, a price can be established for living on a farm or ranch, and a goal can be established for increasing profits.

Credit and money management become crucial during periods of inflation, high interest rates, and relatively low livestock prices. Prudent use of credit can enable a livestock operation to grow more rapidly than it could through the use of reinvested earnings and savings, so long as borrowed funds return more over time than they cost. Thus, farmers and ranchers have to look to credit as a financial tool and learn to use it effectively.

INCOME TAX CONSIDERATIONS

Frequently managers feel that they are ineffective if income taxes are overpaid. Paying little or no income tax should not be a major goal of the operation. A common attitude is reflected in the frequently heard comment of livestock producers that "I've been producing livestock for 20 years and haven't made any money, but I haven't paid any taxes, either."

Well-managed livestock operations pay income taxes if maximizing profitability is a goal. Therefore, it is not poor management to pay income tax but to pay more than is owed.

Tax laws are complex and constantly changing. Most cattle producers should consult a qualified tax adviser for tax reporting and longer-term tax management.

ESTATE AND GIFT-TAX PLANNING

Many livestock operations have a large amount of debt-free capital invested in land, livestock, buildings, and equipment. Adequate knowledge and proper planning are necessary for farmers and ranchers to pass on viable economic units to their heirs.

In recent years, significant changes in estate-tax policy have benefited family operations. For example, the unified credit allows each descendant to pass on a maximum of $600,000 of property to the next generation without paying federal estate taxes. Thus, a husband and wife could pass on $1.2 million as tax-free dollars. Producers can make substantial annual cash gifts to children and grandchildren without paying a federal gift tax.

Livestock producers should review tax plans (estate, gift, and income) and consult with professionals who are knowledgeable about current tax laws.

COMPUTERS

Livestock operators need to keep a voluminous amount of information for financial, production, and inventory records in order to assess management alternatives critically. Some managers with conventional records systems have an innate ability to "use their heads" to make good management decisions with a high degree of accuracy. They are able to use their mind (the most complex computer) to assimilate, store, and recall useful information effectively. However, for most managers, the computer can be a valuable aid.

Small computers (microcomputers) are frequently used as a management tool by farmers and ranchers. Producers must recognize what computers can and cannot do, at the present time and in the future. The technology of computers is changing rapidly; therefore, producers must be ready to accept the frustration of change if they become involved with computers.

Every computer, regardless of size and shape, is basically a fast adding machine and an electronic filing cabinet. A microcomputer system consists primarily of a system of hardware and software. The hardware for microcomputers (Fig. 36.4) consists of a terminal (a typewriter keyboard and an optional television screen), a printer, data-storage devices (the filing cabinets), main memory, and a central processing unit (CPU) (the adding machine). The data-storage devices can be magnetic (similar to cassette tapes), floppy discs (similar to 45-rpm records), or hard discs (large storage capacity in one unit). The devices that read and write the information on these discs are called "disc drives" or "drives."

Software are the programs that make the hardware function. Each program typically consists of thousands of minutely detailed instructions that tell the computer exactly what data to manipulate mathematically, print, store, or display.

Good software programs are the most limiting factor in microcomputer utilization by livestock producers, although more useful programs are becoming available. Software developed for one microcomputer may not function on a different brand machine. Computer utilization is expected to increase rapidly as more compatible programs are developed. The four ways producers can obtain software are (1) purchasing a complete commercial package, (2) hiring someone to do the programming, (3) learning to program the computer themselves, or (4) obtaining it from their land grant university.

FIGURE 36.4.
Microcomputers are becoming more commonly used by livestock producers. Courtesy of *BEEF*.

The three major areas in which microcomputers have the largest potential for livestock producers are (1) business accounting, (2) herd performance, and (3) financial management. A computer that would handle these three functions would need a relatively large memory.

Computers do not simplify a livestock business or cut overhead costs. They can even make a business more complex and more costly. If wisely acquired and properly utilized, a computer can increase profits, but usually not by reducing expenses. The computer will not solve the problem of a poorly organized operation. Well-planned and efficient office management practices must exist and function smoothly before the addition of a computer will do anything but aggravate the organizational problem of the business. The computer cannot assist the producer in managing the business effectively unless the computer receives all the required data in precisely the prescribed manner. Unless the computer can provide the information needed by producers at the appropriate time and in an easily understood form, it should not be part of a management program, regardless of price.

A producer should follow six steps before deciding to purchase a computer: (1) determine what important management decisions need to be made and what information is needed to make these decisions effectively, (2) see what programs are available to meet the management information needs, (3) determine the hardware needed to use the software, (4) contact local computer hardware dealers and evaluate the various alternatives and service, (5) estimate the cost-benefit ratio of the proposed management-information system, and (6) make the final decision after evaluating the experiences of other producers who are using computers in their operations.

MANAGEMENT SYSTEMS

Management-systems analysis provides a method of systematically organizing information needed to make valid management decisions. It permits variables to be more critically assessed and analyzed in terms of their contribution to the desired end point, usually net profit. Individuals who have been educated to think broadly in the framework of management systems can often make valid management decisions without the use of data-processing equipment. A pencil, hand calculator, and a well-trained mind are the primary components required for making competent management decisions. Without question, however, the use of the computer in synthesizing voluminous amounts of information enhances the management system.

Resources are different for each operation; no fixed recipe exists for successful livestock production. The uniqueness of each operation results from such variables as different levels of forage production, varying marketing alternatives, varying energy costs, different types of animals, environmental differences, feed nutrients at various costs, and varying levels of competence in labor and management. All of these variables and their interactions pose challenges to the producer seeking to combine them into sound management decisions for a specific operation.

It is a common practice to increase or maximize production of animals by using known biological relationships. Animal production typically has been maximized without careful consideration of cost-benefit ratios and of how increased productivity relates to land, feed, and management resources. However, recognition is now being given to the need for optimization rather than maximization of animal productivity. Thus, there is an increased interest in management systems that attempt to optimize production with net profit being the primary (and possibly the only) goal involved. As a result, some valid biological relationships will not be useful or applicable because an economic analysis may prevent their inclusion in sound management decisions. For example, it is a well-known biological fact that calves born earlier in the calving season will have heavier weaning weights. Because of this relationship, some ranchers move the calving season to a period earlier in the year without a careful economic assessment. An economic evaluation for one ranch demonstrated that by changing the calving season to match forage availability (in this case about 30 days to grazable forage), profits were increased significantly. Changing calving season alone was estimated to increase the ranch's carrying capacity by 30%–40%, in terms of animal units. In addition, the annual cow cost was reduced 18% per cow because of reduction in winter feed requirements.

In dairy production, there is often a difference between maximum milk production and optimum milk production if producers want to maximize profit. The extra feed and management needed to maximize milk production may cost more than the value of the added milk.

The farmer and rancher are limited in utilizing the computer in management systems because of the lack of software. However, there is increased discussion about and movement toward making more management system software available to producers. Several projections indicate that programs will be used commonly in the next few years. Producers have to make management decisions now. To be competitive, livestock operations will have to be operated more like a business. This means keeping accurate financial and production records for use in making management decisions. The computer is likely to become more important as a tool to improve the effectiveness of the management-decision process. However, until more usable computer programs become available, producers must use the traditional tools (pencil, hand calculator, and a keen mind) more effectively than in the past.

SELECTED REFERENCES

Publications

Bourdon, R. 1985. *The Systems Concept of Beef Production.* Beef Improvement Federation Fact Sheet.

Gosey, J. Matching genetic potential to feed resources. *Cornbelt Cow-Calf Conference,* 25 Feb. 1984.

Harl, N. 1980. *Farm Estate and Business Planning.* 6th ed. Skokie, IL: Century Communications.

Hughes, H. 1981. Dec. *The Computer Explosion. Proceedings: The Range Beef Cow, A Symposium on Production, VII.* Rapid City, SD.

———. 1981. Dec. Six steps to take in making a decision to buy a computer. *BEEF.*

Killcreas, W. E., and Hickel, R. 1982. *A Set of Microcomputer Programs for Swine Record Keeping and Production Management.* Miss. Agric. and Forestry Expt. Stat. AEC Tech. Public. No. 35.

Klinefelter, D. A., and Hottel, B. 1981. *Farmers' and Ranchers' Guide to Borrowing Money.* Texas Agric. Expt. Stat. MP-1494.

Libbin, J. D., and Catlett, L. B. 1987. *Farm and Ranch Financial Records.* New York: Macmillan.

Luft, L. D. Sources of credit and the cost of credit. In *Great Plains Beef Cattle Handbook,* GPE-4351 and 4352.

Maddux, J. 1981. Dec. *The Man in Management. Proceedings: The Range Beef Cow, a Symposium on Production, VII.* Rapid City, SD.

Miller, W. C., Brinks, J. S., and Greathouse, G. A. 1985. A systems analysis model for cattle ranch management. *J. Anim. Sci.* 61(Suppl. 1):177.

Ott, G. Planning for profit with partial budgeting. *Great Plains Beef Cattle Handbook,* GPE-4551.

Sobba, A. 1986, July 22. Focusing on the new tax code: Changes that will affect cattlemen. In *NCA Beef Business Bulletin.*

Wilt, R. W., Jr., and Bell, S. D. 1977. *Use of Financial Cash Flow Statements as a Financial Management Tool.* Ala. Agric. Expt. Sta. Bull.

Visuals

Farm and Ranch Management; and *Agricultural Credit* (sound filmstrips). Vocational Education Productions, California Polytechnic State University, San Luis Obispo, CA 93407.
Finding the Profit in Agriculture (videotape). CEV, P.O. Box 65265, Lubbock, TX 79464–5265.

Computer Software

Swine Management Series One; and *Swine Record Keeping.* Vocational Education Productions, California Polytechnic State University, San Luis Obispo, CA 93407.

CHAPTER 37

Careers and Career Preparation in the Animal Sciences

Millions of domestic animals that provide food, fiber, and recreation for people create many and varied types of career opportunities. A placement survey of approximately 20,000 agriculture graduates of state colleges and universities is shown in Tables 37.1 and 37.2. Animal sciences placement data follow a similar pattern because they compose a high percentage of the graduates shown in these tables.

Beef cattle, dairy cattle, horses, poultry, sheep, and swine are the animals of primary importance in animal science curricula, whereas reproduction, nutrition, breeding (genetics), meats, and live animal appraisal are the specialized topics typically covered in animal science courses. A few animal science programs include studies of pet and companion animals. Most college and university curricula in the animal sciences are designed to assist students in the broad career areas of production, science, agribusiness, and the food industry. Some animal

TABLE 37.1. Postgraduation Activities of Bachelor Degree Recipients in Agriculture

Postgraduation Activity	Percent of Graduates
Agribusiness (industry)	40%
Graduate and professional study	20
Farming and ranching	15
Education, including extension	5
Government (national, state, and local)	10
Miscellaneous (not placed or not seeking employment)	10

Source: Adapted from the National Association of State Universities and Land Grant Colleges, 1989.

TABLE 37.2. Average Starting Salaries of Agriculture Graduates from State Universities

Graduate	Average Annual Starting Salary 1980	1985	1990
Bachelor of Science (B.S.)	$13,848	$17,585	$20,000
Master of Science (M.S.)	17,378	22,020	25,000
Doctor of Philosophy (Ph.D.)	22,472	29,448	35,000

Source: Adapted from the National Association of State Universities and Land Grant Colleges, 1989.

science departments combine production and agribusiness into an industry concentration. The major careers in these areas are shown in Table 37.3.

PRODUCTION

Many individuals are intrigued with animal production because of the possibility of being their own boss and working directly with animals (Fig. 37.1). These ambitions may be somewhat idealistic because the financial investment required in land is typically hundreds of thousands of dollars. Beef cattle, dairy, poultry, sheep, and swine production operations continue to become fewer in number, more specialized, and larger in terms of the amount of capital invested. Those who find a career in the production area usually have a family operation to which they can return. A few others have the needed capital to invest.

Some students who seek employment in animal production are disillusioned with the base salary, benefits, and working hours when production work is compared with agribusiness careers. However, some graduates are anxious and willing to obtain experience, prove they can work, and eventually locate permanent employment in production operations. Some producers of cattle, sheep, swine, and horse operations allow an employee to buy into an operation on a limited basis or own some of the animals after working a year to two.

Certain careers require education and experience in the production area even though the individual will not be producing animals directly. Career opportunities such as breed association and publication positions, fieldpersons, extension agents, and livestock marketing require an understanding of production as one works directly with livestock producers.

SCIENCE

An animal science student who concentrates heavily in science courses is usually preparing for further academic work with a goal of achieving one or more advanced degrees. A minimum grade average of B is usually required for admission into graduate school or a professional veterinary medicine program. Advanced degrees are usually obtained after entrance into graduate school or after being admitted to a professional veterinary medicine program where a Doctor of Veterinary Medicine (D.V.M.) degree is awarded. Table 37.4 shows where graduates of Veterinary medical colleges are employed and their average starting salaries. The two most important employment areas in 1989 were small animal practice and mixed animal practice, whereas 15% of the graduates entered advanced study.

TABLE 37.3. Animal Sciences Careers in Production, Science, Agribusiness, and Food Industry

Animal Sciences			
Production	**Science**	**Agribusiness**	**Food Industry**
Feedlot positions	Graduate school for Master of Science (M.S.) and Doctor of Philosophy (Ph.D) degrees	Sales and management positions with feed companies, packing companies, drug and pharmacy companies, equipment companies, and so on	Food-processing plants
Livestock production operations (beef, dairy, swine, sheep, and horses)	Research (university or industry) in nutrition, reproduction, breeding and genetics, products, and production management	Liverstock publications	Food-ingredient plants
Ranch positions	University or college teaching	Advertising and promotion	Food-manufacturing plants
Breed associations	University extension and area extension	Finance (PCAs, banks, and so on)	Government—protection and regulatory agencies
AI studs and breeding	Management positions in industry	Public relations	Government—Department of Defense (food supply and food service)
Livestock buyers for feeders and packers	Government work	Meat grading (federal government)	Government—Department of Agriculture (research and Information)
County extension agents	International opportunities	International opportunities	University research, teaching, and extension
Meat grading and handling distribution	Laboratory technicians	Graduate school for Master's in business Administration (M.B.A.)	Positions with food companies
Marketing (auctions, Cattle Fax, livestock sales management, and so on)	Veterinary school for Doctor of Veterinary Medicine (D.V.M.)	Foreign agriculture	Research and development with food companies
International opportunities	Private practice	Technical sales and service	
Livestock and meat market reporting (government)	Consulting	Positions in poultry-production units	
Riding instructors	University teaching and research	Companion animals	
Feed manufacturing	Meat inspection		
Companion animals	Industry/commercial		
Boarding	Companion animal research		
Breeding			
Training			
Humane Society			

The Master's of Science (M.S.) and Doctor of Philosophy (Ph.D.) degrees are the advanced degrees received by the science-oriented student. Although the 2-year college certificate or Bachelor of Science (B.S.) degree allows breadth of education, advanced degrees are generally directed to a specialization. These specialized animal science areas are typically in nutrition, reproduction, breeding (genetics and statistics), animal products, and, less frequently, management systems (Figs. 37.2–37.5).

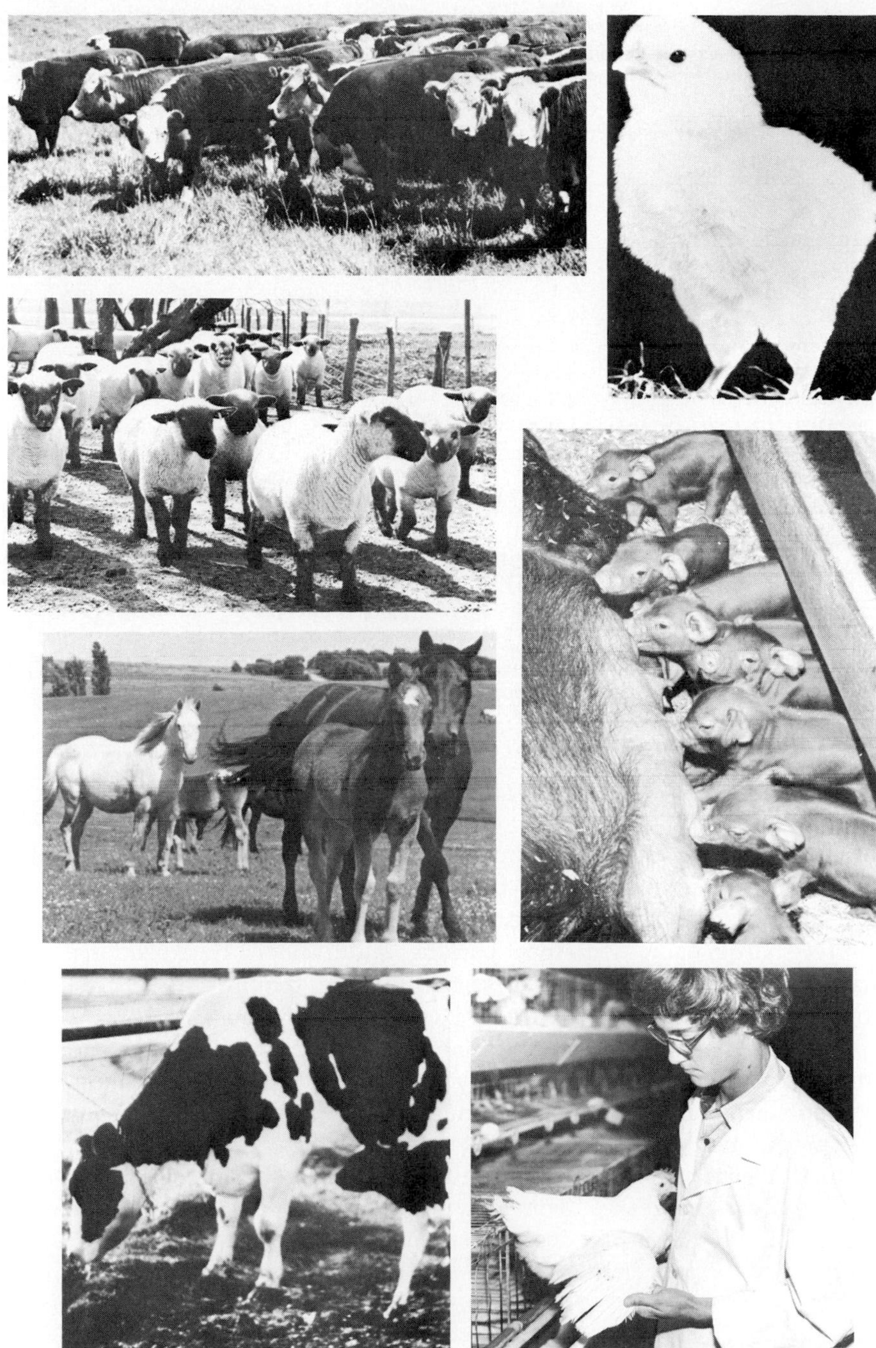

FIGURE 37.1.
There are numerous career opportunities in the production of the various species of farm animals. Some students interested in the production area will not be directly involved in animal production. These students will work for companies, associations, or groups closely associated with the animal producers. Courtesy of Institute of Agriculture and Natural Resources, University of Nebraska; lower left photo courtesy of University of Illinois.

TABLE 37.4. Types of Employment and Starting Incomes of a Large Sample of 1989 U.S. Veterinary Medical College Graduates

Employment Area	Percentage of Graduates	Average Starting Salary (no.)	Average Additional Compensation Expected in 1st Year (no.)
Large animal exclusive	2.3%	$25,210 (20)	$7,308 (12)
Large animal predominant	10.7	26,663 (82)	3,908 (64)
Mixed animal	11.8	23,961 (96)	3,488 (56)
Small animal predominant	9.1	23,736 (64)	3,248 (46)
Small animal exclusive	39.1	24,834 (313)	2,722 (201)
Equine predominant	4.8	23,270 (38)	6,456 (23)
University	1.3	15,320 (11)	1,250 (2)
Federal government	0.8	23,301 (5)	1,000 (1)
Military service	1.0	31,275 (8)	6,000 (1)
State and local government	0.1	26,500 (1)	—
Industry/commercial	0.4	29,000 (4)	3,500 (2)
Advanced study	15.2	16,363 (109)	3,096 (26)
Self-employed	3.0	26,000 (13)	5,390 (10)
Other	0.5	25,637 (4)	2,000 (1)
	100 (924)[a]	$23,627 (768)[a]	$3,565 (445)

[a] 924 reported their employment area, while 768 also disclosed their salaries.
Source: JAVMA (1989) 195:1407.

AGRIBUSINESS

Although the number of individuals employed in livestock and poultry production has decreased, the number of individuals and businesses serving producers has greatly increased. Positions in sales, management, finance, advertising, public relations, and publications are prevalent in feed, drug, equipment, meat packing, and livestock organizations.

Agribusiness careers that relate to the livestock industry require a student to have a foundation of knowledge of livestock along with an excellent comprehension of business, economics, computer science, and effective communication. A graduate should understand people, know how to communicate with people, and enjoy working with people. Extracurricular activities that give students experience in leadership and working with people are invaluable for meaningful career preparation.

Some animal science students who concentrate heavily in business and economics courses will pursue an advanced degree. This is typically a Master's in Business Administration (M.B.A.). A combination of a B.S. degree in Animal Science with an M.B.A. is an excellent preparation for management positions in livestock-oriented businesses.

FOOD INDUSTRY

Red meats, poultry, milk, and eggs—the primary end products of animal production—provide basic nutrition and eating enjoyment for millions of consumers. Career opportunities are numerous in providing one of our basic needs—food. Processing, packaging, and distribution of

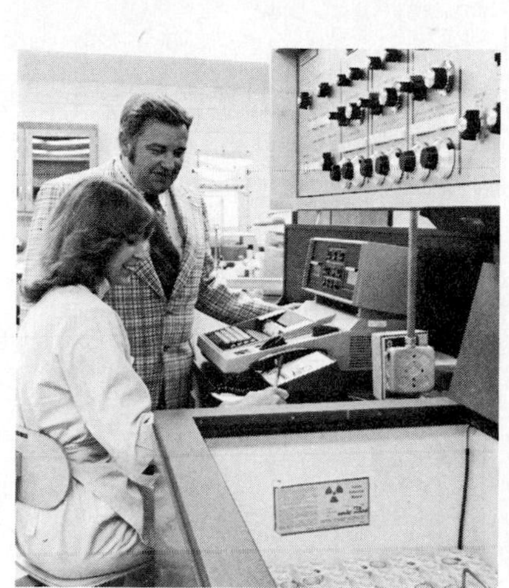

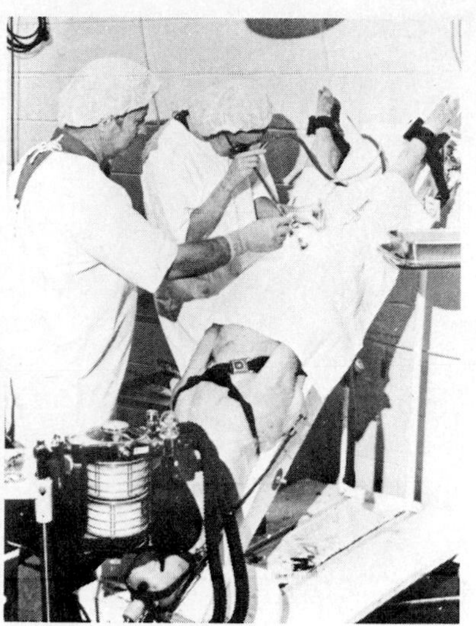

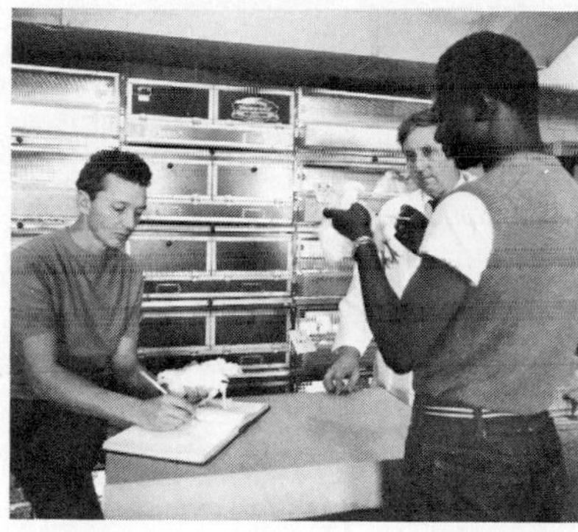

FIGURE 37.2.
Many students concentrating in the sciences are preparing themselves for entrance into graduate school. There they will complete M.S. and Ph.D. degrees, which are primarily research-oriented degrees. A few examples are depicted here. Courtesy of Institute of Agriculture and Natural Resources, University of Nebraska photo; lower left photo courtesy of West Virginia University.

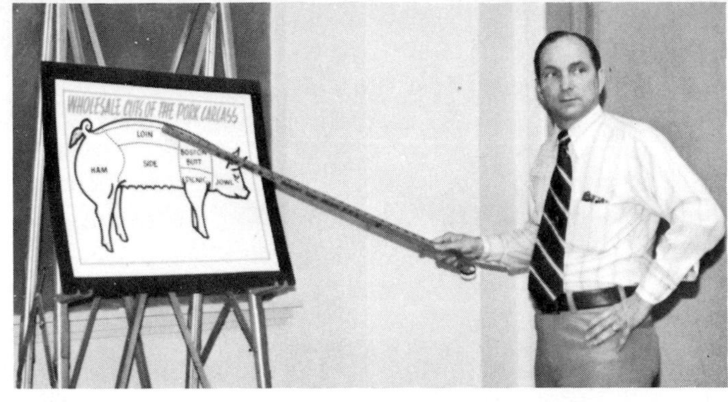

FIGURE 37.3.
A Ph.D. is usually required for teaching in a college or university. Courtesy of Oklahoma State University.

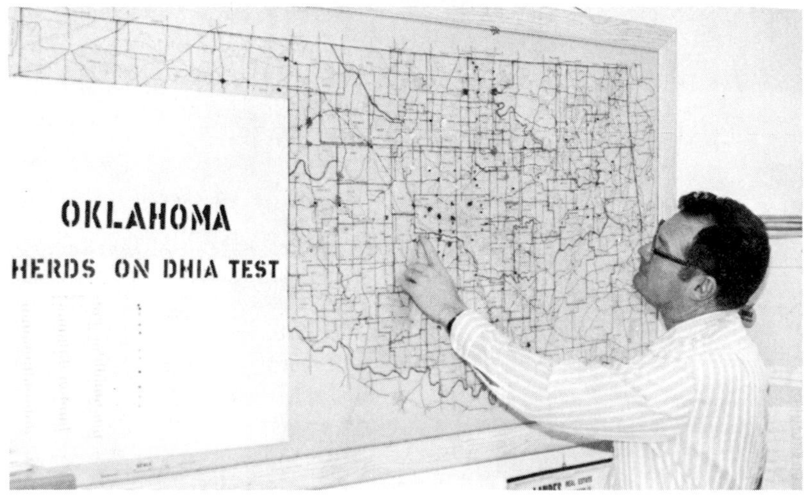

FIGURE 37.4.
University extension personnel need a Ph.D. degree so they can interpret the current research and apply it in off-campus educational programs. Courtesy of Oklahoma State University.

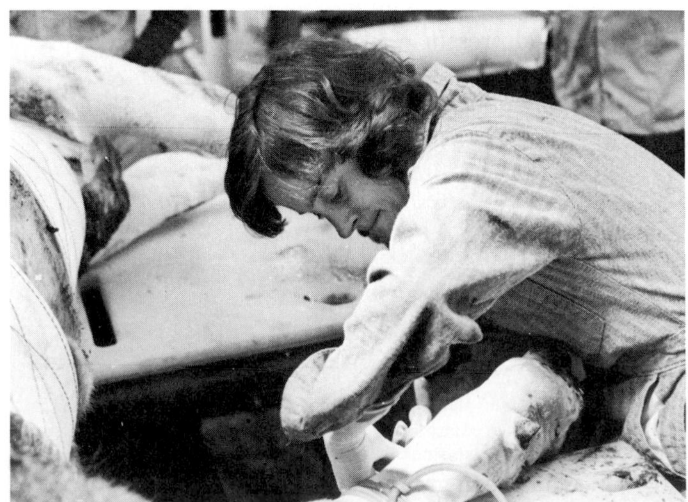

FIGURE 37.5.
Students will usually have a B.S. degree before applying for admission to the College of Veterinary Medicine. Students with high academic performance in the science aspect of animal science are typically well prepared for completing the D.V.M. degree. Courtesy of Colorado State University.

food are important components of the food-production chain. New food products are continually being produced, and new methods of manufacturing and fabricating food are being developed. Electrical stimulation of carcasses for increased tenderization, vacuum packaging of primal cuts for a longer shelf life, and preparation of convenience products are examples of recent innovations in meat processing. A vital and continuing challenge over the next several decades will be to provide a food supply that is nutritious, safe, convenient, attractive, and economical which is also satisfying the consumer (Fig. 37.6).

INTERNATIONAL OPPORTUNITIES

Much has been written during the past decade of the challenge to provide adequate nutrition to an ever-expanding world population. Many countries have tremendous natural resources for expanded food production but lack technical knowledge and adequate capital to develop these resources. Federal government programs, designed to help foreign countries help themselves, offer several career opportunities in organizations, such as the Peace Corps, Vista, and USAID. Many of these opportunities of assisting people in agricultural production in developing countries are open to individuals educated and experienced in the animal sciences.

The Foreign Agricultural Service of the USDA employs people in animal economics, marketing, and administration as attachés and international secretaries. Animal science students take several courses in economics, marketing, foreign languages, and business administration if they wish to qualify for these positions.

Certain private industries offer opportunities in animal production and related businesses in foreign countries. Multinational firms that develop livestock feed companies, drug and pharmaceutical companies, companies that export and import animals and animal products, and consulting companies are some examples.

MANAGEMENT POSITIONS

Management and administrative positions exist in the production, science, agribusiness, and food industry areas of animal science. Because management generally implies less work and more pay than other positions that require more physical labor, young men and women typically desire management positions. Nevertheless, although management and administrative salaries are usually higher, the work load and pressures are usually much greater.

Many college graduates have the impression that once the degree is in hand, it automatically qualifies them for management positions. In actuality, management positions are usually earned based on a person's proven ability to work with people, solve problems, and make effective decisions. After being employed for a few years, individuals having previously learned the academic principles must also experience the component parts of an operation or business. For example, presidents or vice-presidents of feed companies have typically started their initial careers in feed sales. Most successful managers have had a continual series of learning experiences since the end of their formal education. Managers need to understand all aspects of the business they are managing, particularly the products that are produced and sold.

WOMEN IN ANIMAL SCIENCE CAREERS

Women are pursuing and finding career opportunities in all areas of the animal sciences. The number of women majoring in animal science has been growing steadily in most colleges and

FIGURE 37.6.

The demand for animal products creates many industries that support the animals and process the products for human consumption. Courtesy of the University of Nebraska, Colorado State University, and Oklahoma State University.

universities. In the early 1970s, the number of females majoring in animal science was 20%–25% of the total majors. In many universities women now comprise more than half of the animal science and DVM enrollments (Fig. 37.7). Many agricultural employers, especially in the agribusiness, are actively recruiting women with animal science degrees.

In recent years, women have found career opportunities that many felt were reserved for men only. Although some men expressed fear and had serious reservations, many of these women proved they could perform competently. It does, however, appear that some employers in private production agriculture are still reluctant in hiring women on the same basis as men. Nevertheless, women interested in animal science careers should prepare themselves adequately in both education and experience. Many livestock agribusiness companies are actively recruiting women graduates.

Recent observations in a California study showed that women graduates in agriculture were at a disadvantage in salary and job status when compared with men graduating with similar degrees. However, a Colorado State University survey of its women graduates in animal sciences since 1979 revealed that many of them were in high-paying careers. This survey also demonstrated that women desiring employment in the production area had struggled in identifying meaningful employment. The agribusiness area (e.g., Farmer's Home Administration, feed companies, food-processing companies, and drug and pharmaceutical companies) had provided attractive careers for women graduates: several companies reported annual starting salaries were above $20,000.

FUTURE CAREER OPPORTUNITIES

A 1990 USDA national assessment report projected the employment opportunities for food and agricultural sciences graduates through 1995. The estimated number of annual job openings is 48,000 with approximately 43,500 qualified college graduates available each year. The supply of graduates is expected to be approximately 11% less than the available job openings.

Figure 37.8 shows the employment opportunities and the available graduates for six different career areas. The USDA report has the following summary:

> In summary, basic plant and animal research, food and fiber processing, and agribusiness management and marketing are expected to provide the most significant employment opportunities for college graduates with expertise in agriculture, natural resources, and veterinary medicine through 1995. In contrast, college graduates seeking positions in production agriculture, education, and communications are encountering strong competition for somewhat limited employment opportunities within the U.S. food and agricultural system.

CAREER PREPARATION

An education should provide opportunities for people to earn a living, continue learning, and live a full, productive life even beyond the typical retirement years. A broad-based education is important because a person may be preparing for a career that does not presently exist or a career not recognized at the present time. Change has occurred and will no doubt continue to occur, so a person needs to be flexible and adaptable and must be willing to continue learning throughout life.

Occasionally someone chooses a career for which he or she has little real talent or for which she or he is not qualified or properly motivated. These individuals may spend years preparing

A

B

C

D

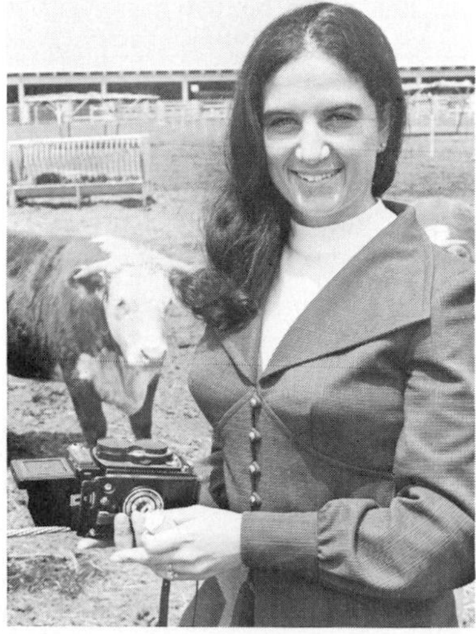
E

FIGURE 37.7.
Women are seeking and finding career opportunities in the animal sciences. The examples shown are (A) teaching equitation, (B) veterinarian's assistant, (C) feedlot manager; (D) researcher, (E) photographer. Courtesy of Colorado State University; University of Illinois; Office of Agricultural Communications; *BEEF;* University of Wyoming; *The American Hereford Journal;* and Oklahoma State University.

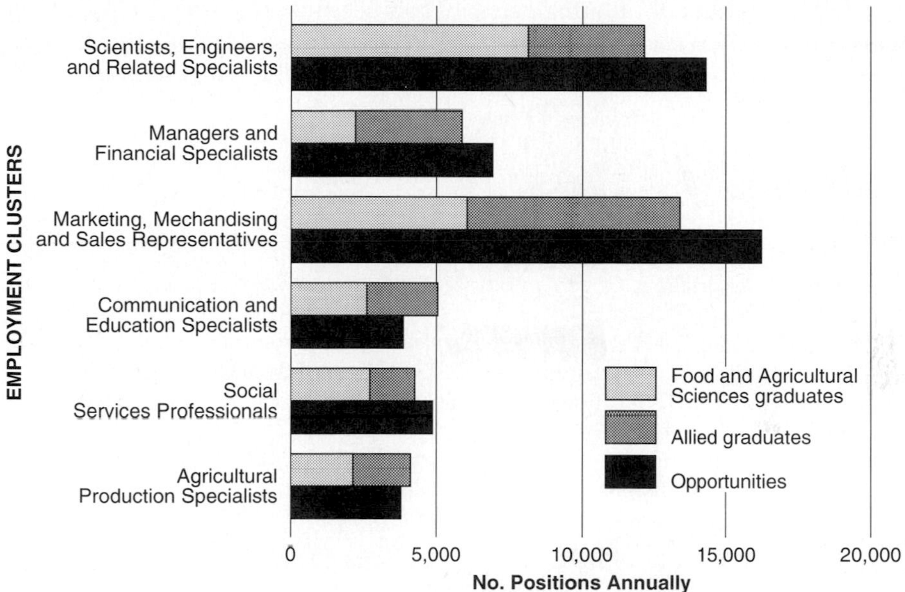

FIGURE 37.8.
Employment opportunities and available graduates (1990–1995). Courtesy of the USDA.

for or achieving partial success when they could have been outstanding in another area. In the animal sciences, students preparing for acceptance into veterinary medicine, graduate school, or another professional school seem to experience this frustration frequently. Individuals are capable of success in several different careers if they receive the appropriate education and experience. A career choice should be consistent with a person's interest, desire, and motivation. A career goal should be established with flexibility for change if it proves to be unrealistic.

After tentatively choosing a career area, it should be pursued vigorously with sustained personal motivation. Students should write and visit with people currently working in the student's chosen career area. Every personal visit or written letter should request another lead or source of further information. Students should continually evaluate the reality of a chosen career. They should think realistically about the facts rather than getting caught up in the glamour of what they have perceived about a career choice. Career interest tests can be helpful in identifying areas to pursue in more detail. However, these tests are not infallible; they can provide direction but they are not the final answer. Students should always temper the results with additional information from several sources before making final decisions.

Employers hire people, not a college major or area of study. The classes a student takes in college are only part of the necessary preparation. Therefore, in addition to academic preparation, students should develop their marketable personal assets, emphasized by employers, as the ability to lead, solve problems, communicate and work with people, and consistently work hard. A person develops many of these personal characteristics through experience, part-time and summer jobs, and extracurricular activities. Internships are especially valuable in obtaining exposure to a career area and developing personal abilities and skills through practical experience. A combination of useful courses, practical experience, effective communication, and excellent work skills is the best assurance of finding and keeping a meaningful career in the animal sciences.

SELECTED REFERENCES

Publications

American Meat Science Association, *Careers in the Meat Industry.* Chicago, IL: American Meat Science Association.

Coulter, K. J., Stanton, M., and Goecker, A. D. 1990. *Employment Opportunities for College Graduates in the Food and Agricultural Sciences.* Washington, DC: USDA, Higher Education Program.

Employment starting salaries and educational indebtedness of 1989 graduates of U.S. veterinary medical colleges. 1989. *JAVMA* 195:1407.

National Association of State Universities and Land Grant Colleges. July 1990. *Survey of Agricultural Degrees Granted and Post-Graduation Activities of Graduates.*

Wood, J. B., Dupre, D. H., and Thompson, O. E. 1981. *Women in the agricultural labor market. California Agriculture* (Sept.–Oct., 16).

Visuals

Careers: Marketing Specialists; Social Service Professionals; Agricultural Producers; Agricultural Scientists; and *Financial Specialists and Managers* (5 videotapes). CEV, P.O. Box 65265, Lubbock, TX 79464–5265.

Careers: Marketing Yourself; the Right Fit; Resumes; Interviews; Getting the Interview; Getting in the Door; Making the Cut; Practice Interviewing; Getting the Offer. (8 videotapes). CEV, P.O. Box 65265, Lubbock, TX 79464–5265.

Job Hunting Skills: Working Toward a Career; Finding and Landing the Right Job; How to Interview for a Job; Interviewing; Resume Writing; The Job Application (6 videotapes). CEV, P.O. Box 65265, Lubbock, TX 79464–5265.

Unbridled Opportunities-Careers in the Horse Industry; American Horse Council, 1700 K Street N.W., Suite 300, Washington, D.C. 20006.

Veterinary Medicine: The Challenge That Lasts a Lifetime (videotape; 13 min.). College of Veterinary Medicine and Biomedical Sciences, Colorado State University, Ft. Collins, CO 80523.

GLOSSARY

abomasum The fourth stomach compartment of ruminant animals that corresponds to the true stomach of monogastric animals.

abortion Delivery of fetus between conception and a few days before normal parturition.

abscess Localized collection of pus in a cavity formed by disintegration of tissues.

absorption The passage of liquid and digested (soluble) food across the gut wall.

accessory organs The seminal vesicles, prostate, and Cowper's glands in the male. These glands add their secretions to the sperm to form semen.

accuracy (ACC) of selection Numerical value, ranging from 0–1.0, denoting the confidence that can be placed in the EPD (expected progeny difference); e.g., high ($\geq$0.70), medium (0.40–0.69), low ($\leq$0.40).

adipose Fat cells or fat tissue.

ad libitum Free choice; allowing animals to eat all they want.

afterbirth The membranes attached to the fetus that are expelled after parturition.

AI Abbreviation for artificial insemination.

air dry Refers to feeds in equilibrium with air; they would contain approximately 10% water or 90% dry matter.

albumen The white of an egg.

alimentary tract Passageway for food and waste products through the body.

alleles Genes occupying corresponding loci in homologous chromosomes that affect the same hereditary trait but in different ways.

allelomimetic behavior Doing the same thing. Animals tend to follow the actions of other animals.

alveolus *(plural, alveoli)* A hollow cluster of cells. In the mammary gland, these cells secrete milk.

amino acid An organic acid in which one or more of the hydrogen atoms has been replaced by the amino group ($—NH_2$). Amino acids are the building blocks in the formation of proteins.

amnion A fluid-filled membrane located next to the fetus.

ampulla The dilated or enlarged upper portion of the vas deferens in bulls, bucks, and rams, where sperm are stored for sudden release at ejaculation.

anabolic A constructive, or "building up," process.

anatomy Science of animal body structure and the relation of the body parts.

androgen A male sex hormone, such as testosterone.

anemia Deficiency of hemoglobin, often accompanied by a reduced number of red blood cells. Usually results from an iron deficiency.

anestrous Period of time when female is not in estrus; the nonbreeding season.

ante mortem Before death.

anterior Situated in front of, or toward the front part of, a point of reference. Toward the head of an animal.

anterior pituitary (AP) The part of the pituitary gland, located at the base of the brain, that produces several hormones.

anthelmintic A drug or chemical agent used to kill or remove internal parasites.

antibiotic A product produced by living organisms, such as yeast, which destroys or inhibits the growth of other microorganisms, especially bacteria.

antibody A specific protein molecule that is produced in response to a foreign protein (antigen) that has been introduced into the body.

antigen A foreign substance that, when introduced into the blood or tissues, causes the formation of antibodies. Antigens may be toxins or native proteins.

antiseptic A chemical agent used on living tissue to control the growth and development of microorganisms.

AP See *anterior pituitary.*

artery Vessel through which blood passes from the heart to all parts of the body.

arteriosclerosis A disease resulting in the thickening and hardening of the artery walls.

artificial insemination The introduction of semen into the female reproductive tract (usually the cervix or uterus) by a technique other than natural service.

artificial vagina A device used to collect semen from a male when he mounts in a normal manner to copulate. The male ejaculates into this device, which simulates the vagina of the female in pressure, temperature, and sensation to the penis.

ascaris Any of the genus (Ascaris) of parasitic roundworms.

as fed Refers to feeding feeds that contain their normal amount of moisture.

assimilation The process of transforming food into living tissue.

atherosclerosis A form of arteriosclerosis involving fatty deposits in the inner walls of the arteries.

atrophy Shrinking or wasting away of a tissue or organ.

auction A market facility where an auctioneer sells animals to the highest bidder.

autopsy A postmortem examination in which the body is dissected to determine the cause of death.

avian Refers to birds, including poultry.

balance sheet A statement of assets owned and liabilities owed in dollar terms that shows the equity or net worth at a specific point in time; i.e., net worth statement.

Bang's disease See *brucellosis.*

barren Not capable of producing offspring.

barrow A male swine that was castrated before reaching puberty.

basal metabolism The chemical changes that occur in an animal's body when the animal is in a thermoneutral environment, resting, and in a postabsorptive state. It is usually determined by measuring oxygen consumption and carbon dioxide production.

beef The meat from cattle (bovine species) other than calves (the meat from calves is called *veal*).

beri-beri A disease caused by a deficiency of vitamin B_1.

biologicals Pharmaceutical products used especially to diagnose and treat diseases.

biotechnology The use of microorganisms, plant cells, animal cells, or parts of cells (such as enzymes) to produce industrially important products or processes.

blemish Any defect or injury that mars the appearance of, but does not impair the usefulness of, an animal.

bloat An abnormal condition in ruminants characterized by a distention of the rumen, usually seen on an animal's upper left side, owing to an accumulation of gases.

blood spots Spots in the egg caused by a rupture of one or more blood vessels in the yolk follicle at the time of ovulation.

BLUP Best linear unbiased prediction, method for estimating breeding values of breeding animals.

boar (1) A male swine of breeding age. (2) Denotes a male pig, which is called a *boar pig.*

bog spavin A soft enlargement of the anterior, inner aspect of the hock.

bolus (1) Regurgitated food. (2) A large pill for dosing animals.

bone spavin A bony (hard) enlargement of the inner aspect of the hock.

bots Any of a number of related flies whose larvae are parasitic in horses and sheep.

bovine A general family grouping of cattle.

boxed beef Cuts of beef put in boxes for shipping from packing plant to retailers. These primal and subprimal cuts are intermediate cuts between the carcass and retail cuts.

boxed lamb See *boxed beef.* Similar process except lamb instead of beef.

break joint Denotes the point on a lamb carcass where the foot and pastern are removed at the cartilaginous junction of the front leg.

bred Female has been mated to the male. Usually implies the female is pregnant.

breech The buttocks. A breech presentation at birth is where the rear portion of the fetus is presented first.
breed Animals of common origin and having characteristics that distinguish them from other groups within the same species.
breeding value A genetic measure for one trait of an animal, calculated by combining into one number several performance values, that have been accumulated on the animal and the animal's relatives.
brisket disease A noninfectious disease of cattle characterized by congestive right heart failure. It affects animals residing at high altitudes (usually above 7,000 ft.)
British Thermal Unit The quantity of heat required to raise the temperature of 1 lb of water 1°F at or near 39.2°F.
brockle-faced White-faced with other colors splotched on the face and head.
broiler A young meat-type chicken of either sex (usually up to 6–8 weeks of age) weighing 3–5 lb. Also referred to as a fryer or young chicken.
broken-mouth Some teeth are missing or broken.
broodiness The desire of a female bird to sit on eggs (incubate).
browse Woody or brushy plants. Livestock feed on tender shoots or twigs.
brucellosis A contagious bacterial disease that results in abortions; also called Bang's disease.
buck A male sheep or goat. This term usually denotes animals of breeding age.
bulbourethral (Cowper's) gland An accessory gland of the male that secretes a fluid which constitutes a portion of the semen.
bull A bovine male. The term usually denotes animals of breeding age.
buller-steer syndrome A behavior problem where a steer has a sexual attraction to other steers in the pen. The steer is ridden by the other steers, resulting in poor performance and injury.
bullock A young bull, typically less than 20 months of age.
buttermilk The fluid remaining after butter has been made from cream. By use of bacteria, cultured buttermilk is also produced from milk.
buttons May refer to cartilage or dorsal processes of the thoracic vertebrae. Also see *cotyledons.*
by-product A product of considerably less value than the major product. For example in U.S. meat animals, the hide, pelt, and offal are by-products whereas meat is the major product.
C-section See *cesarian section.*
calf A young male or female bovine animal under a year of age.
calorie The amount of heat required to raise the temperature of 1 g of water from 15°C to 16 C.
calve Giving birth to a calf. Same as parturition.
calving interval The amount of time (days or months) between the birth of a calf and the birth of a subsequent calf, both from the same cow.
candling The shining of a bright light through an egg to see if it contains a live embryo.
canter A slow, easy gallop.
capon Castrated male chicken. Castration usually occurs between 3 and 4 weeks of age.
capped hocks Hocks that have hard growths that cover, or "cap," their points.
carbohydrates Any foods, including starches, sugars, celluloses, and gums, that are broken down to simple sugars through digestion.
carcass merit The value of a carcass for consumption.
carnivorous Subsisting or feeding on animal tissues.
carotene The orange pigment found in carrots, leafy plants, yellow corn, and other feeds, which can be broken down to form two molecules of vitamin A.
caruncle (1) The red and blue fleshy, unfeathered area of skin on the upper region of the turkey's neck. (2) The "buttons" on the ruminant uterus where the cotyledons on the fetal membranes attach.
casein The major protein of milk.
cash-flow statement A financial statement summarizing all cash receipts and disbursements over the period of time covered by the statement.

castrate (1) To remove the testicles. (2) An animal that has had its testicles removed.
cattalo A cross between domestic cattle and bison.
cecum (ceca) A blind pouch at the junction of the small and large intestine. Poultry have two ceca.
cervix The portion of the female reproductive tract between the vagina and the uterus. It is usually sealed by thick mucus except when the female is in estrus or delivering young.
cesarian section Delivery of fetus through an incision in abdominal and uterine walls.
chalaza A spiral band of thick albumen that helps hold the yolk of an egg in place.
chemotherapeutics Chemical agents used to prevent or treat diseases.
chevon Meat from goats.
chick A young chicken that has recently been hatched.
chorion The outermost layer of fetal membranes.
chromosome A rod-like or string-like body found in the nucleus of the cell that contains genetic information. The chromosome contains the genes.
chyme The thick, liquid mixture of food that passes from the stomach to the small intestine.
chymotrypsin A milk-digesting enzyme secreted by the pancreas into the small intestine.
class A group of animals categorized primarily by sex and age.
clip One season's yield of wool.
clitoris The ventral part of the vulva of the female reproductive tract that is homologous to the penis in the male. It is highly sensory.
cloaca Portion of the lower end of the avian digestive tract that provides a passageway for products of the urinary, digestive, and reproductive tracts.
closed face A condition in which sheep cannot see because wool covers their eyes.
clutch Eggs layed by a hen on consecutive days.
coccidia A protozoan organism that causes an intestinal disease called *coccidiosis.*
coccidiosis A morbid state caused by the presence of organisms called coccidia, which belong to a class of sporozoans.
cock A male chicken; also called a rooster.
cockerel Immature male chicken.
cod Scrotal area of steer remaining after castration.
coefficient of determination Percentage of variation in one trait that is accounted for by variation in another trait.
colic A nonspecific pain of the digestive tract.
colon The large intestine from the end of the ileum and beginning with the cecum to the anus.
colostrum The first milk given by a female after delivery of her young. It is high in antibodies that protects young animals from invading microorganisms.
colt A young male of the horse or donkey species.
comb The fleshy outgrowth on the top of a chicken's head, usually red in color with varying sizes and shapes.
compensatory gain A faster-than-normal rate of gain after a period of restricted gain.
compensatory growth See *compensatory gain.*
composite breed A breed that has been formed by crossing two or more breeds.
concentrate A feed that is high in energy, low in fiber content, and highly digestible.
conception Fertilization of the ovum (egg).
conditioning The treatment of animals by vaccination and other means before putting them in the feedlot.
conformation The physical form of an animal; its shape and arrangement of parts.
contagious disease Infectious disease; a disease that is transmitted from one animal to another.
contemporaries A group of animals of the same sex and breed (or similar breeding) that have been raised under similar environmental conditions (same management group).

contracted heels A condition in which the heels of a horse are pulled in so that expansion of the heel cannot occur when the foot strikes the ground.

core samples Samples (wool, feed, or meat) taken by a coring device to determine the composition of the sample.

corpus luteum A yellowish body in the mammalian ovary. The cells that were follicular cells develop into the corpus luteum, which secretes progesterone. It becomes yellow in color from the yellow lipids that are in the cells.

correlation coefficient A measure of the association of one trait with another.

cost of gain The total cost divided by the total pound gained; usually expressed on a per-pound basis.

cotyledon An area of the placenta that contacts the uterine lining to allow nutrients and wastes to pass from the mother to the developing young. Sometimes referred to as button.

cow A sexually mature female bovine animal—usually has produced a calf.

cow-calf operation A management unit that maintains a breeding herd and produces weaned calves.

cow hocked A condition in which the hocks are close together but the feet stand apart.

creep An enclosure in which young can enter to obtain feed but larger animals cannot enter. This process is called creep feeding.

crimp The waves, or kinks, in a wool fiber.

crossbred An animal produced by crossing two or more breeds.

crossbreeding Mating animals from genetically diverse groups (i.e., breeds) within a species.

crutching See tagging.

cryptorchidism The retention of one or both testicles in the abdominal cavity in animals that typically have the testicles hanging in a scrotal sac.

cud Bolus of feed a ruminant animal regurgitates for further chewing.

cull To eliminate one or more animals from the breeding herd or flock.

curb A hard swelling that occurs just below the point of the hock.

curd Coagulated milk.

cutability Fat, lean, and bone composition of meat animals. Used interchangeably with yield grade. (See also *yield grade.*)

cutting chute A narrow chute where animals go through in single file gates such that animals can be directed into pens along the side of the chute.

cwt An abbreviation for hundredweight (100 lb).

cycling Infers that nonpregnant females have active estrous cycles.

dam Female parent.

dark cutter Color of the lean (muscle) in the carcass has a dark appearance usually caused by stress (excitement, etc.) to the animal before slaughter.

debeaking To remove the tip of the beak of chickens.

dehorn To remove the horns from an animal.

deoxyribonucleic acid (DNA) A complex molecule consisting of deoxyribose (a sugar), phosphoric acid, and four nitrogen bases. (A gene is a piece of DNA.)

depreciation An accounting procedure by which the purchase price of an asset with a useful life of more than 1 year is prorated over time.

dewclaws Hard horny structures above the hoof on the rear surface of the legs of cattle, swine, and sheep.

dewlap Loose skin under the chin and neck of cattle.

DHIA Dairy Herd Improvement Association, an association which dairy producers participate in keeping dairy records. Sanctioned by the National Cooperative Dairy Herd Improvement Program.

DHIR Dairy Herd Improvement Registry, a dairy record-keeping plan sponsored by the breed associations.

digestibility The quality of being digestible. If a high percentage of a given food taken into the digestive tract is absorbed into the body, that food is said to have high digestibility.
digestion The reduction in particle size of feed so that the feed becomes soluble and can pass across the gut wall into the vascular or lymph system.
diploid Having the normal, paired chromosomes of somatic tissue as produced by the doubling of the primary chromosomes of the germ cells at fertilization.
disease Any deviation from a normal state of health.
disinfect To kill, or render ineffective, harmful microorganisms and parasites.
disinfectant A chemical that destroys disease-producing microorganisms or parasites.
distal Position that is distant from the point of attachment of an organ.
DM See *dry matter.*
DNA See *deoxyribonucleic acid.*
dock (1) To cut off the tail. (2) The remaining portion of the tail of a sheep that has been docked. (3) To reduce or lower in value.
doe A female goat or rabbit.
dominance (1) A situation in which one gene of an allelic pair prevents the phenotypic expression of the other member of the allelic pair. (2) A type of social behavior in which an animal exerts influence over one or more other animals.
dominant gene A gene that overpowers and prevents the expression of its recessive allele when the two alleles are present in a heterozygous individual.
down Soft, fluffy type of feather located under the contour feathers. Serves as insulating material.
drake Mature male duck.
drench To give fluid by mouth; e.g., medicated fluid is given to sheep for parasite control.
dressing percentage The percentage of the live animal weight, that becomes the carcass weight at slaughter. It is determined by dividing the carcass weight by the live weight, then multiplying by 100.
drop Body parts removed at slaughter—primarily hide (pelt), head, shanks, and offal.
drop credit Value of the drop.
dry (cow, ewe, sow, mare) Refers to a nonlactating female.
dry matter Feed after water (moisture) has been removed (100% dry).
dubbing The removal of part or all of the soft tissues (comb and wattles) of chickens.
dung The feces (manure) of farm animals.
dwarfism The state of being abnormally undersized. Two kinds of dwarfs are recognized; one is proportionate and the other is disproportionate.
dysentery Severe diarrhea.
dystocia Difficult birth
ectoderm The outermost layer of the three layers of the primitive embryo.
edema Abnormal fluid accumulation in the intercellular tissue spaces of the body.
ejaculation Discharge of semen from the male.
emaciation Thinness; loss of flesh where bony structures (hips, ribs, and vertebrae) become prominant.
embryo Very early stage of individual development within the uterus. The embryo grows and develops into a fetus. In poultry, the embryo develops within the eggshell.
embryo transfer The transfer of fertilized eggs from a donor female to one or more recipient females.
endocrine gland A ductless gland that secretes a hormone into the bloodstream.
endoderm The innermost layer of the three layers of the primitive embryo.
enterotoxemia A disease of the intestinal tract caused by bacterial secretion of toxins. Its symptoms are characteristic of food poisoning.
entropion Turned-in eyelids.
environment The sum total of all external conditions that affect the well-being and performance of an animal.

enzyme A complex protein produced by living cells that causes changes in other substances in the cells without being changed itself and without becoming a part of the product.

EPD See *expected progeny difference.*

epididymis The long, coiled tubule leading from the testis to the vas deferens.

epididymitis An inflammation of the epididymis.

epiphysis A piece of bone separated from a long bone in early life by cartilage, which later becomes part of the larger bone.

epistatis A situation in which a gene or gene pair masks (or controls) the expression of another nonallelic pair of genes.

equine Refers to horses.

equine encephalomyelitis An inflammation of the brain of horses.

eruction (or eructation) The elimination of gas by belching.

esophageal groove A groove in the reticulum between the esophagus and omasum. Directs milk in the nursing young ruminant directly from the esophagus to the omasum.

essential nutrient A nutrient that cannot by synthesized by the body and must be supplied in the diet.

estrogen Any hormone (including estradiol, estriol, and estrone) that causes the female to come physiologically into heat and to be receptive to the male. Estrogens are produced by the follicle of the ovary and by the placenta.

estrous An adjective meaning "heat," which modifies such words as "cycle." The estrous cycle is the heat cycle, or time from one heat to the next.

estrous synchronization Controlling the estrous cycle so that a high percentage of the females in the herd express estrus at approximately the same time.

estrus The period of mating activity in the female mammal. Same as heat.

ET Abbreviation for *embryo transfer.*

ethology Study of animal behavior.

eviscerate The removal of the internal organs during the slaughtering process.

ewe A sexually mature female sheep. A ewe lamb is a female sheep before attaining sexual maturity.

exocrine gland Gland that secretes fluid into a duct.

expected progeny difference (EPD) One-half of the breeding value; the difference in performance to be expected from future progeny of a sire, compared with that expected from future progeny of an average bull in the same test.

family selection Selection based on performance of a family.

farrow To deliver, or give birth to, pigs.

fat Adipose tissue.

FDA See *Food and Drug Administration.*

feather picking The picking of feathers from one bird by another.

feces Bowel movements, excrement from the intestinal tract.

feed additive Ingredient (such as an antibiotic or hormone-like substance) added to a diet to perform a specific role; e.g., to improve gain or feed efficiency.

feed bunk A trough or container used to feed farm animals.

feed efficiency (1) The amount of feed required to produce a unit of weight gain or milk; for poultry, this term can also denote the amount of feed required to produce a given quantity of eggs. (2) The amount of gain made per unit of feed.

feeder Animals (i.e., cattle, lambs, pigs) that need further feeding prior to slaughter.

feeder grades Visual classifications (descriptive and/or numerical) of feeder animals. Most of these grades have been established by the USDA.

felting The process of pressing wool fibers together in conjunction with heat and moisture to produce a fabric.

femininity Well-developed secondary female sex characteristics, udder development and refinement in head and neck.

fertility The capacity to initiate, sustain, and support reproduction. With reference to poultry, the term typically refers to the percentage of eggs that, when incubated, show some degree of embryonic development.

fertilization The process in which a sperm unites with an egg to produce a zygote.

fetus Later stage of individual development within the uterus. Generally, the new individual is regarded as an embryo during the first half of pregnancy, and as a fetus during the last half.

fill The contents of the digestive tract.

filly A young female horse.

fineness A term used to describe the diameter of wool fibers.

finish The degree of fatness of an animal.

Finnsheep A highly prolific breed of sheep introduced into the United States in 1968.

fistula A running sore at the top of the withers of a horse, resulting from a bruise followed by invasion of microorganisms.

flank firmness Firmness of the flank muscle in lamb carcass evaluation.

flank streaking Streaks of fat in the flank muscle of lamb carcasses.

fleece The wool shorn at one time from all parts of the sheep.

flehmen A pattern of behavior expressed in some male animals (e.g., bull, ram, stallion) during sexual activity. The upper lip curls up and the animal inhales in the vicinity of the vulva or urine.

Food and Drug Administration (FDA) A U.S. government agency responsible for protecting the public against impure and unsafe foods, drugs, veterinary products, and other products.

flock A group of sheep or poultry.

flushing Placing females (typically sheep and swine) on a gaining level of nutrition before breeding to stimulate greater ovulation rates.

fly strike An infestation with large numbers of blowfly maggots.

foal A young male or female horse (noun) or the act of giving birth (verb).

follicle A blisterlike, fluid-filled structure in the ovary that contains the egg.

follicle-stimulating hormone (FSH) A hormone produced and released by the anterior pituitary that stimulates the development of the follicle in the ovary.

footrot A disease of the foot in sheep and cattle. In sheep it causes rotting of tissue between the horny part of the foot and the soft tissue underneath.

forb Weedy or broad-leaf plants, as contrasted to grasses, that serve as pasture for animals.

forging The striking of the heel of the front foot with the toe of the hind foot by a horse in action.

founder Nutritional ailment resulting from overeating. Lameness in front feet with excessive hoof growth usually occurs.

frame score A numerical rating of frame size.

frame size A measure of skeletal size. It can be visual or a measurement (usually at shoulders or hips) is taken.

freemartin Female born twin to a bull (approximately 9 of 10 will not conceive).

freshen To give birth to young and initiate milk production. This term is usually used with reference to dairy cattle.

fryer See *broiler.*

FSH See *follicle-stimulating hormone.*

full-mouth Animal has all permanent teeth fully exposed.

full sibs Animals having the same sire and dam.

gallop A three-beat gait in which each of the two front feet and both of the hind feet strike the ground at different times.

gametes Male and female reproductive cells. The sperm and the egg.

gametogenesis The process by which sperm and eggs are produced.

gander Mature male goose.

gelding A male horse that has been castrated.

gene A small piece of chromosome (DNA) that codes for a trait and determines how a trait will develop.

general combining ability The ability of individuals of one line or population to combine favorably or unfavorably with individuals of several other lines or populations.

generation interval Average age of the parents when offspring are born.

generation turnover Length of time from one generation of animals to the next generation.

genetic engineering The technique of removing, modifying, or adding genes to a DNA molecule.

genome All of the genes of a species.

genotype The genetic constitution, or makeup, of an individual. For any pair of alleles, three genotypes (e.g., *AA*, *Aa*, and *aa*) are possible.

gestation The time from breeding or conception of a female until she gives birth to her young.

gilt A young female swine prior to the time that she has produced her first litter.

goiter Enlargement of the thyroid gland, usually caused by iodine-deficient diets.

gonad The testis of the male; the ovary of the female.

gonadotrophin Hormone that stimulates the gonads.

gossypol A toxic product contained in cottonseed.

grading up The continued use of purebred sires of the same breed in a grade herd or flock.

grass tetany A disease of cattle and sheep marked by staggering, convulsions, coma, and frequently death, and caused by a mineral imbalance (magnesium) while grazing lush pasture.

grease wool Wool as it comes from the sheep and prior to cleaning. It contains the natural oils from the sheep.

gross energy The amount of heat, measured in calories, produced when a substance is completely oxidized. It does not reveal the amount of energy that an animal could derive from eating the substance.

growth The increase in protein over its loss in the animal body. Growth occurs by increases in cell numbers, cell size, or both.

habituation The gradual adaptation to a stimulus or to the environment.

half sib Animals having one common parent.

hand mating Same as hand breeding—bringing a female to a male for service (breeding), after which she is removed from the area where the male is located.

hank A measurement of the fineness of wool. A hank is 560 yards of yarn. More hanks of yarn are produced from fine wools than coarse wools.

haploid One-half of the diploid number of chromosomes for a given species, as found in the germ cells.

hatchability A term that indicates the percentage of a given number of eggs set from which viable young hatch, sometimes calculated specifically from the number of fertile eggs set.

heat See *estrus*.

heat increment The increase in heat production after consumption of feed when an animal is in a thermoneutral environment. It includes additional heat generated in fermentation, digestion, and nutrient metabolism.

heaves A respiratory defect in horses during which the animal has difficulty completing the exhalation of inhaled air.

heifer A young female bovine cow before the time that she has produced her first calf.

heiferette A heifer that has calved once then the heifer is fed for slaughter; the calf has usually died or been weaned at an early age.

hemoglobin The iron-containing pigment of the red blood cells. It carries oxygen from the lungs to the tissues.

hen An adult female domestic fowl, such as a chicken or turkey.

herbivorous Subsisting or feeding on plants.

herd A group of animals. Used with beef, dairy, or swine.

heritability The portion of the total variation or phenotypic differences among animals that is due to heredity.

hernia The protrusion of some of the intestine through an opening in the body wall (also commonly called rupture). Two types of hernias, umbilical and scrotal, occur in farm animals.
heterosis Performance of offspring that is greater than the average of the parents. Usually referred to as the amount of superiority of the crossbred over the average of the parental breeds. Also referred to as hybrid vigor.
heterozygous A term designating an individual that possesses unlike genes for a particular trait.
hides Skins from animals such as cattle, horses, and pigs.
hinny The offspring that results from crossing a stallion with a female donkey (jenny).
hobble To tie two of an animal's legs together. An animal is hobbled to prevent it from kicking or moving a long distance.
homeotherm A warm-blooded animal. An animal that maintains its characteristic body temperature even though environmental temperature varies.
homogenized Milk that has had the fat droplets broken into very small particles so that the milk fat stays in suspension in the milk fluids.
homologous corresponding in type of structure and derived from a common primitive origin.
homologous chromosomes Chromosomes having the same size and shape that contain genes affecting the same characters. Homologous chromosomes occur in pairs in typical diploid cells.
homozygous A term designating an individual whose genes for a particular trait are alike.
hormone A chemical substance secreted by a ductless gland. Usually carried by the bloodstream to other places in the body where it has its specific effect on another organ.
hybrid vigor See *heterosis.*
hydrocephalus A condition characterized by an abnormal increase in the amount of cerebral fluid, accompanied by dilation of the cerebral ventricles.
hypertension High blood pressure.
hypothalamus A portion of the brain found in the floor of the third ventricle. It regulates reproduction, hunger, and body temperature and has other functions.
hypoxia A condition resulting from deficient oxygenation of the blood.
immunity The ability of an animal to resist or overcome an infection.
implant To graft or insert material to intact tissues.
implantation The attachment of the fertilized egg to the uterine wall.
imprinting Learning associated with maturational readiness.
inbreeding The mating of individuals who are more closely related than the average individuals in a population. Inbreeding increases homozygosity in the population but it does not change gene frequency.
incisor A front tooth.
incubation period The time that elapses from the time an egg is placed into an incubator until the young is hatched.
independent culling level Selection method in which minimum acceptable phenotypic levels are assigned to several traits.
index (1) An overall merit rating of an animal. (2) A method of predicting the milk-producing ability that a bull will transmit to his daughters.
infection Invasion of the body tissues by microbial agents or parasites other than insects.
infectious Capable of invading and growing in living tissues. Use to describe various pathogenic microorganisms such as viruses, bacteria, protozoa, and fungi.
influenza A virus disease characterized by inflammation of the respiratory tract, high fever, and muscular pain.
ingest Anything taken into the stomach.
inheritance The transmission of genes from parents to offspring.
insemination Deposition of semen in the female reproductive tract.
instinct Inborn behavior.

integration The bringing together of all segments of a livestock or poultry production program under one centrally organized unit.
intelligence The ability to learn to adjust successfully to situations.
interference The striking of the supporting leg by the foot of the striding leg by a horse in action.
interstitial cells The cells between the seminiferous tubules of the testicle that produce testosterone.
intravenous Within the vein. An intravenous injection is an injection into a vein.
in vitro Outside the living body; in a test tube or other artificial environment.
jack A male donkey.
jackass See *jack.*
jennet A female donkey.
jenny A female donkey.
Karakul A breed of fat-tailed sheep having coarse, wiry furlike hair. Used to produce Persian lambskins.
ked An external parasite that affects sheep. Although commonly called sheep tick, it is actually a wingless fly.
kemp Coarse, opaque, hairlike fibers in wool.
ketosis A condition (also called acetonemia) that is characterized by a high concentration of ketone bodies in the body tissues and fluids.
kid Young goat.
kilocalorie (kcal, Kcal) An amount of heat equal to 1,000 calories (See also *calorie.)*
kosher meat Meat from ruminant animals with split hooves where the animals have been slaughtered according to Jewish law.
lactalbumin A nutritive protein of milk.
lactation The secretion and production of milk.
lactose Milk sugar. When digested, it is broken down into one molecule of glucose and one of galactose.
lamb (1) A young male or female sheep, usually an individual less than a year of age. (2) To deliver, or give birth to, a lamb.
lamb dysentery See *dysentery.*
lambing Act of giving birth. Same as parturition.
lambing jug A small pen in which a ewe is put for lambing. It is also used for containing the ewe and her lamb until the lamb is strong enough to run with other ewes and lambs.
laminitis Lameness associated with inflammation of the laminae that attaches the horse's hoof wall to the fleshy part of the foot. Typically related to founder.
lard The fat from pigs that has been produced through a rendering process.
layer A hen that is kept for egg production.
legume Any plant of the family *leguminosae,* such as pea, bean, alfalfa, and clover.
leucocytes White blood cells.
LH See *luteinizing hormone.*
libido Sex drive or the desire to mate on the part of the male.
lice Small, flat, wingless insect with sucking mouth parts that is parasitic on the skin of animals.
linebreeding A mild form of inbreeding that maintains a high genetic relationship to an outstanding ancestor.
line crossing The crossing of inbred lines.
lipid An organic substance that is soluble in alcohol or ether but insoluble in water; used interchangeably with the term *fat.*
litter The young produced by multiparous females such as swine. The young in a litter are called litter mates.
liver flukes A parasitic flatworm found in the liver.
locus The place on a chromosome where a gene is located.
longevity Life span of an animal, usually refers to a long life span.

luteinizing hormone (LH) A protein hormone, produced and released by the anterior pituitary, which stimulates the formation and retention of the corpus luteum. It also initiates ovulation.
lymph Clear yellowish, slightly alkaline fluid contained in lymphatic vessels.
macroclimate The large, general climate in which an animal exists.
macromineral A mineral that is needed in the diet in relatively large amounts.
maintenance A condition in which the body is maintained without an increase or decrease in body weight and with no production or work being done.
mammal Warm-blooded animals that suckle their young.
mammary gland Gland that secretes milk.
management The act, art, or manner of managing, handling, controlling, or directing a resource or integrating several resources.
marbling The distribution of fat in muscular tissue; intramuscular fat.
mare A sexually developed female horse.
market class Animals grouped according to the use to which they will be put, such as slaughter, feeder, or stocker.
market grade Animals grouped within a market class according to their value.
masticate To chew food.
mastitis Inflammation of the mammary gland.
masturbation Ejaculation by a male by some process other than sexual intercourse.
maternal breeding value (MBV) A breeding value which measures primarily milk production in beef cattle.
mean (1) Statistical term for average. (2) Term used to describe animals having bad behavior.
meat The tissues of the animal body that are used for food.
meat spots Spots in the egg that are blood spots which have changed color or tissue sloughed off from the reproductive organs of the hen.
meiosis A special type of cell nuclear division that is undergone in the production of gametes (sperm in the male, ova in the female). As a result of meiosis, each gamete carries half the number of chromosomes of a typical body cell in that species.
melengestrol acetate (MGA) A feed additive that suppresses estrus in heifer and is widely used in the feedlot industry.
mesoderm The middle layer of the three layers of the primitive embryo.
messenger RNA The ribonucleic acid that is the carrier of genetic information from nuclear DNA. It is important in protein synthesis.
metabolism (1) The sum total of chemical changes in the body, including the "building up" and "breaking down" processes. (2) The transformation by which energy is made available for body uses.
metabolizable energy Gross energy in the feed minus the sum of energy in feces, gaseous products of digestion, and energy in urine. Energy that is available for metabolism by the body.
metritis Inflammation (infection) of the uterus.
MGA See *melengestrol acetate.*
microclimate A small, special climate within a macroclimate created by the use of such devices as shelters, heat lamps, and bedding.
microcomputer A small computer that has a smaller memory capacity than a larger or main-frame computer.
micromineral A mineral that is needed in the diet in relatively small amounts. The quantity needed is so small that such a mineral is often called a trace mineral.
milk fat The fat in milk; synonymous with butterfat.
milk fever See *parturient paresis.*
milk letdown The release of milk into the teat cisterns.
Milk Only Records Dairy record system similar to DHI except no milk fat samples are taken.

minimum culling level A selection method in which an animal must meet minimum standards for each trait desired in order to qualify for being retained for breeding purposes.

mites Very small arachnids that are often parasitic upon animals.

mitosis A process in which a cell divides to produce two daughter cells, each of which contains the same chromosome complement as the mother cell from which they came.

modifying genes Genes that modify the expression of other genes.

mohair Fleece of the Angora goat.

monogastric Having only one stomach or only one compartment in the stomach. Examples are swine and poultry.

monoparous A term designating animals that usually produce only one offspring at each pregnancy. Horses and cattle are monoparous.

moon blindness Periodic blindness that occurs in horses.

morbidity Measurement of illness; morbidity rate is the number of individuals in a group that become ill during a specified time.

mortality rate Number of individuals that die from a disease during a specified time, usually 1 year.

mouthed The examination of an animal's teeth.

mule The hybrid that is produced by mating a male donkey with a female horse. They are usually sterile.

mulefoot Having one instead of the expected two toes, on one or more of the feet.

multiparous A term that designates animals that usually produce several young at each pregnancy. Swine are multiparous.

mutation A change in a gene.

mutton The meat from a sheep that is over 1 year old.

muzzle The nose of horse, cattle, or sheep.

myofibrils The primary component part of muscle fibers.

navel The area where the umbilical cord was formerly attached to the body of the offspring.

necropsy Perform a postmortem examination.

net energy Metabolizable energy minus heat increment. The energy available to the animal for maintenance and production.

nicking The way in which certain lines, strains, or breeds perform when mated together. When outstanding offspring result, the parents are said to have nicked well.

nipple See *teat.*

nodular worm An internal parasitic worm that causes the formation of nodules in the intestines.

nonruminant Simple stomached or monagastric animal.

NPN (nonprotein nitrogen) Nitrogen in feeds from substances such as urea and amino acids, but not from preformed proteins.

nucleotide Compound composed of phosphoric acid, sugar, and a base (purine or pyrimadine), all of which constitute a structural unit of nucleic acid.

nutrient (1) A substance that nourishes the metabolic processes of the body. (2) The end product of digestion.

nutrient density Amount of essential nutrients relative to the number of calories in a given amount of food.

obesity An excessive accumulation of body fat.

offal All organs and tissues removed from inside the animal during the slaughtering process.

omasum One of the stomach components of ruminant animals that has many folds.

omnivorous Feeding on both animal and vegetable substances.

on full feed A term that refers to animals that are receiving all the feed they will consume. See also *Ad libitum.*

oogenesis The process by which eggs, or ova, are produced.

open Refers to nonpregnant females.

open-faced Face of sheep that is free from wool, particularly around the eyes.

opportunity costs Returns given up if debt-free resources (e.g., land, livestock, equipment) were used in their next best level of employment.
optimum level of performance The level at which a trait or traits maximizes net profit. Resources are managed to achieve a combined balance of traits that sustains high levels of profitability.
osteopetrosis Abnormal thickening, hardening, and fragility of bones, making them weaker.
osteoporosis An abnormal decrease in bone mass with an increased fragility of the bones.
outbreeding The process of continuously mating females of the herd to unrelated males of the same breed.
outcrossing The mating of an individual to another in the same breed that is not related to it. Outcrossing is a specific type of outbreeding system.
ova Plural of ovum, meaning eggs.
ovary The female reproductive gland in which the eggs are formed and progesterone and estrogenic hormones are produced.
overeating disease A toxic condition caused by the presence of undigested carbohydrates in the intestine, which stimulates harmful bacteria to multiply. When the bacteria die, they release toxins. Called *enterotoxemia* in some animals.
overshot jaw Upper jaw is longer than lower jaw. Also called *parrot mouth.*
oviduct A duct leading from the ovary to the horn of the uterus.
ovine Refers to sheep.
ovulation The shedding, or release, of the egg from the follicle of the ovary.
ovum The egg produced by a female.
Owner-sampler record Dairy record system similar to DHI except milk weights and samples are taken by the dairy producer instead of a DHIA supervisor.
pace A lateral two-beat gait in which the right rear and front feet hit the ground at one time and the left rear and front feet strike the ground at another time.
paddling The outward swinging of the front feet of a horse that toes in.
pale, soft, exudative (PSE) A genetically predisposed condition in swine in which the pork is very light colored, soft, and watery.
palpation Feeling by hand.
parasite An organism that lives a part of its life cycle in or on, and at the expense of, another organism. Parasites of farm animals live at the expense of the farm animals.
parity Number of different times a female has had offspring.
parrot mouth Upper jaw is longer than lower jaw.
parturient paresis Partial paralysis that occurs at or near time of giving birth to young and beginning lactation. The mother mobilizes large amounts of calcium to produce milk to feed newborn, and blood calcium levels drop below the point necessary for impulse transmission along the nerve tracks. Commonly called *milk fever.*
parturition The process of giving birth.
pasteurization The process of heating milk to 161°F and holding it at that temperature for 15 seconds to destroy pathogenic microorganisms.
pasture rotation The rotation of animals from one pasture to another so that some pasture areas have no livestock on them in certain periods.
pathogen Biologic agent—i.e., bacteria, virus, protozoa, nematode—that may produce disease or illness.
paunch Another name for rumen.
pay weight The actual weight for which payment is made. In many cases it is the shrunk weight (actual weight minus pencil shrink).
pedigree The record of the ancestry of an animal.
pelt The natural, whole skin covering, including the wool, hair, or fur.
pencil shrink An arithmetic deduction (% of liveweight) from an animal's weight to account for fill.

pendulous Hanging loosely.
penis The male organ of copulation. It serves both as a channel for passage of urine from the bladder as an extension of the urethra, and as a copulatory organ through which sperm are deposited into the female reproductive tract.
per capita Per person.
performance test The evaluation of an animal according to its performance.
pernicious anemia A chronic type of mycrocitic anemia caused by a deficiency of vitamin B_{12} or a failure of intestinal absorption of vitamin B_{12}.
pharmaceutical A medicinal drug.
phenotype The characteristics of an animal that can be seen and/or measured; e.g., the presence or absence of horns, the color, or the weight of an animal.
pheromones Chemical substances that attract the opposite sex.
photoperiod Time period when light is present.
physiology The science that pertains to the functions of organs, organ systems, or the entire animal.
picking The removal of feathers in dressing poultry.
pigeon toed See *toeing in.*
pin bones In cattle, the posterior ends of the pelvic bones that appear as two raised areas on either side of the tail head.
pink tooth Congenital porphyria, teeth are pink gray and the animals tend to sunburn easily.
pinworms A small nematode worm with unsegmented body found as a parasite in the rectum and large intestine of animals.
pituitary Small endocrine gland located at the base of the brain.
placenta The vascular organ that unites the fetus to the uterus.
pneumonia Inflammation or infection of alveoli of the lungs caused by either bacteria or viruses.
poikilotherm A cold-blooded animal; one whose body temperature varies with that of the environment.
polled Naturally or genetically hornless.
poll evil An abscess behind the ears of a horse.
Polypay A synthetic breed of sheep developed in the United States by combining the Dorset, Targhee, Rambouillet, and Finnsheep breeds.
pork The meat from swine.
postgastric fermentation The fermentation of feed that occurs in the cecum, behind the area where digestion has occurred.
postnatal See *postpartum.*
postpartum After birth.
postpartum interval The length of time from parturition until the dam is pregnant again.
poult A young turkey of either sex, from hatching to approximately 10 weeks of age.
poultry This term includes chickens, turkeys, geese, pigeons, peafowls, guineas, and game birds.
predicted transmitting ability (PTA) Estimate of genetic transmitting ability (i.e., one-half of the breeding value) of dairy bulls. Estimated amount by which daughters of a bull will differ from the breed average.
pregastric fermentation Fermentation that occurs in the rumen of ruminant animals. It occurs before feed passes into the portion of the digestive tract in which digestion actually occurs.
pregnancy disease A metabolic disease in late pregnancy affecting primarily ewes carrying twins or triplets. A form of ketosis. Also called pregnancy toxemia.
pregnancy testing Evaluation of females for pregnancy through palpation or using an ultrasound machine.
prenatal Prior to being born. Before birth.
probe A device used to measure backfat thickness in pigs and cattle.
production testing An evaluation of an animal based on its production record.

progeny testing An evaluation of an animal on the basis of performance of its offspring.
progesterone A hormone produced by the corpus luteum that stimulates progestational proliferation in the uterus of the female.
prolapse Abnormal protrusion of part of an organ, such as uterus or anus.
prostaglandins Chemical mediators that control many physiological and biochemical functions in the body. One prostaglandin ($PGF_{2\alpha}$) can be used to synchronize estrus.
prostate A gland of the male reproductive tract that is located just back of the bladder. It secretes a fluid that becomes part of semen at ejaculation.
protein A substance made up of amino acids that contains approximately 16% nitrogen (based on molecular weight).
protein supplement Any dietary component containing a high concentration (at least 25%) of protein.
PSE See *pale, soft, and exudative.*
PTA See *predicted transmitting ability.*
puberty The age at which the reproductive organs become functionally operative.
pullet Young female chicken from day of hatch through onset of egg production; sometimes the term is used through the first laying year.
purebred An animal eligible for registry with a recognized breed association.
quality grades Animals grouped according to value as prime, choice, etc., based on conformation and fatness of the animals.
rack (1) A rapid four-beat gait of a horse. (2) A wholesale cut of lamb located between the shoulder and loin.
ram A male sheep that is sexually mature.
ration The quantity of feed fed to an animal over a given period of time.
reach See *selection differential.*
realized heritability The portion obtained of what is reached for in selection.
realizer A feeder animal (usually cattle) that has serious health problems or injury. Economics dictate the animal be sold rather than continue the duration of the feeding program.
reasoning The ability of an animal to respond correctly to a stimulus the first time the animal encounters a new situation.
recessive gene A gene that has its phenotype masked by its dominant allele when the two genes are present together in an individual.
reciprocal recurrent selection The selection of breeding animals in two populations based on the performance of their offspring after animals from two population are crossed.
recombinant DNA (rDNA) Isolated DNA molecules that can be inserted into the DNA of another cell. rDNA is used in the genetic-engineering process.
rectal prolapse Protrusion of part of large intestine through the anus.
recurrent selection Selection for general combining ability by selecting males that sire outstanding offspring when mated to females from varying genetic backgrounds.
red meat Meat from cattle, sheep, swine, and goats as contrasted to the white meat of poultry.
registered Recorded in the herdbook of a breed.
regurgitate To cast up digested food to the mouth as is done by ruminants.
reinforcement A reward for making the proper response to a stimulus or condition.
replicate To duplicate, or make another exactly alike, the original.
reproduction The production of live, normal offspring.
retained placenta Placenta remains within the reproductive tract after parturition has occurred.
reticulum One of the stomach components of ruminant animals that is lined with small compartments, giving a honeycomb appearance.
rhinitis Inflammation of the mucous membranes lining the nasal passages.
ribonucleic acid (RNA) An essential component of living cells, composed of long chains of phosphate, ribose sugar, and several bases.
rhinopneumonitis Equine herpes virus-1. It produces acute catarrh upon primary infection.

rickets A disease of disturbed ossification of the bones caused by a lack of vitamin D or unbalanced calcium/phosphorus ratio.
ridgling Another term for cryptorchid.
ringbone An ossification of the lateral cartilage of the foot of a horse all around the foot.
RNA See *ribonucleic acid.*
roughage A feed that is high in fiber, low in digestible nutrients, and low in energy. Such feeds as hay, straw, silage, and pasture are examples.
rumen The large fermentation pouch of the ruminant animal in which bacteria and protozoa break down fibrous plant material that is swallowed by the animal, sometimes referred to as the *paunch.*
ruminant A mammal whose stomach has four parts (rumen, reticulum, omasum, and abomasum). Cattle, sheep, goats, deer, and elk are ruminants.
rumination The regurgitation of undigested food and chewing of it for a second time, after which it is again swallowed.
salmonella Gram-positive, rod-shaped bacteria that cause various disease such as food poisoning in animals.
scale (1) Size. (2) Equipment on which an animal is weighed.
scoured wool Wool that has been cleaned of grease and other foreign material.
scours Diarrhea; a profuse watery discharge from the intestines.
screwworms Larvae of several American flies that infest wounds of animals.
scrotal circumference A measurement (usually cm or in.) of the circumference of both testicles and the scrotal sac that surrounds them.
scrotum A pouch that contains the testes. It is also a thermoregulatory organ that contracts when cold and relaxes when warm, thus tending to keep the testes at a lower temperature than that of the body.
scurs Small growths of hornlike tissue attached to the skin of polled or dehorned animals.
scurvy A deficiency disease in humans that causes spongy gums and loose teeth. It is caused by a lack of vitamin C (ascorbic acid).
seed stock Breeding animals; sometimes used interchangeably with *purebred.*
selection Differentially reproducing what one wants in a herd or flock.
selection differential The difference between the average for a trait in selected animals and the average of the group from which they come; also called reach.
selection index Selection method in which several traits are evaluated and expressed as one total score.
semen The fluid containing the sperm that is ejaculated by the male. Secretions from the seminal vesicles, the prostate gland, the bulbourethral glands, and the urethral glands provide most of the fluid.
seminal vesicles Accessory sex glands of the male that provide a portion of the fluid of semen.
seminiferous tubules Minute tubules in the testicles in which sperm are produced. They comprise about 90% of the mass of the testes.
service To breed or mate.
settle To become pregnant.
sex-limited Exists in only one sex, such as milk production in dairy cattle.
shearing The process of removing the fleece (wool) from a sheep.
sheath rot Inflammation of the prepuce in male sheep.
sheep bot Any of a number of related flies whose larvae are parasitic in sheep. They usually are found in the sinuses.
shipping fever A widespread respiratory disease of cattle and sheep.
shoat A young pig of either sex.
shoe boil Blemish of the horse caused by the horseshoe putting pressure on the elbow when the horse lies down.
shrink Loss of weight—commonly used in the loss in liveweight when animals are marketed or loss in weight from grease wool to clean wool.
sib A brother or sister.

sickle hocks Hocks that have too much set, causing the hind feet to be too far forward and too far under the animal.
side bones Ossification of the lateral cartilages of the foot of a horse.
sigmoid flexure The S-curve in the penis of boars, rams, bucks, and bulls.
silage Forage, corn fodder, or sorghum preserved by fermentation that produces acids similar to the acids that are used to make pickled foods for people.
sire Male parent.
skins See *hides*
sleeping sickness An infectious disease common in tropical Africa and transmitted by the bite of a tsetse fly.
slotted floor Floor having any kind of openings through which excreta may fall.
SNF See *solids-nonfat.*
snood The relatively long, fleshy extension at the base of the turkey's beak.
software Program instructions to make computer hardware function.
soilage Green forage that is cut and brought to animals as food.
solids-nonfat Total milk solids minus fat. It includes protein, lactose, and minerals.
somatotropin The growth hormone from the anterior pituitary that stimulates nitrogen retention and growth.
sore mouth A virus-caused disease affecting primarily lambs.
sow A female swine that has farrowed one litter or has reached 12 months of age.
spay To remove the ovaries.
specific combining ability The ability of a line or population to exhibit superiority or inferiority when combined with other lines or populations.
spermatid The haploid germ cell prior to spermiogenesis.
spermatogenesis The process by which spermatozoa are formed.
spermiogenesis The process by which the spermatid loses most of its cytoplasm and develops a tail to become a mature sperm.
spinning count The number of hanks of yarn that can be spun from a pound of clean wool. One method of evaluating fineness of wool.
splay footed See *toeing out.*
spool joint The joint where the foot and pastern are removed from the front leg. Used to identify a mutton carcass.
spur A sharp projection on the back of a male bird's shank.
stags Castrated male sheep, cattle, goats, or swine that have reached sexual maturity prior to castration.
stallion A sexually mature male horse.
staple length Length of wool fibers.
steer A castrated bovine male that was castrated early in life before puberty.
sterility Inability to produce offspring.
stifle Joint of the hindleg between the femur and tibia.
stifled Injury of the stifle joint.
stillborn Offspring born dead without previously breathing.
stocker Weaned cattle that are fed high-roughage diets (including grazing) before going into the feedlot.
stomach worms *Haemonchus contortus,* or worms of the stomach of cattle, swine, sheep, and goats.
strangles An infectious disease of horses, characterized by inflammation of the mucous membranes of the respiratory tract.
streptococcus Sperical, gram-positive bacteria that divide in only one plane and occur in chains. Some species cause serious disease.
stress An unusual or abnormal influence causing a change in an animal's function, structure, or behavior.
stringhalt A sudden and extreme flexion of the back of a horse, producing a jerking motion of the hind leg in walking.

strongyles Any of various roundworms living as parasites, especially in domestic animals.

stud Usually the same as stallion. Also a place where male animals are maintained; i.e., bull stud.

suckling gain The gain that a young animal makes from birth until it is weaned.

subcutaneous Situated beneath, or occurring beneath, the skin. A subcutaneous injection is an injection made under the skin.

sulfonamides A sulfa drug capable of killing bacteria.

superovulation The hormonally induced ovulation of a greater than normal number of eggs.

sweeny Atrophy of muscle (typically shoulder) in horses.

sweetbread An edible by-product also known as the pancreas.

switch The tuft of long hair at the end of tail (cattle and horses).

syndactyly Union of two or more digits; e.g., in cattle, the two toes would be a solid hoof.

synthetic breeds See *composite breed.*

tagging Clipping wool from the dock, udder, and vulva regions of the ewe prior to breeding and lambing.

tags (1) Wool covered with manure. (2) Abbreviated form of ear tags, used for identification.

tallow The fat of cattle and sheep.

tandem selection Selection for one trait for a given period of time followed by selection for a second trait and continuing in this way until all important traits are selected.

TDN Total digestible nutrients; it includes the total amounts of digestible protein, nitrogen-free extract, fiber, and fat (multiplied by 2.25) all summed together.

teaser ram A ram made incapable of impregnating a ewe by vasectomy or by use of an apron to prevent copulation, which is used to find ewes in heat.

teasing The stallion in the presence of the mare to see if she will mate.

teat The protuberance of the udder through which milk is drawn.

tendon Tough, fibrous connective tissue at ends of muscle bundles that attach muscle to bones or cartilage structures.

terminal sire The sire used in a terminal crossbreeding program. It is intended that all offspring from a terminal sire be sold as market animals.

testicle The male sex gland that produces sperm and testosterone.

testosterone The male sex hormone that stimulates the accessory sex glands, causes the male sex drive, and causes the development of masculine characteristics.

tetanus An acute infectious disease caused by toxin elaborated by the bacterium *Clostridium tetani,* in which toxic spasms of some of the voluntary muscles occur.

tetrad A group of four similar chromotids formed by the splitting longitudinally of a pair of homologous chromosomes during meiotic prophase.

thermoneutral zone (TNZ) Range in temperature where rate and efficiency of gain is maximized. Comfort zone.

thoroughpin A hard swelling that is located between the Achilles tendon and the bone of the hock joint.

toeing in Toes of front feet turn in. Also called *pigeon toed.*

toeing out Toes of front feet turn out. Also called *splay footed.*

tom A male turkey.

TPI Total prediction index used in dairy cattle breeding. It includes the predicted differences for milk production, fat percentage, and type into one figure in a ratio of milk production $\times 3$: fat percentage $\times 1$: type $\times 1$.

transcription The synthesis of RNA from DNA in the nucleus by matching the sequences of the bases.

transgenic animals Animals that contain genes transferred from other animals, usually from a different species.

transmissable gastroenteritis (TGE) A serious, contagious diarrhea disease in baby pigs.

tripe Edible product from walls of ruminant stomach.

trot A diagonal two-beat gait in which the right front and left rear feet strike the ground in unison, and the left front and right rear feet strike the ground in unison.

twist Vertical measurement from top of the rump to point where hind legs separate.
twitch To squeeze tightly the upper lip of a horse by means of a small rope that is twisted.
type (1) The physical conformation of an animal. (2) All those physical attributes that contribute to the value of an animal for a specific purpose.
udder The encased group of mammary glands of mammals.
ultrasound A process used to measure fat thickness and ribeye area in swine and cattle. The machine sends sound waves into the back of the animal and records these waves as they bounce off the tissues. Different wavelengths are recorded for fat than for lean. Also used to diagnose pregnancy.
umbilical cord A cord through which arteries and veins travel from the fetus to and from the placenta, respectively. This cord is broken when the young are born.
undershot jaw Lower jaw is longer than upper jaw.
unsoundness Any defect or injury that interferes with the usefulness of an animal.
urinary calculi Disease where mineral deposits crystallize in the urinary tract. The deposits may block the tract causing difficulty in urination.
uterus That portion of the female reproductive tract where the young develop during pregnancy.
vaccination The act of administering a vaccine or antigens.
vaccine Suspension of attenuated or killed microbes or toxins administered to induce active immunity.
vagina The copulatory portion of the female's reproductive tract. The vestibule portion of the vagina also serves for passage of urine during urination. The vagina also serves as a canal through which young pass when born.
variety meats Edible organ by-products, e.g., liver, heart, tongue, tripe.
vas deferens Ducts that carry sperm from the epididymis to the urethra.
vasectomy The removal of a portion of the vas deferens. As a result, sperm are prevented from traveling from the testicles to become part of the semen.
veal The meat from very young cattle, under 3 months of age.
vein Vessel through which blood passes from various organs or parts back to the heart.
vermifuge A chemical substance given to the animals to kill internal parasitic worms.
VFA See *volatile fatty acids.*
villi Projections of the inner lining of the small intestine.
virus Ultra-microscopic bundle of genetic material capable of multiplying only in living cells. Viruses cause a wide range of disease in plants, animals, and humans, such as rabies and measles.
viscera Internal organs and glands contained in the thoracic and abdominal cavities.
vitamin An organic catalyst, or component thereof, that facilitates specific and necessary functions.
volatile fatty acids (VFA) A group of fatty acids produced from microbial action in the rumen; examples are acetic, propionic, and butyric acids.
vulva The external genitalia of a female mammal.
walk A four-beat gait of a horse in which each foot strikes the ground at a time different from each of the other three feet.
warble The larval stage of the heel fly that burrows out through the hide of cattle in springtime.
wattle Method of identification in cattle where strips of skin (3–6 inches) long are usually cut on the nose, jaw, throat, or brisket.
weaner An animal that has been weaned or is nearing weaning age.
weaning Separating young animals from their dams so that the offspring can no longer suckle.
weaning breeding value (WBV) A breeding value that measures primarily preweaning growth in beef cattle.
wether A male sheep castrated before reaching puberty.
white muscle disease A muscular disease caused by a deficiency of selenium or vitamin E.
winking Indication of estrus in the mare where the vulva opens and closes.
withdrawl time The time before slaughter that a drug should not be given to an animal.
withers Top of the shoulders.

wool The fibers that grow from the skin of sheep.
wool blindness Sheep cannot see owing to wool covering their eyes.
wool top A continuous untwisted strand of combed wool in which the fibers lie parallel and the short fibers have been combed out.
woolens Cloth made from short wool fibers that are intermingled in the making of the cloth by carding.
worsteds Cloth made from wool that is long enough to comb and spin into yarn. The finish of worsteds is harder than woolens, and worsted clothes hold a press better.
yearling Animals that are approximately 1 year old.
yearling breeding value (YBV) A breeding value that measures primarily postweaning growth in beef cattle.
yield Used interchangeably with *dressing percentage.*
yield grades The grouping of animals according to the estimated trimmed lean meat that their carcass would provide; cutability.
yolk (1) The yellow part of the egg. (2) The natural grease (lanolin) of wool.
yolk sac Layer of tissue encompassing the yolk of an egg.
zone of thermoneutrality The environmental temperature (about 65°F) at which heat production and heat elimination are approximately equal for most farm animals.
zygote (1) The cell formed by the union of two gametes. (2) An individual from the time of fertilization until death.

INDEX